AF730974

College Physics for AP® Courses 2e

Volume 1:Chapters 1-19

SENIOR CONTRIBUTING AUTHORS

IRINA LYUBLINSKAYA, CUNY COLLEGE OF STATEN ISLAND
GREGG WOLFE, AVONWORTH HIGH SCHOOL
DOUGLAS INGRAM, TEXAS CHRISTIAN UNIVERSITY
LIZA PUJJI, MANUKAU INSTITUTE OF TECHNOLOGY
SUDHI OBEROI, RAMAN RESEARCH INSTITUTE
NATHAN CZUBA, SABIO ACADEMY

openstax™

ISBN: 978-1-711470-84-9

OpenStax
Rice University
6100 Main Street MS-375
Houston, Texas 77005

To learn more about OpenStax, visit https://openstax.org.
Individual print copies and bulk orders can be purchased through our website.

COLOR PAPERBACK BOOK ISBN-13	978-1-711470-84-9
DIGITAL VERSION ISBN-13	978-1-951693-61-9
ORIGINAL PUBLICATION YEAR	**2022**

1 2 3 4 5 6 7 8 9 10 RS 22

OpenStax

OpenStax provides free, peer-reviewed, openly licensed textbooks for introductory college and Advanced Placement® courses and low-cost, personalized courseware that helps students learn. A nonprofit ed tech initiative based at Rice University, we're committed to helping students access the tools they need to complete their courses and meet their educational goals.

Rice University

OpenStax, OpenStax CNX, and OpenStax Tutor are initiatives of Rice University. As a leading research university with a distinctive commitment to undergraduate education, Rice University aspires to path-breaking research, unsurpassed teaching, and contributions to the betterment of our world. It seeks to fulfill this mission by cultivating a diverse community of learning and discovery that produces leaders across the spectrum of human endeavor.

RICE

Philanthropic Support

OpenStax is grateful for the generous philanthropic partners who advance our mission to improve educational access and learning for everyone. To see the impact of our supporter community and our most updated list of partners, please visit openstax.org/impact.

Arnold Ventures
Chan Zuckerberg Initiative
Chegg, Inc.
Arthur and Carlyse Ciocca Charitable Foundation
Digital Promise
Ann and John Doerr
Bill & Melinda Gates Foundation
Girard Foundation
Google Inc.
The William and Flora Hewlett Foundation
The Hewlett-Packard Company
Intel Inc.
Rusty and John Jaggers
The Calvin K. Kazanjian Economics Foundation
Charles Koch Foundation
Leon Lowenstein Foundation, Inc.
The Maxfield Foundation
Burt and Deedee McMurtry
Michelson 20MM Foundation
National Science Foundation
The Open Society Foundations
Jumee Yhu and David E. Park III
Brian D. Patterson USA-International Foundation
The Bill and Stephanie Sick Fund
Steven L. Smith & Diana T. Go
Stand Together
Robin and Sandy Stuart Foundation
The Stuart Family Foundation
Tammy and Guillermo Treviño
Valhalla Charitable Foundation
White Star Education Foundation
Schmidt Futures
William Marsh Rice University

Contents

CHAPTER 19
Electric Potential and Electric Field 875

CHAPTER 20
Electric Current, Resistance, and Ohm's Law 919

CHAPTER 21
Circuits and DC Instruments 969

CHAPTER 22
Magnetism 1023

CHAPTER 23
Electromagnetic Induction, AC Circuits, and Electrical Technologies 1075

CHAPTER 24
Electromagnetic Waves 1135

CHAPTER 34

PREFACE

Welcome to *College Physics for AP® Courses 2e*, an OpenStax resource. This textbook was written to increase student access to high-quality learning materials, maintaining highest standards of academic rigor at little to no cost.

About OpenStax

OpenStax is a part of rice University, which is a 501(c)(3) nonprofit charitable corporation. As an educational initiative it is our mission to transform learning so that education works for every student. Through our partnerships with philanthropic foundations and our alliance with other educational resource organizations, we're breaking down the most common barriers to learning, because we believe that everyone should and can have access to knowledge.

About OpenStax resources

Customization

College Physics for AP® Courses 2e is licensed under a Creative Commons Attribution 4.0 International (CC BY) license, which means that you can distribute, remix, and build upon the content, as long as you provide attribution to OpenStax and its content contributors.

Because our books are openly licensed, you are free to use the entire book or select only the sections that are most relevant to the needs of your course. Feel free to remix the content by assigning your students certain chapters and sections in your syllabus, in the order that you prefer. You can even provide a direct link in your syllabus to the sections in the web view of your book.

Instructors also have the option of creating a customized version of their OpenStax book. The custom version can be made available to students in low-cost print or digital form through their campus bookstore. Visit the Instructor Resources section of your book page on OpenStax.org for more information.

Art Attribution

In *College Physics for AP® Courses 2e*, most photos and third-party illustrations contain attribution to their creator, rights holder, host platform, and/or license within the caption. Because the art is openly licensed, anyone may reuse the art as long as they provide the same attribution to its original source. To maximize readability and content flow, some art does not include attribution in the text. This art is part of the public domain or under a CC0 or similar license, and can be reused without attribution. For illustrations (e.g., graphs, charts, etc.) that are not credited, use the following attribution: Copyright Rice University, OpenStax, under CC BY 4.0 license.

Errata

All OpenStax textbooks undergo a rigorous review process. However, like any professional-grade textbook, errors sometimes occur. Since our books are web based, we can make updates periodically when deemed pedagogically necessary. If you have a correction to suggest, submit it through the link on your book page on OpenStax.org. Subject matter experts review all errata suggestions. OpenStax is committed to remaining transparent about all updates, so you will also find a list of past errata changes on your book page on OpenStax.org.

Format

You can access this textbook for free in web view or PDF through OpenStax.org, and for a low cost in print.

About *College Physics for AP® Courses 2e*

College Physics for AP® Courses 2e is designed to engage students in their exploration of physics and help them apply these concepts to the Advanced Placement® test. Because physics is integral to modern technology and other sciences, the book also includes content that goes beyond the scope of the AP® course to further student understanding. The AP® Connection in each chapter directs students to the material they should focus on for the AP® exam, and what content — although interesting — is not necessarily part of the AP® curriculum. This book is Learning List-approved for AP® Physics courses.

This content features enhancements from *TEA AP® Physics 1 & 2: Algebra-Based* by TEA (Texas Education Agency).

Coverage, scope, and alignment to the AP® curriculum

The current AP® Physics curriculum framework outlines the two full-year physics courses AP® Physics 1: Algebra-Based and AP® Physics 2: Algebra-Based. These two courses replaced the one-year AP® Physics B course, which over the years had become a fast-paced survey of physics facts and formulas that did not provide in-depth conceptual understanding of major physics ideas and the connections between them.

AP® Physics 1 and 2 courses focus on the big ideas typically included in the first and second semesters of an algebra-based, introductory college-level physics course, providing students with the essential knowledge and skills required to support future advanced course work in physics. The AP® Physics 1 curriculum includes mechanics, mechanical waves, sound, and electrostatics. The AP® Physics 2 curriculum focuses on thermodynamics, fluid statics, dynamics, electromagnetism, geometric and physical optics, quantum physics, atomic physics, and nuclear physics. Seven unifying themes of physics called the Big Ideas each include three to seven enduring understandings (EU), which are themselves composed of essential knowledge (EK) that provides details and context for students as they explore physics.

AP® science practices emphasize inquiry-based learning and development of critical thinking and reasoning skills. Inquiry usually uses a series of steps to gain new knowledge, beginning with an observation and following with a hypothesis to explain the observation; then experiments are conducted to test the hypothesis, gather results, and draw conclusions from data. The AP® framework has identified seven major science practices, which can be described by short phrases: using representations and models to communicate information and solve problems; using mathematics appropriately; engaging in questioning; planning and implementing data collection strategies; analyzing and evaluating data; justifying scientific explanations; and connecting concepts. The framework's Learning Objectives merge content (EU and EK) with one or more of the seven science practices that students should develop as they prepare for the AP® Physics exam.

College Physics for AP® Courses 2e is based on the OpenStax *College Physics* text, adapted to focus on the AP curriculum's concepts and practices. Each chapter of OpenStax *College Physics for AP® Courses 2e* begins with a *Connection for AP® Courses* introduction that explains how the content in the chapter sections align to the Big Ideas, enduring understandings, and essential knowledge in the AP® framework. This textbook contains a wealth of information, and the *Connection for AP® Courses* sections will help you distill the required AP® content from material that, although interesting, exceeds the scope of an introductory-level course.

Each section opens with the program's learning objectives as well as the AP® learning objectives and science practices addressed. We have also developed *Real World Connections* features and *Applying the Science Practices* features that highlight concepts, examples, and practices in the framework.

- 1 Introduction: The Nature of Science and Physics
- 2 Kinematics
- 3 Two-Dimensional Kinematics
- 4 Dynamics: Force and Newton's Laws of Motion
- 5 Further Applications of Newton's Laws: Friction, Drag, and Elasticity
- 6 Gravitation and Uniform Circular Motion
- 7 Work, Energy, and Energy Resources
- 8 Linear Momentum and Collisions
- 9 Statics and Torque
- 10 Rotational Motion and Angular Momentum
- 11 Fluid Statics
- 12 Fluid Dynamics and Its Biological and Medical Applications
- 13 Temperature, Kinetic Theory, and the Gas Laws
- 14 Heat and Heat Transfer Methods
- 15 Thermodynamics
- 16 Oscillatory Motion and Waves
- 17 Physics of Hearing
- 18 Electric Charge and Electric Field
- 19 Electric Potential and Electric Field
- 20 Electric Current, Resistance, and Ohm's Law
- 21 Circuits, Bioelectricity, and DC Instruments
- 22 Magnetism
- 23 Electromagnetic Induction, AC Circuits, and Electrical Technologies
- 24 Electromagnetic Waves
- 25 Geometric Optics
- 26 Vision and Optical Instruments
- 27 Wave Optics
- 28 Special Relativity
- 29 Introduction to Quantum Physics
- 30 Atomic Physics
- 31 Radioactivity and Nuclear Physics
- 32 Medical Applications of Nuclear Physics
- 33 Particle Physics
- 34 Frontiers of Physics
- Appendix A: Atomic Masses
- Appendix B: Selected Radioactive Isotopes
- Appendix C: Useful Information
- Appendix D: Glossary of Key Symbols and Notation

Pedagogical foundation and features

College Physics for AP® Courses 2e is organized so that topics are introduced conceptually with a steady progression to precise definitions and analytical applications. The analytical, problem-solving aspect is tied back to the conceptual before moving on to another topic. Each introductory chapter, for example, opens with an engaging photograph relevant to the subject of the chapter and interesting applications that are easy for most students to visualize.

- **Connections for AP® Courses** introduce each chapter and explain how its content addresses the AP® curriculum.
- **Worked Examples** Examples start with problems based on real-life situations, then describe a strategy for solving the problem that emphasizes key concepts. The subsequent detailed mathematical solution also includes a follow-up discussion.
- **Problem-solving Strategies** are presented independently and subsequently appear at crucial points in the text where students can benefit most from them.
- **Misconception Alerts** address common misconceptions that students may bring to class.
- **Take-Home Investigations** provide the opportunity for students to apply or explore what they have learned with a hands-on activity.
- **Real World Connections** highlight important concepts and examples in the AP® framework.
- **Applying the Science Practices** includes activities and challenging questions that engage students while they apply the AP® science practices.
- **Things Great and Small** explains macroscopic phenomena (such as air pressure) with submicroscopic phenomena (such as atoms bouncing off of walls).
- **PhET Explorations** link students to interactive PHeT physics simulations, developed by the University of Colorado, to help them further explore the physics concepts they have learned about in their book module.

Assessment
College Physics for AP® Courses 2e offers a wealth of assessment options, including the following end-of-module problems:

- **Integrated Concept Problems** challenge students to apply both conceptual knowledge and skills to solve a problem.
- **Unreasonable Results** encourage students to solve a problem and then evaluate why the premise or answer to the problem are unrealistic.
- **Construct Your Own Problem** requires students to construct how to solve a particular problem, justify their starting assumptions, show their steps to find the solution to the problem, and finally discuss the meaning of the result.
- **Test Prep for AP® Courses** includes assessment items with the format and rigor found in the AP® exam to help prepare students for the exam.

AP Physics Collection
College Physics for AP® Courses 2e is a part of the AP Physics Collection. The AP Physics Collection is a free, turnkey solution for your AP® Physics course, brought to you through a collaboration between OpenStax and Rice Online Learning. The integrated collection pairs the OpenStax College Physics for AP® Courses text with Concept Trailer videos, instructional videos, problem solution videos, and a correlation guide to help you align all of your content. The instructional videos and problem solution videos were developed by Rice Professor Jason Hafner and AP® Physics teachers Gigi Nevils-Noe and Matt Wilson through Rice Online Learning. You can access all of this free material through the *College Physics for AP® Courses 2e* page on OpenStax.org.

Changes to the Second Edition

College Physics for AP® Courses 2e builds on the first edition's guiding principle that physics is a discipline undertaken by and for people. Throughout the text, the human impact of physics understanding, phenomena, discoveries, and applications is made clear through widespread examples, scenarios, and explanations. The narrative of physics and scientific discovery has been even further expanded to focus on including more diverse contributors to the field. From Ibn al-Haytham's 11th century foundation of the scientific method to Gladys West's complex models enabling GPS, the second edition broadens the discussion of pioneering and current researchers in an effort to tell a more accurate and inclusive scientific and societal story.

Relevance and Responsiveness

The impact of physics on engineering, urban development, the environment, medicine, energy production, and other aspects of everyday life have been updated and expanded to reflect more student experiences and interests. Techniques and developments in related disciplines are covered in context—not only in opening vignettes—so that students encounter the deep impact of evolving knowledge relevant to their potential fields of study.

Since many introductory physics students are focused on medicine, sections and examples related to biology have been significantly expanded. The section on electric forces in biology (18.6), for example, has been deepened to include Ernest Everett Just's work on electronegativity in ova, as well as the emerging practice of electrical stimulation in wound healing.

Additional biological application narratives include Yalow and Berson's development of radioimmunoassay, and Strickland and Mourou's invention of chirped lasers used in vision correction.

Currency and Accuracy

We have updated sections related to ongoing research, frontiers of physics, and emerging information. In particular, section 4.8 on the four basic forces has been revised with information about recent discoveries and ongoing research, as well as with additional context about the ongoing process of discovery—for example, the progression from Einstein's black hole predictions to the first black hole images produced in 2019. The section on world energy use (7.9), the section on ozone depletion (24.3), and several sections discussing space telescopes have been similarly updated to reflect current research and data.

Over ten years of widespread usage, OpenStax *College Physics* has benefitted from suggestions, corrections, and clarifications submitted by hundreds of faculty and also from students. We have made the requisite corrections and improvements over time, but the second edition unifies those edits for more consistency and ease of use.

Improving Problem-Solving and Deepening Understanding

College Physics for AP® Courses 2e employs the best practices of physics teaching, informed by education research and extensive adopter feedback. In order to unify conceptual, analytical, and calculation skills within the learning process, the authors have integrated a wide array of strategies and supports throughout the text.

Worked Examples

Worked examples have four distinct parts to promote both analytical and conceptual skills. Worked examples are introduced in words, always using some application that should be of interest. This is followed by a Strategy section that emphasizes the concepts involved and how solving the problem relates to those concepts. This is followed by the mathematical Solution and Discussion.

Many worked examples contain multiple-part problems to help the students learn how to approach normal situations, in which problems tend to have multiple parts. Finally, worked examples employ the techniques of the problem-solving strategies so that students can see how those strategies succeed in practice as well as in theory.

About the authors

Senior contributing authors

Irina Lyublinskaya, CUNY College of Staten Island
Gregg Wolfe, Avonworth High School
Douglas Ingram, Trinity Christian University
Liza Pujji, Manukau Institute of Technology, New Zealand
Sudhi Oberoi, Visiting Research Student, QuIC Lab, Raman Research Institute, India
Nathan Czuba, Sabio Academy
Julie Kretchman, Science Writer, BS, University of Toronto
John Stoke, Science Writer, MS, University of Chicago
David Anderson, Science Writer, PhD, College of William and Mary
Erika Gasper, Science Writer, MA, University of California, Santa Cruz
Kenneth Podolak, State University of New York, Plattsburgh
Henry Smith, River Parishes Community College

Advanced Placement teacher reviewers

John Boehringer, Prosper High School
Victor Brazil, Petaluma High School
Michelle Burgess, Avon Lake High School
Bryan Callow, Lindenwold High School
Brian Hastings, Spring Grove Area School District
Alexander Lavy, Xavier High School
Jerome Mass, Glastonbury Public Schools

Faculty reviewers

John Aiken, Georgia Institute of Technology
Robert Arts, University of Pikeville
Anand Batra, Howard University
Michael Ottinger, Missouri Western State University
James Smith, Caldwell University
Ulrich Zurcher, Cleveland State University

Additional resources

Student and instructor resources

We've compiled additional resources for both students and instructors, including Getting Started Guides, an instructor's manual, test bank, and image slides. Instructor resources require a verified instructor account, which you can apply for when you log in or create your account on OpenStax.org. Take advantage of these resources to supplement your OpenStax book.

Instructor's solutions manual The instructor solutions manual contains the instructor-facing answers to the problems and exercises within the textbook. Since many instructors use these questions in graded assignments, we ask that you not post these questions and the answers on any publicly available websites.

PowerPoint lecture slides The PowerPoint slides provide images and descriptions as a starting place for instructors to build their lectures.

Concept Trailer instructor notes These teaching notes support implementation of the OpenStax Physics Concept Trailers. The notes contain tips for usage, clarifications of coverage, and guidance on how to use the trailers in different educational situations.

Academic Integrity

Academic integrity builds trust, understanding, equity, and genuine learning. While students may encounter significant challenges in their courses and their lives, doing their own work and maintaining a high degree of authenticity will result in meaningful outcomes that will extend far beyond their college career. Faculty, administrators, resource providers, and students can work together to maintain a fair and positive experience.

We realize that students benefit when academic integrity ground rules are established early in the course. To that end, OpenStax has created an interactive to aid with academic integrity discussions in your course.

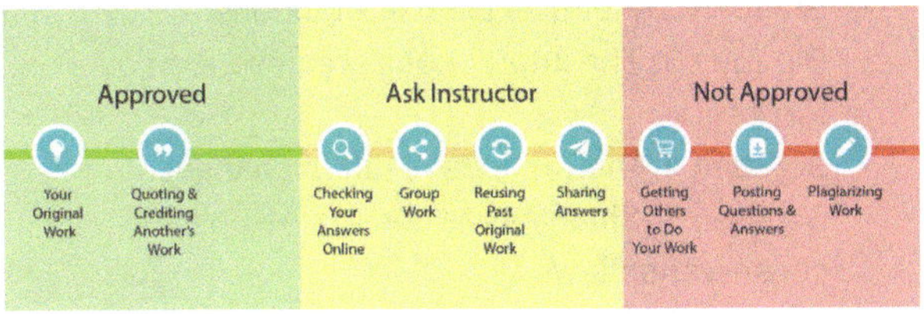

Visit our academic integrity slider (https://view.genial.ly/61e08a7af6db870d591078c1/interactive-image-defining-academic-integrity-interactive-slider). Click and drag icons along the continuum to align these practices with your institution and course policies. You may then include the graphic on your syllabus, present it in your first course meeting, or create a handout for students.

At OpenStax we are also developing resources supporting authentic learning experiences and assessment. Please visit this book's page for updates. For an in-depth review of academic integrity strategies, we highly recommend visiting the International Center of Academic Integrity (ICAI) website at https://academicintegrity.org/ (https://academicintegrity.org/).

Community Hubs

OpenStax partners with the Institute for the Study of Knowledge Management in Education (ISKME) to offer Community Hubs on OER Commons—a platform for instructors to share community-created resources that support OpenStax books, free of charge. Through our Community Hubs, instructors can upload their own materials or download resources to use in their own courses, including additional ancillaries, teaching material, multimedia, and relevant course content. We encourage instructors to join the hubs for the subjects most relevant to your teaching and research as an opportunity both to enrich your courses and to engage with other faculty. To reach the Community Hubs, visit www.oercommons.org/hubs/openstax (https://www.oercommons.org/hubs/openstax).

Technology Partners

As allies in making high-quality learning materials accessible, our technology partners offer optional low-cost tools that are integrated with OpenStax books. To access the technology options for your text, visit your book page on OpenStax.org.

To the AP® Physics student

The fundamental goal of physics is to discover and understand the "laws" that govern observed phenomena in the world around us. Why study physics? If you plan to become a physicist, the answer is obvious—introductory physics provides the foundation for your career; or if you want to become an engineer, physics provides the basis for the engineering principles used to solve applied and practical problems. For example, after the discovery of the photoelectric effect by physicists, engineers developed photocells that are used in solar panels to convert sunlight to electricity. What if you are an aspiring medical doctor? Although the applications of the laws of physics may not be obvious, their understanding is tremendously valuable. Physics is involved in medical diagnostics, such as x-rays, magnetic resonance imaging (MRI), and ultrasonic blood flow measurements. Medical therapy sometimes directly involves physics; cancer radiotherapy uses ionizing radiation. What if you are planning a nonscience career? Learning physics provides you with a well-rounded education and the ability to make important decisions, such as evaluating the pros and cons of energy production sources or voting on decisions about nuclear waste disposal.

This AP® Physics 1 course begins with **kinematics,** the study of motion without considering its causes. Motion is everywhere: from the vibration of atoms to the planetary revolutions around the Sun. Understanding motion is key to understanding other concepts in physics. You will then study **dynamics,** which considers the forces that affect the motion of moving objects and systems. Newton's laws of motion are the foundation of dynamics. These laws provide an example of the breadth and simplicity of the principles under which nature functions. One of the most remarkable simplifications in physics is that only four distinct forces account for all known phenomena. Your journey will continue as you learn about energy. Energy plays an essential role both in everyday events and in scientific phenomena. You can likely name many forms of energy, from that provided by our foods, to the energy we use to run our cars, to the sunlight that warms us on the beach. The next stop is learning about oscillatory motion and waves. All oscillations involve force and energy: you push a child in a swing to get the motion started and you put energy into a guitar string when you pluck it. Some oscillations create waves. For example, a guitar creates sound waves. You will conclude this first physics course with the study of static electricity and electric currents. Many of the characteristics of static electricity can be explored by rubbing things together. Rubbing creates the spark you get from walking across a wool carpet, for example. Similarly, lightning results from air movements under certain weather conditions.

In the AP® Physics 2 course, you will continue your journey by studying **fluid dynamics,** which explains why rising smoke curls and twists and how the body regulates blood flow. The next stop is **thermodynamics,** the study of heat transfer—energy in transit—that can be used to do work. Basic physical laws govern how heat transfers and its efficiency. Then you will learn more about electric phenomena as you delve into **electromagnetism.** An electric current produces a magnetic field; similarly, a magnetic field produces a current. This phenomenon, known as **magnetic induction,** is essential to our technological society. The generators in cars and nuclear plants use magnetism to generate a current. Other devices that use magnetism to induce currents include pickup coils in electric guitars, transformers of every size, certain microphones, airport security gates, and damping mechanisms on sensitive chemical balances. From electromagnetism you will continue your journey to **optics,** the study of light. You already know that visible light is the type of electromagnetic waves to which our eyes respond. Through vision, light can evoke deep emotions, such as when we view a magnificent sunset or glimpse a rainbow breaking through the clouds. Optics is concerned with the generation and propagation of light. The **quantum mechanics, atomic physics,** and **nuclear physics** are at the end of your journey. These areas of physics have been developed at the end of the 19th and early 20th centuries and deal with submicroscopic objects. Because these objects are smaller than we can observe directly with our senses and generally must be observed with the aid of instruments, parts of these physics areas may seem foreign and bizarre to you at first. However, we have experimentally confirmed most of the ideas in these areas of physics.

AP® Physics is a challenging course. After all, you are taking physics at the introductory college level. You will discover that some concepts are more difficult to understand than others; most students, for example, struggle to understand rotational motion and angular momentum or particle-wave duality. The AP® curriculum promotes depth of understanding over breadth of content, and to make your exploration of topics more manageable, concepts are organized around seven major themes called the **Big Ideas** that apply to all levels of physical systems and interactions between them (see web diagram below). Each Big Idea identifies **enduring understandings** (EU), **essential knowledge** (EK), and **illustrative examples** that support key concepts and content. Simple descriptions define the focus of each Big Idea.

- Big Idea 1: Objects and systems have properties.
- Big Idea 2: Fields explain interactions.
- Big Idea 3: The interactions are described by forces.
- Big Idea 4: Interactions result in changes.
- Big Idea 5: Changes are constrained by conservation laws.
- Big Idea 6: Waves can transfer energy and momentum.
- Big Idea 7: The mathematics of probability can to describe the behavior of complex and quantum mechanical systems.

Doing college work is not easy, but completion of AP® classes is a reliable predictor of college success and prepares you for subsequent courses. The more you engage in the subject, the easier your journey through the curriculum will be. Bring your enthusiasm to class every day along with your notebook, pencil, and calculator. Prepare for class the day before, and review concepts daily. Form a peer study group and ask your teacher for extra help if necessary. The AP® lab program focuses on more open-ended, student-directed, and inquiry-based lab investigations designed to make you think, ask questions, and analyze data like scientists. You will develop critical thinking and reasoning skills and apply different means of communicating information. By the time you sit for the AP® exam in May, you will be fluent in the language of physics; because you have been doing real science, you will be ready to show what you have learned. Along the way, you will find the study of the world around us to be one of the most relevant and enjoyable experiences of your high school career.

Irina Lyublinskaya, PhD
Professor of Science Education

To the AP® Physics teacher

The AP® curriculum was designed to allow instructors flexibility in their approach to teaching the physics courses. *College Physics for AP® Courses 2e* helps you orient students as they delve deeper into the world of physics. Each chapter includes a Connection for AP® Courses introduction that describes the AP® Physics Big Ideas, enduring understandings, and essential knowledge addressed in that chapter.

Each section starts with specific AP® learning objectives and includes essential concepts, illustrative examples, and science practices, along with suggestions for applying the learning objectives through take-home experiments, virtual lab investigations, and activities and questions for preparation and review. At the end of each section, students will find the Test Prep for AP® courses with multiple-choice and open-response questions addressing AP® learning objectives to help them prepare for the AP® exam.

College Physics for AP® Courses 2e has been written to engage students in their exploration of physics and help them relate what they learn in the classroom to their lives outside of it. Physics underlies much of what is happening today in other sciences and in technology. Thus, the book content includes interesting facts and ideas that go beyond the scope of the AP® course. The AP® Connection in each chapter directs students to the material they should focus on for the AP® exam, and what content—although interesting—is not part of the AP® curriculum. Physics is a beautiful and fascinating science. It is in your hands to engage and inspire your students to dive into an amazing world of physics, so they can enjoy it beyond just preparation for the AP® exam.

Irina Lyublinskaya, PhD
Professor of Science Education

CHAPTER 1
Introduction: The Nature of Science and Physics

FIGURE 1.1 Galaxies are as immense as atoms are small. Yet the same laws of physics describe both, and all the rest of nature—an indication of the underlying unity in the universe. The laws of physics are surprisingly few in number, implying an underlying simplicity to nature's apparent complexity. (credit: NASA, JPL-Caltech, P. Barmby, Harvard-Smithsonian Center for Astrophysics)

CHAPTER OUTLINE

CONNECTION FOR AP® COURSES What is your first reaction when you hear the word "physics"? Did you imagine working through difficult equations or memorizing formulas that seem to have no real use in life outside the physics classroom? Many people come to the subject of physics with a bit of fear. But as you begin your exploration of this broad-ranging subject, you may soon come to realize that physics plays a much larger role in your life than you first thought, no matter your life goals or career choice.

For example, take a look at the image above. This image is of the Andromeda Galaxy, which contains billions of individual stars, huge clouds of gas, and dust. Two smaller galaxies are also visible as bright blue spots in the background. At a staggering 2.5 million light years from Earth, this galaxy is the nearest one to our own galaxy (which is called the Milky Way). The stars and planets that make up Andromeda might seem to be the furthest thing from most people's regular, everyday lives. But Andromeda is a great starting point to think about the forces that hold together the universe. The forces that cause Andromeda to act as it does are the same forces we contend with here on Earth, whether we are planning to send a rocket into space or simply raise the walls for a new home. The same gravity that causes the stars of Andromeda to rotate and revolve also causes water to flow over hydroelectric dams here on Earth. Tonight, take a moment to look up at the stars. The forces out there are the same as the ones here on Earth. Through a study of physics, you may gain a greater understanding of the interconnectedness of everything we can see and know in this universe.

Think now about all of the technological devices that you use on a regular basis. Computers, smart phones, GPS systems, MP3 players, and satellite radio might come to mind. Next, think about the most exciting modern technologies that you have heard about in the news, such as trains that levitate above tracks, "invisibility cloaks" that bend light around them, and microscopic robots that fight cancer cells in our bodies. All of these groundbreaking advancements, commonplace or unbelievable, rely on the principles of physics. Aside from playing a significant role in technology, professionals such as engineers, pilots, physicians, physical therapists, electricians, and computer programmers apply physics concepts in their daily work. For example, a pilot must understand how wind forces affect a flight path and a physical therapist must understand how the muscles in the body experience forces as they move and bend. As you will learn in this text, physics principles are propelling new, exciting technologies, and these principles are applied in a wide range of careers.

In this text, you will begin to explore the history of the formal study of physics, beginning with natural philosophy and the ancient Greeks, and leading up through a review of Sir Isaac Newton and the laws of physics that bear his name. You will also be introduced to the standards scientists use when they study physical quantities and the interrelated system of measurements most of the scientific community uses to communicate in a single mathematical language. Finally, you will study the limits of our ability to be accurate and precise, and the reasons scientists go to painstaking lengths to be as clear as possible regarding their own limitations.

Chapter 1 introduces many fundamental skills and understandings needed for success with the AP® Learning Objectives. While this chapter does not directly address any Big Ideas, its content will allow for a more meaningful understanding when these Big Ideas are addressed in future chapters. For instance, the discussion of models, theories, and laws will assist you in understanding the concept of fields as addressed in Big Idea 2, and the section titled 'The Evolution of Natural Philosophy into Modern Physics' will help prepare you for the statistical topics addressed in Big Idea 7.

This chapter will also prepare you to understand the Science Practices. In explicitly addressing the role of models in representing and communicating scientific phenomena, Section 1.1 supports Science Practice 1. Additionally, anecdotes about historical investigations and the inset on the scientific method will help you to engage in the scientific questioning referenced in Science Practice 3. The appropriate use of mathematics, as called for in Science Practice 2, is a major focus throughout sections 1.2, 1.3, and 1.4.

1.1 Physics: An Introduction

LEARNING OBJECTIVES

By the end of this section, you will be able to:

- Explain the difference between a principle and a law.
- Explain the difference between a model and a theory.

FIGURE 1.2 The flight formations of migratory birds such as Canada geese are governed by the laws of physics. (credit: David Merrett)

The physical universe is enormously complex in its detail. Every day, each of us observes a great variety of objects and phenomena. Over the centuries, the curiosity of the human race has led us collectively to explore and catalog a tremendous wealth of information. From the flight of birds to the colors of flowers, from lightning to gravity, from quarks to clusters of galaxies, from the flow of time to the mystery of the creation of the universe, we have asked questions and assembled huge arrays of facts. In the face of all these details, we have discovered that a surprisingly small and unified set of physical laws can explain what we observe. As humans, we make generalizations and seek order. We have found that nature is remarkably cooperative—it exhibits the *underlying order and simplicity* we so value.

It is the underlying order of nature that makes science in general, and physics in particular, so enjoyable to study. For example, what do a bag of chips and a car battery have in common? Both contain energy that can be converted to other forms. The law of conservation of energy (which says that energy can change form but is never lost) ties together such topics as food calories, batteries, heat, light, and watch springs. Understanding this law makes it easier to learn about the various forms energy takes and how they relate to one another. Apparently unrelated topics are connected through broadly applicable physical laws, permitting an understanding beyond just the memorization of lists of facts.

The unifying aspect of physical laws and the basic simplicity of nature form the underlying themes of this text. In learning to apply these laws, you will, of course, study the most important topics in physics. More importantly, you will gain analytical abilities that will enable you to apply these laws far beyond the scope of what can be included in a single book. These analytical skills will help you to excel academically, and they will also help you to think critically in any professional career you choose to pursue. This module discusses the realm of physics (to define what physics is), some applications of physics (to illustrate its relevance to other disciplines), and more precisely what constitutes a physical law (to illuminate the importance of experimentation to theory).

Science and the Realm of Physics

Science consists of the theories and laws that are the general truths of nature as well as the body of knowledge they encompass. Scientists are continually trying to expand this body of knowledge and to perfect the expression of the laws that describe it. **Physics** is concerned with describing the interactions of energy, matter, space, and time, and it is especially interested in what fundamental mechanisms underlie every phenomenon. The concern for describing the basic phenomena in nature essentially defines the *realm of physics*.

Physics aims to describe the function of everything around us, from the movement of tiny charged particles to the motion of people, cars, and spaceships. In fact, almost everything around you can be described quite accurately by the laws of physics. Consider a smart phone (Figure 1.3). Physics describes how electricity interacts with the various circuits inside the device. This knowledge helps engineers select the appropriate materials and circuit layout when building the smart phone. Next, consider a GPS system. Physics describes the relationship between the speed of an object, the distance over which it travels, and the time it takes to travel that distance. GPS relies on precise calculations that account for variations in the Earth's landscapes, the exact distance between orbiting satellites, and even the effect of a complex occurrence of time dilation. Most of these calculations are founded on algorithms developed by Gladys West, a mathematician and computer scientist who programmed the first computers capable of highly accurate remote sensing and positioning. When you use a GPS device, it utilizes these algorithms to recognize where you are and how your position relates to other objects on Earth.

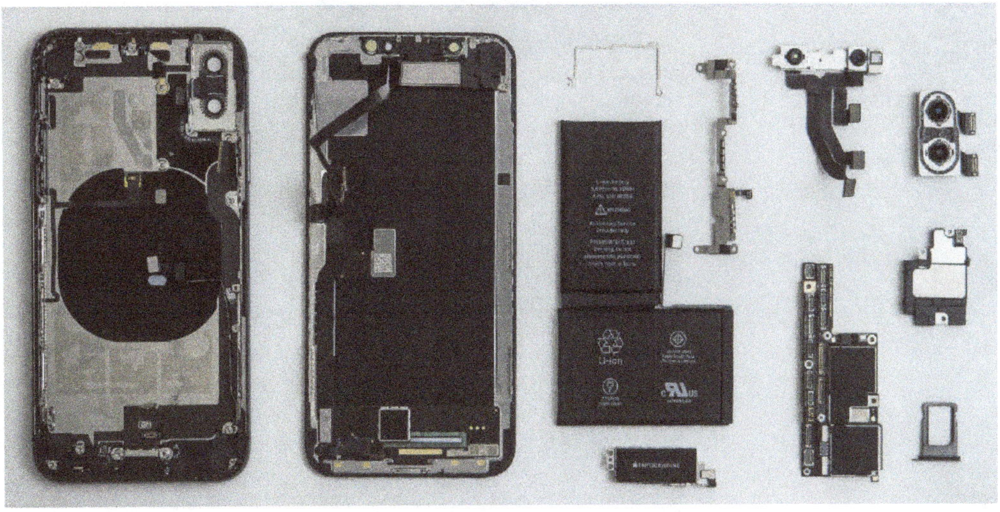

FIGURE 1.3 The Apple iPhone is a common smart phone with a GPS function, sophisticated camera, haptic (vibration) capabilities, and many other functions. Physics describes the way that electricity flows through the circuits of this device. Engineers use their knowledge of physics to construct an iPhone with features that consumers will enjoy. One specific feature of an iPhone is the GPS function. GPS uses physics equations to determine the driving time between two locations on a map. (credit: Tinh tế Photo/Flickr)

Applications of Physics

You need not be a scientist to use physics. On the contrary, knowledge of physics is useful in everyday situations as well as in nonscientific professions. It can help you understand how microwave ovens work, why metals should not be put into them, and why they might affect pacemakers. (See Figure 1.4 and Figure 1.5.) Physics allows you to understand the hazards of radiation and rationally evaluate these hazards more easily. Physics also explains the reason why a black car radiator helps remove heat in a car engine, and it explains why a white roof helps keep the inside of a house cool. Similarly, the operation of a car's ignition system as well as the transmission of electrical signals through our body's nervous system are much easier to understand when you think about them in terms of basic physics.

Physics is the foundation of many important disciplines and contributes directly to others. Chemistry, for example—since it deals with the interactions of atoms and molecules—is rooted in atomic and molecular physics. Most branches of engineering are applied physics. In architecture, physics is at the heart of structural stability, and is involved in the acoustics, heating, lighting, and cooling of buildings. Parts of geology rely heavily on physics, such as radioactive dating of rocks, earthquake analysis, and heat transfer in the Earth. Some disciplines, such as biophysics and geophysics, are hybrids of physics and other disciplines.

Physics has many applications in the biological sciences. On the microscopic level, it helps describe the properties of cell walls and cell membranes (Figure 1.6 and Figure 1.7). On the macroscopic level, it can explain the heat, work, and power associated with the human body. Physics is involved in medical diagnostics, such as x-rays, magnetic resonance imaging (MRI), and ultrasonic blood flow measurements. Medical therapy sometimes directly involves physics; for example, cancer radiotherapy uses ionizing radiation. Physics can also explain sensory phenomena, such as how musical instruments make sound, how the eye detects color, and how lasers can transmit information.

It is not necessary to formally study all applications of physics. What is most useful is knowledge of the basic laws of physics and a skill in the analytical methods for applying them. The study of physics also can improve your problem-solving skills. Furthermore, physics has retained the most basic aspects of science, so it is used by all of the sciences, and the study of physics makes other sciences easier to understand.

FIGURE 1.4 The laws of physics help us understand how common appliances work. For example, the laws of physics can help explain how microwave ovens heat up food, and they also help us understand why it is dangerous to place metal objects in a microwave oven. (credit: MoneyBlogNewz)

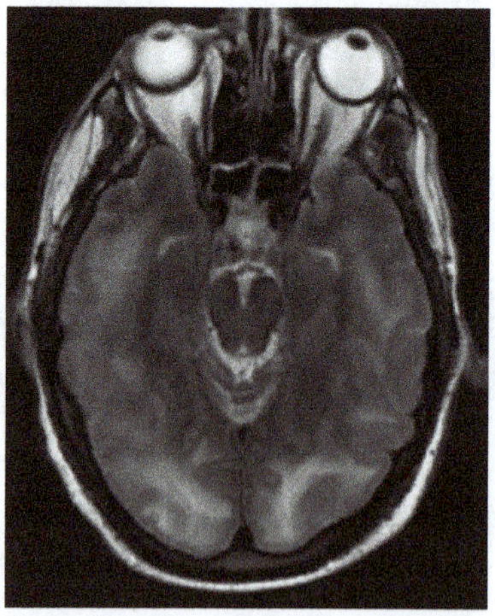

FIGURE 1.5 These two applications of physics have more in common than meets the eye. Microwave ovens use electromagnetic waves to heat food. Magnetic resonance imaging (MRI) also uses electromagnetic waves to yield an image of the brain, from which the exact location of tumors can be determined. (credit: Rashmi Chawla, Daniel Smith, and Paul E. Marik)

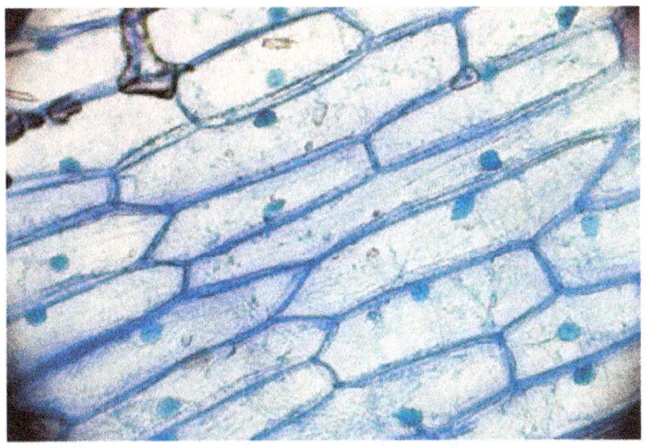

FIGURE 1.6 Physics, chemistry, and biology help describe the properties of cell walls in plant cells, such as the onion cells seen here. (credit: Umberto Salvagnin)

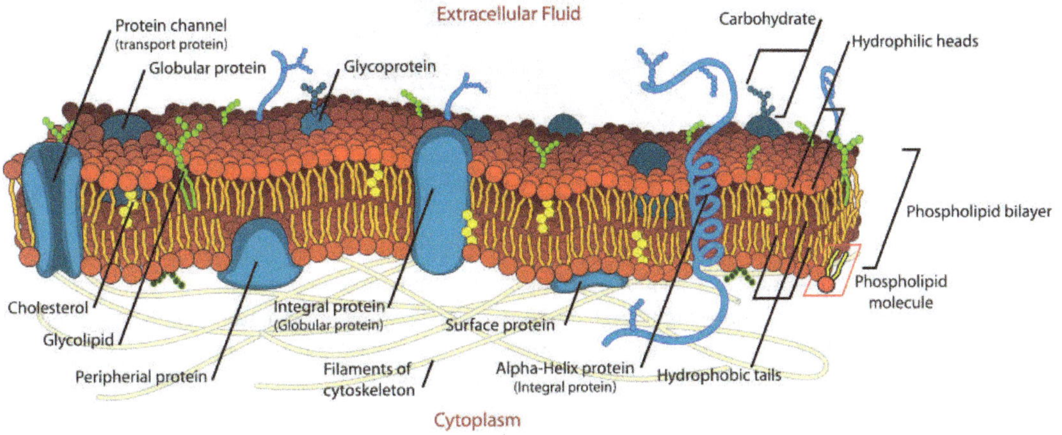

FIGURE 1.7 An artist's rendition of the structure of a cell membrane. Membranes form the boundaries of animal cells and are complex in structure and function. Many of the most fundamental properties of life, such as the firing of nerve cells, are related to membranes. The disciplines of biology, chemistry, and physics all help us understand the membranes of animal cells. (credit: Mariana Ruiz)

Models, Theories, and Laws; The Role of Experimentation

The laws of nature are concise descriptions of the universe around us; they are human statements of the underlying laws or rules that all natural processes follow. Such laws are intrinsic to the universe; humans did not create them and so cannot change them. We can only discover and understand them. Their discovery is a very human endeavor, with all the elements of mystery, imagination, struggle, triumph, and disappointment inherent in any creative effort. (See Figure 1.8 and Figure 1.9.) The cornerstone of discovering natural laws is observation; science must describe the universe as it is, not as we may imagine it to be.

FIGURE 1.8 **Isaac Newton** (1642–1727) was very reluctant to publish his revolutionary work and had to be convinced to do so. In his later years, he stepped down from his academic post and became exchequer of the Royal Mint. He took this post seriously, inventing reeding (or

creating ridges) on the edge of coins to prevent unscrupulous people from trimming the silver off of them before using them as currency. (credit: Arthur Shuster and Arthur E. Shipley: *Britain's Heritage of Science*. London, 1917.)

FIGURE 1.9 **Marie Curie** (1867–1934) sacrificed monetary assets to help finance her early research and damaged her physical well-being with radiation exposure. She is the only person to win Nobel prizes in both physics and chemistry. One of her daughters also won a Nobel Prize. (credit: Wikimedia Commons)

We all are curious to some extent. We look around, make generalizations, and try to understand what we see—for example, we look up and wonder whether one type of cloud signals an oncoming storm. As we become serious about exploring nature, we become more organized and formal in collecting and analyzing data. We attempt greater precision, perform controlled experiments (if we can), and write down ideas about how the data may be organized and unified. We then formulate models, theories, and laws based on the data we have collected and analyzed to generalize and communicate the results of these experiments.

A **model** is a representation of something that is often too difficult (or impossible) to display directly. While a model is justified with experimental proof, it is only accurate under limited situations. An example is the planetary model of the atom in which electrons are pictured as orbiting the nucleus, analogous to the way planets orbit the Sun. (See Figure 1.10.) We cannot observe electron orbits directly, but the mental image helps explain the observations we can make, such as the emission of light from hot gases (atomic spectra). Physicists use models for a variety of purposes. For example, models can help physicists analyze a scenario and perform a calculation, or they can be used to represent a situation in the form of a computer simulation. A **theory** is an explanation for patterns in nature that is supported by scientific evidence and verified multiple times by various groups of researchers. Some theories include models to help visualize phenomena, whereas others do not. Newton's theory of gravity, for example, does not require a model or mental image, because we can observe the objects directly with our own senses. The kinetic theory of gases, on the other hand, is a model in which a gas is viewed as being composed of atoms and molecules. Atoms and molecules are too small to be observed directly with our senses—thus, we picture them mentally to understand what our instruments tell us about the behavior of gases.

A **law** uses concise language to describe a generalized pattern in nature that is supported by scientific evidence and repeated experiments. Often, a law can be expressed in the form of a single mathematical equation. Laws and theories are similar in that they are both scientific statements that result from a tested hypothesis and are supported by scientific evidence. However, the designation *law* is reserved for a concise and very general statement that describes phenomena in nature, such as the law that energy is conserved during any process, or Newton's second law of motion, which relates force, mass, and acceleration by the simple equation $\mathbf{F} = m\mathbf{a}$. A theory, in contrast, is a less concise statement of observed phenomena. For example, the Theory of Evolution and the Theory of Relativity cannot be expressed concisely enough to be considered a law. The biggest difference between a law and a theory is that a theory is much more complex and dynamic. A law describes a single action, whereas a theory explains an entire group of related phenomena. And, whereas a law is a postulate that forms the foundation of the scientific method, a theory is the end result of that process.

Less broadly applicable statements are usually called principles (such as Pascal's principle, which is applicable only in fluids), but the distinction between laws and principles often is not carefully made.

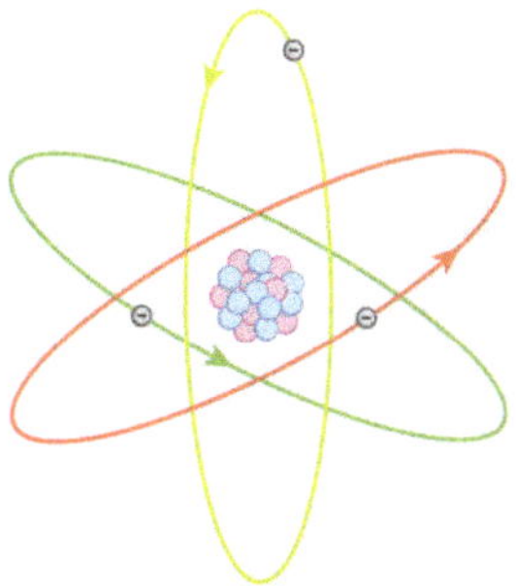

FIGURE 1.10 What is a model? This planetary model of the atom shows electrons orbiting the nucleus. It is a drawing that we use to form a mental image of the atom that we cannot see directly with our eyes because it is too small.

MODELS, THEORIES, AND LAWS

Models, theories, and laws are used to help scientists analyze the data they have already collected. However, often after a model, theory, or law has been developed, it points scientists toward new discoveries they would not otherwise have made.

The models, theories, and laws we devise sometimes *imply the existence of objects or phenomena as yet unobserved.* These predictions are remarkable triumphs and tributes to the power of science. It is the underlying order in the universe that enables scientists to make such spectacular predictions. However, if *experiment* does not verify our predictions, then the theory or law is wrong, no matter how elegant or convenient it is. Laws can never be known with absolute certainty because it is impossible to perform every imaginable experiment in order to confirm a law in every possible scenario. Physicists operate under the assumption that all scientific laws and theories are valid until a counterexample is observed. If a good-quality, verifiable experiment contradicts a well-established law, then the law must be modified or overthrown completely.

The study of science in general and physics in particular is an adventure much like the exploration of uncharted ocean. Discoveries are made; models, theories, and laws are formulated; and the beauty of the physical universe is made more sublime for the insights gained.

THE SCIENTIFIC METHOD

Ibn al-Haytham (sometimes referred to as Alhazen), a 10th-11th century scientist working in Cairo, significantly advanced the understanding of optics and vision. But his contributions go much further. In demonstrating that previous approaches were incorrect, he emphasized that scientists must be ready to reject existing knowledge and become "the enemy" of everything they read; he expressed that scientists must trust only objective evidence. Al-Haytham emphasized repeated experimentation and validation, and acknowledged that senses and predisposition could lead to poor conclusions. His work was a precursor to the scientific method that we use today.

As scientists inquire and gather information about the world, they follow a process called the **scientific method**. This process typically begins with an observation and question that the scientist will research. Next, the scientist typically performs some research about the topic and then devises a hypothesis. Then, the scientist will test the hypothesis by performing an experiment. Finally, the scientist analyzes the results of the experiment and draws a conclusion. Note that the scientific method can be applied to many situations that are not limited to science, and this method can be modified to suit the situation.

Consider an example. Let us say that you try to turn on your car, but it will not start. You undoubtedly wonder: Why will the car not start? You can follow a scientific method to answer this question. First off, you may perform some research to determine a variety of reasons why the car will not start. Next, you will state a hypothesis. For example, you may believe that the car is not starting because it has no engine oil. To test this, you open the hood of the car and examine the oil level. You observe that the oil is at an acceptable level, and you thus conclude that the oil level is not contributing to your car issue. To troubleshoot the issue further, you may devise a new hypothesis to test and then repeat the process again.

The Evolution of Natural Philosophy into Modern Physics

Physics was not always a separate and distinct discipline. It remains connected to other sciences to this day. The word *physics* comes from Greek, meaning nature. The study of nature came to be called "natural philosophy." From ancient times through the Renaissance, natural philosophy encompassed many fields, including astronomy, biology, chemistry, physics, mathematics, and medicine. Over the last few centuries, the growth of knowledge has resulted in ever-increasing specialization and branching of natural philosophy into separate fields, with physics retaining the most basic facets. (See Figure 1.11, Figure 1.12, and Figure 1.13.) Physics as it developed from the Renaissance to the end of the 19th century is called **classical physics**. It was transformed into modern physics by revolutionary discoveries made starting at the beginning of the 20th century.

FIGURE 1.11 Over the centuries, natural philosophy has evolved into more specialized disciplines, as illustrated by the contributions of some of the greatest minds in history. The Greek philosopher **Aristotle** (384–322 B.C.) wrote on a broad range of topics including physics, animals, the soul, politics, and poetry. (credit: Jastrow (2006)/Ludovisi Collection)

FIGURE 1.12 Ibn al-Haytham (965–1040) and Galileo Galilei (1564–1642) were so critical to the advancement of scientific practice and to the fields of mathematics, optics, physics, and astronomy that a later prominent scientist featured them on the cover of his major work. (credit: Johannes Hevelius (author), Adolph Boÿ (artist), J. Falck (engraver); Houghton Library, Harvard University/Wikimedia Commons)

FIGURE 1.13 **Niels Bohr** (1885–1962) made fundamental contributions to the development of quantum mechanics, one part of modern physics. (credit: United States Library of Congress Prints and Photographs Division)

Classical physics is not an exact description of the universe, but it is an excellent approximation under the following conditions: Matter must be moving at speeds less than about 1% of the speed of light, the objects dealt with must be large enough to be seen with a microscope, and only weak gravitational fields, such as the field generated by the Earth, can be involved. Because humans live under such circumstances, classical physics seems intuitively reasonable, while many aspects of modern physics seem bizarre. This is why models are so useful in modern physics—they let us conceptualize phenomena we do not ordinarily experience. We can relate to models in human terms and visualize what happens when objects move at high speeds or imagine what objects too small to observe with our senses might be like. For example, we can understand an atom's properties because we can picture it in our minds, although we have never seen an atom with our eyes. New tools, of course, allow us to better picture phenomena we cannot see. In fact, new instrumentation has allowed us in recent years to actually "picture" the atom.

LIMITS ON THE LAWS OF CLASSICAL PHYSICS

For the laws of classical physics to apply, the following criteria must be met: Matter must be moving at speeds less than about 1% of the speed of light, the objects dealt with must be large enough to be seen with a microscope, and only weak gravitational fields (such as the field generated by the Earth) can be involved.

FIGURE 1.14 Using a scanning tunneling microscope (STM), scientists can see the individual atoms that compose this sheet of gold. (credit: Erwinrossen)

Some of the most spectacular advances in science have been made in modern physics. Many of the laws of classical physics have been modified or rejected, and revolutionary changes in technology, society, and our view of the universe have resulted. Like science fiction, modern physics is filled with fascinating objects beyond our normal experiences, but it has the advantage over science fiction of being very real. Why, then, is the majority of this text devoted to topics of classical physics? There are two main reasons: Classical physics gives an extremely accurate description of the universe under a wide range of everyday circumstances, and knowledge of classical physics is necessary to understand modern physics.

Modern physics itself consists of the two revolutionary theories, relativity and quantum mechanics. These theories deal with the very fast and the very small, respectively. **Relativity** must be used whenever an object is traveling at greater than about 1% of the speed of light or experiences a strong gravitational field such as that near the Sun. **Quantum mechanics** must be used for objects smaller than can be seen with a microscope. The combination of these two theories is *relativistic quantum mechanics,* and it describes the behavior of small objects traveling at high speeds or experiencing a strong gravitational field. Relativistic quantum mechanics is the best universally applicable theory we have. Because of its mathematical complexity, it is used only when necessary, and the other theories are used whenever they will produce sufficiently accurate results. We will find, however, that we can do a great deal of modern physics with the algebra and trigonometry used in this text.

CHECK YOUR UNDERSTANDING

A friend tells you they have learned about a new law of nature. What can you know about the information even before your friend describes the law? How would the information be different if your friend told you they had learned about a scientific theory rather than a law?

Solution

Without knowing the details of the law, you can still infer that the information your friend has learned conforms to the requirements of all laws of nature: it will be a concise description of the universe around us; a statement of the underlying rules that all natural processes follow. If the information had been a theory, you would be able to infer that the information will be a large-scale, broadly applicable generalization.

PHET EXPLORATIONS

Equation Grapher

Learn about graphing polynomials. The shape of the curve changes as the constants are adjusted. View the curves for the individual terms (e.g. $y = bx$) to see how they add to generate the polynomial curve.

Click to view content (https://openstax.org/books/college-physics-ap-courses-2e/pages/1-1-physics-an-introduction)

1.2 Physical Quantities and Units

LEARNING OBJECTIVES

By the end of this section, you will be able to:

- Perform unit conversions both in the SI and English units.
- Explain the most common prefixes in the SI units and be able to write them in scientific notation.

FIGURE 1.15 The distance from Earth to the Moon may seem immense, but it is just a tiny fraction of the distances from Earth to other celestial bodies. (credit: NASA)

The range of objects and phenomena studied in physics is immense. From the incredibly short lifetime of a nucleus to the age of the Earth, from the tiny sizes of sub-nuclear particles to the vast distance to the edges of the known universe, from the force exerted by a jumping flea to the force between Earth and the Sun, there are enough factors of 10 to challenge the imagination of even the most experienced scientist. Giving numerical values for physical quantities and equations for physical principles allows us to understand nature much more deeply than does qualitative description alone. To comprehend these vast ranges, we must also have accepted units in which to express them. And we shall find that (even in the potentially mundane discussion of meters, kilograms, and seconds) a profound simplicity of nature appears—most physical quantities can be expressed as combinations of only four fundamental physical quantities: length, mass, time, and electric current.

We define a **physical quantity** either by *specifying how it is measured* or by *stating how it is calculated* from other measurements. For example, we define distance and time by specifying methods for measuring them, whereas we define *average speed* by stating that it is calculated as distance traveled divided by time of travel.

Measurements of physical quantities are expressed in terms of **units**, which are standardized values. For example, the length of a race, which is a physical quantity, can be expressed in units of meters (for sprinters) or kilometers (for distance runners). Without standardized units, it would be extremely difficult for scientists to express and compare measured values in a meaningful way. (See Figure 1.16.)

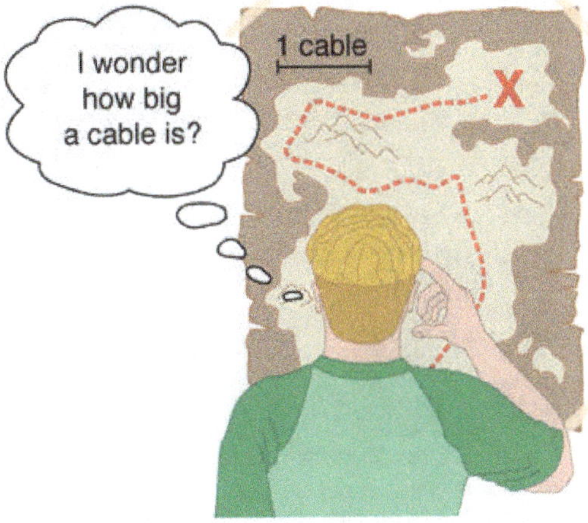

FIGURE 1.16 Distances given in unknown units are maddeningly useless.

There are two major systems of units used in the world: **SI units** (also known as the metric system) and **English units** (also known as the customary or imperial system). **English units** were historically used in nations once ruled by the British Empire and are still widely used in the United States. Virtually every other country in the world now uses SI units as the standard; the metric system is also the standard system agreed upon by scientists and mathematicians. The acronym "SI" is derived from the French *Système International.*

SI Units: Fundamental and Derived Units

Table 1.1 gives the fundamental SI units that are used throughout this textbook. This text uses non-SI units in a few applications where they are in very common use, such as the measurement of blood pressure in millimeters of mercury (mm Hg). Whenever non-SI units are discussed, they will be tied to SI units through conversions.

Length	Mass	Time	Electric Current
meter (m)	kilogram (kg)	second (s)	ampere (A)

TABLE 1.1 Fundamental SI Units

It is an intriguing fact that some physical quantities are more fundamental than others and that the most fundamental physical quantities can be defined *only* in terms of the procedure used to measure them. The units in which they are measured are thus called **fundamental units**. In this textbook, the fundamental physical quantities are taken to be length, mass, time, and electric current. (Note that electric current will not be introduced until much later in this text.) All other physical quantities, such as force and electric charge, can be expressed as algebraic combinations of length, mass, time, and current (for example, speed is length divided by time); these units are called **derived units**.

Units of Time, Length, and Mass: The Second, Meter, and Kilogram

The Second

The SI unit for time, the **second** (abbreviated s), has a long history. For many years it was defined as 1/86,400 of a mean solar day. More recently, a new standard was adopted to gain greater accuracy and to define the second in terms of a non-varying, or constant, physical phenomenon (because the solar day is getting longer due to very gradual slowing of the Earth's rotation). Cesium atoms can be made to vibrate in a very steady way, and these vibrations can be readily observed and counted. In 1967 the second was redefined as the time required for 9,192,631,770 of these vibrations. (See Figure 1.17.) Accuracy in the fundamental units is essential, because all measurements are ultimately expressed in terms of fundamental units and can be no more accurate than are the fundamental units themselves.

FIGURE 1.17 An atomic clock such as this one uses the vibrations of cesium atoms to keep time to a precision of better than a microsecond per year. The fundamental unit of time, the second, is based on such clocks. This image is looking down from the top of an atomic fountain nearly 30 feet tall! (credit: Steve Jurvetson/Flickr)

The Meter

The SI unit for length is the **meter** (abbreviated m); its definition has also changed over time to become more accurate and precise. The meter was first defined in 1791 as 1/10,000,000 of the distance from the equator to the North Pole. This measurement was improved in 1889 by redefining the meter to be the distance between two engraved lines on a platinum-iridium bar now kept near Paris. By 1960, it had become possible to define the meter even more accurately in terms of the wavelength of light, so it was again redefined as 1,650,763.73 wavelengths of orange light emitted by krypton atoms. In 1983, the meter was given its present definition (partly for greater accuracy) as the distance light travels in a vacuum in 1/299,792,458 of a second. (See Figure 1.18.) This change defines the speed of light to be exactly 299,792,458 meters per second. The length of the meter will change if the speed of light is someday measured with greater accuracy.

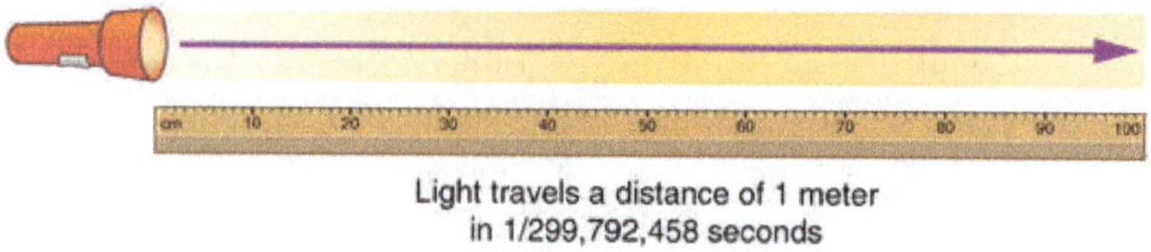

FIGURE 1.18 The meter is defined to be the distance light travels in 1/299,792,458 of a second in a vacuum. Distance traveled is speed multiplied by time.

The Kilogram

The SI unit for mass is the **kilogram** (abbreviated kg); it was previously defined to be the mass of a platinum-iridium cylinder kept with the old meter standard at the International Bureau of Weights and Measures near Paris. Exact replicas of the previously defined kilogram are also kept at the United States' National Institute of Standards and Technology, or NIST, located in Gaithersburg, Maryland outside of Washington D.C., and at other locations around the world. The determination of all other masses could be ultimately traced to a comparison with the standard mass. Even though the platinum-iridium cylinder was resistant to corrosion, airborne contaminants were able to adhere to its surface, slightly changing its mass over time. In May 2019, the scientific community adopted a more stable definition of the kilogram. The kilogram is now defined in terms of the second, the meter, and Planck's constant, *h* (a quantum mechanical value that relates a photon's energy to its frequency).

Electric current and its accompanying unit, the ampere, will be introduced in Electric Current, Resistance, and Ohm's Law when electricity and magnetism are covered. The initial modules in this textbook are concerned with mechanics, fluids, heat, and waves. In these subjects all pertinent physical quantities can be expressed in terms of the fundamental units of length, mass, and time.

Metric Prefixes

SI units are part of the **metric system**. The metric system is convenient for scientific and engineering calculations because the units are categorized by factors of 10. Table 1.2 gives metric prefixes and symbols used to denote various factors of 10.

Metric systems have the advantage that conversions of units involve only powers of 10. There are 100 centimeters in a meter, 1000 meters in a kilometer, and so on. In nonmetric systems, such as the system of U.S. customary units, the relationships are not as simple—there are 12 inches in a foot, 5280 feet in a mile, and so on. Another advantage of the metric system is that the same unit can be used over extremely large ranges of values simply by using an appropriate metric prefix. For example, distances in meters are suitable in construction, while distances in kilometers are appropriate for air travel, and the tiny measure of nanometers are convenient in optical design. With the metric system there is no need to invent new units for particular applications.

The term **order of magnitude** refers to the scale of a value expressed in the metric system. Each power of 10, and so forth are all different orders of magnitude. All quantities that can be expressed as a product of a specific power of 10 are said to be of the *same* order of magnitude. For example, the number 800 can be written as 8×10^2, and the number 450 can be written as 4.5×10^2. Thus, the numbers 800 and 450 are of the same order of magnitude: 10^2. Order of magnitude can be thought of as a ballpark estimate for the scale of a value. The diameter of an atom is on the order of 10^{-10} m, while the diameter of the Sun is on the order of 10^9 m.

THE QUEST FOR MICROSCOPIC STANDARDS FOR BASIC UNITS

The fundamental units described in this chapter are those that produce the greatest accuracy and precision in measurement. There is a sense among physicists that, because there is an underlying microscopic substructure to matter, it would be most satisfying to base our standards of measurement on microscopic objects and fundamental physical phenomena such as the speed of light. A microscopic standard has been accomplished for the standard of time, which is based on the oscillations of the cesium atom.

The standard for length was once based on the wavelength of light (a small-scale length) emitted by a certain type of atom, but it has been supplanted by the more precise measurement of the speed of light. If it becomes possible to measure the mass of atoms or a particular arrangement of atoms such as a silicon sphere to greater precision than the kilogram standard, it may become possible to base mass measurements on the small scale. There are also possibilities that electrical phenomena on the small scale may someday allow us to base a unit of charge on the charge of electrons and protons, but at present current and charge are related to large-scale currents and forces between wires.

Prefix	Symbol	Value	Example (some are approximate)			
exa	E	10^{18}	exameter	Em	10^{18} m	distance light travels in a century
peta	P	10^{15}	petasecond	Ps	10^{15} s	30 million years
tera	T	10^{12}	terawatt	TW	10^{12} W	powerful laser output

TABLE 1.2 Metric Prefixes for Powers of 10 and their Symbols

Prefix	Symbol	Value	Example (some are approximate)			
giga	G	10^9	gigahertz	GHz	10^9 Hz	a microwave frequency
mega	M	10^6	megacurie	MCi	10^6 Ci	high radioactivity
kilo	k	10^3	kilometer	km	10^3 m	about 6/10 mile
hecto	h	10^2	hectoliter	hL	10^2 L	26 gallons
deka	da	10^1	dekagram	dag	10^1 g	teaspoon of butter
–	–	10^0 (=1)				
deci	d	10^{-1}	deciliter	dL	10^{-1} L	less than half a soda
centi	c	10^{-2}	centimeter	cm	10^{-2} m	fingertip thickness
milli	m	10^{-3}	millimeter	mm	10^{-3} m	flea at its shoulders
micro	μ	10^{-6}	micrometer	μm	10^{-6} m	detail in microscope
nano	n	10^{-9}	nanogram	ng	10^{-9} g	small speck of dust
pico	p	10^{-12}	picofarad	pF	10^{-12} F	small capacitor in radio
femto	f	10^{-15}	femtometer	fm	10^{-15} m	size of a proton
atto	a	10^{-18}	attosecond	as	10^{-18} s	time light crosses an atom

TABLE 1.2 Metric Prefixes for Powers of 10 and their Symbols

Known Ranges of Length, Mass, and Time

The vastness of the universe and the breadth over which physics applies are illustrated by the wide range of examples of known lengths, masses, and times in Table 1.3. Examination of this table will give you some feeling for the range of possible topics and numerical values. (See Figure 1.19 and Figure 1.20.)

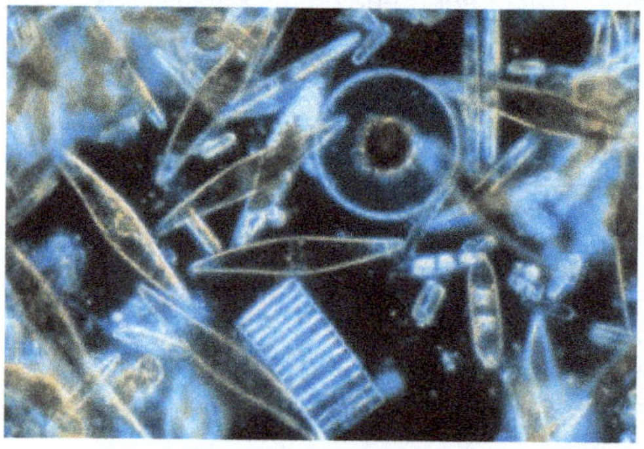

FIGURE 1.19 Tiny phytoplankton swims among crystals of ice in the Antarctic Sea. They range from a few micrometers to as much as 2 millimeters in length. (credit: Prof. Gordon T. Taylor, Stony Brook University; NOAA Corps Collections)

FIGURE 1.20 Galaxies collide 2.4 billion light years away from Earth. The tremendous range of observable phenomena in nature challenges the imagination. (credit: NASA/CXC/UVic./A. Mahdavi et al. Optical/lensing: CFHT/UVic./H. Hoekstra et al.)

Unit Conversion and Dimensional Analysis

It is often necessary to convert from one type of unit to another. For example, if you are reading a European cookbook, some quantities may be expressed in units of liters and you need to convert them to cups. Or, perhaps you are reading walking directions from one location to another and you are interested in how many miles you will be walking. In this case, you will need to convert units of feet to miles.

Let us consider a simple example of how to convert units. Let us say that we want to convert 80 meters (m) to kilometers (km).

The first thing to do is to list the units that you have and the units that you want to convert to. In this case, we have units in *meters* and we want to convert to *kilometers*.

Next, we need to determine a **conversion factor** relating meters to kilometers. A conversion factor is a ratio expressing how many of one unit are equal to another unit. For example, there are 12 inches in 1 foot, 100 centimeters in 1 meter, 60 seconds in 1 minute, and so on. In this case, we know that there are 1,000 meters in 1 kilometer.

Now we can set up our unit conversion. We will write the units that we have and then multiply them by the conversion factor so that the units cancel out, as shown:

$$80\,\cancel{\text{m}} \times \frac{1\text{ km}}{1000\,\cancel{\text{m}}} = 0.080\text{ km}. \qquad (1.1)$$

Note that the unwanted m unit cancels, leaving only the desired km unit. You can use this method to convert between any types of unit.

Click Appendix C for a more complete list of conversion factors.

Lengths in meters		Masses in kilograms (more precise values in parentheses)		Times in seconds (more precise values in parentheses)	
10^{-18}	Present experimental limit to smallest observable detail	10^{-30}	Mass of an electron $(9.11 \times 10^{-31}\text{ kg})$	10^{-23}	Time for light to cross a proton
10^{-15}	Diameter of a proton	10^{-27}	Mass of a hydrogen atom $(1.67 \times 10^{-27}\text{ kg})$	10^{-22}	Mean life of an extremely unstable nucleus

TABLE 1.3 Approximate Values of Length, Mass, and Time

Lengths in meters		Masses in kilograms (more precise values in parentheses)		Times in seconds (more precise values in parentheses)	
10^{-14}	Diameter of a uranium nucleus	10^{-15}	Mass of a bacterium	10^{-15}	Time for one oscillation of visible light
10^{-10}	Diameter of a hydrogen atom	10^{-5}	Mass of a mosquito	10^{-13}	Time for one vibration of an atom in a solid
10^{-8}	Thickness of membranes in cells of living organisms	10^{-2}	Mass of a hummingbird	10^{-8}	Time for one oscillation of an FM radio wave
10^{-6}	Wavelength of visible light	1	Mass of a liter of water (about a quart)	10^{-3}	Duration of a nerve impulse
10^{-3}	Size of a grain of sand	10^{2}	Mass of a person	1	Time for one heartbeat
1	Height of a 4-year-old child	10^{3}	Mass of a car	10^{5}	One day $(8.64 \times 10^4\ \text{s})$
10^{2}	Length of a football field	10^{8}	Mass of a large ship	10^{7}	One year (y) $(3.16 \times 10^7\ \text{s})$
10^{4}	Greatest ocean depth	10^{12}	Mass of a large iceberg	10^{9}	About half the life expectancy of a human
10^{7}	Diameter of the Earth	10^{15}	Mass of the nucleus of a comet	10^{11}	Recorded history
10^{11}	Distance from the Earth to the Sun	10^{23}	Mass of the Moon $(7.35 \times 10^{22}\ \text{kg})$	10^{17}	Age of the Earth
10^{16}	Distance traveled by light in 1 year (a light year)	10^{25}	Mass of the Earth $(5.97 \times 10^{24}\ \text{kg})$	10^{18}	Age of the universe
10^{21}	Diameter of the Milky Way galaxy	10^{30}	Mass of the Sun $(1.99 \times 10^{30}\ \text{kg})$		
10^{22}	Distance from the Earth to the nearest large galaxy (Andromeda)	10^{42}	Mass of the Milky Way galaxy (current upper limit)		
10^{26}	Distance from the Earth to the edges of the known universe	10^{53}	Mass of the known universe (current upper limit)		

TABLE 1.3 Approximate Values of Length, Mass, and Time

EXAMPLE 1.1

Unit Conversions: A Short Drive Home

Suppose that you drive the 10.0 km from your school to home in 20.0 min. Calculate your average speed (a) in kilometers per hour (km/h) and (b) in meters per second (m/s). (Note: Average speed is distance traveled divided by time of travel.)

Strategy

First we calculate the average speed using the given units. Then we can get the average speed into the desired units by picking the correct conversion factor and multiplying by it. The correct conversion factor is the one that cancels the unwanted unit and leaves the desired unit in its place.

Solution for (a)

(1) Calculate average speed. Average speed is distance traveled divided by time of travel. (Take this definition as a given for now—average speed and other motion concepts will be covered in a later module.) In equation form,

$$\text{average speed} = \frac{\text{distance}}{\text{time}}. \tag{1.2}$$

(2) Substitute the given values for distance and time.

$$\text{average speed} = \frac{10.0\text{ km}}{20.0\text{ min}} = 0.500\frac{\text{km}}{\text{min}}. \tag{1.3}$$

(3) Convert km/min to km/h: multiply by the conversion factor that will cancel minutes and leave hours. That conversion factor is 60 min/hr

Discussion for (a)

To check your answer, consider the following:

(1) Be sure that you have properly cancelled the units in the unit conversion. If you have written the unit conversion factor upside down, the units will not cancel properly in the equation. If you accidentally get the ratio upside down, then the units will not cancel; rather, they will give you the wrong units as follows:

$$\frac{\text{km}}{\text{min}} \times \frac{1\text{ hr}}{60\text{ min}} = \frac{1}{60}\frac{\text{km} \cdot \text{hr}}{\text{min}^2}, \tag{1.4}$$

which are obviously not the desired units of km/h.

(2) Check that the units of the final answer are the desired units. The problem asked us to solve for average speed in units of km/h and we have indeed obtained these units.

(3) Check the significant figures. Because each of the values given in the problem has three significant figures, the answer should also have three significant figures. The answer 30.0 km/hr does indeed have three significant figures, so this is appropriate. Note that the significant figures in the conversion factor are not relevant because an hour is *defined* to be 60 minutes, so the precision of the conversion factor is perfect.

(4) Next, check whether the answer is reasonable. Let us consider some information from the problem—if you travel 10 km in a third of an hour (20 min), you would travel three times that far in an hour. The answer does seem reasonable.

Solution for (b)

There are several ways to convert the average speed into meters per second.

(1) Start with the answer to (a) and convert km/h to m/s. Two conversion factors are needed—one to convert hours to seconds, and another to convert kilometers to meters.

(2) Multiplying by these yields

$$\text{Average speed} = 30.0\frac{\text{km}}{\text{h}} \times \frac{1\text{ h}}{3{,}600\text{ s}} \times \frac{1{,}000\text{ m}}{1\text{ km}}, \quad (1.5)$$

$$\text{Average speed} = 8.33\frac{\text{m}}{\text{s}}. \quad (1.6)$$

Discussion for (b)

If we had started with 0.500 km/min, we would have needed different conversion factors, but the answer would have been the same: 8.33 m/s.

You may have noted that the answers in the worked example just covered were given to three digits. Why? When do you need to be concerned about the number of digits in something you calculate? Why not write down all the digits your calculator produces? The module Accuracy, Precision, and Significant Figures will help you answer these questions.

NONSTANDARD UNITS

While there are numerous types of units that we are all familiar with, there are others that are much more obscure. For example, a **firkin** is a unit of volume that was once used to measure beer. One firkin equals about 34 liters. To learn more about nonstandard units, use a dictionary or encyclopedia to research different "weights and measures." Take note of any unusual units, such as a barleycorn, that are not listed in the text. Think about how the unit is defined and state its relationship to SI units.

CHECK YOUR UNDERSTANDING

Some hummingbirds beat their wings more than 50 times per second. A scientist is measuring the time it takes for a hummingbird to beat its wings once. Which fundamental unit should the scientist use to describe the measurement? Which factor of 10 is the scientist likely to use to describe the motion precisely? Identify the metric prefix that corresponds to this factor of 10.

Solution

The scientist will measure the time between each movement using the fundamental unit of seconds. Because the wings beat so fast, the scientist will probably need to measure in milliseconds, or 10^{-3} seconds. (50 beats per second corresponds to 20 milliseconds per beat.)

CHECK YOUR UNDERSTANDING

One cubic centimeter is equal to one milliliter. What does this tell you about the different units in the SI metric system?

Solution

The fundamental unit of length (meter) is probably used to create the derived unit of volume (liter). The measure of a milliliter is dependent on the measure of a centimeter.

1.3 Accuracy, Precision, and Significant Figures

LEARNING OBJECTIVES

By the end of this section, you will be able to:

- Determine the appropriate number of significant figures in both addition and subtraction, as well as multiplication and division calculations.
- Calculate the percent uncertainty of a measurement.

FIGURE 1.21 A double-pan mechanical balance is used to compare different masses. Usually an object with unknown mass is placed in one pan and objects of known mass are placed in the other pan. When the bar that connects the two pans is horizontal, then the masses in both pans are equal. The "known masses" are typically metal cylinders of standard mass such as 1 gram, 10 grams, and 100 grams. (credit: Serge Melki)

FIGURE 1.22 Many mechanical balances, such as double-pan balances, have been replaced by digital scales, which can typically measure the mass of an object more precisely. Whereas a mechanical balance may only read the mass of an object to the nearest tenth of a gram, many digital scales can measure the mass of an object up to the nearest thousandth of a gram. (credit: Karel Jakubec)

Accuracy and Precision of a Measurement

Science is based on observation and experiment—that is, on measurements. **Accuracy** is how close a measurement is to the correct value for that measurement. For example, let us say that you are measuring the length of standard computer paper. The packaging in which you purchased the paper states that it is 11.0 inches long. You measure the length of the paper three times and obtain the following measurements: 11.1 in., 11.2 in., and 10.9 in. These measurements are quite accurate because they are very close to the correct value of 11.0 inches. In contrast, if you had obtained a measurement of 12 inches, your measurement would not be very accurate.

The **precision** of a measurement system refers to how close the agreement is between repeated measurements (which are repeated under the same conditions). Consider the example of the paper measurements. The precision of the measurements refers to the spread of the measured values. One way to analyze the precision of the measurements would be to determine the range, or difference, between the lowest and the highest measured values. In that case, the lowest value was 10.9 in. and the highest value was 11.2 in. Thus, the measured values deviated from each other by at most 0.3 in. These measurements were relatively precise because they did not vary too much in value. However, if the measured values had been 10.9, 11.1, and 11.9, then the measurements would not be very precise because there would be significant variation from one measurement to another.

The measurements in the paper example are both accurate and precise, but in some cases, measurements are accurate but not precise, or they are precise but not accurate. Let us consider an example of a GPS system that is attempting to locate the position of a restaurant in a city. Think of the restaurant location as existing at the center of a bull's-eye target, and think of each GPS attempt to locate the restaurant as a black dot. In Figure 1.23, you can see that the GPS measurements are spread out far apart from each other, but they are all relatively close to the actual location of the restaurant at the center of the target. This indicates a low precision, high accuracy measuring system. However, in Figure 1.24, the GPS measurements are concentrated quite closely to one another, but they are far away from the target location. This indicates a high precision, low accuracy measuring system.

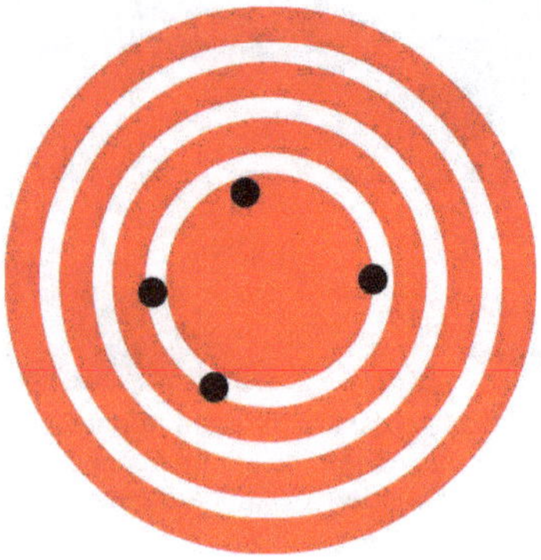

FIGURE 1.23 A GPS system attempts to locate a restaurant at the center of the bull's-eye. The black dots represent each attempt to pinpoint the location of the restaurant. The dots are spread out quite far apart from one another, indicating low precision, but they are each rather close to the actual location of the restaurant, indicating high accuracy. (credit: Dark Evil)

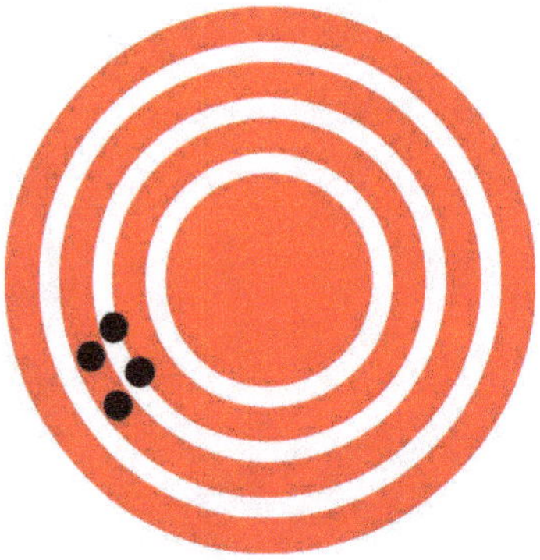

FIGURE 1.24 In this figure, the dots are concentrated rather closely to one another, indicating high precision, but they are rather far away from the actual location of the restaurant, indicating low accuracy. (credit: Dark Evil)

Accuracy, Precision, and Uncertainty

The degree of accuracy and precision of a measuring system are related to the **uncertainty** in the measurements. Uncertainty is a quantitative measure of how much your measured values deviate from a standard or expected value. If your measurements are not very accurate or precise, then the uncertainty of your values will be very high. In more general terms, uncertainty can be thought of as a disclaimer for your measured values. For example, if someone asked you to provide the mileage on your car, you might say that it is 45,000 miles, plus or minus 500 miles. The plus or minus amount is the uncertainty in your value. That is, you are indicating that the actual mileage of your car might be as low as 44,500 miles or as high as 45,500 miles, or anywhere in between. All measurements contain some amount of uncertainty. In our example of measuring the length of the paper, we might say that the length of the paper is 11 in., plus or minus 0.2 in. The uncertainty in a measurement, A, is often denoted as δA ("delta A"), so the measurement result would be recorded as $A \pm \delta A$. In our paper example, the length of the paper could be expressed as $11 \text{ in.} \pm 0.2$.

The factors contributing to uncertainty in a measurement include:

1. Limitations of the measuring device,
2. The skill of the person making the measurement,
3. Irregularities in the object being measured,
4. Any other factors that affect the outcome (highly dependent on the situation).

In our example, such factors contributing to the uncertainty could be the following: the smallest division on the ruler is 0.1 in., the person using the ruler has bad eyesight, or one side of the paper is slightly longer than the other. At any rate, the uncertainty in a measurement must be based on a careful consideration of all the factors that might contribute and their possible effects.

MAKING CONNECTIONS: REAL-WORLD CONNECTIONS – FEVERS OR CHILLS?

Uncertainty is a critical piece of information, both in physics and in many other real-world applications. Imagine you are caring for a sick child. You suspect the child has a fever, so you check their temperature with a thermometer. What if the uncertainty of the thermometer were $3.0°C$? If the child's temperature reading was $37.0°C$ (which is normal body temperature), the "true" temperature could be anywhere from a hypothermic $34.0°C$ to a dangerously high $40.0°C$. A thermometer with an uncertainty of $3.0°C$ would be useless.

Percent Uncertainty

One method of expressing uncertainty is as a percent of the measured value. If a measurement A is expressed with uncertainty, δA, the **percent uncertainty** (%unc) is defined to be

$$\%\ \text{unc} = \frac{\delta A}{A} \times 100\%. \tag{1.7}$$

EXAMPLE 1.2

Calculating Percent Uncertainty: A Bag of Apples

A grocery store sells 5-lb bags of apples. You purchase four bags over the course of a month and weigh the apples each time. You obtain the following measurements:

- Week 1 weight: $4.8\ \text{lb}$
- Week 2 weight: $5.3\ \text{lb}$
- Week 3 weight: $4.9\ \text{lb}$
- Week 4 weight: $5.4\ \text{lb}$

You determine that the weight of the 5-lb bag has an uncertainty of $\pm 0.4\ \text{lb}$. What is the percent uncertainty of the bag's weight?

Strategy

First, observe that the expected value of the bag's weight, A, is 5 lb. The uncertainty in this value, δA, is 0.4 lb. We can use the following equation to determine the percent uncertainty of the weight:

$$\%\ \text{unc} = \frac{\delta A}{A} \times 100\%. \tag{1.8}$$

Solution

Plug the known values into the equation:

$$\%\ \text{unc} = \frac{0.4\ \text{lb}}{5\ \text{lb}} \times 100\% = 8\%. \tag{1.9}$$

Discussion

We can conclude that the weight of the apple bag is $5\ \text{lb} \pm 8\%$. Consider how this percent uncertainty would change if the bag of apples were half as heavy, but the uncertainty in the weight remained the same. Hint for future calculations: when calculating percent uncertainty, always remember that you must multiply the fraction by 100%. If you do not do this, you will have a decimal quantity, not a percent value.

Uncertainties in Calculations

There is an uncertainty in anything calculated from measured quantities. For example, the area of a floor calculated from measurements of its length and width has an uncertainty because the length and width have uncertainties. How big is the uncertainty in something you calculate by multiplication or division? If the measurements going into the calculation have small uncertainties (a few percent or less), then the **method of adding percents** can be used for multiplication or division. This method says that *the percent uncertainty in a quantity calculated by multiplication* *or division is the sum of the percent uncertainties in the items used to make the calculation.* For example, if a floor has a length of 4.00 m and a width of 3.00 m, with uncertainties of 2% and 1%, respectively, then the area of the floor is 12.0 m^2 and has an uncertainty of 3%. (Expressed as an area this is 0.36 m^2, which we round to 0.4 m^2 since the area of the floor is given to a tenth of a square meter.)

CHECK YOUR UNDERSTANDING

A high school track coach has just purchased a new stopwatch. The stopwatch manual states that the stopwatch has an uncertainty of ±0.05 s. The team's top sprinter clocked a 100 meter sprint at 12.04 seconds last week and at 11.96 seconds this week. Can we conclude that this week's time was faster?

Solution
No, the uncertainty in the stopwatch is too great to effectively differentiate between the sprint times.

Precision of Measuring Tools and Significant Figures

An important factor in the accuracy and precision of measurements involves the precision of the measuring tool. In general, a precise measuring tool is one that can measure values in very small increments. For example, a standard ruler can measure length to the nearest millimeter, while a caliper can measure length to the nearest 0.01 millimeter. The caliper is a more precise measuring tool because it can measure extremely small differences in length. The more precise the measuring tool, the more precise and accurate the measurements can be.

When we express measured values, we can only list as many digits as we initially measured with our measuring tool. For example, if you use a standard ruler to measure the length of a stick, you may measure it to be 36.7 cm. You could not express this value as 36.71 cm because your measuring tool was not precise enough to measure a hundredth of a centimeter. It should be noted that the last digit in a measured value has been estimated in some way by the person performing the measurement. For example, the person measuring the length of a stick with a ruler notices that the stick length seems to be somewhere in between 36.6 cm and 36.7 cm, and they must estimate the value of the last digit. Using the method of **significant figures**, the rule is that *the last digit written down in a measurement is the first digit with some uncertainty*. In order to determine the number of significant digits in a value, start with the first measured value at the left and count the number of digits through the last digit written on the right. For example, the measured value 36.7 cm has three digits, or significant figures. Significant figures indicate the precision of a measuring tool that was used to measure a value.

Zeros

Special consideration is given to zeros when counting significant figures. The zeros in 0.053 are not significant, because they are only placekeepers that locate the decimal point. There are two significant figures in 0.053. The zeros in 10.053 are not placekeepers but are significant—this number has five significant figures. The zeros in 1300 may or may not be significant depending on the style of writing numbers. They could mean the number is known to the last digit, or they could be placekeepers. So 1300 could have two, three, or four significant figures. (To avoid this ambiguity, write 1300 in scientific notation.) *Zeros are significant except when they serve only as placekeepers.*

CHECK YOUR UNDERSTANDING

Determine the number of significant figures in the following measurements:

a. 0.0009
b. 15,450.0
c. 6×10^3
d. 87.990
e. 30.42

Solution
(a) 1; the zeros in this number are placekeepers that indicate the decimal point

(b) 6; here, the zeros indicate that a measurement was made to the 0.1 decimal point, so the zeros are significant

(c) 1; the value 10^3 signifies the decimal place, not the number of measured values

(d) 5; the final zero indicates that a measurement was made to the 0.001 decimal point, so it is significant

(e) 4; any zeros located in between significant figures in a number are also significant

Significant Figures in Calculations

When combining measurements with different degrees of accuracy and precision, *the number of significant digits in the final answer can be no greater than the number of significant digits in the least precise measured value.* There are two different rules, one for multiplication and division and the other for addition and subtraction, as discussed below.

1. For multiplication and division: *The result should have the same number of significant figures as the quantity having the least significant figures entering into the calculation.* For example, the area of a circle can be calculated from its radius using $A = \pi r^2$. Let us see how many significant figures the area has if the radius has only two—say, $r = 1.2\text{ m}$. Then,

$$A = \pi r^2 = (3.1415927...) \times (1.2\text{ m})^2 = 4.5238934\text{ m}^2 \quad 1.10$$

is what you would get using a calculator that has an eight-digit output. But because the radius has only two significant figures, it limits the calculated quantity to two significant figures or

$$A = 4.5\text{ m}^2, \quad 1.11$$

even though π is good to at least eight digits.

2. For addition and subtraction: *The answer can contain no more decimal places than the least precise measurement.* Suppose that you buy 7.56-kg of potatoes in a grocery store as measured with a scale with precision 0.01 kg. Then you drop off 6.052-kg of potatoes at your laboratory as measured by a scale with precision 0.001 kg. Finally, you go home and add 13.7 kg of potatoes as measured by a bathroom scale with precision 0.1 kg. How many kilograms of potatoes do you now have, and how many significant figures are appropriate in the answer? The mass is found by simple addition and subtraction:

$$\begin{array}{r} 7.56\ \text{kg} \\ -\ 6.052\ \text{kg} \\ \underline{+13.7\ \ \ \text{kg}} \\ 15.208\ \text{kg} \end{array} = 15.2\text{ kg}. \quad 1.12$$

Next, we identify the least precise measurement: 13.7 kg. This measurement is expressed to the 0.1 decimal place, so our final answer must also be expressed to the 0.1 decimal place. Thus, the answer is rounded to the tenths place, giving us 15.2 kg.

Significant Figures in this Text

In this text, most numbers are assumed to have three significant figures. Furthermore, consistent numbers of significant figures are used in all worked examples. You will note that an answer given to three digits is based on input good to at least three digits, for example. If the input has fewer significant figures, the answer will also have fewer significant figures. Care is also taken that the number of significant figures is reasonable for the situation posed. In some topics, particularly in optics, more accurate numbers are needed and more than three significant figures will be used. Finally, if a number is *exact,* such as the two in the formula for the circumference of a circle, $c = 2\pi r$, it does not affect the number of significant figures in a calculation.

CHECK YOUR UNDERSTANDING

Perform the following calculations and express your answer using the correct number of significant digits.

(a) A woman has two bags weighing 13.5 pounds and one bag with a weight of 10.2 pounds. What is the total weight of the bags?

(b) The force F on an object is equal to its mass m multiplied by its acceleration a. If a wagon with mass 55 kg accelerates at a rate of 0.0255 m/s^2, what is the force on the wagon? (The unit of force is called the newton, and it is expressed with the symbol N.)

Solution

(a) 37.2 pounds; Because the number of bags is an exact value, it is not considered in the significant figures.

(b) 1.4 N; Because the value 55 kg has only two significant figures, the final value must also contain two significant figures.

1.4 Approximation

LEARNING OBJECTIVES

By the end of this section, you will be able to:

- Make reasonable approximations based on given data.

On many occasions, physicists, other scientists, and engineers need to make **approximations** or "guesstimates" for a particular quantity. What is the distance to a certain destination? What is the approximate density of a given item? About how large a current will there be in a circuit? Many approximate numbers are based on formulae in which the input quantities are known only to a limited accuracy. As you develop problem-solving skills (that can be applied to a variety of fields through a study of physics), you will also develop skills at approximating. You will develop these skills through thinking more quantitatively, and by being willing to take risks. As with any endeavor, experience helps, as well as familiarity with units. These approximations allow us to rule out certain scenarios or unrealistic numbers. Approximations also allow us to challenge others and guide us in our approaches to our scientific world. Let us do two examples to illustrate this concept.

EXAMPLE 1.3

Approximate the Height of a Building

Can you approximate the height of one of the buildings on your campus, or in your neighborhood? Let us make an approximation based upon the height of a person. In this example, we will calculate the height of a 39-story building.

Strategy

Think about the average height of an adult male. We can approximate the height of the building by scaling up from the height of a person.

Solution

Based on information in the example, we know there are 39 stories in the building. If we use the fact that the height of one story is approximately equal to about the length of two adult humans (each human is about 2-m tall), then we can estimate the total height of the building to be

$$\frac{2\text{ m}}{1\text{ person}} \times \frac{2\text{ person}}{1\text{ story}} \times 39\text{ stories} = 156\text{ m}. \quad (1.13)$$

Discussion

You can use known quantities to determine an approximate measurement of unknown quantities. If your hand measures 10 cm across, how many hand lengths equal the width of your desk? What other measurements can you approximate besides length?

EXAMPLE 1.4

Approximating Vast Numbers: a Trillion Dollars

FIGURE 1.25 A bank stack contains one-hundred $100 bills, and is worth $10,000. How many bank stacks make up a trillion dollars? (credit: Andrew Magill)

The U.S. federal debt in 2021 was a little more than $28 trillion. Most of us do not have any concept of how much even one trillion actually is. Suppose that you were given a trillion dollars in $100 bills. If you made 100-bill stacks and used them to evenly cover a football field (between the end zones), make an approximation of how high the money pile would become. (We will use feet/inches rather than meters here because football fields are measured in yards.) One of your friends says 3 in., while another says 10 ft. What do you think?

Strategy

When you imagine the situation, you probably envision thousands of small stacks of 100 wrapped $100 bills, such as you might see in movies or at a bank. Since this is an easy-to-approximate quantity, let us start there. We can find the volume of a stack of 100 bills, find out how many stacks make up one trillion dollars, and then set this volume equal to the area of the football field multiplied by the unknown height.

Solution

(1) Calculate the volume of a stack of 100 bills. The dimensions of a single bill are approximately 3 in. by 6 in. A stack of 100 of these is about 0.5 in. thick. So the total volume of a stack of 100 bills is:

$$\begin{aligned} \text{volume of stack} &= \text{length} \times \text{width} \times \text{height}, \\ \text{volume of stack} &= 6 \text{ in.} \times 3 \text{ in.} \times 0.5 \text{ in.}, \\ \text{volume of stack} &= 9 \text{ in.}^3. \end{aligned} \tag{1.14}$$

(2) Calculate the number of stacks. Note that a trillion dollars is equal to $\$1 \times 10^{12}$, and a stack of one-hundred $\$100$ bills is equal to $\$10{,}000$, or $\$1 \times 10^4$. The number of stacks you will have is:

$$\$1 \times 10^{12} (\text{a trillion dollars})/\ \$1 \times 10^4 \text{ per stack} = 1 \times 10^8 \text{ stacks.} \tag{1.15}$$

(3) Calculate the area of a football field in square inches. The area of a football field is $100 \text{ yd} \times 50 \text{ yd}$, which gives $5{,}000 \text{ yd}^2$. Because we are working in inches, we need to convert square yards to square inches:

$$\begin{aligned} \text{Area} &= 5{,}000 \text{ yd}^2 \times \frac{3 \text{ ft}}{1 \text{ yd}} \times \frac{3 \text{ ft}}{1 \text{ yd}} \times \frac{12 \text{ in.}}{1 \text{ ft}} \times \frac{12 \text{ in.}}{1 \text{ ft}} = 6{,}480{,}000 \text{ in.}^2, \\ \text{Area} &\approx 6 \times 10^6 \text{ in.}^2. \end{aligned} \tag{1.16}$$

This conversion gives us $6 \times 10^6 \text{ in.}^2$ for the area of the field. (Note that we are using only one significant figure in these calculations.)

(4) Calculate the total volume of the bills. The volume of all the $\$100$-bill stacks is

$9\ \text{in.}^3/\text{stack} \times 10^8\ \text{stacks} = 9 \times 10^8\ \text{in.}^3.$

(5) Calculate the height. To determine the height of the bills, use the equation:

$$\begin{aligned}\text{volume of bills} &= \text{area of field} \times \text{height of money:}\\ \text{Height of money} &= \frac{\text{volume of bills}}{\text{area of field}},\\ \text{Height of money} &= \frac{9\times10^8\,\text{in.}^3}{6\times10^6\,\text{in.}^2} = 1.33 \times 10^2\,\text{in.},\\ \text{Height of money} &\approx 1 \times 10^2\,\text{in.} = 100\ \text{in.}\end{aligned} \tag{1.17}$$

The height of the money will be about 100 in. high. Converting this value to feet gives

$$100\ \text{in.} \times \frac{1\ \text{ft}}{12\ \text{in.}} = 8.33\ \text{ft} \approx 8\ \text{ft}. \tag{1.18}$$

Discussion

The final approximate value is much higher than the early estimate of 3 in., but the other early estimate of 10 ft (120 in.) was roughly correct. How did the approximation measure up to your first guess? What can this exercise tell you in terms of rough "guesstimates" versus carefully calculated approximations?

CHECK YOUR UNDERSTANDING

Using mental math and your understanding of fundamental units, approximate the area of a regulation basketball court. Describe the process you used to arrive at your final approximation.

Solution

An average male is about two meters tall. It would take approximately 15 males laid out end to end to cover the length, and about 7 to cover the width. That gives an approximate area of $420\ \text{m}^2$.

Glossary

accuracy the degree to which a measured value agrees with correct value for that measurement

approximation an estimated value based on prior experience and reasoning

classical physics physics that was developed from the Renaissance to the end of the 19th century

conversion factor a ratio expressing how many of one unit are equal to another unit

derived units units that can be calculated using algebraic combinations of the fundamental units

English units system of measurement used in the United States; includes units of measurement such as feet, gallons, and pounds

fundamental units units that can only be expressed relative to the procedure used to measure them

kilogram the SI unit for mass, abbreviated (kg)

law a description, using concise language or a mathematical formula, a generalized pattern in nature that is supported by scientific evidence and repeated experiments

meter the SI unit for length, abbreviated (m)

method of adding percents the percent uncertainty in a quantity calculated by multiplication or division is the sum of the percent uncertainties in the items used to make the calculation

metric system a system in which values can be calculated in factors of 10

model representation of something that is often too difficult (or impossible) to display directly

modern physics the study of relativity, quantum mechanics, or both

order of magnitude refers to the size of a quantity as it relates to a power of 10

percent uncertainty the ratio of the uncertainty of a measurement to the measured value, expressed as a percentage

physical quantity a characteristic or property of an object that can be measured or calculated from other measurements

physics the science concerned with describing the interactions of energy, matter, space, and time; it is especially interested in what fundamental mechanisms underlie every phenomenon

precision the degree to which repeated measurements agree with each other

quantum mechanics the study of objects smaller than can be seen with a microscope

relativity the study of objects moving at speeds greater than about 1% of the speed of light, or of objects being affected by a strong gravitational field

scientific method a method that typically begins with an observation and question that the scientist will research; next, the scientist typically performs some research about the topic and then devises a hypothesis; then, the scientist will test the hypothesis by performing an experiment; finally, the scientist analyzes the results of the experiment and draws a conclusion

second the SI unit for time, abbreviated (s)

SI units the international system of units that scientists in most countries have agreed to use; includes units such as meters, liters, and grams

significant figures express the precision of a measuring tool used to measure a value

theory an explanation for patterns in nature that is supported by scientific evidence and verified multiple times by various groups of researchers

uncertainty a quantitative measure of how much your measured values deviate from a standard or expected value

units a standard used for expressing and comparing measurements

Section Summary

1.1 Physics: An Introduction

- Science seeks to discover and describe the underlying order and simplicity in nature.
- Physics is the most basic of the sciences, concerning itself with energy, matter, space and time, and their interactions.
- Scientific laws and theories express the general truths of nature and the body of knowledge they encompass. These laws of nature are rules that all natural processes appear to follow.

1.2 Physical Quantities and Units

- Physical quantities are a characteristic or property of an object that can be measured or calculated from other measurements.
- Units are standards for expressing and comparing the measurement of physical quantities. All units can be expressed as combinations of four fundamental units.
- The four fundamental units we will use in this text are the meter (for length), the kilogram (for mass), the second (for time), and the ampere (for electric current). These units are part of the metric system, which uses powers of 10 to relate quantities over the vast ranges encountered in nature.
- The four fundamental units are abbreviated as follows: meter, m; kilogram, kg; second, s; and

ampere, A. The metric system also uses a standard set of prefixes to denote each order of magnitude greater than or lesser than the fundamental unit itself.

- Unit conversions involve changing a value expressed in one type of unit to another type of unit. This is done by using conversion factors, which are ratios relating equal quantities of different units.

1.3 Accuracy, Precision, and Significant Figures

- Accuracy of a measured value refers to how close a measurement is to the correct value. The uncertainty in a measurement is an estimate of the amount by which the measurement result may differ from this value.
- Precision of measured values refers to how close the agreement is between repeated measurements.
- The precision of a *measuring tool* is related to the size of its measurement increments. The smaller the measurement increment, the more precise the tool.
- Significant figures express the precision of a measuring tool.
- When multiplying or dividing measured values, the final answer can contain only as many significant figures as the least precise value.
- When adding or subtracting measured values, the final answer cannot contain more decimal places than the least precise value.

1.4 Approximation

Scientists often approximate the values of quantities to perform calculations and analyze systems.

Conceptual Questions

1.1 Physics: An Introduction

1. Models are particularly useful in relativity and quantum mechanics, where conditions are outside those normally encountered by humans. What is a model?
2. How does a model differ from a theory?
3. If two different theories describe experimental observations equally well, can one be said to be more valid than the other (assuming both use accepted rules of logic)?
4. What determines the validity of a theory?
5. Certain criteria must be satisfied if a measurement or observation is to be believed. Will the criteria necessarily be as strict for an expected result as for an unexpected result?
6. Can the validity of a model be limited, or must it be universally valid? How does this compare to the required validity of a theory or a law?
7. Classical physics is a good approximation to modern physics under certain circumstances. What are they?
8. When is it *necessary* to use relativistic quantum mechanics?
9. Can classical physics be used to accurately describe a satellite moving at a speed of 7500 m/s? Explain why or why not.

1.2 Physical Quantities and Units

10. Identify some advantages of metric units.

1.3 Accuracy, Precision, and Significant Figures

11. What is the relationship between the accuracy and uncertainty of a measurement?
12. Prescriptions for vision correction are given in units called *diopters* (D). Determine the meaning of that unit. Obtain information (perhaps by calling an optometrist or performing an internet search) on the minimum uncertainty with which corrections in diopters are determined and the accuracy with which corrective lenses can be produced. Discuss the sources of uncertainties in both the prescription and accuracy in the manufacture of lenses.

Problems & Exercises

1.2 Physical Quantities and Units

1. The speed limit on some interstate highways is roughly 100 km/h. (a) What is this in meters per second? (b) How many miles per hour is this?
2. A car is traveling at a speed of 33 m/s. (a) What is its speed in kilometers per hour? (b) Is it exceeding the 90 km/h speed limit?
3. Show that $1.0 \text{ m/s} = 3.6 \text{ km/h}$. Hint: Show the explicit steps involved in converting $1.0 \text{ m/s} = 3.6 \text{ km/h}.$

4. American football is played on a 100-yd-long field, excluding the end zones. How long is the field in meters? (Assume that 1 meter equals 3.281 feet.)

5. Soccer fields vary in size. A large soccer field is 115 m long and 85 m wide. What are its dimensions in feet and inches? (Assume that 1 meter equals 3.281 feet.)

6. What is the height in meters of a person who is 6 ft 1.0 in. tall? (Assume that 1 meter equals 39.37 in.)

7. Mount Everest, at 29,028 feet, is the tallest mountain on the Earth. What is its height in kilometers? (Assume that 1 kilometer equals 3,281 feet.)

8. The speed of sound is measured to be 342 m/s on a certain day. What is this in km/h?

9. Tectonic plates are large segments of the Earth's crust that move slowly. Suppose that one such plate has an average speed of 4.0 cm/year. (a) What distance does it move in 1 s at this speed? (b) What is its speed in kilometers per million years?

10. (a) Refer to Table 1.3 to determine the average distance between the Earth and the Sun. Then calculate the average speed of the Earth in its orbit in kilometers per second. (b) What is this in meters per second?

1.3 Accuracy, Precision, and Significant Figures

Express your answers to problems in this section to the correct number of significant figures and proper units.

11. Suppose that your bathroom scale reads your mass as 65 kg with a 3% uncertainty. What is the uncertainty in your mass (in kilograms)?

12. A good-quality measuring tape can be off by 0.50 cm over a distance of 20 m. What is its percent uncertainty?

13. (a) A car speedometer has a 5.0% uncertainty. What is the range of possible speeds when it reads 90 km/h? (b) Convert this range to miles per hour. $(1 \text{ km} = 0.6214 \text{ mi})$

14. An infant's pulse rate is measured to be 130 ± 5 beats/min. What is the percent uncertainty in this measurement?

15. (a) Suppose that a person has an average heart rate of 72.0 beats/min. How many beats do they have in 2.0 y? (b) In 2.00 y? (c) In 2.000 y?

16. A can contains 375 mL of soda. How much is left after 308 mL is removed?

17. State how many significant figures are proper in the results of the following calculations: (a) $(106.7)(98.2)/(46.210)(1.01)$ (b) $(18.7)^2$ (c) $\left(1.60 \times 10^{-19}\right)(3712)$.

18. (a) How many significant figures are in the numbers 99 and 100? (b) If the uncertainty in each number is 1, what is the percent uncertainty in each? (c) Which is a more meaningful way to express the accuracy of these two numbers, significant figures or percent uncertainties?

19. (a) If your speedometer has an uncertainty of 2.0 km/h at a speed of 90 km/h, what is the percent uncertainty? (b) If it has the same percent uncertainty when it reads 60 km/h, what is the range of speeds you could be going?

20. (a) A person's blood pressure is measured to be $120 \pm 2 \text{ mm Hg}$. What is its percent uncertainty? (b) Assuming the same percent uncertainty, what is the uncertainty in a blood pressure measurement of 80 mm Hg?

21. A person measures their heart rate by counting the number of beats in 30 s. If 40 ± 1 beats are counted in $30.0 \pm 0.5 \text{ s}$, what is the heart rate and its uncertainty in beats per minute?

22. What is the area of a circle 3.102 cm in diameter?

23. If a marathon runner averages 9.5 mi/h, how long does it take him or her to run a 26.22-mi marathon?

24. A marathon runner completes a 42.188-km course in 2 h, 30 min, and 12 s. There is an uncertainty of 25 m in the distance traveled and an uncertainty of 1 s in the elapsed time. (a) Calculate the percent uncertainty in the distance. (b) Calculate the uncertainty in the elapsed time. (c) What is the average speed in meters per second? (d) What is the uncertainty in the average speed?

25. The sides of a small rectangular box are measured to be $1.80 \pm 0.01 \text{ cm}$, $2.05 \pm 0.02 \text{ cm, and } 3.1 \pm 0.1 \text{ cm}$ long. Calculate its volume and uncertainty in cubic centimeters.

26. When non-metric units were used in the United Kingdom, a unit of mass called the *pound-mass* (lbm) was employed, where $1 \text{ lbm} = 0.4539 \text{ kg}$. (a) If there is an uncertainty of 0.0001 kg in the pound-mass unit, what is its percent uncertainty?

(b) Based on that percent uncertainty, what mass in pound-mass has an uncertainty of 1 kg when converted to kilograms?

27. The length and width of a rectangular room are measured to be $3.955 \pm 0.005 \text{ m}$ and $3.050 \pm 0.005 \text{ m}$. Calculate the area of the room and its uncertainty in square meters.

28. A car engine moves a piston with a circular cross section of $7.500 \pm 0.002 \text{ cm}$ diameter a distance of $3.250 \pm 0.001 \text{ cm}$ to compress the gas in the cylinder. (a) By what amount is the gas decreased in volume in cubic centimeters? (b) Find the uncertainty in this volume.

1.4 Approximation

29. How many heartbeats are there in a lifetime?

30. A generation is about one-third of a lifetime. Approximately how many generations have passed since the year 0 AD?

31. How many times longer than the mean life of an extremely unstable atomic nucleus is the lifetime of a human? (Hint: The lifetime of an unstable atomic nucleus is on the order of 10^{-22} s.)

32. Calculate the approximate number of atoms in a bacterium. Assume that the average mass of an atom in the bacterium is ten times the mass of a hydrogen atom. (Hint: The mass of a hydrogen atom is on the order of 10^{-27} kg and the mass of a bacterium is on the order of 10^{-15} kg.)

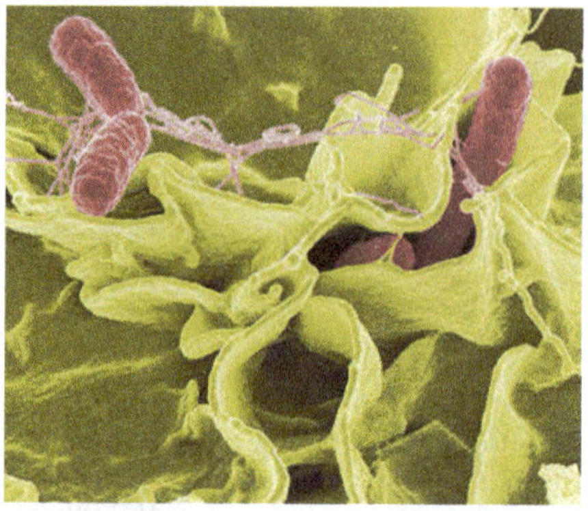

FIGURE 1.26 This color-enhanced photo shows *Salmonella typhimurium* (red) attacking human cells. These bacteria are commonly known for causing foodborne illness. Can you estimate the number of atoms in each bacterium? (credit: Rocky Mountain Laboratories, NIAID, NIH)

33. Approximately how many atoms thick is a cell membrane, assuming all atoms there average about twice the size of a hydrogen atom?

34. (a) What fraction of Earth's diameter is the greatest ocean depth? (b) The greatest mountain height?

35. (a) Calculate the number of cells in a hummingbird assuming the mass of an average cell is ten times the mass of a bacterium. (b) Making the same assumption, how many cells are there in a human?

36. Assuming one nerve impulse must end before another can begin, what is the maximum firing rate of a nerve in impulses per second?

CHAPTER 2
Kinematics

FIGURE 2.1 The motion of an American kestrel through the air can be described by the bird's displacement, speed, velocity, and acceleration. When it flies in a straight line without any change in direction, its motion is said to be one dimensional. (credit: Vince Maidens, Wikimedia Commons)

CHAPTER OUTLINE

CONNECTION FOR AP® COURSES Objects are in motion everywhere we look. Everything from a tennis game to a space-probe flyby of the planet Neptune involves motion. When you are resting, your heart moves blood through your veins. Even in inanimate objects, there is a continuous motion in the vibrations of atoms and molecules. Questions about motion are interesting in and of themselves: *How long will it take for a space probe to get to Mars? Where will a football land if it is thrown at a certain angle?*

Understanding motion will not only provide answers to these questions, but will be key to understanding more advanced concepts in physics. For example, the discussion of force in Chapter 4 will not fully make sense until you understand acceleration. This relationship between force and acceleration is also critical to understanding Big Idea 3.

Additionally, this unit will explore the topic of reference frames, a critical component to quantifying how things move. If you have ever waved to a departing friend at a train station, you are likely familiar with this idea. While you see your friend move away from you at a considerable rate, those sitting with her will likely see her as not moving. The effect that the chosen reference frame has on your observations is substantial, and an understanding of this is needed to grasp both Enduring Understanding 3.A and Essential Knowledge 3.A.1.

Our formal study of physics begins with **kinematics,** which is defined as the *study of motion without considering its causes*. In one- and two-dimensional kinematics we will study only the *motion* of a football, for example, without worrying about what forces cause or change its motion. In this chapter, we examine the simplest type of motion—namely, motion along a straight line, or one-dimensional motion. Later, in two-dimensional kinematics, we apply concepts developed here to study motion along curved paths (two- and three-dimensional motion), for example, that of a car rounding a curve.

The content in this chapter supports:

Big Idea 3 The interactions of an object with other objects can be described by forces.

Enduring Understanding 3.A All forces share certain common characteristics when considered by observers in inertial reference frames.

Essential Knowledge 3.A.1 An observer in a particular reference frame can describe the motion of an object using such quantities as position, displacement, distance, velocity, speed, and acceleration.

Click to view content (https://openstax.org/books/college-physics-ap-courses-2e/pages/2-connection-for-ap-r-courses)

2.1 Displacement

LEARNING OBJECTIVES

By the end of this section, you will be able to:

- Define position, displacement, distance, and distance traveled.
- Explain the relationship between position and displacement.
- Distinguish between displacement and distance traveled.
- Calculate displacement and distance given initial position, final position, and the path between the two.

FIGURE 2.2 These cyclists in Vietnam can be described by their position relative to buildings and a canal. Their motion can be described by their change in position, or displacement, in the frame of reference. (credit: Suzan Black, Fotopedia)

Position

In order to describe the motion of an object, you must first be able to describe its **position**—where it is at any particular time. More precisely, you need to specify its position relative to a convenient reference frame. Earth is often used as a reference frame, and we often describe the position of an object as it relates to stationary objects in that reference frame. For example, a rocket launch would be described in terms of the position of the rocket with respect to the Earth as a whole, while a professor's position could be described in terms of where she is in relation to the nearby white board. (See Figure 2.3.) In other cases, we use reference frames that are not stationary but are in motion relative to the Earth. To describe the position of a person in an airplane, for example, we use the airplane, not the Earth, as the reference frame. (See Figure 2.4.)

Displacement

If an object moves relative to a reference frame (for example, if a professor moves to the right relative to a white board or a passenger moves toward the rear of an airplane), then the object's position changes. This change in position is known as **displacement**. The word "displacement" implies that an object has moved, or has been displaced.

DISPLACEMENT

Displacement is the *change in position* of an object:

$$\Delta x = x_f - x_0, \quad (2.1)$$

where Δx is displacement, x_f is the final position, and x_0 is the initial position.

In this text the upper case Greek letter Δ (delta) always means "change in" whatever quantity follows it; thus, Δx means *change in position*. Always solve for displacement by subtracting initial position x_0 from final position x_f.

Note that the SI unit for displacement is the meter (m) (see Physical Quantities and Units), but sometimes kilometers, miles, feet, and other units of length are used. Keep in mind that when units other than the meter are used in a problem, you may need to convert them into meters to complete the calculation.

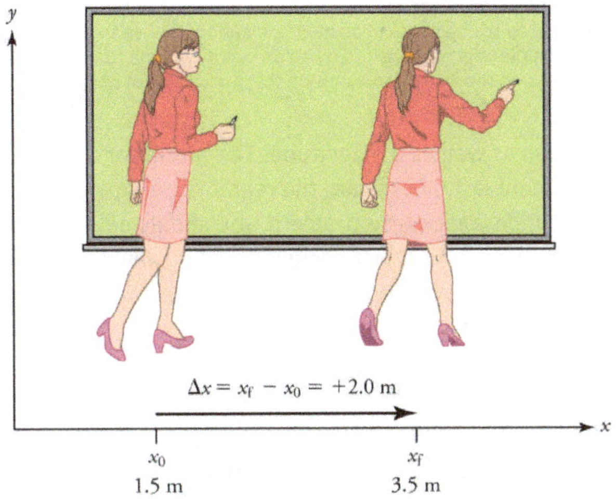

FIGURE 2.3 A professor paces left and right while lecturing. Her position relative to Earth is given by x. The $+2.0\text{ m}$ displacement of the professor relative to Earth is represented by an arrow pointing to the right.

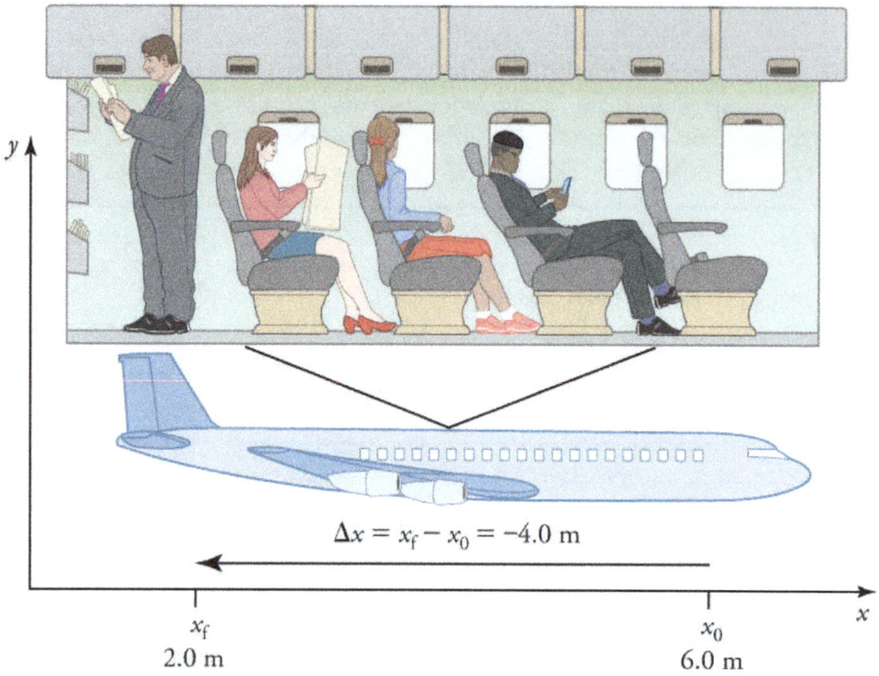

FIGURE 2.4 A passenger moves from his seat to the back of the plane. His location relative to the airplane is given by x. The -4.0-m displacement of the passenger relative to the plane is represented by an arrow toward the rear of the plane. Notice that the arrow representing his displacement is twice as long as the arrow representing the displacement of the professor (he moves twice as far) in Figure 2.3.

Note that displacement has a direction as well as a magnitude. The professor's displacement is 2.0 m to the right, and the airline passenger's displacement is 4.0 m toward the rear. In one-dimensional motion, direction can be specified with a plus or minus sign. When you begin a problem, you should select which direction is positive (usually that will be to the right or up, but you are free to select positive as being any direction). The professor's initial position is $x_0 = 1.5 \text{ m}$ and her final position is $x_f = 3.5 \text{ m}$. Thus her displacement is

$$\Delta x = x_f - x_0 = 3.5 \text{ m} - 1.5 \text{ m} = +2.0 \text{ m}. \quad 2.2$$

In this coordinate system, motion to the right is positive, whereas motion to the left is negative. Similarly, the airplane passenger's initial position is $x_0 = 6.0 \text{ m}$ and his final position is $x_f = 2.0 \text{ m}$, so his displacement is

$$\Delta x = x_f - x_0 = 2.0 \text{ m} - 6.0 \text{ m} = -4.0 \text{ m}. \quad 2.3$$

His displacement is negative because his motion is toward the rear of the plane, or in the negative x direction in our coordinate system.

Distance

Although displacement is described in terms of direction, distance is not. **Distance** is defined to be *the magnitude or size of displacement between two positions.* Note that the distance between two positions is not the same as the distance traveled between them. **Distance traveled** is *the total length of the path traveled between two positions.* Distance has no direction and, thus, no sign. For example, the distance the professor walks is 2.0 m. The distance the airplane passenger walks is 4.0 m.

MISCONCEPTION ALERT: DISTANCE TRAVELED VS. MAGNITUDE OF DISPLACEMENT

It is important to note that the *distance traveled,* however, can be greater than the magnitude of the displacement (by magnitude, we mean just the size of the displacement without regard to its direction; that is, just a number with a unit). For example, the professor could pace back and forth many times, perhaps walking a distance of 150 m during a lecture, yet still end up only 2.0 m to the right of her starting point. In this case her displacement would be +2.0 m, the magnitude of her displacement would be 2.0 m, but the distance she traveled would be 150 m. In kinematics we nearly always deal with displacement and magnitude of displacement, and almost never with distance traveled. One way to think about this is to assume you marked the start of the motion and the end of the motion. The displacement is simply the difference in the position of the two marks and is independent of the path taken in traveling between the two marks. The distance traveled, however, is the total length of the path taken between the two marks.

CHECK YOUR UNDERSTANDING

A cyclist rides 3 km west and then turns around and rides 2 km east. (a) What is their displacement? (b) What distance do they ride? (c) What is the magnitude of their displacement?

Solution

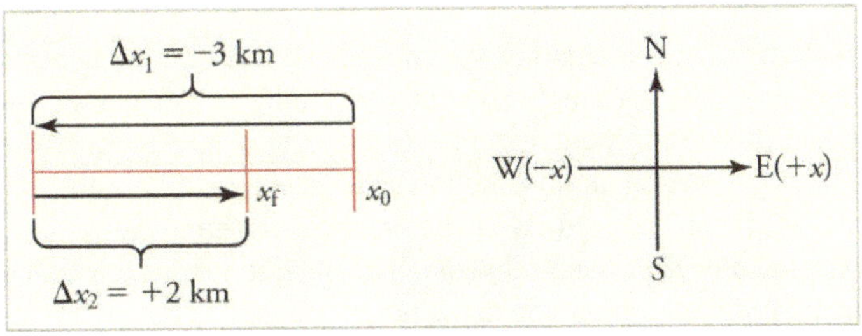

FIGURE 2.5

(a) The rider's displacement is $\Delta x = x_f - x_0 = -1$ km. (The displacement is negative because we take east to be positive and west to be negative.)

(b) The distance traveled is $3 \text{ km} + 2 \text{ km} = 5 \text{ km}$.

(c) The magnitude of the displacement is 1 km.

2.2 Vectors, Scalars, and Coordinate Systems

LEARNING OBJECTIVES

By the end of this section, you will be able to:

- Define and distinguish between scalar and vector quantities.
- Assign a coordinate system for a scenario involving one-dimensional motion.

FIGURE 2.6 The motion of this Eclipse Concept jet can be described in terms of the distance it has traveled (a scalar quantity) or its displacement in a specific direction (a vector quantity). In order to specify the direction of motion, its displacement must be described based on a coordinate system. In this case, it may be convenient to choose motion toward the left as positive motion (it is the forward direction for the plane), although in many cases, the x-coordinate runs from left to right, with motion to the right as positive and motion to the left as negative. (credit: Armchair Aviator, Flickr)

What is the difference between distance and displacement? Whereas displacement is defined by both direction and magnitude, distance is defined only by magnitude. Displacement is an example of a vector quantity. Distance is an example of a scalar quantity. A **vector** is any quantity with both *magnitude and direction*. Other examples of vectors include a velocity of 90 km/h east and a force of 500 newtons straight down.

The direction of a vector in one-dimensional motion is given simply by a plus (+) or minus (−) sign. Vectors are represented graphically by arrows. An arrow used to represent a vector has a length proportional to the vector's magnitude (e.g., the larger the magnitude, the longer the length of the vector) and points in the same direction as the vector.

Some physical quantities, like distance, either have no direction or none is specified. A **scalar** is any quantity that has a magnitude, but no direction. For example, a $20°C$ temperature, the 250 kilocalories (250 Calories) of energy in a candy bar, a 90 km/h speed limit, a person's 1.8 m height, and a distance of 2.0 m are all scalars—quantities with no specified direction. Note, however, that a scalar can be negative, such as a $-20°C$ temperature. In this case, the minus sign indicates a point on a scale rather than a direction. Scalars are never represented by arrows.

Coordinate Systems for One-Dimensional Motion

In order to describe the direction of a vector quantity, you must designate a coordinate system within the reference frame. For one-dimensional motion, this is a simple coordinate system consisting of a one-dimensional coordinate line. In general, when describing horizontal motion, motion to the right is usually considered positive, and motion to the left is considered negative. With vertical motion, motion up is usually positive and motion down is negative. In some cases, however, as with the jet in Figure 2.6, it can be more convenient to switch the positive and negative directions. For example, if you are analyzing the motion of falling objects, it can be useful to define downwards as the positive direction. If people in a race are running to the left, it is useful to define left as the positive direction. It does not matter as long as the system is clear and consistent. Once you assign a positive direction and start solving a problem, you cannot change it.

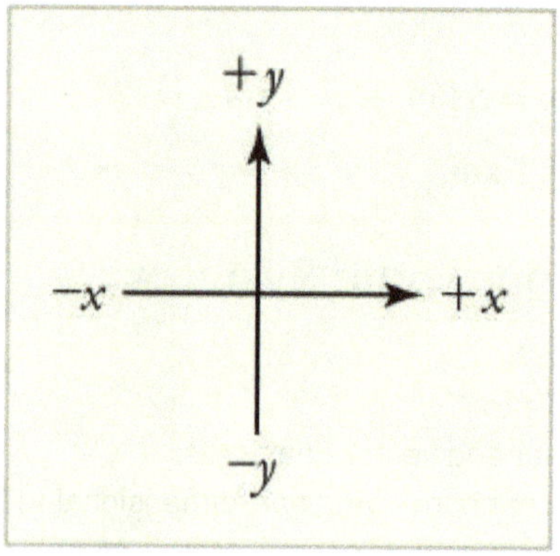

FIGURE 2.7 It is usually convenient to consider motion upward or to the right as positive (+) and motion downward or to the left as negative (−).

CHECK YOUR UNDERSTANDING

A person's speed can stay the same as they round a corner and changes direction. Given this information, is speed a scalar or a vector quantity? Explain.

Solution

Speed is a scalar quantity. It does not change at all with direction changes; therefore, it has magnitude only. If it were a vector quantity, it would change as direction changes (even if its magnitude remained constant).

2.3 Time, Velocity, and Speed

LEARNING OBJECTIVES

By the end of this section, you will be able to:

- Explain the relationships between instantaneous velocity, average velocity, instantaneous speed, average speed, displacement, and time.
- Calculate velocity and speed given initial position, initial time, final position, and final time.
- Derive a graph of velocity vs. time given a graph of position vs. time.
- Interpret a graph of velocity vs. time.

FIGURE 2.8 The motion of these racing snails can be described by their speeds and their velocities. (credit: tobitasflickr, Flickr)

There is more to motion than distance and displacement. Questions such as, "How long does a foot race take?" and "What was the runner's speed?" cannot be answered without an understanding of other concepts. In this section we add definitions of time, velocity, and speed to expand our description of motion.

Time

As discussed in Physical Quantities and Units, the most fundamental physical quantities are defined by how they are measured. This is the case with time. Every measurement of time involves measuring a change in some physical quantity. It may be a number on a digital clock, a heartbeat, or the position of the Sun in the sky. In physics, the definition of time is simple—**time** is *change*, or the interval over which change occurs. It is impossible to know that time has passed unless something changes.

The amount of time or change is calibrated by comparison with a standard. The SI unit for time is the second, abbreviated s. We might, for example, observe that a certain pendulum makes one full swing every 0.75 s. We could then use the pendulum to measure time by counting its swings or, of course, by connecting the pendulum to a clock mechanism that registers time on a dial. This allows us to not only measure the amount of time, but also to determine a sequence of events.

How does time relate to motion? We are usually interested in elapsed time for a particular motion, such as how long it takes an airplane passenger to get from his seat to the back of the plane. To find elapsed time, we note the time at the beginning and end of the motion and subtract the two. For example, a lecture may start at 11:00 A.M. and end at 11:50 A.M., so that the elapsed time would be 50 min. **Elapsed time** Δt is the difference between the ending time and beginning time,

$$\Delta t = t_f - t_0, \tag{2.4}$$

where Δt is the change in time or elapsed time, t_f is the time at the end of the motion, and t_0 is the time at the beginning of the motion. (As usual, the delta symbol, Δ, means the change in the quantity that follows it.)

Life is simpler if the beginning time t_0 is taken to be zero, as when we use a stopwatch. If we were using a stopwatch, it would simply read zero at the start of the lecture and 50 min at the end. If $t_0 = 0$, then $\Delta t = t_f \equiv t$.

In this text, for simplicity's sake,

- motion starts at time equal to zero $(t_0 = 0)$
- the symbol t is used for elapsed time unless otherwise specified $(\Delta t = t_f \equiv t)$

Velocity

Your notion of velocity is probably the same as its scientific definition. You know that if you have a large displacement in a small amount of time you have a large velocity, and that velocity has units of distance divided by time, such as miles per hour or kilometers per hour.

AVERAGE VELOCITY

Average velocity is *displacement (change in position) divided by the time of travel,*

$$\bar{v} = \frac{\Delta x}{\Delta t} = \frac{x_f - x_0}{t_f - t_0}, \quad 2.5$$

where $\bar{v}$ is the *average* (indicated by the bar over the v) velocity, Δx is the change in position (or displacement), and x_f and x_0 are the final and beginning positions at times t_f and t_0, respectively. If the starting time t_0 is taken to be zero, then the average velocity is simply

$$\bar{v} = \frac{\Delta x}{t}. \quad 2.6$$

Notice that this definition indicates that *velocity is a vector because displacement is a vector.* It has both magnitude and direction. The SI unit for velocity is meters per second or m/s, but many other units, such as km/h, mi/h (also written as mph), and cm/s, are in common use. Suppose, for example, an airplane passenger took 5 seconds to move −4 m (the negative sign indicates that displacement is toward the back of the plane). His average velocity would be

$$\bar{v} = \frac{\Delta x}{t} = \frac{-4 \text{ m}}{5 \text{ s}} = -0.8 \text{ m/s}. \quad 2.7$$

The minus sign indicates the average velocity is also toward the rear of the plane.

The average velocity of an object does not tell us anything about what happens to it between the starting point and ending point, however. For example, we cannot tell from average velocity whether the airplane passenger stops momentarily or backs up before he goes to the back of the plane. To get more details, we must consider smaller segments of the trip over smaller time intervals.

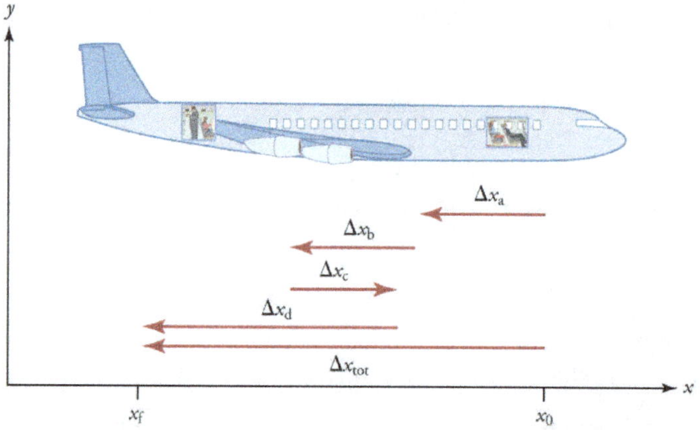

FIGURE 2.9 A more detailed record of an airplane passenger heading toward the back of the plane, showing smaller segments of his trip.

The smaller the time intervals considered in a motion, the more detailed the information. When we carry this process to its logical conclusion, we are left with an infinitesimally small interval. Over such an interval, the average velocity becomes the *instantaneous velocity* or the *velocity at a specific instant.* A car's speedometer, for example, shows the magnitude (but not the direction) of the instantaneous velocity of the car. (Police give tickets based on instantaneous velocity, but when calculating how long it will take to get from one place to another on a road trip, you need to use average velocity.) **Instantaneous velocity** v is the average velocity at a specific instant in time (or over an infinitesimally small time interval).

Mathematically, finding instantaneous velocity, v, at a precise instant t can involve taking a limit, a calculus operation beyond the scope of this text. However, under many circumstances, we can find precise values for instantaneous velocity without calculus.

Speed

In everyday language, most people use the terms "speed" and "velocity" interchangeably. In physics, however, they do not have the same meaning and they are distinct concepts. One major difference is that speed has no direction. Thus *speed is a scalar.* Just as we need to distinguish between instantaneous velocity and average velocity, we also need to distinguish between instantaneous speed and average speed.

Instantaneous speed is the magnitude of instantaneous velocity. For example, suppose the airplane passenger at one instant had an instantaneous velocity of −3.0 m/s (the minus meaning toward the rear of the plane). At that same time his instantaneous speed was 3.0 m/s. Or suppose that at one time during a shopping trip your instantaneous velocity is 40 km/h due north. Your instantaneous speed at that instant would be 40 km/h—the same magnitude but without a direction. Average speed, however, is very different from average velocity. **Average speed** is the distance traveled divided by elapsed time.

We have noted that distance traveled can be greater than the magnitude of displacement. So average speed can be greater than average velocity, which is displacement divided by time. For example, if you drive to a store and return home in half an hour, and your car's odometer shows the total distance traveled was 6 km, then your average speed was 12 km/h. Your average velocity, however, was zero, because your displacement for the round trip is zero. (Displacement is change in position and, thus, is zero for a round trip.) Thus average speed is *not* simply the magnitude of average velocity.

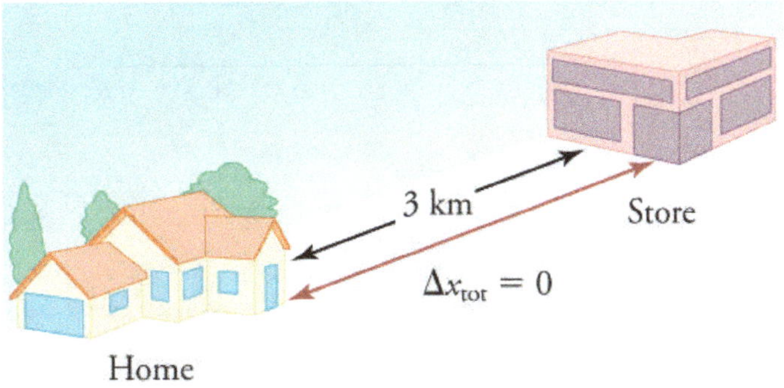

FIGURE 2.10 During a 30-minute round trip to the store, the total distance traveled is 6 km. The average speed is 12 km/h. The displacement for the round trip is zero, since there was no net change in position. Thus the average velocity is zero.

Another way of visualizing the motion of an object is to use a graph. A plot of position or of velocity as a function of time can be very useful. For example, for this trip to the store, the position, velocity, and speed-vs.-time graphs are displayed in Figure 2.11. (Note that these graphs depict a very simplified **model** of the trip. We are assuming that speed is constant during the trip, which is unrealistic given that we'll probably stop at the store. But for simplicity's sake, we will model it with no stops or changes in speed. We are also assuming that the route between the store and the house is a perfectly straight line.)

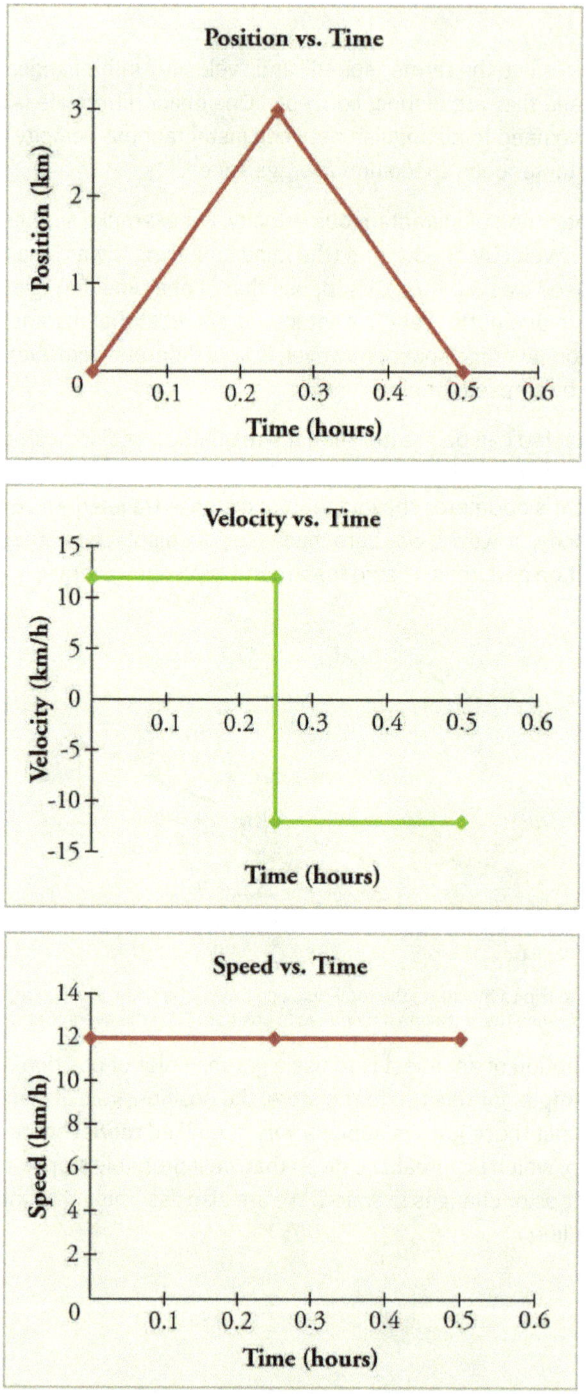

FIGURE 2.11 Position vs. time, velocity vs. time, and speed vs. time on a trip. Note that the velocity for the return trip is negative.

MAKING CONNECTIONS: TAKE-HOME INVESTIGATION—GETTING A SENSE OF SPEED

If you have spent much time driving, you probably have a good sense of speeds between about 10 and 70 miles per hour. But what are these in meters per second? What do we mean when we say that something is moving at 10 m/s? To get a better sense of what these values really mean, do some observations and calculations on your own:

- calculate typical car speeds in meters per second

- estimate jogging and walking speed by timing yourself; convert the measurements into both m/s and mi/h
- determine the speed of an ant, snail, or falling leaf

CHECK YOUR UNDERSTANDING

A commuter train travels from Baltimore to Washington, DC, and back in 1 hour and 45 minutes. The distance between the two stations is approximately 40 miles. What is (a) the average velocity of the train, and (b) the average speed of the train in m/s?

Solution

(a) The average velocity of the train is zero because $x_f = x_0$; the train ends up at the same place it starts.

(b) The average speed of the train is calculated below. Note that the train travels 40 miles one way and 40 miles back, for a total distance of 80 miles.

$$\frac{\text{distance}}{\text{time}} = \frac{80 \text{ miles}}{105 \text{ minutes}} \tag{2.8}$$

$$\frac{80 \text{ miles}}{105 \text{ minutes}} \times \frac{5280 \text{ feet}}{1 \text{ mile}} \times \frac{1 \text{ meter}}{3.28 \text{ feet}} \times \frac{1 \text{ minute}}{60 \text{ seconds}} = 20 \text{ m/s} \tag{2.9}$$

2.4 Acceleration

LEARNING OBJECTIVES

By the end of this section, you will be able to:

- Define and distinguish between instantaneous acceleration, average acceleration, and deceleration.
- Calculate acceleration given initial time, initial velocity, final time, and final velocity.

FIGURE 2.12 A plane decelerates, or slows down, as it comes in for landing in St. Maarten. Its acceleration is opposite in direction to its velocity. (credit: Steve Conry, Flickr)

In everyday conversation, to accelerate means to speed up. The accelerator in a car can in fact cause it to speed up. The greater the **acceleration**, the greater the change in velocity over a given time. The formal definition of acceleration is consistent with these notions, but more inclusive.

AVERAGE ACCELERATION

Average Acceleration is *the rate at which velocity changes,*

$$\bar{a} = \frac{\Delta v}{\Delta t} = \frac{v_f - v_0}{t_f - t_0}, \tag{2.10}$$

where $\bar{a}$ is average acceleration, v is velocity, and t is time. (The bar over the a means *average* acceleration.)

Because acceleration is velocity in m/s divided by time in s, the SI units for acceleration are m/s^2, meters per second squared or meters per second per second, which literally means by how many meters per second the velocity changes every second.

Recall that velocity is a vector—it has both magnitude and direction. This means that a change in velocity can be a change in magnitude (or speed), but it can also be a change in *direction*. For example, if a car turns a corner at constant speed, it is accelerating because its direction is changing. The quicker you turn, the greater the acceleration. So there is an acceleration when velocity changes either in magnitude (an increase or decrease in speed) or in direction, or both.

ACCELERATION AS A VECTOR

Acceleration is a vector in the same direction as the *change* in velocity, Δv. Since velocity is a vector, it can change either in magnitude or in direction. Acceleration is therefore a change in either speed or direction, or both.

Keep in mind that although acceleration is in the direction of the *change* in velocity, it is not always in the direction of *motion*. When an object slows down, its acceleration is opposite to the direction of its motion. This is known as **deceleration**.

FIGURE 2.13 A subway train in Sao Paulo, Brazil, decelerates as it comes into a station. It is accelerating in a direction opposite to its direction of motion. (credit: Yusuke Kawasaki, Flickr)

MISCONCEPTION ALERT: DECELERATION VS. NEGATIVE ACCELERATION

Deceleration always refers to acceleration in the direction opposite to the direction of the velocity. Deceleration always reduces speed. Negative acceleration, however, is acceleration *in the negative direction in the chosen coordinate system*. Negative acceleration may or may not be deceleration, and deceleration may or may not be considered negative acceleration. For example, consider Figure 2.14.

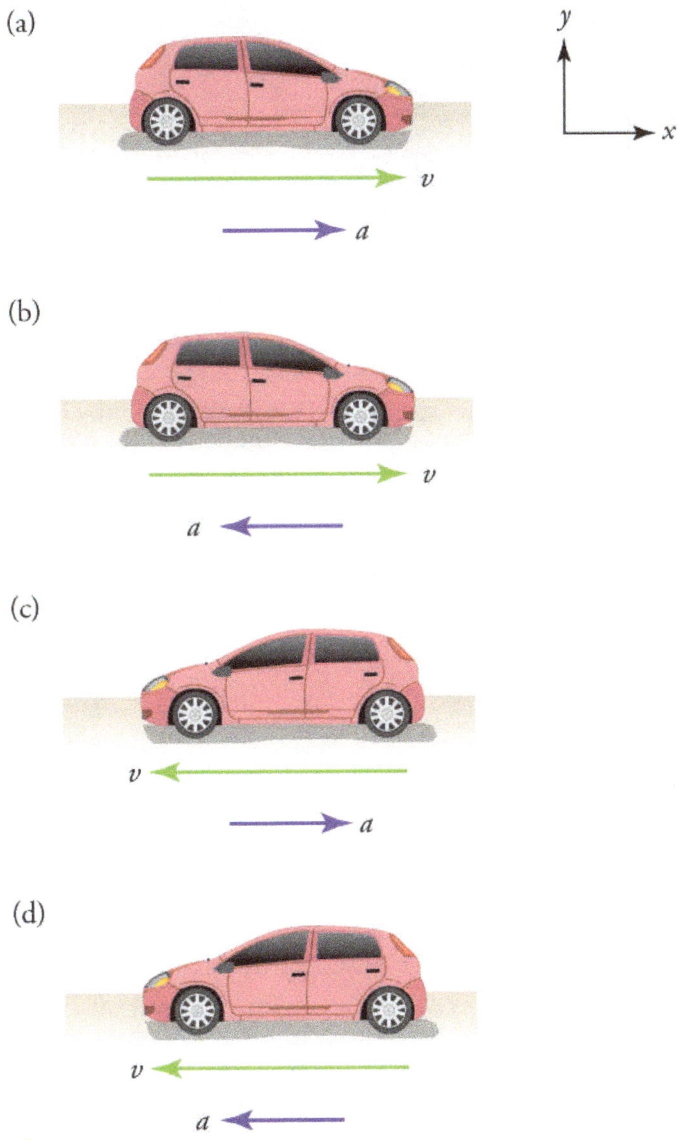

FIGURE 2.14 (a) This car is speeding up as it moves toward the right. It therefore has positive acceleration in our coordinate system. (b) This car is slowing down as it moves toward the right. Therefore, it has negative acceleration in our coordinate system, because its acceleration is toward the left. The car is also decelerating: the direction of its acceleration is opposite to its direction of motion. (c) This car is moving toward the left, but slowing down over time. Therefore, its acceleration is positive in our coordinate system because it is toward the right. However, the car is decelerating because its acceleration is opposite to its motion. (d) This car is speeding up as it moves toward the left. It has negative acceleration because it is accelerating toward the left. However, because its acceleration is in the same direction as its motion, it is speeding up (*not* decelerating).

EXAMPLE 2.1

Calculating Acceleration: A Racehorse Leaves the Gate

A racehorse coming out of the gate accelerates from rest to a velocity of 15.0 m/s due west in 1.80 s. What is its average acceleration?

FIGURE 2.15 (credit: Jon Sullivan, PD Photo.org)

Strategy

First we draw a sketch and assign a coordinate system to the problem. This is a simple problem, but it always helps to visualize it. Notice that we assign east as positive and west as negative. Thus, in this case, we have negative velocity.

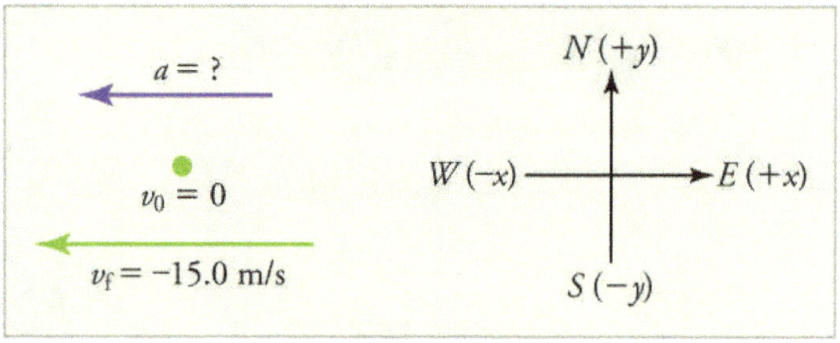

FIGURE 2.16

We can solve this problem by identifying Δv and Δt from the given information and then calculating the average acceleration directly from the equation $\bar{a} = \frac{\Delta v}{\Delta t} = \frac{v_f - v_0}{t_f - t_0}$.

Solution

1. Identify the knowns. $v_0 = 0$, $v_f = -15.0\text{ m/s}$ (the negative sign indicates direction toward the west), $\Delta t = 1.80\text{ s}$.

2. Find the change in velocity. Since the horse is going from zero to -15.0 m/s, its change in velocity equals its final velocity: $\Delta v = v_f = -15.0\text{ m/s}$.

3. Plug in the known values (Δv and Δt) and solve for the unknown $\bar{a}$.

$$\bar{a} = \frac{\Delta v}{\Delta t} = \frac{-15.0\text{ m/s}}{1.80\text{ s}} = -8.33\text{ m/s}^2. \quad (2.11)$$

Discussion

The negative sign for acceleration indicates that acceleration is toward the west. An acceleration of 8.33 m/s^2 due west means that the horse increases its velocity by 8.33 m/s due west each second, that is, 8.33 meters per second per second, which we write as 8.33 m/s^2. This is truly an average acceleration, because the ride is not smooth. We shall see later that an acceleration of this magnitude would require the rider to hang on with a force nearly equal to his weight.

Instantaneous Acceleration

Instantaneous acceleration *a*, or the *acceleration at a specific instant in time*, is obtained by the same process as discussed for instantaneous velocity in Time, Velocity, and Speed—that is, by considering an infinitesimally small interval of time. How do we find instantaneous acceleration using only algebra? The answer is that we choose an average acceleration that is representative of the motion. Figure 2.17 shows graphs of instantaneous acceleration versus time for two very different motions. In Figure 2.17(a), the acceleration varies slightly and the average over the entire interval is nearly the same as the instantaneous acceleration at any time. In this case, we should treat this motion as if it had a constant acceleration equal to the average (in this case about $1.8\ \text{m/s}^2$). In Figure 2.17(b), the acceleration varies drastically over time. In such situations it is best to consider smaller time intervals and choose an average acceleration for each. For example, we could consider motion over the time intervals from 0 to 1.0 s and from 1.0 to 3.0 s as separate motions with accelerations of $+3.0\ \text{m/s}^2$ and $-2.0\ \text{m/s}^2$, respectively.

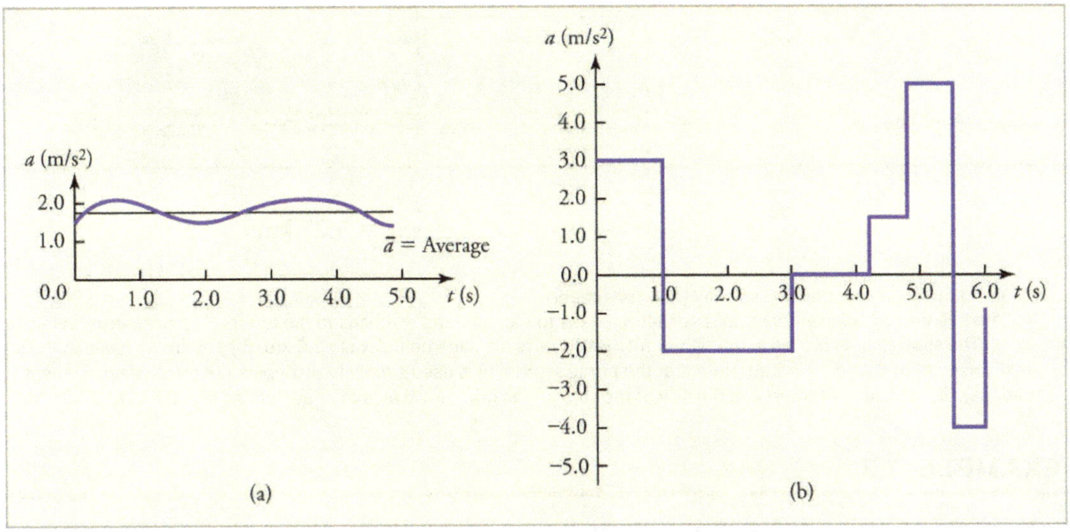

FIGURE 2.17 Graphs of instantaneous acceleration versus time for two different one-dimensional motions. (a) Here acceleration varies only slightly and is always in the same direction, since it is positive. The average over the interval is nearly the same as the acceleration at any given time. (b) Here the acceleration varies greatly, perhaps representing a package on a post office conveyor belt that is accelerated forward and backward as it bumps along. It is necessary to consider small time intervals (such as from 0 to 1.0 s) with constant or nearly constant acceleration in such a situation.

The next several examples consider the motion of the subway train shown in Figure 2.18. In (a) the shuttle moves to the right, and in (b) it moves to the left. The examples are designed to further illustrate aspects of motion and to illustrate some of the reasoning that goes into solving problems.

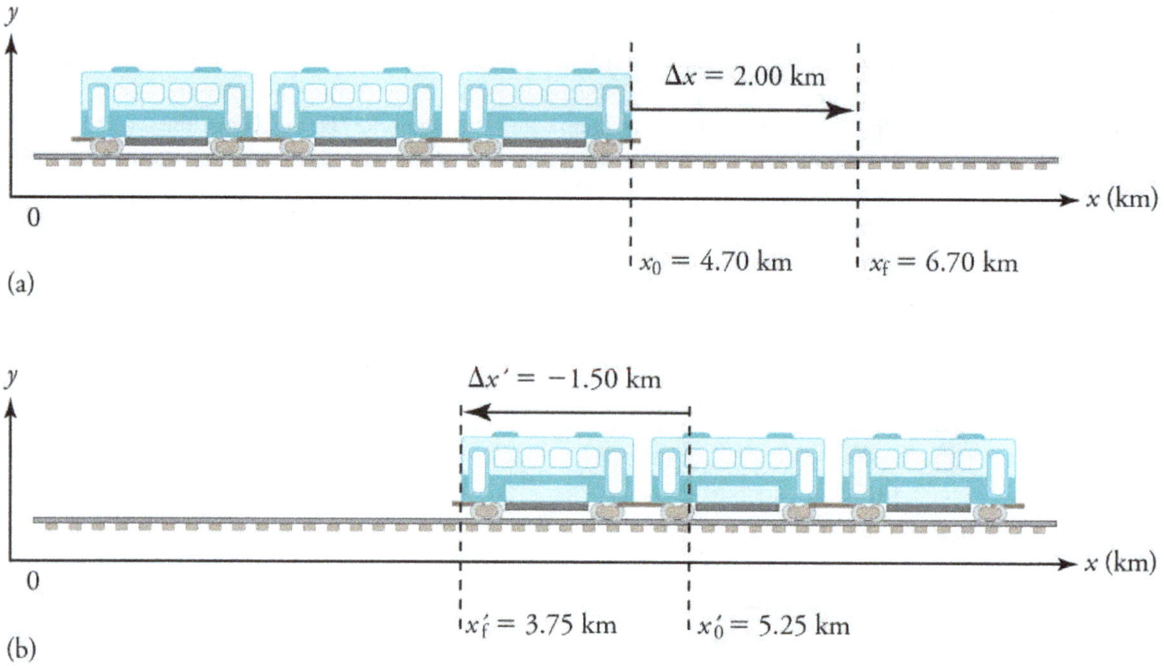

FIGURE 2.18 One-dimensional motion of a subway train considered in Example 2.2, Example 2.3, Example 2.4, Example 2.5, Example 2.6, and Example 2.7. Here we have chosen the x-axis so that + means to the right and − means to the left for displacements, velocities, and accelerations. (a) The subway train moves to the right from x_0 to x_f. Its displacement Δx is +2.0 km. (b) The train moves to the left from x'_0 to x'_f. Its displacement $\Delta x'$ is -1.5 km. (Note that the prime symbol (′) is used simply to distinguish between displacement in the two different situations. The distances of travel and the size of the cars are on different scales to fit everything into the diagram.)

EXAMPLE 2.2

Calculating Displacement: A Subway Train

What are the magnitude and sign of displacements for the motions of the subway train shown in parts (a) and (b) of Figure 2.18?

Strategy

A drawing with a coordinate system is already provided, so we don't need to make a sketch, but we should analyze it to make sure we understand what it is showing. Pay particular attention to the coordinate system. To find displacement, we use the equation $\Delta x = x_f - x_0$. This is straightforward since the initial and final positions are given.

Solution

1. Identify the knowns. In the figure we see that $x_f = 6.70$ km and $x_0 = 4.70$ km for part (a), and $x'_f = 3.75$ km and $x'_0 = 5.25$ km for part (b).

2. Solve for displacement in part (a).

$$\Delta x = x_f - x_0 = 6.70 \text{ km} - 4.70 \text{ km} = +2.00 \text{ km} \tag{2.12}$$

3. Solve for displacement in part (b).

$$\Delta x' = x'_f - x'_0 = 3.75 \text{ km} - 5.25 \text{ km} = -1.50 \text{ km} \tag{2.13}$$

Discussion

The direction of the motion in (a) is to the right and therefore its displacement has a positive sign, whereas motion in (b) is to the left and thus has a negative sign.

EXAMPLE 2.3

Comparing Distance Traveled with Displacement: A Subway Train

What are the distances traveled for the motions shown in parts (a) and (b) of the subway train in Figure 2.18?

Strategy

To answer this question, think about the definitions of distance and distance traveled, and how they are related to displacement. Distance between two positions is defined to be the magnitude of displacement, which was found in Example 2.2. Distance traveled is the total length of the path traveled between the two positions. (See Displacement.) In the case of the subway train shown in Figure 2.18, the distance traveled is the same as the distance between the initial and final positions of the train.

Solution

1. The displacement for part (a) was +2.00 km. Therefore, the distance between the initial and final positions was 2.00 km, and the distance traveled was 2.00 km.

2. The displacement for part (b) was -1.5 km. Therefore, the distance between the initial and final positions was 1.50 km, and the distance traveled was 1.50 km.

Discussion

Distance is a scalar. It has magnitude but no sign to indicate direction.

EXAMPLE 2.4

Calculating Acceleration: A Subway Train Speeding Up

Suppose the train in Figure 2.18(a) accelerates from rest to 30.0 km/h in the first 20.0 s of its motion. What is its average acceleration during that time interval?

Strategy

It is worth it at this point to make a simple sketch:

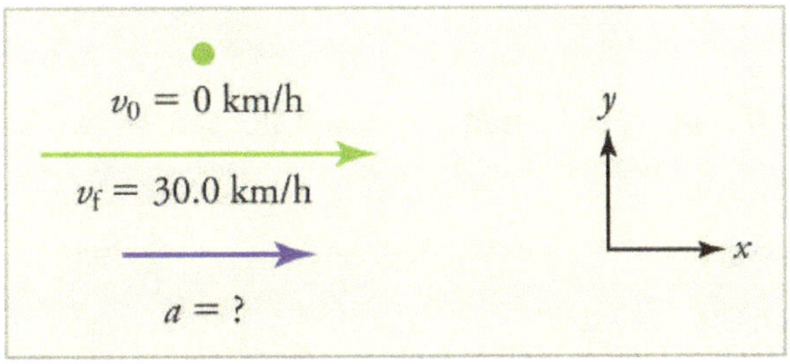

FIGURE 2.19

This problem involves three steps. First we must determine the change in velocity, then we must determine the change in time, and finally we use these values to calculate the acceleration.

Solution

1. Identify the knowns. $v_0 = 0$ (the trains starts at rest), $v_{\text{f}} = 30.0\text{ km/h}$, and $\Delta t = 20.0\text{ s}$.

2. Calculate Δv. Since the train starts from rest, its change in velocity is $\Delta v = +30.0\text{ km/h}$, where the plus sign means velocity to the right.

3. Plug in known values and solve for the unknown, $\bar{a}$.

$$\bar{a} = \frac{\Delta v}{\Delta t} = \frac{+30.0\ \text{km/h}}{20.0\ \text{s}} \quad 2.14$$

4. Since the units are mixed (we have both hours and seconds for time), we need to convert everything into SI units of meters and seconds. (See Physical Quantities and Units for more guidance.)

$$\bar{a} = \left(\frac{+30\ \text{km/h}}{20.0\ \text{s}}\right)\left(\frac{10^3\ \text{m}}{1\ \text{km}}\right)\left(\frac{1\ \text{h}}{3600\ \text{s}}\right) = 0.417\ \text{m/s}^2 \quad 2.15$$

Discussion

The plus sign means that acceleration is to the right. This is reasonable because the train starts from rest and ends up with a velocity to the right (also positive). So acceleration is in the same direction as the *change* in velocity, as is always the case.

EXAMPLE 2.5

Calculate Acceleration: A Subway Train Slowing Down

Now suppose that at the end of its trip, the train in Figure 2.18(a) slows to a stop from a speed of 30.0 km/h in 8.00 s. What is its average acceleration while stopping?

Strategy

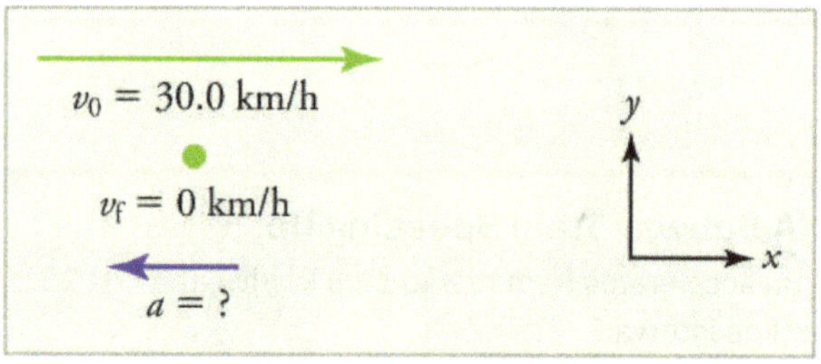

FIGURE 2.20

In this case, the train is decelerating and its acceleration is negative because it is toward the left. As in the previous example, we must find the change in velocity and the change in time and then solve for acceleration.

Solution

1. Identify the knowns. $v_0 = 30.0\ \text{km/h}$, $v_f = 0\ \text{km/h}$ (the train is stopped, so its velocity is 0), and $\Delta t = 8.00\ \text{s}$.

2. Solve for the change in velocity, Δv.

$$\Delta v = v_f - v_0 = 0 - 30.0\ \text{km/h} = -30.0\ \text{km/h} \quad 2.16$$

3. Plug in the knowns, Δv and Δt, and solve for $\bar{a}$.

$$\bar{a} = \frac{\Delta v}{\Delta t} = \frac{-30.0\ \text{km/h}}{8.00\ \text{s}} \quad 2.17$$

4. Convert the units to meters and seconds.

$$\bar{a} = \frac{\Delta v}{\Delta t} = \left(\frac{-30.0\ \text{km/h}}{8.00\ \text{s}}\right)\left(\frac{10^3\ \text{m}}{1\ \text{km}}\right)\left(\frac{1\ \text{h}}{3600\ \text{s}}\right) = -1.04\ \text{m/s}^2. \quad 2.18$$

Discussion

The minus sign indicates that acceleration is to the left. This sign is reasonable because the train initially has a positive velocity in this problem, and a negative acceleration would oppose the motion. Again, acceleration is in the same direction as the *change* in velocity, which is negative here. This acceleration can be called a deceleration because it has a direction opposite to the velocity.

The graphs of position, velocity, and acceleration vs. time for the trains in Example 2.4 and Example 2.5 are displayed in Figure 2.21. (We have taken the velocity to remain constant from 20 to 40 s, after which the train decelerates.)

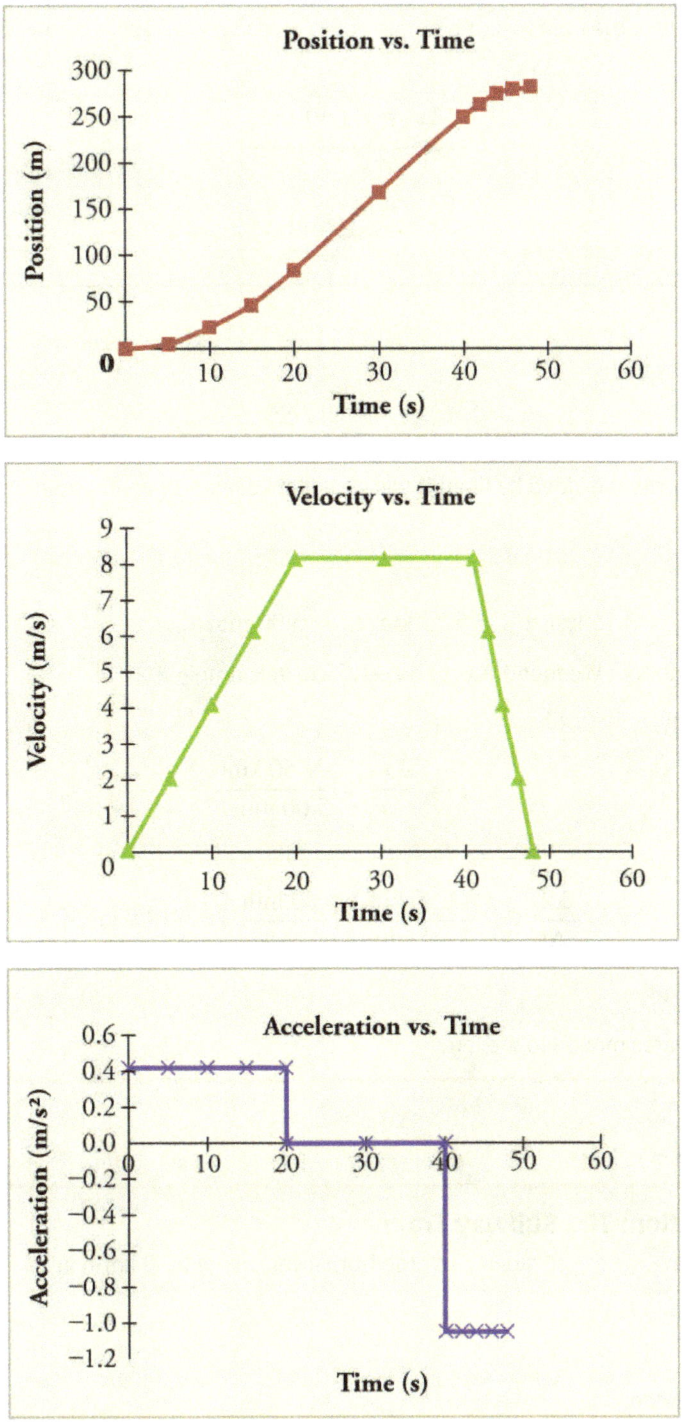

FIGURE 2.21 (a) Position of the train over time. Notice that the train's position changes slowly at the beginning of the journey, then more and more quickly as it picks up speed. Its position then changes more slowly as it slows down at the end of the journey. In the middle of the journey, while the velocity remains constant, the position changes at a constant rate. (b) Velocity of the train over time. The train's velocity increases as it accelerates at the beginning of the journey. It remains the same in the middle of the journey (where there is no acceleration). It decreases as the train decelerates at the end of the journey. (c) The acceleration of the train over time. The train has positive acceleration as it speeds up at the beginning of the journey. It has no acceleration as it travels at constant velocity in the middle of the journey. Its acceleration is negative as it slows down at the end of the journey.

EXAMPLE 2.6

Calculating Average Velocity: The Subway Train

What is the average velocity of the train in part b of Example 2.2, and shown again below, if it takes 5.00 min to make its trip?

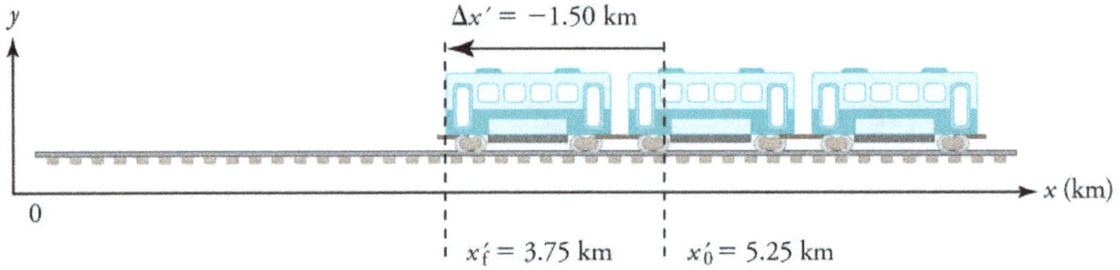

FIGURE 2.22

Strategy

Average velocity is displacement divided by time. It will be negative here, since the train moves to the left and has a negative displacement.

Solution

1. Identify the knowns. $x'_f = 3.75\text{ km}$, $x'_0 = 5.25\text{ km}$, $\Delta t = 5.00\text{ min}$.

2. Determine displacement, $\Delta x'$. We found $\Delta x'$ to be -1.5 km in Example 2.2.

3. Solve for average velocity.

$$\bar{v} = \frac{\Delta x'}{\Delta t} = \frac{-1.50\text{ km}}{5.00\text{ min}} \tag{2.19}$$

4. Convert units.

$$\bar{v} = \frac{\Delta x'}{\Delta t} = \left(\frac{-1.50\text{ km}}{5.00\text{ min}}\right)\left(\frac{60\text{ min}}{1\text{ h}}\right) = -18.0\text{ km/h} \tag{2.20}$$

Discussion

The negative velocity indicates motion to the left.

EXAMPLE 2.7

Calculating Deceleration: The Subway Train

Finally, suppose the train in Figure 2.22 slows to a stop from a velocity of 20.0 km/h in 10.0 s. What is its average acceleration?

Strategy

Once again, let's draw a sketch:

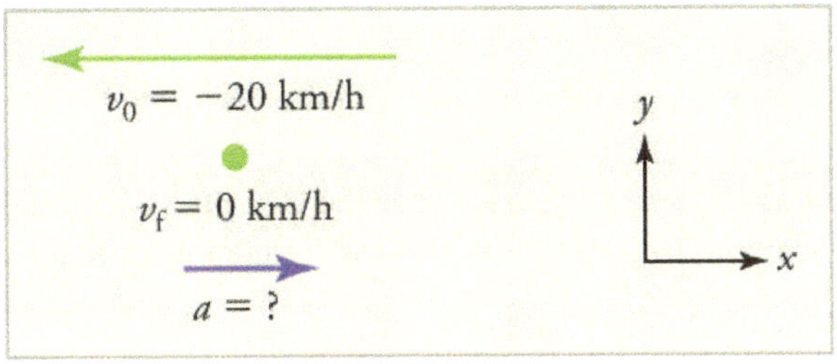

FIGURE 2.23

As before, we must find the change in velocity and the change in time to calculate average acceleration.

Solution

1. Identify the knowns. $v_0 = -20 \text{ km/h}$, $v_f = 0 \text{ km/h}$, $\Delta t = 10.0 \text{ s}$.
2. Calculate Δv. The change in velocity here is actually positive, since

$$\Delta v = v_f - v_0 = 0 - (-20 \text{ km/h}) = +20 \text{ km/h}. \tag{2.21}$$

3. Solve for $\bar{a}$.

$$\bar{a} = \frac{\Delta v}{\Delta t} = \frac{+20.0 \text{ km/h}}{10.0 \text{ s}} \tag{2.22}$$

4. Convert units.

$$\bar{a} = \left(\frac{+20.0 \text{ km/h}}{10.0 \text{ s}}\right)\left(\frac{10^3 \text{ m}}{1 \text{ km}}\right)\left(\frac{1 \text{ h}}{3600 \text{ s}}\right) = +0.556 \text{ m/s}^2 \tag{2.23}$$

Discussion

The plus sign means that acceleration is to the right. This is reasonable because the train initially has a negative velocity (to the left) in this problem and a positive acceleration opposes the motion (and so it is to the right). Again, acceleration is in the same direction as the *change* in velocity, which is positive here. As in Example 2.5, this acceleration can be called a deceleration since it is in the direction opposite to the velocity.

Sign and Direction

Perhaps the most important thing to note about these examples is the signs of the answers. In our chosen coordinate system, plus means the quantity is to the right and minus means it is to the left. This is easy to imagine for displacement and velocity. But it is a little less obvious for acceleration. Most people interpret negative acceleration as the slowing of an object. This was not the case in Example 2.7, where a positive acceleration slowed a negative velocity. The crucial distinction was that the acceleration was in the opposite direction from the velocity. In fact, a negative acceleration will *increase* a negative velocity. For example, the train moving to the left in Figure 2.22 is sped up by an acceleration to the left. In that case, both v and a are negative. The plus and minus signs give the directions of the accelerations. If acceleration has the same sign as the velocity, the object is speeding up. If acceleration has the opposite sign as the velocity, the object is slowing down.

CHECK YOUR UNDERSTANDING

An airplane lands on a runway traveling east. Describe its acceleration.

Solution

If we take east to be positive, then the airplane has negative acceleration, as it is accelerating toward the west. It is also decelerating: its acceleration is opposite in direction to its velocity.

PHET EXPLORATIONS

Moving Man Simulation

Learn about position, velocity, and acceleration graphs. Move the little man back and forth with the mouse and plot his motion. Set the position, velocity, or acceleration and let the simulation move the man for you.

[Click to view content (https://openstax.org/l/02moving_man)](https://openstax.org/l/02moving_man).

2.5 Motion Equations for Constant Acceleration in One Dimension

LEARNING OBJECTIVES

By the end of this section, you will be able to:

- Calculate displacement of an object that is not accelerating, given initial position and velocity.
- Calculate final velocity of an accelerating object, given initial velocity, acceleration, and time.
- Calculate displacement and final position of an accelerating object, given initial position, initial velocity, time, and acceleration.

FIGURE 2.24 Kinematic equations can help us describe and predict the motion of moving objects such as these kayaks racing in Newbury, England. (credit: Barry Skeates, Flickr)

We might know that the greater the acceleration of, say, a car moving away from a stop sign, the greater the displacement in a given time. But we have not developed a specific equation that relates acceleration and displacement. In this section, we develop some convenient equations for kinematic relationships, starting from the definitions of displacement, velocity, and acceleration already covered.

Notation: *t*, *x*, *v*, *a*

First, let us make some simplifications in notation. Taking the initial time to be zero, as if time is measured with a stopwatch, is a great simplification. Since elapsed time is $\Delta t = t_f - t_0$, taking $t_0 = 0$ means that $\Delta t = t_f$, the final time on the stopwatch. When initial time is taken to be zero, we use the subscript 0 to denote initial values of position and velocity. That is, x_0 *is the initial position* and v_0 *is the initial velocity*. We put no subscripts on the final values. That is, t *is the final time*, x *is the final position*, and v *is the final velocity*. This gives a simpler expression for elapsed time—now, $\Delta t = t$. It also simplifies the expression for displacement, which is now $\Delta x = x - x_0$. Also, it simplifies the expression for change in velocity, which is now $\Delta v = v - v_0$. To summarize, using the simplified notation, with the initial time taken to be zero,

$$\left.\begin{array}{rcl}\Delta t & = & t \\ \Delta x & = & x - x_0 \\ \Delta v & = & v - v_0\end{array}\right\} \qquad 2.24$$

where *the subscript 0 denotes an initial value and the absence of a subscript denotes a final value* in whatever motion is under consideration.

We now make the important assumption that *acceleration is constant*. This assumption allows us to avoid using calculus to find instantaneous acceleration. Since acceleration is constant, the average and instantaneous accelerations are equal. That is,

$$\bar{a} = a = \text{constant}, \tag{2.25}$$

so we use the symbol a for acceleration at all times. Assuming acceleration to be constant does not seriously limit the situations we can study nor degrade the accuracy of our treatment. For one thing, acceleration *is* constant in a great number of situations. Furthermore, in many other situations we can accurately describe motion by assuming a constant acceleration equal to the average acceleration for that motion. Finally, in motions where acceleration changes drastically, such as a car accelerating to top speed and then braking to a stop, the motion can be considered in separate parts, each of which has its own constant acceleration.

SOLVING FOR DISPLACEMENT (Δx) AND FINAL POSITION (x) FROM AVERAGE VELOCITY WHEN ACCELERATION (a) IS CONSTANT

To get our first two new equations, we start with the definition of average velocity:

$$\bar{v} = \frac{\Delta x}{\Delta t}. \tag{2.26}$$

Substituting the simplified notation for Δx and Δt yields

$$\bar{v} = \frac{x - x_0}{t}. \tag{2.27}$$

Solving for x yields

$$x = x_0 + \bar{v}t, \tag{2.28}$$

where the average velocity is

$$\bar{v} = \frac{v_0 + v}{2} \text{ (constant } a\text{)}. \tag{2.29}$$

The equation $\bar{v} = \frac{v_0+v}{2}$ reflects the fact that, when acceleration is constant, v is just the simple average of the initial and final velocities. For example, if you steadily increase your velocity (that is, with constant acceleration) from 30 to 60 km/h, then your average velocity during this steady increase is 45 km/h. Using the equation $\bar{v} = \frac{v_0+v}{2}$ to check this, we see that

$$\bar{v} = \frac{v_0 + v}{2} = \frac{30 \text{ km/h} + 60 \text{ km/h}}{2} = 45 \text{ km/h}, \tag{2.30}$$

which seems logical.

EXAMPLE 2.8

Calculating Displacement: How Far does the Jogger Run?

A jogger runs down a straight stretch of road with an average velocity of 4.00 m/s for 2.00 min. What is his final position, taking his initial position to be zero?

Strategy

Draw a sketch.

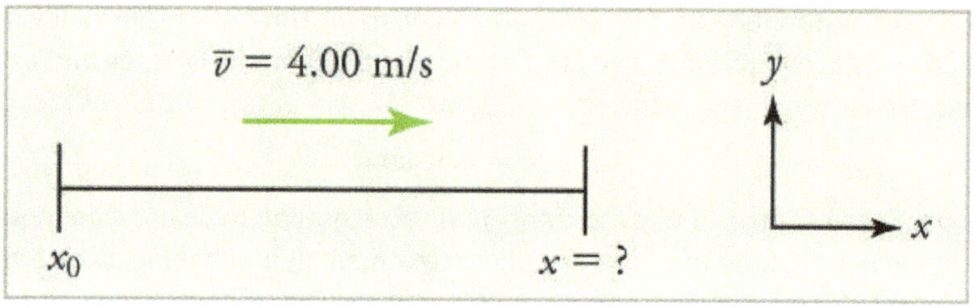

FIGURE 2.25

The final position x is given by the equation

$$x = x_0 + \bar{v}t. \tag{2.31}$$

To find x, we identify the values of x_0, $\bar{v}$, and t from the statement of the problem and substitute them into the equation.

Solution

1. Identify the knowns. $\bar{v} = 4.00\text{ m/s}$, $\Delta t = 2.00\text{ min}$, and $x_0 = 0\text{ m}$.

2. Enter the known values into the equation.

$$x = x_0 + \bar{v}t = 0 + (4.00\text{ m/s})(120\text{ s}) = 480\text{ m} \tag{2.32}$$

Discussion

Velocity and final displacement are both positive, which means they are in the same direction.

The equation $x = x_0 + \bar{v}t$ gives insight into the relationship between displacement, average velocity, and time. It shows, for example, that displacement is a linear function of average velocity. (By linear function, we mean that displacement depends on $\bar{v}$ rather than on $\bar{v}$ raised to some other power, such as $\bar{v}^2$. When graphed, linear functions look like straight lines with a constant slope.) On a car trip, for example, we will get twice as far in a given time if we average 90 km/h than if we average 45 km/h.

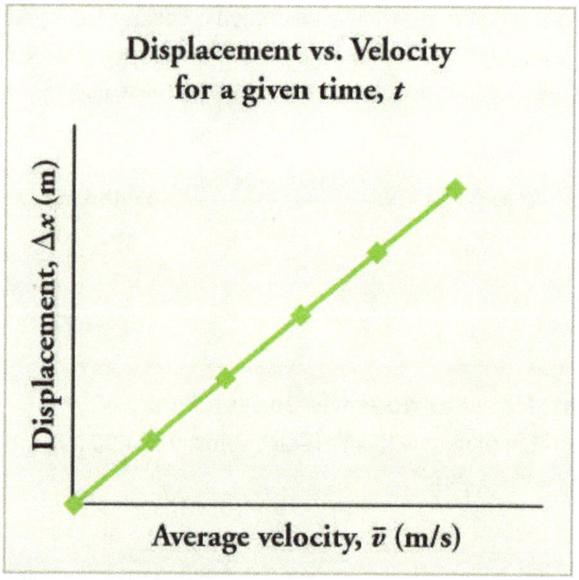

FIGURE 2.26 There is a linear relationship between displacement and average velocity. For a given time t, an object moving twice as fast as another object will move twice as far as the other object.

SOLVING FOR FINAL VELOCITY

We can derive another useful equation by manipulating the definition of acceleration.

$$a = \frac{\Delta v}{\Delta t} \tag{2.33}$$

Substituting the simplified notation for Δv and Δt gives us

$$a = \frac{v - v_0}{t} \text{ (constant } a\text{).} \tag{2.34}$$

Solving for v yields

$$v = v_0 + at \text{ (constant } a\text{).} \tag{2.35}$$

EXAMPLE 2.9

Calculating Final Velocity: An Airplane Slowing Down after Landing

An airplane lands with an initial velocity of 70.0 m/s and then decelerates at 1.50 m/s^2 for 40.0 s. What is its final velocity?

Strategy

Draw a sketch. We draw the acceleration vector in the direction opposite the velocity vector because the plane is decelerating.

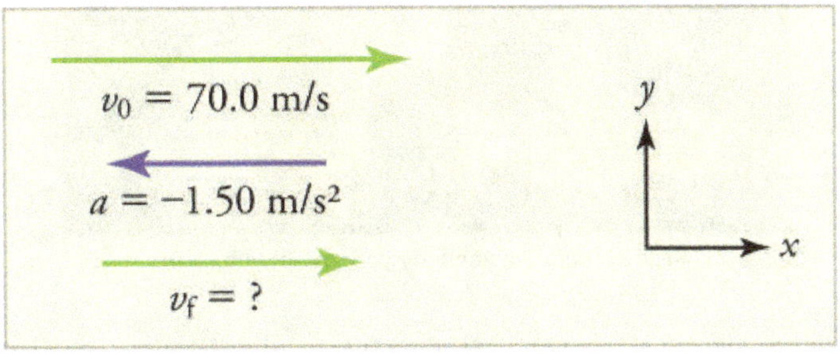

FIGURE 2.27

Solution

1. Identify the knowns. $v_0 = 70.0 \text{ m/s}$, $a = -1.50 \text{ m/s}^2$, $t = 40.0 \text{ s}$.

2. Identify the unknown. In this case, it is final velocity, v_f.

3. Determine which equation to use. We can calculate the final velocity using the equation $v = v_0 + at$.

4. Plug in the known values and solve.

$$v = v_0 + at = 70.0 \text{ m/s} + \left(-1.50 \text{ m/s}^2\right)(40.0 \text{ s}) = 10.0 \text{ m/s} \tag{2.36}$$

Discussion

The final velocity is much less than the initial velocity, as desired when slowing down, but still positive. With jet engines, reverse thrust could be maintained long enough to stop the plane and start moving it backward. That would be indicated by a negative final velocity, which is not the case here.

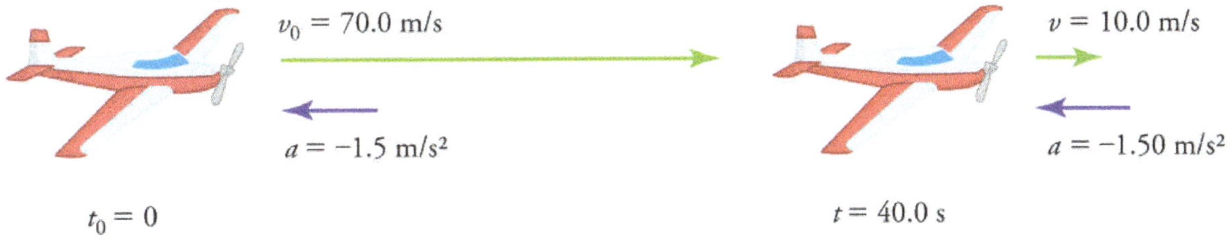

FIGURE 2.28 The airplane lands with an initial velocity of 70.0 m/s and slows to a final velocity of 10.0 m/s before heading for the terminal.

Note that the acceleration is negative because its direction is opposite to its velocity, which is positive.

In addition to being useful in problem solving, the equation $v = v_0 + at$ gives us insight into the relationships among velocity, acceleration, and time. From it we can see, for example, that

- final velocity depends on how large the acceleration is and how long it lasts
- if the acceleration is zero, then the final velocity equals the initial velocity ($v = v_0$), as expected (i.e., velocity is constant)
- if a is negative, then the final velocity is less than the initial velocity

(All of these observations fit our intuition, and it is always useful to examine basic equations in light of our intuition and experiences to check that they do indeed describe nature accurately.)

MAKING CONNECTIONS: REAL-WORLD CONNECTION

FIGURE 2.29 The Space Shuttle *Endeavor* blasts off from the Kennedy Space Center in February 2010. (credit: Matthew Simantov, Flickr)

An intercontinental ballistic missile (ICBM) has a larger average acceleration than the Space Shuttle and achieves a greater velocity in the first minute or two of flight (actual ICBM burn times are classified—short-burn-time missiles are more difficult for an enemy to destroy). But the Space Shuttle obtains a greater final velocity, so that it can orbit the earth rather than come directly back down as an ICBM does. The Space Shuttle does this by accelerating for a longer time.

SOLVING FOR FINAL POSITION WHEN VELOCITY IS NOT CONSTANT ($a \neq 0$)

We can combine the equations above to find a third equation that allows us to calculate the final position of an object experiencing constant acceleration. We start with

$$v = v_0 + at. \tag{2.37}$$

Adding v_0 to each side of this equation and dividing by 2 gives

$$\frac{v_0 + v}{2} = v_0 + \frac{1}{2}at. \tag{2.38}$$

Since $\frac{v_0+v}{2} = \bar{v}$ for constant acceleration, then

$$\bar{v} = v_0 + \frac{1}{2}at. \tag{2.39}$$

Now we substitute this expression for $\bar{v}$ into the equation for displacement, $x = x_0 + \bar{v}t$, yielding

$$x = x_0 + v_0 t + \frac{1}{2}at^2 \text{ (constant } a\text{)}. \tag{2.40}$$

EXAMPLE 2.10

Calculating Displacement of an Accelerating Object: Dragsters

Dragsters can achieve average accelerations of 26.0 m/s^2. Suppose such a dragster accelerates from rest at this rate for 5.56 s. How far does it travel in this time?

FIGURE 2.30 U.S. Army Top Fuel pilot Tony "The Sarge" Schumacher begins a race with a controlled burnout. (credit: Lt. Col. William Thurmond. Photo Courtesy of U.S. Army.)

Strategy

Draw a sketch.

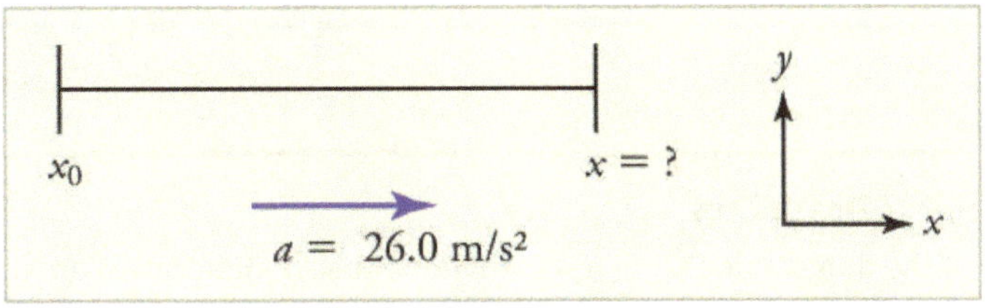

FIGURE 2.31

We are asked to find displacement, which is x if we take x_0 to be zero. (Think about it like the starting line of a race. It can be anywhere, but we call it 0 and measure all other positions relative to it.) We can use the equation $x = x_0 + v_0 t + \frac{1}{2}at^2$ once we identify v_0, a, and t from the statement of the problem.

Solution

1. Identify the knowns. Starting from rest means that $v_0 = 0$, a is given as 26.0 m/s^2 and t is given as 5.56 s.
2. Plug the known values into the equation to solve for the unknown x:

$$x = x_0 + v_0 t + \frac{1}{2}at^2. \tag{2.41}$$

Since the initial position and velocity are both zero, this simplifies to

$$x = \frac{1}{2}at^2. \tag{2.42}$$

Substituting the identified values of a and t gives

$$x = \frac{1}{2}\left(26.0 \text{ m/s}^2\right)(5.56 \text{ s})^2, \tag{2.43}$$

yielding

$$x = 402 \text{ m}. \tag{2.44}$$

Discussion

If we convert 402 m to miles, we find that the distance covered is very close to one quarter of a mile, the standard distance for drag racing. So the answer is reasonable. This is an impressive displacement in only 5.56 s, but top-notch dragsters can do a quarter mile in even less time than this.

What else can we learn by examining the equation $x = x_0 + v_0 t + \frac{1}{2}at^2$? We see that:

- displacement depends on the square of the elapsed time when acceleration is not zero. In Example 2.10, the dragster covers only one fourth of the total distance in the first half of the elapsed time
- if acceleration is zero, then the initial velocity equals average velocity ($v_0 = \overline{v}$) and $x = x_0 + v_0 t + \frac{1}{2}at^2$ becomes $x = x_0 + v_0 t$

SOLVING FOR FINAL VELOCITY WHEN VELOCITY IS NOT CONSTANT ($a \neq 0$)

A fourth useful equation can be obtained from another algebraic manipulation of previous equations.

If we solve $v = v_0 + at$ for t, we get

$$t = \frac{v - v_0}{a}. \tag{2.45}$$

Substituting this and $\overline{v} = \frac{v_0 + v}{2}$ into $x = x_0 + \overline{v}t$, we get

$$v^2 = v_0^2 + 2a(x - x_0) \text{ (constant } a\text{)}. \tag{2.46}$$

EXAMPLE 2.11

Calculating Final Velocity: Dragsters

Calculate the final velocity of the dragster in Example 2.10 without using information about time.

Strategy

Draw a sketch.

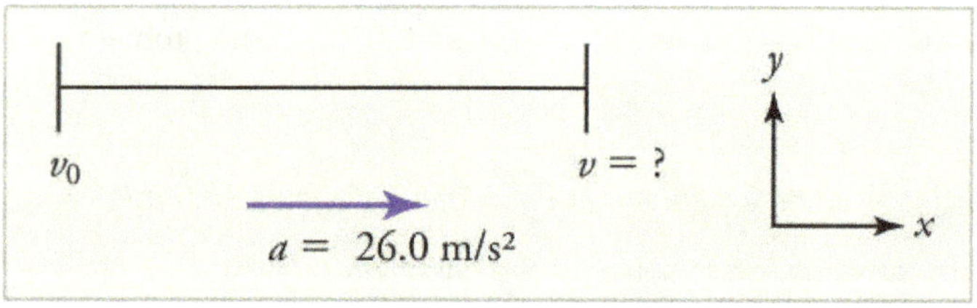

FIGURE 2.32

The equation $v^2 = v_0^2 + 2a(x - x_0)$ is ideally suited to this task because it relates velocities, acceleration, and displacement, and no time information is required.

Solution

1. Identify the known values. We know that $v_0 = 0$, since the dragster starts from rest. Then we note that $x - x_0 = 402 \text{ m}$ (this was the answer in Example 2.10). Finally, the average acceleration was given to be $a = 26.0 \text{ m/s}^2$.

2. Plug the knowns into the equation $v^2 = v_0^2 + 2a(x - x_0)$ and solve for v.

$$v^2 = 0 + 2\left(26.0 \text{ m/s}^2\right)(402 \text{ m}). \tag{2.47}$$

Thus

$$v^2 = 2.09 \times 10^4 \text{ m}^2/\text{s}^2. \tag{2.48}$$

To get v, we take the square root:

$$v = \sqrt{2.09 \times 10^4 \text{ m}^2/\text{s}^2} = 145 \text{ m/s}. \tag{2.49}$$

Discussion

145 m/s is about 522 km/h or about 324 mi/h, but even this breakneck speed is short of the record for the quarter mile. Also, note that a square root has two values; we took the positive value to indicate a velocity in the same direction as the acceleration.

An examination of the equation $v^2 = v_0^2 + 2a(x - x_0)$ can produce further insights into the general relationships among physical quantities:

- The final velocity depends on how large the acceleration is and the distance over which it acts
- For a fixed deceleration, a car that is going twice as fast doesn't simply stop in twice the distance—it takes much further to stop. (This is why we have reduced speed zones near schools.)

Putting Equations Together

In the following examples, we further explore one-dimensional motion, but in situations requiring slightly more algebraic manipulation. The examples also give insight into problem-solving techniques. The box below provides easy reference to the equations needed.

SUMMARY OF KINEMATIC EQUATIONS (CONSTANT a)

$$x = x_0 + \bar{v}t \tag{2.50}$$

$$\bar{v} = \frac{v_0 + v}{2} \tag{2.51}$$

$$v = v_0 + at \tag{2.52}$$

$$x = x_0 + v_0 t + \frac{1}{2}at^2 \tag{2.53}$$

$$v^2 = v_0^2 + 2a(x - x_0) \tag{2.54}$$

EXAMPLE 2.12

Calculating Displacement: How Far Does a Car Go When Coming to a Halt?

On dry concrete, a car can decelerate at a rate of 7.00 m/s^2, whereas on wet concrete it can decelerate at only 5.00 m/s^2. Find the distances necessary to stop a car moving at 30.0 m/s (about 110 km/h) (a) on dry concrete and (b) on wet concrete. (c) Repeat both calculations, finding the displacement from the point where the driver sees a traffic light turn red, taking into account his reaction time of 0.500 s to get his foot on the brake.

Strategy

Draw a sketch.

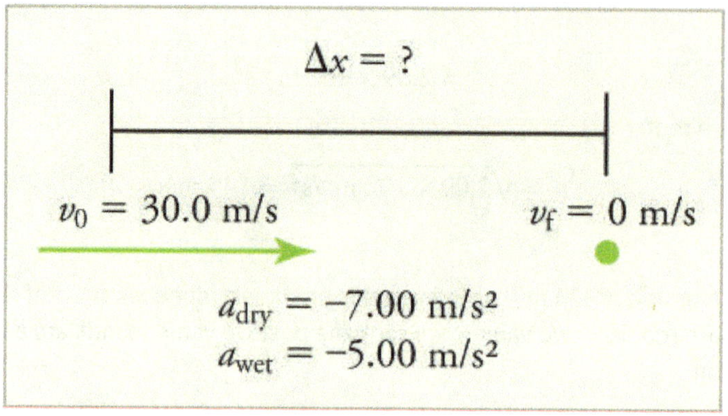

FIGURE 2.33

In order to determine which equations are best to use, we need to list all of the known values and identify exactly what we need to solve for. We shall do this explicitly in the next several examples, using tables to set them off.

Solution for (a)

1. Identify the knowns and what we want to solve for. We know that $v_0 = 30.0\text{ m/s}$; $v = 0$; $a = -7.00\text{ m/s}^2$ (a is negative because it is in a direction opposite to velocity). We take x_0 to be 0. We are looking for displacement Δx, or $x - x_0$.

2. Identify the equation that will help up solve the problem. The best equation to use is

$$v^2 = v_0^2 + 2a(x - x_0). \tag{2.55}$$

This equation is best because it includes only one unknown, x. We know the values of all the other variables in this equation. (There are other equations that would allow us to solve for x, but they require us to know the stopping time, t, which we do not know. We could use them but it would entail additional calculations.)

3. Rearrange the equation to solve for x.

$$x - x_0 = \frac{v^2 - v_0^2}{2a} \tag{2.56}$$

4. Enter known values.

$$x - 0 = \frac{0^2 - (30.0\text{ m/s})^2}{2\left(-7.00\text{ m/s}^2\right)} \tag{2.57}$$

Thus,

$$x = 64.3\text{ m on dry concrete.} \tag{2.58}$$

Solution for (b)

This part can be solved in exactly the same manner as Part A. The only difference is that the deceleration is -5.00 m/s^2. The result is

$$x_{\text{wet}} = 90.0\text{ m on wet concrete.} \tag{2.59}$$

Solution for (c)

Once the driver reacts, the stopping distance is the same as it is in Parts A and B for dry and wet concrete. So to answer this question, we need to calculate how far the car travels during the reaction time, and then add that to the stopping time. It is reasonable to assume that the velocity remains constant during the driver's reaction time.

1. Identify the knowns and what we want to solve for. We know that $\bar{v} = 30.0\text{ m/s}$; $t_{\text{reaction}} = 0.500\text{ s}$; $a_{\text{reaction}} = 0$. We take $x_{0\text{–reaction}}$ to be 0. We are looking for x_{reaction}.

2. Identify the best equation to use.

$x = x_0 + \bar{v}t$ works well because the only unknown value is x, which is what we want to solve for.

3. Plug in the knowns to solve the equation.

$$x = 0 + (30.0\text{ m/s})(0.500\text{ s}) = 15.0\text{ m}. \quad 2.60$$

This means the car travels 15.0 m while the driver reacts, making the total displacements in the two cases of dry and wet concrete 15.0 m greater than if he reacted instantly.

4. Add the displacement during the reaction time to the displacement when braking.

$$x_{\text{braking}} + x_{\text{reaction}} = x_{\text{total}} \quad 2.61$$

a. 64.3 m + 15.0 m = 79.3 m when dry
b. 90.0 m + 15.0 m = 105 m when wet

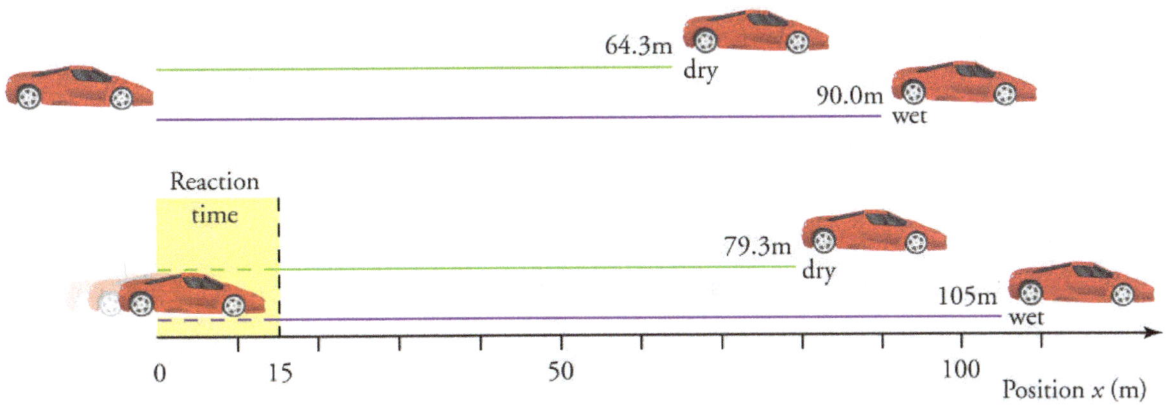

FIGURE 2.34 The distance necessary to stop a car varies greatly, depending on road conditions and driver reaction time. Shown here are the braking distances for dry and wet pavement, as calculated in this example, for a car initially traveling at 30.0 m/s. Also shown are the total distances traveled from the point where the driver first sees a light turn red, assuming a 0.500 s reaction time.

Discussion

The displacements found in this example seem reasonable for stopping a fast-moving car. It should take longer to stop a car on wet rather than dry pavement. It is interesting that reaction time adds significantly to the displacements. But more important is the general approach to solving problems. We identify the knowns and the quantities to be determined and then find an appropriate equation. There is often more than one way to solve a problem. The various parts of this example can in fact be solved by other methods, but the solutions presented above are the shortest.

EXAMPLE 2.13

Calculating Time: A Car Merges into Traffic

Suppose a car merges into freeway traffic on a 200-m-long ramp. If its initial velocity is 10.0 m/s and it accelerates at 2.00 m/s^2, how long does it take to travel the 200 m up the ramp? (Such information might be useful to a traffic engineer.)

Strategy

Draw a sketch.

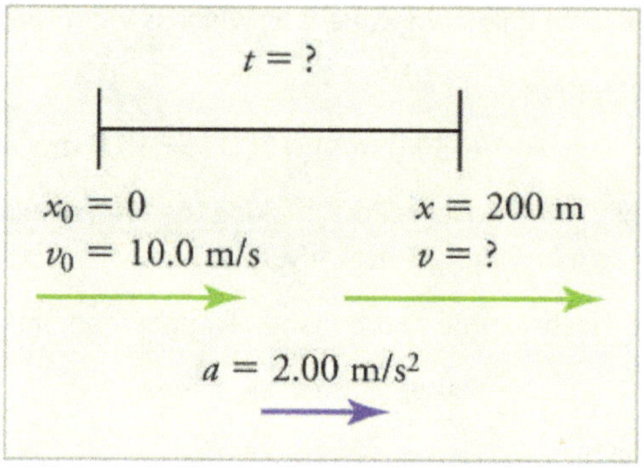

FIGURE 2.35

We are asked to solve for the time t. As before, we identify the known quantities in order to choose a convenient physical relationship (that is, an equation with one unknown, t).

Solution

1. Identify the knowns and what we want to solve for. We know that $v_0 = 10\text{ m/s}$; $a = 2.00\text{ m/s}^2$; and $x = 200\text{ m}$.

2. We need to solve for t. Choose the best equation. $x = x_0 + v_0 t + \frac{1}{2}at^2$ works best because the only unknown in the equation is the variable t for which we need to solve.

3. We will need to rearrange the equation to solve for t. In this case, it will be easier to plug in the knowns first.

$$200\text{ m} = 0\text{ m} + (10.0\text{ m/s})t + \frac{1}{2}\left(2.00\text{ m/s}^2\right)t^2 \tag{2.62}$$

4. Simplify the equation. The units of meters (m) cancel because they are in each term. We can get the units of seconds (s) to cancel by taking $t = t$ s, where t is the magnitude of time and s is the unit. Doing so leaves

$$200 = 10t + t^2. \tag{2.63}$$

5. Use the quadratic formula to solve for t.

(a) Rearrange the equation to get 0 on one side of the equation.

$$t^2 + 10t - 200 = 0 \tag{2.64}$$

This is a quadratic equation of the form

$$at^2 + bt + c = 0, \tag{2.65}$$

where the constants are $a = 1.00$, $b = 10.0$, and $c = -200$.

(b) Its solutions are given by the quadratic formula:

$$t = \frac{-b \pm \sqrt{b^2 - 4ac}}{2a}. \tag{2.66}$$

This yields two solutions for t, which are

$$t = 10.0 \text{ and } -20.0. \tag{2.67}$$

In this case, then, the time is $t = t$ in seconds, or

$$t = 10.0\text{ s and } -20.0\text{ s}. \tag{2.68}$$

A negative value for time is unreasonable, since it would mean that the event happened 20 s before the motion began. We can discard that solution. Thus,

$$t = 10.0\text{ s}. \tag{2.69}$$

Discussion

Whenever an equation contains an unknown squared, there will be two solutions. In some problems both solutions are meaningful, but in others, such as the above, only one solution is reasonable. The 10.0 s answer seems reasonable for a typical freeway on-ramp.

With the basics of kinematics established, we can go on to many other interesting examples and applications. In the process of developing kinematics, we have also glimpsed a general approach to problem solving that produces both correct answers and insights into physical relationships. Problem-Solving Basics discusses problem-solving basics and outlines an approach that will help you succeed in this invaluable task.

MAKING CONNECTIONS: TAKE-HOME EXPERIMENT—BREAKING NEWS

We have been using SI units of meters per second squared to describe some examples of acceleration or deceleration of cars, runners, and trains. To achieve a better feel for these numbers, one can measure the braking deceleration of a car doing a slow (and safe) stop. Recall that, for average acceleration, $\bar{a} = \Delta v/\Delta t$. While traveling in a car, slowly apply the brakes as you come up to a stop sign. Have a passenger note the initial speed in miles per hour and the time taken (in seconds) to stop. From this, calculate the deceleration in miles per hour per second. Convert this to meters per second squared and compare with other decelerations mentioned in this chapter. Calculate the distance traveled in braking.

CHECK YOUR UNDERSTANDING

A rocket accelerates at a rate of $20\ \text{m/s}^2$ during launch. How long does it take the rocket to reach a velocity of 400 m/s?

Solution

To answer this, choose an equation that allows you to solve for time t, given only a, v_0, and v.

$$v = v_0 + at \quad (2.70)$$

Rearrange to solve for t.

$$t = \frac{v - v_0}{a} = \frac{400\ \text{m/s} - 0\ \text{m/s}}{20\ \text{m/s}^2} = 20\ \text{s} \quad (2.71)$$

2.6 Problem-Solving Basics for One-Dimensional Kinematics

LEARNING OBJECTIVES

By the end of this section, you will be able to:

- Apply problem-solving steps and strategies to solve problems of one-dimensional kinematics.
- Apply strategies to determine whether or not the result of a problem is reasonable, and if not, determine the cause.

FIGURE 2.36 Problem-solving skills are essential to your success in Physics. (credit: scui3asteveo, Flickr)

Problem-solving skills are obviously essential to success in a quantitative course in physics. More importantly, the ability to apply broad physical principles, usually represented by equations, to specific situations is a very powerful form of knowledge. It is much more powerful than memorizing a list of facts. Analytical skills and problem-solving abilities can be applied to new situations, whereas a list of facts cannot be made long enough to contain every possible circumstance. Such analytical skills are useful both for solving problems in this text and for applying physics in everyday and professional life.

Problem-Solving Steps

While there is no simple step-by-step method that works for every problem, the following general procedures facilitate problem solving and make it more meaningful. A certain amount of creativity and insight is required as well.

Step 1

Examine the situation to determine which physical principles are involved. It often helps to *draw a simple sketch* at the outset. You will also need to decide which direction is positive and note that on your sketch. Once you have identified the physical principles, it is much easier to find and apply the equations representing those principles. Although finding the correct equation is essential, keep in mind that equations represent physical principles, laws of nature, and relationships among physical quantities. Without a conceptual understanding of a problem, a numerical solution is meaningless.

Step 2

Make a list of what is given or can be inferred from the problem as stated (identify the knowns). Many problems are stated very succinctly and require some inspection to determine what is known. A sketch can also be very useful at this point. Formally identifying the knowns is of particular importance in applying physics to real-world situations. Remember, "stopped" means velocity is zero, and we often can take initial time and position as zero.

Step 3

Identify exactly what needs to be determined in the problem (identify the unknowns). In complex problems, especially, it is not always obvious what needs to be found or in what sequence. Making a list can help.

Step 4

Find an equation or set of equations that can help you solve the problem. Your list of knowns and unknowns can help here. It is easiest if you can find equations that contain only one unknown—that is, all of the other variables are known, so you can easily solve for the unknown. If the equation contains more than one unknown, then an additional equation is needed to solve the problem. In some problems, several unknowns must be determined to get at the one needed most. In such problems it is especially important to keep physical principles in mind to avoid going astray in a sea of equations. You may have to use two (or more) different equations to get the final answer.

Step 5

Substitute the knowns along with their units into the appropriate equation, and obtain numerical solutions complete with units. This step produces the numerical answer; it also provides a check on units that can help you find errors. If the units of the answer are incorrect, then an error has been made. However, be warned that correct units do not guarantee that the numerical part of the answer is also correct.

Step 6

Check the answer to see if it is reasonable: Does it make sense? This final step is extremely important—the goal of physics is to accurately describe nature. To see if the answer is reasonable, check both its magnitude and its sign, in addition to its units. Your judgment will improve as you solve more and more physics problems, and it will become possible for you to make finer and finer judgments regarding whether nature is adequately described by the answer to a problem. This step brings the problem back to its conceptual meaning. If you can judge whether the answer is reasonable, you have a deeper understanding of physics than just being able to mechanically solve a problem.

When solving problems, we often perform these steps in different order, and we also tend to do several steps simultaneously. There is no rigid procedure that will work every time. Creativity and insight grow with experience, and the basics of problem solving become almost automatic. One way to get practice is to work out the text's examples for yourself as you read. Another is to work as many end-of-section problems as possible, starting with the easiest to build confidence and progressing to the more difficult. Once you become involved in physics, you will see it all around you, and you can begin to apply it to situations you encounter outside the classroom, just as is done in many of the applications in this text.

Unreasonable Results

Physics must describe nature accurately. Some problems have results that are unreasonable because one premise is unreasonable or because certain premises are inconsistent with one another. The physical principle applied correctly then produces an unreasonable result. For example, if a person starting a foot race accelerates at $0.40\ \text{m/s}^2$ for 100 s, his final speed will be 40 m/s (about 150 km/h)—clearly unreasonable because the time of 100 s is an unreasonable premise. The physics is correct in a sense, but there is more to describing nature than just manipulating equations correctly. Checking the result of a problem to see if it is reasonable does more than help uncover errors in problem solving—it also builds intuition in judging whether nature is being accurately described.

Use the following strategies to determine whether an answer is reasonable and, if it is not, to determine what is the cause.

Step 1

Solve the problem using strategies as outlined and in the format followed in the worked examples in the text. In the example given in the preceding paragraph, you would identify the givens as the acceleration and time and use the equation below to find the unknown final velocity. That is,

$$v = v_0 + at = 0 + \left(0.40\ \text{m/s}^2\right)(100\ \text{s}) = 40\ \text{m/s}. \tag{2.72}$$

Step 2

Check to see if the answer is reasonable. Is it too large or too small, or does it have the wrong sign, improper units, ...? In this case, you may need to convert meters per second into a more familiar unit, such as miles per hour.

$$\left(\frac{40\ \text{m}}{\text{s}}\right)\left(\frac{3.28\ \text{ft}}{\text{m}}\right)\left(\frac{1\ \text{mi}}{5280\ \text{ft}}\right)\left(\frac{60\ \text{s}}{\text{min}}\right)\left(\frac{60\ \text{min}}{1\ \text{h}}\right) = 89\ \text{mph} \tag{2.73}$$

This velocity is about four times greater than a person can run—so it is too large.

Step 3

If the answer is unreasonable, look for what specifically could cause the identified difficulty. In the example of the runner, there are only two assumptions that are suspect. The acceleration could be too great or the time too long. First look at the acceleration and think about what the number means. If someone accelerates at $0.40\ \text{m/s}^2$, their velocity is increasing by 0.4 m/s each second. Does this seem reasonable? If so, the time must be too long. It is not possible for someone to accelerate at a constant rate of $0.40\ \text{m/s}^2$ for 100 s (almost two minutes).

2.7 Falling Objects

LEARNING OBJECTIVES

By the end of this section, you will be able to:

- Describe the effects of gravity on objects in motion.
- Describe the motion of objects that are in free fall.
- Calculate the position and velocity of objects in free fall.

Falling objects form an interesting class of motion problems. For example, we can estimate the depth of a vertical mine shaft by dropping a rock into it and listening for the rock to hit the bottom. By applying the kinematics developed so far to falling objects, we can examine some interesting situations and learn much about gravity in the process.

Gravity

The most remarkable and unexpected fact about falling objects is that, if air resistance and friction are negligible, then in a given location all objects fall toward the center of Earth with the *same constant acceleration, independent of their mass*. This experimentally determined fact is unexpected, because we are so accustomed to the effects of air resistance and friction that we expect light objects to fall slower than heavy ones.

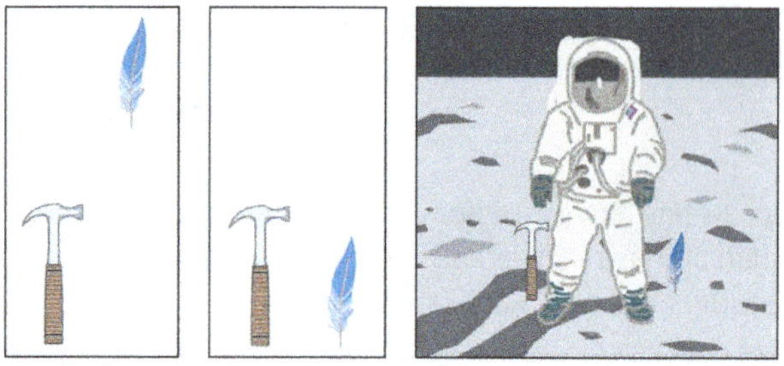

FIGURE 2.37 A hammer and a feather will fall with the same constant acceleration if air resistance is considered negligible. This is a general characteristic of gravity not unique to Earth, as astronaut David R. Scott demonstrated on the Moon in 1971, where the acceleration due to gravity is only 1.67 m/s^2.

In the real world, air resistance can cause a lighter object to fall slower than a heavier object of the same size. A tennis ball will reach the ground after a hard baseball dropped at the same time. (It might be difficult to observe the difference if the height is not large.) Air resistance opposes the motion of an object through the air, while friction between objects—such as between clothes and a laundry chute or between a stone and a pool into which it is dropped—also opposes motion between them. For the ideal situations of these first few chapters, an object *falling without air resistance or friction* is defined to be in **free-fall.**

The force of gravity causes objects to fall toward the center of Earth. The acceleration of free-falling objects is therefore called the **acceleration due to gravity**. The acceleration due to gravity is *constant*, which means we can apply the kinematics equations to any falling object where air resistance and friction are negligible. This opens a broad class of interesting situations to us. The acceleration due to gravity is so important that its magnitude is given its own symbol, g. It is constant at any given location on Earth and has the average value

$$g = 9.80 \text{ m/s}^2. \quad 2.74$$

Although g varies from 9.78 m/s^2 to 9.83 m/s^2, depending on latitude, altitude, underlying geological formations, and local topography, the average value of 9.80 m/s^2 will be used in this text unless otherwise specified. The direction of the acceleration due to gravity is *downward (towards the center of Earth).* In fact, its direction *defines* what we call vertical. Note that whether the acceleration a in the kinematic equations has the value $+g$ or $-g$ depends on how we define our coordinate system. If we define the upward direction as positive, then $a = -g = -9.80 \text{ m/s}^2$, and if we define the downward direction as positive, then $a = g = 9.80 \text{ m/s}^2$.

One-Dimensional Motion Involving Gravity

The best way to see the basic features of motion involving gravity is to start with the simplest situations and then progress toward more complex ones. So we start by considering straight up and down motion with no air resistance or friction. These assumptions mean that the velocity (if there is any) is vertical. If the object is dropped, we know the initial velocity is zero. Once the object has left contact with whatever held or threw it, the object is in free-fall. Under these circumstances, the motion is one-dimensional and has constant acceleration of magnitude g. We will also represent vertical displacement with the symbol y and use x for horizontal displacement.

KINEMATIC EQUATIONS FOR OBJECTS IN FREE-FALL WHERE ACCELERATION = -G

$$v = v_0 - gt \quad 2.75$$

$$y = y_0 + v_0 t - \frac{1}{2} g t^2 \quad 2.76$$

$$v^2 = v_0^2 - 2g(y - y_0) \quad 2.77$$

EXAMPLE 2.14

Calculating Position and Velocity of a Falling Object: A Rock Thrown Upward

A person standing on the edge of a high cliff throws a rock straight up with an initial velocity of 13.0 m/s. The rock misses the edge of the cliff as it falls back to earth. Calculate the position and velocity of the rock 1.00 s, 2.00 s, and 3.00 s after it is thrown, neglecting the effects of air resistance.

Strategy

Draw a sketch.

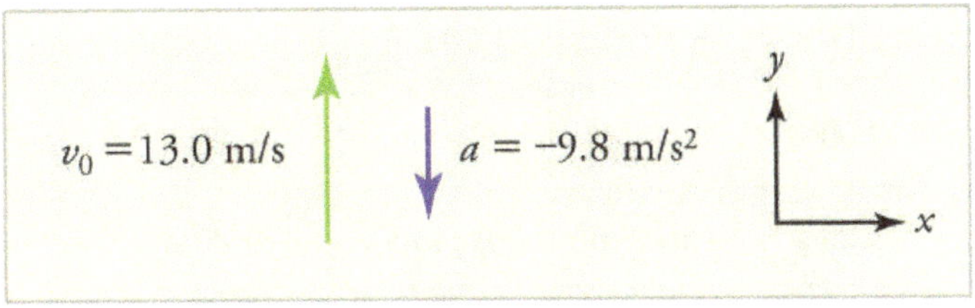

FIGURE 2.38

We are asked to determine the position y at various times. It is reasonable to take the initial position y_0 to be zero. This problem involves one-dimensional motion in the vertical direction. We use plus and minus signs to indicate direction, with up being positive and down negative. Since up is positive, and the rock is thrown upward, the initial velocity must be positive too. The acceleration due to gravity is downward, so a is negative. It is crucial that the initial velocity and the acceleration due to gravity have opposite signs. Opposite signs indicate that the acceleration due to gravity opposes the initial motion and will slow and eventually reverse it.

Since we are asked for values of position and velocity at three times, we will refer to these as y_1 and v_1; y_2 and v_2; and y_3 and v_3.

Solution for Position

y_1

1. Identify the knowns. We know that $y_0 = 0$; $v_0 = 13.0\text{ m/s}$; $a = -g = -9.80\text{ m/s}^2$; and $t = 1.00\text{ s}$.

2. Identify the best equation to use. We will use $y = y_0 + v_0 t + \frac{1}{2}at^2$ because it includes only one unknown, y (or y_1, here), which is the value we want to find.

3. Plug in the known values and solve for y_1.

$$y_1 = 0 + (13.0\text{ m/s})(1.00\text{ s}) + \frac{1}{2}\left(-9.80\text{ m/s}^2\right)(1.00\text{ s})^2 = 8.10\text{ m} \qquad 2.78$$

Discussion

The rock is 8.10 m above its starting point at $t = 1.00$ s, since $y_1 > y_0$. It could be *moving* up or down; the only way to tell is to calculate v_1 and find out if it is positive or negative.

Solution for Velocity

v_1

1. Identify the knowns. We know that $y_0 = 0$; $v_0 = 13.0\text{ m/s}$; $a = -g = -9.80\text{ m/s}^2$; and $t = 1.00\text{ s}$. We also know from the solution above that $y_1 = 8.10\text{ m}$.

2. Identify the best equation to use. The most straightforward is $v = v_0 - gt$ (from $v = v_0 + at$, where $a = \text{gravitational acceleration} = -g$).

3. Plug in the knowns and solve.

$$v_1 = v_0 - gt = 13.0\text{ m/s} - \left(9.80\text{ m/s}^2\right)(1.00\text{ s}) = 3.20\text{ m/s} \qquad 2.79$$

Discussion

The positive value for v_1 means that the rock is still heading upward at $t = 1.00\ \text{s}$. However, it has slowed from its original 13.0 m/s, as expected.

Solution for Remaining Times

The procedures for calculating the position and velocity at $t = 2.00\ \text{s}$ and $3.00\ \text{s}$ are the same as those above. The results are summarized in Table 2.1 and illustrated in Figure 2.39.

Time, *t*	Position, *y*	Velocity, *v*	Acceleration, *a*
$1.00\ \text{s}$	$8.10\ \text{m}$	$3.20\ \text{m/s}$	$-9.80\ \text{m/s}^2$
$2.00\ \text{s}$	$6.40\ \text{m}$	$-6.60\ \text{m/s}$	$-9.80\ \text{m/s}^2$
$3.00\ \text{s}$	$-5.10\ \text{m}$	$-16.4\ \text{m/s}$	$-9.80\ \text{m/s}^2$

TABLE 2.1 Results

Graphing the data helps us understand it more clearly.

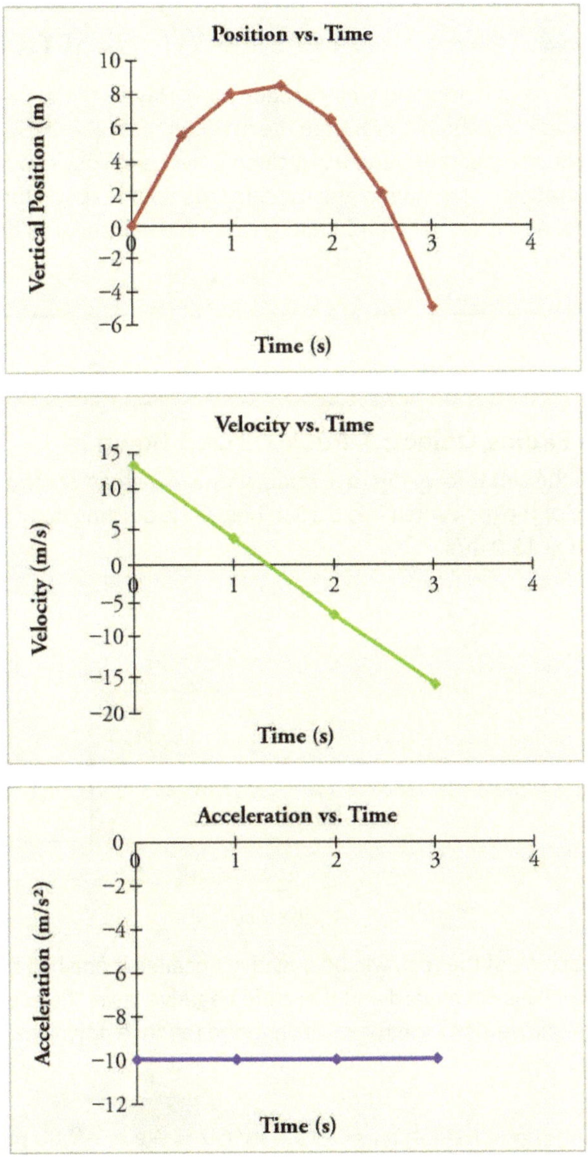

FIGURE 2.39 Vertical position, vertical velocity, and vertical acceleration vs. time for a rock thrown vertically up at the edge of a cliff. Notice that velocity changes linearly with time and that acceleration is constant. *Misconception Alert!* Notice that the position vs. time graph shows vertical position only. It is easy to get the impression that the graph shows some horizontal motion—the shape of the graph looks like the path of a projectile. But this is not the case; the horizontal axis is *time*, not space. The actual path of the rock in space is straight up, and straight down.

Discussion

The interpretation of these results is important. At 1.00 s the rock is above its starting point and heading upward, since y_1 and v_1 are both positive. At 2.00 s, the rock is still above its starting point, but the negative velocity means it is moving downward. At 3.00 s, both y_3 and v_3 are negative, meaning the rock is below its starting point and continuing to move downward. Notice that when the rock is at its highest point (at 1.5 s), its velocity is zero, but its acceleration is still $-9.80\ \text{m/s}^2$. Its acceleration is $-9.80\ \text{m/s}^2$ for the whole trip—while it is moving up and while it is moving down. Note that the values for y are the positions (or displacements) of the rock, not the total distances traveled. Finally, note that free-fall applies to upward motion as well as downward. Both have the same acceleration—the acceleration due to gravity, which remains constant the entire time. Astronauts training in the famous Vomit Comet, for example, experience free-fall while arcing up as well as down, as we will discuss in more detail later.

MAKING CONNECTIONS: TAKE-HOME EXPERIMENT—REACTION TIME

A simple experiment can be done to determine your reaction time. Have a friend hold a ruler between your thumb and index finger, separated by about 1 cm. Note the mark on the ruler that is right between your fingers. Have your friend drop the ruler unexpectedly, and try to catch it between your two fingers. Note the new reading on the ruler. Assuming acceleration is that due to gravity, calculate your reaction time. How far would you travel in a car (moving at 30 m/s) if the time it took your foot to go from the gas pedal to the brake was twice this reaction time?

EXAMPLE 2.15

Calculating Velocity of a Falling Object: A Rock Thrown Down

What happens if the person on the cliff throws the rock straight down, instead of straight up? To explore this question, calculate the velocity of the rock when it is 5.10 m below the starting point, and has been thrown downward with an initial speed of 13.0 m/s.

Strategy

Draw a sketch.

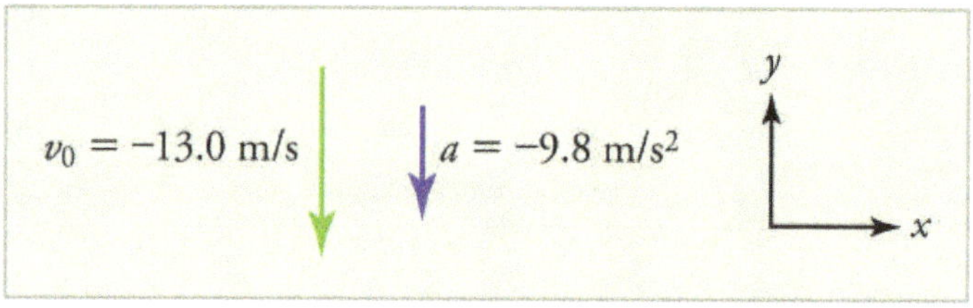

FIGURE 2.40

Since up is positive, the final position of the rock will be negative because it finishes below the starting point at $y_0 = 0$. Similarly, the initial velocity is downward and therefore negative, as is the acceleration due to gravity. We expect the final velocity to be negative since the rock will continue to move downward.

Solution

1. Identify the knowns. $y_0 = 0$; $y_1 = -5.10\text{ m}$; $v_0 = -13.0\text{ m/s}$; $a = -g = -9.80\text{ m/s}^2$.

2. Choose the kinematic equation that makes it easiest to solve the problem. The equation $v^2 = v_0^2 + 2a(y - y_0)$ works well because the only unknown in it is v. (We will plug y_1 in for y.)

3. Enter the known values

$$v^2 = (-13.0\text{ m/s})^2 + 2\left(-9.80\text{ m/s}^2\right)(-5.10\text{ m} - 0\text{ m}) = 268.96\text{ m}^2/\text{s}^2, \tag{2.80}$$

where we have retained extra significant figures because this is an intermediate result.

Taking the square root, and noting that a square root can be positive or negative, gives

$$v = \pm 16.4\text{ m/s}. \tag{2.81}$$

The negative root is chosen to indicate that the rock is still heading down. Thus,

$$v = -16.4\text{ m/s}. \tag{2.82}$$

Discussion

Note that *this is exactly the same velocity the rock had at this position when it was thrown straight upward with the same initial speed.* (See Example 2.14 and Figure 2.41(a).) This is not a coincidental result. Because we only consider the acceleration due to gravity in this problem, the *speed* of a falling object depends only on its initial speed and its vertical position relative to the starting point. For example, if the velocity of the rock is calculated at a height of 8.10 m above the starting point (using the method from Example 2.14) when the initial velocity is 13.0 m/s straight up, a result of ± 3.20 m/s is obtained. Here both signs are meaningful; the positive value occurs when the rock is at 8.10 m and heading up, and the negative value occurs when the rock is at 8.10 m and heading back down. It has the same *speed* but the opposite direction.

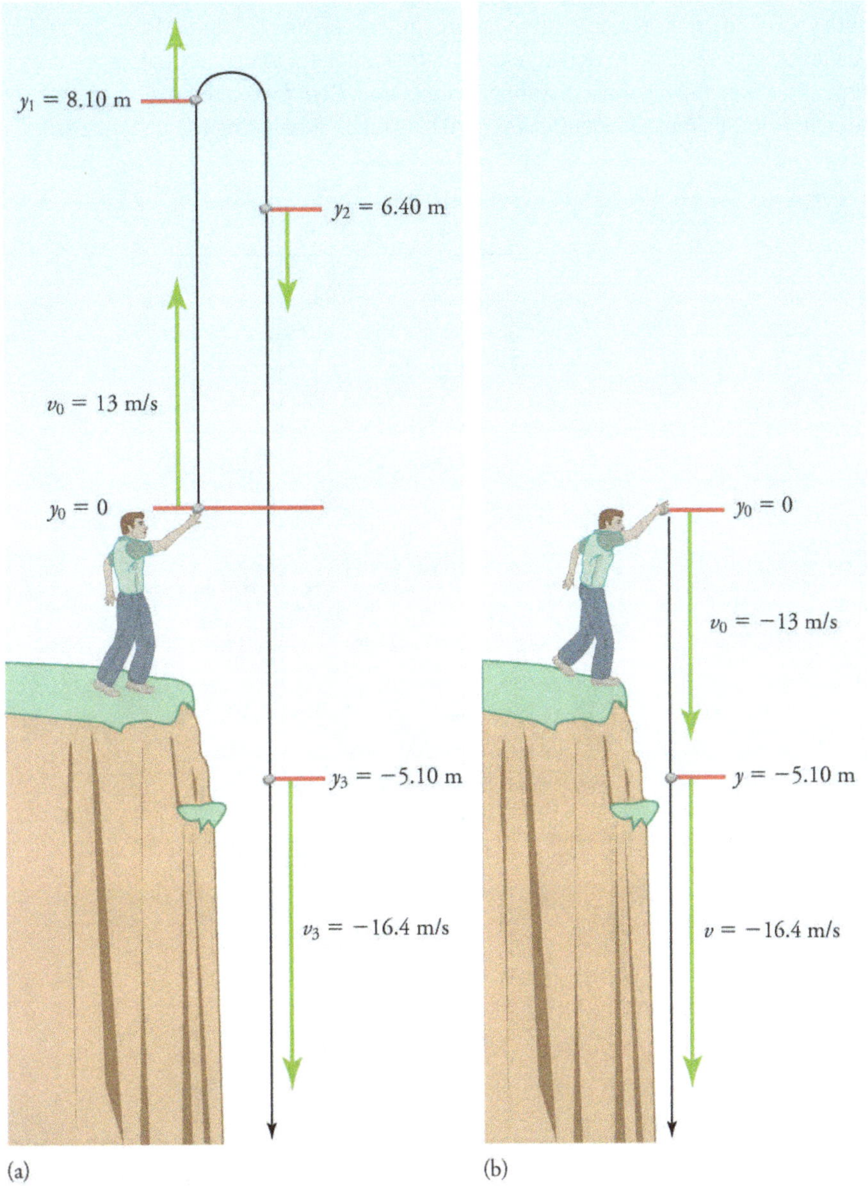

FIGURE 2.41 (a) A person throws a rock straight up, as explored in Example 2.14. The arrows are velocity vectors at 0, 1.00, 2.00, and 3.00 s. (b) A person throws a rock straight down from a cliff with the same initial speed as before, as in Example 2.15. Note that at the same distance below the point of release, the rock has the same velocity in both cases.

Another way to look at it is this: In Example 2.14, the rock is thrown up with an initial velocity of 13.0 m/s. It rises and then falls back down. When its position is $y = 0$ on its way back down, its velocity is -13.0 m/s. That is, it has the same speed on its way down as on its way up. We would then expect its velocity at a position of $y = -5.10$ m to be the same whether we have thrown it upwards at $+13.0$ m/s or thrown it downwards at -13.0 m/s. The velocity of the rock on its way down from $y = 0$ is the same whether we have thrown it up or down to start with, as long as the speed with which it was initially thrown is the same.

EXAMPLE 2.16

Find *g* from Data on a Falling Object

The acceleration due to gravity on Earth differs slightly from place to place, depending on topography (e.g., whether you are on a hill or in a valley) and subsurface geology (whether there is dense rock like iron ore as opposed to light rock like salt beneath you.) The precise acceleration due to gravity can be calculated from data taken in an introductory physics laboratory course. An object, usually a metal ball for which air resistance is negligible, is dropped and the time it takes to fall a known distance is measured. See, for example, Figure 2.42. Very precise results can be produced with this method if sufficient care is taken in measuring the distance fallen and the elapsed time.

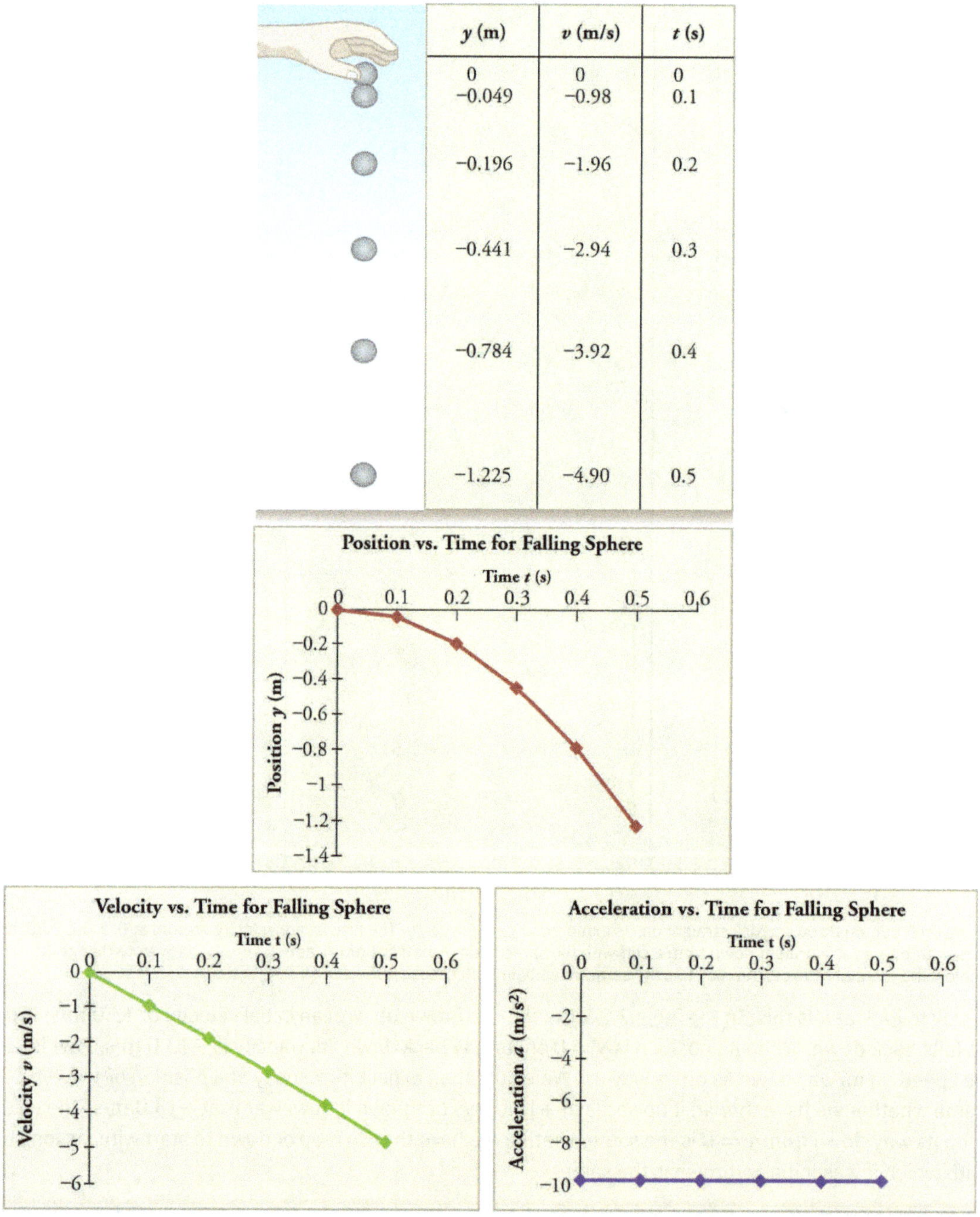

y (m)	v (m/s)	t (s)
0	0	0
−0.049	−0.98	0.1
−0.196	−1.96	0.2
−0.441	−2.94	0.3
−0.784	−3.92	0.4
−1.225	−4.90	0.5

FIGURE 2.42 Positions and velocities of a metal ball released from rest when air resistance is negligible. Velocity is seen to increase linearly with time while displacement increases with time squared. Acceleration is a constant and is equal to gravitational acceleration.

Suppose the ball falls 1.0000 m in 0.45173 s. Assuming the ball is not affected by air resistance, what is the precise acceleration due to gravity at this location?

Strategy

Draw a sketch.

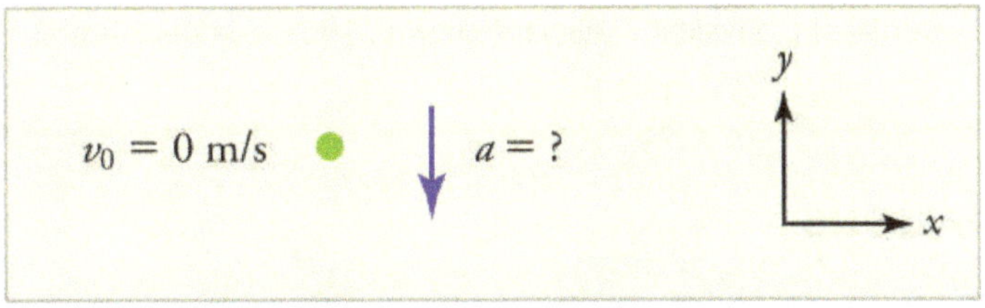

FIGURE 2.43

We need to solve for acceleration a. Note that in this case, displacement is downward and therefore negative, as is acceleration.

Solution

1. Identify the knowns. $y_0 = 0$; $y = -1.0000$ m; $t = 0.45173$; $v_0 = 0$.

2. Choose the equation that allows you to solve for a using the known values.

$$y = y_0 + v_0 t + \frac{1}{2}at^2 \tag{2.83}$$

3. Substitute 0 for v_0 and rearrange the equation to solve for a. Substituting 0 for v_0 yields

$$y = y_0 + \frac{1}{2}at^2. \tag{2.84}$$

Solving for a gives

$$a = \frac{2(y - y_0)}{t^2}. \tag{2.85}$$

4. Substitute known values yields

$$a = \frac{2(-1.0000 \text{ m} - 0)}{(0.45173 \text{ s})^2} = -9.8010 \text{ m/s}^2, \tag{2.86}$$

so, because $a = -g$ with the directions we have chosen,

$$g = 9.8010 \text{ m/s}^2. \tag{2.87}$$

Discussion

The negative value for a indicates that the gravitational acceleration is downward, as expected. We expect the value to be somewhere around the average value of 9.80 m/s^2, so 9.8010 m/s^2 makes sense. Since the data going into the calculation are relatively precise, this value for g is more precise than the average value of 9.80 m/s^2; it represents the local value for the acceleration due to gravity.

CHECK YOUR UNDERSTANDING

A chunk of ice breaks off a glacier and falls 30.0 meters before it hits the water. Assuming it falls freely (there is no air resistance), how long does it take to hit the water?

Solution

We know that initial position $y_0 = 0$, final position $y = -30.0$ m, and $a = -g = -9.80 \text{ m/s}^2$. We can then use the equation $y = y_0 + v_0 t + \frac{1}{2}at^2$ to solve for t. Inserting $a = -g$, we obtain

$$\begin{aligned} y &= 0 + 0 - \tfrac{1}{2}gt^2 \\ t^2 &= \frac{2y}{-g} \\ t &= \pm\sqrt{\frac{2y}{-g}} = \pm\sqrt{\frac{2(-30.0\text{ m})}{-9.80\text{ m/s}^2}} = \pm\sqrt{6.12\text{ s}^2} = 2.47\text{ s} \approx 2.5\text{ s} \end{aligned} \quad (2.88)$$

where we take the positive value as the physically relevant answer. Thus, it takes about 2.5 seconds for the piece of ice to hit the water.

PHET EXPLORATIONS

Equation Grapher

Learn about graphing polynomials. The shape of the curve changes as the constants are adjusted. View the curves for the individual terms (e.g. $y = bx$) to see how they add to generate the polynomial curve.

Click to view content (https://openstax.org/books/college-physics-ap-courses-2e/pages/2-7-falling-objects)

PhET

2.8 Graphical Analysis of One-Dimensional Motion

LEARNING OBJECTIVES

By the end of this section, you will be able to:

- Describe a straight-line graph in terms of its slope and y-intercept.
- Determine average velocity or instantaneous velocity from a graph of position vs. time.
- Determine average or instantaneous acceleration from a graph of velocity vs. time.
- Derive a graph of velocity vs. time from a graph of position vs. time.
- Derive a graph of acceleration vs. time from a graph of velocity vs. time.

A graph, like a picture, is worth a thousand words. Graphs not only contain numerical information; they also reveal relationships between physical quantities. This section uses graphs of position, velocity, and acceleration versus time to illustrate one-dimensional kinematics.

Slopes and General Relationships

First note that graphs in this text have perpendicular axes, one horizontal and the other vertical. When two physical quantities are plotted against one another in such a graph, the horizontal axis is usually considered to be an **independent variable** and the vertical axis a **dependent variable**. If we call the horizontal axis the x-axis and the vertical axis the y-axis, as in Figure 2.44, a straight-line graph has the general form

$$y = mx + b. \quad (2.89)$$

Here m is the **slope**, defined to be the rise divided by the run (as seen in the figure) of the straight line. The letter b is used for the ***y*-intercept**, which is the point at which the line crosses the vertical axis.

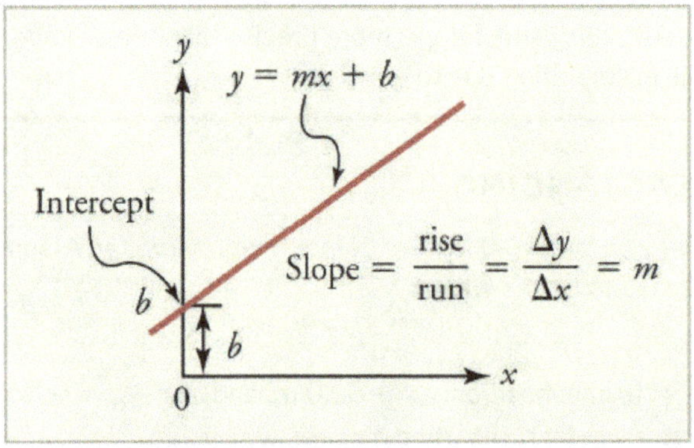

FIGURE 2.44 A straight-line graph. The equation for a straight line is $y = mx + b$.

Graph of Position vs. Time ($a = 0$, so v is constant)

Time is usually an independent variable that other quantities, such as position, depend upon. A graph of position versus time would, thus, have x on the vertical axis and t on the horizontal axis. Figure 2.45 is just such a straight-line graph. It shows a graph of position versus time for a jet-powered car on a very flat dry lake bed in Nevada.

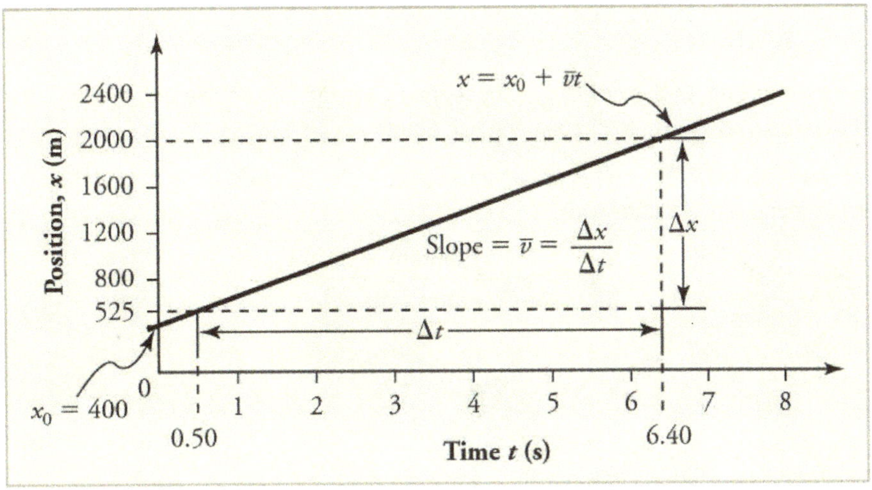

FIGURE 2.45 Graph of position versus time for a jet-powered car on the Bonneville Salt Flats.

Using the relationship between dependent and independent variables, we see that the slope in the graph above is average velocity $\bar{v}$ and the intercept is position at time zero—that is, x_0. Substituting these symbols into $y = mx + b$ gives

$$x = \bar{v}t + x_0 \tag{2.90}$$

or

$$x = x_0 + \bar{v}t. \tag{2.91}$$

Thus a graph of position versus time gives a general relationship among displacement(change in position), velocity, and time, as well as giving detailed numerical information about a specific situation.

THE SLOPE OF *X* VS. *T*

The slope of the graph of position x vs. time t is velocity v.

$$\text{slope} = \frac{\Delta x}{\Delta t} = v \tag{2.92}$$

Notice that this equation is the same as that derived algebraically from other motion equations in Motion Equations for Constant Acceleration in One Dimension.

From the figure we can see that the car has a position of 525 m at 0.50 s and 2000 m at 6.40 s. Its position at other times can be read from the graph; furthermore, information about its velocity and acceleration can also be obtained from the graph.

EXAMPLE 2.17

Determining Average Velocity from a Graph of Position versus Time: Jet Car

Find the average velocity of the car whose position is graphed in Figure 2.45.

Strategy

The slope of a graph of x vs. t is average velocity, since slope equals rise over run. In this case, rise = change in position and run = change in time, so that

$$\text{slope} = \frac{\Delta x}{\Delta t} = \bar{v}. \qquad 2.93$$

Since the slope is constant here, any two points on the graph can be used to find the slope. (Generally speaking, it is most accurate to use two widely separated points on the straight line. This is because any error in reading data from the graph is proportionally smaller if the interval is larger.)

Solution

1. Choose two points on the line. In this case, we choose the points labeled on the graph: (6.4 s, 2000 m) and (0.50 s, 525 m). (Note, however, that you could choose any two points.)

2. Substitute the x and t values of the chosen points into the equation. Remember in calculating change (Δ) we always use final value minus initial value.

$$\bar{v} = \frac{\Delta x}{\Delta t} = \frac{2000\text{ m} - 525\text{ m}}{6.4\text{ s} - 0.50\text{ s}}, \qquad 2.94$$

yielding

$$\bar{v} = 250\text{ m/s}. \qquad 2.95$$

Discussion

This is an impressively large land speed (900 km/h, or about 560 mi/h): much greater than the typical highway speed limit of 60 mi/h (27 m/s or 96 km/h), but considerably shy of the record of 343 m/s (1234 km/h or 766 mi/h) set in 1997.

Graphs of Motion when a is constant but $a \neq 0$

The graphs in Figure 2.46 below represent the motion of the jet-powered car as it accelerates toward its top speed, but only during the time when its acceleration is constant. Time starts at zero for this motion (as if measured with a stopwatch), and the position and velocity are initially 200 m and 15 m/s, respectively.

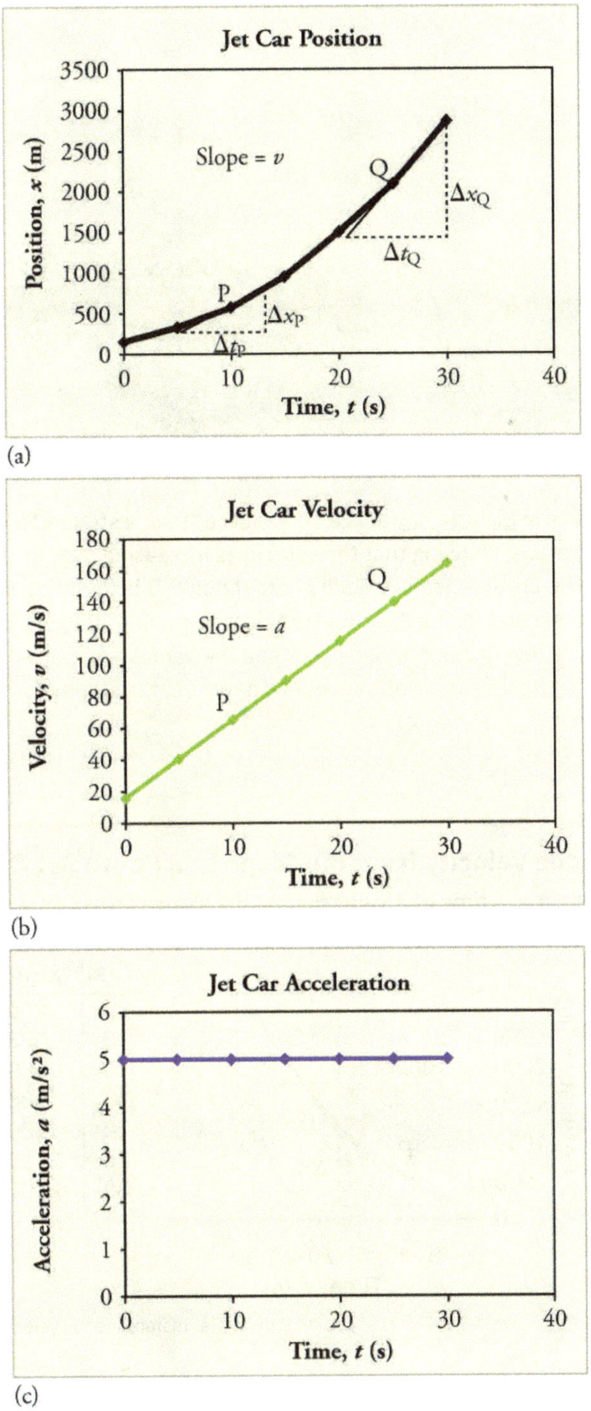

FIGURE 2.46 Graphs of motion of a jet-powered car during the time span when its acceleration is constant. (a) The slope of an x vs. t graph is velocity. This is shown at two points, and the instantaneous velocities obtained are plotted in the next graph. Instantaneous velocity at any point is the slope of the tangent at that point. (b) The slope of the v vs. t graph is constant for this part of the motion, indicating constant acceleration. (c) Acceleration has the constant value of $5.0\ \text{m/s}^2$ over the time interval plotted.

FIGURE 2.47 A U.S. Air Force jet car speeds down a track. (credit: Matt Trostle, Flickr)

The graph of position versus time in Figure 2.46(a) is a curve rather than a straight line. The slope of the curve becomes steeper as time progresses, showing that the velocity is increasing over time. The slope at any point on a position-versus-time graph is the instantaneous velocity at that point. It is found by drawing a straight line tangent to the curve at the point of interest and taking the slope of this straight line. Tangent lines are shown for two points in Figure 2.46(a). If this is done at every point on the curve and the values are plotted against time, then the graph of velocity versus time shown in Figure 2.46(b) is obtained. Furthermore, the slope of the graph of velocity versus time is acceleration, which is shown in Figure 2.46(c).

EXAMPLE 2.18

Determining Instantaneous Velocity from the Slope at a Point: Jet Car

Calculate the velocity of the jet car at a time of 25 s by finding the slope of the x vs. t graph in the graph below.

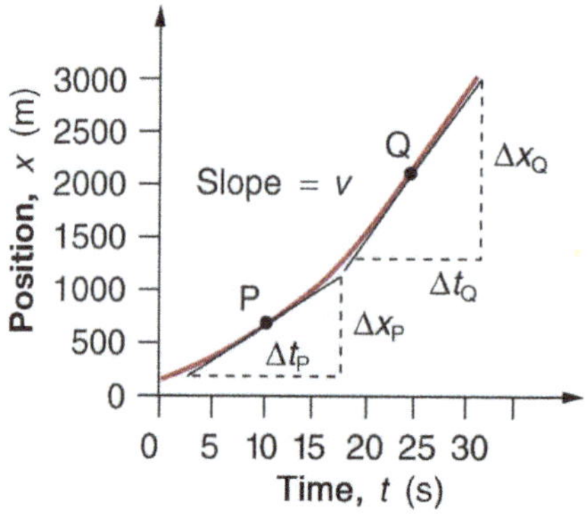

t (s)	x (m)
0	200
5	338
10	600
15	988
20	1500
25	2138
30	2900

FIGURE 2.48 The slope of an x vs. t graph is velocity. This is shown at two points. Instantaneous velocity at any point is the slope of the tangent at that point.

Strategy

The slope of a curve at a point is equal to the slope of a straight line tangent to the curve at that point. This principle is illustrated in Figure 2.48, where Q is the point at $t = 25\text{ s}$.

Solution

1. Find the tangent line to the curve at $t = 25\text{ s}$.

2. Determine the endpoints of the tangent. These correspond to a position of 1300 m at time 19 s and a position of 3120 m at time 32 s.

3. Plug these endpoints into the equation to solve for the slope, v.

$$\text{slope} = v_Q = \frac{\Delta x_Q}{\Delta t_Q} = \frac{(3120\text{ m} - 1300\text{ m})}{(32\text{ s} - 19\text{ s})} \tag{2.96}$$

Thus,

$$v_Q = \frac{1820\text{ m}}{13\text{ s}} = 140\text{ m/s}. \tag{2.97}$$

Discussion

This is the value given in this figure's table for v at $t = 25$ s. The value of 140 m/s for v_Q is plotted in Figure 2.48. The entire graph of v vs. t can be obtained in this fashion.

Carrying this one step further, we note that the slope of a velocity versus time graph is acceleration. Slope is rise divided by run; on a v vs. t graph, rise = change in velocity Δv and run = change in time Δt.

THE SLOPE OF *V* VS. *T*

The slope of a graph of velocity v vs. time t is acceleration a.

$$\text{slope} = \frac{\Delta v}{\Delta t} = a \tag{2.98}$$

Since the velocity versus time graph in Figure 2.46(b) is a straight line, its slope is the same everywhere, implying that acceleration is constant. Acceleration versus time is graphed in Figure 2.46(c).

Additional general information can be obtained from Figure 2.48 and the expression for a straight line, $y = mx + b$.

In this case, the vertical axis y is V, the intercept b is v_0, the slope m is a, and the horizontal axis x is t. Substituting these symbols yields

$$v = v_0 + at. \tag{2.99}$$

A general relationship for velocity, acceleration, and time has again been obtained from a graph. Notice that this equation was also derived algebraically from other motion equations in Motion Equations for Constant Acceleration in One Dimension.

It is not accidental that the same equations are obtained by graphical analysis as by algebraic techniques. In fact, an important way to *discover* physical relationships is to measure various physical quantities and then make graphs of one quantity against another to see if they are correlated in any way. Correlations imply physical relationships and might be shown by smooth graphs such as those above. From such graphs, mathematical relationships can sometimes be postulated. Further experiments are then performed to determine the validity of the hypothesized relationships.

Graphs of Motion Where Acceleration is Not Constant

Now consider the motion of the jet car as it goes from 165 m/s to its top velocity of 250 m/s, graphed in Figure 2.49. Time again starts at zero, and the initial velocity is 165 m/s. (This was the final velocity of the car in the motion graphed in Figure 2.46.) Acceleration gradually decreases from 5.0 m/s^2 to zero when the car hits 250 m/s. The velocity increases until 55 s and then becomes constant, since acceleration decreases to zero at 55 s and remains zero afterward.

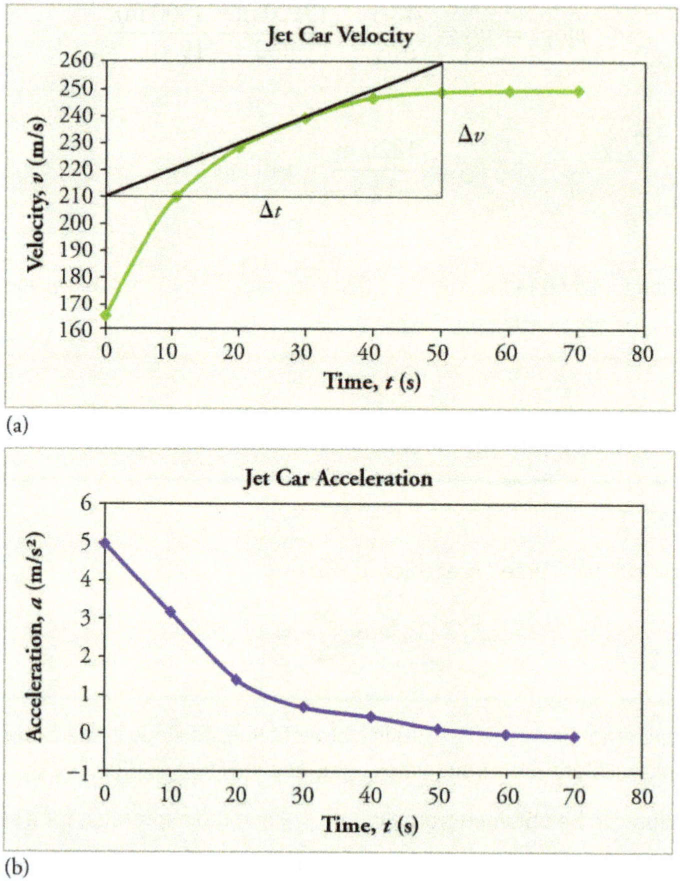

FIGURE 2.49 Graphs of motion of a jet-powered car as it reaches its top velocity. This motion begins where the motion in Figure 2.46 ends. (a) The velocity gradually approaches its top value. The slope of this graph is acceleration. It is plotted in the final graph. (b) Acceleration gradually declines to zero when velocity becomes constant. Notice in each of the three graphs that the acceleration drops down to zero and the velocity levels out. This results in a position-time graph that is almost linear. A close-up of the position time graph would show a slight curvature, as indicated in the velocity graph.

EXAMPLE 2.19

Calculating Acceleration from a Graph of Velocity versus Time

Calculate the acceleration of the jet car at a time of 25 s by finding the slope of the v vs. t graph in Figure 2.49(a).

Strategy

The slope of the curve at $t = 25$ s is equal to the slope of the line tangent at that point, as illustrated in Figure 2.49(a).

Solution

Determine endpoints of the tangent line from the figure, and then plug them into the equation to solve for slope, a.

$$\text{slope} = \frac{\Delta v}{\Delta t} = \frac{(260 \text{ m/s} - 210 \text{ m/s})}{(51 \text{ s} - 1.0 \text{ s})} \quad (2.100)$$

$$a = \frac{50 \text{ m/s}}{50 \text{ s}} = 1.0 \text{ m/s}^2. \quad (2.101)$$

Discussion

Note that this value for a is consistent with the value plotted in Figure 2.49(b) at $t = 25$ s.

A graph of position versus time can be used to generate a graph of velocity versus time, and a graph of velocity versus time can be used to generate a graph of acceleration versus time. We do this by finding the slope of the graphs at every point. If the graph is linear (i.e., a line with a constant slope), it is easy to find the slope at any point and you have the slope for every point. Graphical analysis of motion can be used to describe both specific and general characteristics of kinematics. Graphs can also be used for other topics in physics. An important aspect of exploring physical relationships is to graph them and look for underlying relationships.

CHECK YOUR UNDERSTANDING

A graph of velocity vs. time of a ship coming into a harbor is shown below. (a) Describe the motion of the ship based on the graph. (b)What would a graph of the ship's acceleration look like?

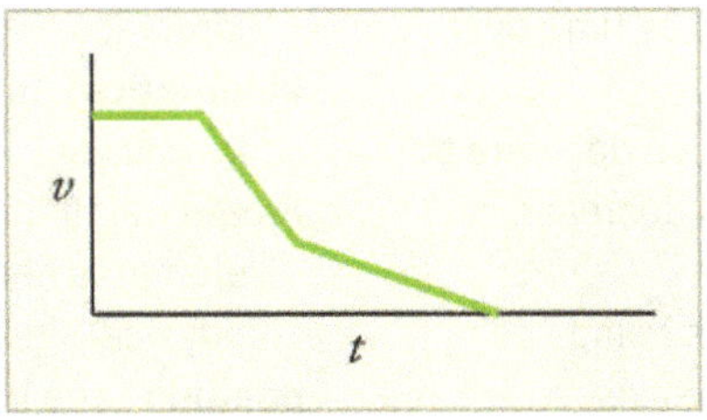

FIGURE 2.50

Solution

(a) The ship moves at constant velocity and then begins to decelerate at a constant rate. At some point, its deceleration rate decreases. It maintains this lower deceleration rate until it stops moving.

(b) A graph of acceleration vs. time would show zero acceleration in the first leg, large and constant negative acceleration in the second leg, and constant negative acceleration.

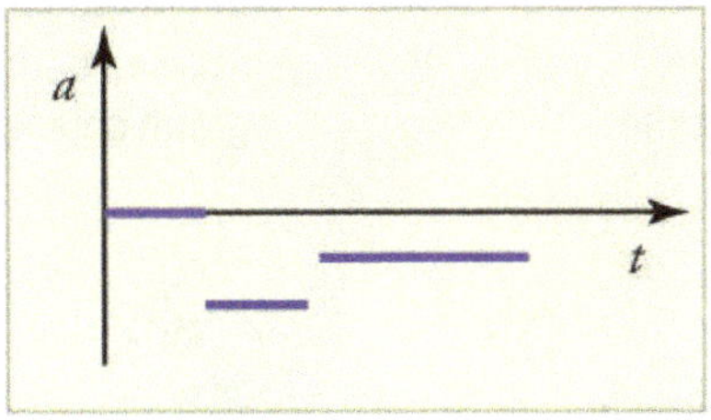

FIGURE 2.51

Glossary

acceleration the rate of change in velocity; the change in velocity over time

acceleration due to gravity acceleration of an object as a result of gravity

average acceleration the change in velocity divided by the time over which it changes

average speed distance traveled divided by time during which motion occurs

average velocity displacement divided by time over which displacement occurs

deceleration acceleration in the direction opposite to velocity; acceleration that results in a decrease in velocity

dependent variable the variable that is being measured; usually plotted along the y-axis

displacement the change in position of an object

distance the magnitude of displacement between two positions

distance traveled the total length of the path traveled between two positions

elapsed time the difference between the ending time and beginning time

free-fall the state of movement that results from gravitational force only

independent variable the variable that the dependent variable is measured with respect to; usually plotted along the x-axis

instantaneous acceleration acceleration at a specific point in time

instantaneous speed magnitude of the instantaneous velocity

instantaneous velocity velocity at a specific instant, or the average velocity over an infinitesimal time interval

kinematics the study of motion without considering its causes

model simplified description that contains only those elements necessary to describe the physics of a physical situation

position the location of an object at a particular time

scalar a quantity that is described by magnitude, but not direction

slope the difference in y-value (the rise) divided by the difference in x-value (the run) of two points on a straight line

time change, or the interval over which change occurs

vector a quantity that is described by both magnitude and direction

y-intercept the y-value when x= 0, or when the graph crosses the y-axis

Section Summary

2.1 Displacement

- Kinematics is the study of motion without considering its causes. In this chapter, it is limited to motion along a straight line, called one-dimensional motion.
- Displacement is the change in position of an object.
- In symbols, displacement Δx is defined to be
  $\Delta x = x_\text{f} - x_0,$
  where x_0 is the initial position and x_f is the final position. In this text, the Greek letter Δ (delta) always means "change in" whatever quantity follows it. The SI unit for displacement is the meter (m). Displacement has a direction as well as a magnitude.
- When you start a problem, assign which direction will be positive.
- Distance is the magnitude of displacement between two positions.
- Distance traveled is the total length of the path traveled between two positions.

2.2 Vectors, Scalars, and Coordinate Systems

- A vector is any quantity that has magnitude and direction.
- A scalar is any quantity that has magnitude but no direction.
- Displacement and velocity are vectors, whereas distance and speed are scalars.
- In one-dimensional motion, direction is specified by a plus or minus sign to signify left or right, up or down, and the like.

2.3 Time, Velocity, and Speed

- Time is measured in terms of change, and its SI unit is the second (s). Elapsed time for an event is
  $\Delta t = t_\text{f} - t_0,$
  where t_f is the final time and t_0 is the initial time. The initial time is often taken to be zero, as if measured with a stopwatch; the elapsed time is then just t.
- Average velocity $\bar{v}$ is defined as displacement divided by the travel time. In symbols, average velocity is

$$\bar{v} = \frac{\Delta x}{\Delta t} = \frac{x_f - x_0}{t_f - t_0}.$$

- The SI unit for velocity is m/s.
- Velocity is a vector and thus has a direction.
- Instantaneous velocity v is the velocity at a specific instant or the average velocity for an infinitesimal interval.
- Instantaneous speed is the magnitude of the instantaneous velocity.
- Instantaneous speed is a scalar quantity, as it has no direction specified.
- Average speed is the total distance traveled divided by the elapsed time. (Average speed is *not* the magnitude of the average velocity.) Speed is a scalar quantity; it has no direction associated with it.

2.4 Acceleration

- Acceleration is the rate at which velocity changes. In symbols, **average acceleration $\bar{a}$** is
$$\bar{a} = \frac{\Delta v}{\Delta t} = \frac{v_f - v_0}{t_f - t_0}.$$
- The SI unit for acceleration is m/s^2.
- Acceleration is a vector, and thus has a both a magnitude and direction.
- Acceleration can be caused by either a change in the magnitude or the direction of the velocity.
- Instantaneous acceleration a is the acceleration at a specific instant in time.
- Deceleration is an acceleration with a direction opposite to that of the velocity.

2.5 Motion Equations for Constant Acceleration in One Dimension

- To simplify calculations we take acceleration to be constant, so that $\bar{a} = a$ at all times.
- We also take initial time to be zero.
- Initial position and velocity are given a subscript 0; final values have no subscript. Thus,
$$\left.\begin{array}{lll} \Delta t & = & t \\ \Delta x & = & x - x_0 \\ \Delta v & = & v - v_0 \end{array}\right\}$$
- The following kinematic equations for motion with constant a are useful:
$$x = x_0 + \bar{v}t$$
$$\bar{v} = \frac{v_0 + v}{2}$$
$$v = v_0 + at$$
$$x = x_0 + v_0 t + \frac{1}{2}at^2$$
$$v^2 = v_0^2 + 2a(x - x_0)$$
- In vertical motion, y is substituted for x.

2.6 Problem-Solving Basics for One-Dimensional Kinematics

- *The six basic problem solving steps for physics are:*
  Step 1. Examine the situation to determine which physical principles are involved.

  Step 2. Make a list of what is given or can be inferred from the problem as stated (identify the knowns).

  Step 3. Identify exactly what needs to be determined in the problem (identify the unknowns).

  Step 4. Find an equation or set of equations that can help you solve the problem.

  Step 5. Substitute the knowns along with their units into the appropriate equation, and obtain numerical solutions complete with units.

  Step 6. Check the answer to see if it is reasonable: Does it make sense?

2.7 Falling Objects

- An object in free-fall experiences constant acceleration if air resistance is negligible.
- On Earth, all free-falling objects have an acceleration due to gravity g, which averages $g = 9.80\ \text{m/s}^2$.
- Whether the acceleration a should be taken as $+g$ or $-g$ is determined by your choice of coordinate system. If you choose the upward direction as positive, $a = -g = -9.80\ \text{m/s}^2$ is negative. In the opposite case, $a = +g = 9.80\ \text{m/s}^2$ is positive. Since acceleration is constant, the kinematic equations above can be applied with the appropriate $+g$ or $-g$ substituted for a.
- For objects in free-fall, up is normally taken as positive for displacement, velocity, and acceleration.

2.8 Graphical Analysis of One-Dimensional Motion

- Graphs of motion can be used to analyze motion.
- Graphical solutions yield identical solutions to mathematical methods for deriving motion equations.
- The slope of a graph of displacement x vs. time t is velocity v.
- The slope of a graph of velocity v vs. time t graph is acceleration a.
- Average velocity, instantaneous velocity, and acceleration can all be obtained by analyzing

graphs.

Conceptual Questions

2.1 Displacement

1. Give an example in which there are clear distinctions among distance traveled, displacement, and magnitude of displacement. Specifically identify each quantity in your example.

2. Under what circumstances does distance traveled equal magnitude of displacement? What is the only case in which magnitude of displacement and displacement are exactly the same?

3. Bacteria move back and forth by using their flagella (structures that look like little tails). Speeds of up to $50\ \mu m/s\ (50 \times 10^{-6}\ m/s)$ have been observed. The total distance traveled by a bacterium is large for its size, while its displacement is small. Why is this?

2.2 Vectors, Scalars, and Coordinate Systems

4. A student writes, "*A bird that is diving for prey has a speed of* $-10\ m/s$." What is wrong with the student's statement? What has the student actually described? Explain.

5. What is the speed of the bird in Exercise 2.4?

6. Acceleration is the change in velocity over time. Given this information, is acceleration a vector or a scalar quantity? Explain.

7. A weather forecast states that the temperature is predicted to be $-5°C$ the following day. Is this temperature a vector or a scalar quantity? Explain.

2.3 Time, Velocity, and Speed

8. Give an example (but not one from the text) of a device used to measure time and identify what change in that device indicates a change in time.

9. There is a distinction between average speed and the magnitude of average velocity. Give an example that illustrates the difference between these two quantities.

10. Does a car's odometer measure distance traveled or displacement? Does its speedometer measure speed or velocity?

11. If you divide the total distance traveled on a car trip (as determined by the odometer) by the time for the trip, are you calculating the average speed or the magnitude of the average velocity? Under what circumstances are these two quantities the same?

12. How are instantaneous velocity and instantaneous speed related to one another? How do they differ?

2.4 Acceleration

13. Is it possible for speed to be constant while acceleration is not zero? Give an example of such a situation.

14. Is it possible for velocity to be constant while acceleration is not zero? Explain.

15. Give an example in which velocity is zero yet acceleration is not.

16. If a subway train is moving to the left (has a negative velocity) and then comes to a stop, what is the direction of its acceleration? Is the acceleration positive or negative?

17. Plus and minus signs are used in one-dimensional motion to indicate direction. What is the sign of an acceleration that reduces the magnitude of a negative velocity? Of a positive velocity?

2.6 Problem-Solving Basics for One-Dimensional Kinematics

18. What information do you need in order to choose which equation or equations to use to solve a problem? Explain.

19. What is the last thing you should do when solving a problem? Explain.

2.7 Falling Objects

20. What is the acceleration of a rock thrown straight upward on the way up? At the top of its flight? On the way down?

21. An object that is thrown straight up falls back to Earth. This is one-dimensional motion. (a) When is its velocity zero? (b) Does its velocity change direction? (c) Does the acceleration due to gravity have the same sign on the way up as on the way down?

22. Suppose you throw a rock nearly straight up at a coconut in a palm tree, and the rock misses on the way up but hits the coconut on the way down. Neglecting air resistance, how does the speed of the rock when it hits the coconut on the way down compare with what it would have been if it had hit

the coconut on the way up? Is it more likely to dislodge the coconut on the way up or down? Explain.

23. If an object is thrown straight up and air resistance is negligible, then its speed when it returns to the starting point is the same as when it was released. If air resistance were not negligible, how would its speed upon return compare with its initial speed? How would the maximum height to which it rises be affected?

24. The severity of a fall depends on your speed when you strike the ground. All factors but the acceleration due to gravity being the same, how many times higher could a safe fall on the Moon be than on Earth (gravitational acceleration on the Moon is about 1/6 that of the Earth)?

25. How many times higher could an astronaut jump on the Moon than on Earth if his takeoff speed is the same in both locations (gravitational acceleration on the Moon is about 1/6 of g on Earth)?

2.8 Graphical Analysis of One-Dimensional Motion

26. (a) Explain how you can use the graph of position versus time in Figure 2.52 to describe the change in velocity over time. Identify (b) the time (t_a, t_b, t_c, t_d, or t_e) at which the instantaneous velocity is greatest, (c) the time at which it is zero, and (d) the time at which it is negative.

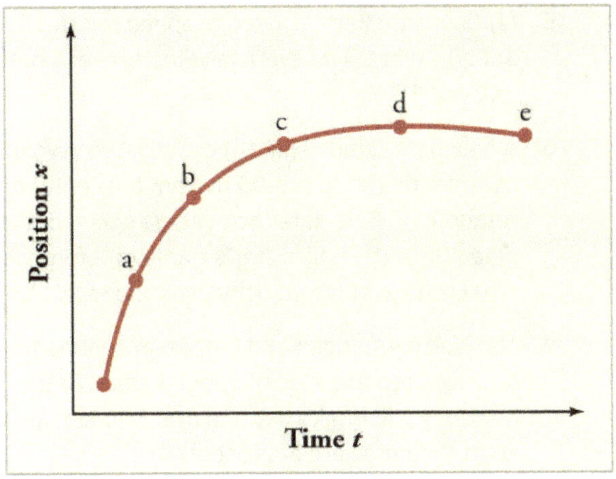

FIGURE 2.52

27. (a) Sketch a graph of velocity versus time corresponding to the graph of position versus time given in Figure 2.53. (b) Identify the time or times (t_a, t_b, t_c, etc.) at which the instantaneous velocity is greatest. (c) At which times is it zero? (d) At which times is it negative?

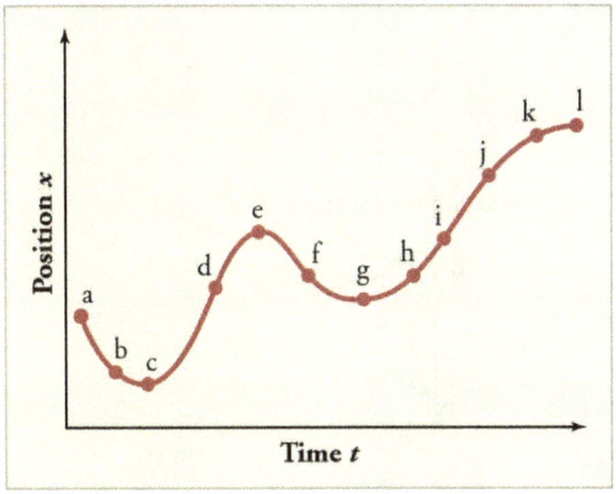

FIGURE 2.53

28. (a) Explain how you can determine the acceleration over time from a velocity versus time graph such as the one in Figure 2.54. (b) Based on the graph, how does acceleration change over time?

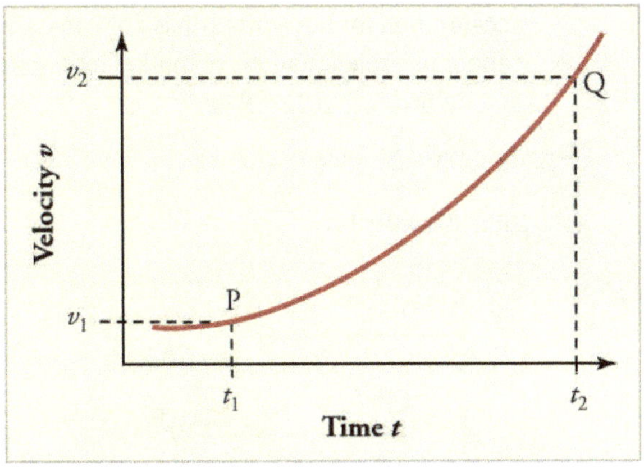

FIGURE 2.54

29. (a) Sketch a graph of acceleration versus time corresponding to the graph of velocity versus time given in Figure 2.55. (b) Identify the time or times (t_a, t_b, t_c, etc.) at which the acceleration is greatest. (c) At which times is it zero? (d) At which times is it negative?

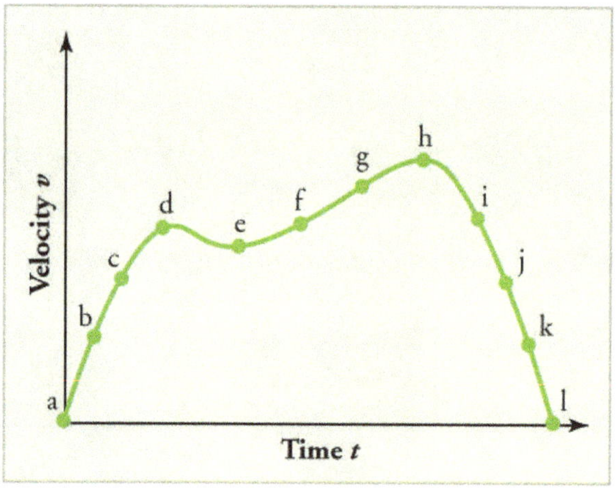

FIGURE 2.55

30. Consider the velocity vs. time graph of a person in an elevator shown in Figure 2.56. Suppose the elevator is initially at rest. It then accelerates for 3 seconds, maintains that velocity for 15 seconds, then decelerates for 5 seconds until it stops. The acceleration for the entire trip is not constant so we cannot use the equations of motion from Motion Equations for Constant Acceleration in One Dimension for the complete trip. (We could, however, use them in the three individual sections where acceleration is a constant.) Sketch graphs of (a) position vs. time and (b) acceleration vs. time for this trip.

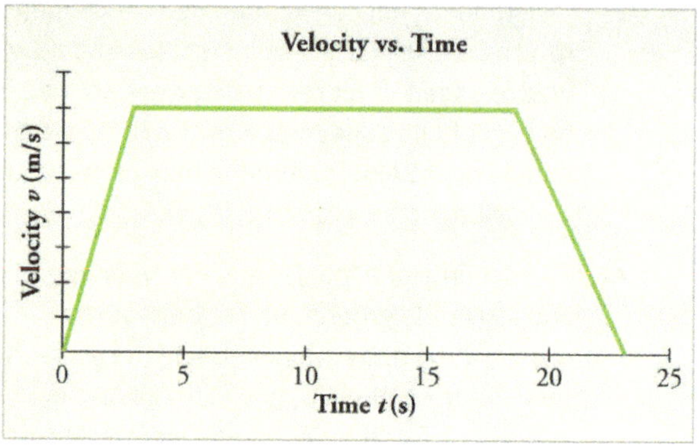

FIGURE 2.56

31. A cylinder is given a push and then rolls up an inclined plane. If the origin is the starting point, sketch the position, velocity, and acceleration of the cylinder vs. time as it goes up and then down the plane.

Problems & Exercises

2.1 Displacement

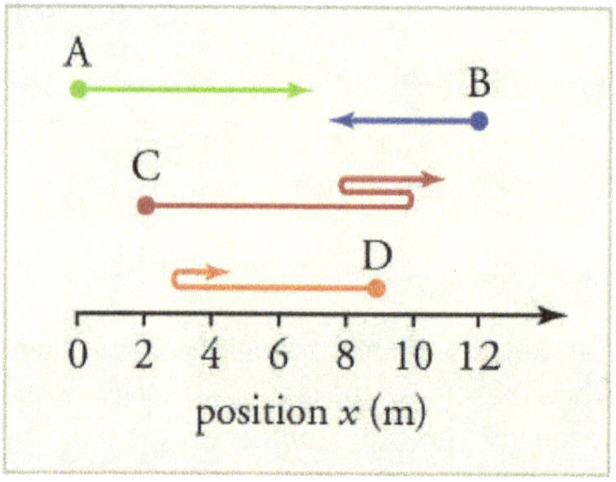

FIGURE 2.57

1. Find the following for path A in Figure 2.57: (a) The distance traveled. (b) The magnitude of the displacement from start to finish. (c) The displacement from start to finish.

2. Find the following for path B in Figure 2.57: (a) The distance traveled. (b) The magnitude of the displacement from start to finish. (c) The displacement from start to finish.

3. Find the following for path C in Figure 2.57: (a) The distance traveled. (b) The magnitude of the displacement from start to finish. (c) The displacement from start to finish.

4. Find the following for path D in Figure 2.57: (a) The distance traveled. (b) The magnitude of the displacement from start to finish. (c) The displacement from start to finish.

2.3 Time, Velocity, and Speed

5. (a) Calculate Earth's average speed relative to the Sun. (b) What is its average velocity over a period of one year?

6. A helicopter blade spins at exactly 100 revolutions per minute. Its tip is 5.00 m from the center of rotation. (a) Calculate the average speed of the blade tip in the helicopter's frame of reference. (b) What is its average velocity over one revolution?

7. The North American and European continents are moving apart at a rate of about 3 cm/y. At this rate how long will it take them to drift 500 km farther apart than they are at present?

8. Land west of the San Andreas fault in southern California is moving at an average velocity of about 6 cm/y northwest relative to land east of the fault. Los Angeles is west of the fault and may thus someday be at the same latitude as San Francisco, which is east of the fault. How far in the future will this occur if the displacement to be made is 590 km northwest, assuming the motion remains constant?

9. On May 26, 1934, a streamlined, stainless steel diesel train called the Zephyr set the world's nonstop long-distance speed record for trains. Its run from Denver to Chicago took 13 hours, 4 minutes, 58 seconds, and was witnessed by more than a million people along the route. The total distance traveled was 1633.8 km. What was its average speed in km/h and m/s?

10. Tidal friction is slowing the rotation of the Earth. As a result, the orbit of the Moon is increasing in radius at a rate of approximately 4 cm/year. Assuming this to be a constant rate, how many years will pass before the radius of the Moon's orbit increases by $3.84 \times 10^6\ \text{m}$ (1%)?

11. A student drove to the university from their home and noted that the odometer reading of their car increased by 12.0 km. The trip took 18.0 min. (a) What was their average speed? (b) If the straight-line distance from their home to the university is 10.3 km in a direction 25.0° south of east, what was their average velocity? (c) If they returned home by the same path 7 h 30 min after they left, what were their average speed and velocity for the entire trip?

12. The speed of propagation of the action potential (an electrical signal) in a nerve cell depends (inversely) on the diameter of the axon (nerve fiber). If the nerve cell connecting the spinal cord to your feet is 1.1 m long, and the nerve impulse speed is 18 m/s, how long does it take for the nerve signal to travel this distance?

13. Conversations with astronauts on the lunar surface were characterized by a kind of echo in which the earthbound person's voice was so loud in the astronaut's space helmet that it was picked up by the astronaut's microphone and transmitted back to Earth. It is reasonable to assume that the echo time equals the time necessary for the radio wave to travel from the Earth to the Moon and back (that is, neglecting any time delays in the electronic equipment). Calculate the distance from Earth to the Moon given that the echo time was 2.56 s and that radio waves travel at the speed of light $(3.00 \times 10^8\ \text{m/s})$.

14. A football quarterback runs 15.0 m straight down the playing field in 2.50 s. He is then hit and pushed 3.00 m straight backward in 1.75 s. He breaks the tackle and runs straight forward another 21.0 m in 5.20 s. Calculate his average velocity (a) for each of the three intervals and (b) for the entire motion.

15. The planetary model of the atom pictures electrons orbiting the atomic nucleus much as planets orbit the Sun. In this model you can view hydrogen, the simplest atom, as having a single electron in a circular orbit $1.06 \times 10^{-10}\ \text{m}$ in diameter. (a) If the average speed of the electron in this orbit is known to be $2.20 \times 10^6\ \text{m/s}$, calculate the number of revolutions per second it makes about the nucleus. (b) What is the electron's average velocity per revolution?

2.4 Acceleration

16. A cheetah can accelerate from rest to a speed of 30.0 m/s in 7.00 s. What is its acceleration?

17. Professional Application
Dr. John Paul Stapp was U.S. Air Force officer who studied the effects of extreme deceleration on the human body. On December 10, 1954, Stapp rode a rocket sled, accelerating from rest to a top speed of 282 m/s (1015 km/h) in 5.00 s, and was brought jarringly back to rest in only 1.40 s! Calculate his (a) acceleration and (b) deceleration. Express each in multiples of $g\ (9.80\ \text{m/s}^2)$ by taking its ratio to the acceleration of gravity.

18. A commuter backs her car out of her garage with an acceleration of $1.40\ \text{m/s}^2$. (a) How long does it take her to reach a speed of 2.00 m/s? (b) If she then brakes to a stop in 0.800 s, what is her deceleration?

19. Assume that an intercontinental ballistic missile goes from rest to a suborbital speed of 6.50 km/s in 60.0 s (the actual speed and time are classified). What is its average acceleration in m/s^2 and in multiples of $g\ (9.80\ \text{m/s}^2)$?

2.5 Motion Equations for Constant Acceleration in One Dimension

20. An Olympic-class sprinter starts a race with an acceleration of $4.50\ \text{m/s}^2$. (a) What is her speed 2.40 s later? (b) Sketch a graph of her position vs. time for this period.

21. A well-thrown ball is caught in a well-padded mitt. If the deceleration of the ball is $2.10 \times 10^4\ \text{m/s}^2$, and 1.85 ms $(1\ \text{ms} = 10^{-3}\ \text{s})$ elapses from the time the ball first touches the mitt until it stops, what was the initial velocity of the ball?

22. A bullet in a gun is accelerated from the firing chamber to the end of the barrel at an average

rate of 6.20×10^5 m/s^2 for 8.10×10^{-4} s. What is its muzzle velocity (that is, its final velocity)?

23. (a) A light-rail commuter train accelerates at a rate of 1.35 m/s^2. How long does it take to reach its top speed of 80.0 km/h, starting from rest? (b) The same train ordinarily decelerates at a rate of 1.65 m/s^2. How long does it take to come to a stop from its top speed? (c) In emergencies the train can decelerate more rapidly, coming to rest from 80.0 km/h in 8.30 s. What is its emergency deceleration in m/s^2?

24. While entering a freeway, a car accelerates from rest at a rate of 2.40 m/s^2 for 12.0 s. (a) Draw a sketch of the situation. (b) List the knowns in this problem. (c) How far does the car travel in those 12.0 s? To solve this part, first identify the unknown, and then discuss how you chose the appropriate equation to solve for it. After choosing the equation, show your steps in solving for the unknown, check your units, and discuss whether the answer is reasonable. (d) What is the car's final velocity? Solve for this unknown in the same manner as in part (c), showing all steps explicitly.

25. At the end of a race, a runner decelerates from a velocity of 9.00 m/s at a rate of 2.00 m/s^2. (a) How far does she travel in the next 5.00 s? (b) What is her final velocity? (c) Evaluate the result. Does it make sense?

26. Professional Application:
Blood is accelerated from rest to 30.0 cm/s in a distance of 1.80 cm by the left ventricle of the heart. (a) Make a sketch of the situation. (b) List the knowns in this problem. (c) How long does the acceleration take? To solve this part, first identify the unknown, and then discuss how you chose the appropriate equation to solve for it. After choosing the equation, show your steps in solving for the unknown, checking your units. (d) Is the answer reasonable when compared with the time for a heartbeat?

27. In a slap shot, a hockey player accelerates the puck from a velocity of 8.00 m/s to 40.0 m/s in the same direction. If this shot takes 3.33×10^{-2} s, calculate the distance over which the puck accelerates.

28. A powerful motorcycle can accelerate from rest to 26.8 m/s (100 km/h) in only 3.90 s. (a) What is its average acceleration? (b) How far does it travel in that time?

29. Freight trains can produce only relatively small accelerations and decelerations. (a) What is the final velocity of a freight train that accelerates at a rate of 0.0500 m/s^2 for 8.00 min, starting with an initial velocity of 4.00 m/s? (b) If the train can slow down at a rate of 0.550 m/s^2, how long will it take to come to a stop from this velocity? (c) How far will it travel in each case?

30. A fireworks shell is accelerated from rest to a velocity of 65.0 m/s over a distance of 0.250 m. (a) How long did the acceleration last? (b) Calculate the acceleration.

31. A swan on a lake gets airborne by flapping its wings and running on top of the water. (a) If the swan must reach a velocity of 6.00 m/s to take off and it accelerates from rest at an average rate of 0.350 m/s^2, how far will it travel before becoming airborne? (b) How long does this take?

32. **Professional Application:**
A woodpecker's brain is specially protected from large decelerations by tendon-like attachments inside the skull. While pecking on a tree, the woodpecker's head comes to a stop from an initial velocity of 0.600 m/s in a distance of only 2.00 mm. (a) Find the acceleration in m/s^2 and in multiples of g $\left(g = 9.80 \text{ m/s}^2\right)$. (b) Calculate the stopping time. (c) The tendons cradling the brain stretch, making its stopping distance 4.50 mm (greater than the head and, hence, less deceleration of the brain). What is the brain's deceleration, expressed in multiples of g?

33. An unwary football player collides with a padded goalpost while running at a velocity of 7.50 m/s and comes to a full stop after compressing the padding and his body 0.350 m. (a) What is his deceleration? (b) How long does the collision last?

34. In World War II, there were several reported cases of airmen who jumped from their flaming airplanes with no parachute to escape certain death. Some fell about 20,000 feet (6000 m), and some of them survived, with few life-threatening injuries. For these lucky pilots, the tree branches and snow drifts on the ground allowed their deceleration to be relatively small. If we assume that a pilot's speed upon impact was 123 mph (54 m/s), then what was his deceleration? Assume that the trees and snow stopped him over a distance of 3.0 m.

35. Consider a grey squirrel falling out of a tree to the ground. (a) If we ignore air resistance in this case (only for the sake of this problem), determine a squirrel's velocity just before hitting the ground, assuming it fell from a height of 3.0 m. (b) If the squirrel stops in a distance of 2.0 cm through bending its limbs, compare its deceleration with that of the airman in the previous problem.

36. An express train passes through a station. It enters with an initial velocity of 22.0 m/s and decelerates at a rate of $0.150\ \text{m/s}^2$ as it goes through. The station is 210 m long. (a) How long did the nose of the train stay in the station? (b) How fast is it going when the nose leaves the station? (c) If the train is 130 m long, when does the end of the train leave the station? (d) What is the velocity of the end of the train as it leaves?

37. Dragsters can actually reach a top speed of 145 m/s in only 4.45 s—considerably less time than given in Example 2.10 and Example 2.11. (a) Calculate the average acceleration for such a dragster. (b) Find the final velocity of this dragster starting from rest and accelerating at the rate found in (a) for 402 m (a quarter mile) without using any information on time. (c) Why is the final velocity greater than that used to find the average acceleration? *Hint*: Consider whether the assumption of constant acceleration is valid for a dragster. If not, discuss whether the acceleration would be greater at the beginning or end of the run and what effect that would have on the final velocity.

38. A bicycle racer sprints at the end of a race to clinch a victory. The racer has an initial velocity of 11.5 m/s and accelerates at the rate of $0.500\ \text{m/s}^2$ for 7.00 s. (a) What is his final velocity? (b) The racer continues at this velocity to the finish line. If he was 300 m from the finish line when he started to accelerate, how much time did he save? (c) One other racer was 5.00 m ahead when the winner started to accelerate, but he was unable to accelerate, and traveled at 11.8 m/s until the finish line. How far ahead of him (in meters and in seconds) did the winner finish?

39. In 1967, New Zealander Burt Munro set the world record for an Indian motorcycle, on the Bonneville Salt Flats in Utah, with a maximum speed of 183.58 mi/h. The one-way course was 5.00 mi long. Acceleration rates are often described by the time it takes to reach 60.0 mi/h from rest. If this time was 4.00 s, and Burt accelerated at this rate until he reached his maximum speed, how long did it take Burt to complete the course?

40. (a) A world record was set for the men's 100-m dash in the 2008 Olympic Games in Beijing by Usain Bolt of Jamaica. Bolt "coasted" across the finish line with a time of 9.69 s. If we assume that Bolt accelerated for 3.00 s to reach his maximum speed, and maintained that speed for the rest of the race, calculate his maximum speed and his acceleration. (b) During the same Olympics, Bolt also set the world record in the 200-m dash with a time of 19.30 s. Using the same assumptions as for the 100-m dash, what was his maximum speed for this race?

2.7 Falling Objects

Assume air resistance is negligible unless otherwise stated.

41. Calculate the displacement and velocity at times of (a) 0.500, (b) 1.00, (c) 1.50, and (d) 2.00 s for a ball thrown straight up with an initial velocity of 15.0 m/s. Take the point of release to be $y_0 = 0$.

42. Calculate the displacement and velocity at times of (a) 0.500, (b) 1.00, (c) 1.50, (d) 2.00, and (e) 2.50 s for a rock thrown straight down with an initial velocity of 14.0 m/s from the Verrazano Narrows Bridge in New York City. The roadway of this bridge is 70.0 m above the water.

43. A basketball referee tosses the ball straight up for the starting tip-off. At what velocity must a basketball player leave the ground to rise 1.25 m above the floor in an attempt to get the ball?

44. A rescue helicopter is hovering over a person whose boat has sunk. One of the rescuers throws a life preserver straight down to the victim with an initial velocity of 1.40 m/s and observes that it takes 1.8 s to reach the water. (a) List the knowns in this problem. (b) How high above the water was the preserver released? Note that the downdraft of the helicopter reduces the effects of air resistance on the falling life preserver, so that an acceleration equal to that of gravity is reasonable.

45. A dolphin in an aquatic show jumps straight up out of the water at a velocity of 13.0 m/s. (a) List the knowns in this problem. (b) How high does his body rise above the water? To solve this part, first note that the final velocity is now a known and identify its value. Then identify the unknown, and discuss how you chose the appropriate equation to solve for it. After choosing the equation, show your steps in solving for the unknown, checking units, and discuss whether the answer is reasonable. (c) How long is the dolphin in the air? Neglect any effects due to his size or orientation.

46. A swimmer bounces straight up from a diving board and falls feet first into a pool. She starts with a velocity of 4.00 m/s, and her takeoff point is 1.80 m above the pool. (a) How long are her feet in the air? (b) What is her highest point above the board? (c) What is her velocity when her feet hit the water?

47. (a) Calculate the height of a cliff if it takes 2.35 s for a rock to hit the ground when it is thrown straight up from the cliff with an initial velocity of 8.00 m/s. (b) How long would it take to reach the ground if it is thrown straight down with the same speed?

48. A very strong, but inept, shot putter puts the shot straight up vertically with an initial velocity of 11.0 m/s. How long does he have to get out of the way if the shot was released at a height of 2.20 m, and he is 1.80 m tall?

49. You throw a ball straight up with an initial velocity of 15.0 m/s. It passes a tree branch on the way up at a height of 7.00 m. How much additional time will pass before the ball passes the tree branch on the way back down?

50. A kangaroo can jump over an object 2.50 m high. (a) Calculate its vertical speed when it leaves the ground. (b) How long is it in the air?

51. Standing at the base of one of the cliffs of Mt. Arapiles in Victoria, Australia, a hiker hears a rock break loose from a height of 105 m. He can't see the rock right away but then does, 1.50 s later. (a) How far above the hiker is the rock when he can see it? (b) How much time does he have to move before the rock hits his head?

52. An object is dropped from a height of 75.0 m above ground level. (a) Determine the distance traveled during the first second. (b) Determine the final velocity at which the object hits the ground. (c) Determine the distance traveled during the last second of motion before hitting the ground.

53. There is a 250-m-high cliff at Half Dome in Yosemite National Park in California. Suppose a boulder breaks loose from the top of this cliff. (a) How fast will it be going when it strikes the ground? (b) Assuming a reaction time of 0.300 s, how long will a tourist at the bottom have to get out of the way after hearing the sound of the rock breaking loose (neglecting the height of the tourist, which would become negligible anyway if hit)? The speed of sound is 335 m/s on this day.

54. A ball is thrown straight up. It passes a 2.00-m-high window 7.50 m off the ground on its path up and takes 0.312 s to go past the window. What was the ball's initial velocity? Hint: First consider only the distance along the window, and solve for the ball's velocity at the bottom of the window. Next, consider only the distance from the ground to the bottom of the window, and solve for the initial velocity using the velocity at the bottom of the window as the final velocity.

55. Suppose you drop a rock into a dark well and, using precision equipment, you measure the time for the sound of a splash to return. (a) Neglecting the time required for sound to travel up the well, calculate the distance to the water if the sound returns in 2.0000 s. (b) Now calculate the distance taking into account the time for sound to travel up the well. The speed of sound is 332.00 m/s in this well.

56. A steel ball is dropped onto a hard floor from a height of 1.50 m and rebounds to a height of 1.45 m. (a) Calculate its velocity just before it strikes the floor. (b) Calculate its velocity just after it leaves the floor on its way back up. (c) Calculate its acceleration during contact with the floor if that contact lasts 0.0800 ms $(8.00 \times 10^{-5}\ \text{s})$. (d) How much did the ball compress during its collision with the floor, assuming the floor is absolutely rigid?

57. A coin is dropped from a hot-air balloon that is 300 m above the ground and rising at 10.0 m/s upward. For the coin, find (a) the maximum height reached, (b) its position and velocity 4.00 s after being released, and (c) the time before it hits the ground.

58. A soft tennis ball is dropped onto a hard floor from a height of 1.50 m and rebounds to a height of 1.10 m. (a) Calculate its velocity just before it strikes the floor. (b) Calculate its velocity just after it leaves the floor on its way back up. (c) Calculate its acceleration during contact with the floor if that contact lasts 3.50 ms $(3.50 \times 10^{-3}\ \text{s})$. (d) How much did the ball compress during its collision with the floor, assuming the floor is absolutely rigid?

2.8 Graphical Analysis of One-Dimensional Motion

Note: There is always uncertainty in numbers taken from graphs. If your answers differ from expected values, examine them to see if they are within data extraction uncertainties estimated by you.

59. (a) By taking the slope of the curve in Figure 2.58, verify that the velocity of the jet car is 115 m/s at $t = 20$ s. (b) By taking the slope of the curve at any point in Figure 2.59, verify that the jet car's acceleration is $5.0\ \text{m/s}^2$.

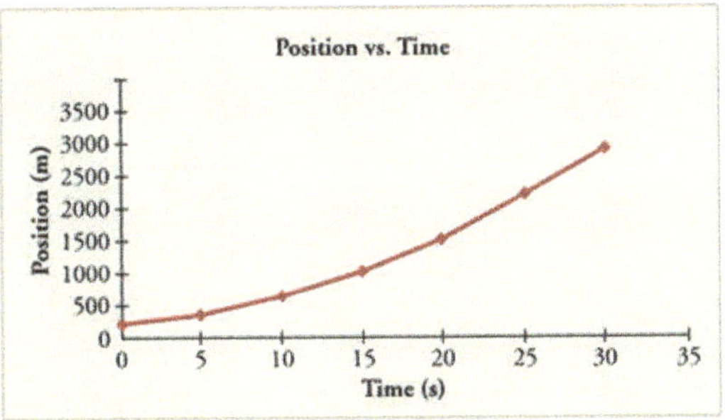

FIGURE 2.58

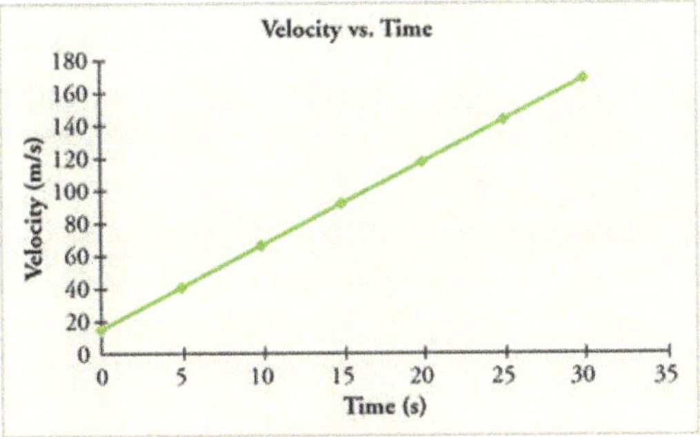

FIGURE 2.59

60. Using approximate values, calculate the slope of the curve in Figure 2.60 to verify that the velocity at $t = 30.0$ s is approximately 0.24 m/s. Assume all values are known to 2 significant figures.

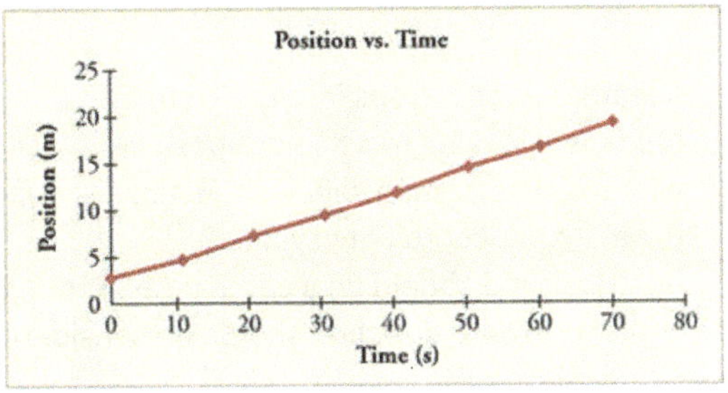

FIGURE 2.60

61. Using approximate values, calculate the slope of the curve in Figure 2.60 to verify that the velocity at $t = 30.0$ s is approximately 0.24 m/s.

62. By taking the slope of the curve in Figure 2.61, verify that the acceleration is $3.2\ \text{m/s}^2$ at $t = 10$ s.

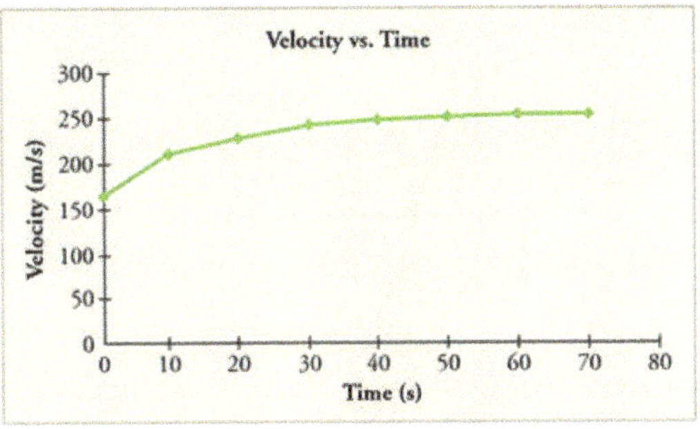

FIGURE 2.61

63. Construct the position graph for the subway shuttle train as shown in Figure 2.18(a). Your graph should show the position of the train, in kilometers, from t = 0 to 20 s. You will need to use the information on acceleration and velocity given in the examples for this figure.

64. (a) Take the slope of the curve in Figure 2.62 to find the jogger's velocity at $t = 2.5$ s. (b) Repeat at 7.5 s. These values must be consistent with the graph in Figure 2.63.

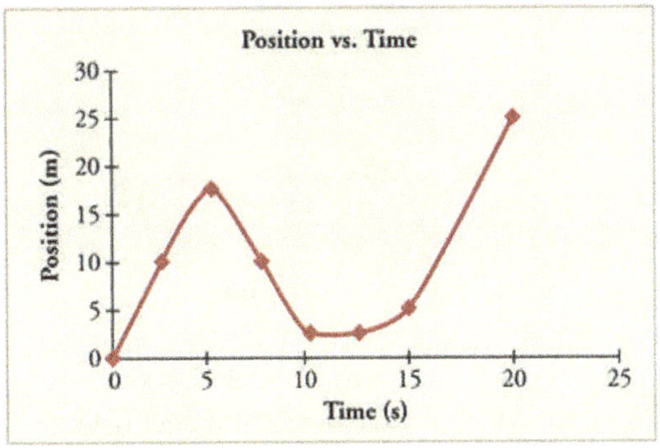

FIGURE 2.62

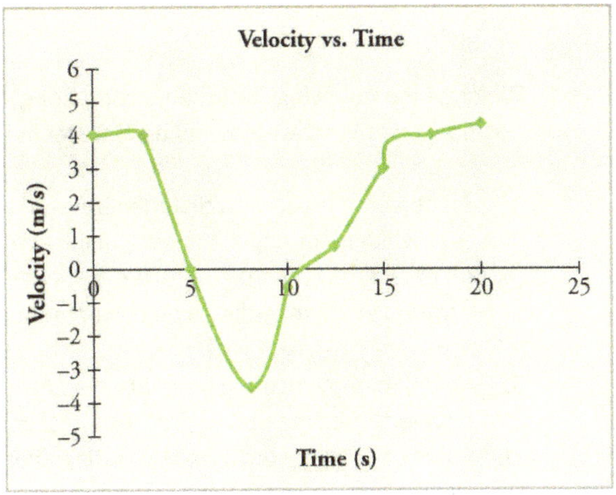

FIGURE 2.63

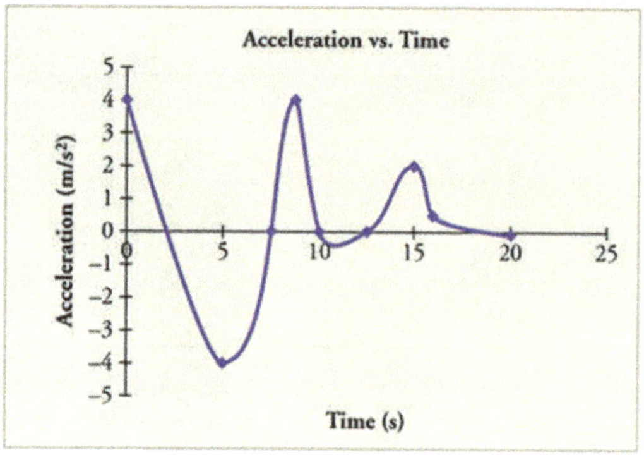

FIGURE 2.64

65. A graph of $v(t)$ is shown for a world-class track sprinter in a 100-m race. (See Figure 2.65). (a) What is his average velocity for the first 4 s? (b) What is his instantaneous velocity at $t = 5$ s? (c) What is his average acceleration between 0 and 4 s? (d) What is his time for the race?

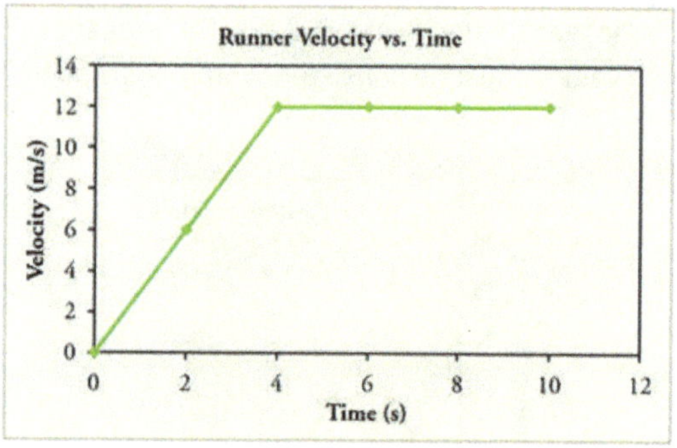

FIGURE 2.65

66. Figure 2.66 shows the position graph for a particle for 6 s. (a) Draw the corresponding Velocity vs. Time graph. (b) What is the acceleration between 0 s and 2 s? (c) What happens to the acceleration at exactly 2 s?

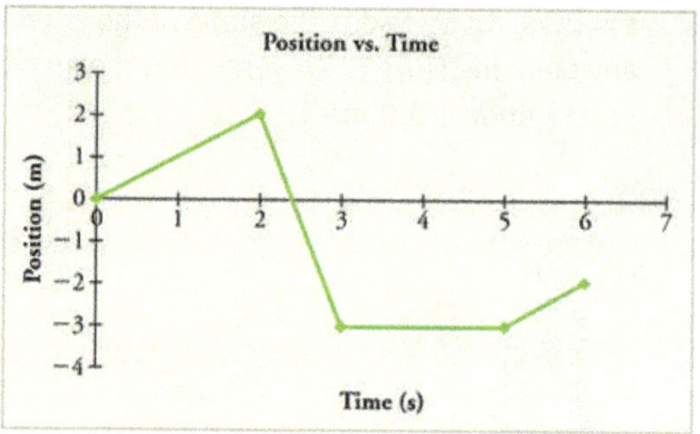

FIGURE 2.66

67. Critical Thinking Two cars are side by side on a path where friction is negligible. Car A starts from rest and has a positive, constant acceleration while car B travels at a constant speed. The cars reach the same check point down the road at the same time. (a) Which car is traveling faster at the check point? Briefly explain your reasoning. (b) Based on experimental data, an equation that fits the data is suggested for the speed of car A at the check point, *V*, which may not be correct: $V = KV_0$, where *K* is a constant with appropriate units and V_0 is the initial velocity of car B. Is this equation consistent with your answer from part a? Explain why or why not. Does this equation make sense? Explain why or why not. (c) Graph the velocity of car A and the velocity of car B vs. distance along the path, starting when the cars are side by side.

Test Prep for AP® Courses

2.1 Displacement

1. Which of the following statements comparing position, distance traveled, and displacement is correct?
   a. An object may record a distance traveled of zero while recording a non-zero displacement.
   b. An object may record a non-zero distance traveled while recording a displacement of zero.
   c. An object may record a non-zero distance traveled while maintaining a position of zero.
   d. An object may record a non-zero displacement while maintaining a position of zero.

2.2 Vectors, Scalars, and Coordinate Systems

2. A student is trying to determine the acceleration of a feather as she drops it to the ground. If the student is looking to achieve a positive velocity and positive acceleration, what is the *most sensible* way to set up her coordinate system?
   a. Her hand should be a coordinate of zero and the upward direction should be considered positive.
   b. Her hand should be a coordinate of zero and the downward direction should be considered positive.
   c. The floor should be a coordinate of zero and the upward direction should be considered positive.
   d. The floor should be a coordinate of zero and the downward direction should be considered positive.

2.3 Time, Velocity, and Speed

3. A group of students has two carts, *A* and *B*, with wheels that turn with negligible friction. The two carts travel along a straight horizontal track and eventually collide. Before the collision, cart *A* travels to the right and cart *B* is initially at rest. After the collision, the carts stick together.

a. Describe an experimental procedure to determine the velocities of the carts before and after the collision, including all the additional equipment you would need. You may include a labeled diagram of your setup to help in your description. Indicate what measurements you would take and how you would take them. Include enough detail so that another student could carry out your procedure.

b. There will be sources of error in the measurements taken in the experiment both before and after the collision. Which velocity will be more greatly affected by this error: the velocity prior to the collision or the velocity after the collision? Or will both sets of data be affected equally? Justify your answer.

2.4 Acceleration

4.

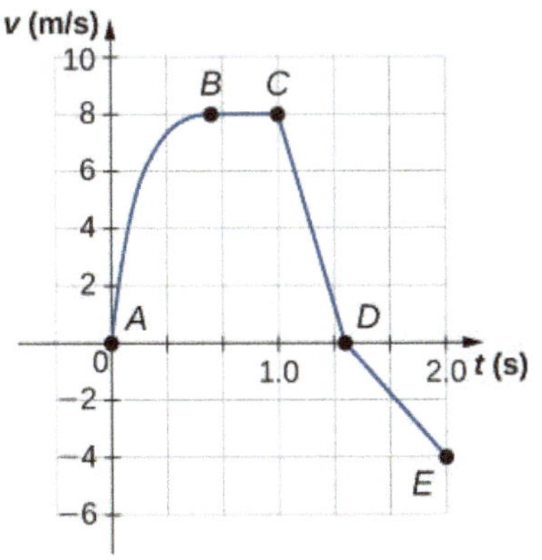

FIGURE 2.68 Graph showing Velocity vs. Time of a cart.

A cart is constrained to move along a straight line. A varying net force along the direction of motion is exerted on the cart. The cart's velocity *v* as a function of time *t* is shown in the graph. The five labeled points divide the graph into four sections. Which of the following correctly ranks the magnitude of the average acceleration of the cart during the four sections of the graph?

a. $a_{CD} > a_{AB} > a_{BC} > a_{DE}$
b. $a_{BC} > a_{AB} > a_{CD} > a_{DE}$
c. $a_{AB} > a_{BC} > a_{DE} > a_{CD}$
d. $a_{CD} > a_{AB} > a_{DE} > a_{BC}$

5. Push a book across a table and observe it slow to a stop.
Draw graphs showing the book's position vs. time and velocity vs. time if the direction of its motion is considered positive.
Draw graphs showing the book's position vs. time and velocity vs. time if the direction of its motion is considered negative.

2.5 Motion Equations for Constant Acceleration in One Dimension

6. A group of students is attempting to determine the average acceleration of a marble released from the top of a long ramp. Below is a set of data representing the marble's position with respect to time.

Position (cm)	Time (s)
0.0	0.0
0.3	0.5
1.25	1.0
2.8	1.5
5.0	2.0
7.75	2.5
11.3	3.0

TABLE 2.2

Use the data table above to construct a graph determining the acceleration of the marble. Select a set of data points from the table and plot those points on the graph. Fill in the blank column in the table for any quantities you graph other than the given data. Label the axes and indicate the scale for each. Draw a best-fit line or curve through your data points.
Using the best-fit line, determine the value of the marble's acceleration.

2.7 Falling Objects

7. Observing a spacecraft land on a distant asteroid, scientists notice that the craft is falling at a rate of 5 m/s. When it is 100 m closer to the surface of the asteroid, the craft reports a velocity of 8 m/s. According to their data, what is the approximate gravitational acceleration on this asteroid?

a. $0\ m/s^2$
b. $0.03\ m/s^2$

c. $0.20\ m/s^2$
d. $0.65\ m/s^2$
e. $33\ m/s^2$

CHAPTER 3
Two-Dimensional Kinematics

FIGURE 3.1 Hitting a tennis ball is difficult enough when it is traveling at high speeds in a relatively straight line. However, most motion is in curved, rather than straight-line, paths. Tennis players must account for the arc of the ball and the impact of its spin, while they also predict how it will bounce and plan the location of their shot. Motion along a curved path is two- or three-dimensional motion, and can be described in a similar fashion to one-dimensional motion. (credit: Edwin Martinez/Flickr)

CHAPTER OUTLINE

CONNECTION FOR AP® COURSES Most instances of motion in everyday life involve changes in displacement and velocity that occur in more than one direction. For example, when you take a long road trip, you drive on different roads in different directions for different amounts of time at different speeds. How can these motions all be combined to determine information about the trip such as the total displacement and average velocity? If you kick a ball from ground level at some angle above the horizontal, how can you describe its motion? To what maximum height does the object rise above the ground? How long is the object in the air? How much horizontal distance is covered before the ball lands? To answer questions such as these, we need to describe motion in two dimensions.

Examining two-dimensional motion requires an understanding of both the scalar and the vector quantities associated with the motion. You will learn how to combine vectors to incorporate both the magnitude and direction of vectors into your analysis. You will learn strategies for simplifying the calculations involved by choosing the appropriate reference frame and by treating each dimension of the motion separately as a one-dimensional problem, but you will also see that the motion itself occurs in the same way regardless of your chosen reference frame (Essential Knowledge 3.A.1).

This chapter lays a necessary foundation for examining interactions of objects described by forces (Big Idea 3). Changes in direction result from acceleration, which necessitates force on an object. In this chapter, you will concentrate on describing motion that involves changes in direction. In later chapters, you will apply this understanding as you learn about how forces cause these motions (Enduring Understanding 3.A). The concepts in this chapter support:

Big Idea 3 The interactions of an object with other objects can be described by forces.

Enduring Understanding 3.A All forces share certain common characteristics when considered by observers in inertial reference frames.

Essential Knowledge 3.A.1 An observer in a particular reference frame can describe the motion of an object using such quantities as position, displacement, distance, velocity, speed, and acceleration.

Click to view content (https://openstax.org/books/college-physics-ap-courses-2e/pages/3-connection-for-ap-r-courses)

3.1 Kinematics in Two Dimensions: An Intr oduction

LEARNING OBJECTIVES

By the end of this section, you will be able to:

- Observe that motion in two dimensions consists of horizontal and vertical components.
- Understand the independence of horizontal and vertical vectors in two-dimensional motion.

FIGURE 3.2 Walkers and drivers in a city like New York are rarely able to travel in straight lines to reach their destinations. Instead, they must follow roads and sidewalks, making two-dimensional, zigzagged paths. (credit: Margaret W. Carruthers)

Two-Dimensional Motion: Walking in a City

Suppose you want to walk from one point to another in a city with uniform square blocks, as pictured in Figure 3.3.

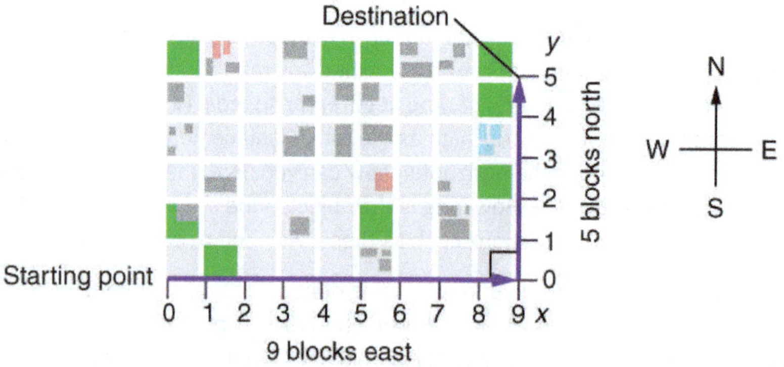

FIGURE 3.3 A pedestrian walks a two-dimensional path between two points in a city. In this scene, all blocks are square and are the same size.

The straight-line path that a helicopter might fly is blocked to you as a pedestrian, and so you are forced to take a two-dimensional path, such as the one shown. You walk 14 blocks in all, 9 east followed by 5 north. What is the straight-line distance?

An old adage states that the shortest distance between two points is a straight line. The two legs of the trip and the straight-line path form a right triangle, and so the Pythagorean theorem, $a^2 + b^2 = c^2$, can be used to find the straight-line distance.

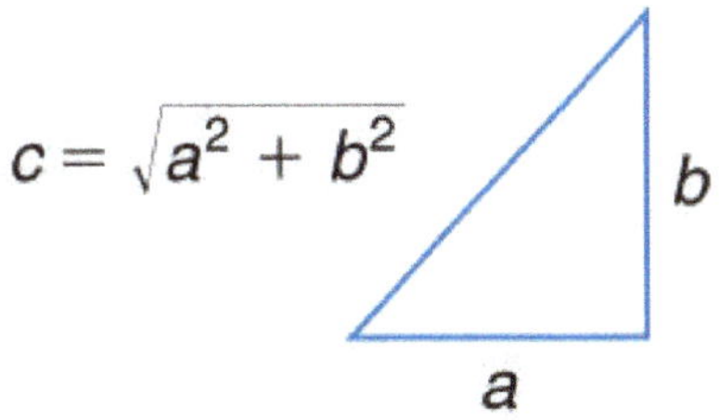

FIGURE 3.4 The Pythagorean theorem relates the length of the legs of a right triangle, labeled a and b, with the hypotenuse, labeled c. The relationship is given by: $a^2 + b^2 = c^2$. This can be rewritten, solving for $c: c = \sqrt{a^2 + b^2}$.

The hypotenuse of the triangle is the straight-line path, and so in this case its length in units of city blocks is $\sqrt{(9 \text{ blocks})^2 + (5 \text{ blocks})^2} = 10.3 \text{ blocks}$, considerably shorter than the 14 blocks you walked. (Note that we are using three significant figures in the answer. Although it appears that "9" and "5" have only one significant digit, they are discrete numbers. In this case "9 blocks" is the same as "9.0 or 9.00 blocks." We have decided to use three significant figures in the answer in order to show the result more precisely.)

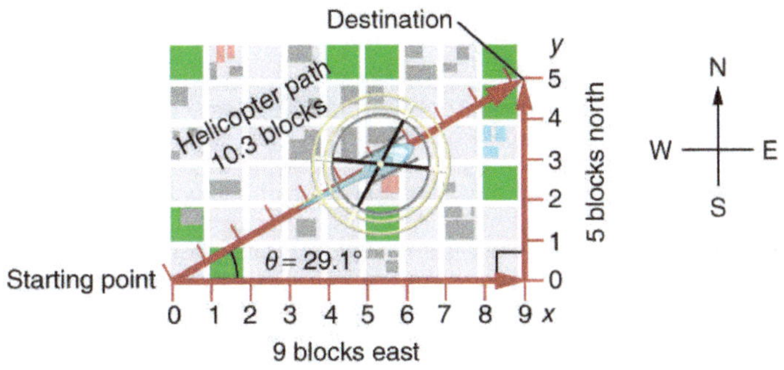

FIGURE 3.5 The straight-line path followed by a helicopter between the two points is shorter than the 14 blocks walked by the pedestrian. All blocks are square and the same size.

The fact that the straight-line distance (10.3 blocks) in Figure 3.5 is less than the total distance walked (14 blocks) is one example of a general characteristic of vectors. (Recall that **vectors** are quantities that have both magnitude and direction.)

As for one-dimensional kinematics, we use arrows to represent vectors. The length of the arrow is proportional to the vector's magnitude. The arrow's length is indicated by hash marks in Figure 3.3 and Figure 3.5. The arrow points in the same direction as the vector. For two-dimensional motion, the path of an object can be represented with three vectors: one vector shows the straight-line path between the initial and final points of the motion, one vector shows the horizontal component of the motion, and one vector shows the vertical component of the motion. The horizontal and vertical components of the motion add together to give the straight-line path. For example, observe the three vectors in Figure 3.5. The first represents a 9-block displacement east. The second represents a 5-block displacement north. These vectors are added to give the third vector, with a 10.3-block total displacement. The third vector is the straight-line path between the two points. Note that in this example, the vectors that we are adding are perpendicular to each other and thus form a right triangle. This means that we can use the Pythagorean theorem to calculate the magnitude of the total displacement. (Note that we cannot use the Pythagorean theorem to add vectors that are not perpendicular. We will develop techniques for adding vectors having any direction, not just those perpendicular to one another, in Vector Addition and Subtraction: Graphical Methods and Vector Addition and Subtraction: Analytical Methods.)

The Independence of Perpendicular Motions

The person taking the path shown in Figure 3.5 walks east and then north (two perpendicular directions). How far they walk east is only affected by their motion eastward. Similarly, how far they walk north is only affected by their motion northward.

INDEPENDENCE OF MOTION

The horizontal and vertical components of two-dimensional motion are independent of each other. Any motion in the horizontal direction does not affect motion in the vertical direction, and vice versa.

This is true in a simple scenario like that of walking in one direction first, followed by another. It is also true of more complicated motion involving movement in two directions at once. For example, let's compare the motions of two baseballs. One baseball is dropped from rest. At the same instant, another is thrown horizontally from the same height and follows a curved path. A stroboscope has captured the positions of the balls at fixed time intervals as they fall.

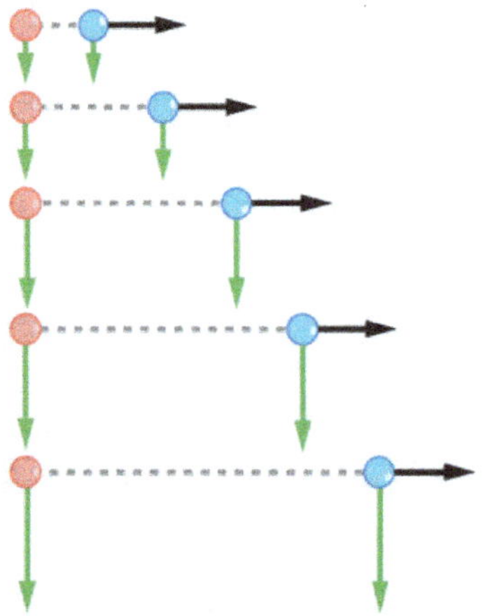

FIGURE 3.6 This shows the motions of two identical balls—one falls from rest, the other has an initial horizontal velocity. Each subsequent position is an equal time interval. Arrows represent horizontal and vertical velocities at each position. The ball on the right has an initial horizontal velocity, while the ball on the left has no horizontal velocity. Despite the difference in horizontal velocities, the vertical velocities and positions are identical for both balls. This shows that the vertical and horizontal motions are independent.

It is remarkable that for each flash of the strobe, the vertical positions of the two balls are the same. This similarity implies that the vertical motion is independent of whether or not the ball is moving horizontally. (Assuming no air resistance, the vertical motion of a falling object is influenced by gravity only, and not by any horizontal forces.) Careful examination of the ball thrown horizontally shows that it travels the same horizontal distance between flashes. This is due to the fact that there are no additional forces on the ball in the horizontal direction after it is thrown. This result means that the horizontal velocity is constant, and affected neither by vertical motion nor by gravity (which is vertical). Note that this case is true only for ideal conditions. In the real world, air resistance will affect the speed of the balls in both directions.

The two-dimensional curved path of the horizontally thrown ball is composed of two independent one-dimensional motions (horizontal and vertical). The key to analyzing such motion, called *projectile motion*, is to *resolve* (break) it into motions along perpendicular directions. Resolving two-dimensional motion into perpendicular components is possible because the components are independent. We shall see how to resolve vectors in Vector Addition and Subtraction: Graphical Methods and Vector Addition and Subtraction: Analytical Methods. We will find such techniques to be useful in many areas of physics.

PHET EXPLORATIONS

Ladybug Motion 2D

Learn about position, velocity and acceleration vectors. Move the ladybug by setting the position, velocity or acceleration, and see how the vectors change. Choose linear, circular or elliptical motion, and record and playback the motion to analyze the behavior.

Click to view content (https://openstax.org/l/28ladybugmotion).

PhET

3.2 Vector Addition and Subtraction: Graphical Methods

LEARNING OBJECTIVES

By the end of this section, you will be able to:

- Understand the rules of vector addition, subtraction, and multiplication.
- Apply graphical methods of vector addition and subtraction to determine the displacement of moving objects.

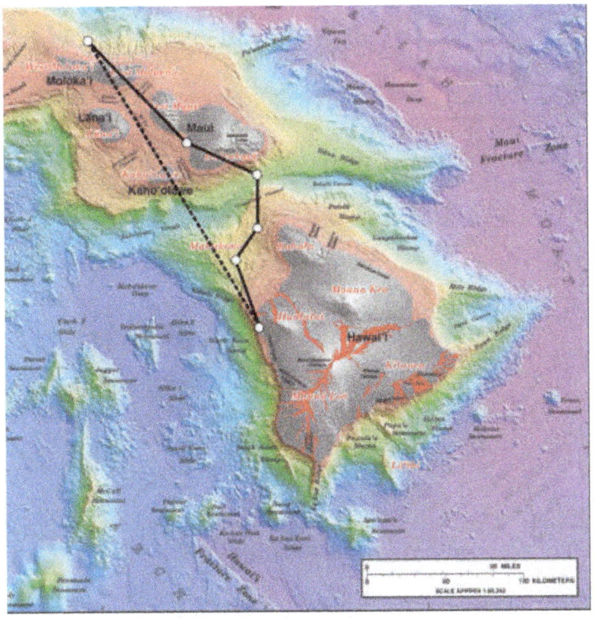

FIGURE 3.7 Displacement can be determined graphically using a scale map, such as this one of the Hawaiian Islands. A journey from Hawai'i to Moloka'i has a number of legs, or journey segments. These segments can be added graphically with a ruler to determine the total two-dimensional displacement of the journey. (credit: US Geological Survey)

Vectors in Two Dimensions

A **vector** is a quantity that has magnitude and direction. Displacement, velocity, acceleration, and force, for example, are all vectors. In one-dimensional, or straight-line, motion, the direction of a vector can be given simply by a plus or minus sign. In two dimensions (2-d), however, we specify the direction of a vector relative to some reference frame (i.e., coordinate system), using an arrow having length proportional to the vector's magnitude and pointing in the direction of the vector.

Figure 3.8 shows such a *graphical representation of a vector*, using as an example the total displacement for the person walking in a city considered in Kinematics in Two Dimensions: An Introduction. We shall use the notation that a boldface symbol, such as $\mathbf{D}$, stands for a vector. Its magnitude is represented by the symbol in italics, D, and its direction by θ.

VECTORS IN THIS TEXT

In this text, we will represent a vector with a boldface variable. For example, we will represent the quantity force with the vector $\mathbf{F}$, which has both magnitude and direction. The magnitude of the vector will be represented by a variable in italics, such as F, and the direction of the variable will be given by an angle θ.

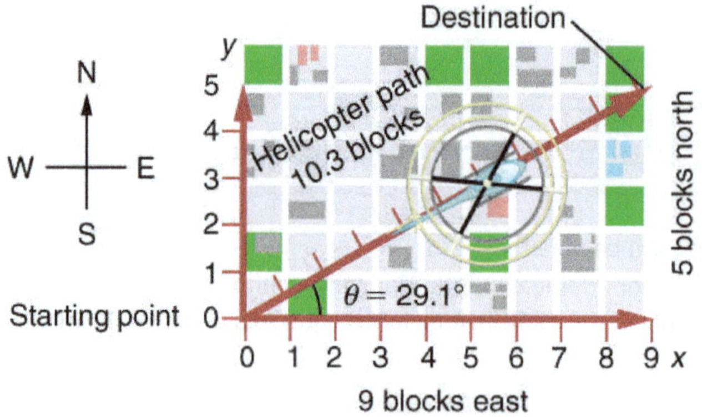

FIGURE 3.8 A person walks 9 blocks east and 5 blocks north. The displacement is 10.3 blocks at an angle 29.1° north of east.

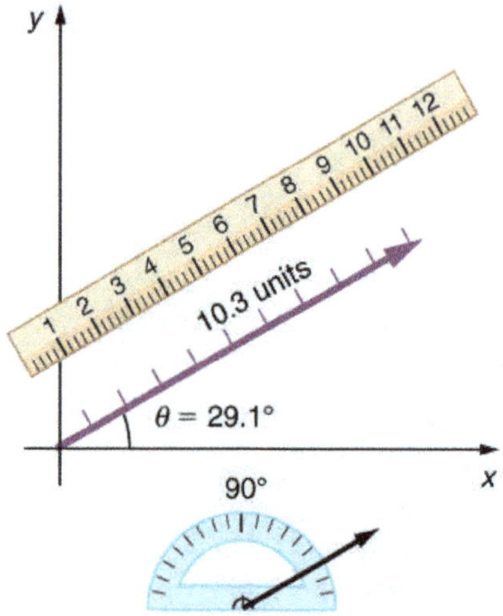

FIGURE 3.9 To describe the resultant vector for the person walking in a city considered in Figure 3.8 graphically, draw an arrow to represent the total displacement vector $\mathbf{D}$. Using a protractor, draw a line at an angle θ relative to the east-west axis. The length D of the arrow is proportional to the vector's magnitude and is measured along the line with a ruler. In this example, the magnitude D of the vector is 10.3 units, and the direction θ is 29.1° north of east.

Vector Addition: Head-to-Tail Method

The **head-to-tail method** is a graphical way to add vectors, described in Figure 3.10 below and in the steps following. The **tail** of the vector is the starting point of the vector, and the **head** (or tip) of a vector is the final, pointed end of the arrow.

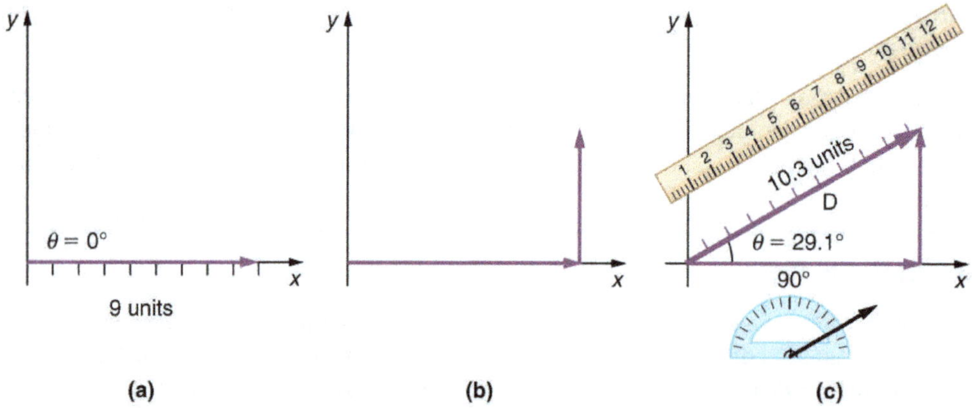

FIGURE 3.10 **Head-to-Tail Method:** The head-to-tail method of graphically adding vectors is illustrated for the two displacements of the person walking in a city considered in Figure 3.8. (a) Draw a vector representing the displacement to the east. (b) Draw a vector representing the displacement to the north. The tail of this vector should originate from the head of the first, east-pointing vector. (c) Draw a line from the tail of the east-pointing vector to the head of the north-pointing vector to form the sum or **resultant vector** $\mathbf{D}$. The length of the arrow $\mathbf{D}$ is proportional to the vector's magnitude and is measured to be 10.3 units . Its direction, described as the angle with respect to the east (or horizontal axis) θ is measured with a protractor to be 29.1°.

Step 1. *Draw an arrow to represent the first vector (9 blocks to the east) using a ruler and protractor.*

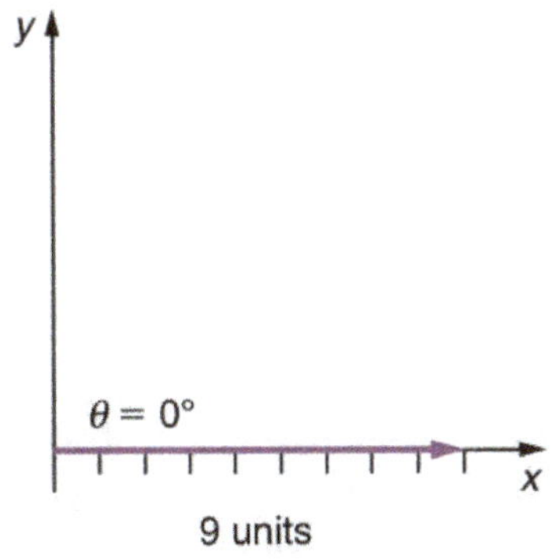

(a)

FIGURE 3.11

Step 2. Now draw an arrow to represent the second vector (5 blocks to the north). *Place the tail of the second vector at the head of the first vector.*

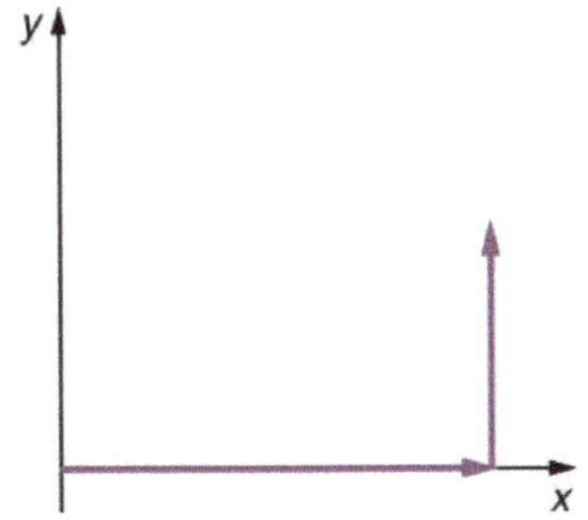

(b)

FIGURE 3.12

Step 3. *If there are more than two vectors, continue this process for each vector to be added. Note that in our example, we have only two vectors, so we have finished placing arrows tip to tail.*

Step 4. *Draw an arrow from the tail of the first vector to the head of the last vector.* This is the **resultant**, or the sum, of the other vectors.

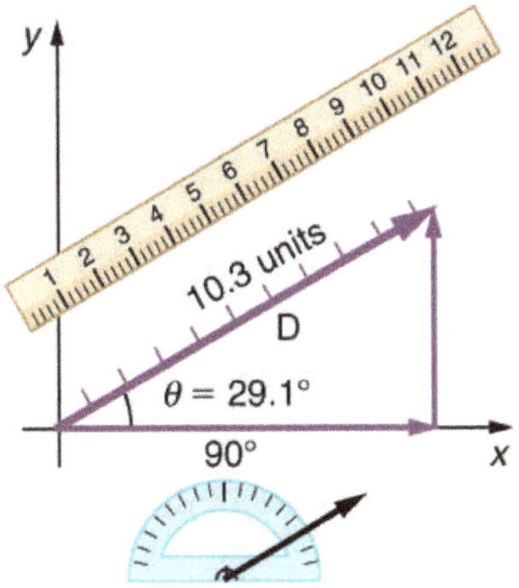

(c)

FIGURE 3.13

Step 5. To get the **magnitude** of the resultant, *measure its length with a ruler. (Note that in most calculations, we* *will use the Pythagorean theorem to determine this length.)*

Step 6. To get the **direction** of the resultant, *measure the angle it makes with the reference frame using a protractor. (Note that in most calculations, we will use trigonometric relationships to determine this angle.)*

The graphical addition of vectors is limited in accuracy only by the precision with which the drawings can be made and the precision of the measuring tools. It is valid for any number of vectors.

EXAMPLE 3.1

Adding Vectors Graphically Using the Head-to-Tail Method: A Woman Takes a Walk

Use the graphical technique for adding vectors to find the total displacement of a person who walks the following three paths (displacements) on a flat field. First, she walks 25.0 m in a direction $49.0°$ north of east. Then, she walks 23.0 m heading $15.0°$ north of east. Finally, she turns and walks 32.0 m in a direction 68.0° south of east.

Strategy

Represent each displacement vector graphically with an arrow, labeling the first $\mathbf{A}$, the second $\mathbf{B}$, and the third $\mathbf{C}$, making the lengths proportional to the distance and the directions as specified relative to an east-west line. The head-to-tail method outlined above will give a way to determine the magnitude and direction of the resultant displacement, denoted $\mathbf{R}$.

Solution

(1) Draw the three displacement vectors.

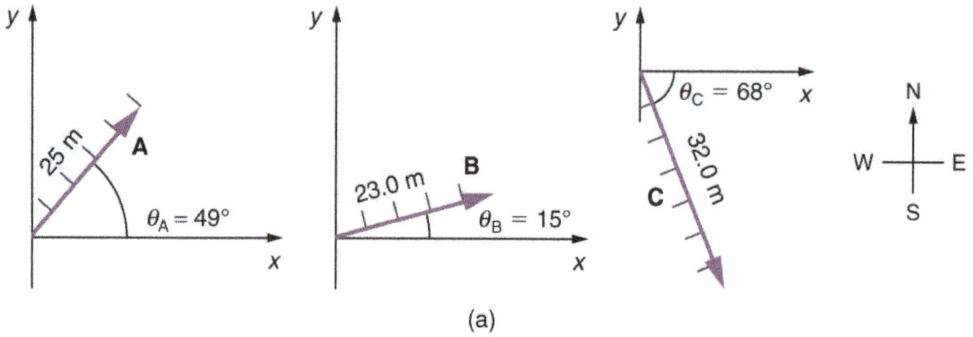

FIGURE 3.14

(2) Place the vectors head to tail retaining both their initial magnitude and direction.

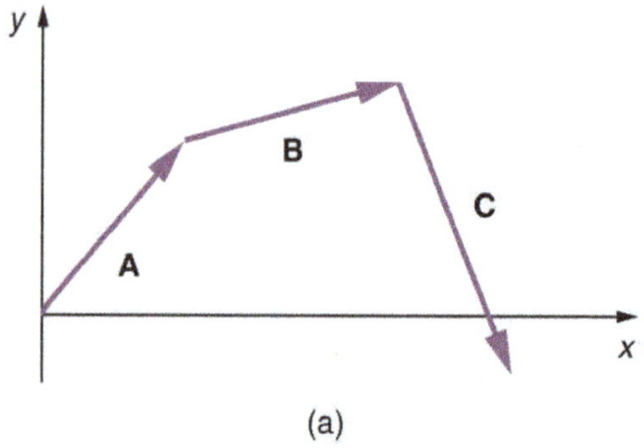

FIGURE 3.15

(3) Draw the resultant vector, $\mathbf{R}$.

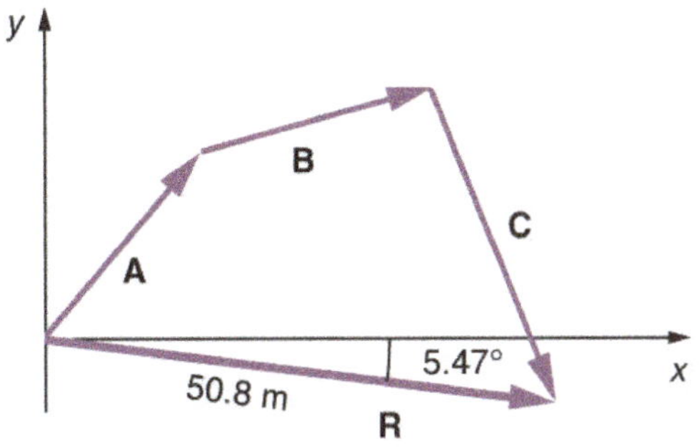

FIGURE 3.16

(4) Use a ruler to measure the magnitude of $\mathbf{R}$, and a protractor to measure the direction of $\mathbf{R}$. While the direction of the vector can be specified in many ways, the easiest way is to measure the angle between the vector and the nearest horizontal or vertical axis. Since the resultant vector is south of the eastward pointing axis, we flip the protractor upside down and measure the angle between the eastward axis and the vector.

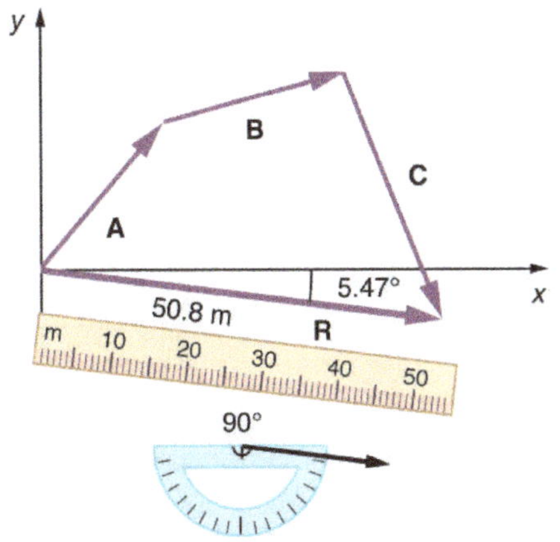

FIGURE 3.17

In this case, the total displacement $\mathbf{R}$ is seen to have a magnitude of 50.8 m and to lie in a direction $5.47°$ south of east. By using its magnitude and direction, this vector can be expressed as $R = 50.8 \text{ m}$ and $\theta = 5.47°$ south of east.

Discussion

The head-to-tail graphical method of vector addition works for any number of vectors. It is also important to note that the resultant is independent of the order in which the vectors are added. Therefore, we could add the vectors in any order as illustrated in Figure 3.18 and we will still get the same solution.

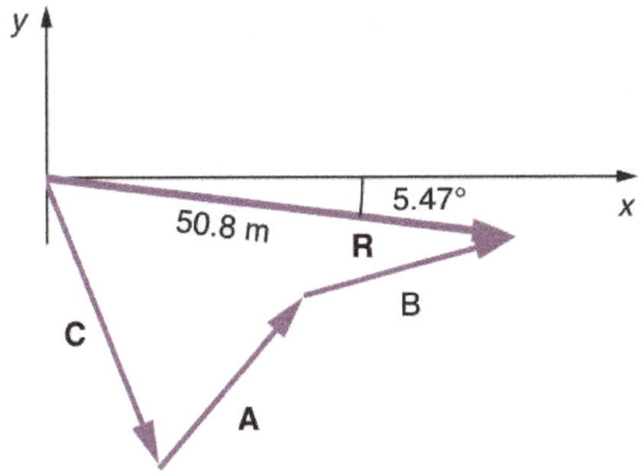

FIGURE 3.18

Here, we see that when the same vectors are added in a different order, the result is the same. This characteristic is true in every case and is an important characteristic of vectors. Vector addition is **commutative**. Vectors can be added in any order.

$$\mathbf{A} + \mathbf{B} = \mathbf{B} + \mathbf{A}. \tag{3.1}$$

(This is true for the addition of ordinary numbers as well—you get the same result whether you add $\mathbf{2} + \mathbf{3}$ or $\mathbf{3} + \mathbf{2}$, for example).

Vector Subtraction

Vector subtraction is a straightforward extension of vector addition. To define subtraction (say we want to subtract $\mathbf{B}$ from $\mathbf{A}$, written $\mathbf{A} - \mathbf{B}$, we must first define what we mean by subtraction. The *negative* of a vector $\mathbf{B}$ is defined to be $-\mathbf{B}$; that is, graphically *the negative of any vector has the same magnitude but the opposite direction*, as shown in Figure 3.19. In other words, $\mathbf{B}$ has the same length as $-\mathbf{B}$, but points in the opposite direction. Essentially, we just flip the vector so it points in the opposite direction.

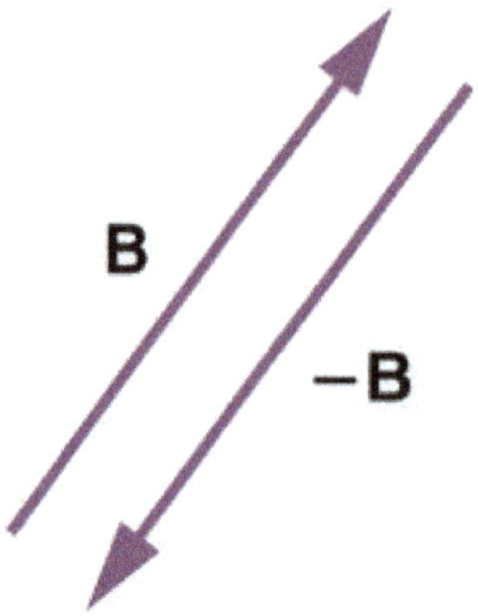

FIGURE 3.19 The negative of a vector is just another vector of the same magnitude but pointing in the opposite direction. So $\mathbf{B}$ is the negative of $-\mathbf{B}$; it has the same length but opposite direction.

The *subtraction* of vector $\mathbf{B}$ from vector $\mathbf{A}$ is then simply defined to be the addition of $-\mathbf{B}$ to $\mathbf{A}$. Note that vector subtraction is the addition of a negative vector. The order of subtraction does not affect the results.

$$\mathbf{A} - \mathbf{B} = \mathbf{A} + (-\mathbf{B}). \tag{3.2}$$

This is analogous to the subtraction of scalars (where, for example, $5 - 2 = 5 + (-2)$). Again, the result is independent of the order in which the subtraction is made. When vectors are subtracted graphically, the techniques outlined above are used, as the following example illustrates.

EXAMPLE 3.2

Subtracting Vectors Graphically: A Woman Sailing a Boat

A woman sailing a boat at night is following directions to a dock. The instructions read to first sail 27.5 m in a direction 66.0° north of east from her current location, and then travel 30.0 m in a direction 112° north of east (or 22.0° west of north). If the woman makes a mistake and travels in the *opposite* direction for the second leg of the trip, where will she end up? Compare this location with the location of the dock.

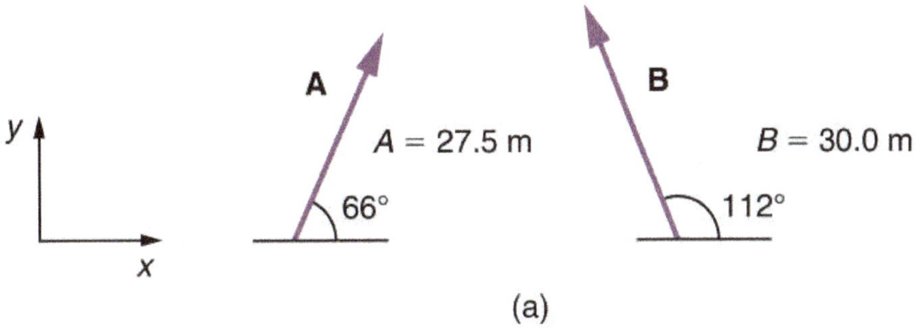

FIGURE 3.20

Strategy

We can represent the first leg of the trip with a vector $\mathbf{A}$, and the second leg of the trip with a vector $\mathbf{B}$. The dock is located at a location $\mathbf{A}+\mathbf{B}$. If the woman mistakenly travels in the *opposite* direction for the second leg of the journey, she will travel a distance B (30.0 m) in the direction $180°-112°=68°$ south of east. We represent this as $-\mathbf{B}$, as shown below. The vector $-\mathbf{B}$ has the same magnitude as $\mathbf{B}$ but is in the opposite direction. Thus, she will end up at a location $\mathbf{A}+(-\mathbf{B})$, or $\mathbf{A}-\mathbf{B}$.

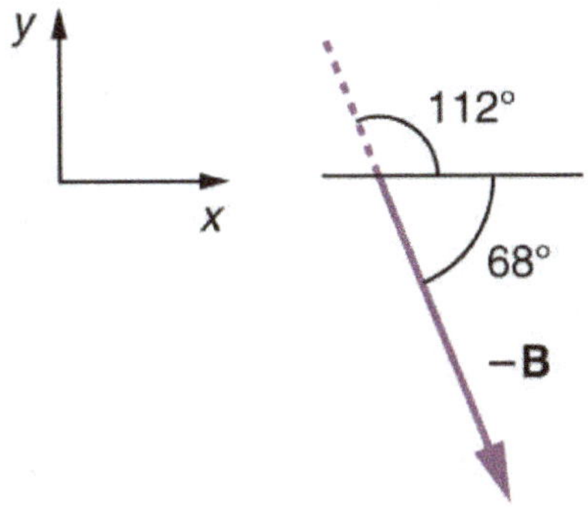

FIGURE 3.21

We will perform vector addition to compare the location of the dock, $\mathbf{A}+\mathbf{B}$, with the location at which the woman mistakenly arrives, $\mathbf{A}+(-\mathbf{B})$.

Solution

(1) To determine the location at which the woman arrives by accident, draw vectors $\mathbf{A}$ and $-\mathbf{B}$.

(2) Place the vectors head to tail.

(3) Draw the resultant vector $\mathbf{R}$.

(4) Use a ruler and protractor to measure the magnitude and direction of $\mathbf{R}$.

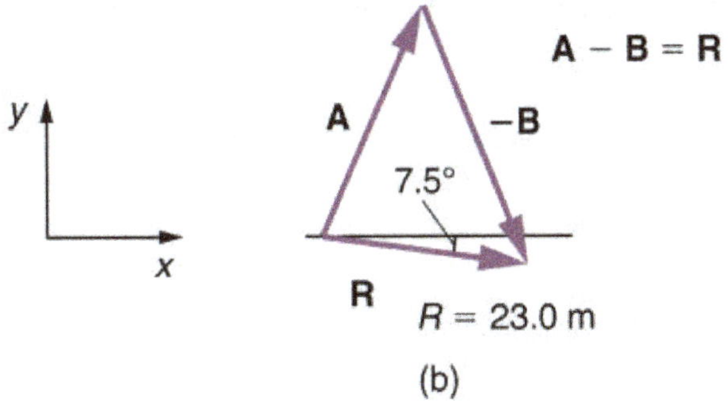

FIGURE 3.22

In this case, $R=23.0\text{ m}$ and $\theta=7.5°$ south of east.

(5) To determine the location of the dock, we repeat this method to add vectors $\mathbf{A}$ and $\mathbf{B}$. We obtain the resultant vector $\mathbf{R}'$:

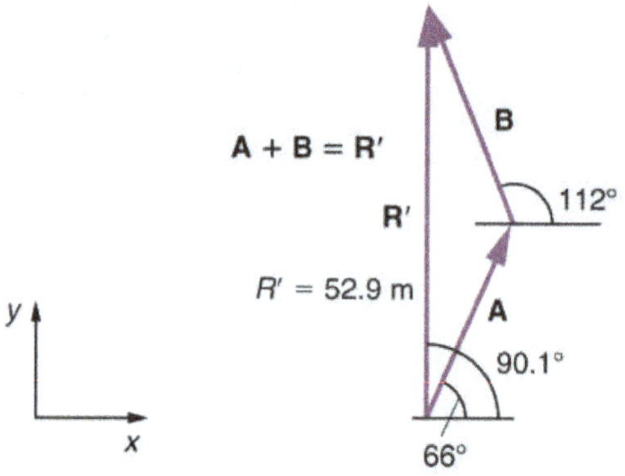

(c)

FIGURE 3.23

In this case $R = 52.9\ \text{m}$ and $\theta = 90.1^{\text{o}}$ north of east.

We can see that the woman will end up a significant distance from the dock if she travels in the opposite direction for the second leg of the trip.

Discussion

Because subtraction of a vector is the same as addition of a vector with the opposite direction, the graphical method of subtracting vectors works the same as for addition.

Multiplication of Vectors and Scalars

If we decided to walk three times as far on the first leg of the trip considered in the preceding example, then we would walk $3\ \times\ 27.5\ \text{m}$, or 82.5 m, in a direction 66.0^{o} north of east. This is an example of multiplying a vector by a positive **scalar**. Notice that the magnitude changes, but the direction stays the same.

If the scalar is negative, then multiplying a vector by it changes the vector's magnitude and gives the new vector the *opposite* direction. For example, if you multiply by –2, the magnitude doubles but the direction changes. We can summarize these rules in the following way: When vector $\mathbf{A}$ is multiplied by a scalar c,

- the magnitude of the vector becomes the absolute value of cA,
- if c is positive, the direction of the vector does not change,
- if c is negative, the direction is reversed.

In our case, $c = 3$ and $A = 27.5\ \text{m}$. Vectors are multiplied by scalars in many situations. Note that division is the inverse of multiplication. For example, dividing by 2 is the same as multiplying by the value (1/2). The rules for multiplication of vectors by scalars are the same for division; simply treat the divisor as a scalar between 0 and 1.

Resolving a Vector into Components

In the examples above, we have been adding vectors to determine the resultant vector. In many cases, however, we will need to do the opposite. We will need to take a single vector and find what other vectors added together produce it. In most cases, this involves determining the perpendicular **components** of a single vector, for example the *x- and y-*components, or the north-south and east-west components.

For example, we may know that the total displacement of a person walking in a city is 10.3 blocks in a direction 29.0^{o} north of east and want to find out how many blocks east and north had to be walked. This method is called *finding the components (or parts)* of the displacement in the east and north directions, and it is the inverse of the process followed to find the total displacement. It is one example of finding the components of a vector. There are many applications in physics where this is a useful thing to do. We will see this soon in Projectile Motion, and much more when we cover **forces** in Dynamics: Newton's Laws of Motion. Most of these involve finding components along perpendicular axes (such as north and east), so that right triangles are involved. The analytical techniques presented in Vector Addition and Subtraction: Analytical Methods are ideal for finding vector components.

PHET EXPLORATIONS

Maze Game

Learn about position, velocity, and acceleration in the "Arena of Pain". Use the green arrow to move the ball. Add more walls to the arena to make the game more difficult. Try to make a goal as fast as you can.

Click to view content (https://openstax.org/l/28mazegame).

3.3 Vector Addition and Subtraction: Analytical Methods

LEARNING OBJECTIVES

By the end of this section, you will be able to:

- Understand the rules of vector addition and subtraction using analytical methods.
- Apply analytical methods to determine vertical and horizontal component vectors.
- Apply analytical methods to determine the magnitude and direction of a resultant vector.

Analytical methods of vector addition and subtraction employ geometry and simple trigonometry rather than the ruler and protractor of graphical methods. Part of the graphical technique is retained, because vectors are still represented by arrows for easy visualization. However, analytical methods are more concise, accurate, and precise than graphical methods, which are limited by the accuracy with which a drawing can be made. Analytical methods are limited only by the accuracy and precision with which physical quantities are known.

Resolving a Vector into Perpendicular Components

Analytical techniques and right triangles go hand-in-hand in physics because (among other things) motions along perpendicular directions are independent. We very often need to separate a vector into perpendicular components. For example, given a vector like $\mathbf{A}$ in Figure 3.24, we may wish to find which two perpendicular vectors, $\mathbf{A}_x$ and $\mathbf{A}_y$, add to produce it.

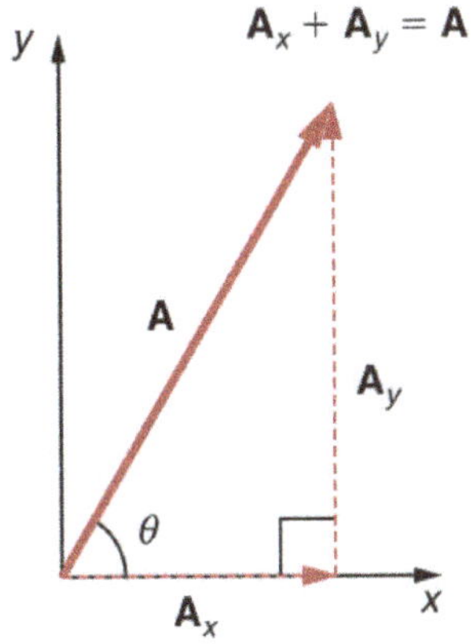

FIGURE 3.24 The vector $\mathbf{A}$, with its tail at the origin of an x, y-coordinate system, is shown together with its x- and y-components, $\mathbf{A}_x$ and $\mathbf{A}_y$. These vectors form a right triangle. The analytical relationships among these vectors are summarized below.

$\mathbf{A}_x$ and $\mathbf{A}_y$ are defined to be the components of $\mathbf{A}$ along the x- and y-axes. The three vectors $\mathbf{A}$, $\mathbf{A}_x$, and $\mathbf{A}_y$ form a right triangle:

$$\mathbf{A}_x + \mathbf{A}_y = \mathbf{A}. \quad (3.3)$$

Note that this relationship between vector components and the resultant vector holds only for vector quantities (which include both magnitude and direction). The relationship does not apply for the magnitudes alone. For example, if $\mathbf{A}_x = 3\text{ m}$ east, $\mathbf{A}_y = 4\text{ m}$ north, and $\mathbf{A} = 5\text{ m}$ north-east, then it is true that the vectors $\mathbf{A}_x + \mathbf{A}_y = \mathbf{A}$. However, it is *not* true that the sum of the magnitudes of the vectors is also equal. That is,

$$3\,\text{m} + 4\,\text{m} \neq 5\,\text{m} \tag{3.4}$$

Thus,

$$A_x + A_y \neq A \tag{3.5}$$

If the vector $\mathbf{A}$ is known, then its magnitude A (its length) and its angle θ (its direction) are known. To find A_x and A_y, its *x*- and *y*-components, we use the following relationships for a right triangle.

$$A_x = A\cos\theta \tag{3.6}$$

and

$$A_y = A\sin\theta. \tag{3.7}$$

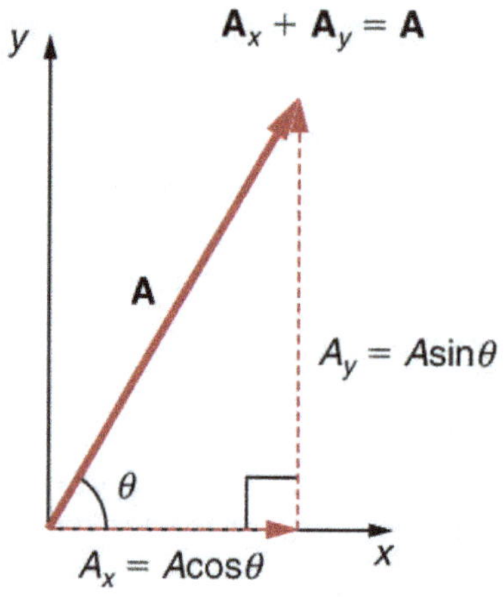

FIGURE 3.25 The magnitudes of the vector components $\mathbf{A}_x$ and $\mathbf{A}_y$ can be related to the resultant vector $\mathbf{A}$ and the angle θ with trigonometric identities. Here we see that $A_x = A\cos\theta$ and $A_y = A\sin\theta$.

Suppose, for example, that $\mathbf{A}$ is the vector representing the total displacement of the person walking in a city considered in Kinematics in Two Dimensions: An Introduction and Vector Addition and Subtraction: Graphical Methods.

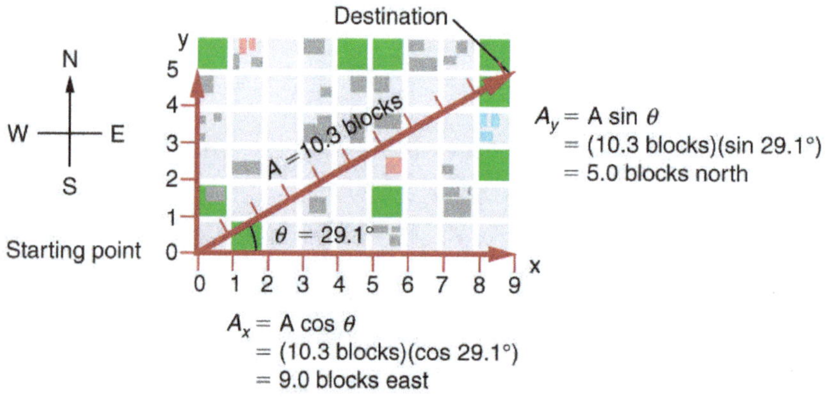

FIGURE 3.26 We can use the relationships $A_x = A\cos\theta$ and $A_y = A\sin\theta$ to determine the magnitude of the horizontal and vertical component vectors in this example.

Then $A = 10.3$ blocks and $\theta = 29.1°$, so that

$$A_x = A\cos\theta = (10.3\text{ blocks})(\cos 29.1°) = 9.0\text{ blocks} \tag{3.8}$$

$$A_y = A\sin\theta = (10.3\text{ blocks})(\sin 29.1°) = 5.0\text{ blocks}. \tag{3.9}$$

Calculating a Resultant Vector

If the perpendicular components $\mathbf{A}_x$ and $\mathbf{A}_y$ of a vector $\mathbf{A}$ are known, then $\mathbf{A}$ can also be found analytically. To find the magnitude A and direction θ of a vector from its perpendicular components $\mathbf{A}_x$ and $\mathbf{A}_y$, relative to the x-axis, we use the following relationships:

$$A = \sqrt{{A_x}^2 + {A_y}^2} \quad 3.10$$

$$\theta = \tan^{-1}(A_y/A_x). \quad 3.11$$

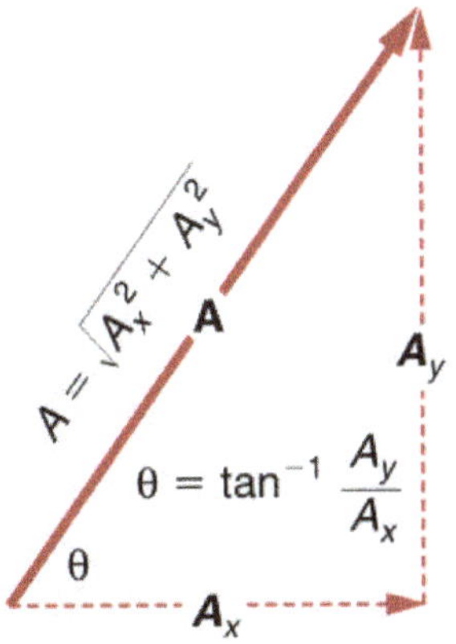

FIGURE 3.27 The magnitude and direction of the resultant vector can be determined once the horizontal and vertical components A_x and A_y have been determined.

Note that the equation $A = \sqrt{A_x^2 + A_y^2}$ is just the Pythagorean theorem relating the legs of a right triangle to the length of the hypotenuse. For example, if A_x and A_y are 9 and 5 blocks, respectively, then $A = \sqrt{9^2+5^2}=10.3$ blocks, again consistent with the example of the person walking in a city. Finally, the direction is $\theta = \tan^{-1}(5/9)=29.1°$, as before.

DETERMINING VECTORS AND VECTOR COMPONENTS WITH ANALYTICAL METHODS

Equations $A_x = A\cos\theta$ and $A_y = A\sin\theta$ are used to find the perpendicular components of a vector—that is, to go from A and θ to A_x and A_y. Equations $A = \sqrt{A_x^2 + A_y^2}$ and $\theta = \tan^{-1}(A_y/A_x)$ are used to find a vector from its perpendicular components—that is, to go from A_x and A_y to A and θ. Both processes are crucial to analytical methods of vector addition and subtraction.

Adding Vectors Using Analytical Methods

To see how to add vectors using perpendicular components, consider Figure 3.28, in which the vectors $\mathbf{A}$ and $\mathbf{B}$ are added to produce the resultant $\mathbf{R}$.

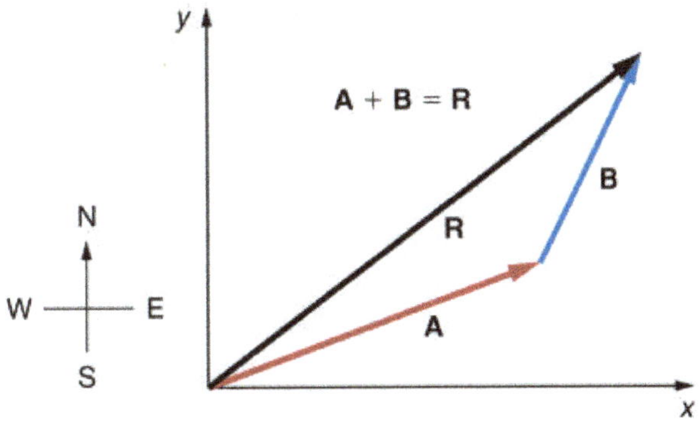

FIGURE 3.28 Vectors $\mathbf{A}$ and $\mathbf{B}$ are two legs of a walk, and $\mathbf{R}$ is the resultant or total displacement. You can use analytical methods to determine the magnitude and direction of $\mathbf{R}$.

If $\mathbf{A}$ and $\mathbf{B}$ represent two legs of a walk (two displacements), then $\mathbf{R}$ is the total displacement. The person taking the walk ends up at the tip of $\mathbf{R}$. There are many ways to arrive at the same point. In particular, the person could have walked first in the *x*-direction and then in the *y*-direction. Those paths are the *x*- and *y*-components of the resultant, $\mathbf{R}_x$ and $\mathbf{R}_y$. If we know $\mathbf{R}_x$ and $\mathbf{R}_y$, we can find R and θ using the equations $A = \sqrt{A_x{}^2 + A_y{}^2}$ and $\theta = \tan^{-1}(A_y/A_x)$. When you use the analytical method of vector addition, you can determine the components or the magnitude and direction of a vector.

Step 1. *Identify the x- and y-axes that will be used in the problem. Then, find the components of each vector to be added along the chosen perpendicular axes.* Use the equations $A_x = A \cos\theta$ and $A_y = A \sin\theta$ to find the components. In Figure 3.29, these components are A_x, A_y, B_x, and B_y. The angles that vectors $\mathbf{A}$ and $\mathbf{B}$ make with the *x*-axis are θ_{A} and θ_{B}, respectively.

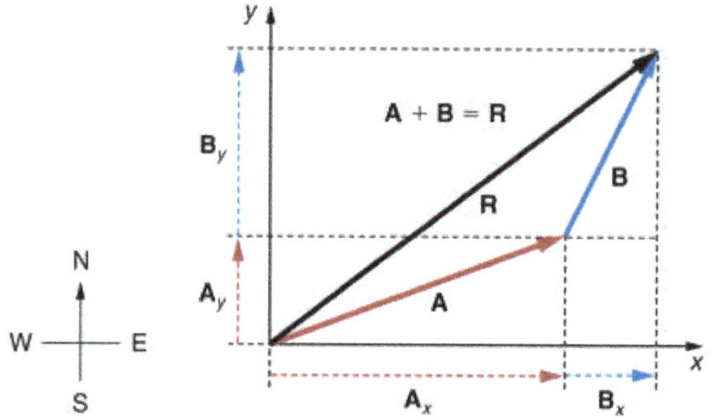

FIGURE 3.29 To add vectors $\mathbf{A}$ and $\mathbf{B}$, first determine the horizontal and vertical components of each vector. These are the dotted vectors $\mathbf{A}_x$, $\mathbf{A}_y$, $\mathbf{B}_x$ and $\mathbf{B}_y$ shown in the image.

Step 2. *Find the components of the resultant along each axis by adding the components of the individual vectors along that axis.* That is, as shown in Figure 3.30,

$$R_x = A_x + B_x \tag{3.12}$$

and

$$R_y = A_y + B_y. \tag{3.13}$$

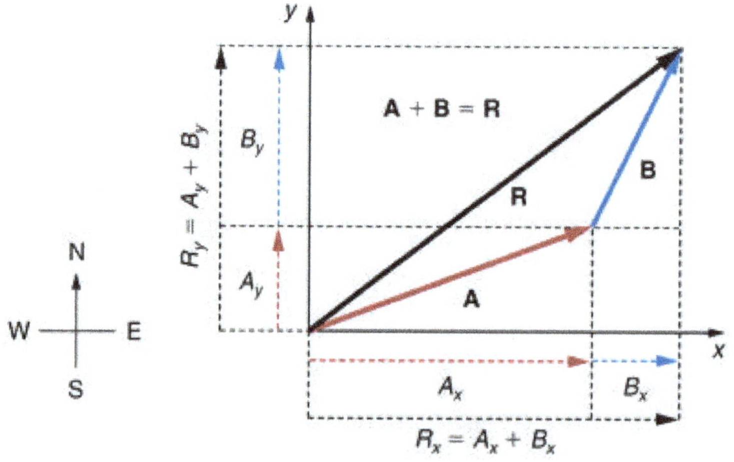

FIGURE 3.30 The magnitude of the vectors $\mathbf{A}_x$ and $\mathbf{B}_x$ add to give the magnitude R_x of the resultant vector in the horizontal direction. Similarly, the magnitudes of the vectors $\mathbf{A}_y$ and $\mathbf{B}_y$ add to give the magnitude R_y of the resultant vector in the vertical direction.

Components along the same axis, say the *x*-axis, are vectors along the same line and, thus, can be added to one another like ordinary numbers. The same is true for components along the *y*-axis. (For example, a 9-block eastward walk could be taken in two legs, the first 3 blocks east and the second 6 blocks east, for a total of 9, because they are along the same direction.) So resolving vectors into components along common axes makes it easier to add them. Now that the components of $\mathbf{R}$ are known, its magnitude and direction can be found.

Step 3. *To get the magnitude* $\mathbf{R}$ *of the resultant, use the Pythagorean theorem:*

$$R = \sqrt{R_x^2 + R_y^2}. \quad (3.14)$$

Step 4. *To get the direction of the resultant relative to the x-axis:*

$$\theta = \tan^{-1}(R_y/R_x). \quad (3.15)$$

The following example illustrates this technique for adding vectors using perpendicular components.

EXAMPLE 3.3

Adding Vectors Using Analytical Methods

Add the vector $\mathbf{A}$ to the vector $\mathbf{B}$ shown in Figure 3.31, using perpendicular components along the *x*- and *y*-axes. The *x*- and *y*-axes are along the east–west and north–south directions, respectively. Vector $\mathbf{A}$ represents the first leg of a walk in which a person walks 53.0 m in a direction 20.0° north of east. Vector $\mathbf{B}$ represents the second leg, a displacement of 34.0 m in a direction 63.0° north of east.

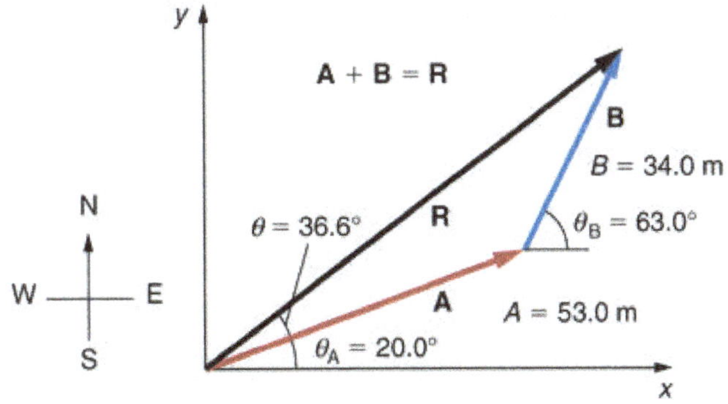

FIGURE 3.31 Vector $\mathbf{A}$ has magnitude 53.0 m and direction 20.0° north of the *x*-axis. Vector $\mathbf{B}$ has magnitude 34.0 m and direction 63.0° north of the *x*-axis. You can use analytical methods to determine the magnitude and direction of $\mathbf{R}$.

Strategy

The components of $\mathbf{A}$ and $\mathbf{B}$ along the *x*- and *y*-axes represent walking due east and due north to get to the same ending point. Once found, they are combined to produce the resultant.

Solution

Following the method outlined above, we first find the components of $\mathbf{A}$ and $\mathbf{B}$ along the *x*- and *y*-axes. Note that $A = 53.0\text{ m}$, $\theta_A = 20.0°$, $B = 34.0\text{ m}$, and $\theta_B = 63.0°$. We find the *x*-components by using $A_x = A\cos\theta$, which gives

$$\begin{aligned} A_x &= A\cos\theta_A = (53.0\text{ m})(\cos 20.0°) \\ &= (53.0\text{ m})(0.940) = 49.8\text{ m} \end{aligned} \quad (3.16)$$

and

$$\begin{aligned} B_x &= B\cos\theta_B = (34.0\text{ m})(\cos 63.0°) \\ &= (34.0\text{ m})(0.454) = 15.4\text{ m}. \end{aligned} \quad (3.17)$$

Similarly, the *y*-components are found using $A_y = A\sin\theta_A$:

$$\begin{aligned} A_y &= A\sin\theta_A = (53.0\text{ m})(\sin 20.0°) \\ &= (53.0\text{ m})(0.342) = 18.1\text{ m} \end{aligned} \quad (3.18)$$

and

$$\begin{aligned} B_y &= B \sin \theta_B = (34.0 \text{ m})(\sin 63.0°) \\ &= (34.0 \text{ m})(0.891) = 30.3 \text{ m}. \end{aligned} \quad 3.19$$

The x- and y-components of the resultant are thus

$$R_x = A_x + B_x = 49.8 \text{ m} + 15.4 \text{ m} = 65.2 \text{ m} \quad 3.20$$

and

$$R_y = A_y + B_y = 18.1 \text{ m} + 30.3 \text{ m} = 48.4 \text{ m}. \quad 3.21$$

Now we can find the magnitude of the resultant by using the Pythagorean theorem:

$$R = \sqrt{R_x^2 + R_y^2} = \sqrt{(65.2)^2 + (48.4)^2 \text{ m}} \quad 3.22$$

so that

$$R = 81.2 \text{ m}. \quad 3.23$$

Finally, we find the direction of the resultant:

$$\theta = \tan^{-1}(R_y/R_x) = +\tan^{-1}(48.4/65.2). \quad 3.24$$

Thus,

$$\theta = \tan^{-1}(0.742) = 36.6°. \quad 3.25$$

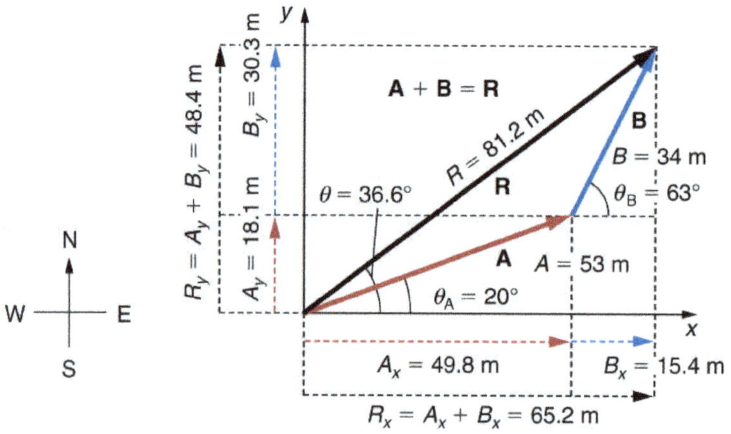

FIGURE 3.32 Using analytical methods, we see that the magnitude of $\mathbf{R}$ is 81.2 m and its direction is $36.6°$ north of east.

Discussion

This example illustrates the addition of vectors using perpendicular components. Vector subtraction using perpendicular components is very similar—it is just the addition of a negative vector.

Subtraction of vectors is accomplished by the addition of a negative vector. That is, $\mathbf{A} - \mathbf{B} \equiv \mathbf{A} + (-\mathbf{B})$. Thus, *the method for the subtraction of vectors using perpendicular components is identical to that for addition.* The components of $-\mathbf{B}$ are the negatives of the components of $\mathbf{B}$. The x- and y-components of the resultant $\mathbf{A} - \mathbf{B} = \mathbf{R}$ are thus

$$R_x = A_x + (-B_x) \quad 3.26$$

and

$$R_y = A_y + (-B_y) \quad 3.27$$

and the rest of the method outlined above is identical to that for addition. (See Figure 3.33.)

Analyzing vectors using perpendicular components is very useful in many areas of physics, because perpendicular quantities are often independent of one another. The next module, Projectile Motion, is one of many in which using perpendicular components helps make the picture clear and simplifies the physics.

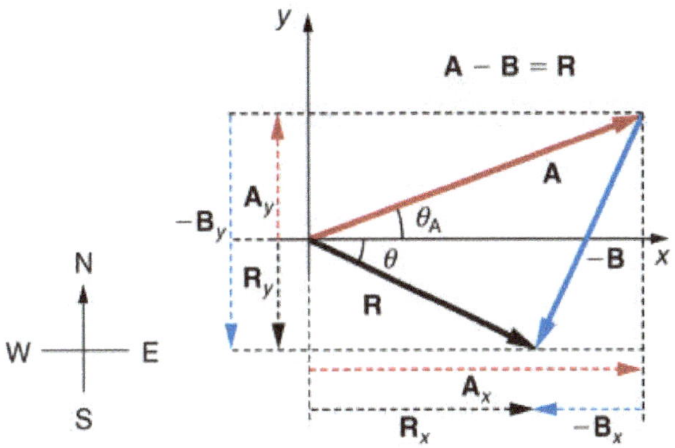

FIGURE 3.33 The subtraction of the two vectors shown in Figure 3.28. The components of **–B** are the negatives of the components of **B**. The method of subtraction is the same as that for addition.

PHET EXPLORATIONS

Vector Addition

Learn how to add vectors. Drag vectors onto a graph, change their length and angle, and sum them together. The magnitude, angle, and components of each vector can be displayed in several formats.

Click to view content (https://openstax.org/books/college-physics-ap-courses-2e/pages/3-3-vector-addition-and-subtraction-analytical-methods)

3.4 Projectile Motion

LEARNING OBJECTIVES

By the end of this section, you will be able to:

- Identify and explain the properties of a projectile, such as acceleration due to gravity, range, maximum height, and trajectory.
- Determine the location and velocity of a projectile at different points in its trajectory.
- Apply the principle of independence of motion to solve projectile motion problems.

Projectile motion is the **motion** of an object thrown or projected into the air, subject to only the acceleration of gravity. The object is called a **projectile**, and its path is called its **trajectory**. The motion of falling objects, as covered in Problem-Solving Basics for One-Dimensional Kinematics, is a simple one-dimensional type of projectile motion in which there is no horizontal movement. In this section, we consider two-dimensional projectile motion, such as that of a football or other object for which **air resistance** *is negligible.*

The most important fact to remember here is that *motions along perpendicular axes are independent* and thus can be analyzed separately. This fact was discussed in Kinematics in Two Dimensions: An Introduction, where vertical and horizontal motions were seen to be independent. The key to analyzing two-dimensional projectile motion is to break it into two motions, one along the horizontal axis and the other along the vertical. (This choice of axes is the most sensible, because acceleration due to gravity is vertical—thus, there will be no acceleration along the horizontal axis when air resistance is negligible.) As is customary, we call the horizontal axis the *x*-axis and the vertical axis the *y*-axis. Figure 3.34 illustrates the notation for displacement, where $\mathbf{s}$ is defined to be the total displacement and $\mathbf{x}$ and $\mathbf{y}$ are its components along the horizontal and vertical axes, respectively. The magnitudes of these vectors are *s*, *x*, and *y*. (Note that in the last section we used the notation $\mathbf{A}$ to represent a vector with components $\mathbf{A}_x$ and $\mathbf{A}_y$. If we continued this format, we would call displacement $\mathbf{s}$ with components $\mathbf{s}_x$ and $\mathbf{s}_y$. However, to simplify the notation, we will simply represent the component vectors as $\mathbf{x}$ and $\mathbf{y}$.)

Of course, to describe motion we must deal with velocity and acceleration, as well as with displacement. We must find their components along the *x*- and *y*-axes, too. We will assume all forces except gravity (such as air resistance and friction, for example) are negligible. The components of acceleration are then very simple:

$a_y = -g = -9.80 \text{ m/s}^2$. (Note that this definition assumes that the upwards direction is defined as the positive direction. If you arrange the coordinate system instead such that the downwards direction is positive, then acceleration due to gravity takes a positive value.) Because gravity is vertical, $a_x = 0$. Both accelerations are constant, so the kinematic equations can be used.

REVIEW OF KINEMATIC EQUATIONS (CONSTANT a)

$$x = x_0 + \bar{v}t \quad (3.28)$$

$$\bar{v} = \frac{v_0 + v}{2} \quad (3.29)$$

$$v = v_0 + at \quad (3.30)$$

$$x = x_0 + v_0 t + \frac{1}{2}at^2 \quad (3.31)$$

$$v^2 = v_0^2 + 2a(x - x_0). \quad (3.32)$$

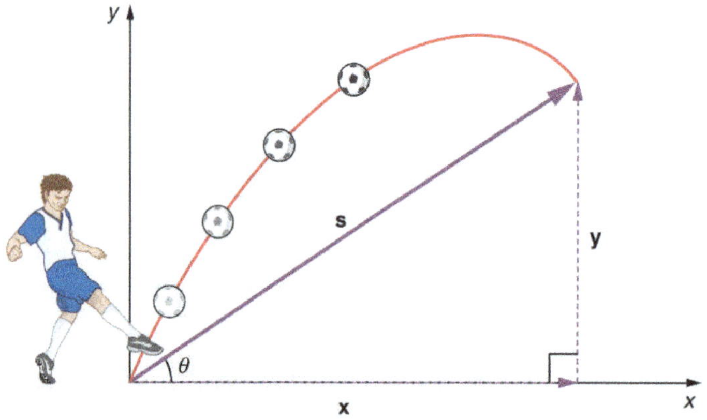

FIGURE 3.34 The total displacement **s** of a soccer ball at a point along its path. The vector **s** has components **x** and **y** along the horizontal and vertical axes. Its magnitude is s, and it makes an angle θ with the horizontal.

Given these assumptions, the following steps are then used to analyze projectile motion:

Step 1. *Resolve or break the motion into horizontal and vertical components along the x- and y-axes.* These axes are perpendicular, so $A_x = A \cos\theta$ and $A_y = A \sin\theta$ are used. The magnitude of the components of displacement **s** along these axes are x and y. The magnitudes of the components of the velocity **v** are $v_x = v \cos\theta$ and $v_y = v \sin\theta$, where v is the magnitude of the velocity and θ is its direction, as shown in Figure 3.35. Initial values are denoted with a subscript 0, as usual.

Step 2. *Treat the motion as two independent one-dimensional motions, one horizontal and the other vertical.* The kinematic equations for horizontal and vertical motion take the following forms:

$$\text{Horizontal Motion}(a_x = 0) \quad (3.33)$$

$$x = x_0 + v_x t \quad (3.34)$$

$$v_x = v_{0x} = v_x = \text{velocity is a constant.} \quad (3.35)$$

$$\text{Vertical Motion (assuming positive is up } a_y = -g = -9.80\text{m/s}^2) \quad (3.36)$$

$$y = y_0 + \frac{1}{2}(v_{0y} + v_y)t \quad (3.37)$$

$$v_y = v_{0y} - gt \quad (3.38)$$

$$y = y_0 + v_{0y}t - \frac{1}{2}gt^2 \quad (3.39)$$

$$v_y^2 = v_{0y}^2 - 2g(y - y_0). \quad 3.40$$

Step 3. *Solve for the unknowns in the two separate motions—one horizontal and one vertical.* Note that the only common variable between the motions is time t. The problem solving procedures here are the same as for one-dimensional **kinematics** and are illustrated in the solved examples below.

Step 4. *Recombine the two motions to find the total displacement* $\mathbf{s}$ *and velocity* $\mathbf{v}$. Because the x - and y -motions are perpendicular, we determine these vectors by using the techniques outlined in the Vector Addition and Subtraction: Analytical Methods and employing $A = \sqrt{A_x^2 + A_y^2}$ and $\theta = \tan^{-1}(A_y/A_x)$ in the following form, where θ is the direction of the displacement $\mathbf{s}$ and θ_v is the direction of the velocity $\mathbf{v}$:

Total displacement and velocity

$$s = \sqrt{x^2 + y^2} \quad 3.41$$

$$\theta = \tan^{-1}(y/x) \quad 3.42$$

$$v = \sqrt{v_x^2 + v_y^2} \quad 3.43$$

$$\theta_v = \tan^{-1}(v_y/v_x). \quad 3.44$$

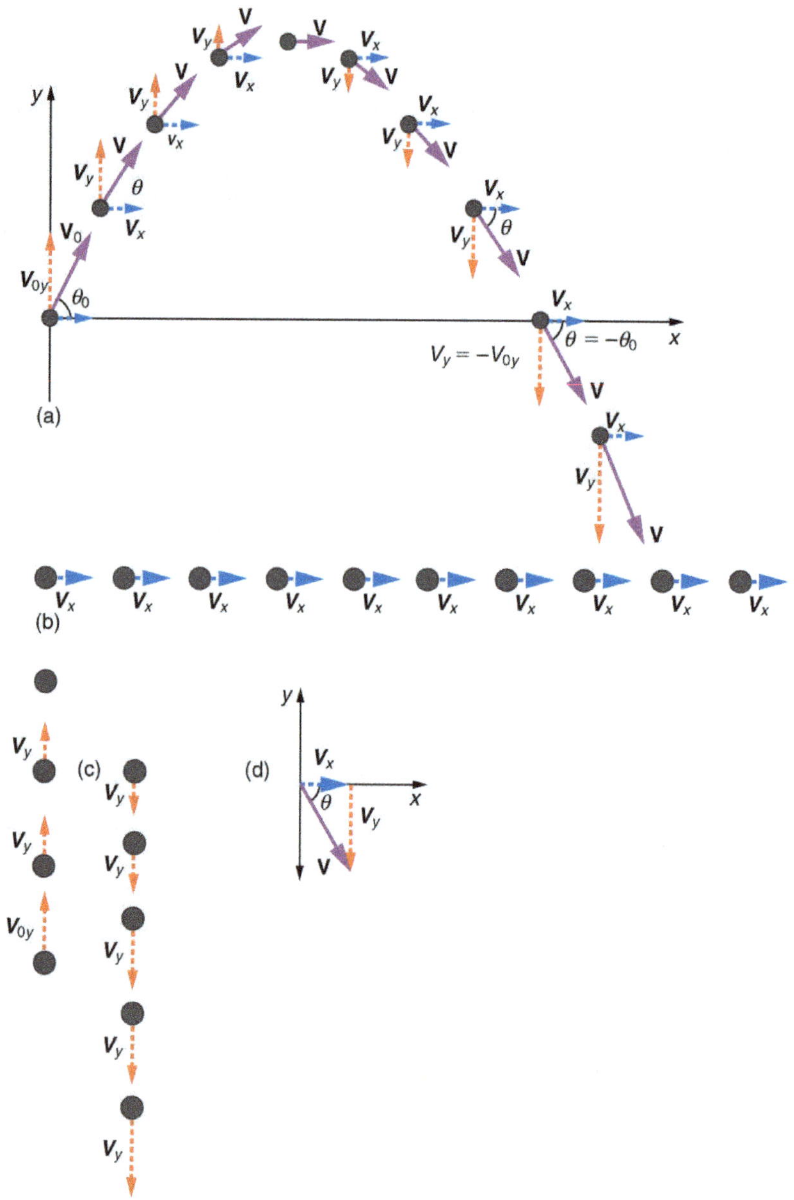

FIGURE 3.35 (a) We analyze two-dimensional projectile motion by breaking it into two independent one-dimensional motions along the vertical and horizontal axes. (b) The horizontal motion is simple, because $a_x = 0$ and v_x is thus constant. (c) The velocity in the vertical direction begins to decrease as the object rises; at its highest point, the vertical velocity is zero. As the object falls towards the Earth again, the vertical velocity increases again in magnitude but points in the opposite direction to the initial vertical velocity. (d) The x- and y-motions are recombined to give the total velocity at any given point on the trajectory.

EXAMPLE 3.4

A Fireworks Projectile Explodes High and Away

During a fireworks display, a shell is shot into the air with an initial speed of 70.0 m/s at an angle of $75.0°$ above the horizontal, as illustrated in Figure 3.36. The fuse is timed to ignite the shell just as it reaches its highest point above the ground. (a) Calculate the height at which the shell explodes. (b) How much time passed between the launch of the shell and the explosion? (c) What is the horizontal displacement of the shell when it explodes?

Strategy

Because air resistance is negligible for the unexploded shell, the analysis method outlined above can be used. The motion can be broken into horizontal and vertical motions in which $a_x = 0$ and $a_y = -g$. We can then define x_0 and y_0 to be zero and solve for the desired quantities.

Solution for (a)

By "height" we mean the altitude or vertical position y above the starting point. The highest point in any trajectory, called the apex, is reached when $v_y = 0$. Since we know the initial and final velocities as well as the initial position, we use the following equation to find y:

$$v_y^2 = v_{0y}^2 - 2g(y - y_0). \tag{3.45}$$

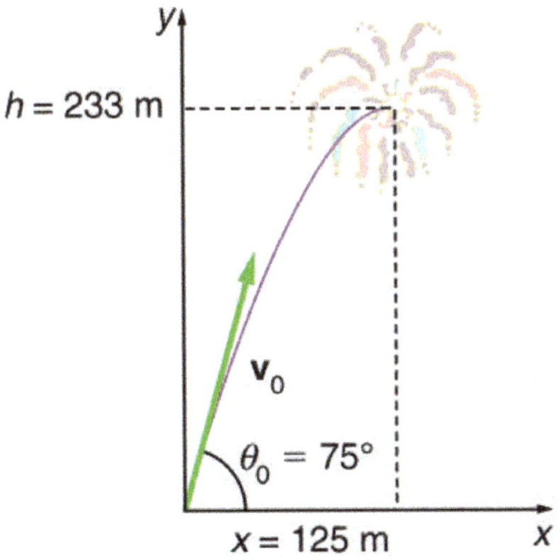

FIGURE 3.36 The trajectory of a fireworks shell. The fuse is set to explode the shell at the highest point in its trajectory, which is found to be at a height of 233 m and 125 m away horizontally.

Because y_0 and v_y are both zero, the equation simplifies to

$$0 = v_{0y}^2 - 2gy. \tag{3.46}$$

Solving for y gives

$$y = \frac{v_{0y}^2}{2g}. \tag{3.47}$$

Now we must find v_{0y}, the component of the initial velocity in the y-direction. It is given by $v_{0y} = v_0 \sin \theta$, where v_{0y} is the initial velocity of 70.0 m/s, and $\theta_0 = 75.0°$ is the initial angle. Thus,

$$v_{0y} = v_0 \sin \theta_0 = (70.0 \text{ m/s})(\sin 75°) = 67.6 \text{ m/s}. \tag{3.48}$$

and y is

$$y = \frac{(67.6 \text{ m/s})^2}{2(9.80 \text{ m/s}^2)}, \tag{3.49}$$

so that

$$y = 233\text{m}. \tag{3.50}$$

Discussion for (a)

Note that because up is positive, the initial velocity is positive, as is the maximum height, but the acceleration due to gravity is negative. Note also that the maximum height depends only on the vertical component of the initial velocity, so that any projectile with a 67.6 m/s initial vertical component of velocity will reach a maximum height of 233 m (neglecting air resistance). The numbers in this example are reasonable for large fireworks displays, the shells of which do reach such heights before exploding. In practice, air resistance is not completely negligible, and so the initial velocity would have to be somewhat larger than that given to reach the same height.

Solution for (b)

As in many physics problems, there is more than one way to solve for the time to the highest point. In this case, the easiest method is to use $y = y_0 + \frac{1}{2}(v_{0y} + v_y)t$. Because y_0 is zero, this equation reduces to simply

$$y = \frac{1}{2}(v_{0y} + v_y)t. \quad \text{3.51}$$

Note that the final vertical velocity, v_y, at the highest point is zero. Thus,

$$\begin{aligned} t &= \frac{2y}{(v_{0y}+v_y)} = \frac{2(233\text{ m})}{(67.6\text{ m/s})} \\ &= 6.90\text{ s}. \end{aligned} \quad \text{3.52}$$

Discussion for (b)

This time is also reasonable for large fireworks. When you are able to see the launch of fireworks, you will notice several seconds pass before the shell explodes. (Another way of finding the time is by using $y = y_0 + v_{0y}t - \frac{1}{2}gt^2$, and solving the quadratic equation for t.)

Solution for (c)

Because air resistance is negligible, $a_x = 0$ and the horizontal velocity is constant, as discussed above. The horizontal displacement is horizontal velocity multiplied by time as given by $x = x_0 + v_x t$, where x_0 is equal to zero:

$$x = v_x t, \quad \text{3.53}$$

where v_x is the x-component of the velocity, which is given by $v_x = v_0 \cos \theta_0$. Now,

$$v_x = v_0 \cos \theta_0 = (70.0\text{ m/s})(\cos 75.0^\circ) = 18.1\text{ m/s}. \quad \text{3.54}$$

The time t for both motions is the same, and so x is

$$x = (18.1\text{ m/s})(6.90\text{ s}) = 125\text{ m}. \quad \text{3.55}$$

Discussion for (c)

The horizontal motion is a constant velocity in the absence of air resistance. The horizontal displacement found here could be useful in keeping the fireworks fragments from falling on spectators. Once the shell explodes, air resistance has a major effect, and many fragments will land directly below.

In solving part (a) of the preceding example, the expression we found for y is valid for any projectile motion where air resistance is negligible. Call the maximum height $y = h$; then,

$$h = \frac{v_{0y}^2}{2g}. \quad \text{3.56}$$

This equation defines the *maximum height of a projectile* and depends only on the vertical component of the initial velocity.

DEFINING A COORDINATE SYSTEM

It is important to set up a coordinate system when analyzing projectile motion. One part of defining the coordinate system is to define an origin for the x and y positions. Often, it is convenient to choose the initial position of the object as the origin such that $x_0 = 0$ and $y_0 = 0$. It is also important to define the positive and negative directions in the x and y directions. Typically, we define the positive vertical direction as upwards, and the positive horizontal direction is usually the direction of the object's motion. When this is the case, the vertical acceleration, g, takes a negative value (since it is directed downwards towards the Earth). However, it is occasionally useful to define the coordinates differently. For example, if you are analyzing the motion of a ball thrown downwards from the top of a cliff, it may make sense to define the positive direction downwards since the motion of the ball is solely in the downwards direction. If this is the case, g takes a positive value.

EXAMPLE 3.5

Calculating Projectile Motion: Hot Rock Projectile

Kilauea in Hawaii is the world's most continuously active volcano. Very active volcanoes characteristically eject red-hot rocks and lava rather than smoke and ash. Suppose a large rock is ejected from the volcano with a speed of 25.0 m/s and at an angle $35.0°$ above the horizontal, as shown in Figure 3.37. The rock strikes the side of the volcano at an altitude 20.0 m lower than its starting point. (a) Calculate the time it takes the rock to follow this path. (b) What are the magnitude and direction of the rock's velocity at impact?

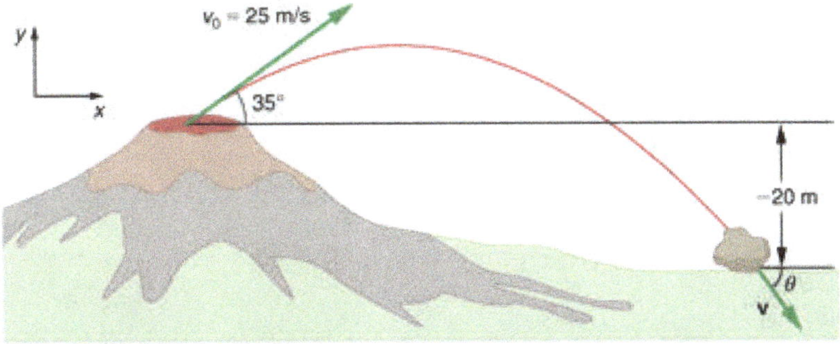

FIGURE 3.37 The trajectory of a rock ejected from the Kilauea volcano.

Strategy

Again, resolving this two-dimensional motion into two independent one-dimensional motions will allow us to solve for the desired quantities. The time a projectile is in the air is governed by its vertical motion alone. We will solve for t first. While the rock is rising and falling vertically, the horizontal motion continues at a constant velocity. This example asks for the final velocity. Thus, the vertical and horizontal results will be recombined to obtain v and θ_v at the final time t determined in the first part of the example.

Solution for (a)

While the rock is in the air, it rises and then falls to a final position 20.0 m lower than its starting altitude. We can find the time for this by using

$$y = y_0 + v_{0y}t - \frac{1}{2}gt^2. \quad 3.57$$

If we take the initial position y_0 to be zero, then the final position is $y = -20.0\text{ m}$. Now the initial vertical velocity is the vertical component of the initial velocity, found from $v_{0y} = v_0 \sin \theta_0 = (25.0\text{ m/s})(\sin 35.0°) = 14.3\text{ m/s}$. Substituting known values yields

$$-20.0\text{ m} = (14.3\text{ m/s})t - \left(4.90\text{ m/s}^2\right)t^2. \quad 3.58$$

Rearranging terms gives a quadratic equation in t:

$$\left(4.90\text{ m/s}^2\right)t^2 - (14.3\text{ m/s})t - (20.0\text{ m}) = 0. \quad 3.59$$

This expression is a quadratic equation of the form $at^2 + bt + c = 0$, where the constants are $a = 4.90$, $b = -14.3$, and $c = -20.0$. Its solutions are given by the quadratic formula:

$$t = \frac{-b \pm \sqrt{b^2 - 4ac}}{2a}. \quad 3.60$$

This equation yields two solutions: $t = 3.96$ and $t = -1.03$. (It is left as an exercise for the reader to verify these solutions.) The time is $t = 3.96$ s or -1.03 s. The negative value of time implies an event before the start of motion, and so we discard it. Thus,

$$t = 3.96\text{ s}. \tag{3.61}$$

Discussion for (a)

The time for projectile motion is completely determined by the vertical motion. So any projectile that has an initial vertical velocity of 14.3 m/s and lands 20.0 m below its starting altitude will spend 3.96 s in the air.

Solution for (b)

From the information now in hand, we can find the final horizontal and vertical velocities v_x and v_y and combine them to find the total velocity v and the angle θ_0 it makes with the horizontal. Of course, v_x is constant so we can solve for it at any horizontal location. In this case, we chose the starting point since we know both the initial velocity and initial angle. Therefore:

$$v_x = v_0 \cos\theta_0 = (25.0\text{ m/s})(\cos 35^\circ) = 20.5\text{ m/s}. \tag{3.62}$$

The final vertical velocity is given by the following equation:

$$v_y = v_{0y} - gt, \tag{3.63}$$

where v_{0y} was found in part (a) to be 14.3 m/s. Thus,

$$v_y = 14.3\text{ m/s} - (9.80\text{ m/s}^2)(3.96\text{ s}) \tag{3.64}$$

so that

$$v_y = -24.5\text{ m/s}. \tag{3.65}$$

To find the magnitude of the final velocity v we combine its perpendicular components, using the following equation:

$$v = \sqrt{v_x^2 + v_y^2} = \sqrt{(20.5\text{ m/s})^2 + (-24.5\text{ m/s})^2}, \tag{3.66}$$

which gives

$$v = 31.9\text{ m/s}. \tag{3.67}$$

The direction θ_v is found from the equation:

$$\theta_v = \tan^{-1}(v_y/v_x) \tag{3.68}$$

so that

$$\theta_v = \tan^{-1}(-24.5/20.5) = \tan^{-1}(-1.19). \tag{3.69}$$

Thus,

$$\theta_v = -50.1^\circ. \tag{3.70}$$

Discussion for (b)

The negative angle means that the velocity is 50.1° below the horizontal. This result is consistent with the fact that the final vertical velocity is negative and hence downward—as you would expect because the final altitude is 20.0 m lower than the initial altitude. (See Figure 3.37.)

One of the most important things illustrated by projectile motion is that vertical and horizontal motions are independent of each other. Galileo was the first person to fully comprehend this characteristic. He used it to predict the range of a projectile. On level ground, we define **range** to be the horizontal distance R traveled by a projectile. Galileo and many others were interested in the range of projectiles primarily for military purposes—such as aiming cannons. However, investigating the range of projectiles can shed light on other interesting phenomena, such as the orbits of satellites around the Earth. Let us consider projectile range further.

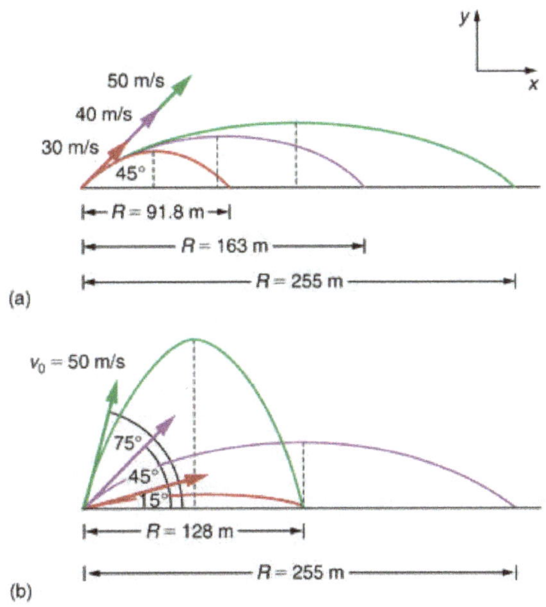

FIGURE 3.38 Trajectories of projectiles on level ground. (a) The greater the initial speed v_0, the greater the range for a given initial angle. (b) The effect of initial angle θ_0 on the range of a projectile with a given initial speed. Note that the range is the same for 15° and 75°, although the maximum heights of those paths are different.

How does the initial velocity of a projectile affect its range? Obviously, the greater the initial speed v_0, the greater the range, as shown in Figure 3.38(a). The initial angle θ_0 also has a dramatic effect on the range, as illustrated in Figure 3.38(b). For a fixed initial speed, such as might be produced by a cannon, the maximum range is obtained with $\theta_0 = 45^\circ$. This is true only for conditions neglecting air resistance. If air resistance is considered, the maximum angle is approximately 38°. Interestingly, for every initial angle except 45°, there are two angles that give the same range—the sum of those angles is 90°. The range also depends on the value of the acceleration of gravity g. The lunar astronaut Alan Shepherd was able to drive a golf ball a great distance on the Moon because gravity is weaker there. The range R of a projectile on *level ground* for which air resistance is negligible is given by

$$R = \frac{v_0^2 \sin 2\theta_0}{g}, \tag{3.71}$$

where v_0 is the initial speed and θ_0 is the initial angle relative to the horizontal. The proof of this equation is left as an end-of-chapter problem (hints are given), but it does fit the major features of projectile range as described.

When we speak of the range of a projectile on level ground, we assume that R is very small compared with the circumference of the Earth. If, however, the range is large, the Earth curves away below the projectile and acceleration of gravity changes direction along the path. The range is larger than predicted by the range equation given above because the projectile has farther to fall than it would on level ground. (See Figure 3.39.) If the initial speed is great enough, the projectile goes into orbit. This possibility was recognized centuries before it could be accomplished. When an object is in orbit, the Earth curves away from underneath the object at the same rate as it falls. The object thus falls continuously but never hits the surface. These and other aspects of orbital motion, such as the rotation of the Earth, will be covered analytically and in greater depth later in this text.

Once again we see that thinking about one topic, such as the range of a projectile, can lead us to others, such as the Earth orbits. In Addition of Velocities, we will examine the addition of velocities, which is another important aspect of two-dimensional kinematics and will also yield insights beyond the immediate topic.

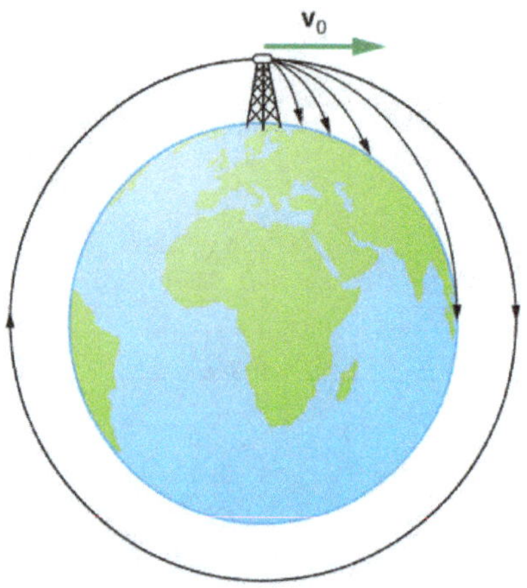

FIGURE 3.39 Hypothetical projectile to satellite. From this theoretical tower, a projectile is launched from a very high tower to avoid air resistance. With increasing initial speed, the range increases and becomes longer than it would be on level ground because the Earth curves away underneath its path. With a large enough initial speed, orbit is achieved.

PHET EXPLORATIONS

Projectile Motion

Blast a Buick out of a cannon! Learn about projectile motion by firing various objects. Set the angle, initial speed, and mass. Add air resistance. Make a game out of this simulation by trying to hit a target.

Click to view content (https://openstax.org/books/college-physics-ap-courses-2e/pages/3-4-projectile-motion)

PhET

3.5 Addition of Velocities

LEARNING OBJECTIVES

By the end of this section, you will be able to:

- Apply principles of vector addition to determine relative velocity.
- Explain the significance of the observer in the measurement of velocity.

Relative Velocity

If a person rows a boat across a rapidly flowing river and tries to head directly for the other shore, the boat instead moves *diagonally* relative to the shore, as in Figure 3.40. The boat does not move in the direction in which it is pointed. The reason, of course, is that the river carries the boat downstream. Similarly, if a small airplane flies overhead in a strong crosswind, you can sometimes see that the plane is not moving in the direction in which it is pointed, as illustrated in Figure 3.41. The plane is moving straight ahead relative to the air, but the movement of the air mass relative to the ground carries it sideways.

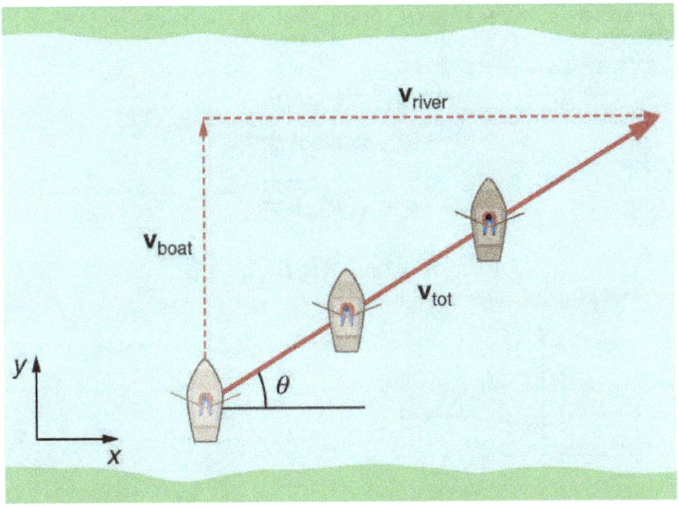

FIGURE 3.40 A boat trying to head straight across a river will actually move diagonally relative to the shore as shown. Its total velocity (solid arrow) relative to the shore is the sum of its velocity relative to the river plus the velocity of the river relative to the shore.

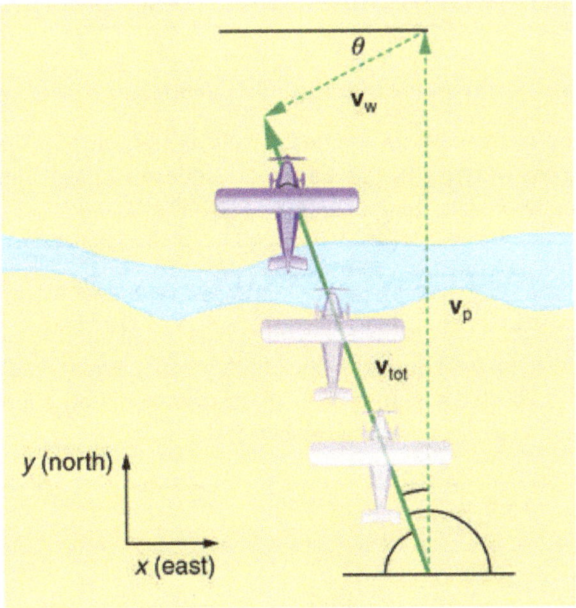

FIGURE 3.41 An airplane heading straight north is instead carried to the west and slowed down by wind. The plane does not move relative to the ground in the direction it points; rather, it moves in the direction of its total velocity (solid arrow).

In each of these situations, an object has a **velocity** relative to a medium (such as a river) and that medium has a velocity relative to an observer on solid ground. The velocity of the object *relative to the observer* is the sum of these velocity vectors, as indicated in Figure 3.40 and Figure 3.41. These situations are only two of many in which it is useful to add velocities. In this module, we first re-examine how to add velocities and then consider certain aspects of what relative velocity means.

How do we add velocities? Velocity is a vector (it has both magnitude and direction); the rules of **vector addition** discussed in Vector Addition and Subtraction: Graphical Methods and Vector Addition and Subtraction: Analytical Methods apply to the addition of velocities, just as they do for any other vectors. In one-dimensional motion, the addition of velocities is simple—they add like ordinary numbers. For example, if a field hockey player is moving at 5 m/s straight toward the goal and drives the ball in the same direction with a velocity of 30 m/s relative to her body, then the velocity of the ball is 35 m/s relative to the stationary, profusely sweating goalkeeper standing in front of the goal.

In two-dimensional motion, either graphical or analytical techniques can be used to add velocities. We will concentrate on analytical techniques. The following equations give the relationships between the magnitude and direction of velocity (v and θ) and its components (v_x and v_y) along the x- and y-axes of an appropriately chosen coordinate system:

$$v_x = v \cos \theta \tag{3.72}$$

$$v_y = v \sin \theta \tag{3.73}$$

$$v = \sqrt{v_x^2 + v_y^2} \tag{3.74}$$

$$\theta = \tan^{-1}(v_y / v_x). \tag{3.75}$$

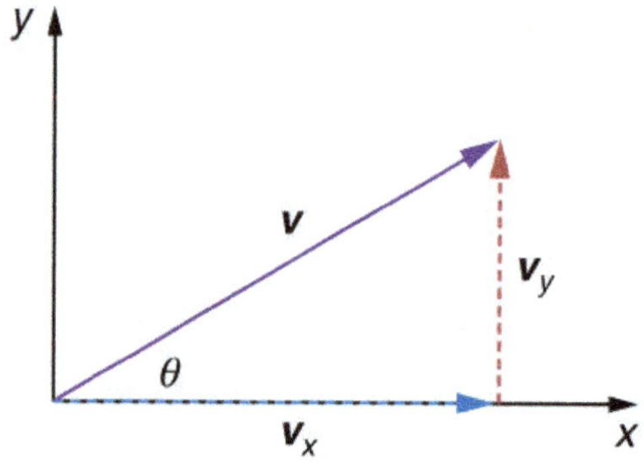

FIGURE 3.42 The velocity, v, of an object traveling at an angle θ to the horizontal axis is the sum of component vectors $\mathbf{v}_x$ and $\mathbf{v}_y$.

These equations are valid for any vectors and are adapted specifically for velocity. The first two equations are used to find the components of a velocity when its magnitude and direction are known. The last two are used to find the magnitude and direction of velocity when its components are known.

TAKE-HOME EXPERIMENT: RELATIVE VELOCITY OF A BOAT

Fill a bathtub half-full of water. Take a toy boat or some other object that floats in water. Unplug the drain so water starts to drain. Try pushing the boat from one side of the tub to the other and perpendicular to the flow of water. Which way do you need to push the boat so that it ends up immediately opposite? Compare the directions of the flow of water, heading of the boat, and actual velocity of the boat.

EXAMPLE 3.6

Adding Velocities: A Boat on a River

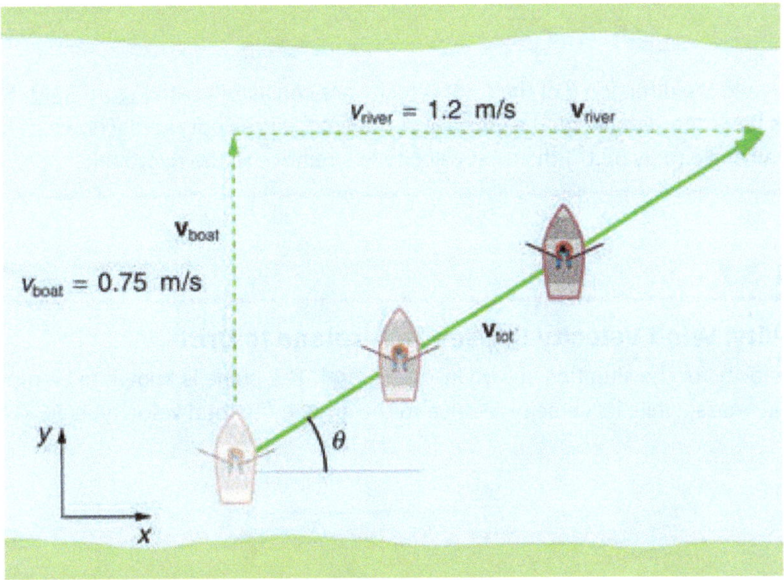

FIGURE 3.43 A boat attempts to travel straight across a river at a speed 0.75 m/s. The current in the river, however, flows at a speed of 1.20 m/s to the right.

Refer to Figure 3.43, which shows a boat trying to go straight across the river. Let us calculate the magnitude and direction of the boat's velocity relative to an observer on the shore, $\mathbf{v}_{tot}$. The velocity of the boat, $\mathbf{v}_{boat}$, is 0.75 m/s in the y-direction relative to the river and the velocity of the river, $\mathbf{v}_{river}$, is 1.20 m/s to the right.

Strategy

We start by choosing a coordinate system with its x-axis parallel to the velocity of the river, as shown in Figure 3.43. Because the boat is directed straight toward the other shore, its velocity relative to the water is parallel to the y-axis and perpendicular to the velocity of the river. Thus, we can add the two velocities by using the equations $v_{tot} = \sqrt{v_x^2 + v_y^2}$ and $\theta = \tan^{-1}(v_y/v_x)$ directly.

Solution

The magnitude of the total velocity is

$$v_{tot} = \sqrt{v_x^2 + v_y^2}, \tag{3.76}$$

where

$$v_x = v_{river} = 1.20 \text{ m/s} \tag{3.77}$$

and

$$v_y = v_{boat} = 0.750 \text{ m/s}. \tag{3.78}$$

Thus,

$$v_{tot} = \sqrt{(1.20 \text{ m/s})^2 + (0.750 \text{ m/s})^2} \tag{3.79}$$

yielding

$$v_{tot} = 1.42 \text{ m/s}. \tag{3.80}$$

The direction of the total velocity θ is given by:

$$\theta = \tan^{-1}(v_y/v_x) = \tan^{-1}(0.750/1.20). \quad 3.81$$

This equation gives

$$\theta = 32.0^\circ. \quad 3.82$$

Discussion

Both the magnitude v and the direction θ of the total velocity are consistent with Figure 3.43. Note that because the velocity of the river is large compared with the velocity of the boat, it is swept rapidly downstream. This result is evidenced by the small angle (only 32.0°) the total velocity has relative to the riverbank.

EXAMPLE 3.7

Calculating Velocity: Wind Velocity Causes an Airplane to Drift

Calculate the wind velocity for the situation shown in Figure 3.44. The plane is known to be moving at 45.0 m/s due north relative to the air mass, while its velocity relative to the ground (its total velocity) is 38.0 m/s in a direction 20.0° west of north.

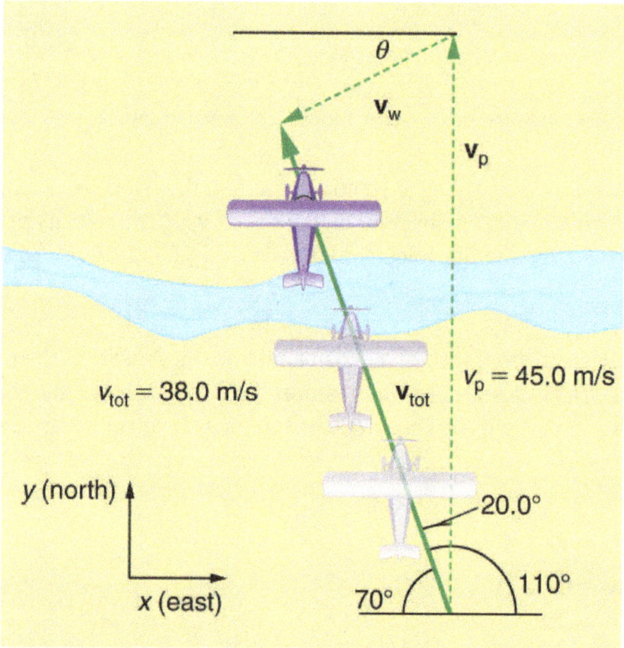

FIGURE 3.44 An airplane is known to be heading north at 45.0 m/s, though its velocity relative to the ground is 38.0 m/s at an angle west of north. What is the speed and direction of the wind?

Strategy

In this problem, somewhat different from the previous example, we know the total velocity $\mathbf{v}_{\text{tot}}$ and that it is the sum of two other velocities, $\mathbf{v}_{\text{w}}$ (the wind) and $\mathbf{v}_{\text{p}}$ (the plane relative to the air mass). The quantity $\mathbf{v}_{\text{p}}$ is known, and we are asked to find $\mathbf{v}_{\text{w}}$. None of the velocities are perpendicular, but it is possible to find their components along a common set of perpendicular axes. If we can find the components of $\mathbf{v}_{\text{w}}$, then we can combine them to solve for its magnitude and direction. As shown in Figure 3.44, we choose a coordinate system with its *x*-axis due east and its *y*-axis due north (parallel to $\mathbf{v}_{\text{p}}$). (You may wish to look back at the discussion of the addition of vectors using perpendicular components in Vector Addition and Subtraction: Analytical Methods.)

Solution

Because $\mathbf{v}_{\text{tot}}$ is the vector sum of the $\mathbf{v}_{\text{w}}$ and $\mathbf{v}_{\text{p}}$, its *x*- and *y*-components are the sums of the *x*- and *y*-components of the wind and plane velocities. Note that the plane only has vertical component of velocity so $v_{\text{px}} = 0$ and

$v_{py} = v_p$. That is,

$$v_{totx} = v_{wx} \tag{3.83}$$

and

$$v_{toty} = v_{wy} + v_p. \tag{3.84}$$

We can use the first of these two equations to find v_{wx}:

$$v_{wx} = v_{totx} = v_{tot}\cos 110^\circ. \tag{3.85}$$

Because $v_{tot} = 38.0\ \text{m/s}$ and $\cos 110^\circ = -0.342$ we have

$$v_{wx} = (38.0\ \text{m/s})(-0.342) = -13\ \text{m/s}. \tag{3.86}$$

The minus sign indicates motion west which is consistent with the diagram.

Now, to find v_{wy} we note that

$$v_{toty} = v_{wy} + v_p \tag{3.87}$$

Here $v_{toty} = v_{tot}\sin 110^\circ$; thus,

$$v_{wy} = (38.0\ \text{m/s})(0.940) - 45.0\ \text{m/s} = -9.29\ \text{m/s}. \tag{3.88}$$

This minus sign indicates motion south which is consistent with the diagram.

Now that the perpendicular components of the wind velocity v_{wx} and v_{wy} are known, we can find the magnitude and direction of $\mathbf{v}_w$. First, the magnitude is

$$\begin{aligned} v_w &= \sqrt{v_{wx}^2 + v_{wy}^2} \\ &= \sqrt{(-13.0\ \text{m/s})^2 + (-9.29\ \text{m/s})^2} \end{aligned} \tag{3.89}$$

so that

$$v_w = 16.0\ \text{m/s}. \tag{3.90}$$

The direction is:

$$\theta = \tan^{-1}(v_{wy}/v_{wx}) = \tan^{-1}(-9.29/-13.0) \tag{3.91}$$

giving

$$\theta = 35.6^\circ. \tag{3.92}$$

Discussion

The wind's speed and direction are consistent with the significant effect the wind has on the total velocity of the plane, as seen in Figure 3.44. Because the plane is fighting a strong combination of crosswind and head-wind, it ends up with a total velocity significantly less than its velocity relative to the air mass as well as heading in a different direction.

Note that in both of the last two examples, we were able to make the mathematics easier by choosing a coordinate system with one axis parallel to one of the velocities. We will repeatedly find that choosing an appropriate coordinate system makes problem solving easier. For example, in projectile motion we always use a coordinate system with one axis parallel to gravity.

Relative Velocities and Classical Relativity

When adding velocities, we have been careful to specify that the *velocity is relative to some reference frame.* These velocities are called **relative velocities**. For example, the velocity of an airplane relative to an air mass is different from its velocity relative to the ground. Both are quite different from the velocity of an airplane relative to its passengers (which should be close to zero). Relative velocities are one aspect of **relativity**, which is defined to be the study of how different observers moving relative to each other measure the same phenomenon.

Nearly everyone has heard of relativity and immediately associates it with Albert Einstein (1879–1955), the greatest physicist of the 20th century. Einstein revolutionized our view of nature with his *modern* theory of relativity, which we shall study in later chapters. The relative velocities in this section are actually aspects of classical relativity, first discussed correctly by Galileo and Isaac Newton. **Classical relativity** is limited to situations where speeds are less than about 1% of the speed of light—that is, less than $3{,}000\ \text{km/s}$. Most things we encounter in daily life move slower than this speed.

Let us consider an example of what two different observers see in a situation analyzed long ago by Galileo. Suppose a sailor at the top of a mast on a moving ship drops their binoculars. Where will it hit the deck? Will it hit at the base of the mast, or will it hit behind the mast because the ship is moving forward? The answer is that if air resistance is negligible, the binoculars will hit at the base of the mast at a point directly below its point of release. Now let us consider what two different observers see when the binoculars drop. One observer is on the ship and the other on shore. The binoculars have no horizontal velocity relative to the observer on the ship, and so he sees them fall straight down the mast. (See Figure 3.45.) To the observer on shore, the binoculars and the ship have the *same* horizontal velocity, so both move the same distance forward while the binoculars are falling. This observer sees the curved path shown in Figure 3.45. Although the paths look different to the different observers, each sees the same result—the binoculars hit at the base of the mast and not behind it. To get the correct description, it is crucial to correctly specify the velocities relative to the observer.

FIGURE 3.45 Classical relativity. The same motion as viewed by two different observers. An observer on the moving ship sees the binoculars dropped from the top of its mast fall straight down. An observer on shore sees the binoculars take the curved path, moving forward with the ship. Both observers see the binoculars strike the deck at the base of the mast. The initial horizontal velocity is different relative to the two observers. (The ship is shown moving rather fast to emphasize the effect.)

EXAMPLE 3.8

Calculating Relative Velocity: An Airline Passenger Drops a Coin

An airline passenger drops a coin while the plane is moving at 260 m/s. What is the velocity of the coin when it strikes the floor 1.50 m below its point of release: (a) Measured relative to the plane? (b) Measured relative to the Earth?

FIGURE 3.46 The motion of a coin dropped inside an airplane as viewed by two different observers. (a) An observer in the plane sees the coin fall straight down. (b) An observer on the ground sees the coin move almost horizontally.

Strategy

Both problems can be solved with the techniques for falling objects and projectiles. In part (a), the initial velocity of the coin is zero relative to the plane, so the motion is that of a falling object (one-dimensional). In part (b), the initial velocity is 260 m/s horizontal relative to the Earth and gravity is vertical, so this motion is a projectile motion. In both parts, it is best to use a coordinate system with vertical and horizontal axes.

Solution for (a)

Using the given information, we note that the initial velocity and position are zero, and the final position is 1.50 m. The final velocity can be found using the equation:

$$v_y{}^2 = v_{0,y}{}^2 - 2g(y - y_0). \tag{3.93}$$

Substituting known values into the equation, we get

$$v_y{}^2 = 0^2 - 2(9.80 \text{ m/s}^2)(-1.50 \text{ m} - 0 \text{ m}) = 29.4 \text{ m}^2/\text{s}^2 \tag{3.94}$$

yielding

$$v_y = -5.42 \text{ m/s}. \tag{3.95}$$

We know that the square root of 29.4 has two roots: 5.42 and -5.42. We choose the negative root because we know that the velocity is directed downwards, and we have defined the positive direction to be upwards. There is no initial horizontal velocity relative to the plane and no horizontal acceleration, and so the motion is straight down relative to the plane.

Solution for (b)

Because the initial vertical velocity is zero relative to the ground and vertical motion is independent of horizontal motion, the final vertical velocity for the coin relative to the ground is $v_y = -5.42$ m/s, the same as found in part (a). In contrast to part (a), there now is a horizontal component of the velocity. However, since there is no horizontal acceleration, the initial and final horizontal velocities are the same and $v_x = 260$ m/s. The *x*- and *y*-components of velocity can be combined to find the magnitude of the final velocity:

$$v = \sqrt{{v_x}^2 + {v_y}^2}. \quad (3.96)$$

Thus,

$$v = \sqrt{(260 \text{ m/s})^2 + (-5.42 \text{ m/s})^2} \quad (3.97)$$

yielding

$$v = 260.06 \text{ m/s}. \quad (3.98)$$

The direction is given by:

$$\theta = \tan^{-1}(v_y/v_x) = \tan^{-1}(-5.42/260) \quad (3.99)$$

so that

$$\theta = \tan^{-1}(-0.0208) = -1.19^\circ. \quad (3.100)$$

Discussion

In part (a), the final velocity relative to the plane is the same as it would be if the coin were dropped from rest on the Earth and fell 1.50 m. This result fits our experience; objects in a plane fall the same way when the plane is flying horizontally as when it is at rest on the ground. This result is also true in moving cars. In part (b), an observer on the ground sees a much different motion for the coin. The plane is moving so fast horizontally to begin with that its final velocity is barely greater than the initial velocity. Once again, we see that in two dimensions, vectors do not add like ordinary numbers—the final velocity v in part (b) is *not* $(260 - 5.42)$ m/s; rather, it is 260.06 m/s. The velocity's magnitude had to be calculated to five digits to see any difference from that of the airplane. The motions as seen by different observers (one in the plane and one on the ground) in this example are analogous to those discussed for the binoculars dropped from the mast of a moving ship, except that the velocity of the plane is much larger, so that the two observers see *very* different paths. (See Figure 3.46.) In addition, both observers see the coin fall 1.50 m vertically, but the one on the ground also sees it move forward 144 m (this calculation is left for the reader). Thus, one observer sees a vertical path, the other a nearly horizontal path.

MAKING CONNECTIONS: RELATIVITY AND EINSTEIN

Because Einstein was able to clearly define how measurements are made (some involve light) and because the speed of light is the same for all observers, the outcomes are spectacularly unexpected. Time varies with observer, energy is stored as increased mass, and more surprises await.

PHET EXPLORATIONS

Motion in 2D

Try the "Motion in 2D" simulation to Learn about position, velocity, and acceleration vectors. Move the ball with the mouse or let the simulation move the ball in four types of motion (2 types of linear, simple harmonic, circle).

Click to view content (https://openstax.org/l/motion-2d).

PhET

Glossary

air resistance a frictional force that slows the motion of objects as they travel through the air; when solving basic physics problems, air resistance is assumed to be zero

analytical method the method of determining the magnitude and direction of a resultant vector using the Pythagorean theorem and trigonometric identities

classical relativity the study of relative velocities in situations where speeds are less than about 1% of the speed of light—that is, less than 3000 km/s

commutative refers to the interchangeability of order in a function; vector addition is commutative because the order in which vectors are added together does not affect the final sum

component (of a 2-d vector) a piece of a vector that points in either the vertical or the horizontal direction; every 2-d vector can be expressed as a sum of two vertical and horizontal vector components

direction (of a vector) the orientation of a vector in space

head (of a vector) the end point of a vector; the location of the tip of the vector's arrowhead; also referred to as the "tip"

head-to-tail method a method of adding vectors in which the tail of each vector is placed at the head of the previous vector

kinematics the study of motion without regard to mass or force

magnitude (of a vector) the length or size of a vector; magnitude is a scalar quantity

motion displacement of an object as a function of time

projectile an object that travels through the air and experiences only acceleration due to gravity

projectile motion the motion of an object that is subject only to the acceleration of gravity

range the maximum horizontal distance that a projectile travels

relative velocity the velocity of an object as observed from a particular reference frame

relativity the study of how different observers moving relative to each other measure the same phenomenon

resultant the sum of two or more vectors

resultant vector the vector sum of two or more vectors

scalar a quantity with magnitude but no direction

tail the start point of a vector; opposite to the head or tip of the arrow

trajectory the path of a projectile through the air

vector a quantity that has both magnitude and direction; an arrow used to represent quantities with both magnitude and direction

vector addition the rules that apply to adding vectors together

velocity speed in a given direction

Section Summary

3.1 Kinematics in Two Dimensions: An Introduction

- The shortest path between any two points is a straight line. In two dimensions, this path can be represented by a vector with horizontal and vertical components.
- The horizontal and vertical components of a vector are independent of one another. Motion in the horizontal direction does not affect motion in the vertical direction, and vice versa.

3.2 Vector Addition and Subtraction: Graphical Methods

- The **graphical method of adding vectors** $\mathbf{A}$ and $\mathbf{B}$ involves drawing vectors on a graph and adding them using the head-to-tail method. The resultant vector $\mathbf{R}$ is defined such that $\mathbf{A} + \mathbf{B} = \mathbf{R}$. The magnitude and direction of $\mathbf{R}$ are then determined with a ruler and protractor, respectively.
- The **graphical method of subtracting vector $\mathbf{B}$** from $\mathbf{A}$ involves adding the opposite of vector $\mathbf{B}$, which is defined as $-\mathbf{B}$. In this case, $\mathbf{A} - \mathbf{B} = \mathbf{A} + (-\mathbf{B}) = \mathbf{R}$. Then, the head-to-tail method of addition is followed in the usual way to obtain the resultant vector $\mathbf{R}$.
- Addition of vectors is **commutative** such that $\mathbf{A} + \mathbf{B} = \mathbf{B} + \mathbf{A}$.
- The **head-to-tail method** of adding vectors involves drawing the first vector on a graph and then placing the tail of each subsequent vector at the head of the previous vector. The resultant vector is then drawn from the tail of the first vector to the head of the final vector.
- If a vector $\mathbf{A}$ is multiplied by a scalar quantity c, the magnitude of the product is given by cA. If c is positive, the direction of the product points in the same direction as $\mathbf{A}$; if c is negative, the direction of the product points in the opposite direction as $\mathbf{A}$.

3.3 Vector Addition and Subtraction: Analytical Methods

- The analytical method of vector addition and subtraction involves using the Pythagorean theorem and trigonometric identities to determine the magnitude and direction of a resultant vector.
- The steps to add vectors **A** and **B** using the analytical method are as follows:
  Step 1: Determine the coordinate system for the vectors. Then, determine the horizontal and vertical components of each vector using the equations

$$A_x = A\cos\theta$$
$$B_x = B\cos\theta$$

and

$$A_y = A\sin\theta$$
$$B_y = B\sin\theta.$$

Step 2: Add the horizontal and vertical components of each vector to determine the components R_x and R_y of the resultant vector, **R**:

$$R_x = A_x + B_x$$

and

$$R_y = A_y + B_y.$$

Step 3: Use the Pythagorean theorem to determine the magnitude, R, of the resultant vector **R**:

$$R = \sqrt{R_x^2 + R_y^2}.$$

Step 4: Use a trigonometric identity to determine the direction, θ, of **R**:

$$\theta = \tan^{-1}(R_y/R_x).$$

3.4 Projectile Motion

- Projectile motion is the motion of an object through the air that is subject only to the acceleration of gravity.
- To solve projectile motion problems, perform the following steps:
  1. Determine a coordinate system. Then, resolve the position and/or velocity of the object in the horizontal and vertical components. The components of position **s** are given by the quantities x and y, and the components of the velocity **v** are given by $v_x = v\cos\theta$ and $v_y = v\sin\theta$, where v is the magnitude of the velocity and θ is its direction.
  2. Analyze the motion of the projectile in the horizontal direction using the following equations:
     Horizontal motion($a_x = 0$)
     $$x = x_0 + v_x t$$
     $$v_x = v_{0x} = \mathbf{v}_x = \text{velocity is a constant.}$$
  3. Analyze the motion of the projectile in the vertical direction using the following equations:
     Vertical Motion
     (assuming positive is up
     $$a_y = -g = -9.80\text{m/s}^2)$$
     $$y = y_0 + \frac{1}{2}(v_{0y} + v_y)t$$
     $$v_y = v_{0y} - gt$$
     $$y = y_0 + v_{0y}t - \frac{1}{2}gt^2$$
     $$v_y^2 = v_{0y}^2 - 2g(y - y_0).$$
  4. Recombine the horizontal and vertical components of location and/or velocity using the following equations:
     $$s = \sqrt{x^2 + y^2}$$
     $$\theta = \tan^{-1}(y/x)$$
     $$v = \sqrt{v_x^2 + v_y^2}$$
     $$\theta_v = \tan^{-1}(v_y/v_x).$$
- The maximum height h of a projectile launched with initial vertical velocity v_{0y} is given by
  $$h = \frac{v_{0y}^2}{2g}.$$
- The maximum horizontal distance traveled by a projectile is called the **range**. The range R of a projectile on level ground launched at an angle θ_0 above the horizontal with initial speed v_0 is given by
  $$R = \frac{v_0^2 \sin 2\theta_0}{g}.$$

3.5 Addition of Velocities

- Velocities in two dimensions are added using the same analytical vector techniques, which are rewritten as
  $$v_x = v\cos\theta$$
  $$v_y = v\sin\theta$$
  $$v = \sqrt{v_x^2 + v_y^2}$$
  $$\theta = \tan^{-1}(v_y/v_x).$$
- Relative velocity is the velocity of an object as observed from a particular reference frame, and it varies dramatically with reference frame.
- **Relativity** is the study of how different observers measure the same phenomenon, particularly when the observers move relative to one another. **Classical relativity** is limited to situations where speed is less than about 1% of the speed of light (3000 km/s).

Conceptual Questions

3.2 Vector Addition and Subtraction: Graphical Methods

1. Which of the following is a vector: a person's height, the altitude on Mt. Everest, the age of the Earth, the boiling point of water, the cost of this book, the Earth's population, the acceleration of gravity?
2. Give a specific example of a vector, stating its magnitude, units, and direction.
3. What do vectors and scalars have in common? How do they differ?
4. Two campers in a national park hike from their cabin to the same spot on a lake, each taking a different path, as illustrated below. The total distance traveled along Path 1 is 7.5 km, and that along Path 2 is 8.2 km. What is the final displacement of each camper?

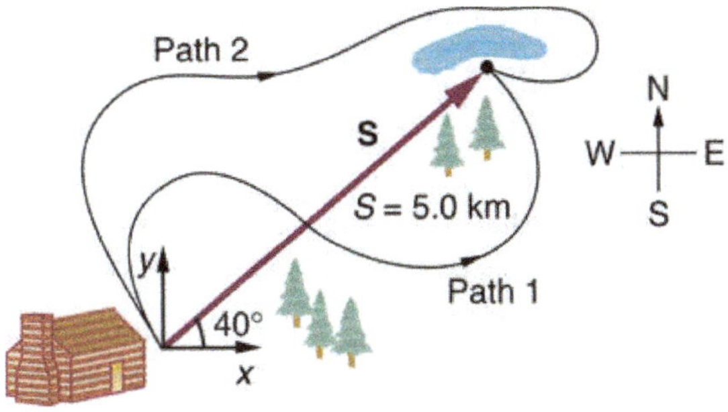

FIGURE 3.47

5. If an airplane pilot is told to fly 123 km in a straight line to get from San Francisco to Sacramento, explain why he could end up anywhere on the circle shown in Figure 3.48. What other information would he need to get to Sacramento?

FIGURE 3.48

6. Suppose you take two steps $\mathbf{A}$ and $\mathbf{B}$ (that is, two nonzero displacements). Under what circumstances can you end up at your starting point? More generally, under what circumstances can two nonzero vectors add to give zero? Is the maximum distance you can end up from the starting point $\mathbf{A} + \mathbf{B}$ the sum of the lengths of the two steps?
7. Explain why it is not possible to add a scalar to a vector.
8. If you take two steps of different sizes, can you end up at your starting point? More generally, can two vectors with different magnitudes ever add to zero? Can three or more?

3.3 Vector Addition and Subtraction: Analytical Methods

9. Suppose you add two vectors $\mathbf{A}$ and $\mathbf{B}$. What relative direction between them produces the resultant with the greatest magnitude? What is the maximum magnitude? What relative direction between them produces the resultant with the smallest magnitude? What is the minimum magnitude?
10. Give an example of a nonzero vector that has a component of zero.
11. Explain why a vector cannot have a component greater than its own magnitude.
12. If the vectors $\mathbf{A}$ and $\mathbf{B}$ are perpendicular, what is

the component of $\mathbf{A}$ along the direction of $\mathbf{B}$? What is the component of $\mathbf{B}$ along the direction of $\mathbf{A}$?

3.4 Projectile Motion

13. Answer the following questions for projectile motion on level ground assuming negligible air resistance (the initial angle being neither 0° nor 90°): (a) Is the velocity ever zero? (b) When is the velocity a minimum? A maximum? (c) Can the velocity ever be the same as the initial velocity at a time other than at $t = 0$? (d) Can the speed ever be the same as the initial speed at a time other than at $t = 0$?

14. Answer the following questions for projectile motion on level ground assuming negligible air resistance (the initial angle being neither 0° nor 90°): (a) Is the acceleration ever zero? (b) Is the acceleration ever in the same direction as a component of velocity? (c) Is the acceleration ever opposite in direction to a component of velocity?

15. For a fixed initial speed, the range of a projectile is determined by the angle at which it is fired. For all but the maximum, there are two angles that give the same range. Considering factors that might affect the ability of an archer to hit a target, such as wind, explain why the smaller angle (closer to the horizontal) is preferable. When would it be necessary for the archer to use the larger angle? Why does the punter in a football game use the higher trajectory?

16. During a lecture demonstration, a professor places two coins on the edge of a table. She then flicks one of the coins horizontally off the table, simultaneously nudging the other over the edge. Describe the subsequent motion of the two coins, in particular discussing whether they hit the floor at the same time.

3.5 Addition of Velocities

17. What frame or frames of reference do you instinctively use when driving a car? When flying in a commercial jet airplane?

18. A basketball player dribbling down the court usually keeps his eyes fixed on the players around him. He is moving fast. Why doesn't he need to keep his eyes on the ball?

19. If someone is riding in the back of a pickup truck and throws a softball straight backward, is it possible for the ball to fall straight down as viewed by a person standing at the side of the road? Under what condition would this occur? How would the motion of the ball appear to the person who threw it?

20. The hat of a jogger running at constant velocity falls off the back of his head. Draw a sketch showing the path of the hat in the jogger's frame of reference. Draw its path as viewed by a stationary observer.

21. A clod of dirt falls from the bed of a moving truck. It strikes the ground directly below the end of the truck. What is the direction of its velocity relative to the truck just before it hits? Is this the same as the direction of its velocity relative to ground just before it hits? Explain your answers.

Problems & Exercises

3.2 Vector Addition and Subtraction: Graphical Methods

Use graphical methods to solve these problems. You may assume data taken from graphs is accurate to three digits.

1. Find the following for path A in Figure 3.49: (a) the total distance traveled, and (b) the magnitude and direction of the displacement from start to finish.

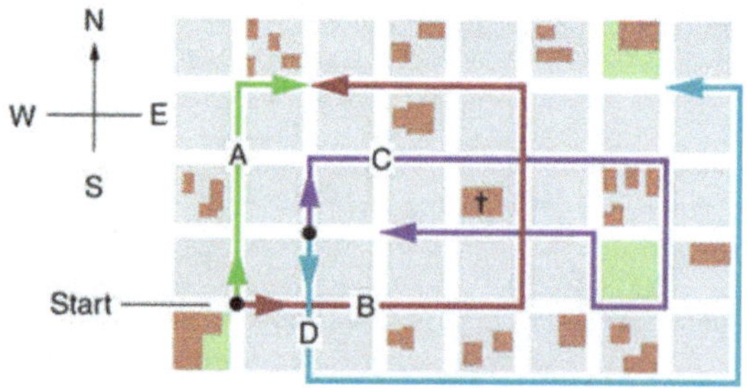

FIGURE 3.49 The various lines represent paths taken by different people walking in a city. All blocks are 120 m on a side.

2. Find the following for path B in Figure 3.49: (a) the total distance traveled, and (b) the magnitude and direction of the displacement from start to finish.

3. Find the north and east components of the

displacement for the hikers shown in Figure 3.47.

4. Suppose you walk 18.0 m straight west and then 25.0 m straight north. How far are you from your starting point, and what is the compass direction of a line connecting your starting point to your final position? (If you represent the two legs of the walk as vector displacements $\mathbf{A}$ and $\mathbf{B}$, as in Figure 3.50, then this problem asks you to find their sum $\mathbf{R} = \mathbf{A} + \mathbf{B}$.)

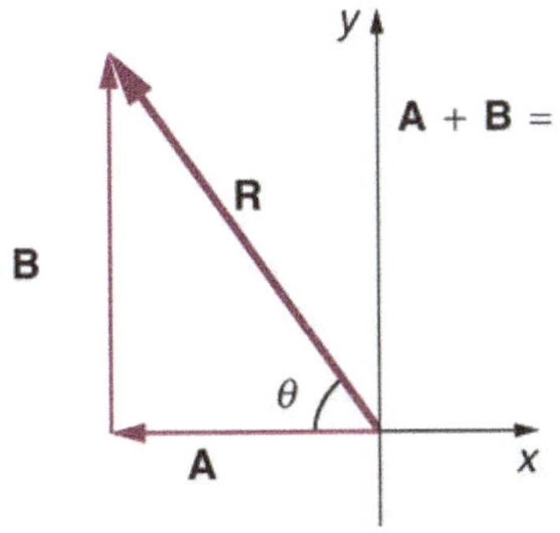

FIGURE 3.50 The two displacements $\mathbf{A}$ and $\mathbf{B}$ add to give a total displacement $\mathbf{R}$ having magnitude R and direction θ.

5. Suppose you first walk 12.0 m in a direction $20°$ west of north and then 20.0 m in a direction $40.0°$ south of west. How far are you from your starting point, and what is the compass direction of a line connecting your starting point to your final position? (If you represent the two legs of the walk as vector displacements $\mathbf{A}$ and $\mathbf{B}$, as in Figure 3.51, then this problem finds their sum $\mathbf{R} = \mathbf{A} + \mathbf{B}$.)

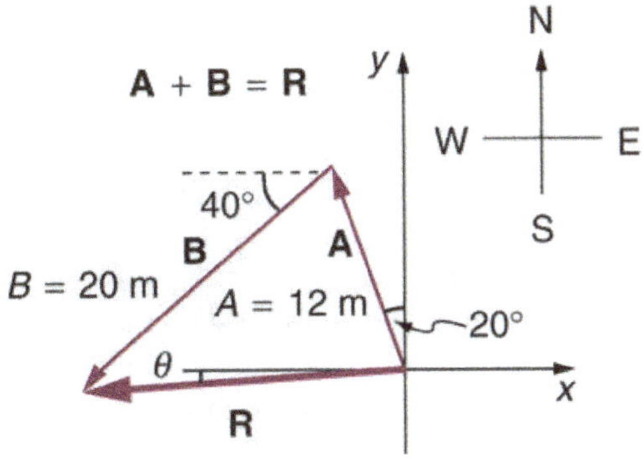

FIGURE 3.51

6. Repeat the problem above, but reverse the order of the two legs of the walk; show that you get the same final result. That is, you first walk leg $\mathbf{B}$, which is 20.0 m in a direction exactly $40°$ south of west, and then leg $\mathbf{A}$, which is 12.0 m in a direction exactly $20°$ west of north. (This problem shows that $\mathbf{A} + \mathbf{B} = \mathbf{B} + \mathbf{A}$.)

7. (a) Repeat the problem two problems prior, but for the second leg you walk 20.0 m in a direction $40.0°$). (b) Repeat the problem two problems prior, but now you first walk 20.0 m in a direction $40.0°$ east of south (which is equivalent to subtracting $\mathbf{A}$ from $\mathbf{B}$ —that is, to finding $\mathbf{R}'' = \mathbf{B} - \mathbf{A} = -\mathbf{R}'$). Show that this is the case.

8. Show that the *order* of addition of three vectors does not affect their sum. Show this property by choosing any three vectors $\mathbf{A}$, $\mathbf{B}$, and $\mathbf{C}$, all having different lengths and directions. Find the sum $\mathbf{A} + \mathbf{B} + \mathbf{C}$ then find their sum when added in a different order and show the result is the same. (There are five other orders in which $\mathbf{A}$, $\mathbf{B}$, and $\mathbf{C}$ can be added; choose only one.)

9. Show that the sum of the vectors discussed in Example 3.2 gives the result shown in Figure 3.23.

10. Find the magnitudes of velocities v_A and v_B in Figure 3.52

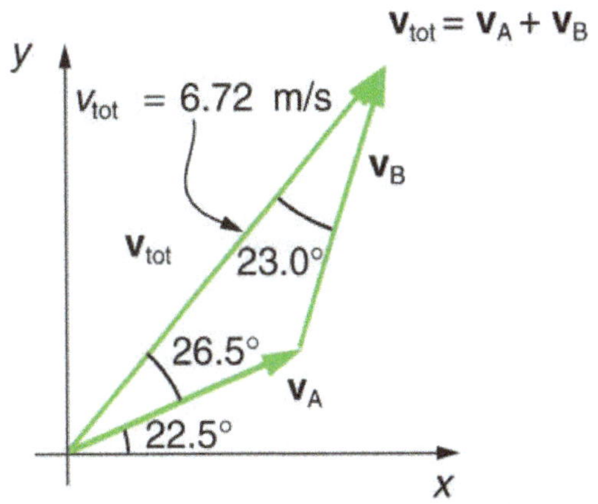

FIGURE 3.52 The two velocities $\mathbf{v}_A$ and $\mathbf{v}_B$ add to give a total $\mathbf{v}_{tot}$.

11. Find the components of v_{tot} along the *x*- and *y*-axes in Figure 3.52.

12. Find the components of v_{tot} along a set of perpendicular axes rotated $30°$ counterclockwise relative to those in Figure 3.52.

3.3 Vector Addition and Subtraction: Analytical Methods

13. Find the following for path C in Figure 3.53: (a) the total distance traveled and (b) the magnitude and direction of the displacement from start to finish. In this part of the problem, explicitly show how you follow the steps of the analytical method of vector addition.

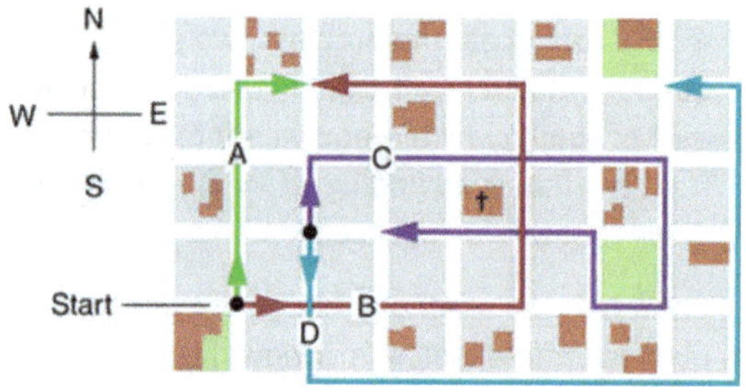

FIGURE 3.53 The various lines represent paths taken by different people walking in a city. All blocks are 120 m on a side.

14. Find the following for path D in Figure 3.53: (a) the total distance traveled and (b) the magnitude and direction of the displacement from start to finish. In this part of the problem, explicitly show how you follow the steps of the analytical method of vector addition.

15. Find the north and east components of the displacement from San Francisco to Sacramento shown in Figure 3.54.

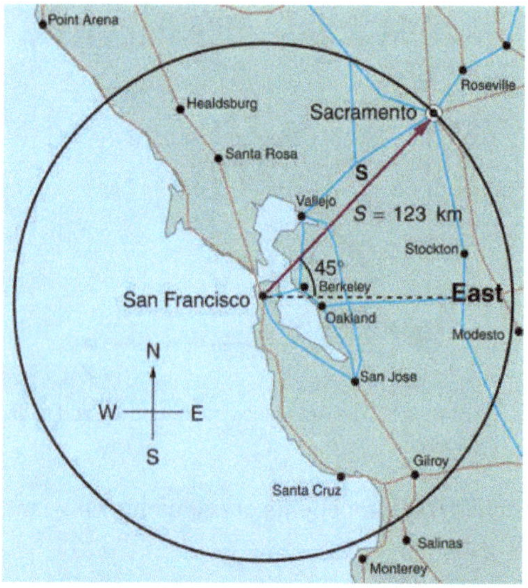

FIGURE 3.54

16. Solve the following problem using analytical techniques: Suppose you walk 18.0 m straight west and then 25.0 m straight north. How far are you from your starting point, and what is the compass direction of a line connecting your starting point to your final position? (If you represent the two legs of the walk as vector displacements $\mathbf{A}$ and $\mathbf{B}$, as in Figure 3.55, then this problem asks you to find their sum $\mathbf{R} = \mathbf{A} + \mathbf{B}$.)

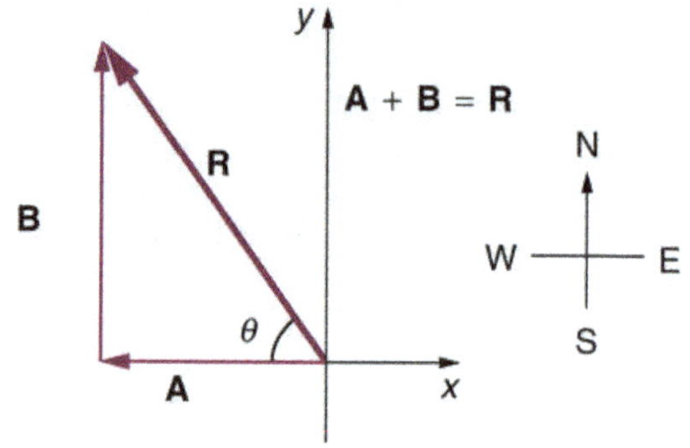

FIGURE 3.55 The two displacements $\mathbf{A}$ and $\mathbf{B}$ add to give a total displacement $\mathbf{R}$ having magnitude R and direction θ.

Note that you can also solve this graphically. Discuss why the analytical technique for solving this problem is potentially more accurate than the graphical technique.

17. Repeat Exercise 3.16 using analytical techniques, but reverse the order of the two legs of the walk and show that you get the same final result. (This problem shows that adding them in reverse order gives the same result—that is, $\mathbf{B} + \mathbf{A} = \mathbf{A} + \mathbf{B}$.) Discuss how taking another path to reach the same point might help to overcome an obstacle blocking your other path.

18. You drive $7.50\ \text{km}$ in a straight line in a direction 15° east of north. (a) Find the distances you would have to drive straight east and then straight north to arrive at the same point. (This determination is equivalent to find the components of the displacement along the east and north directions.) (b) Show that you still arrive at the same point if the east and north legs are reversed in order.

19. Do Exercise 3.16 again using analytical techniques and change the second leg of the walk to $25.0\ \text{m}$ straight south. (This is equivalent to subtracting $\mathbf{B}$ from $\mathbf{A}$ —that is, finding $\mathbf{R}' = \mathbf{A} - \mathbf{B}$) (b) Repeat again, but now you first walk $25.0\ \text{m}$ north and then $18.0\ \text{m}$ east. (This is equivalent to subtract $\mathbf{A}$ from $\mathbf{B}$ —that is, to find $\mathbf{A} = \mathbf{B} + \mathbf{C}$. Is that consistent with your result?)

20. A new landowner has a triangular piece of flat land she wishes to fence. Starting at the west corner, she measures the first side to be 80.0 m long and the next to be 105 m. These sides are represented as displacement vectors $\mathbf{A}$ from $\mathbf{B}$ in Figure 3.56. She then correctly calculates the length and orientation of the third side $\mathbf{C}$. What is her result?

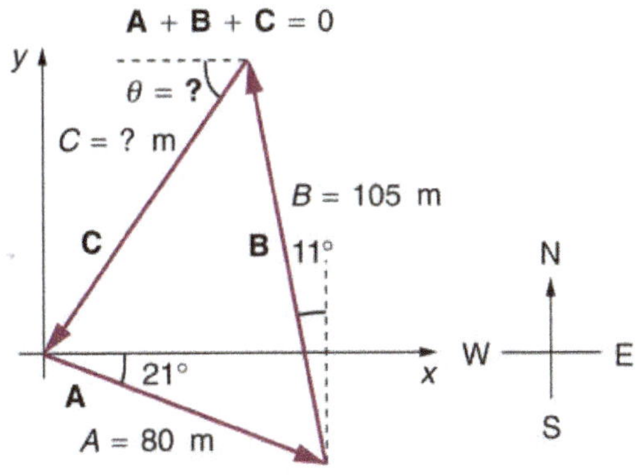

FIGURE 3.56

21. You fly 32.0 km in a straight line in still air in the direction $35.0°$ south of west. (a) Find the distances you would have to fly straight south and then straight west to arrive at the same point. (This determination is equivalent to finding the components of the displacement along the south and west directions.) (b) Find the distances you would have to fly first in a direction $45.0°$ south of west and then in a direction $45.0°$ west of north. These are the components of the displacement along a different set of axes—one rotated $45°$.

22. A farmer wants to fence off a four-sided plot of flat land. They measure the first three sides, shown as **A**, **B**, and **C** in Figure 3.57, and then correctly calculate the length and orientation of the fourth side **D**. What is their result?

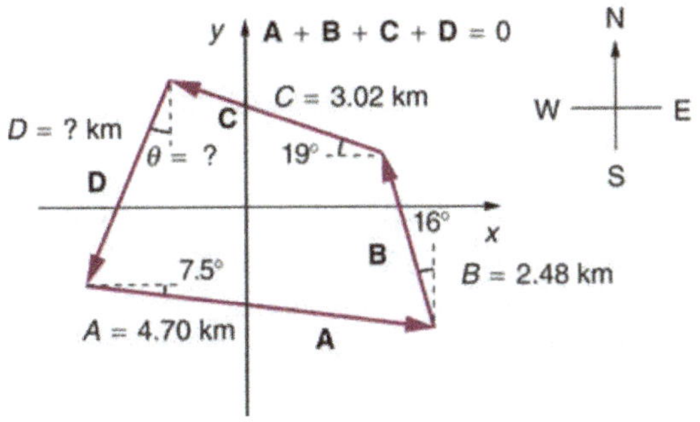

FIGURE 3.57

23. In an attempt to escape his island, Gilligan builds a raft and sets to sea. The wind shifts a great deal during the day, and he is blown along the following straight lines: 2.50 km $45.0°$ north of west; then 4.70 km $60.0°$ south of east; then 1.30 km $25.0°$ south of west; then 5.10 km straight east; then 1.70 km $5.00°$ east of north; then 7.20 km $55.0°$ south of west; and finally 2.80 km $10.0°$ north of east. What is his final position relative to the island?

24. Suppose a pilot flies 40.0 km in a direction $60°$ north of east and then flies 30.0 km in a direction $15°$ north of east as shown in Figure 3.58. Find her total distance R from the starting point and the direction θ of the straight-line path to the final position. Discuss qualitatively how this flight would be altered by a wind from the north and how the effect of the wind would depend on both wind speed and the speed of the plane relative to the air mass.

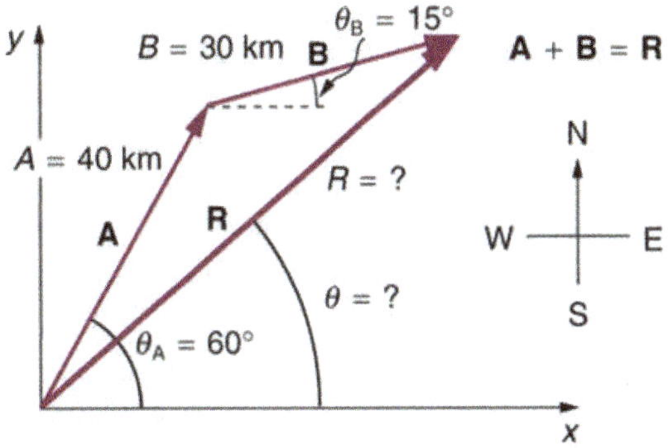

FIGURE 3.58

3.4 Projectile Motion

25. A projectile is launched at ground level with an initial speed of 50.0 m/s at an angle of $30.0°$ above the horizontal. It strikes a target above the ground 3.00 seconds later. What are the x and y distances from where the projectile was launched to where it lands?

26. A ball is kicked with an initial velocity of 16 m/s in the horizontal direction and 12 m/s in the vertical direction. (a) At what speed does the ball hit the ground? (b) For how long does the ball remain in the air? (c)What maximum height is attained by the ball?

27. A ball is thrown horizontally from the top of a 60.0-m building and lands 100.0 m from the base of the building. Ignore air resistance. (a) How long is the ball in the air? (b) What must have been the initial horizontal component of the velocity? (c) What is the vertical component of the velocity just before the ball hits the ground? (d) What is the velocity (including both the horizontal and vertical components) of the ball just before it hits the ground?

28. (a) A daredevil is attempting to jump his motorcycle over a line of buses parked end to end by driving up a $32°$ ramp at a speed of 40.0 m/s (144 km/h). How many buses can he clear if the top of the takeoff ramp is at the same

height as the bus tops and the buses are 20.0 m long? (b) Discuss what your answer implies about the margin of error in this act—that is, consider how much greater the range is than the horizontal distance he must travel to miss the end of the last bus. (Neglect air resistance.)

29. An archer shoots an arrow at a 75.0 m distant target; the bull's-eye of the target is at same height as the release height of the arrow. (a) At what angle must the arrow be released to hit the bull's-eye if its initial speed is 35.0 m/s? In this part of the problem, explicitly show how you follow the steps involved in solving projectile motion problems. (b) There is a large tree halfway between the archer and the target with an overhanging horizontal branch 3.50 m above the release height of the arrow. Will the arrow go over or under the branch?

30. A rugby player passes the ball 7.00 m across the field, where it is caught at the same height as it left his hand. (a) At what angle was the ball thrown if its initial speed was 12.0 m/s, assuming that the smaller of the two possible angles was used? (b) What other angle gives the same range, and why would it not be used? (c) How long did this pass take?

31. Verify the ranges for the projectiles in Figure 3.38(a) for $\theta = 45°$ and the given initial velocities.

32. Verify the ranges shown for the projectiles in Figure 3.38(b) for an initial velocity of 50 m/s at the given initial angles.

33. The cannon on a battleship can fire a shell a maximum distance of 32.0 km. (a) Calculate the initial velocity of the shell. (b) What maximum height does it reach? (At its highest, the shell is above 60% of the atmosphere—but air resistance is not really negligible as assumed to make this problem easier.) (c) The ocean is not flat, because the Earth is curved. Assume that the radius of the Earth is 6.37×10^3 km. How many meters lower will its surface be 32.0 km from the ship along a horizontal line parallel to the surface at the ship? Does your answer imply that error introduced by the assumption of a flat Earth in projectile motion is significant here?

34. An arrow is shot from a height of 1.5 m toward a cliff of height H. It is shot with a velocity of 30 m/s at an angle of $60°$ above the horizontal. It lands on the top edge of the cliff 4.0 s later. (a) What is the height of the cliff? (b) What is the maximum height reached by the arrow along its trajectory? (c) What is the arrow's impact speed just before hitting the cliff?

35. In the standing broad jump, one squats and then pushes off with the legs to see how far one can jump. Suppose the extension of the legs from the crouch position is 0.600 m and the acceleration achieved from this position is 1.25 times the acceleration due to gravity, g. How far can they jump? State your assumptions. (Increased range can be achieved by swinging the arms in the direction of the jump.)

36. The world long jump record is 8.95 m (Mike Powell, USA, 1991). Treated as a projectile, what is the maximum range obtainable by a person if he has a take-off speed of 9.5 m/s? State your assumptions.

37. Serving at a speed of 170 km/h, a tennis player hits the ball at a height of 2.5 m and an angle θ below the horizontal. The base line is 11.9 m from the net, which is 0.91 m high. What is the angle θ such that the ball just crosses the net? Will the ball land in the service box, whose service line is 6.40 m from the net?

38. A football quarterback is moving straight backward at a speed of 2.00 m/s when he throws a pass to a player 18.0 m straight downfield. (a) If the ball is thrown at an angle of $25°$ relative to the ground and is caught at the same height as it is released, what is its initial speed relative to the ground? (b) How long does it take to get to the receiver? (c) What is its maximum height above its point of release?

39. Gun sights are adjusted to aim high to compensate for the effect of gravity, effectively making the gun accurate only for a specific range. (a) If a gun is sighted to hit targets that are at the same height as the gun and 100.0 m away, how low will the bullet hit if aimed directly at a target 150.0 m away? The muzzle velocity of the bullet is 275 m/s. (b) Discuss qualitatively how a larger muzzle velocity would affect this problem and what would be the effect of air resistance.

40. An eagle is flying horizontally at a speed of 3.00 m/s when the fish in her talons wiggles loose and falls into the lake 5.00 m below. Calculate the velocity of the fish relative to the water when it hits the water.

41. An owl is carrying a mouse to the chicks in its nest. Its position at that time is 4.00 m west and

12.0 m above the center of the 30.0 cm diameter nest. The owl is flying east at 3.50 m/s at an angle 30.0° below the horizontal when it accidentally drops the mouse. Is the owl lucky enough to have the mouse hit the nest? To answer this question, calculate the horizontal position of the mouse when it has fallen 12.0 m.

42. Suppose a soccer player kicks the ball from a distance 30 m toward the goal. Find the initial speed of the ball if it just passes over the goal, 2.4 m above the ground, given the initial direction to be 40° above the horizontal.

43. Can a goalkeeper at her/ his goal kick a soccer ball into the opponent's goal without the ball touching the ground? The distance will be about 95 m. A goalkeeper can give the ball a speed of 30 m/s.

44. The free throw line in basketball is 4.57 m (15 ft) from the basket, which is 3.05 m (10 ft) above the floor. A player standing on the free throw line throws the ball with an initial speed of 8.15 m/s, releasing it at a height of 2.44 m (8 ft) above the floor. At what angle above the horizontal must the ball be thrown to exactly hit the basket? Note that most players will use a large initial angle rather than a flat shot because it allows for a larger margin of error. Explicitly show how you follow the steps involved in solving projectile motion problems.

45. In 2007, Michael Carter (U.S.) set a world record in the shot put with a throw of 24.77 m. What was the initial speed of the shot if he released it at a height of 2.10 m and threw it at an angle of 38.0° above the horizontal? (Although the maximum distance for a projectile on level ground is achieved at 45° when air resistance is neglected, the actual angle to achieve maximum range is smaller; thus, 38° will give a longer range than 45° in the shot put.)

46. A basketball player is running at 5.00 m/s directly toward the basket when he jumps into the air to dunk the ball. He maintains his horizontal velocity. (a) What vertical velocity does he need to rise 0.750 m above the floor? (b) How far from the basket (measured in the horizontal direction) must he start his jump to reach his maximum height at the same time as he reaches the basket?

47. A football player punts the ball at a 45.0° angle. Without an effect from the wind, the ball would travel 60.0 m horizontally. (a) What is the initial speed of the ball? (b) When the ball is near its maximum height it experiences a brief gust of wind that reduces its horizontal velocity by 1.50 m/s. What distance does the ball travel horizontally?

48. Prove that the trajectory of a projectile is parabolic, having the form $y = ax + bx^2$. To obtain this expression, solve the equation $x = v_{0x}t$ for t and substitute it into the expression for $y = v_{0y}t - (1/2)gt^2$ (These equations describe the x and y positions of a projectile that starts at the origin.) You should obtain an equation of the form $y = ax + bx^2$ where a and b are constants.

49. Derive $R = \frac{v_0^2 \sin 2\theta_0}{g}$ for the range of a projectile on level ground by finding the time t at which y becomes zero and substituting this value of t into the expression for $x - x_0$, noting that $R = x - x_0$

50. Unreasonable Results (a) Find the maximum range of a super cannon that has a muzzle velocity of 4.0 km/s. (b) What is unreasonable about the range you found? (c) Is the premise unreasonable or is the available equation inapplicable? Explain your answer. (d) If such a muzzle velocity could be obtained, discuss the effects of air resistance, thinning air with altitude, and the curvature of the Earth on the range of the super cannon.

51. Construct Your Own Problem Consider a ball tossed over a fence. Construct a problem in which you calculate the ball's needed initial velocity to just clear the fence. Among the things to determine are; the height of the fence, the distance to the fence from the point of release of the ball, and the height at which the ball is released. You should also consider whether it is possible to choose the initial speed for the ball and just calculate the angle at which it is thrown. Also examine the possibility of multiple solutions given the distances and heights you have chosen.

3.5 Addition of Velocities

52. Bryan Allen pedaled a human-powered aircraft across the English Channel from the cliffs of Dover to Cap Gris-Nez on June 12, 1979. (a) He flew for 169 min at an average velocity of 3.53 m/s in a direction 45° south of east. What was his total displacement? (b) Allen encountered a headwind averaging 2.00 m/s almost precisely in the opposite direction of his motion relative to the Earth. What was his average velocity relative to the air? (c) What was his total displacement relative to the air mass?

53. A seagull flies at a velocity of 9.00 m/s straight into the wind. (a) If it takes the bird 20.0 min to travel 6.00 km relative to the Earth, what is the velocity of the wind? (b) If the bird turns around and flies with the wind, how long will he take to return 6.00 km? (c) Discuss how the wind affects the total round-trip time compared to what it would be with no wind.

54. Near the end of a marathon race, the first two runners are separated by a distance of 45.0 m. The front runner has a velocity of 3.50 m/s, and the second a velocity of 4.20 m/s. (a) What is the velocity of the second runner relative to the first? (b) If the front runner is 250 m from the finish line, who will win the race, assuming they run at constant velocity? (c) What distance ahead will the winner be when she crosses the finish line?

55. Verify that the coin dropped by the airline passenger in the Example 3.8 travels 144 m horizontally while falling 1.50 m in the frame of reference of the Earth.

56. A football quarterback is moving straight backward at a speed of 2.00 m/s when he throws a pass to a player 18.0 m straight downfield. The ball is thrown at an angle of 25.0° relative to the ground and is caught at the same height as it is released. What is the initial velocity of the ball *relative to the quarterback*?

57. A ship sets sail from Rotterdam, The Netherlands, heading due north at 7.00 m/s relative to the water. The local ocean current is 1.50 m/s in a direction 40.0° north of east. What is the velocity of the ship relative to the Earth?

58. (a) A jet airplane flying from Darwin, Australia, has an air speed of 260 m/s in a direction 5.0° south of west. It is in the jet stream, which is blowing at 35.0 m/s in a direction 15° south of east. What is the velocity of the airplane relative to the Earth? (b) Discuss whether your answers are consistent with your expectations for the effect of the wind on the plane's path.

59. (a) In what direction would the ship in Exercise 3.57 have to travel in order to have a velocity straight north relative to the Earth, assuming its speed relative to the water remains 7.00 m/s? (b) What would its speed be relative to the Earth?

60. (a) Another airplane is flying in a jet stream that is blowing at 45.0 m/s in a direction 20° south of east (as in Exercise 3.58). Its direction of motion relative to the Earth is 45.0° south of west, while its direction of travel relative to the air is 5.00° south of west. What is the airplane's speed relative to the air mass? (b) What is the airplane's speed relative to the Earth?

61. A sandal is dropped from the top of a 15.0-m-high mast on a ship moving at 1.75 m/s due south. Calculate the velocity of the sandal when it hits the deck of the ship: (a) relative to the ship and (b) relative to a stationary observer on shore. (c) Discuss how the answers give a consistent result for the position at which the sandal hits the deck.

62. The velocity of the wind relative to the water is crucial to sailboats. Suppose a sailboat is in an ocean current that has a velocity of 2.20 m/s in a direction 30.0° east of north relative to the Earth. It encounters a wind that has a velocity of 4.50 m/s in a direction of 50.0° south of west relative to the Earth. What is the velocity of the wind relative to the water?

63. The great astronomer Edwin Hubble discovered that all distant galaxies are receding from our Milky Way Galaxy with velocities proportional to their distances. It appears to an observer on the Earth that we are at the center of an expanding universe. Figure 3.59 illustrates this for five galaxies lying along a straight line, with the Milky Way Galaxy at the center. Using the data from the figure, calculate the velocities: (a) relative to galaxy 2 and (b) relative to galaxy 5. The results mean that observers on all galaxies will see themselves at the center of the expanding universe, and they would likely be aware of relative velocities, concluding that it is not possible to locate the center of expansion with the given information.

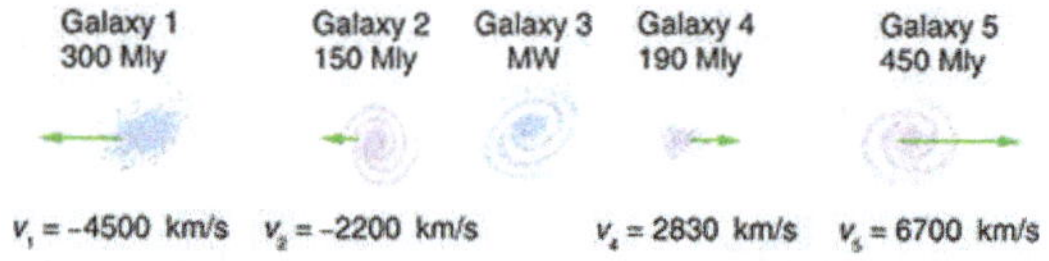

FIGURE 3.59 Five galaxies on a straight line, showing their distances and velocities relative to the Milky Way (MW) Galaxy. The distances are in millions of light years (Mly), where a light year is the distance light travels in one year. The velocities are nearly proportional to the distances. The sizes of the galaxies are greatly exaggerated; an average galaxy is about 0.1 Mly across.

64. (a) Use the distance and velocity data in Figure 3.59 to find the rate of expansion as a function of distance.
(b) If you extrapolate back in time, how long ago would all of the galaxies have been at approximately the same position? The two parts of

this problem give you some idea of how the Hubble constant for universal expansion and the time back to the Big Bang are determined, respectively.

65. An athlete crosses a 25-m-wide river by swimming perpendicular to the water current at a speed of 0.5 m/s relative to the water. They reach the opposite side at a distance 40 m downstream from the starting point. How fast is the water in the river flowing with respect to the ground? What is the speed of the swimmer with respect to a friend at rest on the ground?

66. A ship sailing in the Gulf Stream is heading 25.0° west of north at a speed of 4.00 m/s relative to the water. Its velocity relative to the Earth is 4.80 m/s 5.00° west of north. What is the velocity of the Gulf Stream? (The velocity obtained is typical for the Gulf Stream a few hundred kilometers off the east coast of the United States.)

67. An ice hockey player is moving at 8.00 m/s when they hit the puck toward the goal. The speed of the puck relative to the player is 29.0 m/s. The line between the center of the goal and the player makes a 90.0° angle relative to their path as shown in Figure 3.60. What angle must the puck's velocity make relative to the player (in their frame of reference) to hit the center of the goal?

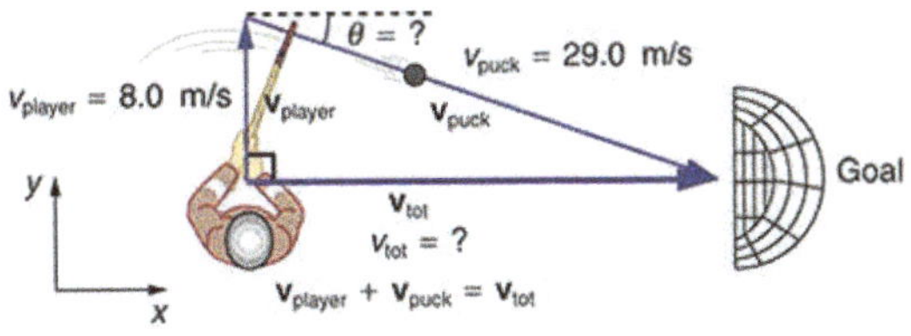

FIGURE 3.60 An ice hockey player moving across the rink must shoot backward to give the puck a velocity toward the goal.

68. Unreasonable Results Suppose you wish to shoot supplies straight up to astronauts in an orbit 36,000 km above the surface of the Earth. (a) At what velocity must the supplies be launched? (b) What is unreasonable about this velocity? (c) Is there a problem with the relative velocity between the supplies and the astronauts when the supplies reach their maximum height? (d) Is the premise unreasonable or is the available equation inapplicable? Explain your answer.

69. Unreasonable Results A commercial airplane has an air speed of 280 m/s due east and flies with a strong tailwind. It travels 3000 km in a direction 5° south of east in 1.50 h. (a) What was the velocity of the plane relative to the ground? (b) Calculate the magnitude and direction of the tailwind's velocity. (c) What is unreasonable about both of these velocities? (d) Which premise is unreasonable?

70. Construct Your Own Problem Consider an airplane headed for a runway in a cross wind. Construct a problem in which you calculate the angle the airplane must fly relative to the air mass in order to have a velocity parallel to the runway. Among the things to consider are the direction of the runway, the wind speed and direction (its velocity) and the speed of the plane relative to the air mass. Also calculate the speed of the airplane relative to the ground. Discuss any last minute maneuvers the pilot might have to perform in order for the plane to land with its wheels pointing straight down the runway.

71. Critical Thinking Two identical spring-loaded launchers are fixed to the end of a table. Launcher A is inclined 40° above the horizontal and launcher B is inclined 50° above the horizontal. (a) Which of these launchers will fire the ball the greatest vertical height above the launcher before it crashes into the ground? (b) Based on experimental data, an equation that fits the data is suggested for the vertical height above the launcher, *y*, which may not be correct: $y = KV_0^{\,2} \sin\theta$, where *K* is a constant with appropriate units, V_0 is the initial velocity of the launcher, and θ is the angle relative to the *x*-axis of the launcher. Is this equation consistent with your answer from part a? Explain why or why not. Does this equation make sense? Explain why or why not. (c) Graph the magnitude of the velocity vs. vertical height for both launcher A and B.

Test Prep for AP® Courses

3.1 Kinematics in Two Dimensions: An Introduction

1. A ball is thrown at an angle of 45 degrees above the horizontal. Which of the following best describes the acceleration of the ball from the instant after it leaves the thrower's hand until the time it hits the ground?

a. Always in the same direction as the motion, initially positive and gradually dropping to zero by the time it hits the ground
b. Initially positive in the upward direction, then

zero at maximum height, then negative from there until it hits the ground
c. Always in the opposite direction as the motion, initially positive and gradually dropping to zero by the time it hits the ground
d. Always in the downward direction with the same constant value

2. In an experiment, a student launches a ball with an initial horizontal velocity at an elevation 2 meters above ground. The ball follows a parabolic trajectory until it hits the ground. Which of the following accurately describes the graph of the ball's vertical acceleration versus time (taking the downward direction to be negative)?
a. A negative value that does not change with time
b. A gradually increasing negative value (straight line)
c. An increasing rate of negative values over time (parabolic curve)
d. Zero at all times since the initial motion is horizontal

3. A student wishes to design an experiment to show that the acceleration of an object is independent of the object's velocity. To do this, ball A is launched horizontally with some initial speed at an elevation 1.5 meters above the ground, ball B is dropped from rest 1.5 meters above the ground, and ball C is launched vertically with some initial speed at an elevation 1.5 meters above the ground. What information would the student need to collect about each ball in order to test the hypothesis?

3.2 Vector Addition and Subtraction: Graphical Methods

4. A ball is launched vertically upward. The vertical position of the ball is recorded at various points in time in the table shown.

Height (m)	Time (sec)
0.490	0.1
0.882	0.2
1.176	0.3
1.372	0.4
1.470	0.5
1.470	0.6
1.372	0.7

TABLE 3.1

Which of the following correctly describes the graph of the ball's vertical velocity versus time?
a. Always positive, steadily decreasing
b. Always positive, constant
c. Initially positive, steadily decreasing, becoming negative at the end
d. Initially zero, steadily getting more and more negative

5.

Height (m)	Time (sec)
0.490	0.1
0.882	0.2
1.176	0.3
1.372	0.4
1.470	0.5
1.470	0.6
1.372	0.7

TABLE 3.2

A ball is launched at an angle of 60 degrees above the horizontal, and the vertical position of the ball is recorded at various points in time in the table shown, assuming the ball was at a height of 0 at time t = 0.
a. Draw a graph of the ball's vertical velocity versus time.
b. Describe the graph of the ball's horizontal velocity.
c. Draw a graph of the ball's vertical acceleration versus time.

3.4 Projectile Motion

6. In an experiment, a student launches a ball with an initial horizontal velocity of 5.00 meters/sec at an elevation 2.00 meters above ground. Draw and

clearly label with appropriate values and units a graph of the ball's horizontal velocity vs. time and the ball's vertical velocity vs. time. The graph should cover the motion from the instant after the ball is launched until the instant before it hits the ground. Assume the downward direction is negative for this problem.

CHAPTER 4

Dynamics: Force and Newton's Laws of Motion

FIGURE 4.1 Newton's laws of motion describe the motion of the dolphin's path. (credit: Jin Jang)

CHAPTER OUTLINE

CONNECTION FOR AP® COURSES Motion draws our attention. Motion itself can be beautiful, causing us to marvel at the forces needed to achieve spectacular motion, such as that of a jumping dolphin, a leaping pole vaulter, a bird in flight, or an orbiting satellite. The study of motion is kinematics, but kinematics only *describes* the way objects move—their velocity and their acceleration. **Dynamics** considers the forces that affect the motion of moving objects and systems. Newton's laws of motion are the foundation of dynamics. These laws provide an example of the breadth and simplicity of principles under which nature functions. They are also universal laws in that they apply to situations on Earth as well as in space.

Isaac Newton's (1642–1727) laws of motion were just one part of the monumental work that has made him legendary. The development of Newton's laws marks the transition from the Renaissance into the modern era. This transition was characterized by a revolutionary change in the way people thought about the physical universe. For many centuries natural philosophers had debated the nature of the universe based largely on certain rules of logic, with great weight given to the thoughts of earlier classical philosophers such as Aristotle (384–322 BC). Among the many great thinkers who contributed to this change were Newton and Galileo Galilei (1564–1647).

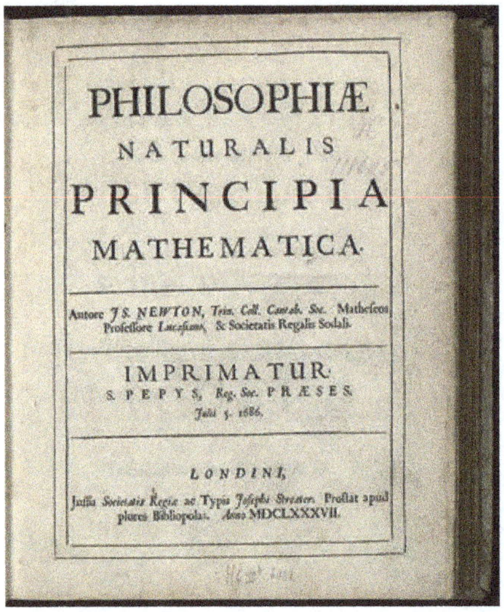

FIGURE 4.2 Isaac Newton's monumental work, *Philosophiae Naturalis Principia Mathematica*, was published in 1687. It proposed scientific laws that are still used today to describe the motion of objects. (credit: Service commun de la documentation de l'Université de Strasbourg)

Galileo was instrumental in establishing *observation* as the absolute determinant of truth, rather than "logical" argument. Galileo's use of the telescope was his most notable achievement in demonstrating the importance of observation. He discovered moons orbiting Jupiter and made other observations that were inconsistent with certain ancient ideas and religious dogma. For this reason, and because of the manner in which he dealt with those in authority, Galileo was tried by the Inquisition and punished. He spent the final years of his life under a form of house arrest. Because others before Galileo had also made discoveries by *observing* the nature of the universe and because repeated observations verified those of Galileo, his work could not be suppressed or denied. After his death, his work was verified by others, and his ideas were eventually accepted by the church and scientific communities.

Galileo also contributed to the formulation of what is now called Newton's first law of motion. Newton made use of the work of his predecessors, which enabled him to develop laws of motion, discover the law of gravity, invent calculus, and make great contributions to the theories of light and color. It is amazing that many of these developments were made by Newton working alone, without the benefit of the usual interactions that take place among scientists today.

Newton's laws are introduced along with Big Idea 3, that interactions can be described by forces. These laws provide a theoretical basis for studying motion depending on interactions between the objects. In particular, Newton's laws are applicable to all forces in inertial frames of references (Enduring Understanding 3.A). We will find that all forces are vectors; that is, forces always have both a magnitude and a direction (Essential Knowledge 3.A.2). Furthermore, we will learn that all forces are a result of interactions between two or more objects (Essential Knowledge 3.A.3). These interactions between any two objects are described by Newton's third law, stating that the forces exerted on these objects are equal in magnitude and opposite in direction to each other (Essential Knowledge 3.A.4).

We will discover that there is an empirical cause-effect relationship between the net force exerted on an object of mass m and its acceleration, with this relationship described by Newton's second law (Enduring Understanding 3.B). This supports Big Idea 1, that inertial mass is a property of an object or a system. The mass of an object or a system is one of the factors affecting changes in motion when an object or a system interacts with other objects or systems (Essential Knowledge 1.C.1). Another is the net force on an object, which is the vector sum of all the forces exerted on the object (Essential Knowledge 3.B.1). To analyze this, we use free-body diagrams to visualize the forces exerted on a given object in order to find the net force and analyze the object's motion (Essential Knowledge 3.B.2).

Thinking of these objects as systems is a concept introduced in this chapter, where a system is a collection of elements that could be considered as a single object without any internal structure (Essential Knowledge 5.A.1). This will support Big Idea 5, that changes that occur to the system due to interactions are governed by conservation laws. These conservation laws will be the focus of later chapters in this book. They explain whether quantities are conserved in the given system or change due to transfer to or from another system due to interactions between the systems (Enduring Understanding 5.A).

Furthermore, when a situation involves more than one object, it is important to define the system and analyze the motion of a whole system, not its elements, based on analysis of external forces on the system. This supports Big Idea 4, that interactions between systems cause changes in those systems. All kinematics variables in this case describe the motion of the center of mass of the system (Essential Knowledge 4.A.1, Essential Knowledge 4.A.2). The internal forces between the elements of the system do not affect the velocity of the center of mass (Essential Knowledge 4.A.3). The velocity of the center of mass will change only if there is a net external force exerted on the system (Enduring Understanding 4.A).

We will learn that some of these interactions can be explained by the existence of fields extending through space, supporting Big Idea 2. For example, any object that has mass creates a gravitational field in space (Enduring Understanding 2.B). Any material object (one that has mass) placed in the gravitational field will experience gravitational force (Essential Knowledge 2.B.1).

Forces may be categorized as contact or long-distance (Enduring Understanding 3.C). In this chapter we will work with both. An example of a long-distance force is gravitation (Essential Knowledge 3.C.1). Contact forces, such as tension, friction, normal force, and the force of a spring, result from interatomic electric forces at the microscopic level (Essential Knowledge 3.C.4).

It was not until the advent of modern physics early in the twentieth century that it was discovered that Newton's laws of motion produce a good approximation to motion only when the objects are moving at speeds much, much less than the speed of light and when those objects are larger than the size of most molecules (about 10^{-9} m in diameter). These constraints define the realm of classical mechanics, as discussed in Introduction to the Nature of Science and Physics. At the beginning of the twentieth century, Albert Einstein (1879–1955) developed the theory of relativity and, along with many other scientists, quantum theory. Quantum theory does not have the constraints present in classical physics. All of the situations we consider in this chapter, and all those preceding the introduction of relativity in **Special Relativity**, are in the realm of classical physics.

The development of special relativity and empirical observations at atomic scales led to the idea that there are four basic forces that account for all known phenomena. These forces are called fundamental (Enduring Understanding 3.G). The properties of gravitational (Essential Knowledge 3.G.1) and electromagnetic (Essential Knowledge 3.G.2) forces are explained in more detail.

Big Idea 1 Objects and systems have properties such as mass and charge. Systems may have internal structure.

Essential Knowledge 1.C.1 Inertial mass is the property of an object or a system that determines how its motion changes when it interacts with other objects or systems.

Big Idea 2 Fields existing in space can be used to explain interactions.

Enduring Understanding 2.A A field associates a value of some physical quantity with every point in space. Field models are useful for describing interactions that occur at a distance (long-range forces) as well as a variety of other physical phenomena.

Essential Knowledge 2.A.1 A vector field gives, as a function of position (and perhaps time), the value of a physical quantity that is described by a vector.

Essential Knowledge 2.A.2 A scalar field gives the value of a physical quantity.

Enduring Understanding 2.B A gravitational field is caused by an object with mass.

Essential Knowledge 2.B.1 A gravitational field g at the location of an object with mass m causes a gravitational force of magnitude *mg* to be exerted on the object in the direction of the field.

Big Idea 3 The interactions of an object with other objects can be described by forces.

Enduring Understanding 3.A All forces share certain common characteristics when considered by observers in inertial reference frames.

Essential Knowledge 3.A.2 Forces are described by vectors.

Essential Knowledge 3.A.3 A force exerted on an object is always due to the interaction of that object with another object.

Essential Knowledge 3.A.4 If one object exerts a force on a second object, the second object always exerts a force of equal magnitude on the first object in the opposite direction.

Enduring Understanding 3.B Classically, the acceleration of an object interacting with other objects can be predicted by using $a = \sum F/m$.

Essential Knowledge 3.B.1 If an object of interest interacts with several other objects, the net force is the vector sum of the individual forces.

Essential Knowledge 3.B.2 Free-body diagrams are useful tools for visualizing the forces being exerted on a single object and writing the equations that represent a physical situation.

Enduring Understanding 3.C At the macroscopic level, forces can be categorized as either long-range (action-at-a-distance) forces or contact forces.

Essential Knowledge 3.C.1 Gravitational force describes the interaction of one object that has mass with another object that has mass.

Essential Knowledge 3.C.4 Contact forces result from the interaction of one object touching another object, and they arise from interatomic electric forces. These forces include tension, friction, normal, spring (Physics 1), and buoyant (Physics 2).

Enduring Understanding 3.G Certain types of forces are considered fundamental.

Essential Knowledge 3.G.1 Gravitational forces are exerted at all scales and dominate at the largest distance and mass scales.

Essential Knowledge 3.G.2 Electromagnetic forces are exerted at all scales and can dominate at the human scale.

Big Idea 4 Interactions between systems can result in changes in those systems.

Enduring Understanding 4.A The acceleration of the center of mass of a system is related to the net force exerted on the system, where $a = \sum F/m$.

Essential Knowledge 4.A.1 The linear motion of a system can be described by the displacement, velocity, and acceleration of its center of mass.

Essential Knowledge 4.A.2 The acceleration is equal to the rate of change of velocity with time, and velocity is equal to the rate of change of position with time.

Essential Knowledge 4.A.3 Forces that systems exert on each other are due to interactions between objects in the systems. If the interacting objects are parts of the same system, there will be no change in the center-of-mass velocity of that system.

Big Idea 5 Changes that occur as a result of interactions are constrained by conservation laws.

Enduring Understanding 5.A Certain quantities are conserved, in the sense that the changes of those quantities in a given system are always equal to the transfer of that quantity to or from the system by all possible interactions with other systems.

Essential Knowledge 5.A.1 A system is an object or a collection of objects. The objects are treated as having no internal structure.

Click to view content (https://openstax.org/books/college-physics-ap-courses-2e/pages/4-connection-for-ap-r-courses)

4.1 Development of Force Concept

LEARNING OBJECTIVES

By the end of this section, you will be able to:

- Understand the definition of force.

Dynamics is the study of the forces that cause objects and systems to move. To understand this, we need a working definition of force. Our intuitive definition of **force**—that is, a push or a pull—is a good place to start. We know that a push or pull has both magnitude and direction (therefore, it is a vector quantity) and can vary considerably in each regard. For example, a cannon exerts a strong force on a cannonball that is launched into the air. In contrast, Earth exerts only a tiny downward pull on a flea. Our everyday experiences also give us a good idea of how multiple forces add. If two people push in different directions on a third person, as illustrated in Figure 4.3, we might expect the total force to be in the direction shown. Since force is a vector, it adds just like other vectors, as illustrated in Figure 4.3(a) for two ice skaters. Forces, like other vectors, are represented by arrows and can be added using the familiar head-to-tail method or by trigonometric methods. These ideas were developed in Two-Dimensional Kinematics.

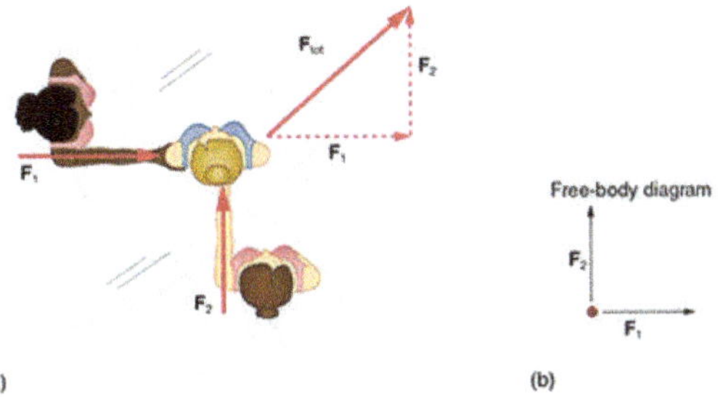

FIGURE 4.3 Part (a) shows an overhead view of two ice skaters pushing on a third. Forces are vectors and add like other vectors, so the total force on the third skater is in the direction shown. In part (b), we see a free-body diagram representing the forces acting on the third skater.

Figure 4.3(b) is our first example of a **free-body diagram**, which is a technique used to illustrate all the **external forces** acting on a body. The body is represented by a single isolated point (or free body), and only those forces acting *on* the body from the outside (external forces) are shown. (These forces are the only ones shown, because only external forces acting on the body affect its motion. We can ignore any internal forces within the body.) Free-body diagrams are very useful in analyzing forces acting on a system and are employed extensively in the study and application of Newton's laws of motion.

A more quantitative definition of force can be based on some standard force, just as distance is measured in units relative to a standard distance. One possibility is to stretch a spring a certain fixed distance, as illustrated in Figure 4.4, and use the force it exerts to pull itself back to its relaxed shape—called a *restoring force*—as a standard. The magnitude of all other forces can be stated as multiples of this standard unit of force. Many other possibilities exist for standard forces. (One that we will encounter in Magnetism is the magnetic force between two wires carrying electric current.) Some alternative definitions of force will be given later in this chapter.

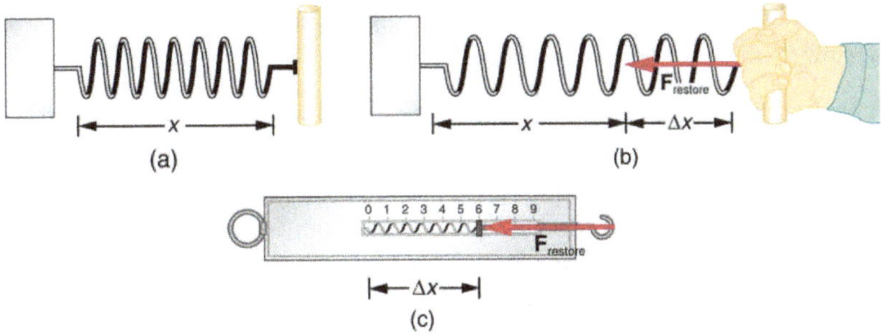

FIGURE 4.4 The force exerted by a stretched spring can be used as a standard unit of force. (a) This spring has a length x when undistorted. (b) When stretched a distance Δx, the spring exerts a restoring force, $\mathbf{F}_{\text{restore}}$, which is reproducible. (c) A spring scale is one device that uses a spring to measure force. The force $\mathbf{F}_{\text{restore}}$ is exerted on whatever is attached to the hook. Here $\mathbf{F}_{\text{restore}}$ has a magnitude of 6 units in the force standard being employed.

TAKE-HOME EXPERIMENT: FORCE STANDARDS

To investigate force standards and cause and effect, get two identical rubber bands. Hang one rubber band vertically on a hook. Find a small household item that could be attached to the rubber band using a paper clip, and use this item as a weight to investigate the stretch of the rubber band. Measure the amount of stretch produced in the rubber band with one, two, and four of these (identical) items suspended from the rubber band. What is the relationship between the number of items and the amount of stretch? How large a stretch would you expect for the same number of items suspended from two rubber bands? What happens to the amount of stretch of the rubber band (with the weights attached) if the weights are also pushed to the side with a pencil?

4.2 Newton's First Law of Motion: Inertia

LEARNING OBJECTIVES

By the end of this section, you will be able to:

- Define mass and inertia.
- Understand Newton's first law of motion.

Experience suggests that an object at rest will remain at rest if left alone, and that an object in motion tends to slow down and stop unless some effort is made to keep it moving. What **Newton's first law of motion** states, however, is the following:

NEWTON'S FIRST LAW OF MOTION

A body at rest remains at rest, or, if in motion, remains in motion at a constant velocity unless acted on by a net external force.

Note the repeated use of the verb "remains." We can think of this law as preserving the status quo of motion.

Rather than contradicting our experience, **Newton's first law of motion** states that there must be a *cause* (which is a net external force) *for there to be any change in velocity (either a change in magnitude or direction).* We will define *net external force* in the next section. An object sliding across a table or floor slows down due to the net force of friction acting on the object. If friction disappeared, would the object still slow down?

The idea of cause and effect is crucial in accurately describing what happens in various situations. For example, consider what happens to an object sliding along a rough horizontal surface. The object quickly grinds to a halt. If we spray the surface with talcum powder to make the surface smoother, the object slides farther. If we make the surface even smoother by rubbing lubricating oil on it, the object slides farther yet. Extrapolating to a frictionless surface, we can imagine the object sliding in a straight line indefinitely. Friction is thus the *cause* of the slowing (consistent with Newton's first law). The object would not slow down at all if friction were completely eliminated. Consider an air hockey table. When the air is turned off, the puck slides only a short distance before friction slows it to a stop. However, when the air is turned on, it creates a nearly frictionless surface, and the puck glides long distances without slowing down. Additionally, if we know enough about the friction, we can accurately predict how quickly the object will slow down. Friction is an external force.

Newton's first law is completely general and can be applied to anything from an object sliding on a table to a satellite in orbit to blood pumped from the heart. Experiments have thoroughly verified that any change in velocity (speed or direction) must be caused by an external force. The idea of *generally applicable or universal laws* is important not only here—it is a basic feature of all laws of physics. Identifying these laws is like recognizing patterns in nature from which further patterns can be discovered. The genius of Galileo, who first developed the idea for the first law, and Newton, who clarified it, was to ask the fundamental question, "What is the cause?" Thinking in terms of cause and effect is a worldview fundamentally different from the typical ancient Greek approach when questions such as "Why does a tiger have stripes?" would have been answered in Aristotelian fashion, "That is the nature of the beast." True perhaps, but not a useful insight.

Mass

The property of a body to remain at rest or to remain in motion with constant velocity is called **inertia**. Newton's first law is often called the **law of inertia**. As we know from experience, some objects have more inertia than others. It is obviously more difficult to change the motion of a large boulder than that of a basketball, for example. The inertia of an object is measured by its **mass**. Roughly speaking, mass is a measure of the amount of "stuff" (or matter) in something. The quantity or amount of matter in an object is determined by the numbers of atoms and molecules of various types it contains. Unlike weight, mass does not vary with location. The mass of an object is the same on Earth, in orbit, or on the surface of the Moon. In practice, it is very difficult to count and identify all of the atoms and molecules in an object, so masses are not often determined in this manner. Operationally, the masses of objects are determined by comparison with the standard kilogram.

CHECK YOUR UNDERSTANDING

Which has more mass: a kilogram of cotton balls or a kilogram of gold?

Solution
They are equal. A kilogram of one substance is equal in mass to a kilogram of another substance. The quantities that might differ between them are volume and density.

4.3 Newton's Second Law of Motion: Concept of a System

LEARNING OBJECTIVES

By the end of this section, you will be able to:

- Define net force, external force, and system.
- Understand Newton's second law of motion.
- Apply Newton's second law to determine the weight of an object.

Newton's second law of motion is closely related to Newton's first law of motion. It mathematically states the cause and effect relationship between force and changes in motion. Newton's second law of motion is more quantitative and is used extensively to calculate what happens in situations involving a force. Before we can write down Newton's second law as a simple equation giving the exact relationship of force, mass, and acceleration, we need to sharpen some ideas that have already been mentioned.

First, what do we mean by a change in motion? The answer is that a change in motion is equivalent to a change in velocity. A change in velocity means, by definition, that there is an **acceleration**. Newton's first law says that a net external force causes a change in motion; thus, we see that a *net external force causes acceleration*.

Another question immediately arises. What do we mean by an external force? An intuitive notion of external is correct—an **external force** acts from outside the **system** of interest. For example, in Figure 4.5(a) the system of interest is the wagon plus the child in it. The two forces exerted by the other children are external forces. An internal force acts between elements of the system. Again looking at Figure 4.5(a), the force the child in the wagon exerts to hang onto the wagon is an internal force between elements of the system of interest. Only external forces affect the motion of a system, according to Newton's first law. (The internal forces actually cancel, as we shall see in the next section.) *You must define the boundaries of the system before you can determine which forces are external.* Sometimes the system is obvious, whereas other times identifying the boundaries of a system is more subtle. The concept of a system is fundamental to many areas of physics, as is the correct application of Newton's laws. This concept will be revisited many times on our journey through physics.

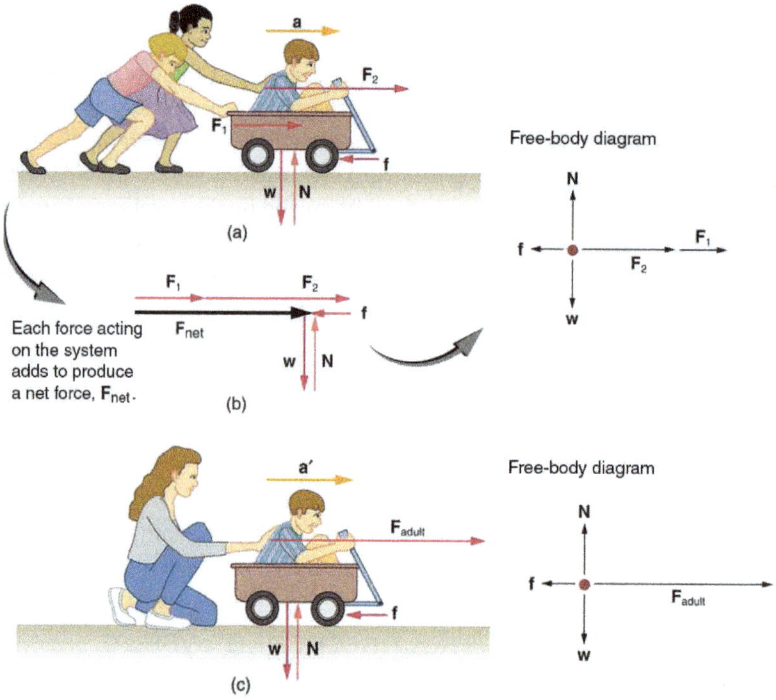

FIGURE 4.5 Different forces exerted on the same mass produce different accelerations. (a) Two children push a wagon with a child in it. Arrows representing all external forces are shown. The system of interest is the wagon and its rider. The weight $\mathbf{w}$ of the system and the support of the ground $\mathbf{N}$ are also shown for completeness and are assumed to cancel. The vector $\mathbf{f}$ represents the friction acting on the wagon, and it acts to the left, opposing the motion of the wagon. (b) All of the external forces acting on the system add together to produce a net force, $\mathbf{F}_{\text{net}}$. The free-body diagram shows all of the forces acting on the system of interest. The dot represents the center of mass of the system. Each force vector extends from this dot. Because there are two forces acting to the right, we draw the vectors collinearly. (c) A larger net external force produces a larger acceleration ($\mathbf{a}' > \mathbf{a}$) when an adult pushes the child.

Now, it seems reasonable that acceleration should be directly proportional to and in the same direction as the net (total) external force acting on a system. This assumption has been verified experimentally and is illustrated in Figure 4.5. In part (a), a smaller force causes a smaller acceleration than the larger force illustrated in part (c). For completeness, the vertical forces are also shown; they are assumed to cancel since there is no acceleration in the vertical direction. The vertical forces are the weight $\mathbf{w}$ and the support of the ground $\mathbf{N}$, and the horizontal force $\mathbf{f}$ represents the force of friction. These will be discussed in more detail in later sections. For now, we will define **friction** as a force that opposes the motion past each other of objects that are touching. Figure 4.5(b) shows how vectors representing the external forces add together to produce a net force, $\mathbf{F}_{\text{net}}$.

To obtain an equation for Newton's second law, we first write the relationship of acceleration and net external force as the proportionality

$$\mathbf{a} \propto \mathbf{F}_{\text{net}}, \tag{4.1}$$

where the symbol $\propto$ means "proportional to," and $\mathbf{F}_{\text{net}}$ is the **net external force**. (The net external force is the vector sum of all external forces and can be determined graphically, using the head-to-tail method, or analytically, using components. The techniques are the same as for the addition of other vectors, and are covered in Two-Dimensional Kinematics.) This proportionality states what we have said in words—*acceleration is directly proportional to the net external force.* Once the system of interest is chosen, it is important to identify the external forces and ignore the internal ones. It is a tremendous simplification not to have to consider the numerous internal forces acting between objects within the system, such as muscular forces within the child's body, let alone the myriad of forces between atoms in the objects, but by doing so, we can easily solve some very complex problems with only minimal error due to our simplification

Now, it also seems reasonable that acceleration should be inversely proportional to the mass of the system. In other words, the larger the mass (the inertia), the smaller the acceleration produced by a given force. And indeed, as illustrated in Figure 4.6, the same net external force applied to a car produces a much smaller acceleration than when applied to a basketball. The proportionality is written as

$$\mathbf{a} \propto \frac{1}{m} \quad 4.2$$

where m is the mass of the system. Experiments have shown that acceleration is exactly inversely proportional to mass, just as it is exactly linearly proportional to the net external force.

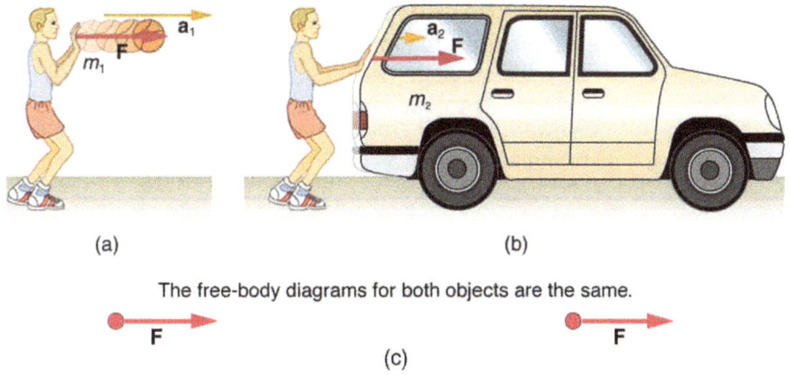

FIGURE 4.6 The same force exerted on systems of different masses produces different accelerations. (a) A basketball player pushes on a basketball to make a pass. (The effect of gravity on the ball is ignored.) (b) The same player exerts an identical force on a stalled SUV and produces a far smaller acceleration (even if friction is negligible). (c) The free-body diagrams are identical, permitting direct comparison of the two situations. A series of patterns for the free-body diagram will emerge as you do more problems.

It has been found that the acceleration of an object depends *only* on the net external force and the mass of the object. Combining the two proportionalities just given yields Newton's second law of motion.

NEWTON'S SECOND LAW OF MOTION

The acceleration of a system is directly proportional to and in the same direction as the net external force acting on the system, and inversely proportional to its mass.

In equation form, Newton's second law of motion is

$$\mathbf{a} = \frac{\mathbf{F}_{\text{net}}}{m}. \quad 4.3$$

This is often written in the more familiar form

$$\mathbf{F}_{\text{net}} = m\mathbf{a}. \quad 4.4$$

When only the magnitude of force and acceleration are considered, this equation is simply

$$F_{\text{net}} = ma. \quad 4.5$$

Although these last two equations are really the same, the first gives more insight into what Newton's second law means. The law is a *cause and effect relationship* among three quantities that is not simply based on their definitions. The validity of the second law is completely based on experimental verification.

Units of Force

$\mathbf{F}_{\text{net}} = m\mathbf{a}$ is used to define the units of force in terms of the three basic units for mass, length, and time. The SI unit of force is called the **newton** (abbreviated N) and is the force needed to accelerate a 1-kg system at the rate of 1m/s^2. That is, since $\mathbf{F}_{\text{net}} = m\mathbf{a}$,

$$1 \text{ N} = 1 \text{ kg} \cdot \text{m/s}^2. \quad 4.6$$

While almost the entire world uses the newton for the unit of force, in the United States the most familiar unit of force is the pound (lb), where 1 N = 0.225 lb.

Weight and the Gravitational Force

When an object is dropped, it accelerates toward the center of Earth. Newton's second law states that a net force on an object is responsible for its acceleration. If air resistance is negligible, the net force on a falling object is the gravitational force, commonly called its **weight w**. Weight can be denoted as a vector **w** because it has a direction; *down* is, by definition, the direction of gravity, and hence weight is a downward force. The magnitude of weight is denoted as w. Galileo was instrumental in showing that, in the absence of air resistance, all objects fall with the same acceleration g. Using Galileo's result and Newton's second law, we can derive an equation for weight.

Consider an object with mass m falling downward toward Earth. It experiences only the downward force of gravity, which has magnitude w. Newton's second law states that the magnitude of the net external force on an object is $F_{\text{net}} = ma$.

Since the object experiences only the downward force of gravity, $F_{\text{net}} = w$. We know that the acceleration of an object due to gravity is g, or $a = g$. Substituting these into Newton's second law gives

WEIGHT

This is the equation for *weight*—the gravitational force on a mass m:

$$w = mg. \tag{4.7}$$

Since $g = 9.80\ \text{m/s}^2$ on Earth, the weight of a 1.0 kg object on Earth is 9.8 N, as we see:

$$w = mg = (1.0\ \text{kg})(9.80\ \text{m/s}^2) = 9.8\ \text{N}. \tag{4.8}$$

Recall that g can take a positive or negative value, depending on the positive direction in the coordinate system. Be sure to take this into consideration when solving problems with weight.

When the net external force on an object is its weight, we say that it is in **free-fall**. That is, the only force acting on the object is the force of gravity. In the real world, when objects fall downward toward Earth, they are never truly in free-fall because there is always some upward force from the air acting on the object.

The acceleration due to gravity g varies slightly over the surface of Earth, so that the weight of an object depends on location and is not an intrinsic property of the object. Weight varies dramatically if one leaves Earth's surface. On the Moon, for example, the acceleration due to gravity is only $1.625\ \text{m/s}^2$. A 1.0-kg mass thus has a weight of 9.8 N on Earth and only about 1.7 N on the Moon.

The broadest definition of weight in this sense is that *the weight of an object is the gravitational force on it from the nearest large body*, such as Earth, the Moon, the Sun, and so on. This is the most common and useful definition of weight in physics. It differs dramatically, however, from the definition of weight used by NASA and the popular media in relation to space travel and exploration. When they speak of "weightlessness" and "microgravity," they are really referring to the phenomenon we call "free-fall" in physics. We shall use the above definition of weight, and we will make careful distinctions between free-fall and actual weightlessness.

It is important to be aware that weight and mass are very different physical quantities, although they are closely related. Mass is the quantity of matter (how much "stuff") and does not vary in classical physics, whereas weight is the gravitational force and does vary depending on gravity. It is tempting to equate the two, since most of our examples take place on Earth, where the weight of an object only varies a little with the location of the object. Furthermore, the terms *mass* and *weight* are used interchangeably in everyday language; for example, our medical records often show our "weight" in kilograms, but never in the correct units of newtons.

COMMON MISCONCEPTIONS: MASS VS. WEIGHT

Mass and weight are often used interchangeably in everyday language. However, in science, these terms are distinctly different from one another. Mass is a measure of how much matter is in an object. The typical measure of mass is the kilogram (or the "slug" in English units). Weight, on the other hand, is a measure of the force of gravity acting on an object. Weight is equal to the mass of an object (m) multiplied by the acceleration due to gravity (g). Like any other force, weight is measured in terms of newtons (or pounds in English units).

Assuming the mass of an object is kept intact, it will remain the same, regardless of its location. However, because weight depends on the acceleration due to gravity, the weight of an object *can change* when the object enters into a region with stronger or weaker gravity. For example, the acceleration due to gravity on the Moon is $1.625\ \mathrm{m/s^2}$ (which is much less than the acceleration due to gravity on Earth, $9.80\ \mathrm{m/s^2}$). If you measured your weight on Earth and then measured your weight on the Moon, you would find that you "weigh" much less, even though you do not look any skinnier. This is because the force of gravity is weaker on the Moon. In fact, when people say that they are "losing weight," they really mean that they are losing "mass" (which in turn causes them to weigh less).

TAKE-HOME EXPERIMENT: MASS AND WEIGHT

What do bathroom scales measure? When you stand on a bathroom scale, what happens to the scale? It depresses slightly. The scale contains springs that compress in proportion to your weight—similar to rubber bands expanding when pulled. The springs provide a measure of your weight (for an object which is not accelerating). This is a force in newtons (or pounds). In most countries, the measurement is divided by 9.80 to give a reading in mass units of kilograms. The scale measures weight but is calibrated to provide information about mass. While standing on a bathroom scale, push down on a table next to you. What happens to the reading? Why? Would your scale measure the same "mass" on Earth as on the Moon?

EXAMPLE 4.1

What Acceleration Can a Person Produce when Pushing a Lawn Mower?

Suppose that the net external force (push minus friction) exerted on a lawn mower is 51 N (about 11 lb) parallel to the ground. The mass of the mower is 24 kg. What is its acceleration?

FIGURE 4.7 The net force on a lawn mower is 51 N to the right. At what rate does the lawn mower accelerate to the right?

Strategy

Since $\mathbf{F}_{\text{net}}$ and m are given, the acceleration can be calculated directly from Newton's second law as stated in $\mathbf{F}_{\text{net}} = m\mathbf{a}$.

Solution

The magnitude of the acceleration a is $a = \frac{F_{\text{net}}}{m}$. Entering known values gives

$$a = \frac{51\ \mathrm{N}}{24\ \mathrm{kg}} \tag{4.9}$$

Substituting the units $\mathrm{kg \cdot m/s^2}$ for N yields

$$a = \frac{51 \text{ kg} \cdot \text{m/s}^2}{24 \text{ kg}} = 2.1 \text{ m/s}^2. \tag{4.10}$$

Discussion

The direction of the acceleration is the same direction as that of the net force, which is parallel to the ground. There is no information given in this example about the individual external forces acting on the system, but we can say something about their relative magnitudes. For example, the force exerted by the person pushing the mower must be greater than the friction opposing the motion (since we know the mower moves forward), and the vertical forces must cancel if there is to be no acceleration in the vertical direction (the mower is moving only horizontally). The acceleration found is small enough to be reasonable for a person pushing a mower. Such an effort would not last too long because the person's top speed would soon be reached.

EXAMPLE 4.2

What Rocket Thrust Accelerates This Sled?

Prior to space flights carrying astronauts, rocket sleds were used to test aircraft, missile equipment, and physiological effects on human subjects at high speeds. They consisted of a platform that was mounted on one or two rails and propelled by several rockets. Calculate the magnitude of force exerted by each rocket, called its thrust $\mathbf{T}$, for the four-rocket propulsion system shown in Figure 4.8. The sled's initial acceleration is 49 m/s^2, the mass of the system is 2100 kg, and the force of friction opposing the motion is known to be 650 N.

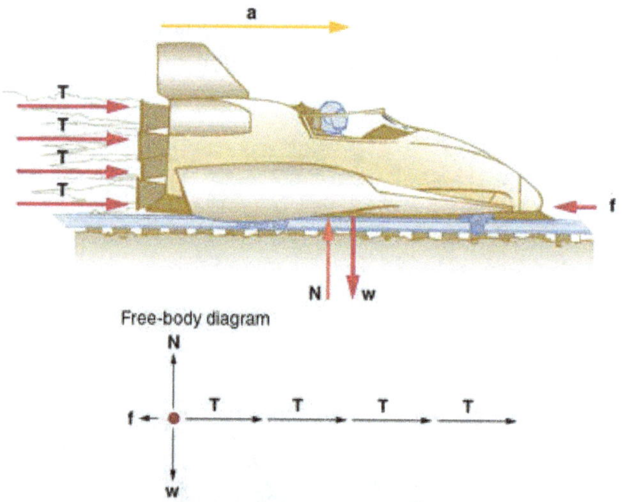

FIGURE 4.8 A sled experiences a rocket thrust that accelerates it to the right. Each rocket creates an identical thrust $\mathbf{T}$. As in other situations where there is only horizontal acceleration, the vertical forces cancel. The ground exerts an upward force $\mathbf{N}$ on the system that is equal in magnitude and opposite in direction to its weight, $\mathbf{w}$. The system here is the sled, its rockets, and rider, so none of the forces *between* these objects are considered. The arrow representing friction ($\mathbf{f}$) is drawn larger than scale.

Strategy

Although there are forces acting vertically and horizontally, we assume the vertical forces cancel since there is no vertical acceleration. This leaves us with only horizontal forces and a simpler one-dimensional problem. Directions are indicated with plus or minus signs, with right taken as the positive direction. See the free-body diagram in the figure.

Solution

Since acceleration, mass, and the force of friction are given, we start with Newton's second law and look for ways to find the thrust of the engines. Since we have defined the direction of the force and acceleration as acting "to the right," we need to consider only the magnitudes of these quantities in the calculations. Hence we begin with

$$F_{\text{net}} = ma, \tag{4.11}$$

where F_{net} is the net force along the horizontal direction. We can see from Figure 4.8 that the engine thrusts add, while friction opposes the thrust. In equation form, the net external force is

$$F_{\text{net}} = 4T - f. \tag{4.12}$$

Substituting this into Newton's second law gives

$$F_{\text{net}} = ma = 4T - f. \tag{4.13}$$

Using a little algebra, we solve for the total thrust 4*T*:

$$4T = ma + f. \tag{4.14}$$

Substituting known values yields

$$4T = ma + f = (2100 \text{ kg})(49 \text{ m/s}^2) + 650 \text{ N}. \tag{4.15}$$

So the total thrust is

$$4T = 1.0 \times 10^5 \text{ N}, \tag{4.16}$$

and the individual thrusts are

$$T = \frac{1.0 \times 10^5 \text{ N}}{4} = 2.6 \times 10^4 \text{ N}. \tag{4.17}$$

Discussion

The numbers are quite large, so the result might surprise you. Experiments such as this were performed in the early 1960s to test the limits of human endurance and the setup designed to protect human subjects in jet fighter emergency ejections. Speeds of 1000 km/h were obtained, with accelerations of 45 g's. (Recall that g, the acceleration due to gravity, is 9.80 m/s^2. When we say that an acceleration is 45 g's, it is $45 \times 9.80 \text{ m/s}^2$, which is approximately 440 m/s^2.) While living subjects are not used any more, land speeds of 10,000 km/h have been obtained with rocket sleds. In this example, as in the preceding one, the system of interest is obvious. We will see in later examples that choosing the system of interest is crucial—and the choice is not always obvious.

Newton's second law of motion is more than a definition; it is a relationship among acceleration, force, and mass. It can help us make predictions. Each of those physical quantities can be defined independently, so the second law tells us something basic and universal about nature. The next section introduces the third and final law of motion.

4.4 Newton's Third Law of Motion: Symmetry in Forces

LEARNING OBJECTIVES

By the end of this section, you will be able to:

- Understand Newton's third law of motion.
- Apply Newton's third law to define systems and solve problems of motion.

Baseball relief pitcher Mariano Rivera was so highly regarded that during his retirement year, opposing teams conducted farewell presentations when he played at their stadiums. The Minnesota Twins offered a unique gift: A chair made of broken bats. Any pitch can break a bat, but with Rivera's signature pitch—known as a cutter—the ball and the bat frequently came together at a point that shattered the hardwood. Typically, we think of a baseball or softball hitter exerting a force on the incoming ball, and baseball analysts focus on the resulting "exit velocity" as a key statistic. But the force of the ball can do its own damage. This is exactly what happens whenever one body exerts a force on another—the first also experiences a force (equal in magnitude and opposite in direction). Numerous common experiences, such as stubbing a toe or pushing off the floor during a jump, confirm this. It is precisely stated in **Newton's third law of motion**.

NEWTON'S THIRD LAW OF MOTION

Whenever one body exerts a force on a second body, the first body experiences a force that is equal in magnitude and opposite in direction to the force that it exerts.

This law represents a certain *symmetry in nature*: Forces always occur in pairs, and one body cannot exert a force on another without experiencing a force itself. We sometimes refer to this law loosely as "action-reaction," where the force exerted is the action and the force experienced as a consequence is the reaction. Newton's third law has practical uses in analyzing the origin of forces and understanding which forces are external to a system.

We can readily see Newton's third law at work by taking a look at how people move about. Consider a swimmer pushing off from the side of a pool, as illustrated in Figure 4.9. She pushes against the pool wall with her feet and accelerates in the direction *opposite* to that of her push. The wall has exerted an equal and opposite force back on the swimmer. You might think that two equal and opposite forces would cancel, but they do not *because they act on different systems*. In this case, there are two systems that we could investigate: the swimmer or the wall. If we select the swimmer to be the system of interest, as in the figure, then $\mathbf{F}_{\text{wall on feet}}$ is an external force on this system and affects its motion. The swimmer moves in the direction of $\mathbf{F}_{\text{wall on feet}}$. In contrast, the force $\mathbf{F}_{\text{feet on wall}}$ acts on the wall and not on our system of interest. Thus $\mathbf{F}_{\text{feet on wall}}$ does not directly affect the motion of the system and does not cancel $\mathbf{F}_{\text{wall on feet}}$. Note that the swimmer pushes in the direction opposite to that in which she wishes to move. The reaction to her push is thus in the desired direction.

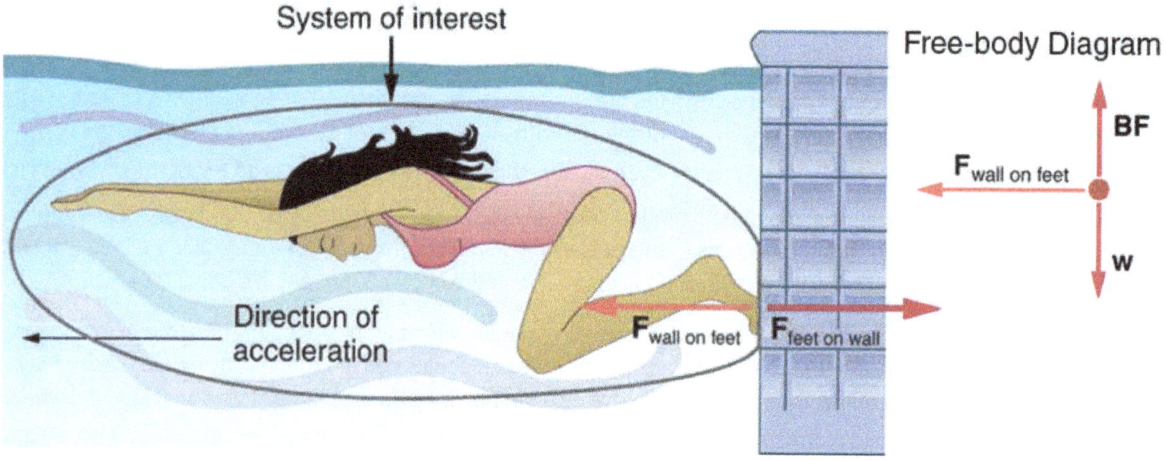

FIGURE 4.9 When the swimmer exerts a force $\mathbf{F}_{\text{feet on wall}}$ on the wall, she accelerates in the direction opposite to that of her push. This means the net external force on her is in the direction opposite to $\mathbf{F}_{\text{feet on wall}}$. This opposition occurs because, in accordance with Newton's third law of motion, the wall exerts a force $\mathbf{F}_{\text{wall on feet}}$ on her, equal in magnitude but in the direction opposite to the one she exerts on it. The line around the swimmer indicates the system of interest. Note that $\mathbf{F}_{\text{feet on wall}}$ does not act on this system (the swimmer) and, thus, does not cancel $\mathbf{F}_{\text{wall on feet}}$. Thus the free-body diagram shows only $\mathbf{F}_{\text{wall on feet}}$, $\mathbf{w}$, the gravitational force, and $\mathbf{BF}$, the buoyant force of the water supporting the swimmer's weight. The vertical forces $\mathbf{w}$ and $\mathbf{BF}$ cancel since there is no vertical motion.

Other examples of Newton's third law are easy to find. As a professor walks in front of a whiteboard, she exerts a force backward on the floor. The floor exerts a reaction force forward on the professor that causes her to accelerate forward. Similarly, a car accelerates because the ground pushes forward on the drive wheels in reaction to the drive wheels pushing backward on the ground. You can see evidence of the wheels pushing backward when tires spin on a gravel road and throw rocks backward. In another example, rockets move forward by expelling gas backward at high velocity. This means the rocket exerts a large backward force on the gas in the rocket combustion chamber, and the gas therefore exerts a large reaction force forward on the rocket. This reaction force is called **thrust**. It is a common misconception that rockets propel themselves by pushing on the ground or on the air behind them. They actually work better in a vacuum, where they can more readily expel the exhaust gases. Helicopters similarly create lift by pushing air down, thereby experiencing an upward reaction force. Birds and airplanes also fly by exerting force on air in a direction opposite to that of whatever force they need. For example, the wings of a bird force air downward and backward in order to get lift and move forward. An octopus propels itself in the water by ejecting water through a funnel from its body, similar to a jet ski. Boxers and other martial arts fighters experience reaction forces when they punch, sometimes breaking their hand by hitting an opponent's body.

EXAMPLE 4.3

Getting Up To Speed: Choosing the Correct System

A physics professor pushes a cart of demonstration equipment to a lecture hall, as seen in Figure 4.10. Her mass is 65.0 kg, the cart's is 12.0 kg, and the equipment's is 7.0 kg. Calculate the acceleration produced when the professor exerts a backward force of 150 N on the floor. All forces opposing the motion, such as friction on the cart's wheels and air resistance, total 24.0 N.

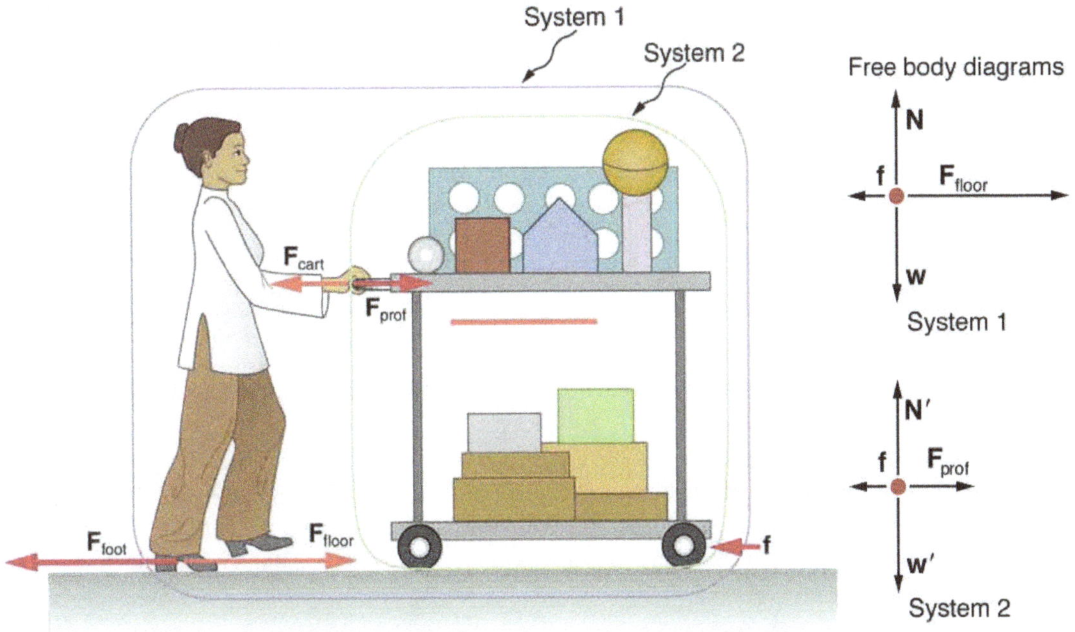

FIGURE 4.10 A professor pushes a cart of demonstration equipment. The lengths of the arrows are proportional to the magnitudes of the forces (except for $\mathbf{f}$, since it is too small to draw to scale). Different questions are asked in each example; thus, the system of interest must be defined differently for each. System 1 is appropriate for this example, since it asks for the acceleration of the entire group of objects. Only $\mathbf{F}_{\text{floor}}$ and $\mathbf{f}$ are external forces acting on System 1 along the line of motion. All other forces either cancel or act on the outside world. System 2 is chosen for Example 4.4 so that $\mathbf{F}_{\text{prof}}$ will be an external force and enter into Newton's second law. Note that the free-body diagrams, which allow us to apply Newton's second law, vary with the system chosen.

Strategy

Since they accelerate as a unit, we define the system to be the professor, cart, and equipment. This is System 1 in Figure 4.10. The professor pushes backward with a force $\mathbf{F}_{\text{foot}}$ of 150 N. According to Newton's third law, the floor exerts a forward reaction force $\mathbf{F}_{\text{floor}}$ of 150 N on System 1. Because all motion is horizontal, we can assume there is no net force in the vertical direction. The problem is therefore one-dimensional along the horizontal direction. As noted, $\mathbf{f}$ opposes the motion and is thus in the opposite direction of $\mathbf{F}_{\text{floor}}$. Note that we do not include the forces $\mathbf{F}_{\text{prof}}$ or $\mathbf{F}_{\text{cart}}$ because these are internal forces, and we do not include $\mathbf{F}_{\text{foot}}$ because it acts on the floor, not on the system. There are no other significant forces acting on System 1. If the net external force can be found from all this information, we can use Newton's second law to find the acceleration as requested. See the free-body diagram in the figure.

Solution

Newton's second law is given by

$$a = \frac{F_{\text{net}}}{m}. \tag{4.18}$$

The net external force on System 1 is deduced from Figure 4.10 and the discussion above to be

$$F_{\text{net}} = F_{\text{floor}} - f = 150\ \text{N} - 24.0\ \text{N} = 126\ \text{N}. \tag{4.19}$$

The mass of System 1 is

$$m = (65.0 + 12.0 + 7.0)\text{ kg} = 84\text{ kg}. \qquad 4.20$$

These values of F_{net} and m produce an acceleration of

$$a = \frac{F_{\text{net}}}{m}, \quad a = \frac{126\text{ N}}{84\text{ kg}} = 1.5\text{ m/s}^2. \qquad 4.21$$

Discussion

None of the forces between components of System 1, such as between the professor's hands and the cart, contribute to the net external force because they are internal to System 1. Another way to look at this is to note that forces between components of a system cancel because they are equal in magnitude and opposite in direction. For example, the force exerted by the professor on the cart results in an equal and opposite force back on her. In this case both forces act on the same system and, therefore, cancel. Thus internal forces (between components of a system) cancel. Choosing System 1 was crucial to solving this problem.

EXAMPLE 4.4

Force on the Cart—Choosing a New System

Calculate the force the professor exerts on the cart in Figure 4.10 using data from the previous example if needed.

Strategy

If we now define the system of interest to be the cart plus equipment (System 2 in Figure 4.10), then the net external force on System 2 is the force the professor exerts on the cart minus friction. The force she exerts on the cart, $\mathbf{F}_{\text{prof}}$, is an external force acting on System 2. $\mathbf{F}_{\text{prof}}$ was internal to System 1, but it is external to System 2 and will enter Newton's second law for System 2.

Solution

Newton's second law can be used to find $\mathbf{F}_{\text{prof}}$. Starting with

$$a = \frac{F_{\text{net}}}{m} \qquad 4.22$$

and noting that the magnitude of the net external force on System 2 is

$$F_{\text{net}} = F_{\text{prof}} - f, \qquad 4.23$$

we solve for F_{prof}, the desired quantity:

$$F_{\text{prof}} = F_{\text{net}} + f. \qquad 4.24$$

The value of f is given, so we must calculate net F_{net}. That can be done since both the acceleration and mass of System 2 are known. Using Newton's second law we see that

$$F_{\text{net}} = ma, \qquad 4.25$$

where the mass of System 2 is 19.0 kg (m= 12.0 kg + 7.0 kg) and its acceleration was found to be $a = 1.5\text{ m/s}^2$ in the previous example. Thus,

$$F_{\text{net}} = ma, \qquad 4.26$$

$$F_{\text{net}} = (19.0\text{ kg})(1.5\text{ m/s}^2) = 29\text{ N}. \qquad 4.27$$

Now we can find the desired force:

$$F_{\text{prof}} = F_{\text{net}} + f, \qquad 4.28$$

$$F_{\text{prof}} = 29\text{ N} + 24.0\text{ N} = 53\text{ N}. \qquad 4.29$$

Discussion

It is interesting that this force is significantly less than the 150-N force the professor exerted backward on the floor. Not all of that 150-N force is transmitted to the cart; some of it accelerates the professor.

The choice of a system is an important analytical step both in solving problems and in thoroughly understanding the physics of the situation (which is not necessarily the same thing).

PHET EXPLORATIONS

Gravity Force Lab

Visualize the gravitational force that two objects exert on each other. Change properties of the objects in order to see how it changes the gravity force.

Click to view content (https://openstax.org/books/college-physics-ap-courses-2e/pages/4-4-newtons-third-law-of-motion-symmetry-in-forces)

4.5 Normal, Tension, and Other Examples of Forces

LEARNING OBJECTIVES

By the end of this section, you will be able to:

- Define normal and tension forces.
- Apply Newton's laws of motion to solve problems involving a variety of forces.
- Use trigonometric identities to resolve weight into components.

Forces are given many names, such as push, pull, thrust, lift, weight, friction, and tension. Traditionally, forces have been grouped into several categories and given names relating to their source, how they are transmitted, or their effects. The most important of these categories are discussed in this section, together with some interesting applications. Further examples of forces are discussed later in this text.

Normal Force

Weight (also called force of gravity) is a pervasive force that acts at all times and must be counteracted to keep an object from falling. You definitely notice that you must support the weight of a heavy object by pushing up on it when you hold it stationary, as illustrated in Figure 4.11(a). But how do inanimate objects like a table support the weight of a mass placed on them, such as shown in Figure 4.11(b)? When the bag of dog food is placed on the table, the table actually sags slightly under the load. This would be noticeable if the load were placed on a card table, but even rigid objects deform when a force is applied to them. Unless the object is deformed beyond its limit, it will exert a restoring force much like a deformed spring (or trampoline or diving board). The greater the deformation, the greater the restoring force. So when the load is placed on the table, the table sags until the restoring force becomes as large as the weight of the load. At this point the net external force on the load is zero. That is the situation when the load is stationary on the table. The table sags quickly, and the sag is slight so we do not notice it. But it is similar to the sagging of a trampoline when you climb onto it.

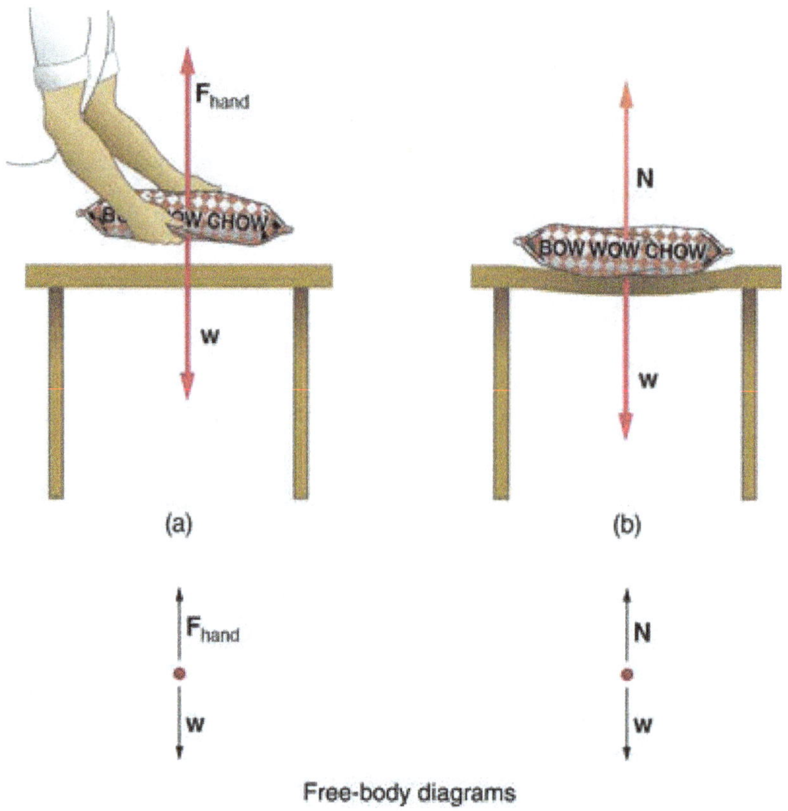

FIGURE 4.11 (a) The person holding the bag of dog food must supply an upward force $\mathbf{F}_{\text{hand}}$ equal in magnitude and opposite in direction to the weight of the food $\mathbf{w}$. (b) The card table sags when the dog food is placed on it, much like a stiff trampoline. Elastic restoring forces in the table grow as it sags until they supply a force $\mathbf{N}$ equal in magnitude and opposite in direction to the weight of the load.

We must conclude that whatever supports a load, be it animate or not, must supply an upward force equal to the weight of the load, as we assumed in a few of the previous examples. If the force supporting a load is perpendicular to the surface of contact between the load and its support, this force is defined to be a **normal force** and here is given the symbol $\mathbf{N}$. (This is not the unit for force N.) The word *normal* means perpendicular to a surface. The normal force can be less than the object's weight if the object is on an incline, as you will see in the next example.

COMMON MISCONCEPTION: NORMAL FORCE (N) VS. NEWTON (N)

In this section we have introduced the quantity normal force, which is represented by the variable $\mathbf{N}$. This should not be confused with the symbol for the newton, which is also represented by the letter N. These symbols are particularly important to distinguish because the units of a normal force ($\mathbf{N}$) happen to be newtons (N). For example, the normal force $\mathbf{N}$ that the floor exerts on a chair might be $\mathbf{N} = 100\text{ N}$. One important difference is that normal force is a vector, while the newton is simply a unit. Be careful not to confuse these letters in your calculations! You will encounter more similarities among variables and units as you proceed in physics. Another example of this is the quantity work (W) and the unit watts (W).

EXAMPLE 4.5

Weight on an Incline, a Two-Dimensional Problem

Consider the skier on a slope shown in Figure 4.12. Her mass including equipment is 60.0 kg. (a) What is her acceleration if friction is negligible? (b) What is her acceleration if friction is known to be 45.0 N?

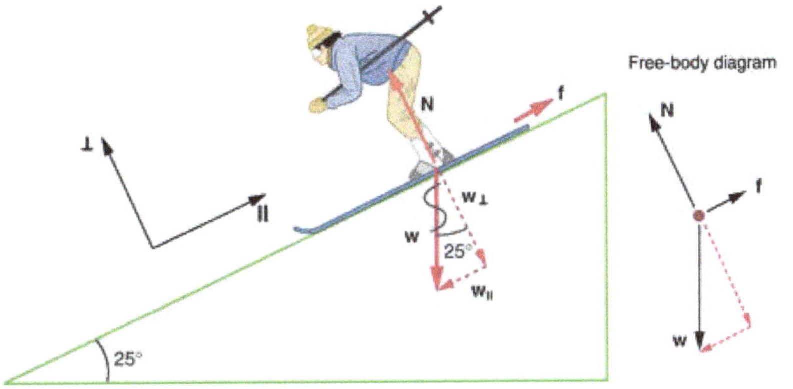

FIGURE 4.12 Since motion and friction are parallel to the slope, it is most convenient to project all forces onto a coordinate system where one axis is parallel to the slope and the other is perpendicular (axes shown to left of skier). **N** is perpendicular to the slope and **f** is parallel to the slope, but **w** has components along both axes, namely $\mathbf{w}_{\perp}$ and $\mathbf{w}_{\parallel}$. **N** is equal in magnitude to $\mathbf{w}_{\perp}$, so that there is no motion perpendicular to the slope, but f is less than $w_{\parallel}$, so that there is a downslope acceleration (along the parallel axis).

Strategy

This is a two-dimensional problem, since the forces on the skier (the system of interest) are not parallel. The approach we have used in two-dimensional kinematics also works very well here. Choose a convenient coordinate system and project the vectors onto its axes, creating *two* connected *one*-dimensional problems to solve. The most convenient coordinate system for motion on an incline is one that has one coordinate parallel to the slope and one perpendicular to the slope. (Remember that motions along mutually perpendicular axes are independent.) We use the symbols ⊥ and || to represent perpendicular and parallel, respectively. This choice of axes simplifies this type of problem, because there is no motion perpendicular to the slope and because friction is always parallel to the surface between two objects. The only external forces acting on the system are the skier's weight, friction, and the support of the slope, respectively labeled **w**, **f**, and **N** in Figure 4.12. **N** is always perpendicular to the slope, and **f** is parallel to it. But **w** is not in the direction of either axis, and so the first step we take is to project it into components along the chosen axes, defining $w_{\parallel}$ to be the component of weight parallel to the slope and $w_{\perp}$ the component of weight perpendicular to the slope. Once this is done, we can consider the two separate problems of forces parallel to the slope and forces perpendicular to the slope.

Solution

The magnitude of the component of the weight parallel to the slope is $w_{\parallel} = w \sin(25°) = mg \sin(25°)$, and the magnitude of the component of the weight perpendicular to the slope is $w_{\perp} = w \cos(25°) = mg \cos(25°)$.

(a) Neglecting friction. Since the acceleration is parallel to the slope, we need only consider forces parallel to the slope. (Forces perpendicular to the slope add to zero, since there is no acceleration in that direction.) The forces parallel to the slope are the amount of the skier's weight parallel to the slope $w_{\parallel}$ and friction f. Using Newton's second law, with subscripts to denote quantities parallel to the slope,

$$a_{\parallel} = \frac{F_{\text{net}\parallel}}{m} \tag{4.30}$$

where $F_{\text{net}\parallel} = w_{\parallel} = mg \sin(25°)$, assuming no friction for this part, so that

$$a_{\parallel} = \frac{F_{\text{net}\parallel}}{m} = \frac{mg \sin(25°)}{m} = g \sin(25°) \tag{4.31}$$

$$(9.80\ \text{m/s}^2)(0.4226) = 4.14\ \text{m/s}^2 \tag{4.32}$$

is the acceleration.

(b) Including friction. We now have a given value for friction, and we know its direction is parallel to the slope and it opposes motion between surfaces in contact. So the net external force is now

$$F_{\text{net}\parallel} = w_{\parallel} - f, \tag{4.33}$$

and substituting this into Newton's second law, $a_{||} = \frac{F_{\text{net}||}}{m}$, gives

$$a_{||} = \frac{F_{\text{net}||}}{m} = \frac{w_{||} - f}{m} = \frac{mg \sin(25^\circ) - f}{m}. \quad 4.34$$

We substitute known values to obtain

$$a_{||} = \frac{(60.0 \text{ kg})(9.80 \text{ m/s}^2)(0.4226) - 45.0 \text{ N}}{60.0 \text{ kg}}, \quad 4.35$$

which yields

$$a_{||} = 3.39 \text{ m/s}^2, \quad 4.36$$

which is the acceleration parallel to the incline when there is 45.0 N of opposing friction.

Discussion

Since friction always opposes motion between surfaces, the acceleration is smaller when there is friction than when there is none. In fact, it is a general result that if friction on an incline is negligible, then the acceleration down the incline is $a = g \sin\theta$, *regardless of mass*. This is related to the previously discussed fact that all objects fall with the same acceleration in the absence of air resistance. Similarly, all objects, regardless of mass, slide down a frictionless incline with the same acceleration (if the angle is the same).

RESOLVING WEIGHT INTO COMPONENTS

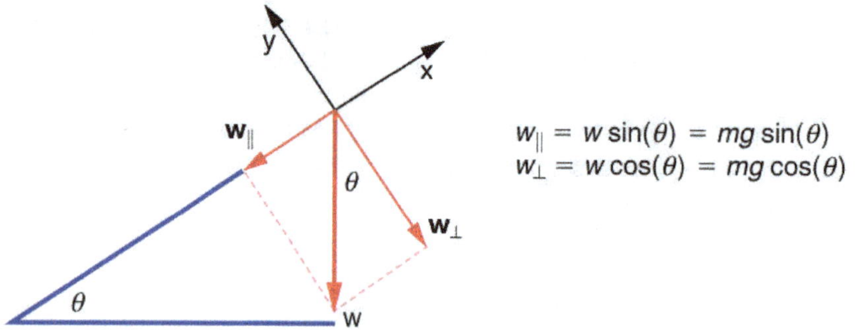

FIGURE 4.13 An object rests on an incline that makes an angle θ with the horizontal.

When an object rests on an incline that makes an angle θ with the horizontal, the force of gravity acting on the object is divided into two components: a force acting perpendicular to the plane, $\mathbf{w}_\perp$, and a force acting parallel to the plane, $\mathbf{w}_{||}$. The perpendicular force of weight, $\mathbf{w}_\perp$, is typically equal in magnitude and opposite in direction to the normal force, $\mathbf{N}$. The force acting parallel to the plane, $\mathbf{w}_{||}$, causes the object to accelerate down the incline. The force of friction, $\mathbf{f}$, opposes the motion of the object, so it acts upward along the plane.

It is important to be careful when resolving the weight of the object into components. If the angle of the incline is at an angle θ to the horizontal, then the magnitudes of the weight components are

$$w_{||} = w \sin(\theta) = mg \sin(\theta) \quad 4.37$$

and

$$w_\perp = w \cos(\theta) = mg \cos(\theta). \quad 4.38$$

Instead of memorizing these equations, it is helpful to be able to determine them from reason. To do this, draw the right triangle formed by the three weight vectors. Notice that the angle θ of the incline is the same as the angle formed between $\mathbf{w}$ and $\mathbf{w}_\perp$. Knowing this property, you can use trigonometry to determine the magnitude of the weight components:

$$\cos(\theta) = \frac{w_{\perp}}{w} \quad (4.39)$$
$$w_{\perp} = w\cos(\theta) = mg\cos(\theta)$$

$$\sin(\theta) = \frac{w_{\parallel}}{w} \quad (4.40)$$
$$w_{\parallel} = w\sin(\theta) = mg\sin(\theta)$$

TAKE-HOME EXPERIMENT: FORCE PARALLEL

To investigate how a force parallel to an inclined plane changes, find a rubber band, some objects to hang from the end of the rubber band, and a board you can position at different angles. How much does the rubber band stretch when you hang the object from the end of the board? Now place the board at an angle so that the object slides off when placed on the board. How much does the rubber band extend if it is lined up parallel to the board and used to hold the object stationary on the board? Try two more angles. What does this show?

Tension

A **tension** is a force along the length of a medium, especially a force carried by a flexible medium, such as a rope or cable. The word "tension" comes from a Latin word meaning "to stretch." Not coincidentally, the flexible cords that carry muscle forces to other parts of the body are called *tendons*. Any flexible connector, such as a string, rope, chain, wire, or cable, can exert pulls only parallel to its length; thus, a force carried by a flexible connector is a tension with direction parallel to the connector. It is important to understand that tension is a pull in a connector. In contrast, consider the phrase: "You can't push a rope." The tension force pulls outward along the two ends of a rope.

Consider a person holding a mass on a rope as shown in Figure 4.14.

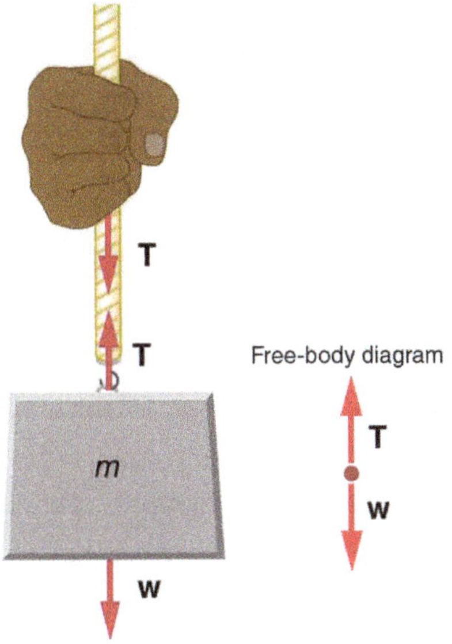

FIGURE 4.14 When a perfectly flexible connector (one requiring no force to bend it) such as this rope transmits a force $\mathbf{T}$, that force must be parallel to the length of the rope, as shown. The pull such a flexible connector exerts is a tension. Note that the rope pulls with equal force but in opposite directions on the hand and the supported mass (neglecting the weight of the rope). This is an example of Newton's third law. The rope is the medium that carries the equal and opposite forces between the two objects. The tension anywhere in the rope between the hand and the mass is equal. Once you have determined the tension in one location, you have determined the tension at all locations along the rope.

Tension in the rope must equal the weight of the supported mass, as we can prove using Newton's second law. If the 5.00-kg mass in the figure is stationary, then its acceleration is zero, and thus $\mathbf{F}_{\text{net}} = 0$. The only external forces acting on the mass are its weight $\mathbf{w}$ and the tension $\mathbf{T}$ supplied by the rope. Thus,

$$F_{\text{net}} = T - w = 0, \quad (4.41)$$

where T and w are the magnitudes of the tension and weight and their signs indicate direction, with up being positive here. Thus, just as you would expect, the tension equals the weight of the supported mass:

$$T = w = mg. \tag{4.42}$$

For a 5.00-kg mass, then (neglecting the mass of the rope) we see that

$$T = mg = (5.00\ \text{kg})(9.80\ \text{m/s}^2) = 49.0\ \text{N}. \tag{4.43}$$

If we cut the rope and insert a spring, the spring would extend a length corresponding to a force of 49.0 N, providing a direct observation and measure of the tension force in the rope.

Flexible connectors are often used to transmit forces around corners, such as in a hospital traction system, a finger joint, or a bicycle brake cable. If there is no friction, the tension is transmitted undiminished. Only its direction changes, and it is always parallel to the flexible connector. This is illustrated in Figure 4.15 (a) and (b).

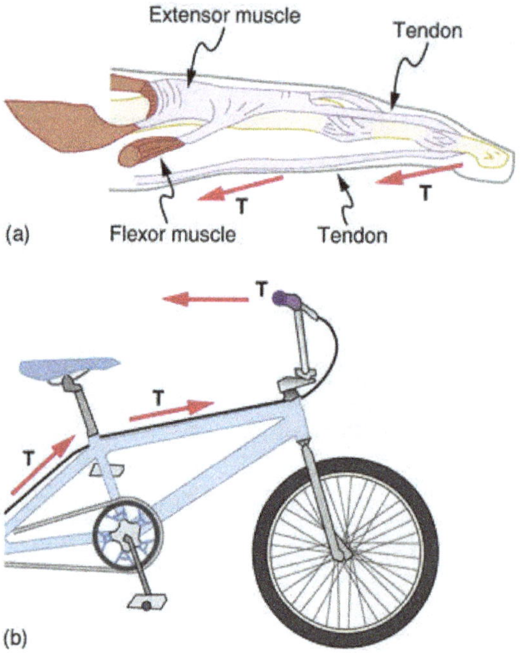

FIGURE 4.15 (a) Tendons in the finger carry force **T** from the muscles to other parts of the finger, usually changing the force's direction, but not its magnitude (the tendons are relatively friction free). (b) The brake cable on a bicycle carries the tension **T** from the handlebars to the brake mechanism. Again, the direction but not the magnitude of **T** is changed.

EXAMPLE 4.6

What Is the Tension in a Tightrope?

Calculate the tension in the wire supporting the 70.0-kg tightrope walker shown in Figure 4.16.

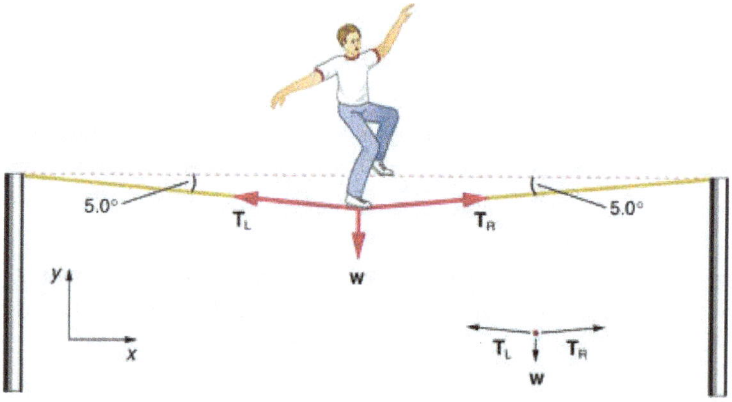

FIGURE 4.16 The weight of a tightrope walker causes a wire to sag by 5.0 degrees. The system of interest here is the point in the wire at which the tightrope walker is standing.

Strategy

As you can see in the figure, the wire is not perfectly horizontal (it cannot be!), but is bent under the person's weight. Thus, the tension on either side of the person has an upward component that can support his weight. As usual, forces are vectors represented pictorially by arrows having the same directions as the forces and lengths proportional to their magnitudes. The system is the tightrope walker, and the only external forces acting on him are his weight $\mathbf{w}$ and the two tensions $\mathbf{T_L}$ (left tension) and $\mathbf{T_R}$ (right tension), as illustrated. It is reasonable to neglect the weight of the wire itself. The net external force is zero since the system is stationary. A little trigonometry can now be used to find the tensions. One conclusion is possible at the outset—we can see from part (b) of the figure that the magnitudes of the tensions T_L and T_R must be equal. This is because there is no horizontal acceleration in the rope, and the only forces acting to the left and right are T_L and T_R. Thus, the magnitude of those forces must be equal so that they cancel each other out.

Whenever we have two-dimensional vector problems in which no two vectors are parallel, the easiest method of solution is to pick a convenient coordinate system and project the vectors onto its axes. In this case the best coordinate system has one axis horizontal and the other vertical. We call the horizontal the x-axis and the vertical the y-axis.

Solution

First, we need to resolve the tension vectors into their horizontal and vertical components. It helps to draw a new free-body diagram showing all of the horizontal and vertical components of each force acting on the system.

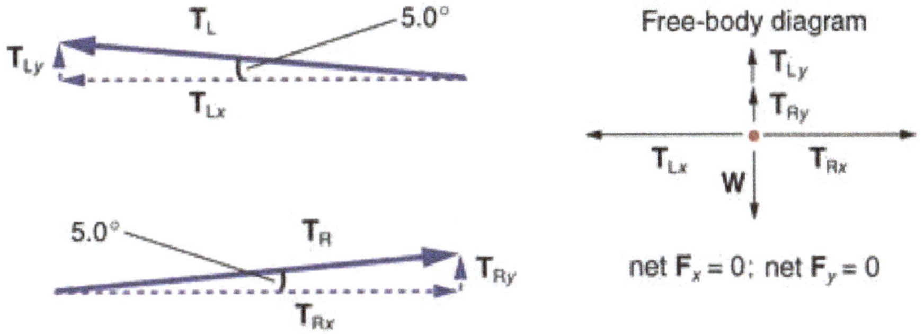

FIGURE 4.17 When the vectors are projected onto vertical and horizontal axes, their components along those axes must add to zero, since the tightrope walker is stationary. The small angle results in T being much greater than w.

Consider the horizontal components of the forces (denoted with a subscript x):

$$F_{\text{net}x} = T_{\text{L}x} - T_{\text{R}x}. \tag{4.44}$$

The net external horizontal force $F_{\text{net}x} = 0$, since the person is stationary. Thus,

$$\begin{aligned} F_{\text{net}x} = 0 &= T_{\text{L}x} - T_{\text{R}x} \\ T_{\text{L}x} &= T_{\text{R}x}. \end{aligned} \tag{4.45}$$

Now, observe Figure 4.17. You can use trigonometry to determine the magnitude of T_L and T_R. Notice that:

$$\begin{aligned} \cos(5.0°) &= \frac{T_{\text{L}x}}{T_\text{L}} \\ T_{\text{L}x} &= T_\text{L}\cos(5.0°) \\ \cos(5.0°) &= \frac{T_{\text{R}x}}{T_\text{R}} \\ T_{\text{R}x} &= T_\text{R}\cos(5.0°). \end{aligned} \tag{4.46}$$

Equating $T_{\text{L}x}$ and $T_{\text{R}x}$:

$$T_\text{L}\cos(5.0°) = T_\text{R}\cos(5.0°). \tag{4.47}$$

Thus,

$$T_\text{L} = T_\text{R} = T, \tag{4.48}$$

as predicted. Now, considering the vertical components (denoted by a subscript y), we can solve for T. Again, since the person is stationary, Newton's second law implies that net $F_y = 0$. Thus, as illustrated in the free-body diagram in Figure 4.17,

$$F_{\text{net}y} = T_{\text{L}y} + T_{\text{R}y} - w = 0. \tag{4.49}$$

Observing Figure 4.17, we can use trigonometry to determine the relationship between $T_{\text{L}y}$, $T_{\text{R}y}$, and T. As we determined from the analysis in the horizontal direction, $T_\text{L} = T_\text{R} = T$:

$$\begin{aligned} \sin(5.0^\circ) &= \frac{T_{\text{L}y}}{T_\text{L}} \\ T_{\text{L}y} = T_\text{L}\sin(5.0^\circ) &= T\sin(5.0^\circ) \\ \sin(5.0^\circ) &= \frac{T_{\text{R}y}}{T_\text{R}} \\ T_{\text{R}y} = T_\text{R}\sin(5.0^\circ) &= T\sin(5.0^\circ). \end{aligned} \tag{4.50}$$

Now, we can substitute the values for $T_{\text{L}y}$ and $T_{\text{R}y}$, into the net force equation in the vertical direction:

$$\begin{aligned} F_{\text{net}y} &= T_{\text{L}y} + T_{\text{R}y} - w = 0 \\ F_{\text{net}y} &= T\sin(5.0^\circ) + T\sin(5.0^\circ) - w = 0 \\ 2\,T\sin(5.0^\circ) - w &= 0 \\ 2\,T\sin(5.0^\circ) &= w \end{aligned} \tag{4.51}$$

and

$$T = \frac{w}{2\sin(5.0^\circ)} = \frac{mg}{2\sin(5.0^\circ)}, \tag{4.52}$$

so that

$$T = \frac{(70.0\text{ kg})(9.80\text{ m/s}^2)}{2(0.0872)}, \tag{4.53}$$

and the tension is

$$T = 3900\text{ N}. \tag{4.54}$$

Discussion

Note that the vertical tension in the wire acts as a normal force that supports the weight of the tightrope walker. The tension is almost six times the 686-N weight of the tightrope walker. Since the wire is nearly horizontal, the vertical component of its tension is only a small fraction of the tension in the wire. The large horizontal components are in opposite directions and cancel, and so most of the tension in the wire is not used to support the weight of the tightrope walker.

If we wish to *create* a very large tension, all we have to do is exert a force perpendicular to a flexible connector, as illustrated in Figure 4.18. As we saw in the last example, the weight of the tightrope walker acted as a force perpendicular to the rope. We saw that the tension in the roped related to the weight of the tightrope walker in the following way:

$$T = \frac{w}{2\sin(\theta)}. \tag{4.55}$$

We can extend this expression to describe the tension T created when a perpendicular force $(\mathbf{F}_\perp)$ is exerted at the middle of a flexible connector:

$$T = \frac{F_\perp}{2\sin(\theta)}. \tag{4.56}$$

Note that θ is the angle between the horizontal and the bent connector. In this case, T becomes very large as θ approaches zero. Even the relatively small weight of any flexible connector will cause it to sag, since an infinite tension would result if it were horizontal (i.e., $\theta = 0$ and $\sin\theta = 0$). (See Figure 4.18.)

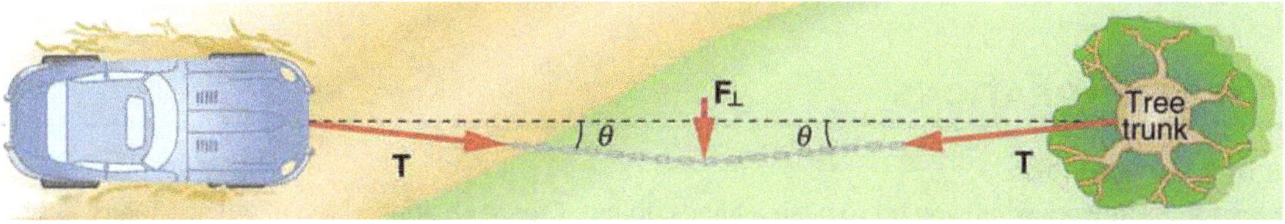

FIGURE 4.18 We can create a very large tension in the chain by pushing on it perpendicular to its length, as shown. Suppose we wish to pull a car out of the mud when no tow truck is available. Each time the car moves forward, the chain is tightened to keep it as nearly straight as possible. The tension in the chain is given by $T = \frac{F_\perp}{2\sin(\theta)}$; since θ is small, T is very large. This situation is analogous to the tightrope walker shown in Figure 4.16, except that the tensions shown here are those transmitted to the car and the tree rather than those acting at the point where $\mathbf{F}_\perp$ is applied.

FIGURE 4.19 Unless an infinite tension is exerted, any flexible connector—such as the chain at the bottom of the picture—will sag under its own weight, giving a characteristic curve when the weight is evenly distributed along the length. Suspension bridges—such as the Golden Gate Bridge shown in this image—are essentially very heavy flexible connectors. The weight of the bridge is evenly distributed along the length of flexible connectors, usually cables, which take on the characteristic shape. (credit: Leaflet, Wikimedia Commons)

Extended Topic: Real Forces and Inertial Frames

There is another distinction among forces in addition to the types already mentioned. Some forces are real, whereas others are not. *Real forces* are those that have some physical origin, such as the gravitational pull. Contrastingly, *fictitious forces* are those that arise simply because an observer is in an accelerating frame of reference, such as one that rotates (like a merry-go-round) or undergoes linear acceleration (like a car slowing down). For example, if a satellite is heading due north above Earth's northern hemisphere, then to an observer on Earth it will appear to experience a force to the west that has no physical origin. Of course, what is happening here is that Earth is rotating toward the east and moves east under the satellite. In Earth's frame this looks like a westward force on the satellite, or it can be interpreted as a violation of Newton's first law (the law of inertia). An **inertial frame of reference** is one in which all forces are real and, equivalently, one in which Newton's laws have the simple forms given in this chapter.

Earth's rotation is slow enough that Earth is nearly an inertial frame. You ordinarily must perform precise experiments to observe fictitious forces and the slight departures from Newton's laws, such as the effect just described. On the large scale, such as for the rotation of weather systems and ocean currents, the effects can be easily observed.

The crucial factor in determining whether a frame of reference is inertial is whether it accelerates or rotates relative to a known inertial frame. Unless stated otherwise, all phenomena discussed in this text are considered in inertial frames.

All the forces discussed in this section are real forces, but there are a number of other real forces, such as lift and thrust, that are not discussed in this section. They are more specialized, and it is not necessary to discuss every type of force. It is natural, however, to ask where the basic simplicity we seek to find in physics is in the long list of forces. Are some more basic than others? Are some different manifestations of the same underlying force? The answer to both questions is yes, as will be seen in the next (extended) section and in the treatment of modern physics later in the text.

PHET EXPLORATIONS

Forces in 1 Dimension

Explore the forces at work when you try to push a filing cabinet. Create an applied force and see the resulting friction force and total force acting on the cabinet. Charts show the forces, position, velocity, and acceleration vs. time. View a free-body diagram of all the forces (including gravitational and normal forces).

Click to view content (https://openstax.org/l/21forcesatwork).

4.6 Problem-Solving Strategies

LEARNING OBJECTIVES

By the end of this section, you will be able to:

- Understand and apply a problem-solving procedure to solve problems using Newton's laws of motion.

Success in problem solving is obviously necessary to understand and apply physical principles, not to mention the more immediate need of passing exams. The basics of problem solving, presented earlier in this text, are followed here, but specific strategies useful in applying Newton's laws of motion are emphasized. These techniques also reinforce concepts that are useful in many other areas of physics. Many problem-solving strategies are stated outright in the worked examples, and so the following techniques should reinforce skills you have already begun to develop.

Problem-Solving Strategy for Newton's Laws of Motion

Step 1. As usual, it is first necessary to identify the physical principles involved. *Once it is determined that Newton's laws of motion are involved (if the problem involves forces), it is particularly important to draw a careful sketch of the situation.* Such a sketch is shown in Figure 4.20(a). Then, as in Figure 4.20(b), use arrows to represent all forces, label them carefully, and make their lengths and directions correspond to the forces they represent (whenever sufficient information exists).

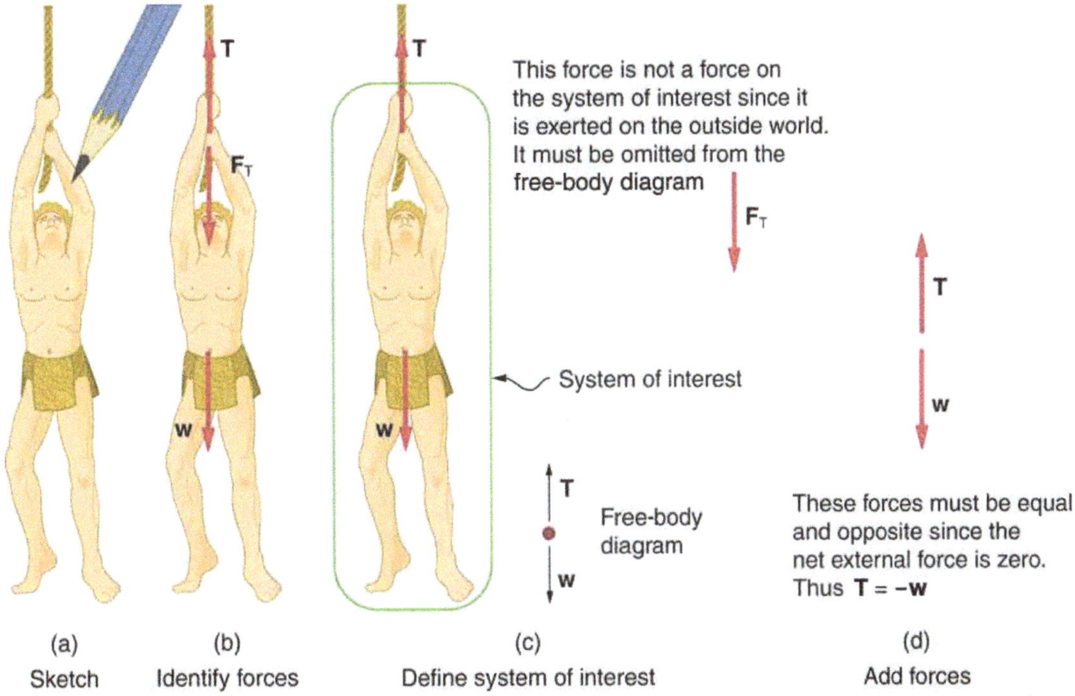

FIGURE 4.20 (a) A sketch of Tarzan hanging from a vine. (b) Arrows are used to represent all forces. $\mathbf{T}$ is the tension in the vine above Tarzan, $\mathbf{F_T}$ is the force he exerts on the vine, and $\mathbf{w}$ is his weight. All other forces, such as the nudge of a breeze, are assumed negligible. (c) Suppose we are given the ape man's mass and asked to find the tension in the vine. We then define the system of interest as shown and draw a free-body diagram. $\mathbf{F_T}$ is no longer shown, because it is not a force acting on the system of interest; rather, $\mathbf{F_T}$ acts on the outside world. (d) Showing only the arrows, the head-to-tail method of addition is used. It is apparent that $\mathbf{T} = -\mathbf{w}$, if Tarzan is stationary.

Step 2. Identify what needs to be determined and what is known or can be inferred from the problem as stated. That is, make a list of knowns and unknowns. *Then carefully determine the system of interest.* This decision is a crucial step, since Newton's second law involves only external forces. Once the system of interest has been identified, it becomes possible to determine which forces are external and which are internal, a necessary step to employ Newton's second law. (See Figure 4.20(c).) Newton's third law may be used to identify whether forces are exerted between components of a system (internal) or between the system and something outside (external). As illustrated earlier in this chapter, the system of interest depends on what question we need to answer. This choice becomes easier with practice, eventually developing into an almost unconscious process. Skill in clearly defining systems will be beneficial in later chapters as well.

A diagram showing the system of interest and all of the external forces is called a **free-body diagram**. Only forces are shown on free-body diagrams, not acceleration or velocity. We have drawn several of these in worked examples. Figure 4.20(c) shows a free-body diagram for the system of interest. Note that no internal forces are shown in a free-body diagram.

Step 3. Once a free-body diagram is drawn, *Newton's second law can be applied to solve the problem.* This is done in Figure 4.20(d) for a particular situation. In general, once external forces are clearly identified in free-body diagrams, it should be a straightforward task to put them into equation form and solve for the unknown, as done in all previous examples. If the problem is one-dimensional—that is, if all forces are parallel—then they add like scalars. If the problem is two-dimensional, then it must be broken down into a pair of one-dimensional problems. This is done by projecting the force vectors onto a set of axes chosen for convenience. As seen in previous examples, the choice of axes can simplify the problem. For example, when an incline is involved, a set of axes with one axis parallel to the incline and one perpendicular to it is most convenient. It is almost always convenient to make one axis parallel to the direction of motion, if this is known.

APPLYING NEWTON'S SECOND LAW

Before you write net force equations, it is critical to determine whether the system is accelerating in a particular direction. If the acceleration is zero in a particular direction, then the net force is zero in that direction. Similarly, if the acceleration is nonzero in a particular direction, then the net force is described by the equation: $F_{\text{net}} = ma$.

For example, if the system is accelerating in the horizontal direction, but it is not accelerating in the vertical direction, then you will have the following conclusions:

$$F_{\text{net }x} = ma, \quad (4.57)$$

$$F_{\text{net }y} = 0. \quad (4.58)$$

You will need this information in order to determine unknown forces acting in a system.

Step 4. As always, *check the solution to see whether it is reasonable.* In some cases, this is obvious. For example, it is reasonable to find that friction causes an object to slide down an incline more slowly than when no friction exists. In practice, intuition develops gradually through problem solving, and with experience it becomes progressively easier to judge whether an answer is reasonable. Another way to check your solution is to check the units. If you are solving for force and end up with units of m/s, then you have made a mistake.

4.7 Further Applications of Newton's Laws of Motion

LEARNING OBJECTIVES

By the end of this section, you will be able to:

- Apply problem-solving techniques to solve for quantities in more complex systems of forces.
- Integrate concepts from kinematics to solve problems using Newton's laws of motion.

There are many interesting applications of Newton's laws of motion, a few more of which are presented in this section. These serve also to illustrate some further subtleties of physics and to help build problem-solving skills.

EXAMPLE 4.7

Drag Force on a Barge

Suppose two tugboats push on a barge at different angles, as shown in Figure 4.21. The first tugboat exerts a force of 2.7×10^5 N in the *x*-direction, and the second tugboat exerts a force of 3.6×10^5 N in the *y*-direction.

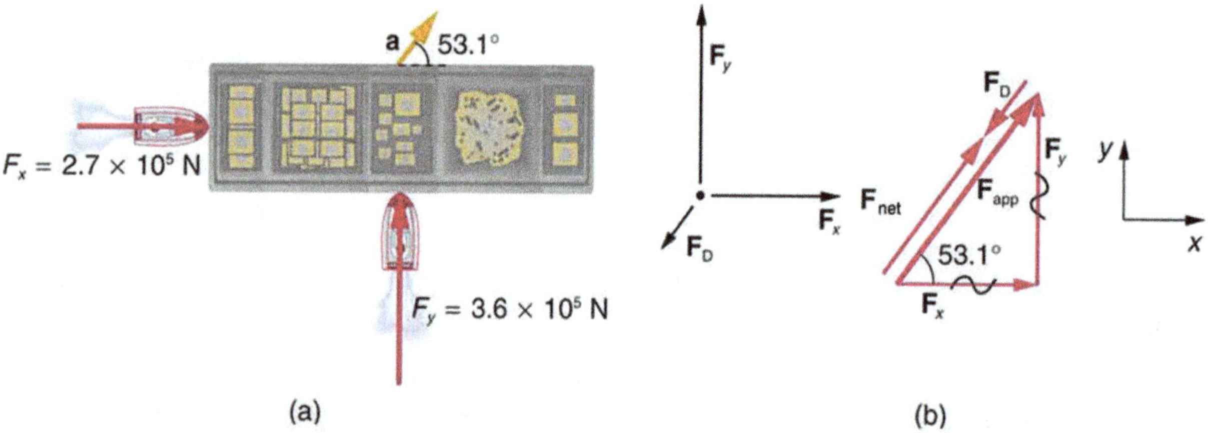

FIGURE 4.21 (a) A view from above of two tugboats pushing on a barge. (b) The free-body diagram for the ship contains only forces acting in the plane of the water. It omits the two vertical forces—the weight of the barge and the buoyant force of the water supporting it cancel and are not shown. Since the applied forces are perpendicular, the *x*- and *y*-axes are in the same direction as $\mathbf{F}_x$ and $\mathbf{F}_y$. The problem quickly becomes a one-dimensional problem along the direction of $\mathbf{F}_{\text{app}}$, since friction is in the direction opposite to $\mathbf{F}_{\text{app}}$.

If the mass of the barge is 5.0×10^6 kg and its acceleration is observed to be 7.5×10^{-2} m/s^2 in the direction shown, what is the drag force of the water on the barge resisting the motion? (Note: drag force is a frictional force exerted by fluids, such as air or water. The drag force opposes the motion of the object.)

Strategy

The directions and magnitudes of acceleration and the applied forces are given in Figure 4.21**(a)**. We will define the total force of the tugboats on the barge as $\mathbf{F}_{\text{app}}$ so that:

$$\mathbf{F}_{\text{app}} = \mathbf{F}_x + \mathbf{F}_y \tag{4.59}$$

Since the barge is flat bottomed, the drag of the water $\mathbf{F}_{\text{D}}$ will be in the direction opposite to $\mathbf{F}_{\text{app}}$, as shown in the free-body diagram in Figure 4.21(b). The system of interest here is the barge, since the forces on *it* are given as well as its acceleration. Our strategy is to find the magnitude and direction of the net applied force $\mathbf{F}_{\text{app}}$, and then apply Newton's second law to solve for the drag force $\mathbf{F}_{\text{D}}$.

Solution

Since $\mathbf{F}_x$ and $\mathbf{F}_y$ are perpendicular, the magnitude and direction of $\mathbf{F}_{\text{app}}$ are easily found. First, the resultant magnitude is given by the Pythagorean theorem:

$$\begin{aligned} F_{\text{app}} &= \sqrt{\mathrm{F}_x^2 + \mathrm{F}_y^2} \\ F_{\text{app}} &= \sqrt{(2.7 \times 10^5\ \text{N})^2 + (3.6 \times 10^5\ \text{N})^2} = 4.5 \times 10^5\ \text{N}. \end{aligned} \tag{4.60}$$

The angle is given by

$$\begin{aligned} \theta &= \tan^{-1}\left(\frac{F_y}{F_x}\right) \\ \theta &= \tan^{-1}\left(\frac{3.6 \times 10^5\ \text{N}}{2.7 \times 10^5\ \text{N}}\right) = 53^\circ, \end{aligned} \tag{4.61}$$

which we know, because of Newton's first law, is the same direction as the acceleration. $\mathbf{F}_{\text{D}}$ is in the opposite direction of $\mathbf{F}_{\text{app}}$, since it acts to slow down the acceleration. Therefore, the net external force is in the same direction as $\mathbf{F}_{\text{app}}$, but its magnitude is slightly less than $\mathbf{F}_{\text{app}}$. The problem is now one-dimensional. From Figure 4.21**(b)**, we can see that

$$F_{\text{net}} = F_{\text{app}} - F_{\text{D}}. \tag{4.62}$$

But Newton's second law states that

$$F_{\text{net}} = ma. \tag{4.63}$$

Thus,

$$F_{\text{app}} - F_{\text{D}} = ma. \tag{4.64}$$

This can be solved for the magnitude of the drag force of the water F_{D} in terms of known quantities:

$$F_{\text{D}} = F_{\text{app}} - ma. \tag{4.65}$$

Substituting known values gives

$$\mathrm{F}_{\text{D}} = (4.5 \times 10^5\ \text{N}) - (5.0 \times 10^6\ \text{kg})(7.5 \times 10^{-2}\ \text{m/s}^2) = 7.5 \times 10^4\ \text{N}. \tag{4.66}$$

The direction of $\mathbf{F}_{\text{D}}$ has already been determined to be in the direction opposite to $\mathbf{F}_{\text{app}}$, or at an angle of 53° south of west.

Discussion

The numbers used in this example are reasonable for a moderately large barge. It is certainly difficult to obtain larger accelerations with tugboats, and small speeds are desirable to avoid running the barge into the docks. Drag is relatively small for a well-designed hull at low speeds, consistent with the answer to this example, where F_{D} is less than 1/600th of the weight of the ship.

In the earlier example of a tightrope walker we noted that the tensions in wires supporting a mass were equal only because the angles on either side were equal. Consider the following example, where the angles are not equal; slightly more trigonometry is involved.

EXAMPLE 4.8

Different Tensions at Different Angles

Consider the traffic light (mass 15.0 kg) suspended from two wires as shown in Figure 4.22. Find the tension in each wire, neglecting the masses of the wires.

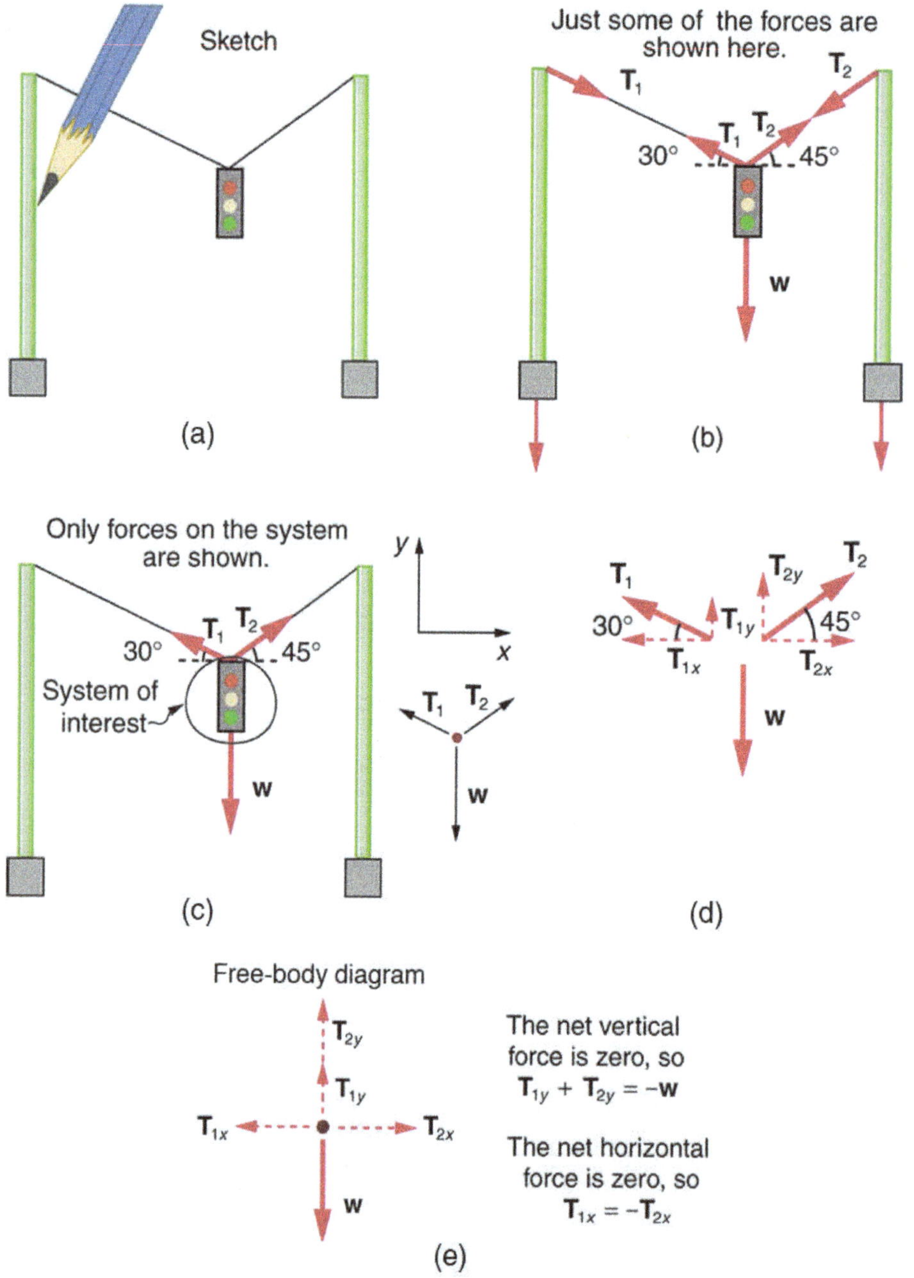

FIGURE 4.22 A traffic light is suspended from two wires. (b) Some of the forces involved. (c) Only forces acting on the system are shown here. The free-body diagram for the traffic light is also shown. (d) The forces projected onto vertical (y) and horizontal (x) axes. The horizontal components of the tensions must cancel, and the sum of the vertical components of the tensions must equal the weight of the traffic light. (e) The free-body diagram shows the vertical and horizontal forces acting on the traffic light.

Strategy

The system of interest is the traffic light, and its free-body diagram is shown in Figure 4.22(c). The three forces involved are not parallel, and so they must be projected onto a coordinate system. The most convenient coordinate system has one axis vertical and one horizontal, and the vector projections on it are shown in part (d) of the figure. There are two unknowns in this problem (T_1 and T_2), so two equations are needed to find them. These two equations come from applying Newton's second law along the vertical and horizontal axes, noting that the net external force is zero along each axis because acceleration is zero.

Solution

First consider the horizontal or *x*-axis:

$$F_{\text{net}x} = T_{2x} - T_{1x} = 0. \tag{4.67}$$

Thus, as you might expect,

$$T_{1x} = T_{2x}. \tag{4.68}$$

This gives us the following relationship between T_1 and T_2:

$$T_1 \cos(30°) = T_2 \cos(45°). \tag{4.69}$$

Thus,

$$T_2 = (1.225)T_1. \tag{4.70}$$

Note that T_1 and T_2 are not equal in this case, because the angles on either side are not equal. It is reasonable that T_2 ends up being greater than T_1, because it is exerted more vertically than T_1.

Now consider the force components along the vertical or *y*-axis:

$$F_{\text{net }y} = T_{1y} + T_{2y} - w = 0. \tag{4.71}$$

This implies

$$T_{1y} + T_{2y} = w. \tag{4.72}$$

Substituting the expressions for the vertical components gives

$$T_1 \sin(30°) + T_2 \sin(45°) = w. \tag{4.73}$$

There are two unknowns in this equation, but substituting the expression for T_2 in terms of T_1 reduces this to one equation with one unknown:

$$T_1(0.500) + (1.225T_1)(0.707) = w = mg, \tag{4.74}$$

which yields

$$(1.366)T_1 = (15.0\text{ kg})(9.80\text{ m/s}^2). \tag{4.75}$$

Solving this last equation gives the magnitude of T_1 to be

$$T_1 = 108\text{ N}. \tag{4.76}$$

Finally, the magnitude of T_2 is determined using the relationship between them, $T_2 = 1.225\,T_1$, found above. Thus we obtain

$$T_2 = 132\text{ N}. \tag{4.77}$$

Discussion

Both tensions would be larger if both wires were more horizontal, and they will be equal if and only if the angles on either side are the same (as they were in the earlier example of a tightrope walker).

The bathroom scale is an excellent example of a normal force acting on a body. It provides a quantitative reading of how much it must push upward to support the weight of an object. But can you predict what you would see on the dial of a bathroom scale if you stood on it during an elevator ride? Will you see a value greater than your weight when the elevator starts up? What about when the elevator moves upward at a constant speed: will the scale still read more than your weight at rest? Consider the following example.

EXAMPLE 4.9

What Does the Bathroom Scale Read in an Elevator?

Figure 4.23 shows a 75.0-kg man (weight of about 165 lb) standing on a bathroom scale in an elevator. Calculate the scale reading: (a) if the elevator accelerates upward at a rate of $1.20\ \text{m/s}^2$, and (b) if the elevator moves upward at a constant speed of 1 m/s.

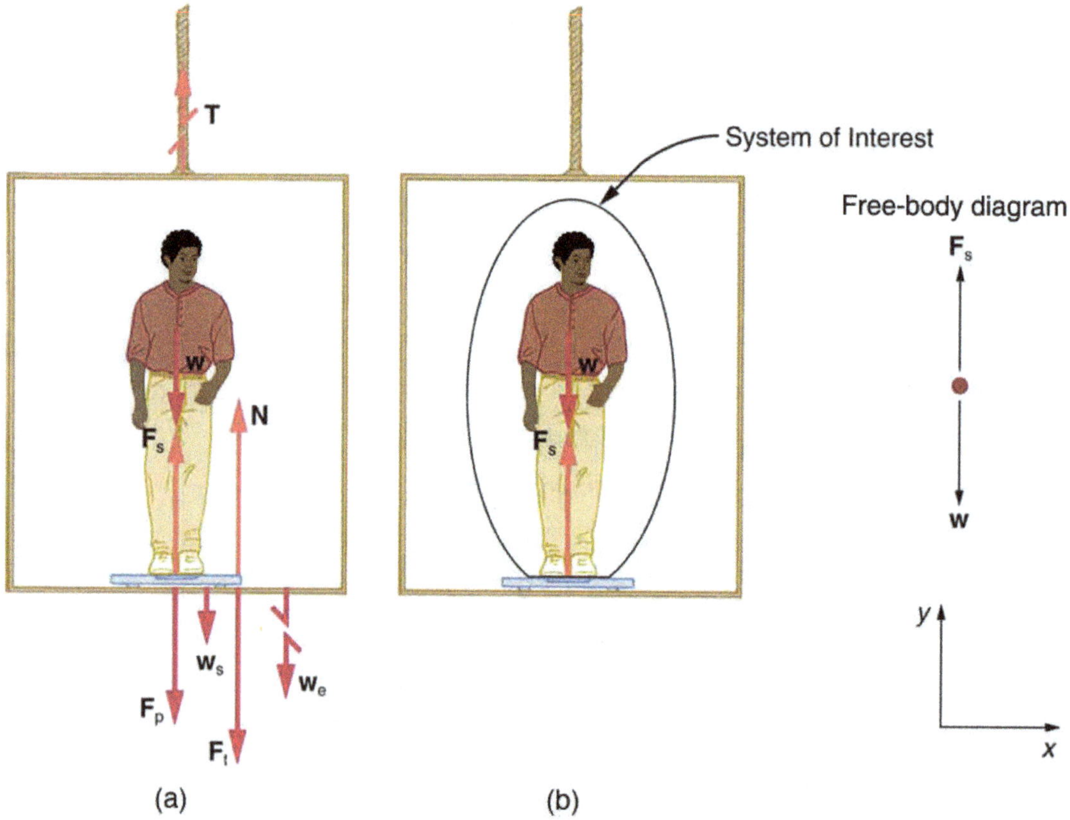

FIGURE 4.23 (a) The various forces acting when a person stands on a bathroom scale in an elevator. The arrows are approximately correct for when the elevator is accelerating upward—broken arrows represent forces too large to be drawn to scale. $\mathbf{T}$ is the weight of the scale, $\mathbf{w_e}$ is the weight of the elevator, $\mathbf{F_s}$ is the force of the scale on the person, $\mathbf{F_p}$ is the force of the person on the scale, $\mathbf{F_t}$ is the force of the scale on the floor of the elevator, and $\mathbf{N}$ is the force of the floor upward on the scale. (b) The free-body diagram shows only the external forces acting on the designated system of interest—the person.

Strategy

If the scale is accurate, its reading will equal F_p, the magnitude of the force the person exerts downward on it. Figure 4.23(a) shows the numerous forces acting on the elevator, scale, and person. It makes this one-dimensional problem look much more formidable than if the person is chosen to be the system of interest and a free-body diagram is drawn as in Figure 4.23(b). Analysis of the free-body diagram using Newton's laws can produce answers to both parts (a) and (b) of this example, as well as some other questions that might arise. The only forces acting on the person are his weight $\mathbf{w}$ and the upward force of the scale $\mathbf{F_s}$. According to Newton's third law $\mathbf{F_p}$ and $\mathbf{F_s}$ are equal in magnitude and opposite in direction, so that we need to find F_s in order to find what the scale reads. We can do this, as usual, by applying Newton's second law,

$$F_{\text{net}} = ma. \tag{4.78}$$

From the free-body diagram we see that $F_{\text{net}} = F_s - w$, so that

$$F_s - w = ma. \quad 4.79$$

Solving for F_s gives an equation with only one unknown:

$$F_s = ma + w, \quad 4.80$$

or, because $w = mg$, simply

$$F_s = ma + mg. \quad 4.81$$

No assumptions were made about the acceleration, and so this solution should be valid for a variety of accelerations in addition to the ones in this exercise.

Solution for (a)

In this part of the problem, $a = 1.20\ \text{m/s}^2$, so that

$$F_s = (75.0\ \text{kg})(1.20\ \text{m/s}^2) + (75.0\ \text{kg})(9.80\ \text{m/s}^2), \quad 4.82$$

yielding

$$F_s = 825\ \text{N}. \quad 4.83$$

Discussion for (a)

This is about 185 lb. What would the scale have read if he were stationary? Since his acceleration would be zero, the force of the scale would be equal to his weight:

$$\begin{aligned} F_{net} &= ma = 0 = F_s - w \\ F_s &= w = mg \\ F_s &= (75.0\ \text{kg})(9.80\ \text{m/s}^2) \\ F_s &= 735\ \text{N}. \end{aligned} \quad 4.84$$

So, the scale reading in the elevator is greater than his 735-N (165 lb) weight. This means that the scale is pushing up on the person with a force greater than his weight, as it must in order to accelerate him upward. Clearly, the greater the acceleration of the elevator, the greater the scale reading, consistent with what you feel in rapidly accelerating versus slowly accelerating elevators.

Solution for (b)

Now, what happens when the elevator reaches a constant upward velocity? Will the scale still read more than his weight? For any constant velocity—up, down, or stationary—acceleration is zero because $a = \frac{\Delta v}{\Delta t}$, and $\Delta v = 0$.

Thus,

$$F_s = ma + mg = 0 + mg. \quad 4.85$$

Now

$$F_s = (75.0\ \text{kg})(9.80\ \text{m/s}^2), \quad 4.86$$

which gives

$$F_s = 735\ \text{N}. \quad 4.87$$

Discussion for (b)

The scale reading is 735 N, which equals the person's weight. This will be the case whenever the elevator has a constant velocity—moving up, moving down, or stationary.

The solution to the previous example also applies to an elevator accelerating downward, as mentioned. When an elevator accelerates downward, a is negative, and the scale reading is *less* than the weight of the person, until a constant downward velocity is reached, at which time the scale reading again becomes equal to the person's weight. If the elevator is in free-fall and accelerating downward at g, then the scale reading will be zero and the person will *appear* to be weightless.

Integrating Concepts: Newton's Laws of Motion and Kinematics

Physics is most interesting and most powerful when applied to general situations that involve more than a narrow set of physical principles. Newton's laws of motion can also be integrated with other concepts that have been discussed previously in this text to solve problems of motion. For example, forces produce accelerations, a topic of kinematics, and hence the relevance of earlier chapters. When approaching problems that involve various types of forces, acceleration, velocity, and/or position, use the following steps to approach the problem:

Problem-Solving Strategy

Step 1. *Identify which physical principles are involved.* Listing the givens and the quantities to be calculated will allow you to identify the principles involved.
Step 2. *Solve the problem using strategies outlined in the text.* If these are available for the specific topic, you should refer to them. You should also refer to the sections of the text that deal with a particular topic. The following worked example illustrates how these strategies are applied to an integrated concept problem.

EXAMPLE 4.10

What Force Must a Soccer Player Exert to Reach Top Speed?

A soccer player starts from rest and accelerates forward, reaching a velocity of 8.00 m/s in 2.50 s. (a) What was his average acceleration? (b) What average force did he exert backward on the ground to achieve this acceleration? The player's mass is 70.0 kg, and air resistance is negligible.

Strategy

1. To solve an *integrated concept problem,* we must first identify the physical principles involved and identify the chapters in which they are found. Part (a) of this example considers *acceleration* along a straight line. This is a topic of *kinematics*. Part (b) deals with *force*, a topic of *dynamics* found in this chapter.
2. The following solutions to each part of the example illustrate how the specific problem-solving strategies are applied. These involve identifying knowns and unknowns, checking to see if the answer is reasonable, and so forth.

Solution for (a)

We are given the initial and final velocities (zero and 8.00 m/s forward); thus, the change in velocity is $\Delta v = 8.00\text{ m/s}$. We are given the elapsed time, and so $\Delta t = 2.50\text{ s}$. The unknown is acceleration, which can be found from its definition:

$$a = \frac{\Delta v}{\Delta t}. \quad (4.88)$$

Substituting the known values yields

$$\begin{aligned} a &= \frac{8.00\text{ m/s}}{2.50\text{ s}} \\ &= 3.20\text{ m/s}^2. \end{aligned} \quad (4.89)$$

Discussion for (a)

This is an attainable acceleration for an athlete in good condition.

Solution for (b)

Here we are asked to find the average force the player exerts backward to achieve this forward acceleration. Neglecting air resistance, this would be equal in magnitude to the net external force on the player, since this force causes his acceleration. Since we now know the player's acceleration and are given his mass, we can use Newton's second law to find the force exerted. That is,

$$F_{\text{net}} = ma. \quad (4.90)$$

Substituting the known values of m and a gives

$$\begin{aligned} F_{\text{net}} &= (70.0\text{ kg})(3.20\text{ m/s}^2) \\ &= 224\text{ N}. \end{aligned} \tag{4.91}$$

Discussion for (b)

This is about 50 pounds, a reasonable average force.

This worked example illustrates how to apply problem-solving strategies to situations that include topics from different chapters. The first step is to identify the physical principles involved in the problem. The second step is to solve for the unknown using familiar problem-solving strategies. These strategies are found throughout the text, and many worked examples show how to use them for single topics. You will find these techniques for integrated concept problems useful in applications of physics outside of a physics course, such as in your profession, in other science disciplines, and in everyday life. The following problems will build your skills in the broad application of physical principles.

4.8 Extended Topic: The Four Basic Forces—An Introduction

LEARNING OBJECTIVES

By the end of this section, you will be able to:

- Understand the four basic forces that underlie the processes in nature.

One of the most remarkable simplifications in physics is that only four distinct forces account for all known phenomena. In fact, nearly all of the forces we experience directly are due to only one basic force, called the electromagnetic force. (The gravitational force is the only force we experience directly that is not electromagnetic.) This is a tremendous simplification of the myriad of *apparently* different forces we can list, only a few of which were discussed in the previous section. As we will see, the basic forces are all thought to act through the exchange of microscopic carrier particles, and the characteristics of the basic forces are determined by the types of particles exchanged. Action at a distance, such as the gravitational force of Earth on the Moon, is explained by the existence of a **force field** rather than by "physical contact."

The *four basic forces* are the gravitational force, the electromagnetic force, the weak nuclear force, and the strong nuclear force. Their properties are summarized in Table 4.1. Since the weak and strong nuclear forces act over an extremely short range, the size of a nucleus or less, we do not experience them directly, although they are crucial to the very structure of matter. These forces determine which nuclei are stable and which decay, and they are the basis of the release of energy in certain nuclear reactions. Nuclear forces determine not only the stability of nuclei, but also the relative abundance of elements in nature. The properties of the nucleus of an atom determine the number of electrons it has and, thus, indirectly determine the chemistry of the atom. More will be said of all of these topics in later chapters.

CONCEPT CONNECTIONS: THE FOUR BASIC FORCES

The four basic forces will be encountered in more detail as you progress through the text. The gravitational force is defined in Uniform Circular Motion and Gravitation, electric force in Electric Charge and Electric Field, magnetic force in Magnetism, and nuclear forces in Radioactivity and Nuclear Physics. On a macroscopic scale, electromagnetism and gravity are the basis for all forces. The nuclear forces are vital to the substructure of matter, but they are not directly experienced on the macroscopic scale.

Force	Approximate Relative Strengths	Range	Attraction/Repulsion	Carrier Particle
Gravitational	10^{-38}	∞	attractive only	Graviton
Electromagnetic	10^{-2}	∞	attractive and repulsive	Photon
Weak nuclear	10^{-6}	$< 10^{-18}\,m$	attractive and repulsive	W^+, W^-, Z^0
Strong nuclear	1	∞	attractive and repulsive	gluons

TABLE 4.1 Properties of the Four Basic Forces[1]

The gravitational force is surprisingly weak—it is only because gravity is always attractive that we notice it at all. Our weight is the gravitational force due to the *entire* Earth acting on us. On the very large scale, as in astronomical systems, the gravitational force is the dominant force determining the motions of moons, planets, stars, and galaxies. The gravitational force also affects the nature of space and time. As we shall see later in the study of general relativity, space is curved in the vicinity of very massive bodies, such as the Sun, and time actually slows down near massive bodies.

Electromagnetic forces can be either attractive or repulsive. They are long-range forces, which act over extremely large distances, and they nearly cancel for macroscopic objects. (Remember that it is the *net* external force that is important.) If they did not cancel, electromagnetic forces would completely overwhelm the gravitational force. The electromagnetic force is a combination of electrical forces (such as those that cause static electricity) and magnetic forces (such as those that affect a compass needle). These two forces were thought to be quite distinct until early in the 19th century, when scientists began to discover that they are different manifestations of the same force. This discovery is a classical case of the *unification of forces*. Similarly, friction, tension, and all of the other classes of forces we experience directly (except gravity, of course) are due to electromagnetic interactions of atoms and molecules. It is still convenient to consider these forces separately in specific applications, however, because of the ways they manifest themselves.

CONCEPT CONNECTIONS: UNIFYING FORCES

Attempts to unify the four basic forces are discussed in relation to elementary particles later in this text. By "unify" we mean finding connections between the forces that show that they are different manifestations of a single force. Even if such unification is achieved, the forces will retain their separate characteristics on the macroscopic scale and may be identical only under extreme conditions such as those existing in the early universe.

Physicists are now exploring whether the four basic forces are in some way related. Attempts to unify all forces into one come under the rubric of Grand Unified Theories (GUTs), with which there has been some success in recent years. It is now known that under conditions of extremely high density and temperature, such as existed in the early universe, the electromagnetic and weak nuclear forces are indistinguishable. They can now be considered to be different manifestations of one force, called the *electroweak* force. So the list of four has been reduced in a sense to only three. Further progress in unifying all forces is proving difficult—especially the inclusion of the gravitational force, which has the special characteristics of affecting the space and time in which the other forces exist.

While the unification of forces will not affect how we discuss forces in this text, it is fascinating that such underlying simplicity exists in the face of the overt complexity of the universe. There is no reason that nature must be simple—it simply is.

1 The graviton is a proposed particle, though it has not yet been observed by scientists. See the discussion of gravitational waves later in this section. The particles W^+, W^-, and Z^0 are called vector bosons; these were predicted by theory and first observed in 1983. There are eight types of gluons proposed by scientists, and their existence is indicated by meson exchange in the nuclei of atoms.

Action at a Distance: Concept of a Field

All forces act at a distance. This is obvious for the gravitational force. Earth and the Moon, for example, interact without coming into contact. It is also true for all other forces. Friction, for example, is an electromagnetic force between atoms that may not actually touch. What is it that carries forces between objects? One way to answer this question is to imagine that a **force field** surrounds whatever object creates the force. A second object (often called a *test object*) placed in this field will experience a force that is a function of location and other variables. The field itself is the "thing" that carries the force from one object to another. The field is defined so as to be a characteristic of the object creating it; the field does not depend on the test object placed in it. Earth's gravitational field, for example, is a function of the mass of Earth and the distance from its center, independent of the presence of other masses. The concept of a field is useful because equations can be written for force fields surrounding objects (for gravity, this yields $w = mg$ at Earth's surface), and motions can be calculated from these equations. (See Figure 4.24.)

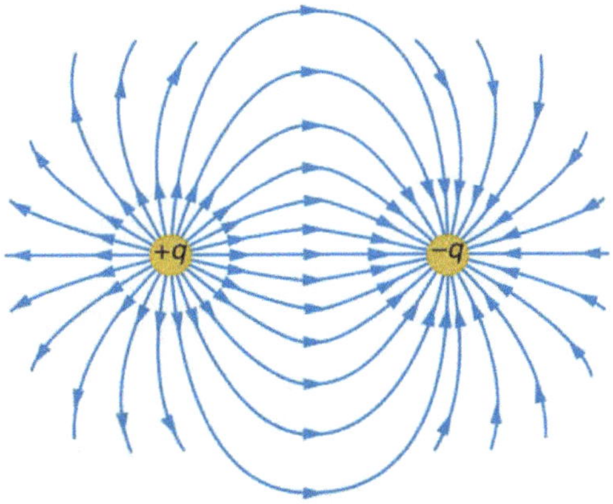

FIGURE 4.24 The electric force field between a positively charged particle and a negatively charged particle. When a positive test charge is placed in the field, the charge will experience a force in the direction of the force field lines.

CONCEPT CONNECTIONS: FORCE FIELDS

The concept of a *force field* is also used in connection with electric charge and is presented in Electric Charge and Electric Field. It is also a useful idea for all the basic forces, as will be seen in Particle Physics. Fields help us to visualize forces and how they are transmitted, as well as to describe them with precision and to link forces with subatomic carrier particles.

The field concept has been applied very successfully; we can calculate motions and describe nature to high precision using field equations. As useful as the field concept is, however, it leaves unanswered the question of what carries the force. It has been proposed in recent decades, starting in 1935 with Hideki Yukawa's (1907–1981) work on the strong nuclear force, that all forces are transmitted by the exchange of elementary particles. We can visualize particle exchange as analogous to macroscopic phenomena such as two people passing a basketball back and forth, thereby exerting a repulsive force without touching one another. (See Figure 4.25.)

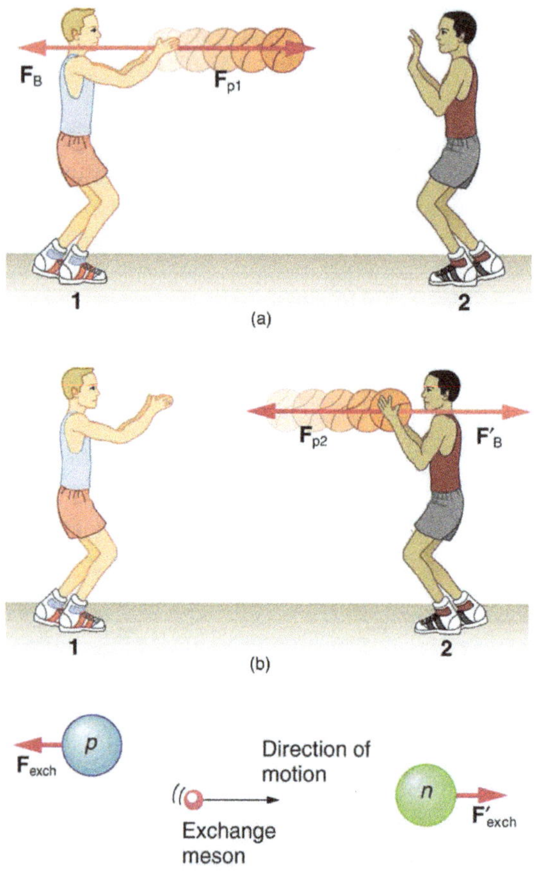

FIGURE 4.25 The exchange of masses resulting in repulsive forces. (a) The person throwing the basketball exerts a force $\mathbf{F}_{p1}$ on it toward the other person and feels a reaction force $\mathbf{F}_B$ away from the second person. (b) The person catching the basketball exerts a force $\mathbf{F}_{p2}$ on it to stop the ball and feels a reaction force $\mathbf{F'}_B$ away from the first person. (c) The analogous exchange of a meson between a proton and a neutron carries the strong nuclear forces $\mathbf{F}_{exch}$ and $\mathbf{F'}_{exch}$ between them. An attractive force can also be exerted by the exchange of a mass—if person 2 pulled the basketball away from the first person as he tried to retain it, then the force between them would be attractive.

This idea of particle exchange deepens rather than contradicts field concepts. It is more satisfying philosophically to think of something physical actually moving between objects acting at a distance. Table 4.1 lists the exchange or **carrier particles**, both observed and proposed, that carry the four forces. But the real fruit of the particle-exchange proposal is that searches for Yukawa's proposed particle found it *and* a number of others that were completely unexpected, stimulating yet more research. All of this research eventually led to the proposal of quarks as the underlying substructure of matter, which is a basic tenet of GUTs. If successful, these theories will explain not only forces, but also the structure of matter itself. Yet physics is an experimental science, so the test of these theories must lie in the domain of the real world. As of this writing, scientists at the CERN laboratory in Switzerland are starting to test these theories using the world's largest particle accelerator: the Large Hadron Collider. This accelerator (27 km in circumference) allows two high-energy proton beams, traveling in opposite directions, to collide. An energy of 14 trillion electron volts will be available. It is anticipated that some new particles, possibly force carrier particles, will be found. (See Figure 4.26.) One of the force carriers of high interest that researchers hope to detect is the Higgs boson. The observation of its properties might tell us why different particles have different masses.

FIGURE 4.26 The world's largest particle accelerator spans the border between Switzerland and France. Two beams, traveling in opposite directions close to the speed of light, collide in a tube similar to the central tube shown here. External magnets determine the beam's path. Special detectors will analyze particles created in these collisions. Questions as broad as what is the origin of mass and what was matter like the first few seconds of our universe will be explored. This accelerator began preliminary operation in 2008. (credit: Frank Hommes)

Tiny particles also have wave-like behavior, something we will explore more in a later chapter. To better understand force-carrier particles from another perspective, let us consider gravity. The search for gravitational waves has been going on for a number of years. Over 100 years ago, Einstein predicted the existence of these waves as part of his general theory of relativity. Gravitational waves are created during the collision of massive stars, in black holes, or in supernova explosions—like shock waves. These gravitational waves will travel through space from such sites much like a pebble dropped into a pond sends out ripples—except these waves move at the speed of light. A detector apparatus has been built in the U.S., consisting of two large installations nearly 3000 km apart—one in Washington state and one in Louisiana! The facility is called the Laser Interferometer Gravitational-Wave Observatory (LIGO). Each installation is designed to use optical lasers to examine any slight shift in the relative positions of two masses due to the effect of gravity waves. The two sites allow simultaneous measurements of these small effects to be separated from other natural phenomena, such as earthquakes. Initial operation of the detectors began in 2002, and work is proceeding on increasing their sensitivity. Similar installations have been built in Italy (VIRGO), Germany (GEO600), and Japan (TAMA300) to provide a worldwide network of gravitational wave detectors.

In September, 2015, LIGO fulfilled its promise and helped prove Einstein's predictions. The system detected the first gravitational waves arising from the merger of two black holes—one 29 times the mass of our Sun and the other 36 times the mass of our Sun—that occurred 1.3 billion years ago. About 3 times the mass of the Sun was converted into gravitational waves in a fraction of a second—with a peak power output about 50 times that of the whole visible universe. Due to the 7 millisecond delay in detection, researchers established that the merger occurred on the southern hemisphere side of Earth. Since then, LIGO and VIRGO have combined to detect about a dozen similar events, with better and more precise measurements. Waves from neutron star mergers and different-sized black holes have deepened our understanding of these objects and their impact on the universe.

International collaboration in this area is moving into space with the joint EU/US project LISA (Laser Interferometer Space Antenna). Earthquakes and other Earthly noises will be no problem for these monitoring spacecraft. LISA will complement LIGO by looking at much more massive black holes through the observation of gravitational-wave sources emitting much larger wavelengths. Three satellites will be placed in space above Earth in an equilateral triangle (with 5,000,000-km sides) (Figure 4.27). The system will measure the relative positions of each satellite to detect passing gravitational waves. Accuracy to within 10% of the size of an atom will be needed to detect any waves. The launch of this project will likely be in the 2030s.

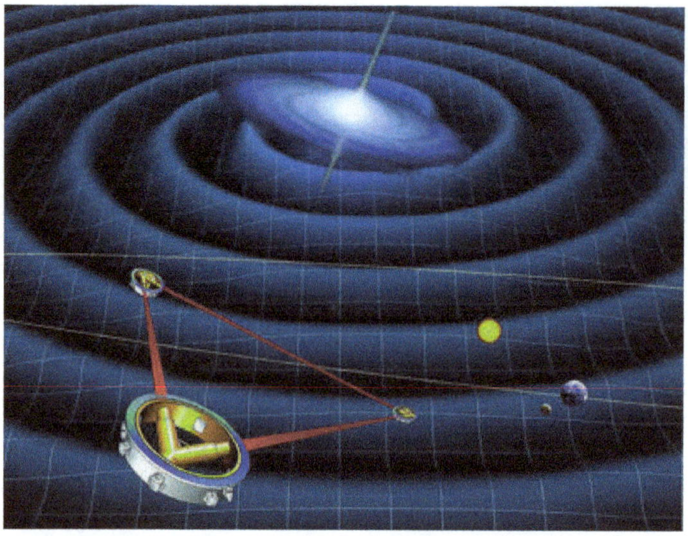

FIGURE 4.27 Space-based future experiments for the measurement of gravitational waves. Shown here is a drawing of LISA's orbit. Each satellite of LISA will consist of a laser source and a mass. The lasers will transmit a signal to measure the distance between each satellite's test mass. The relative motion of these masses will provide information about passing gravitational waves. (credit: NASA)

As you can see above, some of the most groundbreaking developments in physics are made with a relatively long gap from theoretical prediction to experimental detection. This pattern continues the process of science from its earliest days, where early thinkers and researchers made discoveries that only led to more questions. Einstein was unique in many ways, but he was not unique in that later scientists, building on his and each other's work, would prove his theories. Evidence for black holes became more and more concrete as scientists developed new and better ways to look for them. Some of the most prominent have been Roger Penrose, who developed new mathematical models related to black holes, as well as Reinhard Genzel and Andrea Ghez, who independently used telescope observations to identify a region of our galaxy where a massive unseen gravity source (4 million times the size of our Sun) was pulling on stars. And soon after, collaborators on the Event Horizon Telescope project produced the first actual image of a black hole.

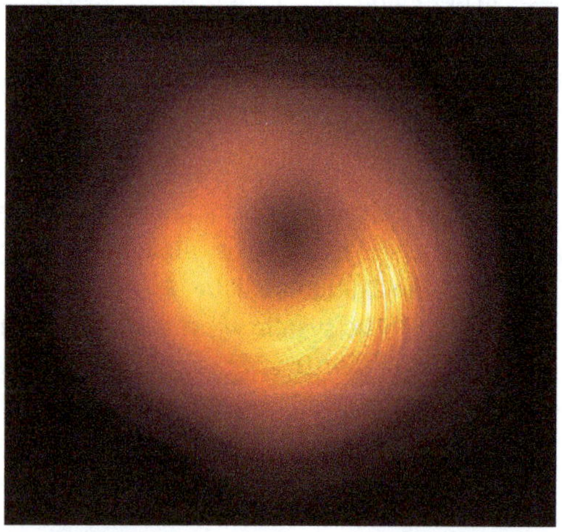

FIGURE 4.28 This updated image of the supermassive black hole at the center of the M87 galaxy shows the polarization created by the powerful magnetic field that surrounds the object. The image was created by the Event Horizon Telescope, which combines data from telescopes around the world. The project involves over 200 researchers and produced the first image of a black hole in 2019. (credit: EHT Collaboration/NASA APOD)

Glossary

acceleration the rate at which an object's velocity changes over a period of time

carrier particle a fundamental particle of nature that is surrounded by a characteristic force field; photons are carrier particles of the electromagnetic force

dynamics the study of how forces affect the motion of objects and systems

external force a force acting on an object or system that originates outside of the object or system

force a push or pull on an object with a specific magnitude and direction; can be represented by vectors; can be expressed as a multiple of a standard force

force field a region in which a test particle will experience a force

free-body diagram a sketch showing all of the external forces acting on an object or system; the system is represented by a dot, and the forces are represented by vectors extending outward from the dot

free-fall a situation in which the only force acting on an object is the force due to gravity

friction a force past each other of objects that are touching; examples include rough surfaces and air resistance

inertia the tendency of an object to remain at rest or remain in motion

inertial frame of reference a coordinate system that is not accelerating; all forces acting in an inertial frame of reference are real forces, as opposed to fictitious forces that are observed due to an accelerating frame of reference

law of inertia see Newton's first law of motion

mass the quantity of matter in a substance; measured in kilograms

net external force the vector sum of all external forces acting on an object or system; causes a mass to accelerate

Newton's first law of motion a body at rest remains at rest, or, if in motion, remains in motion at a constant velocity unless acted on by a net external force; also known as the law of inertia

Newton's second law of motion the net external force $\mathbf{F}_{\text{net}}$ on an object with mass m is proportional to and in the same direction as the acceleration of the object, $\mathbf{a}$, and inversely proportional to the mass; defined mathematically as $\mathbf{a} = \frac{\mathbf{F}_{\text{net}}}{m}$

Newton's third law of motion whenever one body exerts a force on a second body, the first body experiences a force that is equal in magnitude and opposite in direction to the force that the first body exerts

normal force the force that a surface applies to an object to support the weight of the object; acts perpendicular to the surface on which the object rests

system defined by the boundaries of an object or collection of objects being observed; all forces originating from outside of the system are considered external forces

tension the pulling force that acts along a medium, especially a stretched flexible connector, such as a rope or cable; when a rope supports the weight of an object, the force on the object due to the rope is called a tension force

thrust a reaction force that pushes a body forward in response to a backward force; rockets, airplanes, and cars are pushed forward by a thrust reaction force

weight the force $\mathbf{w}$due to gravity acting on an object of mass m; defined mathematically as: $\mathbf{w} = m\mathbf{g}$, where $\mathbf{g}$ is the magnitude and direction of the acceleration due to gravity

Section Summary

4.1 Development of Force Concept

- **Dynamics** is the study of how forces affect the motion of objects.
- **Force** is a push or pull that can be defined in terms of various standards, and it is a vector having both magnitude and direction.
- **External forces** are any outside forces that act on a body. A **free-body diagram** is a drawing of all external forces acting on a body.

4.2 Newton's First Law of Motion: Inertia

- **Newton's first law of motion** states that a body at rest remains at rest, or, if in motion, remains in motion at a constant velocity unless acted on by a net external force. This is also known as the **law of inertia**.
- **Inertia** is the tendency of an object to remain at rest or remain in motion. Inertia is related to an object's mass.
- **Mass** is the quantity of matter in a substance.

4.3 Newton's Second Law of Motion: Concept of a System

- Acceleration, $\mathbf{a}$, is defined as a change in velocity, meaning a change in its magnitude or direction, or both.
- An external force is one acting on a system from outside the system, as opposed to internal forces, which act between components within the system.
- Newton's second law of motion states that the acceleration of a system is directly proportional to and in the same direction as the net external force acting on the system, and inversely proportional to its mass.
- In equation form, Newton's second law of motion is $\mathbf{a} = \frac{\mathbf{F}_{\text{net}}}{m}$.
- This is often written in the more familiar form: $\mathbf{F}_{\text{net}} = m\mathbf{a}$.
- The weight $\mathbf{w}$ of an object is defined as the force of gravity acting on an object of mass m. The object experiences an acceleration due to gravity $\mathbf{g}$: $\mathbf{w} = m\mathbf{g}$.
- If the only force acting on an object is due to gravity, the object is in free fall.
- Friction is a force that opposes the motion past each other of objects that are touching.

4.4 Newton's Third Law of Motion: Symmetry in Forces

- **Newton's third law of motion** represents a basic symmetry in nature. It states: Whenever one body exerts a force on a second body, the first body experiences a force that is equal in magnitude and opposite in direction to the force that the first body exerts.
- A **thrust** is a reaction force that pushes a body forward in response to a backward force. Rockets, airplanes, and cars are pushed forward by a thrust reaction force.

4.5 Normal, Tension, and Other Examples of Forces

- When objects rest on a surface, the surface applies a force to the object that supports the weight of the object. This supporting force acts perpendicular to and away from the surface. It is called a normal force, $\mathbf{N}$.
- When objects rest on a non-accelerating horizontal surface, the magnitude of the normal force is equal to the weight of the object: $N = mg$.
- When objects rest on an inclined plane that makes an angle θ with the horizontal surface, the weight of the object can be resolved into components that act perpendicular ($\mathbf{w}_{\perp}$) and parallel ($\mathbf{w}_{\parallel}$) to the surface of the plane. These components can be calculated using:
  $w_{\parallel} = w \sin(\theta) = mg \sin(\theta)$
  $w_{\perp} = w \cos(\theta) = mg \cos(\theta)$.
- The pulling force that acts along a stretched flexible connector, such as a rope or cable, is called tension, $\mathbf{T}$. When a rope supports the weight of an object that is at rest, the tension in the rope is equal to the weight of the object: $T = mg$.
- In any inertial frame of reference (one that is not accelerated or rotated), Newton's laws have the simple forms given in this chapter and all forces are real forces having a physical origin.

4.6 Problem-Solving Strategies

- To solve problems involving Newton's laws of motion, follow the procedure described:
  1. Draw a sketch of the problem.
  2. Identify known and unknown quantities, and identify the system of interest. Draw a free-body diagram, which is a sketch showing all of the forces acting on an object. The object is represented by a dot, and the forces are represented by vectors extending in different directions from the dot. If vectors act in directions that are not horizontal or vertical, resolve the vectors into horizontal and vertical components and draw them on the free-body diagram.
  3. Write Newton's second law in the horizontal and vertical directions and add the forces acting on the object. If the object does not accelerate in a particular direction (for example, the x -direction) then $F_{\text{net } x} = 0$. If the object does accelerate in that direction, $F_{\text{net } x} = ma$.
  4. Check your answer. Is the answer reasonable? Are the units correct?

4.7 Further Applications of Newton's Laws of Motion

- Newton's laws of motion can be applied in numerous situations to solve problems of motion.
- Some problems will contain multiple force vectors acting in different directions on an object. Be sure to draw diagrams, resolve all force vectors into horizontal and vertical components, and draw a free-body diagram. Always analyze the direction in which an object accelerates so that you can determine whether $F_{\text{net}} = ma$ or $F_{\text{net}} = 0$.
- The normal force on an object is not always equal

in magnitude to the weight of the object. If an object is accelerating, the normal force will be less than or greater than the weight of the object. Also, if the object is on an inclined plane, the normal force will always be less than the full weight of the object.

- Some problems will contain various physical quantities, such as forces, acceleration, velocity, or position. You can apply concepts from kinematics and dynamics in order to solve these problems of motion.

4.8 Extended Topic: The Four Basic Forces—An Introduction

- The various types of forces that are categorized for use in many applications are all manifestations of the *four basic forces* in nature.
- The properties of these forces are summarized in Table 4.1.
- Everything we experience directly without sensitive instruments is due to either electromagnetic forces or gravitational forces. The nuclear forces are responsible for the submicroscopic structure of matter, but they are not directly sensed because of their short ranges. Attempts are being made to show all four forces are different manifestations of a single unified force.
- A force field surrounds an object creating a force and is the carrier of that force.

Conceptual Questions

4.1 Development of Force Concept

1. Propose a force standard different from the example of a stretched spring discussed in the text. Your standard must be capable of producing the same force repeatedly.

2. What properties do forces have that allow us to classify them as vectors?

4.2 Newton's First Law of Motion: Inertia

3. How are inertia and mass related?

4. What is the relationship between weight and mass? Which is an intrinsic, unchanging property of a body?

4.3 Newton's Second Law of Motion: Concept of a System

5. Which statement is correct? (a) Net force causes motion. (b) Net force causes change in motion. Explain your answer and give an example.

6. Why can we neglect forces such as those holding a body together when we apply Newton's second law of motion?

7. Explain how the choice of the "system of interest" affects which forces must be considered when applying Newton's second law of motion.

8. Describe a situation in which the net external force on a system is not zero, yet its speed remains constant.

9. A system can have a nonzero velocity while the net external force on it *is* zero. Describe such a situation.

10. A rock is thrown straight up. What is the net external force acting on the rock when it is at the top of its trajectory?

11. (a) Give an example of different net external forces acting on the same system to produce different accelerations. (b) Give an example of the same net external force acting on systems of different masses, producing different accelerations. (c) What law accurately describes both effects? State it in words and as an equation.

12. If the acceleration of a system is zero, are no external forces acting on it? What about internal forces? Explain your answers.

13. If a constant, nonzero force is applied to an object, what can you say about the velocity and acceleration of the object?

14. The gravitational force on the basketball in Figure 4.6 is ignored. When gravity *is* taken into account, what is the direction of the net external force on the basketball—above horizontal, below horizontal, or still horizontal?

4.4 Newton's Third Law of Motion: Symmetry in Forces

15. When you take off in a jet aircraft, there is a sensation of being pushed back into the seat. Explain why you move backward in the seat—is there really a force backward on you? (The same reasoning explains whiplash injuries, in which the head is apparently thrown backward.)

16. A device used since the 1940s to measure the kick or recoil of the body due to heart beats is the "ballistocardiograph." What physics principle(s) are involved here to measure the force of cardiac contraction? How might we construct such a device?

17. Describe a situation in which one system exerts a force on another and, as a consequence, experiences a force that is equal in magnitude and opposite in direction. Which of Newton's laws of motion apply?

18. Why does an ordinary rifle recoil (kick backward) when fired? The barrel of a recoilless rifle is open at both ends. Describe how Newton's third law applies when one is fired. Can you safely stand close behind one when it is fired?

19. An American football lineman reasons that it is senseless to try to out-push the opposing player, since no matter how hard he pushes he will experience an equal and opposite force from the other player. Use Newton's laws and draw a free-body diagram of an appropriate system to explain how he can still out-push the opposition if he is strong enough.

20. Newton's third law of motion tells us that forces always occur in pairs of equal and opposite magnitude. Explain how the choice of the "system of interest" affects whether one such pair of forces cancels.

4.5 Normal, Tension, and Other Examples of Forces

21. If a leg is suspended by a traction setup as shown in Figure 4.29, what is the tension in the rope?

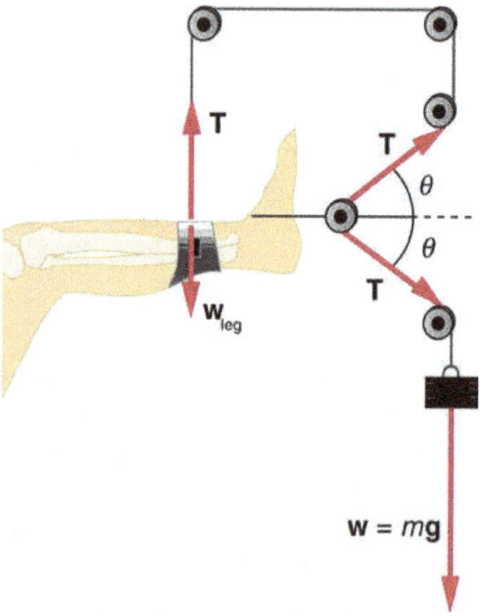

FIGURE 4.29 A leg is suspended by a traction system in which wires are used to transmit forces. Frictionless pulleys change the direction of the force T without changing its magnitude.

22. In a traction setup for a broken bone, with pulleys and rope available, how might we be able to increase the force along the tibia using the same weight? (See Figure 4.29.) (Note that the tibia is the shin bone shown in this image.)

4.7 Further Applications of Newton's Laws of Motion

23. To simulate the apparent weightlessness of space orbit, astronauts are trained in the hold of a cargo aircraft that is accelerating downward at g. Why will they appear to be weightless, as measured by standing on a bathroom scale, in this accelerated frame of reference? Is there any difference between their apparent weightlessness in orbit and in the aircraft?

24. A cartoon shows the hat coming off the head of an elevator passenger when the elevator rapidly stops during an upward ride. Can this really happen without the person being tied to the floor of the elevator? Explain your answer.

4.8 Extended Topic: The Four Basic Forces—An Introduction

25. Explain, in terms of the properties of the four basic forces, why people notice the gravitational force acting on their bodies if it is such a comparatively weak force.

26. What is the dominant force between astronomical objects? Why are the other three basic forces less significant over these very large distances?

27. Give a detailed example of how the exchange of a particle can result in an *attractive* force. (For example, consider one child pulling a toy out of the hands of another.)

Problems & Exercises

4.3 Newton's Second Law of Motion: Concept of a System

You may assume data taken from illustrations is accurate to three digits.

1. A 63.0-kg sprinter starts a race with an acceleration of 4.20 m/s^2. What is the net external force on him?

2. If the sprinter from the previous problem accelerates at that rate for 20 m, and then maintains that velocity for the remainder of the 100-m dash, what will be his time for the race?

3. A cleaner pushes a 4.50-kg laundry cart in such a way that the net external force on it is 60.0 N. Calculate the magnitude of its acceleration.

4. Since astronauts in orbit are apparently weightless, a clever method of measuring their masses is needed to monitor their mass gains or losses to adjust diets. One way to do this is to exert a known force on an astronaut and measure the acceleration produced. Suppose a net external force of 50.0 N is exerted and the astronaut's acceleration is measured to be 0.893 m/s^2. (a) Calculate her mass. (b) By exerting a force on the astronaut, the vehicle in which they orbit experiences an equal and opposite force. Discuss how this would affect the measurement of the astronaut's acceleration. Propose a method in which recoil of the vehicle is avoided.

5. In Figure 4.7, the net external force on the 24-kg mower is stated to be 51 N. If the force of friction opposing the motion is 24 N, what force F (in newtons) is the person exerting on the mower? Suppose the mower is moving at 1.5 m/s when the force F is removed. How far will the mower go before stopping?

6. The same rocket sled drawn in Figure 4.30 is decelerated at a rate of 196 m/s^2. What force is necessary to produce this deceleration? Assume that the rockets are off. The mass of the system is 2100 kg.

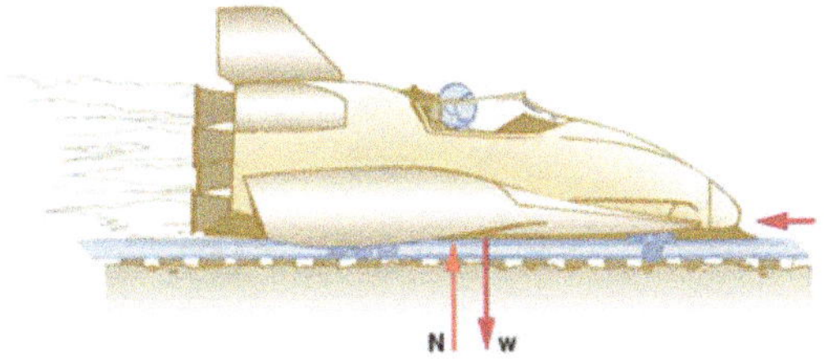

FIGURE 4.30

7. (a) If the rocket sled shown in Figure 4.31 starts with only one rocket burning, what is the magnitude of its acceleration? Assume that the mass of the system is 2100 kg, the thrust T is 2.4×10^4 N, and the force of friction opposing the motion is known to be 650 N. (b) Why is the acceleration not one-fourth of what it is with all rockets burning?

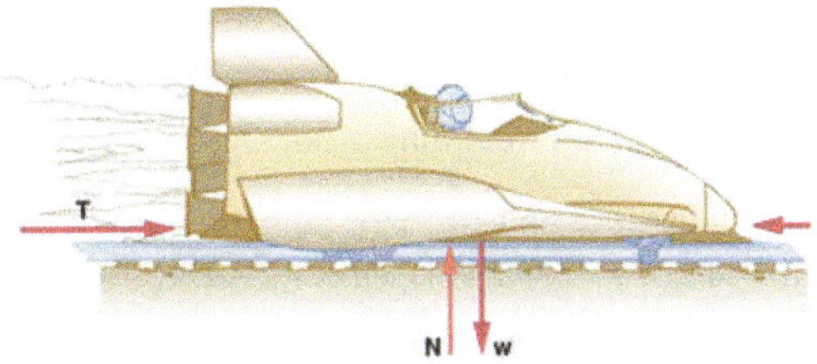

FIGURE 4.31

8. What is the deceleration of the rocket sled if it comes to rest in 1.1 s from a speed of 1000 km/h? (Such deceleration caused one test subject to black out and have temporary blindness.)

9. Suppose two children push horizontally, but in exactly opposite directions, on a third child in a wagon. The first child exerts a force of 75.0 N, the second a force of 90.0 N, friction is 12.0 N, and the mass of the third child plus wagon is 23.0 kg.
   a. What is the system of interest if the acceleration of the child in the wagon is to be calculated?
   b. Draw a free-body diagram, including all forces acting on the system.
   c. Calculate the acceleration.
   d. What would the acceleration be if friction were 15.0 N?

10. A powerful motorcycle can produce an acceleration of 3.50 m/s^2 while traveling at 90.0 km/h. At that speed the forces resisting motion, including friction and air resistance, total 400 N. (Air resistance is analogous to air friction. It always opposes the motion of an object.) What is the magnitude of the force the motorcycle exerts backward on the ground to produce its acceleration if the mass of the motorcycle with rider is 245 kg?

11. The rocket sled shown in Figure 4.32 accelerates at a rate of 49.0 m/s^2. Its passenger has a mass of 75.0 kg. (a) Calculate the horizontal component of the force the seat exerts against his body. Compare this with his weight by using a ratio. (b) Calculate the direction and magnitude of the total force the seat exerts against his body.

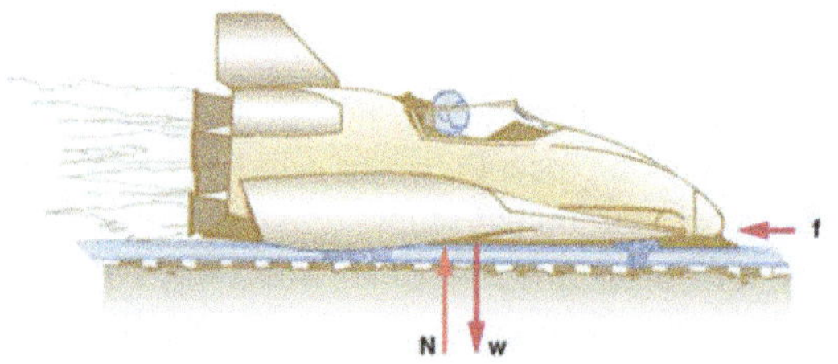

FIGURE 4.32

12. Repeat the previous problem for the situation in which the rocket sled decelerates at a rate of $201\ \text{m/s}^2$. In this problem, the forces are exerted by the seat and restraining belts.

13. The weight of an astronaut plus their space suit on the Moon is only 250 N. How much do they weigh on Earth? What is the mass on the Moon? On Earth?

14. Suppose the mass of a fully loaded module in which astronauts take off from the Moon is 10,000 kg. The thrust of its engines is 30,000 N. (a) Calculate its the magnitude of acceleration in a vertical takeoff from the Moon. (b) Could it lift off from Earth? If not, why not? If it could, calculate the magnitude of its acceleration.

4.4 Newton's Third Law of Motion: Symmetry in Forces

15. What net external force is exerted on a 1100-kg artillery shell fired from a battleship if the shell is accelerated at $2.40\times10^4\ \text{m/s}^2$? What is the magnitude of the force exerted on the ship by the artillery shell?

16. A rugby player is being pushed backward by an opposing player who is exerting a force of 800 N on him. The mass of the losing player plus equipment is 90.0 kg, and he is accelerating at $1.20\ \text{m/s}^2$ backward. (a) What is the force of friction between the losing player's feet and the grass? (b) What force does the winning player exert on the ground to move forward if his mass plus equipment is 110 kg? (c) Draw a sketch of the situation showing the system of interest used to solve each part. For this situation, draw a free-body diagram and write the net force equation.

4.5 Normal, Tension, and Other Examples of Forces

17. Two teams of nine members each engage in a tug of war. Each of the first team's members has an average mass of 68 kg and exerts an average force of 1350 N horizontally. Each of the second team's members has an average mass of 73 kg and exerts an average force of 1365 N horizontally. (a) What is magnitude of the acceleration of the two teams? (b) What is the tension in the section of rope between the teams?

18. What force does a trampoline have to apply to a 45.0-kg gymnast to accelerate her straight up at $7.50\ \text{m/s}^2$? Note that the answer is independent of the velocity of the gymnast—she can be moving either up or down, or be stationary.

19. (a) Calculate the tension in a vertical strand of spider web if a spider of mass 8.00×10^{-5} kg hangs motionless on it. (b) Calculate the tension in a horizontal strand of spider web if the same spider sits motionless in the middle of it much like the tightrope walker in Figure 4.16. The strand sags at an angle of 12° below the horizontal. Compare this with the tension in the vertical strand (find their ratio).

20. Suppose a 60.0-kg gymnast climbs a rope. (a) What is the tension in the rope if they climb at a constant speed? (b) What is the tension in the rope if they accelerate upward at a rate of $1.50\ \text{m/s}^2$?

21. Show that, as stated in the text, a force $\mathbf{F}_\perp$ exerted on a flexible medium at its center and perpendicular to its length (such as on the tightrope wire in Figure 4.16) gives rise to a tension of magnitude $T = \frac{F_\perp}{2\sin(\theta)}$.

22. Consider the baby being weighed in Figure 4.33. (a) What is the mass of the child and basket if a scale reading of 55 N is observed? (b) What is the tension T_1 in the cord attaching the baby to the scale? (c) What is the tension T_2 in the cord attaching the scale to the ceiling, if the scale has a mass of 0.500 kg? (d) Draw a sketch of the situation indicating the system of interest used to solve each part. The masses of the cords are negligible.

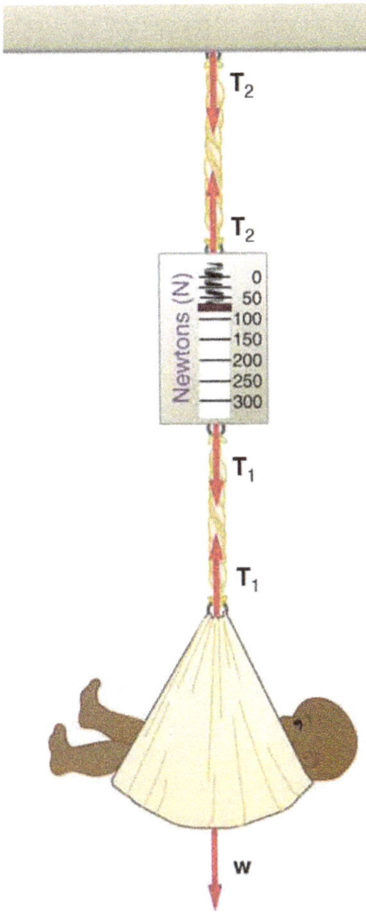

FIGURE 4.33 A baby is weighed using a spring scale.

4.6 Problem-Solving Strategies

23. A 5.00×10^5-kg rocket is accelerating straight up. Its engines produce 1.250×10^7 N of thrust, and air resistance is 4.50×10^6 N. What is the rocket's acceleration? Explicitly show how you follow the steps in the Problem-Solving Strategy for Newton's laws of motion.

24. The wheels of a midsize car exert a force of 2100 N backward on the road to accelerate the car in the forward direction. If the force of friction including air resistance is 250 N and the acceleration of the car is 1.80 m/s^2, what is the mass of the car plus its occupants? Explicitly show how you follow the steps in the Problem-Solving Strategy for Newton's laws of motion. For this situation, draw a free-body diagram and write the net force equation.

25. Calculate the force a 70.0-kg high jumper must exert on the ground to produce an upward acceleration 4.00 times the acceleration due to gravity. Explicitly show how you follow the steps in the Problem-Solving Strategy for Newton's laws of motion.

26. When landing after a spectacular somersault, a 40.0-kg gymnast decelerates by pushing straight down on the mat. Calculate the force she must exert if her deceleration is 7.00 times the acceleration due to gravity. Explicitly show how you follow the steps in the Problem-Solving Strategy for Newton's laws of motion.

27. A freight train consists of two 8.00×10^4-kg engines and 45 cars with average masses of 5.50×10^4 kg. (a) What force must each engine exert backward on the track to accelerate the train at a rate of $5.00 \times 10^{-2} \text{ m/s}^2$ if the force of friction is 7.50×10^5 N, assuming the engines exert identical forces? This is not a large frictional force for such a massive system. Rolling friction for trains is small, and consequently trains are very energy-efficient transportation systems. (b) What is the force in the coupling between the 37th and 38th cars (this is the force each exerts on the other), assuming all cars have the same mass and that friction is evenly distributed among all of the cars and engines?

28. Commercial airplanes are sometimes pushed out of the passenger loading area by a tractor. (a) An 1800-kg tractor exerts a force of 1.75×10^4 N backward on the pavement, and the system experiences forces resisting motion that total 2400 N. If the acceleration is 0.150 m/s^2, what is the mass of the airplane? (b) Calculate the force exerted by the tractor on the airplane, assuming 2200 N of the friction is experienced by the airplane. (c) Draw two sketches showing the systems of interest used to solve each part, including the free-body diagrams for each.

29. A 1100-kg car pulls a boat on a trailer. (a) What total force resists the motion of the car, boat, and trailer, if the car exerts a 1900-N force on the road and produces an acceleration of 0.550 m/s^2? The mass of the boat plus trailer is 700 kg. (b) What is the force in the hitch between the car and the trailer if 80% of the resisting forces are experienced by the boat and trailer?

30. (a) Find the magnitudes of the forces $\mathbf{F}_1$ and $\mathbf{F}_2$ that add to give the total force $\mathbf{F}_{tot}$ shown in Figure 4.34. This may be done either graphically or by using trigonometry. (b) Show graphically that the same total force is obtained independent of the order of addition of $\mathbf{F}_1$ and $\mathbf{F}_2$. (c) Find the direction and magnitude of some other pair of vectors that add to give $\mathbf{F}_{tot}$. Draw these to scale on the same drawing used in part (b) or a similar picture.

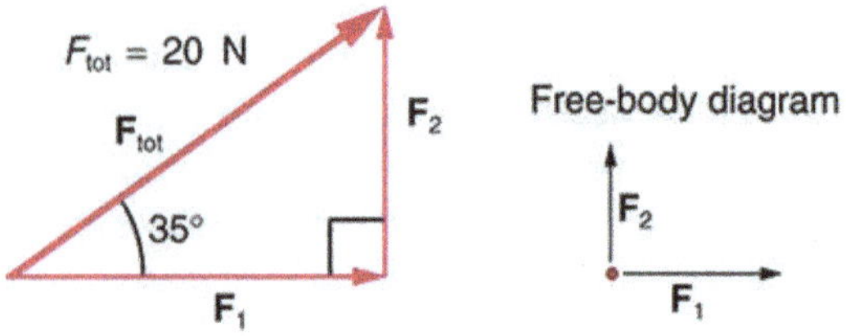

FIGURE 4.34

31. Two children pull a third child on a snow saucer sled exerting forces $\mathbf{F}_1$ and $\mathbf{F}_2$ as shown from above in Figure 4.35. Find the acceleration of the 49.00-kg sled and child system. Note that the direction of the frictional force is unspecified; it will be in the opposite direction of the sum of $\mathbf{F}_1$ and $\mathbf{F}_2$.

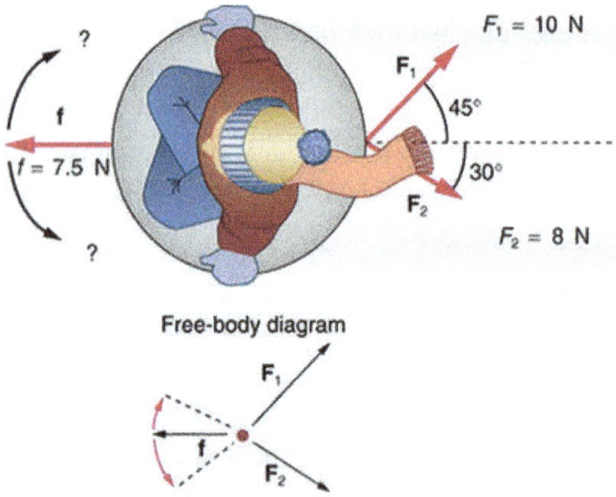

FIGURE 4.35 An overhead view of the horizontal forces acting on a child's snow saucer sled.

32. Suppose your car was mired deeply in the mud and you wanted to use the method illustrated in Figure 4.36 to pull it out. (a) What force would you have to exert perpendicular to the center of the rope to produce a force of 12,000 N on the car if the angle is 2.00°? In this part, explicitly show how you follow the steps in the Problem-Solving Strategy for Newton's laws of motion. (b) Real ropes stretch under such forces. What force would be exerted on the car if the angle increases to 7.00° and you still apply the force found in part (a) to its center?

FIGURE 4.36

33. What force is exerted on the tooth in Figure 4.37 if the tension in the wire is 25.0 N? Note that the force applied to the tooth is smaller than the tension in the wire, but this is necessitated by practical considerations of how force can be applied in the mouth. Explicitly show how you follow steps in the Problem-Solving Strategy for Newton's laws of motion.

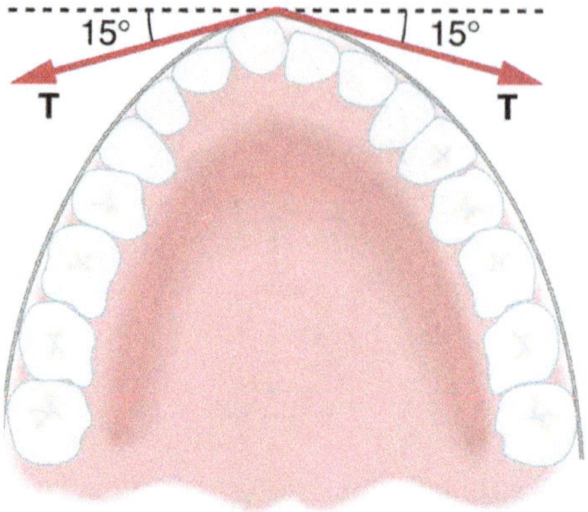

FIGURE 4.37 Braces are used to apply forces to teeth to realign them. Shown in this figure are the tensions applied by the wire to the protruding tooth. The total force applied to the tooth by the wire, $\mathbf{F}_{\text{app}}$, points straight toward the back of the mouth.

34. Figure 4.38 shows Superhero and Trusty Sidekick hanging motionless from a rope. Superhero's mass is 90.0 kg, while Trusty Sidekick's is 55.0 kg, and the mass of the rope is negligible. (a) Draw a free-body diagram of the situation showing all forces acting on Superhero, Trusty Sidekick, and the rope. (b) Find the tension in the rope above Superhero. (c) Find the tension in the rope between Superhero and Trusty Sidekick. Indicate on your free-body diagram the system of interest used to solve each part.

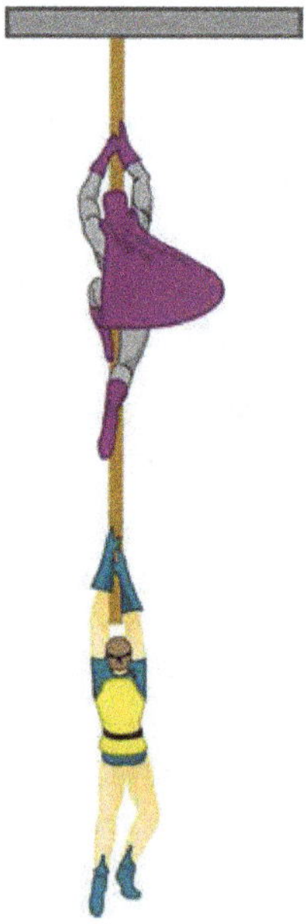

FIGURE 4.38 Superhero and Trusty Sidekick hang motionless on a rope as they try to figure out what to do next. Will the tension be the same everywhere in the rope?

35. A nurse pushes a cart by exerting a force on the handle at a downward angle 35.0° below the horizontal. The loaded cart has a mass of 28.0 kg, and the force of friction is 60.0 N. (a) Draw a free-body diagram for the system of interest. (b) What force must the nurse exert to move at a constant velocity?

36. Construct Your Own Problem Consider the tension in an elevator cable during the time the elevator starts from rest and accelerates its load upward to some cruising velocity. Taking the elevator and its load to be the system of interest, draw a free-body diagram. Then calculate the tension in the cable. Among the things to consider are the mass of the elevator and its load, the final velocity, and the time taken to reach that velocity.

37. Construct Your Own Problem Consider two people pushing a toboggan with four children on it up a snow-covered slope. Construct a problem in which you calculate the acceleration of the toboggan and its load. Include a free-body diagram of the appropriate system of interest as the basis for your analysis. Show vector forces and their components and explain the choice of coordinates. Among the things to be considered are the forces exerted by those pushing, the angle of the slope, and the masses of the toboggan and children.

38. Unreasonable Results (a) Repeat Exercise 4.29, but assume an acceleration of $1.20\ \mathrm{m/s^2}$ is produced. (b) What is unreasonable about the result? (c) Which premise is unreasonable, and why is it unreasonable?

39. Unreasonable Results (a) What is the initial acceleration of a rocket that has a mass of $1.50 \times 10^6\ \mathrm{kg}$ at takeoff, the engines of which produce a thrust of $2.00 \times 10^6\ \mathrm{N}$? Do not neglect gravity. (b) What is unreasonable about the result? (This result has been unintentionally achieved by several real rockets.) (c) Which premise is unreasonable, or which premises are inconsistent? (You may find it useful to compare this problem to the rocket problem earlier in this section.)

4.7 Further Applications of Newton's Laws of Motion

40. A flea jumps by exerting a force of $1.20 \times 10^{-5}\ \mathrm{N}$ straight down on the ground. A breeze blowing on the flea parallel to the ground exerts a force of $0.500 \times 10^{-6}\ \mathrm{N}$ on the flea. Find the direction and magnitude of the acceleration of the flea if its mass is $6.00 \times 10^{-7}\ \mathrm{kg}$. Do not neglect the gravitational force.

41. Two muscles in the back of the leg pull upward on the Achilles tendon, as shown in Figure 4.39. (These muscles are called the medial and lateral heads of the gastrocnemius muscle.) Find the magnitude and direction of the total force on the Achilles tendon. What type of movement could be caused by this force?

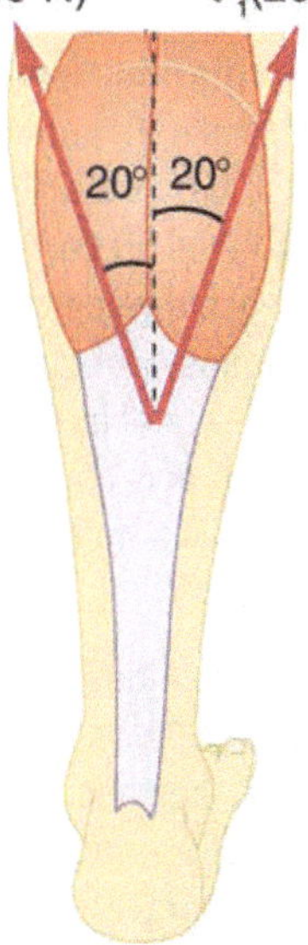

FIGURE 4.39 Achilles tendon

42. A 76.0-kg person is being pulled away from a burning building as shown in Figure 4.40. Calculate the tension in the two ropes if the person is momentarily motionless. Include a free-body diagram in your solution.

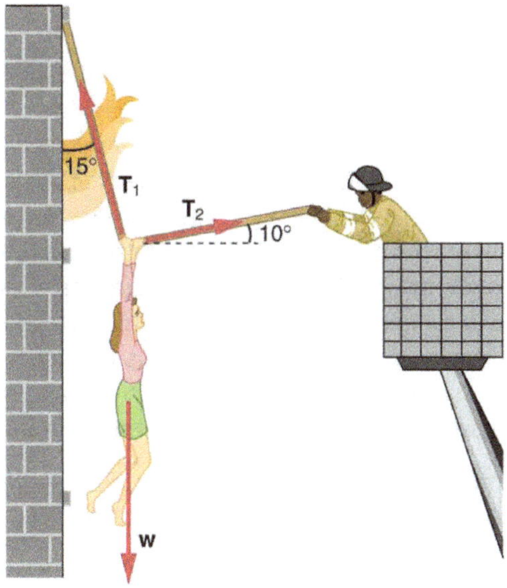

FIGURE 4.40 The force $\mathbf{T}_2$ needed to hold steady the person being rescued from the fire is less than her weight and less than the force $\mathbf{T}_1$ in the other rope, since the more vertical rope supports a greater part of her weight (a vertical force).

43. Integrated Concepts A 35.0-kg dolphin decelerates from 12.0 to 7.50 m/s in 2.30 s to join another dolphin in play. What average force was exerted to slow him if he was moving horizontally? (The gravitational force is balanced by the buoyant force of the water.)

44. Integrated Concepts When starting a foot race, a 70.0-kg sprinter exerts an average force of 650 N backward on the ground for 0.800 s. (a) What is his final speed? (b) How far does he travel?

45. Integrated Concepts A large rocket has a mass of 2.00×10^6 kg at takeoff, and its engines produce a thrust of 3.50×10^7 N. (a) Find its initial acceleration if it takes off vertically. (b) How long does it take to reach a velocity of 120 km/h straight up, assuming constant mass and thrust? (c) In reality, the mass of a rocket decreases significantly as its fuel is consumed. Describe qualitatively how this affects the acceleration and time for this motion.

46. Integrated Concepts A basketball player jumps straight up for a ball. To do this, they lower their body 0.300 m and then accelerate through this distance by forcefully straightening their legs. This player leaves the floor with a vertical velocity sufficient to carry the player 0.900 m above the floor. (a) Calculate the player's velocity when they leave the floor. (b) Calculate their acceleration while they are straightening their legs. They go from zero to the velocity found in part (a) in a distance of 0.300 m. (c) Calculate the force they exert on the floor to do this, given that their mass is 110 kg.

47. Integrated Concepts A 2.50-kg fireworks shell is fired straight up from a mortar and reaches a height of 110 m. (a) Neglecting air resistance (a poor assumption, but we will make it for this example), calculate the shell's velocity when it leaves the mortar. (b) The mortar itself is a tube 0.450 m long. Calculate the average acceleration of the shell in the tube as it goes from zero to the velocity found in (a). (c) What is the average force on the shell in the mortar? Express your answer in newtons and as a ratio to the weight of the shell.

48. Integrated Concepts Repeat Exercise 4.47 for a shell fired at an angle 10.0° from the vertical.

49. Integrated Concepts An elevator filled with passengers has a mass of 1700 kg. (a) The elevator accelerates upward from rest at a rate of 1.20 m/s^2 for 1.50 s. Calculate the tension in the cable supporting the elevator. (b) The elevator continues upward at constant velocity for 8.50 s. What is the tension in the cable during this time? (c) The elevator decelerates at a rate of 0.600 m/s^2 for 3.00 s. What is the tension in the cable during deceleration? (d) How high has the elevator moved above its original starting point, and what is its final velocity?

50. Unreasonable Results (a) What is the final velocity of a car originally traveling at 50.0 km/h that decelerates at a rate of 0.400 m/s^2 for 50.0 s? (b) What is unreasonable about the result? (c) Which premise is unreasonable, or which premises are inconsistent?

51. Unreasonable Results A 75.0-kg man stands on a bathroom scale in an elevator that accelerates from rest to 30.0 m/s in 2.00 s. (a) Calculate the scale reading in newtons and compare it with his weight. (The scale exerts an upward force on him equal to its reading.) (b) What is unreasonable about the result? (c) Which premise is unreasonable, or which premises are inconsistent?

4.8 Extended Topic: The Four Basic Forces—An Introduction

52. (a) What is the strength of the weak nuclear force relative to the strong nuclear force? (b) What is the strength of the weak nuclear force relative to the electromagnetic force? Since the weak nuclear force acts at only very short distances, such as inside nuclei, where the strong and electromagnetic forces also act, it might seem surprising that we have any knowledge of it at all. We have such knowledge because the weak nuclear force is responsible for beta decay, a type of nuclear decay not explained by other forces.

53. (a) What is the ratio of the strength of the gravitational force to that of the strong nuclear force? (b) What is the ratio of the strength of the gravitational force to that of the weak nuclear force? (c) What is the ratio of the strength of the gravitational force to that of the electromagnetic force? What do your answers imply about the influence of the gravitational force on atomic nuclei?

54. What is the ratio of the strength of the strong nuclear force to that of the electromagnetic force? Based on this ratio, you might expect that the strong force dominates the nucleus, which is true for small nuclei. Large nuclei, however, have sizes greater than the range of the strong nuclear force. At these sizes, the electromagnetic force begins to affect nuclear stability. These facts will be used to explain nuclear fusion and fission later in this text.

55. Critical Thinking Two boxes of equal mass slide start from rest and slide with different horizontal applied forces across frictionless surfaces to reach the same distance away. Box A has a horizontal force of three times that of box B. (a) Which box is traveling faster at this distance away from the starting point? Briefly explain your reasoning. (b) Based on experimental data, an equation that fits the data is suggested for the final speed, V, which may not be correct: $V = KF$, where K is a constant with appropriate units and F is the horizontal applied force. Is this equation consistent with your answer from part a? Explain why or why not. Does this equation make sense? Explain why or why not. (c) Now the applied force can be any value and the distance from the starting point is measured when the speed gets to a consistent value. Graph the distance the box gets to at a given speed as a function of the applied force.

Test Prep for AP® Courses

4.1 Development of Force Concept

1.

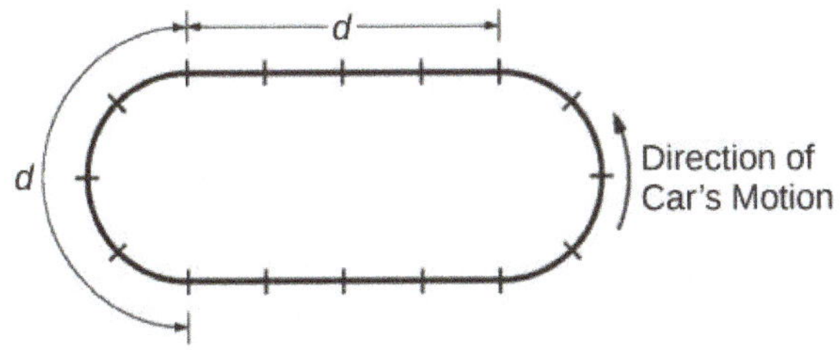

FIGURE 4.42

The figure above represents a racetrack with semicircular sections connected by straight sections. Each section has length d, and markers along the track are spaced $d/4$ apart. Two people drive cars counterclockwise around the track, as shown. Car X goes around the curves at constant speed v_C, increases speed at constant acceleration for half of each straight section to reach a maximum speed of $2v_C$, then brakes at constant acceleration for the other half of each straight section to return to speed v_C. Car Y also goes around the curves at constant speed v_C, increases its speed at constant acceleration for one-fourth of each straight section to reach the same maximum speed $2v_C$, stays at that speed for half of each straight section, then brakes at constant acceleration for the remaining fourth of each straight section to return to speed v_C.

(a) On the figures below, draw an arrow showing the direction of the net force on each of the cars at the positions noted by the dots. If the net force is zero at any position, label the dot with 0.

FIGURE 4.43

The position of the six dots on the Car Y track on the right are as follows:

The first dot on the left center of the track is at the same position as it is on the Car X track.
The second dot is just slight to the right of the Car X dot (less than a dash) past three perpendicular hash marks moving to the right.
The third dot is about one and two-thirds perpendicular hash marks to the right of the center top perpendicular has mark.
The fourth dot is in the same position as the Car X figure (one perpendicular hash mark above the center right perpendicular hash mark).
The fifth dot is about one and two-third perpendicular hash marks to the right of the center bottom perpendicular hash mark.
The sixth dot is in the same position as the Car Y dot (one and two third perpendicular hash marks to the left of the center bottom hash mark).

(b)
i. Indicate which car, if either, completes one trip around the track in less time, and justify your answer qualitatively without using equations.
ii. Justify your answer about which car, if either, completes one trip around the track in less time quantitatively with appropriate equations.

2. Which of the following is an example of a body exerting a force on itself?
a. a person standing up from a seated position
b. a car accelerating while driving
c. both of the above
d. none of the above

3. A hawk accelerates as it glides in the air. Does the force causing the acceleration come from the hawk itself? Explain.

4. What causes the force that moves a boat forward when someone rows it?
a. The force is caused by the rower's arms.

b. The force is caused by an interaction between the oars and gravity.
c. The force is caused by an interaction between the oars and the water the boat is traveling in.
d. The force is caused by friction.

4.4 Newton's Third Law of Motion: Symmetry in Forces

5. What object or objects commonly exert forces on the following objects in motion? (a) a soccer ball being kicked, (b) a dolphin jumping, (c) a parachutist drifting to Earth.

6. A ball with a mass of 0.25 kg hits a gym ceiling with a force of 78.0 N. What is the net force on the ball?
a. 2.50 N downward
b. 75.5 N downward
c. 78.0 N downward
d. 80.5 N downward

7. Which of the following is true?
a. Earth exerts a force due to gravity on your body, and your body exerts a smaller force on the Earth, because your mass is smaller than the mass of the Earth.
b. The Moon orbits the Earth because the Earth exerts a force on the Moon and the Moon exerts a force equal in magnitude and direction on the Earth.
c. A rocket taking off exerts a force on the Earth equal to the force the Earth exerts on the rocket.
d. An airplane cruising at a constant speed is not affected by gravity.

8. Stationary skater A pushes stationary skater B, who then accelerates at 5.0 m/s^2. Skater A does not move. Since forces act in action-reaction pairs, explain why Skater A did not move?

9. The current in a river exerts a force of 9.0 N on a balloon floating in the river. A wind exerts a force of 13.0 N on the balloon in the opposite direction. Draw a free-body diagram to show the forces acting on the balloon. Use your free-body diagram to predict the effect on the balloon.

10. A force is applied to accelerate an object on a smooth icy surface. When the force stops, which of the following will be true? (Assume zero friction.)
a. The object's acceleration becomes zero.
b. The object's speed becomes zero.
c. The object's acceleration continues to increase at a constant rate.
d. The object accelerates, but in the opposite direction.

11. A parachutist's fall to Earth is determined by two opposing forces. A gravitational force of 539 N acts on the parachutist. After 2 s, she opens her parachute and experiences an air resistance of 615 N. At what speed is the parachutist falling after 10 s?

12. A flight attendant pushes a cart down the aisle of a plane in flight. In determining the acceleration of the cart relative to the plane, which factor do you not need to consider?
a. The friction of the cart's wheels.
b. The force with which the flight attendant's feet push on the floor.
c. The velocity of the plane.
d. The mass of the items in the cart.

13. A landscaper is easing a wheelbarrow full of soil down a hill. Define the system you would analyze and list all the forces that you would need to include to calculate the acceleration of the wheelbarrow.

14. Two water-skiers, with masses of 48 kg and 61 kg, are preparing to be towed behind the same boat. When the boat accelerates, the rope the skiers hold onto accelerates with it and exerts a net force of 290 N on the skiers. At what rate will the skiers accelerate?
a. 10.8 m/s^2
b. 2.7 m/s^2
c. 6.0 m/s^2 and 4.8 m/s^2
d. 5.3 m/s^2

15. A figure skater has a mass of 40 kg and her partner's mass is 50 kg. She pushes against the ice with a force of 120 N, causing her and her partner to move forward. Calculate the pair's acceleration. Assume that all forces opposing the motion, such as friction and air resistance, total 5.0 N.

4.5 Normal, Tension, and Other Examples of Forces

16. An archer shoots an arrow straight up with a force of 24.5 N. The arrow has a mass of 0.4 kg. What is the force of gravity on the arrow?
a. 9.8 m/s^2
b. 9.8 N
c. 61.25 N

d. 3.9 N

17. A cable raises a mass of 120.0 kg with an acceleration of 1.3 m/s2. What force of tension is in the cable?

18. A child pulls a wagon along a grassy field. Define the system, the pairs of forces at work, and the results.

19. Two teams are engaging in a tug–of-war. The rope suddenly snaps. Which statement is true about the forces involved?

a. The forces exerted by the two teams are no longer equal; the teams will accelerate in opposite directions as a result.
b. The forces exerted by the players are no longer balanced by the force of tension in the rope; the teams will accelerate in opposite directions as a result.
c. The force of gravity balances the forces exerted by the players; the teams will fall as a result
d. The force of tension in the rope is transferred to the players; the teams will accelerate in opposite directions as a result.

20. The following free-body diagram represents a toboggan on a hill. What acceleration would you expect, and why?

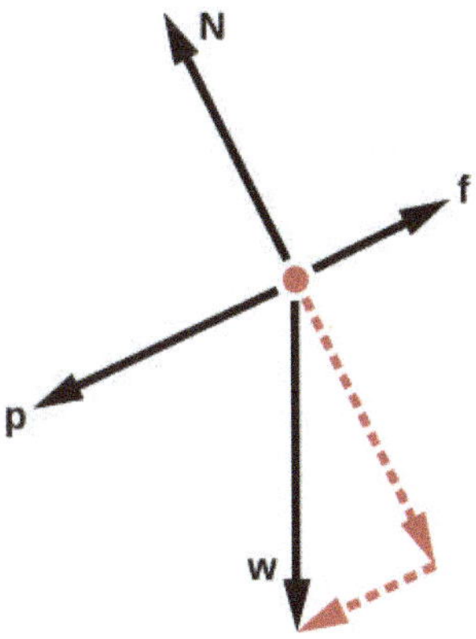

FIGURE 4.46

a. Acceleration down the hill; the force due to being pushed, together with the downhill component of gravity, overcomes the opposing force of friction.
b. Acceleration down the hill; friction is less than the opposing component of force due to gravity.
c. No movement; friction is greater than the force due to being pushed.
d. No movement; friction is greater than the sum of the downhill forces.

21. Draw a free-body diagram to represent the forces acting on a kite on a string that is floating stationary in the air. Label the forces in your diagram.

22. A car is sliding down a hill with a slope of 20°. The mass of the car is 965 kg. When a cable is used to pull the car up the slope, a force of 4215 N is applied. What is the car's acceleration, ignoring friction?

4.6 Problem-Solving Strategies

23. A toboggan with two riders has a total mass of 85.0 kg. A third person is pushing with a horizontal force of 42.5 N on a toboggan moving on a horizontal surface at the top of a hill that has a downward angle of 15°. The force of friction on the toboggan is 31.0 N. Which statement describes an accurate free-body diagram to represent the situation?

a. An arrow of magnitude 10.5 N points down the slope of the hill.
b. An arrow of magnitude 833 N points straight down.
c. An arrow of magnitude 833 N points perpendicular to the slope of the hill.
d. An arrow of magnitude 73.5 N points down the slope of the hill.

24. A mass of 2.0 kg is suspended from the ceiling of an elevator by a rope. What is the tension in the rope when the elevator (i) accelerates upward at 1.5 m/s^2? (ii) accelerates downward at 1.5 m/s^2?

a. (i) 22.6 N; (ii) 16.6 N
b. Because the mass is hanging from the elevator itself, the tension in the rope will not change in either case.
c. (i) 22.6 N; (ii) 19.6 N
d. (i) 16.6 N; (ii) 19.6 N

25. Which statement is true about drawing free-body diagrams?

a. Drawing a free-body diagram should be the last step in solving a problem about forces.
b. Drawing a free-body diagram helps you compare forces quantitatively.
c. The forces in a free-body diagram should always balance.
d. Drawing a free-body diagram can help you determine the net force.

4.7 Further Applications of Newton's Laws of Motion

26. A basketball player jumps as he shoots the ball. Describe the forces that are acting on the ball and on the basketball player. What are the results?

27. Two people push on a boulder to try to move it. The mass of the boulder is 825 kg. One person pushes north with a force of 64 N. The other pushes west with a force of 38 N. Predict the magnitude of the acceleration of the boulder. Assume that friction is negligible.

28.

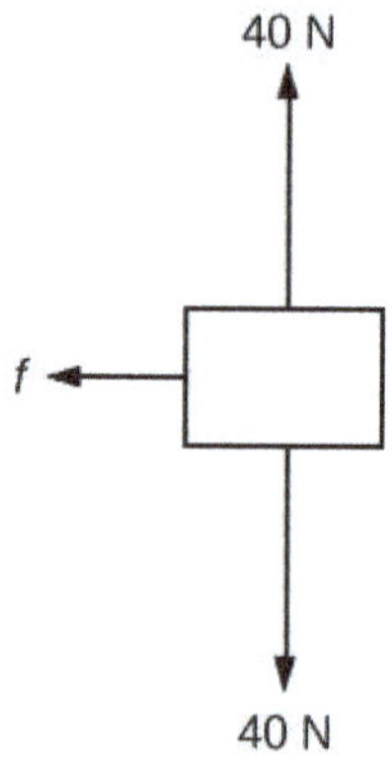

FIGURE 4.48

The figure shows the forces exerted on a block that is sliding on a horizontal surface: the gravitational force of 40 N, the 40 N normal force exerted by the surface, and a frictional force exerted to the left. The coefficient of friction between the block and the surface is 0.20. The acceleration of the block is most nearly

a. 1.0 m/s^2 to the right
b. 1.0 m/s^2 to the left
c. 2.0 m/s^2 to the right
d. 2.0 m/s^2 to the left

4.8 Extended Topic: The Four Basic Forces—An Introduction

29. Which phenomenon correctly describes the direction and magnitude of normal forces?

a. electromagnetic attraction
b. electromagnetic repulsion
c. gravitational attraction
d. gravitational repulsion

30. Explain which of the four fundamental forces is responsible for a ball bouncing off the ground after it hits, and why this force has this effect.

31. Which of the basic forces best explains tension in a rope being pulled between two people? Is the acting force causing attraction or repulsion in this instance?

a. gravity; attraction
b. electromagnetic; attraction
c. weak and strong nuclear; attraction
d. weak and strong nuclear; repulsion

32. Explain how interatomic electric forces produce the normal force, and why it has the direction it does.

33. The gravitational force is the weakest of the four basic forces. In which case can the electromagnetic, strong, and weak forces be ignored because the gravitational force is so strongly dominant?

a. a person jumping on a trampoline
b. a rocket blasting off from Earth
c. a log rolling down a hill
d. all of the above

34. Describe a situation in which gravitational force is the dominant force. Why can the other three basic forces be ignored in the situation you described?

CHAPTER 5

Further Applications of Newton's Laws: Friction, Drag, and Elasticity

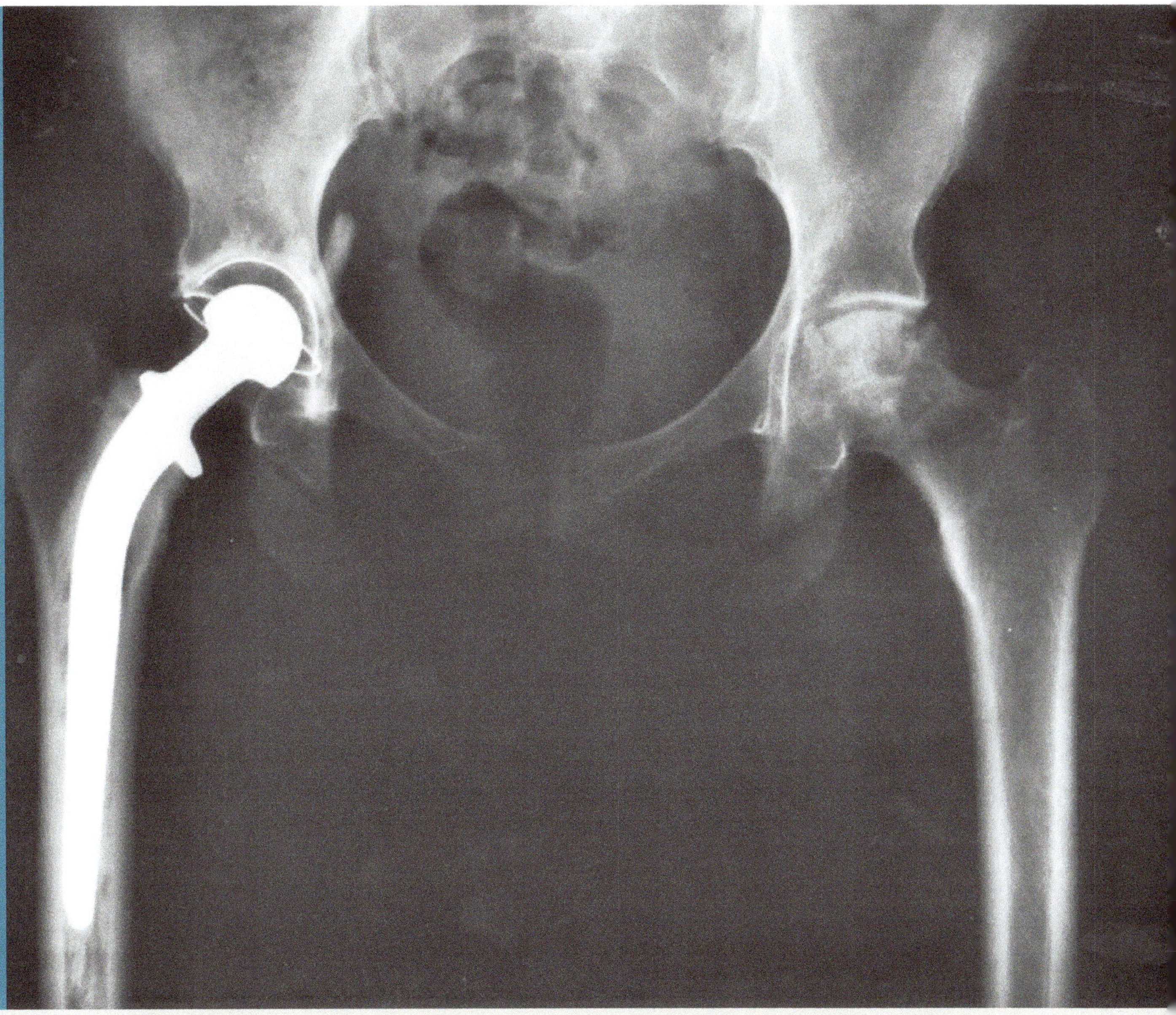

FIGURE 5.1 Total hip replacement surgery has become a common procedure. The head (or ball) of the patient's femur fits into a cup that has a hard plastic-like inner lining. (credit: National Institutes of Health, via Wikimedia Commons)

CHAPTER OUTLINE

CONNECTION FOR AP® COURSES Have you ever wondered why it is difficult to walk on a smooth surface like ice? The interaction between you and the surface is a result of forces that affect your motion. In the previous chapter, you learned Newton's laws of motion and examined how net force affects the motion, position and shape of an object. Now we will look at some interesting and common forces that will provide further applications of Newton's laws of motion.

The information presented in this chapter supports learning objectives covered under Big Idea 3 of the AP Physics Curriculum Framework, which refer to the nature of forces and their roles in interactions among objects. The chapter discusses examples of specific contact forces, such as friction, air or liquid drag, and elasticity that may affect the motion or shape of an object. It also discusses the nature of forces on both macroscopic and microscopic levels (Enduring Understanding 3.C and Essential Knowledge 3.C.4). In addition, Newton's laws are applied to describe the motion of an object (Enduring Understanding 3.B) and to examine relationships between contact forces and other forces exerted on an object (Enduring Understanding 3.A, 3.A.3 and Essential Knowledge 3.A.4). The examples in this chapter give you practice in using vector properties of forces (Essential Knowledge 3.A.2) and free-body diagrams (Essential Knowledge 3.B.2) to determine net force (Essential Knowledge 3.B.1).

Big Idea 3 The interactions of an object with other objects can be described by forces.

Enduring Understanding 3.A All forces share certain common characteristics when considered by observers in inertial reference frames.

Essential Knowledge 3.A.2 Forces are described by vectors.

Essential Knowledge 3.A.3 A force exerted on an object is always due to the interaction of that object with another object.

Essential Knowledge 3.A.4 If one object exerts a force on a second object, the second object always exerts a force of equal magnitude on the first object in the opposite direction.

Enduring Understanding 3.B Classically, the acceleration of an object interacting with other objects can be predicted by using $\vec{a} = \frac{\sum \vec{F}}{m}$.

Essential Knowledge 3.B.1 If an object of interest interacts with several other objects, the net force is the vector sum of the individual forces.

Essential Knowledge 3.B.2 Free-body diagrams are useful tools for visualizing forces being exerted on a single object and writing the equations that represent a physical situation.

Enduring Understanding 3.C At the macroscopic level, forces can be categorized as either long-range (action-at-a-distance) forces or contact forces.

Essential Knowledge 3.C.4 Contact forces result from the interaction of one object touching another object, and they arise from interatomic electric forces. These forces include tension, friction, normal, spring (Physics 1), and buoyant (Physics 2).

Click to view content (https://openstax.org/books/college-physics-ap-courses-2e/pages/5-connection-for-ap-r-courses)

5.1 Friction

LEARNING OBJECTIVES

By the end of this section, you will be able to:

- Discuss the general characteristics of friction.
- Describe the various types of friction.
- Calculate the magnitude of static and kinetic friction.

Friction is a force that is around us all the time that opposes relative motion between surfaces in contact but also allows us to move (which you have discovered if you have ever tried to walk on ice). While a common force, the behavior of friction is actually very complicated and is still not completely understood. We have to rely heavily on observations for whatever understandings we can gain. However, we can still deal with its more elementary general characteristics and understand the circumstances in which it behaves.

FRICTION

Friction is a force that opposes relative motion between surfaces in contact.

One of the simpler characteristics of friction is that it is parallel to the contact surface between surfaces and always in a direction that opposes motion or attempted motion of the systems relative to each other. If two surfaces are in contact and moving relative to one another, then the friction between them is called **kinetic friction**. For example, friction slows a hockey puck sliding on ice. But when objects are stationary, **static friction** can act between them; the static friction is usually greater than the kinetic friction between the surfaces.

KINETIC FRICTION

If two surfaces are in contact and moving relative to one another, then the friction between them is called kinetic friction.

Imagine, for example, trying to slide a heavy crate across a concrete floor—you may push harder and harder on the crate and not move it at all. This means that the static friction responds to what you do—it increases to be equal to and in the opposite direction of your push. But if you finally push hard enough, the crate seems to slip suddenly and starts to move. Once in motion it is easier to keep it in motion than it was to get it started, indicating that the kinetic friction force is less than the static friction force. If you add mass to the crate, say by placing a box on top of it, you need to push even harder to get it started and also to keep it moving. Furthermore, if you oiled the concrete you would find it to be easier to get the crate started and keep it going (as you might expect).

Figure 5.2 is a crude pictorial representation of how friction occurs at the interface between two objects. Close-up inspection of these surfaces shows them to be rough. So when you push to get an object moving (in this case, a crate), you must raise the object until it can skip along with just the tips of the surface hitting, break off the points, or do both. A considerable force can be resisted by friction with no apparent motion. The harder the surfaces are pushed together (such as if another box is placed on the crate), the more force is needed to move them. Part of the friction is due to adhesive forces between the surface molecules of the two objects, which explain the dependence of friction on the nature of the substances. Adhesion varies with substances in contact and is a complicated aspect of surface physics. Once an object is moving, there are fewer points of contact (fewer molecules adhering), so less force is required to keep the object moving. At small but nonzero speeds, friction is nearly independent of speed.

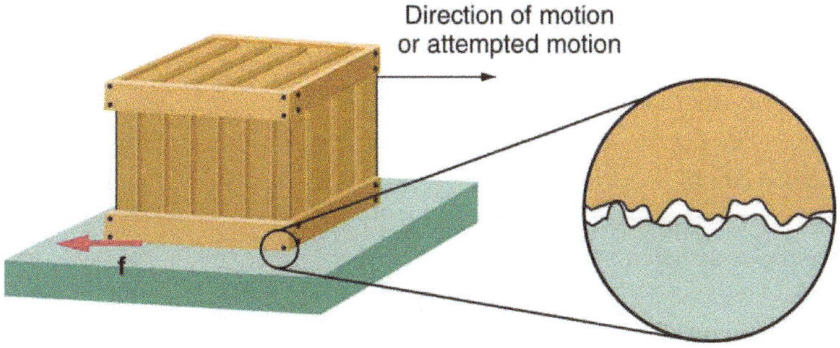

FIGURE 5.2 Frictional forces, such as f, always oppose motion or attempted motion between surfaces in contact. Friction arises in part because of the roughness of the surfaces in contact, as seen in the expanded view. In order for the object to move, it must rise to where the peaks can skip along the bottom surface. Thus a force is required just to set the object in motion. Some of the peaks will be broken off, also requiring a force to maintain motion. Much of the friction is actually due to attractive forces between molecules making up the two objects, so that even perfectly smooth surfaces are not friction-free. Such adhesive forces also depend on the substances the surfaces are made of, explaining, for example, why rubber-soled shoes slip less than those with leather soles.

The magnitude of the frictional force has two forms: one for static situations (static friction), the other for when there is motion (kinetic friction).

When there is no motion between the objects, the **magnitude of static friction $\mathbf{f}_s$** is

$$f_s \leq \mu_s N, \tag{5.1}$$

where μ_s is the coefficient of static friction and N is the magnitude of the normal force (the force perpendicular to the surface).

MAGNITUDE OF STATIC FRICTION

Magnitude of static friction f_s is

$$f_s \leq \mu_s N, \tag{5.2}$$

where μ_s is the coefficient of static friction and N is the magnitude of the normal force.

The symbol ≤ means *less than or equal to,* implying that static friction can have a minimum and a maximum value of $\mu_s N$. Static friction is a responsive force that increases to be equal and opposite to whatever force is exerted, up to its maximum limit. Once the applied force exceeds $f_{s(max)}$, the object will move. Thus

$$f_{s(max)} = \mu_s N. \tag{5.3}$$

Once an object is moving, the **magnitude of kinetic friction $\mathbf{f}_k$** is given by

$$f_k = \mu_k N, \tag{5.4}$$

where μ_k is the coefficient of kinetic friction. A system in which $f_k = \mu_k N$ is described as a system in which *friction behaves simply.*

MAGNITUDE OF KINETIC FRICTION

The magnitude of kinetic friction f_k is given by

$$f_k = \mu_k N, \tag{5.5}$$

where μ_k is the coefficient of kinetic friction.

As seen in Table 5.1, the coefficients of kinetic friction are less than their static counterparts. That values of μ in Table 5.1 are stated to only one or, at most, two digits is an indication of the approximate description of friction given by the above two equations.

System	Static friction μ_s	Kinetic friction μ_k
Rubber on dry concrete	1.0	0.7
Rubber on wet concrete	0.7	0.5
Wood on wood	0.5	0.3
Waxed wood on wet snow	0.14	0.1
Metal on wood	0.5	0.3
Steel on steel (dry)	0.6	0.3
Steel on steel (oiled)	0.05	0.03
Teflon on steel	0.04	0.04
Bone lubricated by synovial fluid	0.016	0.015

TABLE 5.1 Coefficients of Static and Kinetic Friction

System	Static friction μ_s	Kinetic friction μ_k
Shoes on wood	0.9	0.7
Shoes on ice	0.1	0.05
Ice on ice	0.1	0.03
Steel on ice	0.04	0.02

TABLE 5.1 Coefficients of Static and Kinetic Friction

The equations given earlier include the dependence of friction on materials and the normal force. The direction of friction is always opposite that of motion, parallel to the surface between objects, and perpendicular to the normal force. For example, if the crate you try to push (with a force parallel to the floor) has a mass of 100 kg, then the normal force would be equal to its weight, $W = mg = (100 \text{ kg})(9.80 \text{ m/s}^2) = 980 \text{ N}$, perpendicular to the floor. If the coefficient of static friction is 0.45, you would have to exert a force parallel to the floor greater than $f_{s(\max)} = \mu_s N = (0.45)(980 \text{ N}) = 440 \text{ N}$ to move the crate. Once there is motion, friction is less and the coefficient of kinetic friction might be 0.30, so that a force of only 290 N ($f_k = \mu_k N = (0.30)(980 \text{ N}) = 290 \text{ N}$) would keep it moving at a constant speed. If the floor is lubricated, both coefficients are considerably less than they would be without lubrication. Coefficient of friction is a unit less quantity with a magnitude usually between 0 and 1.0. The coefficient of the friction depends on the two surfaces that are in contact.

TAKE-HOME EXPERIMENT

Find a small plastic object (such as a food container) and slide it on a kitchen table by giving it a gentle tap. Now spray water on the table, simulating a light shower of rain. What happens now when you give the object the same-sized tap? Now add a few drops of (vegetable or olive) oil on the surface of the water and give the same tap. What happens now? This latter situation is particularly important for drivers to note, especially after a light rain shower. Why?

Many people have experienced the slipperiness of walking on ice. However, many parts of the body, especially the joints, have much smaller coefficients of friction—often three or four times less than ice. A joint is formed by the ends of two bones, which are connected by thick tissues. The knee joint is formed by the lower leg bone (the tibia) and the thighbone (the femur). The hip is a ball (at the end of the femur) and socket (part of the pelvis) joint. The ends of the bones in the joint are covered by cartilage, which provides a smooth, almost glassy surface. The joints also produce a fluid (synovial fluid) that reduces friction and wear. A damaged or arthritic joint can be replaced by an artificial joint (Figure 5.3). These replacements can be made of metals (stainless steel or titanium) or plastic (polyethylene), also with very small coefficients of friction.

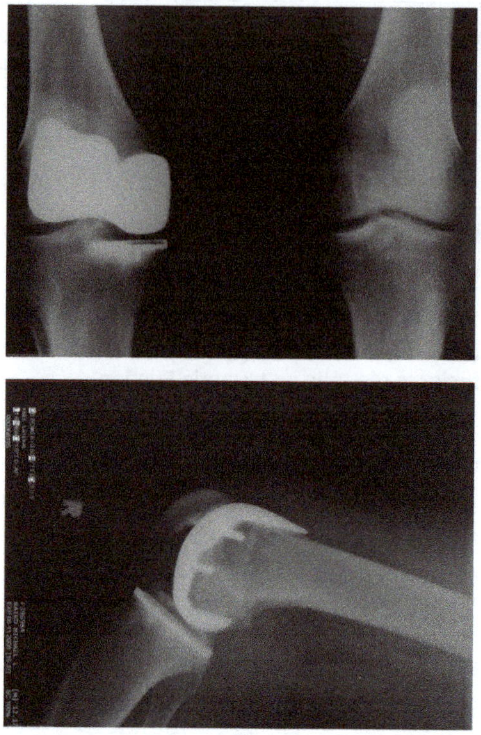

FIGURE 5.3 Artificial knee replacement is a procedure that has been performed for more than 20 years. In this figure, we see the post-op X-rays of the right knee joint replacement. (credit: Mike Baird, Flickr)

Other natural lubricants include saliva produced in our mouths to aid in the swallowing process, and the slippery mucus found between organs in the body, allowing them to move freely past each other during heartbeats, during breathing, and when a person moves. Artificial lubricants are also common in hospitals and doctor's clinics. For example, when ultrasonic imaging is carried out, the gel that couples the transducer to the skin also serves to lubricate the surface between the transducer and the skin—thereby reducing the coefficient of friction between the two surfaces. This allows the transducer to move freely over the skin.

EXAMPLE 5.1

Skiing Exercise

A skier with a mass of 62 kg is sliding down a snowy slope. Find the coefficient of kinetic friction for the skier if friction is known to be 45.0 N.

Strategy

The magnitude of kinetic friction was given in to be 45.0 N. Kinetic friction is related to the normal force $\mathbf{N}$ as $f_\mathrm{k} = \mu_\mathrm{k} N$; thus, the coefficient of kinetic friction can be found if we can find the normal force of the skier on a slope. The normal force is always perpendicular to the surface, and since there is no motion perpendicular to the surface, the normal force should equal the component of the skier's weight perpendicular to the slope. (See the skier and free-body diagram in Figure 5.4.)

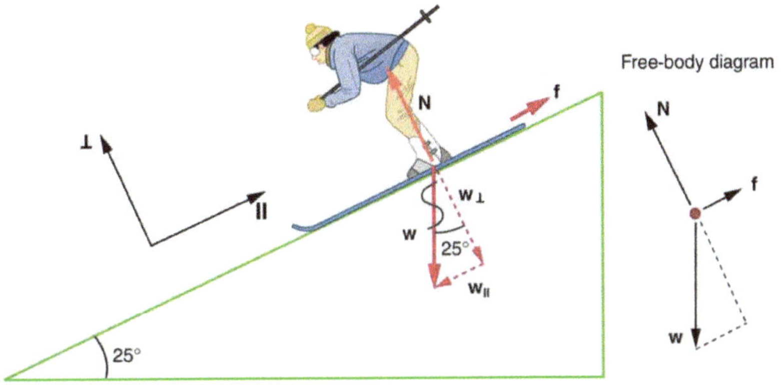

FIGURE 5.4 The motion of the skier and friction are parallel to the slope and so it is most convenient to project all forces onto a coordinate system where one axis is parallel to the slope and the other is perpendicular (axes shown to left of skier). **N** (the normal force) is perpendicular to the slope, and **f** (the friction) is parallel to the slope, but **w** (the skier's weight) has components along both axes, namely $\mathbf{w}_\perp$ and $\mathbf{W}_{//}$. **N** is equal in magnitude to $\mathbf{w}_\perp$, so there is no motion perpendicular to the slope. However, **f** is less than $\mathbf{W}_{//}$ in magnitude, so there is acceleration down the slope (along the *x*-axis).

That is,

$$N = w_\perp = w \cos 25° = mg \cos 25°. \quad (5.6)$$

Substituting this into our expression for kinetic friction, we get

$$f_k = \mu_k mg \cos 25°, \quad (5.7)$$

which can now be solved for the coefficient of kinetic friction μ_k.

Solution

Solving for μ_k gives

$$\mu_k = \frac{f_k}{N} = \frac{f_k}{w \cos 25°} = \frac{f_k}{mg \cos 25°}. \quad (5.8)$$

Substituting known values on the right-hand side of the equation,

$$\mu_k = \frac{45.0\ \text{N}}{(62\ \text{kg})(9.80\ \text{m/s}^2)(0.906)} = 0.082. \quad (5.9)$$

Discussion

This result is a little smaller than the coefficient listed in Table 5.1 for waxed wood on snow, but it is still reasonable since values of the coefficients of friction can vary greatly. In situations like this, where an object of mass m slides down a slope that makes an angle θ with the horizontal, friction is given by $f_k = \mu_k mg \cos\theta$. All objects will slide down a slope with constant acceleration under these circumstances. Proof of this is left for this chapter's Problems and Exercises.

TAKE-HOME EXPERIMENT

An object will slide down an inclined plane at a constant velocity if the net force on the object is zero. We can use this fact to measure the coefficient of kinetic friction between two objects. As shown in Example 5.1, the kinetic friction on a slope $f_k = \mu_k mg \cos\theta$. The component of the weight down the slope is equal to $mg \sin\theta$ (see the free-body diagram in Figure 5.4). These forces act in opposite directions, so when they have equal magnitude, the acceleration is zero. Writing these out:

$$f_k = mg_x \quad (5.10)$$

$$\mu_k mg \cos\theta = mg \sin\theta. \quad (5.11)$$

Solving for μ_k, we find that

$$\mu_k = \frac{mg \sin \theta}{mg \cos \theta} = \tan \theta. \quad 5.12$$

Put a coin on a book and tilt it until the coin slides at a constant velocity down the book. You might need to tap the book lightly to get the coin to move. Measure the angle of tilt relative to the horizontal and find μ_k. Note that the coin will not start to slide at all until an angle greater than θ is attained, since the coefficient of static friction is larger than the coefficient of kinetic friction. Discuss how this may affect the value for μ_k and its uncertainty.

We have discussed that when an object rests on a horizontal surface, there is a normal force supporting it equal in magnitude to its weight. Furthermore, simple friction is always proportional to the normal force.

MAKING CONNECTIONS: SUBMICROSCOPIC EXPLANATIONS OF FRICTION

The simpler aspects of friction dealt with so far are its macroscopic (large-scale) characteristics. Great strides have been made in the atomic-scale explanation of friction during the past several decades. Researchers are finding that the atomic nature of friction seems to have several fundamental characteristics. These characteristics not only explain some of the simpler aspects of friction—they also hold the potential for the development of nearly friction-free environments that could save hundreds of billions of dollars in energy which is currently being converted (unnecessarily) to heat.

Figure 5.5 illustrates one macroscopic characteristic of friction that is explained by microscopic (small-scale) research. We have noted that friction is proportional to the normal force, but not to the area in contact, a somewhat counterintuitive notion. When two rough surfaces are in contact, the actual contact area is a tiny fraction of the total area since only high spots touch. When a greater normal force is exerted, the actual contact area increases, and it is found that the friction is proportional to this area.

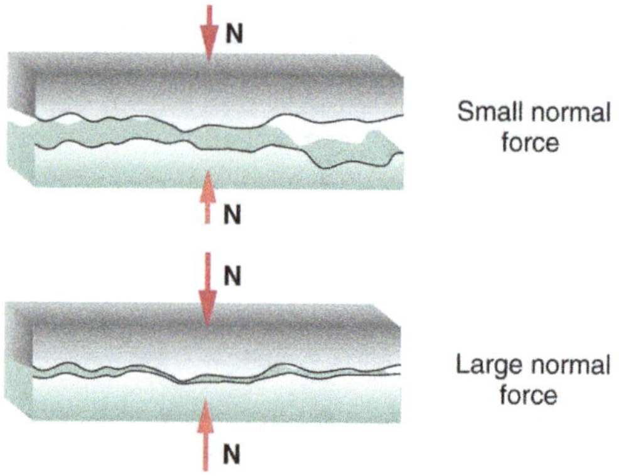

FIGURE 5.5 Two rough surfaces in contact have a much smaller area of actual contact than their total area. When there is a greater normal force as a result of a greater applied force, the area of actual contact increases as does friction.

But the atomic-scale view promises to explain far more than the simpler features of friction. The mechanism for how heat is generated is now being determined. In other words, why do surfaces get warmer when rubbed? Essentially, atoms are linked with one another to form lattices. When surfaces rub, the surface atoms adhere and cause atomic lattices to vibrate—essentially creating sound waves that penetrate the material. The sound waves diminish with distance and their energy is converted into heat. Chemical reactions that are related to frictional wear can also occur between atoms and molecules on the surfaces. Figure 5.6 shows how the tip of a probe drawn across another material is deformed by atomic-scale friction. The force needed to drag the tip can be measured and is found to be related to shear stress, which will be discussed later in this chapter. The variation in shear stress is remarkable (more than a factor of 10^{12}) and difficult to predict theoretically, but shear stress is yielding a fundamental understanding of a large-scale phenomenon known since ancient times—friction.

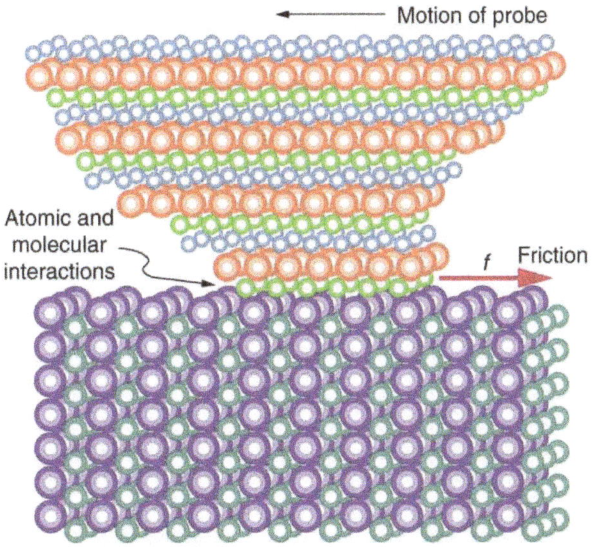

FIGURE 5.6 The tip of a probe is deformed sideways by frictional force as the probe is dragged across a surface. Measurements of how the force varies for different materials are yielding fundamental insights into the atomic nature of friction.

PHET EXPLORATIONS

Forces and Motion

Explore the forces at work when you try to push a filing cabinet. Create an applied force and see the resulting friction force and total force acting on the cabinet. Charts show the forces, position, velocity, and acceleration vs. time. Draw a free-body diagram of all the forces (including gravitational and normal forces).

Click to view content (https://openstax.org/books/college-physics-ap-courses-2e/pages/5-1-friction)

PhET

5.2 Drag Forces

LEARNING OBJECTIVES

By the end of this section, you will be able to:

- Express mathematically the drag force.
- Discuss the applications of drag force.
- Define terminal velocity.
- Determine the terminal velocity given mass.

Another interesting force in everyday life is the force of drag on an object when it is moving in a fluid (either a gas or a liquid). You feel the drag force when you move your hand through water. You might also feel it if you move your hand during a strong wind. The faster you move your hand, the harder it is to move. You feel a smaller drag force when you tilt your hand so only the side goes through the air—you have decreased the area of your hand that faces the direction of motion. Like friction, the **drag force** always opposes the motion of an object. Unlike simple friction, the drag force is proportional to some function of the velocity of the object in that fluid. This functionality is complicated and depends upon the shape of the object, its size, its velocity, and the fluid it is in. For most large objects such as bicyclists, cars, and baseballs not moving too slowly, the magnitude of the drag force F_D is found to be proportional to the square of the speed of the object. We can write this relationship mathematically as $F_D \propto v^2$. When taking into account other factors, this relationship becomes

$$F_D = \frac{1}{2}C\rho Av^2, \tag{5.13}$$

where C is the drag coefficient, A is the area of the object facing the fluid, and ρ is the density of the fluid. (Recall that density is mass per unit volume.) This equation can also be written in a more generalized fashion as $F_D = bv^2$, where b is a constant equivalent to $0.5C\rho A$. We have set the exponent for these equations as 2 because, when an object is moving at high velocity through air, the magnitude of the drag force is proportional to the square of the speed. As we shall see in a few pages on fluid dynamics, for small particles moving at low speeds in a fluid, the exponent is equal to 1.

DRAG FORCE

Drag force F_D is found to be proportional to the square of the speed of the object. Mathematically

$$F_D \propto v^2 \tag{5.14}$$

$$F_D = \frac{1}{2}C\rho A v^2, \tag{5.15}$$

where C is the drag coefficient, A is the area of the object facing the fluid, and ρ is the density of the fluid.

Athletes as well as car designers seek to reduce the drag force to lower their race times. (See Figure 5.7). "Aerodynamic" shaping of an automobile can reduce the drag force and so increase a car's gas mileage.

FIGURE 5.7 From racing cars to bobsled racers, aerodynamic shaping is crucial to achieving top speeds. Bobsleds are designed for speed. They are shaped like a bullet with tapered fins. (credit: U.S. Army, via Wikimedia Commons)

The value of the drag coefficient, C, is determined empirically, usually with the use of a wind tunnel. (See Figure 5.8).

FIGURE 5.8 NASA researchers test a model plane in a wind tunnel. (credit: NASA/Ames)

The drag coefficient can depend upon velocity, but we will assume that it is a constant here. Table 5.2 lists some typical drag coefficients for a variety of objects. Notice that the drag coefficient is a dimensionless quantity. At highway speeds, over 50% of the power of a car is used to overcome air drag. The most fuel-efficient cruising speed is about 70–80 km/h (about 45–50 mi/h). For this reason, during the 1970s oil crisis in the United States, maximum speeds on highways were set at about 90 km/h (55 mi/h).

Object	C
Airfoil	0.05
Toyota Camry	0.28
Ford Focus	0.32
Honda Civic	0.36
Ferrari Testarossa	0.37
Dodge Ram pickup	0.43
Sphere	0.45
Hummer H2 SUV	0.64
Skydiver (feet first)	0.70
Bicycle	0.90
Skydiver (horizontal)	1.0
Circular flat plate	1.12

TABLE 5.2 Drag Coefficient Values Typical values of drag coefficient C.

Substantial research is under way in the sporting world to minimize drag. The dimples on golf balls are being redesigned as are the clothes that athletes wear. Bicycle racers and some swimmers and runners wear full bodysuits. Australian Cathy Freeman wore a full body suit in the 2000 Sydney Olympics, and won the gold medal for the 400 m race. Many swimmers in the 2008 Beijing Olympics wore (Speedo) body suits; it might have made a difference in breaking many world records (See Figure 5.9). Most elite swimmers (and cyclists) shave their body hair. Such innovations can have the effect of slicing away milliseconds in a race, sometimes making the difference between a gold and a silver medal. One consequence is that careful and precise guidelines must be continuously developed to maintain the integrity of the sport.

FIGURE 5.9 Body suits, such as this LZR Racer Suit, have been credited with many world records after their release in 2008. Smoother "skin" and more compression forces on a swimmer's body provide at least 10% less drag. (credit: NASA/Kathy Barnstorff)

Some interesting situations connected to Newton's second law occur when considering the effects of drag forces upon a moving object. For instance, consider a skydiver falling through air under the influence of gravity. The two forces acting on him are the force of gravity and the drag force (ignoring the buoyant force). The downward force of gravity remains constant regardless of the velocity at which the person is moving. However, as the person's velocity increases, the magnitude of the drag force increases until the magnitude of the drag force is equal to the gravitational force, thus producing a net force of zero. A zero net force means that there is no acceleration, as given by Newton's second law. At this point, the person's velocity remains constant and we say that the person has reached his *terminal velocity* (v_t). Since F_D is proportional to the speed, a heavier skydiver must go faster for F_D to equal his weight. Let's see how this works out more quantitatively.

At the terminal velocity,

$$F_{net} = mg - F_D = ma = 0. \tag{5.16}$$

Thus,

$$mg = F_D. \tag{5.17}$$

Using the equation for drag force, we have

$$mg = \frac{1}{2}\rho C A v^2. \tag{5.18}$$

Solving for the velocity, we obtain

$$v = \sqrt{\frac{2mg}{\rho CA}}. \tag{5.19}$$

Assume the density of air is $\rho = 1.21\ \text{kg/m}^3$. A 75-kg skydiver descending head first will have an area approximately $A = 0.18\ \text{m}^2$ and a drag coefficient of approximately $C = 0.70$. We find that

$$\begin{aligned} v &= \sqrt{\frac{2(75\ \text{kg})(9.80\ \text{m/s}^2)}{(1.21\ \text{kg/m}^3)(0.70)(0.18\ \text{m}^2)}} \\ &= 98\ \text{m/s} \\ &= 350\ \text{km/h}. \end{aligned} \tag{5.20}$$

This means a skydiver with a mass of 75 kg achieves a maximum terminal velocity of about 350 km/h while traveling in a headfirst position, minimizing the area and his drag. In a spread-eagle position, that terminal velocity may decrease to about 200 km/h as the area increases. This terminal velocity becomes much smaller after the parachute opens.

TAKE-HOME EXPERIMENT

This interesting activity examines the effect of weight upon terminal velocity. Gather together some nested coffee filters. Leaving them in their original shape, measure the time it takes for one, two, three, four, and five nested filters to fall to the floor from the same height (roughly 2 m). (Note that, due to the way the filters are nested, drag is constant and only mass varies.) They obtain terminal velocity quite quickly, so find this velocity as a function of mass. Plot the terminal velocity v versus mass. Also plot v^2 versus mass. Which of these relationships is more linear? What can you conclude from these graphs?

EXAMPLE 5.2

A Terminal Velocity

Find the terminal velocity of an 85-kg skydiver falling in a spread-eagle position.

Strategy

At terminal velocity, $F_{net} = 0$. Thus the drag force on the skydiver must equal the force of gravity (the person's weight). Using the equation of drag force, we find $mg = \frac{1}{2}\rho CAv^2$.

Thus the terminal velocity v_t can be written as

$$v_t = \sqrt{\frac{2mg}{\rho CA}}. \quad (5.21)$$

Solution

All quantities are known except the person's projected area. This is an adult (85 kg) falling spread eagle. We can estimate the frontal area as

$$A = (2\text{ m})(0.35\text{ m}) = 0.70\text{ m}^2. \quad (5.22)$$

Using our equation for v_t, we find that

$$\begin{aligned} v_t &= \sqrt{\frac{2(85\text{ kg})(9.80\text{ m/s}^2)}{(1.21\text{ kg/m}^3)(1.0)(0.70\text{ m}^2)}} \\ &= 44\text{ m/s}. \end{aligned} \quad (5.23)$$

Discussion

This result is consistent with the value for v_t mentioned earlier. The 75-kg skydiver going feet first had a $v = 98$ m/s. He weighed less but had a smaller frontal area and so a smaller drag due to the air.

The size of the object that is falling through air presents another interesting application of air drag. If you fall from a 5-m high branch of a tree, you will likely get hurt—possibly fracturing a bone. However, a small squirrel does this all the time, without getting hurt. You don't reach a terminal velocity in such a short distance, but the squirrel does.

The following interesting quote on animal size and terminal velocity is from a 1928 essay by a British biologist, J.B.S. Haldane, titled "On Being the Right Size."

To the mouse and any smaller animal, [gravity] presents practically no dangers. You can drop a mouse down a thousand-yard mine shaft; and, on arriving at the bottom, it gets a slight shock and walks away, provided that the ground is fairly soft. A rat is killed, a man is broken, and a horse splashes. For the resistance presented to movement by the air is proportional to the surface of the moving object. Divide an animal's length, breadth, and height each by ten; its weight is reduced to a thousandth, but its surface only to a hundredth. So the resistance to falling in the case of the small animal is relatively ten times greater than the driving force.

The above quadratic dependence of air drag upon velocity does not hold if the object is very small, is going very slow, or is in a denser medium than air. Then we find that the drag force is proportional just to the velocity. This relationship is given by **Stokes' law**, which states that

$$F_s = 6\pi r\eta v, \quad (5.24)$$

where r is the radius of the object, η is the viscosity of the fluid, and v is the object's velocity.

STOKES' LAW

$$F_s = 6\pi r\eta v, \quad (5.25)$$

where r is the radius of the object, η is the viscosity of the fluid, and v is the object's velocity.

Good examples of this law are provided by microorganisms, pollen, and dust particles. Because each of these objects is so small, we find that many of these objects travel unaided only at a constant (terminal) velocity. Terminal velocities for bacteria (size about $1\ \mu\text{m}$) can be about $2\ \mu\text{m/s}$. To move at a greater speed, many bacteria swim using flagella (organelles shaped like little tails) that are powered by little motors embedded in the cell. Sediment in a lake can move at a greater terminal velocity (about $5\ \mu\text{m/s}$), so it can take days to reach the bottom of the lake after being deposited on the surface.

If we compare animals living on land with those in water, you can see how drag has influenced evolution. Fishes, dolphins, and even massive whales are streamlined in shape to reduce drag forces. Birds are streamlined and migratory species that fly large distances often have particular features such as long necks. Flocks of birds fly in the shape of a spear head as the flock forms a streamlined pattern (see Figure 5.10). In humans, one important example of streamlining is the shape of sperm, which need to be efficient in their use of energy.

FIGURE 5.10 Geese fly in a V formation during their long migratory travels. This shape reduces drag and energy consumption for individual birds, and also allows them a better way to communicate. (credit: Julo, Wikimedia Commons)

GALILEO'S EXPERIMENT

Galileo is said to have dropped two objects of different masses from the Tower of Pisa. He measured how long it took each to reach the ground. Since stopwatches weren't readily available, how do you think he measured their fall time? If the objects were the same size, but with different masses, what do you think he should have observed? Would this result be different if done on the Moon?

5.3 Elasticity: Stress and Strain

LEARNING OBJECTIVES

By the end of this section, you will be able to:

- State Hooke's law.
- Explain Hooke's law using graphical representation between deformation and applied force.
- Discuss the three types of deformations such as changes in length, sideways shear and changes in volume.
- Describe with examples the young's modulus, shear modulus and bulk modulus.
- Determine the change in length given mass, length and radius.

We now move from consideration of forces that affect the motion of an object (such as friction and drag) to those that affect an object's shape. If a bulldozer pushes a car into a wall, the car will not move but it will noticeably change shape. A change in shape due to the application of a force is a **deformation**. Even very small forces are known to cause some deformation. For small deformations, two important characteristics are observed. First, the object returns to its original shape when the force is removed—that is, the deformation is elastic for small deformations. Second, the size of the deformation is proportional to the force—that is, for small deformations, Hooke's law is obeyed. In equation form, **Hooke's law** is given by

$$F = k\Delta L, \qquad (5.26)$$

where ΔL is the amount of deformation (the change in length, for example) produced by the force F, and k is a proportionality constant that depends on the shape and composition of the object and the direction of the force. Note that this force is a function of the deformation ΔL —it is not constant as a kinetic friction force is. Rearranging this to

$$\Delta L = \frac{F}{k} \qquad (5.27)$$

makes it clear that the deformation is proportional to the applied force. Figure 5.11 shows the Hooke's law relationship between the extension ΔL of a spring or of a human bone. For metals or springs, the straight line region in which Hooke's law pertains is much larger. Bones are brittle and the elastic region is small and the fracture abrupt. Eventually a large enough stress to the material will cause it to break or fracture. **Tensile strength** is the breaking stress that will cause permanent deformation or fracture of a material.

HOOKE'S LAW

$$F = k\Delta L, \tag{5.28}$$

where ΔL is the amount of deformation (the change in length, for example) produced by the force F, and k is a proportionality constant that depends on the shape and composition of the object and the direction of the force.

$$\Delta L = \frac{F}{k} \tag{5.29}$$

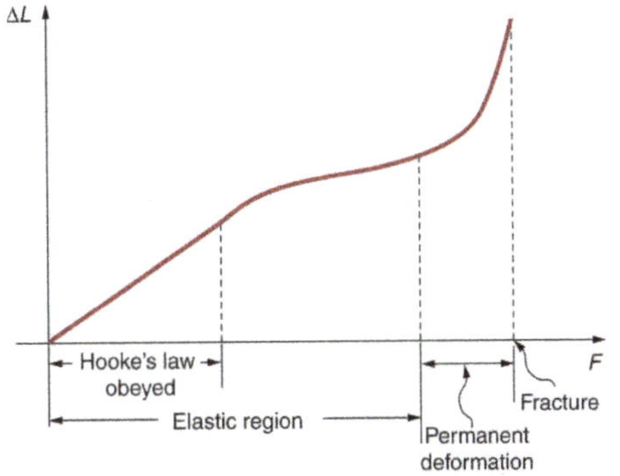

FIGURE 5.11 A graph of deformation ΔL versus applied force F. The straight segment is the linear region where Hooke's law is obeyed. The slope of the straight region is $\frac{1}{k}$. For larger forces, the graph is curved but the deformation is still elastic– ΔL will return to zero if the force is removed. Still greater forces permanently deform the object until it finally fractures. The shape of the curve near fracture depends on several factors, including how the force F is applied. Note that in this graph the slope increases just before fracture, indicating that a small increase in F is producing a large increase in L near the fracture.

The proportionality constant k depends upon a number of factors for the material. For example, a guitar string made of nylon stretches when it is tightened, and the elongation ΔL is proportional to the force applied (at least for small deformations). Thicker nylon strings and ones made of steel stretch less for the same applied force, implying they have a larger k (see Figure 5.12). Finally, all three strings return to their normal lengths when the force is removed, provided the deformation is small. Most materials will behave in this manner if the deformation is less than about 0.1% or about 1 part in 10^3.

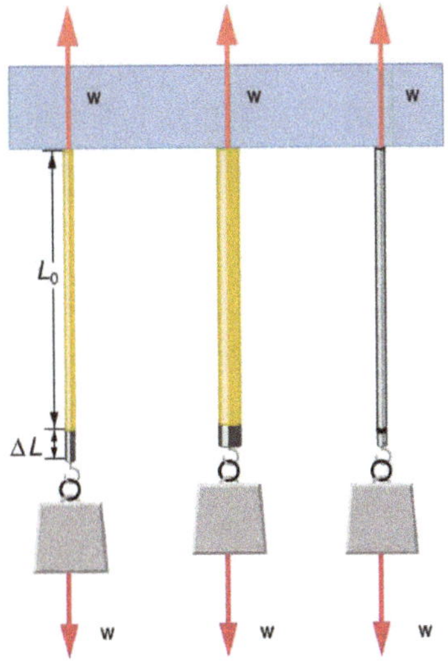

FIGURE 5.12 The same force, in this case a weight (w), applied to three different guitar strings of identical length produces the three different deformations shown as shaded segments. The string on the left is thin nylon, the one in the middle is thicker nylon, and the one on

the right is steel.

STRETCH YOURSELF A LITTLE

How would you go about measuring the proportionality constant k of a rubber band? If a rubber band stretched 3 cm when a 100-g mass was attached to it, then how much would it stretch if two similar rubber bands were attached to the same mass—even if put together in parallel or alternatively if tied together in series?

We now consider three specific types of deformations: changes in length (tension and compression), sideways shear (stress), and changes in volume. All deformations are assumed to be small unless otherwise stated.

Changes in Length—Tension and Compression: Elastic Modulus

A change in length ΔL is produced when a force is applied to a wire or rod parallel to its length L_0, either stretching it (a tension) or compressing it. (See Figure 5.13.)

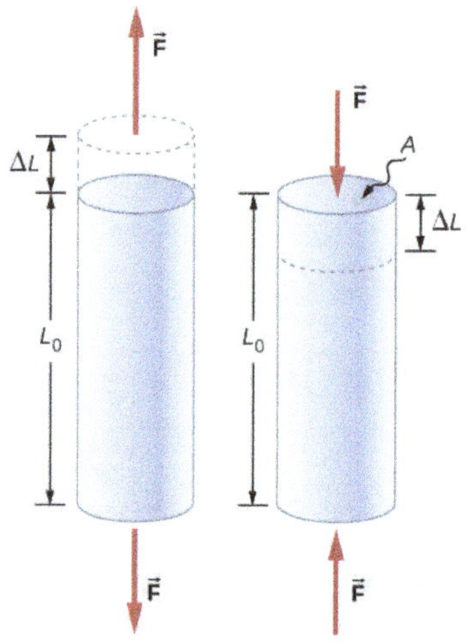

FIGURE 5.13 (a) Tension. The rod is stretched a length ΔL when a force is applied parallel to its length. (b) Compression. The same rod is compressed by forces with the same magnitude in the opposite direction. For very small deformations and uniform materials, ΔL is approximately the same for the same magnitude of tension or compression. For larger deformations, the cross-sectional area changes as the rod is compressed or stretched.

Experiments have shown that the change in length (ΔL) depends on only a few variables. As already noted, ΔL is proportional to the force F and depends on the substance from which the object is made. Additionally, the change in length is proportional to the original length L_0 and inversely proportional to the cross-sectional area of the wire or rod. For example, a long guitar string will stretch more than a short one, and a thick string will stretch less than a thin one. We can combine all these factors into one equation for ΔL:

$$\Delta L = \frac{1}{Y}\frac{F}{A}L_0, \tag{5.30}$$

where ΔL is the change in length, F the applied force, Y is a factor, called the elastic modulus or Young's modulus, that depends on the substance, A is the cross-sectional area, and L_0 is the original length. Table 5.3 lists values of Y for several materials—those with a large Y are said to have a large tensile stiffness because they deform less for a given tension or compression.

Material	Young's modulus (tension–compression) Y $(10^9\ \text{N/m}^2)$	Shear modulus S $(10^9\ \text{N/m}^2)$	Bulk modulus B $(10^9\ \text{N/m}^2)$
Aluminum	70	25	75
Bone – tension	16	80	8
Bone – compression	9		
Brass	90	35	75
Brick	15		
Concrete	20		
Glass	70	20	30
Granite	45	20	45
Hair (human)	10		
Hardwood	15	10	
Iron, cast	100	40	90
Lead	16	5	50
Marble	60	20	70
Nylon	5		
Polystyrene	3		
Silk	6		
Spider thread	3		
Steel	210	80	130
Tendon	1		
Acetone			0.7
Ethanol			0.9
Glycerin			4.5

TABLE 5.3 Elastic Moduli[1]

1 Approximate and average values. Young's moduli Y for tension and compression sometimes differ but are averaged here. Bone has significantly different Young's moduli for tension and compression.

Material	Young's modulus (tension–compression) $Y\,(10^9\ \text{N/m}^2)$	Shear modulus S $(10^9\ \text{N/m}^2)$	Bulk modulus B $(10^9\ \text{N/m}^2)$
Mercury			25
Water			2.2

TABLE 5.3 Elastic Moduli[1]

Young's moduli are not listed for liquids and gases in Table 5.3 because they cannot be stretched or compressed in only one direction. Note that there is an assumption that the object does not accelerate, so that there are actually two applied forces of magnitude F acting in opposite directions. For example, the strings in Figure 5.13 are being pulled down by a force of magnitude w and held up by the ceiling, which also exerts a force of magnitude w.

EXAMPLE 5.3

The Stretch of a Long Cable

Suspension cables are used to carry gondolas at ski resorts. (See Figure 5.14) Consider a suspension cable that includes an unsupported span of 3020 m. Calculate the amount of stretch in the steel cable. Assume that the cable has a diameter of 5.6 cm and the maximum tension it can withstand is 3.0×10^6 N.

FIGURE 5.14 Gondolas travel along suspension cables at the Gala Yuzawa ski resort in Japan. (credit: Rudy Herman, Flickr)

Strategy

The force is equal to the maximum tension, or $F = 3.0 \times 10^6$ N. The cross-sectional area is $\pi r^2 = 2.46 \times 10^{-3}\ \text{m}^2$. The equation $\Delta L = \frac{1}{Y}\frac{F}{A}L_0$ can be used to find the change in length.

Solution

All quantities are known. Thus,

$$\begin{aligned} \Delta L &= \left(\frac{1}{210{\times}10^9\ \text{N/m}^2}\right)\left(\frac{3.0{\times}10^6\ \text{N}}{2.46{\times}10^{-3}\ \text{m}^2}\right)(3020\ \text{m}) \\ &= 18\ \text{m}. \end{aligned} \tag{5.31}$$

Discussion

This is quite a stretch, but only about 0.6% of the unsupported length. Effects of temperature upon length might be important in these environments.

Bones, on the whole, do not fracture due to tension or compression. Rather they generally fracture due to sideways impact or bending, resulting in the bone shearing or snapping. The behavior of bones under tension and compression is important because it determines the load the bones can carry. Bones are classified as weight-bearing structures such as columns in buildings and trees. Weight-bearing structures have special features; columns in building have steel-reinforcing rods while trees and bones are fibrous. The bones in different parts of the body serve different structural functions and are prone to different stresses. Thus the bone in the top of the femur is arranged in thin sheets separated by marrow while in other places the bones can be cylindrical and filled with marrow or just solid. Overweight people have a tendency toward bone damage due to sustained compressions in bone joints and tendons.

Another biological example of Hooke's law occurs in tendons. Functionally, the tendon (the tissue connecting muscle to bone) must stretch easily at first when a force is applied, but offer a much greater restoring force for a greater strain. Figure 5.15 shows a stress-strain relationship for a human tendon. Some tendons have a high collagen content so there is relatively little strain, or length change; others, like support tendons (as in the leg) can change length up to 10%. Note that this stress-strain curve is nonlinear, since the slope of the line changes in different regions. In the first part of the stretch called the toe region, the fibers in the tendon begin to align in the direction of the stress—this is called *uncrimping*. In the linear region, the fibrils will be stretched, and in the failure region individual fibers begin to break. A simple model of this relationship can be illustrated by springs in parallel: different springs are activated at different lengths of stretch. Examples of this are given in the problems at end of this chapter. Ligaments (tissue connecting bone to bone) behave in a similar way.

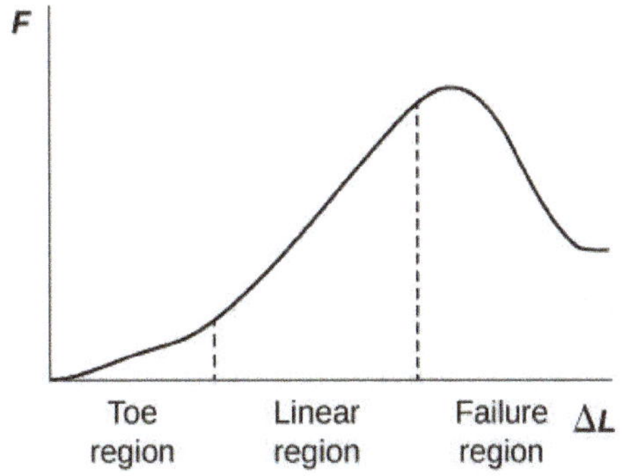

FIGURE 5.15 Typical stress-strain curve for mammalian tendon. Three regions are shown: (1) toe region (2) linear region, and (3) failure region.

Unlike bones and tendons, which need to be strong as well as elastic, the arteries and lungs need to be very stretchable. The elastic properties of the arteries are essential for blood flow. The pressure in the arteries increases and arterial walls stretch when the blood is pumped out of the heart. When the aortic valve shuts, the pressure in the arteries drops and the arterial walls relax to maintain the blood flow. When you feel your pulse, you are feeling exactly this—the elastic behavior of the arteries as the blood gushes through with each pump of the heart. If the arteries were rigid, you would not feel a pulse. The heart is also an organ with special elastic properties. The lungs expand with muscular effort when we breathe in but relax freely and elastically when we breathe out. Our skins are particularly elastic, especially for the young. A young person can go from 100 kg to 60 kg with no visible sag in their skins. The elasticity of all organs reduces with age. Gradual physiological aging through reduction in elasticity starts in the early 20s.

EXAMPLE 5.4

Calculating Deformation: How Much Does Your Leg Shorten When You Stand on It?

Calculate the change in length of the upper leg bone (the femur) when a 70.0 kg man supports 62.0 kg of his mass on it, assuming the bone to be equivalent to a uniform rod that is 40.0 cm long and 2.00 cm in radius.

Strategy

The force is equal to the weight supported, or

$$F = mg = (62.0\ \text{kg})\left(9.80\ \text{m/s}^2\right) = 607.6\ \text{N}, \tag{5.32}$$

and the cross-sectional area is $\pi r^2 = 1.257 \times 10^{-3}\ \text{m}^2$. The equation $\Delta L = \frac{1}{Y}\frac{F}{A}L_0$ can be used to find the change in length.

Solution

All quantities except ΔL are known. Note that the compression value for Young's modulus for bone must be used here. Thus,

$$\begin{aligned}\Delta L &= \left(\frac{1}{9\times10^{9}\ \text{N/m}^2}\right)\left(\frac{607.6\ \text{N}}{1.257\times10^{-3}\ \text{m}^2}\right)(0.400\ \text{m}) \\ &= 2\times10^{-5}\ \text{m}.\end{aligned} \quad 5.33$$

Discussion

This small change in length seems reasonable, consistent with our experience that bones are rigid. In fact, even the rather large forces encountered during strenuous physical activity do not compress or bend bones by large amounts. Although bone is rigid compared with fat or muscle, several of the substances listed in Table 5.3 have larger values of Young's modulus Y. In other words, they are more rigid.

The equation for change in length is traditionally rearranged and written in the following form:

$$\frac{F}{A} = Y\frac{\Delta L}{L_0}. \quad 5.34$$

The ratio of force to area, $\frac{F}{A}$, is defined as **stress** (measured in N/m^2), and the ratio of the change in length to length, $\frac{\Delta L}{L_0}$, is defined as **strain** (a unitless quantity). In other words,

$$\text{stress} = Y \times \text{strain}. \quad 5.35$$

In this form, the equation is analogous to Hooke's law, with stress analogous to force and strain analogous to deformation. If we again rearrange this equation to the form

$$F = YA\frac{\Delta L}{L_0}, \quad 5.36$$

we see that it is the same as Hooke's law with a proportionality constant

$$k = \frac{YA}{L_0}. \quad 5.37$$

This general idea—that force and the deformation it causes are proportional for small deformations—applies to changes in length, sideways bending, and changes in volume.

STRESS

The ratio of force to area, $\frac{F}{A}$, is defined as stress measured in N/m^2.

STRAIN

The ratio of the change in length to length, $\frac{\Delta L}{L_0}$, is defined as strain (a unitless quantity). In other words,

$$\text{stress} = Y \times \text{strain}. \quad 5.38$$

Sideways Stress: Shear Modulus

Figure 5.16 illustrates what is meant by a sideways stress or a *shearing force*. Here the deformation is called Δx and it is perpendicular to L_0, rather than parallel as with tension and compression. Shear deformation behaves similarly to tension and compression and can be described with similar equations. The expression for **shear deformation** is

$$\Delta x = \frac{1}{S}\frac{F}{A}L_0, \quad 5.39$$

where S is the shear modulus (see Table 5.3) and F is the force applied perpendicular to L_0 and parallel to the cross-sectional area A. Again, to keep the object from accelerating, there are actually two equal and opposite forces F applied across opposite faces, as illustrated in Figure 5.16. The equation is logical—for example, it is easier to bend a long thin pencil (small A) than a short thick one, and both are more easily bent than similar steel rods (large S).

SHEAR DEFORMATION

$$\Delta x = \frac{1}{S}\frac{F}{A}L_0, \qquad 5.40$$

where S is the shear modulus and F is the force applied perpendicular to L_0 and parallel to the cross-sectional area A.

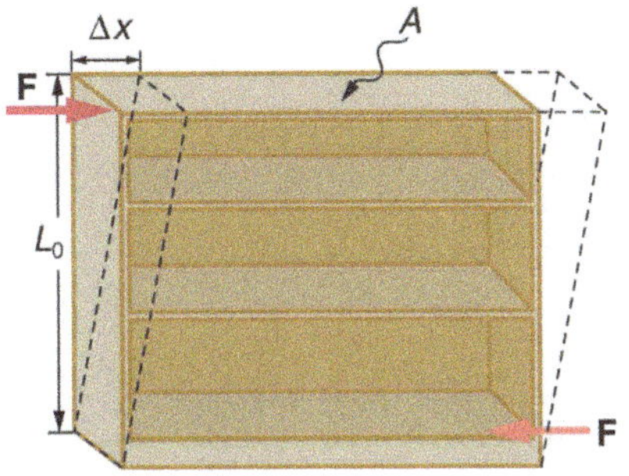

FIGURE 5.16 Shearing forces are applied perpendicular to the length L_0 and parallel to the area A, producing a deformation Δx. Vertical forces are not shown, but it should be kept in mind that in addition to the two shearing forces, $\mathbf{F}$, there must be supporting forces to keep the object from rotating. The distorting effects of these supporting forces are ignored in this treatment. The weight of the object also is not shown, since it is usually negligible compared with forces large enough to cause significant deformations.

Examination of the shear moduli in Table 5.3 reveals some telling patterns. For example, shear moduli are less than Young's moduli for most materials. Bone is a remarkable exception. Its shear modulus is not only greater than its Young's modulus, but it is as large as that of steel. This is why bones are so rigid.

The spinal column (consisting of 26 vertebral segments separated by discs) provides the main support for the head and upper part of the body. The spinal column has normal curvature for stability, but this curvature can be increased, leading to increased shearing forces on the lower vertebrae. Discs are better at withstanding compressional forces than shear forces. Because the spine is not vertical, the weight of the upper body exerts some of both. Pregnant women and people that are overweight (with large abdomens) need to move their shoulders back to maintain balance, thereby increasing the curvature in their spine and so increasing the shear component of the stress. An increased angle due to more curvature increases the shear forces along the plane. These higher shear forces increase the risk of back injury through ruptured discs. The lumbosacral disc (the wedge shaped disc below the last vertebrae) is particularly at risk because of its location.

The shear moduli for concrete and brick are very small; they are too highly variable to be listed. Concrete used in buildings can withstand compression, as in pillars and arches, but is very poor against shear, as might be encountered in heavily loaded floors or during earthquakes. Modern structures were made possible by the use of steel and steel-reinforced concrete. Almost by definition, liquids and gases have shear moduli near zero, because they flow in response to shearing forces.

EXAMPLE 5.5

Calculating Force Required to Deform: That Nail Does Not Bend Much Under a Load

Find the mass of the picture hanging from a steel nail as shown in Figure 5.17, given that the nail bends only $1.80\ \mu\text{m}$. (Assume the shear modulus is known to two significant figures.)

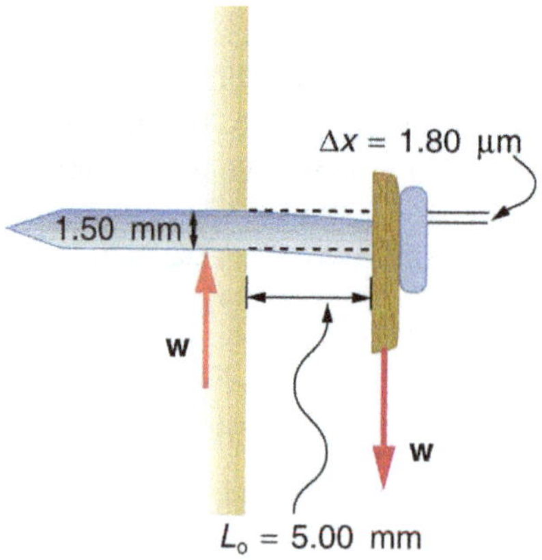

FIGURE 5.17 Side view of a nail with a picture hung from it. The nail flexes very slightly (shown much larger than actual) because of the shearing effect of the supported weight. Also shown is the upward force of the wall on the nail, illustrating that there are equal and opposite forces applied across opposite cross sections of the nail. See Example 5.5 for a calculation of the mass of the picture.

Strategy

The force F on the nail (neglecting the nail's own weight) is the weight of the picture w. If we can find w, then the mass of the picture is just $\frac{w}{g}$. The equation $\Delta x = \frac{1}{S}\frac{F}{A}L_0$ can be solved for F.

Solution

Solving the equation $\Delta x = \frac{1}{S}\frac{F}{A}L_0$ for F, we see that all other quantities can be found:

$$F = \frac{SA}{L_0}\Delta x. \quad 5.41$$

S is found in Table 5.3 and is $S = 80 \times 10^9\ \text{N/m}^2$. The radius r is 0.750 mm (as seen in the figure), so the cross-sectional area is

$$A = \pi r^2 = 1.77 \times 10^{-6}\ \text{m}^2. \quad 5.42$$

The value for L_0 is also shown in the figure. Thus,

$$F = \frac{(80 \times 10^9\ \text{N/m}^2)(1.77 \times 10^{-6}\ \text{m}^2)}{(5.00 \times 10^{-3}\ \text{m})}(1.80 \times 10^{-6}\ \text{m}) = 51\ \text{N}. \quad 5.43$$

This 51 N force is the weight w of the picture, so the picture's mass is

$$m = \frac{w}{g} = \frac{F}{g} = 5.2\ \text{kg}. \quad 5.44$$

Discussion

This is a fairly massive picture, and it is impressive that the nail flexes only $1.80\ \mu\text{m}$—an amount undetectable to the unaided eye.

Changes in Volume: Bulk Modulus

An object will be compressed in all directions if inward forces are applied evenly on all its surfaces as in Figure 5.18. It is relatively easy to compress gases and extremely difficult to compress liquids and solids. For example, air in a wine bottle is compressed when it is corked. But if you try corking a brim-full bottle, you cannot compress the wine—some must be removed if the cork is to be inserted. The reason for these different compressibilities is that atoms and molecules are separated by large empty spaces in gases but packed close together in liquids and solids. To compress a gas, you must force its atoms and molecules closer together. To compress liquids and solids, you must actually compress their atoms and molecules, and very strong electromagnetic forces in them oppose this compression.

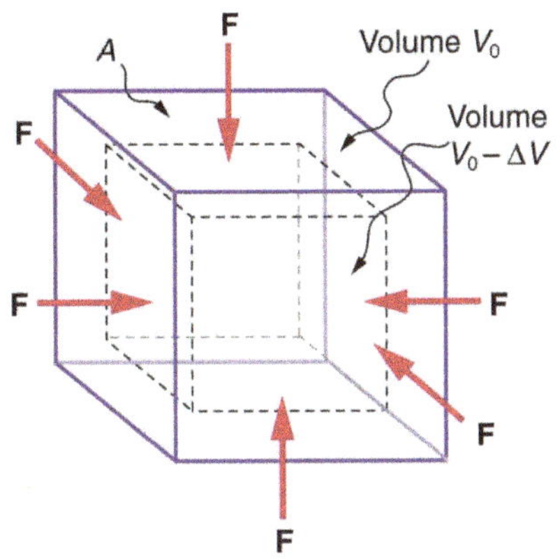

FIGURE 5.18 An inward force on all surfaces compresses this cube. Its change in volume is proportional to the force per unit area and its original volume, and is related to the compressibility of the substance.

We can describe the compression or volume deformation of an object with an equation. First, we note that a force "applied evenly" is defined to have the same stress, or ratio of force to area $\frac{F}{A}$ on all surfaces. The deformation produced is a change in volume ΔV, which is found to behave very similarly to the shear, tension, and compression previously discussed. (This is not surprising, since a compression of the entire object is equivalent to compressing each of its three dimensions.) The relationship of the change in volume to other physical quantities is given by

$$\Delta V = \frac{1}{B}\frac{F}{A}V_0, \quad (5.45)$$

where B is the bulk modulus (see Table 5.3), V_0 is the original volume, and $\frac{F}{A}$ is the force per unit area applied uniformly inward on all surfaces. Note that no bulk moduli are given for gases.

What are some examples of bulk compression of solids and liquids? One practical example is the manufacture of industrial-grade diamonds by compressing carbon with an extremely large force per unit area. The carbon atoms rearrange their crystalline structure into the more tightly packed pattern of diamonds. In nature, a similar process occurs deep underground, where extremely large forces result from the weight of overlying material. Another natural source of large compressive forces is the pressure created by the weight of water, especially in deep parts of the oceans. Water exerts an inward force on all surfaces of a submerged object, and even on the water itself. At great depths, water is measurably compressed, as the following example illustrates.

EXAMPLE 5.6

Calculating Change in Volume with Deformation: How Much Is Water Compressed at Great Ocean Depths?

Calculate the fractional decrease in volume ($\frac{\Delta V}{V_0}$) for seawater at 5.00 km depth, where the force per unit area is $5.00 \times 10^7\ \text{N/m}^2$.

Strategy

Equation $\Delta V = \frac{1}{B}\frac{F}{A}V_0$ is the correct physical relationship. All quantities in the equation except $\frac{\Delta V}{V_0}$ are known.

Solution

Solving for the unknown $\frac{\Delta V}{V_0}$ gives

$$\frac{\Delta V}{V_0} = \frac{1}{B}\frac{F}{A}. \quad (5.46)$$

Substituting known values with the value for the bulk modulus B from Table 5.3,

$$\begin{aligned}\frac{\Delta V}{V_0} &= \frac{5.00\times10^7\ \text{N/m}^2}{2.2\times10^9\ \text{N/m}^2} \\ &= 0.023 = 2.3\%.\end{aligned} \quad 5.47$$

Discussion

Although measurable, this is not a significant decrease in volume considering that the force per unit area is about 500 atmospheres (1 million pounds per square foot). Liquids and solids are extraordinarily difficult to compress.

Conversely, very large forces are created by liquids and solids when they try to expand but are constrained from doing so—which is equivalent to compressing them to less than their normal volume. This often occurs when a contained material warms up, since most materials expand when their temperature increases. If the materials are tightly constrained, they deform or break their container. Another very common example occurs when water freezes. Water, unlike most materials, expands when it freezes, and it can easily fracture a boulder, rupture a biological cell, or crack an engine block that gets in its way.

Other types of deformations, such as torsion or twisting, behave analogously to the tension, shear, and bulk deformations considered here.

PHET EXPLORATIONS

Masses & Springs

Click to view content (https://openstax.org/books/college-physics-ap-courses-2e/pages/5-3-elasticity-stress-and-strain)

Glossary

deformation change in shape due to the application of force

drag force F_D, found to be proportional to the square of the speed of the object; mathematically

$$F_D \propto v^2$$

$$F_D = \frac{1}{2}C\rho Av^2,$$

where C is the drag coefficient, A is the area of the object facing the fluid, and ρ is the density of the fluid

friction a force that opposes relative motion or attempts at motion between systems in contact

Hooke's law proportional relationship between the force F on a material and the deformation ΔL it causes, $F = k\Delta L$

kinetic friction a force that opposes the motion of two systems that are in contact and moving relative to one another

magnitude of kinetic friction $f_k = \mu_k N$, where μ_k is the coefficient of kinetic friction

magnitude of static friction $f_s \le \mu_s N$, where μ_s is the coefficient of static friction and N is the magnitude of the normal force

shear deformation deformation perpendicular to the original length of an object

static friction a force that opposes the motion of two systems that are in contact and are not moving relative to one another

Stokes' law $F_s = 6\pi r\eta v$, where r is the radius of the object, η is the viscosity of the fluid, and v is the object's velocity

strain ratio of change in length to original length

stress ratio of force to area

tensile strength the breaking stress that will cause permanent deformation or fraction of a material

Section Summary

5.1 Friction

- Friction is a contact force between systems that opposes the motion or attempted motion between them. Simple friction is proportional to the normal force N pushing the systems together. (A normal force is always perpendicular to the contact surface between systems.) Friction depends on both of the materials involved. The magnitude of static friction f_s between systems stationary relative to one another is given by
  $f_s \le \mu_s N,$
  where μ_s is the coefficient of static friction, which depends on both of the materials.
- The kinetic friction force f_k between systems moving relative to one another is given by
  $f_k = \mu_k N,$
  where μ_k is the coefficient of kinetic friction, which also depends on both materials.

5.2 Drag Forces

- Drag forces acting on an object moving in a fluid oppose the motion. For larger objects (such as a baseball) moving at a velocity v in air, the drag force is given by
  $$F_D = \frac{1}{2}C\rho Av^2,$$
  where C is the drag coefficient (typical values are given in Table 5.2), A is the area of the object facing the fluid, and ρ is the fluid density.
- For small objects (such as a bacterium) moving in a denser medium (such as water), the drag force is given by Stokes' law,
  $F_s = 6\pi\eta rv,$
  where r is the radius of the object, η is the fluid viscosity, and v is the object's velocity.

5.3 Elasticity: Stress and Strain

- Hooke's law is given by
  $F = k\Delta L,$
  where ΔL is the amount of deformation (the change in length), F is the applied force, and k is a proportionality constant that depends on the shape and composition of the object and the direction of the force. The relationship between the deformation and the applied force can also be written as
  $$\Delta L = \frac{1}{Y}\frac{F}{A}L_0,$$
  where Y is *Young's modulus*, which depends on the substance, A is the cross-sectional area, and L_0 is the original length.
- The ratio of force to area, $\frac{F}{A}$, is defined as *stress*, measured in N/m^2.
- The ratio of the change in length to length, $\frac{\Delta L}{L_0}$, is defined as *strain* (a unitless quantity). In other words,
  $\text{stress} = Y \times \text{strain}.$
- The expression for shear deformation is
  $$\Delta x = \frac{1}{S}\frac{F}{A}L_0,$$
  where S is the shear modulus and F is the force

applied perpendicular to L_0 and parallel to the cross-sectional area A.

- The relationship of the change in volume to other physical quantities is given by

$$\Delta V = \frac{1}{B}\frac{F}{A}V_0,$$

where B is the bulk modulus, V_0 is the original volume, and $\frac{F}{A}$ is the force per unit area applied uniformly inward on all surfaces.

Conceptual Questions

5.1 Friction

1. Define normal force. What is its relationship to friction when friction behaves simply?

2. The glue on a piece of tape can exert forces. Can these forces be a type of simple friction? Explain, considering especially that tape can stick to vertical walls and even to ceilings.

3. When you learn to drive, you discover that you need to let up slightly on the brake pedal as you come to a stop or the car will stop with a jerk. Explain this in terms of the relationship between static and kinetic friction.

4. When you push a piece of chalk across a chalkboard, it sometimes screeches because it rapidly alternates between slipping and sticking to the board. Describe this process in more detail, in particular explaining how it is related to the fact that kinetic friction is less than static friction. (The same slip-grab process occurs when tires screech on pavement.)

5.2 Drag Forces

5. Athletes such as swimmers and bicyclists wear body suits in competition. Formulate a list of pros and cons of such suits.

6. Two expressions were used for the drag force experienced by a moving object in a liquid. One depended upon the speed, while the other was proportional to the square of the speed. In which types of motion would each of these expressions be more applicable than the other one?

7. As cars travel, oil and gasoline leaks onto the road surface. If a light rain falls, what does this do to the control of the car? Does a heavy rain make any difference?

8. Why can a squirrel jump from a tree branch to the ground and run away undamaged, while a human could break a bone in such a fall?

5.3 Elasticity: Stress and Strain

9. The elastic properties of the arteries are essential for blood flow. Explain the importance of this in terms of the characteristics of the flow of blood (pulsating or continuous).

10. What are you feeling when you feel your pulse? Measure your pulse rate for 10 s and for 1 min. Is there a factor of 6 difference?

11. Examine different types of shoes, including sports shoes and thongs. In terms of physics, why are the bottom surfaces designed as they are? What differences will dry and wet conditions make for these surfaces?

12. Would you expect your height to be different depending upon the time of day? Why or why not?

13. Would you expect a large or small stress to be required to deform a spider web? Why is this elasticity an important feature for a spider web?

14. Explain why pregnant women often suffer from back strain late in their pregnancy.

15. An old carpenter's trick to keep nails from bending when they are pounded into hard materials is to grip the center of the nail firmly with pliers. Why does this help?

16. When a glass bottle full of vinegar warms up, both the vinegar and the glass expand, but vinegar expands significantly more with temperature than glass. The bottle will break if it was filled to its tightly capped lid. Explain why, and also explain how a pocket of air above the vinegar would prevent the break. (This is the function of the air above liquids in glass containers.)

Problems & Exercises

5.1 Friction

1. A physics major is cooking breakfast when he notices that the frictional force between his steel spatula and his Teflon frying pan is only 0.200 N. Knowing the coefficient of kinetic friction between the two materials, he quickly calculates the normal force. What is it?

2. (a) When rebuilding her car's engine, a physics

major must exert 300 N of force to insert a dry steel piston into a steel cylinder. What is the magnitude of the normal force between the piston and cylinder? (b) What is the magnitude of the force would she have to exert if the steel parts were oiled?

3. (a) What is the maximum frictional force in the knee joint of a person who supports 66.0 kg of her mass on that knee? (b) During strenuous exercise it is possible to exert forces to the joints that are easily ten times greater than the weight being supported. What is the maximum force of friction under such conditions? The frictional forces in joints are relatively small in all circumstances except when the joints deteriorate, such as from injury or arthritis. Increased frictional forces can cause further damage and pain.

4. Suppose you have a 120-kg wooden crate resting on a wood floor. (a) What maximum force can you exert horizontally on the crate without moving it? (b) If you continue to exert this force once the crate starts to slip, what will the magnitude of its acceleration then be?

5. (a) If half of the weight of a small 1.00×10^3 kg utility truck is supported by its two drive wheels, what is the magnitude of the maximum acceleration it can achieve on dry concrete? (b) Will a metal cabinet lying on the wooden bed of the truck slip if it accelerates at this rate? (c) Solve both problems assuming the truck has four-wheel drive.

6. A team of eight dogs pulls a sled with waxed wood runners on wet snow (mush!). The dogs have average masses of 19.0 kg, and the loaded sled with its rider has a mass of 210 kg. (a) Calculate the magnitude of the acceleration starting from rest if each dog exerts an average force of 185 N backward on the snow. (b) What is the magnitude of the acceleration once the sled starts to move? (c) For both situations, calculate the magnitude of the force in the coupling between the dogs and the sled.

7. Consider the 65.0-kg ice skater being pushed by two others shown in Figure 5.19. (a) Find the direction and magnitude of $\mathbf{F}_{\text{tot}}$, the total force exerted on her by the others, given that the magnitudes F_1 and F_2 are 26.4 N and 18.6 N, respectively. (b) What is her initial acceleration if she is initially stationary and wearing steel-bladed skates that point in the direction of $\mathbf{F}_{\text{tot}}$? (c) What is her acceleration assuming she is already moving in the direction of $\mathbf{F}_{\text{tot}}$? (Remember that friction always acts in the direction opposite that of motion or attempted motion between surfaces in contact.)

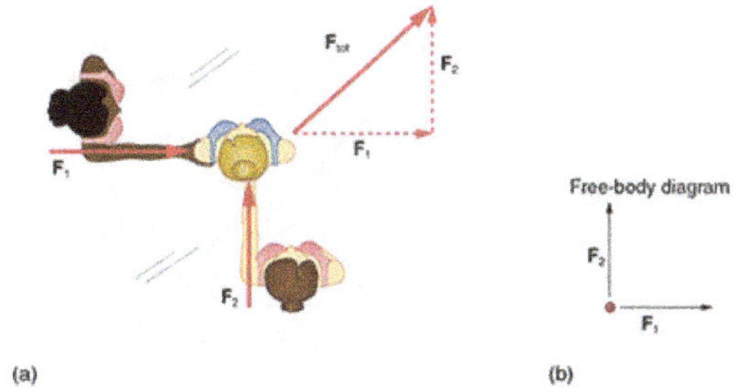

FIGURE 5.19

8. Show that the acceleration of any object down a frictionless incline that makes an angle θ with the horizontal is $a = g \sin \theta$. (Note that this acceleration is independent of mass.)

9. Show that the acceleration of any object down an incline where friction behaves simply (that is, where $f_k = \mu_k N$) is $a = g(\sin \theta - \mu_k \cos \theta)$. Note that the acceleration is independent of mass and reduces to the expression found in the previous problem when friction becomes negligibly small ($\mu_k = 0$).

10. Calculate the deceleration of a snow boarder going up a 5.0°, slope assuming the coefficient of friction for waxed wood on wet snow. The result of Exercise 5.9 may be useful, but be careful to consider the fact that the snow boarder is going uphill. Explicitly show how you follow the steps in Problem-Solving Strategies.

11. (a) Calculate the acceleration of a skier heading down a 10.0° slope, assuming the coefficient of friction for waxed wood on wet snow. (b) Find the angle of the slope down which this skier could coast at a constant velocity. You can neglect air resistance in both parts, and you will find the result of Exercise 5.9 to be useful. Explicitly show how you follow the steps in the Problem-Solving Strategies.

12. If an object is to rest on an incline without slipping, then friction must equal the component of the weight of the object parallel to the incline. This requires greater and greater friction for steeper slopes. Show that the maximum angle of an incline above the horizontal for which an object will not slide down is $\theta = \tan^{-1} \mu_s$. You may use the result of the previous problem. Assume that $a = 0$ and that static friction has reached its maximum value.

13. Calculate the maximum deceleration of a car that is heading down a $6°$ slope (one that makes an angle of $6°$ with the horizontal) under the following road conditions. You may assume that the weight of the car is evenly distributed on all four tires and that the coefficient of static friction is involved—that is, the tires are not allowed to slip during the deceleration. (Ignore rolling.) Calculate for a car: (a) On dry concrete. (b) On wet concrete. (c) On ice, assuming that $\mu_s = 0.100$, the same as for shoes on ice.

14. Calculate the maximum acceleration of a car that is heading up a $4°$ slope (one that makes an angle of $4°$ with the horizontal) under the following road conditions. Assume that only half the weight of the car is supported by the two drive wheels and that the coefficient of static friction is involved—that is, the tires are not allowed to slip during the acceleration. (Ignore rolling.) (a) On dry concrete. (b) On wet concrete. (c) On ice, assuming that $\mu_s = 0.100$, the same as for shoes on ice.

15. Repeat Exercise 5.14 for a car with four-wheel drive.

16. A freight train consists of two 8.00×10^5-kg engines and 45 cars with average masses of 5.50×10^5 kg. (a) What force must each engine exert backward on the track to accelerate the train at a rate of 5.00×10^{-2} m/s^2 if the force of friction is 7.50×10^5 N, assuming the engines exert identical forces? This is not a large frictional force for such a massive system. Rolling friction for trains is small, and consequently trains are very energy-efficient transportation systems. (b) What is the magnitude of the force in the coupling between the 37th and 38th cars (this is the force each exerts on the other), assuming all cars have the same mass and that friction is evenly distributed among all of the cars and engines?

17. Consider the 52.0-kg mountain climber in Figure 5.20. (a) Find the tension in the rope and the force that the mountain climber must exert with her feet on the vertical rock face to remain stationary. Assume that the force is exerted parallel to her legs. Also, assume negligible force exerted by her arms. (b) What is the minimum coefficient of friction between her shoes and the cliff?

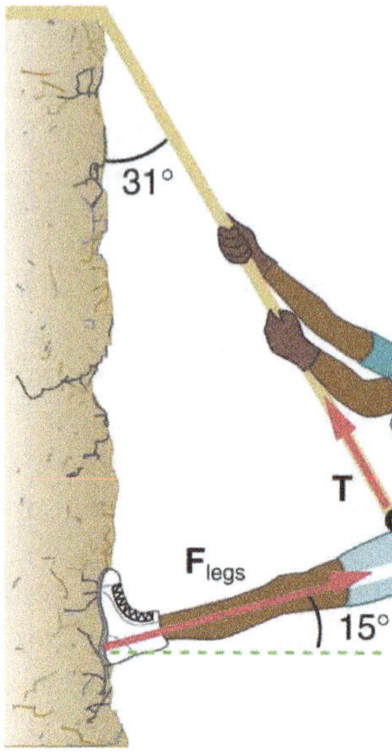

FIGURE 5.20 Part of the climber's weight is supported by her rope and part by friction between her feet and the rock face.

18. A contestant in a winter sporting event pushes a 45.0-kg block of ice across a frozen lake as shown in Figure 5.21(a). (a) Calculate the minimum force F he must exert to get the block moving. (b) What is the magnitude of its acceleration once it starts to move, if that force is maintained?

19. Repeat Exercise 5.18 with the contestant pulling the block of ice with a rope over his shoulder at the same angle above the horizontal as shown in Figure 5.21(b).

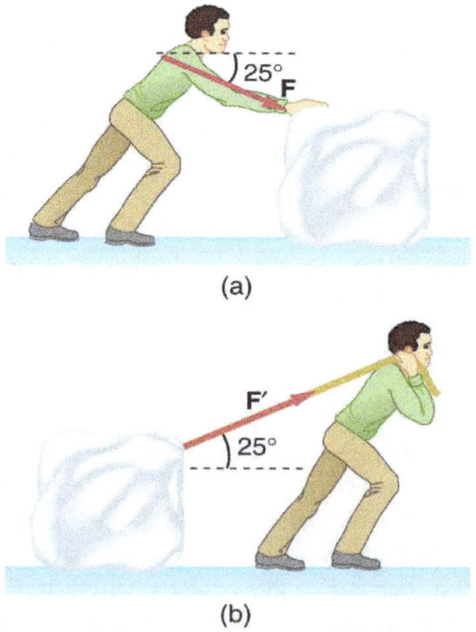

FIGURE 5.21 Which method of sliding a block of ice requires less force—(a) pushing or (b) pulling at the same angle above the horizontal?

5.2 Drag Forces

20. The terminal velocity of a person falling in air depends upon the weight and the area of the person facing the fluid. Find the terminal velocity (in meters per second and kilometers per hour) of an 80.0-kg skydiver falling in a headfirst position with a cross-section area facing the fluid of $0.140\ \text{m}^2$.

21. A 60-kg and a 90-kg skydiver jump from an airplane at an altitude of 6000 m, both falling in a headfirst position. Make some assumption on their frontal areas and calculate their terminal velocities. How long will it take for each skydiver to reach the ground (assuming the time to reach terminal velocity is small)? Assume all values are accurate to three significant digits.

22. A 560-g squirrel with a cross-section area facing the fluid of $144\ \text{cm}^2$ falls from a 5.0-m tree to the ground. Estimate its terminal velocity. (Use a drag coefficient for a horizontal skydiver.) What will be the velocity of a 56-kg person hitting the ground, assuming no drag contribution in such a short distance?

23. To maintain a constant speed, the force provided by a car's engine must equal the drag force plus the force of friction of the road (the rolling resistance). (a) What are the magnitudes of drag forces at 70 km/h and 100 km/h for a Toyota Camry? (Drag area is $0.70\ \text{m}^2$) (b) What is the magnitude of drag force at 70 km/h and 100 km/h for a Hummer H2? (Drag area is $2.44\ \text{m}^2$) Assume all values are accurate to three significant digits.

24. By what factor does the drag force on a car increase as it goes from 65 to 110 km/h?

25. Calculate the speed a spherical rain drop would achieve falling from 5.00 km (a) in the absence of air drag (b) with air drag. Take the size across of the drop to be 4 mm, the density to be $1.00 \times 10^3\ \text{kg/m}^3$, and the cross-section area facing the fluid to be πr^2.

26. Using Stokes' law, verify that the units for viscosity are kilograms per meter per second.

27. Find the terminal velocity of a spherical bacterium (diameter $2.00\ \mu\text{m}$) falling in water. You will first need to note that the drag force is equal to the weight at terminal velocity. Take the density of the bacterium to be $1.10 \times 10^3\ \text{kg/m}^3$.

28. Stokes' law describes sedimentation of particles in liquids and can be used to measure viscosity. Particles in liquids achieve terminal velocity quickly. One can measure the time it takes for a particle to fall a certain distance and then use Stokes' law to calculate the viscosity of the liquid. Suppose a steel ball bearing (density $7.8 \times 10^3\ \text{kg/m}^3$, diameter $3.0\ \text{mm}$) is dropped in a container of motor oil. It takes 12 s to fall a distance of 0.60 m. Calculate the viscosity of the oil.

5.3 Elasticity: Stress and Strain

29. During a circus act, one performer swings upside down hanging from a trapeze holding another, also upside-down, performer by the legs. If the upward force on the lower performer is three times her weight, how much do the bones (the femurs) in her upper legs stretch? You may assume each is equivalent to a uniform rod 35.0 cm long and 1.80 cm in radius. Her mass is 60.0 kg.

30. During a wrestling match, a 150 kg wrestler briefly stands on one hand during a maneuver designed to perplex her adversary. By how much does the upper arm bone shorten in length? The bone can be represented by a uniform rod 38.0 cm in length and 2.10 cm in radius.

31. (a) The "lead" in pencils is a graphite composition with a Young's modulus of about $1 \times 10^9\ \text{N/m}^2$. Calculate the change in length of the lead in an automatic pencil if you tap it straight into the pencil with a force of 4.0 N. The lead is 0.50 mm in diameter and 60 mm long. (b) Is the answer reasonable? That is, does it seem to be consistent with what you have observed when using pencils?

32. TV broadcast antennas are the tallest artificial structures on Earth. In 1987, a 72.0-kg physicist placed himself and 400 kg of equipment at the top of one 610-m high antenna to perform gravity experiments. By how much was the antenna compressed, if we consider it to be equivalent to a steel cylinder 0.150 m in radius?

33. (a) By how much does a 65.0-kg mountain climber stretch her 0.800-cm diameter nylon rope when they hang 35.0 m below a rock outcropping? (b) Does the answer seem to be consistent with what you have observed for nylon ropes? Would it make sense if the rope were actually a bungee cord?

34. A 20.0-m tall hollow aluminum flagpole is equivalent in stiffness to a solid cylinder 4.00 cm in diameter. A strong wind bends the pole much as a horizontal force of 900 N exerted at the top would. How far to the side does the top of the pole flex?

35. As an oil well is drilled, each new section of drill pipe supports its own weight and that of the pipe and drill bit beneath it. Calculate the stretch in a new 6.00 m length of steel pipe that supports 3.00 km of pipe having a mass of 20.0 kg/m and a 100-kg drill bit. The pipe is equivalent in stiffness to a solid cylinder 5.00 cm in diameter.

36. Calculate the force a piano tuner applies to stretch a steel piano wire 8.00 mm, if the wire is originally 0.850 mm in diameter and 1.35 m long.

37. A vertebra is subjected to a shearing force of 500 N. Find the shear deformation, taking the vertebra to be a cylinder 3.00 cm high and 4.00 cm in diameter.

38. A disk between vertebrae in the spine is subjected to a shearing force of 600 N. Find its shear deformation, taking it to have the shear modulus of $1 \times 10^9\ \text{N/m}^2$. The disk is equivalent to a solid cylinder 0.700 cm high and 4.00 cm in diameter.

39. When using a pencil eraser, you exert a vertical force of 6.00 N at a distance of 2.00 cm from the hardwood-eraser joint. The pencil is 6.00 mm in diameter and is held at an angle of 20.0° to the horizontal. (a) By how much does the wood flex perpendicular to its length? (b) How much is it compressed lengthwise?

40. To consider the effect of wires hung on poles, we take data from Example 4.8, in which tensions in wires supporting a traffic light were calculated. The left wire made an angle 30.0° below the horizontal with the top of its pole and carried a tension of 108 N. The 12.0 m tall hollow aluminum pole is equivalent in stiffness to a 4.50 cm diameter solid cylinder. (a) How far is it bent to the side? (b) By how much is it compressed?

41. A farmer making grape juice fills a glass bottle to the brim and caps it tightly. The juice expands more than the glass when it warms up, in such a way that the volume increases by 0.2% (that is, $\Delta V/V_0 = 2 \times 10^{-3}$) relative to the space available. Calculate the magnitude of the normal force exerted by the juice per square centimeter if its bulk modulus is $1.8 \times 10^9\ \text{N/m}^2$, assuming the bottle does not break. In view of your answer, do you think the bottle will survive?

42. (a) When water freezes, its volume increases by 9.05% (that is, $\Delta V/V_0 = 9.05 \times 10^{-2}$). What force per unit area is water capable of exerting on a container when it freezes? (It is acceptable to use the bulk modulus of water in this problem.) (b) Is it surprising that such forces can fracture engine blocks, boulders, and the like?

43. This problem returns to the tightrope walker studied in Example 4.6, who created a tension of $3.94 \times 10^3\ \text{N}$ in a wire making an angle 5.0° below the horizontal with each supporting pole. Calculate how much this tension stretches the steel wire if it was originally 15 m long and 0.50 cm in diameter.

44. The pole in Figure 5.22 is at a 90.0° bend in a power line and is therefore subjected to more shear force than poles in straight parts of the line. The tension in each line is $4.00 \times 10^4\ \text{N}$, at the angles shown. The pole is 15.0 m tall, has an 18.0 cm diameter, and can be considered to have half the stiffness of hardwood. (a) Calculate the compression of the pole. (b) Find how much it bends and in what direction. (c) Find the tension in a guy wire used to keep the pole straight if it is attached to the top of the pole at an angle of 30.0° with the vertical. (Clearly, the guy wire must be in the opposite direction of the bend.)

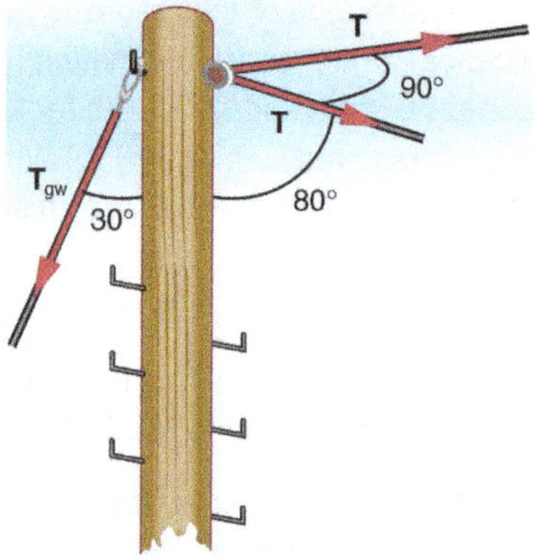

FIGURE 5.22 This telephone pole is at a 90° bend in a power line. A guy wire is attached to the top of the pole at an angle of 30° with the vertical.

45. Critical Thinking Two spherical beads of the same mass fall at a constant speed due to a drag force. Bead A takes twice as long to fall the same distance as bead B. (a) Which of these beads has the larger radius? (b) Based on experimental data, an equation that fits the data is suggested for radius of a bead, *r*, which may not be correct: $r = Kt - \frac{1}{2}$, where *K* is a constant with appropriate units and *t* is the time it takes for a bead to reach a determined distance. Is this equation consistent with your answer from part a?

Explain why or why not. Does this equation make sense? Explain why or why not. (c) Beads of different radii are selected and the time it takes to fall a set distance is recorded. Graph the radius of these beads as a function of the time it takes to fall a determined distance.

Test Prep for AP® Courses

5.1 Friction

1. When a force of 20 N is applied to a stationary box weighing 40 N, the box does not move. This means the coefficient of static friction
   a. is equal to 0.5.
   b. is greater than 0.5.
   c. is less than 0.5.
   d. cannot be determined.

2. A 2-kg block slides down a ramp which is at an incline of 25°. If the frictional force is 4.86 N, what is the coefficient of friction? At what incline will the box slide at a constant velocity? Assume g = 10 m/s^2.

3. A block is given a short push and then slides with constant friction across a horizontal floor. Which statement best explains the direction of the force that friction applies on the moving block?
   a. Friction will be in the same direction as the block's motion because molecular interactions between the block and the floor will deform the block in the direction of motion.
   b. Friction will be in the same direction as the block's motion because thermal energy generated at the interface between the block and the floor adds kinetic energy to the block.
   c. Friction will be in the opposite direction of the block's motion because molecular interactions between the block and the floor will deform the block in the opposite direction of motion.
   d. Friction will be in the opposite direction of the block's motion because thermal energy generated at the interface between the block and the floor converts some of the block's kinetic energy to potential energy.

4. A student pushes a cardboard box across a carpeted floor and afterwards notices that the bottom of the box feels warm. Explain how interactions between molecules in the cardboard and molecules in the carpet produced this heat.

CHAPTER 6

Uniform Circular Motion and Gravitation

FIGURE 6.1 This Australian Grand Prix Formula 1 race car moves in a circular path as it makes the turn. Its wheels also spin rapidly—the latter completing many revolutions, the former only part of one (a circular arc). The same physical principles are involved in each. (credit: Richard Munckton)

CHAPTER OUTLINE

CONNECTION FOR AP® COURSES Many motions, such as the arc of a bird's flight or Earth's path around the Sun, are curved. Recall that Newton's first law tells us that motion is along a straight line at constant speed unless there is a net external force. We will therefore study not only motion along curves, but also the forces that cause it, including gravitational forces. This chapter supports Big Idea 3 that interactions between objects are described by forces, and thus change in motion is a result of a net force exerted on an object. In this chapter, this idea is applied to uniform circular motion. In some ways, this chapter is a continuation of Dynamics: Newton's Laws of Motion as we study more applications of Newton's laws of motion.

This chapter deals with the simplest form of curved motion, **uniform circular motion**, which is motion in a circular path at constant speed. As an object moves on a circular path, the magnitude of its velocity remains constant, but the direction of the velocity is changing. This means there is an acceleration that we will refer to as a "centripetal" acceleration caused by a net external force, also called the "centripetal" force (Enduring Understanding 3.B). The centripetal force is the net force totaling all external forces acting on the object (Essential Knowledge 3.B.1). In order to determine the net force, a free-body diagram may be useful (Essential Knowledge 3.B.2).

Studying this topic illustrates most of the concepts associated with rotational motion and leads to many new topics we group under the name *rotation*. This motion can be described using kinematics variables (Essential Knowledge 3.A.1), but in addition to linear variables, we will introduce angular variables. We use various ways to describe motion, namely, verbally, algebraically and graphically (Learning Objective 3.A.1.1). Pure *rotational motion* occurs when points in an object move in circular paths centered on one point. Pure *translational motion* is motion with no rotation. Some motion combines both types, such as a rotating hockey puck moving over ice. Some combinations of both types of motion are conveniently described with fictitious forces which appear as a result of using a non-inertial frame of reference (Enduring Understanding 3.A).

Furthermore, the properties of uniform circular motion can be applied to the motion of massive objects in a gravitational field. Thus, this chapter supports Big Idea 1 that gravitational mass is an important property of an object or a system.

We have experimental evidence that gravitational and inertial masses are equal (Enduring Understanding 1.C), and that gravitational mass is a measure of the strength of the gravitational interaction (Essential Knowledge 1.C.2). Therefore, this chapter will support Big Idea 2 that fields existing in space can be used to explain interactions, because any massive object creates a gravitational field in space (Enduring Understanding 2.B). Mathematically, we use Newton's universal law of gravitation to provide a model for the gravitational interaction between two massive objects (Essential Knowledge 2.B.2). We will discover that this model describes the interaction of one object with mass with another object with mass (Essential Knowledge 3.C.1), and also that gravitational force is a long-range force (Enduring Understanding 3.C).

The concepts in this chapter support:

Big Idea 1 Objects and systems have properties such as mass and charge. Systems may have internal structure.

Enduring Understanding 1.C Objects and systems have properties of inertial mass and gravitational mass that are experimentally verified to be the same and that satisfy conservation principles.

Essential Knowledge 1.C.2 Gravitational mass is the property of an object or a system that determines the strength of the gravitational interaction with other objects, systems, or gravitational fields.

Essential Knowledge 1.C.3 Objects and systems have properties of inertial mass and gravitational mass that are experimentally verified to be the same and that satisfy conservation principles.

Big Idea 2 Fields existing in space can be used to explain interactions.

Enduring Understanding 2.B A gravitational field is caused by an object with mass.

Essential Knowledge 2.B.2. The gravitational field caused by a spherically symmetric object with mass is radial and, outside the object, varies as the inverse square of the radial distance from the center of that object.

Big Idea 3 The interactions of an object with other objects can be described by forces.

Enduring Understanding 3.A All forces share certain common characteristics when considered by observers in inertial reference frames.

Essential Knowledge 3.A.1. An observer in a particular reference frame can describe the motion of an object using such quantities as position, displacement, distance, velocity, speed, and acceleration.

Essential Knowledge 3.A.3. A force exerted on an object is always due to the interaction of that object with another object.

Enduring Understanding 3.B Classically, the acceleration of an object interacting with other objects can be predicted by using $a = \sum F/m$.

Essential Knowledge 3.B.1 If an object of interest interacts with several other objects, the net force is the vector sum of the individual forces.

Essential Knowledge 3.B.2 Free-body diagrams are useful tools for visualizing forces being exerted on a single object and writing the equations that represent a physical situation.

Enduring Understanding 3.C At the macroscopic level, forces can be categorized as either long-range (action-at-a-distance) forces or contact forces.

Essential Knowledge 3.C.1. Gravitational force describes the interaction of one object that has mass with another object that has mass.

6.1 Rotation Angle and Angular Velocity

LEARNING OBJECTIVES

By the end of this section, you will be able to:

- Define arc length, rotation angle, radius of curvature and angular velocity.
- Calculate the angular velocity of a car wheel spin.

In Kinematics, we studied motion along a straight line and introduced such concepts as displacement, velocity, and acceleration. Two-Dimensional Kinematics dealt with motion in two dimensions. Projectile motion is a special case of two-dimensional kinematics in which the object is projected into the air, while being subject to the gravitational force, and lands a distance away. In this chapter, we consider situations where the object does not land but moves in a curve. We begin the study of uniform circular motion by defining two angular quantities needed to describe rotational motion.

Rotation Angle

When objects rotate about some axis—for example, when the CD (compact disc) in Figure 6.2 rotates about its center—each point in the object follows a circular arc. Consider a line from the center of the CD to its edge. Each **pit** used to record sound along this line moves through the same angle in the same amount of time. The rotation angle is the amount of rotation and is analogous to linear distance. We define the **rotation angle $\Delta\theta$** to be the ratio of the arc length to the radius of curvature:

$$\Delta\theta = \frac{\Delta s}{r}. \tag{6.1}$$

FIGURE 6.2 All points on a CD travel in circular arcs. The pits along a line from the center to the edge all move through the same angle $\Delta\theta$ in a time Δt.

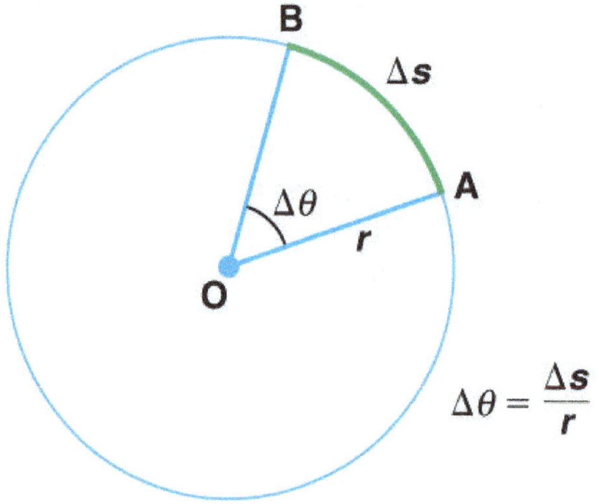

FIGURE 6.3 The radius of a circle is rotated through an angle $\Delta\theta$. The arc length Δs is described on the circumference.

The **arc length** Δs is the distance traveled along a circular path as shown in Figure 6.3 Note that r is the **radius of curvature** of the circular path.

We know that for one complete revolution, the arc length is the circumference of a circle of radius r. The circumference of a circle is $2\pi r$. Thus for one complete revolution the rotation angle is

$$\Delta\theta = \frac{2\pi r}{r} = 2\pi. \tag{6.2}$$

This result is the basis for defining the units used to measure rotation angles, $\Delta\theta$ to be **radians** (rad), defined so that

$$2\pi \text{ rad} = 1 \text{ revolution}. \tag{6.3}$$

A comparison of some useful angles expressed in both degrees and radians is shown in Table 6.1.

Degree Measures	Radian Measure
$30°$	$\frac{\pi}{6}$
$60°$	$\frac{\pi}{3}$
$90°$	$\frac{\pi}{2}$
$120°$	$\frac{2\pi}{3}$
$135°$	$\frac{3\pi}{4}$
$180°$	π

TABLE 6.1 Comparison of Angular Units

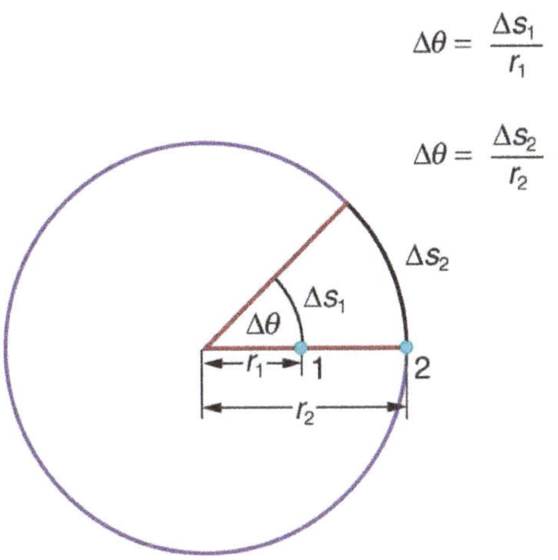

FIGURE 6.4 Points 1 and 2 rotate through the same angle ($\Delta\theta$), but point 2 moves through a greater arc length (Δs) because it is at a greater distance from the center of rotation (r).

If $\Delta\theta = 2\pi$ rad, then the CD has made one complete revolution, and every point on the CD is back at its original position. Because there are $360°$ in a circle or one revolution, the relationship between radians and degrees is thus

$$2\pi \text{ rad} = 360° \tag{6.4}$$

so that

$$1 \text{ rad} = \frac{360°}{2\pi} \approx 57.3°. \tag{6.5}$$

Angular Velocity

How fast is an object rotating? We define **angular velocity** ω as the rate of change of an angle. In symbols, this is

$$\omega = \frac{\Delta\theta}{\Delta t}, \tag{6.6}$$

where an angular rotation $\Delta\theta$ takes place in a time Δt. The greater the rotation angle in a given amount of time, the greater the angular velocity. The units for angular velocity are radians per second (rad/s).

Angular velocity ω is analogous to linear velocity v. To get the precise relationship between angular and linear velocity, we again consider a pit on the rotating CD. This pit moves an arc length Δs in a time Δt, and so it has a linear velocity

$$v = \frac{\Delta s}{\Delta t}. \tag{6.7}$$

From $\Delta\theta = \frac{\Delta s}{r}$ we see that $\Delta s = r\Delta\theta$. Substituting this into the expression for v gives

$$v = \frac{r\Delta\theta}{\Delta t} = r\omega. \tag{6.8}$$

We write this relationship in two different ways and gain two different insights:

$$v = r\omega \text{ or } \omega = \frac{v}{r}. \tag{6.9}$$

The first relationship in $v = r\omega$ or $\omega = \frac{v}{r}$ states that the linear velocity v is proportional to the distance from the center of rotation, thus, it is largest for a point on the rim (largest r), as you might expect. We can also call this linear speed v of a point on the rim the *tangential speed.* The second relationship in $v = r\omega$ or $\omega = \frac{v}{r}$ can be illustrated by considering the tire of a moving car. Note that the speed of a point on the rim of the tire is the same as the speed v of the car. See Figure 6.5. So the faster the car moves, the faster the tire spins—large v means a large ω, because $v = r\omega$. Similarly, a larger-radius tire rotating at the same angular velocity (ω) will produce a greater linear speed (v) for the car.

FIGURE 6.5 A car moving at a velocity v to the right has a tire rotating with an angular velocity ω.The speed of the tread of the tire relative to the axle is v, the same as if the car were jacked up. Thus the car moves forward at linear velocity $v = r\omega$, where r is the tire radius. A larger angular velocity for the tire means a greater velocity for the car.

EXAMPLE 6.1

How Fast Does a Car Tire Spin?

Calculate the angular velocity of a 0.300 m radius car tire when the car travels at 15.0 m/s (about 54 km/h). See Figure 6.5.

Strategy

Because the linear speed of the tire rim is the same as the speed of the car, we have $v = 15.0 \text{ m/s}$. The radius of the tire is given to be $r = 0.300 \text{ m}$. Knowing v and r, we can use the second relationship in $v = r\omega$, $\omega = \frac{v}{r}$ to calculate the angular velocity.

Solution

To calculate the angular velocity, we will use the following relationship:

$$\omega = \frac{v}{r}. \quad (6.10)$$

Substituting the knowns,

$$\omega = \frac{15.0 \text{ m/s}}{0.300 \text{ m}} = 50.0 \text{ rad/s}. \quad (6.11)$$

Discussion

When we cancel units in the above calculation, we get 50.0/s. But the angular velocity must have units of rad/s. Because radians are actually unitless (radians are defined as a ratio of distance), we can simply insert them into the answer for the angular velocity. Also note that if an earth mover with much larger tires, say 1.20 m in radius, were moving at the same speed of 15.0 m/s, its tires would rotate more slowly. They would have an angular velocity

$$\omega = (15.0 \text{ m/s})/(1.20 \text{ m}) = 12.5 \text{ rad/s}. \quad (6.12)$$

Both ω and v have directions (hence they are angular and linear *velocities*, respectively). Angular velocity has only two directions with respect to the axis of rotation—it is either clockwise or counterclockwise. Linear velocity is tangent to the path, as illustrated in Figure 6.6.

TAKE-HOME EXPERIMENT

Tie an object to the end of a string and swing it around in a horizontal circle above your head (swing at your wrist). Maintain uniform speed as the object swings and measure the angular velocity of the motion. What is the approximate speed of the object? Identify a point close to your hand and take appropriate measurements to calculate the linear speed at this point. Identify other circular motions and measure their angular velocities.

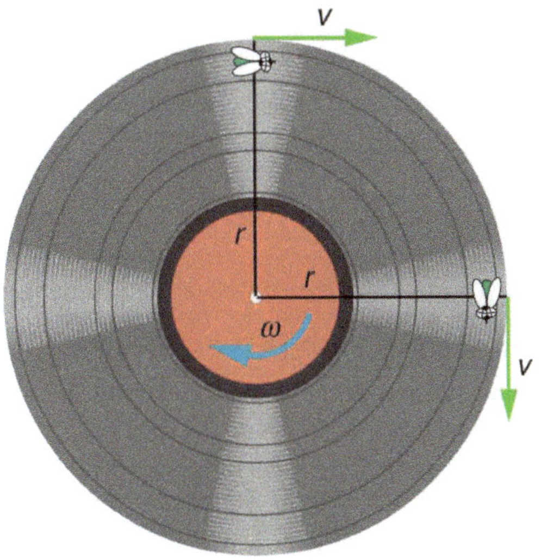

FIGURE 6.6 As an object moves in a circle, here a fly on the edge of an old-fashioned vinyl record, its instantaneous velocity is always tangent to the circle. The direction of the angular velocity is clockwise in this case.

LADYBUG REVOLUTION

Join the ladybug in an exploration of rotational motion. Rotate the merry-go-round to change its angle, or choose a constant angular velocity or angular acceleration. Explore how circular motion relates to the bug's x,y position, velocity, and acceleration using vectors or graphs.

Click to view content (https://openstax.org/l/28ladybugrevolutionrotation).

6.2 Centripetal Acceleration

LEARNING OBJECTIVES

By the end of this section, you will be able to:

- Establish the expression for centripetal acceleration.
- Explain the centrifuge.

We know from kinematics that acceleration is a change in velocity, either in its magnitude or in its direction, or both. In uniform circular motion, the direction of the velocity changes constantly, so there is always an associated acceleration, even though the magnitude of the velocity might be constant. You experience this acceleration yourself when you turn a corner in your car. (If you hold the wheel steady during a turn and move at constant speed, you are in uniform circular motion.) What you notice is a sideways acceleration because you and the car are changing direction. The sharper the curve and the greater your speed, the more noticeable this acceleration will become. In this section we examine the direction and magnitude of that acceleration.

Figure 6.7 shows an object moving in a circular path at constant speed. The direction of the instantaneous velocity is shown at two points along the path. Acceleration is in the direction of the change in velocity, which points directly toward the center of rotation (the center of the circular path). This pointing is shown with the vector diagram in the figure. We call the acceleration of an object moving in uniform circular motion (resulting from a net external force) the **centripetal acceleration**(a_c); centripetal means “toward the center” or “center seeking.”

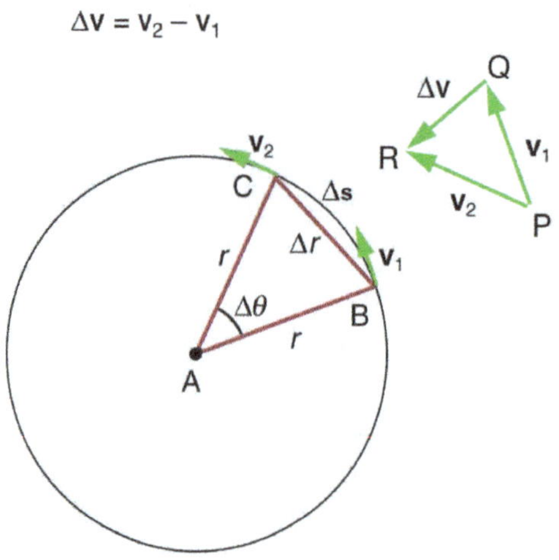

FIGURE 6.7 The directions of the velocity of an object at two different points are shown, and the change in velocity $\Delta \mathbf{v}$ is seen to point directly toward the center of curvature. (See small inset.) Because $\mathbf{a}_c = \Delta \mathbf{v}/\Delta t$, the acceleration is also toward the center; $\mathbf{a}_c$ is called centripetal acceleration. (Because $\Delta\theta$ is very small, the arc length Δs is equal to the chord length Δr for small time differences.)

The direction of centripetal acceleration is toward the center of curvature, but what is its magnitude? Note that the triangle formed by the velocity vectors and the one formed by the radii r and Δs are similar. Both the triangles ABC and PQR are isosceles triangles (two equal sides). The two equal sides of the velocity vector triangle are the speeds $v_1 = v_2 = v$. Using the properties of two similar triangles, we obtain

$$\frac{\Delta v}{v} = \frac{\Delta s}{r}. \qquad 6.13$$

Acceleration is $\Delta v/\Delta t$, and so we first solve this expression for Δv:

$$\Delta v = \frac{v}{r}\Delta s. \qquad 6.14$$

Then we divide this by Δt, yielding

$$\frac{\Delta v}{\Delta t} = \frac{v}{r} \times \frac{\Delta s}{\Delta t}. \qquad 6.15$$

Finally, noting that $\Delta v/\Delta t = a_c$ and that $\Delta s/\Delta t = v$, the linear or tangential speed, we see that the magnitude of the centripetal acceleration is

$$a_c = \frac{v^2}{r}, \qquad 6.16$$

which is the acceleration of an object in a circle of radius r at a speed v. So, centripetal acceleration is greater at high speeds and in sharp curves (smaller radius), as you have noticed when driving a car. But it is a bit surprising that a_c is proportional to speed squared, implying, for example, that it is four times as hard to take a curve at 100 km/h than at 50 km/h. A sharp corner has a small radius, so that a_c is greater for tighter turns, as you have probably noticed.

It is also useful to express a_c in terms of angular velocity. Substituting $v = r\omega$ into the above expression, we find $a_c = (r\omega)^2/r = r\omega^2$. We can express the magnitude of centripetal acceleration using either of two equations:

$$a_c = \frac{v^2}{r};\ a_c = r\omega^2. \qquad 6.17$$

Recall that the direction of a_c is toward the center. You may use whichever expression is more convenient, as illustrated in examples below.

A **centrifuge** (see Figure 6.8b) is a rotating device used to separate specimens of different densities. High centripetal acceleration significantly decreases the time it takes for separation to occur, and makes separation possible with small samples. Centrifuges are used in a variety of applications in science and medicine, including the separation of single cell suspensions such as bacteria, viruses, and blood cells from a liquid medium and the separation of macromolecules, such as DNA and protein, from a solution. Centrifuges are often rated in terms of their centripetal acceleration relative to acceleration due to gravity (g); maximum centripetal acceleration of several hundred thousand g is possible in a vacuum. Human centrifuges, extremely large centrifuges, have been used to test the tolerance of astronauts to the effects of accelerations larger than that of Earth's gravity.

EXAMPLE 6.2

How Does the Centripetal Acceleration of a Car Around a Curve Compare with That Due to Gravity?

What is the magnitude of the centripetal acceleration of a car following a curve of radius 500 m at a speed of 25.0 m/s (about 90 km/h)? Compare the acceleration with that due to gravity for this fairly gentle curve taken at highway speed. See Figure 6.8(a).

Strategy

Because v and r are given, the first expression in $a_c = \frac{v^2}{r}; a_c = r\omega^2$ is the most convenient to use.

Solution

Entering the given values of $v = 25.0 \text{ m/s}$ and $r = 500 \text{ m}$ into the first expression for a_c gives

$$a_c = \frac{v^2}{r} = \frac{(25.0 \text{ m/s})^2}{500 \text{ m}} = 1.25 \text{ m/s}^2. \qquad 6.18$$

Discussion

To compare this with the acceleration due to gravity ($g = 9.80 \text{ m/s}^2$), we take the ratio of $a_c/g = \left(1.25 \text{ m/s}^2\right)/\left(9.80 \text{ m/s}^2\right) = 0.128$. Thus, $a_c = 0.128 \text{ g}$ and is noticeable especially if you were not wearing a seat belt.

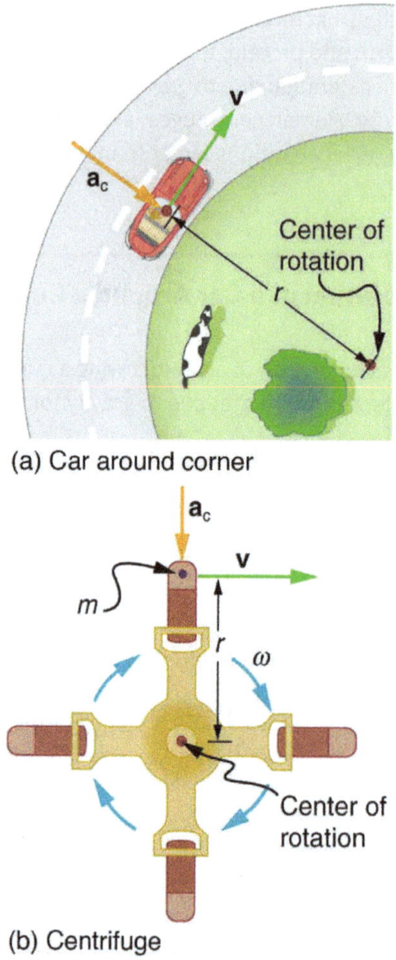

FIGURE 6.8 (a) The car following a circular path at constant speed is accelerated perpendicular to its velocity, as shown. The magnitude of this centripetal acceleration is found in Example 6.2. (b) A particle of mass in a centrifuge is rotating at constant angular velocity . It must be accelerated perpendicular to its velocity or it would continue in a straight line. The magnitude of the necessary acceleration is found in Example 6.3.

EXAMPLE 6.3

How Big Is the Centripetal Acceleration in an Ultracentrifuge?

Calculate the centripetal acceleration of a point 7.50 cm from the axis of an **ultracentrifuge** spinning at 7.5×10^4 rev/min. Determine the ratio of this acceleration to that due to gravity. See Figure 6.8(b).

Strategy

The term rev/min stands for revolutions per minute. By converting this to radians per second, we obtain the angular velocity ω. Because r is given, we can use the second expression in the equation $a_c = \frac{v^2}{r}; a_c = r\omega^2$ to calculate the centripetal acceleration.

Solution

To convert 7.50×10^4 rev/min to radians per second, we use the facts that one revolution is 2πrad and one minute is 60.0 s. Thus,

$$\omega = 7.50 \times 10^4 \frac{\text{rev}}{\text{min}} \times \frac{2\pi \text{ rad}}{1 \text{ rev}} \times \frac{1 \text{ min}}{60.0 \text{ s}} = 7854 \text{ rad/s}. \qquad 6.19$$

Now the centripetal acceleration is given by the second expression in $a_c = \frac{v^2}{r}; a_c = r\omega^2$ as

$$a_c = r\omega^2. \tag{6.20}$$

Converting 7.50 cm to meters and substituting known values gives

$$a_c = (0.0750\ \text{m})(7854\ \text{rad/s})^2 = 4.63 \times 10^6\ \text{m/s}^2. \tag{6.21}$$

Note that the unitless radians are discarded in order to get the correct units for centripetal acceleration. Taking the ratio of a_c to g yields

$$\frac{a_c}{g} = \frac{4.63 \times 10^6}{9.80} = 4.72 \times 10^5. \tag{6.22}$$

Discussion

This last result means that the centripetal acceleration is 472,000 times as strong as g. It is no wonder that such high ω centrifuges are called ultracentrifuges. The extremely large accelerations involved greatly decrease the time needed to cause the sedimentation of blood cells or other materials.

Of course, a net external force is needed to cause any acceleration, just as Newton proposed in his second law of motion. So a net external force is needed to cause a centripetal acceleration. In Centripetal Force, we will consider the forces involved in circular motion.

PHET EXPLORATIONS

Ladybug Motion 2D

Learn about position, velocity and acceleration vectors. Move the ladybug by setting the position, velocity or acceleration, and see how the vectors change. Choose linear, circular or elliptical motion, and record and playback the motion to analyze the behavior.

Click to view content (https://openstax.org/l/28ladybugmotion).

6.3 Centripetal Force

LEARNING OBJECTIVES

By the end of this section, you will be able to:

- Calculate coefficient of friction on a car tire.
- Calculate ideal speed and angle of a car on a turn.

Any force or combination of forces can cause a centripetal or radial acceleration. Just a few examples are the tension in the rope on a tether ball, the force of Earth's gravity on the Moon, friction between roller skates and a rink floor, a banked roadway's force on a car, and forces on the tube of a spinning centrifuge.

Any net force causing uniform circular motion is called a **centripetal force**. The direction of a centripetal force is toward the center of curvature, the same as the direction of centripetal acceleration. According to Newton's second law of motion, net force is mass times acceleration: net $\mathrm{F} = ma$. For uniform circular motion, the acceleration is the centripetal acceleration— $a = a_c$. Thus, the magnitude of centripetal force F_c is

$$\mathrm{F}_c = ma_c. \tag{6.23}$$

By using the expressions for centripetal acceleration a_c from $a_c = \frac{v^2}{r}; a_c = r\omega^2$, we get two expressions for the centripetal force F_c in terms of mass, velocity, angular velocity, and radius of curvature:

$$F_c = m\frac{v^2}{r};\ F_c = mr\omega^2. \tag{6.24}$$

You may use whichever expression for centripetal force is more convenient. Centripetal force F_c is always perpendicular to the path and pointing to the center of curvature, because $\mathbf{a}_c$ is perpendicular to the velocity and pointing to the center of curvature.

Note that if you solve the first expression for r, you get

$$r = \frac{mv^2}{F_c}. \tag{6.25}$$

This implies that for a given mass and velocity, a large centripetal force causes a small radius of curvature—that is, a tight curve.

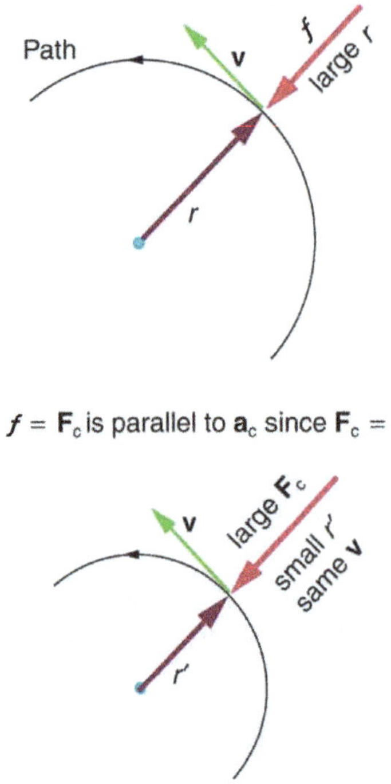

FIGURE 6.9 The frictional force supplies the centripetal force and is numerically equal to it. Centripetal force is perpendicular to velocity and causes uniform circular motion. The larger the $\mathbf{F}_c$, the smaller the radius of curvature r and the sharper the curve. The second curve has the same v, but a larger $\mathbf{F}_c$ produces a smaller r'.

EXAMPLE 6.4

What Coefficient of Friction Do Car Tires Need on a Flat Curve?

(a) Calculate the centripetal force exerted on a 900 kg car that negotiates a 500 m radius curve at 25.0 m/s.

(b) Assuming an unbanked curve, find the minimum static coefficient of friction, between the tires and the road, static friction being the reason that keeps the car from slipping (see Figure 6.10).

Strategy and Solution for (a)

We know that $F_c = \frac{mv^2}{r}$. Thus,

$$F_c = \frac{mv^2}{r} = \frac{(900\text{ kg})(25.0\text{ m/s})^2}{(500\text{ m})} = 1125\text{ N}. \tag{6.26}$$

Strategy for (b)

Figure 6.10 shows the forces acting on the car on an unbanked (level ground) curve. Friction is to the left, keeping the car from slipping, and because it is the only horizontal force acting on the car, the friction is the centripetal force in this case. We know that the maximum static friction (at which the tires roll but do not slip) is $\mu_s N$, where μ_s is the static coefficient of friction and N is the normal force. The normal force equals the car's weight on level ground, so that $N = mg$. Thus the centripetal force in this situation is

$$F_c = f = \mu_s N = \mu_s mg. \tag{6.27}$$

Now we have a relationship between centripetal force and the coefficient of friction. Using the first expression for F_c from the equation

$$\left.\begin{aligned} F_c &= m\frac{v^2}{r} \\ F_c &= mr\omega^2 \end{aligned}\right\}, \tag{6.28}$$

$$m\frac{v^2}{r} = \mu_s mg. \tag{6.29}$$

We solve this for μ_s, noting that mass cancels, and obtain

$$\mu_s = \frac{v^2}{rg}. \tag{6.30}$$

Solution for (b)

Substituting the knowns,

$$\mu_s = \frac{(25.0\ \text{m/s})^2}{(500\ \text{m})(9.80\ \text{m/s}^2)} = 0.13. \tag{6.31}$$

(Because coefficients of friction are approximate, the answer is given to only two digits.)

Discussion

We could also solve part (a) using the first expression in $\left.\begin{aligned} F_c &= m\frac{v^2}{r} \\ F_c &= mr\omega^2 \end{aligned}\right\}$, because $m, v,$ and r are given. The coefficient of friction found in part (b) is much smaller than is typically found between tires and roads. The car will still negotiate the curve if the coefficient is greater than 0.13, because static friction is a responsive force, being able to assume a value less than but no more than $\mu_s N$. A higher coefficient would also allow the car to negotiate the curve at a higher speed, but if the coefficient of friction is less, the safe speed would be less than 25 m/s. Note that mass cancels, implying that in this example, it does not matter how heavily loaded the car is to negotiate the turn. Mass cancels because friction is assumed proportional to the normal force, which in turn is proportional to mass. If the surface of the road were banked, the normal force would be less as will be discussed below.

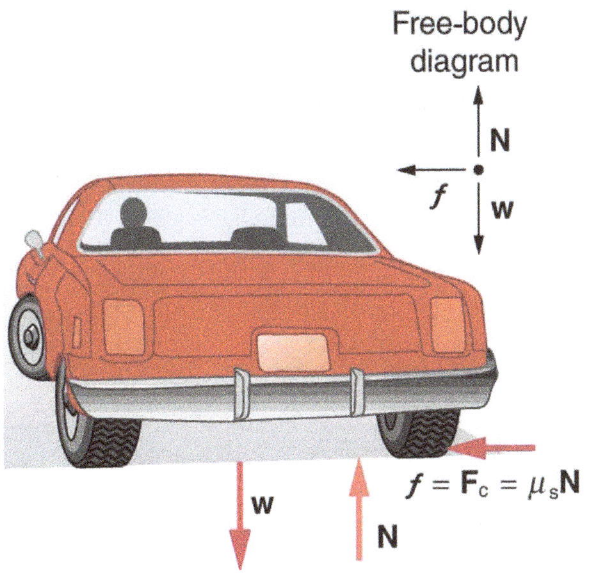

FIGURE 6.10 This car on level ground is moving away and turning to the left. The centripetal force causing the car to turn in a circular path is due to friction between the tires and the road. A minimum coefficient of friction is needed, or the car will move in a larger-radius curve and leave the roadway.

Let us now consider **banked curves**, where the slope of the road helps you negotiate the curve. See Figure 6.11. The greater the angle θ, the faster you can take the curve. Race tracks for bikes as well as cars, for example, often have steeply banked curves. In an "ideally banked curve," the angle θ is such that you can negotiate the curve at a certain speed without the aid of friction between the tires and the road. We will derive an expression for θ for an ideally banked curve and consider an example related to it.

For **ideal banking**, the net external force equals the horizontal centripetal force in the absence of friction. The components of the normal force N in the horizontal and vertical directions must equal the centripetal force and the weight of the car, respectively. In cases in which forces are not parallel, it is most convenient to consider components along perpendicular axes—in this case, the vertical and horizontal directions.

Figure 6.11 shows a free body diagram for a car on a frictionless banked curve. If the angle θ is ideal for the speed and radius, then the net external force will equal the necessary centripetal force. The only two external forces acting on the car are its weight $\mathbf{w}$ and the normal force of the road $\mathbf{N}$. (A frictionless surface can only exert a force perpendicular to the surface—that is, a normal force.) These two forces must add to give a net external force that is horizontal toward the center of curvature and has magnitude $\mathrm{mv^2/r}$. Because this is the crucial force and it is horizontal, we use a coordinate system with vertical and horizontal axes. Only the normal force has a horizontal component, and so this must equal the centripetal force—that is,

$$N \sin\theta = \frac{mv^2}{r}. \tag{6.32}$$

Because the car does not leave the surface of the road, the net vertical force must be zero, meaning that the vertical components of the two external forces must be equal in magnitude and opposite in direction. From the figure, we see that the vertical component of the normal force is $N\cos\theta$, and the only other vertical force is the car's weight. These must be equal in magnitude; thus,

$$N\cos\theta = mg. \tag{6.33}$$

Now we can combine the last two equations to eliminate N and get an expression for θ, as desired. Solving the second equation for $N = mg/(\cos\theta)$, and substituting this into the first yields

$$mg\frac{\sin\theta}{\cos\theta} = \frac{mv^2}{r} \tag{6.34}$$

$$\begin{aligned} mg\tan(\theta) &= \frac{mv^2}{r} \\ \tan\theta &= \frac{v^2}{rg.} \end{aligned} \tag{6.35}$$

Taking the inverse tangent gives

$$\theta = \tan^{-1}\left(\frac{v^2}{rg}\right) \text{ (ideally banked curve, no friction).} \tag{6.36}$$

This expression can be understood by considering how θ depends on v and r. A large θ will be obtained for a large v and a small r. That is, roads must be steeply banked for high speeds and sharp curves. Friction helps, because it allows you to take the curve at greater or lower speed than if the curve is frictionless. Note that θ does not depend on the mass of the vehicle.

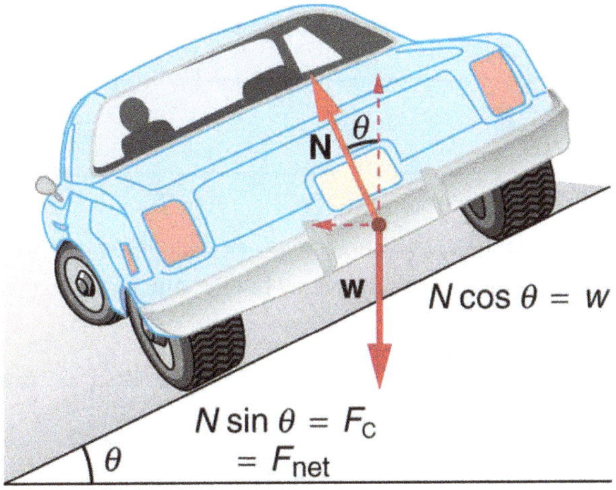

FIGURE 6.11 The car on this banked curve is moving away and turning to the left.

EXAMPLE 6.5

What Is the Ideal Speed to Take a Steeply Banked Tight Curve?

Curves on some test tracks and race courses, such as the Daytona International Speedway in Florida, are very steeply banked. This banking, with the aid of tire friction and very stable car configurations, allows the curves to be taken at very high speed. To illustrate, calculate the speed at which a 100 m radius curve banked at 65.0° should be driven if the road is frictionless.

Strategy

We first note that all terms in the expression for the ideal angle of a banked curve except for speed are known; thus, we need only rearrange it so that speed appears on the left-hand side and then substitute known quantities.

Solution

Starting with

$$\tan\theta = \frac{v^2}{rg} \tag{6.37}$$

we get

$$v = (rg\tan\theta)^{1/2}. \tag{6.38}$$

Noting that tan 65.0° = 2.14, we obtain

$$\begin{aligned} v &= \left[(100\text{ m})(9.80\text{ m/s}^2)(2.14)\right]^{1/2} \\ &= 45.8\text{ m/s}. \end{aligned} \tag{6.39}$$

Discussion

This is just about 165 km/h, consistent with a very steeply banked and rather sharp curve. Tire friction enables a vehicle to take the curve at significantly higher speeds.

Calculations similar to those in the preceding examples can be performed for a host of interesting situations in which centripetal force is involved—a number of these are presented in this chapter's Problems and Exercises.

TAKE-HOME EXPERIMENT

Ask a friend or relative to swing a golf club or a tennis racquet. Take appropriate measurements to estimate the centripetal acceleration of the end of the club or racquet. You may choose to do this in slow motion.

PHET EXPLORATIONS

Gravity and Orbits

Move the sun, earth, moon and space station to see how it affects their gravitational forces and orbital paths. Visualize the sizes and distances between different heavenly bodies, and turn off gravity to see what would happen without it!

Click to view content (https://openstax.org/books/college-physics-ap-courses-2e/pages/6-3-centripetal-force)

6.4 Fictitious Forces and Non-inertial Frames: The Coriolis Force

LEARNING OBJECTIVES

By the end of this section, you will be able to:

- Discuss the inertial frame of reference.
- Discuss the non-inertial frame of reference.
- Describe the effects of the Coriolis force.

What do taking off in a jet airplane, turning a corner in a car, riding a merry-go-round, and the circular motion of a tropical cyclone have in common? Each exhibits fictitious forces—unreal forces that arise from motion and may *seem* real, because the observer's frame of reference is accelerating or rotating.

When taking off in a jet, most people would agree it feels as if you are being pushed back into the seat as the airplane accelerates down the runway. Yet a physicist would say that *you* tend to remain stationary while the *seat* pushes forward on you, and there is no real force backward on you. An even more common experience occurs when you make a tight curve in your car—say, to the right. You feel as if you are thrown (that is, *forced*) toward the left relative to the car. Again, a physicist would say that *you* are going in a straight line but the *car* moves to the right, and there is no real force on you to the left. Recall Newton's first law.

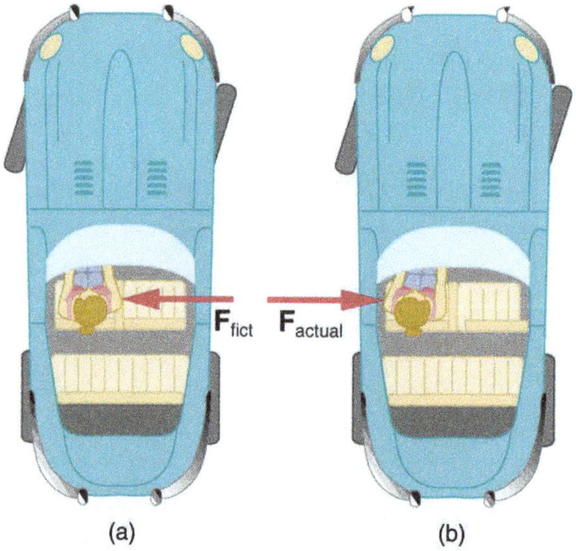

FIGURE 6.12 (a) The car driver feels herself forced to the left relative to the car when she makes a right turn. This is a fictitious force arising from the use of the car as a frame of reference. (b) In the Earth's frame of reference, the driver moves in a straight line, obeying Newton's first law, and the car moves to the right. There is no real force to the left on the driver relative to Earth. There is a real force to the right on the car to make it turn.

We can reconcile these points of view by examining the frames of reference used. Let us concentrate on people in a car. Passengers instinctively use the car as a frame of reference, while a physicist uses Earth. The physicist chooses Earth because it is very nearly an inertial frame of reference—one in which all forces are real (that is, in which all forces have an identifiable physical origin). In such a frame of reference, Newton's laws of motion take the form given in Dynamics: Newton's Laws of Motion The car is a **non-inertial frame of reference** because it is accelerated to the side. The force to the left sensed by car passengers is a **fictitious force** having no physical origin. There is nothing real pushing them left—the car, as well as the driver, is actually accelerating to the right.

Let us now take a mental ride on a merry-go-round—specifically, a rapidly rotating playground merry-go-round. You take the merry-go-round to be your frame of reference because you rotate together. In that non-inertial frame, you feel a fictitious force, named **centrifugal force** (not to be confused with centripetal force), trying to throw you off. You must hang on tightly to counteract the centrifugal force. In Earth's frame of reference, there is no force trying to throw you off. Rather you must hang on to make yourself go in a circle because otherwise you would go in a straight line, right off the merry-go-round.

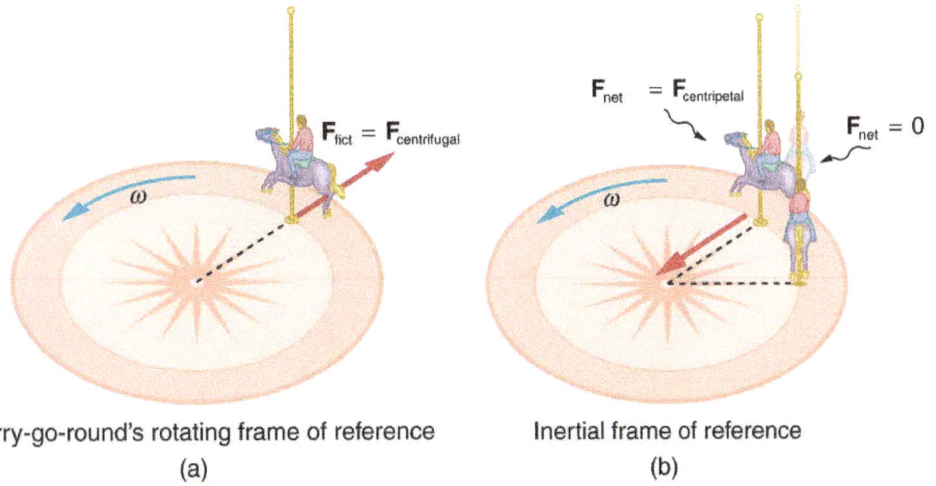

FIGURE 6.13 (a) A rider on a merry-go-round feels as if he is being thrown off. This fictitious force is called the centrifugal force—it explains the rider's motion in the rotating frame of reference. (b) In an inertial frame of reference and according to Newton's laws, it is his inertia that carries him off and not a real force (the unshaded rider has $F_{net} = 0$ and heads in a straight line). A real force, $F_{centripetal}$, is needed to cause a circular path.

This inertial effect, carrying you away from the center of rotation if there is no centripetal force to cause circular motion, is put to good use in centrifuges (see Figure 6.14). A centrifuge spins a sample very rapidly, as mentioned earlier in this chapter. Viewed from the rotating frame of reference, the fictitious centrifugal force throws particles outward, hastening their sedimentation. The greater the angular velocity, the greater the centrifugal force. But what really happens is that the inertia of the particles carries them along a line tangent to the circle while the test tube is forced in a circular path by a centripetal force.

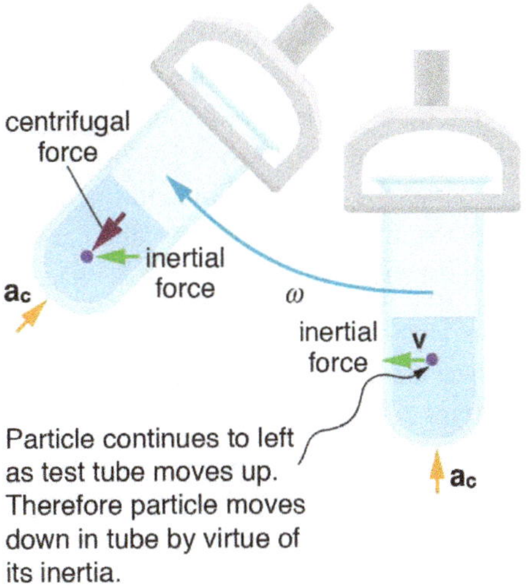

FIGURE 6.14 Centrifuges use inertia to perform their task. Particles in the fluid sediment come out because their inertia carries them away from the center of rotation. The large angular velocity of the centrifuge quickens the sedimentation. Ultimately, the particles will come into contact with the test tube walls, which will then supply the centripetal force needed to make them move in a circle of constant radius.

Let us now consider what happens if something moves in a frame of reference that rotates. For example, what if you slide a ball directly away from the center of the merry-go-round, as shown in Figure 6.15? The ball follows a straight path relative to Earth (assuming negligible friction) and a path curved to the right on the merry-go-round's surface. A person standing next to the merry-go-round sees the ball moving straight and the merry-go-round rotating underneath it. In the merry-go-round's frame of reference, we explain the apparent curve to the right by using a fictitious force, called the **Coriolis force**, that causes the ball to curve to the right. The fictitious Coriolis force can be used by anyone in that frame of reference to explain why objects follow curved paths and allows us to apply Newton's Laws in non-inertial frames of reference.

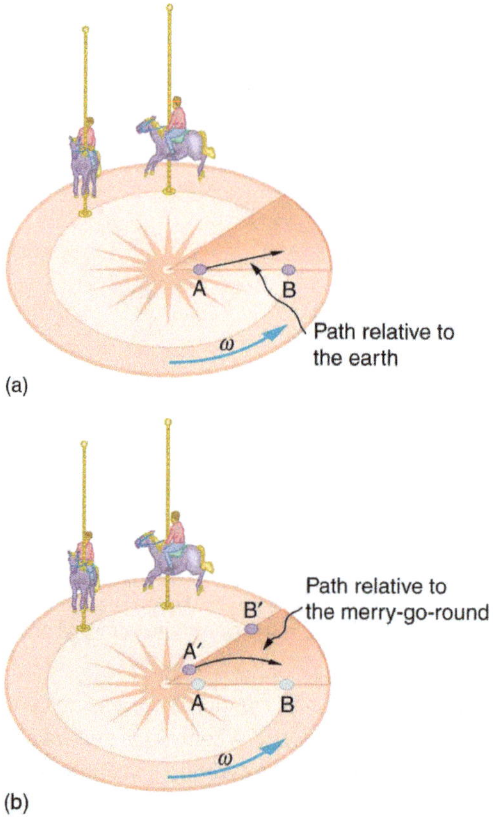

FIGURE 6.15 Looking down on the counterclockwise rotation of a merry-go-round, we see that a ball slid straight toward the edge follows a path curved to the right. The person slides the ball toward point B, starting at point A. Both points rotate to the shaded positions (A' and B') shown in the time that the ball follows the curved path in the rotating frame and a straight path in Earth's frame.

Up until now, we have considered Earth to be an inertial frame of reference with little or no worry about effects due to its rotation. Yet such effects *do* exist—in the rotation of weather systems, for example. Most consequences of Earth's rotation can be qualitatively understood by analogy with the merry-go-round. Viewed from above the North Pole, Earth rotates counterclockwise, as does the merry-go-round in Figure 6.15. As on the merry-go-round, any motion in Earth's northern hemisphere experiences a Coriolis force to the right. Just the opposite occurs in the southern hemisphere; there, the force is to the left. Because Earth's angular velocity is small, the Coriolis force is usually negligible, but for large-scale motions, such as wind patterns, it has substantial effects.

The Coriolis force causes hurricanes in the northern hemisphere to rotate in the counterclockwise direction, while the tropical cyclones (what hurricanes are called below the equator) in the southern hemisphere rotate in the clockwise direction. The terms hurricane, typhoon, and tropical storm are regionally-specific names for tropical cyclones, storm systems characterized by low pressure centers, strong winds, and heavy rains. Figure 6.16 helps show how these rotations take place. Air flows toward any region of low pressure, and tropical cyclones contain particularly low pressures. Thus winds flow toward the center of a tropical cyclone or a low-pressure weather system at the surface. In the northern hemisphere, these inward winds are deflected to the right, as shown in the figure, producing a counterclockwise circulation at the surface for low-pressure zones of any type. Low pressure at the surface is associated with rising air, which also produces cooling and cloud formation, making low-pressure patterns quite visible from space. Conversely, wind circulation around high-pressure zones is clockwise in the northern hemisphere but is less visible because high pressure is associated with sinking air, producing clear skies.

The rotation of tropical cyclones and the path of a ball on a merry-go-round can just as well be explained by inertia and the rotation of the system underneath. When non-inertial frames are used, fictitious forces, such as the Coriolis force, must be invented to explain the curved path. There is no identifiable physical source for these fictitious forces. In an inertial frame, inertia explains the path, and no force is found to be without an identifiable source. Either view allows us to describe nature, but a view in an inertial frame is the simplest and truest, in the sense that all forces have real origins and explanations.

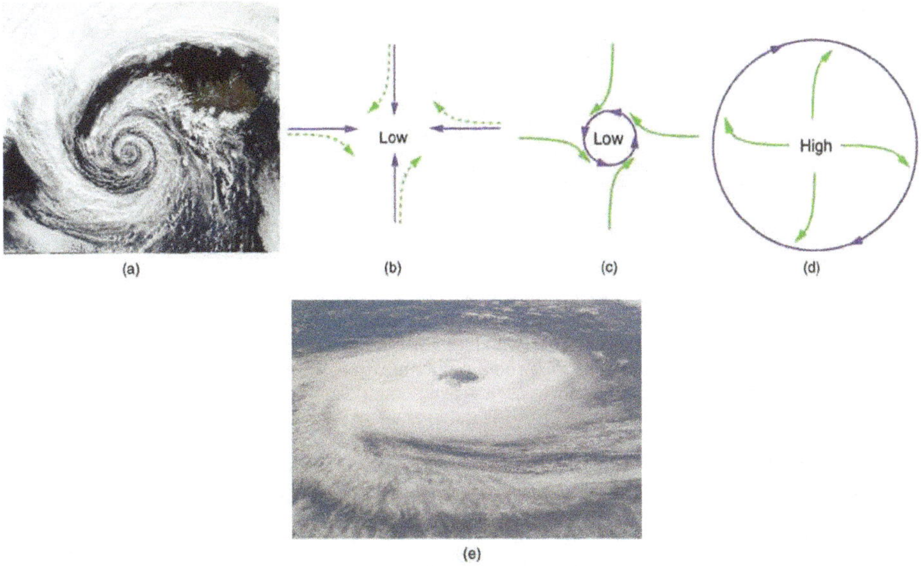

FIGURE 6.16 (a) The counterclockwise rotation of this northern hemisphere hurricane is a major consequence of the Coriolis force. (credit: NASA) (b) Without the Coriolis force, air would flow straight into a low-pressure zone, such as that found in tropical cyclones. (c) The Coriolis force deflects the winds to the right, producing a counterclockwise rotation. (d) Wind flowing away from a high-pressure zone is also deflected to the right, producing a clockwise rotation. (e) The opposite direction of rotation is produced by the Coriolis force in the southern hemisphere, leading to tropical cyclones. (credit: NASA)

6.5 Newton's Universal Law of Gravitation

LEARNING OBJECTIVES

By the end of this section, you will be able to:

- Explain Earth's gravitational force.
- Describe the gravitational effect of the Moon on Earth.
- Discuss weightlessness in space.
- Examine the Cavendish experiment

What do aching feet, a falling apple, and the orbit of the Moon have in common? Each is caused by the gravitational force. Our feet are strained by supporting our weight—the force of Earth's gravity on us. An apple falls from a tree because of the same force acting a few meters above Earth's surface. And the Moon orbits Earth because gravity is able to supply the necessary centripetal force at a distance of hundreds of millions of meters. In fact, the same force causes planets to orbit the Sun, stars to orbit the center of the galaxy, and galaxies to cluster together. Gravity is another example of underlying simplicity in nature. It is the weakest of the four basic forces found in nature, and in some ways the least understood. It is a force that acts at a distance, without physical contact, and is expressed by a formula that is valid everywhere in the universe, for masses and distances that vary from the tiny to the immense.

Sir Isaac Newton was the first scientist to precisely define the gravitational force, and to show that it could explain both falling bodies and astronomical motions. See Figure 6.17. But Newton was not the first to suspect that the same force caused both our weight and the motion of planets. His forerunner Galileo Galilei had contended that falling bodies and planetary motions had the same cause. Some of Newton's contemporaries, such as Robert Hooke, Christopher Wren, and Edmund Halley, had also made some progress toward understanding gravitation. But Newton was the first to propose an exact mathematical form and to use that form to show that the motion of heavenly bodies should be conic sections—circles, ellipses, parabolas, and hyperbolas. This theoretical prediction was a major triumph—it had been known for some time that moons, planets, and comets follow such paths, but no one had been able to propose a mechanism that caused them to follow these paths and not others. Other prominent scientists and mathematicians of the time, particularly those outside of England, were reluctant to accept Newton's principles. It took the work of another prominent philosopher, writer, and scientist, Émilie du Châtelet, to establish the Newtonian gravitation as the accurate and overarching law. Du Châtelet, who had earlier laid the foundation for the understanding of conservation of energy as well as the principle that light had no mass, translated and augmented Newton's key work. She also utilized calculus to explain gravity, which helped lead to its acceptance.

FIGURE 6.17 According to early accounts, Newton was inspired to make the connection between falling bodies and astronomical motions when he saw an apple fall from a tree and realized that if the gravitational force could extend above the ground to a tree, it might also reach the Sun. The inspiration of Newton's apple is a part of worldwide folklore and may even be based in fact. Newton's universal law of gravitation and his laws of motion answered very old questions about nature and gave tremendous support to the notion of underlying simplicity and unity in nature. Like many revolutionary discoveries, it was not immediately accepted. Prominent French scientist and philosopher Émilie du Châtelet helped establish Newton's theory in France and mainland Europe.

The gravitational force is relatively simple. It is always attractive, and it depends only on the masses involved and the distance between them. Stated in modern language, **Newton's universal law of gravitation** states that every particle in the universe attracts every other particle with a force along a line joining them. The force is directly proportional to the product of their masses and inversely proportional to the square of the distance between them.

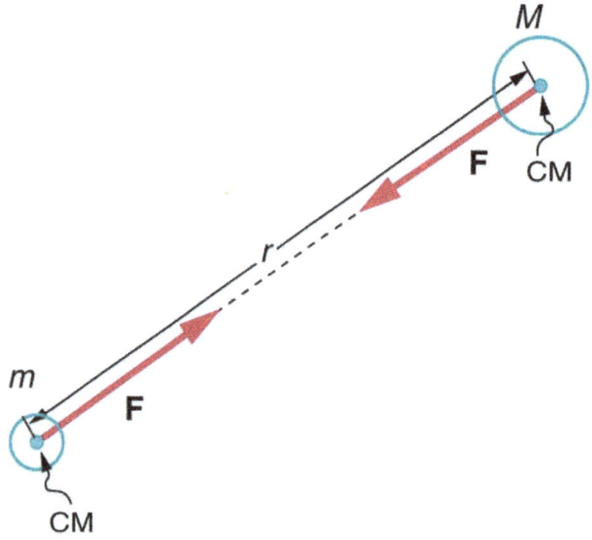

FIGURE 6.18 Gravitational attraction is along a line joining the centers of mass of these two bodies. The magnitude of the force is the same on each, consistent with Newton's third law.

MISCONCEPTION ALERT

The magnitude of the force on each object (one has larger mass than the other) is the same, consistent with Newton's third law.

The bodies we are dealing with tend to be large. To simplify the situation we assume that the body acts as if its entire mass is concentrated at one specific point called the **center of mass** (CM), which will be further explored in Linear Momentum and Collisions. For two bodies having masses m and M with a distance r between their centers of mass, the equation for Newton's universal law of gravitation is

$$F = G\frac{mM}{r^2}, \qquad 6.40$$

where F is the magnitude of the gravitational force and G is a proportionality factor called the **gravitational constant**. G is a universal gravitational constant—that is, it is thought to be the same everywhere in the universe. It has been measured experimentally to be

$$G = 6.674 \times 10^{-11} \frac{\text{N} \cdot \text{m}^2}{\text{kg}^2} \qquad 6.41$$

in SI units. Note that the units of G are such that a force in newtons is obtained from $F = G\frac{mM}{r^2}$, when considering masses in kilograms and distance in meters. For example, two 1.000 kg masses separated by 1.000 m will experience a gravitational attraction of 6.674×10^{-11} N. This is an extraordinarily small force. The small magnitude of the gravitational force is consistent with everyday experience. We are unaware that even large objects like mountains exert gravitational forces on us. In fact, our body weight is the force of attraction of the *entire Earth* on us with a mass of 6×10^{24} kg.

Recall that the acceleration due to gravity g is about $9.80\ \text{m/s}^2$ on Earth. We can now determine why this is so. The weight of an object mg is the gravitational force between it and Earth. Substituting mg for F in Newton's universal law of gravitation gives

$$mg = G\frac{mM}{r^2}, \qquad 6.42$$

where m is the mass of the object, M is the mass of Earth, and r is the distance to the center of Earth (the distance between the centers of mass of the object and Earth). See Figure 6.19. The mass m of the object cancels, leaving an equation for g:

$$g = G\frac{M}{r^2}. \qquad 6.43$$

Substituting known values for Earth's mass and radius (to three significant figures),

$$g = \left(6.67 \times 10^{-11} \frac{\text{N} \cdot \text{m}^2}{\text{kg}^2}\right) \times \frac{5.98 \times 10^{24}\ \text{kg}}{(6.38 \times 10^6\ \text{m})^2}, \qquad 6.44$$

and we obtain a value for the acceleration of a falling body:

$$g = 9.80\ \text{m/s}^2. \qquad 6.45$$

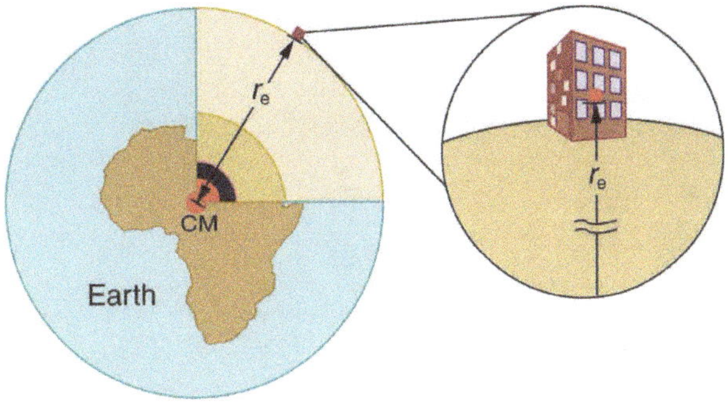

FIGURE 6.19 The distance between the centers of mass of Earth and an object on its surface is very nearly the same as the radius of Earth, because Earth is so much larger than the object.

This is the expected value *and is independent of the body's mass.* Newton's law of gravitation takes Galileo's observation that all masses fall with the same acceleration a step further, explaining the observation in terms of a force that causes objects to fall—in fact, in terms of a universally existing force of attraction between masses.

TAKE-HOME EXPERIMENT

Take a marble, a ball, and a spoon and drop them from the same height. Do they hit the floor at the same time? If you drop a piece of paper as well, does it behave like the other objects? Explain your observations.

MAKING CONNECTIONS

Attempts are still being made to understand the gravitational force. As we shall see in Particle Physics, modern physics is exploring the connections of gravity to other forces, space, and time. General relativity alters our view of gravitation, leading us to think of gravitation as bending space and time.

In the following example, we make a comparison similar to one made by Newton himself. He noted that if the gravitational force caused the Moon to orbit Earth, then the acceleration due to gravity should equal the centripetal acceleration of the Moon in its orbit. Newton found that the two accelerations agreed "pretty nearly."

EXAMPLE 6.6

Earth's Gravitational Force Is the Centripetal Force Making the Moon Move in a Curved Path

(a) Find the acceleration due to Earth's gravity at the distance of the Moon.

(b) Calculate the centripetal acceleration needed to keep the Moon in its orbit (assuming a circular orbit about a fixed Earth), and compare it with the value of the acceleration due to Earth's gravity that you have just found.

Strategy for (a)

This calculation is the same as the one finding the acceleration due to gravity at Earth's surface, except that r is the distance from the center of Earth to the center of the Moon. The radius of the Moon's nearly circular orbit is 3.84×10^8 m.

Solution for (a)

Substituting known values into the expression for g found above, remembering that M is the mass of Earth not the Moon, yields

$$\begin{aligned} g &= G\frac{M}{r^2} = \left(6.67 \times 10^{-11}\ \frac{\text{N}\cdot\text{m}^2}{\text{kg}^2}\right) \times \frac{5.98\times10^{24}\ \text{kg}}{(3.84\times10^8\ \text{m})^2} \\ &= 2.70 \times 10^{-3}\ \text{m/s.}^2 \end{aligned} \qquad 6.46$$

Strategy for (b)

Centripetal acceleration can be calculated using either form of

$$\left.\begin{aligned} a_c &= \frac{v^2}{r} \\ a_c &= r\omega^2 \end{aligned}\right\}. \qquad 6.47$$

We choose to use the second form:

$$a_c = r\omega^2, \qquad 6.48$$

where ω is the angular velocity of the Moon about Earth.

Solution for (b)

Given that the period (the time it takes to make one complete rotation) of the Moon's orbit is 27.3 days, (d) and using

$$1\text{ d} \times 24\frac{\text{hr}}{\text{d}} \times 60\frac{\text{min}}{\text{hr}} \times 60\frac{\text{s}}{\text{min}} = 86{,}400\text{ s} \quad 6.49$$

we see that

$$\omega = \frac{\Delta\theta}{\Delta t} = \frac{2\pi\text{ rad}}{(27.3\text{ d})(86{,}400\text{ s/d})} = 2.66 \times 10^{-6}\frac{\text{rad}}{\text{s}}. \quad 6.50$$

The centripetal acceleration is

$$\begin{aligned} a_c &= r\omega^2 = (3.84 \times 10^8\text{ m})(2.66 \times 10^{-6}\text{ rad/s})^2 \\ &= 2.72 \times 10^{-3}\text{ m/s.}^2 \end{aligned} \quad 6.51$$

The direction of the acceleration is toward the center of the Earth.

Discussion

The centripetal acceleration of the Moon found in (b) differs by less than 1% from the acceleration due to Earth's gravity found in (a). This agreement is approximate because the Moon's orbit is slightly elliptical, and Earth is not stationary (rather the Earth-Moon system rotates about its center of mass, which is located some 1700 km below Earth's surface). The clear implication is that Earth's gravitational force causes the Moon to orbit Earth.

Why does Earth not remain stationary as the Moon orbits it? This is because, as expected from Newton's third law, if Earth exerts a force on the Moon, then the Moon should exert an equal and opposite force on Earth (see Figure 6.20). We do not sense the Moon's effect on Earth's motion, because the Moon's gravity moves our bodies right along with Earth but there are other signs on Earth that clearly show the effect of the Moon's gravitational force as discussed in Satellites and Kepler's Laws: An Argument for Simplicity.

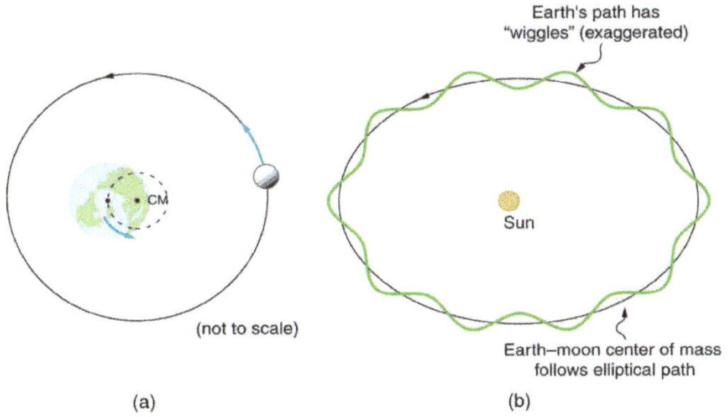

FIGURE 6.20 (a) Earth and the Moon rotate approximately once a month around their common center of mass. (b) Their center of mass orbits the Sun in an elliptical orbit, but Earth's path around the Sun has "wiggles" in it. Similar wiggles in the paths of stars have been observed and are considered direct evidence of planets orbiting those stars. This is important because the planets' reflected light is often too dim to be observed.

Tides

Ocean tides are one very observable result of the Moon's gravity acting on Earth. Figure 6.21 is a simplified drawing of the Moon's position relative to the tides. Because water easily flows on Earth's surface, a high tide is created on the side of Earth nearest to the Moon, where the Moon's gravitational pull is strongest. Why is there also a high tide on the opposite side of Earth? The answer is that Earth is pulled toward the Moon more than the water on the far side, because Earth is closer to the Moon. So the water on the side of Earth closest to the Moon is pulled away from Earth, and Earth is pulled away from water on the far side. As Earth rotates, the tidal bulge (an effect of the tidal forces between an orbiting natural satellite and the primary planet that it orbits) keeps its orientation with the Moon. Thus there are two tides per day (the actual tidal period is about 12 hours and 25.2 minutes), because the Moon moves in its orbit each day as well).

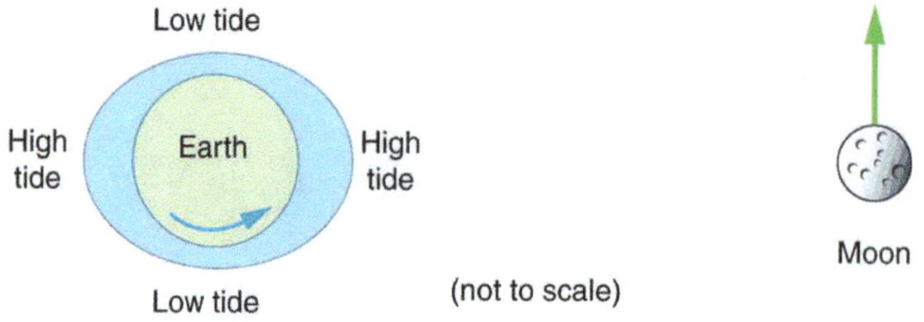

FIGURE 6.21 The Moon causes ocean tides by attracting the water on the near side more than Earth, and by attracting Earth more than the water on the far side. The distances and sizes are not to scale. For this simplified representation of the Earth-Moon system, there are two high and two low tides per day at any location, because Earth rotates under the tidal bulge.

The Sun also affects tides, although it has about half the effect of the Moon. However, the largest tides, called spring tides, occur when Earth, the Moon, and the Sun are aligned. The smallest tides, called neap tides, occur when the Sun is at a 90° angle to the Earth-Moon alignment.

FIGURE 6.22 (a, b) Spring tides: The highest tides occur when Earth, the Moon, and the Sun are aligned. (c) Neap tide: The lowest tides occur when the Sun lies at 90° to the Earth-Moon alignment. Note that this figure is not drawn to scale.

Tides are not unique to Earth but occur in many astronomical systems. The most extreme tides occur where the gravitational force is the strongest and varies most rapidly, such as near black holes (see Figure 6.23). A few likely candidates for black holes have been observed in our galaxy. These have masses greater than the Sun but have diameters only a few kilometers across. The tidal forces near them are so great that they can actually tear matter from a companion star.

FIGURE 6.23 A black hole is an object with such strong gravity that not even light can escape it. This black hole was created by the supernova of one star in a two-star system. The tidal forces created by the black hole are so great that it tears matter from the companion star. This matter is compressed and heated as it is sucked into the black hole, creating light and X-rays observable from Earth.

"Weightlessness" and Microgravity

In contrast to the tremendous gravitational force near black holes is the apparent gravitational field experienced by astronauts orbiting Earth. What is the effect of "weightlessness" upon an astronaut who is in orbit for months? Or what about the effect of weightlessness upon plant growth? Weightlessness doesn't mean that an astronaut is not being acted upon by the gravitational force. There is no "zero gravity" in an astronaut's orbit. The term just means that the astronaut is in free-fall, accelerating with the acceleration due to gravity. If an elevator cable breaks, the passengers inside will be in free fall and will experience weightlessness. You can experience short periods of weightlessness in some rides in amusement parks.

FIGURE 6.24 Astronauts experiencing weightlessness on board the International Space Station. (credit: NASA)

Microgravity refers to an environment in which the apparent net acceleration of a body is small compared with that produced by Earth at its surface. Many interesting biology and physics topics have been studied over the past three decades in the presence of microgravity. Of immediate concern is the effect on astronauts of extended times in outer space, such as at the International Space Station. Researchers have observed that muscles will atrophy (waste away) in this environment. There is also a corresponding loss of bone mass. Study continues on cardiovascular adaptation to space flight. On Earth, blood pressure is usually higher in the feet than in the head, because the higher column of blood exerts a downward force on it, due to gravity. When standing, 70% of your blood is below the level of the heart, while in a horizontal position, just the opposite occurs. What difference does the absence of this pressure differential have upon the heart?

Some findings in human physiology in space can be clinically important to the management of diseases back on

Earth. On a somewhat negative note, spaceflight is known to affect the human immune system, possibly making the crew members more vulnerable to infectious diseases. Experiments flown in space also have shown that some bacteria grow faster in microgravity than they do on Earth. However, on a positive note, studies indicate that microbial antibiotic production can increase by a factor of two in space-grown cultures. One hopes to be able to understand these mechanisms so that similar successes can be achieved on the ground. In another area of physics space research, inorganic crystals and protein crystals have been grown in outer space that have much higher quality than any grown on Earth, so crystallography studies on their structure can yield much better results.

Plants have evolved with the stimulus of gravity and with gravity sensors. Roots grow downward and shoots grow upward. Plants might be able to provide a life support system for long duration space missions by regenerating the atmosphere, purifying water, and producing food. Some studies have indicated that plant growth and development are not affected by gravity, but there is still uncertainty about structural changes in plants grown in a microgravity environment.

The Cavendish Experiment: Then and Now

As previously noted, the universal gravitational constant G is determined experimentally. This definition was first done accurately by Henry Cavendish (1731–1810), an English scientist, in 1798, more than 100 years after Newton published his universal law of gravitation. The measurement of G is very basic and important because it determines the strength of one of the four forces in nature. Cavendish's experiment was very difficult because he measured the tiny gravitational attraction between two ordinary-sized masses (tens of kilograms at most), using apparatus like that in Figure 6.25. Remarkably, his value for G differs by less than 1% from the best modern value.

One important consequence of knowing G was that an accurate value for Earth's mass could finally be obtained. This was done by measuring the acceleration due to gravity as accurately as possible and then calculating the mass of Earth M from the relationship Newton's universal law of gravitation gives

$$mg = G\frac{mM}{r^2}, \tag{6.52}$$

where m is the mass of the object, M is the mass of Earth, and r is the distance to the center of Earth (the distance between the centers of mass of the object and Earth). See Figure 6.18. The mass m of the object cancels, leaving an equation for g:

$$g = G\frac{M}{r^2}. \tag{6.53}$$

Rearranging to solve for M yields

$$M = \frac{gr^2}{G}. \tag{6.54}$$

So M can be calculated because all quantities on the right, including the radius of Earth r, are known from direct measurements. We shall see in Satellites and Kepler's Laws: An Argument for Simplicity that knowing G also allows for the determination of astronomical masses. Interestingly, of all the fundamental constants in physics, G is by far the least well determined.

The Cavendish experiment is also used to explore other aspects of gravity. One of the most interesting questions is whether the gravitational force depends on substance as well as mass—for example, whether one kilogram of lead exerts the same gravitational pull as one kilogram of water. A Hungarian scientist named Roland von Eötvös pioneered this inquiry early in the 20th century. He found, with an accuracy of five parts per billion, that the gravitational force does not depend on the substance. Such experiments continue today, and have improved upon Eötvös' measurements. Cavendish-type experiments such as those of Eric Adelberger and others at the University of Washington, have also put severe limits on the possibility of a fifth force and have verified a major prediction of general relativity—that gravitational energy contributes to rest mass. Ongoing measurements there use a torsion balance and a parallel plate (not spheres, as Cavendish used) to examine how Newton's law of gravitation works over sub-millimeter distances. On this small-scale, do gravitational effects depart from the inverse square law? So far, no deviation has been observed.

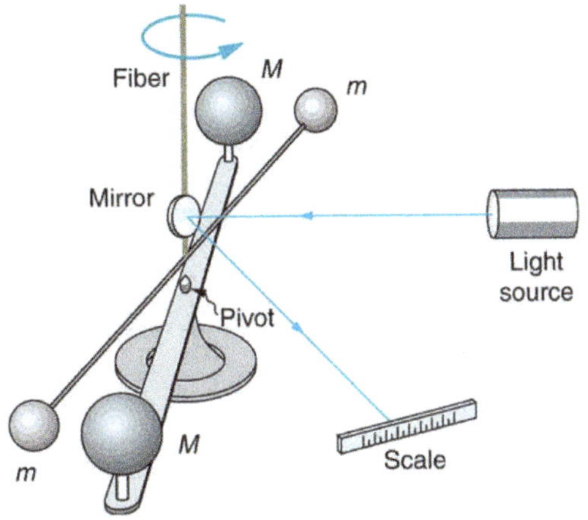

FIGURE 6.25 Cavendish used an apparatus like this to measure the gravitational attraction between the two suspended spheres (m) and the two on the stand (M) by observing the amount of torsion (twisting) created in the fiber. Distance between the masses can be varied to check the dependence of the force on distance. Modern experiments of this type continue to explore gravity.

6.6 Satellites and Kepler's Laws: An Argument for Simplicity

LEARNING OBJECTIVES

By the end of this section, you will be able to:

- State Kepler's laws of planetary motion.
- Derive the third Kepler's law for circular orbits.
- Discuss the Ptolemaic model of the universe.

Examples of gravitational orbits abound. Hundreds of artificial satellites orbit Earth together with thousands of pieces of debris. The Moon's orbit about Earth has intrigued humans from time immemorial. The orbits of planets, asteroids, meteors, and comets about the Sun are no less interesting. If we look further, we see almost unimaginable numbers of stars, galaxies, and other celestial objects orbiting one another and interacting through gravity.

All these motions are governed by gravitational force, and it is possible to describe them to various degrees of precision. Precise descriptions of complex systems must be made with large computers. However, we can describe an important class of orbits without the use of computers, and we shall find it instructive to study them. These orbits have the following characteristics:

1. *A small mass m orbits a much larger mass M.* This allows us to view the motion as if M were stationary—in fact, as if from an inertial frame of reference placed on M —without significant error. Mass m is the satellite of M, if the orbit is gravitationally bound.
2. *The system is isolated from other masses.* This allows us to neglect any small effects due to outside masses.

The conditions are satisfied, to good approximation, by Earth's satellites (including the Moon), by objects orbiting the Sun, and by the satellites of other planets. Historically, planets were studied first, and there is a classical set of three laws, called Kepler's laws of planetary motion, that describe the orbits of all bodies satisfying the two previous conditions (not just planets in our solar system). These descriptive laws are named for the German astronomer Johannes Kepler (1571–1630), who devised them after careful study (over some 20 years) of a large amount of meticulously recorded observations of planetary motion done by Tycho Brahe (1546–1601). Such careful collection and detailed recording of methods and data are hallmarks of good science. Data constitute the evidence from which new interpretations and meanings can be constructed.

Kepler's Laws of Planetary Motion

Kepler's First Law

The orbit of each planet about the Sun is an ellipse with the Sun at one focus.

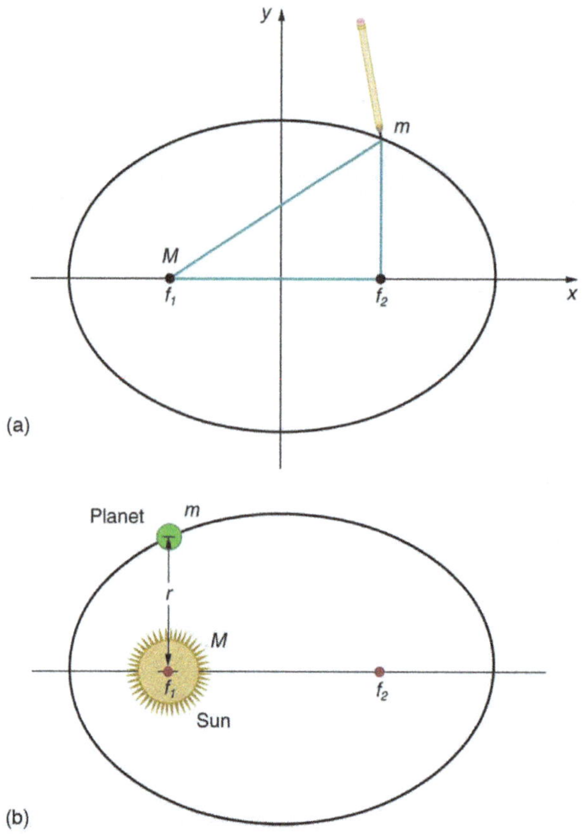

FIGURE 6.26 (a) An ellipse is a closed curve such that the sum of the distances from a point on the curve to the two foci (f_1 and f_2) is a constant. You can draw an ellipse as shown by putting a pin at each focus, and then placing a string around a pencil and the pins and tracing a line on paper. A circle is a special case of an ellipse in which the two foci coincide (thus any point on the circle is the same distance from the center). (b) For any closed gravitational orbit, m follows an elliptical path with M at one focus. Kepler's first law states this fact for planets orbiting the Sun.

Kepler's Second Law

Each planet moves so that an imaginary line drawn from the Sun to the planet sweeps out equal areas in equal times (see Figure 6.27).

Kepler's Third Law

The ratio of the squares of the periods of any two planets about the Sun is equal to the ratio of the cubes of their average distances from the Sun. In equation form, this is

$$\frac{T_1^2}{T_2^2} = \frac{r_1^3}{r_2^3}, \tag{6.55}$$

where T is the period (time for one orbit) and r is the average radius. This equation is valid only for comparing two small masses orbiting the same large one. Most importantly, this is a descriptive equation only, giving no information as to the cause of the equality.

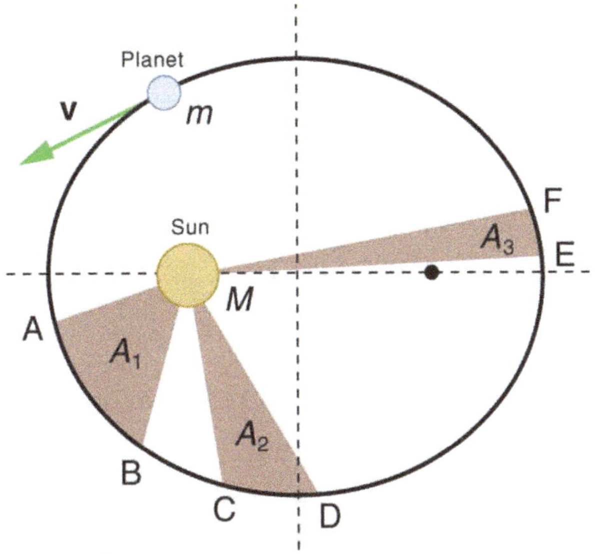

FIGURE 6.27 The shaded regions have equal areas. It takes equal times for m to go from A to B, from C to D, and from E to F. The mass m moves fastest when it is closest to M. Kepler's second law was originally devised for planets orbiting the Sun, but it has broader validity.

Note again that while, for historical reasons, Kepler's laws are stated for planets orbiting the Sun, they are actually valid for all bodies satisfying the two previously stated conditions.

EXAMPLE 6.7

Find the Time for One Orbit of an Earth Satellite

Given that the Moon orbits Earth each 27.3 d and that it is an average distance of 3.84×10^8 m from the center of Earth, calculate the period of an artificial satellite orbiting at an average altitude of 1500 km above Earth's surface.

Strategy

The period, or time for one orbit, is related to the radius of the orbit by Kepler's third law, given in mathematical form in $\frac{T_1^2}{T_2^2} = \frac{r_1^3}{r_2^3}$. Let us use the subscript 1 for the Moon and the subscript 2 for the satellite. We are asked to find T_2. The given information tells us that the orbital radius of the Moon is $r_1 = 3.84 \times 10^8$ m, and that the period of the Moon is $T_1 = 27.3$ d. The height of the artificial satellite above Earth's surface is given, and so we must add the radius of Earth (6380 km) to get $r_2 = (1500 + 6380)\text{ km} = 7880\text{ km}$. Now all quantities are known, and so T_2 can be found.

Solution

Kepler's third law is

$$\frac{T_1^2}{T_2^2} = \frac{r_1^3}{r_2^3}. \qquad 6.56$$

To solve for T_2, we cross-multiply and take the square root, yielding

$$T_2^2 = T_1^2\left(\frac{r_2}{r_1}\right)^3 \qquad 6.57$$

$$T_2 = T_1\left(\frac{r_2}{r_1}\right)^{3/2}. \qquad 6.58$$

Substituting known values yields

$$T_2 = 27.3\text{ d} \times \frac{24.0\text{ h}}{\text{d}} \times \left(\frac{7880\text{ km}}{3.84\times10^5\text{ km}}\right)^{3/2} = 1.93\text{ h}. \quad 6.59$$

Discussion

This is a reasonable period for a satellite in a fairly low orbit. It is interesting that any satellite at this altitude will orbit in the same amount of time. This fact is related to the condition that the satellite's mass is small compared with that of Earth.

People immediately search for deeper meaning when broadly applicable laws, like Kepler's, are discovered. It was Newton who took the next giant step when he proposed the law of universal gravitation. While Kepler was able to discover *what* was happening, Newton discovered that gravitational force was the cause.

Derivation of Kepler's Third Law for Circular Orbits

We shall derive Kepler's third law, starting with Newton's laws of motion and his universal law of gravitation. The point is to demonstrate that the force of gravity is the cause for Kepler's laws (although we will only derive the third one).

Let us consider a circular orbit of a small mass m around a large mass M, satisfying the two conditions stated at the beginning of this section. Gravity supplies the centripetal force to mass m. Starting with Newton's second law applied to circular motion,

$$F_{\text{net}} = ma_c = m\frac{v^2}{r}. \quad 6.60$$

The net external force on mass m is gravity, and so we substitute the force of gravity for F_{net}:

$$G\frac{mM}{r^2} = m\frac{v^2}{r}. \quad 6.61$$

The mass m cancels, yielding

$$G\frac{M}{r} = v^2. \quad 6.62$$

The fact that m cancels out is another aspect of the oft-noted fact that at a given location all masses fall with the same acceleration. Here we see that at a given orbital radius r, all masses orbit at the same speed. (This was implied by the result of the preceding worked example.) Now, to get at Kepler's third law, we must get the period T into the equation. By definition, period T is the time for one complete orbit. Now the average speed v is the circumference divided by the period—that is,

$$v = \frac{2\pi r}{T}. \quad 6.63$$

Substituting this into the previous equation gives

$$G\frac{M}{r} = \frac{4\pi^2 r^2}{T^2}. \quad 6.64$$

Solving for T^2 yields

$$T^2 = \frac{4\pi^2}{GM}r^3. \quad 6.65$$

Using subscripts 1 and 2 to denote two different satellites, and taking the ratio of the last equation for satellite 1 to satellite 2 yields

$$\frac{T_1^2}{T_2^2} = \frac{r_1^3}{r_2^3}. \quad 6.66$$

This is Kepler's third law. Note that Kepler's third law is valid only for comparing satellites of the same parent body, because only then does the mass of the parent body M cancel.

Now consider what we get if we solve $T^2 = \frac{4\pi^2}{GM}r^3$ for the ratio r^3/T^2. We obtain a relationship that can be used to determine the mass M of a parent body from the orbits of its satellites:

$$\frac{r^3}{T^2} = \frac{G}{4\pi^2}M. \tag{6.67}$$

If r and T are known for a satellite, then the mass M of the parent can be calculated. This principle has been used extensively to find the masses of heavenly bodies that have satellites. Furthermore, the ratio r^3/T^2 should be a constant for all satellites of the same parent body (because $r^3/T^2 = GM/4\pi^2$). (See Table 6.2).

It is clear from Table 6.2 that the ratio of r^3/T^2 is constant, at least to the third digit, for all listed satellites of the Sun, and for those of Jupiter. Small variations in that ratio have two causes—uncertainties in the r and T data, and perturbations of the orbits due to other bodies. Interestingly, those perturbations can be—and have been—used to predict the location of new planets and moons. This is another verification of Newton's universal law of gravitation.

MAKING CONNECTIONS

Newton's universal law of gravitation is modified by Einstein's general theory of relativity, as we shall see in Particle Physics. Newton's gravity is not seriously in error—it was and still is an extremely good approximation for most situations. Einstein's modification is most noticeable in extremely large gravitational fields, such as near black holes. However, general relativity also explains such phenomena as small but long-known deviations of the orbit of the planet Mercury from classical predictions.

The Case for Simplicity

The development of the universal law of gravitation by Newton played a pivotal role in the history of ideas. While it is beyond the scope of this text to cover that history in any detail, we note some important points. The definition of planet set in 2006 by the International Astronomical Union (IAU) states that in the solar system, a planet is a celestial body that:

1. is in orbit around the Sun,
2. has sufficient mass to assume hydrostatic equilibrium and
3. has cleared the neighborhood around its orbit.

A non-satellite body fulfilling only the first two of the above criteria is classified as "dwarf planet."

In 2006, Pluto was demoted to a 'dwarf planet' after scientists revised their definition of what constitutes a "true" planet.

Parent	Satellite	Average orbital radius r(km)	Period T(y)	r^3 / T^2 (km^3 / y^2)
Earth	Moon	3.84×10^5	0.07481	1.01×10^{19}
Sun	Mercury	5.79×10^7	0.2409	3.34×10^{24}
	Venus	1.082×10^8	0.6150	3.35×10^{24}
	Earth	1.496×10^8	1.000	3.35×10^{24}
	Mars	2.279×10^8	1.881	3.35×10^{24}

TABLE 6.2 Orbital Data and Kepler's Third Law

Parent	Satellite	Average orbital radius r(km)	Period T(y)	r^3 / T^2 (km^3 / y^2)
	Jupiter	7.783×10^8	11.86	3.35×10^{24}
	Saturn	1.427×10^9	29.46	3.35×10^{24}
	Neptune	4.497×10^9	164.8	3.35×10^{24}
	Pluto	5.90×10^9	248.3	3.33×10^{24}
Jupiter	Io	4.22×10^5	0.00485 (1.77 d)	3.19×10^{21}
	Europa	6.71×10^5	0.00972 (3.55 d)	3.20×10^{21}
	Ganymede	1.07×10^6	0.0196 (7.16 d)	3.19×10^{21}
	Callisto	1.88×10^6	0.0457 (16.19 d)	3.20×10^{21}

TABLE 6.2 Orbital Data and Kepler's Third Law

The universal law of gravitation is a good example of a physical principle that is very broadly applicable. That single equation for the gravitational force describes all situations in which gravity acts. It gives a cause for a vast number of effects, such as the orbits of the planets and moons in the solar system. It epitomizes the underlying unity and simplicity of physics.

Before the discoveries of Kepler, Copernicus, Galileo, Newton, and others, the solar system was thought to revolve around Earth as shown in Figure 6.28(a). This is called the Ptolemaic view, for the Greek philosopher who lived in the second century AD. This model is characterized by a list of facts for the motions of planets with no cause and effect explanation. There tended to be a different rule for each heavenly body and a general lack of simplicity.

Figure 6.28(b) represents the modern or Copernican model. In this model, a small set of rules and a single underlying force explain not only all motions in the solar system, but all other situations involving gravity. The breadth and simplicity of the laws of physics are compelling. As our knowledge of nature has grown, the basic simplicity of its laws has become ever more evident.

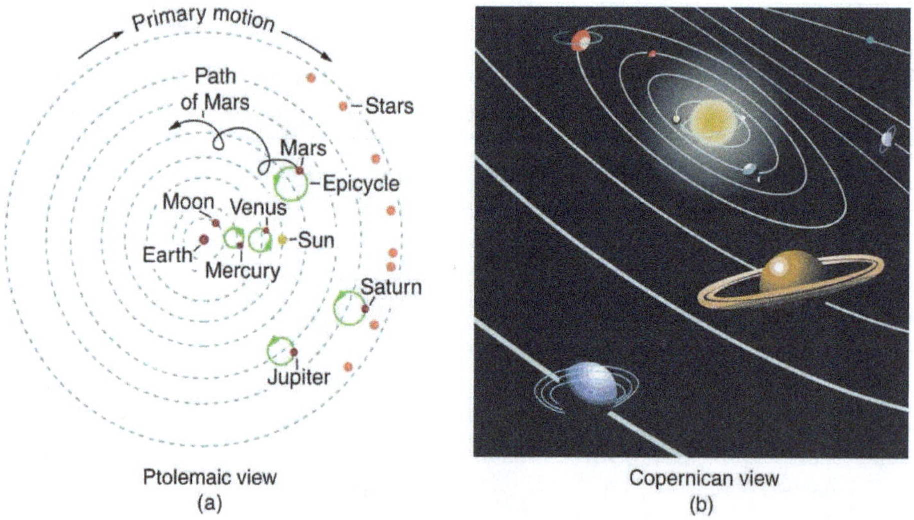

FIGURE 6.28 (a) The Ptolemaic model of the universe has Earth at the center with the Moon, the planets, the Sun, and the stars revolving about it in complex superpositions of circular paths. This geocentric model, which can be made progressively more accurate by adding more circles, is purely descriptive, containing no hints as to what are the causes of these motions. (b) The Copernican model has the Sun at the center of the solar system. It is fully explained by a small number of laws of physics, including Newton's universal law of gravitation.

Glossary

angular velocity ω, the rate of change of the angle with which an object moves on a circular path

arc length Δs, the distance traveled by an object along a circular path

banked curve the curve in a road that is sloping in a manner that helps a vehicle negotiate the curve

center of mass the point where the entire mass of an object can be thought to be concentrated

centrifugal force a fictitious force that tends to throw an object off when the object is rotating in a non-inertial frame of reference

centripetal acceleration the acceleration of an object moving in a circle, directed toward the center

centripetal force any net force causing uniform circular motion

Coriolis force the fictitious force causing the apparent deflection of moving objects when viewed in a rotating frame of reference

fictitious force a force having no physical origin

gravitational constant, *G* a proportionality factor used in the equation for Newton's universal law of gravitation; it is a universal constant—that is, it is thought to be the same everywhere in the universe

ideal angle the angle at which a car can turn safely on a steep curve, which is in proportion to the ideal speed

ideal banking the sloping of a curve in a road, where the angle of the slope allows the vehicle to negotiate the curve at a certain speed without the aid of friction between the tires and the road; the net external force on the vehicle equals the horizontal centripetal force in the absence of friction

ideal speed the maximum safe speed at which a vehicle can turn on a curve without the aid of friction between the tire and the road

microgravity an environment in which the apparent net acceleration of a body is small compared with that produced by Earth at its surface

Newton's universal law of gravitation every particle in the universe attracts every other particle with a force along a line joining them; the force is directly proportional to the product of their masses and inversely proportional to the square of the distance between them

non-inertial frame of reference an accelerated frame of reference

pit a tiny indentation on the spiral track moulded into the top of the polycarbonate layer of CD

radians a unit of angle measurement

radius of curvature radius of a circular path

rotation angle the ratio of the arc length to the radius of curvature on a circular path: $\Delta\theta = \frac{\Delta s}{r}$

ultracentrifuge a centrifuge optimized for spinning a rotor at very high speeds

uniform circular motion the motion of an object in a circular path at constant speed

Section Summary

6.1 Rotation Angle and Angular Velocity

- Uniform circular motion is motion in a circle at constant speed. The rotation angle $\Delta\theta$ is defined as the ratio of the arc length to the radius of curvature:
  $$\Delta\theta = \frac{\Delta s}{r},$$
  where arc length Δs is distance traveled along a circular path and r is the radius of curvature of the circular path. The quantity $\Delta\theta$ is measured in units of radians (rad), for which
  $$2\pi \text{ rad} = 360° = 1 \text{ revolution}.$$
- The conversion between radians and degrees is $1 \text{ rad} = 57.3°$.
- Angular velocity ω is the rate of change of an angle,
  $$\omega = \frac{\Delta\theta}{\Delta t},$$
  where a rotation $\Delta\theta$ takes place in a time Δt. The units of angular velocity are radians per second (rad/s). Linear velocity v and angular velocity ω are related by
  $$v = r\omega \text{ or } \omega = \frac{v}{r}.$$

6.2 Centripetal Acceleration

- Centripetal acceleration a_c is the acceleration experienced while in uniform circular motion. It always points toward the center of rotation. It is perpendicular to the linear velocity v and has the magnitude
  $$a_c = \frac{v^2}{r};\ a_c = r\omega^2.$$
- The unit of centripetal acceleration is m/s^2.

6.3 Centripetal Force

- Centripetal force F_c is any force causing uniform circular motion. It is a "center-seeking" force that always points toward the center of rotation. It is perpendicular to linear velocity v and has

magnitude
$F_c = ma_c,$
which can also be expressed as

$$\left.\begin{array}{c} F_c = m\frac{v^2}{r} \\ \text{or} \\ F_c = mr\omega^2 \end{array}\right\},$$

6.4 Fictitious Forces and Non-inertial Frames: The Coriolis Force

- Rotating and accelerated frames of reference are non-inertial.
- Fictitious forces, such as the Coriolis force, are needed to explain motion in such frames.

6.5 Newton's Universal Law of Gravitation

- Newton's universal law of gravitation: Every particle in the universe attracts every other particle with a force along a line joining them. The force is directly proportional to the product of their masses and inversely proportional to the square of the distance between them. In equation form, this is
  $$F = G\frac{mM}{r^2},$$
  where F is the magnitude of the gravitational force. G is the gravitational constant, given by $G = 6.674 \times 10^{-11}\ \text{N} \cdot \text{m}^2/\text{kg}^2$.
- Newton's law of gravitation applies universally.

6.6 Satellites and Kepler's Laws: An Argument for Simplicity

- Kepler's laws are stated for a small mass m orbiting a larger mass M in near-isolation. Kepler's laws of planetary motion are then as follows:
  Kepler's first law

  The orbit of each planet about the Sun is an ellipse with the Sun at one focus.

  Kepler's second law

  Each planet moves so that an imaginary line drawn from the Sun to the planet sweeps out equal areas in equal times.

  Kepler's third law

  The ratio of the squares of the periods of any two planets about the Sun is equal to the ratio of the cubes of their average distances from the Sun:
  $$\frac{T_1^2}{T_2^2} = \frac{r_1^3}{r_2^3},$$
  where T is the period (time for one orbit) and r is the average radius of the orbit.
- The period and radius of a satellite's orbit about a larger body M are related by
  $$T^2 = \frac{4\pi^2}{GM}r^3$$
  or
  $$\frac{r^3}{T^2} = \frac{G}{4\pi^2}M.$$

Conceptual Questions

6.1 Rotation Angle and Angular Velocity

1. There is an analogy between rotational and linear physical quantities. What rotational quantities are analogous to distance and velocity?

6.2 Centripetal Acceleration

2. Can centripetal acceleration change the speed of circular motion? Explain.

6.3 Centripetal Force

3. If you wish to reduce the stress (which is related to centripetal force) on high-speed tires, would you use large- or small-diameter tires? Explain.

4. Define centripetal force. Can any type of force (for example, tension, gravitational force, friction, and so on) be a centripetal force? Can any combination of forces be a centripetal force?

5. If centripetal force is directed toward the center, why do you feel that you are 'thrown' away from the center as a car goes around a curve? Explain.

6. Race car drivers routinely cut corners as shown in Figure 6.29. Explain how this allows the curve to be taken at the greatest speed.

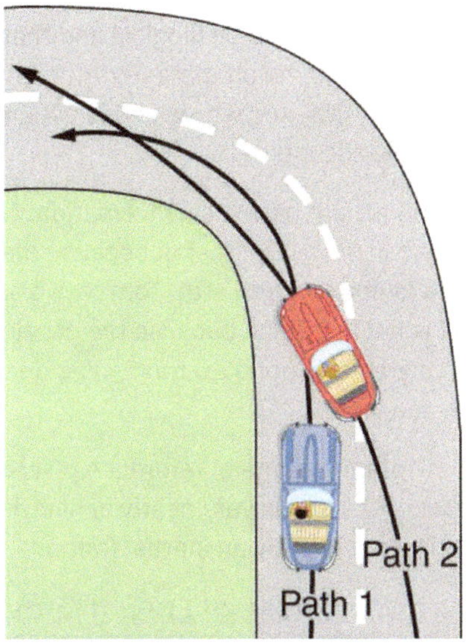

FIGURE 6.29 Two paths around a race track curve are shown. Race car drivers will take the inside path (called cutting the corner) whenever possible because it allows them to take the curve at the highest speed.

7. A number of amusement parks have rides that make vertical loops like the one shown in Figure 6.30. For safety, the cars are attached to the rails in such a way that they cannot fall off. If the car goes over the top at just the right speed, gravity alone will supply the centripetal force. What other force acts and what is its direction if:
(a) The car goes over the top at faster than this speed?
(b)The car goes over the top at slower than this speed?

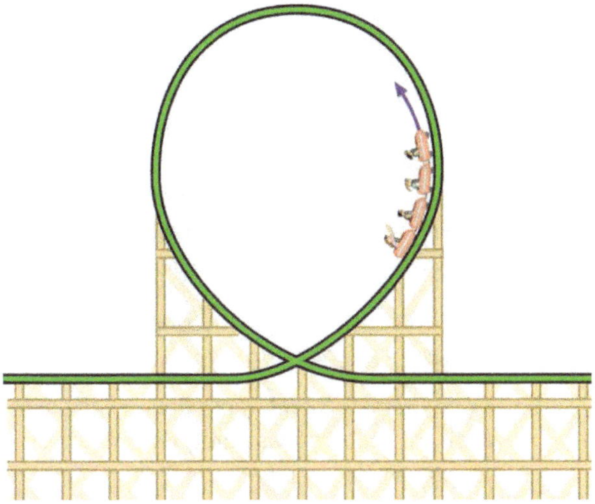

FIGURE 6.30 Amusement rides with a vertical loop are an example of a form of curved motion.

8. What is the direction of the force exerted by the car on the passenger as the car goes over the top of the amusement ride pictured in Figure 6.30 under the following circumstances:
(a) The car goes over the top at such a speed that the gravitational force is the only force acting?
(b) The car goes over the top faster than this speed?
(c) The car goes over the top slower than this speed?

9. As a skater forms a circle, what force is responsible for making her turn? Use a free body diagram in your answer.

10. Suppose a child is riding on a merry-go-round at a distance about halfway between its center and edge. She has a lunch box resting on wax paper, so that there is very little friction between it and the merry-go-round. Which path shown in Figure 6.31 will the lunch box take when she lets go? The lunch box leaves a trail in the dust on the merry-go-round. Is that trail straight, curved to the left, or curved to the right? Explain your answer.

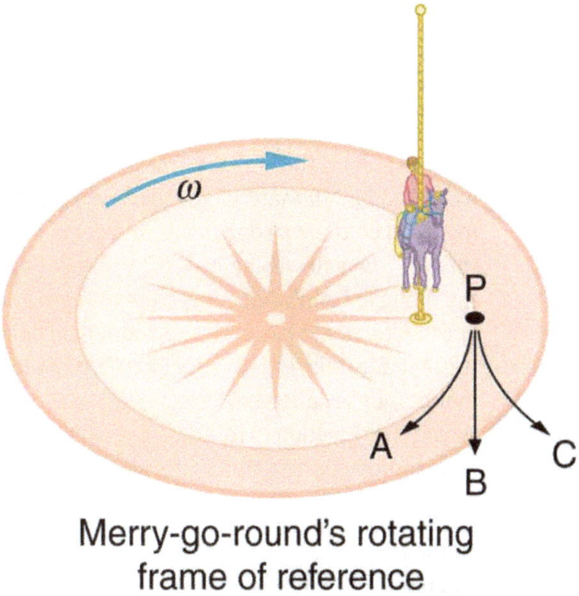

FIGURE 6.31 A child riding on a merry-go-round releases her lunch box at point P. This is a view from above the clockwise rotation. Assuming it slides with negligible friction, will it follow path A, B, or C, as viewed from Earth's frame of reference? What will be the shape of the path it leaves in the dust on the merry-go-round?

11. Do you feel yourself thrown to either side when you negotiate a curve that is ideally banked for your car's speed? What is the direction of the force exerted on you by the car seat?

12. Suppose a mass is moving in a circular path on a frictionless table as shown in figure. In the Earth's frame of reference, there is no centrifugal force pulling the mass away from the centre of rotation, yet there is a very real force stretching the string attaching the mass to the nail. Using concepts

related to centripetal force and Newton's third law, explain what force stretches the string, identifying its physical origin.

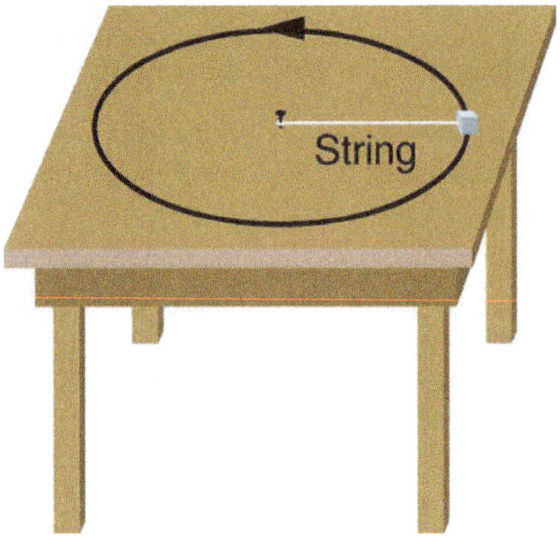

FIGURE 6.32 A mass attached to a nail on a frictionless table moves in a circular path. The force stretching the string is real and not fictional. What is the physical origin of the force on the string?

6.4 Fictitious Forces and Non-inertial Frames: The Coriolis Force

13. When a toilet is flushed or a sink is drained, the water (and other material) begins to rotate about the drain on the way down. Assuming no initial rotation and a flow initially directly straight toward the drain, explain what causes the rotation and which direction it has in the northern hemisphere. (Note that this is a small effect and in most toilets the rotation is caused by directional water jets.) Would the direction of rotation reverse if water were forced up the drain?

14. Is there a real force that throws water from clothes during the spin cycle of a washing machine? Explain how the water is removed.

15. In one amusement park ride, riders enter a large vertical barrel and stand against the wall on its horizontal floor. The barrel is spun up and the floor drops away. Riders feel as if they are pinned to the wall by a force something like the gravitational force. This is a fictitious force sensed and used by the riders to explain events in the rotating frame of reference of the barrel. Explain in an inertial frame of reference (Earth is nearly one) what pins the riders to the wall, and identify all of the real forces acting on them.

16. Action at a distance, such as is the case for gravity, was once thought to be illogical and therefore untrue. What is the ultimate determinant of the truth in physics, and why was this action ultimately accepted?

17. Two friends are having a conversation. Anna says a satellite in orbit is in freefall because the satellite keeps falling toward Earth. Tom says a satellite in orbit is not in freefall because the acceleration due to gravity is not 9.80 m/s^2. Who do you agree with and why?

18. A non-rotating frame of reference placed at the center of the Sun is very nearly an inertial one. Why is it not exactly an inertial frame?

6.5 Newton's Universal Law of Gravitation

19. Action at a distance, such as is the case for gravity, was once thought to be illogical and therefore untrue. What is the ultimate determinant of the truth in physics, and why was this action ultimately accepted?

20. Two friends are having a conversation. Anna says a satellite in orbit is in freefall because the satellite keeps falling toward Earth. Tom says a satellite in orbit is not in freefall because the acceleration due to gravity is not $9.80\ m/s^2$. Who do you agree with and why?

21. Draw a free body diagram for a satellite in an elliptical orbit showing why its speed increases as it approaches its parent body and decreases as it moves away.

22. Newton's laws of motion and gravity were among the first to convincingly demonstrate the underlying simplicity and unity in nature. Many other examples have since been discovered, and we now expect to find such underlying order in complex situations. Is there proof that such order will always be found in new explorations?

6.6 Satellites and Kepler's Laws: An Argument for Simplicity

23. In what frame(s) of reference are Kepler's laws valid? Are Kepler's laws purely descriptive, or do they contain causal information?

Problems & Exercises

6.1 Rotation Angle and Angular Velocity

1. Semi-trailer trucks have an odometer on one hub of a trailer wheel. The hub is weighted so that it does not rotate, but it contains gears to count the number of wheel revolutions—it then calculates the distance traveled. If the wheel has a 1.15 m diameter and goes through 200,000 rotations, how many kilometers should the odometer read?
2. Microwave ovens rotate at a rate of about 6 rev/min. What is this in revolutions per second? What is the angular velocity in radians per second?
3. An automobile with 0.260 m radius tires travels 80,000 km before wearing them out. How many revolutions do the tires make, neglecting any backing up and any change in radius due to wear?
4. (a) What is the period of rotation of Earth in seconds? (b) What is the angular velocity of Earth? (c) Given that Earth has a radius of 6.4×10^6 m at its equator, what is the linear velocity at Earth's surface?
5. A baseball pitcher brings his arm forward during a pitch, rotating the forearm about the elbow. If the velocity of the ball in the pitcher's hand is 35.0 m/s and the ball is 0.300 m from the elbow joint, what is the angular velocity of the forearm?
6. In lacrosse, a ball is thrown from a net on the end of a stick by rotating the stick and forearm about the elbow. If the angular velocity of the ball about the elbow joint is 30.0 rad/s and the ball is 1.30 m from the elbow joint, what is the velocity of the ball?
7. A truck with 0.420-m-radius tires travels at 32.0 m/s. What is the angular velocity of the rotating tires in radians per second? What is this in rev/min?
8. Integrated Concepts When kicking a football, the kicker rotates his leg about the hip joint.
(a) If the velocity of the tip of the kicker's shoe is 35.0 m/s and the hip joint is 1.05 m from the tip of the shoe, what is the shoe tip's angular velocity?
(b) The shoe is in contact with the initially stationary 0.500 kg football for 20.0 ms. What average force is exerted on the football to give it a velocity of 20.0 m/s?
(c) Find the maximum range of the football, neglecting air resistance.
9. Construct Your Own Problem
Consider an amusement park ride in which participants are rotated about a vertical axis in a cylinder with vertical walls. Once the angular velocity reaches its full value, the floor drops away and friction between the walls and the riders prevents them from sliding down. Construct a problem in which you calculate the necessary angular velocity that assures the riders will not slide down the wall. Include a free body diagram of a single rider. Among the variables to consider are the radius of the cylinder and the coefficients of friction between the riders' clothing and the wall.

6.2 Centripetal Acceleration

10. A fairground ride spins its occupants inside a flying saucer-shaped container. If the horizontal circular path the riders follow has an 8.00 m radius, at how many revolutions per minute will the riders be subjected to a centripetal acceleration whose magnitude is 1.50 times that due to gravity?
11. A runner taking part in the 200 m dash must run around the end of a track that has a circular arc with a radius of curvature of 30 m. If the runner completes the 200 m dash in 23.2 s and runs at constant speed throughout the race, what is the magnitude of their centripetal acceleration as they run the curved portion of the track?
12. Taking the age of Earth to be about 4×10^9 years and assuming its orbital radius of 1.5×10^{11} m has not changed and is circular, calculate the approximate total distance Earth has traveled since its birth (in a frame of reference stationary with respect to the Sun).
13. The propeller of a World War II fighter plane is 2.30 m in diameter.
(a) What is its angular velocity in radians per second if it spins at 1200 rev/min?
(b) What is the linear speed of its tip at this angular velocity if the plane is stationary on the tarmac?
(c) What is the centripetal acceleration of the propeller tip under these conditions? Calculate it in meters per second squared and convert to multiples of g.
14. An ordinary workshop grindstone has a radius of 7.50 cm and rotates at 6500 rev/min.
(a) Calculate the magnitude of the centripetal acceleration at its edge in meters per second squared and convert it to multiples of g.
(b) What is the linear speed of a point on its edge?
15. Helicopter blades withstand tremendous stresses.

In addition to supporting the weight of a helicopter, they are spun at rapid rates and experience large centripetal accelerations, especially at the tip.
(a) Calculate the magnitude of the centripetal acceleration at the tip of a 4.00 m long helicopter blade that rotates at 300 rev/min.
(b) Compare the linear speed of the tip with the speed of sound (taken to be 340 m/s).

16. Olympic ice skaters are able to spin at about 5 rev/s.
(a) What is their angular velocity in radians per second?
(b) What is the centripetal acceleration of the skater's nose if it is 0.120 m from the axis of rotation?
(c) An exceptional skater named Dick Button was able to spin much faster in the 1950s than anyone since—at about 9 rev/s. What was the centripetal acceleration of the tip of his nose, assuming it is at 0.120 m radius?
(d) Comment on the magnitudes of the accelerations found. It is reputed that Button ruptured small blood vessels during his spins.

17. What percentage of the acceleration at Earth's surface is the acceleration due to gravity at the position of a satellite located 300 km above Earth?

18. Verify that the linear speed of an ultracentrifuge is about 0.50 km/s, and Earth in its orbit is about 30 km/s by calculating:
(a) The linear speed of a point on an ultracentrifuge 0.100 m from its center, rotating at 50,000 rev/min.
(b) The linear speed of Earth in its orbit about the Sun (use data from the text on the radius of Earth's orbit and approximate it as being circular).

19. A rotating space station is said to create "artificial gravity"—a loosely-defined term used for an acceleration that would be crudely similar to gravity. The outer wall of the rotating space station would become a floor for the astronauts, and centripetal acceleration supplied by the floor would allow astronauts to exercise and maintain muscle and bone strength more naturally than in non-rotating space environments. If the space station is 200 m in diameter, what angular velocity would produce an "artificial gravity" of 9.80 m/s^2 at the rim?

20. At takeoff, a commercial jet has a 60.0 m/s speed. Its tires have a diameter of 0.850 m.
(a) At how many rev/min are the tires rotating?
(b) What is the centripetal acceleration at the edge of the tire?
(c) With what force must a determined 1.00×10^{-15} kg bacterium cling to the rim?
(d) Take the ratio of this force to the bacterium's weight.

21. Integrated Concepts
Riders in an amusement park ride shaped like a Viking ship hung from a large pivot are rotated back and forth like a rigid pendulum. Sometime near the middle of the ride, the ship is momentarily motionless at the top of its circular arc. The ship then swings down under the influence of gravity. The speed at the bottom of the arc is 23.4 m/s.
(a) What is the centripetal acceleration at the bottom of the arc?
(b) Draw a free body diagram of the forces acting on a rider at the bottom of the arc.
(c) Find the force exerted by the ride on a 60.0 kg rider and compare it to her weight.
(d) Discuss whether the answer seems reasonable.

22. Unreasonable Results
A mother pushes her child on a swing so that his speed is 9.00 m/s at the lowest point of his path. The swing is suspended 2.00 m above the child's center of mass.
(a) What is the magnitude of the centripetal acceleration of the child at the low point?
(b) What is the magnitude of the force the child exerts on the seat if his mass is 18.0 kg?
(c) What is unreasonable about these results?
(d) Which premises are unreasonable or inconsistent?

6.3 Centripetal Force

23. (a) A 22.0 kg child is riding a playground merry-go-round that is rotating at 40.0 rev/min. What centripetal force must she exert to stay on if she is 1.25 m from its center?
(b) What centripetal force does she need to stay on an amusement park merry-go-round that rotates at 3.00 rev/min if she is 8.00 m from its center?
(c) Compare each force with her weight.

24. Calculate the centripetal force on the end of a 100 m (radius) wind turbine blade that is rotating at 0.5 rev/s. Assume the mass is 4 kg.

25. What is the ideal banking angle for a gentle turn of 1.20 km radius on a highway with a 105 km/h speed limit (about 65 mi/h), assuming everyone travels at the limit?

26. What is the ideal speed to take a 100 m radius curve banked at a 20.0° angle?

27. (a) What is the radius of a bobsled turn banked at 75.0° and taken at 30.0 m/s, assuming it is ideally banked?
(b) Calculate the centripetal acceleration.
(c) Does this acceleration seem large to you?

28. Part of riding a bicycle involves leaning at the correct angle when making a turn, as seen in Figure 6.33. To be stable, the force exerted by the ground must be on a line going through the center of gravity. The force on the bicycle wheel can be resolved into two perpendicular components—friction parallel to the road (this must supply the centripetal force), and the vertical normal force (which must equal the system's weight).
(a) Show that θ (as defined in the figure) is related to the speed v and radius of curvature r of the turn in the same way as for an ideally banked roadway—that is, $\theta = \tan^{-1} v^2 / rg$
(b) Calculate θ for a 12.0 m/s turn of radius 30.0 m (as in a race).

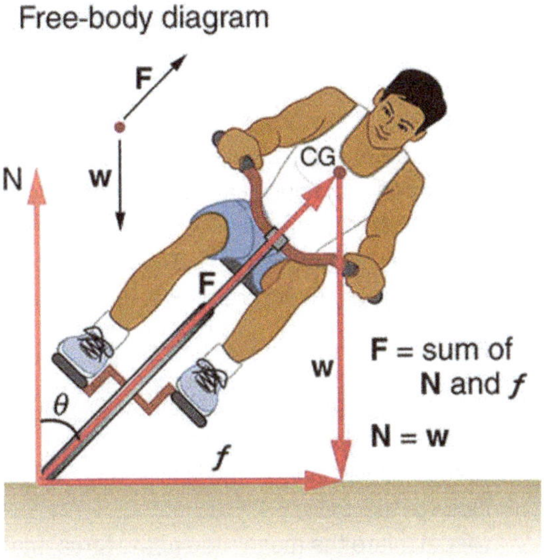

FIGURE 6.33 A bicyclist negotiating a turn on level ground must lean at the correct angle—the ability to do this becomes instinctive. The force of the ground on the wheel needs to be on a line through the center of gravity. The net external force on the system is the centripetal force. The vertical component of the force on the wheel cancels the weight of the system while its horizontal component must supply the centripetal force. This process produces a relationship among the angle θ, the speed v, and the radius of curvature r of the turn similar to that for the ideal banking of roadways.

29. A large centrifuge, like the one shown in Figure 6.34(a), is used to expose aspiring astronauts to accelerations similar to those experienced in rocket launches and atmospheric reentries.
(a) At what angular velocity is the centripetal acceleration $10\ g$ if the rider is 15.0 m from the center of rotation?
(b) The rider's cage hangs on a pivot at the end of the arm, allowing it to swing outward during rotation as shown in Figure 6.34(b). At what angle θ below the horizontal will the cage hang when the centripetal acceleration is $10\ g$? (Hint: The arm supplies centripetal force and supports the weight of the cage. Draw a free body diagram of the forces to see what the angle θ should be.)

(a)

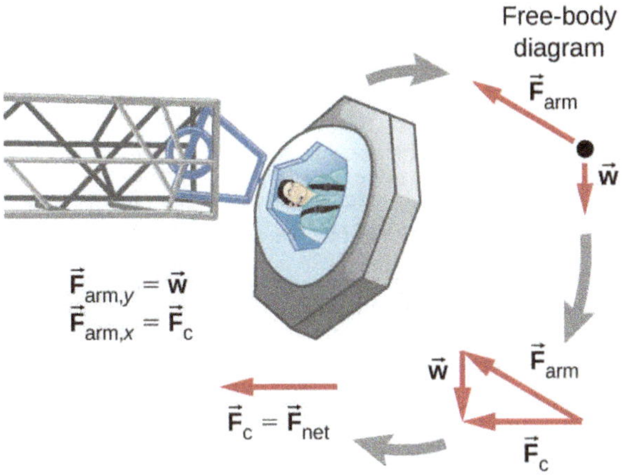

(b)

FIGURE 6.34 (a) NASA centrifuge used to subject trainees to accelerations similar to those experienced in rocket launches and reentries. (credit: NASA) (b) Rider in cage showing how the cage pivots outward during rotation. This allows the total force exerted on the rider by the cage to be along its axis at all times.

30. Integrated Concepts
If a car takes a banked curve at less than the ideal speed, friction is needed to keep it from sliding

toward the inside of the curve (a real problem on icy mountain roads). (a) Calculate the ideal speed to take a 100 m radius curve banked at 15.0°. (b) What is the minimum coefficient of friction needed for a frightened driver to take the same curve at 20.0 km/h?

31. Modern roller coasters have vertical loops like the one shown in Figure 6.35. The radius of curvature is smaller at the top than on the sides so that the downward centripetal acceleration at the top will be greater than the acceleration due to gravity, keeping the passengers pressed firmly into their seats. What is the speed of the roller coaster at the top of the loop if the radius of curvature there is 15.0 m and the downward acceleration of the car is 1.50 g?

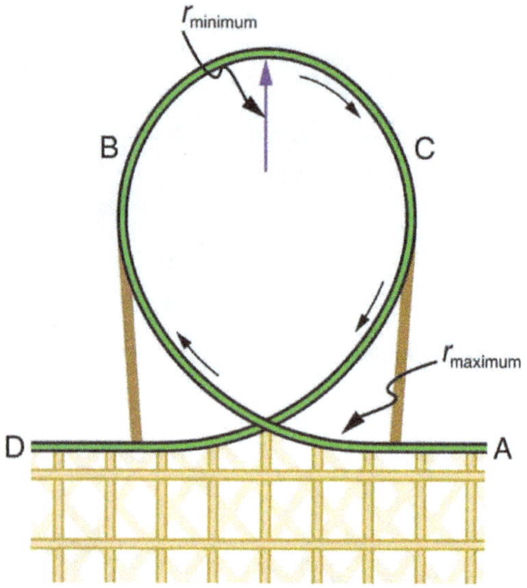

FIGURE 6.35 Teardrop-shaped loops are used in the latest roller coasters so that the radius of curvature gradually decreases to a minimum at the top. This means that the centripetal acceleration builds from zero to a maximum at the top and gradually decreases again. A circular loop would cause a jolting change in acceleration at entry, a disadvantage discovered long ago in railroad curve design. With a small radius of curvature at the top, the centripetal acceleration can more easily be kept greater than g so that the passengers do not lose contact with their seats nor do they need seat belts to keep them in place.

32. Unreasonable Results
(a) Calculate the minimum coefficient of friction needed for a car to negotiate an unbanked 50.0 m radius curve at 30.0 m/s.
(b) What is unreasonable about the result?
(c) Which premises are unreasonable or inconsistent?

6.5 Newton's Universal Law of Gravitation

33. (a) Calculate Earth's mass given the acceleration due to gravity at the North Pole is $9.830\ \text{m/s}^2$ and the radius of the Earth is 6371 km from center to pole.
(b) Compare this with the accepted value of $5.979 \times 10^{24}\ \text{kg}$.

34. (a) Calculate the magnitude of the acceleration due to gravity on the surface of Earth due to the Moon.
(b) Calculate the magnitude of the acceleration due to gravity at Earth due to the Sun.
(c) Take the ratio of the Moon's acceleration to the Sun's and comment on why the tides are predominantly due to the Moon in spite of this number.

35. (a) What is the acceleration due to gravity on the surface of the Moon?
(b) On the surface of Mars? The mass of Mars is $6.418 \times 10^{23}\ \text{kg}$ and its radius is $3.38 \times 10^6\ \text{m}$.

36. (a) Calculate the acceleration due to gravity on the surface of the Sun.
(b) By what factor would your weight increase if you could stand on the Sun? (Never mind that you cannot.)

37. The Moon and Earth rotate about their common center of mass, which is located about 4700 km from the center of Earth. (This is 1690 km below the surface.)
(a) Calculate the magnitude of the acceleration due to the Moon's gravity at that point.
(b) Calculate the magnitude of the centripetal acceleration of the center of Earth as it rotates about that point once each lunar month (about 27.3 d) and compare it with the acceleration found in part (a). Comment on whether or not they are equal and why they should or should not be.

38. Solve part (b) of Example 6.6 using $a_c = v^2/r$.

39. (a) Calculate the magnitude of the gravitational force exerted on a 4.20 kg baby by a 100 kg father 0.200 m away at birth (he is assisting, so he is close to the child).
(b) Calculate the magnitude of the force on the baby due to Jupiter if it is at its closest distance to Earth, some $6.29 \times 10^{11}\ \text{m}$ away. How does the force of Jupiter on the baby compare to the force of the father on the baby? Other objects in the room and the hospital building also exert similar gravitational forces. (Of course, there could be an unknown force acting, but scientists first need to be convinced that there is even an effect, much less that an unknown force causes it.)

40. The existence of the dwarf planet Pluto was

proposed based on irregularities in Neptune's orbit. Pluto was subsequently discovered near its predicted position. But it now appears that the discovery was fortuitous, because Pluto is small and the irregularities in Neptune's orbit were not well known. To illustrate that Pluto has a minor effect on the orbit of Neptune compared with the closest planet to Neptune:
(a) Calculate the acceleration due to gravity at Neptune due to Pluto when they are 4.50×10^{12} m apart, as they are at present. The mass of Pluto is 1.4×10^{22} kg.
(b) Calculate the acceleration due to gravity at Neptune due to Uranus, presently about 2.50×10^{12} m apart, and compare it with that due to Pluto. The mass of Uranus is 8.62×10^{25} kg.

41. (a) The Sun orbits the Milky Way galaxy once each $2.60 \text{ x } 10^8$ y, with a roughly circular orbit averaging $3.00 \text{ x } 10^4$ light years in radius. (A light year is the distance traveled by light in 1 y.) Calculate the centripetal acceleration of the Sun in its galactic orbit. Does your result support the contention that a nearly inertial frame of reference can be located at the Sun?
(b) Calculate the average speed of the Sun in its galactic orbit. Does the answer surprise you?

42. **Unreasonable Result**
A mountain 10.0 km from a person exerts a gravitational force on him equal to 2.00% of his weight.
(a) Calculate the mass of the mountain.
(b) Compare the mountain's mass with that of Earth.
(c) What is unreasonable about these results?
(d) Which premises are unreasonable or inconsistent? (Note that accurate gravitational measurements can easily detect the effect of nearby mountains and variations in local geology.)

6.6 Satellites and Kepler's Laws: An Argument for Simplicity

43. A geosynchronous Earth satellite is one that has an orbital period of precisely 1 day. Such orbits are useful for communication and weather observation because the satellite remains above the same point on Earth (provided it orbits in the equatorial plane in the same direction as Earth's rotation). Calculate the radius of such an orbit based on the data for the moon in Table 6.2.

44. Calculate the mass of the Sun based on data for Earth's orbit and compare the value obtained with the Sun's actual mass.

45. Find the mass of Jupiter based on data for the orbit of one of its moons, and compare your result with its actual mass.

46. Find the ratio of the mass of Jupiter to that of Earth based on data in Table 6.2.

47. Astronomical observations of our Milky Way galaxy indicate that it has a mass of about 8.0×10^{11} solar masses. A star orbiting on the galaxy's periphery is about 6.0×10^4 light years from its center. (a) What should the orbital period of that star be? (b) If its period is 6.0×10^7 years instead, what is the mass of the galaxy? Such calculations are used to imply the existence of "dark matter" in the universe and have indicated, for example, the existence of very massive black holes at the centers of some galaxies.

48. Integrated Concepts
Space debris left from old satellites and their launchers is becoming a hazard to other satellites. (a) Calculate the speed of a satellite in an orbit 900 km above Earth's surface. (b) Suppose a loose rivet is in an orbit of the same radius that intersects the satellite's orbit at an angle of 90° relative to Earth. What is the velocity of the rivet relative to the satellite just before striking it? (c) Given the rivet is 3.00 mm in size, how long will its collision with the satellite last? (d) If its mass is 0.500 g, what is the average force it exerts on the satellite? (e) How much energy in joules is generated by the collision? (The satellite's velocity does not change appreciably, because its mass is much greater than the rivet's.)

49. Unreasonable Results
(a) Based on Kepler's laws and information on the orbital characteristics of the Moon, calculate the orbital radius for an Earth satellite having a period of 1.00 h. (b) What is unreasonable about this result? (c) What is unreasonable or inconsistent about the premise of a 1.00 h orbit?

50. Construct Your Own Problem
On February 14, 2000, the NEAR spacecraft was successfully inserted into orbit around Eros, becoming the first artificial satellite of an asteroid. Construct a problem in which you determine the orbital speed for a satellite near Eros. You will need to find the mass of the asteroid and consider such things as a safe distance for the orbit. Although Eros is not spherical, calculate the

acceleration due to gravity on its surface at a point an average distance from its center of mass. Your instructor may also wish to have you calculate the escape velocity from this point on Eros.

51. Critical Thinking A car travels around a loop with negligible friction at a constant speed and never loses contact with the loop. The top of the loop is labeled A and the bottom of the loop is labeled B. (a) At what point would the normal force be greatest? Briefly explain your reasoning. (b) Based on experimental data, an equation that fits the data is suggested for the normal force, *FN*, which may not be correct: $F_N = Kr^{1/2}$, where *K* is a constant with appropriate units and *r* is the radius of the loop. Is this equation consistent with your answer from part a? Explain why or why not. Does this equation make sense? Explain why or why not. (c) Now the car travels around loops of various radii and the speed at which the car barely makes it around the loop is measured. Graph that speed vs. the radius of the loop.

Test Prep for AP® Courses

6.5 Newton's Universal Law of Gravitation

1. Jupiter has a mass approximately 300 times greater than Earth's and a radius about 11 times greater. How will the gravitational acceleration at the surface of Jupiter compare to that at the surface of the Earth?

a. Greater
b. Less
c. About the same
d. Not enough information

2. Given Newton's universal law of gravitation (Equation 6.40), under what circumstances is the force due to gravity maximized?

3. In the formula $g = \frac{GM}{r^2}$, what does *G* represent?

a. The acceleration due to gravity
b. A gravitational constant that is the same everywhere in the universe
c. A gravitational constant that is inversely proportional to the radius
d. The factor by which you multiply the inertial mass to obtain the gravitational mass

4. Saturn's moon Titan has a radius of 2.58×10^6 m and a measured gravitational field of $1.35\ \text{m/s}^2$. What is its mass?

5. A recently discovered planet has a mass twice as great as Earth's and a radius twice as large as Earth's. What will be the approximate size of its gravitational field?

a. $19\ \text{m/s}^2$
b. $4.9\ \text{m/s}^2$
c. $2.5\ \text{m/s}^2$
d. $9.8\ \text{m/s}^2$

6. 4. Earth is 1.5×10^{11} m from the Sun. Mercury is 5.7×10^{10} m from the Sun. How does the gravitational field of the Sun on Mercury (g_{SM}) compare to the gravitational field of the Sun on Earth (g_{SE})?

CHAPTER 7

Work, Energy, and Energy Resources

FIGURE 7.1 How many forms of energy can you identify in this photograph of a wind farm in Iowa? (credit: Jürgen from Sandesneben, Germany, Wikimedia Commons)

CHAPTER OUTLINE

CONNECTION FOR AP® COURSES **Energy** plays an essential role both in everyday events and in scientific phenomena. You can no doubt name many forms of energy, from that provided by our foods to the energy we use to run our cars and the sunlight that warms us on the beach. You can also cite examples of what people call "energy" that may not be scientific, such as someone having an energetic personality. Not only does energy have many interesting forms, it is involved in almost all phenomena, and is one of the most important concepts of physics.

There is no simple and accurate scientific definition for energy. Energy is characterized by its many forms and the fact that it is conserved. We can loosely define energy as the ability to do **work**, admitting that in some circumstances not all energy is available to do work. Because of the association of energy with work, we begin the chapter with a discussion of work. Work is intimately related to energy and how energy moves from one system to another or changes form. The work-energy theorem supports Big Idea 3, that interactions between objects are described by forces. In particular, exerting a force on an object may do work on it, changing it's energy (Enduring Understanding 3.E). The work-energy theorem, introduced in this chapter, establishes the relationship between work done on an object by an external force and changes in the object's kinetic energy (Essential Knowledge 3.E.1).

Similarly, systems can do work on each other, supporting Big Idea 4, that interactions between systems can result in changes in those systems—in this case, changes in the total energy of the system (Enduring Understanding 4.C). The total energy of the system is the sum of its kinetic energy, potential energy, and microscopic internal energy (Essential Knowledge 4.C.1). In this chapter students learn how to calculate kinetic, gravitational, and elastic potential energy in order to determine the total mechanical energy of a system. The transfer of mechanical energy into or out of a system is equal to the work done on the system by an external force with a nonzero component parallel to the displacement (Essential Knowledge 4.C.2).

An important aspect of energy is that the total amount of energy in the universe is constant. Energy can change forms, but it cannot appear from nothing or disappear without a trace. Energy is thus one of a handful of physical quantities that we say is "conserved." **Conservation of energy** (as physicists call the principle that energy can neither be created nor destroyed) is based on experiment. Even as scientists discovered new forms of energy, conservation of energy has always been found to apply. Perhaps the most dramatic example of this was supplied by Einstein when he suggested that mass is equivalent to energy (his famous equation $E = mc^2$). This is one of the most important applications of Big Idea 5, that changes that occur as a result of interactions are constrained by conservation laws. Specifically, there are many situations where conservation of energy (Enduring Understanding 5.B) is both a useful concept and starting point for calculations related to the system. Note, however, that conservation doesn't necessarily mean that energy in a system doesn't change. Energy may be transferred into or out of the system, and the change must be equal to the amount transferred (Enduring Understanding 5.A). This may occur if there is an external force or a transfer between external objects and the system (Essential Knowledge 5.A.3). Energy is one of the fundamental quantities that are conserved for all systems (Essential Knowledge 5.A.2). The chapter introduces concepts of kinetic energy and potential energy. Kinetic energy is introduced as an energy of motion that can be changed by the amount of work done by an external force. Potential energy can only exist when objects interact with each other via conservative forces according to classical physics (Essential Knowledge 5.B.3). Because of this, a single object can only have kinetic energy and no potential energy (Essential Knowledge 5.B.1). The chapter also introduces the idea that the energy transfer is equal to the work done on the system by external forces and the rate of energy transfer is defined as power (Essential Knowledge 5.B.5).

From a societal viewpoint, energy is one of the major building blocks of modern civilization. Energy resources are key limiting factors to economic growth. The world use of energy resources, especially oil, continues to grow, with ominous consequences economically, socially, politically, and environmentally. We will briefly examine the world's energy use patterns at the end of this chapter.

The concepts in this chapter support:

Big Idea 3 The interactions of an object with other objects can be described by forces.

Enduring Understanding 3.E A force exerted on an object can change the kinetic energy of the object.

Essential Knowledge 3.E.1 The change in the kinetic energy of an object depends on the force exerted on the object and on the displacement of the object during the interval that the force is exerted.

Big Idea 4 Interactions between systems can result in changes in those systems.

Enduring Understanding 4.C Interactions with other objects or systems can change the total energy of a system.

Essential Knowledge 4.C.1 The energy of a system includes its kinetic energy, potential energy, and microscopic internal energy. Examples should include gravitational potential energy, elastic potential energy, and kinetic energy.

Essential Knowledge 4.C.2 Mechanical energy (the sum of kinetic and potential energy) is transferred into or out of a system when an external force is exerted on a system such that a component of the force is parallel to its displacement. The process through which the energy is transferred is called work.

Big Idea 5 Changes that occur as a result of interactions are constrained by conservation laws.

Enduring Understanding 5.A Certain quantities are conserved, in the sense that the changes of those quantities in a given system are always equal to the transfer of that quantity to or from the system by all possible interactions with other systems.

Essential Knowledge 5.A.2 For all systems under all circumstances, energy, charge, linear momentum, and angular momentum are conserved.

Essential Knowledge 5.A.3 An interaction can be either a force exerted by objects outside the system or the transfer of some quantity with objects outside the system.

Enduring Understanding 5.B The energy of a system is conserved.

Essential Knowledge 5.B.1 Classically, an object can only have kinetic energy since potential energy requires an interaction between two or more objects.

Essential Knowledge 5.B.3 A system with internal structure can have potential energy. Potential energy exists within a system if the objects within that system interact with conservative forces.

Essential Knowledge 5.B.5 Energy can be transferred by an external force exerted on an object or system that moves the object or system through a distance; this energy transfer is called work. Energy transfer in mechanical or electrical systems may occur at different rates. Power is defined as the rate of energy transfer into, out of, or within a system.

Click to view content (https://openstax.org/books/college-physics-ap-courses-2e/pages/7-connection-for-ap-r-courses)

7.1 Work: The Scientific Definition

LEARNING OBJECTIVES

By the end of this section, you will be able to:

- Explain how an object must be displaced for a force on it to do work.
- Explain how relative directions of force and displacement determine whether the work done is positive, negative, or zero.

What It Means to Do Work

The scientific definition of work differs in some ways from its everyday meaning. Certain things we think of as hard work, such as writing an exam or carrying a heavy load on level ground, are not work as defined by a scientist. The scientific definition of work reveals its relationship to energy—whenever work is done, energy is transferred.

For work, in the scientific sense, to be done, a force must be exerted and there must be displacement in the direction of the force.

Formally, the **work** done on a system by a constant force is defined to be *the product of the component of the force in the direction of motion times the distance through which the force acts.* For one-way motion in one dimension, this is expressed in equation form as

$$W = |\mathbf{F}|(\cos\theta)|\mathbf{d}|, \quad (7.1)$$

where W is work, $\mathbf{d}$ is the displacement of the system, and θ is the angle between the force vector $\mathbf{F}$ and the displacement vector $\mathbf{d}$, as in Figure 7.2. We can also write this as

$$W = Fd\cos\theta. \quad (7.2)$$

To find the work done on a system that undergoes motion that is not one-way or that is in two or three dimensions, we divide the motion into one-way one-dimensional segments and add up the work done over each segment.

WHAT IS WORK?

The work done on a system by a constant force is *the product of the component of the force in the direction of motion times the distance through which the force acts.* For one-way motion in one dimension, this is expressed in equation form as

$$W = Fd\cos\theta, \quad (7.3)$$

where W is work, F is the magnitude of the force on the system, d is the magnitude of the displacement of the system, and θ is the angle between the force vector $\mathbf{F}$ and the displacement vector $\mathbf{d}$.

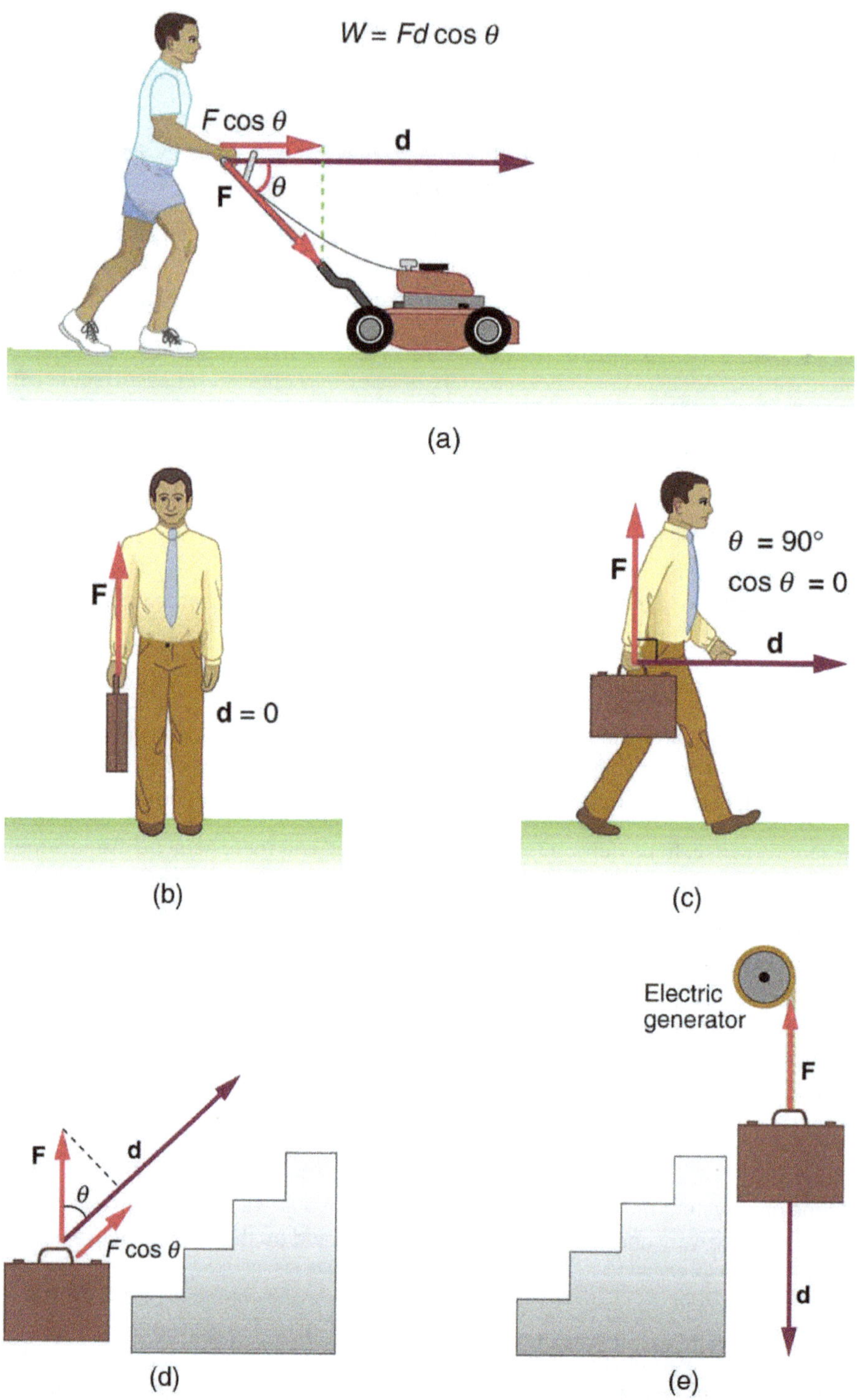

FIGURE 7.2 Examples of work. (a) The work done by the force $\mathbf{F}$ on this lawn mower is $Fd\cos\theta$. Note that $F\cos\theta$ is the component of the force in the direction of motion. (b) A person holding a briefcase does no work on it, because there is no displacement. No energy is transferred to or from the briefcase. (c) The person moving the briefcase horizontally at a constant speed does no work on it, and transfers no energy to it. (d) Work *is* done on the briefcase by carrying it up stairs at constant speed, because there is necessarily a component of force $\mathbf{F}$ in the direction of the motion. Energy is transferred to the briefcase and could in turn be used to do work. (e) When the briefcase is lowered, energy is transferred out of the briefcase and into an electric generator. Here the work done on the briefcase by the generator is negative, removing energy from the briefcase, because $\mathbf{F}$ and $\mathbf{d}$ are in opposite directions.

To examine what the definition of work means, let us consider the other situations shown in Figure 7.2. The person holding the briefcase in Figure 7.2(b) does no work, for example. Here $d = 0$, so $W = 0$. Why is it you get tired just holding a load? The answer is that your muscles are doing work against one another, *but they are doing no work on the system of interest* (the "briefcase-Earth system"—see Gravitational Potential Energy for more details). There must be displacement for work to be done, and there must be a component of the force in the direction of the motion. For example, the person carrying the briefcase on level ground in Figure 7.2(c) does no work on it, because the force is perpendicular to the motion. That is, $\cos 90^\circ = 0$, and so $W = 0$.

In contrast, when a force exerted on the system has a component in the direction of motion, such as in Figure 7.2(d), work *is* done—energy is transferred to the briefcase. Finally, in Figure 7.2(e), energy is transferred from the briefcase to a generator. There are two good ways to interpret this energy transfer. One interpretation is that the briefcase's weight does work on the generator, giving it energy. The other interpretation is that the generator does negative work on the briefcase, thus removing energy from it. The drawing shows the latter, with the force from the generator upward on the briefcase, and the displacement downward. This makes $\theta = 180^\circ$, and $\cos 180^\circ = -1$; therefore, W is negative.

Calculating Work

Work and energy have the same units. From the definition of work, we see that those units are force times distance. Thus, in SI units, work and energy are measured in **newton-meters**. A newton-meter is given the special name **joule** (J), and $1\text{ J} = 1\text{ N}\cdot\text{m} = 1\text{ kg}\cdot\text{m}^2/\text{s}^2$. One joule is not a large amount of energy; it would lift a small 100-gram apple a distance of about 1 meter.

EXAMPLE 7.1

Calculating the Work You Do to Push a Lawn Mower Across a Large Lawn

How much work is done on the lawn mower by the person in Figure 7.2(a) if he exerts a constant force of 75.0 N at an angle 35° below the horizontal and pushes the mower 25.0 m on level ground? Convert the amount of work from joules to kilocalories and compare it with this person's average daily intake of $10{,}000\text{ kJ}$ (about 2400 kcal) of food energy. One *calorie* (1 cal) of heat is the amount required to warm 1 g of water by 1°C, and is equivalent to 4.186 J, while one *food calorie* (1 kcal) is equivalent to 4186 J.

Strategy

We can solve this problem by substituting the given values into the definition of work done on a system, stated in the equation $W = Fd\cos\theta$. The force, angle, and displacement are given, so that only the work W is unknown.

Solution

The equation for the work is

$$W = Fd\cos\theta. \tag{7.4}$$

Substituting the known values gives

$$\begin{aligned} W &= (75.0\text{ N})(25.0\text{ m})\cos(35.0^\circ) \\ &= 1536\text{ J} = 1.54\times10^3\text{ J}. \end{aligned} \tag{7.5}$$

Converting the work in joules to kilocalories yields $W = (1536\text{ J})(1\text{ kcal}/4186\text{ J}) = 0.367\text{ kcal}$. The ratio of the work done to the daily consumption is

$$\frac{W}{2400\text{ kcal}} = 1.53\times10^{-4}. \tag{7.6}$$

Discussion

This ratio is a tiny fraction of what the person consumes, but it is typical. Very little of the energy released in the consumption of food is used to do work. Even when we "work" all day long, less than 10% of our food energy intake is used to do work and more than 90% is converted to thermal energy or stored as chemical energy in fat.

7.2 Kinetic Energy and the Work-Energy Theorem

LEARNING OBJECTIVES

By the end of this section, you will be able to:

- Explain work as a transfer of energy and net work as the work done by the net force.
- Explain and apply the work-energy theorem.

Work Transfers Energy

What happens to the work done on a system? Energy is transferred into the system, but in what form? Does it remain in the system or move on? The answers depend on the situation. For example, if the lawn mower in Figure 7.2(a) is pushed just hard enough to keep it going at a constant speed, then energy put into the mower by the person is removed continuously by friction, and eventually leaves the system in the form of heat transfer. In contrast, work done on the briefcase by the person carrying it up stairs in Figure 7.2(d) is stored in the briefcase-Earth system and can be recovered at any time, as shown in Figure 7.2(e). In fact, the building of the pyramids in ancient Egypt is an example of storing energy in a system by doing work on the system. Some of the energy imparted to the stone blocks in lifting them during construction of the pyramids remains in the stone-Earth system and has the potential to do work.

In this section we begin the study of various types of work and forms of energy. We will find that some types of work leave the energy of a system constant, for example, whereas others change the system in some way, such as making it move. We will also develop definitions of important forms of energy, such as the energy of motion.

Net Work and the Work-Energy Theorem

We know from the study of Newton's laws in Dynamics: Force and Newton's Laws of Motion that net force causes acceleration. We will see in this section that work done by the net force gives a system energy of motion, and in the process we will also find an expression for the energy of motion.

Let us start by considering the total, or net, work done on a system. Net work is defined to be the sum of work on an object. The net work can be written in terms of the net force on an object. $\mathbf{F}_{\text{net}}$. In equation form, this is $W_{\text{net}} = F_{\text{net}} d \cos \theta$ where θ is the angle between the force vector and the displacement vector.

Figure 7.3(a) shows a graph of force versus displacement for the component of the force in the direction of the displacement—that is, an $F \cos \theta$ vs. d graph. In this case, $F \cos \theta$ is constant. You can see that the area under the graph is $Fd \cos \theta$, or the work done. Figure 7.3(b) shows a more general process where the force varies. The area under the curve is divided into strips, each having an average force $(F \cos \theta)_{i(\text{ave})}$. The work done is $(F \cos \theta)_{i(\text{ave})} d_i$ for each strip, and the total work done is the sum of the W_i. Thus the total work done is the total area under the curve, a useful property to which we shall refer later.

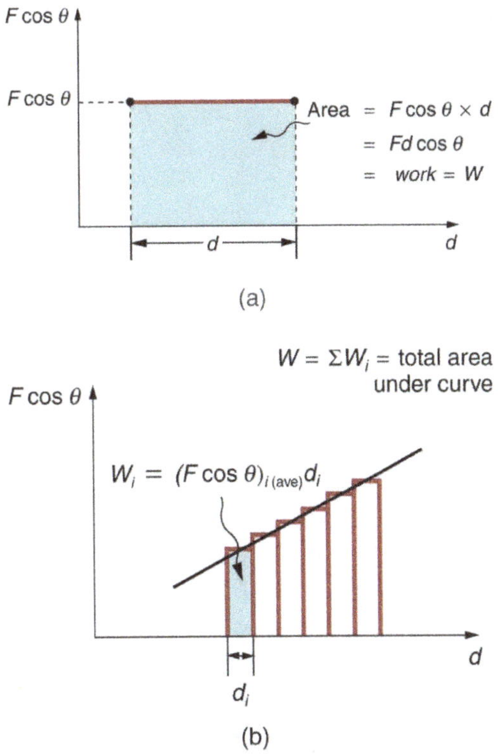

FIGURE 7.3 (a) A graph of $F\cos\theta$ vs. d, when $F\cos\theta$ is constant. The area under the curve represents the work done by the force. (b) A graph of $F\cos\theta$ vs. d in which the force varies. The work done for each interval is the area of each strip; thus, the total area under the curve equals the total work done.

Net work will be simpler to examine if we consider a one-dimensional situation where a force is used to accelerate an object in a direction parallel to its initial velocity. Such a situation occurs for the package on the roller belt conveyor system shown in Figure 7.4.

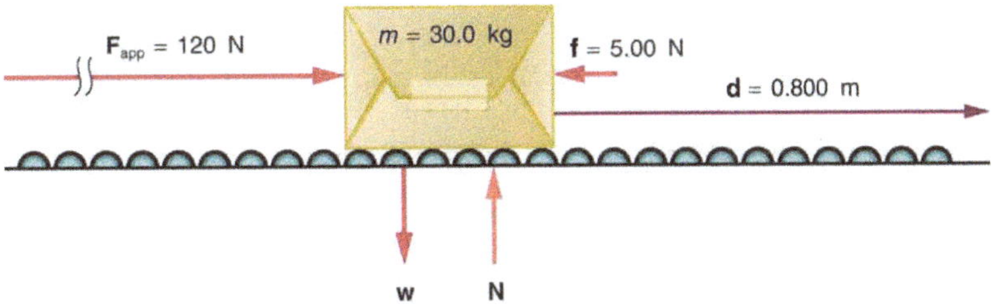

FIGURE 7.4 A package on a roller belt is pushed horizontally through a distance **d**.

The force of gravity and the normal force acting on the package are perpendicular to the displacement and do no work. Moreover, they are also equal in magnitude and opposite in direction so they cancel in calculating the net force. The net force arises solely from the horizontal applied force $\mathbf{F}_{\text{app}}$ and the horizontal friction force $\mathbf{f}$. Thus, as expected, the net force is parallel to the displacement, so that $\theta = 0°$ and $\cos\theta = 1$, and the net work is given by

$$W_{\text{net}} = F_{\text{net}} d. \qquad 7.7$$

The effect of the net force $\mathbf{F}_{\text{net}}$ is to accelerate the package from v_0 to v. The kinetic energy of the package increases, indicating that the net work done on the system is positive. (See Example 7.2.) By using Newton's second law, and doing some algebra, we can reach an interesting conclusion. Substituting $F_{\text{net}} = ma$ from Newton's second law gives

$$W_{\text{net}} = mad. \qquad 7.8$$

To get a relationship between net work and the speed given to a system by the net force acting on it, we take $d = x - x_0$ and use the equation studied in Motion Equations for Constant Acceleration in One Dimension for the change in speed over a distance d if the acceleration has the constant value a; namely, $v^2 = v_0{}^2 + 2ad$ (note that a appears in the expression for the net work). Solving for acceleration gives $a = \frac{v^2 - v_0{}^2}{2d}$. When a is substituted into the preceding expression for W_{net}, we obtain

$$W_{\text{net}} = m\left(\frac{v^2 - v_0{}^2}{2d}\right)d. \quad 7.9$$

The d cancels, and we rearrange this to obtain

$$W_{\text{net}} = \frac{1}{2}mv^2 - \frac{1}{2}mv_0^2. \quad 7.10$$

This expression is called the **work-energy theorem**, and it actually applies *in general* (even for forces that vary in direction and magnitude), although we have derived it for the special case of a constant force parallel to the displacement. The theorem implies that the net work on a system equals the change in the quantity $\frac{1}{2}mv^2$. This quantity is our first example of a form of energy.

THE WORK-ENERGY THEOREM

The net work on a system equals the change in the quantity $\frac{1}{2}mv^2$.

$$W_{\text{net}} = \frac{1}{2}mv^2 - \frac{1}{2}mv_0^2 \quad 7.11$$

The quantity $\frac{1}{2}mv^2$ in the work-energy theorem is defined to be the translational **kinetic energy** (KE) of a mass m moving at a speed v. (*Translational* kinetic energy is distinct from *rotational* kinetic energy, which is considered later.) In equation form, the translational kinetic energy,

$$\text{KE} = \frac{1}{2}mv^2, \quad 7.12$$

is the energy associated with translational motion. Kinetic energy is a form of energy associated with the motion of a particle, single body, or system of objects moving together.

We are aware that it takes energy to get an object, like a car or the package in Figure 7.4, up to speed, but it may be a bit surprising that kinetic energy is proportional to speed squared. This proportionality means, for example, that a car traveling at 100 km/h has four times the kinetic energy it has at 50 km/h, helping to explain why high-speed collisions are so devastating. We will now consider a series of examples to illustrate various aspects of work and energy.

EXAMPLE 7.2

Calculating the Kinetic Energy of a Package

Suppose a 30.0-kg package on the roller belt conveyor system in Figure 7.4 is moving at 0.500 m/s. What is its kinetic energy?

Strategy

Because the mass m and speed v are given, the kinetic energy can be calculated from its definition as given in the equation $\text{KE} = \frac{1}{2}mv^2$.

Solution

The kinetic energy is given by

$$\text{KE} = \frac{1}{2}mv^2. \quad 7.13$$

Entering known values gives

$$\text{KE} = 0.5(30.0\ \text{kg})(0.500\ \text{m/s})^2, \quad 7.14$$

which yields

$$\text{KE} = 3.75\ \text{kg} \cdot \text{m}^2/\text{s}^2 = 3.75\ \text{J}. \quad (7.15)$$

Discussion

Note that the unit of kinetic energy is the joule, the same as the unit of work, as mentioned when work was first defined. It is also interesting that, although this is a fairly massive package, its kinetic energy is not large at this relatively low speed. This fact is consistent with the observation that people can move packages like this without exhausting themselves.

EXAMPLE 7.3

Determining the Work to Accelerate a Package

Suppose that you push on the 30.0-kg package in Figure 7.4 with a constant force of 120 N through a distance of 0.800 m, and that the opposing friction force averages 5.00 N.

(a) Calculate the net work done on the package. (b) Solve the same problem as in part (a), this time by finding the work done by each force that contributes to the net force.

Strategy and Concept for (a)

This is a motion in one dimension problem, because the downward force (from the weight of the package) and the normal force have equal magnitude and opposite direction, so that they cancel in calculating the net force, while the applied force, friction, and the displacement are all horizontal. (See Figure 7.4.) As expected, the net work is the net force times distance.

Solution for (a)

The net force is the push force minus friction, or $F_{\text{net}} = 120\ \text{N} - 5.00\ \text{N} = 115\ \text{N}$. Thus the net work is

$$\begin{aligned} W_{\text{net}} &= F_{\text{net}} d = (115\ \text{N})(0.800\ \text{m}) \\ &= 92.0\ \text{N} \cdot \text{m} = 92.0\ \text{J}. \end{aligned} \quad (7.16)$$

Discussion for (a)

This value is the net work done on the package. The person actually does more work than this, because friction opposes the motion. Friction does negative work and removes some of the energy the person expends and converts it to thermal energy. The net work equals the sum of the work done by each individual force.

Strategy and Concept for (b)

The forces acting on the package are gravity, the normal force, the force of friction, and the applied force. The normal force and force of gravity are each perpendicular to the displacement, and therefore do no work.

Solution for (b)

The applied force does work.

$$\begin{aligned} W_{\text{app}} &= F_{\text{app}} d \cos(0^\circ) = F_{\text{app}} d \\ &= (120\ \text{N})(0.800\ \text{m}) \\ &= 96.0\ \text{J} \end{aligned} \quad (7.17)$$

The friction force and displacement are in opposite directions, so that $\theta = 180^\circ$, and the work done by friction is

$$\begin{aligned} W_{\text{fr}} &= F_{\text{fr}} d \cos(180^\circ) = -F_{\text{fr}} d \\ &= -(5.00\ \text{N})(0.800\ \text{m}) \\ &= -4.00\ \text{J}. \end{aligned} \quad (7.18)$$

So the amounts of work done by gravity, by the normal force, by the applied force, and by friction are, respectively,

$$\begin{aligned} W_{\text{gr}} &= 0, \\ W_{\text{N}} &= 0, \\ W_{\text{app}} &= 96.0\text{ J}, \\ W_{\text{fr}} &= -4.00\text{ J}. \end{aligned} \tag{7.19}$$

The total work done as the sum of the work done by each force is then seen to be

$$W_{\text{total}} = W_{\text{gr}} + W_{\text{N}} + W_{\text{app}} + W_{\text{fr}} = 92.0\text{ J}. \tag{7.20}$$

Discussion for (b)

The calculated total work W_{total} as the sum of the work by each force agrees, as expected, with the work W_{net} done by the net force. The work done by a collection of forces acting on an object can be calculated by either approach.

EXAMPLE 7.4

Determining Speed from Work and Energy

Find the speed of the package in Figure 7.4 at the end of the push, using work and energy concepts.

Strategy

Here the work-energy theorem can be used, because we have just calculated the net work, W_{net}, and the initial kinetic energy, $\frac{1}{2}mv_0{}^2$. These calculations allow us to find the final kinetic energy, $\frac{1}{2}mv^2$, and thus the final speed v.

Solution

The work-energy theorem in equation form is

$$W_{\text{net}} = \frac{1}{2}mv^2 - \frac{1}{2}mv_0{}^2. \tag{7.21}$$

Solving for $\frac{1}{2}mv^2$ gives

$$\frac{1}{2}mv^2 = W_{\text{net}} + \frac{1}{2}mv_0{}^2. \tag{7.22}$$

Thus,

$$\frac{1}{2}mv^2 = 92.0\text{ J} + 3.75\text{ J} = 95.75\text{ J}. \tag{7.23}$$

Solving for the final speed as requested and entering known values gives

$$\begin{aligned} v &= \sqrt{\frac{2(95.75\text{ J})}{m}} = \sqrt{\frac{191.5\text{ kg}\cdot\text{m}^2/\text{s}^2}{30.0\text{ kg}}} \\ &= 2.53\text{ m/s}. \end{aligned} \tag{7.24}$$

Discussion

Using work and energy, we not only arrive at an answer, we see that the final kinetic energy is the sum of the initial kinetic energy and the net work done on the package. This means that the work indeed adds to the energy of the package.

EXAMPLE 7.5

Work and Energy Can Reveal Distance, Too

How far does the package in Figure 7.4 coast after the push, assuming friction remains constant? Use work and energy considerations.

Strategy

We know that once the person stops pushing, friction will bring the package to rest. In terms of energy, friction does negative work until it has removed all of the package's kinetic energy. The work done by friction is the force of friction times the distance traveled times the cosine of the angle between the friction force and displacement; hence, this gives us a way of finding the distance traveled after the person stops pushing.

Solution

The normal force and force of gravity cancel in calculating the net force. The horizontal friction force is then the net force, and it acts opposite to the displacement, so $\theta = 180^\circ$. To reduce the kinetic energy of the package to zero, the work W_{fr} by friction must be minus the kinetic energy that the package started with plus what the package accumulated due to the pushing. Thus $W_{\text{fr}} = -95.75 \text{ J}$. Furthermore, $W_{\text{fr}} = fd' \cos\theta = -fd'$, where d' is the distance it takes to stop. Thus,

$$d' = -\frac{W_{\text{fr}}}{f} = -\frac{-95.75 \text{ J}}{5.00 \text{ N}}, \tag{7.25}$$

and so

$$d' = 19.2 \text{ m}. \tag{7.26}$$

Discussion

This is a reasonable distance for a package to coast on a relatively friction-free conveyor system. Note that the work done by friction is negative (the force is in the opposite direction of motion), so it removes the kinetic energy.

Some of the examples in this section can be solved without considering energy, but at the expense of missing out on gaining insights about what work and energy are doing in this situation. On the whole, solutions involving energy are generally shorter and easier than those using kinematics and dynamics alone.

7.3 Gravitational Potential Energy

LEARNING OBJECTIVES

By the end of this section, you will be able to:

- Explain gravitational potential energy in terms of work done against gravity.
- Show that the gravitational potential energy of an object of mass m at height h on Earth is given by $\text{PE}_\text{g} = mgh$.
- Show how knowledge of the potential energy as a function of position can be used to simplify calculations and explain physical phenomena.

Work Done Against Gravity

Climbing stairs and lifting objects is work in both the scientific and everyday sense—it is work done against the gravitational force. When there is work, there is a transformation of energy. The work done against the gravitational force goes into an important form of stored energy that we will explore in this section.

Let us calculate the work done in lifting an object of mass m through a height h, such as in Figure 7.5. If the object is lifted straight up at constant speed, then the force needed to lift it is equal to its weight mg. The work done on the mass is then $W = Fd = mgh$. We define this to be the **gravitational potential energy** (PE_g) put into (or gained by) the object-Earth system. This energy is associated with the state of separation between two objects that attract each other by the gravitational force. For convenience, we refer to this as the PE_g gained by the object, recognizing that this is energy stored in the gravitational field of Earth. Why do we use the word "system"? Potential energy is a property of a system rather than of a single object—due to its physical position. An object's gravitational potential is due to its position relative to the surroundings within the Earth-object system. The force applied to the object is an external force, from outside the system. When it does positive work it increases the gravitational potential energy of the system. Because gravitational potential energy depends on relative position, we need a reference level at which to set the potential energy equal to 0. We usually choose this point to be Earth's surface, but this point is arbitrary; what is important is the *difference* in gravitational potential energy, because this difference is what relates to the work done. The difference in gravitational potential energy of an object (in the Earth-object system) between two rungs of a ladder will be the same for the first two rungs as for the last two rungs.

Converting Between Potential Energy and Kinetic Energy

Gravitational potential energy may be converted to other forms of energy, such as kinetic energy. If we release the mass, gravitational force will do an amount of work equal to mgh on it, thereby increasing its kinetic energy by that same amount (by the work-energy theorem). We will find it more useful to consider just the conversion of PE_g to KE without explicitly considering the intermediate step of work. (See Example 7.7.) This shortcut makes it is easier to solve problems using energy (if possible) rather than explicitly using forces.

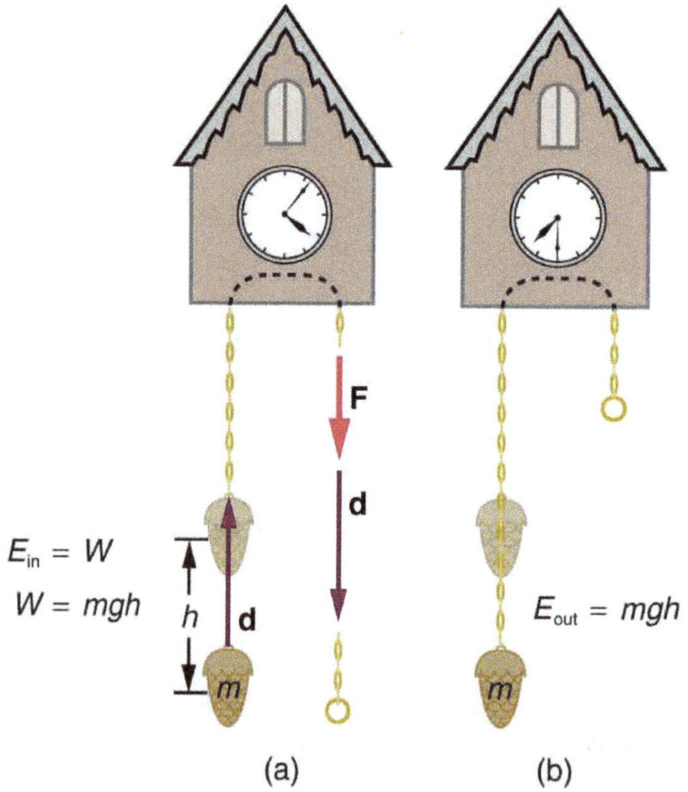

FIGURE 7.5 (a) The work done to lift the weight is stored in the mass-Earth system as gravitational potential energy. (b) As the weight moves downward, this gravitational potential energy is transferred to the cuckoo clock.

More precisely, we define the *change* in gravitational potential energy ΔPE_g to be

$$\Delta\text{PE}_\text{g} = mgh, \tag{7.27}$$

where, for simplicity, we denote the change in height by h rather than the usual Δh. Note that h is positive when the final height is greater than the initial height, and vice versa. For example, if a 0.500-kg mass hung from a cuckoo clock is raised 1.00 m, then its change in gravitational potential energy is

$$\begin{aligned} mgh &= (0.500\text{ kg})(9.80\text{ m/s}^2)(1.00\text{ m}) \\ &= 4.90\text{ kg}\cdot\text{m}^2/\text{s}^2 = 4.90\text{ J}. \end{aligned} \tag{7.28}$$

Note that the units of gravitational potential energy turn out to be joules, the same as for work and other forms of energy. As the clock runs, the mass is lowered. We can think of the mass as gradually giving up its 4.90 J of gravitational potential energy, *without directly considering the force of gravity that does the work.*

Using Potential Energy to Simplify Calculations

The equation $\Delta PE_g = mgh$ applies for any path that has a change in height of h, not just when the mass is lifted straight up. (See Figure 7.6.) It is much easier to calculate mgh (a simple multiplication) than it is to calculate the work done along a complicated path. The idea of gravitational potential energy has the double advantage that it is very broadly applicable and it makes calculations easier. From now on, we will consider that any change in vertical position h of a mass m is accompanied by a change in gravitational potential energy mgh, and we will avoid the equivalent but more difficult task of calculating work done by or against the gravitational force.

FIGURE 7.6 The change in gravitational potential energy (ΔPE_g) between points A and B is independent of the path. $\Delta PE_g = mgh$ for any path between the two points. Gravity is one of a small class of forces where the work done by or against the force depends only on the starting and ending points, not on the path between them.

EXAMPLE 7.6

The Force to Stop Falling

A 60.0-kg person jumps onto the floor from a height of 3.00 m. If he lands stiffly (with his knee joints compressing by 0.500 cm), calculate the force on the knee joints.

Strategy

This person's energy is brought to zero in this situation by the work done on him by the floor as he stops. The initial PE_g is transformed into KE as he falls. The work done by the floor reduces this kinetic energy to zero.

Solution

The work done on the person by the floor as he stops is given by

$$W = Fd\cos\theta = -Fd, \tag{7.29}$$

with a minus sign because the displacement while stopping and the force from floor are in opposite directions $(\cos\theta = \cos 180^\circ = -1)$. The floor removes energy from the system, so it does negative work.

The kinetic energy the person has upon reaching the floor is the amount of potential energy lost by falling through height h:

$$KE = -\Delta PE_g = -mgh, \quad 7.30$$

The distance d that the person's knees bend is much smaller than the height h of the fall, so the additional change in gravitational potential energy during the knee bend is ignored.

The work W done by the floor on the person stops the person and brings the person's kinetic energy to zero:

$$W = -KE = mgh. \quad 7.31$$

Combining this equation with the expression for W gives

$$-Fd = mgh. \quad 7.32$$

Recalling that h is negative because the person fell *down*, the force on the knee joints is given by

$$F = -\frac{mgh}{d} = -\frac{(60.0\text{ kg})(9.80\text{ m/s}^2)(-3.00\text{ m})}{5.00 \times 10^{-3}\text{ m}} = 3.53 \times 10^5\text{ N}. \quad 7.33$$

Discussion

Such a large force (500 times more than the person's weight) over the short impact time is enough to break bones. A much better way to cushion the shock is by bending the legs or rolling on the ground, increasing the time over which the force acts. A bending motion of 0.5 m this way yields a force 100 times smaller than in the example. A kangaroo's hopping shows this method in action. The kangaroo is the only large animal to use hopping for locomotion, but the shock in hopping is cushioned by the bending of its hind legs in each jump.(See Figure 7.7.)

FIGURE 7.7 The work done by the ground upon the kangaroo reduces its kinetic energy to zero as it lands. However, by applying the force of the ground on the hind legs over a longer distance, the impact on the bones is reduced. (credit: Chris Samuel, Flickr)

EXAMPLE 7.7

Finding the Speed of a Roller Coaster from its Height

(a) What is the final speed of the roller coaster shown in Figure 7.8 if it starts from rest at the top of the 20.0 m hill and work done by frictional forces is negligible? (b) What is its final speed (again assuming negligible friction) if its initial speed is 5.00 m/s?

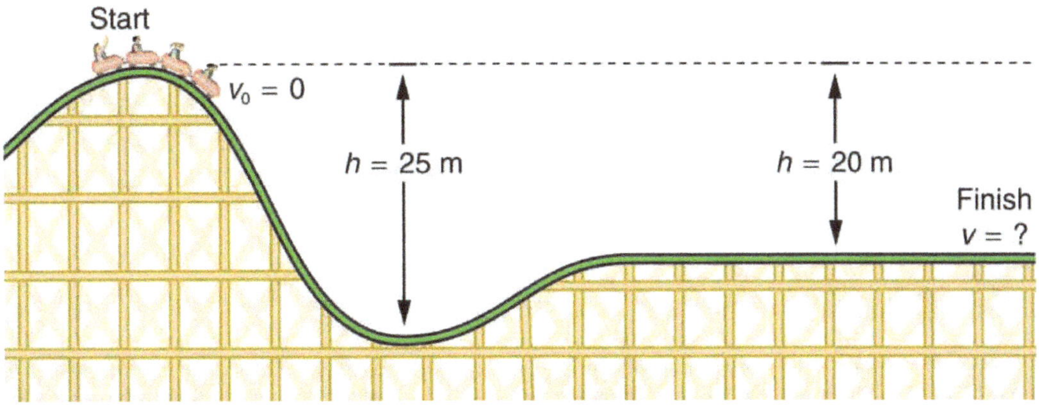

FIGURE 7.8 The speed of a roller coaster increases as gravity pulls it downhill and is greatest at its lowest point. Viewed in terms of energy, the roller-coaster-Earth system's gravitational potential energy is converted to kinetic energy. If work done by friction is negligible, all ΔPE_g is converted to KE.

Strategy

The roller coaster loses potential energy as it goes downhill. We neglect friction, so that the remaining force exerted by the track is the normal force, which is perpendicular to the direction of motion and does no work. The net work on the roller coaster is then done by gravity alone. The *loss* of gravitational potential energy from moving *downward* through a distance h equals the *gain* in kinetic energy. This can be written in equation form as $-\Delta PE_g = \Delta KE$. Using the equations for PE_g and KE, we can solve for the final speed v, which is the desired quantity.

Solution for (a)

Here the initial kinetic energy is zero, so that $\Delta KE = \frac{1}{2}mv^2$. The equation for change in potential energy states that $\Delta PE_g = mgh$. Since h is negative in this case, we will rewrite this as $\Delta PE_g = -mg\,|h|$ to show the minus sign clearly. Thus,

$$-\Delta PE_g = \Delta KE \tag{7.34}$$

becomes

$$mg\,|h| = \frac{1}{2}mv^2. \tag{7.35}$$

Solving for v, we find that mass cancels and that

$$v = \sqrt{2g\,|h|}. \tag{7.36}$$

Substituting known values,

$$\begin{aligned} v &= \sqrt{2(9.80 \text{ m/s}^2)(20.0 \text{ m})} \\ &= 19.8 \text{ m/s}. \end{aligned} \tag{7.37}$$

Solution for (b)

Again $-\Delta PE_g = \Delta KE$. In this case there is initial kinetic energy, so $\Delta KE = \frac{1}{2}mv^2 - \frac{1}{2}mv_0{}^2$. Thus,

$$mg\,|h| = \frac{1}{2}mv^2 - \frac{1}{2}mv_0{}^2. \tag{7.38}$$

Rearranging gives

$$\frac{1}{2}mv^2 = mg\,|h| + \frac{1}{2}mv_0{}^2. \tag{7.39}$$

This means that the final kinetic energy is the sum of the initial kinetic energy and the gravitational potential energy. Mass again cancels, and

$$v = \sqrt{2g|h| + {v_0}^2}. \tag{7.40}$$

This equation is very similar to the kinematics equation $v = \sqrt{{v_0}^2 + 2ad}$, but it is more general—the kinematics equation is valid only for constant acceleration, whereas our equation above is valid for any path regardless of whether the object moves with a constant acceleration. Now, substituting known values gives

$$\begin{aligned} v &= \sqrt{2(9.80\ \text{m/s}^2)(20.0\ \text{m}) + (5.00\ \text{m/s})^2} \\ &= 20.4\ \text{m/s}. \end{aligned} \tag{7.41}$$

Discussion and Implications

First, note that mass cancels. This is quite consistent with observations made in Falling Objects that all objects fall at the same rate if friction is negligible. Second, only the speed of the roller coaster is considered; there is no information about its direction at any point. This reveals another general truth. When friction is negligible, the speed of a falling body depends only on its initial speed and height, and not on its mass or the path taken. For example, the roller coaster will have the same final speed whether it falls 20.0 m straight down or takes a more complicated path like the one in the figure. Third, and perhaps unexpectedly, the final speed in part (b) is greater than in part (a), but by far less than 5.00 m/s. Finally, note that speed can be found at *any* height along the way by simply using the appropriate value of h at the point of interest.

We have seen that work done by or against the gravitational force depends only on the starting and ending points, and not on the path between, allowing us to define the simplifying concept of gravitational potential energy. We can do the same thing for a few other forces, and we will see that this leads to a formal definition of the law of conservation of energy.

MAKING CONNECTIONS: TAKE-HOME INVESTIGATION—CONVERTING POTENTIAL TO KINETIC ENERGY

One can study the conversion of gravitational potential energy into kinetic energy in this experiment. On a smooth, level surface, use a ruler of the kind that has a groove running along its length and a book to make an incline (see Figure 7.9). Place a marble at the 10-cm position on the ruler and let it roll down the ruler. When it hits the level surface, measure the time it takes to roll one meter. Now place the marble at the 20-cm and the 30-cm positions and again measure the times it takes to roll 1 m on the level surface. Find the velocity of the marble on the level surface for all three positions. Plot velocity squared versus the distance traveled by the marble. What is the shape of each plot? If the shape is a straight line, the plot shows that the marble's kinetic energy at the bottom is proportional to its potential energy at the release point.

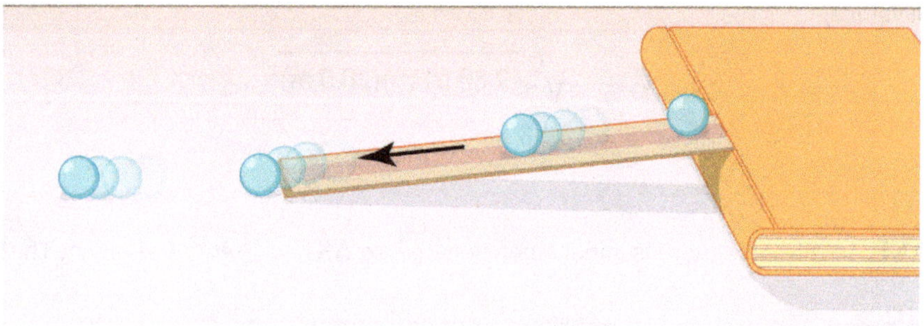

FIGURE 7.9 A marble rolls down a ruler, and its speed on the level surface is measured.

7.4 Conservative Forces and Potential Energy

LEARNING OBJECTIVES

By the end of this section, you will be able to:

- Define conservative force, potential energy, and mechanical energy.
- Explain the potential energy of a spring in terms of its compression when Hooke's law applies.
- Use the work-energy theorem to show how having only conservative forces implies conservation of mechanical energy.

Potential Energy and Conservative Forces

Work is done by a force, and some forces, such as weight, have special characteristics. A **conservative force** is one, like the gravitational force, for which work done by or against it depends only on the starting and ending points of a motion and not on the path taken. We can define a **potential energy** (PE) for any conservative force, just as we did for the gravitational force. For example, when you wind up a toy, an egg timer, or an old-fashioned watch, you do work against its spring and store energy in it. (We treat these springs as ideal, in that we assume there is no friction and no production of thermal energy.) This stored energy is recoverable as work, and it is useful to think of it as potential energy contained in the spring. Indeed, the reason that the spring has this characteristic is that its force is *conservative*. That is, a conservative force results in stored or potential energy. Gravitational potential energy is one example, as is the energy stored in a spring. We will also see how conservative forces are related to the conservation of energy.

POTENTIAL ENERGY AND CONSERVATIVE FORCES

Potential energy is the energy a system has due to position, shape, or configuration. It is stored energy that is completely recoverable.

A conservative force is one for which work done by or against it depends only on the starting and ending points of a motion and not on the path taken.

We can define a potential energy (PE) for any conservative force. The work done against a conservative force to reach a final configuration depends on the configuration, not the path followed, and is the potential energy added.

Potential Energy of a Spring

First, let us obtain an expression for the potential energy stored in a spring $(\mathrm{PE_s})$. We calculate the work done to stretch or compress a spring that obeys Hooke's law. (Hooke's law was examined in Elasticity: Stress and Strain, and states that the magnitude of force F on the spring and the resulting deformation ΔL are proportional, $F = k\Delta L$.) (See Figure 7.10.) For our spring, we will replace ΔL (the amount of deformation produced by a force F) by the distance x that the spring is stretched or compressed along its length. So the force needed to stretch the spring has magnitude $F = kx$, where k is the spring's force constant. The force increases linearly from 0 at the start to kx in the fully stretched position. The average force is $kx/2$. Thus the work done in stretching or compressing the spring is $W_s = Fd = \left(\frac{kx}{2}\right)x = \frac{1}{2}kx^2$. Alternatively, we noted in Kinetic Energy and the Work-Energy Theorem that the area under a graph of F vs. x is the work done by the force. In Figure 7.10(c) we see that this area is also $\frac{1}{2}kx^2$. We therefore define the **potential energy of a spring**, $\mathrm{PE_s}$, to be

$$\mathrm{PE_s} = \frac{1}{2}kx^2, \tag{7.42}$$

where k is the spring's force constant and x is the displacement from its undeformed position. The potential energy represents the work done *on* the spring and the energy stored in it as a result of stretching or compressing it a distance x. The potential energy of the spring $\mathrm{PE_s}$ does not depend on the path taken; it depends only on the stretch or squeeze x in the final configuration.

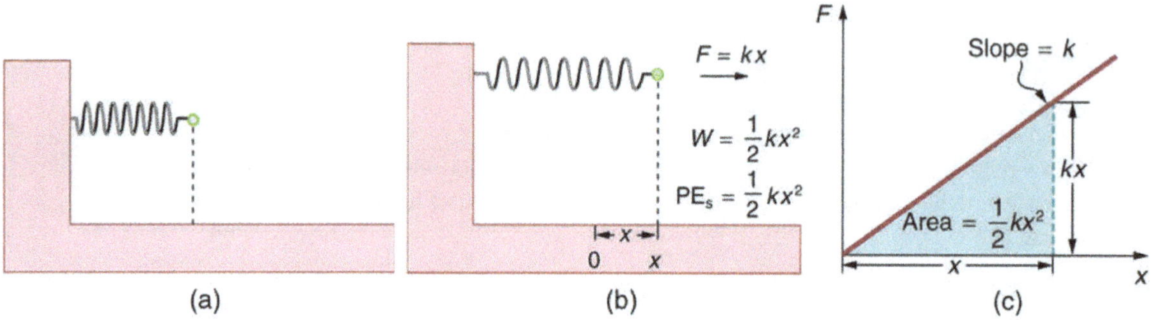

FIGURE 7.10 (a) An undeformed spring has no PE_s stored in it. (b) The force needed to stretch (or compress) the spring a distance x has a magnitude $F = kx$, and the work done to stretch (or compress) it is $\frac{1}{2}kx^2$. Because the force is conservative, this work is stored as potential energy (PE_s) in the spring, and it can be fully recovered. (c) A graph of F vs. x has a slope of k, and the area under the graph is $\frac{1}{2}kx^2$. Thus the work done or potential energy stored is $\frac{1}{2}kx^2$.

The equation $PE_s = \frac{1}{2}kx^2$ has general validity beyond the special case for which it was derived. Potential energy can be stored in any elastic medium by deforming it. Indeed, the general definition of **potential energy** is energy due to position, shape, or configuration. For shape or position deformations, stored energy is $PE_s = \frac{1}{2}kx^2$, where k is the force constant of the particular system and x is its deformation. Another example is seen in Figure 7.11 for a guitar string.

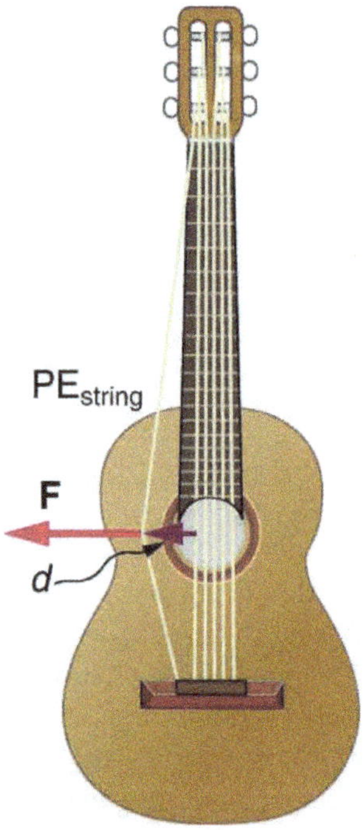

FIGURE 7.11 Work is done to deform the guitar string, giving it potential energy. When released, the potential energy is converted to kinetic energy and back to potential as the string oscillates back and forth. A very small fraction is dissipated as sound energy, slowly removing energy from the string.

Conservation of Mechanical Energy

Let us now consider what form the work-energy theorem takes when only conservative forces are involved. This will lead us to the conservation of energy principle. The work-energy theorem states that the net work done by all forces acting on a system equals its change in kinetic energy. In equation form, this is

$$W_{net} = \frac{1}{2}mv^2 - \frac{1}{2}mv_0{}^2 = \Delta KE. \quad (7.43)$$

If only conservative forces act, then

$$W_{net} = W_c, \quad (7.44)$$

where W_c is the total work done by all conservative forces. Thus,

$$W_c = \Delta KE. \tag{7.45}$$

Now, if the conservative force, such as the gravitational force or a spring force, does work, the system loses potential energy. That is, $W_c = -\Delta PE$. Therefore,

$$-\Delta PE = \Delta KE \tag{7.46}$$

or

$$\Delta KE + \Delta PE = 0. \tag{7.47}$$

This equation means that the total kinetic and potential energy is constant for any process involving only conservative forces. That is,

$$\left.\begin{array}{c} KE + PE = \text{constant} \\ \text{or} \\ KE_i + PE_i = KE_f + PE_f \end{array}\right\} \text{(conservative forces only)}, \tag{7.48}$$

where i and f denote initial and final values. This equation is a form of the work-energy theorem for conservative forces; it is known as the **conservation of mechanical energy** principle. Remember that this applies to the extent that all the forces are conservative, so that friction is negligible. The total kinetic plus potential energy of a system is defined to be its **mechanical energy**, $(KE + PE)$. In a system that experiences only conservative forces, there is a potential energy associated with each force, and the energy only changes form between KE and the various types of PE, with the total energy remaining constant.

EXAMPLE 7.8

Using Conservation of Mechanical Energy to Calculate the Speed of a Toy Car

A 0.100-kg toy car is propelled by a compressed spring, as shown in Figure 7.12. The car follows a track that rises 0.180 m above the starting point. The spring is compressed 4.00 cm and has a force constant of 250.0 N/m. Assuming work done by friction to be negligible, find (a) how fast the car is going before it starts up the slope and (b) how fast it is going at the top of the slope.

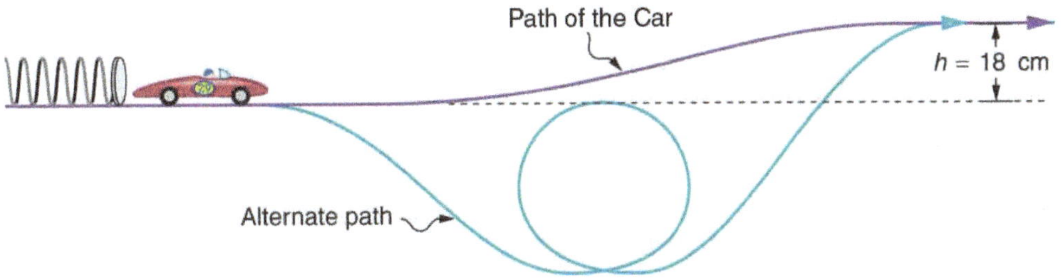

FIGURE 7.12 A toy car is pushed by a compressed spring and coasts up a slope. Assuming negligible friction, the potential energy in the spring is first completely converted to kinetic energy, and then to a combination of kinetic and gravitational potential energy as the car rises. The details of the path are unimportant because all forces are conservative—the car would have the same final speed if it took the alternate path shown.

Strategy

The spring force and the gravitational force are conservative forces, so conservation of mechanical energy can be used. Thus,

$$KE_i + PE_i = KE_f + PE_f \tag{7.49}$$

or

$$\frac{1}{2}mv_i^2 + mgh_i + \frac{1}{2}kx_i^2 = \frac{1}{2}mv_f^2 + mgh_f + \frac{1}{2}kx_f^2, \tag{7.50}$$

where h is the height (vertical position) and x is the compression of the spring. This general statement looks complex but becomes much simpler when we start considering specific situations. First, we must identify the initial and final conditions in a problem; then, we enter them into the last equation to solve for an unknown.

Solution for (a)

This part of the problem is limited to conditions just before the car is released and just after it leaves the spring. Take the initial height to be zero, so that both h_i and h_f are zero. Furthermore, the initial speed v_i is zero and the final compression of the spring x_f is zero, and so several terms in the conservation of mechanical energy equation are zero and it simplifies to

$$\frac{1}{2}kx_i^2 = \frac{1}{2}mv_f^2. \tag{7.51}$$

In other words, the initial potential energy in the spring is converted completely to kinetic energy in the absence of friction. Solving for the final speed and entering known values yields

$$\begin{aligned} v_f &= \sqrt{\frac{k}{m}}x_i \\ &= \sqrt{\frac{250.0 \text{ N/m}}{0.100 \text{ kg}}}(0.0400 \text{ m}) \\ &= 2.00 \text{ m/s}. \end{aligned} \tag{7.52}$$

Solution for (b)

One method of finding the speed at the top of the slope is to consider conditions just before the car is released and just after it reaches the top of the slope, completely ignoring everything in between. Doing the same type of analysis to find which terms are zero, the conservation of mechanical energy becomes

$$\frac{1}{2}kx_i^2 = \frac{1}{2}mv_f^2 + mgh_f. \tag{7.53}$$

This form of the equation means that the spring's initial potential energy is converted partly to gravitational potential energy and partly to kinetic energy. The final speed at the top of the slope will be less than at the bottom. Solving for v_f and substituting known values gives

$$\begin{aligned} v_f &= \sqrt{\frac{kx_i^2}{m} - 2gh_f} \\ &= \sqrt{\left(\frac{250.0 \text{ N/m}}{0.100 \text{ kg}}\right)(0.0400 \text{ m})^2 - 2(9.80 \text{ m/s}^2)(0.180 \text{ m})} \\ &= 0.687 \text{ m/s}. \end{aligned} \tag{7.54}$$

Discussion

Another way to solve this problem is to realize that the car's kinetic energy before it goes up the slope is converted partly to potential energy—that is, to take the final conditions in part (a) to be the initial conditions in part (b).

Note that, for conservative forces, we do not directly calculate the work they do; rather, we consider their effects through their corresponding potential energies, just as we did in Example 7.8. Note also that we do not consider details of the path taken—only the starting and ending points are important (as long as the path is not impossible). This assumption is usually a tremendous simplification, because the path may be complicated and forces may vary along the way.

PHET EXPLORATIONS

Energy Skate Park

Learn about conservation of energy with a skater dude! Build tracks, ramps and jumps for the skater and view the kinetic energy, potential energy and friction as he moves. You can also take the skater to different planets or even space!

Click to view content (https://openstax.org/books/college-physics-ap-courses-2e/pages/7-4-conservative-forces-and-potential-energy)

7.5 Nonconservative Forces

LEARNING OBJECTIVES

By the end of this section, you will be able to:

- Define nonconservative forces and explain how they affect mechanical energy.
- Show how the principle of conservation of energy can be applied by treating the conservative forces in terms of their potential energies and any nonconservative forces in terms of the work they do.

Nonconservative Forces and Friction

Forces are either conservative or nonconservative. Conservative forces were discussed in Conservative Forces and Potential Energy. A **nonconservative force** is one for which work depends on the path taken. Friction is a good example of a nonconservative force. As illustrated in Figure 7.13, work done against friction depends on the length of the path between the starting and ending points. Because of this dependence on path, there is no potential energy associated with nonconservative forces. An important characteristic is that the work done by a nonconservative force *adds or removes mechanical energy from a system*. **Friction**, for example, creates **thermal energy** that dissipates, removing energy from the system. Furthermore, even if the thermal energy is retained or captured, it cannot be fully converted back to work, so it is lost or not recoverable in that sense as well.

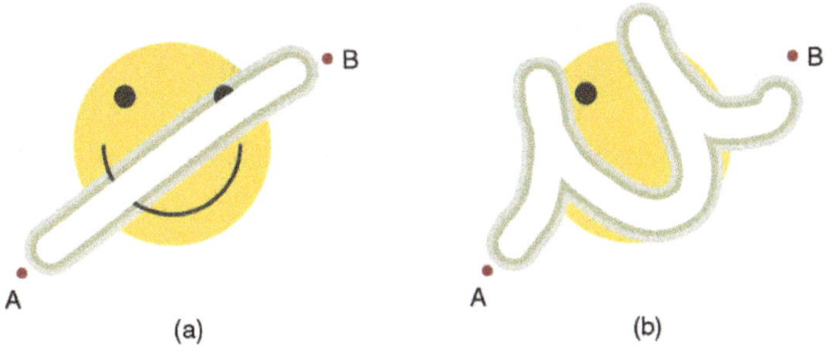

FIGURE 7.13 The amount of the happy face erased depends on the path taken by the eraser between points A and B, as does the work done against friction. Less work is done and less of the face is erased for the path in (a) than for the path in (b). The force here is friction, and most of the work goes into thermal energy that subsequently leaves the system (the happy face plus the eraser). The energy expended cannot be fully recovered.

How Nonconservative Forces Affect Mechanical Energy

Mechanical energy *may* not be conserved when nonconservative forces act. For example, when a car is brought to a stop by friction on level ground, it loses kinetic energy, which is dissipated as thermal energy, reducing its mechanical energy. Figure 7.14 compares the effects of conservative and nonconservative forces. We often choose to understand simpler systems such as that described in Figure 7.14(a) first before studying more complicated systems as in Figure 7.14(b).

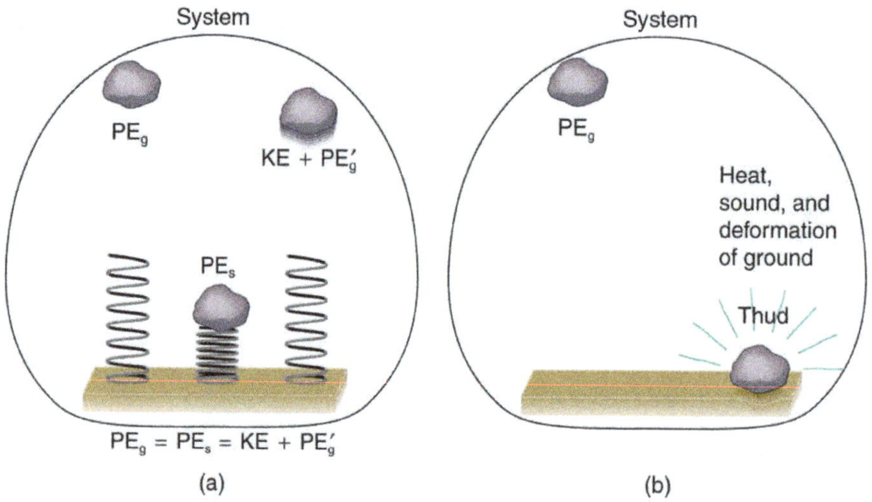

FIGURE 7.14 Comparison of the effects of conservative and nonconservative forces on the mechanical energy of a system. (a) A system with only conservative forces. When a rock is dropped onto a spring, its mechanical energy remains constant (neglecting air resistance) because the force in the spring is conservative. The spring can propel the rock back to its original height, where it once again has only potential energy due to gravity. (b) A system with nonconservative forces. When the same rock is dropped onto the ground, it is stopped by nonconservative forces that dissipate its mechanical energy as thermal energy, sound, and surface distortion. The rock has lost mechanical energy.

How the Work-Energy Theorem Applies

Now let us consider what form the work-energy theorem takes when both conservative and nonconservative forces act. We will see that the work done by nonconservative forces equals the change in the mechanical energy of a system. As noted in Kinetic Energy and the Work-Energy Theorem, the work-energy theorem states that the net work on a system equals the change in its kinetic energy, or $W_{\text{net}} = \Delta\text{KE}$. The net work is the sum of the work by nonconservative forces plus the work by conservative forces. That is,

$$W_{\text{net}} = W_{\text{nc}} + W_{\text{c}}, \quad 7.55$$

so that

$$W_{\text{nc}} + W_{\text{c}} = \Delta\text{KE}, \quad 7.56$$

where W_{nc} is the total work done by all nonconservative forces and W_{c} is the total work done by all conservative forces.

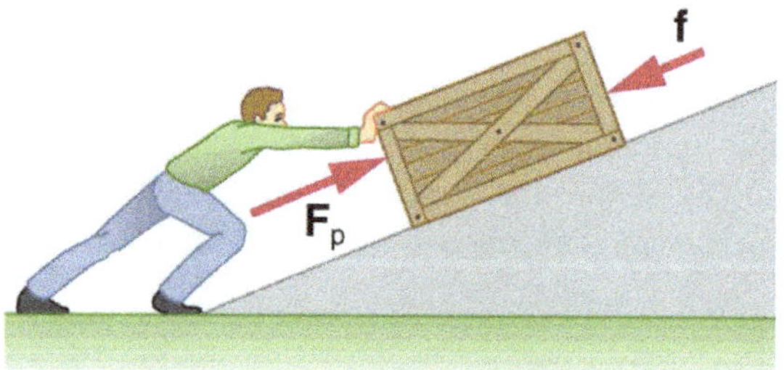

FIGURE 7.15 A person pushes a crate up a ramp, doing work on the crate. Friction and gravitational force (not shown) also do work on the crate; both forces oppose the person's push. As the crate is pushed up the ramp, it gains mechanical energy, implying that the work done by the person is greater than the work done by friction.

Consider Figure 7.15, in which a person pushes a crate up a ramp and is opposed by friction. As in the previous section, we note that work done by a conservative force comes from a loss of gravitational potential energy, so that $W_{\text{c}} = -\Delta\text{PE}$. Substituting this equation into the previous one and solving for W_{nc} gives

$$W_{\text{nc}} = \Delta\text{KE} + \Delta\text{PE}. \quad 7.57$$

This equation means that the total mechanical energy $(\text{KE} + \text{PE})$ changes by exactly the amount of work done by nonconservative forces. In Figure 7.15, this is the work done by the person minus the work done by friction. So even if energy is not conserved for the system of interest (such as the crate), we know that an equal amount of work was done to cause the change in total mechanical energy.

We rearrange $W_{nc} = \Delta KE + \Delta PE$ to obtain

$$KE_i + PE_i + W_{nc} = KE_f + PE_f. \quad 7.58$$

This means that the amount of work done by nonconservative forces adds to the mechanical energy of a system. If W_{nc} is positive, then mechanical energy is increased, such as when the person pushes the crate up the ramp in Figure 7.15. If W_{nc} is negative, then mechanical energy is decreased, such as when the rock hits the ground in Figure 7.14(b). If W_{nc} is zero, then mechanical energy is conserved, and nonconservative forces are balanced. For example, when you push a lawn mower at constant speed on level ground, your work done is removed by the work of friction, and the mower has a constant energy.

Applying Energy Conservation with Nonconservative Forces

When no change in potential energy occurs, applying $KE_i + PE_i + W_{nc} = KE_f + PE_f$ amounts to applying the work-energy theorem by setting the change in kinetic energy to be equal to the net work done on the system, which in the most general case includes both conservative and nonconservative forces. But when seeking instead to find a change in total mechanical energy in situations that involve changes in both potential and kinetic energy, the previous equation $KE_i + PE_i + W_{nc} = KE_f + PE_f$ says that you can start by finding the change in mechanical energy that would have resulted from just the conservative forces, including the potential energy changes, and add to it the work done, with the proper sign, by any nonconservative forces involved.

EXAMPLE 7.9

Calculating Distance Traveled: How Far a Baseball Player Slides

Consider the situation shown in Figure 7.16, where a baseball player slides to a stop on level ground. Using energy considerations, calculate the distance the 65.0-kg baseball player slides, given that his initial speed is 6.00 m/s and the force of friction against him is a constant 450 N.

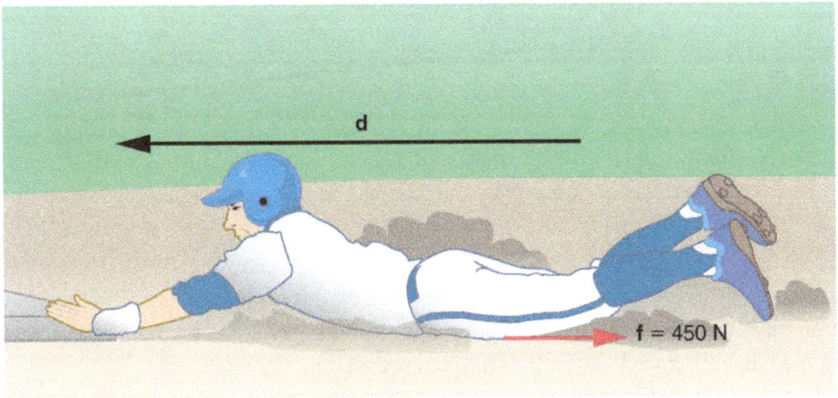

FIGURE 7.16 The baseball player slides to a stop in a distance d. In the process, friction removes the player's kinetic energy by doing an amount of work fd equal to the initial kinetic energy.

Strategy

Friction stops the player by converting his kinetic energy into other forms, including thermal energy. In terms of the work-energy theorem, the work done by friction, which is negative, is added to the initial kinetic energy to reduce it to zero. The work done by friction is negative, because $\mathbf{f}$ is in the opposite direction of the motion (that is, $\theta = 180°$, and so $\cos\theta = -1$). Thus $W_{nc} = -fd$. The equation simplifies to

$$\frac{1}{2}mv_i^2 - fd = 0 \quad 7.59$$

or

$$fd = \frac{1}{2}mv_i^2. \quad 7.60$$

This equation can now be solved for the distance d.

Solution

Solving the previous equation for d and substituting known values yields

$$\begin{aligned} d &= \frac{mv_i^2}{2f} \\ &= \frac{(65.0\text{ kg})(6.00\text{ m/s})^2}{(2)(450\text{ N})} \\ &= 2.60\text{ m.} \end{aligned} \quad 7.61$$

Discussion

The most important point of this example is that the amount of nonconservative work equals the change in mechanical energy. For example, you must work harder to stop a truck, with its large mechanical energy, than to stop a mosquito.

EXAMPLE 7.10

Calculating Distance Traveled: Sliding Up an Incline

Suppose that the player from Example 7.9 is running up a hill having a $5.00°$ incline upward with a surface similar to that in the baseball stadium. The player slides with the same initial speed, and the frictional force is still 450 N. Determine how far he slides.

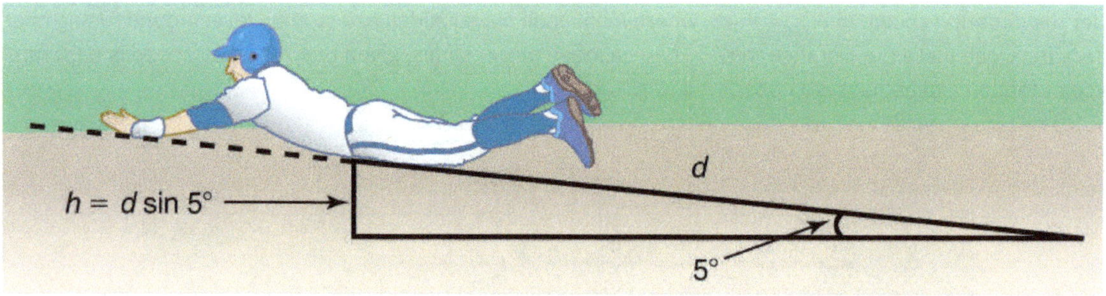

FIGURE 7.17 The same baseball player slides to a stop on a $5.00°$ slope.

Strategy

In this case, the work done by the nonconservative friction force on the player reduces the mechanical energy he has from his kinetic energy at zero height, to the final mechanical energy he has by moving through distance d to reach height h along the hill, with $h = d\sin 5.00°$. This is expressed by the equation

$$\text{KE}_i + \text{PE}_i + W_{nc} = \text{KE}_f + \text{PE}_f. \quad 7.62$$

Solution

The work done by friction is again $W_{nc} = -fd$; initially the potential energy is $\text{PE}_i = mg \cdot 0 = 0$ and the kinetic energy is $\text{KE}_i = \frac{1}{2}mv_i^2$; the final energy contributions are $\text{KE}_f = 0$ for the kinetic energy and $\text{PE}_f = mgh = mgd\sin\theta$ for the potential energy.

Substituting these values gives

$$\frac{1}{2}mv_i^2 + 0 + \left(-fd\right) = 0 + mgd\sin\theta. \quad 7.63$$

Solve this for d to obtain

$$
\begin{aligned}
d &= \frac{\left(\frac{1}{2}\right) m v_{\mathrm{i}}{}^{2}}{f + mg \sin\theta} \\
&= \frac{(0.5)(65.0\text{ kg})(6.00\text{ m/s})^{2}}{450\text{ N} + (65.0\text{ kg})(9.80\text{ m/s}^{2})\sin(5.00^{\circ})} \qquad 7.64 \\
&= 2.31\text{ m.}
\end{aligned}
$$

Discussion

As might have been expected, the player slides a shorter distance by sliding uphill. Note that the problem could also have been solved in terms of the forces directly and the work energy theorem, instead of using the potential energy. This method would have required combining the normal force and force of gravity vectors, which no longer cancel each other because they point in different directions, and friction, to find the net force. You could then use the net force and the net work to find the distance d that reduces the kinetic energy to zero. By applying conservation of energy and using the potential energy instead, we need only consider the gravitational potential energy mgh, without combining and resolving force vectors. This simplifies the solution considerably.

MAKING CONNECTIONS: TAKE-HOME INVESTIGATION—DETERMINING FRICTION FROM THE STOPPING DISTANCE

This experiment involves the conversion of gravitational potential energy into thermal energy. Use the ruler, book, and marble from Take-Home Investigation—Converting Potential to Kinetic Energy. In addition, you will need a foam cup with a small hole in the side, as shown in Figure 7.18. From the 10-cm position on the ruler, let the marble roll into the cup positioned at the bottom of the ruler. Measure the distance d the cup moves before stopping. What forces caused it to stop? What happened to the kinetic energy of the marble at the bottom of the ruler? Next, place the marble at the 20-cm and the 30-cm positions and again measure the distance the cup moves after the marble enters it. Plot the distance the cup moves versus the initial marble position on the ruler. Is this relationship linear?

With some simple assumptions, you can use these data to find the coefficient of kinetic friction μ_{k} of the cup on the table. The force of friction f on the cup is $\mu_{\mathrm{k}} N$, where the normal force N is just the weight of the cup plus the marble. The normal force and force of gravity do no work because they are perpendicular to the displacement of the cup, which moves horizontally. The work done by friction is fd. You will need the mass of the marble as well to calculate its initial kinetic energy.

It is interesting to do the above experiment also with a steel marble (or ball bearing). Releasing it from the same positions on the ruler as you did with the glass marble, is the velocity of this steel marble the same as the velocity of the marble at the bottom of the ruler? Is the distance the cup moves proportional to the mass of the steel and glass marbles?

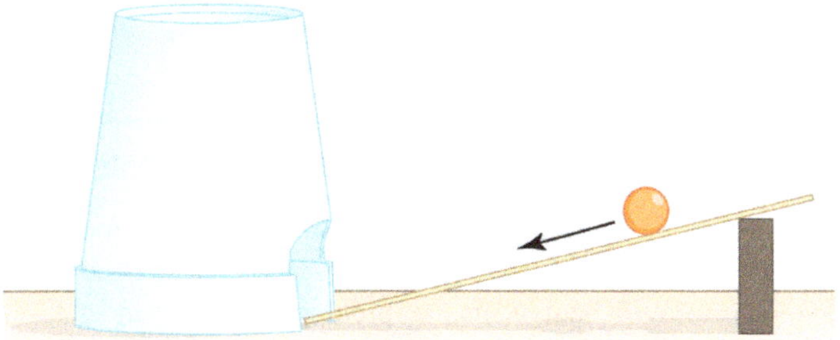

FIGURE 7.18 Rolling a marble down a ruler into a foam cup.

PHET EXPLORATIONS

The Ramp

Explore forces, energy and work as you push household objects up and down a ramp. Lower and raise the ramp to see how the angle of inclination affects the parallel forces acting on the file cabinet. Graphs show forces, energy and work.

Click to view content (https://openstax.org/l/21ramp).

7.6 Conservation of Energy

LEARNING OBJECTIVES

By the end of this section, you will be able to:

- Explain the law of the conservation of energy.
- Describe some of the many forms of energy.
- Define efficiency of an energy conversion process as the fraction left as useful energy or work, rather than being transformed, for example, into thermal energy.

Law of Conservation of Energy

Energy, as we have noted, is conserved, making it one of the most important physical quantities in nature. The **law of conservation of energy** can be stated as follows:

Total energy is constant in any process. It may change in form or be transferred from one system to another, but the total remains the same.

We have explored some forms of energy and some ways it can be transferred from one system to another. This exploration led to the definition of two major types of energy—mechanical energy $(\mathrm{KE} + \mathrm{PE})$ and energy transferred via work done by nonconservative forces (W_{nc}). But energy takes *many* other forms, manifesting itself in *many* different ways, and we need to be able to deal with all of these before we can write an equation for the above general statement of the conservation of energy.

Other Forms of Energy than Mechanical Energy

At this point, we deal with all other forms of energy by lumping them into a single group called other energy (OE). Then we can state the conservation of energy in equation form as

$$\mathrm{KE_i} + \mathrm{PE_i} + W_{\mathrm{nc}} + \mathrm{OE_i} = \mathrm{KE_f} + \mathrm{PE_f} + \mathrm{OE_f}. \tag{7.65}$$

All types of energy and work can be included in this very general statement of conservation of energy. Kinetic energy is KE, work done by a conservative force is represented by PE, work done by nonconservative forces is W_{nc}, and all other energies are included as OE. This equation applies to all previous examples; in those situations OE was constant, and so it subtracted out and was not directly considered.

MAKING CONNECTIONS: USEFULNESS OF THE ENERGY CONSERVATION PRINCIPLE

The fact that energy is conserved and has many forms makes it very important. You will find that energy is discussed in many contexts, because it is involved in all processes. It will also become apparent that many situations are best understood in terms of energy and that problems are often most easily conceptualized and solved by considering energy.

When does OE play a role? One example occurs when a person eats. Food is oxidized with the release of carbon dioxide, water, and energy. Some of this chemical energy is converted to kinetic energy when the person moves, to potential energy when the person changes altitude, and to thermal energy (another form of OE).

Some of the Many Forms of Energy

What are some other forms of energy? You can probably name a number of forms of energy not yet discussed. Many of these will be covered in later chapters, but let us detail a few here. **Electrical energy** is a common form that is converted to many other forms and does work in a wide range of practical situations. Fuels, such as gasoline and food, carry **chemical energy** that can be transferred to a system through oxidation. Chemical fuel can also produce electrical energy, such as in batteries. Batteries can in turn produce light, which is a very pure form of energy. Most energy sources on Earth are in fact stored energy from the energy we receive from the Sun. We sometimes refer to this as **radiant energy**, or electromagnetic radiation, which includes visible light, infrared, and ultraviolet radiation. **Nuclear energy** comes from processes that convert measurable amounts of mass into energy. Nuclear energy is transformed into the energy of sunlight, into electrical energy in power plants, and into the energy of the heat transfer and blast in weapons. Atoms and molecules inside all objects are in random motion. This internal mechanical energy from the random motions is called **thermal energy**, because it is related to the temperature of the object. These and all other forms of energy can be converted into one another and can do work.

Table 7.1 gives the amount of energy stored, used, or released from various objects and in various phenomena. The range of energies and the variety of types and situations is impressive.

PROBLEM-SOLVING STRATEGIES FOR ENERGY

You will find the following problem-solving strategies useful whenever you deal with energy. The strategies help in organizing and reinforcing energy concepts. In fact, they are used in the examples presented in this chapter. The familiar general problem-solving strategies presented earlier—involving identifying physical principles, knowns, and unknowns, checking units, and so on—continue to be relevant here.

Step 1. Determine the system of interest and identify what information is given and what quantity is to be calculated. A sketch will help.

Step 2. Examine all the forces involved and determine whether you know or are given the potential energy from the work done by the forces. Then use step 3 or step 4.

Step 3. If you know the potential energies for the forces that enter into the problem, then forces are all conservative, and you can apply conservation of mechanical energy simply in terms of potential and kinetic energy. The equation expressing conservation of energy is

$$\mathrm{KE_i} + \mathrm{PE_i} = \mathrm{KE_f} + \mathrm{PE_f}. \quad 7.66$$

Step 4. If you know the potential energy for only some of the forces, possibly because some of them are nonconservative and do not have a potential energy, or if there are other energies that are not easily treated in terms of force and work, then the conservation of energy law in its most general form must be used.

$$\mathrm{KE_i} + \mathrm{PE_i} + W_{\mathrm{nc}} + \mathrm{OE_i} = \mathrm{KE_f} + \mathrm{PE_f} + \mathrm{OE_f}. \quad 7.67$$

In most problems, one or more of the terms is zero, simplifying its solution. Do not calculate W_{c}, the work done by conservative forces; it is already incorporated in the PE terms.

Step 5. You have already identified the types of work and energy involved (in step 2). Before solving for the unknown, *eliminate terms wherever possible* to simplify the algebra. For example, choose $h = 0$ at either the initial or final point, so that $\mathrm{PE_g}$ is zero there. Then solve for the unknown in the customary manner.

Step 6. *Check the answer to see if it is reasonable.* Once you have solved a problem, reexamine the forms of work and energy to see if you have set up the conservation of energy equation correctly. For example, work done against friction should be negative, potential energy at the bottom of a hill should be less than that at the top, and so on. Also check to see that the numerical value obtained is reasonable. For example, the final speed of a skateboarder who coasts down a 3-m-high ramp could reasonably be 20 km/h, but *not* 80 km/h.

Transformation of Energy

The transformation of energy from one form into others is happening all the time. The chemical energy in food is converted into thermal energy through metabolism; light energy is converted into chemical energy through photosynthesis. In a larger example, the chemical energy contained in coal is converted into thermal energy as it burns to turn water into steam in a boiler. This thermal energy in the steam in turn is converted to mechanical energy as it spins a turbine, which is connected to a generator to produce electrical energy. (In all of these examples, not all of the initial energy is converted into the forms mentioned. This important point is discussed later in this section.)

Another example of energy conversion occurs in a solar cell. Sunlight impinging on a solar cell (see Figure 7.19) produces electricity, which in turn can be used to run an electric motor. Energy is converted from the primary source of solar energy into electrical energy and then into mechanical energy.

FIGURE 7.19 Solar energy is converted into electrical energy by solar cells, which is used to run a motor in this solar-power aircraft. (credit: NASA)

Object/phenomenon	Energy in joules
Big Bang	10^{68}
Energy released in a supernova	10^{44}
Fusion of all the hydrogen in Earth's oceans	10^{34}
Annual world energy use	4×10^{20}
Large fusion bomb (9 megaton)	3.8×10^{16}
1 kg hydrogen (fusion to helium)	6.4×10^{14}
1 kg uranium (nuclear fission)	8.0×10^{13}
Hiroshima-size fission bomb (10 kiloton)	4.2×10^{13}
90,000-metric ton aircraft carrier at 30 knots	1.1×10^{10}
1 barrel crude oil	5.9×10^{9}
1 ton TNT	4.2×10^{9}

TABLE 7.1 Energy of Various Objects and Phenomena

Object/phenomenon	Energy in joules
1 gallon of gasoline	1.2×10^8
Daily home electricity use (developed countries)	7×10^7
Daily adult food intake (recommended)	1.2×10^7
1000-kg car at 90 km/h	3.1×10^5
1 g fat (9.3 kcal)	3.9×10^4
ATP hydrolysis reaction	3.2×10^4
1 g carbohydrate (4.1 kcal)	1.7×10^4
1 g protein (4.1 kcal)	1.7×10^4
Tennis ball at 100 km/h	22
Mosquito $\left(10^{-2}\text{ g at }0.5\text{ m/s}\right)$	1.3×10^{-6}
Single electron in a TV tube beam	4.0×10^{-15}
Energy to break one DNA strand	10^{-19}

TABLE 7.1 Energy of Various Objects and Phenomena

Efficiency

Even though energy is conserved in an energy conversion process, the output of *useful energy* or work will be less than the energy input. The **efficiency** Eff of an energy conversion process is defined as

$$\text{Efficiency}(Eff) = \frac{\text{useful energy or work output}}{\text{total energy input}} = \frac{W_{\text{out}}}{E_{\text{in}}}. \tag{7.68}$$

Table 7.2 lists some efficiencies of mechanical devices and human activities. In a coal-fired power plant, for example, about 40% of the chemical energy in the coal becomes useful electrical energy. The other 60% transforms into other (perhaps less useful) energy forms, such as thermal energy, which is then released to the environment through combustion gases and cooling towers.

Activity/device	Efficiency (%)[1]
Cycling and climbing	20
Swimming, surface	2

TABLE 7.2 Efficiency of the Human Body and Mechanical Devices

1 Representative values

Activity/device	Efficiency (%)[1]
Swimming, submerged	4
Shoveling	3
Weightlifting	9
Steam engine	17
Gasoline engine	30
Diesel engine	35
Nuclear power plant	35
Coal power plant	42
Electric motor	98
Compact fluorescent light	20
Gas heater (residential)	90
Solar cell	10

TABLE 7.2 Efficiency of the Human Body and Mechanical Devices

PHET EXPLORATIONS

Masses and Springs

A realistic mass and spring laboratory. Hang masses from springs and adjust the spring stiffness and damping. You can even slow time. Transport the lab to different planets. A chart shows the kinetic, potential, and thermal energies for each spring.

Click to view content (https://openstax.org/books/college-physics-ap-courses-2e/pages/7-6-conservation-of-energy)

7.7 Power

LEARNING OBJECTIVES

By the end of this section, you will be able to:

- Calculate power by calculating changes in energy over time.
- Examine power consumption and calculations of the cost of energy consumed.

What is Power?

Power—the word conjures up many images: a professional football player muscling aside his opponent, a dragster roaring away from the starting line, a volcano blowing its lava into the atmosphere, or a rocket blasting off, as in Figure 7.20.

FIGURE 7.20 This powerful rocket on the Space Shuttle *Endeavor* did work and consumed energy at a very high rate. (credit: NASA)

These images of power have in common the rapid performance of work, consistent with the scientific definition of **power** (P) as the rate at which work is done.

POWER

Power is the rate at which work is done.

$$P = \frac{W}{t} \tag{7.69}$$

The SI unit for power is the **watt** (W), where 1 watt equals 1 joule/second ($1\ \text{W} = 1\ \text{J/s}$).

Because work is energy transfer, power is also the rate at which energy is expended. A 60-W light bulb, for example, expends 60 J of energy per second. Great power means a large amount of work or energy developed in a short time. For example, when a powerful car accelerates rapidly, it does a large amount of work and consumes a large amount of fuel in a short time.

Calculating Power from Energy

EXAMPLE 7.11

Calculating the Power to Climb Stairs

What is the power output for a 60.0-kg woman who runs up a 3.00 m high flight of stairs in 3.50 s, starting from rest but having a final speed of 2.00 m/s? (See Figure 7.21.)

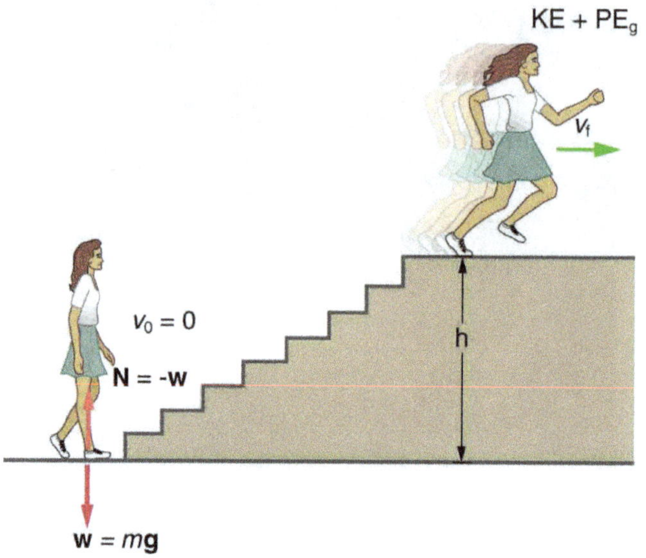

FIGURE 7.21 When this woman runs upstairs starting from rest, she converts the chemical energy originally from food into kinetic energy and gravitational potential energy. Her power output depends on how fast she does this.

Strategy and Concept

The work going into mechanical energy is $W = \text{KE} + \text{PE}$. At the bottom of the stairs, we take both KE and PE_g as initially zero; thus, $W = \text{KE}_\text{f} + \text{PE}_\text{g} = \frac{1}{2}mv_\text{f}^2 + mgh$, where h is the vertical height of the stairs. Because all terms are given, we can calculate W and then divide it by time to get power.

Solution

Substituting the expression for W into the definition of power given in the previous equation, $P = W/t$ yields

$$P = \frac{W}{t} = \frac{\frac{1}{2}mv_\text{f}^2 + mgh}{t}. \tag{7.70}$$

Entering known values yields

$$\begin{aligned} P &= \frac{0.5(60.0\text{ kg})(2.00\text{ m/s})^2 + (60.0\text{ kg})\left(9.80\text{ m/s}^2\right)(3.00\text{ m})}{3.50\text{ s}} \\ &= \frac{120\text{ J} + 1764\text{ J}}{3.50\text{ s}} \\ &= 538\text{ W}. \end{aligned} \tag{7.71}$$

Discussion

The woman does 1764 J of work to move up the stairs compared with only 120 J to increase her kinetic energy; thus, most of her power output is required for climbing rather than accelerating.

It is impressive that this woman's useful power output is slightly less than 1 **horsepower** $(1\text{ hp} = 746\text{ W})$! People can generate more than a horsepower with their leg muscles for short periods of time by rapidly converting available blood sugar and oxygen into work output. (A horse can put out 1 hp for hours on end.) Once oxygen is depleted, power output decreases and the person begins to breathe rapidly to obtain oxygen to metabolize more food—this is known as the *aerobic* stage of exercise. If the woman climbed the stairs slowly, then her power output would be much less, although the amount of work done would be the same.

MAKING CONNECTIONS: TAKE-HOME INVESTIGATION—MEASURE YOUR POWER RATING

Determine your own power rating by measuring the time it takes you to climb a flight of stairs. We will ignore the gain in kinetic energy, as the above example showed that it was a small portion of the energy gain. Don't expect that your output will be more than about 0.5 hp.

Examples of Power

Examples of power are limited only by the imagination, because there are as many types as there are forms of work and energy. (See Table 7.3 for some examples.) Sunlight reaching Earth's surface carries a maximum power of about 1.3 kilowatts per square meter $(\mathrm{kW/m^2})$. A tiny fraction of this is retained by Earth over the long term. Our consumption rate of fossil fuels is far greater than the rate at which they are stored, so it is inevitable that they will be depleted. Power implies that energy is transferred, perhaps changing form. It is never possible to change one form completely into another without losing some of it as thermal energy. For example, a 60-W incandescent bulb converts only 5 W of electrical power to light, with 55 W dissipating into thermal energy. Furthermore, the typical electric power plant converts only 35 to 40% of its fuel into electricity. The remainder becomes a huge amount of thermal energy that must be dispersed as heat transfer, as rapidly as it is created. A coal-fired power plant may produce 1000 megawatts; 1 megawatt (MW) is $10^6\ \mathrm{W}$ of electric power. But the power plant consumes chemical energy at a rate of about 2500 MW, creating heat transfer to the surroundings at a rate of 1500 MW. (See Figure 7.22.)

FIGURE 7.22 Tremendous amounts of electric power are generated by coal-fired power plants such as this one in China, but an even larger amount of power goes into heat transfer to the surroundings. The large cooling towers here are needed to transfer heat as rapidly as it is produced. The transfer of heat is not unique to coal plants but is an unavoidable consequence of generating electric power from any fuel—nuclear, coal, oil, natural gas, or the like. (credit: Kleinolive, Wikimedia Commons)

Object or Phenomenon	Power in Watts
Supernova (at peak)	5×10^{37}
Milky Way galaxy	10^{37}
Crab Nebula pulsar	10^{28}
The Sun	4×10^{26}
Volcanic eruption (maximum)	4×10^{15}
Lightning bolt	2×10^{12}

TABLE 7.3 Power Output or Consumption

Object or Phenomenon	Power in Watts
Nuclear power plant (total electric and heat transfer)	3×10^{9}
Aircraft carrier (total useful and heat transfer)	10^{8}
Dragster (total useful and heat transfer)	2×10^{6}
Car (total useful and heat transfer)	8×10^{4}
Football player (total useful and heat transfer)	5×10^{3}
Clothes dryer	4×10^{3}
Person at rest (all heat transfer)	100
Typical incandescent light bulb (total useful and heat transfer)	60
Heart, person at rest (total useful and heat transfer)	8
Electric clock	3
Pocket calculator	10^{-3}

TABLE 7.3 Power Output or Consumption

Power and Energy Consumption

We usually have to pay for the energy we use. It is interesting and easy to estimate the cost of energy for an electrical appliance if its power consumption rate and time used are known. The higher the power consumption rate and the longer the appliance is used, the greater the cost of that appliance. The power consumption rate is $P = W/t = E/t$, where E is the energy supplied by the electricity company. So the energy consumed over a time t is

$$E = Pt. \tag{7.72}$$

Electricity bills state the energy used in units of **kilowatt-hours** $(\text{kW}\cdot\text{h})$, which is the product of power in kilowatts and time in hours. This unit is convenient because electrical power consumption at the kilowatt level for hours at a time is typical.

EXAMPLE 7.12

Calculating Energy Costs

What is the cost of running a 0.200-kW computer 6.00 h per day for 30.0 d if the cost of electricity is $0.120 per $\text{kW}\cdot\text{h}$?

Strategy

Cost is based on energy consumed; thus, we must find E from $E = Pt$ and then calculate the cost. Because electrical energy is expressed in $\text{kW}\cdot\text{h}$, at the start of a problem such as this it is convenient to convert the units into kW and hours.

Solution

The energy consumed in $\text{kW} \cdot \text{h}$ is

$$\begin{aligned} E &= Pt = (0.200\ \text{kW})(6.00\ \text{h/d})(30.0\ \text{d}) \\ &= 36.0\ \text{kW} \cdot \text{h}, \end{aligned} \tag{7.73}$$

and the cost is simply given by

$$\text{cost} = (36.0\ \text{kW} \cdot \text{h})(\$0.120\ \text{per kW} \cdot \text{h}) = \$4.32\ \text{per month.} \tag{7.74}$$

Discussion

The cost of using the computer in this example is neither exorbitant nor negligible. It is clear that the cost is a combination of power and time. When both are high, such as for an air conditioner in the summer, the cost is high.

The motivation to save energy has become more compelling with its ever-increasing price. Armed with the knowledge that energy consumed is the product of power and time, you can estimate costs for yourself and make the necessary value judgments about where to save energy. Either power or time must be reduced. It is most cost-effective to limit the use of high-power devices that normally operate for long periods of time, such as water heaters and air conditioners. This would not include relatively high power devices like toasters, because they are on only a few minutes per day. It would also not include electric clocks, in spite of their 24-hour-per-day usage, because they are very low power devices. It is sometimes possible to use devices that have greater efficiencies—that is, devices that consume less power to accomplish the same task. One example is the compact fluorescent light bulb, which produces over four times more light per watt of power consumed than its incandescent cousin.

Modern civilization depends on energy, but current levels of energy consumption and production are not sustainable. The likelihood of a link between global warming and fossil fuel use (with its concomitant production of carbon dioxide), has made reduction in energy use as well as a shift to non-fossil fuels of the utmost importance. Even though energy in an isolated system is a conserved quantity, the final result of most energy transformations is waste heat transfer to the environment, which is no longer useful for doing work. As we will discuss in more detail in Thermodynamics, the potential for energy to produce useful work has been "degraded" in the energy transformation.

7.8 Work, Energy, and Power in Humans

LEARNING OBJECTIVES

By the end of this section, you will be able to:

- Explain the human body's consumption of energy when at rest vs. when engaged in activities that do useful work.
- Calculate the conversion of chemical energy in food into useful work.

Energy Conversion in Humans

Our own bodies, like all living organisms, are energy conversion machines. Conservation of energy implies that the chemical energy stored in food is converted into work, thermal energy, and/or stored as chemical energy in fatty tissue. (See Figure 7.23.) The fraction going into each form depends both on how much we eat and on our level of physical activity. If we eat more than is needed to do work and stay warm, the remainder goes into body fat.

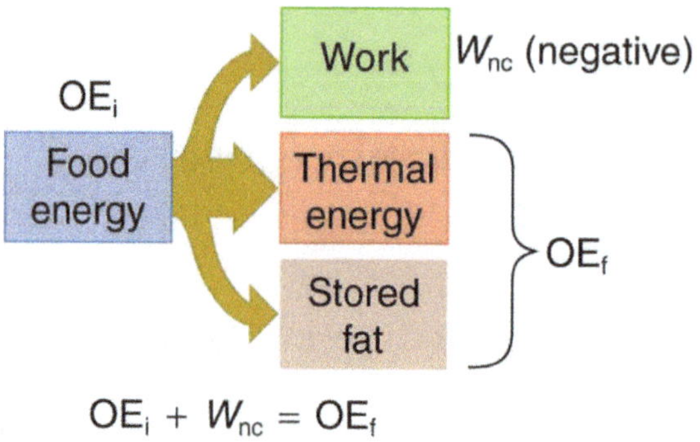

FIGURE 7.23 Energy consumed by humans is converted to work, thermal energy, and stored fat. By far the largest fraction goes to thermal energy, although the fraction varies depending on the type of physical activity.

Power Consumed at Rest

The *rate* at which the body uses food energy to sustain life and to do different activities is called the **metabolic rate**. The total energy conversion rate of a person *at rest* is called the **basal metabolic rate** (BMR) and is divided among various systems in the body, as shown in Table 7.4. The largest fraction goes to the liver and spleen, with the brain coming next. Of course, during vigorous exercise, the energy consumption of the skeletal muscles and heart increase markedly. About 75% of the calories burned in a day go into these basic functions. The BMR is a function of age, gender, total body weight, and amount of muscle mass (which burns more calories than body fat). Athletes have a greater BMR due to this last factor.

Organ	Power consumed at rest (W)	Oxygen consumption (mL/min)	Percent of BMR
Liver & spleen	23	67	27
Brain	16	47	19
Skeletal muscle	15	45	18
Kidney	9	26	10
Heart	6	17	7
Other	16	48	19
Totals	85 W	250 mL/min	100%

TABLE 7.4 Basal Metabolic Rates (BMR)

Energy consumption is directly proportional to oxygen consumption because the digestive process is basically one of oxidizing food. We can measure the energy people use during various activities by measuring their oxygen use. (See Figure 7.24.) Approximately 20 kJ of energy are produced for each liter of oxygen consumed, independent of the type of food. Table 7.5 shows energy and oxygen consumption rates (power expended) for a variety of activities.

Power of Doing Useful Work

Work done by a person is sometimes called **useful work**, which is *work done on the outside world,* such as lifting weights. Useful work requires a force exerted through a distance on the outside world, and so it excludes internal work, such as that done by the heart when pumping blood. Useful work does include that done in climbing stairs or accelerating to a full run, because these are accomplished by exerting forces on the outside world. Forces exerted by the body are nonconservative, so that they can change the mechanical energy $(\mathrm{KE} + \mathrm{PE})$ of the system worked upon, and this is often the goal. A baseball player throwing a ball, for example, increases both the ball's kinetic and potential energy.

If a person needs more energy than they consume, such as when doing vigorous work, the body must draw upon the chemical energy stored in fat. So exercise can be helpful in losing fat. However, the amount of exercise needed to produce a loss in fat, or to burn off extra calories consumed that day, can be large, as Example 7.13 illustrates.

EXAMPLE 7.13

Calculating Weight Loss from Exercising

If a person who normally requires an average of 12,000 kJ (3000 kcal) of food energy per day consumes 13,000 kJ per day, they will steadily add body fat. How much bicycling per day is required to work off this extra 1000 kJ?

Solution

Table 7.5 states that 400 W are used when cycling at a moderate speed. The time required to work off 1000 kJ at this rate is then

$$\text{Time} = \frac{\text{energy}}{\left(\frac{\text{energy}}{\text{time}}\right)} = \frac{1000\ \text{kJ}}{400\ \text{W}} = 2500\ \text{s} = 42\ \text{min}. \tag{7.75}$$

Discussion

If this person uses more energy than they consume, the person's body will obtain the needed energy by metabolizing body fat. If the person uses 13,000 kJ but consumes only 12,000 kJ, then the amount of fat loss will be

$$\text{Fat loss} = (1000\ \text{kJ})\left(\frac{1.0\ \text{g fat}}{39\ \text{kJ}}\right) = 26\ \text{g}, \tag{7.76}$$

assuming the energy content of fat to be 39 kJ/g.

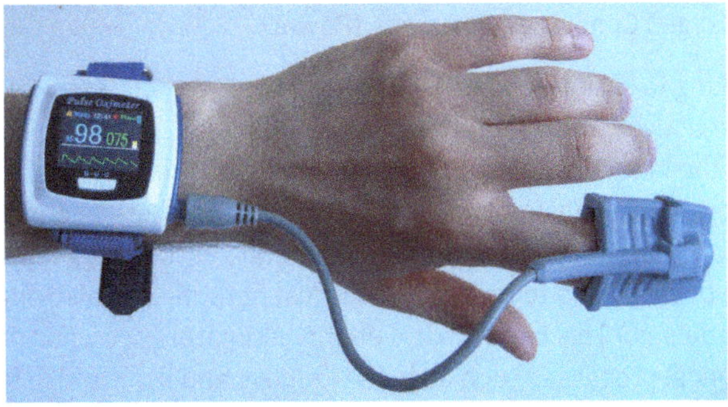

FIGURE 7.24 A pulse oxymeter is an apparatus that measures the amount of oxygen in blood. A knowledge of oxygen and carbon dioxide levels indicates a person's metabolic rate, which is the rate at which food energy is converted to another form. Such measurements can indicate the level of athletic conditioning as well as certain medical problems. (credit: UusiAjaja, Wikimedia Commons)

Activity	Energy consumption in watts	Oxygen consumption in liters O_2/min
Sleeping	83	0.24
Sitting at rest	120	0.34
Standing relaxed	125	0.36
Sitting in class	210	0.60

TABLE 7.5 Energy and Oxygen Consumption Rates[2] (Power)

2 for a 76-kg male with typical metabolic functions

Activity	Energy consumption in watts	Oxygen consumption in liters O_2/min
Walking (5 km/h)	280	0.80
Cycling (13–18 km/h)	400	1.14
Shivering	425	1.21
Playing tennis	440	1.26
Swimming breaststroke	475	1.36
Ice skating (14.5 km/h)	545	1.56
Climbing stairs (116/min)	685	1.96
Cycling (21 km/h)	700	2.00
Running cross-country	740	2.12
Playing basketball	800	2.28
Cycling, professional racer	1855	5.30
Sprinting	2415	6.90

TABLE 7.5 Energy and Oxygen Consumption Rates[2] (Power)

All bodily functions, from thinking to lifting weights, require energy. (See Figure 7.25.) The many small muscle actions accompanying all quiet activity, from sleeping to head scratching, ultimately become thermal energy, as do less visible muscle actions by the heart, lungs, and digestive tract. Shivering, in fact, is an involuntary response to low body temperature that pits muscles against one another to produce thermal energy in the body (and do no work). The kidneys and liver consume a surprising amount of energy, but the biggest surprise of all is that a full 25% of all energy consumed by the body is used to maintain electrical potentials in all living cells. (Nerve cells use this electrical potential in nerve impulses.) This bioelectrical energy ultimately becomes mostly thermal energy, but some is utilized to power chemical processes such as in the kidneys and liver, and in fat production.

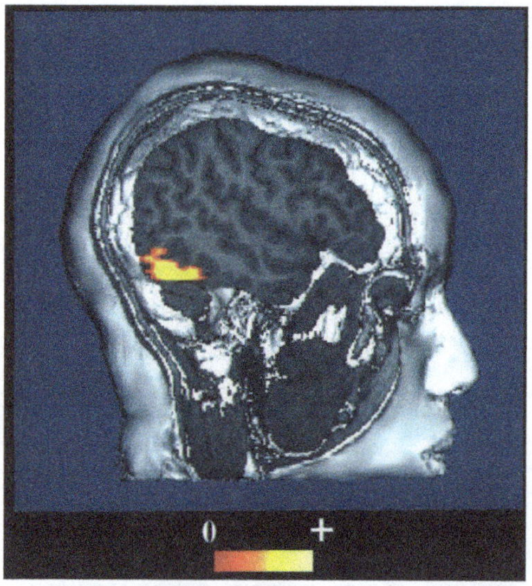

FIGURE 7.25 This fMRI scan shows an increased level of energy consumption in the vision center of the brain. Here, the patient was being

asked to recognize faces. (credit: NIH via Wikimedia Commons)

7.9 World Energy Use

LEARNING OBJECTIVES

By the end of this section, you will be able to:

- Describe the distinction between renewable and nonrenewable energy sources.
- Explain why the inevitable conversion of energy to less useful forms makes it necessary to conserve energy resources.

Energy is an important ingredient in all phases of society. We live in a very interdependent world, and access to adequate and reliable energy resources is crucial for economic growth and for maintaining the quality of our lives. But current levels of energy consumption and production are not sustainable. Depending on the data source, estimates indicate that about 31–35% of the world's energy comes from oil, and much of that goes to transportation uses. This is a reduction by a few percentage points from ten years ago. Oil prices are dependent as much upon new (or foreseen) discoveries as they are upon political events and situations around the world. The U.S., with 4.25% of the world's population, consumes 21% of the world's oil production per year.

Renewable and Nonrenewable Energy Sources

The principal energy resources used in the world are shown in Figure 7.26. The fuel mix has changed over the years but now is dominated by oil, although natural gas and solar contributions are increasing. **Renewable forms of energy** are those sources that cannot be used up, such as water, wind, solar, and biomass. About 85% of our energy comes from nonrenewable **fossil fuels**—oil, natural gas, coal. The likelihood of a link between global warming and fossil fuel use, with its production of carbon dioxide through combustion, has made, in the eyes of many scientists, a shift to non-fossil fuels of utmost importance—but it will not be easy.

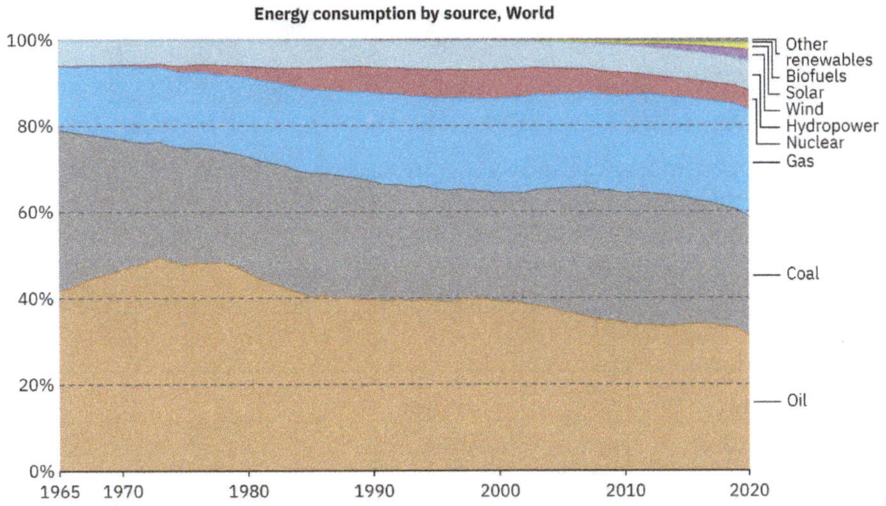

FIGURE 7.26 World energy consumption by source, in billions of kilowatt-hours: 2006. (credit: KVDP)

The World's Growing Energy Needs

World energy consumption continues to rise, especially in the developing countries. (See Figure 7.27.) Global demand for energy has tripled in the past 50 years and might triple again in the next 30 years. While much of this growth will come from the rapidly booming economies of China and India, many of the developed countries, especially those in Europe, are hoping to meet their energy needs by expanding the use of renewable sources. Although presently only a small percentage, renewable energy is growing very fast, especially wind energy. For example, Germany plans to meet 65% of its power and 30% of its overall energy needs with renewable resources by the year 2030. (See Figure 7.28.) Energy is a key constraint in the rapid economic growth of China and India. In 2003, China surpassed Japan as the world's second largest consumer of oil. However, over 1/3 of this is imported. Unlike most Western countries, coal dominates the commercial energy resources of China, accounting for 2/3 of its energy consumption. In 2009 China surpassed the United States as the largest generator of CO_2. In India, the main energy resources are biomass (wood and dung) and coal. Half of India's oil is imported. About 70% of India's electricity is generated by highly polluting coal. Yet there are sizeable strides being made in renewable energy. India has a rapidly growing wind energy base, and it has the largest solar cooking program in the world. China has invested substantially in building solar collection farms as well as hydroelectric plants.

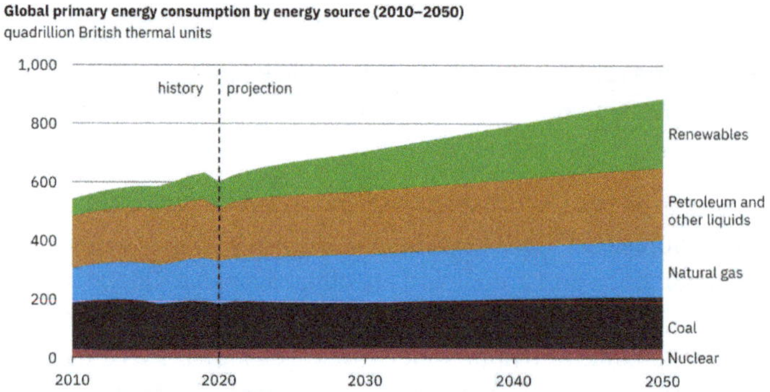

FIGURE 7.27 Past and projected world energy use (source: Based on data from U.S. Energy Information Administration, 2021)

FIGURE 7.28 Solar cell arrays at a power plant in California (credit: Bureau of Land Management, Flickr)

Table 7.6 displays the 2020 commercial energy mix by country for some of the prime energy users in the world. While non-renewable sources dominate, some countries get a sizeable percentage of their electricity from renewable resources. For example, about two-thirds of New Zealand's electricity demand is met by hydroelectric. Only 10% of the U.S. electricity is generated by renewable resources, primarily hydroelectric. It is difficult to determine total sources and consumers of energy in many countries, and estimates vary somewhat by data source and type of measurement.

Country	Consumption, in EJ (10^{18} J)	Oil	Natural Gas	Coal	Nuclear	Hydro	Other Renewables
Australia	5.6	1.8%	1.5%	1.7%	0%	0.1%	0.5%
Brazil	12	4.6%	1.2%	0.6%	0.1%	3.5%	2%
China	145.5	28.5%	11.9%	82.3%	3.3%	11.7%	7.8%
Egypt	3.7	1.3%	2.1%	0.03%	0%	0.1%	0.1%
Germany	12.1	4.2%	3.1%	1.9%	0.6%	0.2%	2.2%
India	31.99	9%	2.2%	17.5%	0.4%	1.5%	1.4%
Indonesia	8.1	2.8%	1.5%	3.3%	0%	0.2%	0.4%

TABLE 7.6 Energy Consumption—Selected Countries (2020)

Country	Consumption, in EJ (10^{18} J)	Oil	Natural Gas	Coal	Nuclear	Hydro	Other Renewables
Japan	17	6.5%	3.8%	4.6%	0.4%	0.7%	1.1%
United Kingdom	6.9	2.4%	2.6%	0.2%	0.5%	0.1%	1.2%
Russia	28.3	6.4%	14.8%	3.2%	1.9%	1.9%	0.5%
U.S.	87.8	32.5%	30%	9.2%	7.4%	2.6%	6.2%
World	**557.1**	**174.2%**	**137.6%**	**151.4%**	**24%**	**38.2%**	**31.7%**

TABLE 7.6 Energy Consumption—Selected Countries (2020)

Energy and Economic Well-being

Economic well-being is dependent upon energy use, and in most countries higher standards of living, as measured by GDP (gross domestic product) per capita, are matched by higher levels of energy consumption per capita. This is borne out in Figure 7.29. Increased efficiency of energy use will change this dependency. A global problem is balancing energy resource development against the harmful effects upon the environment in its extraction and use.

New and diversified energy sources do, however, greatly increase economic opportunity and stability. First, the extensive employment opportunities in renewable energy make it one of the most sustainable and secure fields to enter. Second, renewable energy provides countries and localities with increased levels of resiliency in the face of natural disasters, conflict, or other disruptions. The 21st century has already seen major economic impacts from energy disruptions: Hurricane Katrina, Superstorm Sandy, various wildfires, Hurricane Maria, and the 2021 Texas Winter Storm demonstrate the vulnerability of United States power systems. Diversifying energy sources through renewables and other fossil-fuel alternatives brings power grids and transportation systems back online much more quickly, saving lives and enabling a more swift return to economic operations. And as critical emerging information infrastructure, such as data centers, requires more of the world's energy, supplying those growing systems during normal operations and crises will be increasingly important.

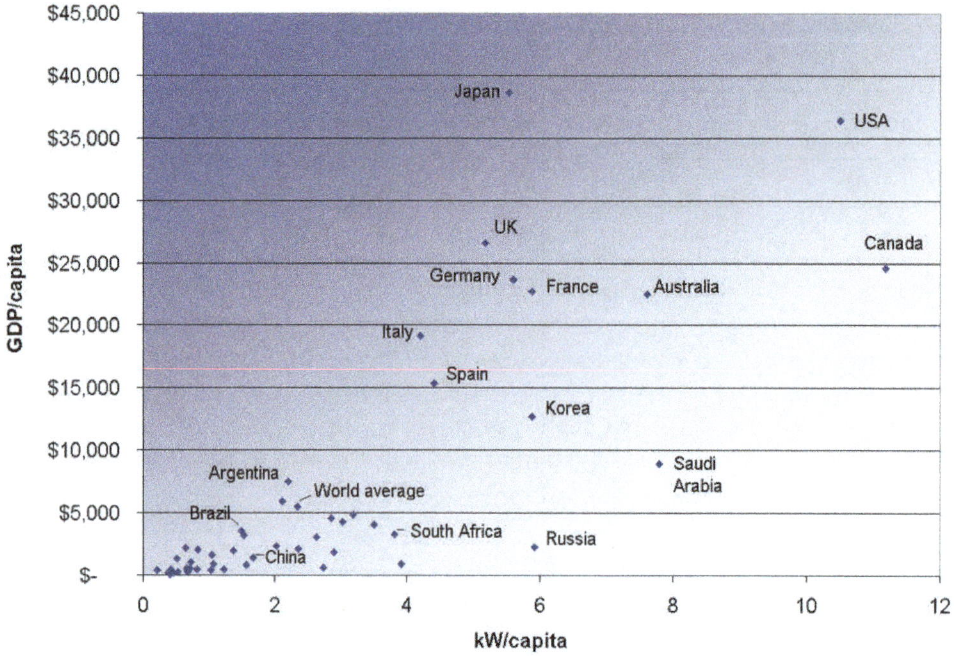

FIGURE 7.29 Power consumption per capita versus GDP per capita for various countries. Note the increase in energy usage with increasing GDP. (2007, credit: Frank van Mierlo, Wikimedia Commons)

Conserving Energy

As we finish this chapter on energy and work, it is relevant to draw some distinctions between two sometimes misunderstood terms in the area of energy use. As has been mentioned elsewhere, the "law of the conservation of energy" is a very useful principle in analyzing physical processes. It is a statement that cannot be proven from basic principles, but is a very good bookkeeping device, and no exceptions have ever been found. It states that the total amount of energy in an isolated system will always remain constant. Related to this principle, but remarkably different from it, is the important philosophy of energy conservation. This concept has to do with seeking to decrease the amount of energy used by an individual or group through (1) reduced activities (e.g., turning down thermostats, driving fewer kilometers) and/or (2) increasing conversion efficiencies in the performance of a particular task—such as developing and using more efficient room heaters, cars that have greater miles-per-gallon ratings, energy-efficient compact fluorescent lights, etc.

Since energy in an isolated system is not destroyed or created or generated, one might wonder why we need to be concerned about our energy resources, since energy is a conserved quantity. The problem is that the final result of most energy transformations is waste heat transfer to the environment and conversion to energy forms no longer useful for doing work. To state it in another way, the potential for energy to produce useful work has been "degraded" in the energy transformation. (This will be discussed in more detail in Thermodynamics.)

Glossary

basal metabolic rate the total energy conversion rate of a person at rest

chemical energy the energy in a substance stored in the bonds between atoms and molecules that can be released in a chemical reaction

conservation of mechanical energy the rule that the sum of the kinetic energies and potential energies remains constant if only conservative forces act on and within a system

conservative force a force that does the same work for any given initial and final configuration, regardless of the path followed

efficiency a measure of the effectiveness of the input of energy to do work; useful energy or work divided by the total input of energy

electrical energy the energy carried by a flow of charge

energy the ability to do work

fossil fuels oil, natural gas, and coal

friction the force between surfaces that opposes one sliding on the other; friction changes mechanical energy into thermal energy

gravitational potential energy the energy an object has due to its position in a gravitational field

horsepower an older non-SI unit of power, with $1\text{ hp} = 746\text{ W}$

joule SI unit of work and energy, equal to one newton-meter

kilowatt-hour $(\text{kW} \cdot \text{h})$ unit used primarily for electrical energy provided by electric utility companies

kinetic energy the energy an object has by reason of its motion, equal to $\frac{1}{2}mv^2$ for the translational (i.e., non-rotational) motion of an object of mass m moving at speed v

law of conservation of energy the general law that total energy is constant in any process; energy may change in form or be transferred from one system to another, but the total remains the same

mechanical energy the sum of kinetic energy and potential energy

metabolic rate the rate at which the body uses food energy to sustain life and to do different activities

net work work done by the net force, or vector sum of all the forces, acting on an object

nonconservative force a force whose work depends on the path followed between the given initial and final configurations

nuclear energy energy released by changes within atomic nuclei, such as the fusion of two light nuclei or the fission of a heavy nucleus

potential energy energy due to position, shape, or configuration

potential energy of a spring the stored energy of a spring as a function of its displacement; when Hooke's law applies, it is given by the expression $\frac{1}{2}kx^2$ where x is the distance the spring is compressed or extended and k is the spring constant

power the rate at which work is done

radiant energy the energy carried by electromagnetic waves

renewable forms of energy those sources that cannot be used up, such as water, wind, solar, and biomass

thermal energy the energy within an object due to the random motion of its atoms and molecules that accounts for the object's temperature

useful work work done on an external system

watt (W) SI unit of power, with $1\text{ W} = 1\text{ J/s}$

work the transfer of energy by a force that causes an object to be displaced; the product of the component of the force in the direction of the displacement and the magnitude of the displacement

work-energy theorem the result, based on Newton's laws, that the net work done on an object is equal to its change in kinetic energy

Section Summary

7.1 Work: The Scientific Definition

- Work is the transfer of energy by a force acting on an object as it is displaced.
- The work W that a force $\mathbf{F}$ does on an object is the product of the magnitude F of the force, times the magnitude d of the displacement, times the cosine of the angle θ between them. In symbols, $W = Fd \cos \theta$.
- The SI unit for work and energy is the joule (J), where $1\text{ J} = 1\text{ N} \cdot \text{m} = 1\text{ kg} \cdot \text{m}^2/\text{s}^2$.
- The work done by a force is zero if the displacement is either zero or perpendicular to the force.
- The work done is positive if the force and displacement have the same direction, and negative if they have opposite direction.

7.2 Kinetic Energy and the Work-Energy Theorem

- The net work W_{net} is the work done by the net

force acting on an object.

- Work done on an object transfers energy to the object.
- The translational kinetic energy of an object of mass m moving at speed v is $\text{KE} = \frac{1}{2}mv^2$.
- The work-energy theorem states that the net work W_{net} on a system changes its kinetic energy, $W_{\text{net}} = \frac{1}{2}mv^2 - \frac{1}{2}mv_0{}^2$.

7.3 Gravitational Potential Energy

- Work done against gravity in lifting an object becomes potential energy of the object-Earth system.
- The change in gravitational potential energy, ΔPE_g, is $\Delta\text{PE}_\text{g} = mgh$, with h being the increase in height and g the acceleration due to gravity.
- The gravitational potential energy of an object near Earth's surface is due to its position in the mass-Earth system. Only differences in gravitational potential energy, ΔPE_g, have physical significance.
- As an object descends without friction, its gravitational potential energy changes into kinetic energy corresponding to increasing speed, so that $\Delta\text{KE} = -\Delta\text{PE}_\text{g}$.

7.4 Conservative Forces and Potential Energy

- A conservative force is one for which work depends only on the starting and ending points of a motion, not on the path taken.
- We can define potential energy (PE) for any conservative force, just as we defined PE_g for the gravitational force.
- The potential energy of a spring is $\text{PE}_\text{s} = \frac{1}{2}kx^2$, where k is the spring's force constant and x is the displacement from its undeformed position.
- Mechanical energy is defined to be $\text{KE} + \text{PE}$ for a conservative force.
- When only conservative forces act on and within a system, the total mechanical energy is constant. In equation form,

$$\left.\begin{array}{c}\text{KE} + \text{PE} = \text{constant} \\ \text{or} \\ \text{KE}_\text{i} + \text{PE}_\text{i} = \text{KE}_\text{f} + \text{PE}_\text{f}\end{array}\right\}\text{(conservative forces only)},$$

where i and f denote initial and final values. This is known as the conservation of mechanical energy.

7.5 Nonconservative Forces

- A nonconservative force is one for which work depends on the path.
- Friction is an example of a nonconservative force that changes mechanical energy into thermal energy.
- Work W_{nc} done by a nonconservative force changes the mechanical energy of a system. In equation form, $W_{\text{nc}} = \Delta\text{KE} + \Delta\text{PE}$ or, equivalently, $\text{KE}_\text{i} + \text{PE}_\text{i} + W_{\text{nc}} = \text{KE}_\text{f} + \text{PE}_\text{f}$.
- When both conservative and nonconservative forces act, energy conservation can be applied and used to calculate motion in terms of the known potential energies of the conservative forces and the work done by nonconservative forces, instead of finding the net work from the net force, or having to directly apply Newton's laws.

7.6 Conservation of Energy

- The law of conservation of energy states that the total energy is constant in any process. Energy may change in form or be transferred from one system to another, but the total remains the same.
- When all forms of energy are considered, conservation of energy is written in equation form as $\text{KE}_\text{i} + \text{PE}_\text{i} + W_{\text{nc}} + \text{OE}_\text{i} = \text{KE}_\text{f} + \text{PE}_\text{f} + \text{OE}_\text{f}$, where OE is all **other forms of energy** besides mechanical energy.
- Commonly encountered forms of energy include electric energy, chemical energy, radiant energy, nuclear energy, and thermal energy.
- Energy is often utilized to do work, but it is not possible to convert all the energy of a system to work.
- The efficiency Eff of a machine or human is defined to be $Eff = \frac{W_{\text{out}}}{E_{\text{in}}}$, where W_{out} is useful work output and E_{in} is the energy consumed.

7.7 Power

- Power is the rate at which work is done, or in equation form, for the average power P for work W done over a time t, $P = W/t$.
- The SI unit for power is the watt (W), where $1 \text{ W} = 1 \text{ J/s}$.
- The power of many devices such as electric motors is also often expressed in horsepower (hp), where $1 \text{ hp} = 746 \text{ W}$.

7.8 Work, Energy, and Power in Humans

- The human body converts energy stored in food into work, thermal energy, and/or chemical energy that is stored in fatty tissue.
- The *rate* at which the body uses food energy to sustain life and to do different activities is called the metabolic rate, and the corresponding rate

when at rest is called the basal metabolic rate (BMR)

- The energy included in the basal metabolic rate is divided among various systems in the body, with the largest fraction going to the liver and spleen, and the brain coming next.
- About 75% of food calories are used to sustain basic body functions included in the basal metabolic rate.
- The energy consumption of people during various activities can be determined by measuring their oxygen use, because the digestive process is basically one of oxidizing food.

7.9 World Energy Use

- The relative use of different fuels to provide energy has changed over the years, but fuel use is currently dominated by oil, although natural gas and solar contributions are increasing.
- Although non-renewable sources dominate, some countries meet a sizeable percentage of their electricity needs from renewable resources.
- The United States obtains only about 10% of its energy from renewable sources, mostly hydroelectric power.
- Economic well-being is dependent upon energy use, and in most countries higher standards of living, as measured by GDP (Gross Domestic Product) per capita, are matched by higher levels of energy consumption per capita.
- Even though, in accordance with the law of conservation of energy, energy can never be created or destroyed, energy that can be used to do work is always partly converted to less useful forms, such as waste heat to the environment, in all of our uses of energy for practical purposes.

Conceptual Questions

7.1 Work: The Scientific Definition

1. Give an example of something we think of as work in everyday circumstances that is not work in the scientific sense. Is energy transferred or changed in form in your example? If so, explain how this is accomplished without doing work.

2. Give an example of a situation in which there is a force and a displacement, but the force does no work. Explain why it does no work.

3. Describe a situation in which a force is exerted for a long time but does no work. Explain.

7.2 Kinetic Energy and the Work-Energy Theorem

4. The person in Figure 7.30 does work on the lawn mower. Under what conditions would the mower gain energy? Under what conditions would it lose energy?

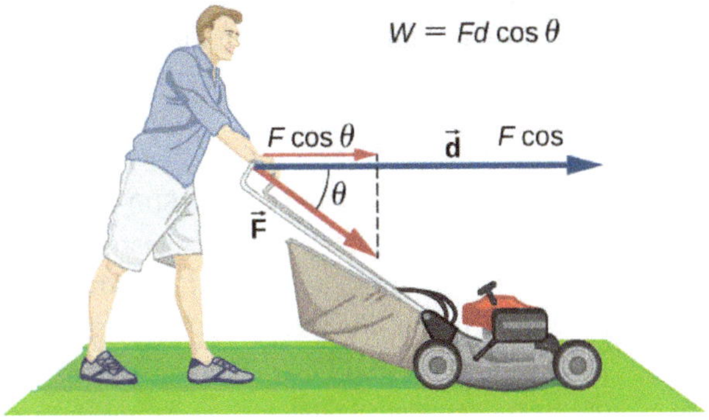

FIGURE 7.30

5. Work done on a system puts energy into it. Work done by a system removes energy from it. Give an example for each statement.

6. When solving for speed in Example 7.4, we kept only the positive root. Why?

7.3 Gravitational Potential Energy

7. In Example 7.7, we calculated the final speed of a roller coaster that descended 20 m in height and had an initial speed of 5 m/s downhill. Suppose the roller coaster had had an initial speed of 5 m/s *uphill* instead, and it coasted uphill, stopped, and then rolled back down to a final point 20 m below the start. We would find in that case that its final speed is the same as its initial speed. Explain in terms of conservation of energy.

8. Does the work you do on a book when you lift it onto a shelf depend on the path taken? On the time taken? On the height of the shelf? On the mass of the book?

7.4 Conservative Forces and Potential Energy

9. What is a conservative force?

10. The force exerted by a diving board is conservative, provided the internal friction is negligible. Assuming friction is negligible, describe changes in the potential energy of a diving board as a swimmer dives from it, starting just before the swimmer steps on the board until just after his feet leave it.

11. Define mechanical energy. What is the relationship of mechanical energy to nonconservative forces?

What happens to mechanical energy if only conservative forces act?

12. What is the relationship of potential energy to conservative force?

7.6 Conservation of Energy

13. Consider the following scenario. A car for which friction is *not* negligible accelerates from rest down a hill, running out of gasoline after a short distance. The driver lets the car coast farther down the hill, then up and over a small crest. He then coasts down that hill into a gas station, where he brakes to a stop and fills the tank with gasoline. Identify the forms of energy the car has, and how they are changed and transferred in this series of events. (See Figure 7.31.)

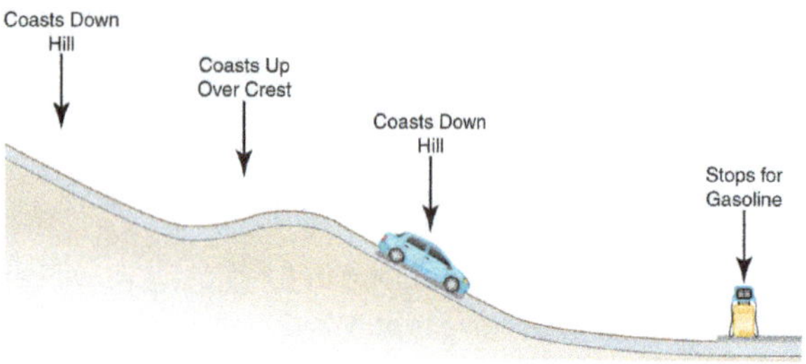

FIGURE 7.31 A car experiencing non-negligible friction coasts down a hill, over a small crest, then downhill again, and comes to a stop at a gas station.

14. Describe the energy transfers and transformations for a javelin, starting from the point at which an athlete picks up the javelin and ending when the javelin is stuck into the ground after being thrown.

15. Do devices with efficiencies of less than one violate the law of conservation of energy? Explain.

16. List four different forms or types of energy. Give one example of a conversion from each of these forms to another form.

17. List the energy conversions that occur when riding a bicycle.

7.7 Power

18. Most electrical appliances are rated in watts. Does this rating depend on how long the appliance is on? (When off, it is a zero-watt device.) Explain in terms of the definition of power.

19. Explain, in terms of the definition of power, why energy consumption is sometimes listed in kilowatt-hours rather than joules. What is the relationship between these two energy units?

20. A spark of static electricity, such as that you might receive from a doorknob on a cold dry day, may carry a few hundred watts of power. Explain why you are not injured by such a spark.

7.8 Work, Energy, and Power in Humans

21. Explain why it is easier to climb a mountain on a zigzag path rather than one straight up the side. Is your increase in gravitational potential energy the same in both cases? Is your energy consumption the same in both?

22. Do you do work on the outside world when you rub your hands together to warm them? What is the efficiency of this activity?

23. Shivering is an involuntary response to lowered body temperature. What is the efficiency of the body when shivering, and is this a desirable value?

24. Discuss the relative impact of dieting and exercise, noting that most athletic activities consume food energy at a rate of 400 to 500 W, while a single cup of yogurt can contain 1360 kJ (325 kcal).

7.9 World Energy Use

25. What is the difference between energy conservation and the law of conservation of energy? Give some examples of each.

26. If the efficiency of a coal-fired electrical generating plant is 35%, then what do we mean when we say that energy is a conserved quantity?

Problems & Exercises

7.1 Work: The Scientific Definition

1. How much work does a supermarket checkout attendant do on a can of soup he pushes 0.600 m horizontally with a force of 5.00 N? Express your answer in joules and kilocalories.

2. A 75.0-kg person climbs stairs, gaining 2.50 meters in height. Find the work done to accomplish this task. (Neglect friction in your calculations.)

3. (a) Calculate the work done on a 1500-kg elevator car by its cable to lift it 40.0 m at constant speed, assuming friction averages 100 N. (b) What is the work done on the elevator car by the gravitational force in this process? (c) What is the total work done on the elevator car?

4. Suppose a car travels 108 km at a speed of 30.0 m/s, and uses 2.0 gal of gasoline. Only 30% of the gasoline goes into useful work by the force that keeps the car moving at constant speed despite friction. (See Table 7.1 for the energy content of gasoline.) (a) What is the magnitude of the force exerted to keep the car moving at constant speed? (b) If the required force is directly proportional to speed, how many gallons will be used to drive 108 km at a speed of 28.0 m/s?

5. Calculate the work done by an 85.0-kg man who pushes a crate 4.00 m up along a ramp that makes an angle of 20.0° with the horizontal. (See Figure 7.32.) He exerts a force of 500 N on the crate parallel to the ramp and moves at a constant speed. Be certain to include the work he does on the crate *and* on his body to get up the ramp.

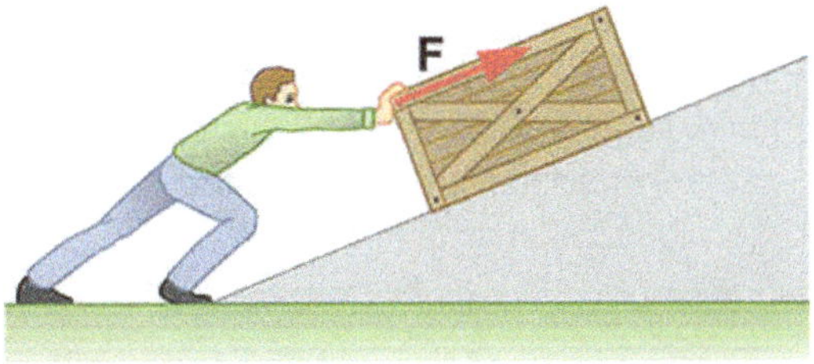

FIGURE 7.32 A man pushes a crate up a ramp.

6. How much work is done by the boy pulling his sister 30.0 m in a wagon as shown in Figure 7.33? Assume no friction acts on the wagon.

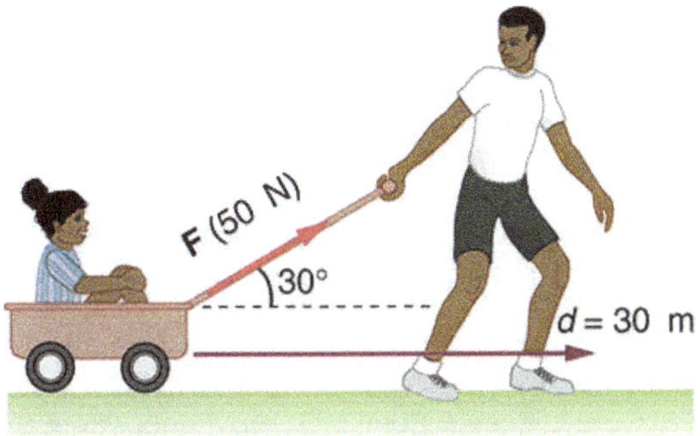

FIGURE 7.33 The boy does work on the system of the wagon and the child when he pulls them as shown.

7. A shopper pushes a grocery cart 20.0 m at constant speed on level ground, against a 35.0 N frictional force. He pushes in a direction 25.0° below the horizontal. (a) What is the work done on the cart by friction? (b) What is the work done on the cart by the gravitational force? (c) What is the work done on the cart by the shopper? (d) Find the force the shopper exerts, using energy considerations. (e) What is the total work done on the cart?

8. Suppose the ski patrol lowers a rescue sled and victim, having a total mass of 90.0 kg, down a 60.0° slope at constant speed, as shown in Figure 7.34. The coefficient of friction between the sled and the snow is 0.100. (a) How much work is done by friction as the sled moves 30.0 m along the hill? (b) How much work is done by the rope on the sled in this distance? (c) What is the work done by the gravitational force on the sled? (d) What is the total work done?

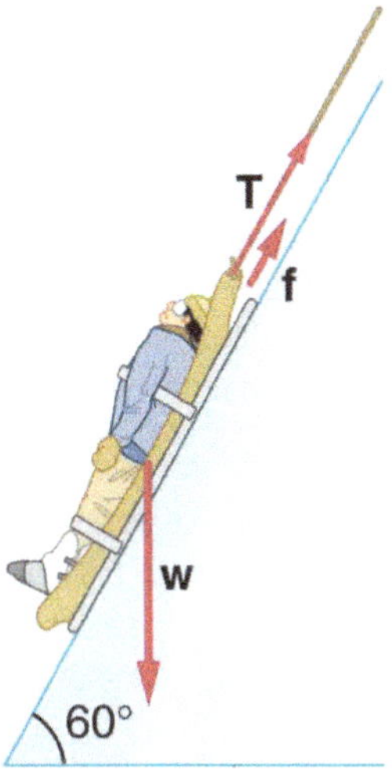

FIGURE 7.34 A rescue sled and victim are lowered down a steep slope.

7.2 Kinetic Energy and the Work-Energy Theorem

9. Compare the kinetic energy of a 20,000-kg truck moving at 110 km/h with that of an 80.0-kg astronaut in orbit moving at 27,500 km/h.

10. (a) How fast must a 3000-kg elephant move to have the same kinetic energy as a 65.0-kg sprinter running at 10.0 m/s? (b) Discuss how the larger energies needed for the movement of larger animals would relate to metabolic rates.

11. Confirm the value given for the kinetic energy of an aircraft carrier in Table 7.1. You will need to look up the definition of a nautical mile (1 knot = 1 nautical mile/h).

12. (a) Calculate the force needed to bring a 950-kg car to rest from a speed of 90.0 km/h in a distance of 120 m (a fairly typical distance for a non-panic stop). (b) Suppose instead the car hits a concrete abutment at full speed and is brought to a stop in 2.00 m. Calculate the force exerted on the car and compare it with the force found in part (a).

13. A car's bumper is designed to withstand a 4.0-km/h (1.12-m/s) collision with an immovable object without damage to the body of the car. The bumper cushions the shock by absorbing the force over a distance. Calculate the magnitude of the average force on a bumper that collapses 0.200 m

while bringing a 900-kg car to rest from an initial speed of 1.12 m/s.

14. Boxing gloves are padded to lessen the force of a blow. (a) Calculate the force exerted by a boxing glove on an opponent's face, if the glove and face compress 7.50 cm during a blow in which the 7.00-kg arm and glove are brought to rest from an initial speed of 10.0 m/s. (b) Calculate the force exerted by an identical blow in the days when no gloves were used and the knuckles and face would compress only 2.00 cm. (c) Discuss the magnitude of the force with glove on. Does it seem high enough to cause damage even though it is lower than the force with no glove?

15. Using energy considerations, calculate the average force a 60.0-kg sprinter exerts backward on the track to accelerate from 2.00 to 8.00 m/s in a distance of 25.0 m, if he encounters a headwind that exerts an average force of 30.0 N against him.

7.3 Gravitational Potential Energy

16. A hydroelectric power facility (see Figure 7.35) converts the gravitational potential energy of water behind a dam to electric energy. (a) What is the gravitational potential energy relative to the generators of a lake of volume 50.0 km^3 $(\text{mass} = 5.00 \times 10^{13}\text{ kg})$, given that the lake has an average height of 40.0 m above the generators? (b) Compare this with the energy stored in a 9-megaton fusion bomb.

FIGURE 7.35 Hydroelectric facility (credit: Denis Belevich, Wikimedia Commons)

17. (a) How much gravitational potential energy (relative to the ground on which it is built) is stored in the Great Pyramid of Cheops, given that its mass is about $7 \times 10^9\text{ kg}$ and its center of mass is 36.5 m above the surrounding ground? (b) How does this energy compare with the daily food intake of a person?

18. Suppose a 350-g kookaburra (a large kingfisher bird) picks up a 75-g snake and raises it 2.5 m from the ground to a branch. (a) How much work did the bird do on the snake? (b) How much work did it do to raise its own center of mass to the branch?

19. In Example 7.7, we found that the speed of a roller coaster that had descended 20.0 m was only slightly greater when it had an initial speed of 5.00 m/s than when it started from rest. This implies that $\Delta\text{PE} >> \text{KE}_\text{i}$. Confirm this statement by taking the ratio of ΔPE to KE_i. (Note that mass cancels.)

20. A 100-g toy car is propelled by a compressed spring that starts it moving. The car follows the curved track in Figure 7.36. Show that the final speed of the toy car is 0.687 m/s if its initial speed is 2.00 m/s and it coasts up the frictionless slope, gaining 0.180 m in altitude.

FIGURE 7.36 A toy car moves up a sloped track. (credit: Leszek Leszczynski, Flickr)

21. In a downhill ski race, surprisingly, little advantage is gained by getting a running start. (This is because the initial kinetic energy is small compared with the gain in gravitational potential energy on even small hills.) To demonstrate this, find the final speed and the time taken for a skier who skies 70.0 m along a 30° slope neglecting friction: (a) Starting from rest. (b) Starting with an initial speed of 2.50 m/s. (c) Does the answer surprise you? Discuss why it is still advantageous to get a running start in very competitive events.

7.4 Conservative Forces and Potential Energy

22. A 5.00×10^5-kg subway train is brought to a stop from a speed of 0.500 m/s in 0.400 m by a large spring bumper at the end of its track. What is the force constant k of the spring?

23. A pogo stick has a spring with a force constant of $2.50 \times 10^4\text{ N/m}$, which can be compressed 12.0

cm. To what maximum height can a child jump on the stick using only the energy in the spring, if the child and stick have a total mass of 40.0 kg? Explicitly show how you follow the steps in the Problem-Solving Strategies for Energy.

7.5 Nonconservative Forces

24. A 60.0-kg skier with an initial speed of 12.0 m/s coasts up a 2.50-m-high rise as shown in Figure 7.37. Find her final speed at the top, given that the coefficient of friction between her skis and the snow is 0.0800. (Hint: Find the distance traveled up the incline assuming a straight-line path as shown in the figure.)

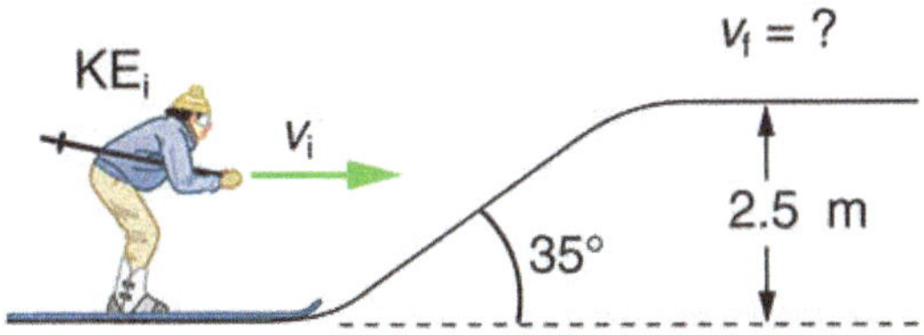

FIGURE 7.37 The skier's initial kinetic energy is partially used in coasting to the top of a rise.

25. (a) How high a hill can a car coast up (engine disengaged) if work done by friction is negligible and its initial speed is 110 km/h? (b) If, in actuality, a 750-kg car with an initial speed of 110 km/h is observed to coast up a hill to a height 22.0 m above its starting point, how much thermal energy was generated by friction? (c) What is the average force of friction if the hill has a slope 2.5° above the horizontal?

7.6 Conservation of Energy

26. Using values from Table 7.1, how many DNA molecules could be broken by the energy carried by a single electron in the beam of an old-fashioned TV tube? (These electrons were not dangerous in themselves, but they did create dangerous x rays. Later model tube TVs had shielding that absorbed x rays before they escaped and exposed viewers.)

27. Using energy considerations and assuming negligible air resistance, show that a rock thrown from a bridge 20.0 m above water with an initial speed of 15.0 m/s strikes the water with a speed of 24.8 m/s independent of the direction thrown.

28. If the energy in fusion bombs were used to supply the energy needs of the world, how many of the 9-megaton variety would be needed for a year's supply of energy (using data from Table 7.1)? This is not as far-fetched as it may sound—there are thousands of nuclear bombs, and their energy can be trapped in underground explosions and converted to electricity, as natural geothermal energy is.

29. (a) Use of hydrogen fusion to supply energy is a dream that may be realized in the next century. Fusion would be a relatively clean and almost limitless supply of energy, as can be seen from Table 7.1. To illustrate this, calculate how many years the present energy needs of the world could be supplied by one millionth of the oceans' hydrogen fusion energy. (b) How does this time compare with historically significant events, such as the duration of stable economic systems?

7.7 Power

30. The Crab Nebula (see Figure 7.38) pulsar is the remnant of a supernova that occurred in A.D. 1054. Using data from Table 7.3, calculate the approximate factor by which the power output of this astronomical object has declined since its explosion.

FIGURE 7.38 Crab Nebula (credit: ESO, via Wikimedia Commons)

31. Suppose a star 1000 times brighter than our Sun (that is, emitting 1000 times the power) suddenly goes supernova. Using data from Table 7.3: (a) By what factor does its power output increase? (b) How many times brighter than our entire Milky Way galaxy is the supernova? (c) Based on your answers, discuss whether it should be possible to observe supernovas in distant galaxies. Note that there are on the order of 10^{11} observable galaxies, the average brightness of which is somewhat less than our own galaxy.

32. A person in good physical condition can put out 100 W of useful power for several hours at a stretch, perhaps by pedaling a mechanism that drives an electric generator. Neglecting any problems of generator efficiency and practical considerations such as resting time: (a) How many people would it take to run a 4.00-kW electric clothes dryer? (b) How many people would it take to replace a large electric power plant that generates 800 MW?

33. What is the cost of operating a 3.00-W electric clock for a year if the cost of electricity is $0.0900 per $\mathrm{kW \cdot h}$?

34. A large household air conditioner may consume 15.0 kW of power. What is the cost of operating this air conditioner 3.00 h per day for 30.0 d if the cost of electricity is $0.110 per $\mathrm{kW \cdot h}$?

35. (a) What is the average power consumption in watts of an appliance that uses $5.00\ \mathrm{kW \cdot h}$ of energy per day? (b) How many joules of energy does this appliance consume in a year?

36. (a) What is the average useful power output of a person who does 6.00×10^6 J of useful work in 8.00 h? (b) Working at this rate, how long will it take this person to lift 2000 kg of bricks 1.50 m to a platform? (Work done to lift his body can be omitted because it is not considered useful output here.)

37. A 500-kg dragster accelerates from rest to a final speed of 110 m/s in 400 m (about a quarter of a mile) and encounters an average frictional force of 1200 N. What is its average power output in watts and horsepower if this takes 7.30 s?

38. (a) How long will it take an 850-kg car with a useful power output of 40.0 hp (1 hp = 746 W) to reach a speed of 15.0 m/s, neglecting friction? (b) How long will this acceleration take if the car also climbs a 3.00-m-high hill in the process?

39. (a) Find the useful power output of an elevator motor that lifts a 2500-kg load a height of 35.0 m in 12.0 s, if it also increases the speed from rest to 4.00 m/s. Note that the total mass of the counterbalanced system is 10,000 kg—so that only 2500 kg is raised in height, but the full 10,000 kg is accelerated. (b) What does it cost, if electricity is $0.0900 per $\mathrm{kW \cdot h}$?

40. (a) What is the available energy content, in joules, of a battery that operates a 2.00-W electric clock for 18 months? (b) How long can a battery that can supply 8.00×10^4 J run a pocket calculator that consumes energy at the rate of 1.00×10^{-3} W?

41. (a) How long would it take a 1.50×10^5-kg airplane with engines that produce 100 MW of power to reach a speed of 250 m/s and an altitude of 12.0 km if air resistance were negligible? (b) If it actually takes 900 s, what is the power? (c) Given this power, what is the average force of air resistance if the airplane takes 1200 s? (Hint: You must find the distance the plane travels in 1200 s assuming constant acceleration.)

42. Calculate the power output needed for a 950-kg car to climb a 2.00° slope at a constant 30.0 m/s while encountering wind resistance and friction totaling 600 N. Explicitly show how you follow the steps in the Problem-Solving Strategies for Energy.

43. (a) Calculate the power per square meter reaching Earth's upper atmosphere from the Sun. (Take the power output of the Sun to be 4.00×10^{26} W.) (b) Part of this is absorbed and reflected by the atmosphere, so that a maximum of $1.30\ \mathrm{kW/m^2}$ reaches Earth's surface. Calculate the area in $\mathrm{km^2}$ of solar energy collectors needed to replace an electric power plant that generates 750 MW if the collectors convert an average of 2.00% of the maximum power into electricity. (This small conversion efficiency is due to the devices themselves, and the fact that the sun is directly overhead only briefly.) With the same assumptions, what area would be needed to meet the United States' energy needs (1.05×10^{20} J)? Australia's energy needs (5.4×10^{18} J)? China's energy needs (6.3×10^{19} J)? (These energy consumption values are from 2006.)

7.8 Work, Energy, and Power in Humans

44. (a) How long can you rapidly climb stairs (116/min) on the 93.0 kcal of energy in a 10.0-g pat of butter? (b) How many flights is this if each flight has 16 stairs?

45. (a) What is the power output in watts and horsepower of a 70.0-kg sprinter who accelerates from rest to 10.0 m/s in 3.00 s? (b) Considering the amount of power generated, do you think a well-trained athlete could do this repetitively for long periods of time?

46. Calculate the power output in watts and

horsepower of a shot-putter who takes 1.20 s to accelerate the 7.27-kg shot from rest to 14.0 m/s, while raising it 0.800 m. (Do not include the power produced to accelerate his body.)

FIGURE 7.39 Shot putter at the Dornoch Highland Gathering in 2007. (credit: John Haslam, Flickr)

47. (a) What is the efficiency of an out-of-condition person who does 2.10×10^5 J of useful work while metabolizing 500 kcal of food energy? (b) How many food calories would a well-conditioned athlete metabolize in doing the same work with an efficiency of 20%?

48. Energy that is not utilized for work or heat transfer is converted to the chemical energy of body fat containing about 39 kJ/g. How many grams of fat will you gain if you eat 10,000 kJ (about 2500 kcal) one day and do nothing but sit relaxed for 16.0 h and sleep for the other 8.00 h? Use data from Table 7.5 for the energy consumption rates of these activities.

49. Using data from Table 7.5, calculate the daily energy needs of a person who sleeps for 7.00 h, walks for 2.00 h, attends classes for 4.00 h, cycles for 2.00 h, sits relaxed for 3.00 h, and studies for 6.00 h. (Studying consumes energy at the same rate as sitting in class.)

50. What is the efficiency of a subject on a treadmill who puts out work at the rate of 100 W while consuming oxygen at the rate of 2.00 L/min? (Hint: See Table 7.5.)

51. Shoveling snow can be extremely taxing because the arms have such a low efficiency in this activity. Suppose a person shoveling a footpath metabolizes food at the rate of 800 W. (a) What is her useful power output? (b) How long will it take her to lift 3000 kg of snow 1.20 m? (This could be the amount of heavy snow on 20 m of footpath.) (c) How much waste heat transfer in kilojoules will she generate in the process?

52. Very large forces are produced in joints when a person jumps from some height to the ground. (a) Calculate the magnitude of the force produced if an 80.0-kg person jumps from a 0.600–m-high ledge and lands stiffly, compressing joint material 1.50 cm as a result. (Be certain to include the weight of the person.) (b) In practice the knees bend almost involuntarily to help extend the distance over which you stop. Calculate the magnitude of the force produced if the stopping distance is 0.300 m. (c) Compare both forces with the weight of the person.

53. Jogging on hard surfaces with insufficiently padded shoes produces large forces in the feet and legs. (a) Calculate the magnitude of the force needed to stop the downward motion of a jogger's leg, if his leg has a mass of 13.0 kg, a speed of 6.00 m/s, and stops in a distance of 1.50 cm. (Be certain to include the weight of the 75.0-kg jogger's body.) (b) Compare this force with the weight of the jogger.

54. (a) Calculate the energy in kJ used by a 55.0-kg person who does 50 deep knee bends in which their center of mass is lowered and raised 0.400 m. (They do work in both directions.) You may assume their efficiency is 20%. (b) What is the average power consumption rate in watts if they do this in 3.00 min?

55. Kanellos Kanellopoulos flew 119 km from Crete to Santorini, Greece, on April 23, 1988, in the *Daedalus 88*, an aircraft powered by a bicycle-type drive mechanism (see Figure 7.40). His useful power output for the 234-min trip was about 350 W. Using the efficiency for cycling from Table 7.2, calculate the food energy in kilojoules he metabolized during the flight.

FIGURE 7.40 The Daedalus 88 in flight. (credit: NASA photo by Beasley)

56. The swimmer shown in Figure 7.41 exerts an average horizontal backward force of 80.0 N with his arm during each 1.80 m long stroke. (a) What is his work output in each stroke? (b) Calculate the power output of his arms if he does 120 strokes per minute.

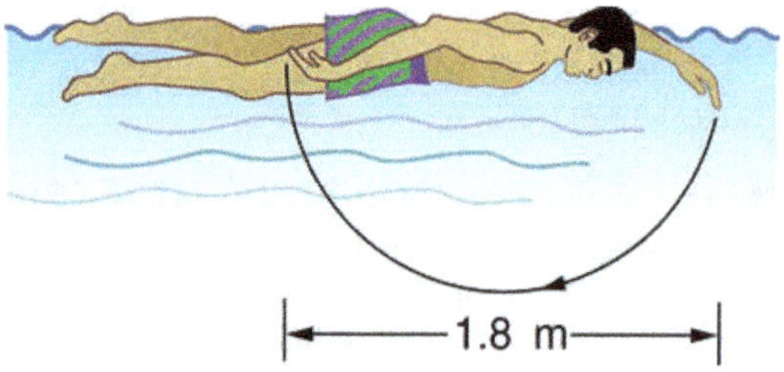

FIGURE 7.41

57. Mountain climbers carry bottled oxygen when at very high altitudes. (a) Assuming that a mountain climber uses oxygen at twice the rate for climbing 116 stairs per minute (because of low air temperature and winds), calculate how many liters of oxygen a climber would need for 10.0 h of climbing. (These are liters at sea level.) Note that only 40% of the inhaled oxygen is utilized; the rest is exhaled. (b) How much useful work does the climber do if he and his equipment have a mass of 90.0 kg and he gains 1000 m of altitude? (c) What is his efficiency for the 10.0-h climb?

58. The awe-inspiring Great Pyramid of Cheops was built more than 4500 years ago. Its square base, originally 230 m on a side, covered 13.1 acres, and it was 146 m high, with a mass of about 7×10^9 kg. (The pyramid's dimensions are slightly different today due to quarrying and some sagging.) Historians estimate that 20,000 workers spent 20 years to construct it, working 12-hour days, 330 days per year. (a) Calculate the gravitational potential energy stored in the pyramid, given its center of mass is at one-fourth its height. (b) Only a fraction of the workers lifted blocks; most were involved in support services such as building ramps (see Figure 7.42), bringing food and water, and hauling blocks to the site. Calculate the efficiency of the workers who did the lifting, assuming there were 1000 of them and they consumed food energy at the rate of 300 kcal/h. What does your answer imply about how much of their work went into block-lifting, versus how much work went into friction and lifting and lowering their own bodies? (c) Calculate the mass of food that had to be supplied each day, assuming that the average worker required 3600 kcal per day and that their diet was 5% protein, 60% carbohydrate, and 35% fat. (These proportions neglect the mass of bulk and nondigestible materials consumed.)

FIGURE 7.42 Ancient pyramids were probably constructed using ramps as simple machines. (credit: Franck Monnier, Wikimedia Commons)

59. (a) How long can you play tennis on the 800 kJ (about 200 kcal) of energy in a candy bar? (b) Does this seem like a long time? Discuss why exercise is necessary but may not be sufficient to cause a person to lose weight.

7.9 World Energy Use

60. Integrated Concepts
(a) Calculate the force the woman in Figure 7.43 exerts to do a push-up at constant speed, taking all data to be known to three digits. (b) How much work does she do if her center of mass rises 0.240 m? (c) What is her useful power output if she does 25 push-ups in 1 min? (Should work done lowering her body be included? See the discussion of useful work in Work, Energy, and Power in Humans.

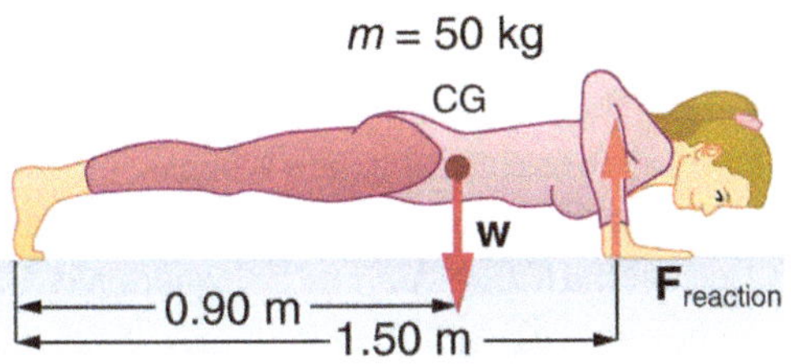

FIGURE 7.43 Forces involved in doing push-ups. The woman's weight acts as a force exerted downward on her center of gravity (CG).

61. Integrated Concepts
A 75.0-kg cross-country skier is climbing a 3.0° slope at a constant speed of 2.00 m/s and encounters air resistance of 25.0 N. Find his power output for work done against the gravitational force and air resistance. (b) What average force does he exert backward on the snow to accomplish this? (c) If he continues to exert this force and to experience the same air resistance when he reaches a level area, how long will it take him to reach a velocity of 10.0 m/s?

62. Integrated Concepts
The 70.0-kg swimmer in Figure 7.41 starts a race with an initial velocity of 1.25 m/s and exerts an average force of 80.0 N backward with his arms during each 1.80 m long stroke. (a) What is his initial acceleration if water resistance is 45.0 N? (b) What is the subsequent average resistance force from the water during the 5.00 s it takes him to reach his top velocity of 2.50 m/s? (c) Discuss whether water resistance seems to increase linearly with velocity.

63. Integrated Concepts
A toy gun uses a spring with a force constant of 300 N/m to propel a 10.0-g steel ball. If the spring is compressed 7.00 cm and friction is negligible: (a) How much force is needed to compress the spring? (b) To what maximum height can the ball be shot? (c) At what angles above the horizontal may a child aim to hit a target 3.00 m away at the same height as the gun? (d) What is the gun's maximum range on level ground?

64. Integrated Concepts
(a) What force must be supplied by an elevator cable to produce an acceleration of 0.800 m/s^2 against a 200-N frictional force, if the mass of the loaded elevator is 1500 kg? (b) How much work is done by the cable in lifting the elevator 20.0 m? (c) What is the final speed of the elevator if it starts from rest? (d) How much work went into thermal energy?

65. Unreasonable Results
A car advertisement claims that its 900-kg car accelerated from rest to 30.0 m/s and drove 100 km, gaining 3.00 km in altitude, on 1.0 gal of gasoline. The average force of friction including air resistance was 700 N. Assume all values are known to three significant figures. (a) Calculate the car's efficiency. (b) What is unreasonable about the result? (c) Which premise is unreasonable, or which premises are inconsistent?

66. Unreasonable Results
Body fat is metabolized, supplying 9.30 kcal/g, when dietary intake is less than needed to fuel metabolism. The manufacturers of an exercise bicycle claim that you can metabolize 0.500 kg of fat per day by vigorously exercising for 2.00 h per day on their machine. (a) How many kcal are supplied by the metabolization of 0.500 kg of fat? (b) Calculate the kcal/min that you would have to utilize to metabolize fat at the rate of 0.500 kg in 2.00 h. (c) What is unreasonable about the results? (d) Which premise is unreasonable, or which premises are inconsistent?

67. Construct Your Own Problem
Consider a person climbing and descending stairs. Construct a problem in which you calculate the long-term rate at which stairs can be climbed considering the mass of the person, his ability to generate power with his legs, and the height of a single stair step. Also consider why the same person can descend stairs at a faster rate for a nearly unlimited time in spite of the fact that very similar forces are exerted going down as going up. (This points to a fundamentally different process for descending versus climbing stairs.)

68. Construct Your Own Problem
Consider humans generating electricity by pedaling a device similar to a stationary bicycle. Construct a problem in which you determine the number of people it would take to replace a large electrical generation facility. Among the things to consider are the power output that is reasonable using the legs, rest time, and the need for electricity 24 hours per day. Discuss the practical implications of your results.

69. Integrated Concepts
A 105-kg basketball player crouches down 0.400 m while waiting to jump. After exerting a force on the floor through this 0.400 m, their feet leave the

floor and their center of gravity rises 0.950 m above its normal standing erect position. (a) Using energy considerations, calculate the player's velocity when they leave the floor. (b) What average force did the player exert on the floor? (Do not neglect the force to support their weight as well as that to accelerate them.) (c) What was the player's power output during the acceleration phase?

70. Critical Thinking Two boxes of the same mass are pressed against pistons that compress and release the boxes on frictionless surfaces. Box A's piston has a constant force F over a distance *x* before the box is released while box B starts at zero force and increases linearly to a force of 2*F* before releasing the box at a distance of 1/2*d*. (a) Which of these boxes has the greatest speed after releasing from the piston? (b) Based on experimental data for trials similar to box A, an equation that fits the data is suggested for the change in kinetic energy, ΔKE, which may not be correct: $\Delta KE = KF^{1/2}x^{1/2}$, where *K* is a constant with appropriate units, *F* is the applied force, and *x* is the distance the piston moves in contact with the box. Is this equation consistent with your answer from part a? Explain why or why not. Does this equation make sense? Explain why or why not. (c) If the applied force of the piston is proportional to the distance in contact with the box, graph the work done on the box vs. the distance in contact with the piston and box.

Test Prep for AP® Courses

7.1 Work: The Scientific Definition

1. Given Table 7.7 about how much force does the rocket engine exert on the 3.0-kg payload?

Distance traveled with rocket engine firing (m)	Payload final velocity (m/s)
500	310
490	300
1020	450
505	312

TABLE 7.7

a. 150 N
b. 300 N
c. 450 N
d. 600 N

2. You have a cart track, a cart, several masses, and a position-sensing pulley. Design an experiment to examine how the force exerted on the cart does work as it moves through a distance.

3. Look at Figure 7.10(c). You compress a spring by *x*, and then release it. Next you compress the spring by 2*x*. How much more work did you do the second time than the first?

a. Half as much
b. The same
c. Twice as much
d. Four times as much

4. You have a cart track, two carts, several masses, a position-sensing pulley, and a piece of carpet (a rough surface) that will fit over the track. Design an experiment to examine how the force exerted on the cart does work as the cart moves through a distance.

5. A crane is lifting construction materials from the ground to an elevation of 60 m. Over the first 10 m, the motor linearly increases the force it exerts from 0 to 10 kN. It exerts that constant force for the next 40 m, and then winds down to 0 N again over the last 10 m, as shown in the figure. What is the total work done on the construction materials?

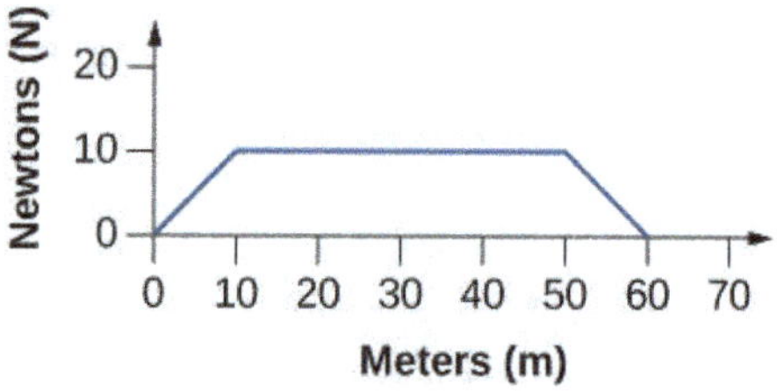

FIGURE 7.45

a. 500 kJ
b. 600 kJ
c. 300 kJ
d. 18 MJ

7.2 Kinetic Energy and the Work-Energy Theorem

6. A toy car is going around a loop-the-loop. Gravity ____ the kinetic energy on the upward side of the loop, ____ the kinetic energy at the top, and ____ the kinetic energy on the downward side of the loop.

a. increases, decreases, has no effect on
b. decreases, has no effect on, increases
c. increases, has no effect on, decreases
d. decreases, increases, has no effect on

7. A roller coaster is set up with a track in the form of a perfect cosine. Describe and graph what happens to the kinetic energy of a cart as it goes through the first full period of the track.

8. If wind is blowing horizontally toward a car with an angle of 30 degrees from the direction of travel, the kinetic energy will ____. If the wind is blowing at a car at 135 degrees from the direction of travel, the kinetic energy will ____.

a. increase, increase
b. increase, decrease
c. decrease, increase
d. decrease, decrease

9. In what direction relative to the direction of travel can a force act on a car (traveling on level ground), and not change the kinetic energy? Can you give examples of such forces?

10. A 2000-kg airplane is coming in for a landing, with a velocity 5 degrees below the horizontal and a drag force of 40 kN acting directly rearward. Ignoring thrust and lift on the plane, kinetic energy will ____ due to the net force of ____.

a. increase, 20 kN
b. decrease, 40 kN
c. increase, 45 kN
d. decrease, 45 kN

11. You are participating in the Iditarod, and your sled dogs are pulling you across a frozen lake with a force of 1200 N while a 300 N wind is blowing at you at 135 degrees from your direction of travel. What is the net force, and will your kinetic energy increase or decrease?

12. A model drag car is being accelerated along its track from rest by a motor with a force of 75 N, but there is a drag force of 30 N due to the track. What is the kinetic energy after 2 m of travel?

a. 90 J
b. 150 J
c. 210 J
d. 60 J

13. You are launching a 0.315-kg potato out of a potato cannon. The cannon is 1.5 m long and is aimed 30.0 degrees above the horizontal. It exerts an average 45 N force on the potato. Ignoring friction, what is the kinetic energy of the potato as it leaves the muzzle of the potato cannon?

14. When the force acting on an object is parallel to the direction of the motion of the center of mass, the mechanical energy ____. When the force acting on an object is antiparallel to the direction of the center of mass, the mechanical energy ____.

a. increases, increases
b. increases, decreases
c. decreases, increases
d. decreases, decreases

15. Describe a system in which the main forces acting are parallel or antiparallel to the center of mass, and justify your answer.

16. A child is pulling two red wagons, with the second one tied to the first by a (non-stretching) rope. Each wagon has a mass of 10 kg. If the child exerts a force of 30 N for 5.0 m, how much has the kinetic energy of the two-wagon system changed?

a. 300 J
b. 150 J
c. 75 J
d. 60 J

17. A child has two red wagons, with the rear one tied to the front by a (non-stretching) rope. If the child pushes on the rear wagon, what happens to the kinetic energy of each of the wagons, and the two-wagon system?

18. Draw a graph of the force parallel to displacement exerted on a stunt motorcycle going through a loop-the-loop versus the distance traveled around the loop. Explain the net change in energy.

7.3 Gravitational Potential Energy

19. A 1.0 kg baseball is flying at 10 m/s. How much kinetic energy does it have? Potential energy?

a. 10 J, 20 J
b. 50 J, 20 J
c. unknown, 50 J
d. 50 J, unknown

20. A 0.305-kg potato has been launched out of a potato cannon at 15.8 m/s. What is the kinetic energy? If you then learn that it is 4.00 m above the ground, what is the total mechanical energy relative to the ground?

a. 12.0 J, 50.1 J
b. 2.41 J, 14.4 J
c. 38.1 J, 50.1 J
d. 12.0 J, 14.4 J

21. You have a 120-g yo-yo that you are swinging at 0.9 m/s. How much energy does it have? How high can it get above the lowest point of the swing without your doing any additional work, on Earth? How high could it get on the Moon, where gravity is 1/6 Earth's?

7.4 Conservative Forces and Potential Energy

22. Two 4.0 kg masses are connected to each other by a spring with a force constant of 25 N/m and a rest length of 1.0 m. If the spring has been compressed to 0.80 m in length and the masses are traveling toward each other at 0.50 m/s (each), what is the total energy in the system?
a. 1.0 J
b. 1.5 J
c. 9.0 J
d. 8.0 J

23. A spring with a force constant of 5000 N/m and a rest length of 3.0 m is used in a catapult. When compressed to 1.0 m, it is used to launch a 50 kg rock. However, there is an error in the release mechanism, so the rock gets launched almost straight up. How high does it go, and how fast is it going when it hits the ground?

24. What information do you need to calculate the kinetic energy and potential energy of a spring? Potential energy due to gravity? How many objects do you need information about for each of these cases?

25. You are loading a toy dart gun, which has two settings, the more powerful with the spring compressed twice as far as the lower setting. If it takes 5.0 J of work to compress the dart gun to the lower setting, how much work does it take for the higher setting?
a. 20 J
b. 10 J
c. 2.5 J
d. 40 J

26. Describe a system you use daily with internal potential energy.

27. Old-fashioned pendulum clocks are powered by masses that need to be wound back to the top of the clock about once a week to counteract energy lost due to friction and to the chimes. One particular clock has three masses: 4.0 kg, 4.0 kg, and 6.0 kg. They can drop 1.3 meters. How much energy does the clock use in a week?
a. 51 J
b. 76 J
c. 127 J
d. 178 J

28. A water tower stores not only water, but (at least part of) the energy to move the water. How much? Make reasonable estimates for how much water is in the tower, and other quantities you need.

29. Old-fashioned pocket watches needed to be wound daily so they wouldn't run down and lose time, due to the friction in the internal components. This required a large number of turns of the winding key, but not much force per turn, and it was possible to overwind and break the watch. How was the energy stored?
a. A small mass raised a long distance
b. A large mass raised a short distance
c. A weak spring deformed a long way
d. A strong spring deformed a short way

30. Some of the very first clocks invented in China were powered by water. Describe how you think this was done.

7.5 Nonconservative Forces

31. You are in a room in a basement with a smooth concrete floor (friction force equals 40 N) and a nice rug (friction force equals 55 N) that is 3 m by 4 m. However, you have to push a very heavy box from one corner of the rug to the opposite corner of the rug. Will you do more work against friction going around the floor or across the rug, and how much extra?
a. Across the rug is 275 J extra
b. Around the floor is 5 J extra
c. Across the rug is 5 J extra
d. Around the floor is 280 J extra

32. In the Appalachians, along the interstate, there are ramps of loose gravel for semis that have had their brakes fail to drive into to stop. Design an experiment to measure how effective this would be.

7.6 Conservation of Energy

33. You do 30 J of work to load a toy dart gun. However, the dart is 10 cm long and feels a frictional force of 10 N while going through the dart gun's barrel. What is the kinetic energy of the fired dart?

a. 30 J
b. 29 J
c. 28 J
d. 27 J

34. When an object is lifted by a crane, it begins and ends its motion at rest. The same is true of an object pushed across a rough surface. Explain why this happens. What are the differences between these systems?

35. A child has two red wagons, with the rear one tied to the front by a stretchy rope (a spring). If the child pulls on the front wagon, the ____ increases.

a. kinetic energy of the wagons
b. potential energy stored in the spring
c. both A and B
d. not enough information

36. A child has two red wagons, with the rear one tied to the front by a stretchy rope (a spring). If the child pulls on the front wagon, the energy stored in the system increases. How do the relative amounts of potential and kinetic energy in this system change over time?

37. Which of the following are closed systems?

a. Earth
b. a car
c. a frictionless pendulum
d. a mass on a spring in a vacuum

38. Describe a real-world example of a closed system.

39. A 5.0-kg rock falls off of a 10 m cliff. If air resistance exerts an average force of 10 N, what is the kinetic energy when the rock hits the ground?

a. 400 J
b. 12.6 m/s
c. 100 J
d. 500 J

40. Hydroelectricity is generated by storing water behind a dam, and then letting some of it run through generators in the dam to turn them. If the system is the water, what is the environment that is doing work on it? If a dam has water 100 m deep behind it, how much energy was generated if 10,000 kg of water exited the dam at 2.0 m/s?

41. Before railroads were invented, goods often traveled along canals, with mules pulling barges from the bank. If a mule is exerting a 1200 N force for 10 km, and the rope connecting the mule to the barge is at a 20 degree angle from the direction of travel, how much work did the mule do on the barge?

a. 12 MJ
b. 11 MJ
c. 4.1 MJ
d. 6 MJ

42. Describe an instance today in which you did work, by the scientific definition. Then calculate how much work you did in that instance, showing your work.

CHAPTER 8
Linear Momentum and Collisions

FIGURE 8.1 "Each rugby player has great momentum, which will affect the outcome of their collisions with each other and the ground. (credit: vjpaul, Flickr)"

CHAPTER OUTLINE

CONNECTION FOR AP® COURSES In this chapter, you will learn about the concept of momentum and the relationship between momentum and force (both vector quantities) applied over a time interval. Have you ever considered why a glass dropped on a tile floor will often break, but a glass dropped on carpet will often remain intact? Both involve changes in momentum, but the actual collision with the floor is different in each case, just as an automobile collision without the benefit of an airbag can have a significantly different outcome than one with an airbag.

You will learn that the interaction of objects (like a glass and the floor or two automobiles) results in forces, which in turn result in changes in the momentum of each object. At the same time, you will see how the law of momentum conservation can be applied to a system to help determine the outcome of a collision.

The content in this chapter supports:

Big Idea 3 The interactions of an object with other objects can be described by forces.

Enduring Understanding 3.D A force exerted on an object can change the momentum of the object.

Essential Knowledge 3.D.2 The change in momentum of an object occurs over a time interval.

Big Idea 4: Interactions between systems can result in changes in those systems.

Enduring Understanding 4.B Interactions with other objects or systems can change the total linear momentum of a system.

Essential Knowledge 4.B.1 The change in linear momentum for a constant-mass system is the product of the mass of the system and the change in velocity of the center of mass.

Big Idea 5 Changes that occur as a result of interactions are constrained by conservation laws.

Enduring Understanding 5.A Certain quantities are conserved, in the sense that the changes of those quantities in a given system are always equal to the transfer of that quantity to or from the system by all possible interactions with other systems.

Essential Knowledge 5.A.2 For all systems under all circumstances, energy, charge, linear momentum, and angular momentum are conserved.

Essential Knowledge 5.D.1 In a collision between objects, linear momentum is conserved. In an elastic collision, kinetic energy is the same before and after.

Essential Knowledge 5.D.2 In a collision between objects, linear momentum is conserved. In an inelastic collision, kinetic energy is not the same before and after the collision.

Click to view content (https://openstax.org/books/college-physics-ap-courses-2e/pages/8-connection-for-ap-r-courses)

8.1 Linear Momentum and F orce

LEARNING OBJECTIVES

By the end of this section, you will be able to:

- Define linear momentum.
- Explain the relationship between momentum and force.
- State Newton's second law of motion in terms of momentum.
- Calculate momentum given mass and velocity.

Linear Momentum

The scientific definition of linear momentum is consistent with most people's intuitive understanding of momentum: a large, fast-moving object has greater momentum than a smaller, slower object. **Linear momentum** is defined as the product of a system's mass multiplied by its velocity. In symbols, linear momentum is expressed as

$$\mathbf{p} = m\mathbf{v}. \tag{8.1}$$

Momentum is directly proportional to the object's mass and also its velocity. Thus the greater an object's mass or the greater its velocity, the greater its momentum. Momentum $\mathbf{p}$ is a vector having the same direction as the velocity $\mathbf{v}$. The SI unit for momentum is $\text{kg} \cdot \text{m/s}$.

LINEAR MOMENTUM

Linear momentum is defined as the product of a system's mass multiplied by its velocity:

$$\mathbf{p} = m\mathbf{v}. \tag{8.2}$$

EXAMPLE 8.1

Calculating Momentum: A Football Player and a Football

(a) Calculate the momentum of a 110-kg football player running at 8.00 m/s. (b) Compare the player's momentum with the momentum of a hard-thrown 0.410-kg football that has a speed of 25.0 m/s.

Strategy

No information is given regarding direction, and so we can calculate only the magnitude of the momentum, p. (As usual, a symbol that is in italics is a magnitude, whereas one that is italicized, boldfaced, and has an arrow is a vector.) In both parts of this example, the magnitude of momentum can be calculated directly from the definition of momentum given in the equation, which becomes

$$p = mv \tag{8.3}$$

when only magnitudes are considered.

Solution for (a)

To determine the momentum of the player, substitute the known values for the player's mass and speed into the equation.

$$p_{\text{player}} = (110 \text{ kg})(8.00 \text{ m/s}) = 880 \text{ kg} \cdot \text{m/s} \tag{8.4}$$

Solution for (b)

To determine the momentum of the ball, substitute the known values for the ball's mass and speed into the equation.

$$p_{\text{ball}} = (0.410 \text{ kg})(25.0 \text{ m/s}) = 10.3 \text{ kg} \cdot \text{m/s} \tag{8.5}$$

The ratio of the player's momentum to that of the ball is

$$\frac{p_{\text{player}}}{p_{\text{ball}}} = \frac{880}{10.3} = 85.9. \tag{8.6}$$

Discussion

Although the ball has greater velocity, the player has a much greater mass. Thus the momentum of the player is much greater than the momentum of the football, as you might guess. As a result, the player's motion is only slightly affected if he catches the ball. We shall quantify what happens in such collisions in terms of momentum in later sections.

Momentum and Newton's Second Law

The importance of momentum, unlike the importance of energy, was recognized early in the development of classical physics. Momentum was deemed so important that it was called the "quantity of motion." Newton actually stated his **second law of motion** in terms of momentum: The net external force equals the change in momentum of a system divided by the time over which it changes. Using symbols, this law is

$$\mathbf{F}_{\text{net}} = \frac{\Delta \mathbf{p}}{\Delta t}, \tag{8.7}$$

where $\mathbf{F}_{\text{net}}$ is the net external force, $\Delta \mathbf{p}$ is the change in momentum, and Δt is the change in time.

NEWTON'S SECOND LAW OF MOTION IN TERMS OF MOMENTUM

The net external force equals the change in momentum of a system divided by the time over which it changes.

$$\mathbf{F}_{\text{net}} = \frac{\Delta \mathbf{p}}{\Delta t} \tag{8.8}$$

> **MAKING CONNECTIONS: FORCE AND MOMENTUM**
>
> Force and momentum are intimately related. Force acting over time can change momentum, and Newton's second law of motion, can be stated in its most broadly applicable form in terms of momentum. Momentum continues to be a key concept in the study of atomic and subatomic particles in quantum mechanics.

This statement of Newton's second law of motion includes the more familiar $\mathbf{F}_{\text{net}}=m\mathbf{a}$ as a special case. We can derive this form as follows. First, note that the change in momentum $\Delta\mathbf{p}$ is given by

$$\Delta\mathbf{p} = \Delta(m\mathbf{v}). \tag{8.9}$$

If the mass of the system is constant, then

$$\Delta(m\mathbf{v}) = m\Delta\mathbf{v}. \tag{8.10}$$

So that for constant mass, Newton's second law of motion becomes

$$\mathbf{F}_{\text{net}} = \frac{\Delta\mathbf{p}}{\Delta t} = \frac{m\Delta\mathbf{v}}{\Delta t}. \tag{8.11}$$

Because $\frac{\Delta\mathbf{v}}{\Delta t} = \mathbf{a}$, we get the familiar equation

$$\mathbf{F}_{\text{net}}=m\mathbf{a} \tag{8.12}$$

when the mass of the system is constant.

Newton's second law of motion stated in terms of momentum is more generally applicable because it can be applied to systems where the mass is changing, such as rockets, as well as to systems of constant mass. We will consider systems with varying mass in some detail; however, the relationship between momentum and force remains useful when mass is constant, such as in the following example.

EXAMPLE 8.2

Calculating Force: Venus Williams' Racquet

During the 2007 French Open, Venus Williams hit the fastest recorded serve in a premier women's match, reaching a speed of 58 m/s (209 km/h). What is the average force exerted on the 0.057-kg tennis ball by Venus Williams' racquet, assuming that the ball's speed just after impact is 58 m/s, that the initial horizontal component of the velocity before impact is negligible, and that the ball remained in contact with the racquet for 5.0 ms (milliseconds)?

Strategy

This problem involves only one dimension because the ball starts from having no horizontal velocity component before impact. Newton's second law stated in terms of momentum is then written as

$$\mathbf{F}_{\text{net}} = \frac{\Delta\mathbf{p}}{\Delta t}. \tag{8.13}$$

As noted above, when mass is constant, the change in momentum is given by

$$\Delta p = m\Delta v = m(v_{\text{f}} - v_{\text{i}}). \tag{8.14}$$

In this example, the velocity just after impact and the change in time are given; thus, once Δp is calculated, $F_{\text{net}} = \frac{\Delta p}{\Delta t}$ can be used to find the force.

Solution

To determine the change in momentum, substitute the values for the initial and final velocities into the equation above.

$$\begin{aligned} \Delta p &= m(v_f - v_i) \\ &= (0.057 \text{ kg})(58 \text{ m/s} - 0 \text{ m/s}) \\ &= 3.306 \text{ kg} \cdot \text{m/s} \approx 3.3 \text{ kg} \cdot \text{m/s} \end{aligned} \quad (8.15)$$

Now the magnitude of the net external force can determined by using $F_{net} = \frac{\Delta p}{\Delta t}$:

$$\begin{aligned} F_{net} &= \frac{\Delta p}{\Delta t} = \frac{3.306 \text{ kg} \cdot \text{m/s}}{5.0 \times 10^{-3} \text{ s}} \\ &= 661 \text{ N} \approx 660 \text{ N}, \end{aligned} \quad (8.16)$$

where we have retained only two significant figures in the final step.

Discussion

This quantity was the average force exerted by Venus Williams' racquet on the tennis ball during its brief impact (note that the ball also experienced the 0.56-N force of gravity, but that force was not due to the racquet). This problem could also be solved by first finding the acceleration and then using $F_{net} = ma$, but one additional step would be required compared with the strategy used in this example.

8.2 Impulse

LEARNING OBJECTIVES

By the end of this section, you will be able to:

- Define impulse.
- Describe effects of impulses in everyday life.
- Determine the average effective force using graphical representation.
- Calculate average force and impulse given mass, velocity, and time.

The effect of a force on an object depends on how long it acts, as well as how great the force is. In Example 8.1, a very large force acting for a short time had a great effect on the momentum of the tennis ball. A small force could cause the same **change in momentum**, but it would have to act for a much longer time. For example, if the ball were thrown upward, the gravitational force (which is much smaller than the tennis racquet's force) would eventually reverse the momentum of the ball. Quantitatively, the effect we are talking about is the change in momentum $\Delta \mathbf{p}$.

By rearranging the equation $\mathbf{F}_{net} = \frac{\Delta \mathbf{p}}{\Delta t}$ to be

$$\Delta \mathbf{p} = \mathbf{F}_{net} \Delta t, \quad (8.17)$$

we can see how the change in momentum equals the average net external force multiplied by the time this force acts. The quantity $\mathbf{F}_{net} \Delta t$ is given the name **impulse**. Impulse is the same as the change in momentum.

IMPULSE: CHANGE IN MOMENTUM

Change in momentum equals the average net external force multiplied by the time this force acts.

$$\Delta \mathbf{p} = \mathbf{F}_{net} \Delta t \quad (8.18)$$

The quantity $\mathbf{F}_{net} \Delta t$ is given the name impulse.

There are many ways in which an understanding of impulse can save lives, or at least limbs. The dashboard padding in a car, and certainly the airbags, allow the net force on the occupants in the car to act over a much longer time when there is a sudden stop. The momentum change is the same for an occupant, whether an air bag is deployed or not, but the force (to bring the occupant to a stop) will be much less if it acts over a larger time. Cars today have many plastic components. One advantage of plastics is their lighter weight, which results in better gas mileage. Another advantage is that a car will crumple in a collision, especially in the event of a head-on collision. A longer collision time means the force on the car will be less. Deaths during car races decreased dramatically when the rigid frames of racing cars were replaced with parts that could crumple or collapse in the event of an accident.

Bones in a body will fracture if the force on them is too large. If you jump onto the floor from a table, the force on your legs can be immense if you land stiff-legged on a hard surface. Rolling on the ground after jumping from the table, or landing with a parachute, extends the time over which the force (on you from the ground) acts.

EXAMPLE 8.3

Calculating Magnitudes of Impulses: Two Billiard Balls Striking a Rigid Wall

Two identical billiard balls strike a rigid wall with the same speed, and are reflected without any change of speed. The first ball strikes perpendicular to the wall. The second ball strikes the wall at an angle of 30° from the perpendicular, and bounces off at an angle of 30° from perpendicular to the wall.

(a) Determine the direction of the force on the wall due to each ball.

(b) Calculate the ratio of the magnitudes of impulses on the two balls by the wall.

Strategy for (a)

In order to determine the force on the wall, consider the force on the ball due to the wall using Newton's second law and then apply Newton's third law to determine the direction. Assume the x-axis to be normal to the wall and to be positive in the initial direction of motion. Choose the y-axis to be along the wall in the plane of the second ball's motion. The momentum direction and the velocity direction are the same.

Solution for (a)

The first ball bounces directly into the wall and exerts a force on it in the $+x$ direction. Therefore the wall exerts a force on the ball in the $-x$ direction. The second ball continues with the same momentum component in the y direction, but reverses its x-component of momentum, as seen by sketching a diagram of the angles involved and keeping in mind the proportionality between velocity and momentum.

These changes mean the change in momentum for both balls is in the $-x$ direction, so the force of the wall on each ball is along the $-x$ direction.

Strategy for (b)

Calculate the change in momentum for each ball, which is equal to the impulse imparted to the ball.

Solution for (b)

Let u be the speed of each ball before and after collision with the wall, and m the mass of each ball. Choose the x-axis and y-axis as previously described, and consider the change in momentum of the first ball which strikes perpendicular to the wall.

$$p_{\text{xi}} = mu;\ p_{\text{yi}} = 0 \tag{8.19}$$

$$p_{\text{xf}} = -mu;\ p_{\text{yf}} = 0 \tag{8.20}$$

Impulse is the change in momentum vector. Therefore the x-component of impulse is equal to $-2mu$ and the y-component of impulse is equal to zero.

Now consider the change in momentum of the second ball.

$$p_{\text{xi}} = mu\cos 30^\circ;\ p_{\text{yi}} = -mu\sin 30^\circ \tag{8.21}$$

$$p_{\text{xf}} =-mu\cos 30^\circ;\ p_{\text{yf}} = -mu\sin 30^\circ \tag{8.22}$$

It should be noted here that while p_{x} changes sign after the collision, p_{y} does not. Therefore the x-component of impulse is equal to $-2mu\cos 30^\circ$ and the y-component of impulse is equal to zero.

The ratio of the magnitudes of the impulse imparted to the balls is

$$\frac{2mu}{2mu \cos 30^\circ} = \frac{2}{\sqrt{3}} = 1.155. \tag{8.23}$$

Discussion

The direction of impulse and force is the same as in the case of (a); it is normal to the wall and along the negative x-direction. Making use of Newton's third law, the force on the wall due to each ball is normal to the wall along the positive x -direction.

Our definition of impulse includes an assumption that the force is constant over the time interval Δt. *Forces are usually not constant.* Forces vary considerably even during the brief time intervals considered. It is, however, possible to find an average effective force F_{eff} that produces the same result as the corresponding time-varying force. Figure 8.2 shows a graph of what an actual force looks like as a function of time for a ball bouncing off the floor. The area under the curve has units of momentum and is equal to the impulse or change in momentum between times t_1 and t_2. That area is equal to the area inside the rectangle bounded by F_{eff}, t_1, and t_2. Thus the impulses and their effects are the same for both the actual and effective forces.

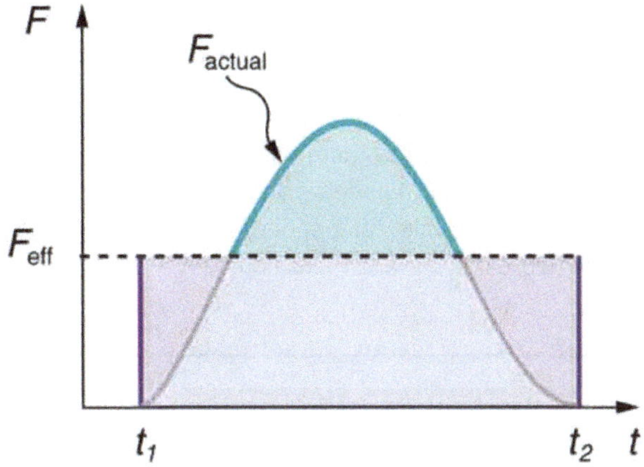

FIGURE 8.2 A graph of force versus time with time along the x-axis and force along the y -axis for an actual force and an equivalent effective force. The areas under the two curves are equal.

MAKING CONNECTIONS: TAKE-HOME INVESTIGATION—HAND MOVEMENT AND IMPULSE

Try catching a ball while "giving" with the ball, pulling your hands toward your body. Then, try catching a ball while keeping your hands still. Hit water in a tub with your full palm. After the water has settled, hit the water again by diving your hand with your fingers first into the water. (Your full palm represents a swimmer doing a belly flop and your diving hand represents a swimmer doing a dive.) Explain what happens in each case and why. Which orientations would you advise people to avoid and why?

MAKING CONNECTIONS: CONSTANT FORCE AND CONSTANT ACCELERATION

The assumption of a constant force in the definition of impulse is analogous to the assumption of a constant acceleration in kinematics. In both cases, nature is adequately described without the use of calculus.

8.3 Conservation of Momentum

LEARNING OBJECTIVES

By the end of this section, you will be able to:

- Describe the principle of conservation of momentum.
- Derive an expression for the conservation of momentum.
- Explain conservation of momentum with examples.
- Explain the principle of conservation of momentum as it relates to atomic and subatomic particles.

Momentum is an important quantity because it is conserved. Yet it was not conserved in the examples in Impulse and Linear Momentum and Force, where large changes in momentum were produced by forces acting on the system of interest. Under what circumstances is momentum conserved?

The answer to this question entails considering a sufficiently large system. It is always possible to find a larger system in which total momentum is constant, even if momentum changes for components of the system. If a football player runs into the goalpost in the end zone, there will be a force on him that causes him to bounce backward. However, the Earth also recoils —conserving momentum—because of the force applied to it through the goalpost. Because Earth is many orders of magnitude more massive than the player, its recoil is immeasurably small and can be neglected in any practical sense, but it is real nevertheless.

Consider what happens if the masses of two colliding objects are more similar than the masses of a football player and Earth—for example, one car bumping into another, as shown in Figure 8.3. Both cars are coasting in the same direction when the lead car (labeled m_2) is bumped by the trailing car (labeled m_1). The only unbalanced force on each car is the force of the collision. (Assume that the effects due to friction are negligible.) Car 1 slows down as a result of the collision, losing some momentum, while car 2 speeds up and gains some momentum. We shall now show that the total momentum of the two-car system remains constant.

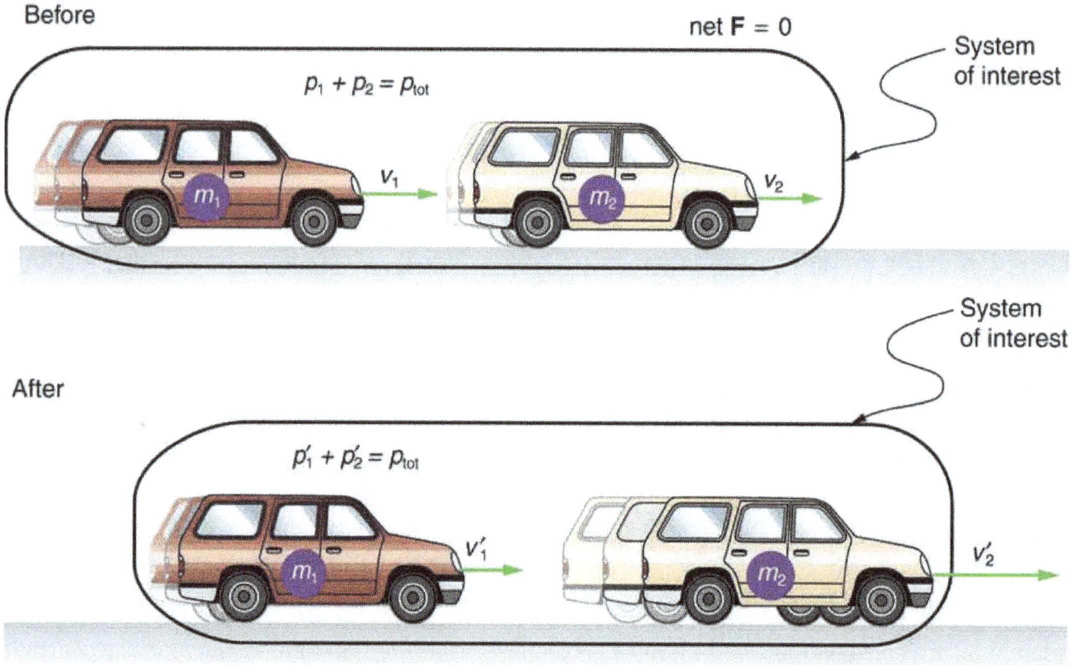

FIGURE 8.3 A car of mass m_1 moving with a velocity of v_1 bumps into another car of mass m_2 and velocity v_2 that it is following. As a result, the first car slows down to a velocity of v'_1 and the second speeds up to a velocity of v'_2. The momentum of each car is changed, but the total momentum p_{tot} of the two cars is the same before and after the collision (if you assume friction is negligible).

Using the definition of impulse, the change in momentum of car 1 is given by

$$\Delta p_1 = F_1 \Delta t, \qquad 8.24$$

where F_1 is the force on car 1 due to car 2, and Δt is the time the force acts (the duration of the collision). Intuitively, it seems obvious that the collision time is the same for both cars, but it is only true for objects traveling at ordinary speeds. This assumption must be modified for objects travelling near the speed of light, without affecting the result that momentum is conserved.

Similarly, the change in momentum of car 2 is

$$\Delta p_2 = F_2 \Delta t, \quad (8.25)$$

where F_2 is the force on car 2 due to car 1, and we assume the duration of the collision Δt is the same for both cars. We know from Newton's third law that $F_2 = -F_1$, and so

$$\Delta p_2 = -F_1 \Delta t = -\Delta p_1. \quad (8.26)$$

Thus, the changes in momentum are equal and opposite, and

$$\Delta p_1 + \Delta p_2 = 0. \quad (8.27)$$

Because the changes in momentum add to zero, the total momentum of the two-car system is constant. That is,

$$p_1 + p_2 = \text{constant}, \quad (8.28)$$

$$p_1 + p_2 = p'_1 + p'_2, \quad (8.29)$$

where p'_1 and p'_2 are the momenta of cars 1 and 2 after the collision. (We often use primes to denote the final state.)

This result—that momentum is conserved—has validity far beyond the preceding one-dimensional case. It can be similarly shown that total momentum is conserved for any isolated system, with any number of objects in it. In equation form, the **conservation of momentum principle** for an isolated system is written

$$\mathbf{p}_{\text{tot}} = \text{constant}, \quad (8.30)$$

or

$$\mathbf{p}_{\text{tot}} = \mathbf{p}'_{\text{tot}}, \quad (8.31)$$

where $\mathbf{p}_{\text{tot}}$ is the total momentum (the sum of the momenta of the individual objects in the system) and $\mathbf{p}'_{\text{tot}}$ is the total momentum some time later. (The total momentum can be shown to be the momentum of the center of mass of the system.) An **isolated system** is defined to be one for which the net external force is zero $(\mathbf{F}_{\text{net}} = 0)$.

CONSERVATION OF MOMENTUM PRINCIPLE

$$\begin{aligned} \mathbf{p}_{\text{tot}} &= \text{constant} \\ \mathbf{p}_{\text{tot}} &= \mathbf{p}'_{\text{tot}} \quad \text{(isolated system)} \end{aligned} \quad (8.32)$$

ISOLATED SYSTEM

An isolated system is defined to be one for which the net external force is zero $(\mathbf{F}_{\text{net}} = 0)$.

Perhaps an easier way to see that momentum is conserved for an isolated system is to consider Newton's second law in terms of momentum, $\mathbf{F}_{\text{net}} = \frac{\Delta \mathbf{p}_{\text{tot}}}{\Delta t}$. For an isolated system, $(\mathbf{F}_{\text{net}} = 0)$; thus, $\Delta \mathbf{p}_{\text{tot}} = 0$, and $\mathbf{p}_{\text{tot}}$ is constant.

We have noted that the three length dimensions in nature—x, y, and z—are independent, and it is interesting to note that momentum can be conserved in different ways along each dimension. For example, during projectile motion and where air resistance is negligible, momentum is conserved in the horizontal direction because horizontal forces are zero and momentum is unchanged. But along the vertical direction, the net vertical force is not zero and the momentum of the projectile is not conserved. (See Figure 8.4.) However, if the momentum of the projectile-Earth system is considered in the vertical direction, we find that the total momentum is conserved.

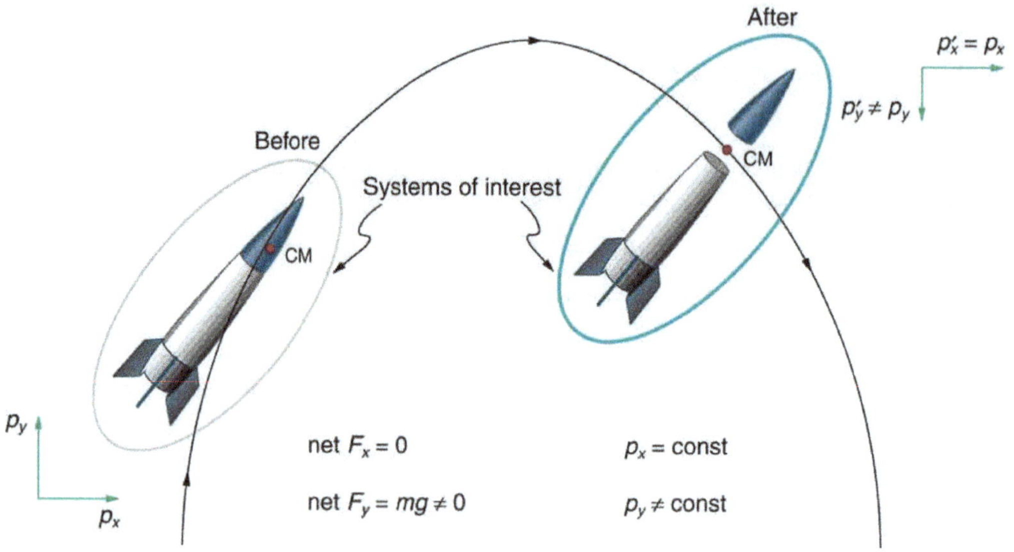

FIGURE 8.4 The horizontal component of a projectile's momentum is conserved if air resistance is negligible, even in this case where a space probe separates. The forces causing the separation are internal to the system, so that the net external horizontal force $F_{x\text{-net}}$ is still zero. The vertical component of the momentum is not conserved, because the net vertical force $F_{y\text{-net}}$ is not zero. In the vertical direction, the space probe-Earth system needs to be considered and we find that the total momentum is conserved. The center of mass of the space probe takes the same path it would if the separation did not occur.

The conservation of momentum principle can be applied to systems as different as a comet striking Earth and a gas containing huge numbers of atoms and molecules. Conservation of momentum is violated only when the net external force is not zero. But another larger system can always be considered in which momentum is conserved by simply including the source of the external force. For example, in the collision of two cars considered above, the two-car system conserves momentum while each one-car system does not.

MAKING CONNECTIONS: TAKE-HOME INVESTIGATION—DROP OF TENNIS BALL AND A BASKETBALL

Hold a tennis ball side by side and in contact with a basketball. Drop the balls together. (Be careful!) What happens? Explain your observations. Now hold the tennis ball above and in contact with the basketball. What happened? Explain your observations. What do you think will happen if the basketball ball is held above and in contact with the tennis ball?

MAKING CONNECTIONS: TAKE-HOME INVESTIGATION—TWO TENNIS BALLS IN A BALLISTIC TRAJECTORY

Tie two tennis balls together with a string about a foot long. Hold one ball and let the other hang down and throw it in a ballistic trajectory. Explain your observations. Now mark the center of the string with bright ink or attach a brightly colored sticker to it and throw again. What happened? Explain your observations.

Some aquatic animals such as jellyfish move around based on the principles of conservation of momentum. A jellyfish fills its umbrella section with water and then pushes the water out resulting in motion in the opposite direction to that of the jet of water. Squids propel themselves in a similar manner but, in contrast with jellyfish, are able to control the direction in which they move by aiming their nozzle forward or backward. Typical squids can move at speeds of 8 to 12 km/h.

The ballistocardiograph (BCG) was a diagnostic tool used in the second half of the 20th century to study the strength of the heart. About once a second, your heart beats, forcing blood into the aorta. A force in the opposite direction is exerted on the rest of your body (recall Newton's third law). A ballistocardiograph is a device that can measure this reaction force. This measurement is done by using a sensor (resting on the person) or by using a moving table suspended from the ceiling. This technique can gather information on the strength of the heart beat and the volume of blood passing from the heart. However, the electrocardiogram (ECG or EKG) and the echocardiogram (cardiac ECHO or ECHO; a technique that uses ultrasound to see an image of the heart) are more widely used in the practice of cardiology.

MAKING CONNECTIONS: CONSERVATION OF MOMENTUM AND COLLISION

Conservation of momentum is quite useful in describing collisions. Momentum is crucial to our understanding of atomic and subatomic particles because much of what we know about these particles comes from collision experiments.

Subatomic Collisions and Momentum

The conservation of momentum principle not only applies to the macroscopic objects, it is also essential to our explorations of atomic and subatomic particles. Giant machines hurl subatomic particles at one another, and researchers evaluate the results by assuming conservation of momentum (among other things).

On the small scale, we find that particles and their properties are invisible to the naked eye but can be measured with our instruments, and models of these subatomic particles can be constructed to describe the results. Momentum is found to be a property of all subatomic particles including massless particles such as photons that compose light. Momentum being a property of particles hints that momentum may have an identity beyond the description of an object's mass multiplied by the object's velocity. Indeed, momentum relates to wave properties and plays a fundamental role in what measurements are taken and how we take these measurements. Furthermore, we find that the conservation of momentum principle is valid when considering systems of particles. We use this principle to analyze the masses and other properties of previously undetected particles, such as the nucleus of an atom and the existence of quarks that make up particles of nuclei. Figure 8.5 below illustrates how a particle scattering backward from another implies that its target is massive and dense. Experiments seeking evidence that **quarks** make up protons (one type of particle that makes up nuclei) scattered high-energy electrons off of protons (nuclei of hydrogen atoms). Electrons occasionally scattered straight backward in a manner that implied a very small and very dense particle makes up the proton—this observation is considered nearly direct evidence of quarks. The analysis was based partly on the same conservation of momentum principle that works so well on the large scale.

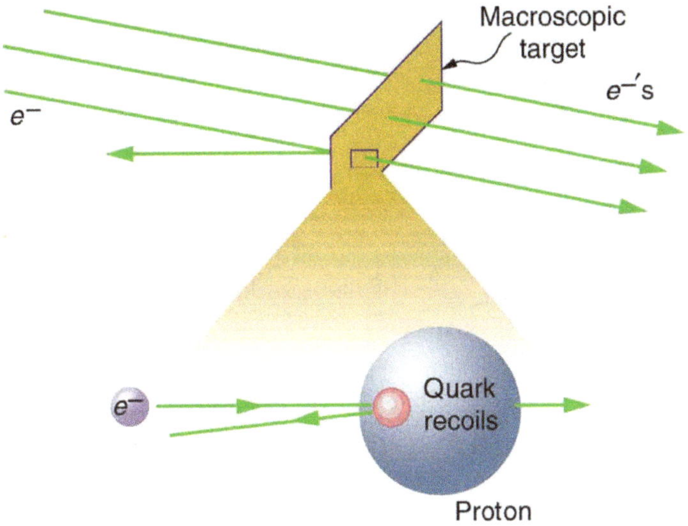

FIGURE 8.5 A subatomic particle scatters straight backward from a target particle. In experiments seeking evidence for quarks, electrons were observed to occasionally scatter straight backward from a proton.

8.4 Elastic Collisions in One Dimension

LEARNING OBJECTIVES

By the end of this section, you will be able to:

- Describe an elastic collision of two objects in one dimension.
- Define internal kinetic energy.
- Derive an expression for conservation of internal kinetic energy in a one dimensional collision.
- Determine the final velocities in an elastic collision given masses and initial velocities.

Let us consider various types of two-object collisions. These collisions are the easiest to analyze, and they illustrate many of the physical principles involved in collisions. The conservation of momentum principle is very useful here, and it can be used whenever the net external force on a system is zero.

We start with the elastic collision of two objects moving along the same line—a one-dimensional problem. An **elastic collision** is one that also conserves internal kinetic energy. **Internal kinetic energy** is the sum of the kinetic energies of the objects in the system. Figure 8.6 illustrates an elastic collision in which internal kinetic energy and momentum are conserved.

Truly elastic collisions can only be achieved with subatomic particles, such as electrons striking nuclei. Macroscopic collisions can be very nearly, but not quite, elastic—some kinetic energy is always converted into other forms of energy such as heat transfer due to friction and sound. One macroscopic collision that is nearly elastic is that of two steel blocks on ice. Another nearly elastic collision is that between two carts with spring bumpers on an air track. Icy surfaces and air tracks are nearly frictionless, more readily allowing nearly elastic collisions on them.

ELASTIC COLLISION

An **elastic collision** is one that conserves internal kinetic energy.

INTERNAL KINETIC ENERGY

Internal kinetic energy is the sum of the kinetic energies of the objects in the system.

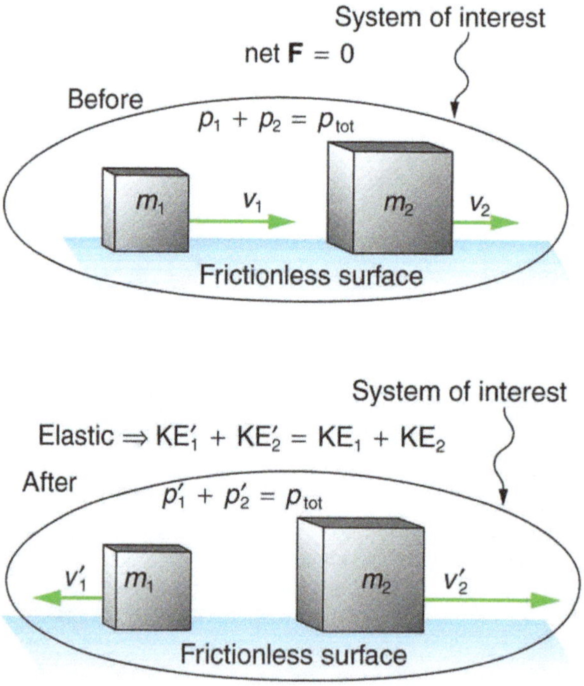

FIGURE 8.6 An elastic one-dimensional two-object collision. Momentum and internal kinetic energy are conserved.

Now, to solve problems involving one-dimensional elastic collisions between two objects we can use the equations for conservation of momentum and conservation of internal kinetic energy. First, the equation for conservation of momentum for two objects in a one-dimensional collision is

$$p_1 + p_2 = p'_1 + p'_2 \quad (F_{\text{net}} = 0) \tag{8.33}$$

or

$$m_1 v_1 + m_2 v_2 = m_1 v'_1 + m_2 v'_2 \quad (F_{\text{net}} = 0), \tag{8.34}$$

where the primes (') indicate values after the collision. By definition, an elastic collision conserves internal kinetic energy, and so the sum of kinetic energies before the collision equals the sum after the collision. Thus,

$$\frac{1}{2}m_1 {v_1}^2 + \frac{1}{2}m_2 {v_2}^2 = \frac{1}{2}m_1 {v'_1}^2 + \frac{1}{2}m_2 {v'_2}^2 \quad \text{(two-object elastic collision)} \tag{8.35}$$

expresses the equation for conservation of internal kinetic energy in a one-dimensional collision.

EXAMPLE 8.4

Calculating Velocities Following an Elastic Collision

Calculate the velocities of two objects following an elastic collision, given that

$$m_1 = 0.500\text{ kg},\ m_2 = 3.50\text{ kg},\ v_1 = 4.00\text{ m/s, and } v_2 = 0. \tag{8.36}$$

Strategy and Concept

First, visualize what the initial conditions mean—a small object strikes a larger object that is initially at rest. This situation is slightly simpler than the situation shown in Figure 8.6 where both objects are initially moving. We are asked to find two unknowns (the final velocities v'_1 and v'_2). To find two unknowns, we must use two independent equations. Because this collision is elastic, we can use the above two equations. Both can be simplified by the fact that object 2 is initially at rest, and thus $v_2 = 0$. Once we simplify these equations, we combine them algebraically to solve for the unknowns.

Solution

For this problem, note that $v_2 = 0$ and use conservation of momentum. Thus,

$$p_1 = p'_1 + p'_2 \tag{8.37}$$

or

$$m_1 v_1 = m_1 v'_1 + m_2 v'_2. \tag{8.38}$$

Using conservation of internal kinetic energy and that $v_2 = 0$,

$$\frac{1}{2}m_1 {v_1}^2 = \frac{1}{2}m_1 {v'_1}^2 + \frac{1}{2}m_2 {v'_2}^2. \tag{8.39}$$

Solving the first equation (momentum equation) for v'_2, we obtain

$$v'_2 = \frac{m_1}{m_2}(v_1 - v'_1). \tag{8.40}$$

Substituting this expression into the second equation (internal kinetic energy equation) eliminates the variable v'_2, leaving only v'_1 as an unknown (the algebra is left as an exercise for the reader). There are two solutions to any quadratic equation; in this example, they are

$$v'_1 = 4.00\text{ m/s} \tag{8.41}$$

and

$$v'_1 = -3.00\text{ m/s}. \tag{8.42}$$

As noted when quadratic equations were encountered in earlier chapters, both solutions may or may not be meaningful. In this case, the first solution is the same as the initial condition. The first solution thus represents the situation before the collision and is discarded. The second solution ($v'_1 = -3.00\text{ m/s}$) is negative, meaning that the first object bounces backward. When this negative value of v'_1 is used to find the velocity of the second object after the collision, we get

$$v'_2 = \frac{m_1}{m_2}(v_1 - v'_1) = \frac{0.500\text{ kg}}{3.50\text{ kg}}[4.00 - (-3.00)]\text{ m/s} \quad (8.43)$$

or

$$v'_2 = 1.00\text{ m/s}. \quad (8.44)$$

Discussion

The result of this example is intuitively reasonable. A small object strikes a larger one at rest and bounces backward. The larger one is knocked forward, but with a low speed. (This is like a compact car bouncing backward off a full-size SUV that is initially at rest.) As a check, try calculating the internal kinetic energy before and after the collision. You will see that the internal kinetic energy is unchanged at 4.00 J. Also check the total momentum before and after the collision; you will find it, too, is unchanged.

The equations for conservation of momentum and internal kinetic energy as written above can be used to describe any one-dimensional elastic collision of two objects. These equations can be extended to more objects if needed.

MAKING CONNECTIONS: TAKE-HOME INVESTIGATION—ICE CUBES AND ELASTIC COLLISION

Find a few ice cubes which are about the same size and a smooth kitchen tabletop or a table with a glass top. Place the ice cubes on the surface several centimeters away from each other. Flick one ice cube toward a stationary ice cube and observe the path and velocities of the ice cubes after the collision. Try to avoid edge-on collisions and collisions with rotating ice cubes. Have you created approximately elastic collisions? Explain the speeds and directions of the ice cubes using momentum.

PHET EXPLORATIONS

Collision Lab

Investigate collisions on an air hockey table. Set up your own experiments: vary the number of discs, masses and initial conditions. Is momentum conserved? Is kinetic energy conserved? Vary the elasticity and see what happens.

[Click to view content (https://openstax.org/books/college-physics-ap-courses-2e/pages/8-4-elastic-collisions-in-one-dimension)](https://openstax.org/books/college-physics-ap-courses-2e/pages/8-4-elastic-collisions-in-one-dimension)

8.5 Inelastic Collisions in One Dimension

LEARNING OBJECTIVES

By the end of this section, you will be able to:

- Define inelastic collision.
- Explain perfectly inelastic collision.
- Apply an understanding of collisions to sports.
- Determine recoil velocity and loss in kinetic energy given mass and initial velocity.

We have seen that in an elastic collision, internal kinetic energy is conserved. An **inelastic collision** is one in which the internal kinetic energy changes (it is not conserved). This lack of conservation means that the forces between colliding objects may remove or add internal kinetic energy. Work done by internal forces may change the forms of energy within a system. For inelastic collisions, such as when colliding objects stick together, this internal work may transform some internal kinetic energy into heat transfer. Or it may convert stored energy into internal kinetic energy, such as when exploding bolts separate a satellite from its launch vehicle.

INELASTIC COLLISION

An inelastic collision is one in which the internal kinetic energy changes (it is not conserved).

Figure 8.7 shows an example of an inelastic collision. Two objects that have equal masses head toward one another at equal speeds and then stick together. Their total internal kinetic energy is initially $\frac{1}{2}mv^2 + \frac{1}{2}mv^2 = mv^2$. The two objects come to rest after sticking together, conserving momentum. But the internal kinetic energy is zero after the collision. A collision in which the objects stick together is sometimes called a **perfectly inelastic collision** because it reduces internal kinetic energy more than does any other type of inelastic collision. In fact, such a collision reduces internal kinetic energy to the minimum it can have while still conserving momentum.

PERFECTLY INELASTIC COLLISION

A collision in which the objects stick together is sometimes called "perfectly inelastic."

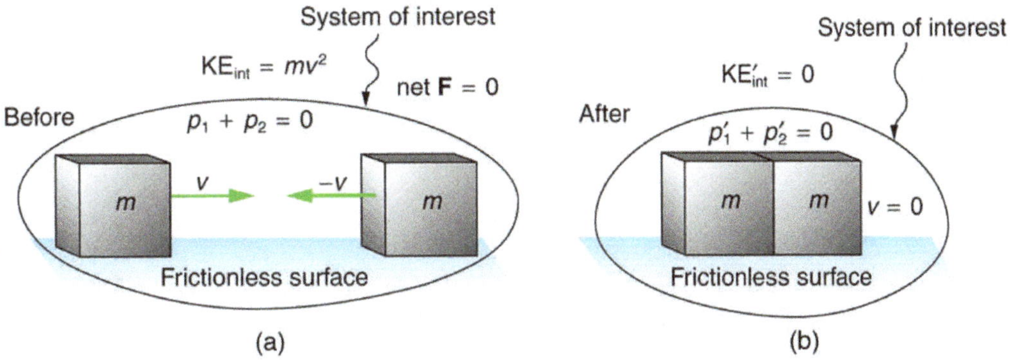

FIGURE 8.7 An inelastic one-dimensional two-object collision. Momentum is conserved, but internal kinetic energy is not conserved. (a) Two objects of equal mass initially head directly toward one another at the same speed. (b) The objects stick together (a perfectly inelastic collision), and so their final velocity is zero. The internal kinetic energy of the system changes in any inelastic collision and is reduced to zero in this example.

EXAMPLE 8.5

Calculating Velocity and Change in Kinetic Energy: Inelastic Collision of a Puck and a Goalie

(a) Find the recoil velocity of a 70.0-kg ice hockey goalie, originally at rest, who catches a 0.150-kg hockey puck slapped at him at a velocity of 35.0 m/s. (b) How much kinetic energy is lost during the collision? Assume friction between the ice and the puck-goalie system is negligible. (See Figure 8.8)

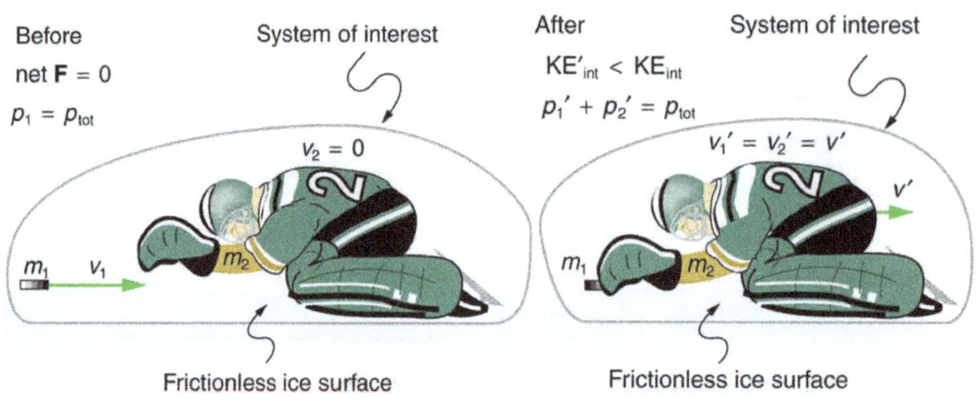

FIGURE 8.8 An ice hockey goalie catches a hockey puck and recoils backward. The initial kinetic energy of the puck is almost entirely converted to thermal energy and sound in this inelastic collision.

Strategy

Momentum is conserved because the net external force on the puck-goalie system is zero. We can thus use conservation of momentum to find the final velocity of the puck and goalie system. Note that the initial velocity of the goalie is zero and that the final velocity of the puck and goalie are the same. Once the final velocity is found, the kinetic energies can be calculated before and after the collision and compared as requested.

Solution for (a)

Momentum is conserved because the net external force on the puck-goalie system is zero.

Conservation of momentum is

$$p_1 + p_2 = p'_1 + p'_2 \tag{8.45}$$

or

$$m_1 v_1 + m_2 v_2 = m_1 v'_1 + m_2 v'_2. \tag{8.46}$$

Because the goalie is initially at rest, we know $v_2 = 0$. Because the goalie catches the puck, the final velocities are equal, or $v'_1 = v'_2 = v'$. Thus, the conservation of momentum equation simplifies to

$$m_1 v_1 = (m_1 + m_2) v'. \tag{8.47}$$

Solving for v' yields

$$v' = \frac{m_1}{m_1 + m_2} v_1. \tag{8.48}$$

Entering known values in this equation, we get

$$v' = \left(\frac{0.150 \text{ kg}}{0.150 \text{ kg} + 70.0 \text{ kg}} \right)(35.0 \text{ m/s}) = 7.48 \times 10^{-2} \text{ m/s}. \tag{8.49}$$

Discussion for (a)

This recoil velocity is small and in the same direction as the puck's original velocity, as we might expect.

Solution for (b)

Before the collision, the internal kinetic energy KE_{int} of the system is that of the hockey puck, because the goalie is initially at rest. Therefore, KE_{int} is initially

$$\begin{aligned} \text{KE}_{\text{int}} &= \tfrac{1}{2} m v^2 = \tfrac{1}{2}(0.150 \text{ kg})(35.0 \text{ m/s})^2 \\ &= 91.9 \text{ J}. \end{aligned} \tag{8.50}$$

After the collision, the internal kinetic energy is

$$\begin{aligned} KE'_{int} &= \tfrac{1}{2}(m+M)v^2 = \tfrac{1}{2}(70.15\text{ kg})\left(7.48 \times 10^{-2}\text{ m/s}\right)^2 \\ &= 0.196\text{ J}. \end{aligned} \quad 8.51$$

The change in internal kinetic energy is thus

$$\begin{aligned} KE'_{int} - KE_{int} &= 0.196\text{ J} - 91.9\text{ J} \\ &= -91.7\text{ J} \end{aligned} \quad 8.52$$

where the minus sign indicates that the energy was lost.

Discussion for (b)

Nearly all of the initial internal kinetic energy is lost in this perfectly inelastic collision. KE_{int} is mostly converted to thermal energy and sound.

During some collisions, the objects do not stick together and less of the internal kinetic energy is removed—such as happens in most automobile accidents. Alternatively, stored energy may be converted into internal kinetic energy during a collision. Figure 8.9 shows a one-dimensional example in which two carts on an air track collide, releasing potential energy from a compressed spring. Example 8.6 deals with data from such a collision.

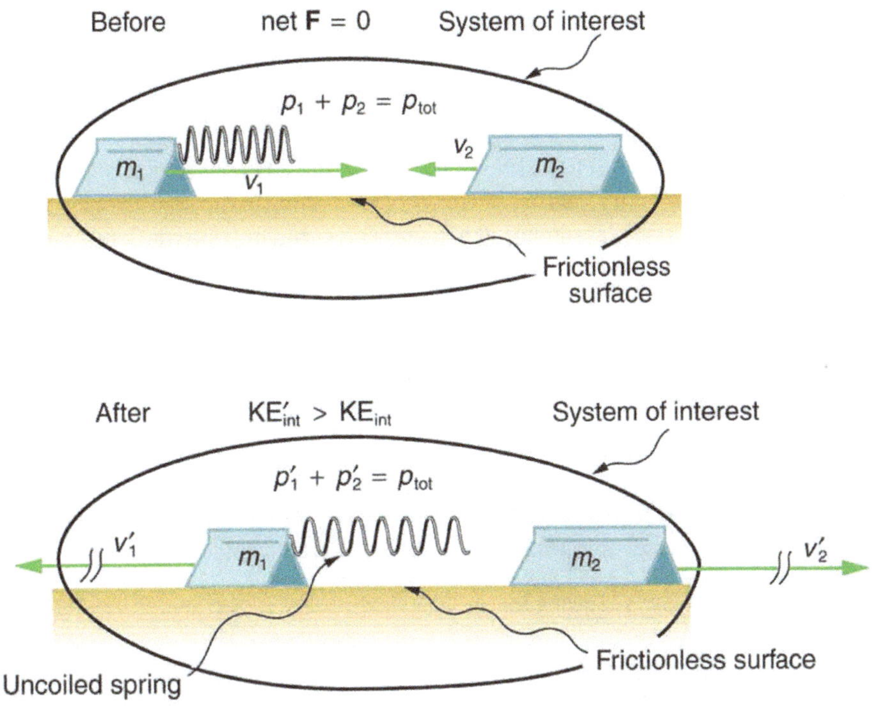

FIGURE 8.9 An air track is nearly frictionless, so that momentum is conserved. Motion is one-dimensional. In this collision, examined in Example 8.6, the potential energy of a compressed spring is released during the collision and is converted to internal kinetic energy.

Collisions are particularly important in sports and the sporting and leisure industry utilizes elastic and inelastic collisions. Let us look briefly at tennis. Recall that in a collision, it is momentum and not force that is important. So, a heavier tennis racquet will have the advantage over a lighter one. This conclusion also holds true for other sports—a lightweight bat (such as a softball bat) cannot hit a hardball very far.

The location of the impact of the tennis ball on the racquet is also important, as is the part of the stroke during which the impact occurs. A smooth motion results in the maximizing of the velocity of the ball after impact and reduces sports injuries such as tennis elbow. A tennis player tries to hit the ball on the "sweet spot" on the racquet, where the vibration and impact are minimized and the ball is able to be given more velocity. Sports science and technologies also use physics concepts such as momentum and rotational motion and vibrations.

TAKE-HOME EXPERIMENT—BOUNCING OF TENNIS BALL

1. Find a racquet (a tennis, badminton, or other racquet will do). Place the racquet on the floor and stand on the handle. Drop a tennis ball on the strings from a measured height. Measure how high the ball bounces. Now ask a friend to hold the racquet firmly by the handle and drop a tennis ball from the same measured height above the racquet. Measure how high the ball bounces and observe what happens to your friend's hand during the collision. Explain your observations and measurements.
2. The coefficient of restitution (c) is a measure of the elasticity of a collision between a ball and an object, and is defined as the ratio of the speeds after and before the collision. A perfectly elastic collision has a c of 1. For a ball bouncing off the floor (or a racquet on the floor), c can be shown to be $c = (h/H)^{1/2}$ where h is the height to which the ball bounces and H is the height from which the ball is dropped. Determine c for the cases in Part 1 and for the case of a tennis ball bouncing off a concrete or wooden floor ($c = 0.85$ for new tennis balls used on a tennis court).

EXAMPLE 8.6

Calculating Final Velocity and Energy Release: Two Carts Collide

In the collision pictured in Figure 8.9, two carts collide inelastically. Cart 1 (denoted m_1 carries a spring which is initially compressed. During the collision, the spring releases its potential energy and converts it to internal kinetic energy. The mass of cart 1 and the spring is 0.350 kg, and the cart and the spring together have an initial velocity of $2.00\ \text{m/s}$. Cart 2 (denoted m_2 in Figure 8.9) has a mass of 0.500 kg and an initial velocity of $-0.500\ \text{m/s}$. After the collision, cart 1 is observed to recoil with a velocity of $-4.00\ \text{m/s}$. (a) What is the final velocity of cart 2? (b) How much energy was released by the spring (assuming all of it was converted into internal kinetic energy)?

Strategy

We can use conservation of momentum to find the final velocity of cart 2, because $F_{\text{net}} = 0$ (the track is frictionless and the force of the spring is internal). Once this velocity is determined, we can compare the internal kinetic energy before and after the collision to see how much energy was released by the spring.

Solution for (a)

As before, the equation for conservation of momentum in a two-object system is

$$m_1 v_1 + m_2 v_2 = m_1 v'_1 + m_2 v'_2. \tag{8.53}$$

The only unknown in this equation is v'_2. Solving for v'_2 and substituting known values into the previous equation yields

$$\begin{aligned} v'_2 &= \frac{m_1 v_1 + m_2 v_2 - m_1 v'_1}{m_2} \\ &= \frac{(0.350\ \text{kg})(2.00\ \text{m/s}) + (0.500\ \text{kg})(-0.500\ \text{m/s})}{0.500\ \text{kg}} - \frac{(0.350\ \text{kg})(-4.00\ \text{m/s})}{0.500\ \text{kg}} \\ &= 3.70\ \text{m/s}. \end{aligned} \tag{8.54}$$

Solution for (b)

The internal kinetic energy before the collision is

$$\begin{aligned} \text{KE}_{\text{int}} &= \tfrac{1}{2} m_1 v_1^2 + \tfrac{1}{2} m_2 v_2^2 \\ &= \tfrac{1}{2}(0.350\ \text{kg})(2.00\ \text{m/s})^2 + \tfrac{1}{2}(0.500\ \text{kg})(-0.500\ \text{m/s})^2 \\ &= 0.763\ \text{J}. \end{aligned} \tag{8.55}$$

After the collision, the internal kinetic energy is

$$\begin{aligned} \text{KE}'_{\text{int}} &= \tfrac{1}{2}m_1 v'^2_1 + \tfrac{1}{2}m_2 v'^2_2 \\ &= \tfrac{1}{2}(0.350\text{ kg})(-4.00\text{ m/s})^2 + \tfrac{1}{2}(0.500\text{ kg})(3.70\text{ m/s})^2 \\ &= 6.22\text{ J.} \end{aligned} \quad 8.56$$

The change in internal kinetic energy is thus

$$\begin{aligned} \text{KE}'_{\text{int}} - \text{KE}_{\text{int}} &= 6.22\text{ J} - 0.763\text{ J} \\ &= 5.46\text{ J.} \end{aligned} \quad 8.57$$

Discussion

The final velocity of cart 2 is large and positive, meaning that it is moving to the right after the collision. The internal kinetic energy in this collision increases by 5.46 J. That energy was released by the spring.

8.6 Collisions of Point Masses in Two Dimensions

LEARNING OBJECTIVES

By the end of this section, you will be able to:

- Discuss two dimensional collisions as an extension of one dimensional analysis.
- Define point masses.
- Derive an expression for conservation of momentum along *x*-axis and *y*-axis.
- Describe elastic collisions of two objects with equal mass.
- Determine the magnitude and direction of the final velocity given initial velocity, and scattering angle.

In the previous two sections, we considered only one-dimensional collisions; during such collisions, the incoming and outgoing velocities are all along the same line. But what about collisions, such as those between billiard balls, in which objects scatter to the side? These are two-dimensional collisions, and we shall see that their study is an extension of the one-dimensional analysis already presented. The approach taken (similar to the approach in discussing two-dimensional kinematics and dynamics) is to choose a convenient coordinate system and resolve the motion into components along perpendicular axes. Resolving the motion yields a pair of one-dimensional problems to be solved simultaneously.

One complication arising in two-dimensional collisions is that the objects might rotate before or after their collision. For example, if two ice skaters hook arms as they pass by one another, they will spin in circles. We will not consider such rotation until later, and so for now we arrange things so that no rotation is possible. To avoid rotation, we consider only the scattering of **point masses**—that is, structureless particles that cannot rotate or spin.

We start by assuming that $\mathbf{F}_{\text{net}} = 0$, so that momentum $\mathbf{p}$ is conserved. The simplest collision is one in which one of the particles is initially at rest. (See Figure 8.10.) The best choice for a coordinate system is one with an axis parallel to the velocity of the incoming particle, as shown in Figure 8.10. Because momentum is conserved, the components of momentum along the x- and y-axes $(p_x \text{ and } p_y)$ will also be conserved, but with the chosen coordinate system, p_y is initially zero and p_x is the momentum of the incoming particle. Both facts simplify the analysis. (Even with the simplifying assumptions of point masses, one particle initially at rest, and a convenient coordinate system, we still gain new insights into nature from the analysis of two-dimensional collisions.)

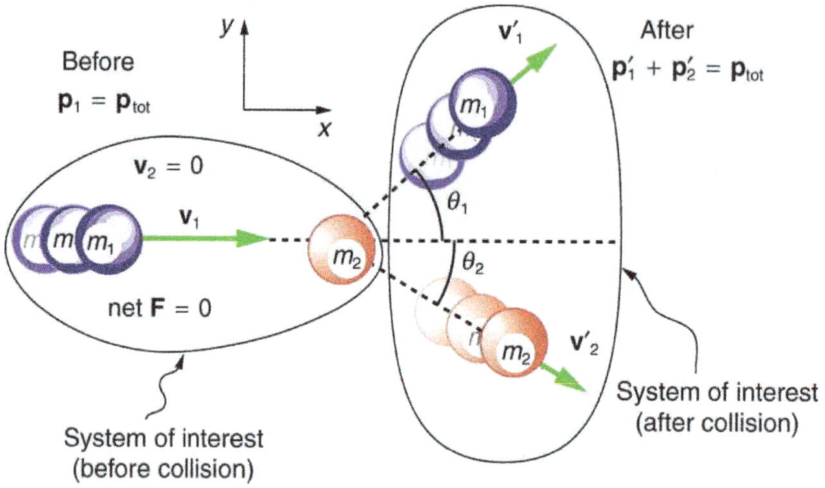

FIGURE 8.10 A two-dimensional collision with the coordinate system chosen so that m_2 is initially at rest and v_1 is parallel to the x -axis. This coordinate system is sometimes called the laboratory coordinate system, because many scattering experiments have a target that is stationary in the laboratory, while particles are scattered from it to determine the particles that make-up the target and how they are bound together. The particles may not be observed directly, but their initial and final velocities are.

Along the x-axis, the equation for conservation of momentum is

$$p_{1x} + p_{2x} = p'_{1x} + p'_{2x}. \tag{8.58}$$

Where the subscripts denote the particles and axes and the primes denote the situation after the collision. In terms of masses and velocities, this equation is

$$m_1 v_{1x} + m_2 v_{2x} = m_1 v'_{1x} + m_2 v'_{2x}. \tag{8.59}$$

But because particle 2 is initially at rest, this equation becomes

$$m_1 v_{1x} = m_1 v'_{1x} + m_2 v'_{2x}. \tag{8.60}$$

The components of the velocities along the x-axis have the form $v \cos \theta$. Because particle 1 initially moves along the x-axis, we find $v_{1x} = v_1$.

Conservation of momentum along the x-axis gives the following equation:

$$m_1 v_1 = m_1 v'_1 \cos \theta_1 + m_2 v'_2 \cos \theta_2, \tag{8.61}$$

where θ_1 and θ_2 are as shown in Figure 8.10.

CONSERVATION OF MOMENTUM ALONG THE x -AXIS

$$m_1 v_1 = m_1 v'_1 \cos \theta_1 + m_2 v'_2 \cos \theta_2 \tag{8.62}$$

Along the y-axis, the equation for conservation of momentum is

$$p_{1y} + p_{2y} = p'_{1y} + p'_{2y} \tag{8.63}$$

or

$$m_1 v_{1y} + m_2 v_{2y} = m_1 v'_{1y} + m_2 v'_{2y}. \tag{8.64}$$

But v_{1y} is zero, because particle 1 initially moves along the x-axis. Because particle 2 is initially at rest, v_{2y} is also zero. The equation for conservation of momentum along the y-axis becomes

$$0 = m_1 v'_{1y} + m_2 v'_{2y}. \tag{8.65}$$

The components of the velocities along the y-axis have the form $v \sin \theta$.

Thus, conservation of momentum along the y-axis gives the following equation:

$$0 = m_1 v'_1 \sin\theta_1 + m_2 v'_2 \sin\theta_2. \quad (8.66)$$

CONSERVATION OF MOMENTUM ALONG THE y-AXIS

$$0 = m_1 v'_1 \sin\theta_1 + m_2 v'_2 \sin\theta_2 \quad (8.67)$$

The equations of conservation of momentum along the x-axis and y-axis are very useful in analyzing two-dimensional collisions of particles, where one is originally stationary (a common laboratory situation). But two equations can only be used to find two unknowns, and so other data may be necessary when collision experiments are used to explore nature at the subatomic level.

EXAMPLE 8.7

Determining the Final Velocity of an Unseen Object from the Scattering of Another Object

Suppose the following experiment is performed. A 0.250-kg object (m_1) is slid on a frictionless surface into a dark room, where it strikes an initially stationary object with mass of 0.400 kg (m_2). The 0.250-kg object emerges from the room at an angle of $45.0°$ with its incoming direction.

The speed of the 0.250-kg object is originally 2.00 m/s and is 1.50 m/s after the collision. Calculate the magnitude and direction of the velocity (v'_2 and θ_2) of the 0.400-kg object after the collision.

Strategy

Momentum is conserved because the surface is frictionless. The coordinate system shown in Figure 8.11 is one in which m_2 is originally at rest and the initial velocity is parallel to the x-axis, so that conservation of momentum along the x- and y-axes is applicable.

Everything is known in these equations except v'_2 and θ_2, which are precisely the quantities we wish to find. We can find two unknowns because we have two independent equations: the equations describing the conservation of momentum in the x- and y-directions.

Solution

Solving $m_1 v_1 = m_1 v'_1 \cos\theta_1 + m_2 v'_2 \cos\theta_2$ for $v'_2 \cos\theta_2$ and $0 = m_1 v'_1 \sin\theta_1 + m_2 v'_2 \sin\theta_2$ for $v'_2 \sin\theta_2$ and taking the ratio yields an equation (in which θ_2 is the only unknown quantity. Applying the identity $\left(\tan\theta = \frac{\sin\theta}{\cos\theta}\right)$, we obtain:

$$\tan\theta_2 = \frac{v'_1 \sin\theta_1}{v'_1 \cos\theta_1 - v_1}. \quad (8.68)$$

Entering known values into the previous equation gives

$$\tan\theta_2 = \frac{(1.50\text{ m/s})(0.7071)}{(1.50\text{ m/s})(0.7071)\text{–}2.00\text{ m/s}} = -1.129. \quad (8.69)$$

Thus,

$$\theta_2 = \tan^{-1}(-1.129) = 311.5° \approx 312°. \quad (8.70)$$

Angles are defined as positive in the counter clockwise direction, so this angle indicates that m_2 is scattered to the right in Figure 8.11, as expected (this angle is in the fourth quadrant). Either equation for the x- or y-axis can now be used to solve for v'_2, but the latter equation is easiest because it has fewer terms.

$$v'_2 = -\frac{m_1}{m_2} v'_1 \frac{\sin\theta_1}{\sin\theta_2} \quad (8.71)$$

Entering known values into this equation gives

$$v'_2 = -\left(\frac{0.250\text{ kg}}{0.400\text{ kg}}\right)(1.50\text{ m/s})\left(\frac{0.7071}{-0.7485}\right). \quad 8.72$$

Thus,

$$v'_2 = 0.886\text{ m/s}. \quad 8.73$$

Discussion

It is instructive to calculate the internal kinetic energy of this two-object system before and after the collision. (This calculation is left as an end-of-chapter problem.) If you do this calculation, you will find that the internal kinetic energy is less after the collision, and so the collision is inelastic. This type of result makes a physicist want to explore the system further.

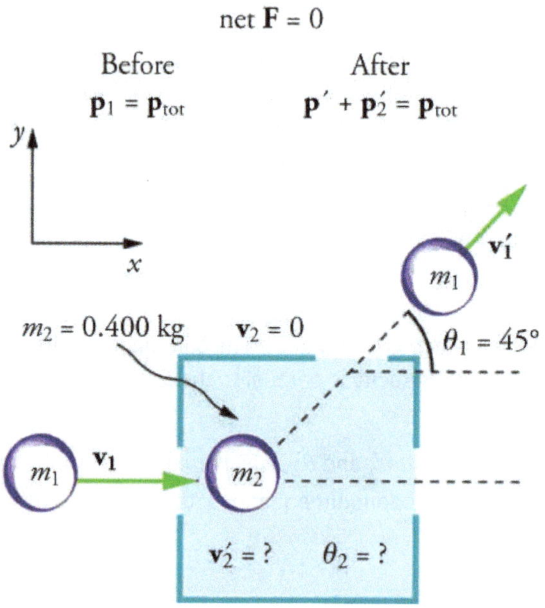

FIGURE 8.11 A collision taking place in a dark room is explored in Example 8.7. The incoming object m_1 is scattered by an initially stationary object. Only the stationary object's mass m_2 is known. By measuring the angle and speed at which m_1 emerges from the room, it is possible to calculate the magnitude and direction of the initially stationary object's velocity after the collision.

Elastic Collisions of Two Objects with Equal Mass

Some interesting situations arise when the two colliding objects have equal mass and the collision is elastic. This situation is nearly the case with colliding billiard balls, and precisely the case with some subatomic particle collisions. We can thus get a mental image of a collision of subatomic particles by thinking about billiards (or pool). (Refer to Figure 8.10 for masses and angles.) First, an elastic collision conserves internal kinetic energy. Again, let us assume object 2 (m_2) is initially at rest. Then, the internal kinetic energy before and after the collision of two objects that have equal masses is

$$\frac{1}{2}mv_1{}^2 = \frac{1}{2}mv'_1{}^2 + \frac{1}{2}mv'_2{}^2. \quad 8.74$$

Because the masses are equal, $m_1 = m_2 = m$. Algebraic manipulation (left to the reader) of conservation of momentum in the x- and y-directions can show that

$$\frac{1}{2}mv_1{}^2 = \frac{1}{2}mv'_1{}^2 + \frac{1}{2}mv'_2{}^2 + mv'_1v'_2\cos(\theta_1 - \theta_2). \quad 8.75$$

(Remember that θ_2 is negative here.) The two preceding equations can both be true only if

$$mv'_1v'_2\cos(\theta_1 - \theta_2) = 0. \quad 8.76$$

There are three ways that this term can be zero. They are

- $v'_1 = 0$: head-on collision; incoming ball stops
- $v'_2 = 0$: no collision; incoming ball continues unaffected
- $\cos(\theta_1 - \theta_2) = 0$: angle of separation $(\theta_1 - \theta_2)$ is 90° after the collision

All three of these ways are familiar occurrences in billiards and pool, although most of us try to avoid the second. If you play enough pool, you will notice that the angle between the balls is very close to 90° after the collision, although it will vary from this value if a great deal of spin is placed on the ball. (Large spin carries in extra energy and a quantity called *angular momentum*, which must also be conserved.) The assumption that the scattering of billiard balls is elastic is reasonable based on the correctness of the three results it produces. This assumption also implies that, to a good approximation, momentum is conserved for the two-ball system in billiards and pool. The problems below explore these and other characteristics of two-dimensional collisions.

CONNECTIONS TO NUCLEAR AND PARTICLE PHYSICS

Two-dimensional collision experiments have revealed much of what we know about subatomic particles, as we shall see in Medical Applications of Nuclear Physics and Particle Physics. Ernest Rutherford, for example, discovered the nature of the atomic nucleus from such experiments.

8.7 Introduction to Rocket Propulsion

LEARNING OBJECTIVES

By the end of this section, you will be able to:

- State Newton's third law of motion.
- Explain the principle involved in propulsion of rockets and jet engines.
- Derive an expression for the acceleration of the rocket and discuss the factors that affect the acceleration.
- Describe the function of a space shuttle.

Rockets range in size from fireworks so small that ordinary people use them to immense Saturn Vs that once propelled massive payloads toward the Moon. The propulsion of all rockets, jet engines, deflating balloons, and even squids and octopuses is explained by the same physical principle—Newton's third law of motion. Matter is forcefully ejected from a system, producing an equal and opposite reaction on what remains. Another common example is the recoil of a gun. The gun exerts a force on a bullet to accelerate it and consequently experiences an equal and opposite force, causing the gun's recoil or kick.

MAKING CONNECTIONS: TAKE-HOME EXPERIMENT—PROPULSION OF A BALLOON

Hold a balloon and fill it with air. Then, let the balloon go. In which direction does the air come out of the balloon and in which direction does the balloon get propelled? If you fill the balloon with water and then let the balloon go, does the balloon's direction change? Explain your answer.

Figure 8.12 shows a rocket accelerating straight up. In part (a), the rocket has a mass m and a velocity v relative to Earth, and hence a momentum mv. In part (b), a time Δt has elapsed in which the rocket has ejected a mass Δm of hot gas at a velocity v_e relative to the rocket. The remainder of the mass $(m - \Delta m)$ now has a greater velocity $(v + \Delta v)$. The momentum of the entire system (rocket plus expelled gas) has actually decreased because the force of gravity has acted for a time Δt, producing a negative impulse $\Delta p = -mg\Delta t$. (Remember that impulse is the net external force on a system multiplied by the time it acts, and it equals the change in momentum of the system.) So, the center of mass of the system is in free fall but, by rapidly expelling mass, part of the system can accelerate upward. It is a commonly held misconception that the rocket exhaust pushes on the ground. If we consider thrust; that is, the force exerted on the rocket by the exhaust gases, then a rocket's thrust is greater in outer space than in the atmosphere or on the launch pad. In fact, gases are easier to expel into a vacuum.

By calculating the change in momentum for the entire system over Δt, and equating this change to the impulse, the following expression can be shown to be a good approximation for the acceleration of the rocket.

$$a = \frac{v_e}{m}\frac{\Delta m}{\Delta t} - g \quad 8.77$$

"The rocket" is that part of the system remaining after the gas is ejected, and g is the acceleration due to gravity.

ACCELERATION OF A ROCKET

Acceleration of a rocket is

$$a = \frac{v_e}{m}\frac{\Delta m}{\Delta t} - g, \quad 8.78$$

where a is the acceleration of the rocket, v_e is the exhaust velocity, m is the mass of the rocket, Δm is the mass of the ejected gas, and Δt is the time in which the gas is ejected.

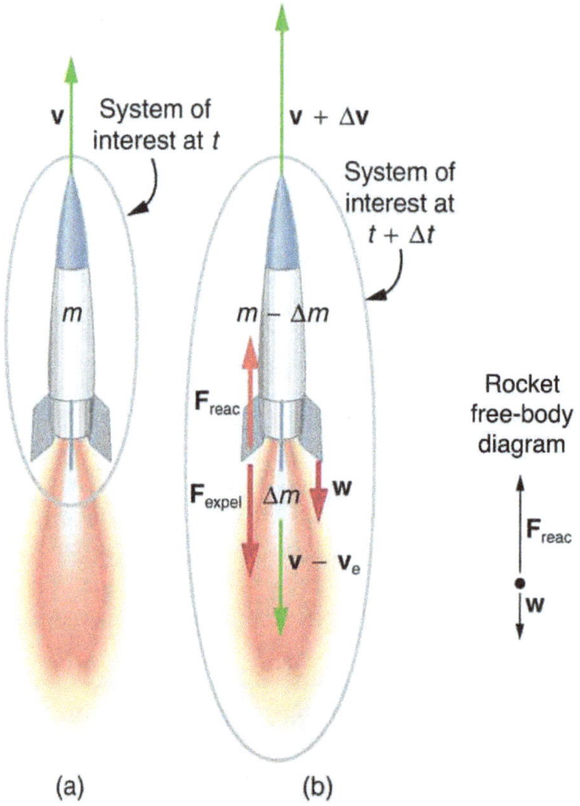

FIGURE 8.12 (a) This rocket has a mass m and an upward velocity v. The net external force on the system is $-mg$, if air resistance is neglected. (b) A time Δt later the system has two main parts, the ejected gas and the remainder of the rocket. The reaction force on the rocket is what overcomes the gravitational force and accelerates it upward.

A rocket's acceleration depends on three major factors, consistent with the equation for acceleration of a rocket . First, the greater the exhaust velocity of the gases relative to the rocket, v_e, the greater the acceleration is. The practical limit for v_e is about 2.5×10^3 m/s for conventional (non-nuclear) hot-gas propulsion systems. The second factor is the rate at which mass is ejected from the rocket. This is the factor $\Delta m/\Delta t$ in the equation. The quantity $(\Delta m/\Delta t)v_e$, with units of newtons, is called "thrust." The faster the rocket burns its fuel, the greater its thrust, and the greater its acceleration. The third factor is the mass m of the rocket. The smaller the mass is (all other factors being the same), the greater the acceleration. The rocket mass m decreases dramatically during flight because most of the rocket is fuel to begin with, so that acceleration increases continuously, reaching a maximum just before the fuel is exhausted.

FACTORS AFFECTING A ROCKET'S ACCELERATION

- The greater the exhaust velocity v_e of the gases relative to the rocket, the greater the acceleration.
- The faster the rocket burns its fuel, the greater its acceleration.
- The smaller the rocket's mass (all other factors being the same), the greater the acceleration.

EXAMPLE 8.8

Calculating Acceleration: Initial Acceleration of a Moon Launch

A Saturn V's mass at liftoff was 2.80×10^6 kg, its fuel-burn rate was 1.40×10^4 kg/s, and the exhaust velocity was 2.40×10^3 m/s. Calculate its initial acceleration.

Strategy

This problem is a straightforward application of the expression for acceleration because a is the unknown and all of the terms on the right side of the equation are given.

Solution

Substituting the given values into the equation for acceleration yields

$$\begin{aligned} a &= \frac{v_e}{m}\frac{\Delta m}{\Delta t} - g \\ &= \frac{2.40\times10^3 \text{ m/s}}{2.80\times10^6 \text{ kg}}\left(1.40\times10^4 \text{ kg/s}\right) - 9.80 \text{ m/s}^2 \\ &= 2.20 \text{ m/s}^2. \end{aligned} \quad 8.79$$

Discussion

This value is fairly small, even for an initial acceleration. The acceleration does increase steadily as the rocket burns fuel, because m decreases while v_e and $\frac{\Delta m}{\Delta t}$ remain constant. Knowing this acceleration and the mass of the rocket, you can show that the thrust of the engines was 3.36×10^7 N.

To achieve the high speeds needed to hop continents, obtain orbit, or escape Earth's gravity altogether, the mass of the rocket other than fuel must be as small as possible. It can be shown that, in the absence of air resistance and neglecting gravity, the final velocity of a one-stage rocket initially at rest is

$$v = v_e \ln \frac{m_0}{m_r}, \quad 8.80$$

where $\ln(m_0/m_r)$ is the natural logarithm of the ratio of the initial mass of the rocket (m_0) to what is left (m_r) after all of the fuel is exhausted. (Note that v is actually the change in velocity, so the equation can be used for any segment of the flight. If we start from rest, the change in velocity equals the final velocity.) For example, let us calculate the mass ratio needed to escape Earth's gravity starting from rest, given that the escape velocity from Earth is about 11.2×10^3 m/s, and assuming an exhaust velocity $v_e = 2.5 \times 10^3$ m/s.

$$\ln \frac{m_0}{m_r} = \frac{v}{v_e} = \frac{11.2 \times 10^3 \text{ m/s}}{2.5 \times 10^3 \text{ m/s}} = 4.48 \quad 8.81$$

Solving for m_0/m_r gives

$$\frac{m_0}{m_r} = e^{4.48} = 88. \quad 8.82$$

Thus, the mass of the rocket is

$$m_r = \frac{m_0}{88}. \quad 8.83$$

This result means that only $1/88$ of the mass is left when the fuel is burnt, and $87/88$ of the initial mass was fuel. Expressed as percentages, 98.9% of the rocket is fuel, while payload, engines, fuel tanks, and other components make up only 1.10%. Taking air resistance and gravitational force into account, the mass m_r remaining can only be about $m_0/180$. It is difficult to build a rocket in which the fuel has a mass 180 times everything else. The solution is multistage rockets. Each stage only needs to achieve part of the final velocity and is discarded after it burns its fuel. The result is that each successive stage can have smaller engines and more payload relative to its fuel. Once out of the atmosphere, the ratio of payload to fuel becomes more favorable, too.

The space shuttle was an attempt at an economical vehicle with some reusable parts, such as the solid fuel boosters and the craft itself. (See Figure 8.13) The shuttle's need to be operated by humans, however, made it at least as costly for launching satellites as expendable, unpiloted rockets. Ideally, the shuttle would only have been used when human activities were required for the success of a mission, such as the repair of the Hubble space telescope. Rockets with satellites can also be launched from airplanes. Using airplanes has the double advantage that the initial velocity is significantly above zero and a rocket can avoid most of the atmosphere's resistance.

FIGURE 8.13 The space shuttle had a number of reusable parts. Solid fuel boosters on either side were recovered and refueled after each flight, and the entire orbiter returned to Earth for use in subsequent flights. The large liquid fuel tank was expended. The space shuttle was a complex assemblage of technologies, employing both solid and liquid fuel and pioneering ceramic tiles as reentry heat shields. As a result, it permitted multiple launches as opposed to single-use rockets. (credit: NASA)

Glossary

change in momentum the difference between the final and initial momentum; the mass times the change in velocity

conservation of momentum principle when the net external force is zero, the total momentum of the system is conserved or constant

elastic collision a collision that also conserves internal kinetic energy

impulse the average net external force times the time it acts; equal to the change in momentum

inelastic collision a collision in which internal kinetic energy is not conserved

internal kinetic energy the sum of the kinetic energies of the objects in a system

isolated system a system in which the net external force is zero

linear momentum the product of mass and velocity

perfectly inelastic collision a collision in which the colliding objects stick together

point masses structureless particles with no rotation or spin

quark fundamental constituent of matter and an elementary particle

second law of motion physical law that states that the net external force equals the change in momentum of a system divided by the time over which it changes

Section Summary

8.1 Linear Momentum and Force

- Linear momentum (*momentum* for brevity) is defined as the product of a system's mass multiplied by its velocity.
- In symbols, linear momentum $\mathbf{p}$ is defined to be
  $\mathbf{p} = m\mathbf{v}$,
  where m is the mass of the system and $\mathbf{v}$ is its velocity.
- The SI unit for momentum is $\text{kg} \cdot \text{m/s}$.
- Newton's second law of motion in terms of momentum states that the net external force equals the change in momentum of a system divided by the time over which it changes.
- In symbols, Newton's second law of motion is defined to be
  $\mathbf{F}_{\text{net}} = \frac{\Delta\mathbf{p}}{\Delta t}$,
  $\mathbf{F}_{\text{net}}$ is the net external force, $\Delta\mathbf{p}$ is the change in momentum, and Δt is the change time.

8.2 Impulse

- Impulse, or change in momentum, equals the average net external force multiplied by the time this force acts:
  $\Delta\mathbf{p} = \mathbf{F}_{\text{net}}\Delta t$.
- Forces are usually not constant over a period of time.

8.3 Conservation of Momentum

- The conservation of momentum principle is written
  $\mathbf{p}_{\text{tot}} = \text{constant}$
  or
  $\mathbf{p}_{\text{tot}} = \mathbf{p}'_{\text{tot}}$ (isolated system),
  $\mathbf{p}_{\text{tot}}$ is the initial total momentum and $\mathbf{p}'_{\text{tot}}$ is the total momentum some time later.
- An isolated system is defined to be one for which the net external force is zero $(\mathbf{F}_{\text{net}} = 0)$.
- During projectile motion and where air resistance is negligible, momentum is conserved in the horizontal direction because horizontal forces are zero.
- Conservation of momentum applies only when the net external force is zero.
- The conservation of momentum principle is valid when considering systems of particles.

8.4 Elastic Collisions in One Dimension

- An elastic collision is one that conserves internal kinetic energy.
- Conservation of kinetic energy and momentum together allow the final velocities to be calculated in terms of initial velocities and masses in one dimensional two-body collisions.

8.5 Inelastic Collisions in One Dimension

- An inelastic collision is one in which the internal kinetic energy changes (it is not conserved).
- A collision in which the objects stick together is sometimes called perfectly inelastic because it reduces internal kinetic energy more than does any other type of inelastic collision.
- Sports science and technologies also use physics concepts such as momentum and rotational motion and vibrations.

8.6 Collisions of Point Masses in Two Dimensions

- The approach to two-dimensional collisions is to choose a convenient coordinate system and break the motion into components along perpendicular axes. Choose a coordinate system with the x-axis parallel to the velocity of the incoming particle.

- Two-dimensional collisions of point masses where mass 2 is initially at rest conserve momentum along the initial direction of mass 1 (the x-axis), stated by $m_1 v_1 = m_1 v'_1 \cos \theta_1 + m_2 v'_2 \cos \theta_2$ and along the direction perpendicular to the initial direction (the y-axis) stated by $0 = m_1 v'_{1y} + m_2 v'_{2y}$.
- The internal kinetic before and after the collision of two objects that have equal masses is $\frac{1}{2}mv_1{}^2 = \frac{1}{2}mv'_1{}^2 + \frac{1}{2}mv'_2{}^2 + mv'_1 v'_2 \cos(\theta_1 - \theta_2)$.
- Point masses are structureless particles that cannot spin.

8.7 Introduction to Rocket Propulsion

- Newton's third law of motion states that to every action, there is an equal and opposite reaction.
- Acceleration of a rocket is $a = \frac{v_e}{m} \frac{\Delta m}{\Delta t} - g$.
- A rocket's acceleration depends on three main factors. They are
  1. The greater the exhaust velocity of the gases, the greater the acceleration.
  2. The faster the rocket burns its fuel, the greater its acceleration.
  3. The smaller the rocket's mass, the greater the acceleration.

Conceptual Questions

8.1 Linear Momentum and Force

1. An object that has a small mass and an object that has a large mass have the same momentum. Which object has the largest kinetic energy?

2. An object that has a small mass and an object that has a large mass have the same kinetic energy. Which mass has the largest momentum?

3. Professional Application
Football coaches advise players to block, hit, and tackle with their feet on the ground rather than by leaping through the air. Using the concepts of momentum, work, and energy, explain how a football player can be more effective with his feet on the ground.

4. How can a small force impart the same momentum to an object as a large force?

8.2 Impulse

5. Professional Application
Explain in terms of impulse how padding reduces forces in a collision. State this in terms of a real example, such as the advantages of a carpeted vs. tile floor for a day care center.

6. While jumping on a trampoline, sometimes you land on your back and other times on your feet. In which case can you reach a greater height and why?

7. Professional Application
Tennis racquets have "sweet spots." If the ball hits a sweet spot then the player's arm is not jarred as much as it would be otherwise. Explain why this is the case.

8.3 Conservation of Momentum

8. Professional Application
If you dive into water, you reach greater depths than if you do a belly flop. Explain this difference in depth using the concept of conservation of energy. Explain this difference in depth using what you have learned in this chapter.

9. Under what circumstances is momentum conserved?

10. Can momentum be conserved for a system if there are external forces acting on the system? If so, under what conditions? If not, why not?

11. Momentum for a system can be conserved in one direction while not being conserved in another. What is the angle between the directions? Give an example.

12. Professional Application
Explain in terms of momentum and Newton's laws how a car's air resistance is due in part to the fact that it pushes air in its direction of motion.

13. Can objects in a system have momentum while the momentum of the system is zero? Explain your answer.

14. Must the total energy of a system be conserved whenever its momentum is conserved? Explain why or why not.

8.4 Elastic Collisions in One Dimension

15. What is an elastic collision?

8.5 Inelastic Collisions in One Dimension

16. What is an inelastic collision? What is a perfectly inelastic collision?

17. Mixed-pair ice skaters performing in a show are standing motionless at arms length just before starting a routine. They reach out, clasp hands, and pull themselves together by only using their arms. Assuming there is no friction between the blades of their skates and the ice, what is their velocity after their bodies meet?

18. A small pickup truck that has a camper shell slowly coasts toward a red light with negligible friction. Two dogs in the back of the truck are moving and making various inelastic collisions with each other and the walls. What is the effect of the dogs on the motion of the center of mass of the system (truck plus entire load)? What is their effect on the motion of the truck?

8.6 Collisions of Point Masses in Two Dimensions

19. Figure 8.14 shows a cube at rest and a small object heading toward it. (a) Describe the directions (angle θ_1) at which the small object can emerge after colliding elastically with the cube. How does θ_1 depend on b, the so-called impact parameter? Ignore any effects that might be due to rotation after the collision, and assume that the cube is much more massive than the small object. (b) Answer the same questions if the small object instead collides with a massive sphere.

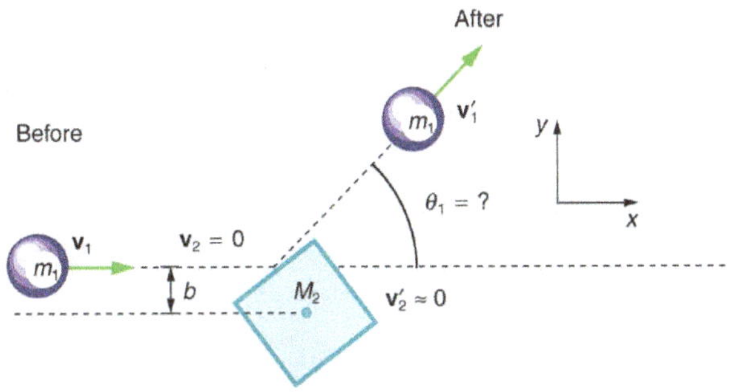

FIGURE 8.14 A small object approaches a collision with a much more massive cube, after which its velocity has the direction θ_1. The angles at which the small object can be scattered are determined by the shape of the object it strikes and the impact parameter b.

8.7 Introduction to Rocket Propulsion

20. Professional Application
Suppose a fireworks shell explodes, breaking into three large pieces for which air resistance is negligible. How is the motion of the center of mass affected by the explosion? How would it be affected if the pieces experienced significantly more air resistance than the intact shell?

21. Professional Application
During a visit to the International Space Station, an astronaut was positioned motionless in the center of the station, out of reach of any solid object on which he could exert a force. Suggest a method by which he could move himself away from this position, and explain the physics involved.

22. Professional Application
It is possible for the velocity of a rocket to be greater than the exhaust velocity of the gases it ejects. When that is the case, the gas velocity and gas momentum are in the same direction as that of the rocket. How is the rocket still able to obtain thrust by ejecting the gases?

Problems & Exercises

8.1 Linear Momentum and Force

1. (a) Calculate the momentum of a 2000-kg elephant charging a hunter at a speed of $7.50\ \text{m/s}$. (b) Compare the elephant's momentum with the momentum of a 0.0400-kg tranquilizer dart fired at a speed of $600\ \text{m/s}$. (c) What is the momentum of the 90.0-kg hunter running at $7.40\ \text{m/s}$ after missing the elephant?

2. (a) What is the mass of a large ship that has a momentum of $1.60 \times 10^9\ \text{kg} \cdot \text{m/s}$, when the ship is moving at a speed of $48.0\ \text{km/h}$? (b) Compare the ship's momentum to the momentum of a 1100-kg artillery shell fired at a speed of $1200\ \text{m/s}$.

3. (a) At what speed would a 2.00×10^4-kg airplane have to fly to have a momentum of $1.60 \times 10^9\ \text{kg} \cdot \text{m/s}$ (the same as the ship's momentum in the problem above)? (b) What is the plane's momentum when it is taking off at a speed of $60.0\ \text{m/s}$? (c) If the ship is an aircraft carrier that launches these airplanes with a catapult, discuss the implications of your answer to (b) as it relates to recoil effects of the catapult on the ship.

4. (a) What is the momentum of a garbage truck that is 1.20×10^4 kg and is moving at 30.0 m/s? (b) At what speed would an 8.00-kg trash can have the same momentum as the truck?

5. A runaway train car that has a mass of 15,000 kg travels at a speed of 5.4 m/s down a track. Compute the time required for a force of 1500 N to bring the car to rest.

6. The mass of Earth is 5.972×10^{24} kg and its orbital radius is an average of 1.496×10^{11} m. Calculate its linear momentum.

8.2 Impulse

7. A bullet is accelerated down the barrel of a gun by hot gases produced in the combustion of gun powder. What is the average force exerted on a 0.0300-kg bullet to accelerate it to a speed of 600.0 m/s in a time of 2.00 ms (milliseconds)?

8. Professional Application
A car moving at 10.0 m/s crashes into a tree and stops in 0.26 s. Calculate the force the seat belt exerts on a passenger in the car to bring him to a halt. The mass of the passenger is 70.0 kg.

9. A person slaps her leg with her hand, bringing her hand to rest in 2.50 milliseconds from an initial speed of 4.00 m/s. (a) What is the average force exerted on the leg, taking the effective mass of the hand and forearm to be 1.50 kg? (b) Would the force be any different if the woman clapped her hands together at the same speed and brought them to rest in the same time? Explain why or why not.

10. Professional Application
A professional boxer hits his opponent with a 1000-N horizontal blow that lasts for 0.150 s. (a) Calculate the impulse imparted by this blow. (b) What is the opponent's final velocity, if his mass is 105 kg and he is motionless in midair when struck near his center of mass? (c) Calculate the recoil velocity of the opponent's 10.0-kg head if hit in this manner, assuming the head does not initially transfer significant momentum to the boxer's body. (d) Discuss the implications of your answers for parts (b) and (c).

11. Professional Application
Suppose a child drives a bumper car head on into the side rail, which exerts a force of 4000 N on the car for 0.200 s. (a) What impulse is imparted by this force? (b) Find the final velocity of the bumper car if its initial velocity was 2.80 m/s and the car plus driver have a mass of 200 kg. You may neglect friction between the car and floor.

12. Professional Application
One hazard of space travel is debris left by previous missions. There are several thousand objects orbiting Earth that are large enough to be detected by radar, but there are far greater numbers of very small objects, such as flakes of paint. Calculate the force exerted by a 0.100-mg chip of paint that strikes a spacecraft window at a relative speed of 4.00×10^3 m/s, given the collision lasts 6.00×10^{-8} s.

13. Professional Application
A 75.0-kg person is riding in a car moving at 20.0 m/s when the car runs into a bridge abutment. (a) Calculate the average force on the person if he is stopped by a padded dashboard that compresses an average of 1.00 cm. (b) Calculate the average force on the person if he is stopped by an air bag that compresses an average of 15.0 cm.

14. Professional Application
Military rifles have a mechanism for reducing the recoil forces of the gun on the person firing it. An internal part recoils over a relatively large distance and is stopped by damping mechanisms in the gun. The larger distance reduces the average force needed to stop the internal part. (a) Calculate the recoil velocity of a 1.00-kg plunger that directly interacts with a 0.0200-kg bullet fired at 600 m/s from the gun. (b) If this part is stopped over a distance of 20.0 cm, what average force is exerted upon it by the gun? (c) Compare this to the force exerted on the gun if the bullet is accelerated to its velocity in 10.0 ms (milliseconds).

15. A cruise ship with a mass of 1.00×10^7 kg strikes a pier at a speed of 0.750 m/s. It comes to rest 6.00 m later, damaging the ship, the pier, and the tugboat captain's finances. Calculate the average force exerted on the pier using the concept of impulse. (Hint: First calculate the time it took to bring the ship to rest.)

16. Calculate the final speed of a 110-kg rugby player who is initially running at 8.00 m/s but collides head-on with a padded goalpost and experiences a backward force of 1.76×10^4 N for 5.50×10^{-2} s.

17. Water from a fire hose is directed horizontally against a wall at a rate of 50.0 kg/s and a speed of 42.0 m/s. Calculate the magnitude of the force exerted on the wall, assuming the water's

horizontal momentum is reduced to zero.

18. A 0.450-kg hammer is moving horizontally at 7.00 m/s when it strikes a nail and comes to rest after driving the nail 1.00 cm into a board. (a) Calculate the duration of the impact. (b) What was the average force exerted on the nail?

19. Starting with the definitions of momentum and kinetic energy, derive an equation for the kinetic energy of a particle expressed as a function of its momentum.

20. A ball with an initial velocity of 10 m/s moves at an angle 60° above the $+x$-direction. The ball hits a vertical wall and bounces off so that it is moving 60° above the $-x$-direction with the same speed. In terms of m, the mass of the ball, what is the impulse delivered by the wall?

21. When serving a tennis ball, a player hits the ball when its velocity is zero (at the highest point of a vertical toss). The racquet exerts a force of 540 N on the ball for 5.00 ms, giving it a final velocity of 45.0 m/s. Using these data, find the mass of the ball.

22. A punter drops a ball from rest vertically 1 meter down onto his foot. The ball leaves the foot with a speed of 18 m/s at an angle 55° above the horizontal. In terms of m, the mass of the ball, what is the impulse delivered by the foot (magnitude and direction)?

8.3 Conservation of Momentum

23. Professional Application
Train cars are coupled together by being bumped into one another. Suppose two loaded train cars are moving toward one another, the first having a mass of 150,000 kg and a velocity of 0.300 m/s, and the second having a mass of 110,000 kg and a velocity of -0.120 m/s. (The minus indicates direction of motion.) What is their final velocity?

24. Suppose a clay model of a koala bear has a mass of 0.200 kg and slides on ice at a speed of 0.750 m/s. It runs into another clay model, which is initially motionless and has a mass of 0.350 kg. Both being soft clay, they naturally stick together. What is their final velocity?

25. Professional Application
Consider the following question: *A car moving at 10 m/s crashes into a tree and stops in 0.26 s. Calculate the force the seatbelt exerts on a passenger in the car to bring him to a halt. The mass of the passenger is 70 kg.* Would the answer to this question be different if the car with the 70-kg passenger had collided with a car that has a mass equal to and is traveling in the opposite direction and at the same speed? Explain your answer.

26. What is the velocity of a 900-kg car initially moving at 30.0 m/s, just after it hits a 150-kg deer initially running at 12.0 m/s in the same direction? Assume the deer remains on the car.

27. A 1.80-kg falcon catches a 0.650-kg dove from behind in midair. What is their velocity after impact if the falcon's velocity is initially 28.0 m/s and the dove's velocity is 7.00 m/s in the same direction?

8.4 Elastic Collisions in One Dimension

28. Two identical objects (such as billiard balls) have a one-dimensional collision in which one is initially motionless. After the collision, the moving object is stationary and the other moves with the same speed as the other originally had. Show that both momentum and kinetic energy are conserved.

29. Professional Application
Two piloted satellites approach one another at a relative speed of 0.250 m/s, intending to dock. The first has a mass of $4.00 \times 10^3\text{ kg}$, and the second a mass of $7.50 \times 10^3\text{ kg}$. If the two satellites collide elastically rather than dock, what is their final relative velocity?

30. A 70.0-kg ice hockey goalie, originally at rest, catches a 0.150-kg hockey puck slapped at him at a velocity of 35.0 m/s. Suppose the goalie and the ice puck have an elastic collision and the puck is reflected back in the direction from which it came. What would their final velocities be in this case?

8.5 Inelastic Collisions in One Dimension

31. A 0.240-kg billiard ball that is moving at 3.00 m/s strikes the bumper of a pool table and bounces straight back at 2.40 m/s (80% of its original speed). The collision lasts 0.0150 s. (a) Calculate the average force exerted on the ball by the bumper. (b) How much kinetic energy in joules is lost during the collision? (c) What percent of the original energy is left?

32. During an ice show, a 60.0-kg skater leaps into the air and is caught by an initially stationary 75.0-kg skater. (a) What is their final velocity assuming negligible friction and that the 60.0-kg skater's original horizontal velocity is 4.00 m/s? (b) How much kinetic energy is lost?

33. Professional Application
Using mass and speed data from Example 8.1 and assuming that the football player catches the ball with his feet off the ground with both of them moving horizontally, calculate: (a) the final velocity if the ball and player are going in the same direction and (b) the loss of kinetic energy in this case. (c) Repeat parts (a) and (b) for the situation in which the ball and the player are going in opposite directions. Might the loss of kinetic energy be related to how much it hurts to catch the pass?

34. A battleship that is 6.00×10^7 kg and is originally at rest fires a 1100-kg artillery shell horizontally with a velocity of 575 m/s. (a) If the shell is fired straight aft (toward the rear of the ship), there will be negligible friction opposing the ship's recoil. Calculate its recoil velocity. (b) Calculate the increase in internal kinetic energy (that is, for the ship and the shell). This energy is less than the energy released by the gun powder—significant heat transfer occurs.

35. Professional Application
Two piloted satellites approaching one another, at a relative speed of 0.250 m/s, intending to dock. The first has a mass of 4.00×10^3 kg, and the second a mass of 7.50×10^3 kg. (a) Calculate the final velocity (after docking) by using the frame of reference in which the first satellite was originally at rest. (b) What is the loss of kinetic energy in this inelastic collision? (c) Repeat both parts by using the frame of reference in which the second satellite was originally at rest. Explain why the change in velocity is different in the two frames, whereas the change in kinetic energy is the same in both.

36. Professional Application
A 30,000-kg freight car is coasting at 0.850 m/s with negligible friction under a hopper that dumps 110,000 kg of scrap metal into it. (a) What is the final velocity of the loaded freight car? (b) How much kinetic energy is lost?

37. Professional Application
Space probes may be separated from their launchers by exploding bolts. (They bolt away from one another.) Suppose a 4800-kg satellite uses this method to separate from the 1500-kg remains of its launcher, and that 5000 J of kinetic energy is supplied to the two parts. What are their subsequent velocities using the frame of reference in which they were at rest before separation?

38. A 0.0250-kg bullet is accelerated from rest to a speed of 550 m/s in a 3.00-kg rifle. The pain of the rifle's kick is much worse if you hold the gun loosely a few centimeters from your shoulder rather than holding it tightly against your shoulder. (a) Calculate the recoil velocity of the rifle if it is held loosely away from the shoulder. (b) How much kinetic energy does the rifle gain? (c) What is the recoil velocity if the rifle is held tightly against the shoulder, making the effective mass 28.0 kg? (d) How much kinetic energy is transferred to the rifle-shoulder combination? The pain is related to the amount of kinetic energy, which is significantly less in this latter situation. (e) Calculate the momentum of a 110-kg football player running at 8.00 m/s. Compare the player's momentum with the momentum of a hard-thrown 0.410-kg football that has a speed of 25.0 m/s. Discuss its relationship to this problem.

39. Professional Application
One of the waste products of a nuclear reactor is plutonium-239 $\left({}^{239}\text{Pu}\right)$. This nucleus is radioactive and decays by splitting into a helium-4 nucleus and a uranium-235 nucleus $\left({}^{4}\text{He} + {}^{235}\text{U}\right)$, the latter of which is also radioactive and will itself decay some time later. The energy emitted in the plutonium decay is 8.40×10^{-13} J and is entirely converted to kinetic energy of the helium and uranium nuclei. The mass of the helium nucleus is 6.68×10^{-27} kg, while that of the uranium is 3.92×10^{-25} kg (note that the ratio of the masses is 4 to 235). (a) Calculate the velocities of the two nuclei, assuming the plutonium nucleus is originally at rest. (b) How much kinetic energy does each nucleus carry away? Note that the data given here are accurate to three digits only.

40. Professional Application
The Moon's craters are remnants of meteorite collisions. Suppose a fairly large asteroid that has a mass of 5.00×10^{12} kg (about a kilometer across) strikes the Moon at a speed of 15.0 km/s. (a) At what speed does the Moon recoil after the perfectly inelastic collision (the mass of the Moon is 7.36×10^{22} kg) ? (b) How much kinetic energy is lost in the collision? Such an event may have been observed by medieval English monks who reported observing a red glow and subsequent haze about the Moon. (c) In October 2009, NASA crashed a rocket into the Moon, and analyzed the

plume produced by the impact. (Significant amounts of water were detected.) Answer part (a) and (b) for this real-life experiment. The mass of the rocket was 2000 kg and its speed upon impact was 9000 km/h. How does the plume produced alter these results?

41. Professional Application
Two football players collide head-on in midair while trying to catch a thrown football. The first player is 95.0 kg and has an initial velocity of 6.00 m/s, while the second player is 115 kg and has an initial velocity of −3.50 m/s. What is their velocity just after impact if they cling together?

42. What is the speed of a garbage truck that is 1.20×10^4 kg and is initially moving at 25.0 m/s just after it hits and adheres to a trash can that is 80.0 kg and is initially at rest?

43. During a circus act, an elderly performer thrills the crowd by catching a cannon ball shot at him. The cannon ball has a mass of 10.0 kg and the horizontal component of its velocity is 8.00 m/s when the 65.0-kg performer catches it. If the performer is on nearly frictionless roller skates, what is his recoil velocity?

44. (a) During an ice skating performance, an initially motionless 80.0-kg clown throws a fake barbell away. The clown's ice skates allow her to recoil frictionlessly. If the clown recoils with a velocity of 0.500 m/s and the barbell is thrown with a velocity of 10.0 m/s, what is the mass of the barbell? (b) How much kinetic energy is gained by this maneuver? (c) Where does the kinetic energy come from?

8.6 Collisions of Point Masses in Two Dimensions

45. Two identical pucks collide on an air hockey table. One puck was originally at rest. (a) If the incoming puck has a speed of 6.00 m/s and scatters to an angle of 30.0°,what is the velocity (magnitude and direction) of the second puck? (You may use the result that $\theta_1 - \theta_2 = 90^\circ$ for elastic collisions of objects that have identical masses.) (b) Confirm that the collision is elastic.

46. Confirm that the results of the example Example 8.7 do conserve momentum in both the x- and y-directions.

47. A 3000-kg cannon is mounted so that it can recoil only in the horizontal direction. (a) Calculate its recoil velocity when it fires a 15.0-kg shell at 480 m/s at an angle of 20.0° above the horizontal. (b) What is the kinetic energy of the cannon? This energy is dissipated as heat transfer in shock absorbers that stop its recoil. (c) What happens to the vertical component of momentum that is imparted to the cannon when it is fired?

48. **Professional Application**
A 5.50-kg bowling ball moving at 9.00 m/s collides with a 0.850-kg bowling pin, which is scattered at an angle of 85.0° to the initial direction of the bowling ball and with a speed of 15.0 m/s. (a) Calculate the final velocity (magnitude and direction) of the bowling ball. (b) Is the collision elastic? (c) Linear kinetic energy is greater after the collision. Discuss how spin on the ball might be converted to linear kinetic energy in the collision.

49. **Professional Application**
Ernest Rutherford (the first New Zealander to be awarded the Nobel Prize in Chemistry) demonstrated that nuclei were very small and dense by scattering helium-4 nuclei $\left({}^4\text{He}\right)$ from gold-197 nuclei $\left({}^{197}\text{Au}\right)$. The energy of the incoming helium nucleus was 8.00×10^{-13} J, and the masses of the helium and gold nuclei were 6.68×10^{-27} kg and 3.29×10^{-25} kg, respectively (note that their mass ratio is 4 to 197). (a) If a helium nucleus scatters to an angle of 120° during an elastic collision with a gold nucleus, calculate the helium nucleus's final speed and the final velocity (magnitude and direction) of the gold nucleus. (b) What is the final kinetic energy of the helium nucleus?

50. Professional Application
Two cars collide at an icy intersection and stick together afterward. The first car has a mass of 1200 kg and is approaching at 8.00 m/s due south. The second car has a mass of 850 kg and is approaching at 17.0 m/s due west. (a) Calculate the final velocity (magnitude and direction) of the cars. (b) How much kinetic energy is lost in the collision? (This energy goes into deformation of the cars.) Note that because both cars have an initial velocity, you cannot use the equations for conservation of momentum along the x-axis and y-axis; instead, you must look for other simplifying aspects.

51. Starting with equations $m_1 v_1 = m_1 v_1' \cos\theta_1 + m_2 v_2' \cos\theta_2$ and $0 = m_1 v_1' \sin\theta_1 + m_2 v_2' \sin\theta_2$ for conservation of momentum in the x- and y-directions and assuming that one object is originally stationary, prove that for an elastic collision of two objects of equal masses,

$$\frac{1}{2}mv_1{}^2 = \frac{1}{2}mv'_1{}^2 + \frac{1}{2}mv'_2{}^2 + mv'_1 v'_2 \cos(\theta_1 - \theta_2)$$

as discussed in the text.

52. Integrated Concepts
A 90.0-kg ice hockey player hits a 0.150-kg puck, giving the puck a velocity of 45.0 m/s. If both are initially at rest and if the ice is frictionless, how far does the player recoil in the time it takes the puck to reach the goal 15.0 m away?

8.7 Introduction to Rocket Propulsion

53. Professional Application
Antiballistic missiles (ABMs) are designed to have very large accelerations so that they may intercept fast-moving incoming missiles in the short time available. What is the takeoff acceleration of a 10,000-kg ABM that expels 196 kg of gas per second at an exhaust velocity of 2.50×10^3 m/s?

54. Professional Application
What is the acceleration of a 5000-kg rocket taking off from the Moon, where the acceleration due to gravity is only 1.6 m/s^2, if the rocket expels 8.00 kg of gas per second at an exhaust velocity of 2.20×10^3 m/s?

55. Professional Application
Calculate the increase in velocity of a 4000-kg space probe that expels 3500 kg of its mass at an exhaust velocity of 2.00×10^3 m/s. You may assume the gravitational force is negligible at the probe's location.

56. Professional Application
Ion-propulsion rockets have been proposed for use in space. They employ atomic ionization techniques and nuclear energy sources to produce extremely high exhaust velocities, perhaps as great as 8.00×10^6 m/s. These techniques allow a much more favorable payload-to-fuel ratio. To illustrate this fact: (a) Calculate the increase in velocity of a 20,000-kg space probe that expels only 40.0-kg of its mass at the given exhaust velocity. (b) These engines are usually designed to produce a very small thrust for a very long time—the type of engine that might be useful on a trip to the outer planets, for example. Calculate the acceleration of such an engine if it expels 4.50×10^{-6} kg/s at the given velocity, assuming the acceleration due to gravity is negligible.

57. Derive the equation for the vertical acceleration of a rocket.

58. Professional Application
(a) Calculate the maximum rate at which a rocket can expel gases if its acceleration cannot exceed seven times that of gravity. The mass of the rocket just as it runs out of fuel is 75,000-kg, and its exhaust velocity is 2.40×10^3 m/s. Assume that the acceleration of gravity is the same as on Earth's surface (9.80 m/s^2). (b) Why might it be necessary to limit the acceleration of a rocket?

59. Given the following data for a fire extinguisher-toy wagon rocket experiment, calculate the average exhaust velocity of the gases expelled from the extinguisher. Starting from rest, the final velocity is 10.0 m/s. The total mass is initially 75.0 kg and is 70.0 kg after the extinguisher is fired.

60. How much of a single-stage rocket that is 100,000 kg can be anything but fuel if the rocket is to have a final speed of 8.00 km/s, given that it expels gases at an exhaust velocity of 2.20×10^3 m/s?

61. Professional Application
(a) A 5.00-kg squid initially at rest ejects 0.250-kg of fluid with a velocity of 10.0 m/s. What is the recoil velocity of the squid if the ejection is done in 0.100 s and there is a 5.00-N frictional force opposing the squid's movement. (b) How much energy is lost to work done against friction?

62. Unreasonable Results
Squids have been reported to jump from the ocean and travel 30.0 m (measured horizontally) before re-entering the water. (a) Calculate the initial speed of the squid if it leaves the water at an angle of 20.0°, assuming negligible lift from the air and negligible air resistance. (b) The squid propels itself by squirting water. What fraction of its mass would it have to eject in order to achieve the speed found in the previous part? The water is ejected at 12.0 m/s; gravitational force and friction are neglected. (c) What is unreasonable about the results? (d) Which premise is unreasonable, or which premises are inconsistent?

63. Construct Your Own Problem
Consider an astronaut in deep space cut free from her space ship and needing to get back to it. The astronaut has a few packages that she can throw away to move herself toward the ship. Construct a problem in which you calculate the time it takes

her to get back by throwing all the packages at one time compared to throwing them one at a time. Among the things to be considered are the masses involved, the force she can exert on the packages through some distance, and the distance to the ship.

64. Construct Your Own Problem
Consider an artillery projectile striking armor plating. Construct a problem in which you find the force exerted by the projectile on the plate. Among the things to be considered are the mass and speed of the projectile and the distance over which its speed is reduced. Your instructor may also wish for you to consider the relative merits of depleted uranium versus lead projectiles based on the greater density of uranium.

Test Prep for AP® Courses

8.1 Linear Momentum and Force

1. A boy standing on a frictionless ice rink is initially at rest. He throws a snowball in the +*x*-direction, and it travels on a ballistic trajectory, hitting the ground some distance away. Which of the following is true about the boy while he is in the act of throwing the snowball?

a. He feels an upward force to compensate for the downward trajectory of the snowball.
b. He feels a backward force exerted by the snowball he is throwing.
c. He feels no net force.
d. He feels a forward force, the same force that propels the snowball.

2. A 150-g baseball is initially moving 80 mi/h in the −*x*-direction. After colliding with a baseball bat for 20 ms, the baseball moves 80 mi/h in the +*x*-direction. What is the magnitude and direction of the average force exerted by the bat on the baseball?

8.2 Impulse

3. A 1.0-kg ball of putty is released from rest and falls vertically 1.5 m until it strikes a hard floor, where it comes to rest in a 0.045-s time interval. What is the magnitude and direction of the average force exerted on the ball by the floor during the collision?

a. 33 N, up
b. 120 N, up
c. 120 N, down
d. 240 N, down

4. A 75-g ball is dropped from rest from a height of 2.2 m. It bounces off the floor and rebounds to a maximum height of 1.7 m. If the ball is in contact with the floor for 0.024 s, what is the magnitude and direction of the average force exerted on the ball by the floor during the collision?

5. A 2.4-kg ceramic bowl falls to the floor. During the 0.018-s impact, the bowl experiences an average force of 750 N from the floor. The bowl is at rest after the impact. From what initial height did the bowl fall?

a. 1.6 m
b. 2.8 m
c. 3.2 m
d. 5.6 m

6. Whether or not an object (such as a plate, glass, or bone) breaks upon impact depends on the average force exerted on that object by the surface. When a 1.2-kg glass figure hits the floor, it will break if it experiences an average force of 330 N. When it hits a tile floor, the glass comes to a stop in 0.015 s. From what minimum height must the glass fall to experience sufficient force to break? How would your answer change if the figure were falling to a padded or carpeted surface? Explain.

7. A 2.5-kg block slides across a frictionless table toward a horizontal spring.As the block bounces off the spring, a probe measures the velocity of the block (initially negative, moving away from the probe) over time as follows:

Velocity (m/s)	Time (s)
−12.0	0
−10.0	0.10
−6.0	0.20
0	0.30
6.0	0.40
10.0	0.50
12.0	0.60

TABLE 8.1

What is the average force exerted on the block by the

spring over the entire 0.60-s time interval of the collision?

a. 50 N
b. 60 N
c. 100 N
d. 120 N

8. During an automobile crash test, the average force exerted by a solid wall on a 2500-kg car that hits the wall is measured to be 740,000 N over a 0.22-s time interval. What was the initial speed of the car prior to the collision, assuming the car is at rest at the end of the time interval?

9. A test car is driving toward a solid crash-test barrier with a speed of 45 mi/h. Two seconds prior to impact, the car begins to brake, but it is still moving when it hits the wall. After the collision with the wall, the car crumples somewhat and comes to a complete stop. In order to estimate the average force exerted by the wall on the car, what information would you need to collect?

a. The (negative) acceleration of the car before it hits the wall and the distance the car travels while braking.
b. The (negative) acceleration of the car before it hits the wall and the velocity of the car just before impact.
c. The velocity of the car just before impact and the duration of the collision with the wall.
d. The duration of the collision with the wall and the distance the car travels while braking.

10. Design an experiment to verify the relationship between the average force exerted on an object and the change in momentum of that object. As part of your explanation, list the equipment you would use and describe your experimental setup. What would you measure and how? How exactly would you verify the relationship? Explain.

11. A 22-g puck hits the wall of an air hockey table perpendicular to the wall with an initial speed of 14 m/s.The puck is in contact with the wall for 0.0055 s, and it rebounds from the wall with a speed of 14 m/s in the opposite direction.What is the magnitude of the average force exerted by the wall on the puck?

a. 0.308 N
b. 0.616 N
c. 56 N
d. 112 N

12. A 22-g puck hits the wall of an air hockey table perpendicular to the wall with an initial speed of 7 m/s. The puck is in contact with the wall for 0.011 s, and the wall exerts an average force of 28 N on the puck during that time. Calculate the magnitude and direction of the change in momentum of the puck.

13.

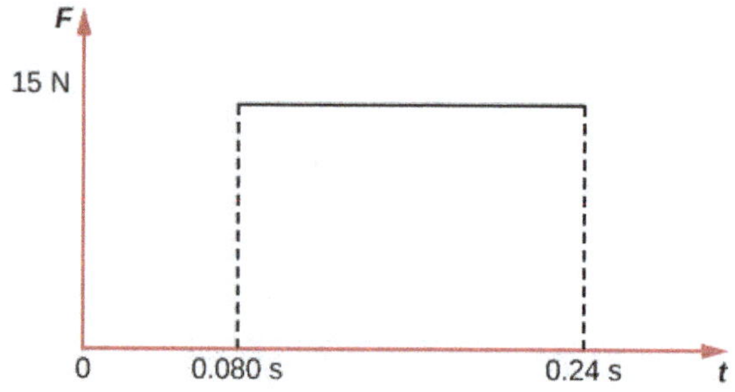

FIGURE 8.15 This is a graph showing the force exerted by a rigid wall versus time.

The graph in Figure 8.15 represents the force exerted on a particle during a collision. What is the magnitude of the change in momentum of the particle as a result of the collision?

a. 1.2 kg • m/s
b. 2.4 kg • m/s
c. 3.6 kg • m/s
d. 4.8 kg • m/s

14.

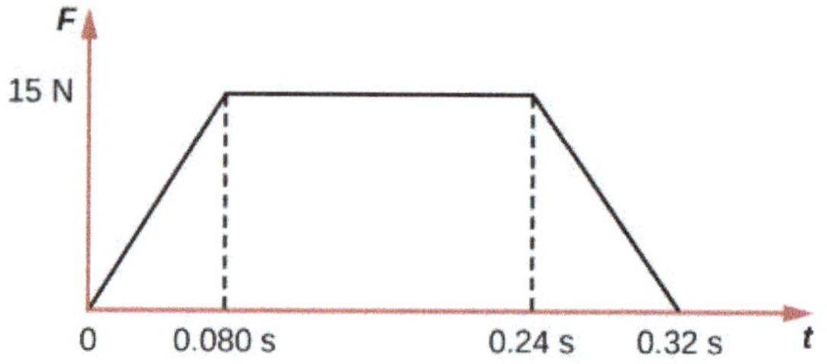

FIGURE 8.16 This is a graph showing the force exerted by a rigid wall versus time.

The graph in Figure 8.16 represents the force exerted on a particle during a collision. What is the magnitude of the change in momentum of the particle as a result of the collision?

8.3 Conservation of Momentum

15. Which of the following is an example of an open system?

a. Two air cars colliding on a track elastically.
b. Two air cars colliding on a track and sticking together.
c. A bullet being fired into a hanging wooden block and becoming embedded in the block, with the system then acting as a ballistic pendulum.
d. A bullet being fired into a hillside and

becoming buried in the earth.

16. A 40-kg girl runs across a mat with a speed of 5.0 m/s and jumps onto a 120-kg hanging platform initially at rest, causing the girl and platform to swing back and forth like a pendulum together after her jump. What is the combined velocity of the girl and platform after the jump? What is the combined momentum of the girl and platform both before and after the collision?
A 50-kg boy runs across a mat with a speed of 6.0 m/s and collides with a soft barrier on the wall, rebounding off the wall and falling to the ground. The boy is at rest after the collision. What is the momentum of the boy before and after the collision? Is momentum conserved in this collision? Explain. Which of these is an example of an open system and which is an example of a closed system? Explain your answer.

17. A student sets up an experiment to measure the momentum of a system of two air cars, A and B, of equal mass, moving on a linear, frictionless track. Before the collision, car A has a certain speed, and car B is at rest. Which of the following will be true about the total momentum of the two cars?
a. It will be greater before the collision.
b. It will be equal before and after the collision.
c. It will be greater after the collision.
d. The answer depends on whether the collision is elastic or inelastic.

18. A group of students has two carts, *A* and *B*, with wheels that turn with negligible friction. The carts can travel along a straight horizontal track. Cart *A* has known mass *mA*. The students are asked to use a one-dimensional collision between the carts to determine the mass of cart *B*. Before the collision, cart *A* travels to the right and cart *B* is initially at rest. After the collision, the carts stick together.
a. Describe an experimental procedure to determine the velocities of the carts before and after a collision, including all the additional equipment you would need. You may include a labeled diagram of your setup to help in your description. Indicate what measurements you would take and how you would take them. Include enough detail so that another student could carry out your procedure.
b. There will be sources of error in the measurements taken in the experiment, both before and after the collision. For your experimental procedure, will the uncertainty in the calculated value of the mass of cart *B* be affected more by the error in the measurements taken before the collision or by those taken after the collision, or will it be equally affected by both sets of measurements? Justify your answer.

A group of students took measurements for one collision. A graph of the students' data is shown below.

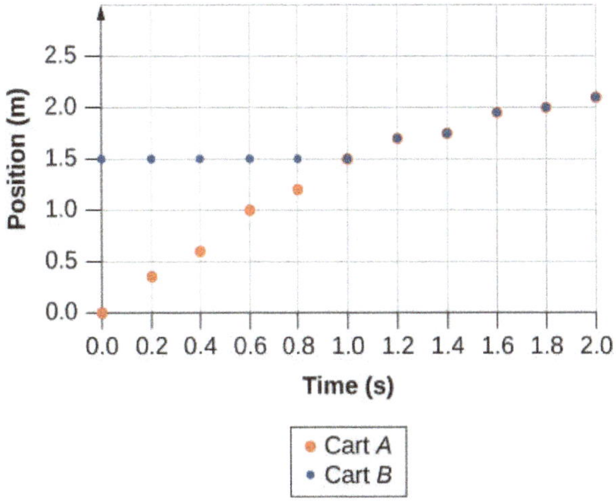

FIGURE 8.17 The image shows a graph with position in meters on the vertical axis and time in seconds on the horizontal axis.

c. Given $m_A = 0.50$ kg, use the graph to calculate the mass of cart *B*. Explicitly indicate the principles used in your calculations.
d. The students are now asked to Consider the kinetic energy changes in an inelastic collision, specifically whether the initial values of one of the physical quantities affect the fraction of mechanical energy dissipated in the collision. How could you modify the experiment to investigate this question? Be sure to explicitly describe the calculations you would make, specifying all equations you would use (but do not actually do any algebra or arithmetic).

19. Cart A is moving with an initial velocity $+v$ (in the positive direction) toward cart B, initially at rest. Both carts have equal mass and are on a frictionless surface. Which of the following statements correctly characterizes the velocity of the center of mass of the system before and after the collision?
a. $\frac{+v}{2}$ before, $\frac{-v}{2}$ after
b. $\frac{+v}{2}$ before, 0 after
c. $\frac{+v}{2}$ before, $\frac{+v}{2}$ after
d. 0 before, 0 after

20. Cart A is moving with a velocity of +10 m/s toward cart B, which is moving with a velocity of +4 m/s. Both carts have equal mass and are moving on a frictionless surface. The two carts have an inelastic collision and stick together after the collision. Calculate the velocity of the center of mass of the system before and after the collision. If there were friction present in this problem, how would this external force affect the center-of-mass velocity both before and after the collision?

8.4 Elastic Collisions in One Dimension

21. Two cars (A and B) of mass 1.5 kg collide. Car A is initially moving at 12 m/s, and car B is initially moving in the same direction with a speed of 6 m/s. The two cars are moving along a straight line before and after the collision. What will be the change in momentum of this system after the collision?
  a. −27 kg • m/s
  b. zero
  c. +27 kg • m/s
  d. It depends on whether the collision is elastic or inelastic.

22. Two cars (A and B) of mass 1.5 kg collide. Car A is initially moving at 24 m/s, and car B is initially moving in the opposite direction with a speed of 12 m/s. The two cars are moving along a straight line before and after the collision. (a) If the two cars have an elastic collision, calculate the change in momentum of the two-car system. (b) If the two cars have a completely inelastic collision, calculate the change in momentum of the two-car system.

23. Puck A (200 g) slides across a frictionless surface to collide with puck B (800 g), initially at rest. The velocity of each puck is measured during the experiment as follows:

Time	Velocity A	Velocity B
0	+8.0 m/s	0
1.0 s	+8.0 m/s	0
2.0 s	−2.0 m/s	+2.5 m/s
3.0 s	−2.0 m/s	+2.5 m/s

TABLE 8.2

What is the change in momentum of the center of mass of the system as a result of the collision?
  a. +1.6 kg•m/s
  b. +0.8 kg•m/s
  c. 0
  d. −1.6 kg•m/s

24. For the table above, calculate the center-of-mass velocity of the system both before and after the collision, then calculate the center-of-mass momentum of the system both before and after the collision. From this, determine the change in the momentum of the system as a result of the collision.

25. Two cars (A and B) of equal mass have an elastic collision. Prior to the collision, car A is moving at 15 m/s in the +*x*-direction, and car B is moving at 10 m/s in the −*x*-direction. Assuming that both cars continue moving along the *x*-axis after the collision, what will be the velocity of car A after the collision?
  a. same as the original 15 m/s speed, opposite direction
  b. equal to car B’s velocity prior to the collision
  c. equal to the average of the two velocities, in its original direction
  d. equal to the average of the two velocities, in the opposite direction

26. Two cars (A and B) of equal mass have an elastic collision. Prior to the collision, car A is moving at 20 m/s in the +*x*-direction, and car B is moving at 10 m/s in the −*x*-direction. Assuming that both cars continue moving along the *x*-axis after the collision, what will be the velocities of each car after the collision?

27. A rubber ball is dropped from rest at a fixed height. It bounces off a hard floor and rebounds upward, but it only reaches 90% of its original fixed height. What is the best way to explain the loss of kinetic energy of the ball during the collision?
  a. Energy was required to deform the ball’s shape during the collision with the floor.
  b. Energy was lost due to work done by the ball pushing on the floor during the collision.
  c. Energy was lost due to friction between the ball and the floor.
  d. Energy was lost due to the work done by gravity during the motion.

28. A tennis ball strikes a wall with an initial speed of 15 m/s. The ball bounces off the wall but rebounds with slightly less speed (14 m/s) after the collision. Explain (a) what else changed its momentum in response to the ball's change in momentum so that overall momentum is conserved, and (b) how some of the ball's kinetic energy was lost.

29. Two objects, A and B, have equal mass. Prior to the collision, mass A is moving 10 m/s in the +*x*-direction, and mass B is moving 4 m/s in the +*x*-direction. Which of the following results represents an inelastic collision between A and B?

a. After the collision, mass A is at rest, and mass B moves 14 m/s in the +*x*-direction.
b. After the collision, mass A moves 4 m/s in the −*x*-direction, and mass B moves 18 m/s in the +*x*-direction.
c. After the collision, the two masses stick together and move 7 m/s in the +*x*-direction.
d. After the collision, mass A moves 4 m/s in the +*x*-direction, and mass B moves 10 m/s in the +*x*-direction.

30. Mass A is three times more massive than mass B. Mass A is initially moving 12 m/s in the +*x*-direction. Mass B is initially moving 12 m/s in the −*x*-direction. Assuming that the collision is elastic, calculate the final velocity of both masses after the collision. Show that your results are consistent with conservation of momentum and conservation of kinetic energy.

31. Two objects (A and B) of equal mass collide elastically. Mass A is initially moving 5.0 m/s in the +*x*-direction prior to the collision. Mass B is initially moving 3.0 m/s in the −*x*-direction prior to the collision. After the collision, mass A will be moving with a velocity of 3.0 m/s in the −*x*-direction. What will be the velocity of mass B after the collision?

a. 3.0 m/s in the +*x*-direction
b. 5.0 m/s in the +*x*-direction
c. 3.0 m/s in the −*x*-direction
d. 5.0 m/s in the −*x*-direction

32. Two objects (A and B) of equal mass collide elastically. Mass A is initially moving 4.0 m/s in the +*x*-direction prior to the collision. Mass B is initially moving 8.0 m/s in the −*x*-direction prior to the collision. After the collision, mass A will be moving with a velocity of 8.0 m/s in the −*x*-direction. (a) Use the principle of conservation of momentum to predict the velocity of mass B after the collision. (b) Use the fact that kinetic energy is conserved in elastic collisions to predict the velocity of mass B after the collision.

33. Two objects of equal mass collide. Object A is initially moving in the +*x*-direction with a speed of 12 m/s, and object B is initially at rest. After the collision, object A is at rest, and object B is moving away with some unknown velocity. There are no external forces acting on the system of two masses. What statement can we make about this collision?

a. Both momentum and kinetic energy are conserved.
b. Momentum is conserved, but kinetic energy is not conserved.
c. Neither momentum nor kinetic energy is conserved.
d. More information is needed in order to determine which is conserved.

34. Two objects of equal mass collide. Object A is initially moving with a velocity of 15 m/s in the +*x*-direction, and object B is initially at rest. After the collision, object A is at rest. There are no external forces acting on the system of two masses. (a) Use momentum conservation to deduce the velocity of object B after the collision. (b) Is this collision elastic? Justify your answer.

35. Which of the following statements is true about an inelastic collision?

a. Momentum is conserved, and kinetic energy is conserved.
b. Momentum is conserved, and kinetic energy is not conserved.
c. Momentum is not conserved, and kinetic energy is conserved.
d. Momentum is not conserved, and kinetic energy is not conserved.

36. Explain how the momentum and kinetic energy of a system of two colliding objects changes as a result of (a) an elastic collision and (b) an inelastic collision.

37.

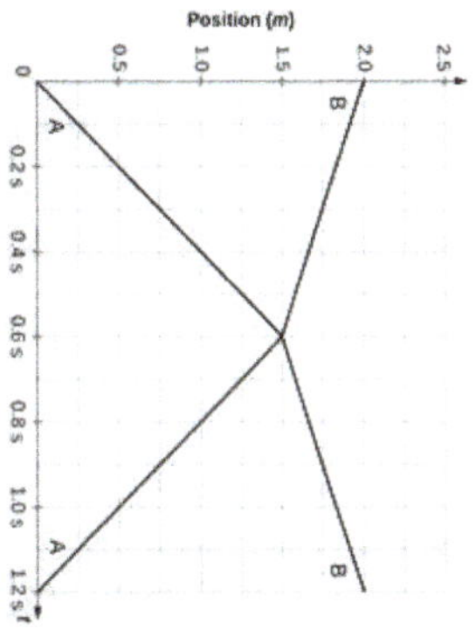

This figure shows the positions of two colliding objects measured before, during, and after a collision. Mass A is 1.0 kg. Mass B is 3.0 kg. Which of the following statements is true?

a. This is an elastic collision, with a total momentum of 0 kg • m/s.
b. This is an elastic collision, with a total momentum of 1.67 kg • m/s.
c. This is an inelastic collision, with a total momentum of 0 kg • m/s.
d. This is an inelastic collision, with a total momentum of 1.67 kg • m/s.

38. For the above graph, determine the initial and final momentum for both objects, assuming mass A is 1.0 kg and mass B is 3.0 kg. Also, determine the initial and final kinetic energies for both objects. Based on your results, explain whether momentum is conserved in this collision, and state whether the collision is elastic or inelastic.

39. Mass A (1.0 kg) slides across a frictionless surface with a velocity of 8 m/s in the positive direction. Mass B (3.0 kg) is initially at rest. The two objects collide and stick together. What will be the change in the center-of-mass velocity of the system as a result of the collision?

a. There will be no change in the center-of-mass velocity.
b. The center-of-mass velocity will decrease by 2 m/s.
c. The center-of-mass velocity will decrease by 6 m/s.
d. The center-of-mass velocity will decrease by 8 m/s.

40. Mass A (1.0 kg) slides across a frictionless surface with a velocity of 4 m/s in the positive direction. Mass B (1.0 kg) slides across the same surface in the opposite direction with a velocity of −8 m/s. The two objects collide and stick together after the collision. Predict how the center-of-mass velocity will change as a result of the collision, and explain your prediction. Calculate the center-of-mass velocity of the system both before and after the collision and explain why it remains the same or why it has changed.

8.5 Inelastic Collisions in One Dimension

41. Mass A (2.0 kg) has an initial velocity of 4 m/s in the $+x$-direction. Mass B (2.0 kg) has an initial velocity of 5 m/s in the $-x$-direction. If the two masses have an elastic collision, what will be the final velocities of the masses after the collision?

a. Both will move 0.5 m/s in the $-x$-direction.
b. Mass A will stop; mass B will move 9 m/s in the $+x$-direction.
c. Mass B will stop; mass A will move 9 m/s in the $-x$-direction.
d. Mass A will move 5 m/s in the $-x$-direction; mass B will move 4 m/s in the $+x$-direction.

42. Mass A has an initial velocity of 22 m/s in the $+x$-direction. Mass B is three times more massive than mass A and has an initial velocity of 22 m/s in the $-x$-direction. If the two masses have an elastic collision, what will be the final velocities of the masses after the collision?

43. Mass A (2.0 kg) is moving with an initial velocity of 15 m/s in the $+x$-direction, and it collides with mass B (5.0 kg), initially at rest. After the collision, the two objects stick together and move as one. What is the change in kinetic energy of the system as a result of the collision?

a. no change
b. decrease by 225 J
c. decrease by 161 J
d. decrease by 64 J

44. Mass A (2.0 kg) is moving with an initial velocity of 15 m/s in the $+x$-direction, and it collides with mass B (4.0 kg), initially moving 7.0 m/s in the $+x$-direction. After the collision, the two objects stick together and move as one. What is the change in kinetic energy of the system as a result of the collision?

45. Mass A slides across a rough table with an initial velocity of 12 m/s in the $+x$-direction. By the time mass A collides with mass B (a stationary object with equal mass), mass A has slowed to 10 m/s. After the collision, the two objects stick together and move as one. Immediately after the collision, the velocity of the system is measured to be 5 m/s in the $+x$-direction, and the system eventually slides to a stop. Which of the following statements is true about this motion?

a. Momentum is conserved during the collision, but it is not conserved during the motion before and after the collision.
b. Momentum is not conserved at any time during this analysis.
c. Momentum is conserved at all times during this analysis.
d. Momentum is not conserved during the collision, but it is conserved during the motion

before and after the collision.

46. Mass A is initially moving with a velocity of 12 m/s in the +*x*-direction. Mass B is twice as massive as mass A and is initially at rest. After the two objects collide, the two masses move together as one with a velocity of 4 m/s in the +*x*-direction. Is momentum conserved in this collision?

47. Mass A is initially moving with a velocity of 24 m/s in the +*x*-direction. Mass B is twice as massive as mass A and is initially at rest. The two objects experience a totally inelastic collision. What is the final speed of both objects after the collision?

a. A is not moving; B is moving 24 m/s in the +*x*-direction.
b. Neither A nor B is moving.
c. A is moving 24 m/s in the −*x*-direction. B is not moving.
d. Both A and B are moving together 8 m/s in the +*x*-direction.

48. Mass A is initially moving with some unknown velocity in the +*x*-direction. Mass B is twice as massive as mass A and initially at rest. The two objects collide, and after the collision, they move together with a speed of 6 m/s in the +*x*-direction. (a) Is this collision elastic or inelastic? Explain. (b) Determine the initial velocity of mass A.

49. Mass A is initially moving with a velocity of 2 m/s in the +*x*-direction. Mass B is initially moving with a velocity of 6 m/s in the −*x*-direction. The two objects have equal masses. After they collide, mass A moves with a speed of 4 m/s in the −*x*-direction. What is the final velocity of mass B after the collision?

a. 6 m/s in the +*x*-direction
b. 4 m/s in the +*x*-direction
c. zero
d. 4 m/s in the −*x*-direction

50. Mass A is initially moving with a velocity of 15 m/s in the +*x*-direction. Mass B is twice as massive and is initially moving with a velocity of 10 m/s in the −*x*-direction. The two objects collide, and after the collision, mass A moves with a speed of 15 m/s in the −*x*-direction. (a) What is the final velocity of mass B after the collision? (b) Calculate the change in kinetic energy as a result of the collision, assuming mass A is 5.0 kg.

8.6 Collisions of Point Masses in Two Dimensions

51. Two cars of equal mass approach an intersection. Car A is moving east at a speed of 45 m/s. Car B is moving south at a speed of 35 m/s. They collide inelastically and stick together after the collision, moving as one object. Which of the following statements is true about the center-of-mass velocity of this system?

a. The center-of-mass velocity will decrease after the collision as a result of lost energy (but not drop to zero).
b. The center-of-mass velocity will remain the same after the collision since momentum is conserved.
c. The center-of-mass velocity will drop to zero since the two objects stick together.
d. The magnitude of the center-of-mass velocity will remain the same, but the direction of the velocity will change.

52. Car A has a mass of 2000 kg and approaches an intersection with a velocity of 38 m/s directed to the east. Car B has a mass of 3500 kg and approaches the intersection with a velocity of 53 m/s directed 63° north of east. The two cars collide and stick together after the collision. Will the center-of-mass velocity change as a result of the collision? Explain why or why not. Calculate the center-of-mass velocity before and after the collision.

CHAPTER 9
Statics and Torque

FIGURE 9.1 On a short time scale, rocks like these in Australia's Kalbarri National Park are static, or motionless relative to the Earth. (credit: Richard Liblanc/Flickr)

CHAPTER OUTLINE

CONNECTION FOR AP® COURSES What might desks, bridges, buildings, trees, and mountains have in common? What do these objects have in common with a car moving at a constant velocity? While it may be apparent that the objects in the first group are all motionless relative to Earth, they also share something with the moving car and all objects moving at a constant velocity. All of these objects, stationary and moving, share an acceleration of zero. How can this be? Consider Newton's second law, $F = ma$. When acceleration is zero, as is the case for both stationary objects and objects moving at a constant velocity, the net external force must also be zero (Big Idea 3). Forces are acting on both stationary objects and on objects moving at a constant velocity, but the forces are balanced. That is, they are in *equilibrium*. In equilibrium, the net force is zero.

The first two sections of this chapter will focus on the two conditions necessary for equilibrium. They will not only help you to distinguish between stationary bridges and cars moving at constant velocity, but will introduce a second equilibrium condition, this time involving rotation. As you explore the second equilibrium condition, you will learn about torque, in support of both Enduring Understanding 3.F and Essential Knowledge 3.F.1. Much like a force, torque provides the capability for acceleration; however, with careful attention, torques may also be balanced and equilibrium can be reached.

The remainder of this chapter will discuss a variety of interesting equilibrium applications. From the art of balancing, to simple machines, to the muscles in your body, the world around you relies upon the principles of equilibrium to remain stable. This chapter will help you to see just how closely related these events truly are.

The content in this chapter supports:

Big Idea 3 The interactions of an object with other objects can be described by forces.

Enduring Understanding 3.F A force exerted on an object can cause a torque on that object.

Essential Knowledge 3.F.1 Only the force component perpendicular to the line connecting the axis of rotation and the point of application of the force results in a torque about that axis.

Click to view content (https://openstax.org/books/college-physics-ap-courses-2e/pages/9-connection-for-ap-r-courses)

9.1 The First Condition for Equilibrium

LEARNING OBJECTIVES

By the end of this section, you will be able to:

- State the first condition of equilibrium.
- Explain static equilibrium.
- Explain dynamic equilibrium.

The first condition necessary to achieve equilibrium is the one already mentioned: the net external force on the system must be zero. Expressed as an equation, this is simply

$$\text{net } \mathbf{F} = 0 \tag{9.1}$$

Note that if net $\mathbf{F}$ is zero, then the net external force in *any* direction is zero. For example, the net external forces along the typical *x*- and *y*-axes are zero. This is written as

$$\text{net } F_x = 0 \text{ and net } F_y = 0 \tag{9.2}$$

Figure 9.2 and Figure 9.3 illustrate situations where net $\mathbf{F} = 0$ for both **static equilibrium** (motionless), and **dynamic equilibrium** (constant velocity).

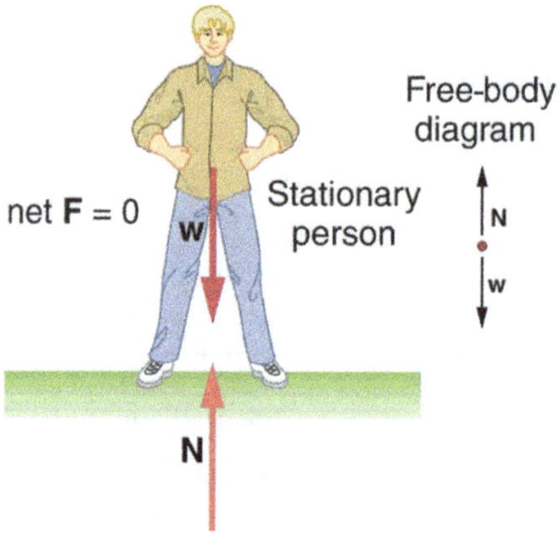

FIGURE 9.2 This motionless person is in static equilibrium. The forces acting on him add up to zero. Both forces are vertical in this case.

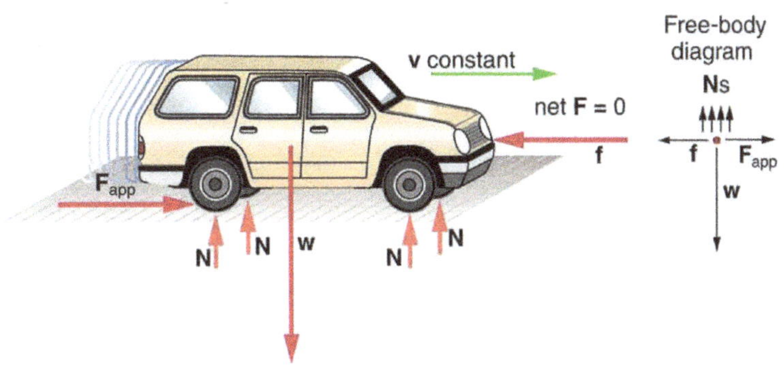

FIGURE 9.3 This car is in dynamic equilibrium because it is moving at constant velocity. There are horizontal and vertical forces, but the net external force in any direction is zero. The applied force $\mathbf{F}_{\text{app}}$ between the tires and the road is balanced by air friction, and the weight of the car is supported by the normal forces, here shown to be equal for all four tires.

However, it is not sufficient for the net external force of a system to be zero for a system to be in equilibrium. Consider the two situations illustrated in Figure 9.4 and Figure 9.5 where forces are applied to an ice hockey stick lying flat on ice. The net external force is zero in both situations shown in the figure; but in one case, equilibrium is achieved, whereas in the other, it is not. In Figure 9.4, the ice hockey stick remains motionless. But in Figure 9.5, with the same forces applied in different places, the stick experiences accelerated rotation. Therefore, we know that the point at which a force is applied is another factor in determining whether or not equilibrium is achieved. This will be explored further in the next section.

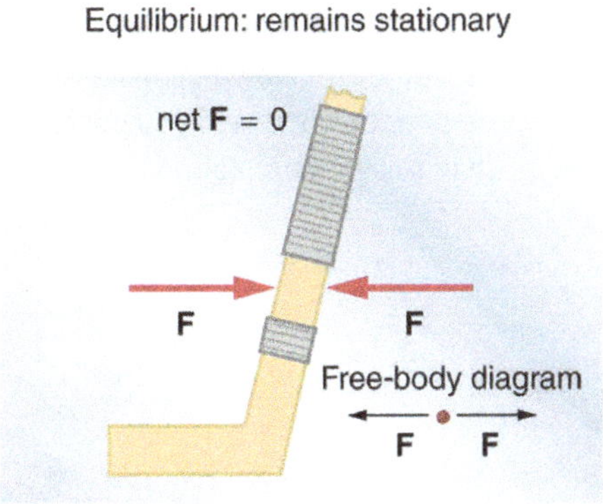

FIGURE 9.4 An ice hockey stick lying flat on ice with two equal and opposite horizontal forces applied to it. Friction is negligible, and the gravitational force is balanced by the support of the ice (a normal force). Thus, net $\mathbf{F} = 0$. Equilibrium is achieved, which is static equilibrium in this case.

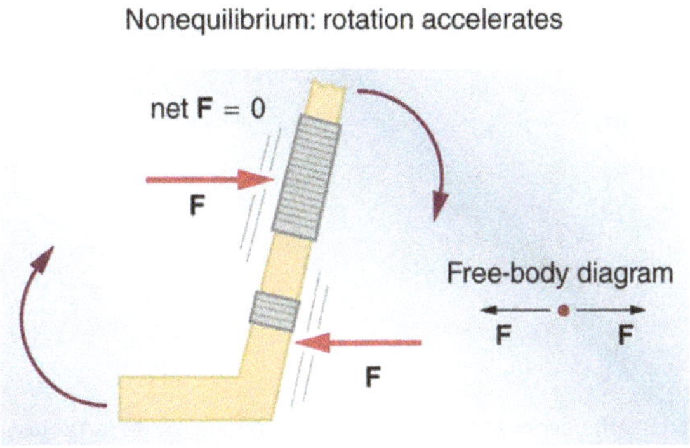

FIGURE 9.5 The same forces are applied at other points and the stick rotates—in fact, it experiences an accelerated rotation. Here net $\mathbf{F} = 0$ but the system is *not* at equilibrium. Hence, the net $\mathbf{F} = 0$ is a necessary—but not sufficient—condition for achieving equilibrium.

PHET EXPLORATIONS

Torque

Investigate how torque causes an object to rotate. Discover the relationships between angular acceleration, moment of inertia, angular momentum and torque.

Click to view content (https://openstax.org/l/21angmomintsim).

PhET

9.2 The Second Condition for Equilibrium

LEARNING OBJECTIVES

By the end of this section, you will be able to:

- State the second condition that is necessary to achieve equilibrium.
- Explain torque and the factors on which it depends.
- Describe the role of torque in rotational mechanics.

TORQUE

The second condition necessary to achieve equilibrium involves avoiding accelerated rotation (maintaining a constant angular velocity). A rotating body or system can be in equilibrium if its rate of rotation is constant and remains unchanged by the forces acting on it. To understand what factors affect rotation, let us think about what happens when you open an ordinary door by rotating it on its hinges.

Several familiar factors determine how effective you are in opening the door. See Figure 9.6. First of all, the larger the force, the more effective it is in opening the door—obviously, the harder you push, the more rapidly the door opens. Also, the point at which you push is crucial. If you apply your force too close to the hinges, the door will open slowly, if at all. Most people have been embarrassed by making this mistake and bumping up against a door when it did not open as quickly as expected. Finally, the direction in which you push is also important. The most effective direction is perpendicular to the door—we push in this direction almost instinctively.

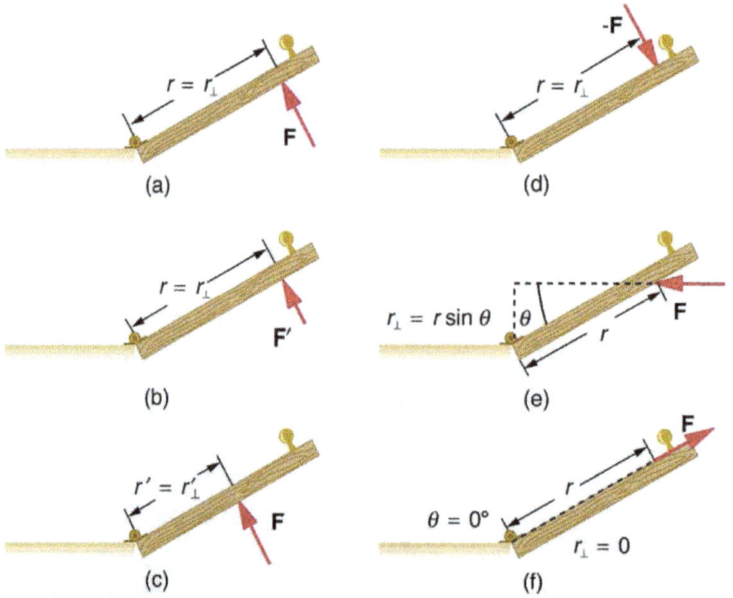

FIGURE 9.6 Torque is the turning or twisting effectiveness of a force, illustrated here for door rotation on its hinges (as viewed from overhead). Torque has both magnitude and direction. (a) Counterclockwise torque is produced by this force, which means that the door will rotate in a counterclockwise due to $\mathbf{F}$. Note that $r_\perp$ is the perpendicular distance of the pivot from the line of action of the force. (b) A smaller counterclockwise torque is produced by a smaller force $\mathbf{F}'$ acting at the same distance from the hinges (the pivot point). (c) The same force as in (a) produces a smaller counterclockwise torque when applied at a smaller distance from the hinges. (d) The same force as in (a), but acting in the opposite direction, produces a clockwise torque. (e) A smaller counterclockwise torque is produced by the same magnitude force acting at the same point but in a different direction. Here, θ is less than $90°$. (f) Torque is zero here since the force just pulls on the hinges, producing no rotation. In this case, $\theta = 0°$.

The magnitude, direction, and point of application of the force are incorporated into the definition of the physical quantity called torque. **Torque** is the rotational equivalent of a force. It is a measure of the effectiveness of a force in changing or accelerating a rotation (changing the angular velocity over a period of time). In equation form, the magnitude of torque is defined to be

$$\tau = rF\sin\theta \quad (9.3)$$

where τ (the Greek letter tau) is the symbol for torque, r is the distance from the pivot point to the point where the force is applied, F is the magnitude of the force, and θ is the angle between the force and the vector directed from the point of application to the pivot point, as seen in Figure 9.6 and Figure 9.7. An alternative expression for torque is given in terms of the **perpendicular lever arm** $r_{\perp}$ as shown in Figure 9.6 and Figure 9.7, which is defined as

$$r_{\perp} = r\sin\theta \quad (9.4)$$

so that

$$\tau = r_{\perp}F. \quad (9.5)$$

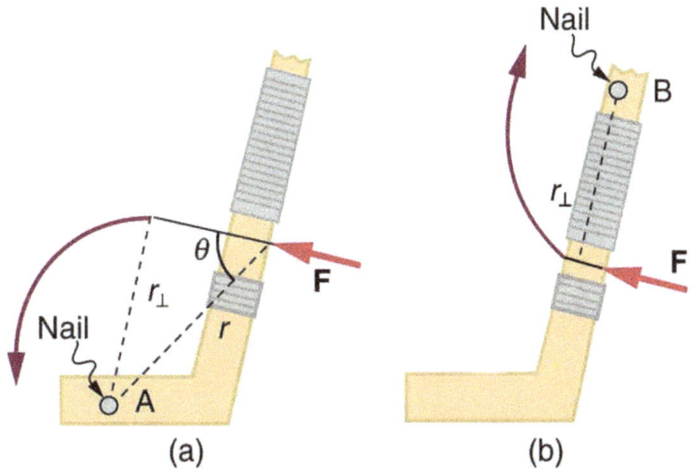

FIGURE 9.7 A force applied to an object can produce a torque, which depends on the location of the pivot point. (a) The three factors $\mathbf{r}$, $\mathbf{F}$, and θ for pivot point A on a body are shown here—$\mathbf{r}$ is the distance from the chosen pivot point to the point where the force $\mathbf{F}$ is applied, and θ is the angle between $\mathbf{F}$ and the vector directed from the point of application to the pivot point. If the object can rotate around point A, it will rotate counterclockwise. This means that torque is counterclockwise relative to pivot A. (b) In this case, point B is the pivot point. The torque from the applied force will cause a clockwise rotation around point B, and so it is a clockwise torque relative to B.

The perpendicular lever arm $r_{\perp}$ is the shortest distance from the pivot point to the line along which $\mathbf{F}$ acts; it is shown as a dashed line in Figure 9.6 and Figure 9.7. Note that the line segment that defines the distance $r_{\perp}$ is perpendicular to $\mathbf{F}$, as its name implies. It is sometimes easier to find or visualize $r_{\perp}$ than to find both r and θ. In such cases, it may be more convenient to use $\tau = r_{\perp}\mathbf{F}$ rather than $\tau = rF\sin\theta$ for torque, but both are equally valid.

The **SI unit of torque** is newtons times meters, usually written as $\mathrm{N \cdot m}$. For example, if you push perpendicular to the door with a force of 40 N at a distance of 0.800 m from the hinges, you exert a torque of 32 N·m(0.800 m × 40 N × sin 90°) relative to the hinges. If you reduce the force to 20 N, the torque is reduced to $16\ \mathrm{N{\cdot}m}$, and so on.

The torque is always calculated with reference to some chosen pivot point. For the same applied force, a different choice for the location of the pivot will give you a different value for the torque, since both r and θ depend on the location of the pivot. Any point in any object can be chosen to calculate the torque about that point. The object may not actually pivot about the chosen "pivot point."

Note that for rotation in a plane, torque has two possible directions. Torque is either clockwise or counterclockwise relative to the chosen pivot point, as illustrated for points B and A, respectively, in Figure 9.7. If the object can rotate about point A, it will rotate counterclockwise, which means that the torque for the force is shown as counterclockwise relative to A. But if the object can rotate about point B, it will rotate clockwise, which means the torque for the force shown is clockwise relative to B. Also, the magnitude of the torque is greater when the lever arm is longer.

Now, *the second condition necessary to achieve equilibrium* is that *the net external torque on a system must be zero*. An external torque is one that is created by an external force. You can choose the point around which the torque is calculated. The point can be the physical pivot point of a system or any other point in space—but it must be the same point for all torques. If the second condition (net external torque on a system is zero) is satisfied for one choice of pivot point, it will also hold true for any other choice of pivot point in or out of the system of interest. (This is true only in an inertial frame of reference.) The second condition necessary to achieve equilibrium is stated in equation form as

$$\text{net } \boldsymbol{\tau} = 0 \tag{9.6}$$

where net means total. Torques, which are in opposite directions are assigned opposite signs. A common convention is to call counterclockwise (ccw) torques positive and clockwise (cw) torques negative.

When two children balance a seesaw as shown in Figure 9.8, they satisfy the two conditions for equilibrium. Most people have perfect intuition about seesaws, knowing that the lighter child must sit farther from the pivot and that a heavier child can keep a lighter one off the ground indefinitely.

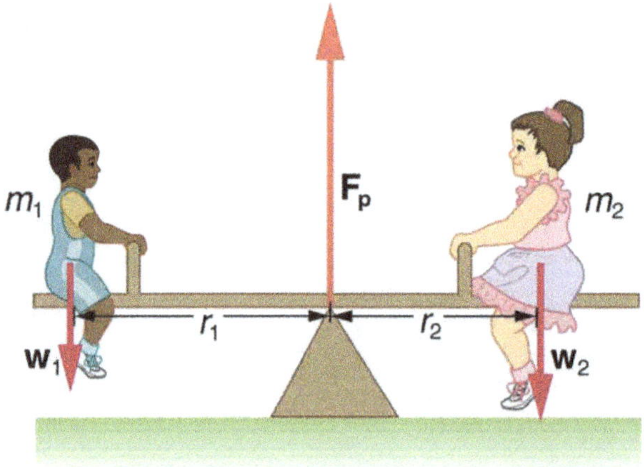

FIGURE 9.8 Two children balancing a seesaw satisfy both conditions for equilibrium. The lighter child sits farther from the pivot to create a torque equal in magnitude to that of the heavier child.

EXAMPLE 9.1

She Saw Torques On A Seesaw

The two children shown in Figure 9.8 are balanced on a seesaw of negligible mass. (This assumption is made to keep the example simple—more involved examples will follow.) The first child has a mass of 26.0 kg and sits 1.60 m from the pivot.(a) If the second child has a mass of 32.0 kg, how far is she from the pivot? (b) What is F_{p}, the supporting force exerted by the pivot?

Strategy

Both conditions for equilibrium must be satisfied. In part (a), we are asked for a distance; thus, the second condition (regarding torques) must be used, since the first (regarding only forces) has no distances in it. To apply the second condition for equilibrium, we first identify the system of interest to be the seesaw plus the two children. We take the supporting pivot to be the point about which the torques are calculated. We then identify all external forces acting on the system.

Solution (a)

The three external forces acting on the system are the weights of the two children and the supporting force of the pivot. Let us examine the torque produced by each. Torque is defined to be

$$\tau = rF\sin\theta. \tag{9.7}$$

Here $\theta = 90^{\text{o}}$, so that $\sin\theta = 1$ for all three forces. That means $r_{\perp} = r$ for all three. The torques exerted by the three forces are first,

$$\tau_1 = r_1 w_1 \tag{9.8}$$

second,

$$\tau_2 = -r_2 w_2 \tag{9.9}$$

and third,

$$\begin{aligned}\tau_p &= r_p F_p \\ &= 0 \cdot F_p \\ &= 0.\end{aligned} \tag{9.10}$$

Note that a minus sign has been inserted into the second equation because this torque is clockwise and is therefore negative by convention. Since F_p acts directly on the pivot point, the distance r_p is zero. A force acting on the pivot cannot cause a rotation, just as pushing directly on the hinges of a door will not cause it to rotate. Now, the second condition for equilibrium is that the sum of the torques on both children is zero. Therefore

$$\tau_2 = -\tau_1, \tag{9.11}$$

or

$$r_2 w_2 = r_1 w_1. \tag{9.12}$$

Weight is mass times the acceleration due to gravity. Entering mg for w, we get

$$r_2 m_2 g = r_1 m_1 g. \tag{9.13}$$

Solve this for the unknown r_2:

$$r_2 = r_1 \frac{m_1}{m_2}. \tag{9.14}$$

The quantities on the right side of the equation are known; thus, r_2 is

$$r_2 = (1.60\text{ m})\frac{26.0\text{ kg}}{32.0\text{ kg}} = 1.30\text{ m}. \tag{9.15}$$

As expected, the heavier child must sit closer to the pivot (1.30 m versus 1.60 m) to balance the seesaw.

Solution (b)

This part asks for a force F_p. The easiest way to find it is to use the first condition for equilibrium, which is

$$\text{net } \mathbf{F} = 0. \tag{9.16}$$

The forces are all vertical, so that we are dealing with a one-dimensional problem along the vertical axis; hence, the condition can be written as

$$\text{net } F_y = 0 \tag{9.17}$$

where we again call the vertical axis the *y*-axis. Choosing upward to be the positive direction, and using plus and minus signs to indicate the directions of the forces, we see that

$$F_p - w_1 - w_2 = 0. \tag{9.18}$$

This equation yields what might have been guessed at the beginning:

$$F_p = w_1 + w_2. \tag{9.19}$$

So, the pivot supplies a supporting force equal to the total weight of the system:

$$F_p = m_1 g + m_2 g. \tag{9.20}$$

Entering known values gives

$$\begin{aligned}F_p &= (26.0\text{ kg})\left(9.80\text{ m/s}^2\right) + (32.0\text{ kg})\left(9.80\text{ m/s}^2\right) \\ &= 568\text{ N}.\end{aligned} \tag{9.21}$$

Discussion

The two results make intuitive sense. The heavier child sits closer to the pivot. The pivot supports the weight of the two children. Part (b) can also be solved using the second condition for equilibrium, since both distances are known, but only if the pivot point is chosen to be somewhere other than the location of the seesaw's actual pivot!

Several aspects of the preceding example have broad implications. First, the choice of the pivot as the point around which torques are calculated simplified the problem. Since F_p is exerted on the pivot point, its lever arm is zero. Hence, the torque exerted by the supporting force F_p is zero relative to that pivot point. The second condition for equilibrium holds for any choice of pivot point, and so we choose the pivot point to simplify the solution of the problem.

Second, the acceleration due to gravity canceled in this problem, and we were left with a ratio of masses. *This will not always be the case.* Always enter the correct forces—do not jump ahead to enter some ratio of masses.

Third, the weight of each child is distributed over an area of the seesaw, yet we treated the weights as if each force were exerted at a single point. This is not an approximation—the distances r_1 and r_2 are the distances to points directly below the **center of gravity** of each child. As we shall see in the next section, the mass and weight of a system can act as if they are located at a single point.

Finally, note that the concept of torque has an importance beyond static equilibrium. *Torque plays the same role in rotational motion that force plays in linear motion.* We will examine this in the next chapter.

TAKE-HOME EXPERIMENT

Take a piece of modeling clay and put it on a table, then mash a cylinder down into it so that a ruler can balance on the round side of the cylinder while everything remains still. Put a penny 8 cm away from the pivot. Where would you need to put two pennies to balance? Three pennies?

9.3 Stability

LEARNING OBJECTIVES

By the end of this section, you will be able to:

- State the types of equilibrium.
- Describe stable and unstable equilibriums.
- Describe neutral equilibrium.

It is one thing to have a system in equilibrium; it is quite another for it to be stable. The toy doll perched on the man's hand in Figure 9.9, for example, is not in stable equilibrium. There are *three types of equilibrium*: *stable*, *unstable*, and *neutral*. Figures throughout this module illustrate various examples.

Figure 9.9 presents a balanced system, such as the toy doll on the man's hand, which has its center of gravity (cg) directly over the pivot, so that the torque of the total weight is zero. This is equivalent to having the torques of the individual parts balanced about the pivot point, in this case the hand. The cgs of the arms, legs, head, and torso are labeled with smaller type.

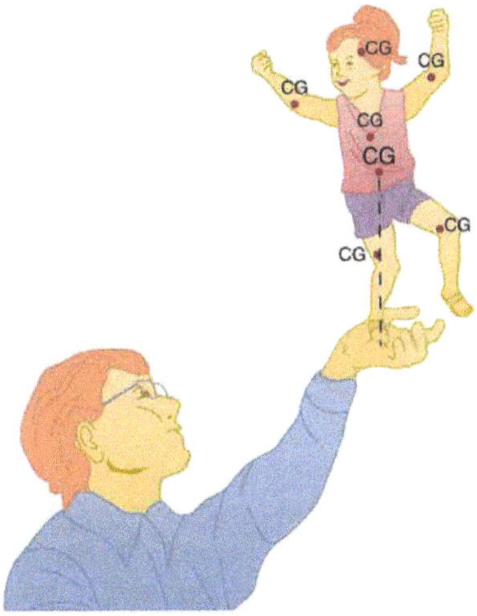

FIGURE 9.9 A man balances a toy doll on one hand.

A system is said to be in **stable equilibrium** if, when displaced from equilibrium, it experiences a net force or torque in a direction opposite to the direction of the displacement. For example, a marble at the bottom of a bowl will experience a *restoring* force when displaced from its equilibrium position. This force moves it back toward the equilibrium position. Most systems are in stable equilibrium, especially for small displacements. For another example of stable equilibrium, see the pencil in Figure 9.10.

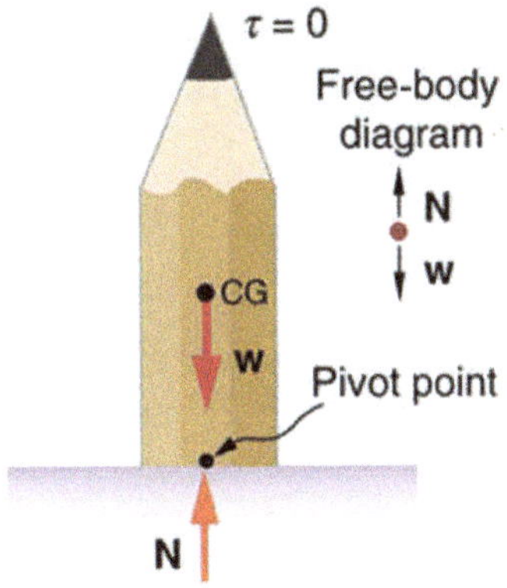

FIGURE 9.10 This pencil is in the condition of equilibrium. The net force on the pencil is zero and the total torque about any pivot is zero.

A system is in **unstable equilibrium** if, when displaced, it experiences a net force or torque in the *same* direction as the displacement from equilibrium. A system in unstable equilibrium accelerates away from its equilibrium position if displaced even slightly. An obvious example is a ball resting on top of a hill. Once displaced, it accelerates away from the crest. See the next several figures for examples of unstable equilibrium.

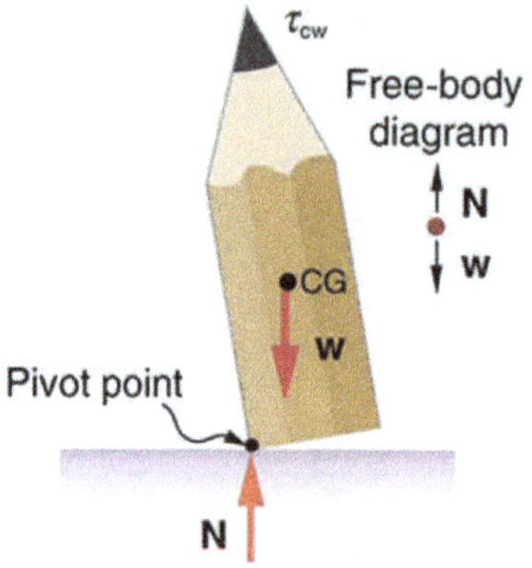

FIGURE 9.11 If the pencil is displaced slightly to the side (counterclockwise), it is no longer in equilibrium. Its weight produces a clockwise torque that returns the pencil to its equilibrium position.

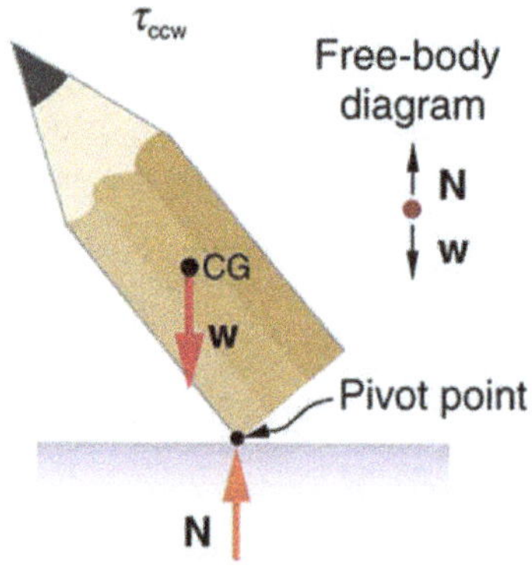

FIGURE 9.12 If the pencil is displaced too far, the torque caused by its weight changes direction to counterclockwise and causes the displacement to increase.

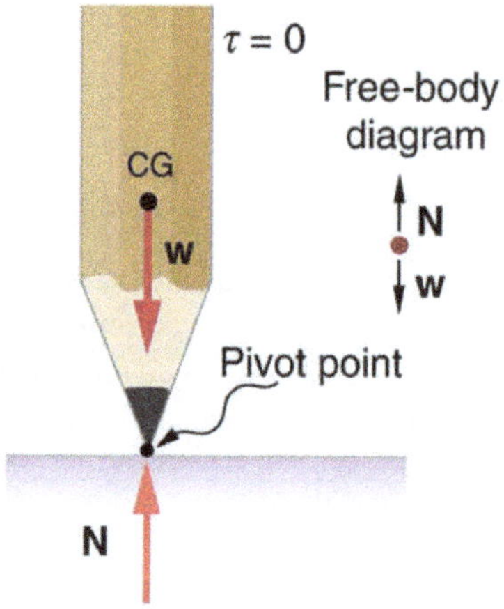

FIGURE 9.13 This figure shows unstable equilibrium, although both conditions for equilibrium are satisfied.

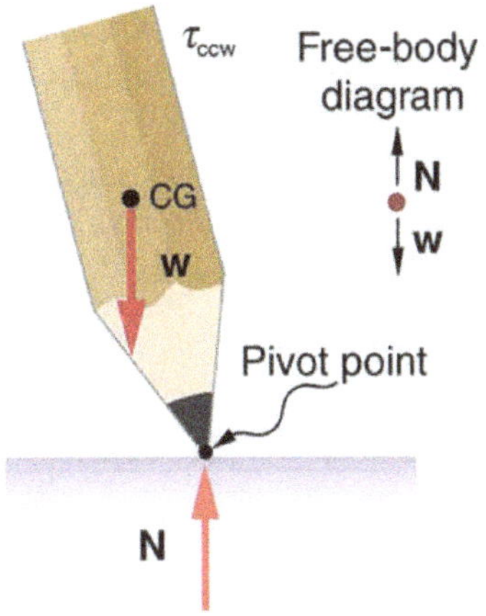

FIGURE 9.14 If the pencil is displaced even slightly, a torque is created by its weight that is in the same direction as the displacement, causing the displacement to increase.

A system is in **neutral equilibrium** if its equilibrium is independent of displacements from its original position. A marble on a flat horizontal surface is an example. Combinations of these situations are possible. For example, a marble on a saddle is stable for displacements toward the front or back of the saddle and unstable for displacements to the side. Figure 9.15 shows another example of neutral equilibrium.

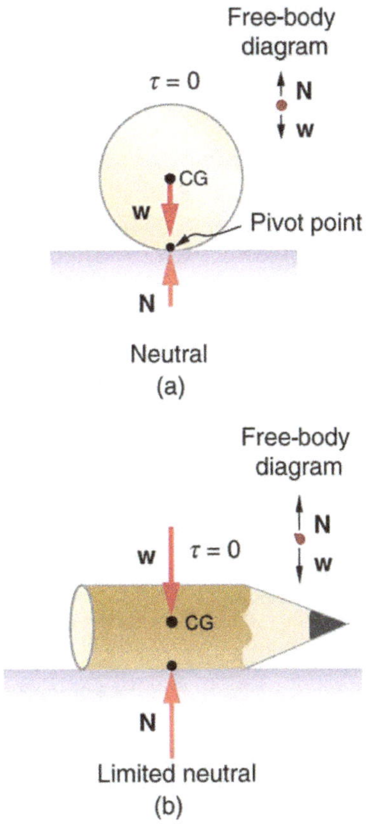

FIGURE 9.15 (a) Here we see neutral equilibrium. The cg of a sphere on a flat surface lies directly above the point of support, independent of the position on the surface. The sphere is therefore in equilibrium in any location, and if displaced, it will remain put. (b) Because it has a circular cross section, the pencil is in neutral equilibrium for displacements perpendicular to its length.

When we consider how far a system in stable equilibrium can be displaced before it becomes unstable, we find that some systems in stable equilibrium are more stable than others. The pencil in Figure 9.10 and the person in Figure 9.16(a) are in stable equilibrium, but become unstable for relatively small displacements to the side. The critical point is reached when the cg is no longer *above* the base of support. Additionally, since the cg of a person's body is above the pivots in the hips, displacements must be quickly controlled. This control is a central nervous system function that is developed when we learn to hold our bodies erect as infants. For increased stability while standing, the feet should be spread apart, giving a larger base of support. Stability is also increased by lowering one's center of gravity by bending the knees, as when a football player prepares to receive a ball or braces themselves for a tackle. A cane, a crutch, or a walker increases the stability of the user, even more as the base of support widens. Usually, the cg of a female is lower (closer to the ground) than a male. Young children have their center of gravity between their shoulders, which increases the challenge of learning to walk.

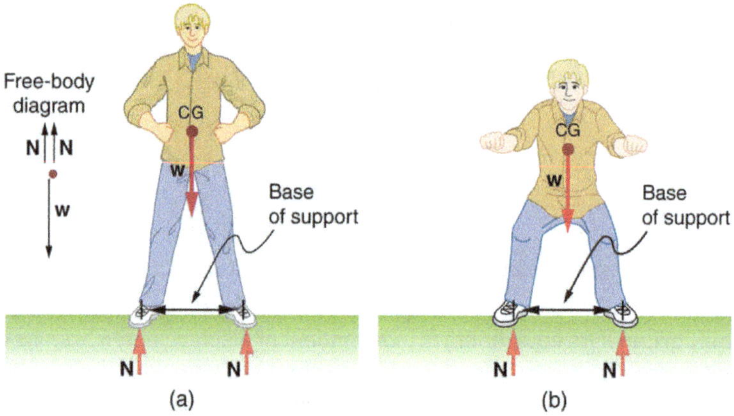

FIGURE 9.16 (a) The center of gravity of an adult is above the hip joints (one of the main pivots in the body) and lies between two narrowly-separated feet. Like a pencil standing on its eraser, this person is in stable equilibrium in relation to sideways displacements, but relatively small displacements take his cg outside the base of support and make him unstable. Humans are less stable relative to forward and backward displacements because the feet are not very long. Muscles are used extensively to balance the body in the front-to-back direction. (b) While bending in the manner shown, stability is increased by lowering the center of gravity. Stability is also increased if the base is expanded by placing the feet farther apart.

Animals such as chickens have easier systems to control. Figure 9.17 shows that the cg of a chicken lies below its hip joints and between its widely separated and broad feet. Even relatively large displacements of the chicken's cg are stable and result in restoring forces and torques that return the cg to its equilibrium position with little effort on the chicken's part. Not all birds are like chickens, of course. Some birds, such as the flamingo, have balance systems that are almost as sophisticated as that of humans.

Figure 9.17 shows that the cg of a chicken is below the hip joints and lies above a broad base of support formed by widely-separated and large feet. Hence, the chicken is in very stable equilibrium, since a relatively large displacement is needed to render it unstable. The body of the chicken is supported from above by the hips and acts as a pendulum between the hips. Therefore, the chicken is stable for front-to-back displacements as well as for side-to-side displacements.

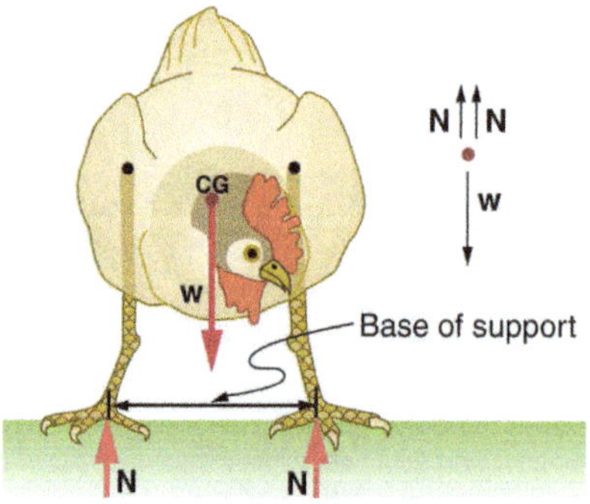

FIGURE 9.17 The center of gravity of a chicken is below the hip joints. The chicken is in stable equilibrium. The body of the chicken is supported from above by the hips and acts as a pendulum between them.

Engineers and architects strive to achieve extremely stable equilibriums for buildings and other systems that must withstand wind, earthquakes, and other forces that displace them from equilibrium. Although the examples in this section emphasize gravitational forces, the basic conditions for equilibrium are the same for all types of forces. The net external force must be zero, and the net torque must also be zero.

TAKE-HOME EXPERIMENT

Stand straight with your heels, back, and head against a wall. Bend forward from your waist, keeping your heels and bottom against the wall, to touch your toes. Can you do this without toppling over? Explain why and what you need to do to be able to touch your toes without losing your balance. Is it easier for a woman to do this?

9.4 Applications of Statics, Including Problem-Solving Strategies

LEARNING OBJECTIVES

By the end of this section, you will be able to:

- Discuss the applications of Statics in real life.
- State and discuss various problem-solving strategies in Statics.

Statics can be applied to a variety of situations, ranging from raising a drawbridge to bad posture and back strain. We begin with a discussion of problem-solving strategies specifically used for statics. Since statics is a special case of Newton's laws, both the general problem-solving strategies and the special strategies for Newton's laws, discussed in Problem-Solving Strategies, still apply.

PROBLEM-SOLVING STRATEGY: STATIC EQUILIBRIUM SITUATIONS

1. The first step is to determine whether or not the system is in **static equilibrium**. This condition is always the case when the *acceleration of the system is zero and accelerated rotation does not occur.*
2. It is particularly important to *draw a free body diagram for the system of interest.* Carefully label all forces, and note their relative magnitudes, directions, and points of application whenever these are known.
3. Solve the problem by applying either or both of the conditions for equilibrium (represented by the equations $\textbf{net F} = 0$ and $\textbf{net}\ \boldsymbol{\tau} = 0$, depending on the list of known and unknown factors. If the second condition is involved, *choose the pivot point to simplify the solution.* Any pivot point can be chosen, but the most useful ones cause torques by unknown forces to be zero. (Torque is zero if the force is applied at the pivot (then $r = 0$), or along a line through the pivot point (then $\theta = 0$)). Always choose a convenient coordinate system for projecting forces.
4. *Check the solution to see if it is reasonable* by examining the magnitude, direction, and units of the answer. The importance of this last step never diminishes, although in unfamiliar applications, it is usually more difficult to judge reasonableness. These judgments become progressively easier with experience.

Now let us apply this problem-solving strategy for the pole vaulter shown in the three figures below. The pole is uniform and has a mass of 5.00 kg. In Figure 9.18, the pole's cg lies halfway between the vaulter's hands. It seems reasonable that the force exerted by each hand is equal to half the weight of the pole, or 24.5 N. This obviously satisfies the first condition for equilibrium $(\textbf{net F} = 0)$. The second condition $(\textbf{net}\ \boldsymbol{\tau} = 0)$ is also satisfied, as we can see by choosing the cg to be the pivot point. The weight exerts no torque about a pivot point located at the cg, since it is applied at that point and its lever arm is zero. The equal forces exerted by the hands are equidistant from the chosen pivot, and so they exert equal and opposite torques. Similar arguments hold for other systems where supporting forces are exerted symmetrically about the cg. For example, the four legs of a uniform table each support one-fourth of its weight.

In Figure 9.18, a pole vaulter holding a pole with its cg halfway between his hands is shown. Each hand exerts a force equal to half the weight of the pole, $F_R = F_L = w/2$. (b) The pole vaulter moves the pole to his left, and the forces that the hands exert are no longer equal. See Figure 9.18. If the pole is held with its cg to the left of the person, then he must push down with his right hand and up with his left. The forces he exerts are larger here because they are in opposite directions and the cg is at a long distance from either hand.

Similar observations can be made using a meter stick held at different locations along its length.

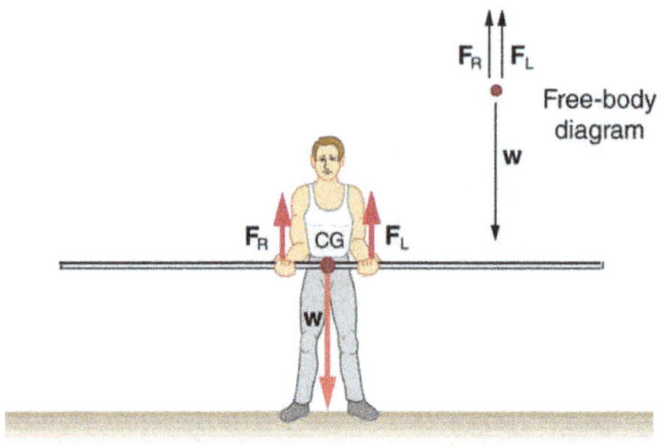

FIGURE 9.18 A pole vaulter holds a pole horizontally with both hands.

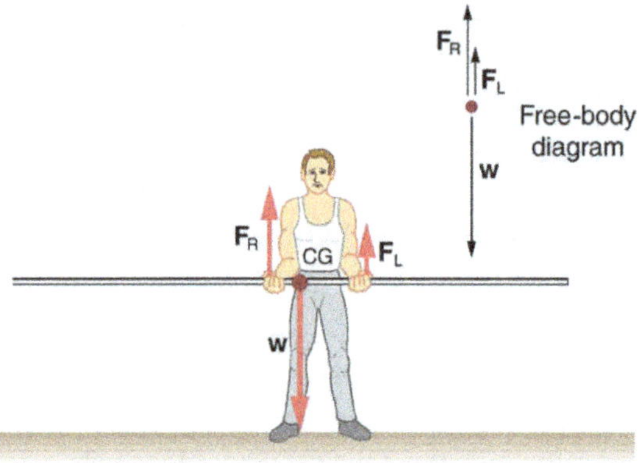

FIGURE 9.19 A pole vaulter is holding a pole horizontally with both hands. The center of gravity is near his right hand.

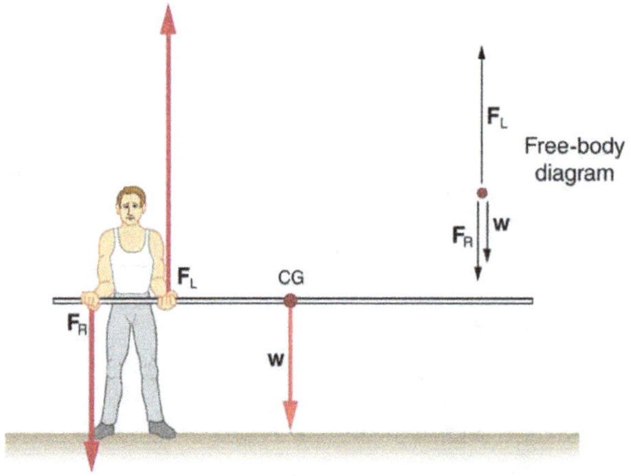

FIGURE 9.20 A pole vaulter is holding a pole horizontally with both hands. The center of gravity is to the left side of the vaulter.

If the pole vaulter holds the pole as shown in Figure 9.19, the situation is not as simple. The total force he exerts is still equal to the weight of the pole, but it is not evenly divided between his hands. (If $F_L = F_R$, then the torques about the cg would not be equal since the lever arms are different.) Logically, the right hand should support more weight, since it is closer to the cg. In fact, if the right hand is moved directly under the cg, it will support all the weight. This situation is exactly analogous to two people carrying a load; the one closer to the cg carries more of its weight. Finding the forces F_L and F_R is straightforward, as the next example shows.

If the pole vaulter holds the pole from near the end of the pole (Figure 9.20), the direction of the force applied by the right hand of the vaulter reverses its direction.

EXAMPLE 9.2

What Force Is Needed to Support a Weight Held Near Its CG?

For the situation shown in Figure 9.19, calculate: (a) F_R , the force exerted by the right hand, and (b) F_L, the force exerted by the left hand. The hands are 0.900 m apart, and the cg of the pole is 0.600 m from the left hand.

Strategy

Figure 9.19 includes a free body diagram for the pole, the system of interest. There is not enough information to use the first condition for equilibrium (net $\mathbf{F} = 0$), since two of the three forces are unknown and the hand forces cannot be assumed to be equal in this case. There is enough information to use the second condition for equilibrium (net $\boldsymbol{\tau} = 0$) if the pivot point is chosen to be at either hand, thereby making the torque from that hand zero. We choose to locate the pivot at the left hand in this part of the problem, to eliminate the torque from the left hand.

Solution for (a)

There are now only two nonzero torques, those from the gravitational force (τ_{w}) and from the push or pull of the right hand (τ_R). Stating the second condition in terms of clockwise and counterclockwise torques,

$$\text{net } \tau_{\text{cw}} = -\text{net } \tau_{\text{ccw}}. \tag{9.22}$$

or the algebraic sum of the torques is zero.

Here this is

$$\tau_R = -\tau_{\text{w}} \tag{9.23}$$

since the weight of the pole creates a counterclockwise torque and the right hand counters with a clockwise torque. Using the definition of torque, $\tau = rF\sin\theta$, noting that $\theta = 90^\circ$, and substituting known values, we obtain

$$(0.900\text{ m})(F_R)=(0.600\text{ m})(mg). \tag{9.24}$$

Thus,

$$\begin{aligned} F_R &= (0.667)(5.00\text{ kg})\left(9.80\text{ m/s}^2\right) \\ &= 32.7\text{ N}. \end{aligned} \tag{9.25}$$

Solution for (b)

The first condition for equilibrium is based on the free body diagram in the figure. This implies that by Newton's second law:

$$F_L + F_R - mg = 0 \tag{9.26}$$

From this we can conclude:

$$F_L + F_R = w = mg \tag{9.27}$$

Solving for F_L, we obtain

$$\begin{aligned} F_L &= mg - F_R \\ &= mg - 32.7\text{ N} \\ &= (5.00\text{ kg})\left(9.80\text{ m/s}^2\right) - 32.7\text{ N} \\ &= 16.3\text{ N} \end{aligned} \tag{9.28}$$

Discussion

F_L is seen to be exactly half of F_R, as we might have guessed, since F_L is applied twice as far from the cg as F_R.

If the pole vaulter holds the pole as he might at the start of a run, shown in Figure 9.20, the forces change again. Both are considerably greater, and one force reverses direction.

TAKE-HOME EXPERIMENT

This is an experiment to perform while standing in a bus or a train. Stand facing sideways. How do you move your body to readjust the distribution of your mass as the bus accelerates and decelerates? Now stand facing forward. How do you move your body to readjust the distribution of your mass as the bus accelerates and decelerates? Why is it easier and safer to stand facing sideways rather than forward? Note: For your safety (and those around you), make sure you are holding onto something while you carry out this activity!

PHET EXPLORATIONS

Balancing Act

Play with objects on a teeter totter to learn about balance. Test what you've learned by trying the Balance Challenge game.

Click to view content (https://openstax.org/books/college-physics-ap-courses-2e/pages/9-4-applications-of-statics-including-problemsolving-strategies)

9.5 Simple Machines

LEARNING OBJECTIVES

By the end of this section, you will be able to:

- Describe different simple machines.
- Calculate the mechanical advantage.

Simple machines are devices that can be used to multiply or augment a force that we apply – often at the expense of a distance through which we apply the force. The word for "machine" comes from the Greek word meaning "to help make things easier." Levers, gears, pulleys, wedges, and screws are some examples of machines. Energy is still conserved for these devices because a machine cannot do more work than the energy put into it. However, machines can reduce the input force that is needed to perform the job. The ratio of output to input force magnitudes for any simple machine is called its **mechanical advantage** (MA).

$$\text{MA} = \frac{F_\text{o}}{F_\text{i}} \tag{9.29}$$

One of the simplest machines is the lever, which is a rigid bar pivoted at a fixed place called the fulcrum. Torques are involved in levers, since there is rotation about a pivot point. Distances from the physical pivot of the lever are crucial, and we can obtain a useful expression for the MA in terms of these distances.

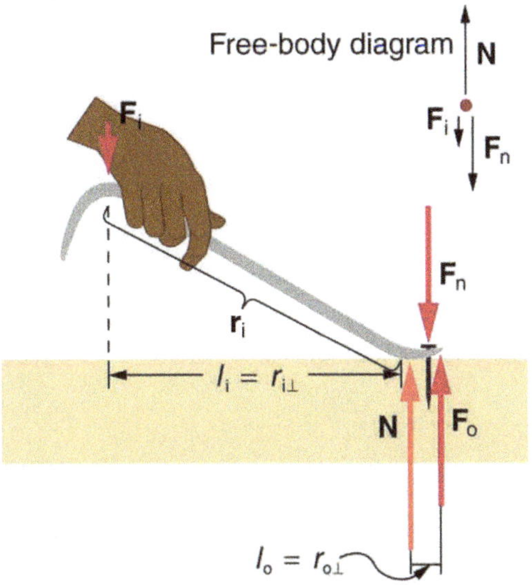

FIGURE 9.21 A nail puller is a lever with a large mechanical advantage. The external forces on the nail puller are represented by solid arrows. The force that the nail puller applies to the nail ($\mathbf{F}_o$) is not a force on the nail puller. The reaction force the nail exerts back on the puller ($\mathbf{F}_n$) is an external force and is equal and opposite to $\mathbf{F}_o$. The perpendicular lever arms of the input and output forces are l_i and l_o.

Figure 9.21 shows a lever type that is used as a nail puller. Crowbars, seesaws, and other such levers are all analogous to this one. $\mathbf{F}_i$ is the input force and $\mathbf{F}_o$ is the output force. There are three vertical forces acting on the nail puller (the system of interest) – these are $\mathbf{F}_i$, $\mathbf{F}_n$, and $\mathbf{N}$. $\mathbf{F}_n$ is the reaction force back on the system, equal and opposite to $\mathbf{F}_o$. (Note that $\mathbf{F}_o$ is not a force on the system.) $\mathbf{N}$ is the normal force upon the lever, and its torque is zero since it is exerted at the pivot. The torques due to $\mathbf{F}_i$ and $\mathbf{F}_n$ must be equal to each other if the nail is not moving, to satisfy the second condition for equilibrium (net $\tau = 0$). (In order for the nail to actually move, the torque due to $\mathbf{F}_i$ must be ever-so-slightly greater than torque due to $\mathbf{F}_n$.) Hence,

$$l_i F_i = l_o F_o \tag{9.30}$$

Notice that $\mathbf{r}_i$ is the distance from the pivot point to the point where the input force $\mathbf{F}_i$ is applied, and $\mathbf{r}_o$ (not labeled on the diagram) is the distance from the pivot point to the point where the output force $\mathbf{F}_o$ is applied. The distances l_i and l_o are the perpendicular components of the distances from where the input and output forces are applied to the pivot, as shown in the figure. Rearranging the last equation gives

$$\frac{F_o}{F_i} = \frac{l_i}{l_o}. \tag{9.31}$$

What interests us most here is that the magnitude of the force exerted by the nail puller, F_o, is much greater than the magnitude of the input force applied to the puller at the other end, F_i. For the nail puller,

$$\text{MA} = \frac{F_o}{F_i} = \frac{l_i}{l_o}. \tag{9.32}$$

This equation is true for levers in general. For the nail puller, the MA is certainly greater than one. The longer the handle on the nail puller, the greater the force you can exert with it.

Two other types of levers that differ slightly from the nail puller are a wheelbarrow and a shovel, shown in Figure 9.22. All these lever types are similar in that only three forces are involved – the input force, the output force, and the force on the pivot – and thus their MAs are given by $\text{MA} = \frac{F_o}{F_i}$ and $\text{MA} = \frac{d_1}{d_2}$, with distances being measured relative to the physical pivot. The wheelbarrow and shovel differ from the nail puller because both the input and output forces are on the same side of the pivot.

In the case of the wheelbarrow, the output force or load is between the pivot (the wheel's axle) and the input or applied force. In the case of the shovel, the input force is between the pivot (at the end of the handle) and the load, but the input lever arm is shorter than the output lever arm. In this case, the MA is less than one.

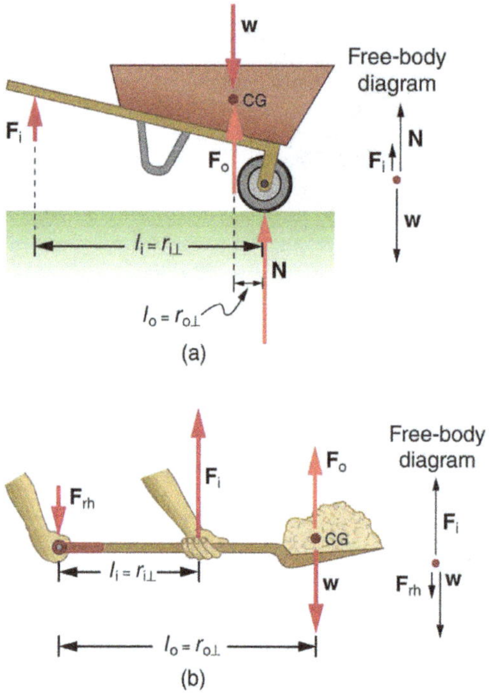

FIGURE 9.22 (a) In the case of the wheelbarrow, the output force or load is between the pivot and the input force. The pivot is the wheel's axle. Here, the output force is greater than the input force. Thus, a wheelbarrow enables you to lift much heavier loads than you could with your body alone. (b) In the case of the shovel, the input force is between the pivot and the load, but the input lever arm is shorter than the output lever arm. The pivot is at the handle held by the right hand. Here, the output force (supporting the shovel's load) is less than the input force (from the hand nearest the load), because the input is exerted closer to the pivot than is the output.

EXAMPLE 9.3

What is the Advantage for the Wheelbarrow?

In the wheelbarrow of Figure 9.22, the load has a perpendicular lever arm of 7.50 cm, while the hands have a perpendicular lever arm of 1.02 m. (a) What upward force must you exert to support the wheelbarrow and its load if their combined mass is 45.0 kg? (b) What force does the wheelbarrow exert on the ground?

Strategy

Here, we use the concept of mechanical advantage.

Solution

(a) In this case, $\frac{F_o}{F_i} = \frac{l_i}{l_o}$ becomes

$$F_i = F_o \frac{l_o}{l_i}. \tag{9.33}$$

Adding values into this equation yields

$$F_i = (45.0 \text{ kg})\left(9.80 \text{ m/s}^2\right)\frac{0.075 \text{ m}}{1.02 \text{ m}} = 32.4 \text{ N}. \tag{9.34}$$

The free-body diagram (see Figure 9.22) gives the following normal force: $F_i + N = W$. Therefore, $N = (45.0 \text{ kg})\left(9.80 \text{ m/s}^2\right) - 32.4 \text{ N} = 409 \text{ N}$. N is the normal force acting on the wheel; by Newton's third law, the force the wheel exerts on the ground is 409 N.

Discussion

An even longer handle would reduce the force needed to lift the load. The MA here is $\text{MA} = 1.02/0.0750 = 13.6$.

Another very simple machine is the inclined plane. Pushing a cart up a plane is easier than lifting the same cart straight up to the top using a ladder, because the applied force is less. However, the work done in both cases (assuming the work done by friction is negligible) is the same. Inclined lanes or ramps were probably used during the construction of the Egyptian pyramids to move large blocks of stone to the top.

A crank is a lever that can be rotated 360° about its pivot, as shown in Figure 9.23. Such a machine may not look like a lever, but the physics of its actions remain the same. The MA for a crank is simply the ratio of the radii r_i/r_0. Wheels and gears have this simple expression for their MAs too. The MA can be greater than 1, as it is for the crank, or less than 1, as it is for the simplified car axle driving the wheels, as shown. If the axle's radius is $2.0\ \text{cm}$ and the wheel's radius is $24.0\ \text{cm}$, then $\text{MA} = 2.0/24.0 = 0.083$ and the axle would have to exert a force of $12{,}000\ \text{N}$ on the wheel to enable it to exert a force of $1000\ \text{N}$ on the ground.

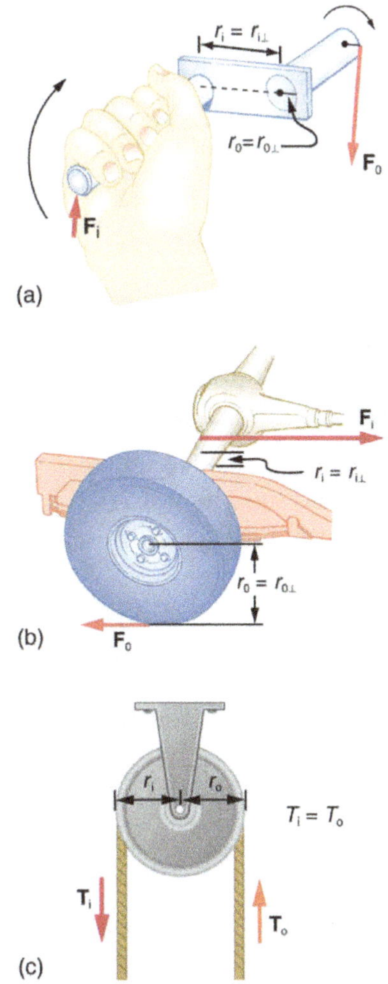

FIGURE 9.23 (a) A crank is a type of lever that can be rotated 360° about its pivot. Cranks are usually designed to have a large MA. (b) A simplified automobile axle drives a wheel, which has a much larger diameter than the axle. The MA is less than 1. (c) An ordinary pulley is used to lift a heavy load. The pulley changes the direction of the force T exerted by the cord without changing its magnitude. Hence, this machine has an MA of 1.

An ordinary pulley has an MA of 1; it only changes the direction of the force and not its magnitude. Combinations of pulleys, such as those illustrated in Figure 9.24, are used to multiply force. If the pulleys are friction-free, then the force output is approximately an integral multiple of the tension in the cable. The number of cables pulling directly upward on the system of interest, as illustrated in the figures given below, is approximately the MA of the pulley system. Since each attachment applies an external force in approximately the same direction as the others, they add, producing a total force that is nearly an integral multiple of the input force T.

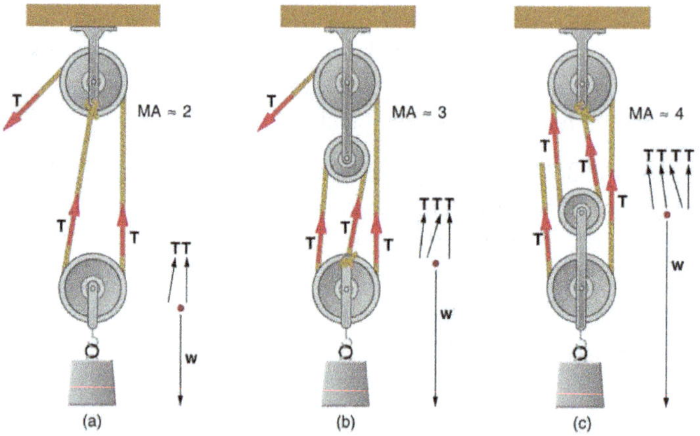

FIGURE 9.24 (a) The combination of pulleys is used to multiply force. The force is an integral multiple of tension if the pulleys are frictionless. This pulley system has two cables attached to its load, thus applying a force of approximately $2T$. This machine has $MA \approx 2$. (b) Three pulleys are used to lift a load in such a way that the mechanical advantage is about 3. Effectively, there are three cables attached to the load. (c) This pulley system applies a force of $4T$, so that it has $MA \approx 4$. Effectively, four cables are pulling on the system of interest.

9.6 Forces and Torques in Muscles and Joints

LEARNING OBJECTIVES

By the end of this section, you will be able to:

- Explain the forces exerted by muscles.
- State how a bad posture causes back strain.
- Discuss the benefits of skeletal muscles attached close to joints.
- Discuss various complexities in the real system of muscles, bones, and joints.

Muscles, bones, and joints are some of the most interesting applications of statics. There are some surprises. Muscles, for example, exert far greater forces than we might think. Figure 9.25 shows a forearm holding a book and a schematic diagram of an analogous lever system. The schematic is a good approximation for the forearm, which looks more complicated than it is, and we can get some insight into the way typical muscle systems function by analyzing it.

Muscles can only contract, so they occur in pairs. In the arm, the biceps muscle is a flexor—that is, it closes the limb. The triceps muscle is an extensor that opens the limb. This configuration is typical of skeletal muscles, bones, and joints in humans and other vertebrates. Most skeletal muscles exert much larger forces within the body than the limbs apply to the outside world. The reason is clear once we realize that most muscles are attached to bones via tendons close to joints, causing these systems to have mechanical advantages much less than one. Viewing them as simple machines, the input force is much greater than the output force, as seen in Figure 9.25.

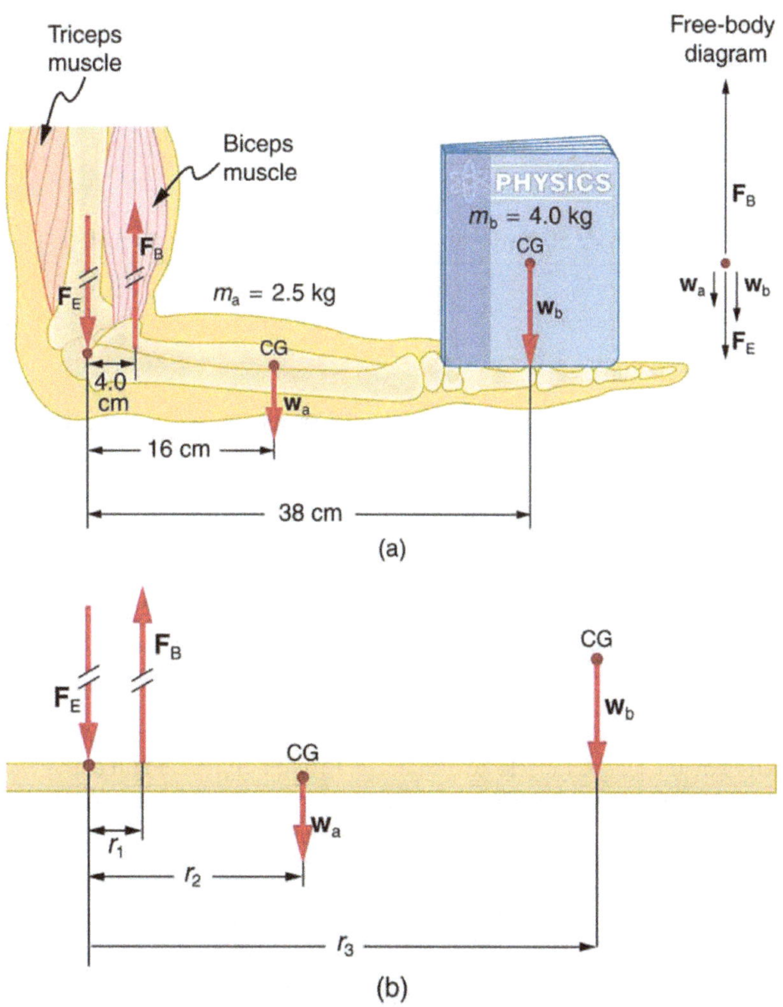

FIGURE 9.25 (a) The figure shows the forearm of a person holding a book. The biceps exert a force $\mathbf{F_B}$ to support the weight of the forearm and the book. The triceps are assumed to be relaxed. (b) Here, you can view an approximately equivalent mechanical system with the pivot at the elbow joint as seen in Example 9.4.

EXAMPLE 9.4

Muscles Exert Bigger Forces Than You Might Think

Calculate the force the biceps muscle must exert to hold the forearm and its load as shown in Figure 9.25, and compare this force with the weight of the forearm plus its load. You may take the data in the figure to be accurate to three significant figures.

Strategy

There are four forces acting on the forearm and its load (the system of interest). The magnitude of the force of the biceps is F_B; that of the elbow joint is F_E; that of the weights of the forearm is w_a, and its load is w_b. Two of these are unknown (F_B and F_E), so that the first condition for equilibrium cannot by itself yield F_B. But if we use the second condition and choose the pivot to be at the elbow, then the torque due to F_E is zero, and the only unknown becomes F_B.

Solution

The torques created by the weights are clockwise relative to the pivot, while the torque created by the biceps is counterclockwise; thus, the second condition for equilibrium (net $\boldsymbol{\tau} = 0$) becomes

$$r_2 w_a + r_3 w_b = r_1 F_B. \tag{9.35}$$

Note that $\sin\theta = 1$ for all forces, since $\theta = 90^\circ$ for all forces. This equation can easily be solved for F_B in terms of known quantities, yielding

$$F_B = \frac{r_2 w_a + r_3 w_b}{r_1}. \quad 9.36$$

Entering the known values gives

$$F_B = \frac{(0.160\text{ m})(2.50\text{ kg})\left(9.80\text{ m/s}^2\right)+(0.380\text{ m})(4.00\text{ kg})\left(9.80\text{ m/s}^2\right)}{0.0400\text{ m}} \quad 9.37$$

which yields

$$F_B = 470\text{ N}. \quad 9.38$$

Now, the combined weight of the arm and its load is $(6.50\text{ kg})\left(9.80\text{ m/s}^2\right) = 63.7\text{ N}$, so that the ratio of the force exerted by the biceps to the total weight is

$$\frac{F_B}{w_a + w_b} = \frac{470}{63.7} = 7.38. \quad 9.39$$

Discussion

This means that the biceps muscle is exerting a force 7.38 times the weight supported.

In the above example of the biceps muscle, the angle between the forearm and upper arm is 90°. If this angle changes, the force exerted by the biceps muscle also changes. In addition, the length of the biceps muscle changes. The force the biceps muscle can exert depends upon its length; it is smaller when it is shorter than when it is stretched.

Very large forces are also created in the joints. In the previous example, the downward force F_E exerted by the humerus at the elbow joint equals 407 N, or 6.38 times the total weight supported. (The calculation of F_E is straightforward and is left as an end-of-chapter problem.) Because muscles can contract, but not expand beyond their resting length, joints and muscles often exert forces that act in opposite directions and thus subtract. (In the above example, the upward force of the muscle minus the downward force of the joint equals the weight supported—that is, $470\text{ N} - 407\text{ N} = 63\text{ N}$, approximately equal to the weight supported.) Forces in muscles and joints are largest when their load is a long distance from the joint, as the book is in the previous example.

In racquet sports such as tennis the constant extension of the arm during game play creates large forces in this way. The mass times the lever arm of a tennis racquet is an important factor, and many players use the heaviest racquet they can handle. It is no wonder that joint deterioration and damage to the tendons in the elbow, such as "tennis elbow," can result from repetitive motion, undue torques, and possibly poor racquet selection in such sports. Various tried techniques for holding and using a racquet or bat or stick not only increases sporting prowess but can minimize fatigue and long-term damage to the body. For example, tennis balls correctly hit at the "sweet spot" on the racquet will result in little vibration or impact force being felt in the racquet and the body—less torque as explained in Collisions of Extended Bodies in Two Dimensions. Twisting the hand to provide top spin on the ball or using an extended rigid elbow in a backhand stroke can also aggravate the tendons in the elbow.

Training coaches and physical therapists use the knowledge of relationships between forces and torques in the treatment of muscles and joints. In physical therapy, an exercise routine can apply a particular force and torque which can, over a period of time, revive muscles and joints. Some exercises are designed to be carried out under water, because this requires greater forces to be exerted, further strengthening muscles. However, connecting tissues in the limbs, such as tendons and cartilage as well as joints are sometimes damaged by the large forces they carry. Often, this is due to accidents, but heavily muscled athletes, such as weightlifters, can tear muscles and connecting tissue through effort alone.

The back is considerably more complicated than the arm or leg, with various muscles and joints between vertebrae, all having mechanical advantages less than 1. Back muscles must, therefore, exert very large forces, which are borne by the spinal column. Discs crushed by mere exertion are very common. The jaw is somewhat exceptional—the masseter muscles that close the jaw have a mechanical advantage greater than 1 for the back teeth, allowing us to exert very large forces with them. A cause of stress headaches is persistent clenching of teeth where the sustained large force translates into fatigue in muscles around the skull.

Figure 9.26 shows how bad posture causes back strain. In part (a), we see a person with good posture. Note that her upper body's cg is directly above the pivot point in the hips, which in turn is directly above the base of support at her feet. Because of this, her upper body's weight exerts no torque about the hips. The only force needed is a vertical force at the hips equal to the weight supported. No muscle action is required, since the bones are rigid and transmit this force from the floor. This is a position of unstable equilibrium, but only small forces are needed to bring the upper body back to vertical if it is slightly displaced. Bad posture is shown in part (b); we see that the upper body's cg is in front of the pivot in the hips. This creates a clockwise torque around the hips that is counteracted by muscles in the lower back. These muscles must exert large forces, since they have typically small mechanical advantages. (In other words, the perpendicular lever arm for the muscles is much smaller than for the cg.) Poor posture can also cause muscle strain for people sitting at their desks using computers. Special chairs are available that allow the body's CG to be more easily situated above the seat, to reduce back pain. Prolonged muscle action produces muscle strain. Note that the cg of the entire body is still directly above the base of support in part (b) of Figure 9.26. This is compulsory; otherwise the person would not be in equilibrium. We lean forward for the same reason when carrying a load on our backs, to the side when carrying a load in one arm, and backward when carrying a load in front of us, as seen in Figure 9.27.

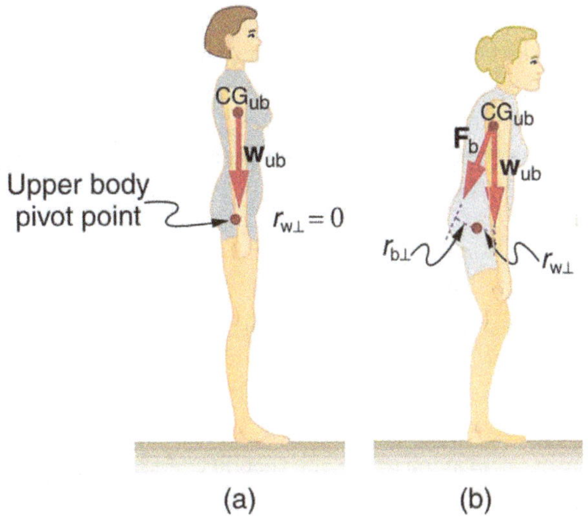

FIGURE 9.26 (a) Good posture places the upper body's cg over the pivots in the hips, eliminating the need for muscle action to balance the body. (b) Poor posture requires exertion by the back muscles to counteract the clockwise torque produced around the pivot by the upper body's weight. The back muscles have a small effective perpendicular lever arm, $r_{b\perp}$, and must therefore exert a large force $\mathbf{F}_b$. Note that the legs lean backward to keep the cg of the entire body above the base of support in the feet.

You have probably been warned against lifting objects with your back. This action, even more than bad posture, can cause muscle strain and damage discs and vertebrae, since abnormally large forces are created in the back muscles and spine.

FIGURE 9.27 People adjust their stance to maintain balance. (a) A father carrying his son piggyback leans forward to position their overall cg above the base of support at his feet. (b) A student carrying a shoulder bag leans to the side to keep the overall cg over their feet. (c) Another student carrying a load of books in her arms leans backward for the same reason.

EXAMPLE 9.5

Do Not Lift with Your Back

Consider the person lifting a heavy box with his back, shown in Figure 9.28. (a) Calculate the magnitude of the force F_B– in the back muscles that is needed to support the upper body plus the box and compare this with his weight. The mass of the upper body is 55.0 kg and the mass of the box is 30.0 kg. (b) Calculate the magnitude and direction of the force $\mathbf{F}_V$– exerted by the vertebrae on the spine at the indicated pivot point. Again, data in the figure may be taken to be accurate to three significant figures.

Strategy

By now, we sense that the second condition for equilibrium is a good place to start, and inspection of the known values confirms that it can be used to solve for F_B– if the pivot is chosen to be at the hips. The torques created by $\mathbf{w}_{ub}$ and $\mathbf{w}_{box}$– are clockwise, while that created by $\mathbf{F}_B$– is counterclockwise.

Solution for (a)

Using the perpendicular lever arms given in the figure, the second condition for equilibrium (net $\boldsymbol{\tau} = 0$) becomes

$$(0.350\text{ m})(55.0\text{ kg})\left(9.80\text{ m/s}^2\right)+(0.500\text{ m})(30.0\text{ kg})\left(9.80\text{ m/s}^2\right)=(0.0800\text{ m})F_B. \quad 9.40$$

Solving for F_B yields

$$F_B = 4.20 \times 10^3\text{ N}. \quad 9.41$$

The ratio of the force the back muscles exert to the weight of the upper body plus its load is

$$\frac{F_B}{w_{ub} + w_{box}} = \frac{4200\text{ N}}{833\text{ N}} = 5.04. \quad 9.42$$

This force is considerably larger than it would be if the load were not present.

Solution for (b)

More important in terms of its damage potential is the force on the vertebrae $\mathbf{F}_V$. The first condition for equilibrium (net $\mathbf{F} = 0$) can be used to find its magnitude and direction. Using y for vertical and x for horizontal, the condition for the net external forces along those axes to be zero

$$\text{net } F_y = 0 \text{ and net } F_x = 0. \quad 9.43$$

Starting with the vertical (y) components, this yields

$$F_{Vy} - w_{ub} - w_{box} - F_B \sin 29.0^\circ = 0. \quad 9.44$$

Thus,

$$\begin{aligned} F_{Vy} &= w_{ub} + w_{box} + F_B \sin 29.0^\circ \\ &= 833\text{ N} + (4200\text{ N}) \sin 29.0^\circ \end{aligned} \quad 9.45$$

yielding

$$F_{Vy} = 2.87 \times 10^3 \text{ N}. \quad 9.46$$

Similarly, for the horizontal (x) components,

$$F_{Vx} - F_B \cos 29.0^\circ = 0 \quad 9.47$$

yielding

$$F_{Vx} = 3.67 \times 10^3 \text{ N}. \quad 9.48$$

The magnitude of $\mathbf{F}_V$ is given by the Pythagorean theorem:

$$F_V = \sqrt{F_{Vx}^2 + F_{Vy}^2} = 4.66 \times 10^3 \text{ N}. \quad 9.49$$

The direction of $\mathbf{F}_V$ is

$$\theta = \tan^{-1}\left(\frac{F_{Vy}}{F_{Vx}}\right) = 38.0^\circ. \quad 9.50$$

Note that the ratio of F_V to the weight supported is

$$\frac{F_V}{w_{ub} + w_{box}} = \frac{4660\text{ N}}{833\text{ N}} = 5.59. \quad 9.51$$

Discussion

This force is about 5.6 times greater than it would be if the person were standing erect. The trouble with the back is not so much that the forces are large—because similar forces are created in our hips, knees, and ankles—but that our spines are relatively weak. Proper lifting, performed with the back erect and using the legs to raise the body and load, creates much smaller forces in the back—in this case, about 5.6 times smaller.

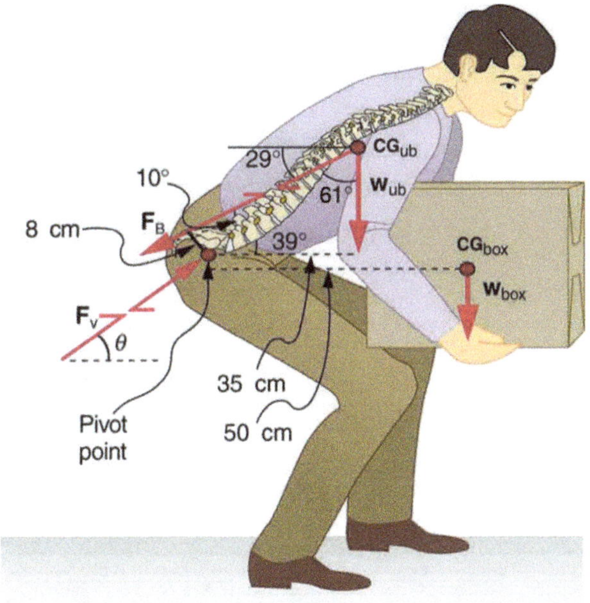

FIGURE 9.28 This figure shows that large forces are exerted by the back muscles and experienced in the vertebrae when a person lifts with their back, since these muscles have small effective perpendicular lever arms. The data shown here are analyzed in the preceding example, Example 9.5.

What are the benefits of having most skeletal muscles attached so close to joints? One advantage is speed because small muscle contractions can produce large movements of limbs in a short period of time. Other advantages are flexibility and agility, made possible by the large numbers of joints and the ranges over which they function. For example, it is difficult to imagine a system with biceps muscles attached at the wrist that would be capable of the broad range of movement we vertebrates possess.

There are some interesting complexities in real systems of muscles, bones, and joints. For instance, the pivot point in many joints changes location as the joint is flexed, so that the perpendicular lever arms and the mechanical advantage of the system change, too. Thus the force the biceps muscle must exert to hold up a book varies as the forearm is flexed. Similar mechanisms operate in the legs, which explain, for example, why there is less leg strain when a bicycle seat is set at the proper height. The methods employed in this section give a reasonable description of real systems provided enough is known about the dimensions of the system. There are many other interesting examples of force and torque in the body—a few of these are the subject of end-of-chapter problems.

Glossary

center of gravity the point where the total weight of the body is assumed to be concentrated

dynamic equilibrium a state of equilibrium in which the net external force and torque on a system moving with constant velocity are zero

mechanical advantage the ratio of output to input forces for any simple machine

neutral equilibrium a state of equilibrium that is independent of a system's displacements from its original position

perpendicular lever arm the shortest distance from the pivot point to the line along which $\mathbf{F}$ lies

SI units of torque newton times meters, usually written as N·m

stable equilibrium a system, when displaced, experiences a net force or torque in a direction opposite to the direction of the displacement

static equilibrium a state of equilibrium in which the net external force and torque acting on a system is zero

static equilibrium equilibrium in which the acceleration of the system is zero and accelerated rotation does not occur

torque turning or twisting effectiveness of a force

unstable equilibrium a system, when displaced, experiences a net force or torque in the same direction as the displacement from equilibrium

Section Summary

9.1 The First Condition for Equilibrium

- Statics is the study of forces in equilibrium.
- Two conditions must be met to achieve equilibrium, which is defined to be motion without linear or rotational acceleration.
- The first condition necessary to achieve equilibrium is that the net external force on the system must be zero, so that $\text{net } \mathbf{F} = 0$.

9.2 The Second Condition for Equilibrium

- The second condition assures those torques are also balanced. Torque is the rotational equivalent of a force in producing a rotation and is defined to be
  $\tau = rF \sin\theta$
  where τ is torque, r is the distance from the pivot point to the point where the force is applied, F is the magnitude of the force, and θ is the angle between $\mathbf{F}$ and the vector directed from the point where the force acts to the pivot point. The perpendicular lever arm $r_\perp$ is defined to be

  $r_\perp = r \sin\theta$
  so that

  $\tau = r_\perp F.$
- The perpendicular lever arm $r_\perp$ is the shortest distance from the pivot point to the line along which F acts. The SI unit for torque is newton-meter (N·m). The second condition necessary to achieve equilibrium is that the net external torque on a system must be zero:
  $\text{net } \boldsymbol{\tau} = 0$
  By convention, counterclockwise torques are positive, and clockwise torques are negative.

9.3 Stability

- A system is said to be in stable equilibrium if, when displaced from equilibrium, it experiences a net force or torque in a direction opposite the direction of the displacement.
- A system is in unstable equilibrium if, when displaced from equilibrium, it experiences a net force or torque in the same direction as the displacement from equilibrium.
- A system is in neutral equilibrium if its equilibrium is independent of displacements from its original position.

9.4 Applications of Statics, Including Problem-Solving Strategies

- Statics can be applied to a variety of situations, ranging from raising a drawbridge to bad posture and back strain. We have discussed the problem-solving strategies specifically useful for statics. Statics is a special case of Newton's laws, both the general problem-solving strategies and the special strategies for Newton's laws, discussed in Problem-Solving Strategies, still apply.

9.5 Simple Machines

- Simple machines are devices that can be used to multiply or augment a force that we apply – often at the expense of a distance through which we have to apply the force.
- The ratio of output to input forces for any simple machine is called its mechanical advantage
- A few simple machines are the lever, nail puller, wheelbarrow, crank, etc.

9.6 Forces and Torques in Muscles and Joints

- Statics plays an important part in understanding everyday strains in our muscles and bones.
- Many lever systems in the body have a mechanical advantage of significantly less than one, as many of our muscles are attached close to joints.
- Someone with good posture stands or sits in such a way that the person's center of gravity lies directly above the pivot point in the hips, thereby avoiding back strain and damage to disks.

Conceptual Questions

9.1 The First Condition for Equilibrium

1. What can you say about the velocity of a moving body that is in dynamic equilibrium? Draw a sketch of such a body using clearly labeled arrows to represent all external forces on the body.
2. Under what conditions can a rotating body be in equilibrium? Give an example.

9.2 The Second Condition for Equilibrium

3. What three factors affect the torque created by a force relative to a specific pivot point?
4. A wrecking ball is being used to knock down a building. One tall unsupported concrete wall remains standing. If the wrecking ball hits the wall near the top, is the wall more likely to fall over by rotating at its base or by falling straight down? Explain your answer. How is it most likely to fall if it is struck with the same force at its base? Note that this depends on how firmly the wall is attached at its base.
5. Mechanics sometimes put a length of pipe over the handle of a wrench when trying to remove a very tight bolt. How does this help? (It is also hazardous since it can break the bolt.)

9.3 Stability

6. A round pencil lying on its side as in Figure 9.12 is in neutral equilibrium relative to displacements perpendicular to its length. What is its stability relative to displacements parallel to its length?
7. Explain the need for tall towers on a suspension bridge to ensure stable equilibrium.

9.4 Applications of Statics, Including Problem-Solving Strategies

8. When visiting some countries, you may see a person balancing a load on the head. Explain why the center of mass of the load needs to be directly above the person's neck vertebrae.

9.5 Simple Machines

9. Scissors are like a double-lever system. Which of the simple machines in Figure 9.21 and Figure 9.22 is most analogous to scissors?
10. Suppose you pull a nail at a constant rate using a nail puller as shown in Figure 9.21. Is the nail puller in equilibrium? What if you pull the nail with some acceleration – is the nail puller in equilibrium then? In which case is the force applied to the nail puller larger and why?
11. Explain the mechanical advantage of a wheelbarrow and how it explains why moving a heavy load is easier with a wheelbarrow.
12. How does a pulley enable a person to lift a load as heavy as a piano with little effort?

9.6 Forces and Torques in Muscles and Joints

13. Why are the forces exerted on the outside world by the limbs of our bodies usually much smaller than the forces exerted by muscles inside the body?
14. Explain why the forces in our joints are several times larger than the forces we exert on the outside world with our limbs. Can these forces be even greater than muscle forces?
15. Certain types of dinosaurs were bipedal (walked on two legs). What is a good reason that these creatures invariably had long tails if they had long necks?
16. Swimmers and athletes during competition need to go through certain postures at the beginning of the race. Consider the balance of the person and why start-offs are so important for races.
17. If the maximum force the biceps muscle can exert is 1000 N, can we pick up an object that weighs 1000 N? Explain your answer.
18. Suppose the biceps muscle was attached through tendons to the upper arm close to the elbow and the forearm near the wrist. What would be the advantages and disadvantages of this type of construction for the motion of the arm?

19. Explain one of the reasons why pregnant women often suffer from back strain late in their pregnancy.

Problems & Exercises

9.2 The Second Condition for Equilibrium

1. (a) When opening a door, you push on it perpendicularly with a force of 55.0 N at a distance of 0.850m from the hinges. What torque are you exerting relative to the hinges? (b) Does it matter if you push at the same height as the hinges?

2. When tightening a bolt, you push perpendicularly on a wrench with a force of 165 N at a distance of 0.140 m from the center of the bolt. (a) How much torque are you exerting in newton × meters (relative to the center of the bolt)? (b) Convert this torque to footpounds.

3. Two children push on opposite sides of a door during play. Both push horizontally and perpendicular to the door. One child pushes with a force of 17.5 N at a distance of 0.600 m from the hinges, and the second child pushes at a distance of 0.450 m. What force must the second child exert to keep the door from moving? Assume friction is negligible.

4. Use the second condition for equilibrium $(\text{net } \tau = 0)$ to calculate F_p in Example 9.1, employing any data given or solved for in part (a) of the example.

5. Repeat the seesaw problem in Example 9.1 with the center of mass of the seesaw 0.160 m to the left of the pivot (on the side of the lighter child) and assuming a mass of 12.0 kg for the seesaw. The other data given in the example remain unchanged. Explicitly show how you follow the steps in the Problem-Solving Strategy for static equilibrium.

9.3 Stability

6. Suppose a horse leans against a wall as in Figure 9.29, emulating a scene in the comedy movie *Cat Ballou*. Calculate the force exerted on the wall assuming that force is horizontal while using the data in the schematic representation of the situation. Note that the force exerted on the wall is equal in magnitude and opposite in direction to the force exerted on the horse, keeping it in equilibrium. The total mass of the horse and rider is 500 kg. Take the data to be accurate to three digits.

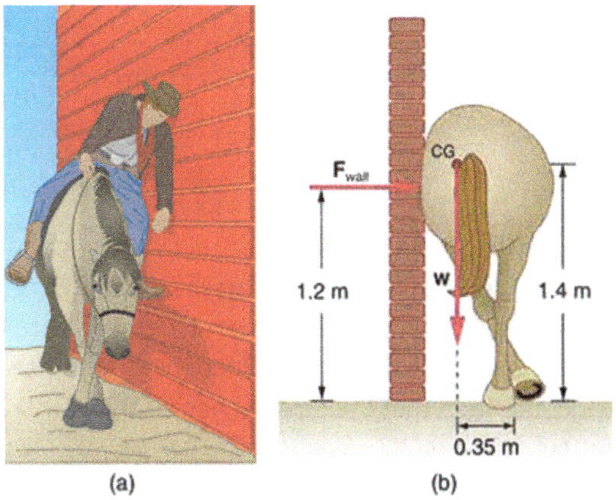

FIGURE 9.29

7. Two children of mass 20.0 kg and 30.0 kg sit balanced on a seesaw with the pivot point located at the center of the seesaw. If the children are separated by a distance of 3.00 m, at what distance from the pivot point is the small child sitting in order to maintain the balance?

8. (a) Calculate the magnitude and direction of the force on each foot of the horse in Figure 9.29 (two are on the ground), assuming the center of mass of the horse is midway between the feet. The total mass of the horse and rider is 500kg. (b) What is the minimum coefficient of friction between the hooves and ground? Note that the force exerted by the wall is horizontal.

9. A person carries a plank of wood 2.00 m long with one hand pushing down on it at one end with a force $\mathrm{F_1}$ and the other hand holding it up at .500 m from the end of the plank with force $\mathrm{F_2}$. If the plank has a mass of 20.0 kg and its center of gravity is at the middle of the plank, what are the magnitudes of the forces $\mathrm{F_1}$ and $\mathrm{F_2}$?

10. A 17.0-m-high and 11.0-m-long wall under construction and its bracing are shown in Figure 9.30. The wall is in stable equilibrium without the bracing but can pivot at its base. Calculate the force exerted by each of the 10 braces if a strong wind exerts a horizontal force of 650 N on each square meter of the wall. Assume that the net force from the wind acts at a height halfway up the wall and that all braces exert equal forces parallel to their lengths. Neglect the thickness of the wall.

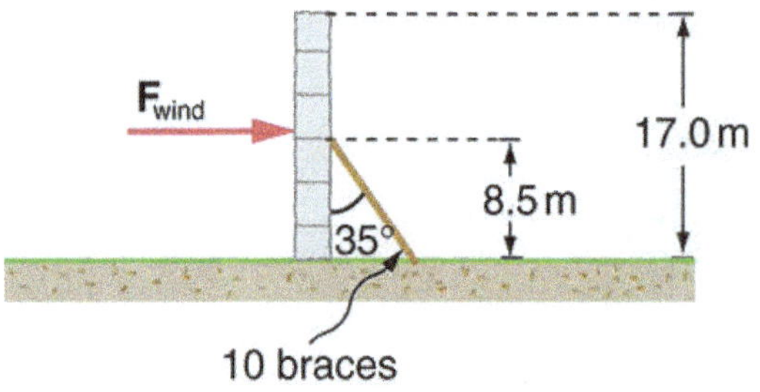

FIGURE 9.30

11. (a) What force must be exerted by the wind to support a 2.50-kg chicken in the position shown in Figure 9.31? (b) What is the ratio of this force to the chicken's weight? (c) Does this support the contention that the chicken has a relatively stable construction?

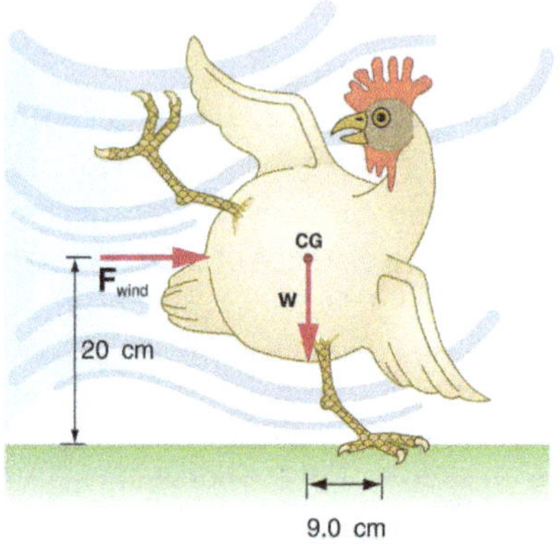

FIGURE 9.31

12. Suppose the weight of the drawbridge in Figure 9.32 is supported entirely by its hinges and the opposite shore, so that its cables are slack. The mass of the bridge is 2500 kg. (a) What fraction of the weight is supported by the opposite shore if the point of support is directly beneath the cable attachments? (b) What is the direction and magnitude of the force the hinges exert on the bridge under these circumstances?

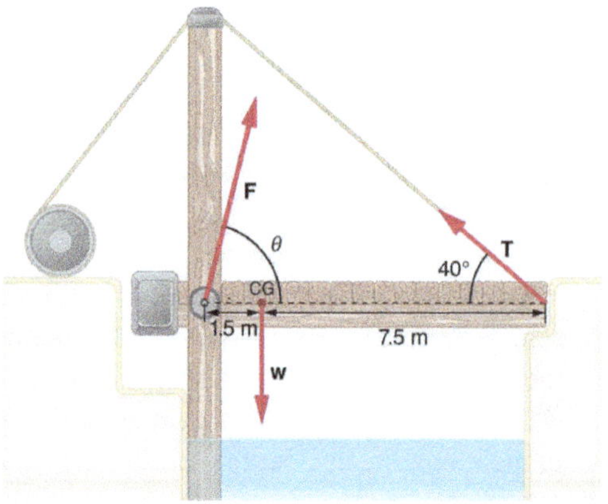

FIGURE 9.32 A small drawbridge, showing the forces on the hinges (F), its weight (w), and the tension in its wires (T).

13. Suppose a 900-kg car is on the bridge in Figure 9.32 with its center of mass halfway between the hinges and the cable attachments. (The bridge is supported by the cables and hinges only.) (a) Find the force in the cables. (b) Find the direction and magnitude of the force exerted by the hinges on the bridge.

14. A sandwich board advertising sign is constructed as shown in Figure 9.33. The sign's mass is 8.00 kg. (a) Calculate the tension in the chain assuming no friction between the legs and the sidewalk. (b) What force is exerted by each side on the hinge?

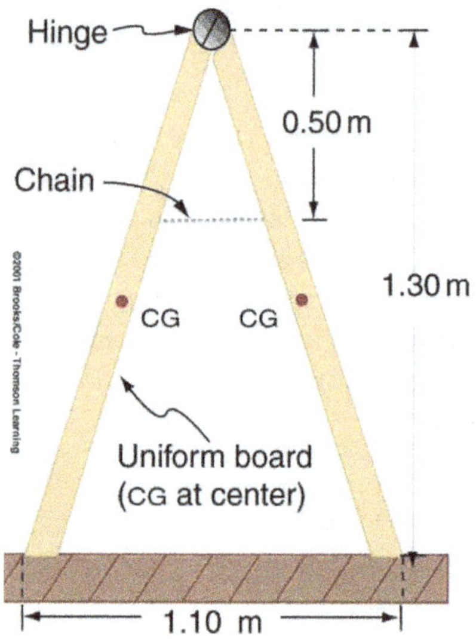

FIGURE 9.33 A sandwich board advertising sign demonstrates tension.

15. (a) What minimum coefficient of friction is needed between the legs and the ground to keep the sign in Figure 9.33 in the position shown if the chain breaks? (b) What force is exerted by each side on the hinge?

16. An athlete is attempting to perform splits. From the information given in Figure 9.34, calculate the magnitude and direction of the force exerted on each foot by the floor.

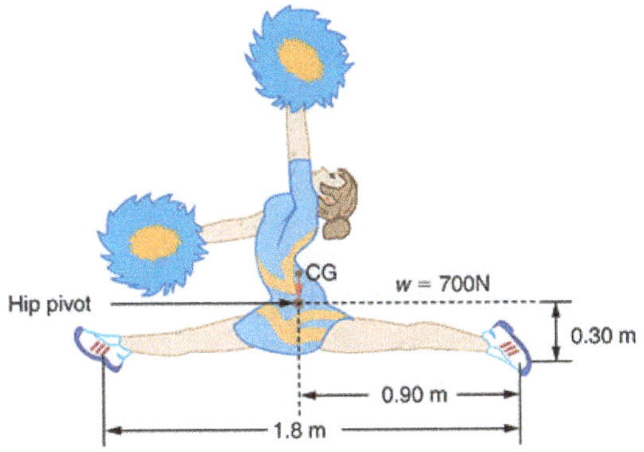

FIGURE 9.34 An athlete performs full split. The center of gravity and the various distances from it are shown.

9.4 Applications of Statics, Including Problem-Solving Strategies

17. To get up on the roof, a person (mass 70.0 kg) places a 6.00-m aluminum ladder (mass 10.0 kg) against the house on a concrete pad with the base of the ladder 2.00 m from the house. The ladder rests against a plastic rain gutter, which we can assume to be frictionless. The center of mass of the ladder is 2 m from the bottom. The person is standing 3 m from the bottom. What are the magnitudes of the forces on the ladder at the top and bottom?

18. In Figure 9.20, the cg of the pole held by the pole vaulter is 2.00 m from the left hand, and the hands are 0.700 m apart. Calculate the force exerted by (a) his right hand and (b) his left hand. (c) If each hand supports half the weight of the pole in Figure 9.18, show that the second condition for equilibrium $(\text{net } \tau = 0)$ is satisfied for a pivot other than the one located at the center of gravity of the pole. Explicitly show how you follow the steps in the Problem-Solving Strategy for static equilibrium described above.

9.5 Simple Machines

19. What is the mechanical advantage of a nail puller—similar to the one shown in Figure 9.21—where you exert a force $45\ \text{cm}$ from the pivot and the nail is $1.8\ \text{cm}$ on the other side? What minimum force must you exert to apply a force of $1250\ \text{N}$ to the nail?

20. Suppose you needed to raise a 250-kg mower a distance of 6.0 cm above the ground to change a tire. If you had a 2.0-m long lever, where would you place the fulcrum if your force was limited to 300 N?

21. a) What is the mechanical advantage of a wheelbarrow, such as the one in Figure 9.22, if the center of gravity of the wheelbarrow and its load has a perpendicular lever arm of 5.50 cm, while the hands have a perpendicular lever arm of 1.02 m? (b) What upward force should you exert to support the wheelbarrow and its load if their combined mass is 55.0 kg? (c) What force does the wheel exert on the ground?

22. A typical car has an axle with $1.10\ \text{cm}$ radius driving a tire with a radius of $27.5\ \text{cm}$. What is its mechanical advantage assuming the very simplified model in Figure 9.23(b)?

23. What force does the nail puller in Exercise 9.19 exert on the supporting surface? The nail puller has a mass of 2.10 kg.

24. If you used an ideal pulley of the type shown in Figure 9.24(a) to support a car engine of mass $115\ \text{kg}$, (a) What would be the tension in the rope? (b) What force must the ceiling supply, assuming you pull straight down on the rope? Neglect the pulley system's mass.

25. Repeat Exercise 9.24 for the pulley shown in Figure 9.24(c), assuming you pull straight up on the rope. The pulley system's mass is $7.00\ \text{kg}$.

9.6 Forces and Torques in Muscles and Joints

26. Verify that the force in the elbow joint in Example 9.4 is 407 N, as stated in the text.

27. Two muscles in the back of the leg pull on the Achilles tendon as shown in Figure 9.35. What total force do they exert?

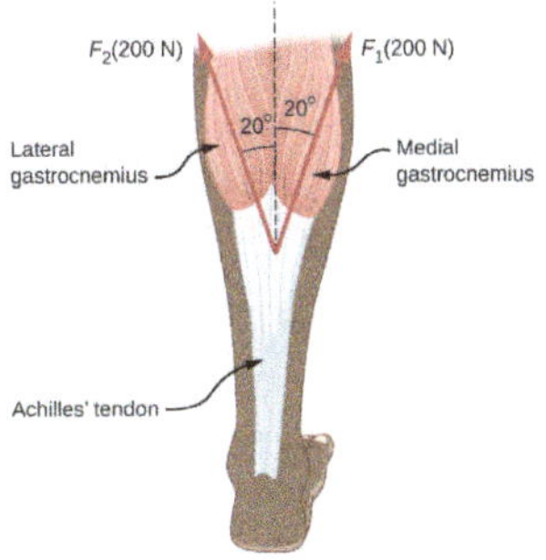

FIGURE 9.35 The Achilles tendon of the posterior leg serves to attach plantaris, gastrocnemius, and soleus muscles to calcaneus bone.

28. The upper leg muscle (quadriceps) exerts a force of 1250 N, which is carried by a tendon over the kneecap (the patella) at the angles shown in Figure 9.36. Find the direction and magnitude of the force exerted by the kneecap on the upper leg bone (the femur).

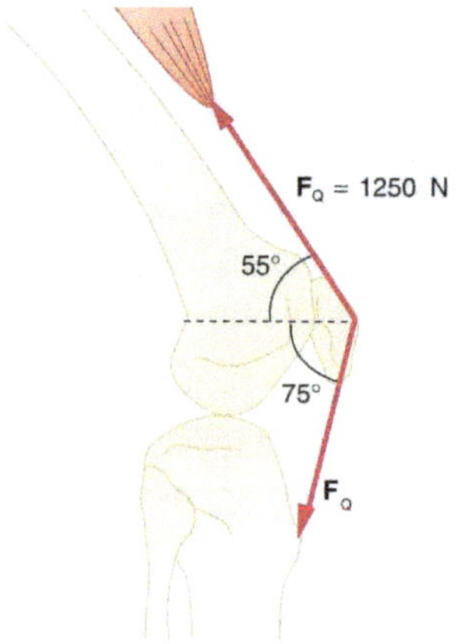

FIGURE 9.36 The knee joint works like a hinge to bend and straighten the lower leg. It permits a person to sit, stand, and pivot.

29. A device for exercising the upper leg muscle is shown in Figure 9.37, together with a schematic representation of an equivalent lever system. Calculate the force exerted by the upper leg muscle to lift the mass at a constant speed. Explicitly show how you follow the steps in the Problem-Solving Strategy for static equilibrium in Applications of Statistics, Including Problem-Solving Strategies.

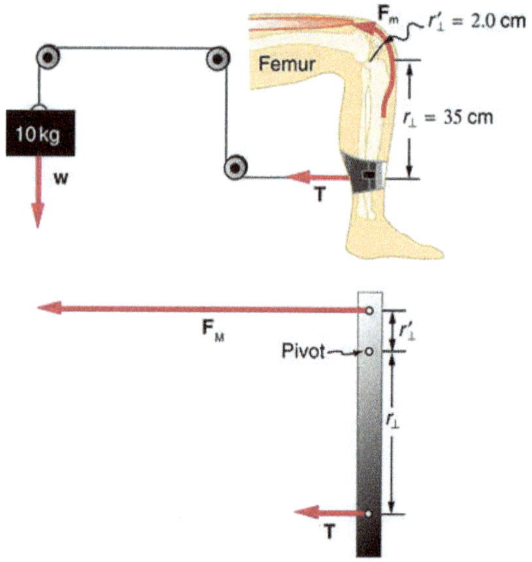

FIGURE 9.37 A mass is connected by pulleys and wires to the ankle in this exercise device.

30. A person working at a drafting board may hold her head as shown in Figure 9.38, requiring muscle action to support the head. The three major acting forces are shown. Calculate the direction and magnitude of the force supplied by the upper vertebrae $\mathbf{F_V}$ to hold the head stationary, assuming that this force acts along a line through the center of mass as do the weight and muscle force.

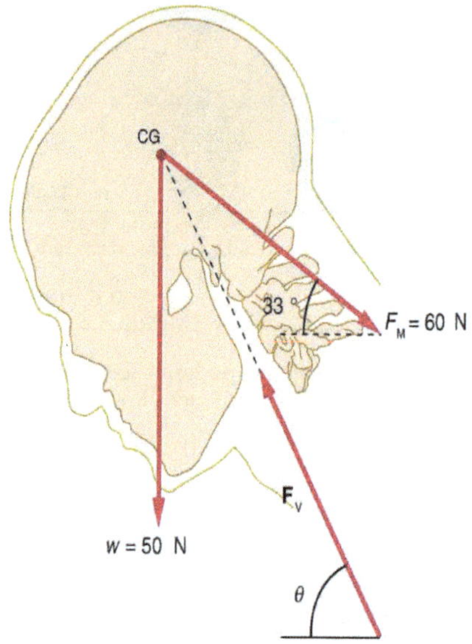

FIGURE 9.38

31. We analyzed the biceps muscle example with the angle between forearm and upper arm set at $90°$. Using the same numbers as in Example 9.4, find the force exerted by the biceps muscle when the angle is $120°$ and the forearm is in a downward position.

32. Even when the head is held erect, as in Figure 9.39, its center of mass is not directly over the principal point of support (the atlanto-occipital joint). The muscles at the back of the neck should therefore exert a force to keep the head erect. That is why your head falls forward when you fall asleep in the class. (a) Calculate the force exerted by these muscles using the information in the figure. (b) What is the force exerted by the pivot on the head?

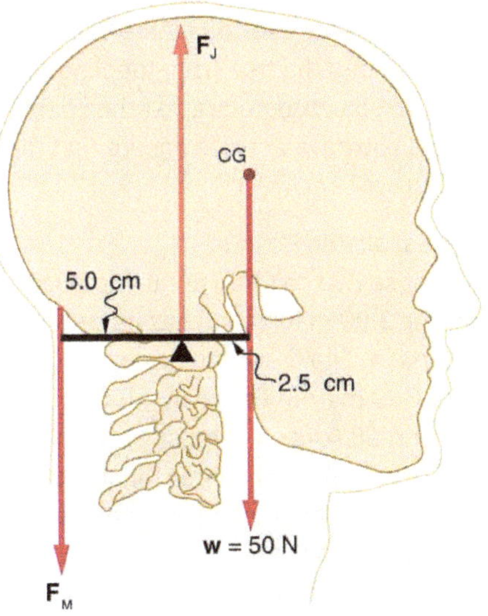

FIGURE 9.39 The center of mass of the head lies in front of its major point of support, requiring muscle action to hold the head erect. A simplified lever system is shown.

33. A 75-kg man stands on his toes by exerting an upward force through the Achilles tendon, as in Figure 9.40. (a) What is the force in the Achilles tendon if he stands on one foot? (b) Calculate the force at the pivot of the simplified lever system shown—that force is representative of forces in the ankle joint.

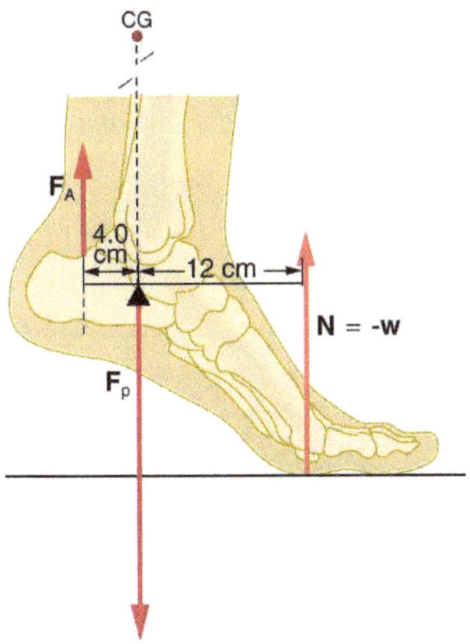

FIGURE 9.40 The muscles in the back of the leg pull the Achilles tendon when one stands on one's toes. A simplified lever system is shown.

34. A father lifts his child as shown in Figure 9.41. What force should the upper leg muscle exert to lift the child at a constant speed?

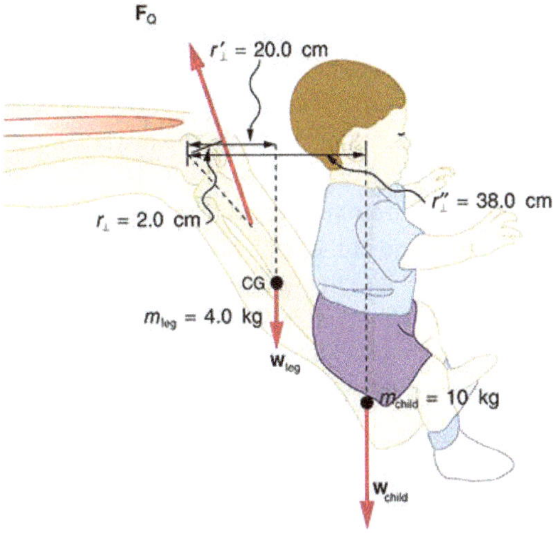

FIGURE 9.41 A child being lifted by a father's lower leg.

35. Unlike most of the other muscles in our bodies, the masseter muscle in the jaw, as illustrated in Figure 9.42, is attached relatively far from the joint, enabling large forces to be exerted by the back teeth. (a) Using the information in the figure, calculate the force exerted by the lower teeth on the bullet. (b) Calculate the force on the joint.

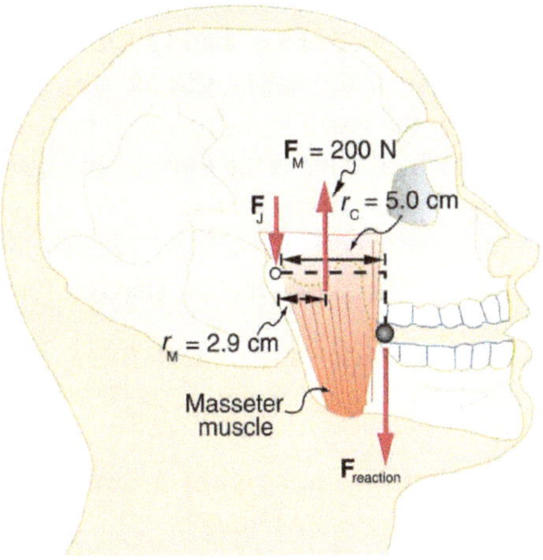

FIGURE 9.42 A person clenching a bullet between his teeth.

36. Integrated Concepts
Suppose we replace the 4.0-kg book in Exercise 9.31 of the biceps muscle with an elastic exercise rope that obeys Hooke's Law. Assume its force constant $k = 600\ \text{N/m}$. (a) How much is the rope stretched (past equilibrium) to provide the same force F_B as in this example? Assume the rope is held in the hand at the same location as the book. (b) What force is on the biceps muscle if the exercise rope is pulled straight up so that the forearm makes an angle of $25°$ with the horizontal? Assume the biceps muscle is still perpendicular to the forearm.

37. (a) What force should the woman in Figure 9.43 exert on the floor with each hand to do a push-up? Assume that she moves up at a constant speed. (b) The triceps muscle at the back of her upper arm has an effective lever arm of 1.75 cm, and she exerts force on the floor at a horizontal distance of 20.0 cm from the elbow joint. Calculate the magnitude of the force in each triceps muscle, and compare it to her weight. (c) How much work does she do if her center of mass rises 0.240 m? (d) What is her useful power output if she does 25 pushups in one minute?

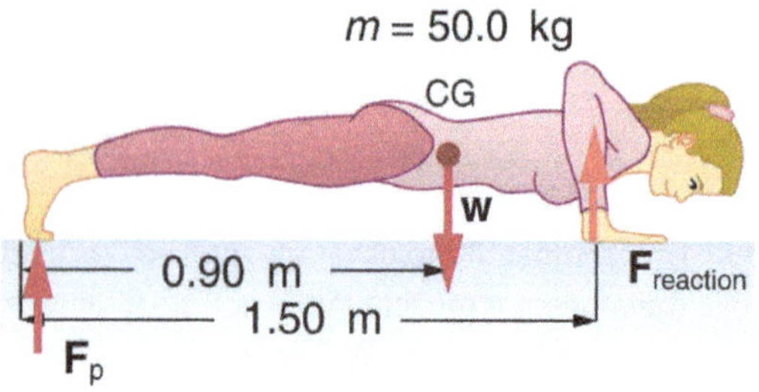

FIGURE 9.43 A woman doing pushups.

38. You have just planted a sturdy 2-m-tall palm tree in your front lawn for your mother's birthday. Your brother kicks a 500 g ball, which hits the top of the tree at a speed of 5 m/s and stays in contact with it for 10 ms. The ball falls to the ground near the base of the tree and the recoil of the tree is minimal. (a) What is the force on the tree? (b) The length of the sturdy section of the root is only 20 cm. Furthermore, the soil around the roots is loose and we can assume that an effective force is applied at the tip of the 20 cm length. What is the effective force exerted by the end of the tip of the root to keep the tree from toppling? Assume the tree will be uprooted rather than bend. (c) What could you have done to ensure that the tree does not uproot easily?

39. Unreasonable Results
Suppose two children are using a uniform seesaw that is 3.00 m long and has its center of mass over the pivot. The first child has a mass of 30.0 kg and sits 1.40 m from the pivot. (a) Calculate where the second 18.0 kg child must sit to balance the seesaw. (b) What is unreasonable about the result? (c) Which premise is unreasonable, or which premises are inconsistent?

40. Construct Your Own Problem
Consider a method for measuring the mass of a person's arm in anatomical studies. The subject lies on her back, extends her relaxed arm to the side and two scales are placed below the arm. One is placed under the elbow and the other under the back of her hand. Construct a problem in which you calculate the mass of the arm and find its center of mass based on the scale readings and the distances of the scales from the shoulder joint. You must include a free body diagram of the arm to direct the analysis. Consider changing the position of the scale under the hand to provide more information, if needed. You may wish to consult references to obtain reasonable mass values.

Test Prep for AP® Courses

9.2 The Second Condition for Equilibrium

1. Which of the following is not an example of an object undergoing a torque?
   a. A car is rounding a bend at a constant speed.
   b. A merry-go-round increases from rest to a constant rotational speed.
   c. A pendulum swings back and forth.
   d. A bowling ball rolls down a bowling alley.

2. Five forces of equal magnitude, labeled ***A–E***, are applied to the object shown below. If the object is anchored at point ***P***, which force will provide the greatest torque?

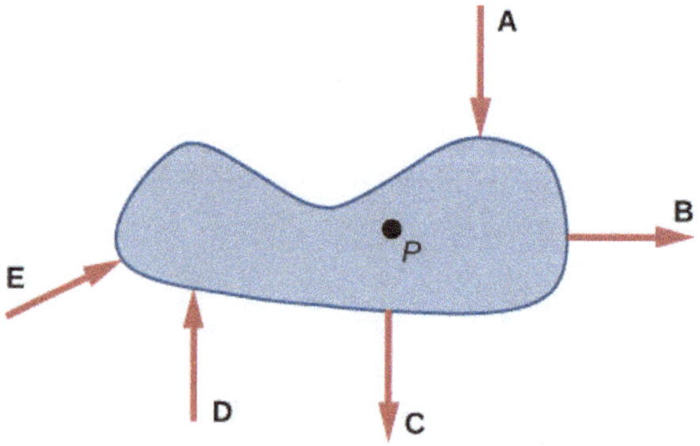

FIGURE 9.44 Five forces acting on an object.

   a. Force ***A***
   b. Force ***B***
   c. Force ***C***
   d. Force ***D***
   e. Force ***E***

9.3 Stability

3. Using the concept of torque, explain why a traffic cone placed on its base is in stable equilibrium, while a traffic cone placed on its tip is in unstable equilibrium.

9.4 Applications of Statics, Including Problem-Solving Strategies

4. A child sits on the end of a playground see-saw. Which of the following values is the most appropriate estimate of the torque created by the child?
   a. 6 N•m
   b. 60 N•m
   c. 600 N•m
   d. 6000 N•m

5. A group of students is stacking a set of identical books, each one overhanging the one below it by 1 inch. They would like to estimate how many books they could place on top of each other before the stack tipped. What information below would they need to know to make this calculation?

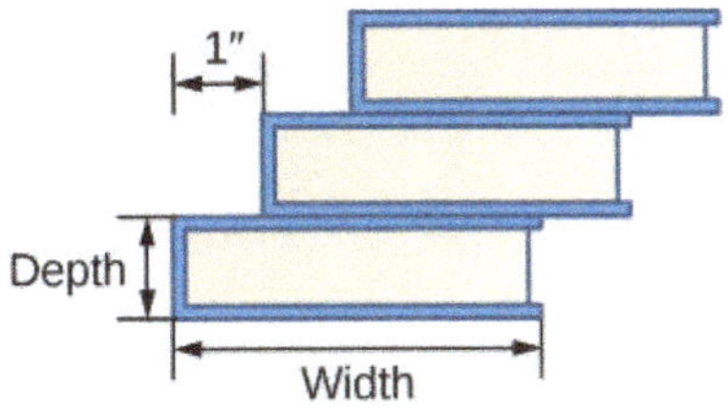

FIGURE 9.45 3 overlapping stacked books.

I. The mass of each book
II. The width of each book
III. The depth of each book

   a. I only
   b. I and II only
   c. I and III only
   d. II only
   e. I, II, and III

6. A 10 N board of uniform density is 5 meters long. It is supported on the left by a string bearing a 3 N upward force. In order to prevent the string from breaking, a person must place an upward force of 7 N at a position along the bottom surface of the board. At what distance from its left edge would they need to place this force in order for the board to be in static equilibrium?
   a. $\frac{3}{7}$ m
   b. $\frac{5}{2}$ m
   c. $\frac{25}{7}$ m
   d. $\frac{30}{7}$ m
   e. 5 m

7. A bridge is supported by two piers located 20 meters apart. Both the left and right piers provide an upward force on the bridge, labeled $\mathbf{F}_L$ and $\mathbf{F}_R$ respectively.
   a. If a 1000 kg car comes to rest at a point 5 meters from the left pier, how much force will the bridge provide to the left and right piers?
   b. How will $\mathbf{F}_L$ and $\mathbf{F}_R$ change as the car drives to the right side of the bridge?

8. An object of unknown mass is provided to a student. Without using a scale, design an experimental procedure detailing how the magnitude of this mass could be experimentally found. Your explanation must include the concept of torque and all steps should be provided in an orderly sequence. You may include a labeled diagram of your setup to help in your description. Include enough detail so that another student could carry out your procedure.

9.5 Simple Machines

9. As a young student, you likely learned that simple machines are capable of increasing the ability to lift and move objects. Now, as an educated AP Physics student, you are aware that this capability is governed by the relationship between force and torque.
   In the space below, explain why torque is integral to the increase in force created by a simple machine. You may use an example or diagram to assist in your explanation. Be sure to cite the mechanical advantage in your explanation as well.

10. Figure 9.24(a) shows a wheelbarrow being lifted by an applied force $\mathbf{F}_i$. If the wheelbarrow is filled with twenty bricks massing 3 kg each, estimate the value of the applied force $\mathbf{F}_i$. Provide an explanation behind the total weight $\boldsymbol{w}$ and any reasoning toward your final answer. Additionally, provide a range of values over which you feel the force could exist.

9.6 Forces and Torques in Muscles and Joints

11. When you use your hand to raise a 20 lb dumbbell in a curling motion, the force on your bicep muscle is not equal to 20 lb.
    a. Compare the size of the force placed on your

bicep muscle to the force of the 20 lb dumbbell lifted by your hand. Using the concept of torque, which force is greater and explain why the two forces are not identical.

b. Does the force placed on your bicep muscle change as you curl the weight closer toward your body? (In other words, is the force on your muscle different when your forearm is 90° to your upper arm than when it is 45° to your upper arm?) Explain your answer using torque.

CHAPTER 10
Rotational Motion and Angular Momentum

FIGURE 10.1 The mention of a tornado conjures up images of raw destructive power. Tornadoes blow houses away as if they were made of paper and have been known to pierce tree trunks with pieces of straw. They descend from clouds in funnel-like shapes that spin violently, particularly at the bottom where they are most narrow, producing winds as high as 500 km/h. (credit: Daphne Zaras, U.S. National Oceanic and Atmospheric Administration)

CHAPTER OUTLINE

CONNECTION FOR AP® COURSES Why do tornados spin? And why do tornados spin so rapidly? The answer is that the air masses that produce tornados are themselves rotating, and when the radii of the air masses decrease, their rate of rotation increases. An ice skater increases her spin in an exactly analogous manner, as seen in Figure 10.2. The skater starts her rotation with outstretched limbs and increases her rate of spin by pulling them in toward her body. The same physics describes the exhilarating spin of a skater and the wrenching force of a tornado. We will find that this is another example of the importance of conservation laws and their role in determining how changes happen in a system, supporting Big Idea 5. The idea that a change of a conserved quantity is always equal to the transfer of that quantity between interacting systems (Enduring Understanding 5.A) is presented for both energy and angular momentum (Enduring Understanding 5.E). The conservation of **angular momentum** in relation to the external net **torque** (Essential Knowledge 5.E.1) parallels that of linear momentum conservation in relation to the external net force. The concept of **rotational inertia** is introduced, a concept that takes into account not only the mass of an object or a system, but also the distribution of mass within the object or system. Therefore, changes in the rotational inertia of a system could lead to changes in the motion (Essential Knowledge 5.E.2) of the system. We shall see that all important aspects of rotational motion either have already been defined for linear motion or have exact analogues in linear motion.

Clearly, therefore, force, energy, and power are associated with rotational motion. This supports Big Idea 3, that interactions are described by forces. The ability of forces to cause torques (Enduring Understanding 3.F) is extended to the interactions between objects that result in nonzero net torque. This nonzero net torque in turn causes changes in the rotational motion of an object (Essential Knowledge 3.F.2) and results in changes of the angular momentum of an object (Essential Knowledge 3.F.3).

Similarly, Big Idea 4, that interactions between systems cause changes in those systems, is supported by the empirical observation that when torques are exerted on rigid bodies these torques cause changes in the angular momentum of the system (Enduring Understanding 4.D).

Again, there is a clear analogy between linear and rotational motion in this interaction. Both the angular kinematics variables (angular displacement, angular velocity, and **angular acceleration**) and the dynamics variables (torque and angular momentum) are vectors with direction depending on whether the rotation is clockwise or counterclockwise with respect to an axis of rotation (Essential Knowledge 4.D.1). The angular momentum of the system can change due to interactions (Essential Knowledge 4.D.2). This change is defined as the product of the average torque and the time interval during which torque is exerted (Essential Knowledge 4.D.3), analogous to the impulse-momentum theorem for linear motion.

The concepts in this chapter support:

Big Idea 3. The interactions of an object with other objects can be described by forces.

Enduring Understanding 3.F. A force exerted on an object can cause a torque on that object.

Extended Knowledge 3.F.2. The presence of a net torque along any axis will cause a rigid system to change its rotational motion or an object to change its rotational motion about that axis.

Extended Knowledge 3.F.3. A torque exerted on an object can change the angular momentum of an object.

Big Idea 4. Interactions between systems can result in changes in those systems.

Enduring Understanding 4.D. A net torque exerted on a system by other objects or systems will change the angular momentum of the system.

Extended Knowledge 4.D.1. Torque, angular velocity, angular acceleration, and angular momentum are vectors and can be characterized as positive or negative depending upon whether they give rise to or correspond to counterclockwise or clockwise rotation with respect to an axis.

Extended Knowledge 4.D.2. The angular momentum of a system may change due to interactions with other objects or systems.

Extended Knowledge 4.D.3. The change in angular momentum is given by the product of the average torque and the time interval during which the torque is exerted.

Big Idea 5. Changes that occur as a result of interactions are constrained by conservation laws.

Enduring Understanding 5.A. Certain quantities are conserved, in the sense that the changes of those quantities in a given system are always equal to the transfer of that quantity to or from the system by all possible interactions with other systems.

Extended Knowledge 5.A.2. For all systems under all circumstances, energy, charge, linear momentum, and angular momentum are conserved.

Enduring Understanding 5.E. The angular momentum of a system is conserved.

Extended Knowledge 5.E.1. If the net external torque exerted on the system is zero, the angular momentum of the system does not change.

Extended Knowledge 5.E.2. The angular momentum of a system is determined by the locations and velocities of the objects that make up the system. The rotational inertia of an object or system depends upon the distribution of mass within the object or system. Changes in the radius of a system or in the distribution of mass within the system result in changes in the system's rotational inertia, and hence in its angular velocity and linear speed for a given angular momentum. Examples should include elliptical orbits in an Earth-satellite system. Mathematical expressions for the moments of inertia will be provided where needed. Students will not be expected to know the parallel axis theorem.

FIGURE 10.2 This figure skater increases her rate of spin by pulling her arms and her extended leg closer to her axis of rotation. (credit: Luu, Wikimedia Commons)

Click to view content (https://openstax.org/books/college-physics-ap-courses-2e/pages/10-connection-for-ap-r-courses)

10.1 Angular Acceleration

LEARNING OBJECTIVES

By the end of this section, you will be able to:

- Describe uniform circular motion.
- Explain non-uniform circular motion.
- Calculate angular acceleration of an object.
- Observe the link between linear and angular acceleration.

Uniform Circular Motion and Gravitation discussed only uniform circular motion, which is motion in a circle at constant speed and, hence, constant angular velocity. Recall that angular velocity ω was defined as the time rate of change of angle θ:

$$\omega = \frac{\Delta\theta}{\Delta t}, \tag{10.1}$$

where θ is the angle of rotation as seen in Figure 10.3. The relationship between angular velocity ω and linear velocity v was also defined in Rotation Angle and Angular Velocity as

$$v = r\omega \tag{10.2}$$

or

$$\omega = \frac{v}{r}, \tag{10.3}$$

where r is the radius of curvature, also seen in Figure 10.3. According to the sign convention, the counter clockwise direction is considered as positive direction and clockwise direction as negative

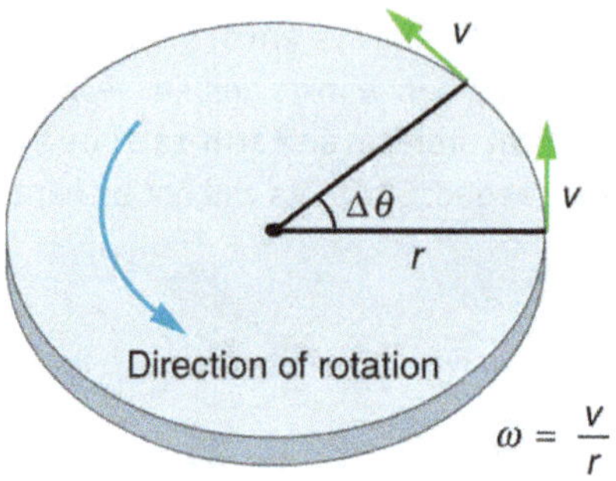

FIGURE 10.3 This figure shows uniform circular motion and some of its defined quantities.

Angular velocity is not constant when a skater pulls in her arms, when a child starts up a merry-go-round from rest, or when a computer's hard disk slows to a halt when switched off. In all these cases, there is an **angular acceleration**, in which ω changes. The faster the change occurs, the greater the angular acceleration. Angular acceleration α is defined as the rate of change of angular velocity. In equation form, angular acceleration is expressed as follows:

$$\alpha = \frac{\Delta\omega}{\Delta t}, \tag{10.4}$$

where $\Delta\omega$ is the **change in angular velocity** and Δt is the change in time. The units of angular acceleration are (rad/s)/s, or rad/s^2. If ω increases, then α is positive. If ω decreases, then α is negative.

EXAMPLE 10.1

Calculating the Angular Acceleration and Deceleration of a Bike Wheel

Suppose a teenager puts her bicycle on its back and starts the rear wheel spinning from rest to a final angular velocity of 250 rpm in 5.00 s. (a) Calculate the angular acceleration in rad/s^2. (b) If she now slams on the brakes, causing an angular acceleration of $-87.3\ \text{rad/s}^2$, how long does it take the wheel to stop?

Strategy for (a)

The angular acceleration can be found directly from its definition in $\alpha = \frac{\Delta\omega}{\Delta t}$ because the final angular velocity and time are given. We see that $\Delta\omega$ is 250 rpm and Δt is 5.00 s.

Solution for (a)

Entering known information into the definition of angular acceleration, we get

$$\begin{aligned} \alpha &= \frac{\Delta\omega}{\Delta t} \\ &= \frac{250\ \text{rpm}}{5.00\ \text{s}}. \end{aligned} \tag{10.5}$$

Because $\Delta\omega$ is in revolutions per minute (rpm) and we want the standard units of rad/s^2 for angular acceleration, we need to convert $\Delta\omega$ from rpm to rad/s:

$$\begin{aligned} \Delta\omega &= 250\frac{\text{rev}}{\text{min}} \cdot \frac{2\pi\ \text{rad}}{\text{rev}} \cdot \frac{1\ \text{min}}{60\ \text{s}} \\ &= 26.2\frac{\text{rad}}{\text{s}}. \end{aligned} \tag{10.6}$$

Entering this quantity into the expression for α, we get

$$\begin{aligned} \alpha &= \frac{\Delta\omega}{\Delta t} \\ &= \frac{26.2\ \text{rad/s}}{5.00\ \text{s}} \\ &= 5.24\ \text{rad/s}^2. \end{aligned} \tag{10.7}$$

Strategy for (b)

In this part, we know the angular acceleration and the initial angular velocity. We can find the stoppage time by using the definition of angular acceleration and solving for Δt, yielding

$$\Delta t = \frac{\Delta \omega}{\alpha}. \tag{10.8}$$

Solution for (b)

Here the angular velocity decreases from 26.2 rad/s (250 rpm) to zero, so that $\Delta\omega$ is -26.2 rad/s, and α is given to be -87.3 rad/s^2. Thus,

$$\begin{aligned} \Delta t &= \frac{-26.2 \text{ rad/s}}{-87.3 \text{ rad/s}^2} \\ &= 0.300 \text{ s}. \end{aligned} \tag{10.9}$$

Discussion

Note that the angular acceleration as the girl spins the wheel is small and positive; it takes 5 s to produce an appreciable angular velocity. When she hits the brake, the angular acceleration is large and negative. The angular velocity quickly goes to zero. In both cases, the relationships are analogous to what happens with linear motion. For example, there is a large deceleration when you crash into a brick wall—the velocity change is large in a short time interval.

If the bicycle in the preceding example had been on its wheels instead of upside-down, it would first have accelerated along the ground and then come to a stop. This connection between circular motion and linear motion needs to be explored. For example, it would be useful to know how linear and angular acceleration are related. In circular motion, linear acceleration is *tangent* to the circle at the point of interest, as seen in Figure 10.4. Thus, linear acceleration is called **tangential acceleration** a_t.

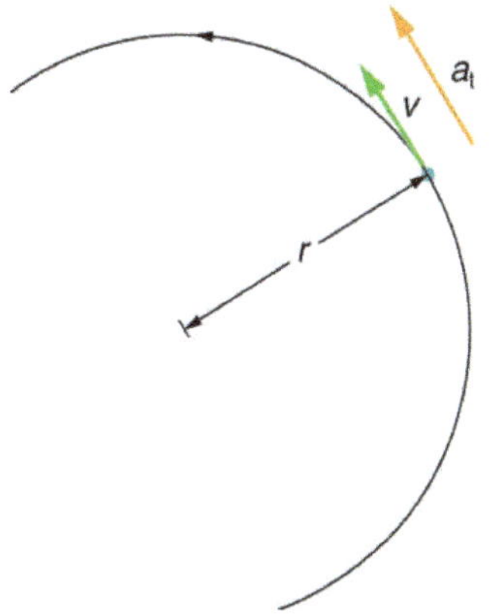

FIGURE 10.4 In circular motion, linear acceleration a, occurs as the magnitude of the velocity changes: a is tangent to the motion. In the context of circular motion, linear acceleration is also called tangential acceleration a_t.

Linear or tangential acceleration refers to changes in the magnitude of velocity but not its direction. We know from Uniform Circular Motion and Gravitation that in circular motion centripetal acceleration, a_c, refers to changes in the direction of the velocity but not its magnitude. An object undergoing circular motion experiences centripetal acceleration, as seen in Figure 10.5. Thus, a_t and a_c are perpendicular and independent of one another. Tangential acceleration a_t is directly related to the angular acceleration α and is linked to an increase or decrease in the velocity, but not its direction.

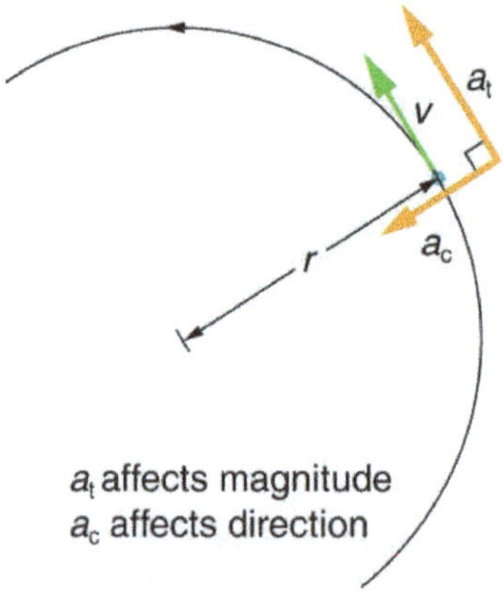

FIGURE 10.5 Centripetal acceleration a_c occurs as the direction of velocity changes; it is perpendicular to the circular motion. Centripetal and tangential acceleration are thus perpendicular to each other.

Now we can find the exact relationship between linear acceleration a_t and angular acceleration α. Because linear acceleration is proportional to a change in the magnitude of the velocity, it is defined (as it was in One-Dimensional Kinematics) to be

$$a_t = \frac{\Delta v}{\Delta t}. \tag{10.10}$$

For circular motion, note that $v = r\omega$, so that

$$a_t = \frac{\Delta(r\omega)}{\Delta t}. \tag{10.11}$$

The radius r is constant for circular motion, and so $\Delta(r\omega) = r(\Delta\omega)$. Thus,

$$a_t = r\frac{\Delta\omega}{\Delta t}. \tag{10.12}$$

By definition, $\alpha = \frac{\Delta\omega}{\Delta t}$. Thus,

$$a_t = r\alpha, \tag{10.13}$$

or

$$\alpha = \frac{a_t}{r}. \tag{10.14}$$

These equations mean that linear acceleration and angular acceleration are directly proportional. The greater the angular acceleration is, the larger the linear (tangential) acceleration is, and vice versa. For example, the greater the angular acceleration of a car's drive wheels, the greater the acceleration of the car. The radius also matters. For example, the smaller a wheel, the smaller its linear acceleration for a given angular acceleration α.

EXAMPLE 10.2

Calculating the Angular Acceleration of a Motorcycle Wheel

A powerful motorcycle can accelerate from 0 to 30.0 m/s (about 108 km/h) in 4.20 s. What is the angular acceleration of its 0.320-m-radius wheels? (See Figure 10.6.)

FIGURE 10.6 The linear acceleration of a motorcycle is accompanied by an angular acceleration of its wheels.

Strategy

We are given information about the linear velocities of the motorcycle. Thus, we can find its linear acceleration a_t. Then, the expression $\alpha = \frac{a_t}{r}$ can be used to find the angular acceleration.

Solution

The linear acceleration is

$$\begin{aligned} a_t &= \frac{\Delta v}{\Delta t} \\ &= \frac{30.0 \text{ m/s}}{4.20 \text{ s}} \\ &= 7.14 \text{ m/s}^2. \end{aligned} \quad (10.15)$$

We also know the radius of the wheels. Entering the values for a_t and r into $\alpha = \frac{a_t}{r}$, we get

$$\begin{aligned} \alpha &= \frac{a_t}{r} \\ &= \frac{7.14 \text{ m/s}^2}{0.320 \text{ m}} \\ &= 22.3 \text{ rad/s}^2. \end{aligned} \quad (10.16)$$

Discussion

Units of radians are dimensionless and appear in any relationship between angular and linear quantities.

So far, we have defined three rotational quantities— θ, ω, and α. These quantities are analogous to the translational quantities x, v, and a. Table 10.1 displays rotational quantities, the analogous translational quantities, and the relationships between them.

Rotational	Translational	Relationship
θ	x	$\theta = \frac{x}{r}$
ω	v	$\omega = \frac{v}{r}$
α	a	$\alpha = \frac{a_t}{r}$

TABLE 10.1 Rotational and Translational Quantities

MAKING CONNECTIONS: TAKE-HOME EXPERIMENT

Sit down with your feet on the ground on a chair that rotates. Lift one of your legs such that it is unbent (straightened out). Using the other leg, begin to rotate yourself by pushing on the ground. Stop using your leg to push the ground but allow the chair to rotate. From the origin where you began, sketch the angle, angular velocity, and angular acceleration of your leg as a function of time in the form of three separate graphs. Estimate the magnitudes of these quantities.

CHECK YOUR UNDERSTANDING

Angular acceleration is a vector, having both magnitude and direction. How do we denote its magnitude and direction? Illustrate with an example.

Solution

The magnitude of angular acceleration is α and its most common units are rad/s^2. The direction of angular acceleration along a fixed axis is denoted by a + or a – sign, just as the direction of linear acceleration in one dimension is denoted by a + or a – sign. For example, consider a gymnast doing a forward flip. Her angular momentum would be parallel to the mat and to her left. The magnitude of her angular acceleration would be proportional to her angular velocity (spin rate) and her moment of inertia about her spin axis.

LADYBUG REVOLUTION

Join the ladybug in an exploration of rotational motion. Rotate the merry-go-round to change its angle, or choose a constant angular velocity or angular acceleration. Explore how circular motion relates to the bug's x,y position, velocity, and acceleration using vectors or graphs.

Click to view content (https://openstax.org/l/28ladybugrevolutionrotation).

10.2 Kinematics of Rotational Motion

LEARNING OBJECTIVES

By the end of this section, you will be able to:

- Observe the kinematics of rotational motion.
- Derive rotational kinematic equations.
- Evaluate problem solving strategies for rotational kinematics.

Just by using our intuition, we can begin to see how rotational quantities like θ, ω, and α are related to one another. For example, if a motorcycle wheel has a large angular acceleration for a fairly long time, it ends up spinning rapidly and rotates through many revolutions. In more technical terms, if the wheel's angular acceleration α is large for a long period of time t, then the final angular velocity ω and angle of rotation θ are large. The wheel's rotational motion is exactly analogous to the fact that the motorcycle's large translational acceleration produces a large final velocity, and the distance traveled will also be large.

Kinematics is the description of motion. The **kinematics of rotational motion** describes the relationships among rotation angle, angular velocity, angular acceleration, and time. Let us start by finding an equation relating ω, α, and t. To determine this equation, we recall a familiar kinematic equation for translational, or straight-line, motion:

$$v = v_0 + at \qquad (\text{constant } a) \tag{10.17}$$

Note that in rotational motion $a = a_\text{t}$, and we shall use the symbol a for tangential or linear acceleration from now on. As in linear kinematics, we assume a is constant, which means that angular acceleration α is also a constant, because $a = r\alpha$. Now, let us substitute $v = r\omega$ and $a = r\alpha$ into the linear equation above:

$$r\omega = r\omega_0 + r\alpha t. \tag{10.18}$$

The radius r cancels in the equation, yielding

$$\omega = \omega_0 + \alpha t \qquad (\text{constant } \alpha), \tag{10.19}$$

where ω_0 is the initial angular velocity. This last equation is a *kinematic relationship* among ω, α, and t —that is, it describes their relationship without reference to forces or masses that may affect rotation. It is also precisely analogous in form to its translational counterpart.

MAKING CONNECTIONS

Kinematics for rotational motion is completely analogous to translational kinematics, first presented in One-Dimensional Kinematics. Kinematics is concerned with the description of motion without regard to force or mass. We will find that translational kinematic quantities, such as displacement, velocity, and acceleration have direct analogs in rotational motion.

Starting with the four kinematic equations we developed in One-Dimensional Kinematics, we can derive the following four rotational kinematic equations (presented together with their translational counterparts):

Rotational	Translational	
$\theta = \bar{\omega} t$	$x = \bar{v} t$	
$\omega = \omega_0 + \alpha t$	$v = v_0 + at$	(constant α, a)
$\theta = \omega_0 t + \frac{1}{2}\alpha t^2$	$x = v_0 t + \frac{1}{2}at^2$	(constant α, a)
$\omega^2 = \omega_0{}^2 + 2\alpha\theta$	$v^2 = v_0{}^2 + 2ax$	(constant α, a)

TABLE 10.2 Rotational Kinematic Equations

In these equations, the subscript 0 denotes initial values (θ_0, x_0, and t_0 are initial values), and the average angular velocity $\bar{\omega}$ and average velocity $\bar{v}$ are defined as follows:

$$\bar{\omega} = \frac{\omega_0 + \omega}{2} \text{ and } \bar{v} = \frac{v_0 + v}{2}. \quad 10.20$$

The equations given above in Table 10.2 can be used to solve any rotational or translational kinematics problem in which a and α are constant.

PROBLEM-SOLVING STRATEGY FOR ROTATIONAL KINEMATICS

1. *Examine the situation to determine that rotational kinematics (rotational motion) is involved.* Rotation must be involved, but without the need to consider forces or masses that affect the motion.
2. *Identify exactly what needs to be determined in the problem (identify the unknowns).* A sketch of the situation is useful.
3. *Make a list of what is given or can be inferred from the problem as stated (identify the knowns).*
4. *Solve the appropriate equation or equations for the quantity to be determined (the unknown).* It can be useful to think in terms of a translational analog because by now you are familiar with such motion.
5. *Substitute the known values along with their units into the appropriate equation, and obtain numerical solutions complete with units.* Be sure to use units of radians for angles.
6. *Check your answer to see if it is reasonable: Does your answer make sense?*

EXAMPLE 10.3

Calculating the Acceleration of a Fishing Reel

A deep-sea fisherman hooks a big fish that swims away from the boat pulling the fishing line from his fishing reel. The whole system is initially at rest and the fishing line unwinds from the reel at a radius of 4.50 cm from its axis of rotation. The reel is given an angular acceleration of 110 rad/s^2 for 2.00 s as seen in Figure 10.7.

(a) What is the final angular velocity of the reel?

(b) At what speed is fishing line leaving the reel after 2.00 s elapses?

(c) How many revolutions does the reel make?

(d) How many meters of fishing line come off the reel in this time?

Strategy

In each part of this example, the strategy is the same as it was for solving problems in linear kinematics. In particular, known values are identified and a relationship is then sought that can be used to solve for the unknown.

Solution for (a)

Here α and t are given and ω needs to be determined. The most straightforward equation to use is $\omega = \omega_0 + \alpha t$ because the unknown is already on one side and all other terms are known. That equation states that

$$\omega = \omega_0 + \alpha t. \tag{10.21}$$

We are also given that $\omega_0 = 0$ (it starts from rest), so that

$$\omega = 0 + \left(110\ \text{rad/s}^2\right)(2.00\text{s}) = 220\ \text{rad/s}. \tag{10.22}$$

Solution for (b)

Now that ω is known, the speed v can most easily be found using the relationship

$$v = r\omega, \tag{10.23}$$

where the radius r of the reel is given to be 4.50 cm; thus,

$$v = (0.0450\ \text{m})(220\ \text{rad/s}) = 9.90\ \text{m/s}. \tag{10.24}$$

Note again that radians must always be used in any calculation relating linear and angular quantities. Also, because radians are dimensionless, we have $\text{m} \times \text{rad} = \text{m}$.

Solution for (c)

Here, we are asked to find the number of revolutions. Because $1\ \text{rev} = 2\pi\ \text{rad}$, we can find the number of revolutions by finding θ in radians. We are given α and t, and we know ω_0 is zero, so that θ can be obtained using $\theta = \omega_0 t + \frac{1}{2}\alpha t^2$.

$$\begin{aligned} \theta &= \omega_0 t + \tfrac{1}{2}\alpha t^2 \\ &= 0 + (0.500)\left(110\ \text{rad/s}^2\right)(2.00\ \text{s})^2 = 220\ \text{rad}. \end{aligned} \tag{10.25}$$

Converting radians to revolutions gives

$$\theta = (220\ \text{rad})\frac{1\ \text{rev}}{2\pi\ \text{rad}} = 35.0\ \text{rev}. \tag{10.26}$$

Solution for (d)

The number of meters of fishing line is x, which can be obtained through its relationship with θ:

$$x = r\theta = (0.0450\ \text{m})(220\ \text{rad}) = 9.90\ \text{m}. \tag{10.27}$$

Discussion

This example illustrates that relationships among rotational quantities are highly analogous to those among linear quantities. We also see in this example how linear and rotational quantities are connected. The answers to the questions are realistic. After unwinding for two seconds, the reel is found to spin at 220 rad/s, which is 2100 rpm. (No wonder reels sometimes make high-pitched sounds.) The amount of fishing line played out is 9.90 m, about right for when the big fish bites.

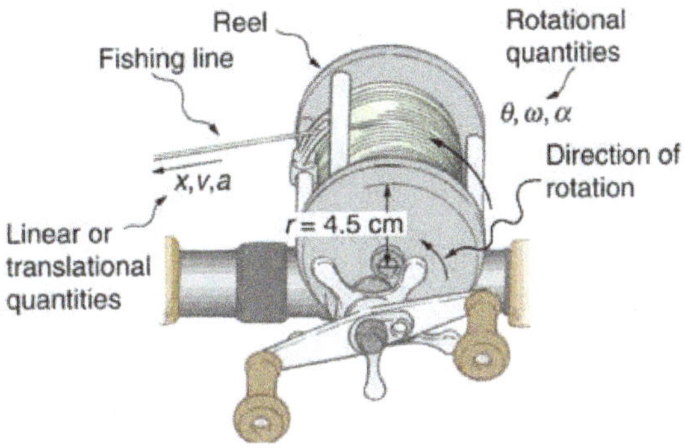

FIGURE 10.7 Fishing line coming off a rotating reel moves linearly. Example 10.3 and Example 10.4 consider relationships between rotational and linear quantities associated with a fishing reel.

EXAMPLE 10.4

Calculating the Duration When the Fishing Reel Slows Down and Stops

Now let us consider what happens if the fisherman applies a brake to the spinning reel, achieving an angular acceleration of $-300\ \text{rad/s}^2$. How long does it take the reel to come to a stop?

Strategy

We are asked to find the time t for the reel to come to a stop. The initial and final conditions are different from those in the previous problem, which involved the same fishing reel. Now we see that the initial angular velocity is $\omega_0 = 220\ \text{rad/s}$ and the final angular velocity ω is zero. The angular acceleration is given to be $\alpha = -300\ \text{rad/s}^2$. Examining the available equations, we see all quantities but t are known in $\omega = \omega_0 + \alpha t$, making it easiest to use this equation.

Solution

The equation states

$$\omega = \omega_0 + \alpha t. \qquad 10.28$$

We solve the equation algebraically for t, and then substitute the known values as usual, yielding

$$t = \frac{\omega - \omega_0}{\alpha} = \frac{0 - 220\ \text{rad/s}}{-300\ \text{rad/s}^2} = 0.733\ \text{s}. \qquad 10.29$$

Discussion

Note that care must be taken with the signs that indicate the directions of various quantities. Also, note that the time to stop the reel is fairly small because the acceleration is rather large. Fishing lines sometimes snap because of the accelerations involved, and fishermen often let the fish swim for a while before applying brakes on the reel. A tired fish will be slower, requiring a smaller acceleration.

EXAMPLE 10.5

Calculating the Slow Acceleration of Trains and Their Wheels

Large freight trains accelerate very slowly. Suppose one such train accelerates from rest, giving its 0.350-m-radius wheels an angular acceleration of $0.250\ \text{rad/s}^2$. After the wheels have made 200 revolutions (assume no slippage): (a) How far has the train moved down the track? (b) What are the final angular velocity of the wheels and the linear velocity of the train?

Strategy

In part (a), we are asked to find x, and in (b) we are asked to find ω and v. We are given the number of revolutions θ, the radius of the wheels r, and the angular acceleration α.

Solution for (a)

The distance x is very easily found from the relationship between distance and rotation angle:

$$\theta = \frac{x}{r}. \quad (10.30)$$

Solving this equation for x yields

$$x = r\theta. \quad (10.31)$$

Before using this equation, we must convert the number of revolutions into radians, because we are dealing with a relationship between linear and rotational quantities:

$$\theta = (200 \text{ rev})\frac{2\pi \text{ rad}}{1 \text{ rev}} = 1257 \text{ rad}. \quad (10.32)$$

Now we can substitute the known values into $x = r\theta$ to find the distance the train moved down the track:

$$x = r\theta = (0.350 \text{ m})(1257 \text{ rad}) = 440 \text{ m}. \quad (10.33)$$

Solution for (b)

We cannot use any equation that incorporates t to find ω, because the equation would have at least two unknown values. The equation $\omega^2 = {\omega_0}^2 + 2\alpha\theta$ will work, because we know the values for all variables except ω:

$$\omega^2 = {\omega_0}^2 + 2\alpha\theta \quad (10.34)$$

Taking the square root of this equation and entering the known values gives

$$\begin{aligned} \omega &= \left[0 + 2(0.250 \text{ rad/s}^2)(1257 \text{ rad})\right]^{1/2} \\ &= 25.1 \text{ rad/s}. \end{aligned} \quad (10.35)$$

We can find the linear velocity of the train, v, through its relationship to ω:

$$v = r\omega = (0.350 \text{ m})(25.1 \text{ rad/s}) = 8.77 \text{ m/s}. \quad (10.36)$$

Discussion

The distance traveled is fairly large and the final velocity is fairly slow (just under 32 km/h).

There is translational motion even for something spinning in place, as the following example illustrates. Figure 10.8 shows a fly on the edge of a rotating microwave oven plate. The example below calculates the total distance it travels.

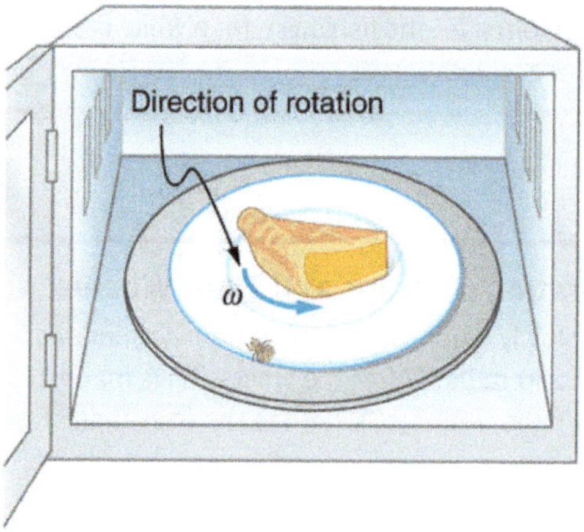

FIGURE 10.8 The image shows a microwave plate. The fly makes revolutions while the food is heated (along with the fly).

EXAMPLE 10.6

Calculating the Distance Traveled by a Fly on the Edge of a Microwave Oven Plate

A person decides to use a microwave oven to reheat some lunch. In the process, a fly accidentally flies into the microwave and lands on the outer edge of the rotating plate and remains there. If the plate has a radius of 0.15 m and rotates at 6.0 rpm, calculate the total distance traveled by the fly during a 2.0-min cooking period. (Ignore the start-up and slow-down times.)

Strategy

First, find the total number of revolutions θ, and then the linear distance x traveled. $\theta = \bar{\omega}t$ can be used to find θ because $\bar{\omega}$ is given to be 6.0 rpm.

Solution

Entering known values into $\theta = \bar{\omega}t$ gives

$$\theta = \bar{\omega}t = (6.0 \text{ rpm})(2.0 \text{ min}) = 12 \text{ rev}. \tag{10.37}$$

As always, it is necessary to convert revolutions to radians before calculating a linear quantity like x from an angular quantity like θ:

$$\theta = (12 \text{ rev})\left(\frac{2\pi \text{ rad}}{1 \text{ rev}}\right) = 75.4 \text{ rad}. \tag{10.38}$$

Now, using the relationship between x and θ, we can determine the distance traveled:

$$x = r\theta = (0.15 \text{ m})(75.4 \text{ rad}) = 11 \text{ m}. \tag{10.39}$$

Discussion

Quite a trip (if it survives)! Note that this distance is the total distance traveled by the fly. Displacement is actually zero for complete revolutions because they bring the fly back to its original position. The distinction between total distance traveled and displacement was first noted in One-Dimensional Kinematics.

CHECK YOUR UNDERSTANDING

Rotational kinematics has many useful relationships, often expressed in equation form. Are these relationships laws of physics or are they simply descriptive? (Hint: the same question applies to linear kinematics.)

Solution

Rotational kinematics (just like linear kinematics) is descriptive and does not represent laws of nature. With kinematics, we can describe many things to great precision but kinematics does not consider causes. For example, a large angular acceleration describes a very rapid change in angular velocity without any consideration of its cause.

10.3 Dynamics of Rotational Motion: Rotational Inertia

LEARNING OBJECTIVES

By the end of this section, you will be able to:

- Understand the relationship between force, mass and acceleration.
- Study the turning effect of force.
- Study the analogy between force and torque, mass and moment of inertia, and linear acceleration and angular acceleration.

If you have ever spun a bike wheel or pushed a merry-go-round, you know that force is needed to change angular velocity as seen in Figure 10.9. In fact, your intuition is reliable in predicting many of the factors that are involved. For example, we know that a door opens slowly if we push too close to its hinges. Furthermore, we know that the more massive the door, the more slowly it opens. The first example implies that the farther the force is applied from the pivot, the greater the angular acceleration; another implication is that angular acceleration is inversely proportional to mass. These relationships should seem very similar to the familiar relationships among force, mass, and acceleration embodied in Newton's second law of motion. There are, in fact, precise rotational analogs to both force and mass.

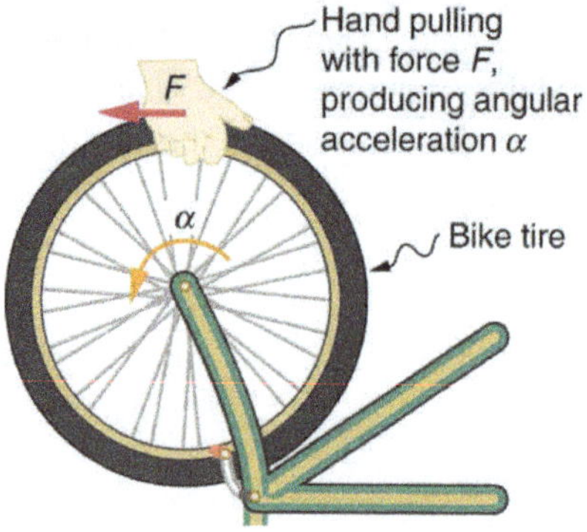

FIGURE 10.9 Force is required to spin the bike wheel. The greater the force, the greater the angular acceleration produced. The more massive the wheel, the smaller the angular acceleration. If you push on a spoke closer to the axle, the angular acceleration will be smaller.

To develop the precise relationship among force, mass, radius, and angular acceleration, consider what happens if we exert a force F on a point mass m that is at a distance r from a pivot point, as shown in Figure 10.10. Because the force is perpendicular to r, an acceleration $a = \frac{F}{m}$ is obtained in the direction of F. We can rearrange this equation such that $F = ma$ and then look for ways to relate this expression to expressions for rotational quantities. We note that $a = r\alpha$, and we substitute this expression into $F = ma$, yielding

$$F = mr\alpha. \tag{10.40}$$

Recall that **torque** is the turning effectiveness of a force. In this case, because $\mathbf{F}$ is perpendicular to r, torque is simply $\tau = Fr$. So, if we multiply both sides of the equation above by r, we get torque on the left-hand side. That is,

$$rF = mr^2\alpha \tag{10.41}$$

or

$$\tau = mr^2\alpha. \tag{10.42}$$

This last equation is the rotational analog of Newton's second law ($F = ma$), where torque is analogous to force, angular acceleration is analogous to translational acceleration, and mr^2 is analogous to mass (or inertia). The quantity mr^2 is called the **rotational inertia** or **moment of inertia** of a point mass m a distance r from the center of rotation.

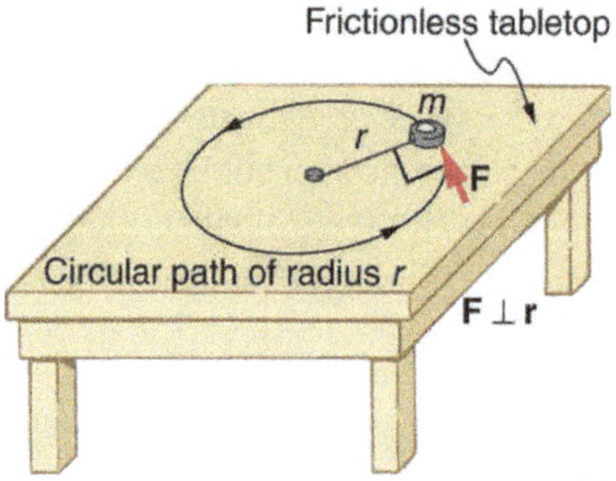

FIGURE 10.10 An object is supported by a horizontal frictionless table and is attached to a pivot point by a cord that supplies centripetal force. A force F is applied to the object perpendicular to the radius r, causing it to accelerate about the pivot point. The force is kept perpendicular to r.

MAKING CONNECTIONS: ROTATIONAL MOTION DYNAMICS

Dynamics for rotational motion is completely analogous to linear or translational dynamics. Dynamics is concerned with force and mass and their effects on motion. For rotational motion, we will find direct analogs to force and mass that behave just as we would expect from our earlier experiences.

Rotational Inertia and Moment of Inertia

Before we can consider the rotation of anything other than a point mass like the one in Figure 10.10, we must extend the idea of rotational inertia to all types of objects. To expand our concept of rotational inertia, we define the **moment of inertia** I of an object to be the sum of mr^2 for all the point masses of which it is composed. That is, $I = \sum mr^2$. Here I is analogous to m in translational motion. Because of the distance r, the moment of inertia for any object depends on the chosen axis. Actually, calculating I is beyond the scope of this text except for one simple case—that of a hoop, which has all its mass at the same distance from its axis. A hoop's moment of inertia around its axis is therefore MR^2, where M is its total mass and R its radius. (We use M and R for an entire object to distinguish them from m and r for point masses.) In all other cases, we must consult Figure 10.11 (note that the table is piece of artwork that has shapes as well as formulae) for formulas for I that have been derived from integration over the continuous body. Note that I has units of mass multiplied by distance squared ($\mathrm{kg} \cdot \mathrm{m}^2$), as we might expect from its definition.

The general relationship among torque, moment of inertia, and angular acceleration is

$$\text{net } \tau = I\alpha \tag{10.43}$$

or

$$\alpha = \frac{\text{net } \tau}{I}, \tag{10.44}$$

where net τ is the total torque from all forces relative to a chosen axis. For simplicity, we will only consider torques exerted by forces in the plane of the rotation. Such torques are either positive or negative and add like ordinary numbers. The relationship in $\tau = I\alpha,\ \alpha = \frac{\text{net } \tau}{I}$ is the rotational analog to Newton's second law and is very generally applicable. This equation is actually valid for *any* torque, applied to *any* object, relative to *any* axis.

As we might expect, the larger the torque is, the larger the angular acceleration is. For example, the harder a child pushes on a merry-go-round, the faster it accelerates. Furthermore, the more massive a merry-go-round, the slower it accelerates for the same torque. The basic relationship between moment of inertia and angular acceleration is that the larger the moment of inertia, the smaller is the angular acceleration. But there is an additional twist. The moment of inertia depends not only on the mass of an object, but also on its *distribution* of mass relative to the axis around which it rotates. For example, it will be much easier to accelerate a merry-go-round full of children if they stand close to its axis than if they all stand at the outer edge. The mass is the same in both cases, but the moment of inertia is much larger when the children are at the edge.

TAKE-HOME EXPERIMENT

Cut out a circle that has about a 10 cm radius from stiff cardboard. Near the edge of the circle, write numbers 1 to 12 like hours on a clock face. Position the circle so that it can rotate freely about a horizontal axis through its center, like a wheel. (You could loosely nail the circle to a wall.) Hold the circle stationary and with the number 12 positioned at the top, attach a lump of blue putty (sticky material used for fixing posters to walls) at the number 3. How large does the lump need to be to just rotate the circle? Describe how you can change the moment of inertia of the circle. How does this change affect the amount of blue putty needed at the number 3 to just rotate the circle? Change the circle's moment of inertia and then try rotating the circle by using different amounts of blue putty. Repeat this process several times.

PROBLEM-SOLVING STRATEGY FOR ROTATIONAL DYNAMICS

1. *Examine the situation to determine that torque and mass are involved in the rotation.* Draw a careful sketch of the situation.
2. *Determine the system of interest.*
3. *Draw a free body diagram.* That is, draw and label all external forces acting on the system of interest.
4. *Apply* $\text{net } \tau = I\alpha,\ \alpha = \frac{\text{net } \tau}{I}$*, the rotational equivalent of Newton's second law, to solve the problem.* Care

must be taken to use the correct moment of inertia and to consider the torque about the point of rotation.

5. *As always, check the solution to see if it is reasonable.*

MAKING CONNECTIONS

In statics, the net torque is zero, and there is no angular acceleration. In rotational motion, net torque is the cause of angular acceleration, exactly as in Newton's second law of motion for rotation.

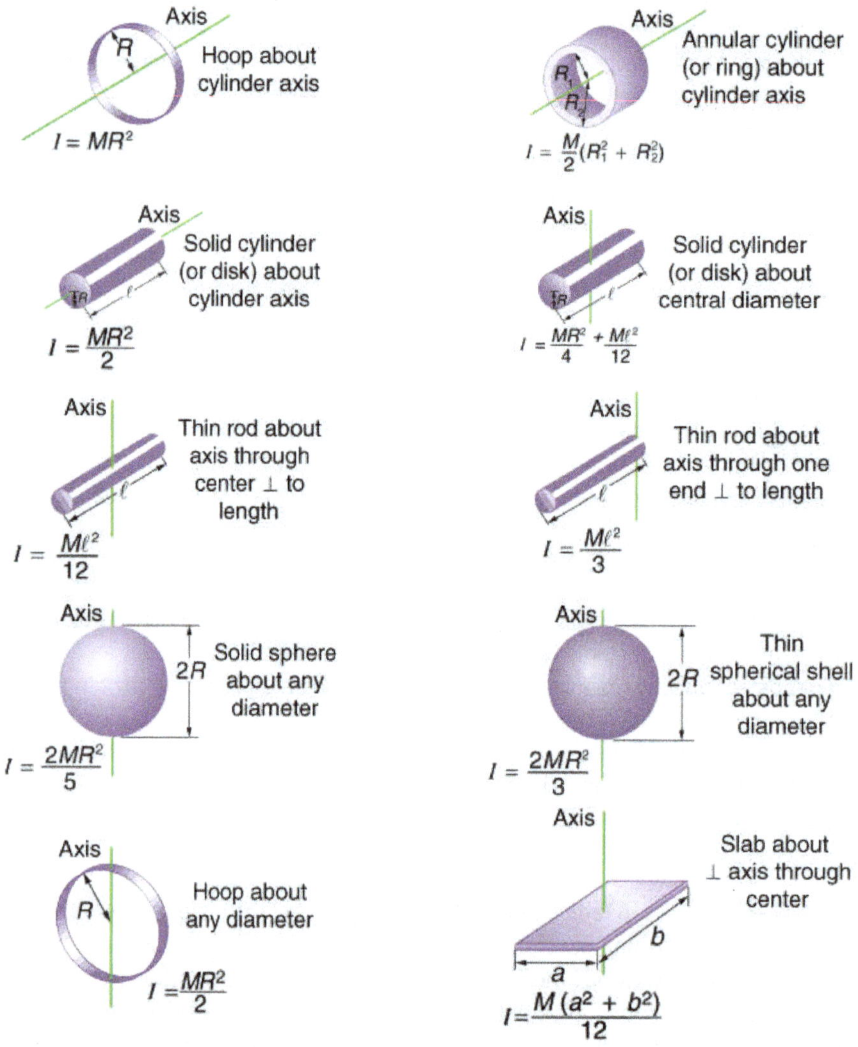

FIGURE 10.11 Some rotational inertias.

EXAMPLE 10.7

Calculating the Effect of Mass Distribution on a Merry-Go-Round

Consider the father pushing a playground merry-go-round in Figure 10.12. He exerts a force of 250 N at the edge of the 50.0-kg merry-go-round, which has a 1.50 m radius. Calculate the angular acceleration produced (a) when no one is on the merry-go-round and (b) when an 18.0-kg child sits 1.25 m away from the center. Consider the merry-go-round itself to be a uniform disk with negligible retarding friction.

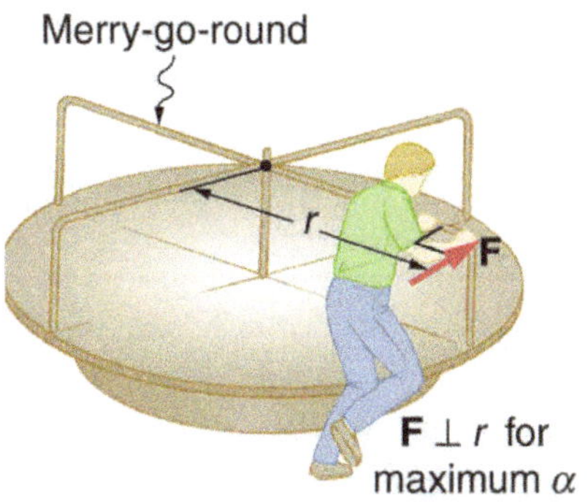

FIGURE 10.12 A father pushes a playground merry-go-round at its edge and perpendicular to its radius to achieve maximum torque.

Strategy

Angular acceleration is given directly by the expression $\alpha = \frac{\text{net } \tau}{I}$:

$$\alpha = \frac{\tau}{I}. \tag{10.45}$$

To solve for α, we must first calculate the torque τ (which is the same in both cases) and moment of inertia I (which is greater in the second case). To find the torque, we note that the applied force is perpendicular to the radius and friction is negligible, so that

$$\tau = rF \sin\theta = (1.50 \text{ m})(250 \text{ N}) = 375 \text{ N} \cdot \text{m}. \tag{10.46}$$

Solution for (a)

The moment of inertia of a solid disk about this axis is given in Figure 10.11 to be

$$\frac{1}{2}MR^2, \tag{10.47}$$

where $M = 50.0 \text{ kg}$ and $R = 1.50 \text{ m}$, so that

$$I = (0.500)(50.0 \text{ kg})(1.50 \text{ m})^2 = 56.25 \text{ kg} \cdot \text{m}^2. \tag{10.48}$$

Now, after we substitute the known values, we find the angular acceleration to be

$$\alpha = \frac{\tau}{I} = \frac{375 \text{ N} \cdot \text{m}}{56.25 \text{ kg} \cdot \text{m}^2} = 6.67 \frac{\text{rad}}{\text{s}^2}. \tag{10.49}$$

Solution for (b)

We expect the angular acceleration for the system to be less in this part, because the moment of inertia is greater when the child is on the merry-go-round. To find the total moment of inertia I, we first find the child's moment of inertia I_c by considering the child to be equivalent to a point mass at a distance of 1.25 m from the axis. Then,

$$I_c = MR^2 = (18.0 \text{ kg})(1.25 \text{ m})^2 = 28.13 \text{ kg} \cdot \text{m}^2. \tag{10.50}$$

The total moment of inertia is the sum of moments of inertia of the merry-go-round and the child (about the same axis). To justify this sum to yourself, examine the definition of I:

$$I = 28.13 \text{ kg} \cdot \text{m}^2 + 56.25 \text{ kg} \cdot \text{m}^2 = 84.38 \text{ kg} \cdot \text{m}^2. \tag{10.51}$$

Substituting known values into the equation for α gives

$$\alpha = \frac{\tau}{I} = \frac{375 \text{ N} \cdot \text{m}}{84.38 \text{ kg} \cdot \text{m}^2} = 4.44 \frac{\text{rad}}{\text{s}^2}. \tag{10.52}$$

Discussion

The angular acceleration is less when the child is on the merry-go-round than when the merry-go-round is empty, as expected. The angular accelerations found are quite large, partly due to the fact that friction was considered to be negligible. If, for example, the father kept pushing perpendicularly for 2.00 s, he would give the merry-go-round an angular velocity of 13.3 rad/s when it is empty but only 8.89 rad/s when the child is on it. In terms of revolutions per second, these angular velocities are 2.12 rev/s and 1.41 rev/s, respectively. The father would end up running at about 50 km/h in the first case. Summer Olympics, here he comes! Confirmation of these numbers is left as an exercise for the reader.

CHECK YOUR UNDERSTANDING

Torque is the analog of force and moment of inertia is the analog of mass. Force and mass are physical quantities that depend on only one factor. For example, mass is related solely to the numbers of atoms of various types in an object. Are torque and moment of inertia similarly simple?

Solution

No. Torque depends on three factors: force magnitude, force direction, and point of application. Moment of inertia depends on both mass and its distribution relative to the axis of rotation. So, while the analogies are precise, these rotational quantities depend on more factors.

10.4 Rotational Kinetic Energy: Work and Energy Revisited

LEARNING OBJECTIVES

By the end of this section, you will be able to:

- Derive the equation for rotational work.
- Calculate rotational kinetic energy.
- Demonstrate the Law of Conservation of Energy.

In this module, we will learn about work and energy associated with rotational motion. Figure 10.13 shows a worker using an electric grindstone propelled by a motor. Sparks are flying, and noise and vibration are created as layers of steel are pared from the pole. The stone continues to turn even after the motor is turned off, but it is eventually brought to a stop by friction. Clearly, the motor had to work to get the stone spinning. This work went into heat, light, sound, vibration, and considerable **rotational kinetic energy**.

FIGURE 10.13 The motor works in spinning the grindstone, giving it rotational kinetic energy. That energy is then converted to heat, light, sound, and vibration. (credit: U.S. Navy photo by Mass Communication Specialist Seaman Zachary David Bell)

Work must be done to rotate objects such as grindstones or merry-go-rounds. Work was defined in Uniform Circular Motion and Gravitation for translational motion, and we can build on that knowledge when considering work done in rotational motion. The simplest rotational situation is one in which the net force is exerted perpendicular to the radius of a disk (as shown in Figure 10.14) and remains perpendicular as the disk starts to rotate. The force is parallel to the displacement, and so the net work done is the product of the force times the arc length traveled:

$$\text{net } W = (\text{net } F)\Delta s. \tag{10.53}$$

To get torque and other rotational quantities into the equation, we multiply and divide the right-hand side of the equation by r, and gather terms:

$$\text{net } W = (r \text{ net } F)\frac{\Delta s}{r}. \tag{10.54}$$

We recognize that r net F = net τ and $\Delta s/r = \theta$, so that

$$\text{net } W = (\text{net } \tau)\theta. \quad 10.55$$

This equation is the expression for rotational work. It is very similar to the familiar definition of translational work as force multiplied by distance. Here, torque is analogous to force, and angle is analogous to distance. The equation net $W = (\text{net } \tau)\theta$ is valid in general, even though it was derived for a special case.

To get an expression for rotational kinetic energy, we must again perform some algebraic manipulations. The first step is to note that net $\tau = I\alpha$, so that

$$\text{net } W = I\alpha\theta. \quad 10.56$$

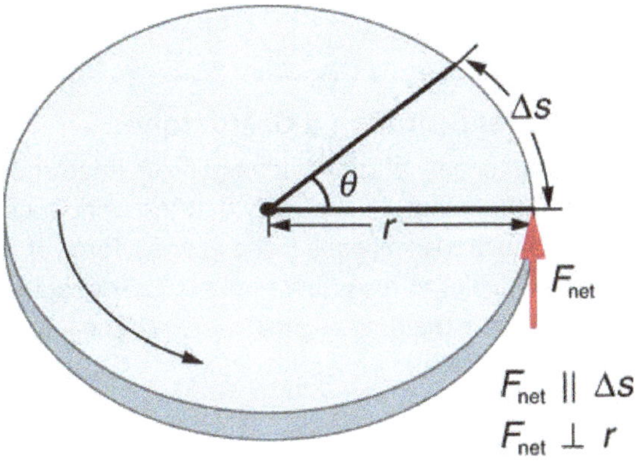

FIGURE 10.14 The net force on this disk is kept perpendicular to its radius as the force causes the disk to rotate. The net work done is thus (net F)Δs. The net work goes into rotational kinetic energy.

MAKING CONNECTIONS

Work and energy in rotational motion are completely analogous to work and energy in translational motion, first presented in Uniform Circular Motion and Gravitation.

Now, we solve one of the rotational kinematics equations for $\alpha\theta$. We start with the equation

$$\omega^2 = {\omega_0}^2 + 2\alpha\theta. \quad 10.57$$

Next, we solve for $\alpha\theta$:

$$\alpha\theta = \frac{\omega^2 - {\omega_0}^2}{2}. \quad 10.58$$

Substituting this into the equation for net W and gathering terms yields

$$\text{net } W = \frac{1}{2}I\omega^2 - \frac{1}{2}I{\omega_0}^2. \quad 10.59$$

This equation is the **work-energy theorem** for rotational motion only. As you may recall, net work changes the kinetic energy of a system. Through an analogy with translational motion, we define the term $\left(\frac{1}{2}\right)I\omega^2$ to be **rotational kinetic energy** KE_{rot} for an object with a moment of inertia I and an angular velocity ω:

$$\text{KE}_{\text{rot}} = \frac{1}{2}I\omega^2. \quad 10.60$$

The expression for rotational kinetic energy is exactly analogous to translational kinetic energy, with I being analogous to m and ω to v. Rotational kinetic energy has important effects. Flywheels, for example, can be used to store large amounts of rotational kinetic energy in a vehicle, as seen in Figure 10.15.

FIGURE 10.15 Experimental vehicles, such as this bus, have been constructed in which rotational kinetic energy is stored in a large flywheel. When the bus goes down a hill, its transmission converts its gravitational potential energy into KE_{rot}. It can also convert translational kinetic energy, when the bus stops, into KE_{rot}. The flywheel's energy can then be used to accelerate, to go up another hill, or to keep the bus from slowing down due to friction.

EXAMPLE 10.8

Calculating the Work and Energy for Spinning a Grindstone

Consider a person who spins a large grindstone by placing her hand on its edge and exerting a force through part of a revolution as shown in Figure 10.16. In this example, we verify that the work done by the torque she exerts equals the change in rotational energy. (a) How much work is done if she exerts a force of 200 N through a rotation of $1.00\text{ rad}(57.3°)$? The force is kept perpendicular to the grindstone's 0.320-m radius at the point of application, and the effects of friction are negligible. (b) What is the final angular velocity if the grindstone has a mass of 85.0 kg? (c) What is the final rotational kinetic energy? (It should equal the work.)

Strategy

To find the work, we can use the equation $\text{net } W = (\text{net } \tau)\theta$. We have enough information to calculate the torque and are given the rotation angle. In the second part, we can find the final angular velocity using one of the kinematic relationships. In the last part, we can calculate the rotational kinetic energy from its expression in $KE_{rot} = \frac{1}{2}I\omega^2$.

Solution for (a)

The net work is expressed in the equation

$$\text{net } W = (\text{net } \tau)\theta, \tag{10.61}$$

where net τ is the applied force multiplied by the radius (rF) because there is no retarding friction, and the force is perpendicular to r. The angle θ is given. Substituting the given values in the equation above yields

$$\begin{aligned}\text{net } W &= rF\theta = (0.320\text{ m})(200\text{ N})(1.00\text{ rad}) \\ &= 64.0\text{ N}\cdot\text{m}.\end{aligned} \tag{10.62}$$

Noting that $1\text{ N}\cdot\text{m} = 1\text{ J}$,

$$\text{net } W = 64.0\text{ J}. \tag{10.63}$$

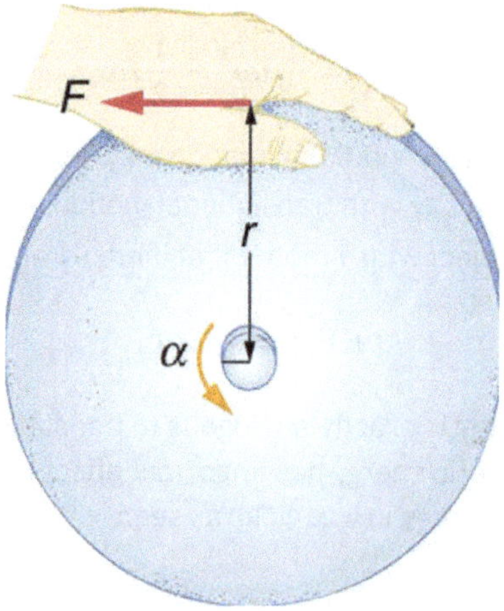

FIGURE 10.16 A large grindstone is given a spin by a person grasping its outer edge.

Solution for (b)

To find ω from the given information requires more than one step. We start with the kinematic relationship in the equation

$$\omega^2 = \omega_0{}^2 + 2\alpha\theta. \tag{10.64}$$

Note that $\omega_0 = 0$ because we start from rest. Taking the square root of the resulting equation gives

$$\omega = (2\alpha\theta)^{1/2}. \tag{10.65}$$

Now we need to find α. One possibility is

$$\alpha = \frac{\text{net } \tau}{I}, \tag{10.66}$$

where the torque is

$$\text{net } \tau = rF = (0.320 \text{ m})(200 \text{ N}) = 64.0 \text{ N} \cdot \text{m}. \tag{10.67}$$

The formula for the moment of inertia for a disk is found in Figure 10.11:

$$I = \frac{1}{2}MR^2 = 0.5(85.0 \text{ kg})(0.320 \text{ m})^2 = 4.352 \text{ kg} \cdot \text{m}^2. \tag{10.68}$$

Substituting the values of torque and moment of inertia into the expression for α, we obtain

$$\alpha = \frac{64.0 \text{ N} \cdot \text{m}}{4.352 \text{ kg} \cdot \text{m}^2} = 14.7 \frac{\text{rad}}{\text{s}^2}. \tag{10.69}$$

Now, substitute this value and the given value for θ into the above expression for ω:

$$\omega = (2\alpha\theta)^{1/2} = \left[2\left(14.7 \frac{\text{rad}}{\text{s}^2}\right)(1.00 \text{ rad})\right]^{1/2} = 5.42 \frac{\text{rad}}{\text{s}}. \tag{10.70}$$

Solution for (c)

The final rotational kinetic energy is

$$\text{KE}_{\text{rot}} = \frac{1}{2}I\omega^2. \tag{10.71}$$

Both I and ω were found above. Thus,

$$\text{KE}_{\text{rot}} = (0.5)\left(4.352 \text{ kg} \cdot \text{m}^2\right)(5.42 \text{ rad/s})^2 = 64.0 \text{ J}. \tag{10.72}$$

Discussion

The final rotational kinetic energy equals the work done by the torque, which confirms that the work done went into rotational kinetic energy. We could, in fact, have used an expression for energy instead of a kinematic relation to solve part (b). We will do this in later examples.

Helicopter pilots are quite familiar with rotational kinetic energy. They know, for example, that a point of no return will be reached if they allow their blades to slow below a critical angular velocity during flight. The blades lose lift, and it is impossible to immediately get the blades spinning fast enough to regain it. Rotational kinetic energy must be supplied to the blades to get them to rotate faster, and enough energy cannot be supplied in time to avoid a crash. Because of weight limitations, helicopter engines are too small to supply both the energy needed for lift and to replenish the rotational kinetic energy of the blades once they have slowed down. The rotational kinetic energy is put into them before takeoff and must not be allowed to drop below this crucial level. One possible way to avoid a crash is to use the gravitational potential energy of the helicopter to replenish the rotational kinetic energy of the blades by losing altitude and aligning the blades so that the helicopter is spun up in the descent. Of course, if the helicopter's altitude is too low, then there is insufficient time for the blade to regain lift before reaching the ground.

PROBLEM-SOLVING STRATEGY FOR ROTATIONAL ENERGY

1. *Determine that energy or work is involved in the rotation.*
2. *Determine the system of interest.* A sketch usually helps.
3. *Analyze the situation to determine the types of work and energy involved.*
4. *For closed systems, mechanical energy is conserved.* That is, $\text{KE}_\text{i} + \text{PE}_\text{i} = \text{KE}_\text{f} + \text{PE}_\text{f}$. Note that KE_i and KE_f may each include translational and rotational contributions.
5. *For open systems,* mechanical energy may not be conserved, and other forms of energy (referred to previously as OE), such as heat transfer, may enter or leave the system. Determine what they are, and calculate them as necessary.
6. *Eliminate terms wherever possible to simplify the algebra.*
7. *Check the answer to see if it is reasonable.*

EXAMPLE 10.9

Calculating Helicopter Energies

A typical small rescue helicopter, similar to the one in Figure 10.17, has four blades, each is 4.00 m long and has a mass of 50.0 kg. The blades can be approximated as thin rods that rotate about one end of an axis perpendicular to their length. The helicopter has a total loaded mass of 1000 kg. (a) Calculate the rotational kinetic energy in the blades when they rotate at 300 rpm. (b) Calculate the translational kinetic energy of the helicopter when it flies at 20.0 m/s, and compare it with the rotational energy in the blades. (c) To what height could the helicopter be raised if all of the rotational kinetic energy could be used to lift it?

Strategy

Rotational and translational kinetic energies can be calculated from their definitions. The last part of the problem relates to the idea that energy can change form, in this case from rotational kinetic energy to gravitational potential energy.

Solution for (a)

The rotational kinetic energy is

$$\text{KE}_\text{rot} = \frac{1}{2}I\omega^2. \tag{10.73}$$

We must convert the angular velocity to radians per second and calculate the moment of inertia before we can find KE_rot. The angular velocity ω is

$$\omega = \frac{300\text{ rev}}{1.00\text{ min}} \cdot \frac{2\pi\text{ rad}}{1\text{ rev}} \cdot \frac{1.00\text{ min}}{60.0\text{ s}} = 31.4\frac{\text{rad}}{\text{s}}. \tag{10.74}$$

The moment of inertia of one blade will be that of a thin rod rotated about its end, found in Figure 10.11. The total I is four times this moment of inertia, because there are four blades. Thus,

$$I = 4\frac{M\ell^2}{3} = 4 \times \frac{(50.0\text{ kg})(4.00\text{ m})^2}{3} = 1067\text{ kg}\cdot\text{m}^2. \tag{10.75}$$

Entering ω and I into the expression for rotational kinetic energy gives

$$\begin{aligned}\text{KE}_\text{rot} &= 0.5(1067\text{ kg}\cdot\text{m}^2)(31.4\text{ rad/s})^2 \\ &= 5.26 \times 10^5\text{ J}\end{aligned} \tag{10.76}$$

Solution for (b)

Translational kinetic energy was defined in Uniform Circular Motion and Gravitation. Entering the given values of mass and velocity, we obtain

$$KE_{trans} = \frac{1}{2}mv^2 = (0.5)(1000\ \text{kg})(20.0\ \text{m/s})^2 = 2.00 \times 10^5\ \text{J}. \tag{10.77}$$

To compare kinetic energies, we take the ratio of translational kinetic energy to rotational kinetic energy. This ratio is

$$\frac{2.00 \times 10^5\ \text{J}}{5.26 \times 10^5\ \text{J}} = 0.380. \tag{10.78}$$

Solution for (c)

At the maximum height, all rotational kinetic energy will have been converted to gravitational energy. To find this height, we equate those two energies:

$$KE_{rot} = PE_{grav} \tag{10.79}$$

or

$$\frac{1}{2}I\omega^2 = mgh. \tag{10.80}$$

We now solve for h and substitute known values into the resulting equation

$$h = \frac{\frac{1}{2}I\omega^2}{mg} = \frac{5.26 \times 10^5\ \text{J}}{(1000\ \text{kg})(9.80\ \text{m/s}^2)} = 53.7\ \text{m}. \tag{10.81}$$

Discussion

The ratio of translational energy to rotational kinetic energy is only 0.380. This ratio tells us that most of the kinetic energy of the helicopter is in its spinning blades—something you probably would not suspect. The 53.7 m height to which the helicopter could be raised with the rotational kinetic energy is also impressive, again emphasizing the amount of rotational kinetic energy in the blades.

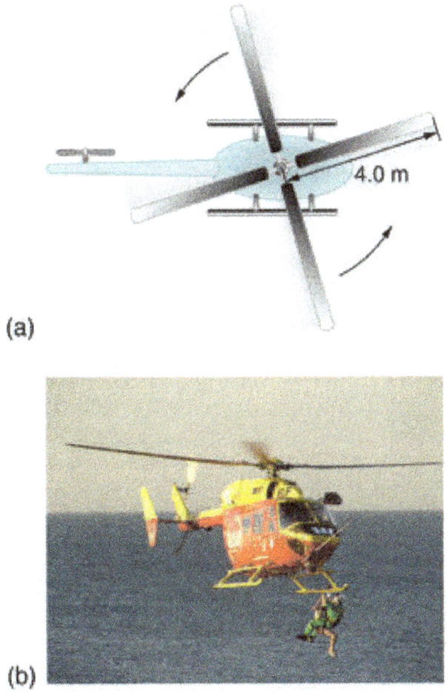

FIGURE 10.17 The first image shows how helicopters store large amounts of rotational kinetic energy in their blades. This energy must be put into the blades before takeoff and maintained until the end of the flight. The engines do not have enough power to simultaneously provide lift and put significant rotational energy into the blades. The second image shows a helicopter from the Auckland Westpac Rescue Helicopter Service. Over 50,000 lives have been saved since its operations beginning in 1973. Here, a water rescue operation is shown. (credit: 111 Emergency, Flickr)

MAKING CONNECTIONS

Conservation of energy includes rotational motion, because rotational kinetic energy is another form of KE. Uniform Circular Motion and Gravitation has a detailed treatment of conservation of energy.

How Thick Is the Soup? Or Why Don't All Objects Roll Downhill at the Same Rate?

One of the quality controls in a tomato soup factory consists of rolling filled cans down a ramp. If they roll too fast, the soup is too thin. Why should cans of identical size and mass roll down an incline at different rates? And why should the thickest soup roll the slowest?

The easiest way to answer these questions is to consider energy. Suppose each can starts down the ramp from rest. Each can starting from rest means each starts with the same gravitational potential energy PE_{grav}, which is converted entirely to KE, provided each rolls without slipping. KE, however, can take the form of KE_{trans} or KE_{rot}, and total KE is the sum of the two. If a can rolls down a ramp, it puts part of its energy into rotation, leaving less for translation. Thus, the can goes slower than it would if it slid down. Furthermore, the thin soup does not rotate, whereas the thick soup does, because it sticks to the can. The thick soup thus puts more of the can's original gravitational potential energy into rotation than the thin soup, and the can rolls more slowly, as seen in Figure 10.18.

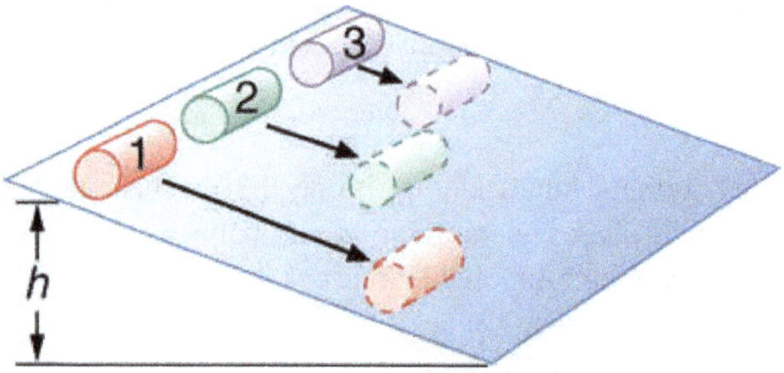

FIGURE 10.18 Three cans of soup with identical masses race down an incline. The first can has a low friction coating and does not roll but just slides down the incline. It wins because it converts its entire PE into translational KE. The second and third cans both roll down the incline without slipping. The second can contains thin soup and comes in second because part of its initial PE goes into rotating the can (but not the thin soup). The third can contains thick soup. It comes in third because the soup rotates along with the can, taking even more of the initial PE for rotational KE, leaving less for translational KE.

Assuming no losses due to friction, there is only one force doing work—gravity. Therefore the total work done is the change in kinetic energy. As the cans start moving, the potential energy is changing into kinetic energy. Conservation of energy gives

$$\text{PE}_{\text{i}} = \text{KE}_{\text{f}}. \quad (10.82)$$

More specifically,

$$\text{PE}_{\text{grav}} = \text{KE}_{\text{trans}} + \text{KE}_{\text{rot}} \quad (10.83)$$

or

$$mgh = \frac{1}{2}mv^2 + \frac{1}{2}I\omega^2. \quad (10.84)$$

So, the initial mgh is divided between translational kinetic energy and rotational kinetic energy; and the greater I is, the less energy goes into translation. If the can slides down without friction, then $\omega = 0$ and all the energy goes into translation; thus, the can goes faster.

TAKE-HOME EXPERIMENT

Locate several cans each containing different types of food. First, predict which can will win the race down an inclined plane and explain why. See if your prediction is correct. You could also do this experiment by collecting several empty cylindrical containers of the same size and filling them with different materials such as wet or dry sand.

EXAMPLE 10.10

Calculating the Speed of a Cylinder Rolling Down an Incline

Calculate the final speed of a solid cylinder that rolls down a 2.00-m-high incline. The cylinder starts from rest, has a mass of 0.750 kg, and has a radius of 4.00 cm.

Strategy

We can solve for the final velocity using conservation of energy, but we must first express rotational quantities in terms of translational quantities to end up with v as the only unknown.

Solution

Conservation of energy for this situation is written as described above:

$$mgh = \frac{1}{2}mv^2 + \frac{1}{2}I\omega^2. \tag{10.85}$$

Before we can solve for v, we must get an expression for I from Figure 10.11. Because v and ω are related (note here that the cylinder is rolling without slipping), we must also substitute the relationship $\omega = v/R$ into the expression. These substitutions yield

$$mgh = \frac{1}{2}mv^2 + \frac{1}{2}\left(\frac{1}{2}mR^2\right)\left(\frac{v^2}{R^2}\right). \tag{10.86}$$

Interestingly, the cylinder's radius R and mass m cancel, yielding

$$gh = \frac{1}{2}v^2 + \frac{1}{4}v^2 = \frac{3}{4}v^2. \tag{10.87}$$

Solving algebraically, the equation for the final velocity v gives

$$v = \left(\frac{4gh}{3}\right)^{1/2}. \tag{10.88}$$

Substituting known values into the resulting expression yields

$$v = \left[\frac{4(9.80\ \text{m/s}^2)(2.00\ \text{m})}{3}\right]^{1/2} = 5.11\ \text{m/s}. \tag{10.89}$$

Discussion

Because m and R cancel, the result $v = \left(\frac{4}{3}gh\right)^{1/2}$ is valid for any solid cylinder, implying that all solid cylinders will roll down an incline at the same rate independent of their masses and sizes. (Rolling cylinders down inclines is what Galileo actually did to show that objects fall at the same rate independent of mass.) Note that if the cylinder slid without friction down the incline without rolling, then the entire gravitational potential energy would go into translational kinetic energy. Thus, $\frac{1}{2}mv^2 = mgh$ and $v = (2gh)^{1/2}$, which is 22% greater than $(4gh/3)^{1/2}$. That is, the cylinder would go faster at the bottom.

CHECK YOUR UNDERSTANDING

Analogy of Rotational and Translational Kinetic Energy Is rotational kinetic energy completely analogous to translational kinetic energy? What, if any, are their differences? Give an example of each type of kinetic energy.

Solution

Yes, rotational and translational kinetic energy are exact analogs. They both are the energy of motion involved with the coordinated (non-random) movement of mass relative to some reference frame. The only difference between rotational and translational kinetic energy is that translational is straight line motion while rotational is not. An example of both kinetic and translational kinetic energy is found in a bike tire while being ridden down a bike path. The rotational motion of the tire means it has rotational kinetic energy while the movement of the bike along the path means the tire also has translational kinetic energy. If you were to lift the front wheel of the bike and spin it while the bike is stationary, then the wheel would have only rotational kinetic energy relative to the Earth.

10.5 Angular Momentum and Its Conservation

LEARNING OBJECTIVES

By the end of this section, you will be able to:

- Understand the analogy between angular momentum and linear momentum.
- Observe the relationship between torque and angular momentum.
- Apply the law of conservation of angular momentum.

Why does Earth keep on spinning? What started it spinning to begin with? And how does an ice skater manage to spin faster and faster simply by pulling her arms in? Why does she not have to exert a torque to spin faster? Questions like these have answers based in angular momentum, the rotational analog to linear momentum.

By now the pattern is clear—every rotational phenomenon has a direct translational analog. It seems quite reasonable, then, to define **angular momentum** L as

$$L = I\omega. \quad (10.90)$$

This equation is an analog to the definition of linear momentum as $p = mv$. Units for linear momentum are $\text{kg} \cdot \text{m/s}$ while units for angular momentum are $\text{kg} \cdot \text{m}^2/\text{s}$. As we would expect, an object that has a large moment of inertia I, such as Earth, has a very large angular momentum. An object that has a large angular velocity ω, such as a centrifuge, also has a rather large angular momentum.

MAKING CONNECTIONS

Angular momentum is completely analogous to linear momentum, first presented in Uniform Circular Motion and Gravitation. It has the same implications in terms of carrying rotation forward, and it is conserved when the net external torque is zero. Angular momentum, like linear momentum, is also a property of the atoms and subatomic particles.

EXAMPLE 10.11

Calculating Angular Momentum of the Earth

Strategy

No information is given in the statement of the problem; so we must look up pertinent data before we can calculate $L = I\omega$. First, according to Figure 10.11, the formula for the moment of inertia of a sphere is

$$I = \frac{2MR^2}{5} \quad (10.91)$$

so that

$$L = I\omega = \frac{2MR^2\omega}{5}. \quad (10.92)$$

Earth's mass M is 5.979×10^{24} kg and its radius R is 6.376×10^6 m. The Earth's angular velocity ω is, of course, exactly one revolution per day, but we must covert ω to radians per second to do the calculation in SI units.

Solution

Substituting known information into the expression for L and converting ω to radians per second gives

$$\begin{aligned} L &= 0.4\left(5.979 \times 10^{24}\text{ kg}\right)\left(6.376 \times 10^{6}\text{ m}\right)^{2}\left(\tfrac{1\text{ rev}}{\text{d}}\right) \\ &= 9.72 \times 10^{37}\text{ kg} \cdot \text{m}^{2} \cdot \text{rev/d}. \end{aligned} \quad 10.93$$

Substituting 2π rad for 1 rev and 8.64×10^{4} s for 1 day gives

$$\begin{aligned} L &= \left(9.72 \times 10^{37}\text{ kg} \cdot \text{m}^{2}\right)\left(\frac{2\pi\text{ rad/rev}}{8.64\times10^{4}\text{ s/d}}\right)(1\text{ rev/d}) \\ &= 7.07 \times 10^{33}\text{ kg} \cdot \text{m}^{2}/\text{s}. \end{aligned} \quad 10.94$$

Discussion

This number is large, demonstrating that Earth, as expected, has a tremendous angular momentum. The answer is approximate, because we have assumed a constant density for Earth in order to estimate its moment of inertia.

When you push a merry-go-round, spin a bike wheel, or open a door, you exert a torque. If the torque you exert is greater than opposing torques, then the rotation accelerates, and angular momentum increases. The greater the net torque, the more rapid the increase in L. The relationship between torque and angular momentum is

$$\text{net } \tau = \frac{\Delta L}{\Delta t}. \quad 10.95$$

This expression is exactly analogous to the relationship between force and linear momentum, $F = \Delta p/\Delta t$. The equation $\text{net } \tau = \frac{\Delta L}{\Delta t}$ is very fundamental and broadly applicable. It is, in fact, the rotational form of Newton's second law.

EXAMPLE 10.12

Calculating the Torque Putting Angular Momentum Into a Rotating Food Tray

Figure 10.19 shows a rotating food tray, often called a lazy Susan, being turned by a person in quest of sustenance. Suppose the person exerts a 2.50 N force perpendicular to the lazy Susan's 0.260-m radius for 0.150 s. (a) What is the final angular momentum of the lazy Susan if it starts from rest, assuming friction is negligible? (b) What is the final angular velocity of the lazy Susan, given that its mass is 4.00 kg and assuming its moment of inertia is that of a disk?

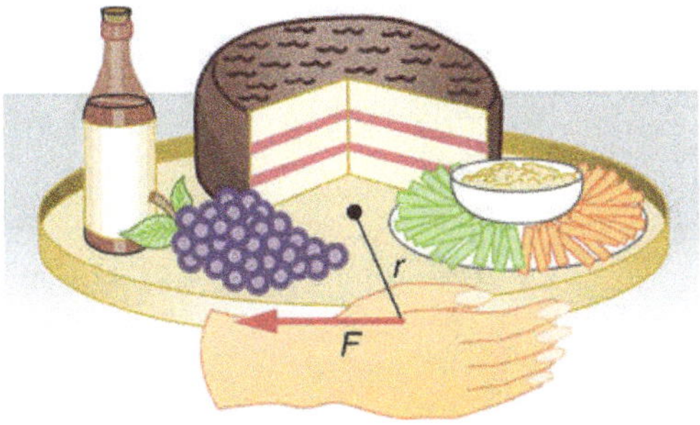

FIGURE 10.19 A partygoer exerts a torque on a lazy Susan to make it rotate. The equation $\text{net } \tau = \frac{\Delta L}{\Delta t}$ gives the relationship between torque and the angular momentum produced.

Strategy

We can find the angular momentum by solving $\text{net } \tau = \frac{\Delta L}{\Delta t}$ for ΔL, and using the given information to calculate the torque. The final angular momentum equals the change in angular momentum, because the lazy Susan starts from rest. That is, $\Delta L = L$. To find the final velocity, we must calculate ω from the definition of L in $L = I\omega$.

Solution for (a)

Solving $\text{net } \tau = \frac{\Delta L}{\Delta t}$ for ΔL gives

$$\Delta L = (\text{net } \tau)\Delta t. \quad 10.96$$

Because the force is perpendicular to r, we see that $\text{net } \tau = rF$, so that

$$\begin{aligned} L &= \text{rF}\Delta t = (0.260 \text{ m})(2.50 \text{ N})(0.150 \text{ s}) \\ &= 9.75 \times 10^{-2} \text{ kg} \cdot \text{m}^2/\text{s}. \end{aligned} \tag{10.97}$$

Solution for (b)

The final angular velocity can be calculated from the definition of angular momentum,

$$L = I\omega. \tag{10.98}$$

Solving for ω and substituting the formula for the moment of inertia of a disk into the resulting equation gives

$$\omega = \frac{L}{I} = \frac{L}{\frac{1}{2}MR^2}. \tag{10.99}$$

And substituting known values into the preceding equation yields

$$\omega = \frac{9.75 \times 10^{-2} \text{ kg} \cdot \text{m}^2/\text{s}}{(0.500)(4.00 \text{ kg})(0.260 \text{ m})^2} = 0.721 \text{ rad/s}. \tag{10.100}$$

Discussion

Note that the imparted angular momentum does not depend on any property of the object but only on torque and time. The final angular velocity is equivalent to one revolution in 8.71 s (determination of the time period is left as an exercise for the reader), which is about right for a lazy Susan.

EXAMPLE 10.13

Calculating the Torque in a Kick

The person whose leg is shown in Figure 10.20 kicks his leg by exerting a 2000-N force with his upper leg muscle. The effective perpendicular lever arm is 2.20 cm. Given the moment of inertia of the lower leg is $1.25 \text{ kg} \cdot \text{m}^2$, (a) find the angular acceleration of the leg. (b) Neglecting the gravitational force, what is the rotational kinetic energy of the leg after it has rotated through $57.3°$ (1.00 rad)?

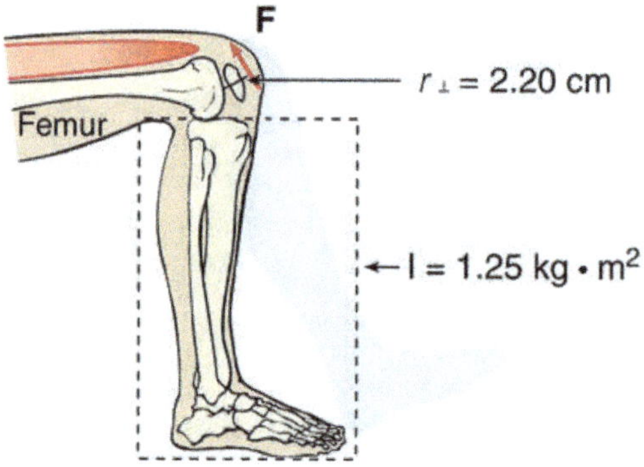

FIGURE 10.20 The muscle in the upper leg gives the lower leg an angular acceleration and imparts rotational kinetic energy to it by exerting a torque about the knee. **F** is a vector that is perpendicular to r. This example examines the situation.

Strategy

The angular acceleration can be found using the rotational analog to Newton's second law, or $\alpha = \text{net } \tau/I$. The moment of inertia I is given and the torque can be found easily from the given force and perpendicular lever arm. Once the angular acceleration α is known, the final angular velocity and rotational kinetic energy can be calculated.

Solution to (a)

From the rotational analog to Newton's second law, the angular acceleration α is

$$\alpha = \frac{\text{net } \tau}{I}. \quad 10.101$$

Because the force and the perpendicular lever arm are given and the leg is vertical so that its weight does not create a torque, the net torque is thus

$$\begin{aligned} \text{net } \tau &= r_{\perp}F \\ &= (0.0220 \text{ m})(2000 \text{ N}) \\ &= 44.0 \text{ N} \cdot \text{m}. \end{aligned} \quad 10.102$$

Substituting this value for the torque and the given value for the moment of inertia into the expression for α gives

$$\alpha = \frac{44.0 \text{ N} \cdot \text{m}}{1.25 \text{ kg} \cdot \text{m}^2} = 35.2 \text{ rad/s}^2. \quad 10.103$$

Solution to (b)

The final angular velocity can be calculated from the kinematic expression

$$\omega^2 = \omega_0{}^2 + 2\alpha\theta \quad 10.104$$

or

$$\omega^2 = 2\alpha\theta \quad 10.105$$

because the initial angular velocity is zero. The kinetic energy of rotation is

$$\text{KE}_{\text{rot}} = \frac{1}{2}I\omega^2 \quad 10.106$$

so it is most convenient to use the value of ω^2 just found and the given value for the moment of inertia. The kinetic energy is then

$$\begin{aligned} \text{KE}_{\text{rot}} &= 0.5\left(1.25 \text{ kg} \cdot \text{m}^2\right)\left(70.4 \text{ rad}^2/\text{s}^2\right) \\ &= 44.0 \text{ J} \end{aligned}. \quad 10.107$$

Discussion

These values are reasonable for a person kicking his leg starting from the position shown. The weight of the leg can be neglected in part (a) because it exerts no torque when the center of gravity of the lower leg is directly beneath the pivot in the knee. In part (b), the force exerted by the upper leg is so large that its torque is much greater than that created by the weight of the lower leg as it rotates. The rotational kinetic energy given to the lower leg is enough that it could give a ball a significant velocity by transferring some of this energy in a kick.

MAKING CONNECTIONS: CONSERVATION LAWS

Angular momentum, like energy and linear momentum, is conserved. This universally applicable law is another sign of underlying unity in physical laws. Angular momentum is conserved when net external torque is zero, just as linear momentum is conserved when the net external force is zero.

Conservation of Angular Momentum

We can now understand why Earth keeps on spinning. As we saw in the previous example, $\Delta L = (\text{net } \tau)\Delta t$. This equation means that, to change angular momentum, a torque must act over some period of time. Because Earth has a large angular momentum, a large torque acting over a long time is needed to change its rate of spin. So what external torques are there? Tidal friction exerts torque that is slowing Earth's rotation, but tens of millions of years must pass before the change is very significant. Recent research indicates the length of the day was 18 h some 900 million years ago. Only the tides exert significant retarding torques on Earth, and so it will continue to spin, although ever more slowly, for many billions of years.

What we have here is, in fact, another conservation law. If the net torque is *zero*, then angular momentum is constant or *conserved*. We can see this rigorously by considering $\text{net } \tau = \frac{\Delta L}{\Delta t}$ for the situation in which the net torque is zero. In that case,

$$\text{net}\tau = 0 \tag{10.108}$$

implying that

$$\frac{\Delta L}{\Delta t} = 0. \tag{10.109}$$

If the change in angular momentum ΔL is zero, then the angular momentum is constant; thus,

$$L = \text{constant (net } \tau = 0) \tag{10.110}$$

or

$$L = L'(\text{net}\tau = 0). \tag{10.111}$$

These expressions are the **law of conservation of angular momentum**. Conservation laws are as scarce as they are important.

An example of conservation of angular momentum is seen in Figure 10.21, in which an ice skater is executing a spin. The net torque on her is very close to zero, because there is relatively little friction between her skates and the ice and because the friction is exerted very close to the pivot point. (Both F and r are small, and so τ is negligibly small.) Consequently, she can spin for quite some time. She can do something else, too. She can increase her rate of spin by pulling her arms and legs in. Why does pulling her arms and legs in increase her rate of spin? The answer is that her angular momentum is constant, so that

$$L = L'. \tag{10.112}$$

Expressing this equation in terms of the moment of inertia,

$$I\omega = I'\omega', \tag{10.113}$$

where the primed quantities refer to conditions after she has pulled in her arms and reduced her moment of inertia. Because I' is smaller, the angular velocity ω' must increase to keep the angular momentum constant. The change can be dramatic, as the following example shows.

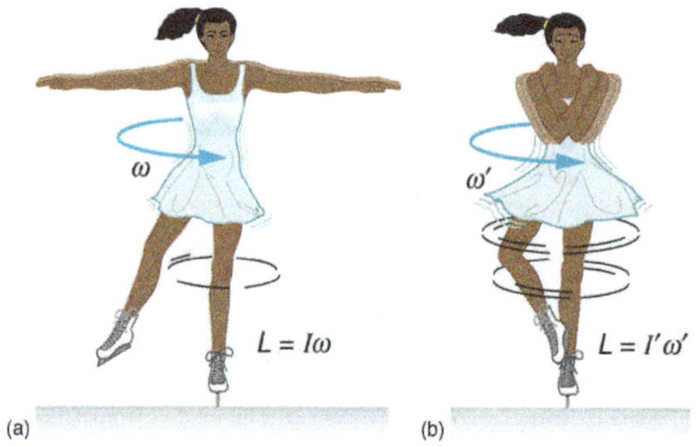

FIGURE 10.21 (a) An ice skater is spinning on the tip of her skate with her arms extended. Her angular momentum is conserved because the net torque on her is negligibly small. In the next image, her rate of spin increases greatly when she pulls in her arms, decreasing her moment of inertia. The work she does to pull in her arms results in an increase in rotational kinetic energy.

EXAMPLE 10.14

Calculating the Angular Momentum of a Spinning Skater

Suppose an ice skater, such as the one in Figure 10.21, is spinning at 0.800 rev/ s with her arms extended. She has a moment of inertia of $2.34 \text{ kg} \cdot \text{m}^2$ with her arms extended and of $0.363 \text{ kg} \cdot \text{m}^2$ with her arms close to her body. (These moments of inertia are based on reasonable assumptions about a 60.0-kg skater.) (a) What is her angular velocity in revolutions per second after she pulls in her arms? (b) What is her rotational kinetic energy before and after she does this?

Strategy

In the first part of the problem, we are looking for the skater's angular velocity ω' after she has pulled in her arms. To find this quantity, we use the conservation of angular momentum and note that the moments of inertia and initial angular velocity are given. To find the initial and final kinetic energies, we use the definition of rotational kinetic energy given by

$$\text{KE}_{\text{rot}} = \frac{1}{2}I\omega^2. \tag{10.114}$$

Solution for (a)

Because torque is negligible (as discussed above), the conservation of angular momentum given in $I\omega = I'\omega'$ is applicable. Thus,

$$L = L' \tag{10.115}$$

or

$$I\omega = I'\omega' \tag{10.116}$$

Solving for $\omega'$and substituting known values into the resulting equation gives

$$\begin{aligned} \omega' &= \frac{I}{I'}\omega = \left(\frac{2.34 \text{ kg}\cdot\text{m}^2}{0.363 \text{ kg}\cdot\text{m}^2}\right)(0.800 \text{ rev/s}) \\ &= 5.16 \text{ rev/s}. \end{aligned} \tag{10.117}$$

Solution for (b)

Rotational kinetic energy is given by

$$\text{KE}_{\text{rot}} = \frac{1}{2}I\omega^2. \tag{10.118}$$

The initial value is found by substituting known values into the equation and converting the angular velocity to rad/s:

$$\begin{aligned} \text{KE}_{\text{rot}} &= (0.5)\left(2.34 \text{ kg}\cdot\text{m}^2\right)((0.800 \text{ rev/s})(2\pi \text{ rad/rev}))^2 \\ &= 29.6 \text{ J}. \end{aligned} \tag{10.119}$$

The final rotational kinetic energy is

$$\text{KE}_{\text{rot}}' = \frac{1}{2}I'\omega'^2. \tag{10.120}$$

Substituting known values into this equation gives

$$\begin{aligned} KE_{\text{rot}}' &= (0.5)\left(0.363 \text{ kg}\cdot\text{m}^2\right)[(5.16 \text{ rev/s})(2\pi \text{ rad/rev})]^2 \\ &= 191 \text{ J}. \end{aligned} \tag{10.121}$$

Discussion

In both parts, there is an impressive increase. First, the final angular velocity is large, although most world-class skaters can achieve spin rates about this great. Second, the final kinetic energy is much greater than the initial kinetic energy. The increase in rotational kinetic energy comes from work done by the skater in pulling in her arms. This work is internal work that depletes some of the skater's food energy.

There are several other examples of objects that increase their rate of spin because something reduced their moment of inertia. Tornadoes are one example. Storm systems that create tornadoes are slowly rotating. When the radius of rotation narrows, even in a local region, angular velocity increases, sometimes to the furious level of a tornado. Earth is another example. Our planet was born from a huge cloud of gas and dust, the rotation of which came from turbulence in an even larger cloud. Gravitational forces caused the cloud to contract, and the rotation rate increased as a result. (See Figure 10.22.)

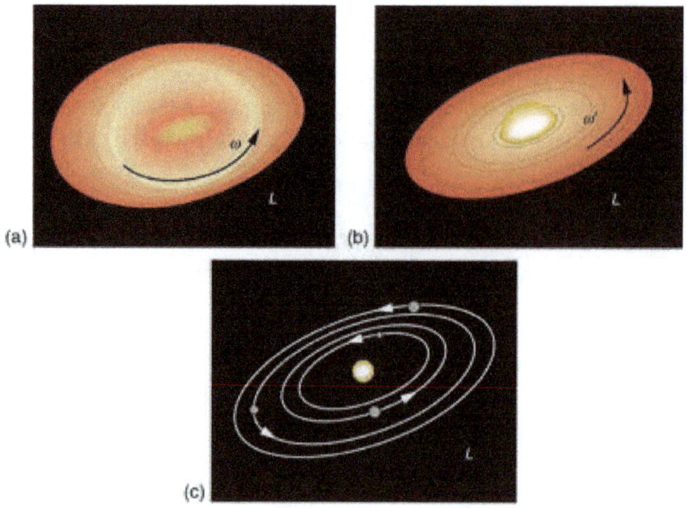

FIGURE 10.22 The Solar System coalesced from a cloud of gas and dust that was originally rotating. The orbital motions and spins of the planets are in the same direction as the original spin and conserve the angular momentum of the parent cloud.

In case of human motion, one would not expect angular momentum to be conserved when a body interacts with the environment as its foot pushes off the ground. Astronauts floating in space aboard the International Space Station have no angular momentum relative to the inside of the ship if they are motionless. Their bodies will continue to have this zero value no matter how they twist about as long as they do not give themselves a push off the side of the vessel.

CHECK YOUR UNDERSTANDING

Is angular momentum completely analogous to linear momentum? What, if any, are their differences?

Solution
Yes, angular and linear momentums are completely analogous. While they are exact analogs they have different units and are not directly inter-convertible like forms of energy are.

10.6 Collisions of Extended Bodies in Two Dimensions

LEARNING OBJECTIVES

By the end of this section, you will be able to:

- Observe collisions of extended bodies in two dimensions.
- Examine collision at the point of percussion.

Bowling pins are sent flying and spinning when hit by a bowling ball—angular momentum as well as linear momentum and energy have been imparted to the pins. (See Figure 10.23). Many collisions involve angular momentum. Cars, for example, may spin and collide on ice or a wet surface. Baseball pitchers throw curves by putting spin on the baseball. A tennis player can put a lot of top spin on the tennis ball which causes it to dive down onto the court once it crosses the net. We now take a brief look at what happens when objects that can rotate collide.

Consider the relatively simple collision shown in Figure 10.24, in which a disk strikes and adheres to an initially motionless stick nailed at one end to a frictionless surface. After the collision, the two rotate about the nail. There is an unbalanced external force on the system at the nail. This force exerts no torque because its lever arm r is zero. Angular momentum is therefore conserved in the collision. Kinetic energy is not conserved, because the collision is inelastic. It is possible that momentum is not conserved either because the force at the nail may have a component in the direction of the disk's initial velocity. Let us examine a case of rotation in a collision in Example 10.15.

FIGURE 10.23 The bowling ball causes the pins to fly, some of them spinning violently. (credit: Tinou Bao, Flickr)

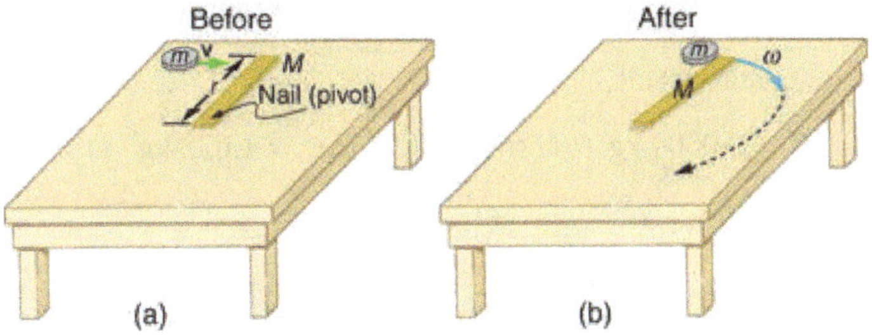

FIGURE 10.24 (a) A disk slides toward a motionless stick on a frictionless surface. (b) The disk hits the stick at one end and adheres to it, and they rotate together, pivoting around the nail. Angular momentum is conserved for this inelastic collision because the surface is frictionless and the unbalanced external force at the nail exerts no torque.

EXAMPLE 10.15

Rotation in a Collision

Suppose the disk in Figure 10.24 has a mass of 50.0 g and an initial velocity of 30.0 m/s when it strikes the stick that is 1.20 m long and 2.00 kg.

(a) What is the angular velocity of the two after the collision?

(b) What is the kinetic energy before and after the collision?

(c) What is the total linear momentum before and after the collision?

Strategy for (a)

We can answer the first question using conservation of angular momentum as noted. Because angular momentum is $I\omega$, we can solve for angular velocity.

Solution for (a)

Conservation of angular momentum states

$$L = L', \qquad (10.122)$$

where primed quantities stand for conditions after the collision and both momenta are calculated relative to the pivot point. The initial angular momentum of the system of stick-disk is that of the disk just before it strikes the stick. That is,

$$L = I\omega, \qquad (10.123)$$

where I is the moment of inertia of the disk and ω is its angular velocity around the pivot point. Now, $I = mr^2$ (taking the disk to be approximately a point mass) and $\omega = v/r$, so that

$$L = mr^2 \frac{v}{r} = mvr. \qquad (10.124)$$

After the collision,

$$L' = I'\omega'. \quad (10.125)$$

It is ω' that we wish to find. Conservation of angular momentum gives

$$I'\omega' = mvr. \quad (10.126)$$

Rearranging the equation yields

$$\omega' = \frac{mvr}{I'}, \quad (10.127)$$

where I' is the moment of inertia of the stick and disk stuck together, which is the sum of their individual moments of inertia about the nail. Figure 10.11 gives the formula for a rod rotating around one end to be $I = Mr^2/3$. Thus,

$$I' = mr^2 + \frac{Mr^2}{3} = \left(m + \frac{M}{3}\right)r^2. \quad (10.128)$$

Entering known values in this equation yields,

$$I' = (0.0500\text{ kg} + 0.667\text{ kg})(1.20\text{ m})^2 = 1.032\text{ kg}\cdot\text{m}^2. \quad (10.129)$$

The value of I' is now entered into the expression for ω', which yields

$$\begin{aligned}\omega' &= \frac{mvr}{I'} = \frac{(0.0500\text{ kg})(30.0\text{ m/s})(1.20\text{ m})}{1.032\text{ kg}\cdot\text{m}^2} \\ &= 1.744\text{ rad/s} \approx 1.74\text{ rad/s}.\end{aligned} \quad (10.130)$$

Strategy for (b)

The kinetic energy before the collision is the incoming disk's translational kinetic energy, and after the collision, it is the rotational kinetic energy of the two stuck together.

Solution for (b)

First, we calculate the translational kinetic energy by entering given values for the mass and speed of the incoming disk.

$$\text{KE} = \frac{1}{2}mv^2 = (0.500)(0.0500\text{ kg})(30.0\text{ m/s})^2 = 22.5\text{ J} \quad (10.131)$$

After the collision, the rotational kinetic energy can be found because we now know the final angular velocity and the final moment of inertia. Thus, entering the values into the rotational kinetic energy equation gives

$$\begin{aligned}\text{KE}' &= \tfrac{1}{2}I'\omega'^2 = (0.5)\left(1.032\text{ kg}\cdot\text{m}^2\right)\left(1.744\tfrac{\text{rad}}{\text{s}}\right)^2 \\ &= 1.57\text{ J}.\end{aligned} \quad (10.132)$$

Strategy for (c)

The linear momentum before the collision is that of the disk. After the collision, it is the sum of the disk's momentum and that of the center of mass of the stick.

Solution of (c)

Before the collision, then, linear momentum is

$$p = mv = (0.0500\text{ kg})(30.0\text{ m/s}) = 1.50\text{ kg}\cdot\text{m/s}. \quad (10.133)$$

After the collision, the disk and the stick's center of mass move in the same direction. The total linear momentum is that of the disk moving at a new velocity $v' = r\omega'$ plus that of the stick's center of mass,

which moves at half this speed because $v_{\text{CM}} = \left(\frac{r}{2}\right)\omega' = \frac{v'}{2}$. Thus,

$$p' = mv' + Mv_{\text{CM}} = mv' + \frac{Mv'}{2}. \quad (10.134)$$

Gathering similar terms in the equation yields,

$$p' = \left(m + \frac{M}{2}\right)v' \tag{10.135}$$

so that

$$p' = \left(m + \frac{M}{2}\right)r\omega'. \tag{10.136}$$

Substituting known values into the equation,

$$p' = (1.050 \text{ kg})(1.20 \text{ m})(1.744 \text{ rad/s}) = 2.20 \text{ kg} \cdot \text{m/s}. \tag{10.137}$$

Discussion

First note that the kinetic energy is less after the collision, as predicted, because the collision is inelastic. More surprising is that the momentum after the collision is actually greater than before the collision. This result can be understood if you consider how the nail affects the stick and vice versa. Apparently, the stick pushes backward on the nail when first struck by the disk. The nail's reaction (consistent with Newton's third law) is to push forward on the stick, imparting momentum to it in the same direction in which the disk was initially moving, thereby increasing the momentum of the system.

The above example has other implications. For example, what would happen if the disk hit very close to the nail? Obviously, a force would be exerted on the nail in the forward direction. So, when the stick is struck at the end farthest from the nail, a backward force is exerted on the nail, and when it is hit at the end nearest the nail, a forward force is exerted on the nail. Thus, striking it at a certain point in between produces no force on the nail. This intermediate point is known as the *percussion point*.

An analogous situation occurs in tennis as seen in Figure 10.25. If you hit a ball with the end of your racquet, the handle is pulled away from your hand. If you hit a ball much farther down, for example, on the shaft of the racquet, the handle is pushed into your palm. And if you hit the ball at the racquet's percussion point (what some people call the "sweet spot"), then little or *no* force is exerted on your hand, and there is less vibration, reducing chances of a tennis elbow. The same effect occurs for a baseball bat.

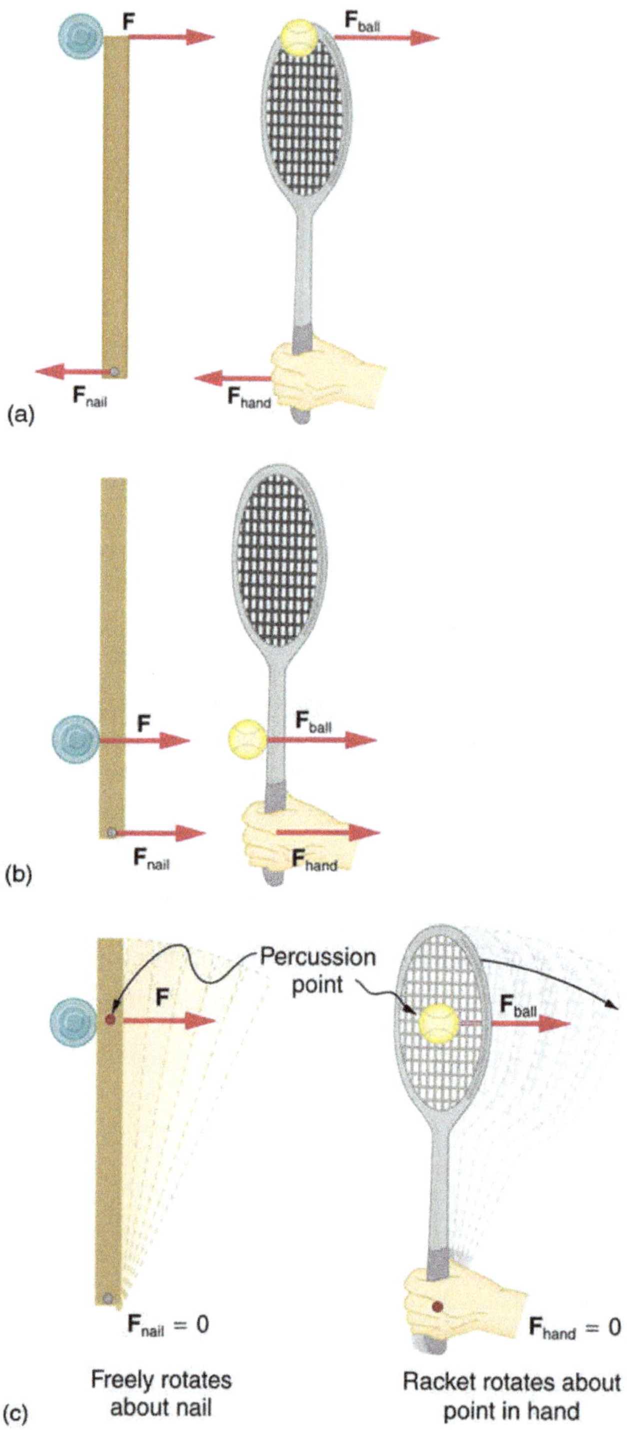

FIGURE 10.25 A disk hitting a stick is compared to a tennis ball being hit by a racquet. (a) When the ball strikes the racquet near the end, a backward force is exerted on the hand. (b) When the racquet is struck much farther down, a forward force is exerted on the hand. (c) When the racquet is struck at the percussion point, no force is delivered to the hand.

CHECK YOUR UNDERSTANDING

Is rotational kinetic energy a vector? Justify your answer.

Solution

No, energy is always scalar whether motion is involved or not. No form of energy has a direction in space and you can see that rotational kinetic energy does not depend on the direction of motion just as linear kinetic energy is independent of the direction of motion.

10.7 Gyroscopic Effects: Vector Aspects of Angular Momentum

LEARNING OBJECTIVES

By the end of this section, you will be able to:

- Describe the right-hand rule to find the direction of angular velocity, momentum, and torque.
- Explain the gyroscopic effect.
- Study how Earth acts like a gigantic gyroscope.

Angular momentum is a vector and, therefore, *has direction as well as magnitude*. Torque affects both the direction and the magnitude of angular momentum. What is the direction of the angular momentum of a rotating object like the disk in Figure 10.26? The figure shows the **right-hand rule** used to find the direction of both angular momentum and angular velocity. Both $\mathbf{L}$ and $\boldsymbol{\omega}$ are vectors—each has direction and magnitude. Both can be represented by arrows. The right-hand rule defines both to be perpendicular to the plane of rotation in the direction shown. Because angular momentum is related to angular velocity by $\mathbf{L} = I\boldsymbol{\omega}$, the direction of $\mathbf{L}$ is the same as the direction of $\boldsymbol{\omega}$. Notice in the figure that both point along the axis of rotation.

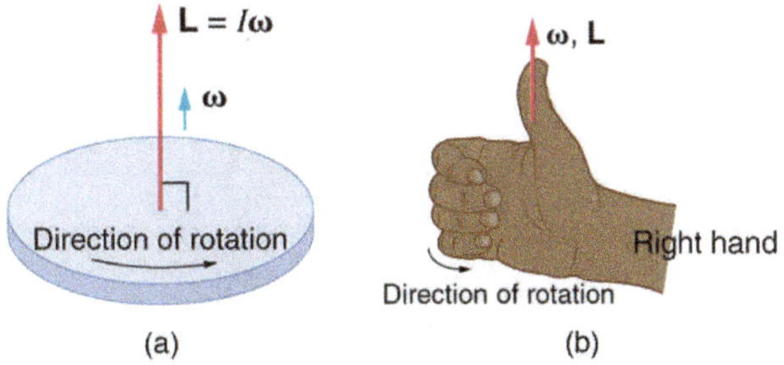

FIGURE 10.26 Figure (a) shows a disk is rotating counterclockwise when viewed from above. Figure (b) shows the right-hand rule. The direction of angular velocity $\boldsymbol{\omega}$ size and angular momentum $\mathbf{L}$ are defined to be the direction in which the thumb of your right hand points when you curl your fingers in the direction of the disk's rotation as shown.

Now, recall that torque changes angular momentum as expressed by

$$\text{net } \boldsymbol{\tau} = \frac{\Delta \mathbf{L}}{\Delta t}. \tag{10.138}$$

This equation means that the direction of $\Delta\mathbf{L}$ is the same as the direction of the torque $\boldsymbol{\tau}$ that creates it. This result is illustrated in Figure 10.27, which shows the direction of torque and the angular momentum it creates.

Let us now consider a bicycle wheel with a couple of handles attached to it, as shown in Figure 10.28. (This device is popular in demonstrations among physicists, because it does unexpected things.) With the wheel rotating as shown, its angular momentum is to the woman's left. Suppose the person holding the wheel tries to rotate it as in the figure. Her natural expectation is that the wheel will rotate in the direction she pushes it—but what happens is quite different. The forces exerted create a torque that is horizontal toward the person, as shown in Figure 10.28(a). This torque creates a change in angular momentum $\mathbf{L}$ in the same direction, perpendicular to the original angular momentum $\mathbf{L}$, thus changing the direction of $\mathbf{L}$ but not the magnitude of $\mathbf{L}$. Figure 10.28 shows how $\Delta\mathbf{L}$ and $\mathbf{L}$ add, giving a new angular momentum with direction that is inclined more toward the person than before. The axis of the wheel has thus moved *perpendicular to the forces exerted on it*, instead of in the expected direction.

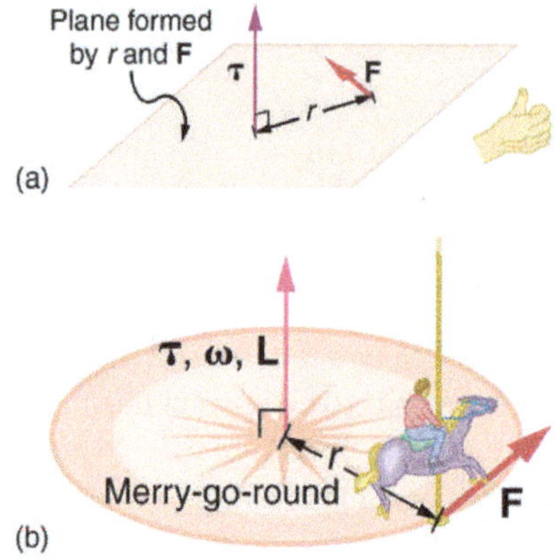

FIGURE 10.27 In figure (a), the torque is perpendicular to the plane formed by r and $\mathbf{F}$ and is the direction your right thumb would point to if you curled your fingers in the direction of $\mathbf{F}$. Figure (b) shows that the direction of the torque is the same as that of the angular momentum it produces.

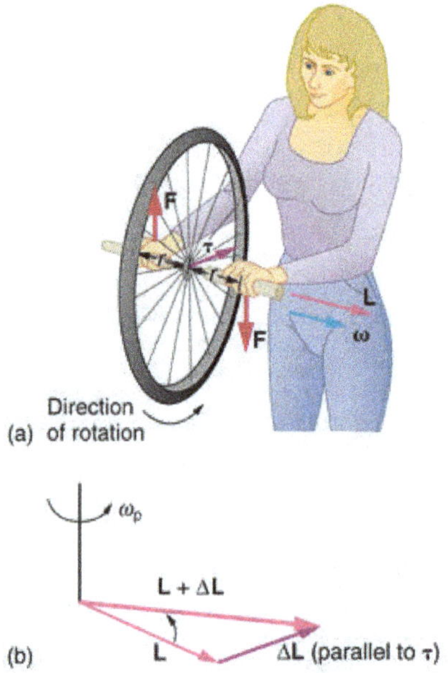

FIGURE 10.28 In figure (a), a person holding the spinning bike wheel lifts it with her right hand and pushes down with her left hand in an attempt to rotate the wheel. This action creates a torque directly toward her. This torque causes a change in angular momentum $\Delta \mathbf{L}$ in exactly the same direction. Figure (b) shows a vector diagram depicting how $\Delta \mathbf{L}$ and $\mathbf{L}$ add, producing a new angular momentum pointing more toward the person. The wheel moves toward the person, perpendicular to the forces she exerts on it.

This same logic explains the behavior of gyroscopes. Figure 10.29 shows the two forces acting on a spinning gyroscope. The torque produced is perpendicular to the angular momentum, thus the direction of the torque is changed, but not its magnitude. The gyroscope *precesses* around a vertical axis, since the torque is always horizontal and perpendicular to $\mathbf{L}$. If the gyroscope is *not* spinning, it acquires angular momentum in the direction of the torque ($\mathbf{L} = \Delta \mathbf{L}$), and it rotates around a horizontal axis, falling over just as we would expect.

Earth itself acts like a gigantic gyroscope. Its angular momentum is along its axis and points at Polaris, the North Star. But Earth is slowly precessing (once in about 26,000 years) due to the torque of the Sun and the Moon on its nonspherical shape.

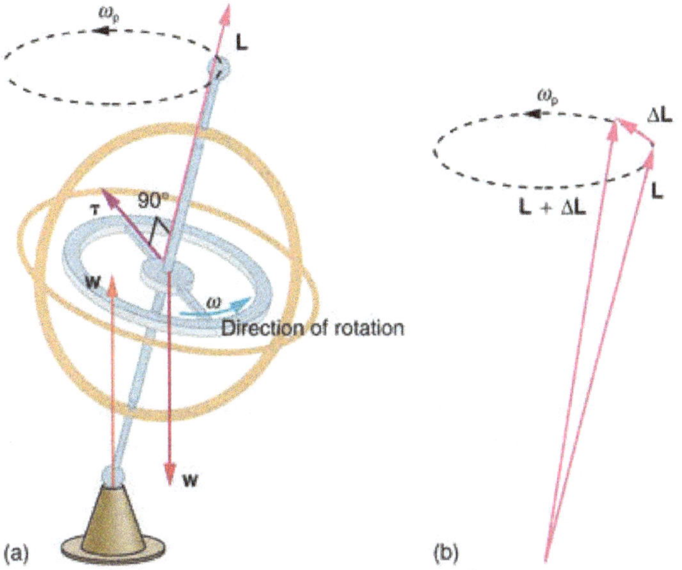

FIGURE 10.29 As seen in figure (a), the forces on a spinning gyroscope are its weight and the supporting force from the stand. These forces create a horizontal torque on the gyroscope, which create a change in angular momentum $\mathbf{\Delta L}$ that is also horizontal. In figure (b), $\mathbf{\Delta L}$ and $\mathbf{L}$ add to produce a new angular momentum with the same magnitude, but different direction, so that the gyroscope precesses in the direction shown instead of falling over.

CHECK YOUR UNDERSTANDING

Rotational kinetic energy is associated with angular momentum? Does that mean that rotational kinetic energy is a vector?

Solution

No, energy is always a scalar whether motion is involved or not. No form of energy has a direction in space and you can see that rotational kinetic energy does not depend on the direction of motion just as linear kinetic energy is independent of the direction of motion.

Glossary

angular acceleration the rate of change of angular velocity with time

angular momentum the product of moment of inertia and angular velocity

change in angular velocity the difference between final and initial values of angular velocity

kinematics of rotational motion describes the relationships among rotation angle, angular velocity, angular acceleration, and time

law of conservation of angular momentum angular momentum is conserved, i.e., the initial angular momentum is equal to the final angular momentum when no external torque is applied to the system

moment of inertia mass times the square of perpendicular distance from the rotation axis; for a point mass, it is $I = mr^2$ and, because any object can be built up from a collection of point masses, this relationship is the basis for all other moments of inertia

right-hand rule direction of angular velocity ω and angular momentum L in which the thumb of your right hand points when you curl your fingers in the direction of the disk's rotation

rotational inertia resistance to change of rotation. The more rotational inertia an object has, the harder it is to rotate

rotational kinetic energy the kinetic energy due to the rotation of an object. This is part of its total kinetic energy

tangential acceleration the acceleration in a direction tangent to the circle at the point of interest in circular motion

torque the turning effectiveness of a force

work-energy theorem if one or more external forces act upon a rigid object, causing its kinetic energy to change from KE_1 to KE_2, then the work W done by the net force is equal to the change in kinetic energy

Section Summary

10.1 Angular Acceleration

- Uniform circular motion is the motion with a constant angular velocity $\omega = \frac{\Delta\theta}{\Delta t}$.
- In non-uniform circular motion, the velocity changes with time and the rate of change of angular velocity (i.e. angular acceleration) is $\alpha = \frac{\Delta\omega}{\Delta t}$.
- Linear or tangential acceleration refers to changes in the magnitude of velocity but not its direction, given as $a_{\mathrm{t}} = \frac{\Delta v}{\Delta t}$.
- For circular motion, note that $v = r\omega$, so that
$$a_{\mathrm{t}} = \frac{\Delta(r\omega)}{\Delta t}.$$
- The radius r is constant for circular motion, and so $\Delta(r\omega) = r\Delta\omega$. Thus,
$$a_{\mathrm{t}} = r\frac{\Delta\omega}{\Delta t}.$$
- By definition, $\Delta\omega/\Delta t = \alpha$. Thus,
$$a_{\mathrm{t}} = r\alpha$$
or
$$\alpha = \frac{a_{\mathrm{t}}}{r}.$$

10.2 Kinematics of Rotational Motion

- Kinematics is the description of motion.
- The kinematics of rotational motion describes the relationships among rotation angle, angular velocity, angular acceleration, and time.
- Starting with the four kinematic equations we developed in the One-Dimensional Kinematics, we can derive the four rotational kinematic equations (presented together with their translational counterparts) seen in Table 10.2.
- In these equations, the subscript 0 denotes initial values (x_0 and t_0 are initial values), and the average angular velocity $\overline{\omega}$ and average velocity $\overline{v}$ are defined as follows:
$$\overline{\omega} = \frac{\omega_0 + \omega}{2} \text{ and } \overline{v} = \frac{v_0 + v}{2}.$$

10.3 Dynamics of Rotational Motion: Rotational Inertia

- The farther the force is applied from the pivot, the greater is the angular acceleration; angular acceleration is inversely proportional to mass.
- If we exert a force F on a point mass m that is at a distance r from a pivot point and because the force is perpendicular to r, an acceleration $a = F/m$ is obtained in the direction of F. We can rearrange this equation such that
$F = ma$,
and then look for ways to relate this expression to expressions for rotational quantities. We note that $a = r\alpha$, and we substitute this expression into $F = ma$, yielding

$F = mr\alpha$
- Torque is the turning effectiveness of a force. In this case, because F is perpendicular to r, torque is simply $\tau = rF$. If we multiply both sides of the equation above by r, we get torque on the left-

hand side. That is,
$rF = mr^2\alpha$
or

$\tau = mr^2\alpha.$

- The moment of inertia I of an object is the sum of MR^2 for all the point masses of which it is composed. That is,
$I = \sum mr^2.$
- The general relationship among torque, moment of inertia, and angular acceleration is
$\tau = I\alpha$
or

$\alpha = \frac{\text{net }\tau}{I}.$

10.4 Rotational Kinetic Energy: Work and Energy Revisited

- The rotational kinetic energy KE_{rot} for an object with a moment of inertia I and an angular velocity ω is given by
$KE_{rot} = \frac{1}{2}I\omega^2.$
- Helicopters store large amounts of rotational kinetic energy in their blades. This energy must be put into the blades before takeoff and maintained until the end of the flight. The engines do not have enough power to simultaneously provide lift and put significant rotational energy into the blades.
- Work and energy in rotational motion are completely analogous to work and energy in translational motion.
- The equation for the **work-energy theorem** for rotational motion is,
$\text{net }W = \frac{1}{2}I\omega^2 - \frac{1}{2}I\omega_0{}^2.$

10.5 Angular Momentum and Its Conservation

- Every rotational phenomenon has a direct translational analog , likewise angular momentum L can be defined as $L = I\omega$.
- This equation is an analog to the definition of linear momentum as $p = mv$. The relationship between torque and angular momentum is
$\text{net }\tau = \frac{\Delta L}{\Delta t}.$
- Angular momentum, like energy and linear momentum, is conserved. This universally applicable law is another sign of underlying unity in physical laws. Angular momentum is conserved when net external torque is zero, just as linear momentum is conserved when the net external force is zero.

10.6 Collisions of Extended Bodies in Two Dimensions

- Angular momentum L is analogous to linear momentum and is given by $L = I\omega$.
- Angular momentum is changed by torque, following the relationship $\text{net }\tau = \frac{\Delta L}{\Delta t}$.
- Angular momentum is conserved if the net torque is zero $L = \text{constant }(\text{net }\tau = 0)$ or $L = L'\ (\text{net }\tau = 0)$. This equation is known as the law of conservation of angular momentum, which may be conserved in collisions.

10.7 Gyroscopic Effects: Vector Aspects of Angular Momentum

- Torque is perpendicular to the plane formed by r and $\mathbf{F}$ and is the direction your right thumb would point if you curled the fingers of your right hand in the direction of $\mathbf{F}$. The direction of the torque is thus the same as that of the angular momentum it produces.
- The gyroscope precesses around a vertical axis, since the torque is always horizontal and perpendicular to $\mathbf{L}$. If the gyroscope is not spinning, it acquires angular momentum in the direction of the torque ($\mathbf{L} = \Delta\mathbf{L}$), and it rotates about a horizontal axis, falling over just as we would expect.
- Earth itself acts like a gigantic gyroscope. Its angular momentum is along its axis and points at Polaris, the North Star.

Conceptual Questions

10.1 Angular Acceleration

1. Analogies exist between rotational and translational physical quantities. Identify the rotational term analogous to each of the following: acceleration, force, mass, work, translational kinetic energy, linear momentum, impulse.

2. Explain why centripetal acceleration changes the direction of velocity in circular motion but not its magnitude.

3. In circular motion, a tangential acceleration can change the magnitude of the velocity but not its direction. Explain your answer.

4. Suppose a piece of food is on the edge of a rotating

microwave oven plate. Does it experience nonzero tangential acceleration, centripetal acceleration, or both when: (a) The plate starts to spin? (b) The plate rotates at constant angular velocity? (c) The plate slows to a halt?

10.3 Dynamics of Rotational Motion: Rotational Inertia

5. The moment of inertia of a long rod spun around an axis through one end perpendicular to its length is $ML^2/3$. Why is this moment of inertia greater than it would be if you spun a point mass M at the location of the center of mass of the rod (at $L/2$)? (That would be $ML^2/4$.)

6. Why is the moment of inertia of a hoop that has a mass M and a radius R greater than the moment of inertia of a disk that has the same mass and radius? Why is the moment of inertia of a spherical shell that has a mass M and a radius R greater than that of a solid sphere that has the same mass and radius?

7. Give an example in which a small force exerts a large torque. Give another example in which a large force exerts a small torque.

8. While reducing the mass of a racing bike, the greatest benefit is realized from reducing the mass of the tires and wheel rims. Why does this allow a racer to achieve greater accelerations than would an identical reduction in the mass of the bicycle's frame?

FIGURE 10.30 The image shows a side view of a racing bicycle. Can you see evidence in the design of the wheels on this racing bicycle that their moment of inertia has been purposely reduced? (credit: Jesús Rodriguez)

9. A ball slides up a frictionless ramp. It is then rolled without slipping and with the same initial velocity up another frictionless ramp (with the same slope angle). In which case does it reach a greater height, and why?

10.4 Rotational Kinetic Energy: Work and Energy Revisited

10. Describe the energy transformations involved when a yo-yo is thrown downward and then climbs back up its string to be caught in the user's hand.

11. What energy transformations are involved when a dragster engine is revved, its clutch let out rapidly, its tires spun, and it starts to accelerate forward? Describe the source and transformation of energy at each step.

12. The Earth has more rotational kinetic energy now than did the cloud of gas and dust from which it formed. Where did this energy come from?

FIGURE 10.31 An immense cloud of rotating gas and dust contracted under the influence of gravity to form the Earth and in the process rotational kinetic energy increased. (credit: NASA)

10.5 Angular Momentum and Its Conservation

13. When you start the engine of your car with the transmission in neutral, you notice that the car rocks in the opposite sense of the engine's rotation. Explain in terms of conservation of angular momentum. Is the angular momentum of the car conserved for long (for more than a few seconds)?

14. Suppose a child walks from the outer edge of a rotating merry-go round to the inside. Does the angular velocity of the merry-go-round increase, decrease, or remain the same? Explain your answer.

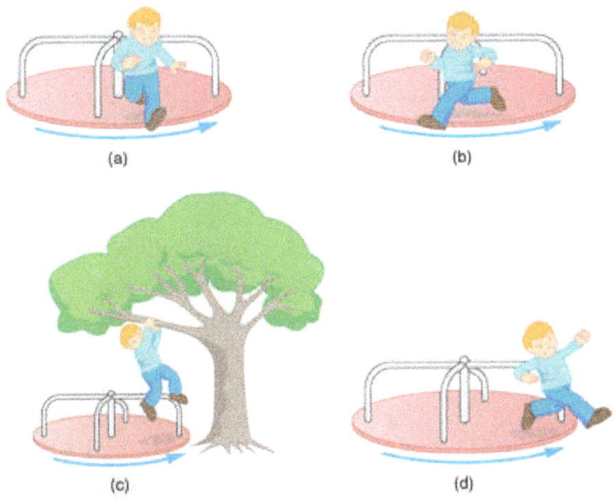

FIGURE 10.32 A child may jump off a merry-go-round in a variety of directions.

15. Suppose a child gets off a rotating merry-go-round. Does the angular velocity of the merry-go-round increase, decrease, or remain the same if: (a) He jumps off radially? (b) He jumps backward to land motionless? (c) He jumps straight up and hangs onto an overhead tree branch? (d) He jumps off forward, tangential to the edge? Explain your answers. (Refer to Figure 10.32).

16. Helicopters have a small propeller on their tail to keep them from rotating in the opposite direction of their main lifting blades. Explain in terms of Newton's third law why the helicopter body rotates in the opposite direction to the blades.

17. Whenever a helicopter has two sets of lifting blades, they rotate in opposite directions (and there will be no tail propeller). Explain why it is best to have the blades rotate in opposite directions.

18. Describe how work is done by a skater pulling in her arms during a spin. In particular, identify the force she exerts on each arm to pull it in and the distance each moves, noting that a component of the force is in the direction moved. Why is angular momentum not increased by this action?

19. When there is a global heating trend on Earth, the atmosphere expands and the length of the day increases very slightly. Explain why the length of a day increases.

20. Nearly all conventional piston engines have flywheels on them to smooth out engine vibrations caused by the thrust of individual piston firings. Why does the flywheel have this effect?

21. Jet turbines spin rapidly. They are designed to fly apart if something makes them seize suddenly, rather than transfer angular momentum to the plane's wing, possibly tearing it off. Explain how flying apart conserves angular momentum without transferring it to the wing.

22. An astronaut tightens a bolt on a satellite in orbit. He rotates in a direction opposite to that of the bolt, and the satellite rotates in the same direction as the bolt. Explain why. If a handhold is available on the satellite, can this counter-rotation be prevented? Explain your answer.

23. Competitive divers pull their limbs in and curl up their bodies when they do flips. Just before entering the water, they fully extend their limbs to enter straight down. Explain the effect of both actions on their angular velocities. Also explain the effect on their angular momenta.

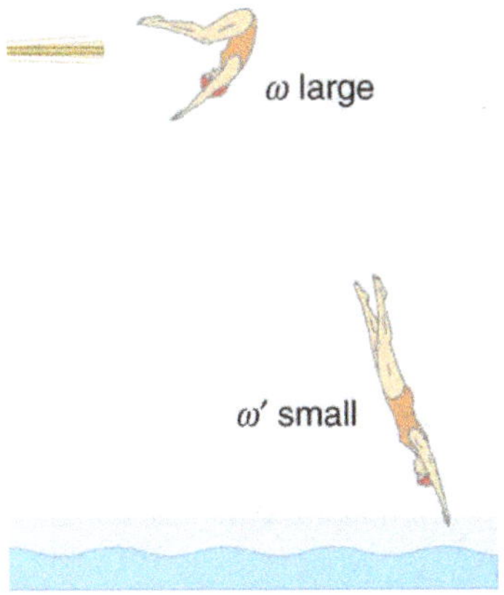

FIGURE 10.33 The diver spins rapidly when curled up and slows when she extends her limbs before entering the water.

24. Draw a free body diagram to show how a diver gains angular momentum when leaving the diving board.

25. In terms of angular momentum, what is the advantage of giving a football or a rifle bullet a spin when throwing or releasing it?

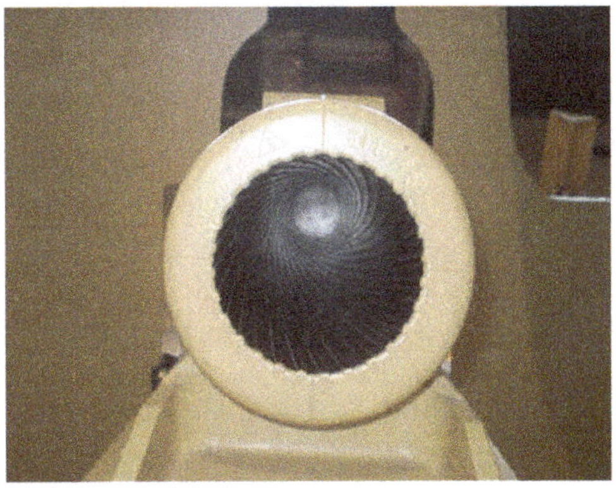

FIGURE 10.34 The image shows a view down the barrel of a

cannon, emphasizing its rifling. Rifling in the barrel of a canon causes the projectile to spin just as is the case for rifles (hence the name for the grooves in the barrel). (credit: Elsie esq., Flickr)

10.6 Collisions of Extended Bodies in Two Dimensions

26. Describe two different collisions—one in which angular momentum is conserved, and the other in which it is not. Which condition determines whether or not angular momentum is conserved in a collision?

27. Suppose an ice hockey puck strikes a hockey stick that lies flat on the ice and is free to move in any direction. Which quantities are likely to be conserved: angular momentum, linear momentum, or kinetic energy (assuming the puck and stick are very resilient)?

28. While driving his motorcycle at highway speed, a physics student notices that pulling back lightly on the right handlebar tips the cycle to the left and produces a left turn. Explain why this happens.

10.7 Gyroscopic Effects: Vector Aspects of Angular Momentum

29. While driving his motorcycle at highway speed, a physics student notices that pulling back lightly on the right handlebar tips the cycle to the left and produces a left turn. Explain why this happens.

30. Gyroscopes used in guidance systems to indicate directions in space must have an angular momentum that does not change in direction. Yet they are often subjected to large forces and accelerations. How can the direction of their angular momentum be constant when they are accelerated?

Problems & Exercises

10.1 Angular Acceleration

1. At its peak, a tornado is 60.0 m in diameter and carries 500 km/h winds. What is its angular velocity in revolutions per second?

2. Integrated Concepts
An ultracentrifuge accelerates from rest to 100,000 rpm in 2.00 min. (a) What is its angular acceleration in rad/s^2? (b) What is the tangential acceleration of a point 9.50 cm from the axis of rotation? (c) What is the radial acceleration in m/s^2 and multiples of g of this point at full rpm?

3. Integrated Concepts
You have a grindstone (a disk) that is 90.0 kg, has a 0.340-m radius, and is turning at 90.0 rpm, and you press a steel axe against it with a radial force of 20.0 N. (a) Assuming the kinetic coefficient of friction between steel and stone is 0.20, calculate the angular acceleration of the grindstone. (b) How many turns will the stone make before coming to rest?

4. Unreasonable Results
You are told that a basketball player spins the ball with an angular acceleration of $100\ \text{rad/s}^2$. (a) What is the ball's final angular velocity if the ball starts from rest and the acceleration lasts 2.00 s? (b) What is unreasonable about the result? (c) Which premises are unreasonable or inconsistent?

10.2 Kinematics of Rotational Motion

5. With the aid of a string, a gyroscope is accelerated from rest to 32 rad/s in 0.40 s.
(a) What is its angular acceleration in rad/s^2?
(b) How many revolutions does it go through in the process?

6. Suppose a piece of dust finds itself on a CD. If the spin rate of the CD is 500 rpm, and the piece of dust is 4.3 cm from the center, what is the total distance traveled by the dust in 3 minutes? (Ignore accelerations due to getting the CD rotating.)

7. A gyroscope slows from an initial rate of 32.0 rad/s at a rate of $0.700\ \text{rad/s}^2$.
(a) How long does it take to come to rest?
(b) How many revolutions does it make before stopping?

8. During a very quick stop, a car decelerates at $7.00\ \text{m/s}^2$.
(a) What is the angular acceleration of its 0.280-m-radius tires, assuming they do not slip on the pavement?
(b) How many revolutions do the tires make before coming to rest, given their initial angular velocity is $95.0\ \text{rad/s}$?
(c) How long does the car take to stop completely?
(d) What distance does the car travel in this time?
(e) What was the car's initial velocity?
(f) Do the values obtained seem reasonable, considering that this stop happens very quickly?

FIGURE 10.35 Yo-yos are amusing toys that display significant physics and are engineered to enhance performance based on physical laws. (credit: Beyond Neon, Flickr)

9. Everyday application: Suppose a yo-yo has a center shaft that has a 0.250 cm radius and that its string is being pulled.
(a) If the string is stationary and the yo-yo accelerates away from it at a rate of $1.50\ \mathrm{m/s^2}$, what is the angular acceleration of the yo-yo?
(b) What is the angular velocity after 0.750 s if it starts from rest?
(c) The outside radius of the yo-yo is 3.50 cm. What is the tangential acceleration of a point on its edge?

10.3 Dynamics of Rotational Motion: Rotational Inertia

10. This problem considers additional aspects of example Calculating the Effect of Mass Distribution on a Merry-Go-Round. (a) How long does it take the father to give the merry-go-round an angular velocity of 1.50 rad/s? (b) How many revolutions must he go through to generate this velocity? (c) If he exerts a slowing force of 300 N at a radius of 1.35 m, how long would it take him to stop them?

11. Calculate the moment of inertia of a skater given the following information. (a) The 60.0-kg skater is approximated as a cylinder that has a 0.110-m radius. (b) The skater with arms extended is approximately a cylinder that is 52.5 kg, has a 0.110-m radius, and has two 0.900-m-long arms which are 3.75 kg each and extend straight out from the cylinder like rods rotated about their ends.

12. The triceps muscle in the back of the upper arm extends the forearm. This muscle in a professional boxer exerts a force of $2.00 \times 10^3\ \mathrm{N}$ with an effective perpendicular lever arm of 3.00 cm, producing an angular acceleration of the forearm of $120\ \mathrm{rad/s^2}$. What is the moment of inertia of the boxer's forearm?

13. A soccer player extends her lower leg in a kicking motion by exerting a force with the muscle above the knee in the front of her leg. She produces an angular acceleration of $30.00\ \mathrm{rad/s^2}$ and her lower leg has a moment of inertia of $0.750\ \mathrm{kg \cdot m^2}$. What is the force exerted by the muscle if its effective perpendicular lever arm is 1.90 cm?

14. Suppose you exert a force of 180 N tangential to a 0.280-m-radius 75.0-kg grindstone (a solid disk). (a)What torque is exerted? (b) What is the angular acceleration assuming negligible opposing friction? (c) What is the angular acceleration if there is an opposing frictional force of 20.0 N exerted 1.50 cm from the axis?

15. Consider the 12.0 kg motorcycle wheel shown in Figure 10.36. Assume it to be approximately an annular ring with an inner radius of 0.280 m and an outer radius of 0.330 m. The motorcycle is on its center stand, so that the wheel can spin freely. (a) If the drive chain exerts a force of 2200 N at a radius of 5.00 cm, what is the angular acceleration of the wheel? (b) What is the tangential acceleration of a point on the outer edge of the tire? (c) How long, starting from rest, does it take to reach an angular velocity of 80.0 rad/s?

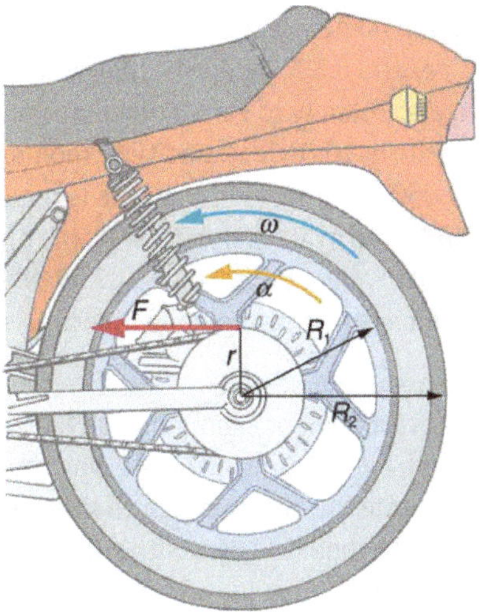

FIGURE 10.36 A motorcycle wheel has a moment of inertia approximately that of an annular ring.

16. Zorch, an archenemy of Superman, decides to slow Earth's rotation to once per 28.0 h by exerting an opposing force at and parallel to the equator. Superman is not immediately concerned, because he knows Zorch can only exert a force of $4.00 \times 10^7\ \mathrm{N}$ (a little greater than a Saturn V rocket's thrust). How long must Zorch push with this force to accomplish his goal? (This period gives Superman time to devote to other villains.)

Explicitly show how you follow the steps found in Problem-Solving Strategy for Rotational Dynamics.

17. An automobile engine can produce 200 N • m of torque. Calculate the angular acceleration produced if 95.0% of this torque is applied to the drive shaft, axle, and rear wheels of a car, given the following information. The car is suspended so that the wheels can turn freely. Each wheel acts like a 15.0 kg disk that has a 0.180 m radius. The walls of each tire act like a 2.00-kg annular ring that has inside radius of 0.180 m and outside radius of 0.320 m. The tread of each tire acts like a 10.0-kg hoop of radius 0.330 m. The 14.0-kg axle acts like a rod that has a 2.00-cm radius. The 30.0-kg drive shaft acts like a rod that has a 3.20-cm radius.

18. Starting with the formula for the moment of inertia of a rod rotated around an axis through one end perpendicular to its length $\left(I = M\ell^2/3\right)$, prove that the moment of inertia of a rod rotated about an axis through its center perpendicular to its length is $I = M\ell^2/12$. You will find the graphics in Figure 10.11 useful in visualizing these rotations.

19. Unreasonable Results
A gymnast doing a forward flip lands on the mat and exerts a 500-N • m torque to slow their angular velocity to zero. Their initial angular velocity is 10.0 rad/s, and their moment of inertia is $0.050\ \text{kg} \cdot \text{m}^2$. (a) What time is required for the gymnast to exactly stop their spin? (b) What is unreasonable about the result? (c) Which premises are unreasonable or inconsistent?

20. Unreasonable Results
An advertisement claims that an 800-kg car is aided by its 20.0-kg flywheel, which can accelerate the car from rest to a speed of 30.0 m/s. The flywheel is a disk with a 0.150-m radius. (a) Calculate the angular velocity the flywheel must have if 95.0% of its rotational energy is used to get the car up to speed. (b) What is unreasonable about the result? (c) Which premise is unreasonable or which premises are inconsistent?

10.4 Rotational Kinetic Energy: Work and Energy Revisited

21. This problem considers energy and work aspects of Example 10.7—use data from that example as needed. (a) Calculate the rotational kinetic energy in the merry-go-round plus child when they have an angular velocity of 20.0 rpm. (b) Using energy considerations, find the number of revolutions the father will have to push to achieve this angular velocity starting from rest. (c) Again, using energy considerations, calculate the force the father must exert to stop the merry-go-round in two revolutions

22. What is the final velocity of a hoop that rolls without slipping down a 5.00-m-high hill, starting from rest?

23. (a) Calculate the rotational kinetic energy of Earth on its axis. (b) What is the rotational kinetic energy of Earth in its orbit around the Sun?

24. Calculate the rotational kinetic energy in the motorcycle wheel (Figure 10.36) if its angular velocity is 120 rad/s. Assume M = 12.0 kg, R_1 = 0.280 m, and R_2 = 0.330 m.

25. A baseball pitcher throws the ball in a motion where there is rotation of the forearm about the elbow joint as well as other movements. If the linear velocity of the ball relative to the elbow joint is 20.0 m/s at a distance of 0.480 m from the joint and the moment of inertia of the forearm is $0.500\ \text{kg} \cdot \text{m}^2$, what is the rotational kinetic energy of the forearm?

26. While punting a football, a kicker rotates her leg about the hip joint. The moment of inertia of the leg is $3.75\ \text{kg} \cdot \text{m}^2$ and its rotational kinetic energy is 175 J. (a) What is the angular velocity of the leg? (b) What is the velocity of tip of the punter's shoe if it is 1.05 m from the hip joint? (c) Explain how the football can be given a velocity greater than the tip of the shoe (necessary for a decent kick distance).

27. A bus contains a 1500 kg flywheel (a disk that has a 0.600 m radius) and has a total mass of 10,000 kg. (a) Calculate the angular velocity the flywheel must have to contain enough energy to take the bus from rest to a speed of 20.0 m/s, assuming 90.0% of the rotational kinetic energy can be transformed into translational energy. (b) How high a hill can the bus climb with this stored energy and still have a speed of 3.00 m/s at the top of the hill? Explicitly show how you follow the steps in the Problem-Solving Strategy for Rotational Energy.

28. A ball with an initial velocity of 8.00 m/s rolls up a hill without slipping. Treating the ball as a spherical shell, calculate the vertical height it reaches. (b) Repeat the calculation for the same ball if it slides up the hill without rolling.

29. While exercising in a fitness center, a man lies face down on a bench and lifts a weight with one lower leg by contacting the muscles in the back of the upper leg. (a) Find the angular acceleration produced given the mass lifted is 10.0 kg at a distance of 28.0 cm from the knee joint, the moment of inertia of the lower leg is $0.900 \text{ kg} \cdot \text{m}^2$, the muscle force is 1500 N, and its effective perpendicular lever arm is 3.00 cm. (b) How much work is done if the leg rotates through an angle of 20.0° with a constant force exerted by the muscle?

30. To develop muscle tone, a woman lifts a 2.00-kg weight held in her hand. She uses her biceps muscle to flex the lower arm through an angle of 60.0°. (a) What is the angular acceleration if the weight is 24.0 cm from the elbow joint, her forearm has a moment of inertia of $0.250 \text{ kg} \cdot \text{m}^2$, and the net force she exerts is 750 N at an effective perpendicular lever arm of 2.00 cm? (b) How much work does she do?

31. Consider two cylinders that start down identical inclines from rest except that one is frictionless. Thus one cylinder rolls without slipping, while the other slides frictionlessly without rolling. They both travel a short distance at the bottom and then start up another incline. (a) Show that they both reach the same height on the other incline, and that this height is equal to their original height. (b) Find the ratio of the time the rolling cylinder takes to reach the height on the second incline to the time the sliding cylinder takes to reach the height on the second incline. (c) Explain why the time for the rolling motion is greater than that for the sliding motion.

32. What is the moment of inertia of an object that rolls without slipping down a 2.00-m-high incline starting from rest, and has a final velocity of 6.00 m/s? Express the moment of inertia as a multiple of MR^2, where M is the mass of the object and R is its radius.

33. Suppose a 200-kg motorcycle has two wheels like, the one described in Problem 10.15 and is heading toward a hill at a speed of 30.0 m/s. (a) How high can it coast up the hill, if you neglect friction? (b) How much energy is lost to friction if the motorcycle only gains an altitude of 35.0 m before coming to rest?

34. In softball, the pitcher throws with the arm fully extended (straight at the elbow). In a fast pitch the ball leaves the hand with a speed of 139 km/h. (a) Find the rotational kinetic energy of the pitcher's arm and ball together given that the arm's moment of inertia is $0.720 \text{ kg} \cdot \text{m}^2$ and the ball leaves the hand at a distance of 0.600 m from the pivot at the shoulder. (b) What force did the muscles exert to cause the arm to rotate if their effective perpendicular lever arm is 4.00 cm and the ball is 0.156 kg?

35. Construct Your Own Problem
Consider the work done by a spinning skater pulling his arms in to increase his rate of spin. Construct a problem in which you calculate the work done with a "force multiplied by distance" calculation and compare it to the skater's increase in kinetic energy.

10.5 Angular Momentum and Its Conservation

36. (a) Calculate the angular momentum of the Earth in its orbit around the Sun.
(b) Compare this angular momentum with the angular momentum of Earth on its axis.

37. (a) What is the angular momentum of the Moon in its orbit around Earth?
(b) How does this angular momentum compare with the angular momentum of the Moon on its axis? Remember that the Moon keeps one side toward Earth at all times.
(c) Discuss whether the values found in parts (a) and (b) seem consistent with the fact that tidal effects with Earth have caused the Moon to rotate with one side always facing Earth.

38. Suppose you start an antique car by exerting a force of 300 N on its crank for 0.250 s. What angular momentum is given to the engine if the handle of the crank is 0.300 m from the pivot and the force is exerted to create maximum torque the entire time?

39. A playground merry-go-round has a mass of 120 kg and a radius of 1.80 m and it is rotating with an angular velocity of 0.500 rev/s. What is its angular velocity after a 22.0-kg child gets onto it by grabbing its outer edge? The child is initially at rest.

40. Three children are riding on the edge of a merry-go-round that is 100 kg, has a 1.60-m radius, and is spinning at 20.0 rpm. The children have masses of 22.0, 28.0, and 33.0 kg. If the child who has a mass of 28.0 kg moves to the center of the merry-go-round, what is the new angular velocity in rpm?

41. (a) Calculate the angular momentum of an ice skater spinning at 6.00 rev/s given his moment of inertia is $0.400 \text{ kg} \cdot \text{m}^2$. (b) He reduces his rate of spin (his angular velocity) by extending his arms and increasing his moment of inertia. Find the value of his moment of inertia if his angular velocity decreases to 1.25 rev/s. (c) Suppose instead he keeps his arms in and allows friction of the ice to slow him to 3.00 rev/s. What average torque was exerted if this takes 15.0 s?

42. Construct Your Own Problem Consider the Earth-Moon system. Construct a problem in which you calculate the total angular momentum of the system including the spins of the Earth and the Moon on their axes and the orbital angular momentum of the Earth-Moon system in its nearly monthly rotation. Calculate what happens to the Moon's orbital radius if the Earth's rotation decreases due to tidal drag. Among the things to be considered are the amount by which the Earth's rotation slows and the fact that the Moon will continue to have one side always facing the Earth.

10.6 Collisions of Extended Bodies in Two Dimensions

43. Repeat Example 10.15 in which the disk strikes and adheres to the stick 0.100 m from the nail.

44. Repeat Example 10.15 in which the disk originally spins clockwise at 1000 rpm and has a radius of 1.50 cm.

45. Twin skaters approach one another as shown in Figure 10.37 and lock hands. (a) Calculate their final angular velocity, given each had an initial speed of 2.50 m/s relative to the ice. Each has a mass of 70.0 kg, and each has a center of mass located 0.800 m from their locked hands. You may approximate their moments of inertia to be that of point masses at this radius. (b) Compare the initial kinetic energy and final kinetic energy.

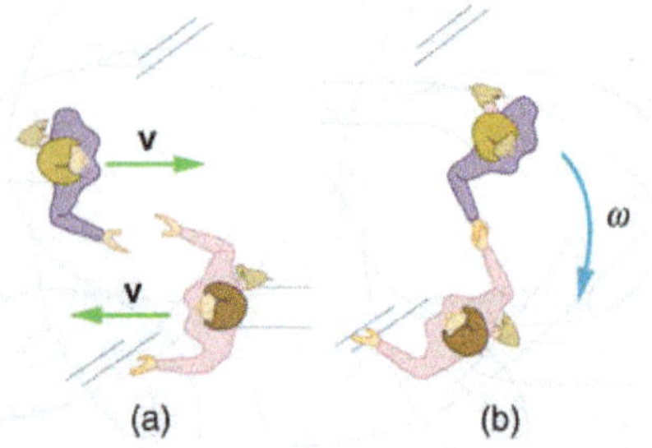

FIGURE 10.37 Twin skaters approach each other with identical speeds. Then, the skaters lock hands and spin.

46. Suppose a 0.250-kg ball is thrown at 15.0 m/s to a motionless person standing on ice who catches it with an outstretched arm as shown in Figure 10.38.
(a) Calculate the final linear velocity of the person, given his mass is 70.0 kg.
(b) What is his angular velocity if each arm is 5.00 kg? You may treat the ball as a point mass and treat the person's arms as uniform rods (each has a length of 0.900 m) and the rest of his body as a uniform cylinder of radius 0.180 m. Neglect the effect of the ball on his center of mass so that his center of mass remains in his geometrical center.
(c) Compare the initial and final total kinetic energies.

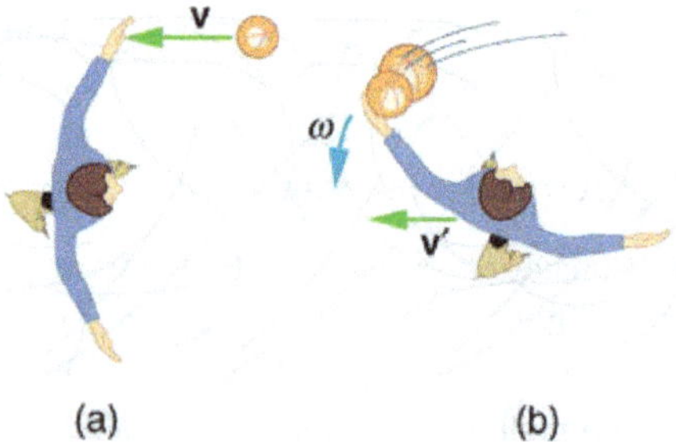

FIGURE 10.38 The figure shows the overhead view of a person standing motionless on ice about to catch a ball. Both arms are outstretched. After catching the ball, the skater recoils and rotates.

47. Repeat Example 10.15 in which the stick is free to have translational motion as well as rotational motion.

10.7 Gyroscopic Effects: Vector Aspects of Angular Momentum

48. Integrated Concepts
The axis of Earth makes a 23.5° angle with a direction perpendicular to the plane of Earth's orbit. As shown in Figure 10.39, this axis precesses, making one complete rotation in 25,780 y.
(a) Calculate the change in angular momentum in half this time.
(b) What is the average torque producing this change in angular momentum?
(c) If this torque were created by a single force (it is not) acting at the most effective point on the equator, what would its magnitude be?

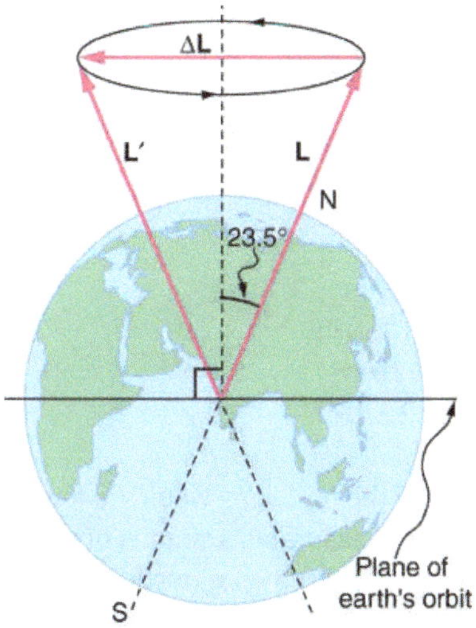

FIGURE 10.39 The Earth's axis slowly precesses, always making an angle of 23.5° with the direction perpendicular to the plane of Earth's orbit. The change in angular momentum for the two shown positions is quite large, although the magnitude **L** is unchanged.

Test Prep for AP® Courses

10.3 Dynamics of Rotational Motion: Rotational Inertia

1. A piece of wood can be carved by spinning it on a motorized lathe and holding a sharp chisel to the edge of the wood as it spins. How does the angular velocity of a piece of wood with a radius of 0.2 m spinning on a lathe change when a chisel is held to the wood's edge with a force of 50 N?

a. It increases by 0.1 N•m multiplied by the moment of inertia of the wood.
b. It decreases by 0.1 N•m divided by the moment of inertia of the wood-and-lathe system.
c. It decreases by 0.1 N•m multiplied by the moment of inertia of the wood.
d. It decreases by 0.1 m/s^2.

2. A Ferris wheel is loaded with people in the chairs at the following positions: 4 o'clock, 1 o'clock, 9 o'clock, and 6 o'clock. As the wheel begins to turn, what forces are acting on the system? How will each force affect the angular velocity and angular momentum?

3. A lever is placed on a fulcrum. A rock is placed on the left end of the lever and a downward (clockwise) force is applied to the right end of the lever. What measurements would be most effective to help you determine the angular momentum of the system? (Assume the lever itself has negligible mass.)

a. the angular velocity and mass of the rock
b. the angular velocity and mass of the rock, and the radius of the lever
c. the velocity of the force, the radius of the lever, and the mass of the rock
d. the mass of the rock, the length of the lever on both sides of the fulcrum, and the force applied on the right side of the lever

4. You can use the following setup to determine angular acceleration and angular momentum: A lever is placed on a fulcrum. A rock is placed on the left end of the lever and a known downward (clockwise) force is applied to the right end of the lever. What calculations would you perform? How would you account for gravity in your calculations?

5. Consider two sizes of disk, both of mass *M*. One size of disk has radius *R*; the other has radius 2*R*. System A consists of two of the larger disks rigidly connected to each other with a common axis of rotation. System B consists of one of the larger disks and a number of the smaller disks rigidly connected with a common axis of rotation. If the moment of inertia for system A equals the moment of inertia for system B, how many of the smaller disks are in system B?

a. 1
b. 2
c. 3
d. 4

6. You are given a thin rod of length 1.0 m and mass 2.0 kg, a small lead weight of 0.50 kg, and a not-so-small lead weight of 1.0 kg. The rod has three holes, one in each end and one through the middle, which may either hold a pivot point or one of the small lead weights. How do you arrange these objects so that the resulting system has the maximum possible moment of inertia? What is that moment of inertia? do you arrange these objects so that the resulting system has the maximum possible moment of inertia? What is that moment of inertia?

10.4 Rotational Kinetic Energy: Work and Energy Revisited

7. Gear A, which turns clockwise, meshes with gear B, which turns counterclockwise. When more force is applied through gear A, torque is created. How does the angular velocity of gear B change as a result?
   a. It increases in magnitude.
   b. It decreases in magnitude.
   c. It changes direction.
   d. It stays the same.

8. Which will cause a greater increase in the angular velocity of a disk: doubling the torque applied or halving the radius at which the torque is applied? Explain.

9. Which measure would not be useful to help you determine the change in angular velocity when the torque on a fishing reel is increased?
   a. the radius of the reel
   b. the amount of line that unspools
   c. the angular momentum of the fishing line
   d. the time it takes the line to unspool

10. What data could you collect to study the change in angular velocity when two people push a merry-go-round instead of one, providing twice as much torque? How would you use the data you collect?

10.5 Angular Momentum and Its Conservation

11. Which rotational system would be best to use as a model to measure how angular momentum changes when forces on the system are changed?
   a. a fishing reel
   b. a planet and its moon
   c. a figure skater spinning
   d. a person's lower leg

12. You are collecting data to study changes in the angular momentum of a bicycle wheel when a force is applied to it. Which of the following measurements would be least helpful to you?
   a. the time for which the force is applied
   b. the radius at which the force is applied
   c. the angular velocity of the wheel when the force is applied
   d. the direction of the force

13. Which torque applied to a disk with radius 7.0 cm for 3.5 s will produce an angular momentum of 25 N•m•s?
   a. 7.1 N•m
   b. 357.1 N•m
   c. 3.6 N•m
   d. 612.5 N•m

14. Which of the following would be the best way to produce measurable amounts of torque on a system to test the relationship between the angular momentum of the system, the average torque applied to the system, and the time for which the torque is applied?
   a. having different numbers of people push on a merry-go-round
   b. placing known masses on one end of a seesaw
   c. touching the outer edge of a bicycle wheel to a treadmill that is moving at different speeds
   d. hanging known masses from a string that is wound around a spool suspended horizontally on an axle

15.

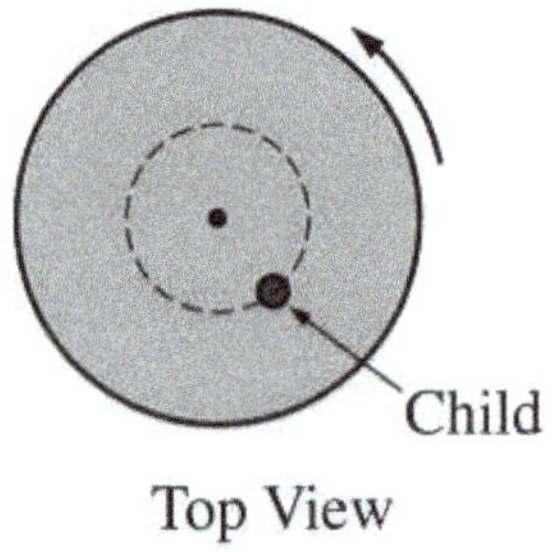

FIGURE 10.40 A curved arrow lies at the side of a gray disk. There is a point at the center of the disk, and around the point there is a dashed circle. There is a point labeled "Child" on the dashed circle. Below the disc is a label saying "Top View".

The diagram above shows a top view of a child of mass M on a circular platform of mass $2M$ that is rotating counterclockwise. Assume the platform rotates without friction. Which of the following describes an action by the child that will increase the angular speed of the platform-child system and why?
   a. The child moves toward the center of the platform, increasing the total angular momentum of the system.
   b. The child moves toward the center of the platform, decreasing the rotational inertia of

the system.
c. The child moves away from the center of the platform, increasing the total angular momentum of the system.
d. The child moves away from the center of the platform, decreasing the rotational inertia of the system.

16.

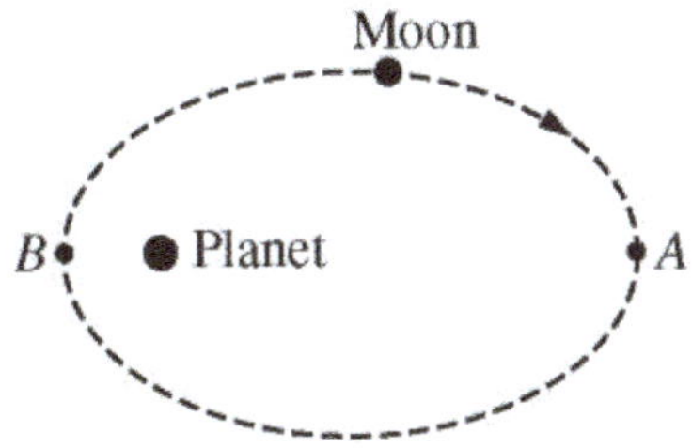

FIGURE 10.41 A point labeled "Moon" lies on a dashed ellipse. Two other points, labeled "A" and "B", lie at opposite ends of the ellipse. A point labeled "Planet" lies inside the ellipse.

A moon is in an elliptical orbit about a planet as shown above. At point *A* the moon has speed *uA* and is at distance *RA* from the planet. At point *B* the moon has speed *uB*. Has the moon's angular momentum changed? Explain your answer.

17. A hamster sits 0.10 m from the center of a lazy Susan of negligible mass. The wheel spins with a frequency of 1.0 rev/s. How will the frequency of the lazy Susan change if the hamster walks to 0.30 m from the center of rotation? Assume zero friction and no external torque.
a. It will speed up to 2.0 rev/s.
b. It will speed up to 9.0 rev/s.
c. It will slow to 0.11 rev/s.
d. It will slow to 0.22 rev/s.

18. Earth has a mass of 6.0×10^{24} kg, a radius of 6.4×10^{6} m, and a rotational frequency of 1.2×10^{-5} rev/s. How would the planet's rotational frequency change if a layer of Earth with mass 1.0×10^{23} kg broke off of the Earth, decreasing Earth's radius by 0.2×10^{6} m? Assume no friction.

19. Consider system A, consisting of two disks of radius *R*, with both rotating clockwise. Now consider system B, consisting of one disk of radius *R* rotating counterclockwise and another disk of radius 2*R* rotating clockwise. All of the disks have the same mass, and all have the same magnitude of angular velocity.
Which system has the greatest angular momentum?
a. A
b. B
c. They're equal.
d. Not enough information

20. Assume that a baseball bat being swung at 3π rad/s by a batting machine is equivalent to a 1.1 m thin rod with a mass of 1.0 kg. How fast would a 0.15 kg baseball that squarely hits the very tip of the bat have to be going for the net angular momentum of the bat-ball system to be zero?

10.6 Collisions of Extended Bodies in Two Dimensions

21. A box with a mass of 2.0 kg rests on one end of a seesaw. The seesaw is 6.0 m long, and we can assume it has negligible mass. Approximately what angular momentum will the box have if someone with a mass of 65 kg sits on the other end of the seesaw quickly, with a velocity of 1.2 m/s?
a. 702 kg•m^2/s
b. 39 kg•m^2/s
c. 18 kg•m^2/s
d. 1.2 kg•m^2/s

22. A spinner in a board game can be thought of as a thin rod that spins about an axis at its center. The spinner in a certain game is 12 cm long and has a mass of 10 g. How will its angular velocity change when it is flicked at one end with a force equivalent to 15 g travelling at 5.0 m/s if all the energy of the collision is transferred to the spinner? (You can use the table in Figure 10.12 to estimate the rotational inertia of the spinner.)

23. A cyclist pedals to exert a torque on the rear wheel of the bicycle. When the cyclist changes to a higher gear, the torque increases. Which of the following would be the most effective strategy to help you determine the change in angular momentum of the bicycle wheel?
a. multiplying the ratio between the two torques by the mass of the bicycle and rider
b. adding the two torques together, and multiplying by the time for which both torques are applied
c. multiplying the difference in the two torques by the time for which the new torque is applied
d. multiplying both torques by the mass of the bicycle and rider

24. An electric screwdriver has two speeds, each of which exerts a different torque on a screw.

Describe what calculations you could use to help you compare the angular momentum of a screw at each speed. What measurements would you need to make in order to calculate this?

25. Why is it important to consider the shape of an object when determining the object's angular momentum?

a. The shape determines the location of the center of mass. The location of the center of mass in turn determines the angular velocity of the object.
b. The shape helps you determine the location of the object's outer edge, where rotational velocity will be greatest.
c. The shape helps you determine the location of the center of rotation.
d. The shape determines the location of the center of mass. The location of the center of mass contributes to the object's rotational inertia, which contributes to its angular momentum.

26. How could you collect and analyze data to test the difference between the torques provided by two speeds on a tabletop fan?

27. Describe a rotational system you could use to demonstrate the effect on the system's angular momentum of applying different amounts of external torque.

28. How could you use simple equipment such as balls and string to study the changes in angular momentum of a system when it interacts with another system?

10.7 Gyroscopic Effects: Vector Aspects of Angular Momentum

29. A globe (model of the Earth) is a hollow sphere with a radius of 16 cm. By wrapping a cord around the equator of a globe and pulling on it, a person exerts a torque on the globe of 120 N • m for 1.2 s. What angular momentum does the globe have after 1.2 s?

30. How could you use a fishing reel to test the relationship between the torque applied to a system, the time for which the torque was applied, and the resulting angular momentum of the system? How would you measure angular momentum?

CHAPTER 11
Fluid Statics

FIGURE 11.1 The fluid essential to all life has a beauty of its own. It also helps support the weight of this swimmer. (credit: 12019, Pixabay)

CHAPTER OUTLINE

CONNECTION FOR AP® COURSES Much of what we value in life is fluid: a breath of fresh winter air; the water we drink, swim in, and bathe in; the blood in our veins. But what exactly is a fluid? Can we understand fluids with the laws already presented, or will new laws emerge from their study?

As you read this chapter, you will learn how the arrangement and interaction of the particles—atoms and molecules—that make up a fluid define many of its macroscopic characteristics, like density and pressure (Big Idea

1, Enduring Understanding 1.E, Essential Knowledge 1.E.1). While the number of particles in a fluid is often immense, you will be able to use a probabilistic approach in order to explain how a fluid affects its environment in a variety of ways (Big Idea 7, Enduring Understanding 7.A, Essential Knowledge 7.A.1). From the pressure a fluid places on the walls of a hydraulic system to a variety of biological and medical applications, understanding a fluid's properties begins with understanding its internal structure.

Big Idea 1 Objects and systems have properties such as mass and charge. Systems may have internal structure.

Enduring Understanding 1.E Materials have many macroscopic properties that result from the arrangement and interactions of the atoms and molecules that make up the material.

Essential Knowledge 1.E.1 Matter has a property called density.

Big Idea 7 The mathematics of probability can be used to describe the behavior of complex systems and to interpret the behavior of quantum mechanical systems.

Enduring Understanding 7.A The properties of an ideal gas can be explained in terms of a small number of macroscopic variables including temperature and pressure.

Essential Knowledge 7.A.1 The pressure of a system determines the force that the system exerts on the walls of its container and is a measure of the average change in the momentum or impulse of the molecules colliding with the walls of the container. The pressure also exists inside the system itself, not just at the walls of the container.

Click to view content (https://openstax.org/books/college-physics-ap-courses-2e/pages/11-connection-for-ap-r-courses)

11.1 What Is a Fluid?

LEARNING OBJECTIVES

By the end of this section, you will be able to:

- State the common phases of matter.
- Explain the physical characteristics of solids, liquids, and gases.
- Describe the arrangement of atoms in solids, liquids, and gases.

Matter most commonly exists as a solid, liquid, gas, or plasma; these states are known as the common *phases of matter*. Solids have a definite shape and a specific volume, liquids have a definite volume but their shape changes depending on the container in which they are held, gases have neither a definite shape nor a specific volume as their molecules move to fill the container in which they are held, and plasmas also have neither definite shape nor volume. (See Figure 11.2.) Liquids, gases, and plasmas are considered to be fluids because they yield to shearing forces, whereas solids resist them. Note that the extent to which fluids yield to shearing forces (and hence flow easily and quickly) depends on a quantity called the viscosity which is discussed in detail in Viscosity and Laminar Flow; Poiseuille's Law. We can understand the phases of matter and what constitutes a fluid by considering the forces between atoms that make up matter in the three phases.

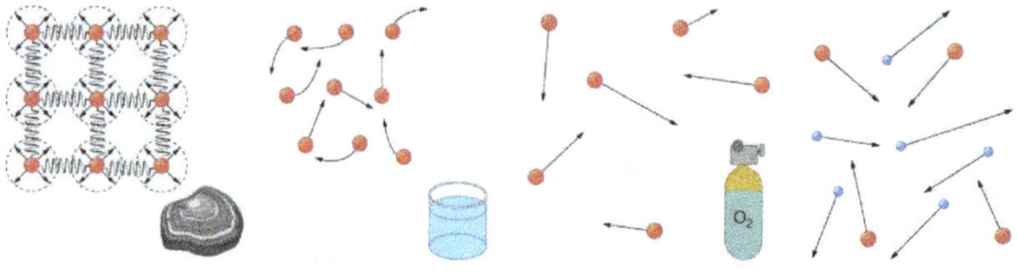

FIGURE 11.2 (a) Atoms in a solid always have the same neighbors, held near home by forces represented here by springs. These atoms are essentially in contact with one another. A rock is an example of a solid. This rock retains its shape because of the forces holding its atoms together. (b) Atoms in a liquid are also in close contact but can slide over one another. Forces between them strongly resist attempts to push them closer together and also hold them in close contact. Water is an example of a liquid. Water can flow, but it also remains in an open container because of the forces between its atoms. (c) Atoms in a gas are separated by distances that are considerably larger than the size of the atoms themselves, and they move about freely. A gas must be held in a closed container to prevent it from moving out freely. (d) A plasma is composed of electrons, protons, and ions that, like gases, are spaced far apart and move about freely.

Atoms in *solids* are in close contact, with forces between them that allow the atoms to vibrate but not to change positions with neighboring atoms. (These forces can be thought of as springs that can be stretched or compressed, but not easily broken.) Thus a solid *resists* all types of stress. A solid cannot be easily deformed because the atoms that make up the solid are not able to move about freely. Solids also resist compression, because their atoms form part of a lattice structure in which the atoms are a relatively fixed distance apart. Under compression, the atoms would be forced into one another. Most of the examples we have studied so far have involved solid objects which deform very little when stressed.

CONNECTIONS: SUBMICROSCOPIC EXPLANATION OF SOLIDS AND LIQUIDS

Atomic and molecular characteristics explain and underlie the macroscopic characteristics of solids and fluids. This submicroscopic explanation is one theme of this text and is highlighted in the Things Great and Small features in Conservation of Momentum. See, for example, microscopic description of collisions and momentum or microscopic description of pressure in a gas. This present section is devoted entirely to the submicroscopic explanation of solids and liquids.

In contrast, *liquids* deform easily when stressed and do not spring back to their original shape once the force is removed because the atoms are free to slide about and change neighbors—that is, they *flow* (so they are a type of fluid), with the molecules held together by their mutual attraction. When a liquid is placed in a container with no lid on, it remains in the container (providing the container has no holes below the surface of the liquid!). Because the atoms are closely packed, liquids, like solids, resist compression.

Atoms in *gases* and charged particles in *plasmas* are separated by distances that are large compared with the size of the particles. The forces between the particles are therefore very weak, except when they collide with one another. Gases and plasmas thus not only flow (and are therefore considered to be fluids) but they are relatively easy to compress because there is much space and little force between the particles. When placed in an open container gases, unlike liquids, will escape. The major distinction is that gases are easily compressed, whereas liquids are not. Plasmas are difficult to contain because they have so much energy. When discussing how substances flow, we shall generally refer to both gases and liquids simply as **fluids**, and make a distinction between them only when they behave differently.

PHET EXPLORATIONS

States of Matter—Basics

Heat, cool, and compress atoms and molecules and watch as they change between solid, liquid, and gas phases.

Click to view content (https://openstax.org/books/college-physics-ap-courses-2e/pages/11-1-what-is-a-fluid)

11.2 Density

LEARNING OBJECTIVES

By the end of this section, you will be able to:

- Define density.
- Calculate the mass of a reservoir from its density.
- Compare and contrast the densities of various substances.

Which weighs more, a ton of feathers or a ton of bricks? This old riddle plays with the distinction between mass and density. A ton is a ton, of course; but bricks have much greater density than feathers, and so we are tempted to think of them as heavier. (See Figure 11.3.)

Density, as you will see, is an important characteristic of substances. It is crucial, for example, in determining whether an object sinks or floats in a fluid. Density is the mass per unit volume of a substance or object. In equation form, density is defined as

$$\rho = \frac{m}{V}, \tag{11.1}$$

where the Greek letter ρ (rho) is the symbol for density, m is the mass, and V is the volume occupied by the substance.

DENSITY

Density is mass per unit volume.

$$\rho = \frac{m}{V}, \quad (11.2)$$

where ρ is the symbol for density, m is the mass, and V is the volume occupied by the substance.

In the riddle regarding the feathers and bricks, the masses are the same, but the volume occupied by the feathers is much greater, since their density is much lower. The SI unit of density is kg/m^3, representative values are given in Table 11.1. The metric system was originally devised so that water would have a density of $1\ g/cm^3$, equivalent to $10^3\ kg/m^3$. Thus the basic mass unit, the kilogram, was first devised to be the mass of 1000 mL of water, which has a volume of 1000 cm^3.

Substance	$\rho(\times 10^3\ kg/m^3$ or $g/mL)$	Substance	$\rho(10^3\ kg/m^3$ or $g/mL)$	Substance	$\rho(10^3\ kg/m^3$ or $g/mL)$
Solids		**Liquids**		**Gases**	
Aluminum	2.7	Water (4°C)	1.000	Air	1.29×10^{-3}
Brass	8.44	Blood	1.05	Carbon dioxide	1.98×10^{-3}
Copper (average)	8.8	Sea water	1.025	Carbon monoxide	1.25×10^{-3}
Gold	19.32	Mercury	13.6	Hydrogen	0.090×10^{-3}
Iron or steel	7.8	Ethyl alcohol	0.79	Helium	0.18×10^{-3}
Lead	11.3	Gasoline	0.68	Methane	0.72×10^{-3}
Polystyrene	0.10	Glycerin	1.26	Nitrogen	1.25×10^{-3}
Tungsten	19.30	Olive oil	0.92	Nitrous oxide	1.98×10^{-3}
Uranium	18.70			Oxygen	1.43×10^{-3}
Concrete	2.30–3.0			Steam (100° C)	0.60×10^{-3}
Cork	0.24				

TABLE 11.1 Densities of Various Substances

Substance	$\rho(\times 10^3\ \text{kg/m}^3$ or g/mL)	Substance	$\rho(10^3\ \text{kg/m}^3$ or g/mL)	Substance	$\rho(10^3\ \text{kg/m}^3$ or g/mL)
Glass, common (average)	2.6				
Granite	2.7				
Earth's crust	3.3				
Wood	0.3–0.9				
Ice (0°C)	0.917				
Bone	1.7–2.0				
Silver	10.49				

TABLE 11.1 Densities of Various Substances

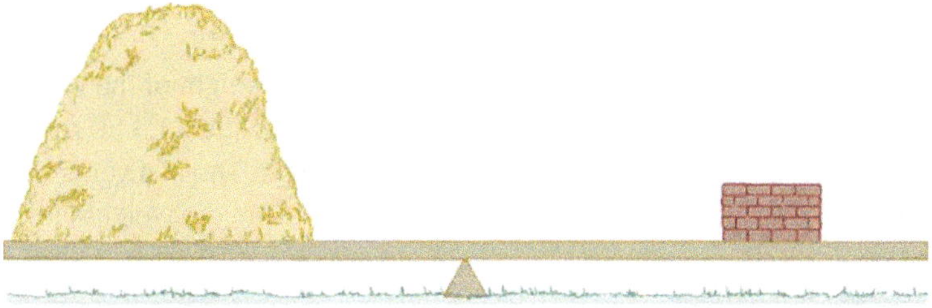

FIGURE 11.3 A ton of feathers and a ton of bricks have the same mass, but the feathers make a much bigger pile because they have a much lower density.

As you can see by examining Table 11.1, the density of an object may help identify its composition. The density of gold, for example, is about 2.5 times the density of iron, which is about 2.5 times the density of aluminum. Density also reveals something about the phase of the matter and its substructure. Notice that the densities of liquids and solids are roughly comparable, consistent with the fact that their atoms are in close contact. The densities of gases are much less than those of liquids and solids, because the atoms in gases are separated by large amounts of empty space.

TAKE-HOME EXPERIMENT SUGAR AND SALT

A pile of sugar and a pile of salt look pretty similar, but which weighs more? If the volumes of both piles are the same, any difference in mass is due to their different densities (including the air space between crystals). Which do you think has the greater density? What values did you find? What method did you use to determine these values?

EXAMPLE 11.1

Calculating the Mass of a Reservoir From Its Volume

A reservoir has a surface area of $50.0\ \text{km}^2$ and an average depth of 40.0 m. What mass of water is held behind the dam? (See Figure 11.4 for a view of a large reservoir—the Three Gorges Dam site on the Yangtze River in central China.)

Strategy

We can calculate the volume V of the reservoir from its dimensions, and find the density of water ρ in Table 11.1. Then the mass m can be found from the definition of density

$$\rho = \frac{m}{V}. \tag{11.3}$$

Solution

Solving equation $\rho = m/V$ for m gives $m = \rho V$.

The volume V of the reservoir is its surface area A times its average depth h:

$$\begin{aligned} V &= Ah = (50.0\ \text{km}^2)(40.0\ \text{m}) \\ &= \left[(50.0\ \text{km}^2)\left(\frac{10^3\ \text{m}}{1\ \text{km}}\right)^2\right](40.0\ \text{m}) = 2.00 \times 10^9\ \text{m}^3 \end{aligned} \tag{11.4}$$

The density of water ρ from Table 11.1 is $1.000 \times 10^3\ \text{kg/m}^3$. Substituting V and ρ into the expression for mass gives

$$\begin{aligned} m &= (1.00 \times 10^3\ \text{kg/m}^3)(2.00 \times 10^9\ \text{m}^3) \\ &= 2.00 \times 10^{12}\ \text{kg}. \end{aligned} \tag{11.5}$$

Discussion

A large reservoir contains a very large mass of water. In this example, the weight of the water in the reservoir is $mg = 1.96 \times 10^{13}\ \text{N}$, where g is the acceleration due to the Earth's gravity (about $9.80\ \text{m/s}^2$). It is reasonable to ask whether the dam must supply a force equal to this tremendous weight. The answer is no. As we shall see in the following sections, the force the dam must supply can be much smaller than the weight of the water it holds back.

FIGURE 11.4 Three Gorges Dam in central China. When completed in 2008, this became the world's largest hydroelectric plant, generating power equivalent to that generated by 22 average-sized nuclear power plants. The concrete dam is 181 m high and 2.3 km across. The reservoir made by this dam is 660 km long. Over 1 million people were displaced by the creation of the reservoir. (credit: Le Grand Portage)

11.3 Pressure

LEARNING OBJECTIVES

By the end of this section, you will be able to:

- Define pressure.
- Explain the relationship between pressure and force.
- Calculate force given pressure and area.

You have no doubt heard the word **pressure** being used in relation to blood (high or low blood pressure) and in relation to the weather (high- and low-pressure weather systems). These are only two of many examples of pressures in fluids. Pressure P is defined as

$$P = \frac{F}{A} \tag{11.6}$$

where F is a force applied to an area A that is perpendicular to the force.

PRESSURE

Pressure is defined as the force divided by the area perpendicular to the force over which the force is applied, or

$$P = \frac{F}{A}. \tag{11.7}$$

A given force can have a significantly different effect depending on the area over which the force is exerted, as shown in Figure 11.5. The SI unit for pressure is the *pascal*, where

$$1 \text{ Pa} = 1 \text{ N/m}^2. \tag{11.8}$$

In addition to the pascal, there are many other units for pressure that are in common use. In meteorology, atmospheric pressure is often described in units of millibar (mb), where

$$100 \text{ mb} = 1 \times 10^4 \text{ Pa}. \tag{11.9}$$

Pounds per square inch $\left(\text{lb/in}^2 \text{ or psi}\right)$ is still sometimes used as a measure of tire pressure, and millimeters of mercury (mm Hg) is still often used in the measurement of blood pressure. Pressure is defined for all states of matter but is particularly important when discussing fluids.

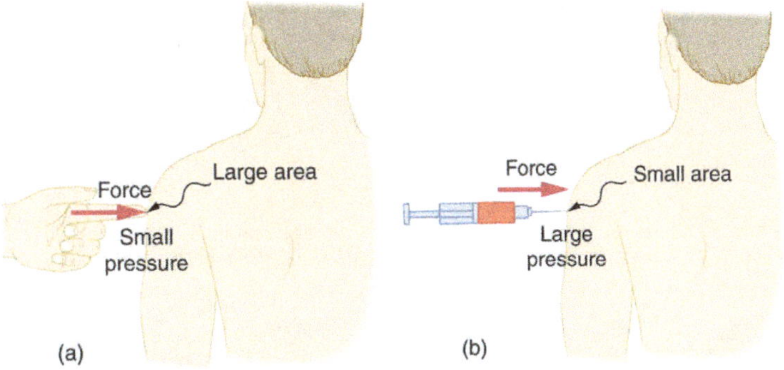

FIGURE 11.5 (a) While the person being poked with the finger might be irritated, the force has little lasting effect. (b) In contrast, the same force applied to an area the size of the sharp end of a needle is great enough to break the skin.

EXAMPLE 11.2

Calculating Force Exerted by the Air: What Force Does a Pressure Exert?

An astronaut is working outside the International Space Station where the atmospheric pressure is essentially zero. The pressure gauge on her air tank reads 6.90×10^6 Pa. What force does the air inside the tank exert on the flat end of the cylindrical tank, a disk 0.150 m in diameter?

Strategy

We can find the force exerted from the definition of pressure given in $P = \frac{F}{A}$, provided we can find the area A acted upon.

Solution

By rearranging the definition of pressure to solve for force, we see that

$$F = PA. \tag{11.10}$$

Here, the pressure P is given, as is the area of the end of the cylinder A, given by $A = \pi r^2$. Thus,

$$\begin{aligned} F &= \left(6.90 \times 10^6 \text{ N/m}^2\right)(3.14)(0.0750 \text{ m})^2 \\ &= 1.22 \times 10^5 \text{ N}. \end{aligned} \tag{11.11}$$

Discussion

Wow! No wonder the tank must be strong. Since we found $F = PA$, we see that the force exerted by a pressure is directly proportional to the area acted upon as well as the pressure itself.

The force exerted on the end of the tank is perpendicular to its inside surface. This direction is because the force is exerted by a static or stationary fluid. We have already seen that fluids cannot *withstand* shearing (sideways) forces; they cannot *exert* shearing forces, either. Fluid pressure has no direction, being a scalar quantity. The forces due to pressure have well-defined directions: they are always exerted perpendicular to any surface. (See the tire in Figure 11.6, for example.) Finally, note that pressure is exerted on all surfaces. Swimmers, as well as the tire, feel pressure on all sides. (See Figure 11.7.)

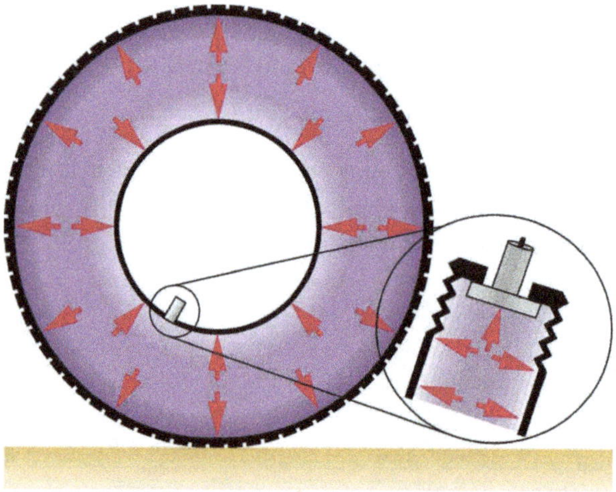

FIGURE 11.6 Pressure inside this tire exerts forces perpendicular to all surfaces it contacts. The arrows give representative directions and magnitudes of the forces exerted at various points. Note that static fluids do not exert shearing forces.

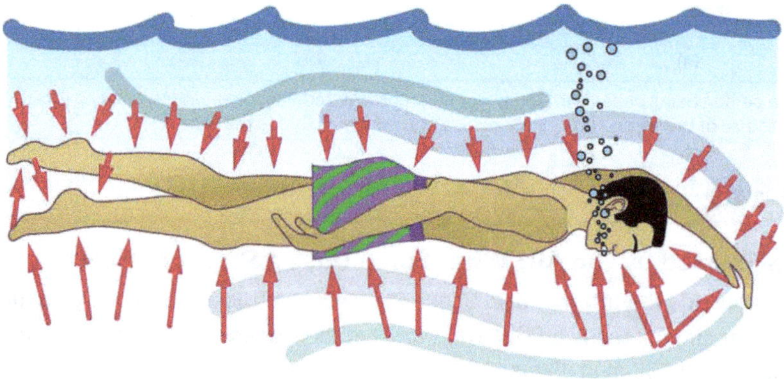

FIGURE 11.7 Pressure is exerted on all sides of this swimmer, since the water would flow into the space he occupies if he were not there. The arrows represent the directions and magnitudes of the forces exerted at various points on the swimmer. Note that the forces are larger underneath, due to greater depth, giving a net upward or buoyant force that is balanced by the weight of the swimmer.

PHET EXPLORATIONS

Gas Properties

Pump gas molecules to a box and see what happens as you change the volume, add or remove heat, change gravity, and more. Measure the temperature and pressure, and discover how the properties of the gas vary in relation to each other.

Click to view content (https://openstax.org/books/college-physics-ap-courses-2e/pages/11-3-pressure)

PhET

11.4 Variation of Pressure with Depth in a Fluid

LEARNING OBJECTIVES

By the end of this section, you will be able to:

- Define pressure in terms of weight.
- Explain the variation of pressure with depth in a fluid.
- Calculate density given pressure and altitude.

If your ears have ever popped on a plane flight or ached during a deep dive in a swimming pool, you have experienced the effect of depth on pressure in a fluid. At the Earth's surface, the air pressure exerted on you is a result of the weight of air above you. This pressure is reduced as you climb up in altitude and the weight of air above you decreases. Under water, the pressure exerted on you increases with increasing depth. In this case, the pressure being exerted upon you is a result of both the weight of water above you *and* that of the atmosphere above you. You may notice an air pressure change on an elevator ride that transports you many stories, but you need only dive a meter or so below the surface of a pool to feel a pressure increase. The difference is that water is much denser than air, about 775 times as dense.

Consider the container in Figure 11.8. Its bottom supports the weight of the fluid in it. Let us calculate the pressure exerted on the bottom by the weight of the fluid. That **pressure** is the weight of the fluid mg divided by the area A supporting it (the area of the bottom of the container):

$$P = \frac{mg}{A}. \tag{11.12}$$

We can find the mass of the fluid from its volume and density:

$$m = \rho V. \tag{11.13}$$

The volume of the fluid V is related to the dimensions of the container. It is

$$V = Ah, \tag{11.14}$$

where A is the cross-sectional area and h is the depth. Combining the last two equations gives

$$m = \rho Ah. \tag{11.15}$$

If we enter this into the expression for pressure, we obtain

$$P = \frac{(\rho Ah)g}{A}. \tag{11.16}$$

The area cancels, and rearranging the variables yields

$$P = h\rho g. \tag{11.17}$$

This value is the *pressure due to the weight of a fluid*. The equation has general validity beyond the special conditions under which it is derived here. Even if the container were not there, the surrounding fluid would still exert this pressure, keeping the fluid static. Thus the equation $P = h\rho g$ represents the pressure due to the weight of any fluid of *average density* ρ at any depth h below its surface. For liquids, which are nearly incompressible, this equation holds to great depths. For gases, which are quite compressible, one can apply this equation as long as the density changes are small over the depth considered. Example 11.4 illustrates this situation.

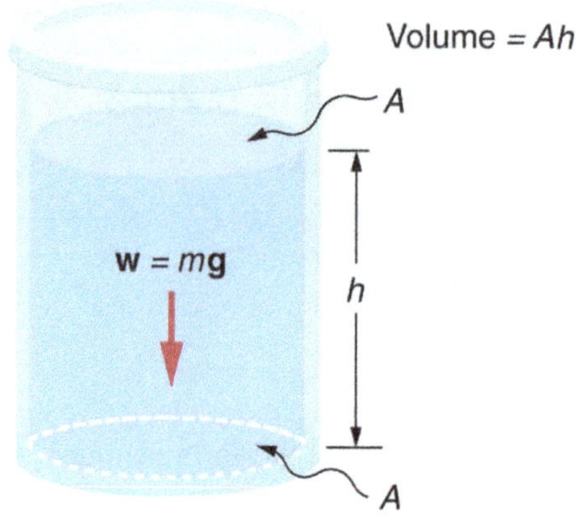

FIGURE 11.8 The bottom of this container supports the entire weight of the fluid in it. The vertical sides cannot exert an upward force on the fluid (since it cannot withstand a shearing force), and so the bottom must support it all.

EXAMPLE 11.3

Calculating the Average Pressure and Force Exerted: What Force Must a Dam Withstand?

In Example 11.1, we calculated the mass of water in a large reservoir. We will now consider the pressure and force acting on the dam retaining water. (See Figure 11.9.) The dam is 500 m wide, and the water is 80.0 m deep at the dam. (a) What is the average pressure on the dam due to the water? (b) Calculate the force exerted against the dam and compare it with the weight of water in the dam (previously found to be 1.96×10^{13} N).

Strategy for (a)

The average pressure $\bar{P}$ due to the weight of the water is the pressure at the average depth $\bar{h}$ of 40.0 m, since pressure increases linearly with depth.

Solution for (a)

The average pressure due to the weight of a fluid is

$$\bar{P} = \bar{h}\rho g. \tag{11.18}$$

Entering the density of water from Table 11.1 and taking $\bar{h}$ to be the average depth of 40.0 m, we obtain

$$\begin{aligned} \bar{P} &= (40.0\text{ m})\left(10^3\ \frac{\text{kg}}{\text{m}^3}\right)\left(9.80\ \frac{\text{m}}{\text{s}^2}\right) \\ &= 3.92 \times 10^5\ \frac{\text{N}}{\text{m}^2} = 392\text{ kPa}. \end{aligned} \tag{11.19}$$

Strategy for (b)

The force exerted on the dam by the water is the average pressure times the area of contact:

$$F = \bar{P}A. \tag{11.20}$$

Solution for (b)

We have already found the value for $\bar{P}$. The area of the dam is $A = 80.0\text{ m} \times 500\text{ m} = 4.00 \times 10^4\text{ m}^2$, so that

$$\begin{aligned} F &= (3.92 \times 10^5\text{ N/m}^2)(4.00 \times 10^4\text{ m}^2) \\ &= 1.57 \times 10^{10}\text{ N}. \end{aligned} \tag{11.21}$$

Discussion

Although this force seems large, it is small compared with the 1.96×10^{13} N weight of the water in the reservoir—in fact, it is only 0.0800% of the weight. Note that the pressure found in part (a) is completely independent of the width and length of the lake—it depends only on its average depth at the dam. Thus the force depends only on the water's average depth and the dimensions of the dam, *not* on the horizontal extent of the reservoir. In the diagram, the thickness of the dam increases with depth to balance the increasing force due to the increasing pressure.epth to balance the increasing force due to the increasing pressure.

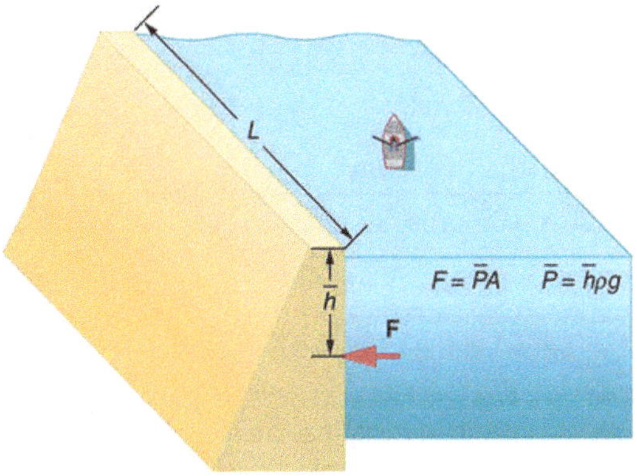

FIGURE 11.9 The dam must withstand the force exerted against it by the water it retains. This force is small compared with the weight of the water behind the dam.

Atmospheric pressure is another example of pressure due to the weight of a fluid, in this case due to the weight of *air* above a given height. The atmospheric pressure at the Earth's surface varies a little due to the large-scale flow of the atmosphere induced by the Earth's rotation (this creates weather "highs" and "lows"). However, the average pressure at sea level is given by the *standard atmospheric pressure* P_{atm}, measured to be

$$1 \text{ atmosphere (atm)} = P_{atm} = 1.01 \times 10^5 \text{ N/m}^2 = 101 \text{ kPa}. \tag{11.22}$$

This relationship means that, on average, at sea level, a column of air above 1.00 m^2 of the Earth's surface has a weight of 1.01×10^5 N, equivalent to 1 atm. (See Figure 11.10.)

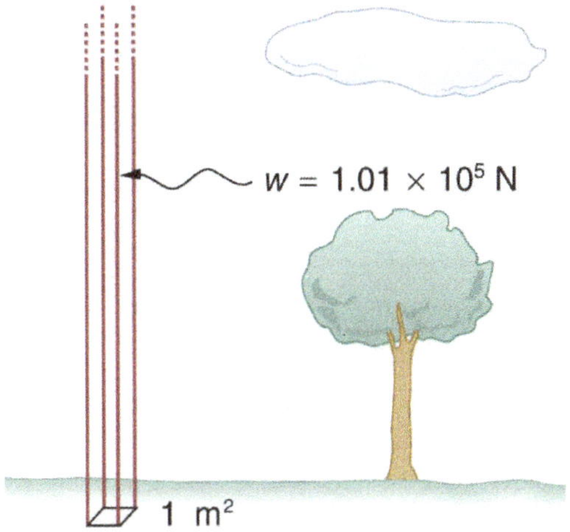

FIGURE 11.10 Atmospheric pressure at sea level averages 1.01×10^5 Pa (equivalent to 1 atm), since the column of air over this 1 m^2, extending to the top of the atmosphere, weighs 1.01×10^5 N.

EXAMPLE 11.4

Calculating Average Density: How Dense Is the Air?

Calculate the average density of the atmosphere, given that it extends to an altitude of 120 km. Compare this density with that of air listed in Table 11.1.

Strategy

If we solve $P = h\rho g$ for density, we see that

$$\bar{\rho} = \frac{P}{hg}. \tag{11.23}$$

We then take P to be atmospheric pressure, h is given, and g is known, and so we can use this to calculate $\bar{\rho}$.

Solution

Entering known values into the expression for $\bar{\rho}$ yields

$$\bar{\rho} = \frac{1.01 \times 10^5 \text{ N/m}^2}{(120 \times 10^3 \text{ m})(9.80 \text{ m/s}^2)} = 8.59 \times 10^{-2} \text{ kg/m}^3. \tag{11.24}$$

Discussion

This result is the average density of air between the Earth's surface and the top of the Earth's atmosphere, which essentially ends at 120 km. The density of air at sea level is given in Table 11.1 as 1.29 kg/m^3 —about 15 times its average value. Because air is so compressible, its density has its highest value near the Earth's surface and declines rapidly with altitude.

EXAMPLE 11.5

Calculating Depth Below the Surface of Water: What Depth of Water Creates the Same Pressure as the Entire Atmosphere?

Calculate the depth below the surface of water at which the pressure due to the weight of the water equals 1.00 atm.

Strategy

We begin by solving the equation $P = h\rho g$ for depth h:

$$h = \frac{P}{\rho g}. \tag{11.25}$$

Then we take P to be 1.00 atm and ρ to be the density of the water that creates the pressure.

Solution

Entering the known values into the expression for h gives

$$h = \frac{1.01 \times 10^5 \text{ N/m}^2}{(1.00 \times 10^3 \text{ kg/m}^3)(9.80 \text{ m/s}^2)} = 10.3 \text{ m}. \tag{11.26}$$

Discussion

Just 10.3 m of water creates the same pressure as 120 km of air. Since water is nearly incompressible, we can neglect any change in its density over this depth.

What do you suppose is the *total* pressure at a depth of 10.3 m in a swimming pool? Does the atmospheric pressure on the water's surface affect the pressure below? The answer is yes. This seems only logical, since both the water's weight and the atmosphere's weight must be supported. So the *total* pressure at a depth of 10.3 m is 2 atm—half from the water above and half from the air above. We shall see in Pascal's Principle that fluid pressures always add in this way.

11.5 Pascal's Principle

LEARNING OBJECTIVES

By the end of this section, you will be able to:

- Define pressure.
- State Pascal's principle.
- Understand applications of Pascal's principle.
- Derive relationships between forces in a hydraulic system.

Pressure is defined as force per unit area. Can pressure be increased in a fluid by pushing directly on the fluid? Yes, but it is much easier if the fluid is enclosed. The heart, for example, increases blood pressure by pushing directly on the blood in an enclosed system (valves closed in a chamber). If you try to push on a fluid in an open system, such as a river, the fluid flows away. An enclosed fluid cannot flow away, and so pressure is more easily increased by an applied force.

What happens to a pressure in an enclosed fluid? Since atoms in a fluid are free to move about, they transmit the pressure to all parts of the fluid and to the walls of the container. Remarkably, the pressure is transmitted *undiminished*. This phenomenon is called **Pascal's principle**, because it was first clearly stated by the French philosopher and scientist Blaise Pascal (1623–1662): A change in pressure applied to an enclosed fluid is transmitted undiminished to all portions of the fluid and to the walls of its container.

PASCAL'S PRINCIPLE

A change in pressure applied to an enclosed fluid is transmitted undiminished to all portions of the fluid and to the walls of its container.

Pascal's principle, an experimentally verified fact, is what makes pressure so important in fluids. Since a change in pressure is transmitted undiminished in an enclosed fluid, we often know more about pressure than other physical quantities in fluids. Moreover, Pascal's principle implies that *the total pressure in a fluid is the sum of the pressures from different sources.* We shall find this fact—that pressures add—very useful.

Blaise Pascal had an interesting life in that he was home-schooled by his father who removed all of the mathematics textbooks from his house and forbade him to study mathematics until the age of 15. This, of course, raised the boy's curiosity, and by the age of 12, he started to teach himself geometry. Despite this early deprivation, Pascal went on to make major contributions in the mathematical fields of probability theory, number theory, and geometry. He is also well known for being the inventor of the first mechanical digital calculator, in addition to his contributions in the field of fluid statics.

Application of Pascal's Principle

One of the most important technological applications of Pascal's principle is found in a *hydraulic system*, which is an enclosed fluid system used to exert forces. The most common hydraulic systems are those that operate car brakes. Let us first consider the simple hydraulic system shown in Figure 11.11.

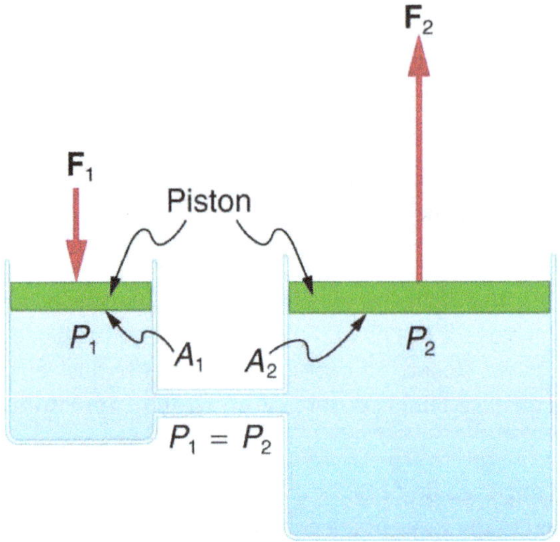

FIGURE 11.11 A typical hydraulic system with two fluid-filled cylinders, capped with pistons and connected by a tube called a hydraulic line. A downward force $\mathbf{F}_1$ on the left piston creates a pressure that is transmitted undiminished to all parts of the enclosed fluid. This results in an upward force $\mathbf{F}_2$ on the right piston that is larger than $\mathbf{F}_1$ because the right piston has a larger area.

Relationship Between Forces in a Hydraulic System

We can derive a relationship between the forces in the simple hydraulic system shown in Figure 11.11 by applying Pascal's principle. Note first that the two pistons in the system are at the same height, and so there will be no difference in pressure due to a difference in depth. Now the pressure due to F_1 acting on area A_1 is simply $P_1 = \frac{F_1}{A_1}$, as defined by $P = \frac{F}{A}$. According to Pascal's principle, this pressure is transmitted undiminished throughout the fluid and to all walls of the container. Thus, a pressure P_2 is felt at the other piston that is equal to P_1. That is $P_1 = P_2$.

But since $P_2 = \frac{F_2}{A_2}$, we see that $\frac{F_1}{A_1} = \frac{F_2}{A_2}$.

This equation relates the ratios of force to area in any hydraulic system, providing the pistons are at the same vertical height and that friction in the system is negligible. Hydraulic systems can increase or decrease the force applied to them. To make the force larger, the pressure is applied to a larger area. For example, if a 100-N force is applied to the left cylinder in Figure 11.11 and the right one has an area five times greater, then the force out is 500 N. Hydraulic systems are analogous to simple levers, but they have the advantage that pressure can be sent through tortuously curved lines to several places at once.

EXAMPLE 11.6

Calculating Force of Wheel Cylinders: Pascal Puts on the Brakes

Consider the automobile hydraulic system shown in Figure 11.12.

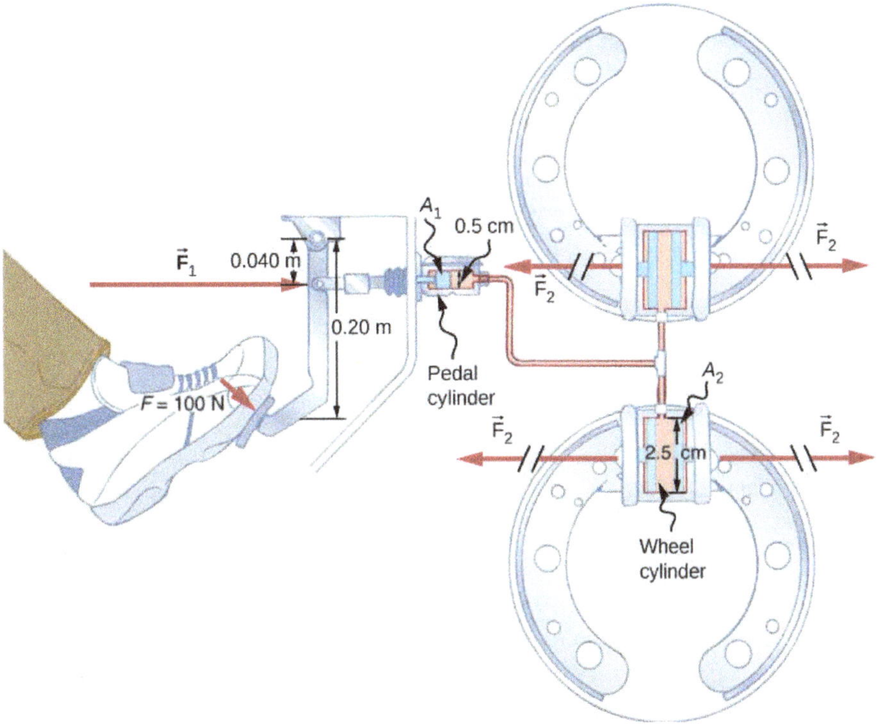

FIGURE 11.12 Hydraulic brakes use Pascal's principle. The driver exerts a force of 100 N on the brake pedal. This force is increased by the simple lever and again by the hydraulic system. Each of the identical wheel cylinders receives the same pressure and, therefore, creates the same force output F_2. The circular cross-sectional areas of the pedal and wheel cylinders are represented by A_1 and A_2, respectively

A force of 100 N is applied to the brake pedal, which acts on the pedal cylinder through a lever. A force of 500 N is exerted on the pedal cylinder. (The reader can verify that the force is 500 N using techniques of statics from Applications of Statics, Including Problem-Solving Strategies.) Pressure created in the pedal cylinder is transmitted to four wheel cylinders. The pedal cylinder has a diameter of 0.500 cm, and each wheel cylinder has a diameter of 2.50 cm. Calculate the force F_2 created at each of the wheel cylinders.

Strategy

We are given the force F_1 that is applied to the pedal cylinder. The cross-sectional areas A_1 and A_2 can be calculated from their given diameters. Then $\frac{F_1}{A_1} = \frac{F_2}{A_2}$ can be used to find the force F_2. Manipulate this algebraically to get F_2 on one side and substitute known values:

Solution

Pascal's principle applied to hydraulic systems is given by $\frac{F_1}{A_1} = \frac{F_2}{A_2}$:

$$F_2 = \frac{A_2}{A_1}F_1 = \frac{\pi r_2^2}{\pi r_1^2}F_1 = \frac{(1.25 \text{ cm})^2}{(0.250 \text{ cm})^2} \times 500 \text{ N} = 1.25 \times 10^4 \text{ N}. \quad (11.27)$$

Discussion

This value is the force exerted by each of the four wheel cylinders. Note that we can add as many wheel cylinders as we wish. If each has a 2.50-cm diameter, each will exert 1.25×10^4 N.

A simple hydraulic system, such as a simple machine, can increase force but cannot do more work than done on it. Work is force times distance moved, and the wheel cylinder moves through a smaller distance than the pedal cylinder. Furthermore, the more wheels added, the smaller the distance each moves. Many hydraulic systems—such as power brakes and those in bulldozers—have a motorized pump that actually does most of the work in the system. The movement of the legs of a spider is achieved partly by hydraulics. Using hydraulics, a jumping spider can create a force that makes it capable of jumping 25 times its length!

MAKING CONNECTIONS: CONSERVATION OF ENERGY

Conservation of energy applied to a hydraulic system tells us that the system cannot do more work than is done on it. Work transfers energy, and so the work output cannot exceed the work input. Power brakes and other similar hydraulic systems use pumps to supply extra energy when needed.

11.6 Gauge Pressure, Absolute Pressure, and Pressure Measurement

LEARNING OBJECTIVES

By the end of this section, you will be able to:

- Define gauge pressure and absolute pressure.
- Understand the working of aneroid and open-tube barometers.

If you limp into a gas station with a nearly flat tire, you will notice the tire gauge on the airline reads nearly zero when you begin to fill it. In fact, if there were a gaping hole in your tire, the gauge would read zero, even though atmospheric pressure exists in the tire. Why does the gauge read zero? There is no mystery here. Tire gauges are simply designed to read zero at atmospheric pressure and positive when pressure is greater than atmospheric.

Similarly, atmospheric pressure adds to blood pressure in every part of the circulatory system. (As noted in Pascal's Principle, the total pressure in a fluid is the sum of the pressures from different sources—here, the heart and the atmosphere.) But atmospheric pressure has no net effect on blood flow since it adds to the pressure coming out of the heart and going back into it, too. What is important is how much *greater* blood pressure is than atmospheric pressure. Blood pressure measurements, like tire pressures, are thus made relative to atmospheric pressure.

In brief, it is very common for pressure gauges to ignore atmospheric pressure—that is, to read zero at atmospheric pressure. We therefore define **gauge pressure** to be the pressure relative to atmospheric pressure. Gauge pressure is positive for pressures above atmospheric pressure, and negative for pressures below it.

GAUGE PRESSURE

Gauge pressure is the pressure relative to atmospheric pressure. Gauge pressure is positive for pressures above atmospheric pressure, and negative for pressures below it.

In fact, atmospheric pressure does add to the pressure in any fluid not enclosed in a rigid container. This happens because of Pascal's principle. The total pressure, or **absolute pressure**, is thus the sum of gauge pressure and atmospheric pressure: $P_{\text{abs}} = P_{\text{g}} + P_{\text{atm}}$ where P_{abs} is absolute pressure, P_{g} is gauge pressure, and P_{atm} is atmospheric pressure. For example, if your tire gauge reads 34 psi (pounds per square inch), then the absolute pressure is 34 psi plus 14.7 psi (P_{atm} in psi), or 48.7 psi (equivalent to 336 kPa).

ABSOLUTE PRESSURE

Absolute pressure is the sum of gauge pressure and atmospheric pressure.

For reasons we will explore later, in most cases the absolute pressure in fluids cannot be negative. Fluids push rather than pull, so the smallest absolute pressure is zero. (A negative absolute pressure is a pull.) Thus the smallest possible gauge pressure is $P_{\text{g}} = -P_{\text{atm}}$ (this makes P_{abs} zero). There is no theoretical limit to how large a gauge pressure can be.

There are a host of devices for measuring pressure, ranging from tire gauges to blood pressure cuffs. Pascal's principle is of major importance in these devices. The undiminished transmission of pressure through a fluid allows precise remote sensing of pressures. Remote sensing is often more convenient than putting a measuring device into a system, such as a person's artery.

Figure 11.13 shows one of the many types of mechanical pressure gauges in use today. In all mechanical pressure gauges, pressure results in a force that is converted (or transduced) into some type of readout.

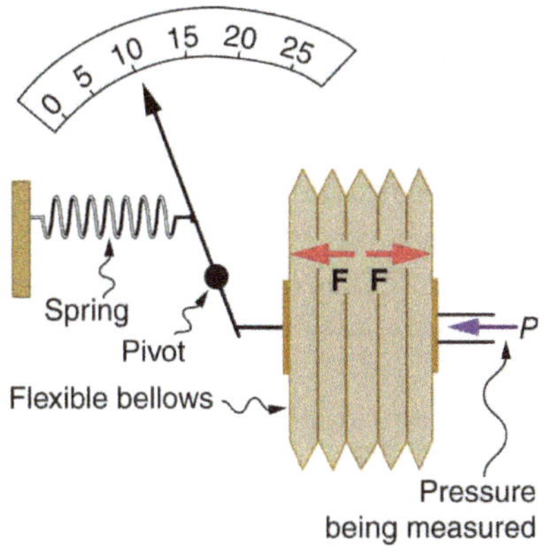

FIGURE 11.13 This aneroid gauge utilizes flexible bellows connected to a mechanical indicator to measure pressure.

An entire class of gauges uses the property that pressure due to the weight of a fluid is given by $P = h\rho g$. Consider the U-shaped tube shown in Figure 11.14, for example. This simple tube is called a *manometer*. In Figure 11.14(a), both sides of the tube are open to the atmosphere. Atmospheric pressure therefore pushes down on each side equally so its effect cancels. If the fluid is deeper on one side, there is a greater pressure on the deeper side, and the fluid flows away from that side until the depths are equal.

Let us examine how a manometer is used to measure pressure. Suppose one side of the U-tube is connected to some source of pressure P_{abs} such as the toy balloon in Figure 11.14(b) or the vacuum-packed peanut jar shown in Figure 11.14(c). Pressure is transmitted undiminished to the manometer, and the fluid levels are no longer equal. In Figure 11.14(b), P_{abs} is greater than atmospheric pressure, whereas in Figure 11.14(c), P_{abs} is less than atmospheric pressure. In both cases, P_{abs} differs from atmospheric pressure by an amount $h\rho g$, where ρ is the density of the fluid in the manometer. In Figure 11.14(b), P_{abs} can support a column of fluid of height h, and so it must exert a pressure $h\rho g$ greater than atmospheric pressure (the gauge pressure P_g is positive). In Figure 11.14(c), atmospheric pressure can support a column of fluid of height h, and so P_{abs} is less than atmospheric pressure by an amount $h\rho g$ (the gauge pressure P_g is negative). A manometer with one side open to the atmosphere is an ideal device for measuring gauge pressures. The gauge pressure is $P_g = h\rho g$ and is found by measuring h.

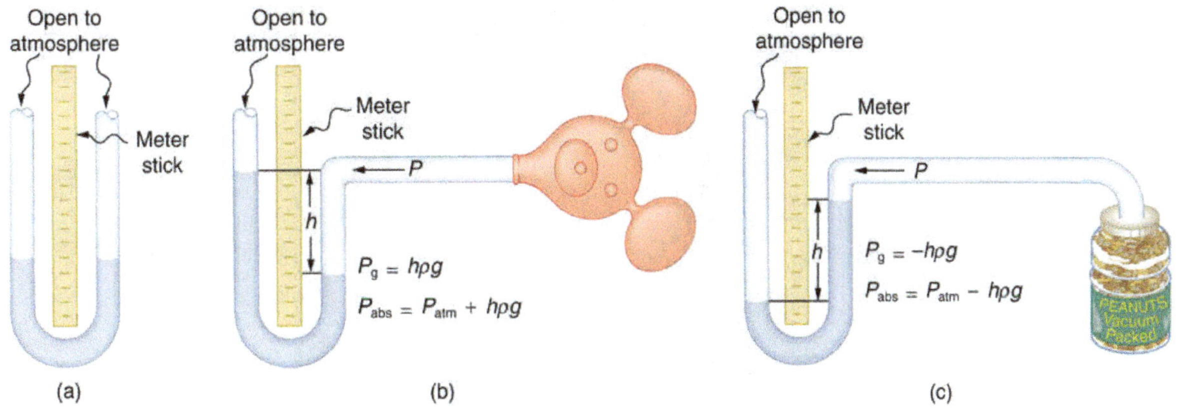

FIGURE 11.14 An open-tube manometer has one side open to the atmosphere. (a) Fluid depth must be the same on both sides, or the pressure each side exerts at the bottom will be unequal and there will be flow from the deeper side. (b) A positive gauge pressure $P_g = h\rho g$ transmitted to one side of the manometer can support a column of fluid of height h. (c) Similarly, atmospheric pressure is greater than a negative gauge pressure P_g by an amount $h\rho g$. The jar's rigidity prevents atmospheric pressure from being transmitted to the peanuts.

Mercury manometers are often used to measure arterial blood pressure. An inflatable cuff is placed on the upper arm as shown in Figure 11.15. By squeezing the bulb, the person making the measurement exerts pressure, which is transmitted undiminished to both the main artery in the arm and the manometer. When this applied pressure exceeds blood pressure, blood flow below the cuff is cut off. The person making the measurement then slowly lowers the applied pressure and listens for blood flow to resume. Blood pressure pulsates because of the pumping action of the heart, reaching a maximum, called **systolic pressure**, and a minimum, called **diastolic pressure**, with each heartbeat. Systolic pressure is measured by noting the value of h when blood flow first begins as cuff pressure is lowered. Diastolic pressure is measured by noting h when blood flows without interruption. The typical blood pressure of a young adult raises the mercury to a height of 120 mm at systolic and 80 mm at diastolic. This is commonly quoted as 120 over 80, or 120/80. The first pressure is representative of the maximum output of the heart; the second is due to the elasticity of the arteries in maintaining the pressure between beats. The density of the mercury fluid in the manometer is 13.6 times greater than water, so the height of the fluid will be 1/13.6 of that in a water manometer. This reduced height can make measurements difficult, so mercury manometers are used to measure larger pressures, such as blood pressure. The density of mercury is such that $1.0 \text{ mm Hg} = 133 \text{ Pa}$.

SYSTOLIC PRESSURE

Systolic pressure is the maximum blood pressure.

DIASTOLIC PRESSURE

Diastolic pressure is the minimum blood pressure.

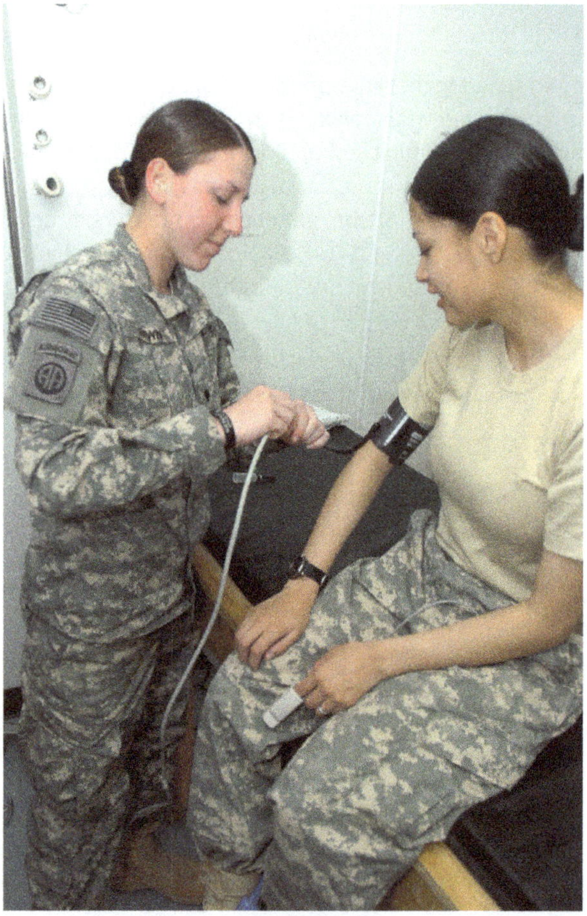

FIGURE 11.15 In routine blood pressure measurements, an inflatable cuff is placed on the upper arm at the same level as the heart. Blood flow is detected just below the cuff, and corresponding pressures are transmitted to a mercury-filled manometer. (credit: U.S. Army photo by Spc. Micah E. Clare\4TH BCT)

EXAMPLE 11.7

Calculating Height of IV Bag: Blood Pressure and Intravenous Infusions

Intravenous infusions are usually made with the help of the gravitational force. Assuming that the density of the fluid being administered is 1.00 g/ml, at what height should the IV bag be placed above the entry point so that the fluid just enters the vein if the blood pressure in the vein is 18 mm Hg above atmospheric pressure? Assume that the IV bag is collapsible.

Strategy for (a)

For the fluid to just enter the vein, its pressure at entry must exceed the blood pressure in the vein (18 mm Hg above atmospheric pressure). We therefore need to find the height of fluid that corresponds to this gauge pressure.

Solution

We first need to convert the pressure into SI units. Since $1.0\text{ mm Hg} = 133\text{ Pa}$,

$$P = 18\text{ mm Hg} \times \frac{133\text{ Pa}}{1.0\text{ mm Hg}} = 2400\text{ Pa}. \tag{11.28}$$

Rearranging $P_g = h\rho g$ for h gives $h = \frac{P_g}{\rho g}$. Substituting known values into this equation gives

$$\begin{aligned} h &= \frac{2400\text{ N/m}^2}{\left(1.0\times10^3\text{ kg/m}^3\right)\left(9.80\text{ m/s}^2\right)} \\ &= 0.24\text{ m}. \end{aligned} \tag{11.29}$$

Discussion

The IV bag must be placed at 0.24 m above the entry point into the arm for the fluid to just enter the arm. Generally, IV bags are placed higher than this. You may have noticed that the bags used for blood collection are placed below the donor to allow blood to flow easily from the arm to the bag, which is the opposite direction of flow than required in the example presented here.

A *barometer* is a device that measures atmospheric pressure. A mercury barometer is shown in Figure 11.16. This device measures atmospheric pressure, rather than gauge pressure, because there is a nearly pure vacuum above the mercury in the tube. The height of the mercury is such that $h\rho g = P_{atm}$. When atmospheric pressure varies, the mercury rises or falls, giving important clues to weather forecasters. The barometer can also be used as an altimeter, since average atmospheric pressure varies with altitude. Mercury barometers and manometers are so common that units of mm Hg are often quoted for atmospheric pressure and blood pressures. Table 11.2 gives conversion factors for some of the more commonly used units of pressure.

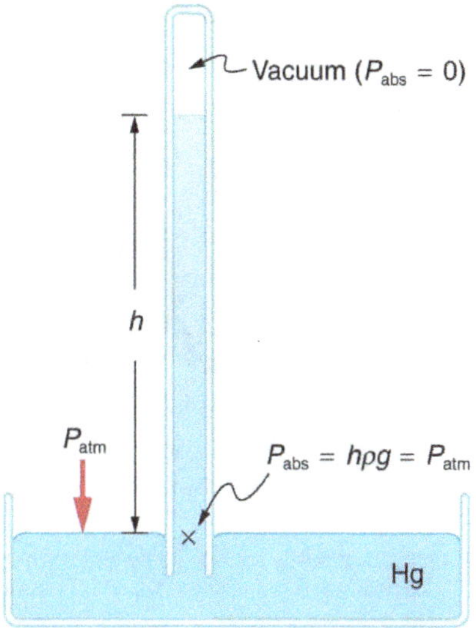

FIGURE 11.16 A mercury barometer measures atmospheric pressure. The pressure due to the mercury's weight, $h\rho g$, equals atmospheric pressure. The atmosphere is able to force mercury in the tube to a height h because the pressure above the mercury is zero.

Conversion to N/m^2 (Pa)	Conversion from atm
$1.0 \text{ atm} = 1.013 \times 10^5 \text{ N/m}^2$	$1.0 \text{ atm} = 1.013 \times 10^5 \text{ N/m}^2$
$1.0 \text{ dyne/cm}^2 = 0.10 \text{ N/m}^2$	$1.0 \text{ atm} = 1.013 \times 10^6 \text{ dyne/cm}^2$
$1.0 \text{ kg/cm}^2 = 9.8 \times 10^4 \text{ N/m}^2$	$1.0 \text{ atm} = 1.013 \text{ kg/cm}^2$
$1.0 \text{ lb/in.}^2 = 6.90 \times 10^3 \text{ N/m}^2$	$1.0 \text{ atm} = 14.7 \text{ lb/in.}^2$
$1.0 \text{ mm Hg} = 133 \text{ N/m}^2$	$1.0 \text{ atm} = 760 \text{ mm Hg}$
$1.0 \text{ cm Hg} = 1.33 \times 10^3 \text{ N/m}^2$	$1.0 \text{ atm} = 76.0 \text{ cm Hg}$
$1.0 \text{ cm water} = 98.1 \text{ N/m}^2$	$1.0 \text{ atm} = 1.03 \times 10^3 \text{ cm water}$
$1.0 \text{ bar} = 1.000 \times 10^5 \text{ N/m}^2$	$1.0 \text{ atm} = 1.013 \text{ bar}$
$1.0 \text{ millibar} = 1.000 \times 10^2 \text{ N/m}^2$	$1.0 \text{ atm} = 1013 \text{ millibar}$

TABLE 11.2 Conversion Factors for Various Pressure Units

11.7 Archimedes' Principle

LEARNING OBJECTIVES

By the end of this section, you will be able to:

- Define buoyant force.
- State Archimedes' principle.
- Understand why objects float or sink.
- Understand the relationship between density and Archimedes' principle.

When you rise from lounging in a warm bath, your arms feel strangely heavy. This is because you no longer have the buoyant support of the water. Where does this buoyant force come from? Why is it that some things float and others do not? Do objects that sink get any support at all from the fluid? Is your body buoyed by the atmosphere, or are only helium balloons affected? (See Figure 11.17.)

FIGURE 11.17 (a) Even objects that sink, like this anchor, are partly supported by water when submerged. (b) Submarines have adjustable density (ballast tanks) so that they may float or sink as desired. (credit: Allied Navy) (c) Helium-filled balloons tug upward on their strings, demonstrating air's buoyant effect. (credit: Crystl)

Answers to all these questions, and many others, are based on the fact that pressure increases with depth in a fluid. This means that the upward force on the bottom of an object in a fluid is greater than the downward force on the top of the object. There is a net upward, or **buoyant force** on any object in any fluid. (See Figure 11.18.) If the buoyant force is greater than the object's weight, the object will rise to the surface and float. If the buoyant force is less than the object's weight, the object will sink. If the buoyant force equals the object's weight, the object will remain suspended at that depth. The buoyant force is always present whether the object floats, sinks, or is suspended in a fluid.

BUOYANT FORCE

The buoyant force is the net upward force on any object in any fluid.

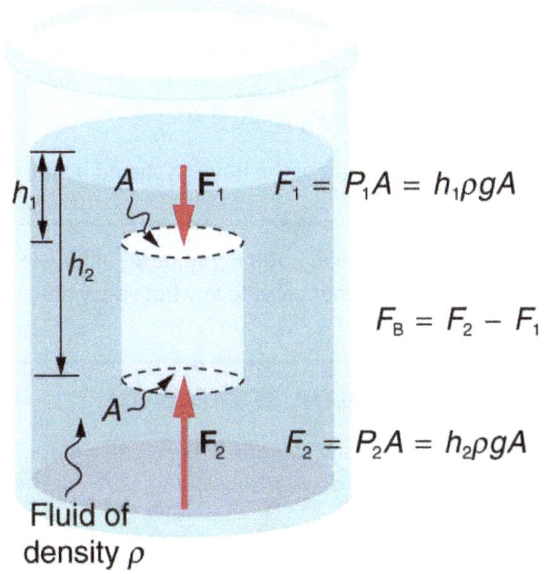

FIGURE 11.18 Pressure due to the weight of a fluid increases with depth since $P = h\rho g$. This pressure and associated upward force on the bottom of the cylinder are greater than the downward force on the top of the cylinder. Their difference is the buoyant force $\mathbf{F_B}$. (Horizontal forces cancel.)

Just how great is this buoyant force? To answer this question, think about what happens when a submerged object is removed from a fluid, as in Figure 11.19.

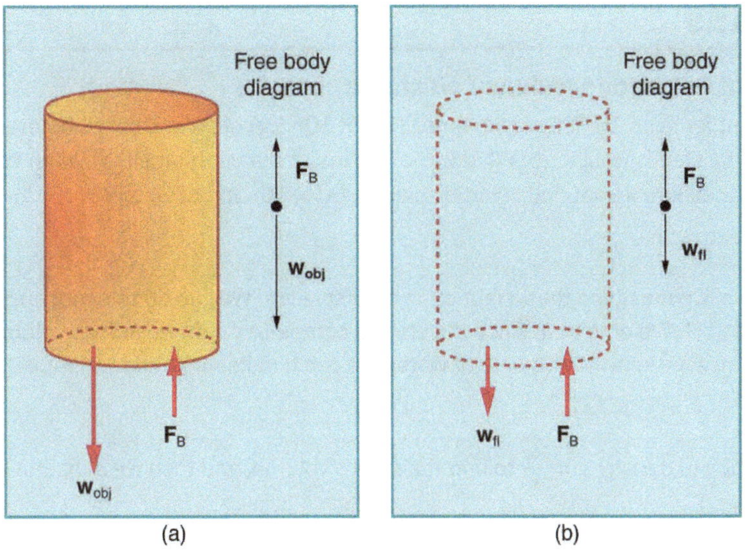

FIGURE 11.19 (a) An object submerged in a fluid experiences a buoyant force F_B. If F_B is greater than the weight of the object, the object will rise. If F_B is less than the weight of the object, the object will sink. (b) If the object is removed, it is replaced by fluid having weight w_{fl}. Since this weight is supported by surrounding fluid, the buoyant force must equal the weight of the fluid displaced. That is, $F_B = w_{fl}$,a statement of Archimedes' principle.

The space it occupied is filled by fluid having a weight w_{fl}. This weight is supported by the surrounding fluid, and so the buoyant force must equal w_{fl}, the weight of the fluid displaced by the object. It is a tribute to the genius of the

Greek mathematician and inventor Archimedes (ca. 287–212 B.C.) that he stated this principle long before concepts of force were well established. Stated in words, **Archimedes' principle** is as follows: The buoyant force on an object equals the weight of the fluid it displaces. In equation form, Archimedes' principle is

$$F_B = w_{fl}, \quad (11.30)$$

where F_B is the buoyant force and w_{fl} is the weight of the fluid displaced by the object. Archimedes' principle is valid in general, for any object in any fluid, whether partially or totally submerged.

ARCHIMEDES' PRINCIPLE

According to this principle the buoyant force on an object equals the weight of the fluid it displaces. In equation form, Archimedes' principle is

$$F_B = w_{fl}, \quad (11.31)$$

where F_B is the buoyant force and w_{fl} is the weight of the fluid displaced by the object.

Humm ... High-tech body swimsuits were introduced in 2008 in preparation for the Beijing Olympics. One concern (and international rule) was that these suits should not provide any buoyancy advantage. How do you think that this rule could be verified?

MAKING CONNECTIONS: TAKE-HOME INVESTIGATION

The density of aluminum foil is 2.7 times the density of water. Take a piece of foil, roll it up into a ball and drop it into water. Does it sink? Why or why not? Can you make it sink?

Floating and Sinking

Drop a lump of clay in water. It will sink. Then mold the lump of clay into the shape of a boat, and it will float. Because of its shape, the boat displaces more water than the lump and experiences a greater buoyant force. The same is true of steel ships.

EXAMPLE 11.8

Calculating buoyant force: dependency on shape

(a) Calculate the buoyant force on 10,000 metric tons $(1.00 \times 10^7 \text{ kg})$ of solid steel completely submerged in water, and compare this with the steel's weight. (b) What is the maximum buoyant force that water could exert on this same steel if it were shaped into a boat that could displace $1.00 \times 10^5 \text{ m}^3$ of water?

Strategy for (a)

To find the buoyant force, we must find the weight of water displaced. We can do this by using the densities of water and steel given in Table 11.1. We note that, since the steel is completely submerged, its volume and the water's volume are the same. Once we know the volume of water, we can find its mass and weight.

Solution for (a)

First, we use the definition of density $\rho = \frac{m}{V}$ to find the steel's volume, and then we substitute values for mass and density. This gives

$$V_{st} = \frac{m_{st}}{\rho_{st}} = \frac{1.00 \times 10^7 \text{ kg}}{7.8 \times 10^3 \text{ kg/m}^3} = 1.28 \times 10^3 \text{ m}^3. \quad (11.32)$$

Because the steel is completely submerged, this is also the volume of water displaced, V_w. We can now find the mass of water displaced from the relationship between its volume and density, both of which are known. This gives

$$\begin{aligned} m_{\text{w}} &= \rho_{\text{w}} V_{\text{w}} = (1.000 \times 10^3\ \text{kg/m}^3)(1.28 \times 10^3\ \text{m}^3) \\ &= 1.28 \times 10^6\ \text{kg}. \end{aligned} \qquad 11.33$$

By Archimedes' principle, the weight of water displaced is $m_{\text{w}} g$, so the buoyant force is

$$\begin{aligned} F_{\text{B}} &= w_{\text{w}} = m_{\text{w}} g = \left(1.28 \times 10^6\ \text{kg}\right)\left(9.80\ \text{m/s}^2\right) \\ &= 1.3 \times 10^7\ \text{N}. \end{aligned} \qquad 11.34$$

The steel's weight is $m_{\text{w}} g = 9.80 \times 10^7\ \text{N}$, which is much greater than the buoyant force, so the steel will remain submerged. Note that the buoyant force is rounded to two digits because the density of steel is given to only two digits.

Strategy for (b)

Here we are given the maximum volume of water the steel boat can displace. The buoyant force is the weight of this volume of water.

Solution for (b)

The mass of water displaced is found from its relationship to density and volume, both of which are known. That is,

$$\begin{aligned} m_{\text{w}} &= \rho_{\text{w}} V_{\text{w}} = \left(1.000 \times 10^3\ \text{kg/m}^3\right)\left(1.00 \times 10^5\ \text{m}^3\right) \\ &= 1.00 \times 10^8\ \text{kg}. \end{aligned} \qquad 11.35$$

The maximum buoyant force is the weight of this much water, or

$$\begin{aligned} F_{\text{B}} &= w_{\text{w}} = m_{\text{w}} g = \left(1.00 \times 10^8\ \text{kg}\right)\left(9.80\ \text{m/s}^2\right) \\ &= 9.80 \times 10^8\ \text{N}. \end{aligned} \qquad 11.36$$

Discussion

The maximum buoyant force is ten times the weight of the steel, meaning the ship can carry a load nine times its own weight without sinking.

MAKING CONNECTIONS: TAKE-HOME INVESTIGATION

A piece of household aluminum foil is 0.016 mm thick. Use a piece of foil that measures 10 cm by 15 cm. (a) What is the mass of this amount of foil? (b) If the foil is folded to give it four sides, and paper clips or washers are added to this "boat," what shape of the boat would allow it to hold the most "cargo" when placed in water? Test your prediction.

Density and Archimedes' Principle

Density plays a crucial role in Archimedes' principle. The average density of an object is what ultimately determines whether it floats. If its average density is less than that of the surrounding fluid, it will float. This is because the fluid, having a higher density, contains more mass and hence more weight in the same volume. The buoyant force, which equals the weight of the fluid displaced, is thus greater than the weight of the object. Likewise, an object denser than the fluid will sink.

The extent to which a floating object is submerged depends on how the object's density is related to that of the fluid. In Figure 11.20, for example, the unloaded ship has a lower density and less of it is submerged compared with the same ship loaded. We can derive a quantitative expression for the fraction submerged by considering density. The fraction submerged is the ratio of the volume submerged to the volume of the object, or

$$\text{fraction submerged} = \frac{V_{\text{sub}}}{V_{\text{obj}}} = \frac{V_{\text{fl}}}{V_{\text{obj}}}. \qquad 11.37$$

The volume submerged equals the volume of fluid displaced, which we call V_{fl}. Now we can obtain the relationship between the densities by substituting $\rho = \frac{m}{V}$ into the expression. This gives

$$\frac{V_{\text{fl}}}{V_{\text{obj}}} = \frac{m_{\text{fl}}/\rho_{\text{fl}}}{m_{\text{obj}}/\bar{\rho}_{\text{obj}}}, \tag{11.38}$$

where $\bar{\rho}_{\text{obj}}$ is the average density of the object and ρ_{fl} is the density of the fluid. Since the object floats, its mass and that of the displaced fluid are equal, and so they cancel from the equation, leaving

$$\text{fraction submerged} = \frac{\bar{\rho}_{\text{obj}}}{\rho_{\text{fl}}}. \tag{11.39}$$

(a) (b)

FIGURE 11.20 An unloaded ship (a) floats higher in the water than a loaded ship (b).

We use this last relationship to measure densities. This is done by measuring the fraction of a floating object that is submerged—for example, with a hydrometer. It is useful to define the ratio of the density of an object to a fluid (usually water) as **specific gravity**:

$$\text{specific gravity} = \frac{\bar{\rho}}{\rho_{\text{w}}}, \tag{11.40}$$

where $\bar{\rho}$ is the average density of the object or substance and ρ_{w} is the density of water at 4.00°C. Specific gravity is dimensionless, independent of whatever units are used for ρ. If an object floats, its specific gravity is less than one. If it sinks, its specific gravity is greater than one. Moreover, the fraction of a floating object that is submerged equals its specific gravity. If an object's specific gravity is exactly 1, then it will remain suspended in the fluid, neither sinking nor floating. Scuba divers try to obtain this state so that they can hover in the water. We measure the specific gravity of fluids, such as battery acid, radiator fluid, and urine, as an indicator of their condition. One device for measuring specific gravity is shown in Figure 11.21.

SPECIFIC GRAVITY

Specific gravity is the ratio of the density of an object to a fluid (usually water).

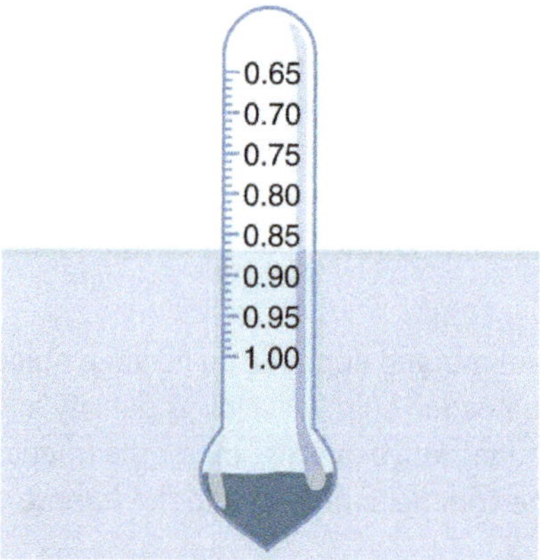

FIGURE 11.21 This hydrometer is floating in a fluid of specific gravity 0.87. The glass hydrometer is filled with air and weighted with lead at the bottom. It floats highest in the densest fluids and has been calibrated and labeled so that specific gravity can be read from it directly.

EXAMPLE 11.9

Calculating Average Density: Floating Woman

Suppose a 60.0-kg woman floats in freshwater with 97.0% of her volume submerged when her lungs are full of air. What is her average density?

Strategy

We can find the woman's density by solving the equation

$$\text{fraction submerged} = \frac{\bar{\rho}_{\text{obj}}}{\rho_{\text{fl}}} \tag{11.41}$$

for the density of the object. This yields

$$\bar{\rho}_{\text{obj}} = \bar{\rho}_{\text{person}} = (\text{fraction submerged}) \cdot \rho_{\text{fl}}. \tag{11.42}$$

We know both the fraction submerged and the density of water, and so we can calculate the woman's density.

Solution

Entering the known values into the expression for her density, we obtain

$$\bar{\rho}_{\text{person}} = 0.970 \cdot \left(10^3 \frac{\text{kg}}{\text{m}^3}\right) = 970 \frac{\text{kg}}{\text{m}^3}. \tag{11.43}$$

Discussion

Her density is less than the fluid density. We expect this because she floats. Body density is one indicator of a person's percent body fat, of interest in medical diagnostics and athletic training. (See Figure 11.22.)

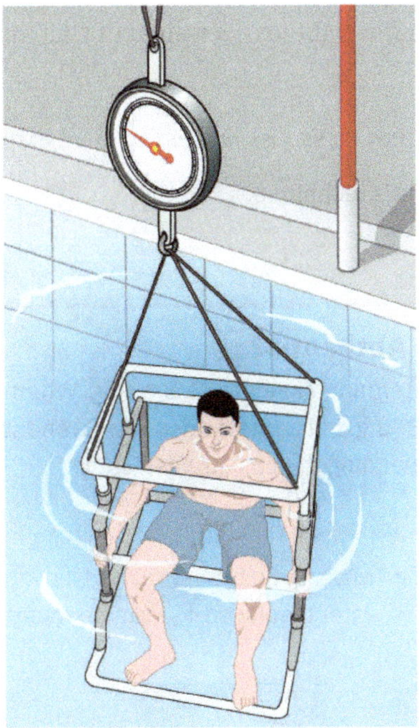

FIGURE 11.22 Subject in a hydrostatis weighing device, where they are weighed while completely submerged as part of a body density determination. The subject must completely empty their lungs and hold a metal weight in order to sink. Corrections are made for the residual air in the lungs (measured separately) and the metal weight. Their corrected submerged weight, their weight in air, and pinch tests of strategic fatty areas are used to calculate the percent body fat.

There are many obvious examples of lower-density objects or substances floating in higher-density fluids—oil on water, a hot-air balloon, a bit of cork in wine, an iceberg, and hot wax in a "lava lamp," to name a few. Less obvious examples include lava rising in a volcano and mountain ranges floating on the higher-density crust and mantle beneath them. Even seemingly solid Earth has fluid characteristics.

More Density Measurements

One of the most common techniques for determining density is shown in Figure 11.23.

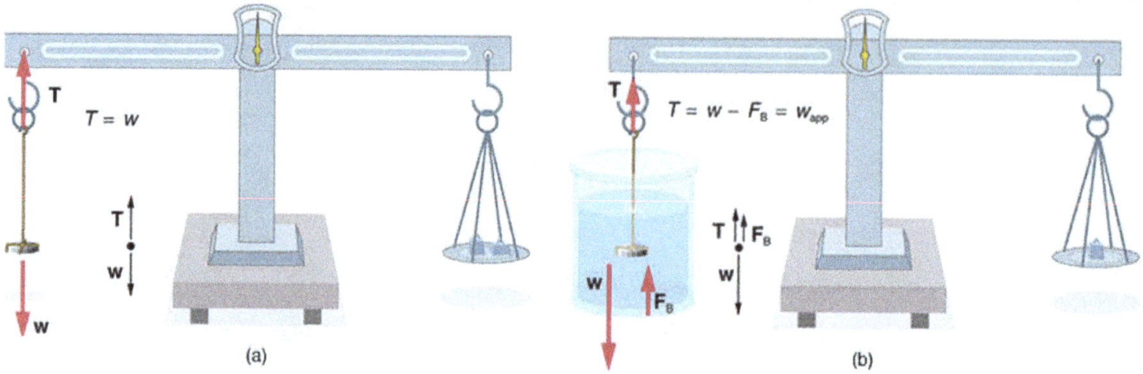

FIGURE 11.23 (a) A coin is weighed in air. (b) The apparent weight of the coin is determined while it is completely submerged in a fluid of known density. These two measurements are used to calculate the density of the coin.

An object, here a coin, is weighed in air and then weighed again while submerged in a liquid. The density of the coin, an indication of its authenticity, can be calculated if the fluid density is known. This same technique can also be used to determine the density of the fluid if the density of the coin is known. All of these calculations are based on Archimedes' principle.

Archimedes' principle states that the buoyant force on the object equals the weight of the fluid displaced. This, in turn, means that the object *appears* to weigh less when submerged; we call this measurement the object's *apparent weight*. The object suffers an *apparent weight loss* equal to the weight of the fluid displaced. Alternatively, on balances that measure mass, the object suffers an *apparent mass loss* equal to the mass of fluid displaced. That is

$$\text{apparent weight loss} = \text{weight of fluid displaced} \qquad 11.44$$

or

$$\text{apparent mass loss} = \text{mass of fluid displaced.} \qquad 11.45$$

The next example illustrates the use of this technique.

EXAMPLE 11.10

Calculating Density: Is the Coin Authentic?

The mass of an ancient Greek coin is determined in air to be 8.630 g. When the coin is submerged in water as shown in Figure 11.23, its apparent mass is 7.800 g. Calculate its density, given that water has a density of $1.000\ \text{g/cm}^3$ and that effects caused by the wire suspending the coin are negligible.

Strategy

To calculate the coin's density, we need its mass (which is given) and its volume. The volume of the coin equals the volume of water displaced. The volume of water displaced V_w can be found by solving the equation for density $\rho = \frac{m}{V}$ for V.

Solution

The volume of water is $V_\text{w} = \frac{m_\text{w}}{\rho_\text{w}}$ where m_w is the mass of water displaced. As noted, the mass of the water displaced equals the apparent mass loss, which is $m_\text{w} = 8.630\ \text{g} - 7.800\ \text{g} = 0.830\ \text{g}$. Thus the volume of water is $V_\text{w} = \frac{0.830\ \text{g}}{1.000\ \text{g/cm}^3} = 0.830\ \text{cm}^3$. This is also the volume of the coin, since it is completely submerged. We can now find the density of the coin using the definition of density:

$$\rho_c = \frac{m_c}{V_c} = \frac{8.630 \text{ g}}{0.830 \text{ cm}^3} = 10.4 \text{ g/cm}^3. \qquad 11.46$$

Discussion

You can see from Table 11.1 that this density is very close to that of pure silver, appropriate for this type of ancient coin. Most modern counterfeits are not pure silver.

This brings us back to Archimedes' principle and how it came into being. As the story goes, the king of Syracuse gave Archimedes the task of determining whether the royal crown maker was supplying a crown of pure gold. The purity of gold is difficult to determine by color (it can be diluted with other metals and still look as yellow as pure gold), and other analytical techniques had not yet been conceived. Even ancient peoples, however, realized that the density of gold was greater than that of any other then-known substance. Archimedes purportedly agonized over his task and had his inspiration one day while at the public baths, pondering the support the water gave his body. He came up with his now-famous principle, saw how to apply it to determine density, and ran naked down the streets of Syracuse crying "Eureka!" (Greek for "I have found it"). Similar behavior can be observed in contemporary physicists from time to time!

11.8 Cohesion and Adhesion in Liquids: Surface Tension and Capillary Action

LEARNING OBJECTIVES

By the end of this section, you will be able to:

- Understand cohesive and adhesive forces.
- Define surface tension.
- Understand capillary action.

Cohesion and Adhesion in Liquids

Children blow soap bubbles and play in the spray of a sprinkler on a hot summer day. (See Figure 11.24.) An underwater spider keeps his air supply in a shiny bubble he carries wrapped around him. A technician draws blood into a small-diameter tube just by touching it to a drop on a pricked finger. A premature infant struggles to inflate her lungs. What is the common thread? All these activities are dominated by the attractive forces between atoms and molecules in liquids—both within a liquid and between the liquid and its surroundings.

Attractive forces between molecules of the same type are called **cohesive forces**. Liquids can, for example, be held in open containers because cohesive forces hold the molecules together. Attractive forces between molecules of different types are called **adhesive forces**. Such forces cause liquid drops to cling to window panes, for example. In this section we examine effects directly attributable to cohesive and adhesive forces in liquids.

COHESIVE FORCES

Attractive forces between molecules of the same type are called cohesive forces.

ADHESIVE FORCES

Attractive forces between molecules of different types are called adhesive forces.

FIGURE 11.24 The soap bubbles in this photograph are caused by cohesive forces among molecules in liquids. (credit: Steve Ford Elliott)

Surface Tension

Cohesive forces between molecules cause the surface of a liquid to contract to the smallest possible surface area. This general effect is called **surface tension**. Molecules on the surface are pulled inward by cohesive forces, reducing the surface area. Molecules inside the liquid experience zero net force, since they have neighbors on all sides.

SURFACE TENSION

Cohesive forces between molecules cause the surface of a liquid to contract to the smallest possible surface area. This general effect is called surface tension.

MAKING CONNECTIONS: SURFACE TENSION

Forces between atoms and molecules underlie the macroscopic effect called surface tension. These attractive forces pull the molecules closer together and tend to minimize the surface area. This is another example of a submicroscopic explanation for a macroscopic phenomenon.

The model of a liquid surface acting like a stretched elastic sheet can effectively explain surface tension effects. For example, some insects can walk on water (as opposed to floating in it) as we would walk on a trampoline—they dent the surface as shown in Figure 11.25(a). Figure 11.25(b) shows another example, where a needle rests on a water surface. The iron needle cannot, and does not, float, because its density is greater than that of water. Rather, its weight is supported by forces in the stretched surface that try to make the surface smaller or flatter. If the needle were placed point down on the surface, its weight acting on a smaller area would break the surface, and it would sink.

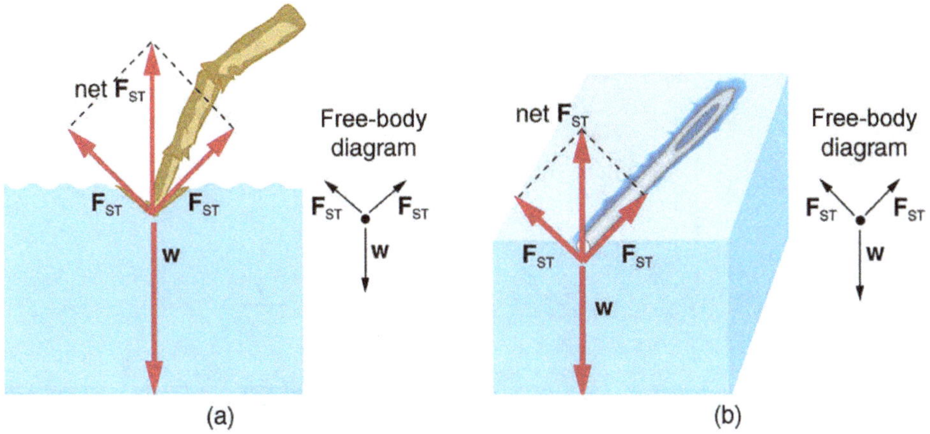

FIGURE 11.25 Surface tension supporting the weight of an insect and an iron needle, both of which rest on the surface without penetrating it. They are not floating; rather, they are supported by the surface of the liquid. (a) An insect leg dents the water surface. F_{ST} is a restoring force (surface tension) parallel to the surface. (b) An iron needle similarly dents a water surface until the restoring force (surface tension) grows to equal its weight.

Surface tension is proportional to the strength of the cohesive force, which varies with the type of liquid. Surface tension γ is defined to be the force F per unit length L exerted by a stretched liquid membrane:

$$\gamma = \frac{F}{L}. \tag{11.47}$$

Table 11.3 lists values of γ for some liquids. For the insect of Figure 11.25(a), its weight w is supported by the upward components of the surface tension force: $w = \gamma L \sin\theta$, where L is the circumference of the insect's foot in contact with the water. Figure 11.26 shows one way to measure surface tension. The liquid film exerts a force on the movable wire in an attempt to reduce its surface area. The magnitude of this force depends on the surface tension of the liquid and can be measured accurately.

Surface tension is the reason why liquids form bubbles and droplets. The inward surface tension force causes bubbles to be approximately spherical and raises the pressure of the gas trapped inside relative to atmospheric pressure outside. It can be shown that the gauge pressure P inside a spherical bubble is given by

$$P = \frac{4\gamma}{r}, \tag{11.48}$$

where r is the radius of the bubble. Thus the pressure inside a bubble is greatest when the bubble is the smallest. Another bit of evidence for this is illustrated in Figure 11.27. When air is allowed to flow between two balloons of unequal size, the smaller balloon tends to collapse, filling the larger balloon.

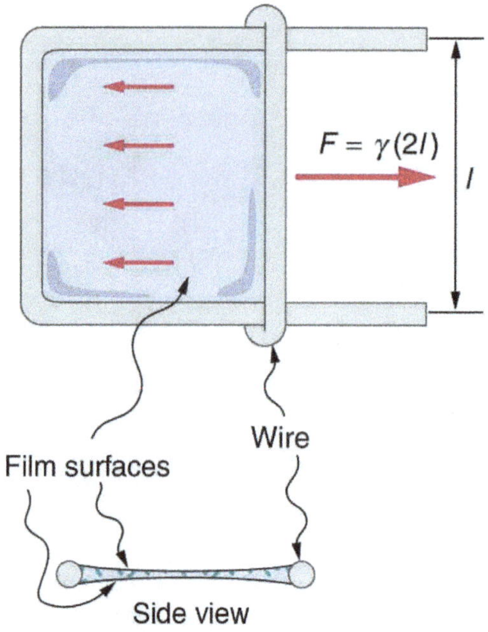

FIGURE 11.26 Sliding wire device used for measuring surface tension; the device exerts a force to reduce the film's surface area. The force needed to hold the wire in place is $F = \gamma L = \gamma(2l)$, since there are *two* liquid surfaces attached to the wire. This force remains nearly constant as the film is stretched, until the film approaches its breaking point.

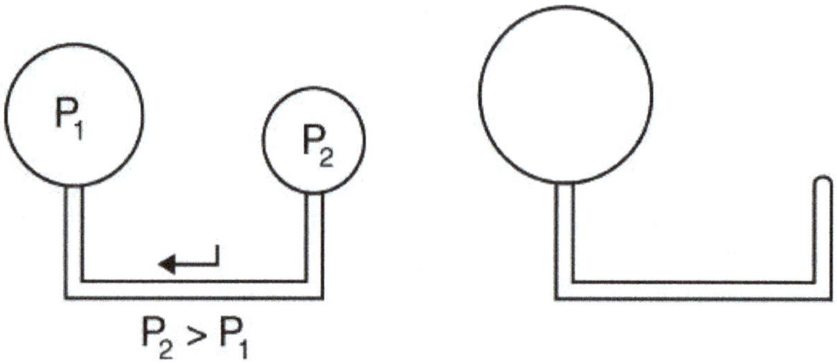

FIGURE 11.27 With the valve closed, two balloons of different sizes are attached to each end of a tube. Upon opening the valve, the smaller balloon decreases in size with the air moving to fill the larger balloon. The pressure in a spherical balloon is inversely proportional to its radius, so that the smaller balloon has a greater internal pressure than the larger balloon, resulting in this flow.

Liquid	Surface tension γ(N/m)
Water at $0°C$	0.0756
Water at $20°C$	0.0728
Water at $100°C$	0.0589
Soapy water (typical)	0.0370
Ethyl alcohol	0.0223
Glycerin	0.0631
Mercury	0.465

TABLE 11.3 Surface Tension of Some Liquids[1]

1 At 20°C unless otherwise stated.

Liquid	Surface tension γ(N/m)
Olive oil	0.032
Tissue fluids (typical)	0.050
Blood, whole at 37°C	0.058
Blood plasma at 37°C	0.073
Gold at 1070°C	1.000
Oxygen at -193°C	0.0157
Helium at -269°C	0.00012

TABLE 11.3 Surface Tension of Some Liquids[1]

EXAMPLE 11.11

Surface Tension: Pressure Inside a Bubble

Calculate the gauge pressure inside a soap bubble $2.00 \times 10^{-4}\ \text{m}$ in radius using the surface tension for soapy water in Table 11.3. Convert this pressure to mm Hg.

Strategy

The radius is given and the surface tension can be found in Table 11.3, and so P can be found directly from the equation $P = \frac{4\gamma}{r}$.

Solution

Substituting r and γ into the equation $P = \frac{4\gamma}{r}$, we obtain

$$P = \frac{4\gamma}{r} = \frac{4(0.037\ \text{N/m})}{2.00 \times 10^{-4}\ \text{m}} = 740\ \text{N/m}^2 = 740\ \text{Pa}. \tag{11.49}$$

We use a conversion factor to get this into units of mm Hg:

$$P = \left(740\ \text{N/m}^2\right)\frac{1.00\ \text{mm Hg}}{133\ \text{N/m}^2} = 5.56\ \text{mm Hg}. \tag{11.50}$$

Discussion

Note that if a hole were to be made in the bubble, the air would be forced out, the bubble would decrease in radius, and the gauge pressure would reduce to zero, and the absolute pressure inside would *decrease* to atmospheric pressure (760 mm Hg).

Our lungs contain hundreds of millions of mucus-lined sacs called *alveoli*, which are very similar in size, and about 0.1 mm in diameter. (See Figure 11.28.) You can exhale without muscle action by allowing surface tension to contract these sacs. Medical patients whose breathing is aided by a positive pressure respirator have air blown into the lungs, but are generally allowed to exhale on their own. Even if there is paralysis, surface tension in the alveoli will expel air from the lungs. Since pressure increases as the radii of the alveoli decrease, an occasional deep cleansing breath is needed to fully reinflate the alveoli. Respirators are programmed to do this and we find it natural, as do our companion dogs and cats, to take a cleansing breath before settling into a nap.

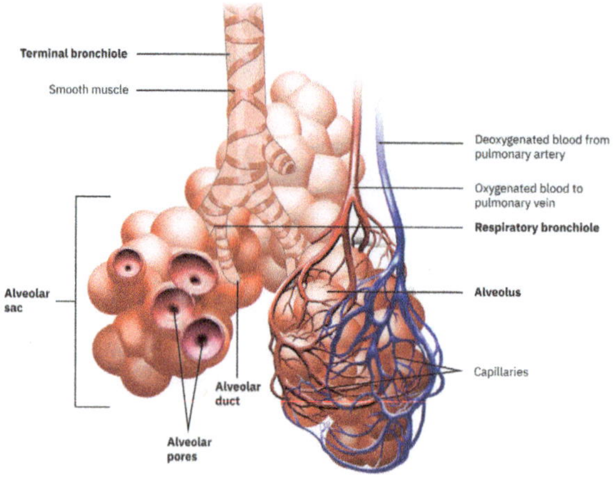

FIGURE 11.28 Bronchial tubes in the lungs branch into ever-smaller structures, finally ending in alveoli. The alveoli act like tiny bubbles. The surface tension of their mucous lining aids in exhalation and can prevent inhalation if too great.

The tension in the walls of the alveoli results from the membrane tissue and a liquid on the walls of the alveoli containing a long lipoprotein that acts as a surfactant (a surface-tension reducing substance). The need for the surfactant results from the tendency of small alveoli to collapse and the air to fill into the larger alveoli making them even larger (as demonstrated in Figure 11.27). During inhalation, the lipoprotein molecules are pulled apart and the wall tension increases as the radius increases (increased surface tension). During exhalation, the molecules slide back together and the surface tension decreases, helping to prevent a collapse of the alveoli. The surfactant therefore serves to change the wall tension so that small alveoli don't collapse and large alveoli are prevented from expanding too much. This tension change is a unique property of these surfactants, and is not shared by detergents (which simply lower surface tension). (See Figure 11.29.)

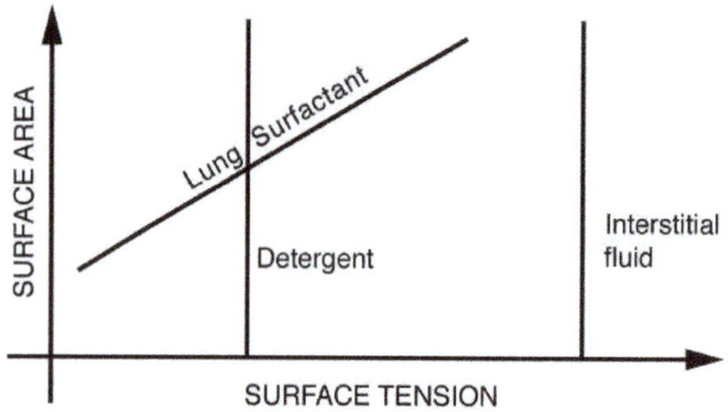

FIGURE 11.29 Surface tension as a function of surface area. The surface tension for lung surfactant decreases with decreasing area. This ensures that small alveoli don't collapse and large alveoli are not able to over expand.

If water gets into the lungs, the surface tension is too great and you cannot inhale. This is a severe problem in resuscitating drowning victims. A similar problem occurs in newborn infants who are born without this surfactant—their lungs are very difficult to inflate. This condition is known as *hyaline membrane disease* and is a leading cause of death for infants, particularly in premature births. Some success has been achieved in treating hyaline membrane disease by spraying a surfactant into the infant's breathing passages. Emphysema produces the opposite problem with alveoli. Alveolar walls of emphysema victims deteriorate, and the sacs combine to form larger sacs. Because pressure produced by surface tension decreases with increasing radius, these larger sacs produce smaller pressure, reducing the ability of emphysema victims to exhale. A common test for emphysema is to measure the pressure and volume of air that can be exhaled.

MAKING CONNECTIONS: TAKE-HOME INVESTIGATION

(1) Try floating a sewing needle on water. In order for this activity to work, the needle needs to be very clean as even the oil from your fingers can be sufficient to affect the surface properties of the needle. (2) Place the bristles of a paint brush into water. Pull the brush out and notice that for a short while, the bristles will stick

together. The surface tension of the water surrounding the bristles is sufficient to hold the bristles together. As the bristles dry out, the surface tension effect dissipates. (3) Place a loop of thread on the surface of still water in such a way that all of the thread is in contact with the water. Note the shape of the loop. Now place a drop of detergent into the middle of the loop. What happens to the shape of the loop? Why? (4) Sprinkle pepper onto the surface of water. Add a drop of detergent. What happens? Why? (5) Float two matches parallel to each other and add a drop of detergent between them. What happens? Note: For each new experiment, the water needs to be replaced and the bowl washed to free it of any residual detergent.

Adhesion and Capillary Action

Why is it that water beads up on a waxed car but does not on bare paint? The answer is that the adhesive forces between water and wax are much smaller than those between water and paint. Competition between the forces of adhesion and cohesion are important in the macroscopic behavior of liquids. An important factor in studying the roles of these two forces is the angle θ between the tangent to the liquid surface and the surface. (See Figure 11.30.) The **contact angle** θ is directly related to the relative strength of the cohesive and adhesive forces. The larger the strength of the cohesive force relative to the adhesive force, the larger θ is, and the more the liquid tends to form a droplet. The smaller θ is, the smaller the relative strength, so that the adhesive force is able to flatten the drop. Table 11.4 lists contact angles for several combinations of liquids and solids.

CONTACT ANGLE

The angle θ between the tangent to the liquid surface and the surface is called the contact angle.

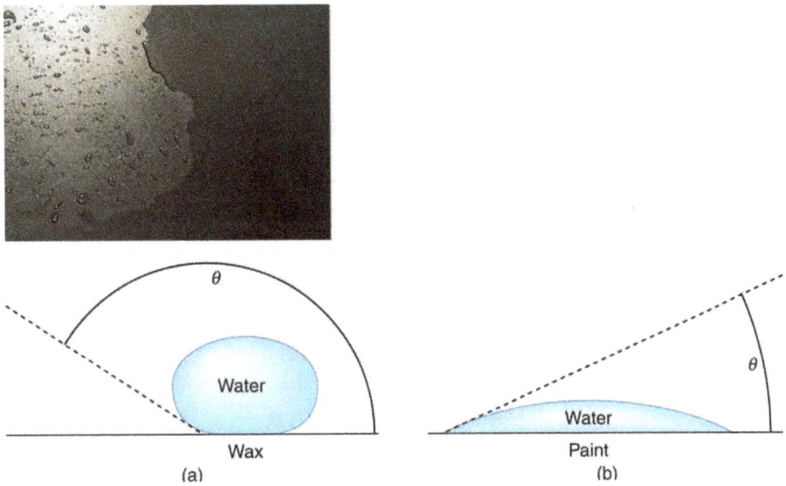

FIGURE 11.30 In the photograph, water beads on the waxed car paint and flattens on the unwaxed paint. (a) Water forms beads on the waxed surface because the cohesive forces responsible for surface tension are larger than the adhesive forces, which tend to flatten the drop. (b) Water beads on bare paint are flattened considerably because the adhesive forces between water and paint are strong, overcoming surface tension. The contact angle θ is directly related to the relative strengths of the cohesive and adhesive forces. The larger θ is, the larger the ratio of cohesive to adhesive forces. (credit: P. P. Urone)

One important phenomenon related to the relative strength of cohesive and adhesive forces is **capillary action**—the tendency of a fluid to be raised or suppressed in a narrow tube, or *capillary tube*. This action causes blood to be drawn into a small-diameter tube when the tube touches a drop.

CAPILLARY ACTION

The tendency of a fluid to be raised or suppressed in a narrow tube, or capillary tube, is called capillary action.

If a capillary tube is placed vertically into a liquid, as shown in Figure 11.31, capillary action will raise or suppress the liquid inside the tube depending on the combination of substances. The actual effect depends on the relative strength of the cohesive and adhesive forces and, thus, the contact angle θ given in the table. If θ is less than $90°$, then the fluid will be raised; if θ is greater than 90°, it will be suppressed. Mercury, for example, has a very large surface tension and a large contact angle with glass. When placed in a tube, the surface of a column of mercury curves downward, somewhat like a drop. The curved surface of a fluid in a tube is called a **meniscus**. The tendency of surface tension is always to reduce the surface area. Surface tension thus flattens the curved liquid surface in a capillary tube. This results in a downward force in mercury and an upward force in water, as seen in Figure 11.31.

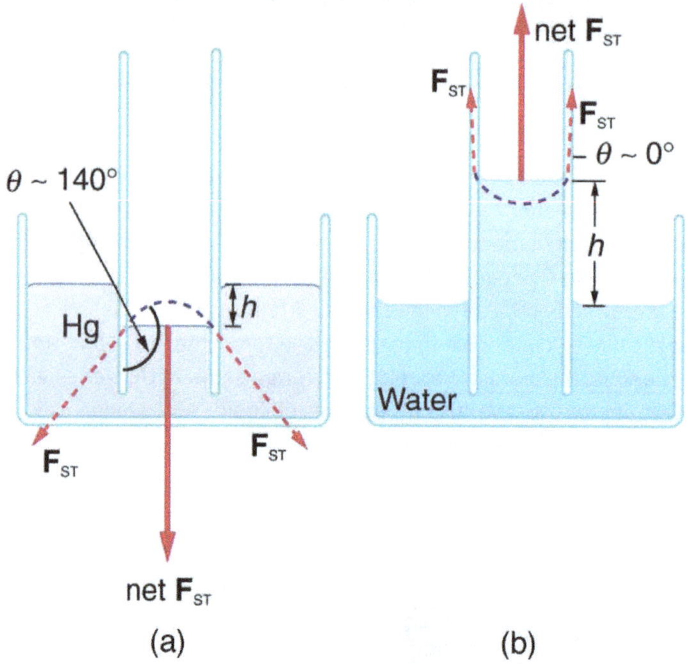

FIGURE 11.31 (a) Mercury is suppressed in a glass tube because its contact angle is greater than 90°. Surface tension exerts a downward force as it flattens the mercury, suppressing it in the tube. The dashed line shows the shape the mercury surface would have without the flattening effect of surface tension. (b) Water is raised in a glass tube because its contact angle is nearly 0°. Surface tension therefore exerts an upward force when it flattens the surface to reduce its area.

Interface	Contact angle Θ
Mercury–glass	140°
Water–glass	0°
Water–paraffin	107°
Water–silver	90°
Organic liquids (most)–glass	0°
Ethyl alcohol–glass	0°
Kerosene–glass	26°

TABLE 11.4 Contact Angles of Some Substances

Capillary action can move liquids horizontally over very large distances, but the height to which it can raise or suppress a liquid in a tube is limited by its weight. It can be shown that this height h is given by

$$h = \frac{2\gamma \cos \theta}{\rho g r}. \quad 11.51$$

If we look at the different factors in this expression, we might see how it makes good sense. The height is directly proportional to the surface tension γ, which is its direct cause. Furthermore, the height is inversely proportional to tube radius—the smaller the radius r, the higher the fluid can be raised, since a smaller tube holds less mass. The height is also inversely proportional to fluid density ρ, since a larger density means a greater mass in the same volume. (See Figure 11.32.)

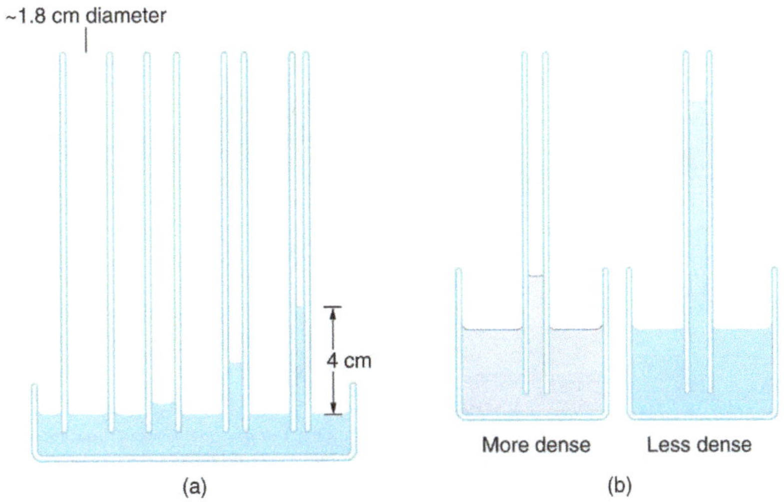

FIGURE 11.32 (a) Capillary action depends on the radius of a tube. The smaller the tube, the greater the height reached. The height is negligible for large-radius tubes. (b) A denser fluid in the same tube rises to a smaller height, all other factors being the same.

EXAMPLE 11.12

Calculating Radius of a Capillary Tube: Capillary Action: Tree Sap

Can capillary action be solely responsible for sap rising in trees? To answer this question, calculate the radius of a capillary tube that would raise sap 100 m to the top of a giant redwood, assuming that sap's density is 1050 kg/m^3, its contact angle is zero, and its surface tension is the same as that of water at 20.0° C.

Strategy

The height to which a liquid will rise as a result of capillary action is given by $h = \dfrac{2\gamma \cos \theta}{\rho g r}$, and every quantity is known except for r.

Solution

Solving for r and substituting known values produces

$$\begin{aligned} r &= \frac{2\gamma \cos \theta}{\rho g h} = \frac{2(0.0728 \text{ N/m})\cos(0^\circ)}{\left(1050 \text{ kg/m}^3\right)\left(9.80 \text{ m/s}^2\right)(100 \text{ m})} \\ &= 1.41 \times 10^{-7} \text{ m}. \end{aligned} \quad 11.52$$

Discussion

This result is unreasonable. Sap in trees moves through the *xylem*, which forms tubes with radii as small as 2.5×10^{-5} m. This value is about 180 times as large as the radius found necessary here to raise sap 100 m. This means that capillary action alone cannot be solely responsible for sap getting to the tops of trees.

How *does* sap get to the tops of tall trees? (Recall that a column of water can only rise to a height of 10 m when there is a vacuum at the top—see Example 11.5.) The question has not been completely resolved, but it appears that it is pulled up like a chain held together by cohesive forces. As each molecule of sap enters a leaf and evaporates (a process called transpiration), the entire chain is pulled up a notch. So a negative pressure created by water evaporation must be present to pull the sap up through the xylem vessels. In most situations, *fluids can push but can exert only negligible pull*, because the cohesive forces seem to be too small to hold the molecules tightly together. But in this case, the cohesive force of water molecules provides a very strong pull. Figure 11.33 shows one device for studying negative pressure. Some experiments have demonstrated that negative pressures sufficient to pull sap to the tops of the tallest trees *can* be achieved.

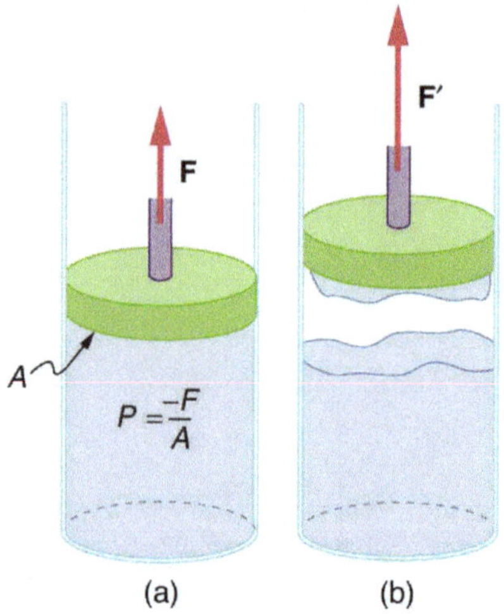

FIGURE 11.33 (a) When the piston is raised, it stretches the liquid slightly, putting it under tension and creating a negative absolute pressure $P = -F/A$. (b) The liquid eventually separates, giving an experimental limit to negative pressure in this liquid.

11.9 Pressures in the Body

LEARNING OBJECTIVES

By the end of this section, you will be able to:

- Explain the concept of pressure the in human body.
- Explain systolic and diastolic blood pressures.
- Describe pressures in the eye, lungs, spinal column, bladder, and skeletal system.

Pressure in the Body

Next to taking a person's temperature and weight, measuring blood pressure is the most common of all medical examinations. Control of high blood pressure is largely responsible for the significant decreases in heart attack and stroke fatalities achieved in the last three decades. The pressures in various parts of the body can be measured and often provide valuable medical indicators. In this section, we consider a few examples together with some of the physics that accompanies them.

Table 11.5 lists some of the measured pressures in mm Hg, the units most commonly quoted.

Body system	Gauge pressure in mm Hg
Blood pressures in large arteries (resting)	
Maximum (systolic)	100–140
Minimum (diastolic)	60–90
Blood pressure in large veins	4–15
Eye	12–24
Brain and spinal fluid (lying down)	5–12
Bladder	

TABLE 11.5 Typical Pressures in Humans

Body system	Gauge pressure in mm Hg
While filling	0–25
When full	100–150
Chest cavity between lungs and ribs	−8 to −4
Inside lungs	−2 to +3
Digestive tract	
Esophagus	−2
Stomach	0–20
Intestines	10–20
Middle ear	<1

TABLE 11.5 Typical Pressures in Humans

Blood Pressure

Common arterial blood pressure measurements typically produce values of 120 mm Hg and 80 mm Hg, respectively, for systolic and diastolic pressures. Both pressures have health implications. When systolic pressure is chronically high, the risk of stroke and heart attack is increased. If, however, it is too low, fainting is a problem. **Systolic pressure** increases dramatically during exercise to increase blood flow and returns to normal afterward. This change produces no ill effects and, in fact, may be beneficial to the tone of the circulatory system. **Diastolic pressure** can be an indicator of fluid balance. When low, it may indicate that a person is hemorrhaging internally and needs a transfusion. Conversely, high diastolic pressure indicates a ballooning of the blood vessels, which may be due to the transfusion of too much fluid into the circulatory system. High diastolic pressure is also an indication that blood vessels are not dilating properly to pass blood through. This can seriously strain the heart in its attempt to pump blood.

Blood leaves the heart at about 120 mm Hg but its pressure continues to decrease (to almost 0) as it goes from the aorta to smaller arteries to small veins (see Figure 11.34). The pressure differences in the circulation system are caused by blood flow through the system as well as the position of the person. For a person standing up, the pressure in the feet will be larger than at the heart due to the weight of the blood ($P = h\rho g$). If we assume that the distance between the heart and the feet of a person in an upright position is 1.4 m, then the increase in pressure in the feet relative to that in the heart (for a static column of blood) is given by

$$\Delta P = \Delta h\rho g = (1.4\text{ m})\left(1050\text{ kg/m}^3\right)\left(9.80\text{ m/s}^2\right) = 1.4 \times 10^4\text{ Pa} = 108\text{ mm Hg}. \quad 11.53$$

INCREASE IN PRESSURE IN THE FEET OF A PERSON

$$\Delta P = \Delta h\rho g = (1.4\text{ m})\left(1050\text{ kg/m}^3\right)\left(9.80\text{ m/s}^2\right) = 1.4 \times 10^4\text{ Pa} = 108\text{ mm Hg}. \quad 11.54$$

Standing a long time can lead to an accumulation of blood in the legs and swelling. This is the reason why soldiers who are required to stand still for long periods of time have been known to faint. Elastic bandages around the calf can help prevent this accumulation and can also help provide increased pressure to enable the veins to send blood back up to the heart. For similar reasons, doctors recommend tight stockings for long-haul flights.

Blood pressure may also be measured in the major veins, the heart chambers, arteries to the brain, and the lungs.

But these pressures are usually only monitored during surgery or for patients in intensive care since the measurements are invasive. To obtain these pressure measurements, qualified health care workers thread thin tubes, called catheters, into appropriate locations to transmit pressures to external measuring devices.

The heart consists of two pumps—the right side forcing blood through the lungs and the left causing blood to flow through the rest of the body (Figure 11.34). Right-heart failure, for example, results in a rise in the pressure in the vena cavae and a drop in pressure in the arteries to the lungs. Left-heart failure results in a rise in the pressure entering the left side of the heart and a drop in aortal pressure. Implications of these and other pressures on flow in the circulatory system will be discussed in more detail in Fluid Dynamics and Its Biological and Medical Applications.

TWO PUMPS OF THE HEART

The heart consists of two pumps—the right side forcing blood through the lungs and the left causing blood to flow through the rest of the body.

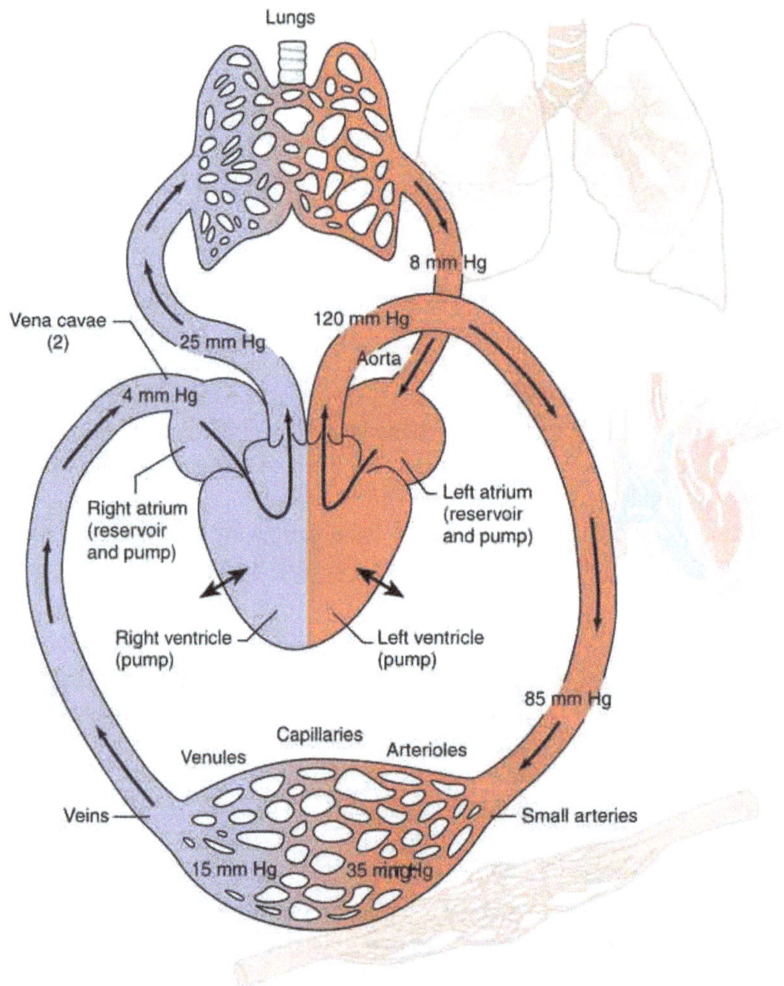

FIGURE 11.34 Schematic of the circulatory system showing typical pressures. The two pumps in the heart increase pressure and that pressure is reduced as the blood flows through the body. Long-term deviations from these pressures have medical implications discussed in some detail in the Fluid Dynamics and Its Biological and Medical Applications. Only aortal or arterial blood pressure can be measured noninvasively.

Pressure in the Eye

The shape of the eye is maintained by fluid pressure, called **intraocular pressure**, which is normally in the range of 12.0 to 24.0 mm Hg. When the circulation of fluid in the eye is blocked, it can lead to a buildup in pressure, a condition called **glaucoma**. The net pressure can become as great as 85.0 mm Hg, an abnormally large pressure that can permanently damage the optic nerve. To get an idea of the force involved, suppose the back of the eye has an area of $6.0\ \text{cm}^2$, and the net pressure is 85.0 mm Hg. Force is given by $F = PA$. To get F in newtons, we convert the area to m^2 ($1\ \text{m}^2 = 10^4\ \text{cm}^2$). Then we calculate as follows:

$$F = h\rho g A = \left(85.0 \times 10^{-3}\ \text{m}\right)\left(13.6 \times 10^3\ \text{kg/m}^3\right)\left(9.80\ \text{m/s}^2\right)\left(6.0 \times 10^{-4}\ \text{m}^2\right) = 6.8\ \text{N}. \quad 11.55$$

EYE PRESSURE

The shape of the eye is maintained by fluid pressure, called intraocular pressure. When the circulation of fluid in the eye is blocked, it can lead to a buildup in pressure, a condition called glaucoma. The force is calculated as

$$F = h\rho g A = \left(85.0 \times 10^{-3}\ \text{m}\right)\left(13.6 \times 10^3\ \text{kg/m}^3\right)\left(9.80\ \text{m/s}^2\right)\left(6.0 \times 10^{-4}\ \text{m}^2\right) = 6.8\ \text{N}. \quad 11.56$$

This force is the weight of about a 680-g mass. A mass of 680 g resting on the eye (imagine 1.5 lb resting on your eye) would be sufficient to cause it damage. (A normal force here would be the weight of about 120 g, less than one-quarter of our initial value.)

People over 40 years of age are at greatest risk of developing glaucoma and should have their intraocular pressure tested routinely. Most measurements involve exerting a force on the (anesthetized) eye over some area (a pressure) and observing the eye's response. A noncontact approach uses a puff of air and a measurement is made of the force needed to indent the eye (Figure 11.35). If the intraocular pressure is high, the eye will deform less and rebound more vigorously than normal. Excessive intraocular pressures can be detected reliably and sometimes controlled effectively.

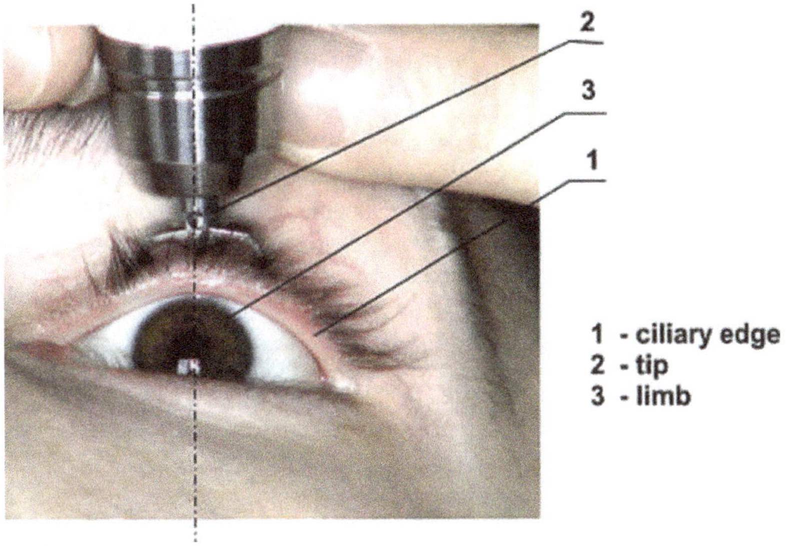

FIGURE 11.35 The intraocular eye pressure can be read with a tonometer. (credit: DevelopAll at the Wikipedia Project.)

EXAMPLE 11.13

Calculating Gauge Pressure and Depth: Damage to the Eardrum

Suppose a 3.00-N force can rupture an eardrum. (a) If the eardrum has an area of $1.00\ \text{cm}^2$, calculate the maximum tolerable gauge pressure on the eardrum in newtons per meter squared and convert it to millimeters of mercury. (b) At what depth in freshwater would this person's eardrum rupture, assuming the gauge pressure in the middle ear is zero?

Strategy for (a)

The pressure can be found directly from its definition since we know the force and area. We are looking for the gauge pressure.

Solution for (a)

$$P_g = F/A = 3.00\ \text{N}/(1.00 \times 10^{-4}\ \text{m}^2) = 3.00 \times 10^4\ \text{N/m}^2. \quad (11.57)$$

We now need to convert this to units of mm Hg:

$$P_g = 3.0 \times 10^4\ \text{N/m}^2 \left(\frac{1.0\ \text{mm Hg}}{133\ \text{N/m}^2} \right) = 226\ \text{mm Hg}. \quad (11.58)$$

Strategy for (b)

Here we will use the fact that the water pressure varies linearly with depth h below the surface.

Solution for (b)

$P = h\rho g$ and therefore $h = P/\rho g$. Using the value above for P, we have

$$h = \frac{3.0 \times 10^4\ \text{N/m}^2}{(1.00 \times 10^3\ \text{kg/m}^3)(9.80\ \text{m/s}^2)} = 3.06\ \text{m}. \quad (11.59)$$

Discussion

Similarly, increased pressure exerted upon the eardrum from the middle ear can arise when an infection causes a fluid buildup.

Pressure Associated with the Lungs

The pressure inside the lungs increases and decreases with each breath. The pressure drops to below atmospheric pressure (negative gauge pressure) when you inhale, causing air to flow into the lungs. It increases above atmospheric pressure (positive gauge pressure) when you exhale, forcing air out.

Lung pressure is controlled by several mechanisms. Muscle action in the diaphragm and rib cage is necessary for inhalation; this muscle action increases the volume of the lungs thereby reducing the pressure within them Figure 11.36. Surface tension in the alveoli creates a positive pressure opposing inhalation. (See Cohesion and Adhesion in Liquids: Surface Tension and Capillary Action.) You can exhale without muscle action by letting surface tension in the alveoli create its own positive pressure. Muscle action can add to this positive pressure to produce forced exhalation, such as when you blow up a balloon, blow out a candle, or cough.

The lungs, in fact, would collapse due to the surface tension in the alveoli, if they were not attached to the inside of the chest wall by liquid adhesion. The gauge pressure in the liquid attaching the lungs to the inside of the chest wall is thus negative, ranging from -4 to $-8\ \text{mm Hg}$ during exhalation and inhalation, respectively. If air is allowed to enter the chest cavity, it breaks the attachment, and one or both lungs may collapse. Suction is applied to the chest cavity of surgery patients and trauma victims to reestablish negative pressure and inflate the lungs.

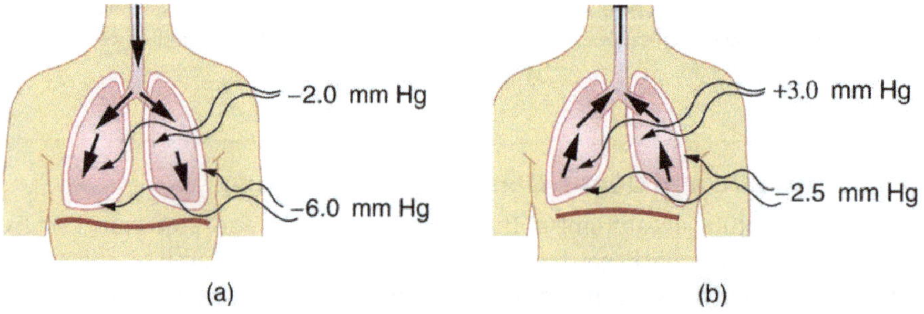

FIGURE 11.36 (a) During inhalation, muscles expand the chest, and the diaphragm moves downward, reducing pressure inside the lungs to less than atmospheric (negative gauge pressure). Pressure between the lungs and chest wall is even lower to overcome the positive pressure created by surface tension in the lungs. (b) During gentle exhalation, the muscles simply relax and surface tension in the alveoli creates a positive pressure inside the lungs, forcing air out. Pressure between the chest wall and lungs remains negative to keep them attached to the chest wall, but it is less negative than during inhalation.

Other Pressures in the Body

Spinal Column and Skull

Normally, there is a 5- to12-mm Hg pressure in the fluid surrounding the brain and filling the spinal column. This cerebrospinal fluid serves many purposes, one of which is to supply flotation to the brain. The buoyant force supplied by the fluid nearly equals the weight of the brain, since their densities are nearly equal. If there is a loss of fluid, the brain rests on the inside of the skull, causing severe headaches, constricted blood flow, and serious damage. Spinal fluid pressure is measured by means of a needle inserted between vertebrae that transmits the pressure to a suitable measuring device.

Bladder Pressure

This bodily pressure is one of which we are often aware. In fact, there is a relationship between our awareness of this pressure and a subsequent increase in it. Bladder pressure climbs steadily from zero to about 25 mm Hg as the bladder fills to its normal capacity of 500 cm^3. This pressure triggers the **micturition reflex**, which stimulates the feeling of needing to urinate. What is more, it also causes muscles around the bladder to contract, raising the pressure to over 100 mm Hg, accentuating the sensation. Coughing, straining, tensing in cold weather, wearing tight clothes, and experiencing simple nervous tension all can increase bladder pressure and trigger this reflex. So can the weight of a pregnant woman's fetus, especially if it is kicking vigorously or pushing down with its head! Bladder pressure can be measured by a catheter or by inserting a needle through the bladder wall and transmitting the pressure to an appropriate measuring device. One hazard of high bladder pressure (sometimes created by an obstruction), is that such pressure can force urine back into the kidneys, causing potentially severe damage.

Pressures in the Skeletal System

These pressures are the largest in the body, due both to the high values of initial force, and the small areas to which this force is applied, such as in the joints.. For example, when a person lifts an object improperly, a force of 5000 N may be created between vertebrae in the spine, and this may be applied to an area as small as 10 cm^2. The pressure created is $P = F/A = (5000\text{ N})/(10^{-3}\text{ m}^2) = 5.0 \times 10^6\text{ N/m}^2$ or about 50 atm! This pressure can damage both the spinal discs (the cartilage between vertebrae), as well as the bony vertebrae themselves. Even under normal circumstances, forces between vertebrae in the spine are large enough to create pressures of several atmospheres. Most causes of excessive pressure in the skeletal system can be avoided by lifting properly and avoiding extreme physical activity. (See Forces and Torques in Muscles and Joints.)

There are many other interesting and medically significant pressures in the body. For example, pressure caused by various muscle actions drives food and waste through the digestive system. Stomach pressure behaves much like bladder pressure and is tied to the sensation of hunger. Pressure in the relaxed esophagus is normally negative because pressure in the chest cavity is normally negative. Positive pressure in the stomach may thus force acid into the esophagus, causing "heartburn." Pressure in the middle ear can result in significant force on the eardrum if it differs greatly from atmospheric pressure, such as while scuba diving. The decrease in external pressure is also noticeable during plane flights (due to a decrease in the weight of air above relative to that at the Earth's surface). The Eustachian tubes connect the middle ear to the throat and allow us to equalize pressure in the middle ear to avoid an imbalance of force on the eardrum.

Many pressures in the human body are associated with the flow of fluids. Fluid flow will be discussed in detail in the Fluid Dynamics and Its Biological and Medical Applications.

Glossary

absolute pressure the sum of gauge pressure and atmospheric pressure

adhesive forces the attractive forces between molecules of different types

Archimedes' principle the buoyant force on an object equals the weight of the fluid it displaces

buoyant force the net upward force on any object in any fluid

capillary action the tendency of a fluid to be raised or lowered in a narrow tube

cohesive forces the attractive forces between molecules of the same type

contact angle the angle θ between the tangent to the liquid surface and the surface

density the mass per unit volume of a substance or object

diastolic pressure minimum arterial blood pressure; indicator for the fluid balance

diastolic pressure the minimum blood pressure in the artery

fluids liquids and gases; a fluid is a state of matter that yields to shearing forces

gauge pressure the pressure relative to atmospheric pressure

glaucoma condition caused by the buildup of fluid pressure in the eye

intraocular pressure fluid pressure in the eye

micturition reflex stimulates the feeling of needing to urinate, triggered by bladder pressure

Pascal's Principle a change in pressure applied to an enclosed fluid is transmitted undiminished to all portions of the fluid and to the walls of its container

pressure the force per unit area perpendicular to the force, over which the force acts

pressure the weight of the fluid divided by the area supporting it

specific gravity the ratio of the density of an object to a fluid (usually water)

surface tension the cohesive forces between molecules which cause the surface of a liquid to contract to the smallest possible surface area

systolic pressure maximum arterial blood pressure; indicator for the blood flow

systolic pressure the maximum blood pressure in the artery

Section Summary

11.1 What Is a Fluid?

- A fluid is a state of matter that yields to sideways or shearing forces. Liquids and gases are both fluids. Fluid statics is the physics of stationary fluids.

11.2 Density

- Density is the mass per unit volume of a substance or object. In equation form, density is defined as
  $\rho = \frac{m}{V}$.
- The SI unit of density is kg/m^3.

11.3 Pressure

- Pressure is the force per unit perpendicular area over which the force is applied. In equation form, pressure is defined as
  $P = \frac{F}{A}$.
- The SI unit of pressure is pascal and
  $1\ \text{Pa} = 1\ \text{N/m}^2$.

11.4 Variation of Pressure with Depth in a Fluid

- Pressure is the weight of the fluid mg divided by the area A supporting it (the area of the bottom of the container):
  $P = \frac{mg}{A}$.
- Pressure due to the weight of a liquid is given by
  $P = h\rho g,$
  where P is the pressure, h is the height of the liquid, ρ is the density of the liquid, and g is the acceleration due to gravity.

11.5 Pascal's Principle

- Pressure is force per unit area.
- A change in pressure applied to an enclosed fluid is transmitted undiminished to all portions of the fluid and to the walls of its container.
- A hydraulic system is an enclosed fluid system used to exert forces.

11.6 Gauge Pressure, Absolute Pressure, and Pressure Measurement

- Gauge pressure is the pressure relative to atmospheric pressure.
- Absolute pressure is the sum of gauge pressure and atmospheric pressure.
- Aneroid gauge measures pressure using a bellows-and-spring arrangement connected to the pointer of a calibrated scale.
- Open-tube manometers have U-shaped tubes and

one end is always open. It is used to measure pressure.
- A mercury barometer is a device that measures atmospheric pressure.

11.7 Archimedes' Principle

- Buoyant force is the net upward force on any object in any fluid. If the buoyant force is greater than the object's weight, the object will rise to the surface and float. If the buoyant force is less than the object's weight, the object will sink. If the buoyant force equals the object's weight, the object will remain suspended at that depth. The buoyant force is always present whether the object floats, sinks, or is suspended in a fluid.
- Archimedes' principle states that the buoyant force on an object equals the weight of the fluid it displaces.
- Specific gravity is the ratio of the density of an object to a fluid (usually water).

11.8 Cohesion and Adhesion in Liquids: Surface Tension and Capillary Action

- Attractive forces between molecules of the same type are called cohesive forces.
- Attractive forces between molecules of different types are called adhesive forces.
- Cohesive forces between molecules cause the surface of a liquid to contract to the smallest possible surface area. This general effect is called surface tension.
- Capillary action is the tendency of a fluid to be raised or suppressed in a narrow tube, or capillary tube which is due to the relative strength of cohesive and adhesive forces.

11.9 Pressures in the Body

- Measuring blood pressure is among the most common of all medical examinations.
- The pressures in various parts of the body can be measured and often provide valuable medical indicators.
- The shape of the eye is maintained by fluid pressure, called intraocular pressure.
- When the circulation of fluid in the eye is blocked, it can lead to a buildup in pressure, a condition called glaucoma.
- Some of the other pressures in the body are spinal and skull pressures, bladder pressure, pressures in the skeletal system.

Conceptual Questions

11.1 What Is a Fluid?

1. What physical characteristic distinguishes a fluid from a solid?
2. Which of the following substances are fluids at room temperature: air, mercury, water, glass?
3. Why are gases easier to compress than liquids and solids?
4. How do gases differ from liquids?

11.2 Density

5. Approximately how does the density of air vary with altitude?
6. Give an example in which density is used to identify the substance composing an object. Would information in addition to average density be needed to identify the substances in an object composed of more than one material?
7. Figure 11.37 shows a glass of ice water filled to the brim. Will the water overflow when the ice melts? Explain your answer.

FIGURE 11.37

11.3 Pressure

8. How is pressure related to the sharpness of a knife and its ability to cut?
9. Why does a dull hypodermic needle hurt more than a sharp one?
10. The outward force on one end of an air tank was calculated in Example 11.2. How is this force balanced? (The tank does not accelerate, so the force must be balanced.)
11. Why is force exerted by static fluids always perpendicular to a surface?

12. In a remote location near the North Pole, an iceberg floats in a lake. Next to the lake (assume it is not frozen) sits a comparably sized glacier sitting on land. If both chunks of ice should melt due to rising global temperatures (and the melted ice all goes into the lake), which ice chunk would give the greatest increase in the level of the lake water, if any?

13. How do jogging on soft ground and wearing padded shoes reduce the pressures to which the feet and legs are subjected?

14. Toe dancing (as in ballet) is much harder on toes than normal dancing or walking. Explain in terms of pressure.

15. How do you convert pressure units like millimeters of mercury, centimeters of water, and inches of mercury into units like newtons per meter squared without resorting to a table of pressure conversion factors?

11.4 Variation of Pressure with Depth in a Fluid

16. Atmospheric pressure exerts a large force (equal to the weight of the atmosphere above your body—about 10 tons) on the top of your body when you are lying on the beach sunbathing. Why are you able to get up?

17. Why does atmospheric pressure decrease more rapidly than linearly with altitude?

18. What are two reasons why mercury rather than water is used in barometers?

19. Figure 11.38 shows how sandbags placed around a leak outside a river levee can effectively stop the flow of water under the levee. Explain how the small amount of water inside the column formed by the sandbags is able to balance the much larger body of water behind the levee.

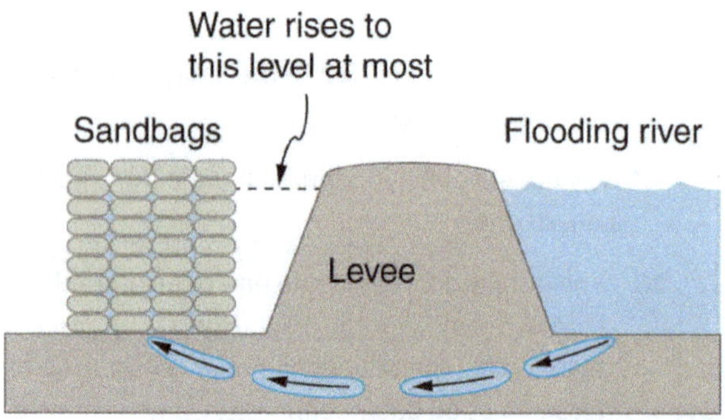

FIGURE 11.38 Because the river level is very high, it has started to leak under the levee. Sandbags are placed around the leak, and the water held by them rises until it is the same level as the river, at which point the water there stops rising.

20. Why is it difficult to swim under water in the Great Salt Lake?

21. Is there a net force on a dam due to atmospheric pressure? Explain your answer.

22. Does atmospheric pressure add to the gas pressure in a rigid tank? In a toy balloon? When, in general, does atmospheric pressure *not* affect the total pressure in a fluid?

23. You can break a strong wine bottle by pounding a cork into it with your fist, but the cork must press directly against the liquid filling the bottle—there can be no air between the cork and liquid. Explain why the bottle breaks, and why it will not if there is air between the cork and liquid.

11.5 Pascal's Principle

24. Suppose the pedal cylinder in a hydraulic system is at a greater height than the wheel cylinder. Explain how this will affect the force produced at the wheel cylinder.

11.6 Gauge Pressure, Absolute Pressure, and Pressure Measurement

25. Explain why the fluid reaches equal levels on either side of a manometer if both sides are open to the atmosphere, even if the tubes are of different diameters.

26. Figure 11.15 shows how a common measurement of arterial blood pressure is made. Is there any effect on the measured pressure if the manometer is lowered? What is the effect of raising the arm above the shoulder? What is the effect of placing the cuff on the upper leg with the person standing? Explain your answers in terms of pressure created by the weight of a fluid.

27. Considering the magnitude of typical arterial blood pressures, why are mercury rather than water manometers used for these measurements?

11.7 Archimedes' Principle

28. More force is required to pull the plug in a full bathtub than when it is empty. Does this contradict Archimedes' principle? Explain your answer.

29. Do fluids exert buoyant forces in a "weightless" environment, such as in the space shuttle? Explain your answer.

30. Will the same ship float higher in salt water than in freshwater? Explain your answer.

31. Marbles dropped into a partially filled bathtub sink to the bottom. Part of their weight is supported by buoyant force, yet the downward force on the bottom of the tub increases by exactly the weight of the marbles. Explain why.

11.8 Cohesion and Adhesion in Liquids: Surface Tension and Capillary Action

32. The density of oil is less than that of water, yet a loaded oil tanker sits lower in the water than an empty one. Why?

33. Is surface tension due to cohesive or adhesive forces, or both?

34. Is capillary action due to cohesive or adhesive forces, or both?

35. Birds such as ducks, geese, and swans have greater densities than water, yet they are able to sit on its surface. Explain this ability, noting that water does not wet their feathers and that they cannot sit on soapy water.

36. Water beads up on an oily sunbather, but not on her neighbor, whose skin is not oiled. Explain in terms of cohesive and adhesive forces.

37. Could capillary action be used to move fluids in a "weightless" environment, such as in an orbiting space probe?

38. What effect does capillary action have on the reading of a manometer with uniform diameter? Explain your answer.

39. Pressure between the inside chest wall and the outside of the lungs normally remains negative. Explain how pressure inside the lungs can become positive (to cause exhalation) without muscle action.

Problems & Exercises

11.2 Density

1. Gold is sold by the troy ounce (31.103 g). What is the volume of 1 troy ounce of pure gold?

2. Mercury is commonly supplied in flasks containing 34.5 kg (about 76 lb). What is the volume in liters of this much mercury?

3. (a) What is the mass of a deep breath of air having a volume of 2.00 L? (b) Discuss the effect taking such a breath has on your body's volume and density.

4. A straightforward method of finding the density of an object is to measure its mass and then measure its volume by submerging it in a graduated cylinder. What is the density of a 240-g rock that displaces $89.0\ \text{cm}^3$ of water? (Note that the accuracy and practical applications of this technique are more limited than a variety of others that are based on Archimedes' principle.)

5. Suppose you have a coffee mug with a circular cross section and vertical sides (uniform radius). What is its inside radius if it holds 375 g of coffee when filled to a depth of 7.50 cm? Assume coffee has the same density as water.

6. (a) A rectangular gasoline tank can hold 50.0 kg of gasoline when full. What is the depth of the tank if it is 0.500-m wide by 0.900-m long? (b) Discuss whether this gas tank has a reasonable volume for a passenger car.

7. A trash compactor can reduce the volume of its contents to 0.350 their original value. Neglecting the mass of air expelled, by what factor is the density of the rubbish increased?

8. A 2.50-kg steel gasoline can holds 20.0 L of gasoline when full. What is the average density of the full gas can, taking into account the volume occupied by steel as well as by gasoline?

9. What is the density of 18.0-karat gold that is a mixture of 18 parts gold, 5 parts silver, and 1 part copper? (These values are parts by mass, not volume.) Assume that this is a simple mixture having an average density equal to the weighted densities of its constituents.

10. There is relatively little empty space between atoms in solids and liquids, so that the average density of an atom is about the same as matter on a macroscopic scale—approximately $10^3\ \text{kg/m}^3$. The nucleus of an atom has a radius about 10^{-5} that of the atom and contains nearly all the mass of the entire atom. (a) What is the approximate density of a nucleus? (b) One remnant of a supernova, called a neutron star, can have the density of a nucleus. What would be the radius of a neutron star with a mass 10 times that of our Sun (the radius of the Sun is $7 \times 10^8\ \text{m}$)?

11.3 Pressure

11. As a woman walks, her entire weight is

momentarily placed on one heel of her high-heeled shoes. Calculate the pressure exerted on the floor by the heel if it has an area of $1.50\ \text{cm}^2$ and the woman's mass is 55.0 kg. Express the pressure in Pa. (In the early days of commercial flight, women were not allowed to wear high-heeled shoes because aircraft floors were too thin to withstand such large pressures.)

12. The pressure exerted by a phonograph needle on a record is surprisingly large. If the equivalent of 1.00 g is supported by a needle, the tip of which is a circle 0.200 mm in radius, what pressure is exerted on the record in N/m^2?

13. Nail tips exert tremendous pressures when they are hit by hammers because they exert a large force over a small area. What force must be exerted on a nail with a circular tip of 1.00 mm diameter to create a pressure of $3.00 \times 10^9\ \text{N/m}^2$?(This high pressure is possible because the hammer striking the nail is brought to rest in such a short distance.)

11.4 Variation of Pressure with Depth in a Fluid

14. What depth of mercury creates a pressure of 1.00 atm?

15. The greatest ocean depths on the Earth are found in the Marianas Trench near the Philippines. Calculate the pressure due to the ocean at the bottom of this trench, given its depth is 11.0 km and assuming the density of seawater is constant all the way down.

16. Verify that the SI unit of $h\rho g$ is N/m^2.

17. Water towers store water above the level of consumers for times of heavy use, eliminating the need for high-speed pumps. How high above a user must the water level be to create a gauge pressure of $3.00 \times 10^5\ \text{N/m}^2$?

18. The aqueous humor in a person's eye is exerting a force of 0.300 N on the 1.10-cm^2 area of the cornea. (a) What pressure is this in mm Hg? (b) Is this value within the normal range for pressures in the eye?

19. How much force is exerted on one side of an 8.50 cm by 11.0 cm sheet of paper by the atmosphere? How can the paper withstand such a force?

20. What pressure is exerted on the bottom of a 0.500-m-wide by 0.900-m-long gas tank that can hold 50.0 kg of gasoline by the weight of the gasoline in it when it is full?

21. Calculate the average pressure exerted on the palm of a shot-putter's hand by the shot if the area of contact is $50.0\ \text{cm}^2$ and he exerts a force of 800 N on it. Express the pressure in N/m^2 and compare it with the $1.00 \times 10^6\ \text{Pa}$ pressures sometimes encountered in the skeletal system.

22. The left side of the heart creates a pressure of 120 mm Hg by exerting a force directly on the blood over an effective area of $15.0\ \text{cm}^2$. What force does it exert to accomplish this?

23. Show that the total force on a rectangular dam due to the water behind it increases with the *square* of the water depth. In particular, show that this force is given by $F = \rho g h^2 L/2$, where ρ is the density of water, h is its depth at the dam, and L is the length of the dam. You may assume the face of the dam is vertical. (Hint: Calculate the average pressure exerted and multiply this by the area in contact with the water. (See Figure 11.39.)

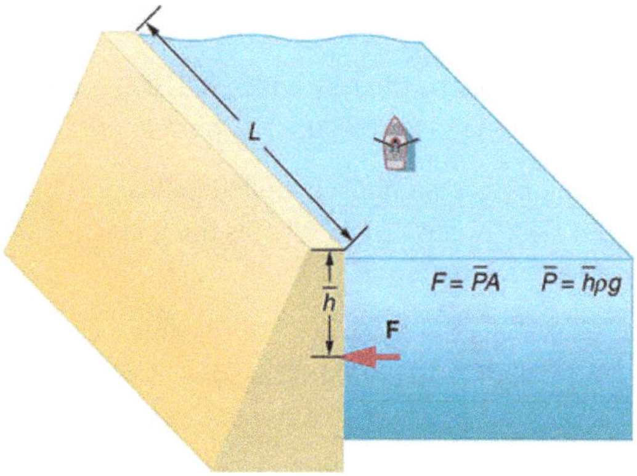

FIGURE 11.39

11.5 Pascal's Principle

24. How much pressure is transmitted in the hydraulic system considered in Example 11.6? Express your answer in pascals and in atmospheres.

25. What force must be exerted on the pedal cylinder of a hydraulic lift to support the weight of a 2000-kg car (a large car) resting on the wheel cylinder? The pedal cylinder has a 2.00-cm diameter and the wheel has a 24.0-cm diameter.

26. A crass host pours the remnants of several bottles of wine into a jug after a party. He then inserts a cork with a 2.00-cm diameter into the bottle, placing it in direct contact with the wine. He is amazed when he pounds the cork into place and the bottom of the jug (with a 14.0-cm diameter) breaks away. Calculate the extra force exerted against the bottom if he pounded the cork with a 120-N force.

27. A certain hydraulic system is designed to exert a force 100 times as large as the one put into it. (a) What must be the ratio of the area of the wheel cylinder to the area of the pedal cylinder? (b) What must be the ratio of their diameters? (c) By what factor is the distance through which the output force moves reduced relative to the distance through which the input force moves? Assume no losses to friction.

28. (a) Verify that work input equals work output for a hydraulic system assuming no losses to friction. Do this by showing that the distance the output force moves is reduced by the same factor that the output force is increased. Assume the volume of the fluid is constant. (b) What effect would friction within the fluid and between components in the system have on the output force? How would this depend on whether or not the fluid is moving?

11.6 Gauge Pressure, Absolute Pressure, and Pressure Measurement

29. Find the gauge and absolute pressures in the balloon and peanut jar shown in Figure 11.14, assuming the manometer connected to the balloon uses water whereas the manometer connected to the jar contains mercury. Express in units of centimeters of water for the balloon and millimeters of mercury for the jar, taking $h = 0.0500\text{ m}$ for each.

30. (a) Convert normal blood pressure readings of 120 over 80 mm Hg to newtons per meter squared using the relationship for pressure due to the weight of a fluid $(P = h\rho g)$ rather than a conversion factor. (b) Discuss why blood pressures for an infant could be smaller than those for an adult. Specifically, consider the smaller height to which blood must be pumped.

31. How tall must a water-filled manometer be to measure blood pressures as high as 300 mm Hg?

32. Pressure cookers have been around for more than 300 years, although their use has strongly declined in recent years (early models had a nasty habit of exploding). How much force must the latches holding the lid onto a pressure cooker be able to withstand if the circular lid is 25.0 cm in diameter and the gauge pressure inside is 300 atm? Neglect the weight of the lid.

33. Suppose you measure a standing person's blood pressure by placing the cuff on his leg 0.500 m below the heart. Calculate the pressure you would observe (in units of mm Hg) if the pressure at the heart were 120 over 80 mm Hg. Assume that there is no loss of pressure due to resistance in the circulatory system (a reasonable assumption, since major arteries are large).

34. A submarine is stranded on the bottom of the ocean with its hatch 25.0 m below the surface. Calculate the force needed to open the hatch from the inside, given it is circular and 0.450 m in diameter. Air pressure inside the submarine is 1.00 atm.

35. Assuming bicycle tires are perfectly flexible and support the weight of bicycle and rider by pressure alone, calculate the total area of the tires in contact with the ground. The bicycle plus rider has a mass of 80.0 kg, and the gauge pressure in the tires is $3.50 \times 10^5\text{ Pa}$.

11.7 Archimedes' Principle

36. What fraction of ice is submerged when it floats in freshwater, given the density of water at 0°C is very close to 1000 kg/m^3?

37. Logs sometimes float vertically in a lake because one end has become water-logged and denser than the other. What is the average density of a uniform-diameter log that floats with 20.0% of its length above water?

38. Find the density of a fluid in which a hydrometer having a density of 0.750 g/mL floats with 92.0% of its volume submerged.

39. If your body has a density of 995 kg/m^3, what fraction of you will be submerged when floating gently in: (a) freshwater? (b) salt water, which has a density of 1027 kg/m^3?

40. Bird bones have air pockets in them to reduce their weight—this also gives them an average density significantly less than that of the bones of other animals. Suppose an ornithologist weighs a bird bone in air and in water and finds its mass is 45.0 g and its apparent mass when submerged is 3.60 g (the bone is watertight). (a) What mass of water is displaced? (b) What is the volume of the bone? (c) What is its average density?

41. A rock with a mass of 540 g in air is found to have an apparent mass of 342 g when submerged in water. (a) What mass of water is displaced? (b)

What is the volume of the rock? (c) What is its average density? Is this consistent with the value for granite?

42. Archimedes' principle can be used to calculate the density of a fluid as well as that of a solid. Suppose a chunk of iron with a mass of 390.0 g in air is found to have an apparent mass of 350.5 g when completely submerged in an unknown liquid. (a) What mass of fluid does the iron displace? (b) What is the volume of iron, using its density as given in Table 11.1 (c) Calculate the fluid's density and identify it.

43. In an immersion measurement of a woman's density, she is found to have a mass of 62.0 kg in air and an apparent mass of 0.0850 kg when completely submerged with lungs empty. (a) What mass of water does she displace? (b) What is her volume? (c) Calculate her density. (d) If her lung capacity is 1.75 L, is she able to float without treading water with her lungs filled with air?

44. Some fish have a density slightly less than that of water and must exert a force (swim) to stay submerged. What force must an 85.0-kg grouper exert to stay submerged in salt water if its body density is $1015\ \text{kg/m}^3$?

45. (a) Calculate the buoyant force on a 2.00-L helium balloon. (b) Given the mass of the rubber in the balloon is 1.50 g, what is the net vertical force on the balloon if it is let go? You can neglect the volume of the rubber.

46. (a) What is the density of a woman who floats in freshwater with 4.00% of her volume above the surface? This could be measured by placing her in a tank with marks on the side to measure how much water she displaces when floating and when held under water (briefly). (b) What percent of her volume is above the surface when she floats in seawater?

47. A certain man has a mass of 80 kg and a density of $955\ \text{kg/m}^3$ (excluding the air in his lungs). (a) Calculate his volume. (b) Find the buoyant force air exerts on him. (c) What is the ratio of the buoyant force to his weight?

48. A simple compass can be made by placing a small bar magnet on a cork floating in water. (a) What fraction of a plain cork will be submerged when floating in water? (b) If the cork has a mass of 10.0 g and a 20.0-g magnet is placed on it, what fraction of the cork will be submerged? (c) Will the bar magnet and cork float in ethyl alcohol?

49. What fraction of an iron anchor's weight will be supported by buoyant force when submerged in saltwater?

50. Scurrilous con artists have been known to represent gold-plated tungsten ingots as pure gold and sell them at prices much below gold value but deservedly far above the cost of tungsten. With what accuracy must you be able to measure the mass of such an ingot in and out of water to tell that it is almost pure tungsten rather than pure gold?

51. A twin-sized air mattress used for camping has dimensions of 100 cm by 200 cm by 15 cm when blown up. The weight of the mattress is 2 kg. How heavy a person could the air mattress hold if it is placed in freshwater?

52. Referring to Figure 11.19, prove that the buoyant force on the cylinder is equal to the weight of the fluid displaced (Archimedes' principle). You may assume that the buoyant force is $F_2 - F_1$ and that the ends of the cylinder have equal areas A. Note that the volume of the cylinder (and that of the fluid it displaces) equals $(h_2 - h_1)A$.

53. (a) A 75.0-kg man floats in freshwater with 3.00% of his volume above water when his lungs are empty, and 5.00% of his volume above water when his lungs are full. Calculate the volume of air he inhales—called his lung capacity—in liters. (b) Does this lung volume seem reasonable?

11.8 Cohesion and Adhesion in Liquids: Surface Tension and Capillary Action

54. What is the pressure inside an alveolus having a radius of $2.50 \times 10^{-4}\ \text{m}$ if the surface tension of the fluid-lined wall is the same as for soapy water? You may assume the pressure is the same as that created by a spherical bubble.

55. (a) The pressure inside an alveolus with a 2.00×10^{-4}-m radius is $1.40 \times 10^3\ \text{Pa}$, due to its fluid-lined walls. Assuming the alveolus acts like a spherical bubble, what is the surface tension of the fluid? (b) Identify the likely fluid. (You may need to extrapolate between values in Table 11.3.)

56. What is the gauge pressure in millimeters of mercury inside a soap bubble 0.100 m in diameter?

57. Calculate the force on the slide wire in Figure 11.26 if it is 3.50 cm long and the fluid is ethyl alcohol.

58. Figure 11.32(a) shows the effect of tube radius on the height to which capillary action can raise a fluid. (a) Calculate the height h for water in a glass tube with a radius of 0.900 cm—a rather large tube like the one on the left. (b) What is the radius of the glass tube on the right if it raises water to 4.00 cm?

59. We stated in Example 11.12 that a xylem tube is of radius 2.50×10^{-5} m. Verify that such a tube raises sap less than a meter by finding h for it, making the same assumptions that sap's density is 1050 kg/m^3, its contact angle is zero, and its surface tension is the same as that of water at 20.0° C.

60. What fluid is in the device shown in Figure 11.26 if the force is 3.16×10^{-3} N and the length of the wire is 2.50 cm? Calculate the surface tension γ and find a likely match from Table 11.3.

61. If the gauge pressure inside a rubber balloon with a 10.0-cm radius is 1.50 cm of water, what is the effective surface tension of the balloon?

62. Calculate the gauge pressures inside 2.00-cm-radius bubbles of water, alcohol, and soapy water. Which liquid forms the most stable bubbles, neglecting any effects of evaporation?

63. Suppose water is raised by capillary action to a height of 5.00 cm in a glass tube. (a) To what height will it be raised in a paraffin tube of the same radius? (b) In a silver tube of the same radius?

64. Calculate the contact angle θ for olive oil if capillary action raises it to a height of 7.07 cm in a glass tube with a radius of 0.100 mm. Is this value consistent with that for most organic liquids?

65. When two soap bubbles touch, the larger is inflated by the smaller until they form a single bubble. (a) What is the gauge pressure inside a soap bubble with a 1.50-cm radius? (b) Inside a 4.00-cm-radius soap bubble? (c) Inside the single bubble they form if no air is lost when they touch?

66. Calculate the ratio of the heights to which water and mercury are raised by capillary action in the same glass tube.

67. What is the ratio of heights to which ethyl alcohol and water are raised by capillary action in the same glass tube?

11.9 Pressures in the Body

68. During forced exhalation, such as when blowing up a balloon, the diaphragm and chest muscles create a pressure of 60.0 mm Hg between the lungs and chest wall. What force in newtons does this pressure create on the 600 cm^2 surface area of the diaphragm?

69. You can chew through very tough objects with your incisors because they exert a large force on the small area of a pointed tooth. What pressure in pascals can you create by exerting a force of 500 N with your tooth on an area of 1.00 mm^2?

70. One way to force air into an unconscious person's lungs is to squeeze on a balloon appropriately connected to the subject. What force must you exert on the balloon with your hands to create a gauge pressure of 4.00 cm water, assuming you squeeze on an effective area of 50.0 cm^2?

71. Heroes in movies hide beneath water and breathe through a hollow reed (villains never catch on to this trick). In practice, you cannot inhale in this manner if your lungs are more than 60.0 cm below the surface. What is the maximum negative gauge pressure you can create in your lungs on dry land, assuming you can achieve -3.00 cm water pressure with your lungs 60.0 cm below the surface?

72. Gauge pressure in the fluid surrounding an infant's brain may rise as high as 85.0 mm Hg (5 to 12 mm Hg is normal), creating an outward force large enough to make the skull grow abnormally large. (a) Calculate this outward force in newtons on each side of an infant's skull if the effective area of each side is 70.0 cm^2. (b) What is the net force acting on the skull?

73. A full-term fetus typically has a mass of 3.50 kg. (a) What pressure does the weight of such a fetus create if it rests on the mother's bladder, supported on an area of 90.0 cm^2? (b) Convert this pressure to millimeters of mercury and determine if it alone is great enough to trigger the micturition reflex (it will add to any pressure already existing in the bladder).

74. If the pressure in the esophagus is -2.00 mm Hg while that in the stomach is $+20.0$ mm Hg, to what height could stomach fluid rise in the esophagus, assuming a density of 1.10 g/mL? (This movement will not occur if the muscle closing the lower end of the esophagus is working

properly.)

75. Pressure in the spinal fluid is measured as shown in Figure 11.40. If the pressure in the spinal fluid is 10.0 mm Hg: (a) What is the reading of the water manometer in cm water? (b) What is the reading if the person sits up, placing the top of the fluid 60 cm above the tap? The fluid density is 1.05 g/mL.

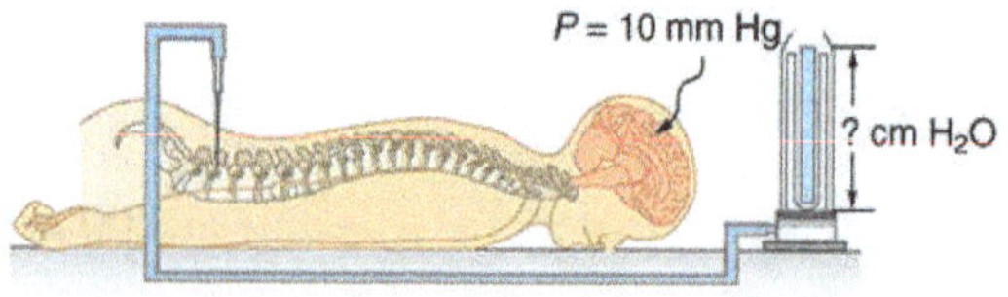

FIGURE 11.40 A water manometer used to measure pressure in the spinal fluid. The height of the fluid in the manometer is measured relative to the spinal column, and the manometer is open to the atmosphere. The measured pressure will be considerably greater if the person sits up.

76. Calculate the maximum force in newtons exerted by the blood on an aneurysm, or ballooning, in a major artery, given the maximum blood pressure for this person is 150 mm Hg and the effective area of the aneurysm is $20.0\ \text{cm}^2$. Note that this force is great enough to cause further enlargement and subsequently greater force on the ever-thinner vessel wall.

77. During heavy lifting, a disk between spinal vertebrae is subjected to a 5000-N compressional force. (a) What pressure is created, assuming that the disk has a uniform circular cross section 2.00 cm in radius? (b) What deformation is produced if the disk is 0.800 cm thick and has a Young's modulus of $1.5 \times 10^9\ \text{N/m}^2$?

78. When a person sits erect, increasing the vertical position of their brain by 36.0 cm, the heart must continue to pump blood to the brain at the same rate. (a) What is the gain in gravitational potential energy for 100 mL of blood raised 36.0 cm? (b) What is the drop in pressure, neglecting any losses due to friction? (c) Discuss how the gain in gravitational potential energy and the decrease in pressure are related.

79. (a) How high will water rise in a glass capillary tube with a 0.500-mm radius? (b) How much gravitational potential energy does the water gain? (c) Discuss possible sources of this energy.

80. A negative pressure of 25.0 atm can sometimes be achieved with the device in Figure 11.41 before the water separates. (a) To what height could such a negative gauge pressure raise water? (b) How much would a steel wire of the same diameter and length as this capillary stretch if suspended from above?

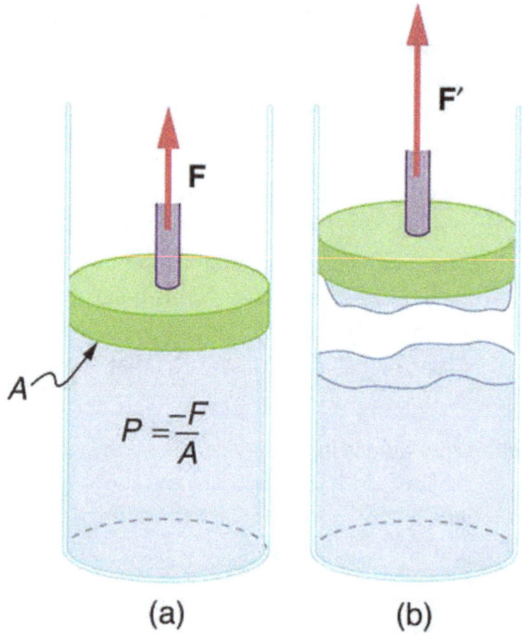

FIGURE 11.41 (a) When the piston is raised, it stretches the liquid slightly, putting it under tension and creating a negative absolute pressure $P = -F/A$ (b) The liquid eventually separates, giving an experimental limit to negative pressure in this liquid.

81. Suppose you hit a steel nail with a 0.500-kg hammer, initially moving at $15.0\ \text{m/s}$ and brought to rest in 2.80 mm. (a) What average force is exerted on the nail? (b) How much is the nail compressed if it is 2.50 mm in diameter and 6.00-cm long? (c) What pressure is created on the 1.00-mm-diameter tip of the nail?

82. Calculate the pressure due to the ocean at the bottom of the Marianas Trench near the Philippines, given its depth is $11.0\ \text{km}$ and assuming the density of sea water is constant all the way down. (b) Calculate the percent decrease in volume of sea water due to such a pressure, assuming its bulk modulus is the same as water and is constant. (c) What would be the percent increase in its density? Is the assumption of constant density valid? Will the actual pressure be greater or smaller than that calculated under this assumption?

83. The hydraulic system of a backhoe is used to lift a load as shown in Figure 11.42. (a) Calculate the force F the secondary cylinder must exert to support the 400-kg load and the 150-kg brace and shovel. (b) What is the pressure in the hydraulic fluid if the secondary cylinder is 2.50 cm in diameter? (c) What force would you have to exert on a lever with a mechanical advantage of 5.00 acting on a primary cylinder 0.800 cm in diameter to create this pressure?

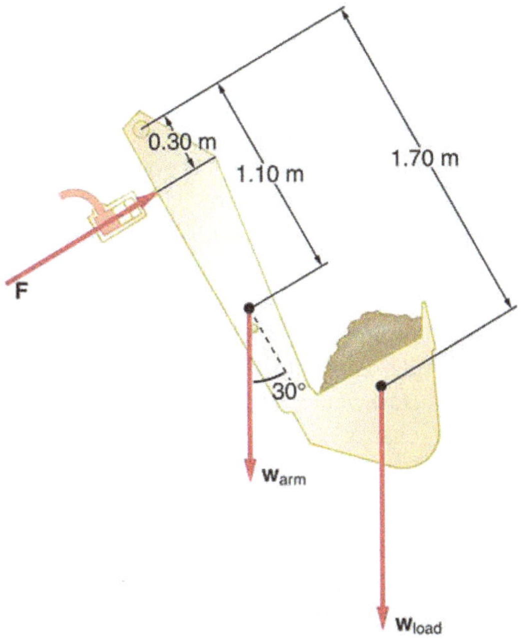

FIGURE 11.42 Hydraulic and mechanical lever systems are used in heavy machinery such as this back hoe.

84. Some miners wish to remove water from a mine shaft. A pipe is lowered to the water 90 m below, and a negative pressure is applied to raise the water. (a) Calculate the pressure needed to raise the water. (b) What is unreasonable about this pressure? (c) What is unreasonable about the premise?

85. You are pumping up a bicycle tire with a hand pump, the piston of which has a 2.00-cm radius. (a) What force in newtons must you exert to create a pressure of 6.90×10^5 Pa (b) What is unreasonable about this (a) result? (c) Which premises are unreasonable or inconsistent?

86. Consider a group of people trying to stay afloat after their boat strikes a log in a lake. Construct a problem in which you calculate the number of people that can cling to the log and keep their heads out of the water. Among the variables to be considered are the size and density of the log, and what is needed to keep a person's head and arms above water without swimming or treading water.

87. The alveoli in emphysema victims are damaged and effectively form larger sacs. Construct a problem in which you calculate the loss of pressure due to surface tension in the alveoli because of their larger average diameters. (Part of the lung's ability to expel air results from pressure created by surface tension in the alveoli.) Among the things to consider are the normal surface tension of the fluid lining the alveoli, the average alveolar radius in normal individuals and its average in emphysema sufferers.

Test Prep for AP® Courses

11.2 Density

1. An under-inflated volleyball is pumped full of air so that its radius increases by 10%. Ignoring the mass of the air inserted into the ball, what will happen to the volleyball's density?

a. The density of the volleyball will increase by approximately 25%.
b. The density of the volleyball will increase by approximately 10%.
c. The density of the volleyball will decrease by approximately 10%.
d. The density of the volleyball will decrease by approximately 17%.
e. The density of the volleyball will decrease by approximately 25%.

2. A piece of aluminum foil has a known surface density of 15 g/cm^2. If a 100-gram hollow cube were constructed using this foil, determine the approximate side length of this cube.

a. 1.05 cm
b. 1.10 cm
c. 2.6 cm
d. 6.67 cm
e. 15 cm

3. A cube of polystyrene measuring 10 cm per side lies partially submerged in a large container of water.

a. If 90% of the polystyrene floats above the surface of the water, what is the density of the polystyrene? (Note: The density of water is 1000 kg/m^3.)
b. A 0.5 kg mass is placed on the block of polystyrene. What percentage of the block now remains above water?
c. The water is poured out of the container and replaced with ethyl alcohol (density = 790 kg/m^3).
   i. Will the block be able to remain partially

submerged in this new fluid? Explain.

ii. Will the block be able to remain partially submerged in this new fluid with the 0.5 kg mass placed on top? Explain.

d. Without using a container of water, explain how you could determine the density of the polystyrene mentioned above if the material instead were spherical.

4. Four spheres are hung from a variety of different springs. The table below describes the characteristics of both the spheres and the springs from which they are hung. Use this information to rank the density of each sphere from least to greatest. Show work supporting your ranking.

Material Type	Radius of Sphere	Stretch of Spring (from equilibrium)	Spring Constant
A	10 cm	5 cm	2 N/m
B	5 cm	8 cm	8 N/m
C	8 cm	10 cm	6 N/m
D	8 cm	12 cm	10 N/m

TABLE 11.6

Rank the densities of the objects listed above, from greatest to least. Show work supporting your ranking.

11.3 Pressure

5. A cylindrical drum of radius 0.5 m is used to hold 400 liters of petroleum ether (density = .68 g/mL or 680 kg/m^3).
(Note: 1 liter = 0.001 m^3)

a. Determine the amount of pressure applied to the walls of the drum if the petroleum ether fills the drum to its top.

b. Determine the amount of pressure applied to the floor of the drum if the petroleum ether fills the drum to its top.

c. If the drum were redesigned to hold 800 liters of petroleum ether:

i. How would the pressure on the walls change?
Would it increase, decrease, or stay the same?

ii. How would the pressure on the floor change?
Would it increase, decrease, or stay the same?

CHAPTER 12
Fluid Dynamics and Its Biological and Medical Applications

FIGURE 12.1 Many fluids are flowing in this scene. Water from the hose and smoke from the fire are visible flows. Less visible are the flow of air and the flow of fluids on the ground and within the people fighting the fire. (credit: Andrew Magill, Flickr)

CHAPTER OUTLINE

CONNECTION FOR AP® COURSES How do planes fly? How do we model blood flow? How do sprayers work for paints or aerosols? What is the purpose of a water tower? To answer these questions, we will examine fluid dynamics. The equations governing fluid dynamics are derived from the same equations that represent energy conservation. One of the most powerful equations in fluid dynamics is Bernoulli's equation, which governs the relationship between fluid pressure, kinetic energy, and potential energy (Essential Knowledge 5.B.10). We will see how Bernoulli's equation explains the pressure difference that provides lift for airplanes and provides the means for fluids (like water or paint or perfume) to move in useful ways.

The content in this chapter supports:

Big Idea 5 Changes that occur as a result of interactions are constrained by conservation laws.

Enduring Understanding 5.B The energy of a system is conserved.

Essential Knowledge 5.B.10 Bernoulli's equation describes the conservation of energy in a fluid flow.

Enduring Understanding 5.F Classically, the mass of a system is conserved.

Essential Knowledge 5.F.1 The continuity equation describes conservation of mass flow rate in fluids.

Click to view content (https://openstax.org/books/college-physics-ap-courses-2e/pages/12-connection-for-ap-r-courses)

12.1 Flow Rate and Its R elation to Velocity

LEARNING OBJECTIVES

By the end of this section, you will be able to:

- Calculate flow rate.
- Define units of volume.
- Describe incompressible fluids.
- Explain the consequences of the equation of continuity.

Flow rate Q is defined to be the volume of fluid passing by some location through an area during a period of time, as seen in Figure 12.2. In symbols, this can be written as

$$Q = \frac{V}{t}, \tag{12.1}$$

where V is the volume and t is the elapsed time.

The SI unit for flow rate is $\text{m}^3\text{/s}$, but a number of other units for Q are in common use. For example, the heart of a resting adult pumps blood at a rate of 5.00 liters per minute (L/min). Note that a **liter** (L) is 1/1000 of a cubic meter or 1000 cubic centimeters ($10^{-3}\ \text{m}^3$ or $10^3\ \text{cm}^3$). In this text we shall use whatever metric units are most convenient for a given situation.

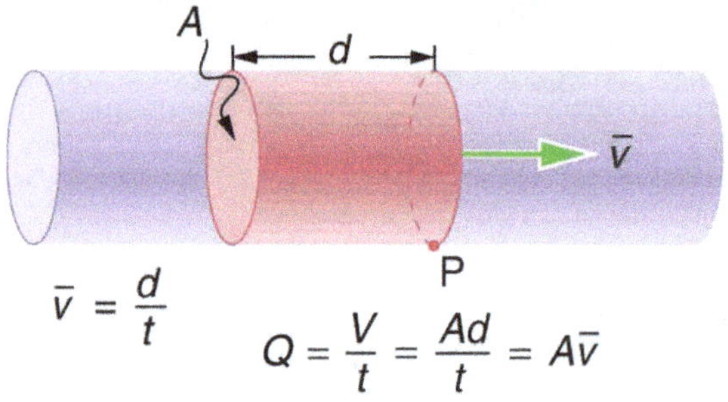

FIGURE 12.2 Flow rate is the volume of fluid per unit time flowing past a point through the area A. Here the shaded cylinder of fluid flows past point P in a uniform pipe in time t. The volume of the cylinder is Ad and the average velocity is $\bar{v} = d/t$ so that the flow rate is $Q = Ad/t = A\bar{v}$.

EXAMPLE 12.1

Calculating Volume from Flow Rate: The Heart Pumps a Lot of Blood in a Lifetime

How many cubic meters of blood does the heart pump in a 75-year lifetime, assuming the average flow rate is 5.00 L/min?

Strategy

Time and flow rate Q are given, and so the volume V can be calculated from the definition of flow rate.

Solution

Solving $Q = V/t$ for volume gives

$$V = Qt. \tag{12.2}$$

Substituting known values yields

$$\begin{aligned} V &= \left(\frac{5.00\ \text{L}}{1\ \text{min}}\right)(75\ \text{y})\left(\frac{1\ \text{m}^3}{10^3\ \text{L}}\right)\left(5.26 \times 10^5\ \frac{\text{min}}{\text{y}}\right) \\ &= 2.0 \times 10^5\ \text{m}^3. \end{aligned} \tag{12.3}$$

Discussion

This amount is about 200,000 tons of blood. For comparison, this value is equivalent to about 200 times the volume of water contained in a 6-lane 50-m lap pool.

Flow rate and velocity are related, but quite different, physical quantities. To make the distinction clear, think about the flow rate of a river. The greater the velocity of the water, the greater the flow rate of the river. But flow rate also depends on the size of the river. A rapid mountain stream carries far less water than the Amazon River in Brazil, for example. The precise relationship between flow rate Q and velocity $\bar{v}$ is

$$Q = A\bar{v}, \tag{12.4}$$

where A is the cross-sectional area and $\bar{v}$ is the average velocity. This equation seems logical enough. The relationship tells us that flow rate is directly proportional to both the magnitude of the average velocity (hereafter referred to as the speed) and the size of a river, pipe, or other conduit. The larger the conduit, the greater its cross-sectional area. Figure 12.2 illustrates how this relationship is obtained. The shaded cylinder has a volume

$$V = Ad, \tag{12.5}$$

which flows past the point $\mathbf{P}$ in a time t. Dividing both sides of this relationship by t gives

$$\frac{V}{t} = \frac{Ad}{t}. \tag{12.6}$$

We note that $Q = V/t$ and the average speed is $\bar{v} = d/t$. Thus the equation becomes $Q = A\bar{v}$.

Figure 12.3 shows an incompressible fluid flowing along a pipe of decreasing radius. Because the fluid is incompressible, the same amount of fluid must flow past any point in the tube in a given time to ensure continuity of flow. In this case, because the cross-sectional area of the pipe decreases, the velocity must necessarily increase. This logic can be extended to say that the flow rate must be the same at all points along the pipe. In particular, for points 1 and 2,

$$\left.\begin{aligned} Q_1 &= Q_2 \\ A_1\bar{v}_1 &= A_2\bar{v}_2 \end{aligned}\right\}. \tag{12.7}$$

This is called the equation of continuity and is valid for any incompressible fluid. The consequences of the equation of continuity can be observed when water flows from a hose into a narrow spray nozzle: it emerges with a large speed—that is the purpose of the nozzle. Conversely, when a river empties into one end of a reservoir, the water slows considerably, perhaps picking up speed again when it leaves the other end of the reservoir. In other words, speed increases when cross-sectional area decreases, and speed decreases when cross-sectional area increases.

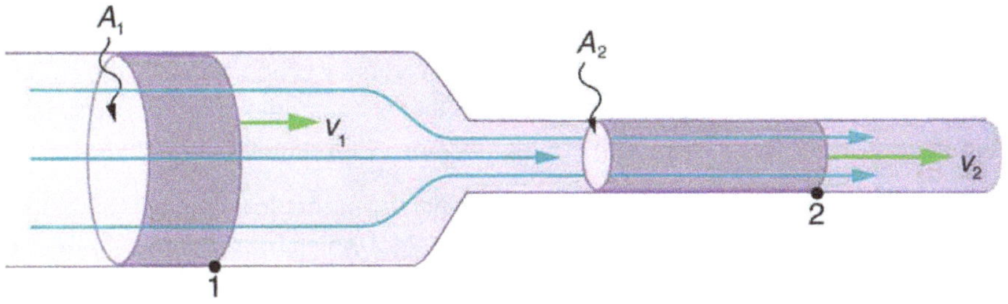

FIGURE 12.3 When a tube narrows, the same volume occupies a greater length. For the same volume to pass points 1 and 2 in a given time, the speed must be greater at point 2. The process is exactly reversible. If the fluid flows in the opposite direction, its speed will decrease when the tube widens. (Note that the relative volumes of the two cylinders and the corresponding velocity vector arrows are not drawn to scale.)

Since liquids are essentially incompressible, the equation of continuity is valid for all liquids. However, gases are compressible, and so the equation must be applied with caution to gases if they are subjected to compression or expansion.

EXAMPLE 12.2

Calculating Fluid Speed: Speed Increases When a Tube Narrows

A nozzle with a radius of 0.250 cm is attached to a garden hose with a radius of 0.900 cm. The flow rate through hose and nozzle is 0.500 L/s. Calculate the speed of the water (a) in the hose and (b) in the nozzle.

Strategy

We can use the relationship between flow rate and speed to find both velocities. We will use the subscript 1 for the hose and 2 for the nozzle.

Solution for (a)

First, we solve $Q = A\bar{v}$ for v_1 and note that the cross-sectional area is $A = \pi r^2$, yielding

$$\bar{v}_1 = \frac{Q}{A_1} = \frac{Q}{\pi r_1^2}. \tag{12.8}$$

Substituting known values and making appropriate unit conversions yields

$$\bar{v}_1 = \frac{(0.500 \text{ L/s})(10^{-3} \text{ m}^3/\text{L})}{\pi(9.00 \times 10^{-3} \text{ m})^2} = 1.96 \text{ m/s}. \tag{12.9}$$

Solution for (b)

We could repeat this calculation to find the speed in the nozzle $\bar{v}_2$, but we will use the equation of continuity to give a somewhat different insight. Using the equation which states

$$A_1\bar{v}_1 = A_2\bar{v}_2, \tag{12.10}$$

solving for $\bar{v}_2$ and substituting πr^2 for the cross-sectional area yields

$$\bar{v}_2 = \frac{A_1}{A_2}\bar{v}_1 = \frac{\pi r_1^2}{\pi r_2^2}\bar{v}_1 = \frac{r_{1}{}^2}{r_{2}{}^2}\bar{v}_1. \tag{12.11}$$

Substituting known values,

$$\bar{v}_2 = \frac{(0.900 \text{ cm})^2}{(0.250 \text{ cm})^2}1.96 \text{ m/s} = 25.5 \text{ m/s}. \tag{12.12}$$

Discussion

A speed of 1.96 m/s is about right for water emerging from a nozzleless hose. The nozzle produces a considerably faster stream merely by constricting the flow to a narrower tube.

The solution to the last part of the example shows that speed is inversely proportional to the *square* of the radius of the tube, making for large effects when radius varies. We can blow out a candle at quite a distance, for example, by pursing our lips, whereas blowing on a candle with our mouth wide open is quite ineffective.

In many situations, including in the cardiovascular system, branching of the flow occurs. The blood is pumped from the heart into arteries that subdivide into smaller arteries (arterioles) which branch into very fine vessels called capillaries. In this situation, continuity of flow is maintained but it is the *sum* of the flow rates in each of the branches in any portion along the tube that is maintained. The equation of continuity in a more general form becomes

$$n_1 A_1\bar{v}_1 = n_2 A_2\bar{v}_2, \tag{12.13}$$

where n_1 and n_2 are the number of branches in each of the sections along the tube.

EXAMPLE 12.3

Calculating Flow Speed and Vessel Diameter: Branching in the Cardiovascular System

The aorta is the principal blood vessel through which blood leaves the heart in order to circulate around the body. (a) Calculate the average speed of the blood in the aorta if the flow rate is 5.0 L/min. The aorta has a radius of 10 mm. (b) Blood also flows through smaller blood vessels known as capillaries. When the rate of blood flow in the aorta is 5.0 L/min, the speed of blood in the capillaries is about 0.33 mm/s. Given that the average diameter of a capillary is $8.0\ \mu\text{m}$, calculate the number of capillaries in the blood circulatory system.

Strategy

We can use $Q = A\bar{v}$ to calculate the speed of flow in the aorta and then use the general form of the equation of continuity to calculate the number of capillaries as all of the other variables are known.

Solution for (a)

The flow rate is given by $Q = A\bar{v}$ or $\bar{v} = \frac{Q}{\pi r^2}$ for a cylindrical vessel.

Substituting the known values (converted to units of meters and seconds) gives

$$\bar{v} = \frac{(5.0\ \text{L/min})\left(10^{-3}\ \text{m}^3/\text{L}\right)(1\ \text{min}/60\ \text{s})}{\pi(0.010\ \text{m})^2} = 0.27\ \text{m/s}. \quad 12.14$$

Solution for (b)

Using $n_1 A_1 \bar{v}_1 = n_2 A_2 \bar{v}_1$, assigning the subscript 1 to the aorta and 2 to the capillaries, and solving for n_2 (the number of capillaries) gives $n_2 = \frac{n_1 A_1 \bar{v}_1}{A_2 \bar{v}_2}$. Converting all quantities to units of meters and seconds and substituting into the equation above gives

$$n_2 = \frac{(1)(\pi)\left(10 \times 10^{-3}\ \text{m}\right)^2(0.27\ \text{m/s})}{(\pi)\left(4.0 \times 10^{-6}\ \text{m}\right)^2\left(0.33 \times 10^{-3}\ \text{m/s}\right)} = 5.0 \times 10^9\ \text{capillaries}. \quad 12.15$$

Discussion

Note that the speed of flow in the capillaries is considerably reduced relative to the speed in the aorta due to the significant increase in the total cross-sectional area at the capillaries. This low speed is to allow sufficient time for effective exchange to occur although it is equally important for the flow not to become stationary in order to avoid the possibility of clotting. Does this large number of capillaries in the body seem reasonable? In active muscle, one finds about 200 capillaries per mm^3, or about 200×10^6 per 1 kg of muscle. For 20 kg of muscle, this amounts to about 4×10^9 capillaries.

12.2 Bernoulli's Equation

LEARNING OBJECTIVES

By the end of this section, you will be able to:

- Explain the terms in Bernoulli's equation.
- Explain how Bernoulli's equation is related to conservation of energy.
- Explain how to derive Bernoulli's principle from Bernoulli's equation.
- Calculate with Bernoulli's principle.
- List some applications of Bernoulli's principle.

When a fluid flows into a narrower channel, its speed increases. That means its kinetic energy also increases. Where does that change in kinetic energy come from? The increased kinetic energy comes from the net work done on the fluid to push it into the channel and the work done on the fluid by the gravitational force, if the fluid changes vertical position. Recall the work-energy theorem,

$$W_{\text{net}} = \frac{1}{2}mv^2 - \frac{1}{2}mv_0^2. \qquad 12.16$$

There is a pressure difference when the channel narrows. This pressure difference results in a net force on the fluid: recall that pressure times area equals force. The net work done increases the fluid's kinetic energy. As a result, the *pressure will drop in a rapidly-moving fluid*, whether or not the fluid is confined to a tube.

There are a number of common examples of pressure dropping in rapidly-moving fluids. Shower curtains have a disagreeable habit of bulging into the shower stall when the shower is on. The high-velocity stream of water and air creates a region of lower pressure inside the shower, and standard atmospheric pressure on the other side. The pressure difference results in a net force inward pushing the curtain in. You may also have noticed that when passing a truck on the highway, your car tends to veer toward it. The reason is the same—the high velocity of the air between the car and the truck creates a region of lower pressure, and the vehicles are pushed together by greater pressure on the outside. (See Figure 12.4.) This effect was observed as far back as the mid-1800s, when it was found that trains passing in opposite directions tipped precariously toward one another.

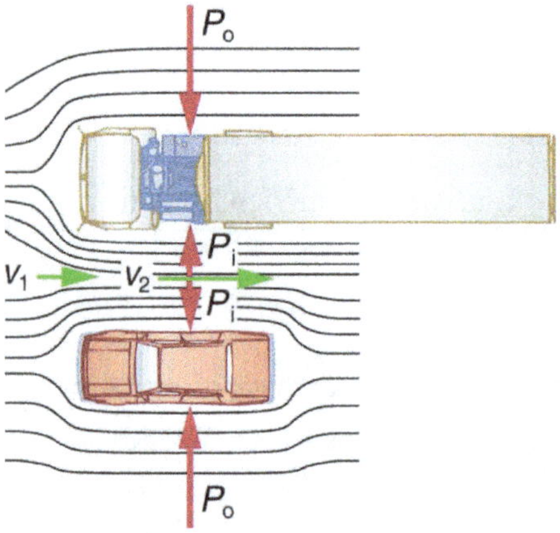

FIGURE 12.4 An overhead view of a car passing a truck on a highway. Air passing between the vehicles flows in a narrower channel and must increase its speed (v_2 is greater than v_1), causing the pressure between them to drop (P_i is less than P_o). Greater pressure on the outside pushes the car and truck together.

MAKING CONNECTIONS: TAKE-HOME INVESTIGATION WITH A SHEET OF PAPER

Hold the short edge of a sheet of paper parallel to your mouth with one hand on each side of your mouth. The page should slant downward over your hands. Blow over the top of the page. Describe what happens and explain the reason for this behavior.

Bernoulli's Equation

The relationship between pressure and velocity in fluids is described quantitatively by **Bernoulli's equation**, named after its discoverer, the Swiss scientist Daniel Bernoulli (1700–1782). Bernoulli's equation states that for an incompressible, frictionless fluid, the following sum is constant:

$$P + \frac{1}{2}\rho v^2 + \rho g h = \text{constant}, \qquad 12.17$$

where P is the absolute pressure, ρ is the fluid density, v is the velocity of the fluid, h is the height above some reference point, and g is the acceleration due to gravity. If we follow a small volume of fluid along its path, various quantities in the sum may change, but the total remains constant. Let the subscripts 1 and 2 refer to any two points along the path that the bit of fluid follows; Bernoulli's equation becomes

$$P_1 + \frac{1}{2}\rho v_1^2 + \rho g h_1 = P_2 + \frac{1}{2}\rho v_2^2 + \rho g h_2\,. \qquad 12.18$$

Bernoulli's equation is a form of the conservation of energy principle. Note that the second and third terms are the kinetic and potential energy with m replaced by ρ. In fact, each term in the equation has units of energy per unit volume. We can prove this for the second term by substituting $\rho = m/V$ into it and gathering terms:

$$\frac{1}{2}\rho v^2 = \frac{\frac{1}{2}mv^2}{V} = \frac{\text{KE}}{V}. \tag{12.19}$$

So $\frac{1}{2}\rho v^2$ is the kinetic energy per unit volume. Making the same substitution into the third term in the equation, we find

$$\rho gh = \frac{mgh}{V} = \frac{\text{PE}_{\text{g}}}{V}, \tag{12.20}$$

so ρgh is the gravitational potential energy per unit volume. Note that pressure P has units of energy per unit volume, too. Since $P = F/A$, its units are N/m^2. If we multiply these by m/m, we obtain $\text{N} \cdot \text{m/m}^3 = \text{J/m}^3$, or energy per unit volume. Bernoulli's equation is, in fact, just a convenient statement of conservation of energy for an incompressible fluid in the absence of friction.

MAKING CONNECTIONS: CONSERVATION OF ENERGY

Conservation of energy applied to fluid flow produces Bernoulli's equation. The net work done by the fluid's pressure results in changes in the fluid's KE and PE_{g} per unit volume. If other forms of energy are involved in fluid flow, Bernoulli's equation can be modified to take these forms into account. Such forms of energy include thermal energy dissipated because of fluid viscosity.

The general form of Bernoulli's equation has three terms in it, and it is broadly applicable. To understand it better, we will look at a number of specific situations that simplify and illustrate its use and meaning.

Bernoulli's Equation for Static Fluids

Let us first consider the very simple situation where the fluid is static—that is, $v_1 = v_2 = 0$. Bernoulli's equation in that case is

$$P_1 + \rho gh_1 = P_2 + \rho gh_2 . \tag{12.21}$$

We can further simplify the equation by taking $h_2 = 0$ (we can always choose some height to be zero, just as we often have done for other situations involving the gravitational force, and take all other heights to be relative to this). In that case, we get

$$P_2 = P_1 + \rho gh_1 . \tag{12.22}$$

This equation tells us that, in static fluids, pressure increases with depth. As we go from point 1 to point 2 in the fluid, the depth increases by h_1, and consequently, P_2 is greater than P_1 by an amount ρgh_1. In the very simplest case, P_1 is zero at the top of the fluid, and we get the familiar relationship $P = \rho gh$. (Recall that $P = \rho gh$ and $\Delta\text{PE}_{\text{g}} = mgh$.) Bernoulli's equation includes the fact that the pressure due to the weight of a fluid is ρgh. Although we introduce Bernoulli's equation for fluid flow, it includes much of what we studied for static fluids in the preceding chapter.

Bernoulli's Principle—Bernoulli's Equation at Constant Depth

Another important situation is one in which the fluid moves but its depth is constant—that is, $h_1 = h_2$. Under that condition, Bernoulli's equation becomes

$$P_1 + \frac{1}{2}\rho v_1^2 = P_2 + \frac{1}{2}\rho v_2^2. \tag{12.23}$$

Situations in which fluid flows at a constant depth are so important that this equation is often called **Bernoulli's principle**. It is Bernoulli's equation for fluids at constant depth. (Note again that this applies to a small volume of fluid as we follow it along its path.) As we have just discussed, pressure drops as speed increases in a moving fluid. We can see this from Bernoulli's principle. For example, if v_2 is greater than v_1 in the equation, then P_2 must be less than P_1 for the equality to hold.

EXAMPLE 12.4

Calculating Pressure: Pressure Drops as a Fluid Speeds Up

In Example 12.2, we found that the speed of water in a hose increased from 1.96 m/s to 25.5 m/s going from the hose to the nozzle. Calculate the pressure in the hose, given that the absolute pressure in the nozzle is $1.01 \times 10^5\ \text{N/m}^2$ (atmospheric, as it must be) and assuming level, frictionless flow.

Strategy

Level flow means constant depth, so Bernoulli's principle applies. We use the subscript 1 for values in the hose and 2 for those in the nozzle. We are thus asked to find P_1.

Solution

Solving Bernoulli's principle for P_1 yields

$$P_1 = P_2 + \frac{1}{2}\rho v_2^2 - \frac{1}{2}\rho v_1^2 = P_2 + \frac{1}{2}\rho(v_2^2 - v_1^2). \tag{12.24}$$

Substituting known values,

$$\begin{aligned} P_1 &= 1.01 \times 10^5\ \text{N/m}^2 \\ &\quad + \tfrac{1}{2}(10^3\ \text{kg/m}^3)\left[(25.5\ \text{m/s})^2 - (1.96\ \text{m/s})^2\right] \\ &= 4.24 \times 10^5\ \text{N/m}^2. \end{aligned} \tag{12.25}$$

Discussion

This absolute pressure in the hose is greater than in the nozzle, as expected since v is greater in the nozzle. The pressure P_2 in the nozzle must be atmospheric since it emerges into the atmosphere without other changes in conditions.

Applications of Bernoulli's Principle

There are a number of devices and situations in which fluid flows at a constant height and, thus, can be analyzed with Bernoulli's principle.

Entrainment

People have long put the Bernoulli principle to work by using reduced pressure in high-velocity fluids to move things about. With a higher pressure on the outside, the high-velocity fluid forces other fluids into the stream. This process is called *entrainment*. Entrainment devices have been in use since ancient times, particularly as pumps to raise water small heights, as in draining swamps, fields, or other low-lying areas. Some other devices that use the concept of entrainment are shown in Figure 12.5.

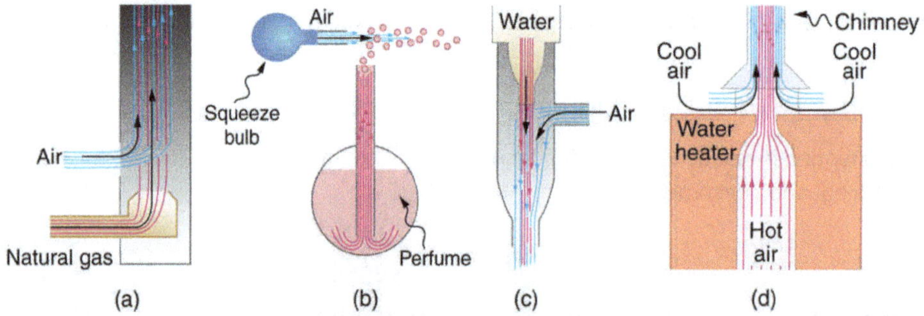

FIGURE 12.5 Examples of entrainment devices that use increased fluid speed to create low pressures, which then entrain one fluid into another. (a) A Bunsen burner uses an adjustable gas nozzle, entraining air for proper combustion. (b) An atomizer uses a squeeze bulb to create a jet of air that entrains drops of perfume. Paint sprayers and carburetors use very similar techniques to move their respective liquids. (c) A common aspirator uses a high-speed stream of water to create a region of lower pressure. Aspirators may be used as suction pumps in dental and surgical situations or for draining a flooded basement or producing a reduced pressure in a vessel. (d) The chimney of a water heater is designed to entrain air into the pipe leading through the ceiling.

Wings and Sails

The airplane wing is a beautiful example of Bernoulli's principle in action. Figure 12.6(a) shows the characteristic shape of a wing. The wing is tilted upward at a small angle and the upper surface is longer, causing air to flow faster over it. The pressure on top of the wing is therefore reduced, creating a net upward force or lift. (Wings can also gain lift by pushing air downward, utilizing the conservation of momentum principle. The deflected air molecules result in an upward force on the wing — Newton's third law.) Sails also have the characteristic shape of a wing. (See Figure 12.6(b).) The pressure on the front side of the sail, P_{front}, is lower than the pressure on the back of the sail, P_{back}. This results in a forward force and even allows you to sail into the wind.

MAKING CONNECTIONS: TAKE-HOME INVESTIGATION WITH TWO STRIPS OF PAPER

For a good illustration of Bernoulli's principle, make two strips of paper, each about 15 cm long and 4 cm wide. Hold the small end of one strip up to your lips and let it drape over your finger. Blow across the paper. What happens? Now hold two strips of paper up to your lips, separated by your fingers. Blow between the strips. What happens?

Velocity measurement

Figure 12.7 shows two devices that measure fluid velocity based on Bernoulli's principle. The manometer in Figure 12.7(a) is connected to two tubes that are small enough not to appreciably disturb the flow. The tube facing the oncoming fluid creates a dead spot having zero velocity ($v_1 = 0$) in front of it, while fluid passing the other tube has velocity v_2. This means that Bernoulli's principle as stated in $P_1 + \frac{1}{2}\rho v_1^2 = P_2 + \frac{1}{2}\rho v_2^2$ becomes

$$P_1 = P_2 + \frac{1}{2}\rho v_2^2. \qquad (12.26)$$

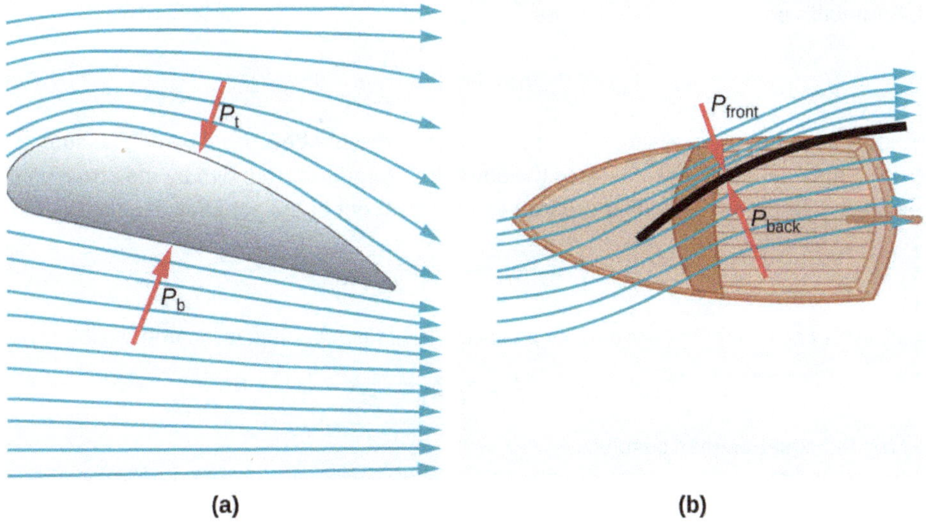

FIGURE 12.6 (a) The Bernoulli principle helps explain lift generated by a wing. (b) Sails use the same technique to generate part of their thrust.

Thus pressure P_2 over the second opening is reduced by $\frac{1}{2}\rho v_2^2$, and so the fluid in the manometer rises by h on the side connected to the second opening, where

$$h \propto \frac{1}{2}\rho v_2^2. \qquad (12.27)$$

(Recall that the symbol $\propto$ means "proportional to.") Solving for v_2, we see that

$$v_2 \propto \sqrt{h}. \qquad (12.28)$$

Figure 12.7(b) shows a version of this device that is in common use for measuring various fluid velocities; such devices are frequently used as air speed indicators in aircraft.

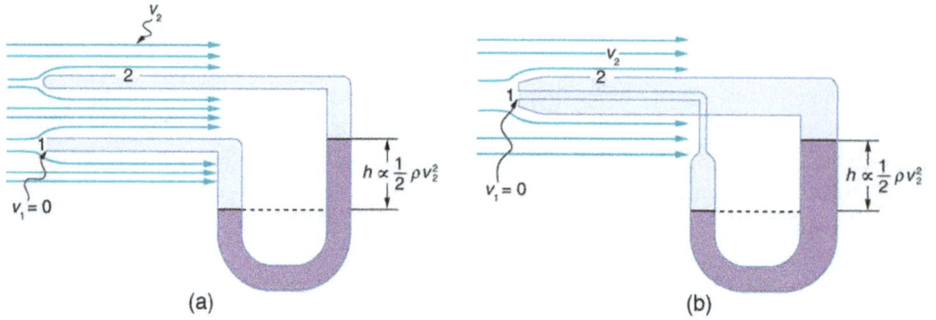

FIGURE 12.7 Measurement of fluid speed based on Bernoulli's principle. (a) A manometer is connected to two tubes that are close together and small enough not to disturb the flow. Tube 1 is open at the end facing the flow. A dead spot having zero speed is created there. Tube 2 has an opening on the side, and so the fluid has a speed v across the opening; thus, pressure there drops. The difference in pressure at the manometer is $\frac{1}{2}\rho v_2^2$, and so h is proportional to $\frac{1}{2}\rho v_2^2$. (b) This type of velocity measuring device is a Prandtl tube, also known as a pitot tube.

12.3 The Most General Applications of Bernoulli's Equation

LEARNING OBJECTIVES

By the end of this section, you will be able to:

- Calculate using Torricelli's theorem.
- Calculate power in fluid flow.

Torricelli's Theorem

Figure 12.8 shows water gushing from a large tube through a dam. What is its speed as it emerges? Interestingly, if resistance is negligible, the speed is just what it would be if the water fell a distance h from the surface of the reservoir; the water's speed is independent of the size of the opening. Let us check this out. Bernoulli's equation must be used since the depth is not constant. We consider water flowing from the surface (point 1) to the tube's outlet (point 2). Bernoulli's equation as stated in previously is

$$P_1 + \frac{1}{2}\rho v_1^2 + \rho g h_1 = P_2 + \frac{1}{2}\rho v_2^2 + \rho g h_2. \qquad 12.29$$

Both P_1 and P_2 equal atmospheric pressure (P_1 is atmospheric pressure because it is the pressure at the top of the reservoir. P_2 must be atmospheric pressure, since the emerging water is surrounded by the atmosphere and cannot have a pressure different from atmospheric pressure.) and subtract out of the equation, leaving

$$\frac{1}{2}\rho v_1^2 + \rho g h_1 = \frac{1}{2}\rho v_2^2 + \rho g h_2. \qquad 12.30$$

Solving this equation for v_2^2, noting that the density ρ cancels (because the fluid is incompressible), yields

$$v_2^2 = v_1^2 + 2g(h_1 - h_2). \qquad 12.31$$

We let $h = h_1 - h_2$; the equation then becomes

$$v_2^2 = v_1^2 + 2gh \qquad 12.32$$

where h is the height dropped by the water. This is simply a kinematic equation for any object falling a distance h with negligible resistance. In fluids, this last equation is called *Torricelli's theorem*. Note that the result is independent of the velocity's direction, just as we found when applying conservation of energy to falling objects.

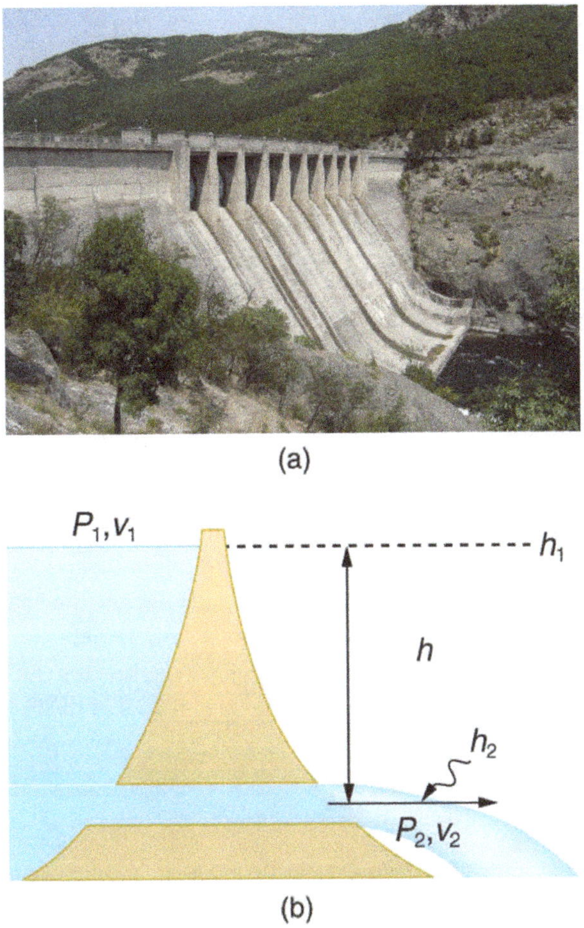

FIGURE 12.8 (a) Water gushes from the base of the Studen Kladenetz dam in Bulgaria. (credit: Kiril Kapustin; http://www.ImagesFromBulgaria.com) (b) In the absence of significant resistance, water flows from the reservoir with the same speed it would have if it fell the distance h without friction. This is an example of Torricelli's theorem.

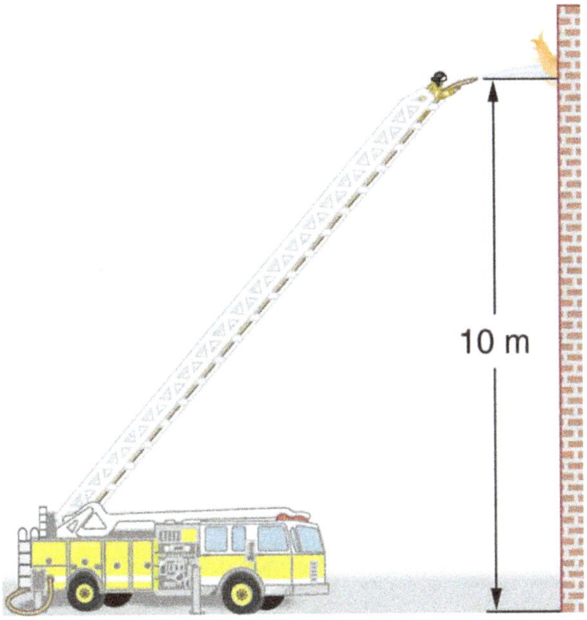

FIGURE 12.9 Pressure in the nozzle of this fire hose is less than at ground level for two reasons: the water has to go uphill to get to the nozzle, and speed increases in the nozzle. In spite of its lowered pressure, the water can exert a large force on anything it strikes, by virtue of its kinetic energy. Pressure in the water stream becomes equal to atmospheric pressure once it emerges into the air.

All preceding applications of Bernoulli's equation involved simplifying conditions, such as constant height or constant pressure. The next example is a more general application of Bernoulli's equation in which pressure, velocity, and height all change. (See Figure 12.9.)

EXAMPLE 12.5

Calculating Pressure: A Fire Hose Nozzle

Fire hoses used in major structure fires have inside diameters of 6.40 cm. Suppose such a hose carries a flow of 40.0 L/s starting at a gauge pressure of $1.62 \times 10^6\ \text{N/m}^2$. The hose goes 10.0 m up a ladder to a nozzle having an inside diameter of 3.00 cm. Assuming negligible resistance, what is the pressure in the nozzle?

Strategy

Here we must use Bernoulli's equation to solve for the pressure, since depth is not constant.

Solution

Bernoulli's equation states

$$P_1 + \frac{1}{2}\rho v_1^2 + \rho g h_1 = P_2 + \frac{1}{2}\rho v_2^2 + \rho g h_2, \tag{12.33}$$

where the subscripts 1 and 2 refer to the initial conditions at ground level and the final conditions inside the nozzle, respectively. We must first find the speeds v_1 and v_2. Since $Q = A_1 v_1$, we get

$$v_1 = \frac{Q}{A_1} = \frac{40.0 \times 10^{-3}\ \text{m}^3/\text{s}}{\pi(3.20 \times 10^{-2}\ \text{m})^2} = 12.434\ \text{m/s}. \tag{12.34}$$

Similarly, we find

$$v_2 = 56.588\ \text{m/s}. \tag{12.35}$$

(This rather large speed is helpful in reaching the fire.) Now, taking h_1 to be zero, we solve Bernoulli's equation for P_2:

$$P_2 = P_1 + \frac{1}{2}\rho\left(v_1^2 - v_2^2\right) - \rho g h_2. \tag{12.36}$$

Substituting known values yields

$$\begin{aligned} P_2 &= \\ &1.62 \times 10^6\ \text{N/m}^2 + \tfrac{1}{2}(1000\ \text{kg/m}^3)\left[(12.434\ \text{m/s})^2 - (56.588\ \text{m/s})^2\right] - (1000\ \text{kg/m}^3)(9.80\ \text{m/s}^2)(10.0\ \text{m}) \\ &\approx 1800\ \text{N/m}^2. \end{aligned} \tag{12.37}$$

Discussion

This value is a gauge pressure, since the initial pressure was given as a gauge pressure. Thus the nozzle pressure is very close to atmospheric pressure, as it must because the water exits into the atmosphere without changes in its conditions.

Power in Fluid Flow

Power is the *rate* at which work is done or energy in any form is used or supplied. To see the relationship of power to fluid flow, consider Bernoulli's equation:

$$P + \frac{1}{2}\rho v^2 + \rho g h = \text{constant}. \tag{12.38}$$

All three terms have units of energy per unit volume, as discussed in the previous section. Now, considering units, if we multiply energy per unit volume by flow rate (volume per unit time), we get units of power. That is, $(E/V)(V/t) = E/t$. This means that if we multiply Bernoulli's equation by flow rate Q, we get power. In equation form, this is

$$\left(P + \frac{1}{2}\rho v^2 + \rho g h\right)Q = \text{power}. \quad 12.39$$

Each term has a clear physical meaning. For example, PQ is the power supplied to a fluid, perhaps by a pump, to give it its pressure P. Similarly, $\frac{1}{2}\rho v^2 Q$ is the power supplied to a fluid to give it its kinetic energy. And $\rho g h Q$ is the power going to gravitational potential energy.

MAKING CONNECTIONS: POWER

Power is defined as the rate of energy transferred, or E/t. Fluid flow involves several types of power. Each type of power is identified with a specific type of energy being expended or changed in form.

EXAMPLE 12.6

Calculating Power in a Moving Fluid

Suppose the fire hose in the previous example is fed by a pump that receives water through a hose with a 6.40-cm diameter coming from a hydrant with a pressure of $0.700 \times 10^6\ \text{N/m}^2$. What power does the pump supply to the water?

Strategy

Here we must consider energy forms as well as how they relate to fluid flow. Since the input and output hoses have the same diameters and are at the same height, the pump does not change the speed of the water nor its height, and so the water's kinetic energy and gravitational potential energy are unchanged. That means the pump only supplies power to increase water pressure by $0.92 \times 10^6\ \text{N/m}^2$ (from $0.700 \times 10^6\ \text{N/m}^2$ to $1.62 \times 10^6\ \text{N/m}^2$).

Solution

As discussed above, the power associated with pressure is

$$\begin{aligned} \text{power} &= PQ \\ &= \left(0.920 \times 10^6\ \text{N/m}^2\right)\left(40.0 \times 10^{-3}\ \text{m}^3/\text{s}\right).. \\ &= 3.68 \times 10^4\ \text{W} = 36.8\ \text{kW} \end{aligned} \quad 12.40$$

Discussion

Such a substantial amount of power requires a large pump, such as is found on some fire trucks. (This kilowatt value converts to about 50 hp.) The pump in this example increases only the water's pressure. If a pump—such as the heart—directly increases velocity and height as well as pressure, we would have to calculate all three terms to find the power it supplies.

12.4 Viscosity and Laminar Flow; Poiseuille's Law

LEARNING OBJECTIVES

By the end of this section, you will be able to:

- Define laminar flow and turbulent flow.
- Explain what viscosity is.
- Calculate flow and resistance with Poiseuille's law.
- Explain how pressure drops due to resistance.

Laminar Flow and Viscosity

When you pour yourself a glass of juice, the liquid flows freely and quickly. But when you pour syrup on your pancakes, that liquid flows slowly and sticks to the pitcher. The difference is fluid friction, both within the fluid itself and between the fluid and its surroundings. We call this property of fluids *viscosity*. Juice has low viscosity, whereas syrup has high viscosity. In the previous sections we have considered ideal fluids with little or no viscosity. In this section, we will investigate what factors, including viscosity, affect the rate of fluid flow.

The precise definition of viscosity is based on *laminar*, or nonturbulent, flow. Before we can define viscosity, then, we need to define laminar flow and turbulent flow. Figure 12.10 shows both types of flow. **Laminar** flow is characterized by the smooth flow of the fluid in layers that do not mix. Turbulent flow, or **turbulence**, is characterized by eddies and swirls that mix layers of fluid together.

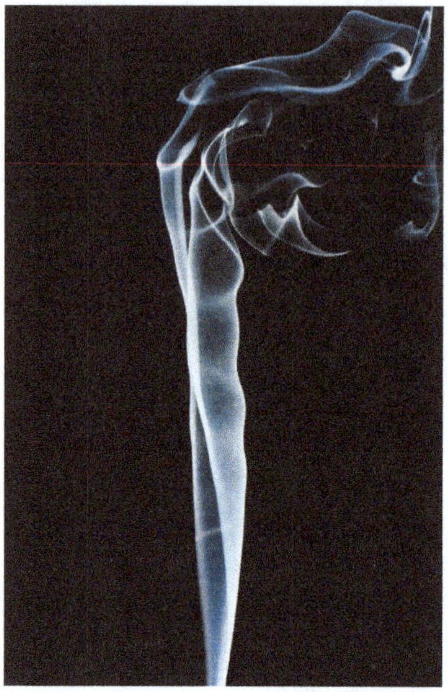

FIGURE 12.10 Smoke rises smoothly for a while and then begins to form swirls and eddies. The smooth flow is called laminar flow, whereas the swirls and eddies typify turbulent flow. If you watch the smoke (being careful not to breathe on it), you will notice that it rises more rapidly when flowing smoothly than after it becomes turbulent, implying that turbulence poses more resistance to flow. (credit: Creativity103)

Figure 12.11 shows schematically how laminar and turbulent flow differ. Layers flow without mixing when flow is laminar. When there is turbulence, the layers mix, and there are significant velocities in directions other than the overall direction of flow. The lines that are shown in many illustrations are the paths followed by small volumes of fluids. These are called *streamlines*. Streamlines are smooth and continuous when flow is laminar, but break up and mix when flow is turbulent. Turbulence has two main causes. First, any obstruction or sharp corner, such as in a faucet, creates turbulence by imparting velocities perpendicular to the flow. Second, high speeds cause turbulence. The drag both between adjacent layers of fluid and between the fluid and its surroundings forms swirls and eddies, if the speed is great enough. We shall concentrate on laminar flow for the remainder of this section, leaving certain aspects of turbulence for later sections.

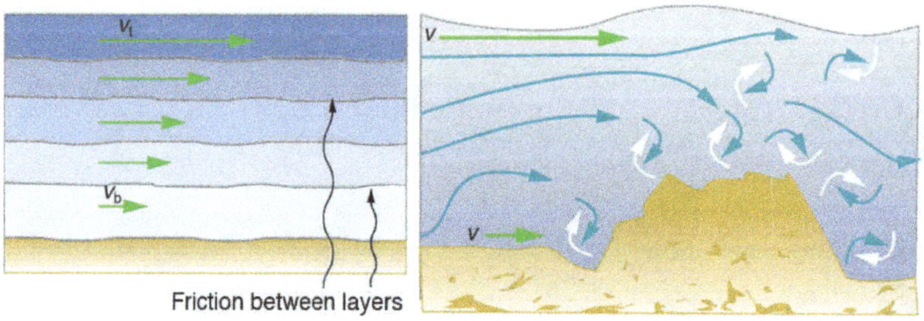

FIGURE 12.11 (a) Laminar flow occurs in layers without mixing. Notice that viscosity causes drag between layers as well as with the fixed surface. (b) An obstruction in the vessel produces turbulence. Turbulent flow mixes the fluid. There is more interaction, greater heating, and more resistance than in laminar flow.

MAKING CONNECTIONS: TAKE-HOME EXPERIMENT: GO DOWN TO THE RIVER

Try dropping simultaneously two sticks into a flowing river, one near the edge of the river and one near the middle. Which one travels faster? Why?

Figure 12.12 shows how viscosity is measured for a fluid. Two parallel plates have the specific fluid between them. The bottom plate is held fixed, while the top plate is moved to the right, dragging fluid with it. The layer (or lamina) of fluid in contact with either plate does not move relative to the plate, and so the top layer moves at v while the bottom layer remains at rest. Each successive layer from the top down exerts a force on the one below it, trying to drag it along, producing a continuous variation in speed from v to 0 as shown. Care is taken to insure that the flow is laminar; that is, the layers do not mix. The motion in Figure 12.12 is like a continuous shearing motion. Fluids have zero shear strength, but the *rate* at which they are sheared is related to the same geometrical factors A and L as is shear deformation for solids.

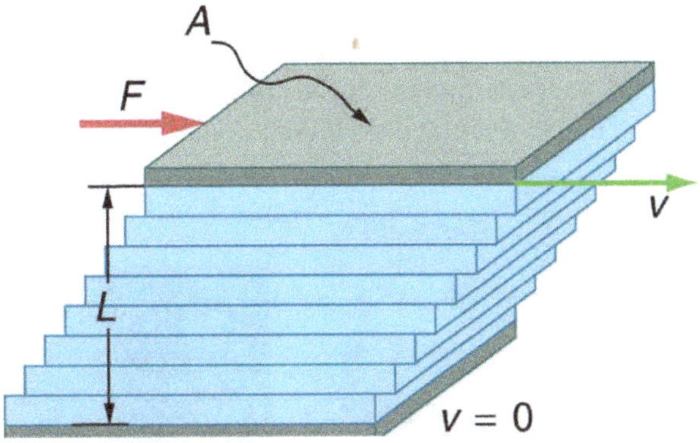

FIGURE 12.12 The graphic shows laminar flow of fluid between two plates of area A. The bottom plate is fixed. When the top plate is pushed to the right, it drags the fluid along with it.

A force F is required to keep the top plate in Figure 12.12 moving at a constant velocity v, and experiments have shown that this force depends on four factors. First, F is directly proportional to v (until the speed is so high that turbulence occurs—then a much larger force is needed, and it has a more complicated dependence on v). Second, F is proportional to the area A of the plate. This relationship seems reasonable, since A is directly proportional to the amount of fluid being moved. Third, F is inversely proportional to the distance between the plates L. This relationship is also reasonable; L is like a lever arm, and the greater the lever arm, the less force that is needed. Fourth, F is directly proportional to *the coefficient of viscosity*, η. The greater the viscosity, the greater the force required. These dependencies are combined into the equation

$$F = \eta \frac{vA}{L}, \qquad 12.41$$

which gives us a working definition of fluid **viscosity** η. Solving for η gives

$$\eta = \frac{FL}{vA}, \qquad 12.42$$

which defines viscosity in terms of how it is measured. The SI unit of viscosity is $\mathrm{N \cdot m/[(m/s)m^2\,] {=} (N/m^2)s}$ or $\mathrm{Pa \cdot s}$. Table 12.1 lists the coefficients of viscosity for various fluids.

Viscosity varies from one fluid to another by several orders of magnitude. As you might expect, the viscosities of gases are much less than those of liquids, and these viscosities are often temperature dependent. The viscosity of blood can be reduced by aspirin consumption, allowing it to flow more easily around the body. (When used over the long term in low doses, aspirin can help prevent heart attacks, and reduce the risk of blood clotting.)

Laminar Flow Confined to Tubes—Poiseuille's Law

What causes flow? The answer, not surprisingly, is pressure difference. In fact, there is a very simple relationship between horizontal flow and pressure. Flow rate Q is in the direction from high to low pressure. The greater the pressure differential between two points, the greater the flow rate. This relationship can be stated as

$$Q = \frac{P_2 - P_1}{R}, \qquad 12.43$$

where P_1 and P_2 are the pressures at two points, such as at either end of a tube, and R is the resistance to flow. The resistance R includes everything, except pressure, that affects flow rate. For example, R is greater for a long tube than for a short one. The greater the viscosity of a fluid, the greater the value of R. Turbulence greatly increases R, whereas increasing the diameter of a tube decreases R.

If viscosity is zero, the fluid is frictionless and the resistance to flow is also zero. Comparing frictionless flow in a tube to viscous flow, as in Figure 12.13, we see that for a viscous fluid, speed is greatest at midstream because of drag at the boundaries. We can see the effect of viscosity in a Bunsen burner flame, even though the viscosity of natural gas is small.

The resistance R to laminar flow of an incompressible fluid having viscosity η through a horizontal tube of uniform radius r and length l, such as the one in Figure 12.14, is given by

$$R = \frac{8\eta l}{\pi r^4}. \qquad 12.44$$

This equation is called **Poiseuille's law for resistance** after the French scientist J. L. Poiseuille (1799–1869), who derived it in an attempt to understand the flow of blood, an often turbulent fluid.

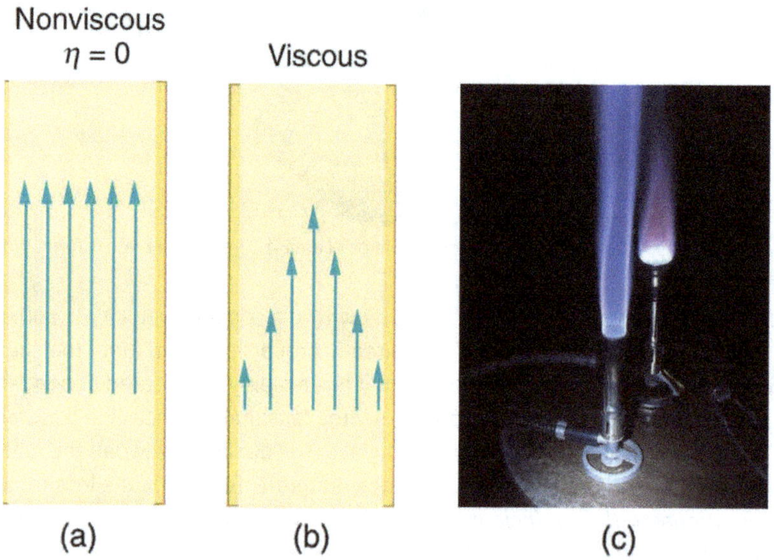

FIGURE 12.13 (a) If fluid flow in a tube has negligible resistance, the speed is the same all across the tube. (b) When a viscous fluid flows through a tube, its speed at the walls is zero, increasing steadily to its maximum at the center of the tube. (c) The shape of the Bunsen burner flame is due to the velocity profile across the tube. (credit: Jason Woodhead)

Let us examine Poiseuille's expression for R to see if it makes good intuitive sense. We see that resistance is directly proportional to both fluid viscosity η and the length l of a tube. After all, both of these directly affect the amount of friction encountered—the greater either is, the greater the resistance and the smaller the flow. The radius r of a tube affects the resistance, which again makes sense, because the greater the radius, the greater the flow (all other factors remaining the same). But it is surprising that r is raised to the *fourth* power in Poiseuille's law. This exponent means that any change in the radius of a tube has a very large effect on resistance. For example, doubling the radius of a tube decreases resistance by a factor of $2^4 = 16$.

Taken together, $Q = \frac{P_2 - P_1}{R}$ and $R = \frac{8\eta l}{\pi r^4}$ give the following expression for flow rate:

$$Q = \frac{(P_2 - P_1)\pi r^4}{8\eta l}. \qquad 12.45$$

This equation describes laminar flow through a tube. It is sometimes called Poiseuille's law for laminar flow, or simply **Poiseuille's law**.

EXAMPLE 12.7

Using Flow Rate: Plaque Deposits Reduce Blood Flow

Suppose the flow rate of blood in a coronary artery has been reduced to half its normal value by plaque deposits. By what factor has the radius of the artery been reduced, assuming no turbulence occurs?

Strategy

Assuming laminar flow, Poiseuille's law states that

$$Q = \frac{(P_2 - P_1)\pi r^4}{8\eta l}. \tag{12.46}$$

We need to compare the artery radius before and after the flow rate reduction.

Solution

With a constant pressure difference assumed and the same length and viscosity, along the artery we have

$$\frac{Q_1}{r_1^4} = \frac{Q_2}{r_2^4}. \tag{12.47}$$

So, given that $Q_2 = 0.5Q_1$, we find that $r_2^4 = 0.5r_1^4$.

Therefore, $r_2 = (0.5)^{0.25} r_1 = 0.841 r_1$, a decrease in the artery radius of 16%.

Discussion

This decrease in radius is surprisingly small for this situation. To restore the blood flow in spite of this buildup would require an increase in the pressure difference $(P_2 - P_1)$ of a factor of two, with subsequent strain on the heart.

Fluid	Temperature (°C)	Viscosity η (mPa·s)
Gases		
Air	0	0.0171
	20	0.0181
	40	0.0190
	100	0.0218
Ammonia	20	0.00974
Carbon dioxide	20	0.0147
Helium	20	0.0196
Hydrogen	0	0.0090
Mercury	20	0.0450
Oxygen	20	0.0203

TABLE 12.1 Coefficients of Viscosity of Various Fluids

Fluid	Temperature (°C)	Viscosity η (mPa·s)
Steam	100	0.0130
Liquids		
Water	0	1.792
	20	1.002
	37	0.6947
	40	0.653
	100	0.282
Whole blood[1]	20	3.015
	37	2.084
Blood plasma[2]	20	1.810
	37	1.257
Ethyl alcohol	20	1.20
Methanol	20	0.584
Oil (heavy machine)	20	660
Oil (motor, SAE 10)	30	200
Oil (olive)	20	138
Glycerin	20	1500
Honey	20	2000–10000
Maple Syrup	20	2000–3000
Milk	20	3.0
Oil (Corn)	20	65

TABLE 12.1 Coefficients of Viscosity of Various Fluids

The circulatory system provides many examples of Poiseuille's law in action—with blood flow regulated by changes in vessel size and blood pressure. Blood vessels are not rigid but elastic. Adjustments to blood flow are primarily made by varying the size of the vessels, since the resistance is so sensitive to the radius. During vigorous exercise, blood vessels are selectively dilated to important muscles and organs and blood pressure increases. This creates both greater overall blood flow and increased flow to specific areas. Conversely, decreases in vessel radii, perhaps

1 The ratios of the viscosities of blood to water are nearly constant between 0°C and 37°C.
2 See note on Whole Blood.

from plaques in the arteries, can greatly reduce blood flow. If a vessel's radius is reduced by only 5% (to 0.95 of its original value), the flow rate is reduced to about $(0.95)^4 = 0.81$ of its original value. A 19% decrease in flow is caused by a 5% decrease in radius. The body may compensate by increasing blood pressure by 19%, but this presents hazards to the heart and any vessel that has weakened walls. Another example comes from automobile engine oil. If you have a car with an oil pressure gauge, you may notice that oil pressure is high when the engine is cold. Motor oil has greater viscosity when cold than when warm, and so pressure must be greater to pump the same amount of cold oil.

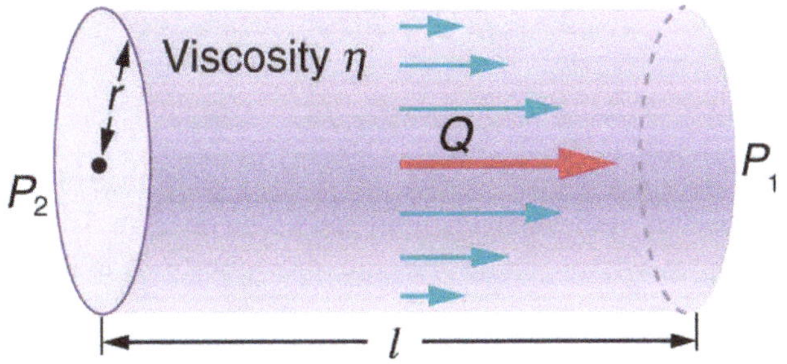

FIGURE 12.14 Poiseuille's law applies to laminar flow of an incompressible fluid of viscosity η through a tube of length l and radius r. The direction of flow is from greater to lower pressure. Flow rate Q is directly proportional to the pressure difference $P_2 - P_1$, and inversely proportional to the length l of the tube and viscosity η of the fluid. Flow rate increases with r^4, the fourth power of the radius.

EXAMPLE 12.8

What Pressure Produces This Flow Rate?

An intravenous (IV) system is supplying saline solution to a patient at the rate of $0.120\ \text{cm}^3/\text{s}$ through a needle of radius 0.150 mm and length 2.50 cm. What pressure is needed at the entrance of the needle to cause this flow, assuming the viscosity of the saline solution to be the same as that of water? The gauge pressure of the blood in the patient's vein is 8.00 mm Hg. (Assume that the temperature is 20°C .)

Strategy

Assuming laminar flow, Poiseuille's law applies. This is given by

$$Q = \frac{(P_2 - P_1)\pi r^4}{8\eta l}, \qquad 12.48$$

where P_2 is the pressure at the entrance of the needle and P_1 is the pressure in the vein. The only unknown is P_2.

Solution

Solving for P_2 yields

$$P_2 = \frac{8\eta l}{\pi r^4} Q + P_1. \qquad 12.49$$

P_1 is given as 8.00 mm Hg, which converts to $1.066 \times 10^3\ \text{N/m}^2$. Substituting this and the other known values yields

$$\begin{aligned} P_2 &= \left[\frac{8(1.00\times10^{-3}\ \text{N}\cdot\text{s/m}^2)(2.50\times10^{-2}\ \text{m})}{\pi(0.150\times10^{-3}\ \text{m})^4}\right](1.20\times10^{-7}\ \text{m}^3/\text{s}) + 1.066\times10^3\ \text{N/m}^2 \\ &= 1.62\times10^4\ \text{N/m}^2. \end{aligned} \qquad 12.50$$

Discussion

This pressure could be supplied by an IV bottle with the surface of the saline solution 1.61 m above the entrance to the needle (this is left for you to solve in this chapter's Problems and Exercises), assuming that there is negligible pressure drop in the tubing leading to the needle.

Flow and Resistance as Causes of Pressure Drops

You may have noticed that water pressure in your home might be lower than normal on hot summer days when there is more use. This pressure drop occurs in the water main before it reaches your home. Let us consider flow through the water main as illustrated in Figure 12.15. We can understand why the pressure P_1 to the home drops during times of heavy use by rearranging

$$Q = \frac{P_2 - P_1}{R} \qquad 12.51$$

to

$$P_2 - P_1 = RQ, \qquad 12.52$$

where, in this case, P_2 is the pressure at the water works and R is the resistance of the water main. During times of heavy use, the flow rate Q is large. This means that $P_2 - P_1$ must also be large. Thus P_1 must decrease. It is correct to think of flow and resistance as causing the pressure to drop from P_2 to P_1. $P_2 - P_1 = RQ$ is valid for both laminar and turbulent flows.

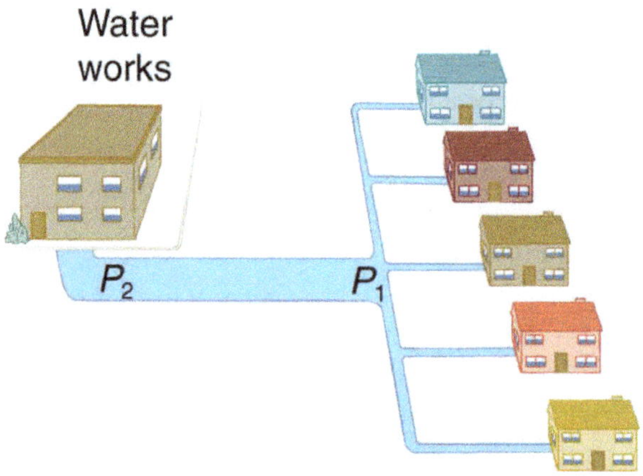

FIGURE 12.15 During times of heavy use, there is a significant pressure drop in a water main, and P_1 supplied to users is significantly less than P_2 created at the water works. If the flow is very small, then the pressure drop is negligible, and $P_2 \approx P_1$.

We can use $P_2 - P_1 = RQ$ to analyze pressure drops occurring in more complex systems in which the tube radius is not the same everywhere. Resistance will be much greater in narrow places, such as an obstructed coronary artery. For a given flow rate Q, the pressure drop will be greatest where the tube is most narrow. This is how water faucets control flow. Additionally, R is greatly increased by turbulence, and a constriction that creates turbulence greatly reduces the pressure downstream. Plaque in an artery reduces pressure and hence flow, both by its resistance and by the turbulence it creates.

Figure 12.16 is a schematic of the human circulatory system, showing average blood pressures in its major parts for an adult at rest. Pressure created by the heart's two pumps, the right and left ventricles, is reduced by the resistance of the blood vessels as the blood flows through them. The left ventricle increases arterial blood pressure that drives the flow of blood through all parts of the body except the lungs. The right ventricle receives the lower pressure blood from two major veins and pumps it through the lungs for gas exchange with atmospheric gases – the disposal of carbon dioxide from the blood and the replenishment of oxygen. Only one major organ is shown schematically, with typical branching of arteries to ever smaller vessels, the smallest of which are the capillaries, and rejoining of small veins into larger ones. Similar branching takes place in a variety of organs in the body, and the circulatory system has considerable flexibility in flow regulation to these organs by the dilation and constriction of the arteries leading to them and the capillaries within them. The sensitivity of flow to tube radius makes this flexibility possible over a large range of flow rates.

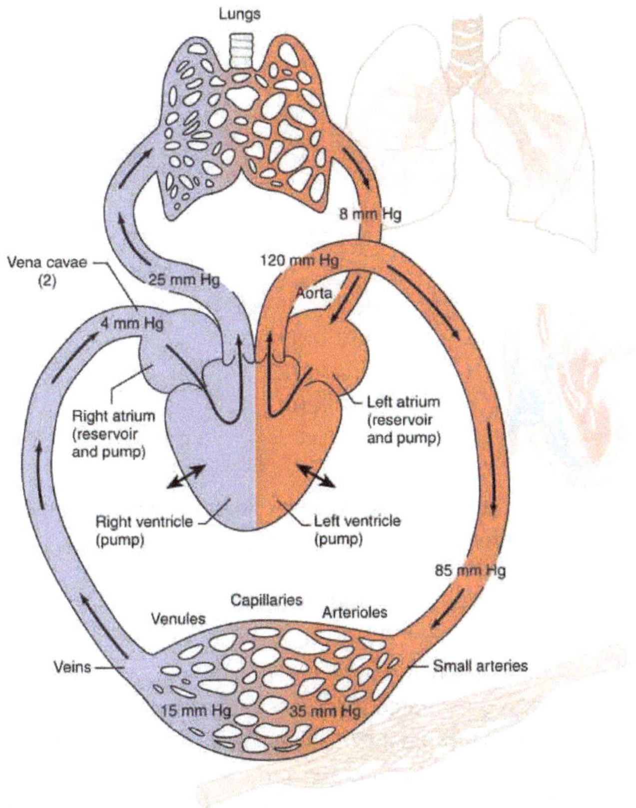

FIGURE 12.16 Schematic of the circulatory system. Pressure difference is created by the two pumps in the heart and is reduced by resistance in the vessels. Branching of vessels into capillaries allows blood to reach individual cells and exchange substances, such as oxygen and waste products, with them. The system has an impressive ability to regulate flow to individual organs, accomplished largely by varying vessel diameters.

Each branching of larger vessels into smaller vessels increases the total cross-sectional area of the tubes through which the blood flows. For example, an artery with a cross section of $1\ \text{cm}^2$ may branch into 20 smaller arteries, each with cross sections of $0.5\ \text{cm}^2$, with a total of $10\ \text{cm}^2$. In that manner, the resistance of the branchings is reduced so that pressure is not entirely lost. Moreover, because $Q = A\bar{v}$ and A increases through branching, the average velocity of the blood in the smaller vessels is reduced. The blood velocity in the aorta $(\text{diameter} = 1\ \text{cm})$ is about 25 cm/s, while in the capillaries $(20 \mu\text{m}$ in diameter) the velocity is about 1 mm/s. This reduced velocity allows the blood to exchange substances with the cells in the capillaries and alveoli in particular.

12.5 The Onset of Turbulence

LEARNING OBJECTIVES

By the end of this section, you will be able to:

- Calculate Reynolds number.
- Use the Reynolds number for a system to determine whether it is laminar or turbulent.

Sometimes we can predict if flow will be laminar or turbulent. We know that flow in a very smooth tube or around a smooth, streamlined object will be laminar at low velocity. We also know that at high velocity, even flow in a smooth tube or around a smooth object will experience turbulence. In between, it is more difficult to predict. In fact, at intermediate velocities, flow may oscillate back and forth indefinitely between laminar and turbulent.

An occlusion, or narrowing, of an artery, such as shown in Figure 12.17, is likely to cause turbulence because of the irregularity of the blockage, as well as the complexity of blood as a fluid. Turbulence in the circulatory system is noisy and can sometimes be detected with a stethoscope, such as when measuring diastolic pressure in the upper arm's partially collapsed brachial artery. These turbulent sounds, at the onset of blood flow when the cuff pressure becomes sufficiently small, are called *Korotkoff sounds*. Aneurysms, or ballooning of arteries, create significant turbulence and can sometimes be detected with a stethoscope. Heart murmurs, consistent with their name, are sounds produced by turbulent flow around damaged and insufficiently closed heart valves. Ultrasound can also be used to detect turbulence as a medical indicator in a process analogous to Doppler-shift radar used to detect storms.

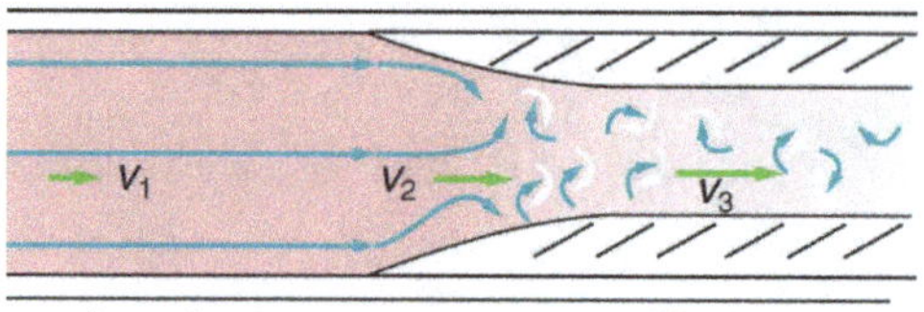

FIGURE 12.17 Flow is laminar in the large part of this blood vessel and turbulent in the part narrowed by plaque, where velocity is high. In the transition region, the flow can oscillate chaotically between laminar and turbulent flow.

An indicator called the **Reynolds number** N_R can reveal whether flow is laminar or turbulent. For flow in a tube of uniform diameter, the Reynolds number is defined as

$$N_R = \frac{2\rho v r}{\eta}\text{(flow in tube)}, \tag{12.53}$$

where ρ is the fluid density, v its speed, η its viscosity, and r the tube radius. The Reynolds number is a unitless quantity. Experiments have revealed that N_R is related to the onset of turbulence. For N_R below about 2000, flow is laminar. For N_R above about 3000, flow is turbulent. For values of N_R between about 2000 and 3000, flow is unstable—that is, it can be laminar, but small obstructions and surface roughness can make it turbulent, and it may oscillate randomly between being laminar and turbulent. The blood flow through most of the body is a quiet, laminar flow. The exception is in the aorta, where the speed of the blood flow rises above a critical value of 35 m/s and becomes turbulent.

EXAMPLE 12.9

Is This Flow Laminar or Turbulent?

Calculate the Reynolds number for flow in the needle considered in Example 12.8 to verify the assumption that the flow is laminar. Assume that the density of the saline solution is 1025 kg/m^3.

Strategy

We have all of the information needed, except the fluid speed v, which can be calculated from $\bar{v} = Q/A = 1.70 \text{ m/s}$ (verification of this is in this chapter's Problems and Exercises).

Solution

Entering the known values into $N_R = \frac{2\rho v r}{\eta}$ gives

$$\begin{aligned} N_R &= \frac{2\rho v r}{\eta} \\ &= \frac{2(1025 \text{ kg/m}^3)(1.70 \text{ m/s})(0.150\times10^{-3} \text{ m})}{1.00\times10^{-3} \text{ N}\cdot\text{s/m}^2} \\ &= 523. \end{aligned} \tag{12.54}$$

Discussion

Since N_R is well below 2000, the flow should indeed be laminar.

TAKE-HOME EXPERIMENT: INHALATION

Under the conditions of normal activity, an adult inhales about 1 L of air during each inhalation. With the aid of a watch, determine the time for one of your own inhalations by timing several breaths and dividing the total length by the number of breaths. Calculate the average flow rate Q of air traveling through the trachea during each inhalation.

The topic of chaos has become quite popular over the last few decades. A system is defined to be *chaotic* when its behavior is so sensitive to some factor that it is extremely difficult to predict. The field of *chaos* is the study of chaotic behavior. A good example of chaotic behavior is the flow of a fluid with a Reynolds number between 2000 and 3000. Whether or not the flow is turbulent is difficult, but not impossible, to predict—the difficulty lies in the extremely sensitive dependence on factors like roughness and obstructions on the nature of the flow. A tiny variation in one factor has an exaggerated (or nonlinear) effect on the flow. Phenomena as disparate as turbulence, the orbit of Pluto, and the onset of irregular heartbeats are chaotic and can be analyzed with similar techniques.

12.6 Motion of an Object in a Viscous Fluid

LEARNING OBJECTIVES

By the end of this section, you will be able to:

- Calculate the Reynolds number for an object moving through a fluid.
- Explain whether the Reynolds number indicates laminar or turbulent flow.
- Describe the conditions under which an object has a terminal speed.

A moving object in a viscous fluid is equivalent to a stationary object in a flowing fluid stream. (For example, when you ride a bicycle at 10 m/s in still air, you feel the air in your face exactly as if you were stationary in a 10-m/s wind.) Flow of the stationary fluid around a moving object may be laminar, turbulent, or a combination of the two. Just as with flow in tubes, it is possible to predict when a moving object creates turbulence. We use another form of the Reynolds number N'_R, defined for an object moving in a fluid to be

$$N'_R = \frac{\rho v L}{\eta}\text{(object in fluid)}, \tag{12.55}$$

where L is a characteristic length of the object (a sphere's diameter, for example), ρ the fluid density, η its viscosity, and v the object's speed in the fluid. If N'_R is less than about 1, flow around the object can be laminar, particularly if the object has a smooth shape. The transition to turbulent flow occurs for N'_R between 1 and about 10, depending on surface roughness and so on. Depending on the surface, there can be a *turbulent wake* behind the object with some laminar flow over its surface. For an N'_R between 10 and 10^6, the flow may be either laminar or turbulent and may oscillate between the two. For N'_R greater than about 10^6, the flow is entirely turbulent, even at the surface of the object. (See Figure 12.18.) Laminar flow occurs mostly when the objects in the fluid are small, such as raindrops, pollen, and blood cells in plasma.

EXAMPLE 12.10

Does a Ball Have a Turbulent Wake?

Calculate the Reynolds number N'_R for a ball with a 7.40-cm diameter thrown at 40.0 m/s.

Strategy

We can use $N'_R = \frac{\rho v L}{\eta}$ to calculate N'_R, since all values in it are either given or can be found in tables of density and viscosity.

Solution

Substituting values into the equation for N'_R yields

$$\begin{aligned} N'_R &= \frac{\rho v L}{\eta} = \frac{(1.29\ \text{kg/m}^3)(40.0\ \text{m/s})(0.0740\ \text{m})}{1.81{\times}10^{-5}\ 1.00\ \text{Pa}{\cdot}\text{s}} \\ &= 2.11 \times 10^5. \end{aligned} \quad 12.56$$

Discussion

This value is sufficiently high to imply a turbulent wake. Most large objects, such as airplanes and sailboats, create significant turbulence as they move. As noted before, the Bernoulli principle gives only qualitatively-correct results in such situations.

One of the consequences of viscosity is a resistance force called **viscous drag** F_V that is exerted on a moving object. This force typically depends on the object's speed (in contrast with simple friction). Experiments have shown that for laminar flow (N'_R less than about one) viscous drag is proportional to speed, whereas for N'_R between about 10 and 10^6, viscous drag is proportional to speed squared. (This relationship is a strong dependence and is pertinent to bicycle racing, where even a small headwind causes significantly increased drag on the racer. Cyclists take turns being the leader in the pack for this reason.) For N'_R greater than 10^6, drag increases dramatically and behaves with greater complexity. For laminar flow around a sphere, F_V is proportional to fluid viscosity η, the object's characteristic size L, and its speed v. All of which makes sense—the more viscous the fluid and the larger the object, the more drag we expect. Recall Stoke's law $F_\text{S} = 6\pi r\eta v$. For the special case of a small sphere of radius R moving slowly in a fluid of viscosity η, the drag force F_S is given by

$$F_\text{S} = 6\pi R\eta v. \quad 12.57$$

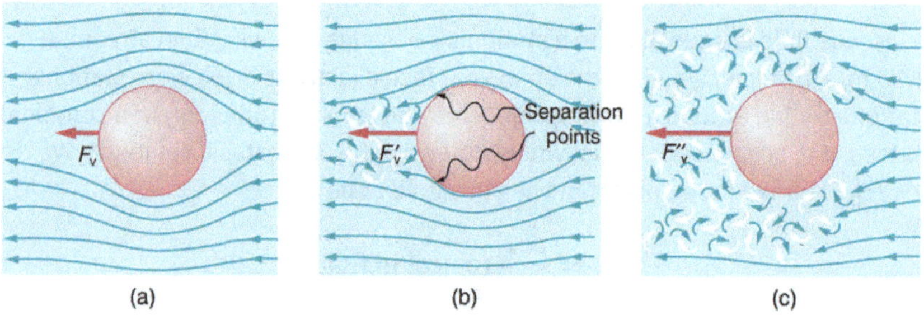

FIGURE 12.18 (a) Motion of this sphere to the right is equivalent to fluid flow to the left. Here the flow is laminar with N'_R less than 1. There is a force, called viscous drag F_V, to the left on the ball due to the fluid's viscosity. (b) At a higher speed, the flow becomes partially turbulent, creating a wake starting where the flow lines separate from the surface. Pressure in the wake is less than in front of the sphere, because fluid speed is less, creating a net force to the left F'_V that is significantly greater than for laminar flow. Here N'_R is greater than 10. (c) At much higher speeds, where N'_R is greater than 10^6, flow becomes turbulent everywhere on the surface and behind the sphere. Drag increases dramatically.

An interesting consequence of the increase in F_V with speed is that an object falling through a fluid will not continue to accelerate indefinitely (as it would if we neglect air resistance, for example). Instead, viscous drag increases, slowing acceleration, until a critical speed, called the **terminal speed**, is reached and the acceleration of the object becomes zero. Once this happens, the object continues to fall at constant speed (the terminal speed). This is the case for particles of sand falling in the ocean, cells falling in a centrifuge, and sky divers falling through the air. Figure 12.19 shows some of the factors that affect terminal speed. There is a viscous drag on the object that depends on the viscosity of the fluid and the size of the object. But there is also a buoyant force that depends on the density of the object relative to the fluid. Terminal speed will be greatest for low-viscosity fluids and objects with high densities and small sizes. Thus a skydiver falls more slowly with outspread limbs than when they are in a pike position—head first with hands at their side and legs together.

TAKE-HOME EXPERIMENT: DON'T LOSE YOUR MARBLES

By measuring the terminal speed of a slowly moving sphere in a viscous fluid, one can find the viscosity of that fluid (at that temperature). It can be difficult to find small ball bearings around the house, but a small marble will do. Gather two or three fluids (syrup, motor oil, honey, olive oil, etc.) and a thick, tall clear glass or vase. Drop the marble into the center of the fluid and time its fall (after letting it drop a little to reach its terminal speed).

Compare your values for the terminal speed and see if they are inversely proportional to the viscosities as listed in Table 12.1. Does it make a difference if the marble is dropped near the side of the glass?

Knowledge of terminal speed is useful for estimating sedimentation rates of small particles. We know from watching mud settle out of dirty water that sedimentation is usually a slow process. Centrifuges are used to speed sedimentation by creating accelerated frames in which gravitational acceleration is replaced by centripetal acceleration, which can be much greater, increasing the terminal speed.

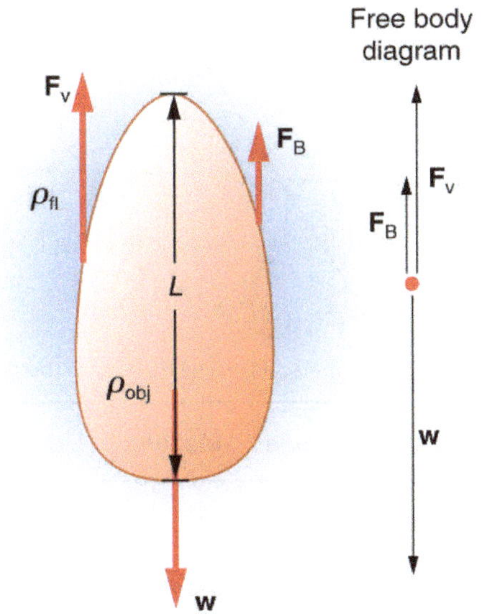

FIGURE 12.19 There are three forces acting on an object falling through a viscous fluid: its weight w, the viscous drag F_V, and the buoyant force $\mathbf{F_B}$.

12.7 Molecular Transport Phenomena: Diffusion, Osmosis, and Related Processes

LEARNING OBJECTIVES

By the end of this section, you will be able to:

- Define diffusion, osmosis, dialysis, and active transport.
- Calculate diffusion rates.

Diffusion

There is something fishy about the ice cube from your freezer—how did it pick up those food odors? How does soaking a sprained ankle in Epsom salt reduce swelling? The answer to these questions are related to atomic and molecular transport phenomena—another mode of fluid motion. Atoms and molecules are in constant motion at any temperature. In fluids they move about randomly even in the absence of macroscopic flow. This motion is called a random walk and is illustrated in Figure 12.20. **Diffusion** is the movement of substances due to random thermal molecular motion. Fluids, like fish fumes or odors entering ice cubes, can even diffuse through solids.

Diffusion is a slow process over macroscopic distances. The densities of common materials are great enough that molecules cannot travel very far before having a collision that can scatter them in any direction, including straight backward. It can be shown that the average distance x_{rms} that a molecule travels is proportional to the square root of time:

$$x_{rms} = \sqrt{2Dt}, \qquad 12.58$$

where x_{rms} stands for the **root-mean-square distance** and is the statistical average for the process. The quantity D is the diffusion constant for the particular molecule in a specific medium. Table 12.2 lists representative values of D for various substances, in units of m^2/s.

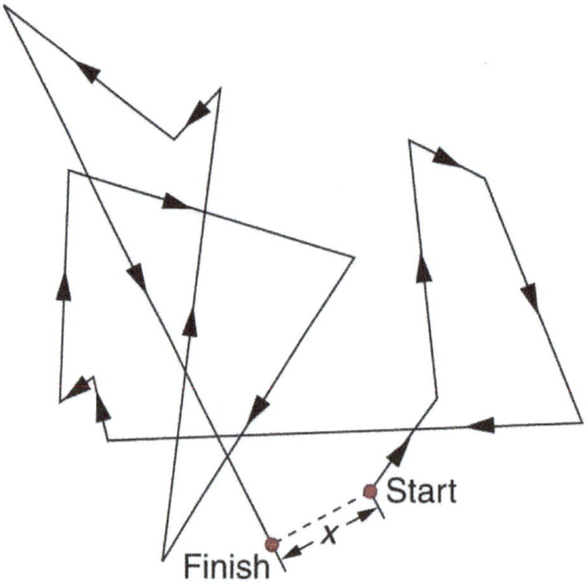

FIGURE 12.20 The random thermal motion of a molecule in a fluid in time t. This type of motion is called a random walk.

Diffusing molecule	Medium	D (m^2/s)
Hydrogen (H_2)	Air	6.4×10^{-5}
Oxygen (O_2)	Air	1.8×10^{-5}
Oxygen (O_2)	Water	1.0×10^{-9}
Glucose ($C_6H_{12}O_6$)	Water	6.7×10^{-10}
Hemoglobin	Water	6.9×10^{-11}
DNA	Water	1.3×10^{-12}

TABLE 12.2 Diffusion Constants for Various Molecules[3]

Note that D gets progressively smaller for more massive molecules. This decrease is because the average molecular speed at a given temperature is inversely proportional to molecular mass. Thus the more massive molecules diffuse more slowly. Another interesting point is that D for oxygen in air is much greater than D for oxygen in water. In water, an oxygen molecule makes many more collisions in its random walk and is slowed considerably. In water, an oxygen molecule moves only about $40\ \mu\text{m}$ in 1 s. (Each molecule actually collides about 10^{10} times per second!). Finally, note that diffusion constants increase with temperature, because average molecular speed increases with temperature. This is because the average kinetic energy of molecules, $\frac{1}{2}mv^2$, is proportional to absolute temperature.

EXAMPLE 12.11

Calculating Diffusion: How Long Does Glucose Diffusion Take?

Calculate the average time it takes a glucose molecule to move 1.0 cm in water.

3 At 20°C and 1 atm

Strategy

We can use $x_{rms} = \sqrt{2Dt}$, the expression for the average distance moved in time t, and solve it for t. All other quantities are known.

Solution

Solving for t and substituting known values yields

$$\begin{aligned} t &= \frac{x_{rms}^2}{2D} = \frac{(0.010\ \text{m})^2}{2(6.7\times10^{-10}\ \text{m}^2/\text{s})} \\ &= 7.5\times10^4\ \text{s} = 21\ \text{h}. \end{aligned} \quad 12.59$$

Discussion

This is a remarkably long time for glucose to move a mere centimeter! For this reason, we stir sugar into water rather than waiting for it to diffuse.

Because diffusion is typically very slow, its most important effects occur over small distances. For example, the cornea of the eye gets most of its oxygen by diffusion through the thin tear layer covering it.

The Rate and Direction of Diffusion

If you very carefully place a drop of food coloring in a still glass of water, it will slowly diffuse into the colorless surroundings until its concentration is the same everywhere. This type of diffusion is called free diffusion, because there are no barriers inhibiting it. Let us examine its direction and rate. Molecular motion is random in direction, and so simple chance dictates that more molecules will move out of a region of high concentration than into it. The net rate of diffusion is higher initially than after the process is partially completed. (See Figure 12.21.)

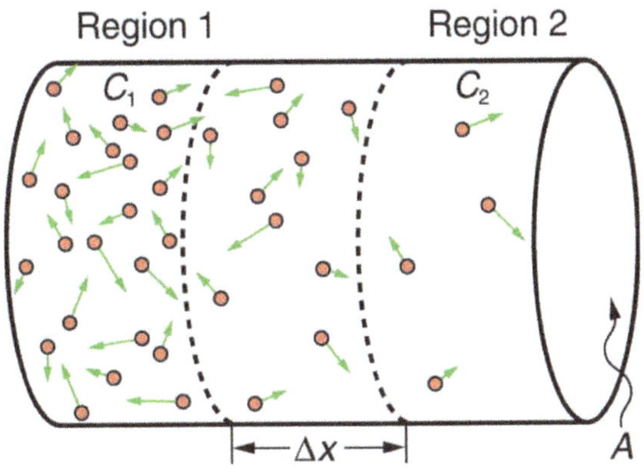

FIGURE 12.21 Diffusion proceeds from a region of higher concentration to a lower one. The net rate of movement is proportional to the difference in concentration.

The net rate of diffusion is proportional to the concentration difference. Many more molecules will leave a region of high concentration than will enter it from a region of low concentration. In fact, if the concentrations were the same, there would be *no* net movement. The net rate of diffusion is also proportional to the diffusion constant D, which is determined experimentally. The farther a molecule can diffuse in a given time, the more likely it is to leave the region of high concentration. Many of the factors that affect the rate are hidden in the diffusion constant D. For example, temperature and cohesive and adhesive forces all affect values of D.

Diffusion is the dominant mechanism by which the exchange of nutrients and waste products occur between the blood and tissue, and between air and blood in the lungs. In the evolutionary process, as organisms became larger, they needed quicker methods of transportation than net diffusion, because of the larger distances involved in the transport, leading to the development of circulatory systems. Less sophisticated, single-celled organisms still rely totally on diffusion for the removal of waste products and the uptake of nutrients.

Osmosis and Dialysis—Diffusion across Membranes

Some of the most interesting examples of diffusion occur through barriers that affect the rates of diffusion. For example, when you soak a swollen ankle in Epsom salt, water diffuses through your skin. Many substances regularly move through cell membranes; oxygen moves in, carbon dioxide moves out, nutrients go in, and wastes go out, for example. Because membranes are thin structures (typically 6.5×10^{-9} to 10×10^{-9} m across) diffusion rates through them can be high. Diffusion through membranes is an important method of transport.

Membranes are generally selectively permeable, or **semipermeable**. (See Figure 12.22.) One type of semipermeable membrane has small pores that allow only small molecules to pass through. In other types of membranes, the molecules may actually dissolve in the membrane or react with molecules in the membrane while moving across. Membrane function, in fact, is the subject of much current research, involving not only physiology but also chemistry and physics.

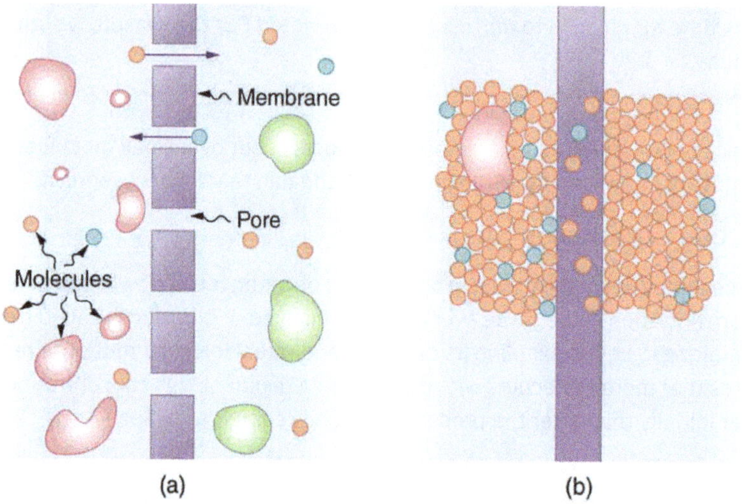

FIGURE 12.22 (a) A semipermeable membrane with small pores that allow only small molecules to pass through. (b) Certain molecules dissolve in this membrane and diffuse across it.

Osmosis is the transport of water through a semipermeable membrane from a region of high concentration to a region of low concentration. Osmosis is driven by the imbalance in water concentration. For example, water is more concentrated in your body than in Epsom salt. When you soak a swollen ankle in Epsom salt, the water moves out of your body into the lower-concentration region in the salt. Similarly, **dialysis** is the transport of any other molecule through a semipermeable membrane due to its concentration difference. Both osmosis and dialysis are used by the kidneys to cleanse the blood.

Osmosis can create a substantial pressure. Consider what happens if osmosis continues for some time, as illustrated in Figure 12.23. Water moves by osmosis from the left into the region on the right, where it is less concentrated, causing the solution on the right to rise. This movement will continue until the pressure ρgh created by the extra height of fluid on the right is large enough to stop further osmosis. This pressure is called a *back pressure*. The back pressure ρgh that stops osmosis is also called the **relative osmotic pressure** if neither solution is pure water, and it is called the **osmotic pressure** if one solution is pure water. Osmotic pressure can be large, depending on the size of the concentration difference. For example, if pure water and sea water are separated by a semipermeable membrane that passes no salt, osmotic pressure will be 25.9 atm. This value means that water will diffuse through the membrane until the salt water surface rises 268 m above the pure-water surface! One example of pressure created by osmosis is turgor in plants (many wilt when too dry). Turgor describes the condition of a plant in which the fluid in a cell exerts a pressure against the cell wall. This pressure gives the plant support. Dialysis can similarly cause substantial pressures.

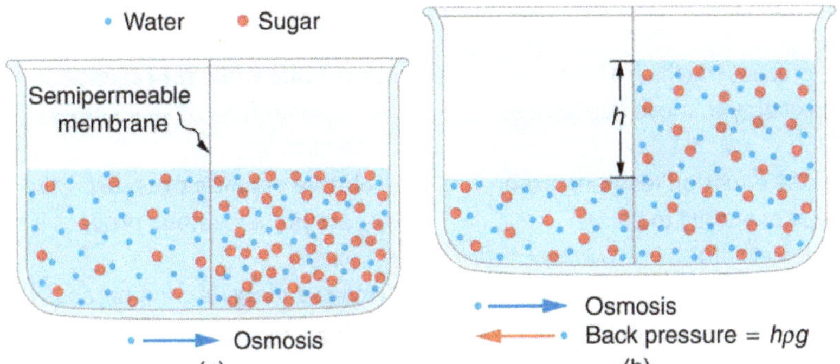

FIGURE 12.23 (a) Two sugar-water solutions of different concentrations, separated by a semipermeable membrane that passes water but not sugar. Osmosis will be to the right, since water is less concentrated there. (b) The fluid level rises until the back pressure ρgh equals the relative osmotic pressure; then, the net transfer of water is zero.

Reverse osmosis and **reverse dialysis** (also called filtration) are processes that occur when back pressure is sufficient to reverse the normal direction of substances through membranes. Back pressure can be created naturally as on the right side of Figure 12.23. (A piston can also create this pressure.) Reverse osmosis can be used to desalinate water by simply forcing it through a membrane that will not pass salt. Similarly, reverse dialysis can be used to filter out any substance that a given membrane will not pass.

One further example of the movement of substances through membranes deserves mention. We sometimes find that substances pass in the direction opposite to what we expect. Cypress tree roots, for example, extract pure water from salt water, although osmosis would move it in the opposite direction. This is not reverse osmosis, because there is no back pressure to cause it. What is happening is called **active transport**, a process in which a living membrane expends energy to move substances across it. Many living membranes move water and other substances by active transport. The kidneys, for example, not only use osmosis and dialysis—they also employ significant active transport to move substances into and out of blood. In fact, it is estimated that at least 25% of the body's energy is expended on active transport of substances at the cellular level. The study of active transport carries us into the realms of microbiology, biophysics, and biochemistry and it is a fascinating application of the laws of nature to living structures.

Glossary

active transport the process in which a living membrane expends energy to move substances across

Bernoulli's equation the equation resulting from applying conservation of energy to an incompressible frictionless fluid: $P + 1/2pv^2 + pgh =$ constant , through the fluid

Bernoulli's principle Bernoulli's equation applied at constant depth: $P_1 + 1/2pv_1{}^2 = P_2 + 1/2pv_2{}^2$

dialysis the transport of any molecule other than water through a semipermeable membrane from a region of high concentration to one of low concentration

diffusion the movement of substances due to random thermal molecular motion

flow rate abbreviated Q, it is the volume V that flows past a particular point during a time t, or $Q = V/t$

fluid dynamics the physics of fluids in motion

laminar a type of fluid flow in which layers do not mix

liter a unit of volume, equal to 10^{-3} m^3

osmosis the transport of water through a semipermeable membrane from a region of high concentration to one of low concentration

osmotic pressure the back pressure which stops the osmotic process if one solution is pure water

Poiseuille's law the rate of laminar flow of an incompressible fluid in a tube: $Q = (P_2 - P_1)\pi r^4/8\eta l$

Poiseuille's law for resistance the resistance to laminar flow of an incompressible fluid in a tube: $R = 8\eta l/\pi r^4$

relative osmotic pressure the back pressure which stops the osmotic process if neither solution is pure water

reverse dialysis the process that occurs when back pressure is sufficient to reverse the normal direction of dialysis through membranes

reverse osmosis the process that occurs when back pressure is sufficient to reverse the normal direction of osmosis through membranes

Reynolds number a dimensionless parameter that can reveal whether a particular flow is laminar or turbulent

semipermeable a type of membrane that allows only certain small molecules to pass through

terminal speed the speed at which the viscous drag of an object falling in a viscous fluid is equal to the other forces acting on the object (such as gravity), so that the acceleration of the object is zero

turbulence fluid flow in which layers mix together via eddies and swirls

viscosity the friction in a fluid, defined in terms of the friction between layers

viscous drag a resistance force exerted on a moving object, with a nontrivial dependence on velocity

Section Summary

12.1 Flow Rate and Its Relation to Velocity

- Flow rate Q is defined to be the volume V flowing past a point in time t, or $Q = \frac{V}{t}$ where V is volume and t is time.
- The SI unit of volume is m^3.
- Another common unit is the liter (L), which is $10^{-3}\ \mathrm{m}^3$.
- Flow rate and velocity are related by $Q = A\bar{v}$ where A is the cross-sectional area of the flow and $\bar{v}$ is its average velocity.
- For incompressible fluids, flow rate at various points is constant. That is,

$$\left.\begin{aligned} Q_1 &= Q_2 \\ A_1\bar{v}_1 &= A_2\bar{v}_2 \\ n_1A_1\bar{v}_1 &= n_2A_2\bar{v}_2 \end{aligned}\right\}.$$

12.2 Bernoulli's Equation

- Bernoulli's equation states that the sum on each side of the following equation is constant, or the same at any two points in an incompressible frictionless fluid:

$$P_1 + \frac{1}{2}\rho v_1^2 + \rho gh_1 = P_2 + \frac{1}{2}\rho v_2^2 + \rho gh_2.$$

- Bernoulli's principle is Bernoulli's equation applied to situations in which depth is constant. The terms involving depth (or height h) subtract out, yielding

$$P_1 + \frac{1}{2}\rho v_1^2 = P_2 + \frac{1}{2}\rho v_2^2.$$

- Bernoulli's principle has many applications, including entrainment, wings and sails, and velocity measurement.

12.3 The Most General Applications of Bernoulli's Equation

- Power in fluid flow is given by the equation $\left(P_1 + \frac{1}{2}\rho v^2 + \rho gh\right)Q = \text{power}$, where the first term is power associated with pressure, the second is power associated with velocity, and the third is power associated with height.

12.4 Viscosity and Laminar Flow; Poiseuille's Law

- Laminar flow is characterized by smooth flow of

the fluid in layers that do not mix.

- Turbulence is characterized by eddies and swirls that mix layers of fluid together.
- Fluid viscosity η is due to friction within a fluid. Representative values are given in Table 12.1. Viscosity has units of $(\text{N/m}^2)\text{s}$ or $\text{Pa} \cdot \text{s}$.
- Flow is proportional to pressure difference and inversely proportional to resistance:
  $$Q = \frac{P_2 - P_1}{R}.$$
- For laminar flow in a tube, Poiseuille's law for resistance states that
  $$R = \frac{8\eta l}{\pi r^4}.$$
- Poiseuille's law for flow in a tube is
  $$Q = \frac{(P_2 - P_1)\pi r^4}{8\eta l}.$$
- The pressure drop caused by flow and resistance is given by
  $$P_2 - P_1 = RQ.$$

12.5 The Onset of Turbulence

- The Reynolds number N_R can reveal whether flow is laminar or turbulent. It is
  $$N_R = \frac{2\rho v r}{\eta}.$$
- For N_R below about 2000, flow is laminar. For N_R above about 3000, flow is turbulent. For values of N_R between 2000 and 3000, it may be either or both.

12.6 Motion of an Object in a Viscous Fluid

- When an object moves in a fluid, there is a different form of the Reynolds number $N'_R = \frac{\rho v L}{\eta}(\text{object in fluid})$, which indicates whether flow is laminar or turbulent.
- For N'_R less than about one, flow is laminar.
- For N'_R greater than 10^6, flow is entirely turbulent.

12.7 Molecular Transport Phenomena: Diffusion, Osmosis, and Related Processes

- Diffusion is the movement of substances due to random thermal molecular motion.
- The average distance x_{rms} a molecule travels by diffusion in a given amount of time is given by
  $$x_{rms} = \sqrt{2Dt},$$
  where D is the diffusion constant, representative values of which are found in Table 12.2.

- Osmosis is the transport of water through a semipermeable membrane from a region of high concentration to a region of low concentration.
- Dialysis is the transport of any other molecule through a semipermeable membrane due to its concentration difference.
- Both processes can be reversed by back pressure.
- Active transport is a process in which a living membrane expends energy to move substances across it.

Conceptual Questions

12.1 Flow Rate and Its Relation to Velocity

1. What is the difference between flow rate and fluid velocity? How are they related?

2. Many figures in the text show streamlines. Explain why fluid velocity is greatest where streamlines are closest together. (Hint: Consider the relationship between fluid velocity and the cross-sectional area through which it flows.)

3. Identify some substances that are incompressible and some that are not.

12.2 Bernoulli's Equation

4. You can squirt water a considerably greater distance by placing your thumb over the end of a garden hose and then releasing, than by leaving it completely uncovered. Explain how this works.

5. Water is shot nearly vertically upward in a decorative fountain and the stream is observed to broaden as it rises. Conversely, a stream of water falling straight down from a faucet narrows. Explain why, and discuss whether surface tension enhances or reduces the effect in each case.

6. Look back to Figure 12.4. Answer the following two questions. Why is P_o less than atmospheric? Why is P_o greater than P_i?

7. Give an example of entrainment not mentioned in the text.

8. Many entrainment devices have a constriction, called a Venturi, such as shown in Figure 12.24. How does this bolster entrainment?

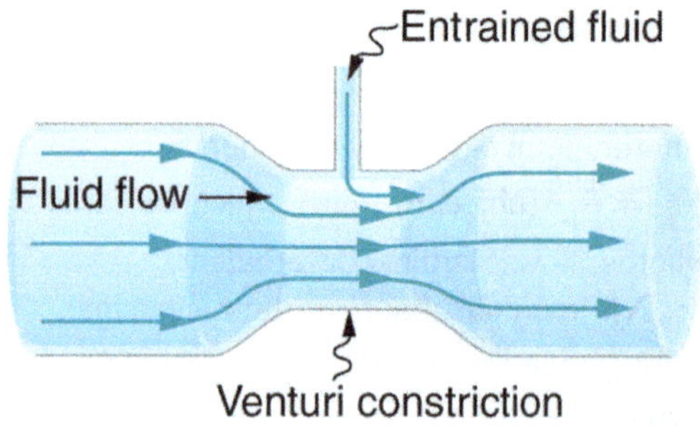

FIGURE 12.24 A tube with a narrow segment designed to enhance entrainment is called a Venturi. These are very commonly used in carburetors and aspirators.

9. Some chimney pipes have a T-shape, with a crosspiece on top that helps draw up gases whenever there is even a slight breeze. Explain how this works in terms of Bernoulli's principle.

10. Is there a limit to the height to which an entrainment device can raise a fluid? Explain your answer.

11. Why is it preferable for airplanes to take off into the wind rather than with the wind?

12. Roofs are sometimes pushed off vertically during a tropical cyclone, and buildings sometimes explode outward when hit by a tornado. Use Bernoulli's principle to explain these phenomena.

13. Why does a sailboat need a keel?

14. It is dangerous to stand close to railroad tracks when a rapidly moving commuter train passes. Explain why atmospheric pressure would push you toward the moving train.

15. Water pressure inside a hose nozzle can be less than atmospheric pressure due to the Bernoulli effect. Explain in terms of energy how the water can emerge from the nozzle against the opposing atmospheric pressure.

16. A perfume bottle or atomizer sprays a fluid that is in the bottle. (Figure 12.25.) How does the fluid rise up in the vertical tube in the bottle?

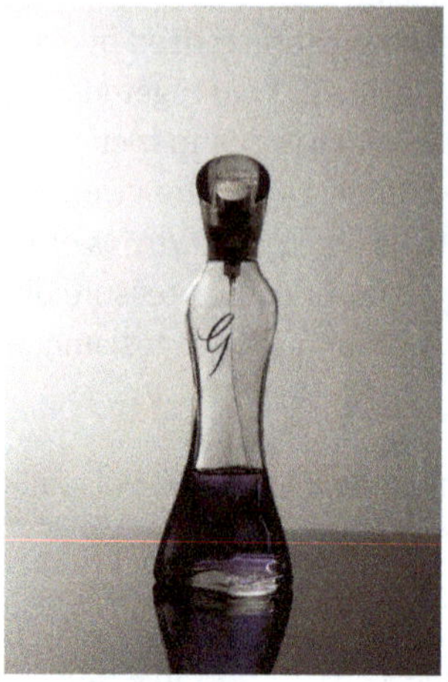

FIGURE 12.25 Atomizer: perfume bottle with tube to carry perfume up through the bottle. (credit: Antonia Foy, Flickr)

17. If you lower the window on a car while moving, an empty plastic bag can sometimes fly out the window. Why does this happen?

12.3 The Most General Applications of Bernoulli's Equation

18. Based on Bernoulli's equation, what are three forms of energy in a fluid? (Note that these forms are conservative, unlike heat transfer and other dissipative forms not included in Bernoulli's equation.)

19. Water that has emerged from a hose into the atmosphere has a gauge pressure of zero. Why? When you put your hand in front of the emerging stream you feel a force, yet the water's gauge pressure is zero. Explain where the force comes from in terms of energy.

20. The old rubber boot shown in Figure 12.26 has two leaks. To what maximum height can the water squirt from Leak 1? How does the velocity of water emerging from Leak 2 differ from that of leak 1? Explain your responses in terms of energy.

FIGURE 12.26 Water emerges from two leaks in an old boot.

21. Water pressure inside a hose nozzle can be less than atmospheric pressure due to the Bernoulli effect. Explain in terms of energy how the water can emerge from the nozzle against the opposing atmospheric pressure.

12.4 Viscosity and Laminar Flow; Poiseuille's Law

22. Explain why the viscosity of a liquid decreases with temperature—that is, how might increased temperature reduce the effects of cohesive forces in a liquid? Also explain why the viscosity of a gas increases with temperature—that is, how does increased gas temperature create more collisions between atoms and molecules?

23. When paddling a canoe upstream, it is wisest to travel as near to the shore as possible. When canoeing downstream, it may be best to stay near the middle. Explain why.

24. Why does flow decrease in your shower when someone flushes the toilet?

25. Plumbing usually includes air-filled tubes near water faucets, as shown in Figure 12.27. Explain why they are needed and how they work.

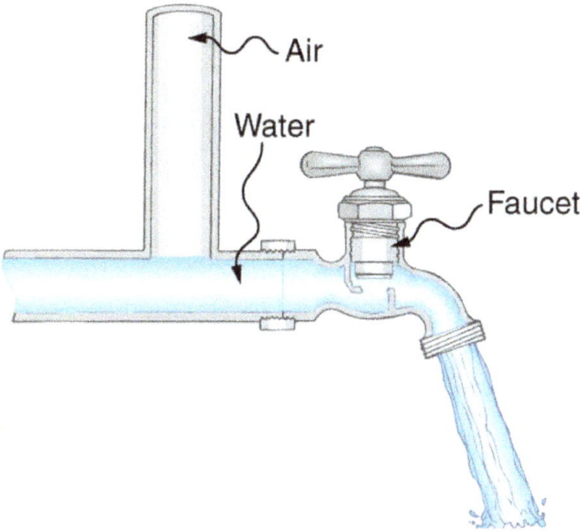

FIGURE 12.27 The vertical tube near the water tap remains full of air and serves a useful purpose.

12.5 The Onset of Turbulence

26. Doppler ultrasound can be used to measure the speed of blood in the body. If there is a partial constriction of an artery, where would you expect blood speed to be greatest, at or nearby the constriction? What are the two distinct causes of higher resistance in the constriction?

27. Sink drains often have a device such as that shown in Figure 12.28 to help speed the flow of water. How does this work?

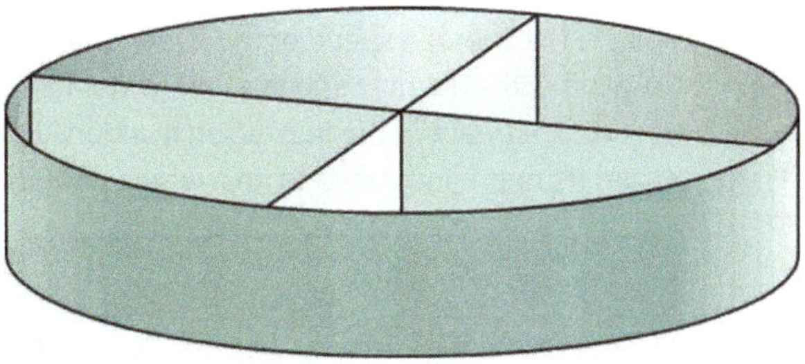

FIGURE 12.28 You will find devices such as this in many drains. They significantly increase flow rate.

28. Some ceiling fans have decorative wicker reeds on their blades. Discuss whether these fans are as quiet and efficient as those with smooth blades.

12.6 Motion of an Object in a Viscous Fluid

29. What direction will a helium balloon move inside a car that is slowing down—toward the front or back? Explain your answer.

30. Will identical raindrops fall more rapidly in $5° \text{ C}$ air or $25° \text{ C}$ air, neglecting any differences in air density? Explain your answer.

31. If you took two marbles of different sizes, what would you expect to observe about the relative magnitudes of their terminal velocities?

12.7 Molecular Transport Phenomena: Diffusion, Osmosis, and Related Processes

32. Why would you expect the rate of diffusion to increase with temperature? Can you give an example, such as the fact that you can dissolve sugar more rapidly in hot water?

33. How are osmosis and dialysis similar? How do they differ?

Problems & Exercises

12.1 Flow Rate and Its Relation to Velocity

1. What is the average flow rate in $\mathrm{cm^3/s}$ of gasoline to the engine of a car traveling at 100 km/h if it averages 10.0 km/L?

2. The heart of a resting adult pumps blood at a rate of 5.00 L/min. (a) Convert this to $\mathrm{cm^3/s}$. (b) What is this rate in $\mathrm{m^3/s}$?

3. Blood is pumped from the heart at a rate of 5.0 L/min into the aorta (of radius 1.0 cm). Determine the speed of blood through the aorta.

4. Blood is flowing through an artery of radius 2 mm at a rate of 40 cm/s. Determine the flow rate and the volume that passes through the artery in a period of 30 s.

5. The Huka Falls on the Waikato River is one of New Zealand's most visited natural tourist attractions (see Figure 12.29). On average the river has a flow rate of about 300,000 L/s. At the gorge, the river narrows to 20 m wide and averages 20 m deep. (a) What is the average speed of the river in the gorge? (b) What is the average speed of the water in the river downstream of the falls when it widens to 60 m and its depth increases to an average of 40 m?

FIGURE 12.29 The Huka Falls in Taupo, New Zealand, demonstrate flow rate. (credit: RaviGogna, Flickr)

6. A major artery with a cross-sectional area of $1.00\ \mathrm{cm^2}$ branches into 18 smaller arteries, each with an average cross-sectional area of $0.400\ \mathrm{cm^2}$. By what factor is the average velocity of the blood reduced when it passes into these branches?

7. (a) As blood passes through the capillary bed in an organ, the capillaries join to form venules (small veins). If the blood speed increases by a factor of 4.00 and the total cross-sectional area of the venules is $10.0\ \mathrm{cm^2}$, what is the total cross-sectional area of the capillaries feeding these venules? (b) How many capillaries are involved if their average diameter is $10.0\ \mu\mathrm{m}$?

8. The human circulation system has approximately 1×10^9 capillary vessels. Each vessel has a diameter of about $8\ \mu\mathrm{m}$. Assuming cardiac output is 5 L/min, determine the average velocity of blood flow through each capillary vessel.

9. (a) Estimate the time it would take to fill a private swimming pool with a capacity of 80,000 L using a garden hose delivering 60 L/min. (b) How long would it take to fill if you could divert a moderate size river, flowing at $5000\ \mathrm{m^3/s}$, into it?

10. The flow rate of blood through a 2.00×10^{-6}-m-radius capillary is $3.80 \times 10^{-9}\ \mathrm{cm^3/s}$. (a) What is the speed of the blood flow? (This small speed allows time for diffusion of materials to and from the blood.) (b) Assuming all the blood in the body passes through capillaries, how many of them must there be to carry a total flow of $90.0\ \mathrm{cm^3/s}$? (The large number obtained is an overestimate, but it is still reasonable.)

11. (a) What is the fluid speed in a fire hose with a 9.00-cm diameter carrying 80.0 L of water per second? (b) What is the flow rate in cubic meters per second? (c) Would your answers be different if salt water replaced the fresh water in the fire hose?

12. The main uptake air duct of a forced air gas heater is 0.300 m in diameter. What is the average speed of air in the duct if it carries a volume equal to that of the house's interior every 15 min? The inside volume of the house is equivalent to a rectangular solid 13.0 m wide by 20.0 m long by 2.75 m high.

13. Water is moving at a velocity of 2.00 m/s through a hose with an internal diameter of 1.60 cm. (a) What is the flow rate in liters per second? (b) The fluid velocity in this hose's nozzle is 15.0 m/s. What is the nozzle's inside diameter?

14. Prove that the speed of an incompressible fluid through a constriction, such as in a Venturi tube, increases by a factor equal to the square of the factor by which the diameter decreases. (The converse applies for flow out of a constriction into a larger-diameter region.)

15. Water emerges straight down from a faucet with a 1.80-cm diameter at a speed of 0.500 m/s. (Because of the construction of the faucet, there is no variation in speed across the stream.) (a) What is the flow rate in cm^3/s? (b) What is the diameter of the stream 0.200 m below the faucet? Neglect any effects due to surface tension.

16. Unreasonable Results
A mountain stream is 10.0 m wide and averages 2.00 m in depth. During the spring runoff, the flow in the stream reaches $100{,}000\ \text{m}^3/\text{s}$. (a) What is the average velocity of the stream under these conditions? (b) What is unreasonable about this velocity? (c) What is unreasonable or inconsistent about the premises?

12.2 Bernoulli's Equation

17. Verify that pressure has units of energy per unit volume.

18. Suppose you have a wind speed gauge like the pitot tube shown in Example 12.2(b). By what factor must wind speed increase to double the value of h in the manometer? Is this independent of the moving fluid and the fluid in the manometer?

19. If the pressure reading of your pitot tube is 15.0 mm Hg at a speed of 200 km/h, what will it be at 700 km/h at the same altitude?

20. Calculate the maximum height to which water could be squirted with the hose in Example 12.2 example if it: (a) Emerges from the nozzle. (b) Emerges with the nozzle removed, assuming the same flow rate.

21. Every few years, winds in Boulder, Colorado, attain sustained speeds of 45.0 m/s (about 100 mi/h) when the jet stream descends during early spring. Approximately what is the force due to the Bernoulli effect on a roof having an area of $220\ \text{m}^2$? Typical air density in Boulder is $1.14\ \text{kg/m}^3$, and the corresponding atmospheric pressure is $8.89 \times 10^4\ \text{N/m}^2$. (Bernoulli's principle as stated in the text assumes laminar flow. Using the principle here produces only an approximate result, because there is significant turbulence.)

22. (a) Calculate the approximate force on a square meter of sail, given the horizontal velocity of the wind is 6.00 m/s parallel to its front surface and 3.50 m/s along its back surface. Take the density of air to be $1.29\ \text{kg/m}^3$. (The calculation, based on Bernoulli's principle, is approximate due to the effects of turbulence.) (b) Discuss whether this force is great enough to be effective for propelling a sailboat.

23. (a) What is the pressure drop due to the Bernoulli effect as water goes into a 3.00-cm-diameter nozzle from a 9.00-cm-diameter fire hose while carrying a flow of 40.0 L/s? (b) To what maximum height above the nozzle can this water rise? (The actual height will be significantly smaller due to air resistance.)

24. (a) Using Bernoulli's equation, show that the measured fluid speed v for a pitot tube, like the one in Figure 12.7(b), is given by $v = \left(\frac{2\rho' gh}{\rho}\right)^{1/2}$, where h is the height of the manometer fluid, ρ' is the density of the manometer fluid, ρ is the density of the moving fluid, and g is the acceleration due to gravity. (Note that v is indeed proportional to the square root of h, as stated in the text.) (b) Calculate v for moving air if a mercury manometer's h is 0.200 m.

12.3 The Most General Applications of Bernoulli's Equation

25. Hoover Dam on the Colorado River is the highest dam in the United States at 221 m, with an output of 1300 MW. The dam generates electricity with water taken from a depth of 150 m and an average flow rate of $650\ \text{m}^3/\text{s}$. (a) Calculate the power in this flow. (b) What is the ratio of this power to the facility's average of 680 MW?

26. A frequently quoted rule of thumb in aircraft design is that wings should produce about 1000 N of lift per square meter of wing. (The fact that a wing has a top and bottom surface does not double its area.) (a) At takeoff, an aircraft travels at 60.0 m/s, so that the air speed relative to the bottom of the wing is 60.0 m/s. Given the sea level density of air to be $1.29\ \text{kg/m}^3$, how fast must it move over the upper surface to create the ideal lift? (b) How fast must air move over the upper surface at a cruising speed of 245 m/s and at an altitude where air density is one-fourth that at sea level? (Note that this is not all of the aircraft's lift—some comes from the body of the plane, some from engine thrust, and so on. Furthermore, Bernoulli's principle gives an approximate answer because flow over the wing creates turbulence.)

27. The left ventricle of a resting adult's heart pumps blood at a flow rate of $83.0\ \text{cm}^3/\text{s}$, increasing its pressure by 110 mm Hg, its speed from zero to 30.0 cm/s, and its height by 5.00 cm. (All numbers are averaged over the entire heartbeat.) Calculate the total power output of the left ventricle. Note that most of the power is used to increase blood pressure.

28. A sump pump (used to drain water from the basement of houses built below the water table) is draining a flooded basement at the rate of 0.750 L/s, with an output pressure of $3.00 \times 10^5\ \text{N/m}^2$. (a) The water enters a hose with a 3.00-cm inside diameter and rises 2.50 m above the pump. What is its pressure at this point? (b) The hose goes over the foundation wall, losing 0.500 m in height, and widens to 4.00 cm in diameter. What is the pressure now? You may neglect frictional losses in both parts of the problem.

12.4 Viscosity and Laminar Flow; Poiseuille's Law

29. (a) Calculate the retarding force due to the viscosity of the air layer between a cart and a level air track given the following information—air temperature is $20^\circ\ \text{C}$, the cart is moving at 0.400 m/s, its surface area is $2.50 \times 10^{-2}\ \text{m}^2$, and the thickness of the air layer is $6.00 \times 10^{-5}\ \text{m}$. (b) What is the ratio of this force to the weight of the 0.300-kg cart?

30. What force is needed to pull one microscope slide over another at a speed of 1.00 cm/s, if there is a 0.500-mm-thick layer of $20^\circ\ \text{C}$ water between them and the contact area is $8.00\ \text{cm}^2$?

31. A glucose solution being administered with an IV has a flow rate of $4.00\ \text{cm}^3/\text{min}$. What will the new flow rate be if the glucose is replaced by whole blood having the same density but a viscosity 2.50 times that of the glucose? All other factors remain constant.

32. The pressure drop along a length of artery is 100 Pa, the radius is 10 mm, and the flow is laminar. The average speed of the blood is 15 mm/s. (a) What is the net force on the blood in this section of artery? (b) What is the power expended maintaining the flow?

33. A small artery has a length of $1.1 \times 10^{-3}\ \text{m}$ and a radius of $2.5 \times 10^{-5}\ \text{m}$. If the pressure drop across the artery is 1.3 kPa, what is the flow rate through the artery? (Assume that the temperature is $37^\circ\ \text{C}$.)

34. Fluid originally flows through a tube at a rate of $100\ \text{cm}^3/\text{s}$. To illustrate the sensitivity of flow rate to various factors, calculate the new flow rate for the following changes with all other factors remaining the same as in the original conditions. (a) Pressure difference increases by a factor of 1.50. (b) A new fluid with 3.00 times greater viscosity is substituted. (c) The tube is replaced by one having 4.00 times the length. (d) Another tube is used with a radius 0.100 times the original. (e) Yet another tube is substituted with a radius 0.100 times the original and half the length, *and* the pressure difference is increased by a factor of 1.50.

35. The arterioles (small arteries) leading to an organ, constrict in order to decrease flow to the organ. To shut down an organ, blood flow is reduced naturally to 1.00% of its original value. By what factor did the radii of the arterioles constrict? Penguins do this when they stand on ice to reduce the blood flow to their feet.

36. Angioplasty is a technique in which arteries partially blocked with plaque are dilated to increase blood flow. By what factor must the radius of an artery be increased in order to increase blood flow by a factor of 10?

37. (a) Suppose a blood vessel's radius is decreased to 90.0% of its original value by plaque deposits and the body compensates by increasing the pressure difference along the vessel to keep the flow rate constant. By what factor must the pressure difference increase? (b) If turbulence is created by the obstruction, what additional effect would it have on the flow rate?

38. A spherical particle falling at a terminal speed in a liquid must have the gravitational force balanced by the drag force and the buoyant force. The buoyant force is equal to the weight of the displaced fluid, while the drag force is assumed to be given by Stokes Law, $F_s = 6\pi r\eta v$. Show that

the terminal speed is given by
$v = \frac{2R^2 g}{9\eta}(\rho_s - \rho_1)$, where R is the radius of the sphere, ρ_s is its density, and ρ_1 is the density of the fluid and η the coefficient of viscosity.

39. Using the equation of the previous problem, find the viscosity of motor oil in which a steel ball of radius 0.8 mm falls with a terminal speed of 4.32 cm/s. The densities of the ball and the oil are 7.86 and 0.88 g/mL, respectively.

40. A skydiver will reach a terminal velocity when the air drag equals their weight. For a skydiver with high speed and a large body, turbulence is a factor. The drag force then is approximately proportional to the square of the velocity. Taking the drag force to be $F_D = \frac{1}{2}\rho Av^2$ and setting this equal to the person's weight, find the terminal speed for a person falling "spread eagle." Find both a formula and a number for v_t, with assumptions as to size.

41. A layer of oil 1.50 mm thick is placed between two microscope slides. Researchers find that a force of 5.50×10^{-4} N is required to glide one over the other at a speed of 1.00 cm/s when their contact area is 6.00 cm^2. What is the oil's viscosity? What type of oil might it be?

42. (a) Verify that a 19.0% decrease in laminar flow through a tube is caused by a 5.00% decrease in radius, assuming that all other factors remain constant, as stated in the text. (b) What increase in flow is obtained from a 5.00% increase in radius, again assuming all other factors remain constant?

43. Example 12.8 dealt with the flow of saline solution in an IV system. (a) Verify that a pressure of $1.62 \times 10^4 \text{ N/m}^2$ is created at a depth of 1.61 m in a saline solution, assuming its density to be that of sea water. (b) Calculate the new flow rate if the height of the saline solution is decreased to 1.50 m. (c) At what height would the direction of flow be reversed? (This reversal can be a problem when patients stand up.)

44. When physicians diagnose arterial blockages, they quote the reduction in flow rate. If the flow rate in an artery has been reduced to 10.0% of its normal value by a blood clot and the average pressure difference has increased by 20.0%, by what factor has the clot reduced the radius of the artery?

45. During a marathon race, a runner's blood flow increases to 10.0 times her resting rate. Her blood's viscosity has dropped to 95.0% of its normal value, and the blood pressure difference across the circulatory system has increased by 50.0%. By what factor has the average radii of her blood vessels increased?

46. Water supplied to a house by a water main has a pressure of $3.00 \times 10^5 \text{ N/m}^2$ early on a summer day when neighborhood use is low. This pressure produces a flow of 20.0 L/min through a garden hose. Later in the day, pressure at the exit of the water main and entrance to the house drops, and a flow of only 8.00 L/min is obtained through the same hose. (a) What pressure is now being supplied to the house, assuming resistance is constant? (b) By what factor did the flow rate in the water main increase in order to cause this decrease in delivered pressure? The pressure at the entrance of the water main is $5.00 \times 10^5 \text{ N/m}^2$, and the original flow rate was 200 L/min. (c) How many more users are there, assuming each would consume 20.0 L/min in the morning?

47. An oil gusher shoots crude oil 25.0 m into the air through a pipe with a 0.100-m diameter. Neglecting air resistance but not the resistance of the pipe, and assuming laminar flow, calculate the gauge pressure at the entrance of the 50.0-m-long vertical pipe. Take the density of the oil to be 900 kg/m^3 and its viscosity to be $1.00 \text{ (N/m}^2\text{)·s}$ (or $1.00 \text{ Pa} \cdot \text{s}$). Note that you must take into account the pressure due to the 50.0-m column of oil in the pipe.

48. Concrete is pumped from a cement mixer to the place it is being laid, instead of being carried in wheelbarrows. The flow rate is 200.0 L/min through a 50.0-m-long, 8.00-cm-diameter hose, and the pressure at the pump is $8.00 \times 10^6 \text{ N/m}^2$. (a) Calculate the resistance of the hose. (b) What is the viscosity of the concrete, assuming the flow is laminar? (c) How much power is being supplied, assuming the point of use is at the same level as the pump? You may neglect the power supplied to increase the concrete's velocity.

49. Construct Your Own Problem
Consider a coronary artery constricted by arteriosclerosis. Construct a problem in which you calculate the amount by which the diameter of the artery is decreased, based on an assessment of the decrease in flow rate.

50. Consider a river that spreads out in a delta region on its way to the sea. Construct a problem in which you calculate the average speed at which water moves in the delta region, based on the speed at which it was moving up river. Among the things to consider are the size and flow rate of the river before it spreads out and its size once it has spread out. You can construct the problem for the river spreading out into one large river or into multiple smaller rivers.

12.5 The Onset of Turbulence

51. Verify that the flow of oil is laminar (barely) for an oil gusher that shoots crude oil 25.0 m into the air through a pipe with a 0.100-m diameter. The vertical pipe is 50 m long. Take the density of the oil to be 900 kg/m^3 and its viscosity to be $1.00 \text{ (N/m}^2)\cdot\text{s}$ (or $1.00 \text{ Pa} \cdot \text{s}$).

52. Show that the Reynolds number N_R is unitless by substituting units for all the quantities in its definition and cancelling.

53. Calculate the Reynolds numbers for the flow of water through (a) a nozzle with a radius of 0.250 cm and (b) a garden hose with a radius of 0.900 cm, when the nozzle is attached to the hose. The flow rate through hose and nozzle is 0.500 L/s. Can the flow in either possibly be laminar?

54. A fire hose has an inside diameter of 6.40 cm. Suppose such a hose carries a flow of 40.0 L/s starting at a gauge pressure of $1.62 \times 10^6 \text{ N/m}^2$. The hose goes 10.0 m up a ladder to a nozzle having an inside diameter of 3.00 cm. Calculate the Reynolds numbers for flow in the fire hose and nozzle to show that the flow in each must be turbulent.

55. Concrete is pumped from a cement mixer to the place it is being laid, instead of being carried in wheelbarrows. The flow rate is 200.0 L/min through a 50.0-m-long, 8.00-cm-diameter hose, and the pressure at the pump is $8.00 \times 10^6 \text{ N/m}^2$. Verify that the flow of concrete is laminar taking concrete's viscosity to be $48.0 \text{ (N/m}^2) \cdot \text{s}$, and given its density is 2300 kg/m^3.

56. At what flow rate might turbulence begin to develop in a water main with a 0.200-m diameter? Assume a $20° \text{ C}$ temperature.

57. What is the greatest average speed of blood flow at $37° \text{ C}$ in an artery of radius 2.00 mm if the flow is to remain laminar? What is the corresponding flow rate? Take the density of blood to be 1025 kg/m^3.

58. In Take-Home Experiment: Inhalation, we measured the average flow rate Q of air traveling through the trachea during each inhalation. Now calculate the average air speed in meters per second through your trachea during each inhalation. The radius of the trachea in adult humans is approximately 10^{-2} m. From the data above, calculate the Reynolds number for the air flow in the trachea during inhalation. Do you expect the air flow to be laminar or turbulent?

59. Gasoline is piped underground from refineries to major users. The flow rate is $3.00 \times 10^{-2} \text{ m}^3\text{/s}$ (about 500 gal/min), the viscosity of gasoline is $1.00 \times 10^{-3} \text{ (N/m}^2)\cdot\text{s}$, and its density is 680 kg/m^3. (a) What minimum diameter must the pipe have if the Reynolds number is to be less than 2000? (b) What pressure difference must be maintained along each kilometer of the pipe to maintain this flow rate?

60. Assuming that blood is an ideal fluid, calculate the critical flow rate at which turbulence is a certainty in the aorta. Take the diameter of the aorta to be 2.50 cm. (Turbulence will actually occur at lower average flow rates, because blood is not an ideal fluid. Furthermore, since blood flow pulses, turbulence may occur during only the high-velocity part of each heartbeat.)

61. Unreasonable Results
A fairly large garden hose has an internal radius of 0.600 cm and a length of 23.0 m. The nozzleless horizontal hose is attached to a faucet, and it delivers 50.0 L/s. (a) What water pressure is supplied by the faucet? (b) What is unreasonable about this pressure? (c) What is unreasonable about the premise? (d) What is the Reynolds number for the given flow? (Take the viscosity of water as $1.005 \times 10^{-3} \left(\text{N/m}^2\right) \cdot \text{s}$.)

12.7 Molecular Transport Phenomena: Diffusion, Osmosis, and Related Processes

62. You can smell perfume very shortly after opening the bottle. To show that it is not reaching your nose by diffusion, calculate the average distance a perfume molecule moves in one second in air, given its diffusion constant D to be $1.00 \times 10^{-6} \text{ m}^2\text{/s}$.

63. What is the ratio of the average distances that oxygen will diffuse in a given time in air and water? Why is this distance less in water (equivalently, why is D less in water)?

64. Oxygen reaches the veinless cornea of the eye by diffusing through its tear layer, which is 0.500-mm thick. How long does it take the average oxygen molecule to do this?

65. (a) Find the average time required for an oxygen molecule to diffuse through a 0.200-mm-thick tear layer on the cornea. (b) How much time is required to diffuse 0.500 cm^3 of oxygen to the cornea if its surface area is 1.00 cm^2?

66. Suppose hydrogen and oxygen are diffusing through air. A small amount of each is released simultaneously. How much time passes before the hydrogen is 1.00 s ahead of the oxygen? Such differences in arrival times are used as an analytical tool in gas chromatography.

Test Prep for AP® Courses

12.1 Flow Rate and Its Relation to Velocity

1. Water flows through a small horizontal pipe with a speed of 12 m/s into a larger part of the pipe for which the diameter of the pipe is doubled. What is the speed of the water in the larger part of the pipe?
   a. 0.75 m/s
   b. 3.0 m/s
   c. 6.0 m/s
   d. 12 m/s

2. A popular pool toy allows the user to push a plunger to compress water in a barrel with a diameter of 3.0 cm. The water is compressed with a speed of 1.2 m/s and emerges from a small opening with a speed of 15 m/s. What is the diameter of the opening? Assume the toy is oriented horizontally.

12.2 Bernoulli's Equation

3. At what depth beneath the surface of the lake is the pressure in the water equal to twice atmospheric pressure?
   a. 10 m
   b. 100 m
   c. 1000 m
   d. 10,000 m

4. A pump provides pressure to the lower end of a long pipeline that supplies water from a reservoir to a house located on a hill 150 m vertically upward from the lower end of the pipe (where the water is initially at rest before being pumped). The pipeline has a constant diameter of 3.5 cm, and the upper end of the pipeline is open to the atmosphere. What pressure must the pump provide for water to flow from the upper end of the pipeline at a rate of 5.0 m/s?

5. According to Bernoulli's equation, if the pressure in a given fluid is constant and the kinetic energy per unit volume of a fluid increases, which of the following is true?
   a. The potential energy per unit volume of the fluid decreases.
   b. The potential energy per unit volume of the fluid increases.
   c. The fluid must no longer be considered incompressible.
   d. The flow rate of the fluid increases.

6. Consider the following circumstances within a fluid, and determine the answer using Bernoulli's equation. (a) The pressure and kinetic energy per unit volume along a fluid path increases. What must be true about the potential energy per unit volume of the fluid along the fluid path? Explain. (b) The pressure along a fluid path increases, and the kinetic energy per unit volume remains constant. What must be true about the potential energy per unit volume of the fluid along the fluid path? Explain.

12.3 The Most General Applications of Bernoulli's Equation

7. A horizontally oriented pipe has a diameter of 5.6 cm and is filled with water. The pipe draws water from a reservoir that is initially at rest. A manually operated plunger provides a force of 440 N in the pipe. Assuming that the other end of the pipe is open to the air, with what speed does the water emerge from the pipe?
   a. 12 m/s
   b. 19 m/s
   c. 150 m/s
   d. 190 m/s

8. A 3.5-cm-diameter pipe contains a pumping mechanism that provides a force of 320 N to push water up into a tall building. Upon entering the piston mechanism, the water is flowing at a rate of 2.5 m/s. The water is then pumped to a level 21 m higher where the other end of the pipe is open to the air. With what speed does water leave the pipe?

9. A large container of water is open to the air, and it develops a hole of area 10 cm^2 at a point 5 m below

the surface of the water. What is the flow rate (m^3/s) of the water emerging from this hole?

a. 99 m^3/s
b. 9.9 m^3/s
c. 0.099 m^3/s
d. 0.0099 m^3/s

10. A pipe is tapered so that the large end has a diameter twice as large as the small end. What must be the gauge pressure (the difference between pressure at the large end and pressure at the small end) in order for water to emerge from the small end with a speed of 12 m/s if the small end is elevated 8 m above the large end of the pipe?

CHAPTER 13
Temperature, Kinetic Theory, and the Gas Laws

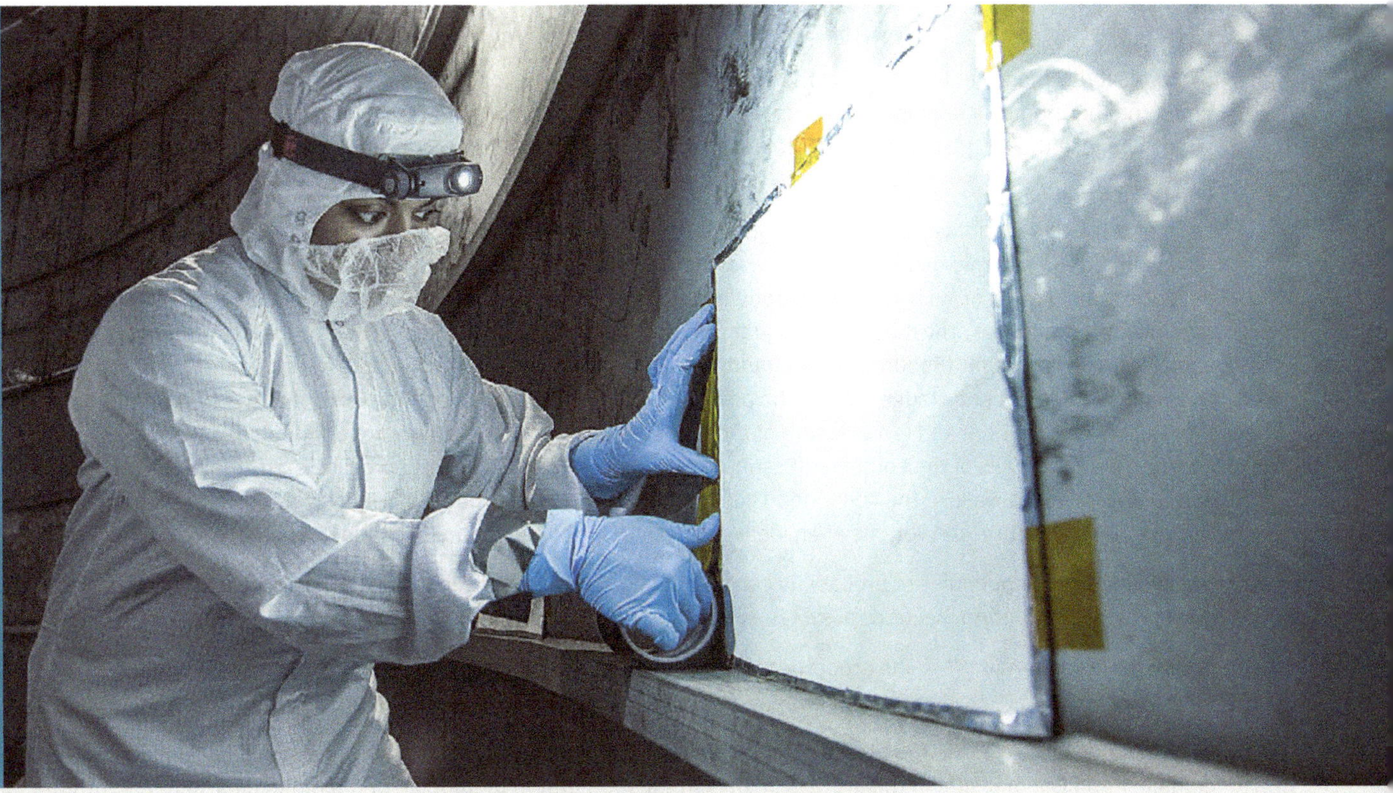

FIGURE 13.1 Molecules dissolved in surfaces undergo a process of outgassing, or release into the space around them. In a car, this leads to the famous "new car smell." In precision instruments like telescopes, this leads to major distortions due to contamination. NASA engineer Nithin Abraham created a coating to absorb these contaminants. Here she is pictured securing a coated panel beneath the Johnson Space Center's Chamber A, where it was used during testing of the James Webb Space Telescope. (credit: NASA, Chris Gunn/Flickr)

CHAPTER OUTLINE

CONNECTION FOR AP® COURSES Heat is something familiar to each of us. We feel the warmth of the summer sun, the chill of a clear summer night, the heat of coffee after a winter stroll, and the cooling effect of our sweat. Heat transfer is maintained by temperature differences. Manifestations of heat transfer—the movement of heat energy from one place or material to another—are apparent throughout the universe. Heat from beneath Earth's surface is brought to the surface in flows of incandescent lava. The Sun warms Earth's surface and is the source of much of the energy we find on it. Rising levels of atmospheric carbon dioxide threaten to trap more of the Sun's energy, perhaps fundamentally altering the ecosphere. In space, supernovas explode, briefly radiating more heat than an entire galaxy does.

In this chapter several concepts related to heat are discussed – what is heat, how is it related to temperature, what are heat's effects, and how is it related to other forms of energy and to work. We will find that, in spite of the richness of the phenomena, there is a small set of underlying physical principles that unite the subjects and tie them to other fields.

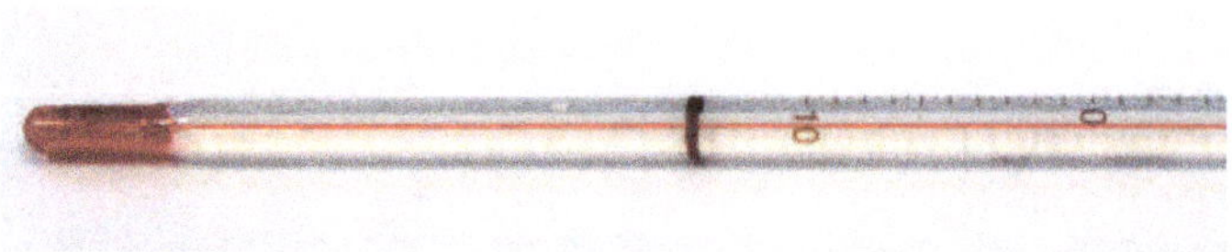

FIGURE 13.2 Alcohol thermometer with red dye. (credit: Chemical Engineer, Wikimedia Commons).

In a typical thermometer like this one, the alcohol, with a red dye, expands more rapidly than the glass containing it. When the thermometer's temperature increases, the liquid from the bulb is forced into the narrow tube, producing a large change in the length of the column for a small change in temperature.

The learning objectives covered under Big Idea 7 of the AP Physics Curriculum Framework are supported in this chapter through descriptive, algebraic, and graphical representations. Complex systems with internal structure can be described by both microscopic and macroscopic quantities. Big Idea 7 corresponds to the use of probability to describe the behavior of such systems by reducing large number of microscopic quantities to a small number of macroscopic quantities. The macroscopic quantities for an ideal gas, including temperature and pressure, are explained in this chapter (Enduring Understanding 7.A). The temperature represents average kinetic energy of gas molecules (Essential Knowledge 7.A.2). The pressure of a system determines the force that the system exerts on the walls of its container and is a measure of the average change in the momentum or impulse of the molecules colliding with the walls of the container (Essential Knowledge 7.A.1). The pressure also exists inside the system itself, not just at the walls of the container. This chapter discussed the "ideal gas law" which relates the temperature, pressure, and volume of an ideal gas using a simple equation (Essential Knowledge 7.A.3).

Big Idea 7 The mathematics of probability can be used to describe the behavior of complex systems and to interpret the behavior of quantum mechanical systems.

Enduring Understanding 7.A The properties of an ideal gas can be explained in terms of a small number of macroscopic variables including temperature and pressure.

Essential Knowledge 7.A.1 The pressure of a system determines the force that the system exerts on the walls of its container and is a measure of the average change in the momentum or impulse of the molecules colliding with the walls of the container. The pressure also exists inside the system itself, not just at the walls of the container.

Essential Knowledge 7.A.2 The temperature of a system characterizes the average kinetic energy of its molecules.

Essential Knowledge 7.A.3 In an ideal gas, the macroscopic (average) pressure (P), temperature (T), and volume (V), are related by the equation $PV = nRT$.

13.1 Temperature

LEARNING OBJECTIVES

By the end of this section, you will be able to:

- Define temperature.
- Convert temperatures between the Celsius, Fahrenheit, and Kelvin scales.
- Define thermal equilibrium.
- State the zeroth law of thermodynamics.

The concept of temperature has evolved from the common concepts of hot and cold. Human perception of what feels hot or cold is a relative one. For example, if you place one hand in hot water and the other in cold water, and then place both hands in tepid water, the tepid water will feel cool to the hand that was in hot water, and warm to the one that was in cold water. The scientific definition of temperature is less ambiguous than your senses of hot and cold. **Temperature** is operationally defined to be what we measure with a thermometer. (Many physical quantities are defined solely in terms of how they are measured. We shall see later how temperature is related to the kinetic energies of atoms and molecules, a more physical explanation.) Two accurate thermometers, one placed in hot water and the other in cold water, will show the hot water to have a higher temperature. If they are then placed in the tepid water, both will give identical readings (within measurement uncertainties). In this section, we discuss temperature, its measurement by thermometers, and its relationship to thermal equilibrium. Again, temperature is the quantity measured by a thermometer.

MISCONCEPTION ALERT: HUMAN PERCEPTION VS. REALITY

On a cold winter morning, the wood on a porch feels warmer than the metal of your bike. The wood and bicycle are in thermal equilibrium with the outside air, and are thus the same temperature. They *feel* different because of the difference in the way that they conduct heat away from your skin. The metal conducts heat away from your body faster than the wood does (see more about conductivity in Conduction). This is just one example demonstrating that the human sense of hot and cold is not determined by temperature alone.

Another factor that affects our perception of temperature is humidity. Most people feel much hotter on hot, humid days than on hot, dry days. This is because on humid days, sweat does not evaporate from the skin as efficiently as it does on dry days. It is the evaporation of sweat (or water from a sprinkler or pool) that cools us off.

Any physical property that depends on temperature, and whose response to temperature is reproducible, can be used as the basis of a thermometer. Because many physical properties depend on temperature, the variety of thermometers is remarkable. For example, volume increases with temperature for most substances. This property is the basis for the common alcohol thermometer, the old mercury thermometer, and the bimetallic strip (Figure 13.3). Other properties used to measure temperature include electrical resistance and color, as shown in Figure 13.4, and the emission of infrared radiation, as shown in Figure 13.5.

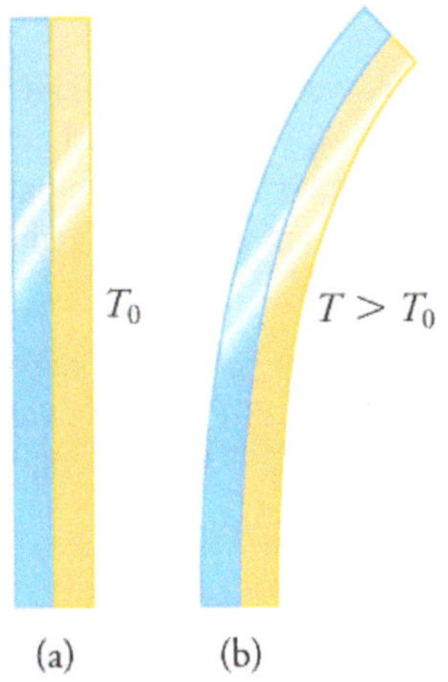

FIGURE 13.3 The curvature of a bimetallic strip depends on temperature. (a) The strip is straight at the starting temperature, where its two components have the same length. (b) At a higher temperature, this strip bends to the right, because the metal on the left has expanded more than the metal on the right.

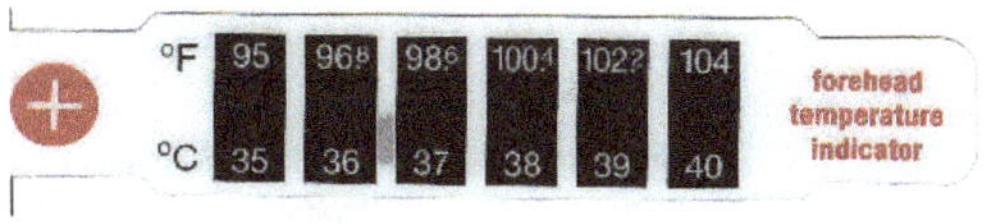

FIGURE 13.4 Each of the six squares on this plastic (liquid crystal) thermometer contains a film of a different heat-sensitive liquid crystal material. Below $95°F$, all six squares are black. When the plastic thermometer is exposed to temperature that increases to $95°F$, the first liquid crystal square changes color. When the temperature increases above $96.8°F$ the second liquid crystal square also changes color, and so forth. (credit: Arkrishna, Wikimedia Commons)

FIGURE 13.5 Fireman Jason Ormand uses a pyrometer to check the temperature of an aircraft carrier's ventilation system. Infrared radiation (whose emission varies with temperature) from the vent is measured and a temperature readout is quickly produced. Infrared measurements are also frequently used as a measure of body temperature. These modern thermometers, placed in the ear canal, are more accurate than alcohol thermometers placed under the tongue or in the armpit. (credit: Lamel J. Hinton/U.S. Navy)

Temperature Scales

Thermometers are used to measure temperature according to well-defined scales of measurement, which use pre-defined reference points to help compare quantities. The three most common temperature scales are the Fahrenheit, Celsius, and Kelvin scales. A temperature scale can be created by identifying two easily reproducible temperatures. The freezing and boiling temperatures of water at standard atmospheric pressure are commonly used.

The **Celsius** scale (which replaced the slightly different *centigrade* scale) has the freezing point of water at $0^{\circ}C$ and the boiling point at $100^{\circ}C$. Its unit is the **degree Celsius**($^{\circ}C$). On the **Fahrenheit** scale (still the most frequently used in the United States), the freezing point of water is at $32^{\circ}F$ and the boiling point is at $212^{\circ}F$. The unit of temperature on this scale is the **degree Fahrenheit**($^{\circ}F$). Note that a temperature difference of one degree Celsius is greater than a temperature difference of one degree Fahrenheit. Only 100 Celsius degrees span the same range as 180 Fahrenheit degrees, thus one degree on the Celsius scale is 1.8 times larger than one degree on the Fahrenheit scale $180/100 = 9/5$.

The **Kelvin** scale is the temperature scale that is commonly used in science. It is an *absolute temperature* scale defined to have 0 K at the lowest possible temperature, called **absolute zero**. The official temperature unit on this scale is the *kelvin*, which is abbreviated K, and is not accompanied by a degree sign. The freezing and boiling points of water are 273.15 K and 373.15 K, respectively. Thus, the magnitude of temperature differences is the same in units of kelvins and degrees Celsius. Unlike other temperature scales, the Kelvin scale is an absolute scale. It is used extensively in scientific work because a number of physical quantities, such as the volume of an ideal gas, are directly related to absolute temperature. The kelvin is the SI unit used in scientific work.

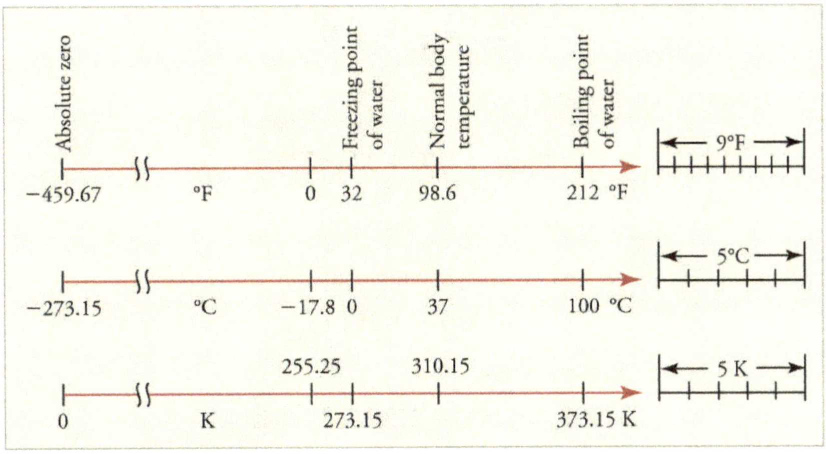

FIGURE 13.6 Relationships between the Fahrenheit, Celsius, and Kelvin temperature scales, rounded to the nearest degree. The relative sizes of the scales are also shown.

The relationships between the three common temperature scales is shown in Figure 13.6. Temperatures on these scales can be converted using the equations in Table 13.1.

To convert from . . .	Use this equation . . .	Also written as . . .
Celsius to Fahrenheit	$T(°\text{F}) = \frac{9}{5}T(°\text{C}) + 32$	$T_{°\text{F}} = \frac{9}{5}T_{°\text{C}} + 32$
Fahrenheit to Celsius	$T(°\text{C}) = \frac{5}{9}(T(°\text{F}) - 32)$	$T_{°\text{C}} = \frac{5}{9}(T_{°\text{F}} - 32)$
Celsius to Kelvin	$T(\text{K}) = T(°\text{C}) + 273.15$	$T_\text{K} = T_{°\text{C}} + 273.15$
Kelvin to Celsius	$T(°\text{C}) = T(\text{K}) - 273.15$	$T_{°\text{C}} = T_\text{K} - 273.15$
Fahrenheit to Kelvin	$T(\text{K}) = \frac{5}{9}(T(°\text{F}) - 32) + 273.15$	$T_\text{K} = \frac{5}{9}(T_{°\text{F}} - 32) + 273.15$
Kelvin to Fahrenheit	$T(°\text{F}) = \frac{9}{5}(T(\text{K}) - 273.15) + 32$	$T_{°\text{F}} = \frac{9}{5}(T_\text{K} - 273.15) + 32$

TABLE 13.1 Temperature Conversions

Notice that the conversions between Fahrenheit and Kelvin look quite complicated. In fact, they are simple combinations of the conversions between Fahrenheit and Celsius, and the conversions between Celsius and Kelvin.

EXAMPLE 13.1

Converting between Temperature Scales: Room Temperature

"Room temperature" is generally defined to be $25°\text{C}$. (a) What is room temperature in $°\text{F}$? (b) What is it in K?

Strategy

To answer these questions, all we need to do is choose the correct conversion equations and plug in the known values.

Solution for (a)

1. Choose the right equation. To convert from $°\text{C}$ to $°\text{F}$, use the equation

$$T_{°F} = \frac{9}{5}T_{°C} + 32. \quad (13.1)$$

2. Plug the known value into the equation and solve:

$$T_{°F} = \frac{9}{5}25°C + 32 = 77°F. \quad (13.2)$$

Solution for (b)

1. Choose the right equation. To convert from °C to K, use the equation

$$T_K = T_{°C} + 273.15. \quad (13.3)$$

2. Plug the known value into the equation and solve:

$$T_K = 25°C + 273.15 = 298\,K. \quad (13.4)$$

EXAMPLE 13.2

Converting between Temperature Scales: the Reaumur Scale

The Reaumur scale is a temperature scale that was used widely in Europe in the 18th and 19th centuries. On the Reaumur temperature scale, the freezing point of water is $0°R$ and the boiling temperature is $80°R$. If "room temperature" is $25°C$ on the Celsius scale, what is it on the Reaumur scale?

Strategy

To answer this question, we must compare the Reaumur scale to the Celsius scale. The difference between the freezing point and boiling point of water on the Reaumur scale is $80°R$. On the Celsius scale it is $100°C$. Therefore $100°C = 80°R$. Both scales start at $0°$ for freezing, so we can derive a simple formula to convert between temperatures on the two scales.

Solution

1. Derive a formula to convert from one scale to the other:

$$T_{°R} = \frac{0.8°R}{°C} \times T_{°C}. \quad (13.5)$$

2. Plug the known value into the equation and solve:

$$T_{°R} = \frac{0.8°R}{°C} \times 25°C = 20°R. \quad (13.6)$$

Temperature Ranges in the Universe

Figure 13.8 shows the wide range of temperatures found in the universe. Human beings have been known to survive with body temperatures within a small range, from $24°C$ to $44°C$ ($75°F$ to $111°F$). The average normal body temperature is usually given as $37.0°C$ ($98.6°F$), and variations in this temperature can indicate a medical condition: a fever, an infection, a tumor, or circulatory problems (see Figure 13.7).

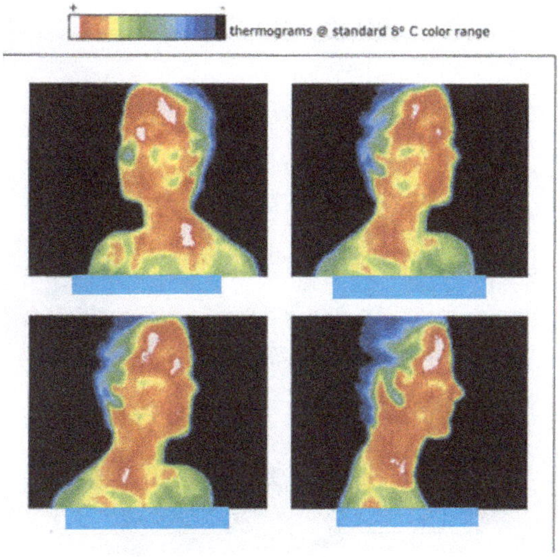

FIGURE 13.7 This image of radiation from a person's body (an infrared thermograph) shows the location of temperature abnormalities in the upper body. Dark blue corresponds to cold areas and red to white corresponds to hot areas. An elevated temperature might be an indication of malignant tissue (a cancerous tumor in the breast, for example), while a depressed temperature might be due to a decline in blood flow from a clot. In this case, the abnormalities are caused by a condition called hyperhidrosis. (credit: Porcelina81, Wikimedia Commons)

The lowest temperatures ever recorded have been measured during laboratory experiments: 4.5×10^{-10} K at the Massachusetts Institute of Technology (USA), and 1.0×10^{-10} K at Helsinki University of Technology (Finland). In comparison, the coldest recorded place on Earth's surface is Vostok, Antarctica at 183 K (–89°C), and the coldest place (outside the lab) known in the universe is the Boomerang Nebula, with a temperature of 1 K.

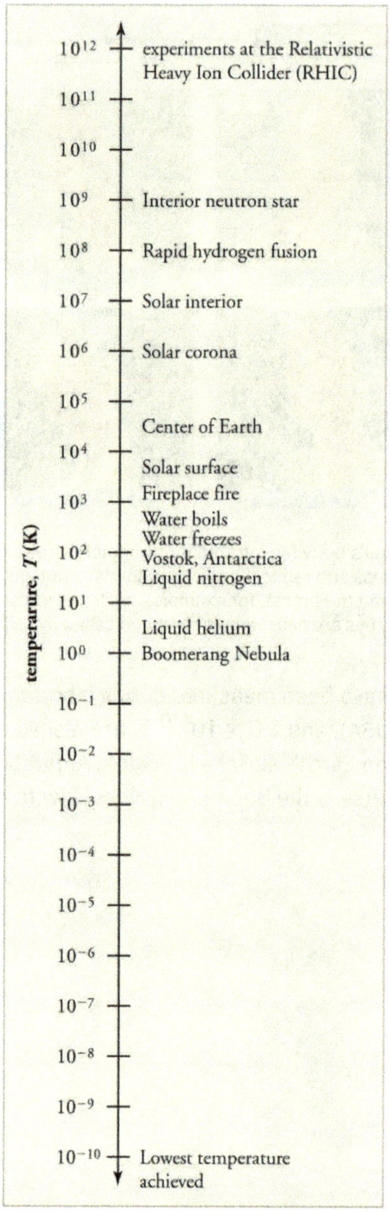

FIGURE 13.8 Each increment on this logarithmic scale indicates an increase by a factor of ten, and thus illustrates the tremendous range of temperatures in nature. Note that zero on a logarithmic scale would occur off the bottom of the page at infinity.

MAKING CONNECTIONS: ABSOLUTE ZERO

What is absolute zero? Absolute zero is the temperature at which all molecular motion has ceased. The concept of absolute zero arises from the behavior of gases. Figure 13.9 shows how the pressure of gases at a constant volume decreases as temperature decreases. Various scientists have noted that the pressures of gases extrapolate to zero at the same temperature, –273.15ºC. This extrapolation implies that there is a lowest temperature. This temperature is called *absolute zero.* Today we know that most gases first liquefy and then freeze, and it is not actually possible to reach absolute zero. The numerical value of absolute zero temperature is –273.15ºC or 0 K.

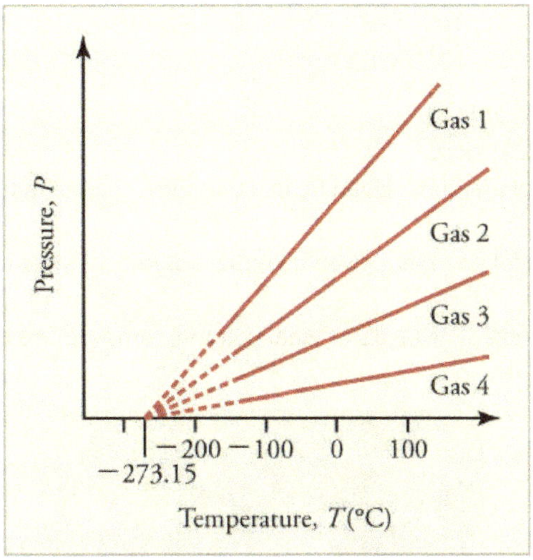

FIGURE 13.9 Graph of pressure versus temperature for various gases kept at a constant volume. Note that all of the graphs extrapolate to zero pressure at the same temperature.

Thermal Equilibrium and the Zeroth Law of Thermodynamics

Thermometers actually take their *own* temperature, not the temperature of the object they are measuring. This raises the question of how we can be certain that a thermometer measures the temperature of the object with which it is in contact. It is based on the fact that any two systems placed in *thermal contact* (meaning heat transfer can occur between them) will reach the same temperature. That is, heat will flow from the hotter object to the cooler one until they have exactly the same temperature. The objects are then in **thermal equilibrium**, and no further changes will occur. The systems interact and change because their temperatures differ, and the changes stop once their temperatures are the same. Thus, if enough time is allowed for this transfer of heat to run its course, the temperature a thermometer registers *does* represent the system with which it is in thermal equilibrium. Thermal equilibrium is established when two bodies are in contact with each other and can freely exchange energy.

Furthermore, experimentation has shown that if two systems, A and B, are in thermal equilibrium with each another, and B is in thermal equilibrium with a third system C, then A is also in thermal equilibrium with C. This conclusion may seem obvious, because all three have the same temperature, but it is basic to thermodynamics. It is called the **zeroth law of thermodynamics**.

THE ZEROTH LAW OF THERMODYNAMICS

If two systems, A and B, are in thermal equilibrium with each other, and B is in thermal equilibrium with a third system, C, then A is also in thermal equilibrium with C.

This law was postulated in the 1930s, after the first and second laws of thermodynamics had been developed and named. It is called the *zeroth law* because it comes logically before the first and second laws (discussed in Thermodynamics). Suppose, for example, a cold metal block and a hot metal block are both placed on a metal plate at room temperature. Eventually the cold block and the plate will be in thermal equilibrium. In addition, the hot block and the plate will be in thermal equilibrium. By the zeroth law, we can conclude that the cold block and the hot block are also in thermal equilibrium.

CHECK YOUR UNDERSTANDING

Does the temperature of a body depend on its size?

Solution

No, the system can be divided into smaller parts each of which is at the same temperature. We say that the temperature is an *intensive* quantity. Intensive quantities are independent of size.

13.2 Thermal Expansion of Solids and Liquids

LEARNING OBJECTIVES

By the end of this section, you will be able to:

- Define and describe thermal expansion.
- Calculate the linear expansion of an object given its initial length, change in temperature, and coefficient of linear expansion.
- Calculate the volume expansion of an object given its initial volume, change in temperature, and coefficient of volume expansion.
- Calculate thermal stress on an object given its original volume, temperature change, volume change, and bulk modulus.

FIGURE 13.10 Thermal expansion joints like these in the Auckland Harbour Bridge in New Zealand allow bridges to change length without buckling. (credit: Ingolfson, Wikimedia Commons)

The expansion of alcohol in a thermometer is one of many commonly encountered examples of **thermal expansion**, the change in size or volume of a given mass with temperature. Hot air rises because its volume increases, which causes the hot air's density to be smaller than the density of surrounding air, causing a buoyant (upward) force on the hot air. The same happens in all liquids and gases, driving natural heat transfer upwards in homes, oceans, and weather systems. Solids also undergo thermal expansion. Railroad tracks and bridges, for example, have expansion joints to allow them to freely expand and contract with temperature changes.

What are the basic properties of thermal expansion? First, thermal expansion is clearly related to temperature change. The greater the temperature change, the more a bimetallic strip will bend. Second, it depends on the material. In a thermometer, for example, the expansion of alcohol is much greater than the expansion of the glass containing it.

What is the underlying cause of thermal expansion? As is discussed in Kinetic Theory: Atomic and Molecular Explanation of Pressure and Temperature, an increase in temperature implies an increase in the kinetic energy of the individual atoms. In a solid, unlike in a gas, the atoms or molecules are closely packed together, but their kinetic energy (in the form of small, rapid vibrations) pushes neighboring atoms or molecules apart from each other. This neighbor-to-neighbor pushing results in a slightly greater distance, on average, between neighbors, and adds up to a larger size for the whole body. For most substances under ordinary conditions, there is no preferred direction, and an increase in temperature will increase the solid's size by a certain fraction in each dimension.

LINEAR THERMAL EXPANSION—THERMAL EXPANSION IN ONE DIMENSION

The change in length ΔL is proportional to length L. The dependence of thermal expansion on temperature, substance, and length is summarized in the equation

$$\Delta L = \alpha L \Delta T, \tag{13.7}$$

where ΔL is the change in length L, ΔT is the change in temperature, and α is the **coefficient of linear expansion**, which varies slightly with temperature.

Table 13.2 lists representative values of the coefficient of linear expansion, which may have units of $1/°C$ or 1/K. Because the size of a kelvin and a degree Celsius are the same, both α and ΔT can be expressed in units of kelvins or degrees Celsius. The equation $\Delta L = \alpha L \Delta T$ is accurate for small changes in temperature and can be used for large changes in temperature if an average value of α is used.

Material	Coefficient of linear expansion $\alpha(1/°C)$	Coefficient of volume expansion $\beta(1/°C)$
Solids		
Aluminum	25×10^{-6}	75×10^{-6}
Brass	19×10^{-6}	56×10^{-6}
Copper	17×10^{-6}	51×10^{-6}
Gold	14×10^{-6}	42×10^{-6}
Iron or Steel	12×10^{-6}	35×10^{-6}
Invar (Nickel-iron alloy)	0.9×10^{-6}	2.7×10^{-6}
Lead	29×10^{-6}	87×10^{-6}
Silver	18×10^{-6}	54×10^{-6}
Glass (ordinary)	9×10^{-6}	27×10^{-6}
Glass (Pyrex®)	3×10^{-6}	9×10^{-6}
Quartz	0.4×10^{-6}	1×10^{-6}
Concrete, Brick	$\sim 12 \times 10^{-6}$	$\sim 36 \times 10^{-6}$
Marble (average)	7×10^{-6}	2.1×10^{-5}
Liquids		
Ether		1650×10^{-6}
Ethyl alcohol		1100×10^{-6}
Petrol		950×10^{-6}

TABLE 13.2 Thermal Expansion Coefficients at $20°C$ [1]

1 Values for liquids and gases are approximate.

Material	Coefficient of linear expansion $\alpha(1/°\text{C})$	Coefficient of volume expansion $\beta(1/°\text{C})$
Glycerin		500×10^{-6}
Mercury		180×10^{-6}
Water		210×10^{-6}
Gases		
Air and most other gases at atmospheric pressure		3400×10^{-6}

TABLE 13.2 Thermal Expansion Coefficients at $20°\text{C}$ [1]

EXAMPLE 13.3

Calculating Linear Thermal Expansion: The Golden Gate Bridge

The main span of San Francisco's Golden Gate Bridge is 1275 m long at its coldest. The bridge is exposed to temperatures ranging from $-15°\text{C}$ to $40°\text{C}$. What is its change in length between these temperatures? Assume that the bridge is made entirely of steel.

Strategy

Use the equation for linear thermal expansion $\Delta L = \alpha L \Delta T$ to calculate the change in length , ΔL. Use the coefficient of linear expansion, α, for steel from Table 13.2, and note that the change in temperature, ΔT, is $55°\text{C}$.

Solution

Plug all of the known values into the equation to solve for ΔL.

$$\Delta L = \alpha L \Delta T = \left(\frac{12 \times 10^{-6}}{°\text{C}}\right)(1275 \text{ m})(55°\text{C}) = 0.84 \text{ m}. \quad (13.8)$$

Discussion

Although not large compared with the length of the bridge, this change in length is observable. It is generally spread over many expansion joints so that the expansion at each joint is small.

Thermal Expansion in Two and Three Dimensions

Objects expand in all dimensions, as illustrated in Figure 13.11. That is, their areas and volumes, as well as their lengths, increase with temperature. Holes also get larger with temperature. If you cut a hole in a metal plate, the remaining material will expand exactly as it would if the plug was still in place. The plug would get bigger, and so the hole must get bigger too. (Think of the ring of neighboring atoms or molecules on the wall of the hole as pushing each other farther apart as temperature increases. Obviously, the ring of neighbors must get slightly larger, so the hole gets slightly larger).

THERMAL EXPANSION IN TWO DIMENSIONS

For small temperature changes, the change in area ΔA is given by

$$\Delta A = 2\alpha A \Delta T, \quad (13.9)$$

where ΔA is the change in area A, ΔT is the change in temperature, and α is the coefficient of linear expansion, which varies slightly with temperature.

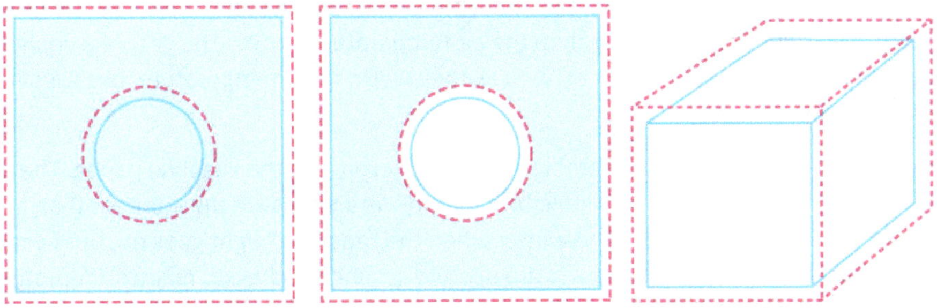

FIGURE 13.11 In general, objects expand in all directions as temperature increases. In these drawings, the original boundaries of the objects are shown with solid lines, and the expanded boundaries with dashed lines. (a) Area increases because both length and width increase. The area of a circular plug also increases. (b) If the plug is removed, the hole it leaves becomes larger with increasing temperature, just as if the expanding plug were still in place. (c) Volume also increases, because all three dimensions increase.

THERMAL EXPANSION IN THREE DIMENSIONS

The change in volume ΔV is very nearly $\Delta V = 3\alpha V\Delta T$. This equation is usually written as

$$\Delta V = \beta V\Delta T, \quad 13.10$$

where β is the **coefficient of volume expansion** and $\beta \approx 3\alpha$. Note that the values of β in Table 13.2 are almost exactly equal to 3α.

In general, objects will expand with increasing temperature. Water is the most important exception to this rule. Water expands with increasing temperature (its density *decreases*) when it is at temperatures greater than $4^\circ C (40^\circ F)$. However, it expands with *decreasing* temperature when it is between $+4^\circ C$ and $0^\circ C (40^\circ F$ to $32^\circ F)$. Water is densest at $+4^\circ C$. (See Figure 13.12.) Perhaps the most striking effect of this phenomenon is the freezing of water in a pond. When water near the surface cools down to $4^\circ C$ it is denser than the remaining water and thus will sink to the bottom. This "turnover" results in a layer of warmer water near the surface, which is then cooled. Eventually the pond has a uniform temperature of $4^\circ C$. If the temperature in the surface layer drops below $4^\circ C$, the water is less dense than the water below, and thus stays near the top. As a result, the pond surface can completely freeze over. The ice on top of liquid water provides an insulating layer from winter's harsh exterior air temperatures. Fish and other aquatic life can survive in $4^\circ C$ water beneath ice, due to this unusual characteristic of water. It also produces circulation of water in the pond that is necessary for a healthy ecosystem of the body of water.

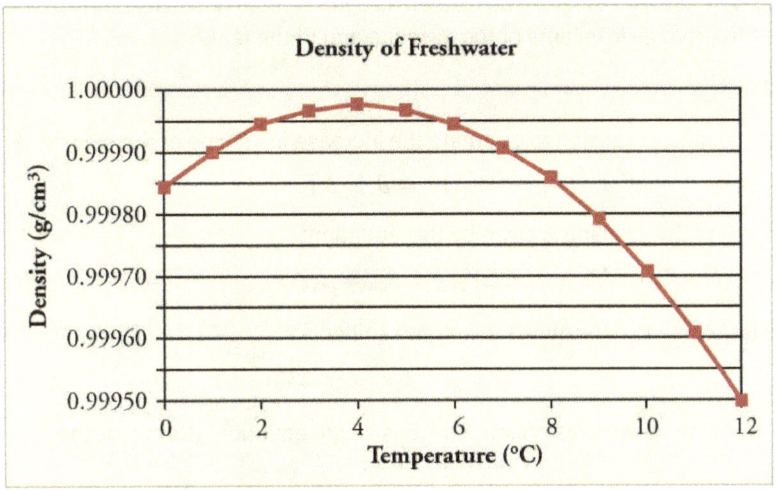

FIGURE 13.12 The density of water as a function of temperature. Note that the thermal expansion is actually very small. The maximum density at $+4^\circ C$ is only *0.0075%* greater than the density at $2^\circ C$, and *0.012%* greater than that at $0^\circ C$.

MAKING CONNECTIONS: REAL-WORLD CONNECTIONS—FILLING THE TANK

Differences in the thermal expansion of materials can lead to interesting effects at the gas station. One example is the dripping of gasoline from a freshly filled tank on a hot day. Gasoline starts out at the temperature of the ground under the gas station, which is cooler than the air temperature above. The gasoline cools the steel tank when it is filled. Both gasoline and steel tank expand as they warm to air temperature, but gasoline expands much more than steel, and so it may overflow.

This difference in expansion can also cause problems when interpreting the gasoline gauge. The actual amount (mass) of gasoline left in the tank when the gauge hits "empty" is a lot less in the summer than in the winter. The gasoline has the same volume as it does in the winter when the "add fuel" light goes on, but because the gasoline has expanded, there is less mass. If you are used to getting another 40 miles on "empty" in the winter, beware—you will probably run out much more quickly in the summer.

FIGURE 13.13 Because the gas expands more than the gas tank with increasing temperature, you can't drive as many miles on "empty" in the summer as you can in the winter. (credit: Hector Alejandro, Flickr)

EXAMPLE 13.4

Calculating Thermal Expansion: Gas vs. Gas Tank

Suppose your 60.0-L (15.9-gal) steel gasoline tank is full of gas, so both the tank and the gasoline have a temperature of 15.0°C. How much gasoline has spilled by the time they warm to 35.0°C?

Strategy

The tank and gasoline increase in volume, but the gasoline increases more, so the amount spilled is the difference in their volume changes. (The gasoline tank can be treated as solid steel.) We can use the equation for volume expansion to calculate the change in volume of the gasoline and of the tank.

Solution

1. Use the equation for volume expansion to calculate the increase in volume of the steel tank:

$$\Delta V_{\text{s}} = \beta_{\text{s}} V_{\text{s}} \Delta T. \tag{13.11}$$

2. The increase in volume of the gasoline is given by this equation:

$$\Delta V_{\text{gas}} = \beta_{\text{gas}} V_{\text{gas}} \Delta T. \tag{13.12}$$

3. Find the difference in volume to determine the amount spilled as

$$V_{\text{spill}} = \Delta V_{\text{gas}} - \Delta V_{\text{s}}. \tag{13.13}$$

Alternatively, we can combine these three equations into a single equation. (Note that the original volumes are equal.)

$$\begin{aligned} V_{\text{spill}} &= (\beta_{\text{gas}} - \beta_{\text{s}})V\Delta T \\ &= \left[(950 - 35)\times 10^{-6}/^\circ\text{C}\right](60.0\text{ L})(20.0^\circ\text{C}) \\ &= 1.10\text{ L}. \end{aligned} \quad 13.14$$

Discussion

This amount is significant, particularly for a 60.0-L tank. The effect is so striking because the gasoline and steel expand quickly. The rate of change in thermal properties is discussed in Heat and Heat Transfer Methods.

If you try to cap the tank tightly to prevent overflow, you will find that it leaks anyway, either around the cap or by bursting the tank. Tightly constricting the expanding gas is equivalent to compressing it, and both liquids and solids resist being compressed with extremely large forces. To avoid rupturing rigid containers, these containers have air gaps, which allow them to expand and contract without stressing them.

Thermal Stress

Thermal stress is created by thermal expansion or contraction (see Elasticity: Stress and Strain for a discussion of stress and strain). Thermal stress can be destructive, such as when expanding gasoline ruptures a tank. It can also be useful, for example, when two parts are joined together by heating one in manufacturing, then slipping it over the other and allowing the combination to cool. Thermal stress can explain many phenomena, such as the weathering of rocks and pavement by the expansion of ice when it freezes.

EXAMPLE 13.5

Calculating Thermal Stress: Gas Pressure

What pressure would be created in the gasoline tank considered in Example 13.4, if the gasoline increases in temperature from 15.0°C to 35.0°C without being allowed to expand? Assume that the bulk modulus B for gasoline is $1.00 \times 10^9\ \text{N/m}^2$. (For more on bulk modulus, see Elasticity: Stress and Strain.)

Strategy

To solve this problem, we must use the following equation, which relates a change in volume ΔV to pressure:

$$\Delta V = \frac{1}{B}\frac{F}{A}V_0, \quad 13.15$$

where F/A is pressure, V_0 is the original volume, and B is the bulk modulus of the material involved. We will use the amount spilled in Example 13.4 as the change in volume, ΔV.

Solution

1. Rearrange the equation for calculating pressure:

$$P = \frac{F}{A} = \frac{\Delta V}{V_0}B. \quad 13.16$$

2. Insert the known values. The bulk modulus for gasoline is $B = 1.00\times 10^9\ \text{N/m}^2$. In the previous example, the change in volume $\Delta V = 1.10\ \text{L}$ is the amount that would spill. Here, $V_0 = 60.0\ \text{L}$ is the original volume of the gasoline. Substituting these values into the equation, we obtain

$$P = \frac{1.10\text{ L}}{60.0\text{ L}}\left(1.00 \times 10^9\text{ Pa}\right) = 1.83 \times 10^7\text{ Pa}. \quad 13.17$$

Discussion

This pressure is about $2500\ \text{lb/in}^2$, *much* more than a gasoline tank can handle.

Forces and pressures created by thermal stress are typically as great as that in the example above. Railroad tracks and roadways can buckle on hot days if they lack sufficient expansion joints. (See Figure 13.14.) Power lines sag more in the summer than in the winter, and will snap in cold weather if there is insufficient slack. Cracks open and close in plaster walls as a house warms and cools. Glass cooking pans will crack if cooled rapidly or unevenly, because of differential contraction and the stresses it creates. (Pyrex® is less susceptible because of its small coefficient of thermal expansion.) Nuclear reactor pressure vessels are threatened by overly rapid cooling, and although none have failed, several have been cooled faster than considered desirable. Biological cells are ruptured when foods are frozen, detracting from their taste. Repeated thawing and freezing accentuate the damage. Even the oceans can be affected. A significant portion of the rise in sea level that is resulting from global warming is due to the thermal expansion of sea water.

FIGURE 13.14 Thermal stress contributes to the formation of potholes. (credit: Editor5807, Wikimedia Commons)

Metal is regularly used in the human body for hip and knee implants. Most implants need to be replaced over time because, among other things, metal does not bond with bone. Researchers are trying to find better metal coatings that would allow metal-to-bone bonding. One challenge is to find a coating that has an expansion coefficient similar to that of metal. If the expansion coefficients are too different, the thermal stresses during the manufacturing process lead to cracks at the coating-metal interface.

Another example of thermal stress is found in the mouth. Dental fillings can expand differently from tooth enamel. It can give pain when eating ice cream or having a hot drink. Cracks might occur in the filling. Metal fillings (gold, silver, etc.) are being replaced by composite fillings (porcelain), which have smaller coefficients of expansion, and are closer to those of teeth.

CHECK YOUR UNDERSTANDING

Two blocks, A and B, are made of the same material. Block A has dimensions $l \times w \times h = L \times 2L \times L$ and Block B has dimensions $2L \times 2L \times 2L$. If the temperature changes, what is (a) the change in the volume of the two blocks, (b) the change in the cross-sectional area $l \times w$, and (c) the change in the height h of the two blocks?

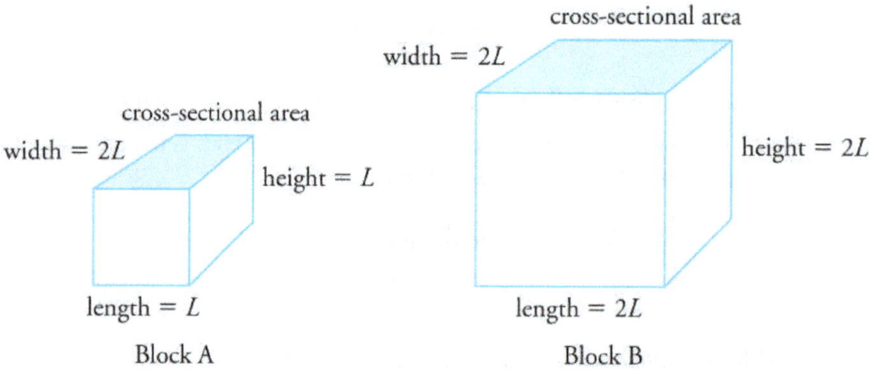

FIGURE 13.15

Solution

(a) The change in volume is proportional to the original volume. Block A has a volume of $L \times 2L \times L = 2L^3$. Block B has a volume of $2L \times 2L \times 2L = 8L^3$, which is 4 times that of Block A. Thus the change in volume of Block B should be 4 times the change in volume of Block A.

(b) The change in area is proportional to the area. The cross-sectional area of Block A is $L \times 2L = 2L^2$, while that of Block B is $2L \times 2L = 4L^2$. Because cross-sectional area of Block B is twice that of Block A, the change in the cross-sectional area of Block B is twice that of Block A.

(c) The change in height is proportional to the original height. Because the original height of Block B is twice that of A, the change in the height of Block B is twice that of Block A.

13.3 The Ideal Gas Law

LEARNING OBJECTIVES

By the end of this section, you will be able to:

- State the ideal gas law in terms of molecules and in terms of moles.
- Use the ideal gas law to calculate pressure change, temperature change, volume change, or the number of molecules or moles in a given volume.
- Use Avogadro's number to convert between number of molecules and number of moles.

FIGURE 13.16 The air inside this hot air balloon flying over Putrajaya, Malaysia, is hotter than the ambient air. As a result, the balloon experiences a buoyant force pushing it upward. (credit: Kevin Poh, Flickr)

In this section, we continue to explore the thermal behavior of gases. In particular, we examine the characteristics of atoms and molecules that compose gases. (Most gases, for example nitrogen, N_2, and oxygen, O_2, are composed of two or more atoms. We will primarily use the term "molecule" in discussing a gas because the term can also be applied to monatomic gases, such as helium.)

Gases are easily compressed. We can see evidence of this in Table 13.2, where you will note that gases have the *largest* coefficients of volume expansion. The large coefficients mean that gases expand and contract very rapidly with temperature changes. In addition, you will note that most gases expand at the *same* rate, or have the same β. This raises the question as to why gases should all act in nearly the same way, when liquids and solids have widely varying expansion rates.

The answer lies in the large separation of atoms and molecules in gases, compared to their sizes, as illustrated in Figure 13.17. Because atoms and molecules have large separations, forces between them can be ignored, except when they collide with each other during collisions. The motion of atoms and molecules (at temperatures well above the boiling temperature) is fast, such that the gas occupies all of the accessible volume and the expansion of gases is rapid. In contrast, in liquids and solids, atoms and molecules are closer together and are quite sensitive to the forces between them.

FIGURE 13.17 Atoms and molecules in a gas are typically widely separated, as shown. Because the forces between them are quite weak at these distances, the properties of a gas depend more on the number of atoms per unit volume and on temperature than on the type of atom.

To get some idea of how pressure, temperature, and volume of a gas are related to one another, consider what happens when you pump air into an initially deflated tire. The tire's volume first increases in direct proportion to the amount of air injected, without much increase in the tire pressure. Once the tire has expanded to nearly its full size, the walls limit volume expansion. If we continue to pump air into it, the pressure increases. The pressure will further increase when the car is driven and the tires move. Most manufacturers specify optimal tire pressure for cold tires. (See Figure 13.18.)

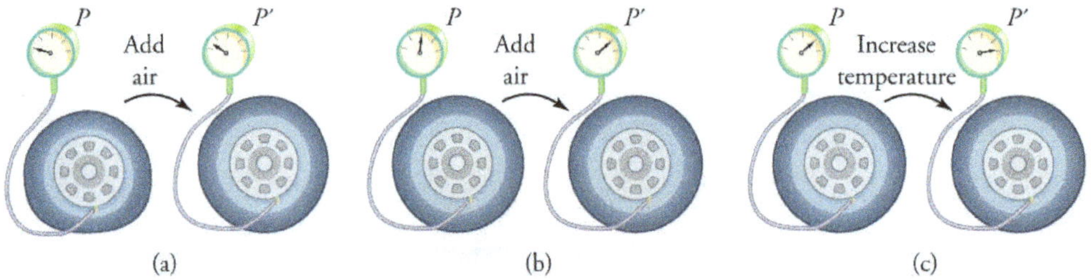

FIGURE 13.18 (a) When air is pumped into a deflated tire, its volume first increases without much increase in pressure. (b) When the tire is filled to a certain point, the tire walls resist further expansion and the pressure increases with more air. (c) Once the tire is inflated, its pressure increases with temperature.

At room temperatures, collisions between atoms and molecules can be ignored. In this case, the gas is called an ideal gas, in which case the relationship between the pressure, volume, and temperature is given by the equation of state called the ideal gas law.

IDEAL GAS LAW

The **ideal gas law** states that

$$PV = NkT, \tag{13.18}$$

where P is the absolute pressure of a gas, V is the volume it occupies, N is the number of atoms and molecules in the gas, and T is its absolute temperature. The constant k is called the **Boltzmann constant** in honor of Austrian physicist Ludwig Boltzmann (1844–1906) and has the value

$$k = 1.38 \times 10^{-23}\text{ J/K}. \tag{13.19}$$

The ideal gas law can be derived from basic principles, but was originally deduced from experimental measurements of Charles' law (that volume occupied by a gas is proportional to temperature at a fixed pressure) and from Boyle's law (that for a fixed temperature, the product PV is a constant). In the ideal gas model, the volume occupied by its atoms and molecules is a negligible fraction of V. The ideal gas law describes the behavior of real gases under most conditions. (Note, for example, that N is the total number of atoms and molecules, independent of the type of gas.)

Let us see how the ideal gas law is consistent with the behavior of filling the tire when it is pumped slowly and the temperature is constant. At first, the pressure P is essentially equal to atmospheric pressure, and the volume V increases in direct proportion to the number of atoms and molecules N put into the tire. Once the volume of the tire is constant, the equation $PV = NkT$ predicts that the pressure should increase in proportion to *the number N of atoms and molecules.*

EXAMPLE 13.6

Calculating Pressure Changes Due to Temperature Changes: Tire Pressure

Suppose your bicycle tire is fully inflated, with an absolute pressure of 7.00×10^5 Pa (a gauge pressure of just under $90.0\ \text{lb/in}^2$) at a temperature of 18.0°C. What is the pressure after its temperature has risen to 35.0°C? Assume that there are no appreciable leaks or changes in volume.

Strategy

The pressure in the tire is changing only because of changes in temperature. First we need to identify what we know and what we want to know, and then identify an equation to solve for the unknown.

We know the initial pressure $P_0 = 7.00 \times 10^5$ Pa, the initial temperature $T_0 = 18.0^\circ\text{C}$, and the final temperature $T_\text{f} = 35.0^\circ\text{C}$. We must find the final pressure P_f. How can we use the equation $PV = NkT$? At first, it may seem that not enough information is given, because the volume V and number of atoms N are not specified. What we can do is use the equation twice: $P_0V_0 = NkT_0$ and $P_\text{f}V_\text{f} = NkT_\text{f}$. If we divide $P_\text{f}V_\text{f}$ by P_0V_0 we can come up with an equation that allows us to solve for P_f.

$$\frac{P_\text{f}V_\text{f}}{P_0V_0} = \frac{N_\text{f}kT_\text{f}}{N_0kT_0} \qquad 13.20$$

Since the volume is constant, V_f and V_0 are the same and they cancel out. The same is true for N_f and N_0, and k, which is a constant. Therefore,

$$\frac{P_\text{f}}{P_0} = \frac{T_\text{f}}{T_0}. \qquad 13.21$$

We can then rearrange this to solve for P_f:

$$P_\text{f} = P_0\frac{T_\text{f}}{T_0}, \qquad 13.22$$

where the temperature must be in units of kelvins, because T_0 and T_f are absolute temperatures.

Solution

1. Convert temperatures from Celsius to Kelvin.

$$\begin{aligned} T_0 &= (18.0 + 273)\text{K} = 291\ \text{K} \\ T_\text{f} &= (35.0 + 273)\text{K} = 308\ \text{K} \end{aligned} \qquad 13.23$$

2. Substitute the known values into the equation.

$$P_\text{f} = P_0\frac{T_\text{f}}{T_0} = 7.00 \times 10^5\ \text{Pa}\left(\frac{308\ \text{K}}{291\ \text{K}}\right) = 7.41 \times 10^5\ \text{Pa} \qquad 13.24$$

Discussion

The final temperature is about 6% greater than the original temperature, so the final pressure is about 6% greater as well. Note that *absolute* pressure and *absolute* temperature must be used in the ideal gas law.

MAKING CONNECTIONS: TAKE-HOME EXPERIMENT—REFRIGERATING A BALLOON

Inflate a balloon at room temperature. Leave the inflated balloon in the refrigerator overnight. What happens to the balloon, and why?

EXAMPLE 13.7

Calculating the Number of Molecules in a Cubic Meter of Gas

How many molecules are in a typical object, such as gas in a tire or water in a drink? We can use the ideal gas law to give us an idea of how large N typically is.

Calculate the number of molecules in a cubic meter of gas at standard temperature and pressure (STP), which is defined to be 0°C and atmospheric pressure.

Strategy

Because pressure, volume, and temperature are all specified, we can use the ideal gas law $PV = NkT$, to find N.

Solution

1. Identify the knowns.

$$\begin{aligned} T &= 0^\circ\text{C} = 273\ \text{K} \\ P &= 1.01 \times 10^5\ \text{Pa} \\ V &= 1.00\ \text{m}^3 \\ k &= 1.38 \times 10^{-23}\ \text{J/K} \end{aligned} \tag{13.25}$$

2. Identify the unknown: number of molecules, N.

3. Rearrange the ideal gas law to solve for N.

$$\begin{aligned} PV &= NkT \\ N &= \tfrac{PV}{kT} \end{aligned} \tag{13.26}$$

4. Substitute the known values into the equation and solve for N.

$$N = \frac{PV}{kT} = \frac{\left(1.01 \times 10^5\ \text{Pa}\right)\left(1.00\ \text{m}^3\right)}{\left(1.38 \times 10^{-23}\ \text{J/K}\right)(273\ \text{K})} = 2.68 \times 10^{25}\ \text{molecules} \tag{13.27}$$

Discussion

This number is undeniably large, considering that a gas is mostly empty space. N is huge, even in small volumes. For example, $1\ \text{cm}^3$ of a gas at STP has 2.68×10^{19} molecules in it. Once again, note that N is the same for all types or mixtures of gases.

Moles and Avogadro's Number

It is sometimes convenient to work with a unit other than molecules when measuring the amount of substance. A **mole** (abbreviated mol) is defined to be the amount of a substance that contains as many atoms or molecules as there are atoms in exactly 12 grams (0.012 kg) of carbon-12. The actual number of atoms or molecules in one mole is called **Avogadro's number**(N_A), in recognition of Italian scientist Amedeo Avogadro (1776–1856). He developed the concept of the mole, based on the hypothesis that equal volumes of gas, at the same pressure and temperature, contain equal numbers of molecules. That is, the number is independent of the type of gas. This hypothesis has been confirmed, and the value of Avogadro's number is

$$N_\text{A} = 6.02 \times 10^{23}\ \text{mol}^{-1}. \tag{13.28}$$

AVOGADRO'S NUMBER

One mole always contains 6.02×10^{23} particles (atoms or molecules), independent of the element or substance. A mole of any substance has a mass in grams equal to its molecular mass, which can be calculated from the atomic masses given in the periodic table of elements.

$$N_A = 6.02 \times 10^{23}\ \text{mol}^{-1} \quad (13.29)$$

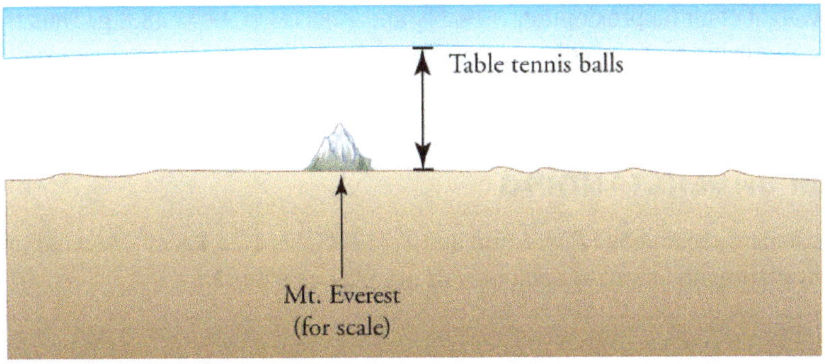

FIGURE 13.19 How big is a mole? On a macroscopic level, one mole of table tennis balls would cover the Earth to a depth of about 40 km.

CHECK YOUR UNDERSTANDING

The active ingredient in a Tylenol pill is 325 mg of acetaminophen ($C_8H_9NO_2$). Find the number of active molecules of acetaminophen in a single pill.

Solution

We first need to calculate the molar mass (the mass of one mole) of acetaminophen. To do this, we need to multiply the number of atoms of each element by the element's atomic mass.

$$\begin{aligned}&(8\text{ moles of carbon})(12\text{ grams/mole}) + (9\text{ moles hydrogen})(1\text{ gram/mole})\\&+(1\text{ mole nitrogen})(14\text{ grams/mole}) + (2\text{ moles oxygen})(16\text{ grams/mole}) = 151\text{ g}\end{aligned} \quad (13.30)$$

Then we need to calculate the number of moles in 325 mg.

$$\left(\frac{325\text{ mg}}{151\text{ grams/mole}}\right)\left(\frac{1\text{ gram}}{1000\text{ mg}}\right) = 2.15 \times 10^{-3}\text{ moles} \quad (13.31)$$

Then use Avogadro's number to calculate the number of molecules.

$$N = \left(2.15 \times 10^{-3}\text{ moles}\right)\left(6.02 \times 10^{23}\text{ molecules/mole}\right) = 1.30 \times 10^{21}\text{ molecules} \quad (13.32)$$

EXAMPLE 13.8

Calculating Moles per Cubic Meter and Liters per Mole

Calculate: (a) the number of moles in $1.00\ \text{m}^3$ of gas at STP, and (b) the number of liters of gas per mole.

Strategy and Solution

(a) We are asked to find the number of moles per cubic meter, and we know from Example 13.7 that the number of molecules per cubic meter at STP is 2.68×10^{25}. The number of moles can be found by dividing the number of molecules by Avogadro's number. We let n stand for the number of moles,

$$n\text{ mol/m}^3 = \frac{N\text{ molecules/m}^3}{6.02 \times 10^{23}\text{ molecules/mol}} = \frac{2.68 \times 10^{25}\text{ molecules/m}^3}{6.02 \times 10^{23}\text{ molecules/mol}} = 44.5\text{ mol/m}^3. \quad (13.33)$$

(b) Using the value obtained for the number of moles in a cubic meter, and converting cubic meters to liters, we obtain

$$\frac{\left(10^3\text{ L/m}^3\right)}{44.5\text{ mol/m}^3} = 22.5\text{ L/mol}. \quad (13.34)$$

Discussion

This value is very close to the accepted value of 22.4 L/mol. The slight difference is due to rounding errors caused by using three-digit input. Again this number is the same for all gases. In other words, it is independent of the gas.

The (average) molar weight of air (approximately 80% N_2 and 20% O_2 is $M = 28.8\text{ g}$. Thus the mass of one cubic meter of air is 1.28 kg. If a living room has dimensions $5\text{ m} \times 5\text{ m} \times 3\text{ m}$, the mass of air inside the room is 96 kg, which is the typical mass of a human.

CHECK YOUR UNDERSTANDING

The density of air at standard conditions ($P = 1\text{ atm}$ and $T = 20^{\circ}\text{C}$) is 1.28 kg/m^3. At what pressure is the density 0.64 kg/m^3 if the temperature and number of molecules are kept constant?

Solution

The best way to approach this question is to think about what is happening. If the density drops to half its original value and no molecules are lost, then the volume must double. If we look at the equation $PV = NkT$, we see that when the temperature is constant, the pressure is inversely proportional to volume. Therefore, if the volume doubles, the pressure must drop to half its original value, and $P_{\text{f}} = 0.50\text{ atm}$.

The Ideal Gas Law Restated Using Moles

A very common expression of the ideal gas law uses the number of moles, n, rather than the number of atoms and molecules, N. We start from the ideal gas law,

$$PV = NkT, \tag{13.35}$$

and multiply and divide the equation by Avogadro's number N_{A}. This gives

$$PV = \frac{N}{N_{\text{A}}} N_{\text{A}} kT. \tag{13.36}$$

Note that $n = N/N_{\text{A}}$ is the number of moles. We define the universal gas constant $R = N_{\text{A}}k$, and obtain the ideal gas law in terms of moles.

IDEAL GAS LAW (IN TERMS OF MOLES)

The ideal gas law (in terms of moles) is

$$PV = nRT. \tag{13.37}$$

The numerical value of R in SI units is

$$R = N_{\text{A}}k = \left(6.02 \times 10^{23}\text{ mol}^{-1}\right)\left(1.38 \times 10^{-23}\text{ J/K}\right) = 8.31\text{ J/mol}\cdot\text{K}. \tag{13.38}$$

In other units,

$$\begin{aligned} R &= 1.99\text{ cal/mol}\cdot\text{K} \\ R &= 0.0821\text{ L}\cdot\text{atm/mol}\cdot\text{K}. \end{aligned} \tag{13.39}$$

You can use whichever value of R is most convenient for a particular problem.

EXAMPLE 13.9

Calculating Number of Moles: Gas in a Bike Tire

How many moles of gas are in a bike tire with a volume of $2.00 \times 10^{-3}\text{ m}^3 (2.00\text{ L})$, a pressure of $7.00 \times 10^5\text{ Pa}$ (a gauge pressure of just under 90.0 lb/in^2), and at a temperature of 18.0°C?

Strategy

Identify the knowns and unknowns, and choose an equation to solve for the unknown. In this case, we solve the ideal gas law, $PV = nRT$, for the number of moles n.

Solution

1. Identify the knowns.

$$\begin{aligned} P &= 7.00 \times 10^5 \text{ Pa} \\ V &= 2.00 \times 10^{-3} \text{ m}^3 \\ T &= 18.0^\circ\text{C} = 291 \text{ K} \\ R &= 8.31 \text{ J/mol} \cdot \text{K} \end{aligned} \tag{13.40}$$

2. Rearrange the equation to solve for n and substitute known values.

$$\begin{aligned} n &= \frac{PV}{RT} = \frac{\left(7.00 \times 10^5 \text{ Pa}\right)\left(2.00 \times 10^{-3} \text{ m}^3\right)}{(8.31 \text{ J/mol} \cdot \text{K})(291 \text{ K})} \\ &= 0.579 \text{ mol} \end{aligned} \tag{13.41}$$

Discussion

The most convenient choice for R in this case is $8.31 \text{ J/mol} \cdot \text{K}$, because our known quantities are in SI units. The pressure and temperature are obtained from the initial conditions in Example 13.6, but we would get the same answer if we used the final values.

The ideal gas law can be considered to be another manifestation of the law of conservation of energy (see Conservation of Energy). Work done on a gas results in an increase in its energy, increasing pressure and/or temperature, or decreasing volume. This increased energy can also be viewed as increased internal kinetic energy, given the gas's atoms and molecules.

The Ideal Gas Law and Energy

Let us now examine the role of energy in the behavior of gases. When you inflate a bike tire by hand, you do work by repeatedly exerting a force through a distance. This energy goes into increasing the pressure of air inside the tire and increasing the temperature of the pump and the air.

The ideal gas law is closely related to energy: the units on both sides are joules. The right-hand side of the ideal gas law in $PV = NkT$ is NkT. This term is roughly the amount of translational kinetic energy of N atoms or molecules at an absolute temperature T, as we shall see formally in Kinetic Theory: Atomic and Molecular Explanation of Pressure and Temperature. The left-hand side of the ideal gas law is PV, which also has the units of joules. We know from our study of fluids that pressure is one type of potential energy per unit volume, so pressure multiplied by volume is energy. The important point is that there is energy in a gas related to both its pressure and its volume. The energy can be changed when the gas is doing work as it expands—something we explore in Heat and Heat Transfer Methods—similar to what occurs in gasoline or steam engines and turbines.

PROBLEM-SOLVING STRATEGY: THE IDEAL GAS LAW

Step 1 Examine the situation to determine that an ideal gas is involved. Most gases are nearly ideal.

Step 2 Make a list of what quantities are given, or can be inferred from the problem as stated (identify the known quantities). Convert known values into proper SI units (K for temperature, Pa for pressure, m^3 for volume, molecules for N, and moles for n).

Step 3 Identify exactly what needs to be determined in the problem (identify the unknown quantities). A written list is useful.

Step 4 Determine whether the number of molecules or the number of moles is known, in order to decide which form of the ideal gas law to use. The first form is $PV = NkT$ and involves N, the number of atoms or molecules. The second form is $PV = nRT$ and involves n, the number of moles.

Step 5 Solve the ideal gas law for the quantity to be determined (the unknown quantity). You may need to take a ratio of final states to initial states to eliminate the unknown quantities that are kept fixed.

Step 6 Substitute the known quantities, along with their units, into the appropriate equation, and obtain numerical solutions complete with units. Be certain to use absolute temperature and absolute pressure.

Step 7 Check the answer to see if it is reasonable: Does it make sense?

CHECK YOUR UNDERSTANDING

Liquids and solids have densities about 1000 times greater than gases. Explain how this implies that the distances between atoms and molecules in gases are about 10 times greater than the size of their atoms and molecules.

Solution
Atoms and molecules are close together in solids and liquids. In gases they are separated by empty space. Thus gases have lower densities than liquids and solids. Density is mass per unit volume, and volume is related to the size of a body (such as a sphere) cubed. So if the distance between atoms and molecules increases by a factor of 10, then the volume occupied increases by a factor of 1000, and the density decreases by a factor of 1000.

13.4 Kinetic Theory: Atomic and Molecular Explanation of Pressure and Temperature

LEARNING OBJECTIVES

By the end of this section, you will be able to:

- Express the ideal gas law in terms of molecular mass and velocity.
- Define thermal energy.
- Calculate the kinetic energy of a gas molecule, given its temperature.
- Describe the relationship between the temperature of a gas and the kinetic energy of atoms and molecules.
- Describe the distribution of speeds of molecules in a gas.

We have developed macroscopic definitions of pressure and temperature. Pressure is the force divided by the area on which the force is exerted, and temperature is measured with a thermometer. We gain a better understanding of pressure and temperature from the kinetic theory of gases, which assumes that atoms and molecules are in continuous random motion.

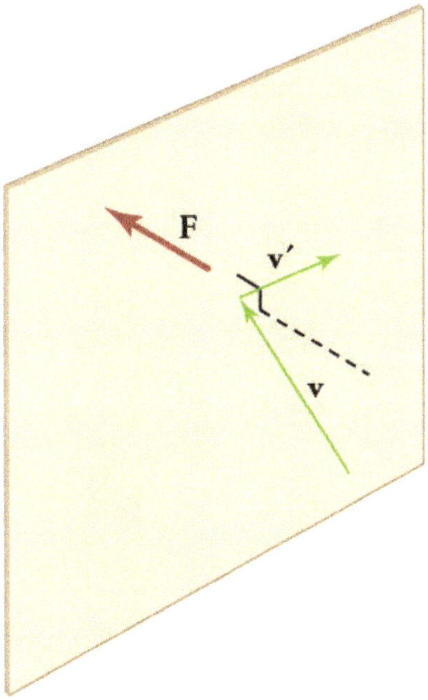

FIGURE 13.20 When a molecule collides with a rigid wall, the component of its momentum perpendicular to the wall is reversed. A force is thus exerted on the wall, creating pressure.

Figure 13.20 shows an elastic collision of a gas molecule with the wall of a container, so that it exerts a force on the wall (by Newton's third law). Because a huge number of molecules will collide with the wall in a short time, we observe an average force per unit area. These collisions are the source of pressure in a gas. As the number of molecules increases, the number of collisions and thus the pressure increase. Similarly, the gas pressure is higher if the average velocity of molecules is higher. The actual relationship is derived in the Things Great and Small feature below. The following relationship is found:

$$PV = \frac{1}{3}Nm\overline{v}^2, \tag{13.42}$$

where P is the pressure (average force per unit area), V is the volume of gas in the container, N is the number of molecules in the container, m is the mass of a molecule, and $\overline{v}^2$ is the average of the molecular speed squared.

What can we learn from this atomic and molecular version of the ideal gas law? We can derive a relationship between temperature and the average translational kinetic energy of molecules in a gas. Recall the previous expression of the ideal gas law:

$$PV = NkT. \tag{13.43}$$

Equating the right-hand side of this equation with the right-hand side of $PV = \frac{1}{3}Nm\overline{v}^2$ gives

$$\frac{1}{3}Nm\overline{v}^2 = NkT. \tag{13.44}$$

MAKING CONNECTIONS: THINGS GREAT AND SMALL—ATOMIC AND MOLECULAR ORIGIN OF PRESSURE IN A GAS

Figure 13.21 shows a box filled with a gas. We know from our previous discussions that putting more gas into the box produces greater pressure, and that increasing the temperature of the gas also produces a greater pressure. But why should increasing the temperature of the gas increase the pressure in the box? A look at the atomic and molecular scale gives us some answers, and an alternative expression for the ideal gas law.

The figure shows an expanded view of an elastic collision of a gas molecule with the wall of a container. Calculating the average force exerted by such molecules will lead us to the ideal gas law, and to the connection between temperature and molecular kinetic energy. We assume that a molecule is small compared with the separation of molecules in the gas, and that its interaction with other molecules can be ignored. We also assume the wall is rigid and that the molecule's direction changes, but that its speed remains constant (and hence its kinetic energy and the magnitude of its momentum remain constant as well). This assumption is not always valid, but the same result is obtained with a more detailed description of the molecule's exchange of energy and momentum with the wall.

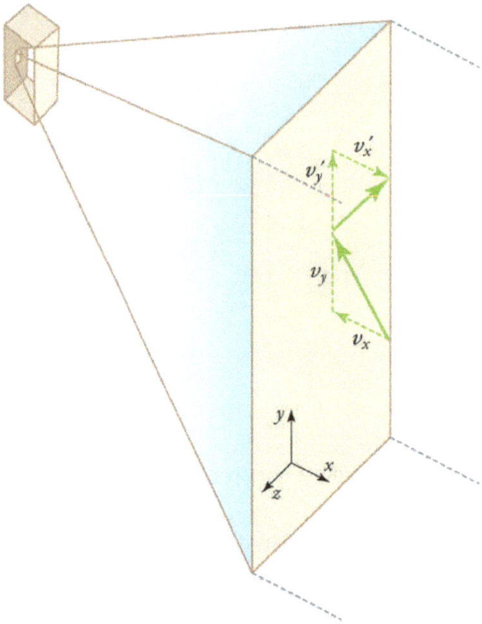

FIGURE 13.21 Gas in a box exerts an outward pressure on its walls. A molecule colliding with a rigid wall has the direction of its velocity and momentum in the x-direction reversed. This direction is perpendicular to the wall. The components of its velocity momentum in the y- and z-directions are not changed, which means there is no force parallel to the wall.

If the molecule's velocity changes in the x-direction, its momentum changes from $-mv_x$ to $+mv_x$. Thus, its change in momentum is $\Delta mv = +mv_x-(-mv_x)= 2mv_x$. The force exerted on the molecule is given by

$$F = \frac{\Delta p}{\Delta t} = \frac{2mv_x}{\Delta t}. \qquad 13.45$$

There is no force between the wall and the molecule until the molecule hits the wall. During the short time of the collision, the force between the molecule and wall is relatively large. We are looking for an average force; we take Δt to be the average time between collisions of the molecule with this wall. It is the time it would take the molecule to go across the box and back (a distance $2l$) at a speed of v_x. Thus $\Delta t = 2l/v_x$, and the expression for the force becomes

$$F = \frac{2mv_x}{2l/v_x} = \frac{mv_x^2}{l}. \qquad 13.46$$

This force is due to *one* molecule. We multiply by the number of molecules N and use their average squared velocity to find the force

$$F = N\frac{m\overline{v_x^2}}{l}, \qquad 13.47$$

where the bar over a quantity means its average value. We would like to have the force in terms of the speed v, rather than the x-component of the velocity. We note that the total velocity squared is the sum of the squares of its components, so that

$$\overline{v^2} = \overline{v_x^2} + \overline{v_y^2} + \overline{v_z^2}. \qquad 13.48$$

Because the velocities are random, their average components in all directions are the same:

$$\overline{v_x^2} = \overline{v_y^2} = \overline{v_z^2}. \tag{13.49}$$

Thus,

$$\overline{v^2} = 3\overline{v_x^2}, \tag{13.50}$$

or

$$\overline{v_x^2} = \frac{1}{3}\overline{v^2}. \tag{13.51}$$

Substituting $\frac{1}{3}\overline{v^2}$ into the expression for F gives

$$F = N\frac{m\overline{v^2}}{3l}. \tag{13.52}$$

The pressure is F/A, so that we obtain

$$P = \frac{F}{A} = N\frac{m\overline{v^2}}{3Al} = \frac{1}{3}\frac{Nm\overline{v^2}}{V}, \tag{13.53}$$

where we used $V = Al$ for the volume. This gives the important result.

$$PV = \frac{1}{3}Nm\overline{v^2} \tag{13.54}$$

This equation is another expression of the ideal gas law.

We can get the average kinetic energy of a molecule, $\frac{1}{2}m\overline{v^2}$, from the right-hand side of the equation by canceling N and multiplying by 3/2. This calculation produces the result that the average kinetic energy of a molecule is directly related to absolute temperature.

$$\overline{\text{KE}} = \frac{1}{2}m\overline{v^2} = \frac{3}{2}kT \tag{13.55}$$

The average translational kinetic energy of a molecule, $\overline{\text{KE}}$, is called **thermal energy.** The equation $\overline{\text{KE}} = \frac{1}{2}m\overline{v^2} = \frac{3}{2}kT$ is a molecular interpretation of temperature, and it has been found to be valid for gases and reasonably accurate in liquids and solids. It is another definition of temperature based on an expression of the molecular energy.

It is sometimes useful to rearrange $\overline{\text{KE}} = \frac{1}{2}m\overline{v^2} = \frac{3}{2}kT$, and solve for the average speed of molecules in a gas in terms of temperature,

$$\sqrt{\overline{v^2}} = v_{\text{rms}} = \sqrt{\frac{3kT}{m}}, \tag{13.56}$$

where v_{rms} stands for root-mean-square (rms) speed.

EXAMPLE 13.10

Calculating Kinetic Energy and Speed of a Gas Molecule

(a) What is the average kinetic energy of a gas molecule at 20.0ºC (room temperature)? (b) Find the rms speed of a nitrogen molecule (N_2) at this temperature.

Strategy for (a)

The known in the equation for the average kinetic energy is the temperature.

$$\overline{\text{KE}} = \frac{1}{2}m\overline{v^2} = \frac{3}{2}kT \tag{13.57}$$

Before substituting values into this equation, we must convert the given temperature to kelvins. This conversion gives $T = (20.0 + 273)\text{ K} = 293\text{ K}$.

Solution for (a)

The temperature alone is sufficient to find the average translational kinetic energy. Substituting the temperature into the translational kinetic energy equation gives

$$\overline{\text{KE}} = \frac{3}{2}kT = \frac{3}{2}\left(1.38 \times 10^{-23}\text{ J/K}\right)(293\text{ K}) = 6.07 \times 10^{-21}\text{ J}. \tag{13.58}$$

Strategy for (b)

Finding the rms speed of a nitrogen molecule involves a straightforward calculation using the equation

$$\sqrt{\overline{v^2}} = v_{\text{rms}} = \sqrt{\frac{3kT}{m}}, \tag{13.59}$$

but we must first find the mass of a nitrogen molecule. Using the molecular mass of nitrogen N_2 from the periodic table,

$$m = \frac{2(14.0067)\times 10^{-3}\text{ kg/mol}}{6.02 \times 10^{23}\text{ mol}^{-1}} = 4.65 \times 10^{-26}\text{ kg}. \tag{13.60}$$

Solution for (b)

Substituting this mass and the value for k into the equation for v_{rms} yields

$$v_{\text{rms}} = \sqrt{\frac{3kT}{m}} = \sqrt{\frac{3\left(1.38 \times 10^{-23}\text{ J/K}\right)(293\text{ K})}{4.65 \times 10^{-26}\text{ kg}}} = 511\text{ m/s}. \tag{13.61}$$

Discussion

Note that the average kinetic energy of the molecule is independent of the type of molecule. The average translational kinetic energy depends only on absolute temperature. The kinetic energy is very small compared to macroscopic energies, so that we do not feel when an air molecule is hitting our skin. The rms velocity of the nitrogen molecule is surprisingly large. These large molecular velocities do not yield macroscopic movement of air, since the molecules move in all directions with equal likelihood. The *mean free path* (the distance a molecule can move on average between collisions) of molecules in air is very small, and so the molecules move rapidly but do not get very far in a second. The high value for rms speed is reflected in the speed of sound, however, which is about 340 m/s at room temperature. The faster the rms speed of air molecules, the faster that sound vibrations can be transferred through the air. The speed of sound increases with temperature and is greater in gases with small molecular masses, such as helium. (See Figure 13.22.)

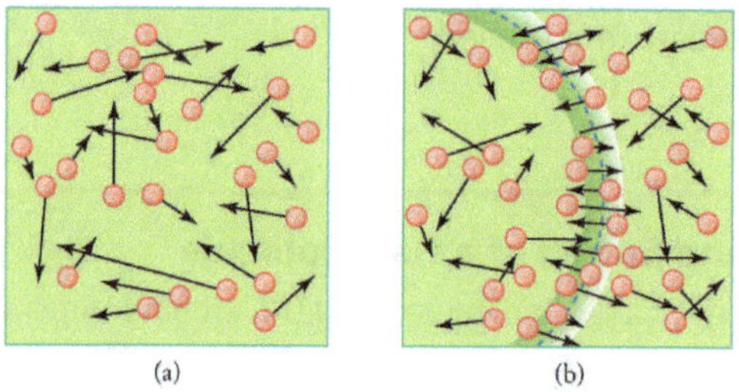

FIGURE 13.22 (a) There are many molecules moving so fast in an ordinary gas that they collide a billion times every second. (b) Individual molecules do not move very far in a small amount of time, but disturbances like sound waves are transmitted at speeds related to the molecular speeds.

MAKING CONNECTIONS: HISTORICAL NOTE—KINETIC THEORY OF GASES

The kinetic theory of gases was developed by Daniel Bernoulli (1700–1782), who is best known in physics for his work on fluid flow (hydrodynamics). Bernoulli's work predates the atomistic view of matter established by Dalton.

Distribution of Molecular Speeds

The motion of molecules in a gas is random in magnitude and direction for individual molecules, but a gas of many molecules has a predictable distribution of molecular speeds. This distribution is called the *Maxwell-Boltzmann distribution*, after its originators, who calculated it based on kinetic theory, and has since been confirmed experimentally. (See Figure 13.23.) The distribution has a long tail, because a few molecules may go several times the rms speed. The most probable speed v_p is less than the rms speed v_{rms}. Figure 13.24 shows that the curve is shifted to higher speeds at higher temperatures, with a broader range of speeds.

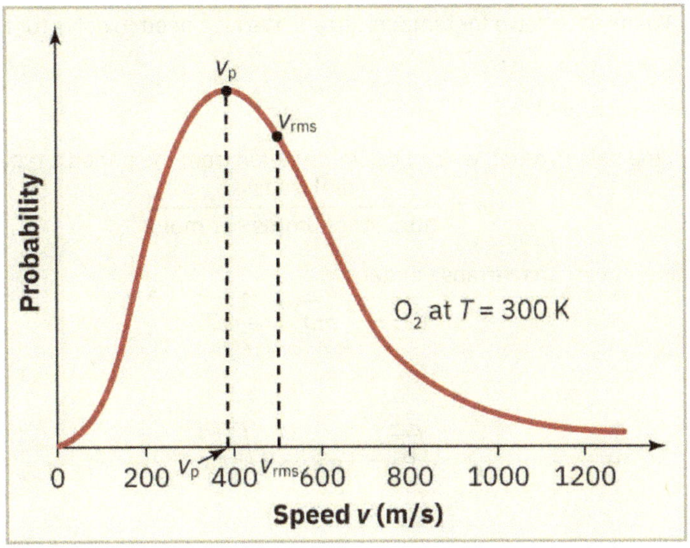

FIGURE 13.23 The Maxwell-Boltzmann distribution of molecular speeds in an ideal gas. The most likely speed v_p is less than the rms speed v_{rms}. Although very high speeds are possible, only a tiny fraction of the molecules have speeds that are an order of magnitude greater than v_{rms}.

The distribution of thermal speeds depends strongly on temperature. As temperature increases, the speeds are shifted to higher values and the distribution is broadened.

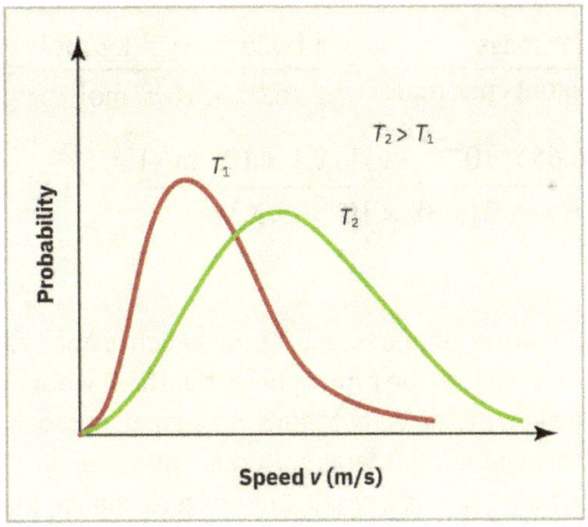

FIGURE 13.24 The Maxwell-Boltzmann distribution is shifted to higher speeds and is broadened at higher temperatures.

What is the implication of the change in distribution with temperature shown in Figure 13.24 for humans? All other things being equal, if a person has a fever, they are likely to lose more water molecules, particularly from linings along moist cavities such as the lungs and mouth, creating a dry sensation in the mouth.

EXAMPLE 13.11

Calculating Temperature: Escape Velocity of Helium Atoms

In order to escape Earth's gravity, an object near the top of the atmosphere (at an altitude of 100 km) must travel away from Earth at 11.1 km/s. This speed is called the *escape velocity*. At what temperature would helium atoms have an rms speed equal to the escape velocity?

Strategy

Identify the knowns and unknowns and determine which equations to use to solve the problem.

Solution

1. Identify the knowns: v is the escape velocity, 11.1 km/s.

2. Identify the unknowns: We need to solve for temperature, T. We also need to solve for the mass m of the helium atom.

3. Determine which equations are needed.

- To solve for mass m of the helium atom, we can use information from the periodic table:

$$m = \frac{\text{molar mass}}{\text{number of atoms per mole}}. \tag{13.62}$$

- To solve for temperature T, we can rearrange either

$$\overline{\text{KE}} = \frac{1}{2}m\overline{v^2} = \frac{3}{2}kT \tag{13.63}$$

or

$$\sqrt{\overline{v^2}} = v_{\text{rms}} = \sqrt{\frac{3kT}{m}} \tag{13.64}$$

to yield

$$T = \frac{m\overline{v^2}}{3k}, \tag{13.65}$$

where k is the Boltzmann constant and m is the mass of a helium atom.

4. Plug the known values into the equations and solve for the unknowns.

$$m = \frac{\text{molar mass}}{\text{number of atoms per mole}} = \frac{4.0026 \times 10^{-3}\ \text{kg/mol}}{6.02 \times 10^{23}\ \text{mol}} = 6.65 \times 10^{-27}\ \text{kg} \tag{13.66}$$

$$T = \frac{\left(6.65 \times 10^{-27}\ \text{kg}\right)\left(11.1 \times 10^{3}\ \text{m/s}\right)^2}{3\left(1.38 \times 10^{-23}\ \text{J/K}\right)} = 1.98 \times 10^{4}\ \text{K} \tag{13.67}$$

Discussion

This temperature is much higher than atmospheric temperature, which is approximately 250 K (–25ºC or –10ºF) at high altitude. Very few helium atoms are left in the atmosphere, but there were many when the atmosphere was formed. The reason for the loss of helium atoms is that there are a small number of helium atoms with speeds higher than Earth's escape velocity even at normal temperatures. The speed of a helium atom changes from one instant to the next, so that at any instant, there is a small, but nonzero chance that the speed is greater than the escape speed and the molecule escapes from Earth's gravitational pull. Heavier molecules, such as oxygen, nitrogen, and water (very little of which reach a very high altitude), have smaller rms speeds, and so it is much less likely that any of them will have speeds greater than the escape velocity. In fact, so few have speeds above the escape velocity that billions of years are required to lose significant amounts of the atmosphere. Figure 13.25 shows the impact of a lack of an atmosphere on the Moon. Because the gravitational pull of the Moon is much weaker, it has lost almost its entire atmosphere. The comparison between Earth and the Moon is discussed in this chapter's Problems and Exercises.

FIGURE 13.25 This photograph of Apollo 17 Commander Eugene Cernan driving the lunar rover on the Moon in 1972 looks as though it was taken at night with a large spotlight. In fact, the light is coming from the Sun. Because the acceleration due to gravity on the Moon is so low (about 1/6 that of Earth), the Moon's escape velocity is much smaller. As a result, gas molecules escape very easily from the Moon, leaving it with virtually no atmosphere. Even during the daytime, the sky is black because there is no gas to scatter sunlight. (credit: Harrison H. Schmitt/NASA)

CHECK YOUR UNDERSTANDING

If you consider a very small object such as a grain of pollen, in a gas, then the number of atoms and molecules striking its surface would also be relatively small. Would the grain of pollen experience any fluctuations in pressure due to statistical fluctuations in the number of gas atoms and molecules striking it in a given amount of time?

Solution

Yes. Such fluctuations actually occur for a body of any size in a gas, but since the numbers of atoms and molecules are immense for macroscopic bodies, the fluctuations are a tiny percentage of the number of collisions, and the averages spoken of in this section vary imperceptibly. Roughly speaking the fluctuations are proportional to the inverse square root of the number of collisions, so for small bodies they can become significant. This was actually observed in the 19th century for pollen grains in water, and is known as the Brownian effect.

PHET EXPLORATIONS

Gas Properties

Pump gas molecules into a box and see what happens as you change the volume, add or remove heat, change gravity, and more. Measure the temperature and pressure, and discover how the properties of the gas vary in relation to each other.

Click to view content (https://openstax.org/books/college-physics-ap-courses-2e/pages/13-4-kinetic-theory-atomic-and-molecular-explanation-of-pressure-and-temperature)

PhET

13.5 Phase Changes

LEARNING OBJECTIVES

By the end of this section, you will be able to:

- Interpret a phase diagram.
- State Dalton's law.
- Identify and describe the triple point of a gas from its phase diagram.
- Describe the state of equilibrium between a liquid and a gas, a liquid and a solid, and a gas and a solid.

Up to now, we have considered the behavior of ideal gases. Real gases are like ideal gases at high temperatures. At lower temperatures, however, the interactions between the molecules and their volumes cannot be ignored. The molecules are very close (condensation occurs) and there is a dramatic decrease in volume, as seen in Figure 13.26. The substance changes from a gas to a liquid. When a liquid is cooled to even lower temperatures, it becomes a solid. The volume never reaches zero because of the finite volume of the molecules.

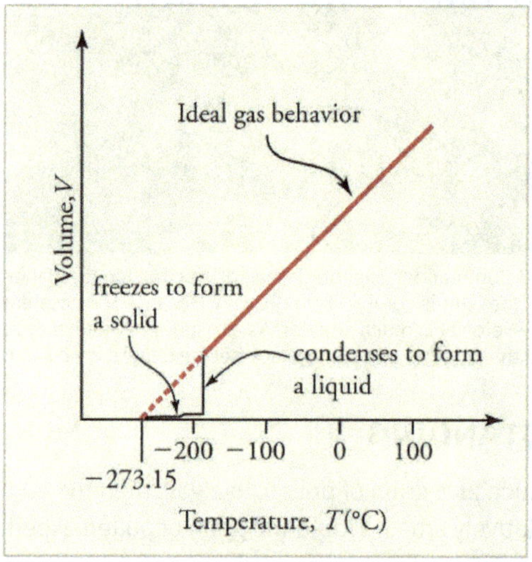

FIGURE 13.26 A sketch of volume versus temperature for a real gas at constant pressure. The linear (straight line) part of the graph represents ideal gas behavior—volume and temperature are directly and positively related and the line extrapolates to zero volume at $-273.15°C$, or absolute zero. When the gas becomes a liquid, however, the volume actually decreases precipitously at the liquefaction point. The volume decreases slightly once the substance is solid, but it never becomes zero.

High pressure may also cause a gas to change phase to a liquid. Carbon dioxide, for example, is a gas at room temperature and atmospheric pressure, but becomes a liquid under sufficiently high pressure. If the pressure is reduced, the temperature drops and the liquid carbon dioxide solidifies into a snow-like substance at the temperature $-78°C$. Solid CO_2 is called "dry ice." Another example of a gas that can be in a liquid phase is liquid nitrogen (LN_2). LN_2 is made by liquefaction of atmospheric air (through compression and cooling). It boils at 77 K $(-196°C)$ at atmospheric pressure. LN_2 is useful as a refrigerant and allows for the preservation of blood, sperm, and other biological materials. It is also used to reduce noise in electronic sensors and equipment, and to help cool down their current-carrying wires. In dermatology, LN_2 is used to freeze and painlessly remove warts and other growths from the skin.

PV Diagrams

We can examine aspects of the behavior of a substance by plotting a graph of pressure versus volume, called a ***PV* diagram**. When the substance behaves like an ideal gas, the ideal gas law describes the relationship between its pressure and volume. That is,

$$PV = NkT \text{ (ideal gas).} \quad 13.68$$

Now, assuming the number of molecules and the temperature are fixed,

$$PV = \text{constant (ideal gas, constant temperature).} \quad 13.69$$

For example, the volume of the gas will decrease as the pressure increases. If you plot the relationship $PV = \text{constant}$ on a PV diagram, you find a hyperbola. Figure 13.27 shows a graph of pressure versus volume. The hyperbolas represent ideal-gas behavior at various fixed temperatures, and are called *isotherms*. At lower temperatures, the curves begin to look less like hyperbolas—the gas is not behaving ideally and may even contain liquid. There is a **critical point**—that is, a **critical temperature**—above which liquid cannot exist. At sufficiently high pressure above the critical point, the gas will have the density of a liquid but will not condense. Carbon dioxide, for example, cannot be liquefied at a temperature above $31.0^{\circ}C$. **Critical pressure** is the minimum pressure needed for liquid to exist at the critical temperature. Table 13.3 lists representative critical temperatures and pressures.

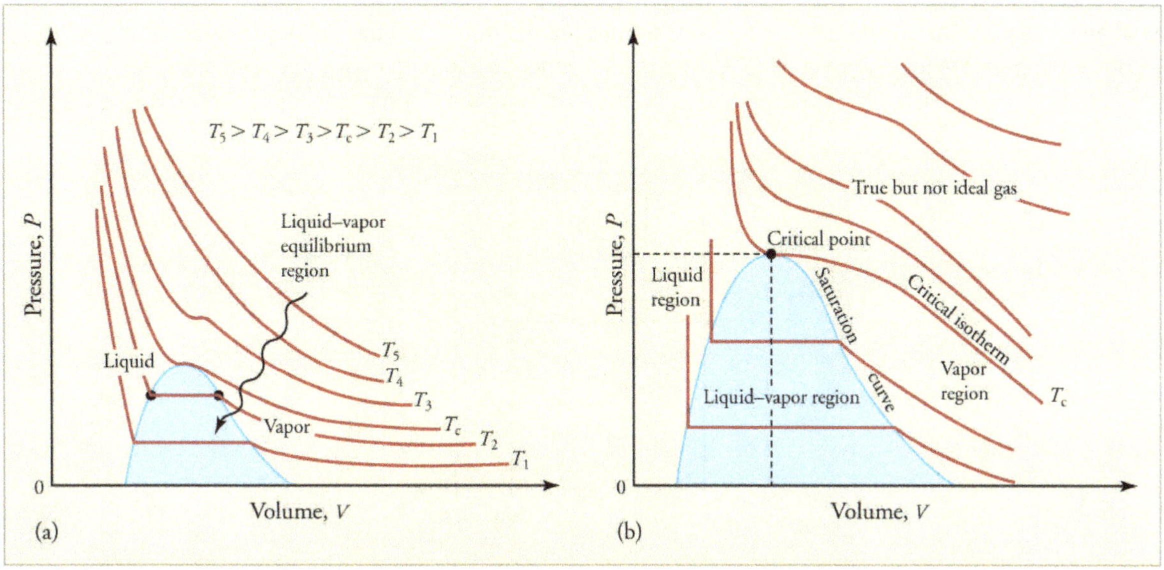

FIGURE 13.27 *PV* diagrams. (a) Each curve (isotherm) represents the relationship between P and V at a fixed temperature; the upper curves are at higher temperatures. The lower curves are not hyperbolas, because the gas is no longer an ideal gas. (b) An expanded portion of the *PV* diagram for low temperatures, where the phase can change from a gas to a liquid. The term "vapor" refers to the gas phase when it exists at a temperature below the boiling temperature.

Substance	Critical temperature		Critical pressure	
	K	°C	Pa	atm
Water	647.4	374.3	22.12×10^6	219.0
Sulfur dioxide	430.7	157.6	7.88×10^6	78.0
Ammonia	405.5	132.4	11.28×10^6	111.7
Carbon dioxide	304.2	31.1	7.39×10^6	73.2
Oxygen	154.8	−118.4	5.08×10^6	50.3
Nitrogen	126.2	−146.9	3.39×10^6	33.6
Hydrogen	33.3	−239.9	1.30×10^6	12.9
Helium	5.3	−267.9	0.229×10^6	2.27

TABLE 13.3 Critical Temperatures and Pressures

Phase Diagrams

The plots of pressure versus temperatures provide considerable insight into thermal properties of substances. There are well-defined regions on these graphs that correspond to various phases of matter, so *PT* graphs are called

phase diagrams. Figure 13.28 shows the phase diagram for water. Using the graph, if you know the pressure and temperature you can determine the phase of water. The solid lines—boundaries between phases—indicate temperatures and pressures at which the phases coexist (that is, they exist together in ratios, depending on pressure and temperature). For example, the boiling point of water is $100^\circ C$ at 1.00 atm. As the pressure increases, the boiling temperature rises steadily to $374^\circ C$ at a pressure of 218 atm. A pressure cooker (or even a covered pot) will cook food faster because the water can exist as a liquid at temperatures greater than $100^\circ C$ without all boiling away. The curve ends at a point called the *critical point*, because at higher temperatures the liquid phase does not exist at any pressure. The critical point occurs at the critical temperature, as you can see for water from Table 13.3. The critical temperature for oxygen is $-118^\circ C$, so oxygen cannot be liquefied above this temperature.

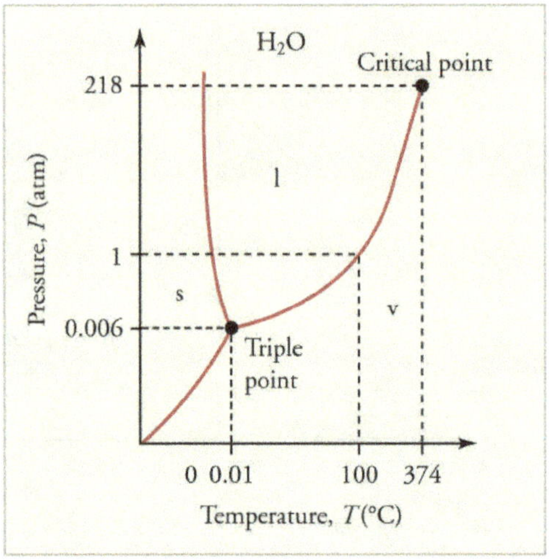

FIGURE 13.28 The phase diagram (PT graph) for water. Note that the axes are nonlinear and the graph is not to scale. This graph is simplified—there are several other exotic phases of ice at higher pressures.

Similarly, the curve between the solid and liquid regions in Figure 13.28 gives the melting temperature at various pressures. For example, the melting point is $0^\circ C$ at 1.00 atm, as expected. Note that, at a fixed temperature, you can change the phase from solid (ice) to liquid (water) by increasing the pressure. Ice melts from pressure in the hands of a snowball maker. From the phase diagram, we can also say that the melting temperature of ice falls with increased pressure. When a car is driven over snow, the increased pressure from the tires melts the snowflakes; afterwards the water refreezes and forms an ice layer.

At sufficiently low pressures there is no liquid phase, but the substance can exist as either gas or solid. For water, there is no liquid phase at pressures below 0.00600 atm. The phase change from solid to gas is called **sublimation**. It accounts for large losses of snow pack that never make it into a river, the routine automatic defrosting of a freezer, and the freeze-drying process applied to many foods. Carbon dioxide, on the other hand, sublimates at standard atmospheric pressure of 1 atm. (The solid form of CO_2 is known as dry ice because it does not melt. Instead, it moves directly from the solid to the gas state.)

All three curves on the phase diagram meet at a single point, the **triple point**, where all three phases exist in equilibrium. For water, the triple point occurs at 273.16 K ($0.01^\circ C$), and is a more accurate calibration temperature than the melting point of water at 1.00 atm, or 273.15 K ($0.0^\circ C$). See Table 13.4 for the triple point values of other substances.

Equilibrium

Liquid and gas phases are in equilibrium at the boiling temperature. (See Figure 13.29.) If a substance is in a closed container at the boiling point, then the liquid is boiling and the gas is condensing at the same rate without net change in their relative amount. Molecules in the liquid escape as a gas at the same rate at which gas molecules stick to the liquid, or form droplets and become part of the liquid phase. The combination of temperature and pressure has to be "just right"; if the temperature and pressure are increased, equilibrium is maintained by the same increase of boiling and condensation rates.

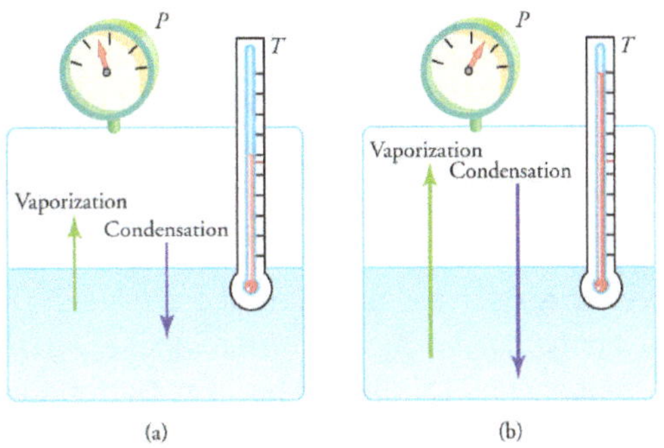

FIGURE 13.29 Equilibrium between liquid and gas at two different boiling points inside a closed container. (a) The rates of boiling and condensation are equal at this combination of temperature and pressure, so the liquid and gas phases are in equilibrium. (b) At a higher temperature, the boiling rate is faster and the rates at which molecules leave the liquid and enter the gas are also faster. Because there are more molecules in the gas, the gas pressure is higher and the rate at which gas molecules condense and enter the liquid is faster. As a result the gas and liquid are in equilibrium at this higher temperature.

Substance	Temperature		Pressure	
	K	°C	Pa	atm
Water	273.16	0.01	6.10×10^2	0.00600
Carbon dioxide	216.55	−56.60	5.16×10^5	5.11
Sulfur dioxide	197.68	−75.47	1.67×10^3	0.0167
Ammonia	195.40	−77.75	6.06×10^3	0.0600
Nitrogen	63.18	−210.0	1.25×10^4	0.124
Oxygen	54.36	−218.8	1.52×10^2	0.00151
Hydrogen	13.84	−259.3	7.04×10^3	0.0697

TABLE 13.4 Triple Point Temperatures and Pressures

One example of equilibrium between liquid and gas is that of water and steam at $100°C$ and 1.00 atm. This temperature is the boiling point at that pressure, so they should exist in equilibrium. Why does an open pot of water at $100°C$ boil completely away? The gas surrounding an open pot is not pure water: it is mixed with air. If pure water and steam are in a closed container at $100°C$ and 1.00 atm, they would coexist—but with air over the pot, there are fewer water molecules to condense, and water boils. What about water at $20.0°C$ and 1.00 atm? This temperature and pressure correspond to the liquid region, yet an open glass of water at this temperature will completely evaporate. Again, the gas around it is air and not pure water vapor, so that the reduced evaporation rate is greater than the condensation rate of water from dry air. If the glass is sealed, then the liquid phase remains. We call the gas phase a **vapor** when it exists, as it does for water at $20.0°C$, at a temperature below the boiling temperature.

CHECK YOUR UNDERSTANDING

Explain why a cup of water (or soda) with ice cubes stays at $0°C$, even on a hot summer day.

Solution

The ice and liquid water are in thermal equilibrium, so that the temperature stays at the freezing temperature as long as ice remains in the liquid. (Once all of the ice melts, the water temperature will start to rise.)

Vapor Pressure, Partial Pressure, and Dalton's Law

Vapor pressure is defined as the pressure at which a gas coexists with its solid or liquid phase. Vapor pressure is created by faster molecules that break away from the liquid or solid and enter the gas phase. The vapor pressure of a substance depends on both the substance and its temperature—an increase in temperature increases the vapor pressure.

Partial pressure is defined as the pressure a gas would create if it occupied the total volume available. In a mixture of gases, *the total pressure is the sum of partial pressures of the component gases*, assuming ideal gas behavior and no chemical reactions between the components. This law is known as **Dalton's law of partial pressures**, after the English scientist John Dalton (1766–1844), who proposed it. Dalton's law is based on kinetic theory, where each gas creates its pressure by molecular collisions, independent of other gases present. It is consistent with the fact that pressures add according to Pascal's Principle. Thus water evaporates and ice sublimates when their vapor pressures exceed the partial pressure of water vapor in the surrounding mixture of gases. If their vapor pressures are less than the partial pressure of water vapor in the surrounding gas, liquid droplets or ice crystals (frost) form.

CHECK YOUR UNDERSTANDING

Is energy transfer involved in a phase change? If so, will energy have to be supplied to change phase from solid to liquid and liquid to gas? What about gas to liquid and liquid to solid? Why do they spray the orange trees with water in Florida when the temperatures are near or just below freezing?

Solution

Yes, energy transfer is involved in a phase change. We know that atoms and molecules in solids and liquids are bound to each other because we know that force is required to separate them. So in a phase change from solid to liquid and liquid to gas, a force must be exerted, perhaps by collision, to separate atoms and molecules. Force exerted through a distance is work, and energy is needed to do work to go from solid to liquid and liquid to gas. This is intuitively consistent with the need for energy to melt ice or boil water. The converse is also true. Going from gas to liquid or liquid to solid involves atoms and molecules pushing together, doing work and releasing energy.

PHET EXPLORATIONS

States of Matter—Basics

Heat, cool, and compress atoms and molecules and watch as they change between solid, liquid, and gas phases.

Click to view content (https://openstax.org/books/college-physics-ap-courses-2e/pages/13-5-phase-changes)

13.6 Humidity, Evaporation, and Boiling

LEARNING OBJECTIVES

By the end of this section, you will be able to:

- Explain the relationship between vapor pressure of water and the capacity of air to hold water vapor.
- Explain the relationship between relative humidity and partial pressure of water vapor in the air.
- Calculate vapor density using vapor pressure.
- Calculate humidity and dew point.

FIGURE 13.30 Dew drops like these, on a banana leaf photographed just after sunrise, form when the air temperature drops to or below the dew point. At the dew point, the rate at which water molecules join together is greater than the rate at which they separate, and some of the water condenses to form droplets. (credit: Aaron Escobar, Flickr)

The expression "it's not the heat, it's the humidity" makes a valid point. We keep cool in hot weather by evaporating sweat from our skin and water from our breathing passages. Because evaporation is inhibited by high humidity, we feel hotter at a given temperature when the humidity is high. Low humidity, on the other hand, can cause discomfort from excessive drying of mucous membranes and can lead to an increased risk of respiratory infections.

When we say humidity, we really mean **relative humidity**. Relative humidity tells us how much water vapor is in the air compared with the maximum possible. At its maximum, denoted as **saturation**, the relative humidity is 100%, and evaporation is inhibited. The amount of water vapor in the air depends on temperature. For example, relative humidity rises in the evening, as air temperature declines, sometimes reaching the **dew point**. At the dew point temperature, relative humidity is 100%, and fog may result from the condensation of water droplets if they are small enough to stay in suspension. Conversely, if you wish to dry something (perhaps your hair), it is more effective to blow hot air over it rather than cold air, because, among other things, the increase in temperature increases the energy of the molecules, so the rate of evaporation increases.

The amount of water vapor in the air depends on the vapor pressure of water. The liquid and solid phases are continuously giving off vapor because some of the molecules have high enough speeds to enter the gas phase; see Figure 13.31(a). If a lid is placed over the container, as in Figure 13.31(b), evaporation continues, increasing the pressure, until sufficient vapor has built up for condensation to balance evaporation. Then equilibrium has been achieved, and the vapor pressure is equal to the partial pressure of water in the container. Vapor pressure increases with temperature because molecular speeds are higher as temperature increases. Table 13.5 gives representative values of water vapor pressure over a range of temperatures.

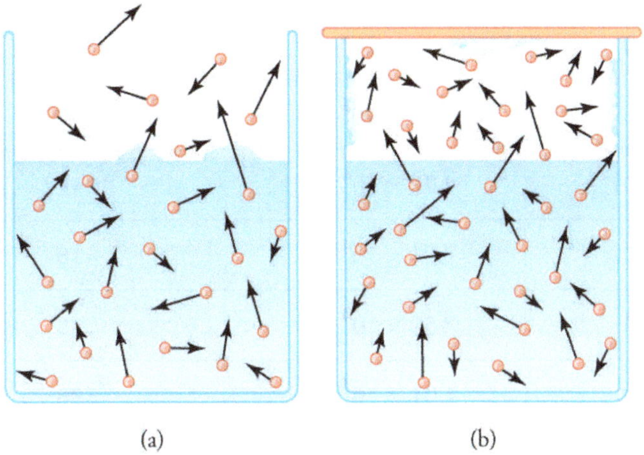

FIGURE 13.31 (a) Because of the distribution of speeds and kinetic energies, some water molecules can break away to the vapor phase even at temperatures below the ordinary boiling point. (b) If the container is sealed, evaporation will continue until there is enough vapor density for the condensation rate to equal the evaporation rate. This vapor density and the partial pressure it creates are the saturation values. They increase with temperature and are independent of the presence of other gases, such as air. They depend only on the vapor pressure of water.

Relative humidity is related to the partial pressure of water vapor in the air. At 100% humidity, the partial pressure is equal to the vapor pressure, and no more water can enter the vapor phase. If the partial pressure is less than the vapor pressure, then evaporation will take place, as humidity is less than 100%. If the partial pressure is greater than the vapor pressure, condensation takes place. In everyday language, people sometimes refer to the capacity of air to "hold" water vapor, but this is not actually what happens. The water vapor is not held by the air. The amount of water in air is determined by the vapor pressure of water and has nothing to do with the properties of air.

Temperature (ºC)	Vapor pressure (Pa)	Saturation vapor density (g/m³)
-50	4.0	0.039
-20	1.04×10^2	0.89
-10	2.60×10^2	2.36
0	6.10×10^2	4.84
5	8.68×10^2	6.80
10	1.19×10^3	9.40
15	1.69×10^3	12.8
20	2.33×10^3	17.2
25	3.17×10^3	23.0
30	4.24×10^3	30.4
37	6.31×10^3	44.0
40	7.34×10^3	51.1
50	1.23×10^4	82.4
60	1.99×10^4	130
70	3.12×10^4	197
80	4.73×10^4	294
90	7.01×10^4	418
95	8.59×10^4	505
100	$\mathbf{1.01 \times 10^5}$	**598**
120	1.99×10^5	1095
150	4.76×10^5	2430

TABLE 13.5 Saturation Vapor Density of Water

Temperature (°C)	Vapor pressure (Pa)	Saturation vapor density (g/m^3)
200	1.55×10^6	7090
220	2.32×10^6	10,200

TABLE 13.5 Saturation Vapor Density of Water

EXAMPLE 13.12

Calculating Density Using Vapor Pressure

Table 13.5 gives the vapor pressure of water at $20.0°C$ as 2.33×10^3 Pa. Use the ideal gas law to calculate the density of water vapor in g/m^3 that would create a partial pressure equal to this vapor pressure. Compare the result with the saturation vapor density given in the table.

Strategy

To solve this problem, we need to break it down into a two steps. The partial pressure follows the ideal gas law,

$$PV = nRT, \quad (13.70)$$

where n is the number of moles. If we solve this equation for n/V to calculate the number of moles per cubic meter, we can then convert this quantity to grams per cubic meter as requested. To do this, we need to use the molecular mass of water, which is given in the periodic table.

Solution

1. Identify the knowns and convert them to the proper units:

   a. temperature $T = 20°C = 293\text{ K}$
   b. vapor pressure P of water at $20°C$ is 2.33×10^3 Pa
   c. molecular mass of water is 18.0 g/mol

2. Solve the ideal gas law for n/V.

$$\frac{n}{V} = \frac{P}{RT} \quad (13.71)$$

3. Substitute known values into the equation and solve for n/V.

$$\frac{n}{V} = \frac{P}{RT} = \frac{2.33 \times 10^3\text{ Pa}}{(8.31\text{ J/mol}\cdot\text{K})(293\text{ K})} = 0.957\text{ mol/m}^3 \quad (13.72)$$

4. Convert the density in moles per cubic meter to grams per cubic meter.

$$\rho = \left(0.957\frac{\text{mol}}{\text{m}^3}\right)\left(\frac{18.0\text{ g}}{\text{mol}}\right) = 17.2\text{ g/m}^3 \quad (13.73)$$

Discussion

The density is obtained by assuming a pressure equal to the vapor pressure of water at $20.0°C$. The density found is identical to the value in Table 13.5, which means that a vapor density of 17.2 g/m^3 at $20.0°C$ creates a partial pressure of 2.33×10^3 Pa, equal to the vapor pressure of water at that temperature. If the partial pressure is equal to the vapor pressure, then the liquid and vapor phases are in equilibrium, and the relative humidity is 100%. Thus, there can be no more than 17.2 g of water vapor per m^3 at $20.0°C$, so that this value is the saturation vapor density at that temperature. This example illustrates how water vapor behaves like an ideal gas: the pressure and density are consistent with the ideal gas law (assuming the density in the table is correct). The saturation vapor densities listed in Table 13.5 are the maximum amounts of water vapor that air can hold at various temperatures.

PERCENT RELATIVE HUMIDITY

We define **percent relative humidity** as the ratio of vapor density to saturation vapor density, or

$$\text{percent relative humidity} = \frac{\text{vapor density}}{\text{saturation vapor density}} \times 100 \quad 13.74$$

We can use this and the data in Table 13.5 to do a variety of interesting calculations, keeping in mind that relative humidity is based on the comparison of the partial pressure of water vapor in air and ice.

EXAMPLE 13.13

Calculating Humidity and Dew Point

(a) Calculate the percent relative humidity on a day when the temperature is 25.0°C and the air contains 9.40 g of water vapor per m^3. (b) At what temperature will this air reach 100% relative humidity (the saturation density)? This temperature is the dew point. (c) What is the humidity when the air temperature is 25.0°C and the dew point is -10.0°C?

Strategy and Solution

(a) Percent relative humidity is defined as the ratio of vapor density to saturation vapor density.

$$\text{percent relative humidity} = \frac{\text{vapor density}}{\text{saturation vapor density}} \times 100 \quad 13.75$$

The first is given to be $9.40\ \text{g/m}^3$, and the second is found in Table 13.5 to be $23.0\ \text{g/m}^3$. Thus,

$$\text{percent relative humidity} = \frac{9.40\ \text{g/m}^3}{23.0\ \text{g/m}^3} \times 100 = 40.9.\% \quad 13.76$$

(b) The air contains $9.40\ \text{g/m}^3$ of water vapor. The relative humidity will be 100% at a temperature where $9.40\ \text{g/m}^3$ is the saturation density. Inspection of Table 13.5 reveals this to be the case at 10.0°C, where the relative humidity will be 100%. That temperature is called the dew point for air with this concentration of water vapor.

(c) Here, the dew point temperature is given to be -10.0°C. Using Table 13.5, we see that the vapor density is $2.36\ \text{g/m}^3$, because this value is the saturation vapor density at -10.0°C. The saturation vapor density at 25.0°C is seen to be $23.0\ \text{g/m}^3$. Thus, the relative humidity at 25.0°C is

$$\text{percent relative humidity} = \frac{2.36\ \text{g/m}^3}{23.0\ \text{g/m}^3} \times 100 = 10.3\%. \quad 13.77$$

Discussion

The importance of dew point is that air temperature cannot drop below 10.0°C in part (b), or -10.0°C in part (c), without water vapor condensing out of the air. If condensation occurs, considerable transfer of heat occurs (discussed in Heat and Heat Transfer Methods), which prevents the temperature from further dropping. When dew points are below 0°C, freezing temperatures are a greater possibility, which explains why farmers keep track of the dew point. Low humidity in deserts means low dew-point temperatures. Thus condensation is unlikely. If the temperature drops, vapor does not condense in liquid drops. Because no heat is released into the air, the air temperature drops more rapidly compared to air with higher humidity. Likewise, at high temperatures, liquid droplets do not evaporate, so that no heat is removed from the gas to the liquid phase. This explains the large range of temperature in arid regions.

Why does water boil at 100°C? You will note from Table 13.5 that the vapor pressure of water at 100°C is 1.01×10^5 Pa, or 1.00 atm. Thus, it can evaporate without limit at this temperature and pressure. But why does it form bubbles when it boils? This is because water ordinarily contains significant amounts of dissolved air and other impurities, which are observed as small bubbles of air in a glass of water. If a bubble starts out at the bottom of the container at $20°C$, it contains water vapor (about 2.30%). The pressure inside the bubble is fixed at 1.00 atm (we ignore the slight pressure exerted by the water around it). As the temperature rises, the amount of air in the bubble stays the same, but the water vapor increases; the bubble expands to keep the pressure at 1.00 atm. At $100°C$, water vapor enters the bubble continuously since the partial pressure of water is equal to 1.00 atm in equilibrium. It cannot reach this pressure, however, since the bubble also contains air and total pressure is 1.00 atm. The bubble grows in size and thereby increases the buoyant force. The bubble breaks away and rises rapidly to the surface—we call this boiling! (See Figure 13.32.)

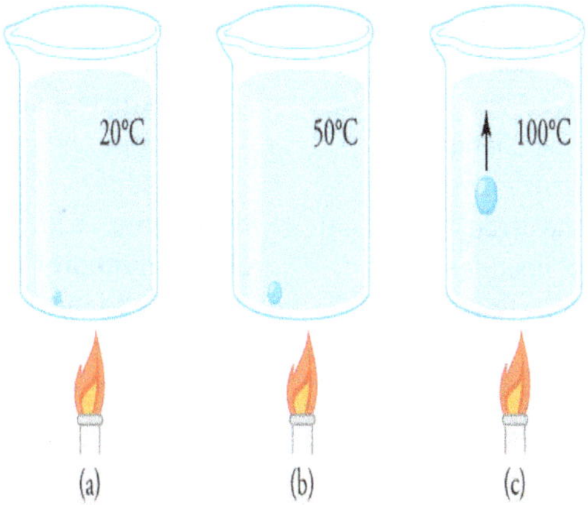

FIGURE 13.32 (a) An air bubble in water starts out saturated with water vapor at $20°C$. (b) As the temperature rises, water vapor enters the bubble because its vapor pressure increases. The bubble expands to keep its pressure at 1.00 atm. (c) At $100°C$, water vapor enters the bubble continuously because water's vapor pressure exceeds its partial pressure in the bubble, which must be less than 1.00 atm. The bubble grows and rises to the surface.

CHECK YOUR UNDERSTANDING

Freeze drying is a process in which substances, such as foods, are dried by placing them in a vacuum chamber and lowering the atmospheric pressure around them. How does the lowered atmospheric pressure speed the drying process, and why does it cause the temperature of the food to drop?

Solution

Decreased the atmospheric pressure results in decreased partial pressure of water, hence a lower humidity. So evaporation of water from food, for example, will be enhanced. The molecules of water most likely to break away from the food will be those with the greatest velocities. Those remaining thus have a lower average velocity and a lower temperature. This can (and does) result in the freezing and drying of the food; hence the process is aptly named freeze drying.

PHET EXPLORATIONS

States of Matter

Watch different types of molecules form a solid, liquid, or gas. Add or remove heat and watch the phase change. Change the temperature or volume of a container and see a pressure-temperature diagram respond in real time. Relate the interaction potential to the forces between molecules.

Click to view content (https://openstax.org/books/college-physics-ap-courses-2e/pages/13-6-humidity-evaporation-and-boiling)

Glossary

absolute zero the lowest possible temperature; the temperature at which all molecular motion ceases

Avogadro's number N_A , the number of molecules or atoms in one mole of a substance; $N_A = 6.02 \times 10^{23}$ particles/mole

Boltzmann constant k , a physical constant that relates energy to temperature; $k = 1.38 \times 10^{-23}$ J/K

Celsius scale temperature scale in which the freezing point of water is $0^\circ C$ and the boiling point of water is $100^\circ C$

coefficient of linear expansion α, the change in length, per unit length, per $1^\circ C$ change in temperature; a constant used in the calculation of linear expansion; the coefficient of linear expansion depends on the material and to some degree on the temperature of the material

coefficient of volume expansion β, the change in volume, per unit volume, per $1^\circ C$ change in temperature

critical point the temperature above which a liquid cannot exist

critical pressure the minimum pressure needed for a liquid to exist at the critical temperature

critical temperature the temperature above which a liquid cannot exist

Dalton's law of partial pressures the physical law that states that the total pressure of a gas is the sum of partial pressures of the component gases

degree Celsius unit on the Celsius temperature scale

degree Fahrenheit unit on the Fahrenheit temperature scale

dew point the temperature at which relative humidity is 100%; the temperature at which water starts to condense out of the air

Fahrenheit scale temperature scale in which the freezing point of water is $32^\circ F$ and the boiling point of water is $212^\circ F$

ideal gas law the physical law that relates the pressure and volume of a gas to the number of gas molecules or number of moles of gas and the temperature of the gas

Kelvin scale temperature scale in which 0 K is the lowest possible temperature, representing absolute zero

mole the quantity of a substance whose mass (in grams) is equal to its molecular mass

partial pressure the pressure a gas would create if it occupied the total volume of space available

percent relative humidity the ratio of vapor density to saturation vapor density

phase diagram a graph of pressure vs. temperature of a particular substance, showing at which pressures and temperatures the three phases of the substance occur

***PV* diagram** a graph of pressure vs. volume

relative humidity the amount of water in the air relative to the maximum amount the air can hold

saturation the condition of 100% relative humidity

sublimation the phase change from solid to gas

temperature the quantity measured by a thermometer

thermal energy $\overline{\text{KE}}$, the average translational kinetic energy of a molecule

thermal equilibrium the condition in which heat no longer flows between two objects that are in contact; the two objects have the same temperature

thermal expansion the change in size or volume of an object with change in temperature

thermal stress stress caused by thermal expansion or contraction

triple point the pressure and temperature at which a substance exists in equilibrium as a solid, liquid, and gas

vapor a gas at a temperature below the boiling temperature

vapor pressure the pressure at which a gas coexists with its solid or liquid phase

zeroth law of thermodynamics law that states that if two objects are in thermal equilibrium, and a third object is in thermal equilibrium with one of those objects, it is also in thermal equilibrium with the other object

Section Summary

13.1 Temperature

- Temperature is the quantity measured by a thermometer.
- Temperature is related to the average kinetic energy of atoms and molecules in a system.
- Absolute zero is the temperature at which there is no molecular motion.
- There are three main temperature scales: Celsius, Fahrenheit, and Kelvin.
- Temperatures on one scale can be converted to temperatures on another scale using the following equations:

$$T_{^\circ F} = \frac{9}{5} T_{^\circ C} + 32$$

$$T_{°C} = \frac{5}{9}(T_{°F} - 32)$$
$$T_K = T_{°C} + 273.15$$
$$T_{°C} = T_K - 273.15$$

- Systems are in thermal equilibrium when they have the same temperature.
- Thermal equilibrium occurs when two bodies are in contact with each other and can freely exchange energy.
- The zeroth law of thermodynamics states that when two systems, A and B, are in thermal equilibrium with each other, and B is in thermal equilibrium with a third system, C, then A is also in thermal equilibrium with C.

13.2 Thermal Expansion of Solids and Liquids

- Thermal expansion is the increase, or decrease, of the size (length, area, or volume) of a body due to a change in temperature.
- Thermal expansion is large for gases, and relatively small, but not negligible, for liquids and solids.
- Linear thermal expansion is
  $\Delta L = \alpha L \Delta T$,
  where ΔL is the change in length L, ΔT is the change in temperature, and α is the coefficient of linear expansion, which varies slightly with temperature.
- The change in area due to thermal expansion is
  $\Delta A = 2\alpha A \Delta T$,
  where ΔA is the change in area.
- The change in volume due to thermal expansion is
  $\Delta V = \beta V \Delta T$,
  where β is the coefficient of volume expansion and $\beta \approx 3\alpha$. Thermal stress is created when thermal expansion is constrained.

13.3 The Ideal Gas Law

- The ideal gas law relates the pressure and volume of a gas to the number of gas molecules and the temperature of the gas.
- The ideal gas law can be written in terms of the number of molecules of gas:
  $PV = NkT$,
  where P is pressure, V is volume, T is temperature, N is number of molecules, and k is the Boltzmann constant
  $k = 1.38 \times 10^{-23}$ J/K.
- A mole is the number of atoms in a 12-g sample of carbon-12.
- The number of molecules in a mole is called Avogadro's number N_A,
  $N_A = 6.02 \times 10^{23}\ \text{mol}^{-1}$.
- A mole of any substance has a mass in grams equal to its molecular weight, which can be determined from the periodic table of elements.
- The ideal gas law can also be written and solved in terms of the number of moles of gas:
  $PV = nRT$,
  where n is number of moles and R is the universal gas constant,
  $R = 8.31$ J/mol · K.
- The ideal gas law is generally valid at temperatures well above the boiling temperature.

13.4 Kinetic Theory: Atomic and Molecular Explanation of Pressure and Temperature

- Kinetic theory is the atomistic description of gases as well as liquids and solids.
- Kinetic theory models the properties of matter in terms of continuous random motion of atoms and molecules.
- The ideal gas law can also be expressed as
  $PV = \frac{1}{3}Nm\overline{v^2}$,
  where P is the pressure (average force per unit area), V is the volume of gas in the container, N is the number of molecules in the container, m is the mass of a molecule, and $\overline{v^2}$ is the average of the molecular speed squared.
- Thermal energy is defined to be the average translational kinetic energy $\overline{\text{KE}}$ of an atom or molecule.
- The temperature of gases is proportional to the average translational kinetic energy of atoms and molecules.
  $$\overline{\text{KE}} = \frac{1}{2}m\overline{v^2} = \frac{3}{2}kT$$
  or
  $$\sqrt{\overline{v^2}} = v_{\text{rms}} = \sqrt{\frac{3kT}{m}}.$$
- The motion of individual molecules in a gas is random in magnitude and direction. However, a gas of many molecules has a predictable distribution of molecular speeds, known as the *Maxwell-Boltzmann distribution*.

13.5 Phase Changes

- Most substances have three distinct phases: gas, liquid, and solid.
- Phase changes among the various phases of matter depend on temperature and pressure.
- The existence of the three phases with respect to pressure and temperature can be described in a phase diagram.

- Two phases coexist (i.e., they are in thermal equilibrium) at a set of pressures and temperatures. These are described as a line on a phase diagram.
- The three phases coexist at a single pressure and temperature. This is known as the triple point and is described by a single point on a phase diagram.
- A gas at a temperature below its boiling point is called a vapor.
- Vapor pressure is the pressure at which a gas coexists with its solid or liquid phase.
- Partial pressure is the pressure a gas would create if it existed alone.
- Dalton's law states that the total pressure is the sum of the partial pressures of all of the gases present.

13.6 Humidity, Evaporation, and Boiling

- Relative humidity is the fraction of water vapor in a gas compared to the saturation value.
- The saturation vapor density can be determined from the vapor pressure for a given temperature.
- Percent relative humidity is defined to be $$\text{percent relative humidity} = \frac{\text{vapor density}}{\text{saturation vapor density}} \times 100.$$
- The dew point is the temperature at which air reaches 100% relative humidity.

Conceptual Questions

13.1 Temperature

1. What does it mean to say that two systems are in thermal equilibrium?

2. Give an example of a physical property that varies with temperature and describe how it is used to measure temperature.

3. When a cold alcohol thermometer is placed in a hot liquid, the column of alcohol goes *down* slightly before going up. Explain why.

4. If you add boiling water to a cup at room temperature, what would you expect the final equilibrium temperature of the unit to be? You will need to include the surroundings as part of the system. Consider the zeroth law of thermodynamics.

13.2 Thermal Expansion of Solids and Liquids

5. Thermal stresses caused by uneven cooling can easily break glass cookware. Explain why Pyrex®, a glass with a small coefficient of linear expansion, is less susceptible.

6. Water expands significantly when it freezes: a volume increase of about 9% occurs. As a result of this expansion and because of the formation and growth of crystals as water freezes, anywhere from 10% to 30% of biological cells are burst when animal or plant material is frozen. Discuss the implications of this cell damage for the prospect of preserving human bodies by freezing so that they can be thawed at some future date when it is hoped that all diseases are curable.

7. One method of getting a tight fit, say of a metal peg in a hole in a metal block, is to manufacture the peg slightly larger than the hole. The peg is then inserted when at a different temperature than the block. Should the block be hotter or colder than the peg during insertion? Explain your answer.

8. Does it really help to run hot water over a tight metal lid on a glass jar before trying to open it? Explain your answer.

9. Liquids and solids expand with increasing temperature, because the kinetic energy of a body's atoms and molecules increases. Explain why some materials *shrink* with increasing temperature.

13.3 The Ideal Gas Law

10. Find out the human population of Earth. Is there a mole of people inhabiting Earth? If the average mass of a person is 60 kg, calculate the mass of a mole of people. How does the mass of a mole of people compare with the mass of Earth?

11. Under what circumstances would you expect a gas to behave significantly differently than predicted by the ideal gas law?

12. A constant-volume gas thermometer contains a fixed amount of gas. What property of the gas is measured to indicate its temperature?

13.4 Kinetic Theory: Atomic and Molecular Explanation of Pressure and Temperature

13. How is momentum related to the pressure exerted by a gas? Explain on the atomic and molecular level, considering the behavior of atoms and molecules.

13.5 Phase Changes

14. A pressure cooker contains water and steam in equilibrium at a pressure greater than

atmospheric pressure. How does this greater pressure increase cooking speed?

15. Why does condensation form most rapidly on the coldest object in a room—for example, on a glass of ice water?

16. What is the vapor pressure of solid carbon dioxide (dry ice) at $-78.5°C$?

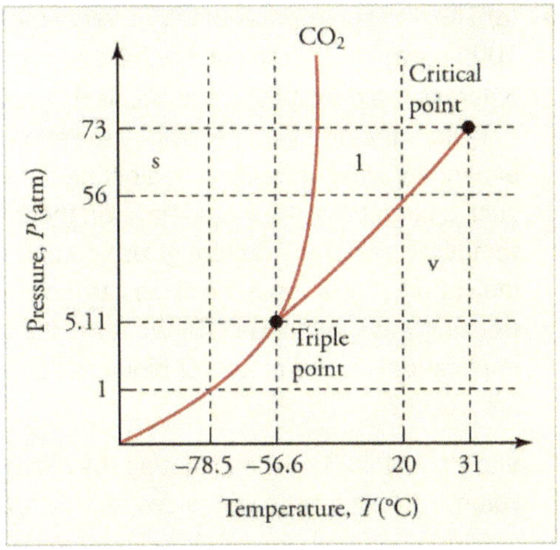

FIGURE 13.33 The phase diagram for carbon dioxide. The axes are nonlinear, and the graph is not to scale. Dry ice is solid carbon dioxide and has a sublimation temperature of $-78.5°C$.

17. Can carbon dioxide be liquefied at room temperature $(20°C)$? If so, how? If not, why not? (See Figure 13.33.)

18. Oxygen cannot be liquefied at room temperature by placing it under a large enough pressure to force its molecules together. Explain why this is.

19. What is the distinction between gas and vapor?

13.6 Humidity, Evaporation, and Boiling

20. Because humidity depends only on water's vapor pressure and temperature, are the saturation vapor densities listed in Table 13.5 valid in an atmosphere of helium at a pressure of $1.01 \times 10^5\ N/m^2$, rather than air? Are those values affected by altitude on Earth?

21. Why does a beaker of $40.0°C$ water placed in a vacuum chamber start to boil as the chamber is evacuated (air is pumped out of the chamber)? At what pressure does the boiling begin? Would food cook any faster in such a beaker?

22. Why does rubbing alcohol evaporate much more rapidly than water at STP (standard temperature and pressure)?

Problems & Exercises

13.1 Temperature

1. What is the Fahrenheit temperature of a person with a $39.0°C$ fever?

2. Frost damage to most plants occurs at temperatures of $28.0°F$ or lower. What is this temperature on the Kelvin scale?

3. To conserve energy, room temperatures are kept at $68.0°F$ in the winter and $78.0°F$ in the summer. What are these temperatures on the Celsius scale?

4. A tungsten light bulb filament may operate at 2900 K. What is its Fahrenheit temperature? What is this on the Celsius scale?

5. The surface temperature of the Sun is about 5750 K. What is this temperature on the Fahrenheit scale?

6. One of the hottest temperatures ever recorded on the surface of Earth was $134°F$ in Death Valley, CA. What is this temperature in Celsius degrees? What is this temperature in Kelvin?

7. (a) Suppose a cold front blows into your locale and drops the temperature by 40.0 Fahrenheit degrees. How many degrees Celsius does the temperature decrease when there is a $40.0°F$ decrease in temperature? (b) Show that any change in temperature in Fahrenheit degrees is nine-fifths the change in Celsius degrees.

8. (a) At what temperature do the Fahrenheit and Celsius scales have the same numerical value? (b) At what temperature do the Fahrenheit and Kelvin scales have the same numerical value?

13.2 Thermal Expansion of Solids and Liquids

9. The height of the Washington Monument is measured to be 170 m on a day when the temperature is $35.0°C$. What will its height be on a day when the temperature falls to $-10.0°C$? Although the monument is made of limestone, assume that its thermal coefficient of expansion is the same as marble's.

10. How much taller does the Eiffel Tower become at the end of a day when the temperature has increased by $15°C$? Its original height is 321 m and you can assume it is made of steel.

11. What is the change in length of a 3.00-cm-long column of mercury if its temperature changes from $37.0°C$ to $40.0°C$, assuming the mercury is unconstrained?

12. How large an expansion gap should be left between steel railroad rails if they may reach a maximum temperature $35.0°C$ greater than when they were laid? Their original length is 10.0 m.

13. You are looking to purchase a small piece of land in Hong Kong. The price is "only" $60,000 per square meter! The land title says the dimensions are $20\ m \times 30\ m$. By how much would the total price change if you measured the parcel with a steel tape measure on a day when the temperature was $20°C$ above normal?

14. Global warming will produce rising sea levels partly due to melting ice caps but also due to the expansion of water as average ocean temperatures rise. To get some idea of the size of this effect, calculate the change in length of a column of water 1.00 km high for a temperature increase of $1.00°C$. Note that this calculation is only approximate because ocean warming is not uniform with depth.

15. Show that 60.0 L of gasoline originally at $15.0°C$ will expand to 61.1 L when it warms to $35.0°C$, as claimed in Example 13.4.

16. (a) Suppose a meter stick made of steel and one made of invar (an alloy of iron and nickel) are the same length at $0°C$. What is their difference in length at $22.0°C$? (b) Repeat the calculation for two 30.0-m-long surveyor's tapes.

17. (a) If a 500-mL glass beaker is filled to the brim with ethyl alcohol at a temperature of $5.00°C$, how much will overflow when its temperature reaches $22.0°C$? (b) How much less water would overflow under the same conditions?

18. Most automobiles have a coolant reservoir to catch radiator fluid that may overflow when the engine is hot. A radiator is made of copper and is filled to its 16.0-L capacity when at $10.0°C$. What volume of radiator fluid will overflow when the radiator and fluid reach their $95.0°C$ operating temperature, given that the fluid's volume coefficient of expansion is $\beta = 400 \times 10^{-6}/°C$?

Note that this coefficient is approximate, because most car radiators have operating temperatures of greater than $95.0°C$.

19. A physicist makes a cup of instant coffee and notices that, as the coffee cools, its level drops 3.00 mm in the glass cup. Show that this decrease cannot be due to thermal contraction by calculating the decrease in level if the $350\ cm^3$ of coffee is in a 7.00-cm-diameter cup and decreases in temperature from $95.0°C$ to $45.0°C$. (Most of the drop in level is actually due to escaping bubbles of air.)

20. (a) The density of water at $0°C$ is very nearly $1000\ kg/m^3$ (it is actually $999.84\ kg/m^3$), whereas the density of ice at $0°C$ is $917\ kg/m^3$. Calculate the pressure necessary to keep ice from expanding when it freezes, neglecting the effect such a large pressure would have on the freezing temperature. (This problem gives you only an indication of how large the forces associated with freezing water might be.) (b) What are the implications of this result for biological cells that are frozen?

21. Show that $\beta \approx 3\alpha$, by calculating the change in volume ΔV of a cube with sides of length L.

13.3 The Ideal Gas Law

22. The gauge pressure in your car tires is $2.50 \times 10^5\ N/m^2$ at a temperature of $35.0°C$ when you drive it onto a ferry boat to Alaska. What is their gauge pressure later, when their temperature has dropped to $-40.0°C$?

23. Convert an absolute pressure of $7.00 \times 10^5\ N/m^2$ to gauge pressure in lb/in^2. (This value was stated to be just less than $90.0\ lb/in^2$ in Example 13.9. Is it?)

24. Suppose a gas-filled incandescent light bulb is manufactured so that the gas inside the bulb is at atmospheric pressure when the bulb has a temperature of $20.0°C$. (a) Find the gauge pressure inside such a bulb when it is hot, assuming its average temperature is $60.0°C$ (an approximation) and neglecting any change in volume due to thermal expansion or gas leaks. (b) The actual final pressure for the light bulb will be less than calculated in part (a) because the glass bulb will expand. What will the actual final pressure be, taking this into account? Is this a negligible difference?

25. To test a balloon, it is placed in a lab and filled with helium. The temperature of the helium is $10.0°C$ and the pressure is 1.00 atmosphere. The pressure in the lab is maintained. Assume the membrane of the balloon provides a negligible inward pressure, so it is not considered significant. (a) What is the pressure inside the balloon if the helium is replaced with helium that is at $-50.0°C$? and the balloon is filled until it has a volume of 20.0 times its original volume? (b) What is the gauge pressure? (Assume the pressure in the lab remains at 1.00 atmosphere during the experiment.)

26. Confirm that the units of nRT are those of energy for each value of R: (a) $8.31\ \text{J/mol} \cdot \text{K}$, (b) $1.99\ \text{cal/mol} \cdot \text{K}$, and (c) $0.0821\ \text{L} \cdot \text{atm/mol} \cdot \text{K}$.

27. In the text, it was shown that $N/V = 2.68 \times 10^{25}\ \text{m}^{-3}$ for gas at STP. (a) Show that this quantity is equivalent to $N/V = 2.68 \times 10^{19}\ \text{cm}^{-3}$, as stated. (b) About how many atoms are there in one μm^3 (a cubic micrometer) at STP? (c) What does your answer to part (b) imply about the separation of atoms and molecules?

28. Calculate the number of moles in the 2.00-L volume of air in the lungs of the average person. Note that the air is at $37.0°C$ (body temperature).

29. An airplane passenger has $100\ \text{cm}^3$ of air in his stomach just before the plane takes off from a sea-level airport. What volume will the air have at cruising altitude if cabin pressure drops to $7.50 \times 10^4\ \text{N/m}^2$?

30. (a) What is the volume (in km^3) of Avogadro's number of sand grains if each grain is a cube and has sides that are 1.0 mm long? (b) How many kilometers of beaches in length would this cover if the beach averages 100 m in width and 10.0 m in depth? Neglect air spaces between grains.

31. An expensive vacuum system can achieve a pressure as low as $1.00 \times 10^{-7}\ \text{N/m}^2$ at $20°C$. How many atoms are there in a cubic centimeter at this pressure and temperature?

32. The number density of gas atoms at a certain location in the space above our planet is about $1.00 \times 10^{11}\ \text{m}^{-3}$, and the pressure is $2.75 \times 10^{-10}\ \text{N/m}^2$ in this space. What is the temperature there?

33. A bicycle tire has a pressure of $7.00 \times 10^5\ \text{N/m}^2$ at a temperature of $18.0°C$ and contains 2.00 L of gas. What will its pressure be if you let out an amount of air that has a volume of $100\ \text{cm}^3$ at atmospheric pressure? Assume tire temperature and volume remain constant.

34. A high-pressure gas cylinder contains 50.0 L of toxic gas at a pressure of $1.40 \times 10^7\ \text{N/m}^2$ and a temperature of $25.0°C$. Its valve leaks after the cylinder is dropped. The cylinder is cooled to dry ice temperature ($-78.5°C$) to reduce the leak rate and pressure so that it can be safely repaired. (a) What is the final pressure in the tank, assuming a negligible amount of gas leaks while being cooled and that there is no phase change? (b) What is the final pressure if one-tenth of the gas escapes? (c) To what temperature must the tank be cooled to reduce the pressure to 1.00 atm (assuming the gas does not change phase and that there is no leakage during cooling)? (d) Does cooling the tank appear to be a practical solution?

35. Find the number of moles in 2.00 L of gas at $35.0°C$ and under $7.41 \times 10^7\ \text{N/m}^2$ of pressure.

36. Calculate the depth to which Avogadro's number of table tennis balls would cover Earth. Each ball has a diameter of 3.75 cm. Assume the space between balls adds an extra 25.0% to their volume and assume they are not crushed by their own weight.

37. (a) What is the gauge pressure in a $25.0°C$ car tire containing 3.60 mol of gas in a 30.0 L volume? (b) What will its gauge pressure be if you add 1.00 L of gas originally at atmospheric pressure and $25.0°C$? Assume the temperature returns to $25.0°C$ and the volume remains constant.

38. (a) In the deep space between galaxies, the density of atoms is as low as $10^6\ \text{atoms/m}^3$, and the temperature is a frigid 2.7 K. What is the pressure? (b) What volume (in m^3) is occupied by 1 mol of gas? (c) If this volume is a cube, what is the length of its sides in kilometers?

13.4 Kinetic Theory: Atomic and Molecular Explanation of Pressure and Temperature

39. Some incandescent light bulbs are filled with argon gas. What is v_{rms} for argon atoms near the filament, assuming their temperature is 2500 K?

40. Average atomic and molecular speeds (v_{rms}) are large, even at low temperatures. What is v_{rms} for helium atoms at 5.00 K, just one degree above helium's liquefaction temperature?

41. (a) What is the average kinetic energy in joules of hydrogen atoms on the $5500°C$ surface of the Sun? (b) What is the average kinetic energy of helium atoms in a region of the solar corona where the temperature is $6.00 \times 10^5\ \text{K}$?

42. The escape velocity of any object from Earth is 11.2 km/s. (a) Express this speed in m/s and km/h. (b) At what temperature would oxygen molecules (molecular mass is equal to 32.0 g/mol) have an average velocity v_{rms} equal to Earth's escape velocity of 11.1 km/s?

43. The escape velocity from the Moon is much smaller than from Earth and is only 2.38 km/s. At what temperature would hydrogen molecules (molecular mass is equal to 2.016 g/mol) have an average velocity v_{rms} equal to the Moon's escape velocity?

44. Nuclear fusion, the energy source of the Sun, hydrogen bombs, and fusion reactors, occurs much more readily when the average kinetic energy of the atoms is high—that is, at high temperatures. Suppose you want the atoms in your fusion experiment to have average kinetic energies of 6.40×10^{-14} J. What temperature is needed?

45. Suppose that the average velocity (v_{rms}) of carbon dioxide molecules (molecular mass is equal to 44.0 g/mol) in a flame is found to be 1.05×10^5 m/s. What temperature does this represent?

46. Hydrogen molecules (molecular mass is equal to 2.016 g/mol) have an average velocity v_{rms} equal to 193 m/s. What is the temperature?

47. Much of the gas near the Sun is atomic hydrogen. Its temperature would have to be 1.5×10^7 K for the average velocity v_{rms} to equal the escape velocity from the Sun. What is that velocity?

48. There are two important isotopes of uranium—^{235}U and ^{238}U; these isotopes are nearly identical chemically but have different atomic masses. Only ^{235}U is very useful in nuclear reactors. One of the techniques for separating them (gas diffusion) is based on the different average velocities v_{rms} of uranium hexafluoride gas, UF_6. (a) The molecular masses for $^{235}U\ UF_6$ and $^{238}U\ UF_6$ are 349.0 g/mol and 352.0 g/mol, respectively. What is the ratio of their average velocities? (b) At what temperature would their average velocities differ by 1.00 m/s? (c) Do your answers in this problem imply that this technique may be difficult?

13.6 Humidity, Evaporation, and Boiling

49. Dry air is 78.1% nitrogen. What is the partial pressure of nitrogen when the atmospheric pressure is 1.01×10^5 N/m^2?

50. (a) What is the vapor pressure of water at 20.0ºC? (b) What percentage of atmospheric pressure does this correspond to? (c) What percent of 20.0ºC air is water vapor if it has 100% relative humidity? (The density of dry air at 20.0ºC is 1.20 kg/m^3.)

51. Pressure cookers increase cooking speed by raising the boiling temperature of water above its value at atmospheric pressure. (a) What pressure is necessary to raise the boiling point to 120.0ºC? (b) What gauge pressure does this correspond to?

52. (a) At what temperature does water boil at an altitude of 1500 m (about 5000 ft) on a day when atmospheric pressure is 8.59×10^4 N/m^2? (b) What about at an altitude of 3000 m (about 10,000 ft) when atmospheric pressure is 7.00×10^4 N/m^2?

53. What is the atmospheric pressure on top of Mt. Everest on a day when water boils there at a temperature of 70.0ºC?

54. At a spot in the high Andes, water boils at 80.0ºC, greatly reducing the cooking speed of potatoes, for example. What is atmospheric pressure at this location?

55. What is the relative humidity on a 25.0ºC day when the air contains 18.0 g/m^3 of water vapor?

56. What is the density of water vapor in g/m^3 on a hot dry day in the desert when the temperature is 40.0ºC and the relative humidity is 6.00%?

57. A deep-sea diver should breathe a gas mixture that has the same oxygen partial pressure as at sea level, where dry air contains 20.9% oxygen and has a total pressure of 1.01×10^5 N/m^2. (a) What is the partial pressure of oxygen at sea level? (b) If the diver breathes a gas mixture at a pressure of 2.00×10^6 N/m^2, what percent oxygen should it be to have the same oxygen partial pressure as at sea level?

58. The vapor pressure of water at 40.0ºC is 7.34×10^3 N/m^2. Using the ideal gas law, calculate the density of water vapor in g/m^3 that creates a partial pressure equal to this vapor pressure. The result should be the same as the saturation vapor density at that temperature (51.1 g/m^3).

59. Air in human lungs has a temperature of 37.0ºC and a saturation vapor density of 44.0 g/m^3. (a) If

2.00 L of air is exhaled and very dry air inhaled, what is the maximum loss of water vapor by the person? (b) Calculate the partial pressure of water vapor having this density, and compare it with the vapor pressure of $6.31 \times 10^3\ \text{N/m}^2$.

60. If the relative humidity is 90.0% on a muggy summer morning when the temperature is $20.0°\text{C}$, what will it be later in the day when the temperature is $30.0°\text{C}$, assuming the water vapor density remains constant?

61. Late on an autumn day, the relative humidity is 45.0% and the temperature is $20.0°\text{C}$. What will the relative humidity be that evening when the temperature has dropped to $10.0°\text{C}$, assuming constant water vapor density?

62. Atmospheric pressure atop Mt. Everest is $3.30 \times 10^4\ \text{N/m}^2$. (a) What is the partial pressure of oxygen there if it is 20.9% of the air? (b) What percent oxygen should a mountain climber breathe so that its partial pressure is the same as at sea level, where atmospheric pressure is $1.01 \times 10^5\ \text{N/m}^2$? (c) One of the most severe problems for those climbing very high mountains is the extreme drying of breathing passages. Why does this drying occur?

63. What is the dew point (the temperature at which 100% relative humidity would occur) on a day when relative humidity is 39.0% at a temperature of $20.0°\text{C}$?

64. On a certain day, the temperature is $25.0°\text{C}$ and the relative humidity is 90.0%. How many grams of water must condense out of each cubic meter of air if the temperature falls to $15.0°\text{C}$? Such a drop in temperature can, thus, produce heavy dew or fog.

65. Integrated Concepts
The boiling point of water increases with depth because pressure increases with depth. At what depth will fresh water have a boiling point of $150°\text{C}$, if the surface of the water is at sea level?

66. Integrated Concepts
(a) At what depth in fresh water is the critical pressure of water reached, given that the surface is at sea level? (b) At what temperature will this water boil? (c) Is a significantly higher temperature needed to boil water at a greater depth?

67. Integrated Concepts
To get an idea of the small effect that temperature has on Archimedes' principle, calculate the fraction of a copper block's weight that is supported by the buoyant force in $0°\text{C}$ water and compare this fraction with the fraction supported in $95.0°\text{C}$ water.

68. Integrated Concepts
If you want to cook in water at $150°\text{C}$, you need a pressure cooker that can withstand the necessary pressure. (a) What pressure is required for the boiling point of water to be this high? (b) If the lid of the pressure cooker is a disk 25.0 cm in diameter, what force must it be able to withstand at this pressure?

69. Unreasonable Results
(a) How many moles per cubic meter of an ideal gas are there at a pressure of $1.00 \times 10^{14}\ \text{N/m}^2$ and at $0°\text{C}$? (b) What is unreasonable about this result? (c) Which premise or assumption is responsible?

70. Unreasonable Results
(a) An automobile mechanic claims that an aluminum rod fits loosely into its hole on an aluminum engine block because the engine is hot and the rod is cold. If the hole is 10.0% bigger in diameter than the $22.0°\text{C}$ rod, at what temperature will the rod be the same size as the hole? (b) What is unreasonable about this temperature? (c) Which premise is responsible?

71. Unreasonable Results
The temperature inside a supernova explosion is said to be $2.00 \times 10^{13}\ \text{K}$. (a) What would the average velocity v_{rms} of hydrogen atoms be? (b) What is unreasonable about this velocity? (c) Which premise or assumption is responsible?

72. Unreasonable Results
Suppose the relative humidity is 80% on a day when the temperature is $30.0°\text{C}$. (a) What will the relative humidity be if the air cools to $25.0°\text{C}$ and the vapor density remains constant? (b) What is unreasonable about this result? (c) Which premise is responsible?

Test Prep for AP® Courses

13.3 The Ideal Gas Law

1. A fixed amount of ideal gas is kept in a container of fixed volume. The absolute pressure *P*, in pascals, of the gas is plotted as a function of its temperature

T, in degrees Celsius. Which of the following are properties of a best fit curve to the data? Select *two* answers.

a. Having a positive slope
b. Passing through the origin
c. Having zero pressure at a certain negative temperature
d. Approaching zero pressure as temperature approaches infinity

2.

FIGURE 13.34

This figure shows a clear plastic container with a movable piston that contains a fixed amount of gas. A group of students is asked to determine whether the gas is ideal. The students design and conduct an experiment. They measure the three quantities recorded in the data table below.

Trial	Absolute Gas Pressure (x10m^5 Pa)	Volume (m^3)	Temp. (K)		
1	1.1	0.020	270		
2	1.4	0.016	270		
3	1.9	0.012	270		
4	2.2	0.010	270		
5	2.8	0.008	270		
6	1.2	0.020	290		
7	1.5	0.016	290		
8	2.0	0.012	290		
9	2.4	0.010	290		
10	3.0	0.008	290		
11	1.3	0.020	310		
12	1.6	0.016	310		
13	2.1	0.012	310		
14	2.6	0.010	310		
15	3.2	0.008	310		

TABLE 13.6

TABLE 13.6

a. Select a set of data points from the table and plot those points on a graph to determine whether the gas exhibits properties of an ideal gas. Fill in blank columns in the table for any quantities you graph other than the given data. Label the axes and indicate the scale for each. Draw a best-fit line or curve through your data points.
b. Indicate whether the gas exhibits properties of an ideal gas, and explain what characteristic of your graph provides the evidence.
c. The students repeat their experiment with an identical container that contains half as much gas. They take data for the same values of volume and temperature as in the table. Would the new data result in a different conclusion about whether the gas is ideal? Justify your answer in terms of interactions between the molecules of the gas and the container walls.

13.4 Kinetic Theory: Atomic and Molecular Explanation of Pressure and Temperature

3. Two samples of ideal gas in separate containers have the same number of molecules and the same temperature, but the molecular mass of gas X is greater than that of gas Y. Which of the following correctly compares the average speed of the molecules of the gases and the average force the gases exert on their respective containers?

	Average Speed of Molecules	Average Force on Container
(a)	Greater for gas X	Greater for gas X
(b)	Greater for gas X	The forces cannot be compared without knowing the volumes of the gases.
(c)	Greater for gas Y	Greater for gas Y
(d)	Greater for gas Y	The forces cannot be compared without knowing the volumes of the gases.

TABLE 13.7

4. How will the average kinetic energy of a gas molecule change if its temperature is increased from 20°C to 313°C?
   a. It will become sixteen times its original value.
   b. It will become four times its original value
   c. It will become double its original value
   d. It will remain unchanged.

5.

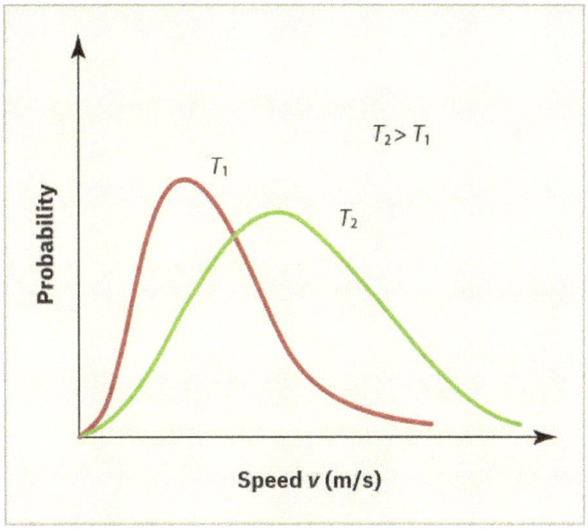

FIGURE 13.35

This graph shows the Maxwell-Boltzmann distribution of molecular speeds in an ideal gas for two temperatures, T_1 and T_2. Which of the following statements is false?
   a. T_1 is lower than T_2
   b. The *rms* speed at T_1 is higher than that at T_2.
   c. The peak of each graph shows the most probable speed at the corresponding temperature.
   d. None of the above.

6. Suppose you have gas in a cylinder with a movable piston which has an area of 0.40 m^2. The pressure of the gas is 150 Pa when the height of the piston is 0.02 m. Find the force exerted by the gas on the piston. How does this force change if the piston is moved to a height of 0.03 m? Assume temperature remains constant.

7. What is the average kinetic energy of a nitrogen molecule (N_2) if its *rms* speed is 560 m/s? At what temperature is this *rms* speed achieved?

8. What will be the ratio of kinetic energies and *rms* speeds of a nitrogen molecule and a helium atom at the same temperature?

CHAPTER 14
Heat and Heat Transfer Methods

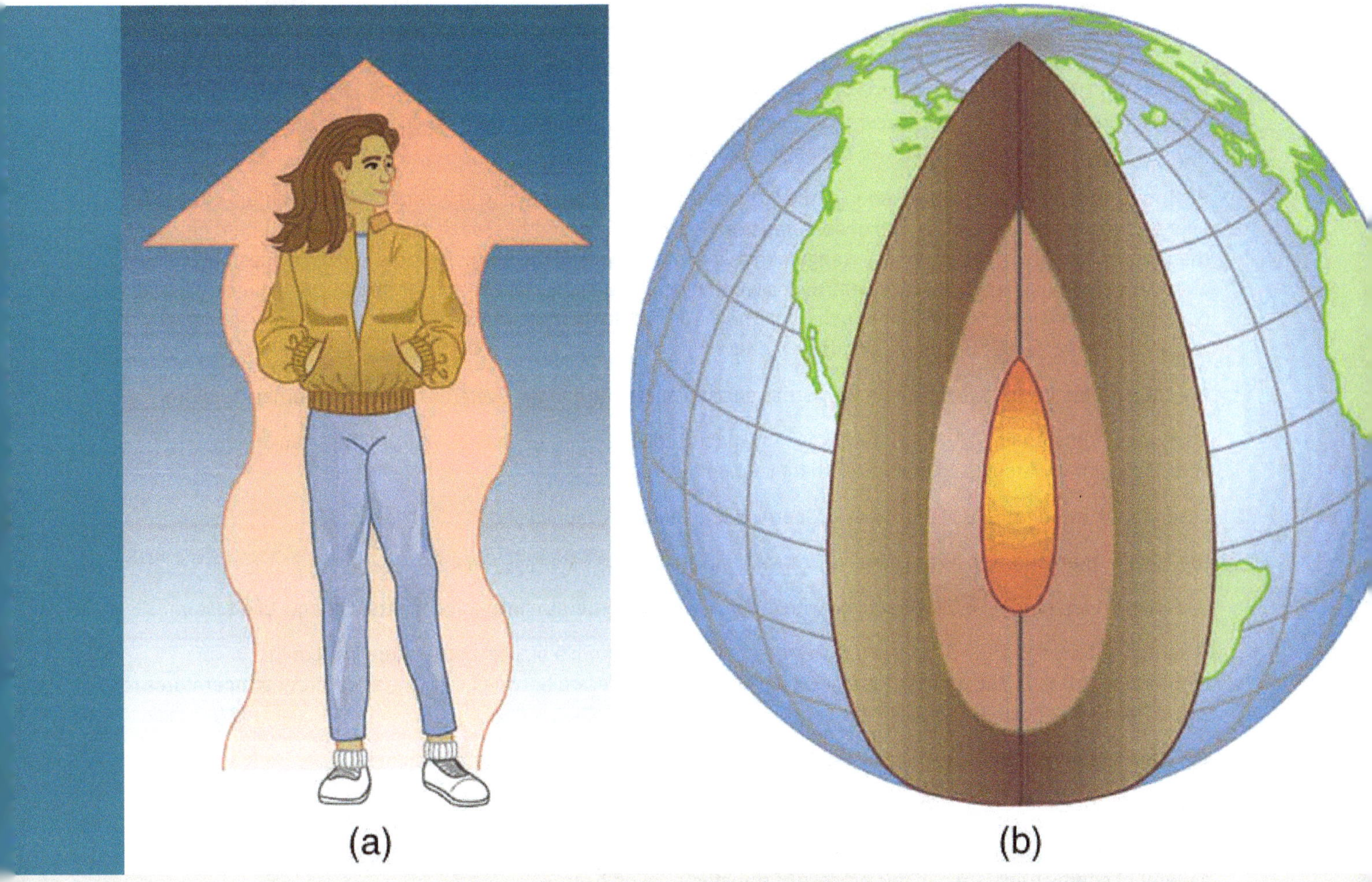

FIGURE 14.1 (a) The chilling effect of a clear breezy night is produced by the wind and by radiative heat transfer to cold outer space. (b) There was once great controversy about the Earth's age, but it is now generally accepted to be about 4.5 billion years old. Much of the debate is centered on the Earth's molten interior. According to our understanding of heat transfer, if the Earth is really that old, its center should have cooled off long ago. The discovery of radioactivity in rocks revealed the source of energy that keeps the Earth's interior molten, despite heat transfer to the surface, and from there to cold outer space.

CHAPTER OUTLINE

CONNECTION FOR AP® COURSES Heat is one of the most intriguing of the many ways in which energy goes from one place to another. Heat is often hidden, as it only exists when energy is in transit, and the methods of transfer are distinctly different. Energy transfer by heat touches every aspect of our lives, and helps us to understand how the universe functions. It explains the chill you feel on a clear breezy night, and why Earth's core has yet to cool.

In this chapter, the ideas of temperature and thermal energy are used to examine and define heat, how heat is affected by the thermal properties of materials, and how the various mechanisms of heat transfer function. These topics are fundamental and practical, and will be returned to in future chapters. Big Idea 4 of the AP® Physics Curriculum Framework is supported by a discussion of how systems interact through energy transfer by heat and how this leads to changes in the energy of each system. Big Idea 5 is supported by exploration of the law of energy conservation that governs any changes in the energy of a system. Heat involves the transfer of thermal energy, or internal energy, from one system to another or to its surroundings, and so leads to a change in the internal energy of the system. This is analogous to the way work transfers mechanical energy to a mass to change its kinetic or potential energy. However, heat occurs as a spontaneous process, in which thermal energy is transferred from a higher temperature system to a lower temperature system.

Big Idea 1 is supported by examination of the internal structure of systems, which determines the nature of those energy changes and the mechanism of heat transfer. Macroscopic properties, such as heat capacity, latent heat, and thermal conductivity, depend on the arrangements and interactions of the atoms or molecules in a substance. The arrangement of these particles also determines whether thermal energy will be transferred through direct physical contact between systems (conduction), through the motion of fluids with different temperatures (convection), or through emission or absorption of radiation.

Big Idea 1 Objects and systems have properties such as mass and charge. Systems may have internal structure.

Enduring Understanding 1.E Materials have many macroscopic properties that result from the arrangement and interactions of the atoms and molecules that make up the material.

Essential Knowledge 1.E.3 Matter has a property called thermal conductivity.

Big Idea 4 Interactions between systems can result in changes in those systems.

Enduring Understanding 4.C Interactions with other objects or systems can change the total energy of a system.

Essential Knowledge 4.C.3 Energy is transferred spontaneously from a higher temperature system to a lower temperature system. The process through which energy is transferred between systems at different temperatures is called heat.

Big Idea 5 Changes that occur as a result of interactions are constrained by conservation laws.

Enduring Understanding 5.B The energy of a system is conserved.

Essential Knowledge 5.B.6 Energy can be transferred by thermal processes involving differences in temperature; the amount of energy transferred in this process of transfer is called heat.

14.1 Heat

LEARNING OBJECTIVES

By the end of this section, you will be able to:

- Define heat as transfer of energy.

In Work, Energy, and Energy Resources, we defined work as force times distance and learned that work done on an object changes its kinetic energy. We also saw in Temperature, Kinetic Theory, and the Gas Laws that temperature is proportional to the (average) kinetic energy of atoms and molecules. We say that a thermal system has a certain internal energy: its internal energy is higher if the temperature is higher. If two objects at different temperatures are brought in contact with each other, energy is transferred from the hotter to the colder object until equilibrium is reached and the bodies reach thermal equilibrium (i.e., they are at the same temperature). No work is done by either object, because no force acts through a distance. The transfer of energy is caused by the temperature difference, and ceases once the temperatures are equal. These observations lead to the following definition of **heat**: Heat is the spontaneous transfer of energy due to a temperature difference.

As noted in Temperature, Kinetic Theory, and the Gas Laws, heat is often confused with temperature. For example, we may say the heat was unbearable, when we actually mean that the temperature was high. Heat is a form of energy, whereas temperature is not. The misconception arises because we are sensitive to the flow of heat, rather than the temperature.

Owing to the fact that heat is a form of energy, it has the SI unit of *joule* (J). The *calorie* (cal) is a common unit of energy, defined as the energy needed to change the temperature of 1.00 g of water by 1.00°C —specifically, between 14.5°C and 15.5°C, since there is a slight temperature dependence. Perhaps the most common unit of heat is the **kilocalorie** (kcal), which is the energy needed to change the temperature of 1.00 kg of water by 1.00°C. Since mass is most often specified in kilograms, kilocalorie is commonly used. Food calories (given the notation Cal, and sometimes called "big calorie") are actually kilocalories ($1\ \text{kilocalorie} = 1000\ \text{calories}$), a fact not easily determined from package labeling.

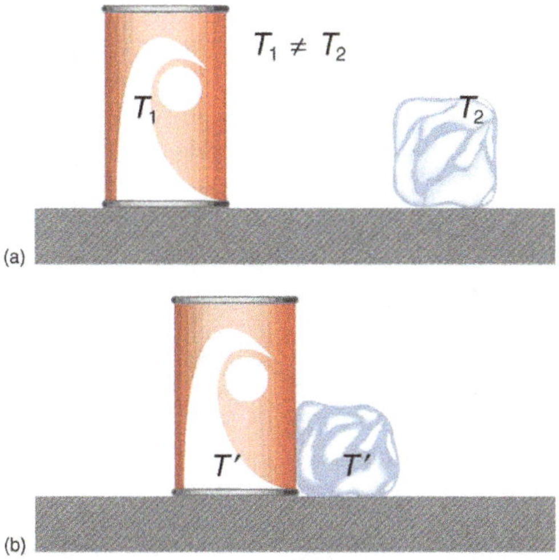

FIGURE 14.2 In figure (a) the soft drink and the ice have different temperatures, T_1 and T_2, and are not in thermal equilibrium. In figure (b), when the soft drink and ice are allowed to interact, energy is transferred until they reach the same temperature T', achieving equilibrium. Heat transfer occurs due to the difference in temperatures. In fact, since the soft drink and ice are both in contact with the surrounding air and bench, the equilibrium temperature will be the same for both.

Mechanical Equivalent of Heat

It is also possible to change the temperature of a substance by doing work. Work can transfer energy into or out of a system. This realization helped establish the fact that heat is a form of energy. James Prescott Joule (1818–1889) performed many experiments to establish the **mechanical equivalent of heat**—*the work needed to produce the same effects as heat transfer*. In terms of the units used for these two terms, the best modern value for this equivalence is

$$1.000\ \text{kcal} = 4186\ \text{J}. \tag{14.1}$$

We consider this equation as the conversion between two different units of energy.

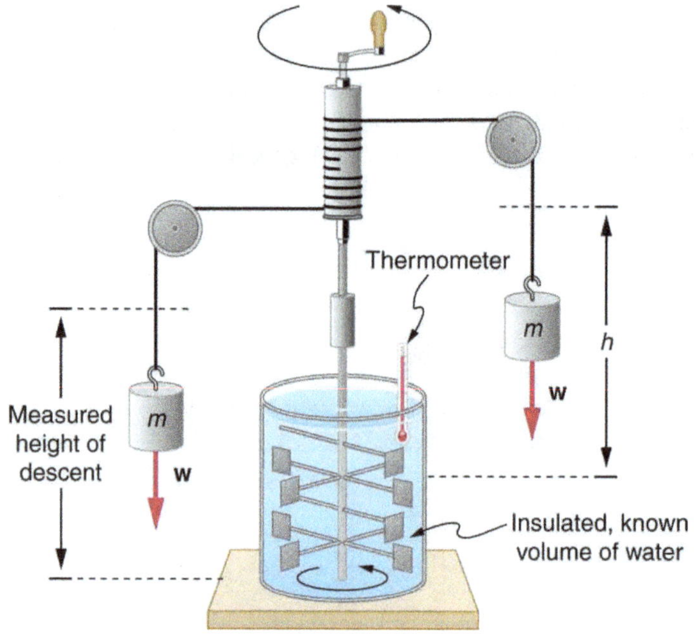

FIGURE 14.3 Schematic depiction of Joule's experiment that established the equivalence of heat and work.

The figure above shows one of Joule's most famous experimental setups for demonstrating the mechanical equivalent of heat. It demonstrated that work and heat can produce the same effects, and helped establish the principle of conservation of energy. Gravitational potential energy (PE) (work done by the gravitational force) is converted into kinetic energy (KE), and then randomized by viscosity and turbulence into increased average kinetic energy of atoms and molecules in the system, producing a temperature increase. His contributions to the field of thermodynamics were so significant that the SI unit of energy was named after him.

Heat added or removed from a system changes its internal energy and thus its temperature. Such a temperature increase is observed while cooking. However, adding heat does not necessarily increase the temperature. An example is melting of ice; that is, when a substance changes from one phase to another. Work done on the system or by the system can also change the internal energy of the system. Joule demonstrated that the temperature of a system can be increased by stirring. If an ice cube is rubbed against a rough surface, work is done by the frictional force. A system has a well-defined internal energy, but we cannot say that it has a certain "heat content" or "work content". We use the phrase "heat transfer" to emphasize its nature.

CHECK YOUR UNDERSTANDING

Two samples (A and B) of the same substance are kept in a lab. Someone adds 10 kilojoules (kJ) of heat to one sample, while 10 kJ of work is done on the other sample. How can you tell to which sample the heat was added?

Solution

Heat and work both change the internal energy of the substance. However, the properties of the sample only depend on the internal energy so that it is impossible to tell whether heat was added to sample A or B.

14.2 Temperature Change and Heat Capacity

LEARNING OBJECTIVES

By the end of this section, you will be able to:

- Observe heat transfer and change in temperature and mass.
- Calculate final temperature after heat transfer between two objects.

One of the major effects of heat transfer is temperature change: heating increases the temperature while cooling decreases it. We assume that there is no phase change and that no work is done on or by the system. Experiments show that the transferred heat depends on three factors—the change in temperature, the mass of the system, and the substance and phase of the substance.

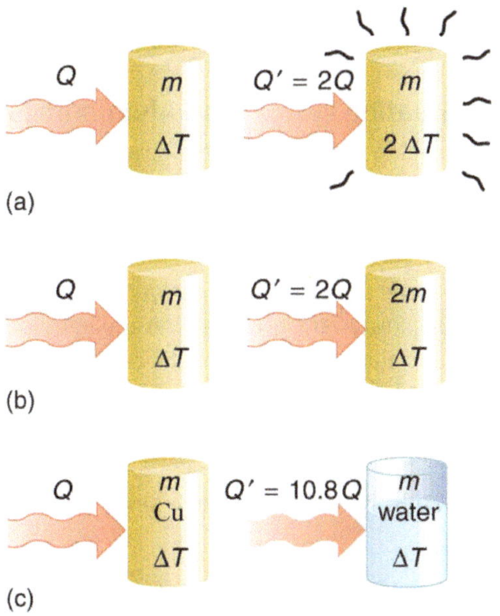

FIGURE 14.4 The heat Q transferred to cause a temperature change depends on the magnitude of the temperature change, the mass of the system, and the substance and phase involved. (a) The amount of heat transferred is directly proportional to the temperature change. To double the temperature change of a mass m, you need to add twice the heat. (b) The amount of heat transferred is also directly proportional to the mass. To cause an equivalent temperature change in a doubled mass, you need to add twice the heat. (c) The amount of heat transferred depends on the substance and its phase. If it takes an amount Q of heat to cause a temperature change ΔT in a given mass of copper, it will take 10.8 times that amount of heat to cause the equivalent temperature change in the same mass of water assuming no phase change in either substance.

The dependence on temperature change and mass are easily understood. Owing to the fact that the (average) kinetic energy of an atom or molecule is proportional to the absolute temperature, the internal energy of a system is proportional to the absolute temperature and the number of atoms or molecules. Owing to the fact that the transferred heat is equal to the change in the internal energy, the heat is proportional to the mass of the substance and the temperature change. The transferred heat also depends on the substance so that, for example, the heat necessary to raise the temperature is less for alcohol than for water. For the same substance, the transferred heat also depends on the phase (gas, liquid, or solid).

HEAT TRANSFER AND TEMPERATURE CHANGE

The quantitative relationship between heat transfer and temperature change contains all three factors:

$$Q = mc\Delta T, \tag{14.2}$$

where Q is the symbol for heat transfer, m is the mass of the substance, and ΔT is the change in temperature. The symbol c stands for **specific heat** and depends on the material and phase. The specific heat is the amount of heat necessary to change the temperature of 1.00 kg of mass by 1.00°C. The specific heat c is a property of the substance; its SI unit is $\text{J/(kg} \cdot \text{K)}$ or $\text{J/(kg}\cdot{}^\circ\text{C)}$. Recall that the temperature change (ΔT) is the same in units of kelvin and degrees Celsius. If heat transfer is measured in kilocalories, then *the unit of specific heat* is $\text{kcal/(kg}\cdot{}^\circ\text{C)}$.

Values of specific heat must generally be looked up in tables, because there is no simple way to calculate them. In general, the specific heat also depends on the temperature. Table 14.1 lists representative values of specific heat for various substances. Except for gases, the temperature and volume dependence of the specific heat of most substances is weak. We see from this table that the specific heat of water is five times that of glass and ten times that of iron, which means that it takes five times as much heat to raise the temperature of water the same amount as for glass and ten times as much heat to raise the temperature of water as for iron. In fact, water has one of the largest specific heats of any material, which is important for sustaining life on Earth.

EXAMPLE 14.1

Calculating the Required Heat: Heating Water in an Aluminum Pan

A 0.500 kg aluminum pan on a stove is used to heat 0.250 liters of water from 20.0°C to 80.0°C. (a) How much heat is required? What percentage of the heat is used to raise the temperature of (b) the pan and (c) the water?

Strategy

The pan and the water are always at the same temperature. When you put the pan on the stove, the temperature of the water and the pan is increased by the same amount. We use the equation for the heat transfer for the given temperature change and mass of water and aluminum. The specific heat values for water and aluminum are given in Table 14.1.

Solution

Because water is in thermal contact with the aluminum, the pan and the water are at the same temperature.

1. Calculate the temperature difference:

$$\Delta T = T_\text{f} - T_\text{i} = 60.0\text{°C}. \tag{14.3}$$

2. Calculate the mass of water. Because the density of water is $1000\ \text{kg/m}^3$, one liter of water has a mass of 1 kg, and the mass of 0.250 liters of water is $m_\text{w} = 0.250\ \text{kg}$.
3. Calculate the heat transferred to the water. Use the specific heat of water in Table 14.1:

$$Q_\text{w} = m_\text{w} c_\text{w} \Delta T = (0.250\ \text{kg})(4186\ \text{J/kg°C})(60.0\text{°C}) = 62.8\ \text{kJ}. \tag{14.4}$$

4. Calculate the heat transferred to the aluminum. Use the specific heat for aluminum in Table 14.1:

$$Q_\text{Al} = m_\text{Al} c_\text{Al} \Delta T = (0.500\ \text{kg})(900\ \text{J/kg°C})(60.0\text{°C}) = 27.0 \times 10^4\ \text{J} = 27.0\ \text{kJ}. \tag{14.5}$$

5. Compare the percentage of heat going into the pan versus that going into the water. First, find the total transferred heat:

$$Q_\text{Total} = Q_\text{W} + Q_\text{Al} = 62.8\ \text{kJ} + 27.0\ \ \text{kJ} = 89.8\ \text{kJ}. \tag{14.6}$$

Thus, the amount of heat going into heating the pan is

$$\frac{27.0\ \text{kJ}}{89.8\ \text{kJ}} \times 100\% = 30.1\%, \tag{14.7}$$

and the amount going into heating the water is

$$\frac{62.8\ \text{kJ}}{89.8\ \text{kJ}} \times 100\% = 69.9\%. \tag{14.8}$$

Discussion

In this example, the heat transferred to the container is a significant fraction of the total transferred heat. Although the mass of the pan is twice that of the water, the specific heat of water is over four times greater than that of aluminum. Therefore, it takes a bit more than twice the heat to achieve the given temperature change for the water as compared to the aluminum pan.

FIGURE 14.5 The smoking brakes on this truck are a visible evidence of the mechanical equivalent of heat.

EXAMPLE 14.2

Calculating the Temperature Increase from the Work Done on a Substance: Truck Brakes Overheat on Downhill Runs

Truck brakes used to control speed on a downhill run do work, converting gravitational potential energy into increased internal energy (higher temperature) of the brake material. This conversion prevents the gravitational potential energy from being converted into kinetic energy of the truck. The problem is that the mass of the truck is large compared with that of the brake material absorbing the energy, and the temperature increase may occur too fast for sufficient heat to transfer from the brakes to the environment.

Calculate the temperature increase of 100 kg of brake material with an average specific heat of $800\ \text{J(kg°C)}$ if the material retains 10% of the energy from a 10,000-kg truck descending 75.0 m (in vertical displacement) at a constant speed.

Strategy

If the brakes are not applied, gravitational potential energy is converted into kinetic energy. When brakes are applied, gravitational potential energy is converted into internal energy of the brake material. We first calculate the gravitational potential energy (Mgh) that the entire truck loses in its descent and then find the temperature increase produced in the brake material alone.

Solution

1. Calculate the change in gravitational potential energy as the truck goes downhill

$$Mgh = (10{,}000\ \text{kg})\left(9.80\ \text{m/s}^2\right)(75.0\ \text{m}) = 7.35 \times 10^6\ \text{J}. \tag{14.9}$$

2. Calculate the temperature from the heat transferred using $Q = Mgh$ and

$$\Delta T = \frac{Q}{mc}, \tag{14.10}$$

where m is the mass of the brake material. Insert the values $m = 100\ \text{kg}$ and $c = 800\ \text{J(kg°C)}$ to find

$$\Delta T = \frac{\left(7.35 \times 10^6\ \text{J}\right)}{(100\ \text{kg})(800\ \text{J(kg°C)})} = 92\text{°C}. \tag{14.11}$$

Discussion

This same idea underlies the recent hybrid technology of cars, where mechanical energy (gravitational potential energy) is converted by the brakes into electrical energy (battery).

Substances	Specific heat (c)	
Solids	J(kg°C)	kcal(kg°C)[1]
Aluminum	900	0.215
Asbestos	800	0.19
Concrete, granite (average)	840	0.20
Copper	387	0.0924
Glass	840	0.20
Gold	129	0.0308
Human body (average at 37 °C)	3500	0.83
Ice (average, -50°C to 0°C)	2090	0.50
Iron, steel	452	0.108
Lead	128	0.0305
Silver	235	0.0562
Wood	1700	0.4
Liquids		
Benzene	1740	0.415
Ethanol	2450	0.586
Glycerin	2410	0.576
Mercury	139	0.0333
Water (15.0 °C)	4186	1.000
Gases[2]	$C_v(C_p)$	$C_v(C_p)$
Air (dry)	721 (1015)	0.172 (0.242)
Ammonia	1670 (2190)	0.399 (0.523)
Carbon dioxide	638 (833)	0.152 (0.199)
Nitrogen	739 (1040)	0.177 (0.248)

1 These values are identical in units of cal/g·°C.

2 c_v at constant volume and at 20.0°C, except as noted, and at 1.00 atm average pressure. Values in parentheses are c_p at a constant

Substances	Specific heat (c)	
Oxygen	651 (913)	0.156 (0.218)
Steam (100°C)	1520 (2020)	0.363 (0.482)

TABLE 14.1 Specific Heats[3] of Various Substances

Note that Example 14.2 is an illustration of the mechanical equivalent of heat. Alternatively, the temperature increase could be produced by a blow torch instead of mechanically.

EXAMPLE 14.3

Calculating the Final Temperature When Heat Is Transferred Between Two Bodies: Pouring Cold Water in a Hot Pan

Suppose you pour 0.250 kg of $20.0°C$ water (about a cup) into a 0.500-kg aluminum pan off the stove with a temperature of $150°C$. Assume that the pan is placed on an insulated pad and that a negligible amount of water boils off. What is the temperature when the water and pan reach thermal equilibrium a short time later?

Strategy

The pan is placed on an insulated pad so that little heat transfer occurs with the surroundings. Originally the pan and water are not in thermal equilibrium: the pan is at a higher temperature than the water. Heat transfer then restores thermal equilibrium once the water and pan are in contact. Because heat transfer between the pan and water takes place rapidly, the mass of evaporated water is negligible and the magnitude of the heat lost by the pan is equal to the heat gained by the water. The exchange of heat stops once a thermal equilibrium between the pan and the water is achieved. The heat exchange can be written as $|Q_{\text{hot}}| = Q_{\text{cold}}$.

Solution

1. Use the equation for heat transfer $Q = mc\Delta T$ to express the heat lost by the aluminum pan in terms of the mass of the pan, the specific heat of aluminum, the initial temperature of the pan, and the final temperature:
$$Q_{\text{hot}} = m_{\text{Al}}c_{\text{Al}}(T_{\text{f}} - 150°\text{C}). \tag{14.12}$$

2. Express the heat gained by the water in terms of the mass of the water, the specific heat of water, the initial temperature of the water and the final temperature:
$$Q_{\text{cold}} = m_{\text{W}}c_{\text{W}}(T_{\text{f}} - 20.0°\text{C}). \tag{14.13}$$

3. Note that $Q_{\text{hot}} < 0$ and $Q_{\text{cold}} > 0$ and that they must sum to zero because the heat lost by the hot pan must be the same as the heat gained by the cold water:
$$\begin{aligned} Q_{\text{cold}} + Q_{\text{hot}} &= 0, \\ Q_{\text{cold}} &= -Q_{\text{hot}}, \\ m_{\text{W}}c_{\text{W}}(T_{\text{f}} - 20.0°\text{C}) &= -m_{\text{Al}}c_{\text{Al}}(T_{\text{f}} - 150°\text{C}.) \end{aligned} \tag{14.14}$$

4. Bring all terms involving T_{f} on the left hand side and all other terms on the right hand side. Solve for T_{f},
$$T_{\text{f}} = \frac{m_{\text{Al}}c_{\text{Al}}(150°\text{C}) + m_{\text{W}}c_{\text{W}}(20.0°\text{C})}{m_{\text{Al}}c_{\text{Al}} + m_{\text{W}}c_{\text{W}}}, \tag{14.15}$$

   and insert the numerical values:
$$\begin{aligned} T_{\text{f}} &= \frac{(0.500\text{ kg})(900\text{ J(kg°C)})(150°\text{C}) + (0.250\text{ kg})(4186\text{ J(kg°C)})(20.0°\text{C})}{(0.500\text{ kg})(900\text{ J(kg°C)}) + (0.250\text{ kg})(4186\text{ J(kg°C)})} \\ &= \frac{88430\text{ J}}{1496.5\text{ J/°C}} \\ &= 59.1°\text{C}. \end{aligned} \tag{14.16}$$

pressure of 1.00 atm.

Discussion

This is a typical *calorimetry* problem—two bodies at different temperatures are brought in contact with each other and exchange heat until a common temperature is reached. Why is the final temperature so much closer to 20.0°C than 150°C? The reason is that water has a greater specific heat than most common substances and thus undergoes a small temperature change for a given heat transfer. A large body of water, such as a lake, requires a large amount of heat to increase its temperature appreciably. This explains why the temperature of a lake stays relatively constant during a day even when the temperature change of the air is large. However, the water temperature does change over longer times (e.g., summer to winter).

TAKE-HOME EXPERIMENT: TEMPERATURE CHANGE OF LAND AND WATER

What heats faster, land or water?

To study differences in heat capacity:

- Place equal masses of dry sand (or soil) and water at the same temperature into two small jars. (The average density of soil or sand is about 1.6 times that of water, so you can achieve approximately equal masses by using 50% more water by volume.)
- Heat both (using an oven or a heat lamp) for the same amount of time.
- Record the final temperature of the two masses.
- Now bring both jars to the same temperature by heating for a longer period of time.
- Remove the jars from the heat source and measure their temperature every 5 minutes for about 30 minutes.

Which sample cools off the fastest? This activity replicates the phenomena responsible for land breezes and sea breezes.

CHECK YOUR UNDERSTANDING

If 25 kJ is necessary to raise the temperature of a block from 25°C to 30°C, how much heat is necessary to heat the block from 45°C to 50°C?

Solution

The heat transfer depends only on the temperature difference. Since the temperature differences are the same in both cases, the same 25 kJ is necessary in the second case.

14.3 Phase Change and Latent Heat

LEARNING OBJECTIVES

By the end of this section, you will be able to:

- Examine heat transfer.
- Calculate final temperature from heat transfer.

So far we have discussed temperature change due to heat transfer. No temperature change occurs from heat transfer if ice melts and becomes liquid water (i.e., during a phase change). For example, consider water dripping from icicles melting on a roof warmed by the Sun. Conversely, water freezes in an ice tray cooled by lower-temperature surroundings.

FIGURE 14.6 Heat from the air transfers to the ice causing it to melt. (credit: Mike Brand)

Energy is required to melt a solid because the cohesive bonds between the molecules in the solid must be broken apart such that, in the liquid, the molecules can move around at comparable kinetic energies; thus, there is no rise in temperature. Similarly, energy is needed to vaporize a liquid, because molecules in a liquid interact with each other via attractive forces. There is no temperature change until a phase change is complete. The temperature of a cup of soda initially at $0°C$ stays at $0°C$ until all the ice has melted. Conversely, energy is released during freezing and condensation, usually in the form of thermal energy. Work is done by cohesive forces when molecules are brought together. The corresponding energy must be given off (dissipated) to allow them to stay together Figure 14.7.

The energy involved in a phase change depends on two major factors: the number and strength of bonds or force pairs. The number of bonds is proportional to the number of molecules and thus to the mass of the sample. The strength of forces depends on the type of molecules. The heat Q required to change the phase of a sample of mass m is given by

$$Q = mL_{\text{f}} \text{ (melting/freezing)}, \quad 14.17$$

$$Q = mL_{\text{v}} \text{ (vaporization/condensation)}, \quad 14.18$$

where the latent heat of fusion, L_{f}, and latent heat of vaporization, L_{v}, are material constants that are determined experimentally. See (Table 14.2).

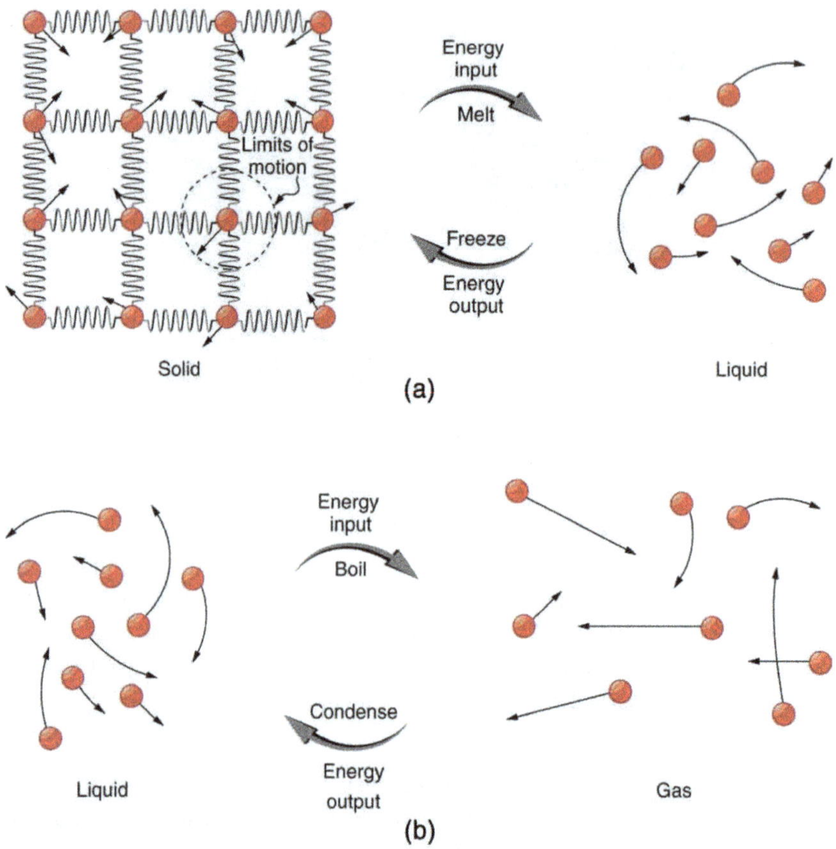

FIGURE 14.7 (a) Energy is required to partially overcome the attractive forces between molecules in a solid to form a liquid. That same energy must be removed for freezing to take place. (b) Molecules are separated by large distances when going from liquid to vapor, requiring significant energy to overcome molecular attraction. The same energy must be removed for condensation to take place. There is no temperature change until a phase change is complete.

Latent heat is measured in units of J/kg. Both L_f and L_v depend on the substance, particularly on the strength of its molecular forces as noted earlier. L_f and L_v are collectively called **latent heat coefficients**. They are *latent*, or hidden, because in phase changes, energy enters or leaves a system without causing a temperature change in the system; so, in effect, the energy is hidden. Table 14.2 lists representative values of L_f and L_v, together with melting and boiling points.

The table shows that significant amounts of energy are involved in phase changes. Let us look, for example, at how much energy is needed to melt a kilogram of ice at $0°C$ to produce a kilogram of water at $0°C$. Using the equation for a change in temperature and the value for water from Table 14.2, we find that $Q = mL_f = (1.0\text{ kg})(334\text{ kJ/kg}) = 334\text{ kJ}$ is the energy to melt a kilogram of ice. This is a lot of energy as it represents the same amount of energy needed to raise the temperature of 1 kg of liquid water from $0°C$ to $79.8°C$. Even more energy is required to vaporize water; it would take 2256 kJ to change 1 kg of liquid water at the normal boiling point ($100°C$ at atmospheric pressure) to steam (water vapor). This example shows that the energy for a phase change is enormous compared to energy associated with temperature changes without a phase change.

		L_f			L_v	
Substance	**Melting point (°C)**	**kJ/kg**	**kcal/kg**	**Boiling point (°C)**	**kJ/kg**	**kcal/kg**
Helium	−269.7	5.23	1.25	−268.9	20.9	4.99
Hydrogen	−259.3	58.6	14.0	−252.9	452	108

TABLE 14.2 Heats of Fusion and Vaporization [6]

6 Values quoted at the normal melting and boiling temperatures at standard atmospheric pressure (1 atm).

		L_f			L_v	
Nitrogen	−210.0	25.5	6.09	−195.8	201	48.0
Oxygen	−218.8	13.8	3.30	−183.0	213	50.9
Ethanol	−114	104	24.9	78.3	854	204
Ammonia	−75		108	−33.4	1370	327
Mercury	−38.9	11.8	2.82	357	272	65.0
Water	0.00	334	79.8	100.0	2430[4]	580[5]
Sulfur	119	38.1	9.10	444.6	326	77.9
Lead	327	24.5	5.85	1750	871	208
Antimony	631	165	39.4	1440	561	134
Aluminum	660	380	90	2450	11400	2720
Silver	961	88.3	21.1	2193	2336	558
Gold	1063	64.5	15.4	2660	1578	377
Copper	1083	134	32.0	2595	5069	1211
Uranium	1133	84	20	3900	1900	454
Tungsten	3410	184	44	5900	4810	1150

TABLE 14.2 Heats of Fusion and Vaporization[6]

Phase changes can have a tremendous stabilizing effect even on temperatures that are not near the melting and boiling points, because evaporation and condensation (conversion of a gas into a liquid state) occur even at temperatures below the boiling point. Take, for example, the fact that air temperatures in humid climates rarely go above $35.0°C$, which is because most heat transfer goes into evaporating water into the air. Similarly, temperatures in humid weather rarely fall below the dew point because enormous heat is released when water vapor condenses.

We examine the effects of phase change more precisely by considering adding heat into a sample of ice at $-20°C$ (Figure 14.8). The temperature of the ice rises linearly, absorbing heat at a constant rate of $0.50\ \text{cal/g} \cdot° \text{C}$ until it reaches $0°C$. Once at this temperature, the ice begins to melt until all the ice has melted, absorbing 79.8 cal/g of heat. The temperature remains constant at $0°C$ during this phase change. Once all the ice has melted, the temperature of the liquid water rises, absorbing heat at a new constant rate of $1.00\ \text{cal/g} \cdot° \text{C}$. At $100°C$, the water begins to boil and the temperature again remains constant while the water absorbs 539 cal/g of heat during this phase change. When all the liquid has become steam vapor, the temperature rises again, absorbing heat at a rate of $0.482\ \text{cal/g} \cdot° \text{C}$.

4 At $37.0°C$ (body temperature), the heat of vaporization L_v for water is 2430 kJ/kg or 580 kcal/kg
5 At $37.0°C$ (body temperature), the heat of vaporization L_v for water is 2430 kJ/kg or 580 kcal/kg

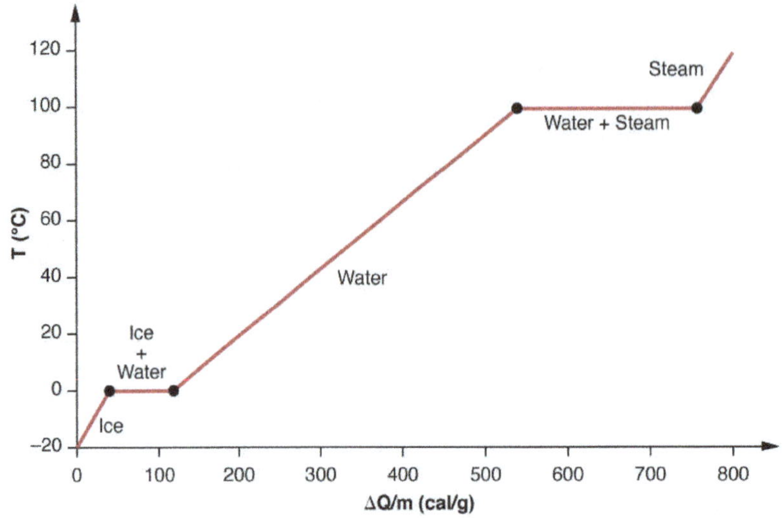

FIGURE 14.8 A graph of temperature versus energy added. The system is constructed so that no vapor evaporates while ice warms to become liquid water, and so that, when vaporization occurs, the vapor remains in of the system. The long stretches of constant temperature values at $0°C$ and $100°C$ reflect the large latent heat of melting and vaporization, respectively.

Water can evaporate at temperatures below the boiling point. More energy is required than at the boiling point, because the kinetic energy of water molecules at temperatures below $100°C$ is less than that at $100°C$, hence less energy is available from random thermal motions. Take, for example, the fact that, at body temperature, perspiration from the skin requires a heat input of 2428 kJ/kg, which is about 10 percent higher than the latent heat of vaporization at $100°C$. This heat comes from the skin, and thus provides an effective cooling mechanism in hot weather. High humidity inhibits evaporation, so that body temperature might rise, leaving unevaporated sweat on your brow.

EXAMPLE 14.4

Calculate Final Temperature from Phase Change: Cooling Soda with Ice Cubes

Three ice cubes are used to chill a soda at $20°C$ with mass $m_{\text{soda}} = 0.25\text{ kg}$. The ice is at $0°C$ and each ice cube has a mass of 6.0 g. Assume that the soda is kept in a foam container so that heat loss can be ignored. Assume the soda has the same heat capacity as water. Find the final temperature when all ice has melted.

Strategy

The ice cubes are at the melting temperature of $0°C$. Heat is transferred from the soda to the ice for melting. Melting of ice occurs in two steps: first the phase change occurs and solid (ice) transforms into liquid water at the melting temperature, then the temperature of this water rises. Melting yields water at $0°C$, so more heat is transferred from the soda to this water until the water plus soda system reaches thermal equilibrium,

$$Q_{\text{ice}} = -Q_{\text{soda}}. \tag{14.19}$$

The heat transferred to the ice is $Q_{\text{ice}} = m_{\text{ice}}L_f + m_{\text{ice}}c_W(T_f - 0°C)$. The heat given off by the soda is $Q_{\text{soda}} = m_{\text{soda}}c_W(T_f - 20°C)$. Since no heat is lost, $Q_{\text{ice}} = -Q_{\text{soda}}$, so that

$$m_{\text{ice}}L_f + m_{\text{ice}}c_W(T_f - 0°C) = -m_{\text{soda}}c_W(T_f - 20°C). \tag{14.20}$$

Bring all terms involving T_f on the left-hand-side and all other terms on the right-hand-side. Solve for the unknown quantity T_f:

$$T_f = \frac{m_{\text{soda}}c_W(20°C) - m_{\text{ice}}L_f}{(m_{\text{soda}} + m_{\text{ice}})c_W}. \tag{14.21}$$

Solution

1. Identify the known quantities. The mass of ice is $m_{\text{ice}} = 3\times6.0\text{ g} = 0.018\text{ kg}$ and the mass of soda is $m_{\text{soda}} = 0.25\text{ kg}$.

2. Calculate the terms in the numerator:

$$m_{\text{soda}}c_{\text{W}}(20^\circ\text{C}) = (0.25\text{ kg})(4186\text{ J(kg}^\circ\text{C))}(20^\circ\text{C}) = 20{,}930\text{ J} \tag{14.22}$$

and

$$m_{\text{ice}}L_{\text{f}} = (0.018\text{ kg})(334{,}000\text{ J/kg}) = 6012\text{ J}. \tag{14.23}$$

3. Calculate the denominator:

$$(m_{\text{soda}} + m_{\text{ice}})c_{\text{W}} = (0.25\text{ kg} + 0.018\text{ kg})(4186\text{ K/(kg}\cdot{}^\circ\text{C}) = 1122\text{ J/}^\circ\text{C}. \tag{14.24}$$

4. Calculate the final temperature:

$$T_{\text{f}} = \frac{20{,}930\text{ J} - 6012\text{ J}}{1122\text{ J/}^\circ\text{C}} = 13^\circ\text{C}. \tag{14.25}$$

Discussion

This example illustrates the enormous energies involved during a phase change. The mass of ice is about 7 percent the mass of water but leads to a noticeable change in the temperature of soda. Although we assumed that the ice was at the freezing temperature, this is incorrect: the typical temperature is -6°C. However, this correction gives a final temperature that is essentially identical to the result we found. Can you explain why?

We have seen that vaporization requires heat transfer to a liquid from the surroundings, so that energy is released by the surroundings. Condensation is the reverse process, increasing the temperature of the surroundings. This increase may seem surprising, since we associate condensation with cold objects—the glass in the figure, for example. However, energy must be removed from the condensing molecules to make a vapor condense. The energy is exactly the same as that required to make the phase change in the other direction, from liquid to vapor, and so it can be calculated from $Q = mL_{\text{V}}$.

FIGURE 14.9 Condensation forms on this glass of iced tea because the temperature of the nearby air is reduced to below the dew point. The rate at which water molecules join together exceeds the rate at which they separate, and so water condenses. Energy is released when the water condenses, speeding the melting of the ice in the glass. (credit: Jenny Downing)

REAL-WORLD APPLICATION

Energy is also released when a liquid freezes. This phenomenon is used by fruit growers in Florida to protect oranges when the temperature is close to the freezing point (0°C). Growers spray water on the plants in orchards so that the water freezes and heat is released to the growing oranges on the trees. This prevents the temperature inside the orange from dropping below freezing, which would damage the fruit.

FIGURE 14.10 The ice on these trees released large amounts of energy when it froze, helping to prevent the temperature of the trees from dropping below $0^{\circ}C$. Water is intentionally sprayed on orchards to help prevent hard frosts. (credit: Hermann Hammer)

Sublimation is the transition from solid to vapor phase. You may have noticed that snow can disappear into thin air without a trace of liquid water, or the disappearance of ice cubes in a freezer. The reverse is also true: Frost can form on very cold windows without going through the liquid stage. A popular effect is the making of "smoke" from dry ice, which is solid carbon dioxide. Sublimation occurs because the equilibrium vapor pressure of solids is not zero. Certain air fresheners use the sublimation of a solid to inject a perfume into the room. Moth balls are a slightly toxic example of a phenol (an organic compound) that sublimates, while some solids, such as osmium tetroxide, are so toxic that they must be kept in sealed containers to prevent human exposure to their sublimation-produced vapors.

FIGURE 14.11 Direct transitions between solid and vapor are common, sometimes useful, and even beautiful. (a) Dry ice sublimates directly to carbon dioxide gas. The visible vapor is made of water droplets. (credit: Windell Oskay) (b) Frost forms patterns on a very cold window, an example of a solid formed directly from a vapor. (credit: Liz West)

All phase transitions involve heat. In the case of direct solid-vapor transitions, the energy required is given by the equation $Q = mL_s$, where L_s is the **heat of sublimation**, which is the energy required to change 1.00 kg of a substance from the solid phase to the vapor phase. L_s is analogous to L_f and L_v, and its value depends on the substance. Sublimation requires energy input, so that dry ice is an effective coolant, whereas the reverse process (i.e., frosting) releases energy. The amount of energy required for sublimation is of the same order of magnitude as that for other phase transitions.

The material presented in this section and the preceding section allows us to calculate any number of effects related to temperature and phase change. In each case, it is necessary to identify which temperature and phase changes are taking place and then to apply the appropriate equation. Keep in mind that heat transfer and work can cause both temperature and phase changes.

Problem-Solving Strategies for the Effects of Heat Transfer

1. *Examine the situation to determine that there is a change in the temperature or phase. Is there heat transfer into or out of the system?* When the presence or absence of a phase change is not obvious, you may wish to first solve the problem as if there were no phase changes, and examine the temperature change obtained. If it is sufficient to take you past a boiling or melting point, you should then go back and do the problem in steps—temperature change, phase change, subsequent temperature change, and so on.
2. *Identify and list all objects that change temperature and phase.*
3. *Identify exactly what needs to be determined in the problem (identify the unknowns).* A written list is useful.
4. *Make a list of what is given or what can be inferred from the problem as stated (identify the knowns).*
5. *Solve the appropriate equation for the quantity to be determined (the unknown).* If there is a temperature change, the transferred heat depends on the specific heat (see Table 14.1) whereas, for a phase change, the transferred heat depends on the latent heat. See Table 14.2.
6. *Substitute the knowns along with their units into the appropriate equation and obtain numerical solutions complete with units.* You will need to do this in steps if there is more than one stage to the process (such as a temperature change followed by a phase change).
7. *Check the answer to see if it is reasonable: Does it make sense?* As an example, be certain that the temperature change does not also cause a phase change that you have not taken into account.

CHECK YOUR UNDERSTANDING

Why does snow remain on mountain slopes even when daytime temperatures are higher than the freezing temperature?

Solution
Snow is formed from ice crystals and thus is the solid phase of water. Because enormous heat is necessary for phase changes, it takes a certain amount of time for this heat to be accumulated from the air, even if the air is above $0°C$. The warmer the air is, the faster this heat exchange occurs and the faster the snow melts.

14.4 Heat Transfer Methods

LEARNING OBJECTIVES

By the end of this section, you will be able to:
- Discuss the different methods of heat transfer.

Equally as interesting as the effects of heat transfer on a system are the methods by which this occurs. Whenever there is a temperature difference, heat transfer occurs. Heat transfer may occur rapidly, such as through a cooking pan, or slowly, such as through the walls of a picnic ice chest. We can control rates of heat transfer by choosing materials (such as thick wool clothing for the winter), controlling air movement (such as the use of weather stripping around doors), or by choice of color (such as a white roof to reflect summer sunlight). So many processes involve heat transfer, so that it is hard to imagine a situation where no heat transfer occurs. Yet every process involving heat transfer takes place by only three methods:

1. **Conduction** is heat transfer through stationary matter by physical contact. (The matter is stationary on a macroscopic scale—we know there is thermal motion of the atoms and molecules at any temperature above absolute zero.) Heat transferred between the electric burner of a stove and the bottom of a pan is transferred by conduction.
2. **Convection** is the heat transfer by the macroscopic movement of a fluid. This type of transfer takes place in a forced-air furnace and in weather systems, for example.
3. Heat transfer by **radiation** occurs when microwaves, infrared radiation, visible light, or another form of

electromagnetic radiation is emitted or absorbed. An obvious example is the warming of the Earth by the Sun. A less obvious example is thermal radiation from the human body.

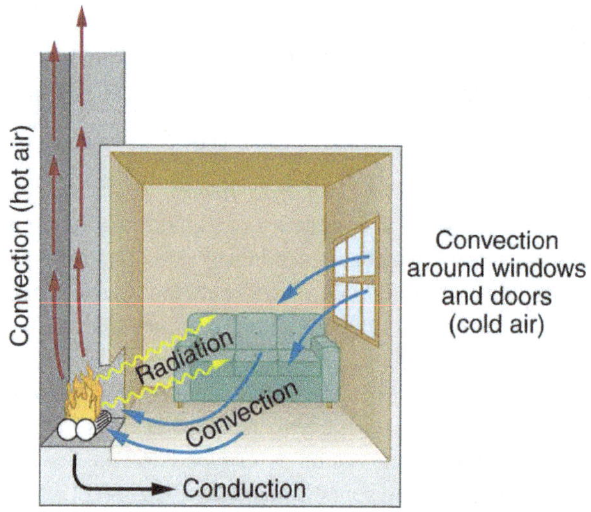

FIGURE 14.12 In a fireplace, heat transfer occurs by all three methods: conduction, convection, and radiation. Radiation is responsible for most of the heat transferred into the room. Heat transfer also occurs through conduction into the room, but at a much slower rate. Heat transfer by convection also occurs through cold air entering the room around windows and hot air leaving the room by rising up the chimney.

We examine these methods in some detail in the three following modules. Each method has unique and interesting characteristics, but all three do have one thing in common: they transfer heat solely because of a temperature difference Figure 14.12.

CHECK YOUR UNDERSTANDING

Name an example from daily life (different from the text) for each mechanism of heat transfer.

Solution

Conduction: Heat transfers into your hands as you hold a hot cup of coffee.

Convection: Heat transfers as the barista "steams" cold milk to make hot *cocoa*.

Radiation: Reheating a cold cup of coffee in a microwave oven.

14.5 Conduction

LEARNING OBJECTIVES

By the end of this section, you will be able to:

- Calculate thermal conductivity.
- Observe conduction of heat in collisions.
- Study thermal conductivities of common substances.

FIGURE 14.13 Insulation is used to limit the conduction of heat from the inside to the outside (in winters) and from the outside to the inside (in summers). (credit: Giles Douglas)

Your feet feel cold as you walk barefoot across the living room carpet in your cold house and then step onto the kitchen tile floor. This result is intriguing, since the carpet and tile floor are both at the same temperature. The different sensation you feel is explained by the different rates of heat transfer: the heat loss during the same time interval is greater for skin in contact with the tiles than with the carpet, so the temperature drop is greater on the tiles.

Some materials conduct thermal energy faster than others. In general, good conductors of electricity (metals like copper, aluminum, gold, and silver) are also good heat conductors, whereas insulators of electricity (wood, plastic, and rubber) are poor heat conductors. Figure 14.14 shows molecules in two bodies at different temperatures. The (average) kinetic energy of a molecule in the hot body is higher than in the colder body. If two molecules collide, an energy transfer from the molecule with greater kinetic energy to the molecule with less kinetic energy occurs. The cumulative effect from all collisions results in a net flux of heat from the hot body to the colder body. The heat flux thus depends on the temperature difference $\Delta T = T_{\text{hot}} - T_{\text{cold}}$. Therefore, you will get a more severe burn from boiling water than from hot tap water. Conversely, if the temperatures are the same, the net heat transfer rate falls to zero, and equilibrium is achieved. Owing to the fact that the number of collisions increases with increasing area, heat conduction depends on the cross-sectional area. If you touch a cold wall with your palm, your hand cools faster than if you just touch it with your fingertip.

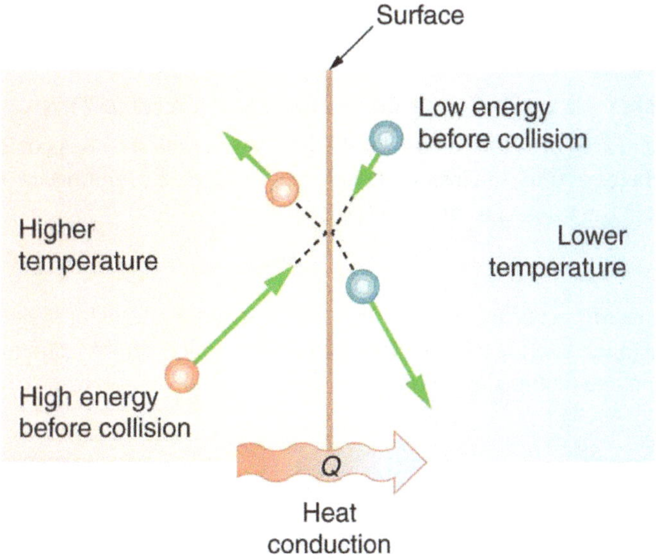

FIGURE 14.14 The molecules in two bodies at different temperatures have different average kinetic energies. Collisions occurring at the contact surface tend to transfer energy from high-temperature regions to low-temperature regions. In this illustration, a molecule in the lower temperature region (right side) has low energy before collision, but its energy increases after colliding with the contact surface. In contrast, a molecule in the higher temperature region (left side) has high energy before collision, but its energy decreases after colliding

with the contact surface.

A third factor in the mechanism of conduction is the thickness of the material through which heat transfers. The figure below shows a slab of material with different temperatures on either side. Suppose that T_2 is greater than T_1, so that heat is transferred from left to right. Heat transfer from the left side to the right side is accomplished by a series of molecular collisions. The thicker the material, the more time it takes to transfer the same amount of heat. This model explains why thick clothing is warmer than thin clothing in winters, and why Arctic mammals protect themselves with thick blubber.

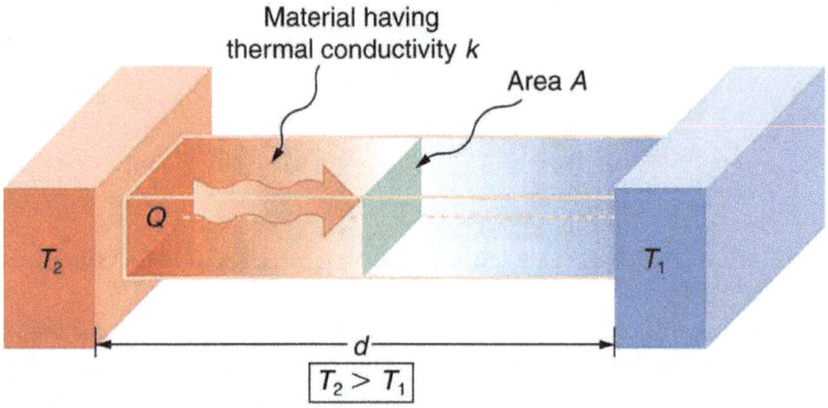

FIGURE 14.15 Heat conduction occurs through any material, represented here by a rectangular bar, whether window glass or walrus blubber. The temperature of the material is T_2 on the left and T_1 on the right, where T_2 is greater than T_1. The rate of heat transfer by conduction is directly proportional to the surface area A, the temperature difference $T_2 - T_1$, and the substance's conductivity k. The rate of heat transfer is inversely proportional to the thickness d.

Lastly, the heat transfer rate depends on the material properties described by the coefficient of thermal conductivity. All four factors are included in a simple equation that was deduced from and is confirmed by experiments. The **rate of conductive heat transfer** through a slab of material, such as the one in Figure 14.15, is given by

$$\frac{Q}{t} = \frac{kA(T_2 - T_1)}{d}, \qquad 14.26$$

where Q/t is the rate of heat transfer in watts or kilocalories per second, k is the **thermal conductivity** of the material, A and d are its surface area and thickness, as shown in Figure 14.15, and $(T_2 - T_1)$ is the temperature difference across the slab. Table 14.3 gives representative values of thermal conductivity.

EXAMPLE 14.5

Calculating Heat Transfer Through Conduction: Conduction Rate Through an Ice Box

A Styrofoam ice box has a total area of $0.950\ \text{m}^2$ and walls with an average thickness of 2.50 cm. The box contains ice, water, and canned beverages at $0°\text{C}$. The inside of the box is kept cold by melting ice. How much ice melts in one day if the ice box is kept in the trunk of a car at $35.0°\text{C}$?

Strategy

This question involves both heat for a phase change (melting of ice) and the transfer of heat by conduction. To find the amount of ice melted, we must find the net heat transferred. This value can be obtained by calculating the rate of heat transfer by conduction and multiplying by time.

Solution

1. Identify the knowns.

$$\begin{aligned} A &= 0.950\ \text{m}^2; \\ d &= 2.50\ \text{cm} = 0.0250\ \text{m}; \\ T_1 &= 0°\text{C}; \\ T_2 &= 35.0°\text{C},\ t = 1\ \text{day} = 24\ \text{hours} = 86{,}400\ \text{s}. \end{aligned} \quad (14.27)$$

2. Identify the unknowns. We need to solve for the mass of the ice, m. We will also need to solve for the net heat transferred to melt the ice, Q.
3. Determine which equations to use. The rate of heat transfer by conduction is given by

$$\frac{Q}{t} = \frac{kA(T_2 - T_1)}{d}. \quad (14.28)$$

4. The heat is used to melt the ice: $Q = mL_\text{f}$.
5. Insert the known values:

$$\frac{Q}{t} = \frac{(0.010\ \text{J/s} \cdot \text{m} \cdot °\text{C})(0.950\ \text{m}^2)(35.0°\text{C} - 0°\text{C})}{0.0250\ \text{m}} = 13.3\ \text{J/s}. \quad (14.29)$$

6. Multiply the rate of heat transfer by the time ($1\ \text{day} = 86{,}400\ \text{s}$):

$$Q = (Q/t)t = (13.3\ \text{J/s})(86{,}400\ \text{s}) = 1.15 \times 10^6\ \text{J}. \quad (14.30)$$

7. Set this equal to the heat transferred to melt the ice: $Q = mL_\text{f}$. Solve for the mass m:

$$m = \frac{Q}{L_\text{f}} = \frac{1.15 \times 10^6\ \text{J}}{334 \times 10^3\ \text{J/kg}} = 3.44\text{kg}. \quad (14.31)$$

Discussion

The result of 3.44 kg, or about 7.6 lbs, seems about right, based on experience. You might expect to use about a 4 kg (7–10 lb) bag of ice per day. A little extra ice is required if you add any warm food or beverages.

Inspecting the conductivities in Table 14.3 shows that Styrofoam is a very poor conductor and thus a good insulator. Other good insulators include fiberglass, wool, and goose-down feathers. Like Styrofoam, these all incorporate many small pockets of air, taking advantage of air's poor thermal conductivity.

Substance	Thermal conductivity k (J/s · m · °C)
Silver	420
Copper	390
Gold	318
Aluminum	220
Steel iron	80
Steel (stainless)	14
Ice	2.2
Glass (average)	0.84
Concrete brick	0.84

TABLE 14.3 Thermal Conductivities of Common Substances[7]

7 At temperatures near 0°C.

Substance	Thermal conductivity k (J/s · m · °C)
Water	0.6
Fatty tissue (without blood)	0.2
Asbestos	0.16
Plasterboard	0.16
Wood	0.08–0.16
Snow (dry)	0.10
Cork	0.042
Glass wool	0.042
Wool	0.04
Down feathers	0.025
Air	0.023
Styrofoam	0.010

TABLE 14.3 Thermal Conductivities of Common Substances[7]

A combination of material and thickness is often manipulated to develop good insulators—the smaller the conductivity k and the larger the thickness d, the better. The ratio of d/k will thus be large for a good insulator. The ratio d/k is called the R **factor**. The rate of conductive heat transfer is inversely proportional to R. The larger the value of R, the better the insulation. R factors are most commonly quoted for household insulation, refrigerators, and the like—unfortunately, it is still in non-metric units of ft^2·°F·h/Btu, although the unit usually goes unstated (1 British thermal unit [Btu] is the amount of energy needed to change the temperature of 1.0 lb of water by 1.0 °F). A couple of representative values are an R factor of 11 for 3.5-in-thick fiberglass batts (pieces) of insulation and an R factor of 19 for 6.5-in-thick fiberglass batts. Walls are usually insulated with 3.5-in batts, while ceilings are usually insulated with 6.5-in batts. In cold climates, thicker batts may be used in ceilings and walls.

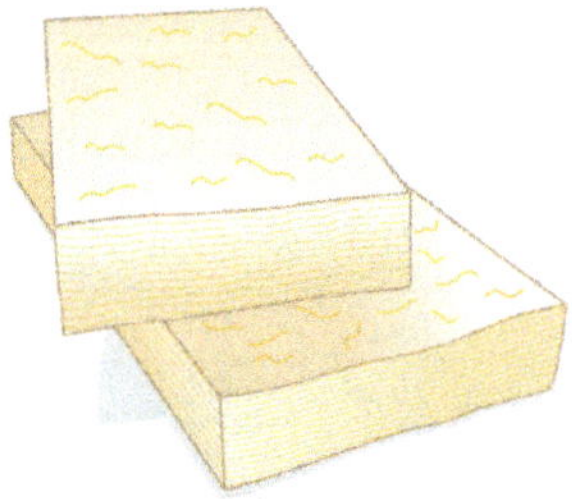

FIGURE 14.16 The fiberglass batt is used for insulation of walls and ceilings to prevent heat transfer between the inside of the building and the outside environment.

Note that in Table 14.3, the best thermal conductors—silver, copper, gold, and aluminum—are also the best electrical conductors, again related to the density of free electrons in them. Cooking utensils are typically made from good conductors.

EXAMPLE 14.6

Calculating the Temperature Difference Maintained by a Heat Transfer: Conduction Through an Aluminum Pan

Water is boiling in an aluminum pan placed on an electrical element on a stovetop. The sauce pan has a bottom that is 0.800 cm thick and 14.0 cm in diameter. The boiling water is evaporating at the rate of 1.00 g/s. What is the temperature difference across (through) the bottom of the pan?

Strategy

Conduction through the aluminum is the primary method of heat transfer here, and so we use the equation for the rate of heat transfer and solve for the temperature difference.

$$T_2 - T_1 = \frac{Q}{t}\left(\frac{d}{kA}\right). \qquad 14.32$$

Solution

1. Identify the knowns and convert them to the SI units.
   The thickness of the pan, $d = 0.800 \text{ cm} = 8.0 \times 10^{-3} \text{ m}$, the area of the pan, $A = \pi(0.14/2)^2 \text{ m}^2 = 1.54 \times 10^{-2} \text{ m}^2$, and the thermal conductivity, $k = 220 \text{ J/s} \cdot \text{m}\cdot°\text{C}$.
2. Calculate the necessary heat of vaporization of 1 g of water:
   $$Q = mL_\text{v} = \left(1.00 \times 10^{-3} \text{ kg}\right)\left(2256 \times 10^3 \text{ J/kg}\right) = 2256 \text{ J}. \qquad 14.33$$
3. Calculate the rate of heat transfer given that 1 g of water melts in one second:
   $$Q/t = 2256 \text{ J/s or } 2.26 \text{ kW}. \qquad 14.34$$
4. Insert the knowns into the equation and solve for the temperature difference:
   $$T_2 - T_1 = \frac{Q}{t}\left(\frac{d}{kA}\right) = (2256 \text{ J/s})\frac{8.00 \times 10^{-3}\text{m}}{(220 \text{ J/s} \cdot \text{m}\cdot°\text{C})\left(1.54 \times 10^{-2} \text{ m}^2\right)} = 5.33°\text{C}. \qquad 14.35$$

Discussion

The value for the heat transfer $Q/t = 2.26\text{kW}$ or 2256 J/s is typical for an electric stove. This value gives a remarkably small temperature difference between the stove and the pan. Consider that the stove burner is red hot while the inside of the pan is nearly $100°\text{C}$ because of its contact with boiling water. This contact effectively cools the bottom of the pan in spite of its proximity to the very hot stove burner. Aluminum is such a good conductor that it only takes this small temperature difference to produce a heat transfer of 2.26 kW into the pan.

Conduction is caused by the random motion of atoms and molecules. As such, it is an ineffective mechanism for heat transport over macroscopic distances and short time distances. Take, for example, the temperature on the Earth, which would be unbearably cold during the night and extremely hot during the day if heat transport in the atmosphere was to be only through conduction. In another example, car engines would overheat unless there was a more efficient way to remove excess heat from the pistons.

CHECK YOUR UNDERSTANDING

How does the rate of heat transfer by conduction change when all spatial dimensions are doubled?

Solution

Because area is the product of two spatial dimensions, it increases by a factor of four when each dimension is doubled $\left(A_\text{final} = (2d)^2 = 4d^2 = 4A_\text{initial}\right)$. The distance, however, simply doubles. Because the temperature difference and the coefficient of thermal conductivity are independent of the spatial dimensions, the rate of heat transfer by conduction increases by a factor of four divided by two, or two:

$$\left(\frac{Q}{t}\right)_{\text{final}} = \frac{kA_{\text{final}}(T_2 - T_1)}{d_{\text{final}}} = \frac{k(4\text{A}_{\text{initial}})(T_2 - T_1)}{2\text{d}_{\text{initial}}} = 2\frac{kA_{\text{initial}}(T_2 - T_1)}{d_{\text{initial}}} = 2\left(\frac{Q}{t}\right)_{\text{initial}}. \quad 14.36$$

14.6 Convection

LEARNING OBJECTIVES

By the end of this section, you will be able to:

- Discuss the method of heat transfer by convection.

Convection is driven by large-scale flow of matter. In the case of Earth, the atmospheric circulation is caused by the flow of hot air from the tropics to the poles, and the flow of cold air from the poles toward the tropics. (Note that Earth's rotation causes the observed easterly flow of air in the northern hemisphere). Car engines are kept cool by the flow of water in the cooling system, with the water pump maintaining a flow of cool water to the pistons. The circulatory system is used the body: when the body overheats, the blood vessels in the skin expand (dilate), which increases the blood flow to the skin where it can be cooled by sweating. These vessels become smaller when it is cold outside and larger when it is hot (so more fluid flows, and more energy is transferred).

The body also loses a significant fraction of its heat through the breathing process.

While convection is usually more complicated than conduction, we can describe convection and do some straightforward, realistic calculations of its effects. Natural convection is driven by buoyant forces: hot air rises because density decreases as temperature increases. The house in Figure 14.17 is kept warm in this manner, as is the pot of water on the stove in Figure 14.18. Ocean currents and large-scale atmospheric circulation transfer energy from one part of the globe to another. Both are examples of natural convection.

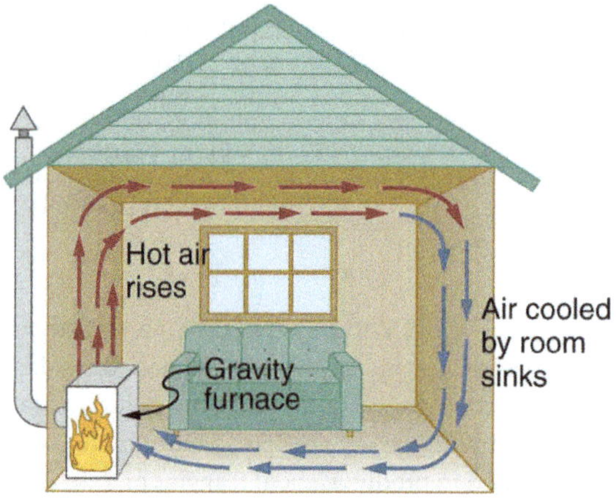

FIGURE 14.17 Air heated by the so-called gravity furnace expands and rises, forming a convective loop that transfers energy to other parts of the room. As the air is cooled at the ceiling and outside walls, it contracts, eventually becoming denser than room air and sinking to the floor. A properly designed heating system using natural convection, like this one, can be quite efficient in uniformly heating a home.

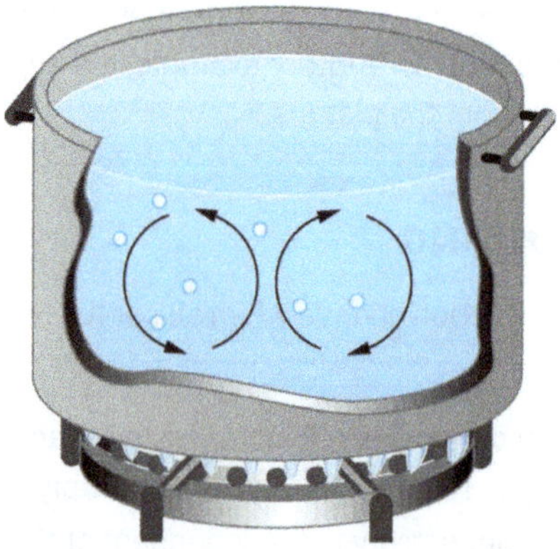

FIGURE 14.18 Convection plays an important role in heat transfer inside this pot of water. Once conducted to the inside, heat transfer to other parts of the pot is mostly by convection. The hotter water expands, decreases in density, and rises to transfer heat to other regions of the water, while colder water sinks to the bottom. This process keeps repeating.

TAKE-HOME EXPERIMENT: CONVECTION ROLLS IN A HEATED PAN

Take two small pots of water and use an eye dropper to place a drop of food coloring near the bottom of each. Leave one on a bench top and heat the other over a stovetop. Watch how the color spreads and how long it takes the color to reach the top. Watch how convective loops form.

EXAMPLE 14.7

Calculating Heat Transfer by Convection: Convection of Air Through the Walls of a House

Most houses are not airtight: air goes in and out around doors and windows, through cracks and crevices, following wiring to switches and outlets, and so on. The air in a typical house is completely replaced in less than an hour. Suppose that a moderately-sized house has inside dimensions $12.0\text{m} \times 18.0\text{m} \times 3.00\text{m}$ high, and that all air is replaced in 30.0 min. Calculate the heat transfer per unit time in watts needed to warm the incoming cold air by 10.0°C, thus replacing the heat transferred by convection alone.

Strategy

Heat is used to raise the temperature of air so that $Q = mc\Delta T$. The rate of heat transfer is then Q/t, where t is the time for air turnover. We are given that ΔT is 10.0°C, but we must still find values for the mass of air and its specific heat before we can calculate Q. The specific heat of air is a weighted average of the specific heats of nitrogen and oxygen, which gives $c = c_{\text{p}} \cong 1000\ \text{J/kg·°C}$ from Table 14.1 (note that the specific heat at constant pressure must be used for this process).

Solution

1. Determine the mass of air from its density and the given volume of the house. The density is given from the density ρ and the volume

$$m = \rho V = \left(1.29\ \text{kg/m}^3\right)(12.0\ \text{m} \times 18.0\ \text{m} \times 3.00\ \text{m}) = 836\ \text{kg}. \tag{14.37}$$

2. Calculate the heat transferred from the change in air temperature: $Q = mc\Delta T$ so that

$$Q = (836\ \text{kg})(1000\ \text{J/kg·°C})(10.0\text{°C}) = 8.36 \times 10^6\ \text{J}. \tag{14.38}$$

3. Calculate the heat transfer from the heat Q and the turnover time t. Since air is turned over in $t = 0.500\ \text{h} = 1800\ \text{s}$, the heat transferred per unit time is

$$\frac{Q}{t} = \frac{8.36 \times 10^6\ \text{J}}{1800\ \text{s}} = 4.64\ \text{kW}. \tag{14.39}$$

Discussion

This rate of heat transfer is equal to the power consumed by about forty-six 100-W light bulbs. Newly constructed homes are designed for a turnover time of 2 hours or more, rather than 30 minutes for the house of this example. Weather stripping, caulking, and improved window seals are commonly employed. More extreme measures are sometimes taken in very cold (or hot) climates to achieve a tight standard of more than 6 hours for one air turnover. Still longer turnover times are unhealthy, because a minimum amount of fresh air is necessary to supply oxygen for breathing and to dilute household pollutants. The term used for the process by which outside air leaks into the house from cracks around windows, doors, and the foundation is called "air infiltration."

A cold wind is much more chilling than still cold air, because convection combines with conduction in the body to increase the rate at which energy is transferred away from the body. The table below gives approximate wind-chill factors, which are the temperatures of still air that produce the same rate of cooling as air of a given temperature and speed. Wind-chill factors are a dramatic reminder of convection's ability to transfer heat faster than conduction. For example, a 15.0 m/s wind at 0°C has the chilling equivalent of still air at about -18°C.

Moving air temperature	Wind speed (m/s)				
(°C)	2	5	10	15	20
5	3	−1	−8	−10	−12
2	0	−7	−12	−16	−18
0	−2	−9	−15	−18	−20
−5	−7	−15	−22	−26	−29
−10	−12	−21	−29	−34	−36
−20	−23	−34	−44	−50	−52
−40	−44	−59	−73	−82	−84

TABLE 14.4 Wind-Chill Factors

Although air can transfer heat rapidly by convection, it is a poor conductor and thus a good insulator. The amount of available space for airflow determines whether air acts as an insulator or conductor. The space between the inside and outside walls of a house, for example, is about 9 cm (3.5 in) —large enough for convection to work effectively. The addition of wall insulation prevents airflow, so heat loss (or gain) is decreased. Similarly, the gap between the two panes of a double-paned window is about 1 cm, which prevents convection and takes advantage of air's low conductivity to prevent greater loss. Fur, fiber, and fiberglass also take advantage of the low conductivity of air by trapping it in spaces too small to support convection, as shown in the figure. Fur and feathers are lightweight and thus ideal for the protection of animals.

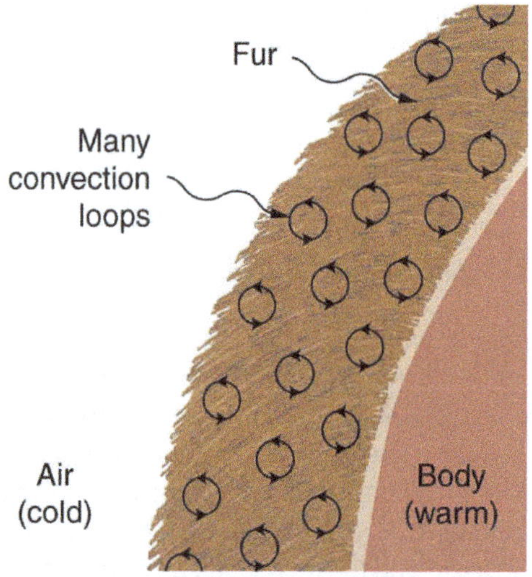

FIGURE 14.19 Fur is filled with air, breaking it up into many small pockets. Convection is very slow here, because the loops are so small. The low conductivity of air makes fur a very good lightweight insulator.

Some interesting phenomena happen *when convection is accompanied by a phase change.* It allows us to cool off by sweating, even if the temperature of the surrounding air exceeds body temperature. Heat from the skin is required for sweat to evaporate from the skin, but without air flow, the air becomes saturated and evaporation stops. Air flow caused by convection replaces the saturated air by dry air and evaporation continues.

EXAMPLE 14.8

Calculate the Flow of Mass during Convection: Sweat-Heat Transfer away from the Body

The average person produces heat at the rate of about 120 W when at rest. At what rate must water evaporate from the body to get rid of all this energy? (This evaporation might occur when a person is sitting in the shade and surrounding temperatures are the same as skin temperature, eliminating heat transfer by other methods.)

Strategy

Energy is needed for a phase change ($Q = mL_V$). Thus, the energy loss per unit time is

$$\frac{Q}{t} = \frac{mL_V}{t} = 120 \text{ W} = 120 \text{ J/s}. \tag{14.40}$$

We divide both sides of the equation by L_V to find that the mass evaporated per unit time is

$$\frac{m}{t} = \frac{120 \text{ J/s}}{L_V}. \tag{14.41}$$

Solution

(1) Insert the value of the latent heat from Table 14.2, $L_V = 2430 \text{ kJ/kg} = 2430 \text{ J/g}$. This yields

$$\frac{m}{t} = \frac{120 \text{ J/s}}{2430 \text{ J/g}} = 0.0494 \text{ g/s} = 2.96 \text{ g/min}. \tag{14.42}$$

Discussion

Evaporating about 3 g/min seems reasonable. This would be about 180 g (about 7 oz) per hour. If the air is very dry, the sweat may evaporate without even being noticed. A significant amount of evaporation also takes place in the lungs and breathing passages.

Another important example of the combination of phase change and convection occurs when water evaporates from the oceans. Heat is removed from the ocean when water evaporates. If the water vapor condenses in liquid droplets as clouds form, heat is released in the atmosphere. Thus, there is an overall transfer of heat from the ocean to the atmosphere. This process is the driving power behind thunderheads, those great cumulus clouds that rise as much as 20.0 km into the stratosphere. Water vapor carried in by convection condenses, releasing tremendous amounts of energy. This energy causes the air to expand and rise, where it is colder. More condensation occurs in these colder regions, which in turn drives the cloud even higher. Such a mechanism is called positive feedback, since the process reinforces and accelerates itself. These systems sometimes produce violent storms, with lightning and hail, and constitute the mechanism driving hurricanes.

FIGURE 14.20 Cumulus clouds are caused by water vapor that rises because of convection. The rise of clouds is driven by a positive feedback mechanism. (credit: Mike Love)

FIGURE 14.21 Convection accompanied by a phase change releases the energy needed to drive this thunderhead into the stratosphere. (credit: Gerardo García Moretti)

FIGURE 14.22 The phase change that occurs when this iceberg melts involves tremendous heat transfer. (credit: Dominic Alves)

The movement of icebergs is another example of convection accompanied by a phase change. Suppose an iceberg drifts from Greenland into warmer Atlantic waters. Heat is removed from the warm ocean water when the ice melts and heat is released to the land mass when the iceberg forms on Greenland.

CHECK YOUR UNDERSTANDING

Explain why using a fan in the summer feels refreshing!

Solution

Using a fan increases the flow of air: warm air near your body is replaced by cooler air from elsewhere. Convection increases the rate of heat transfer so that moving air "feels" cooler than still air.

14.7 Radiation

LEARNING OBJECTIVES

By the end of this section, you will be able to:

- Discuss heat transfer by radiation.
- Explain the power of different materials.

You can feel the heat transfer from a fire and from the Sun. Similarly, you can sometimes tell that the oven is hot without touching its door or looking inside—it may just warm you as you walk by. The space between the Earth and the Sun is largely empty, without any possibility of heat transfer by convection or conduction. In these examples, heat is transferred by radiation. That is, the hot body emits electromagnetic waves that are absorbed by our skin: no medium is required for electromagnetic waves to propagate. Different names are used for electromagnetic waves of different wavelengths: radio waves, microwaves, infrared **radiation**, visible light, ultraviolet radiation, X-rays, and gamma rays.

FIGURE 14.23 Most of the heat transfer from this fire to the observers is through infrared radiation. The visible light, although dramatic, transfers relatively little thermal energy. Convection transfers energy away from the observers as hot air rises, while conduction is negligibly slow here. Skin is very sensitive to infrared radiation, so that you can sense the presence of a fire without looking at it directly. (credit: Daniel X. O'Neil)

The energy of electromagnetic radiation depends on the wavelength (color) and varies over a wide range: a smaller wavelength (or higher frequency) corresponds to a higher energy. Because more heat is radiated at higher temperatures, a temperature change is accompanied by a color change. Take, for example, an electrical element on a stove, which glows from red to orange, while the higher-temperature steel in a blast furnace glows from yellow to white. The radiation you feel is mostly infrared, which corresponds to a lower temperature than that of the electrical element and the steel. The radiated energy depends on its intensity, which is represented in the figure below by the height of the distribution.

Electromagnetic Waves explains more about the electromagnetic spectrum and Introduction to Quantum Physics discusses how the decrease in wavelength corresponds to an increase in energy.

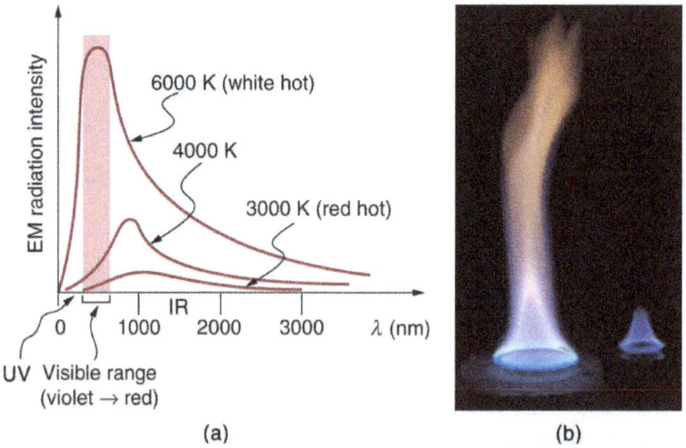

FIGURE 14.24 (a) A graph of the spectra of electromagnetic waves emitted from an ideal radiator at three different temperatures. The intensity or rate of radiation emission increases dramatically with temperature, and the spectrum shifts toward the visible and ultraviolet parts of the spectrum. The shaded portion denotes the visible part of the spectrum. It is apparent that the shift toward the ultraviolet with temperature makes the visible appearance shift from red to white to blue as temperature increases. (b) Note the variations in color corresponding to variations in flame temperature. (credit: Tuohirulla)

All objects absorb and emit electromagnetic radiation. The rate of heat transfer by radiation is largely determined by the color of the object. Black is the most effective, and white is the least effective. People living in hot climates generally avoid wearing black clothing, for instance. Similarly, black asphalt in a parking lot will be hotter than adjacent gray sidewalk on a summer day, because black absorbs better than gray. The reverse is also true—black radiates better than gray. Thus, on a clear summer night, the asphalt will be colder than the gray sidewalk, because black radiates the energy more rapidly than gray. An *ideal radiator* is the same color as an *ideal absorber*, and captures all the radiation that falls on it. In contrast, white is a poor absorber and is also a poor radiator. A white object reflects all radiation, like a mirror. (A perfect, polished white surface is mirror-like in appearance, and a crushed mirror looks white.)

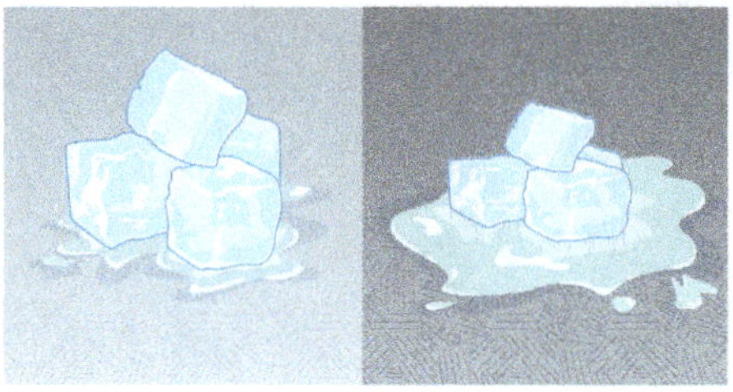

FIGURE 14.25 This illustration shows that the darker pavement is hotter than the lighter pavement (much more of the ice on the right has melted), although both have been in the sunlight for the same time. The thermal conductivities of the pavements are the same.

Gray objects have a uniform ability to absorb all parts of the electromagnetic spectrum. Colored objects behave in similar but more complex ways, which gives them a particular color in the visible range and may make them special in other ranges of the nonvisible spectrum. Take, for example, the strong absorption of infrared radiation by the skin, which allows us to be very sensitive to it.

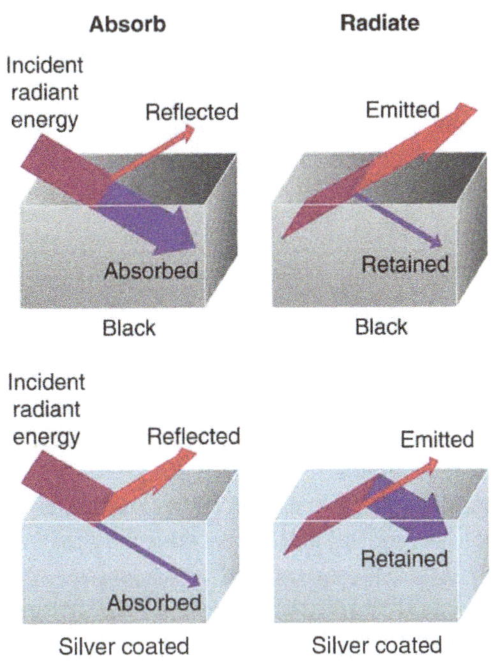

FIGURE 14.26 A black object is a good absorber and a good radiator, while a white (or silver) object is a poor absorber and a poor radiator. It is as if radiation from the inside is reflected back into the silver object, whereas radiation from the inside of the black object is "absorbed" when it hits the surface and finds itself on the outside and is strongly emitted.

The rate of heat transfer by emitted radiation is determined by the **Stefan-Boltzmann law of radiation**:

$$\frac{Q}{t} = \sigma e A T^4, \tag{14.43}$$

where $\sigma = 5.67 \times 10^{-8}\ \text{J/s} \cdot \text{m}^2 \cdot \text{K}^4$ is the Stefan-Boltzmann constant, A is the surface area of the object, and T is its absolute temperature in kelvin. The symbol e stands for the **emissivity** of the object, which is a measure of how well it radiates. An ideal jet-black (or black body) radiator has $e = 1$, whereas a perfect reflector has $e = 0$. Real objects fall between these two values. Take, for example, tungsten light bulb filaments which have an e of about 0.5, and carbon black (a material used in printer toner), which has the (greatest known) emissivity of about 0.99.

The radiation rate is directly proportional to the *fourth power* of the absolute temperature—a remarkably strong temperature dependence. Furthermore, the radiated heat is proportional to the surface area of the object. If you knock apart the coals of a fire, there is a noticeable increase in radiation due to an increase in radiating surface area.

FIGURE 14.27 A thermograph of part of a building shows temperature variations, indicating where heat transfer to the outside is most severe. Windows are a major region of heat transfer to the outside of homes. (credit: U.S. Army)

Skin is a remarkably good absorber and emitter of infrared radiation, having an emissivity of 0.97 in the infrared spectrum. Thus, we are all nearly (jet) black in the infrared, in spite of the obvious variations in skin color. This high infrared emissivity is why we can so easily feel radiation on our skin. It is also the basis for the use of night scopes used by law enforcement and the military to detect human beings. Even small temperature variations can be detected because of the T^4 dependence. Images, called *thermographs*, can be used medically to detect regions of abnormally high temperature in the body, perhaps indicative of disease. Similar techniques can be used to detect heat leaks in homes Figure 14.27, optimize performance of blast furnaces, improve comfort levels in work environments, and even remotely map the Earth's temperature profile.

All objects emit and absorb radiation. The *net* rate of heat transfer by radiation (absorption minus emission) is related to both the temperature of the object and the temperature of its surroundings. Assuming that an object with a temperature T_1 is surrounded by an environment with uniform temperature T_2, the **net rate of heat transfer by radiation** is

$$\frac{Q_{\text{net}}}{t} = \sigma e A\left(T_2^4 - T_1^4\right), \tag{14.44}$$

where e is the emissivity of the object alone. In other words, it does not matter whether the surroundings are white, gray, or black; the balance of radiation into and out of the object depends on how well it emits and absorbs radiation. When $T_2 > T_1$, the quantity Q_{net}/t is positive; that is, the net heat transfer is from hot to cold.

TAKE-HOME EXPERIMENT: TEMPERATURE IN THE SUN

Place a thermometer out in the sunshine and shield it from direct sunlight using an aluminum foil. What is the reading? Now remove the shield, and note what the thermometer reads. Take a handkerchief soaked in nail polish remover, wrap it around the thermometer and place it in the sunshine. What does the thermometer read?

EXAMPLE 14.9

Calculate the Net Heat Transfer of a Person: Heat Transfer by Radiation

What is the rate of heat transfer by radiation, with an unclothed person standing in a dark room whose ambient temperature is 22.0°C. The person has a normal skin temperature of 33.0°C and a surface area of $1.50\ \text{m}^2$. The emissivity of skin is 0.97 in the infrared, where the radiation takes place.

Strategy

We can solve this by using the equation for the rate of radiative heat transfer.

Solution

Insert the temperatures values $T_2 = 295\ \text{K}$ and $T_1 = 306\ \text{K}$, so that

$$\frac{Q}{t} = \sigma e A\left(T_2^4 - T_1^4\right) \tag{14.45}$$

$$= \left(5.67 \times 10^{-8}\ \text{J/s} \cdot \text{m}^2 \cdot \text{K}^4\right)(0.97)\left(1.50\ \text{m}^2\right)\left[(295\ \text{K})^4 - (306\ \text{K})^4\right] \tag{14.46}$$

$$= -99\ \text{J/s} = -99\ \text{W}. \tag{14.47}$$

Discussion

This value is a significant rate of heat transfer to the environment (note the minus sign), considering that a person at rest may produce energy at the rate of 125 W and that conduction and convection will also be transferring energy to the environment. Indeed, we would probably expect this person to feel cold. Clothing significantly reduces heat transfer to the environment by many methods, because clothing slows down both conduction and convection, and has a lower emissivity (especially if it is white) than skin.

The Earth receives almost all its energy from radiation of the Sun and reflects some of it back into outer space. Because the Sun is hotter than the Earth, the net energy flux is from the Sun to the Earth. However, the rate of energy transfer is less than the equation for the radiative heat transfer would predict because the Sun does not fill the sky. The average emissivity (e) of the Earth is about 0.65, but the calculation of this value is complicated by the fact that the highly reflective cloud coverage varies greatly from day to day. There is a negative feedback (one in which a change produces an effect that opposes that change) between clouds and heat transfer; greater temperatures evaporate more water to form more clouds, which reflect more radiation back into space, reducing the temperature. The often mentioned **greenhouse effect** is directly related to the variation of the Earth's emissivity with radiation type (see the figure given below). The greenhouse effect is a natural phenomenon responsible for providing temperatures suitable for life on Earth. The Earth's relatively constant temperature is a result of the energy balance between the incoming solar radiation and the energy radiated from the Earth. Most of the infrared radiation emitted from the Earth is absorbed by carbon dioxide (CO_2) and water (H_2O) in the atmosphere and then re-radiated back to the Earth or into outer space. Re-radiation back to the Earth maintains its surface temperature about $40°C$ higher than it would be if there was no atmosphere, similar to the way glass increases temperatures in a greenhouse.

The greenhouse effect and its causes were first predicted by Eunice Newton Foote after she designed and conducted experiments on heating of different gases. After filling flasks with carbon dioxide, hydrogen, and regular air, then also modifying moisture, she placed them in the sun and carefully measured their heating and, especially, their heat retention. She discovered that the CO_2 flask gained the most temperature and held it the longest. After subsequent research, her paper "Circumstances affecting the Heat of the Sun's Rays" included conclusions that an atmosphere consisting of more carbon dioxide would be hotter resulting from the gas trapping radiation.

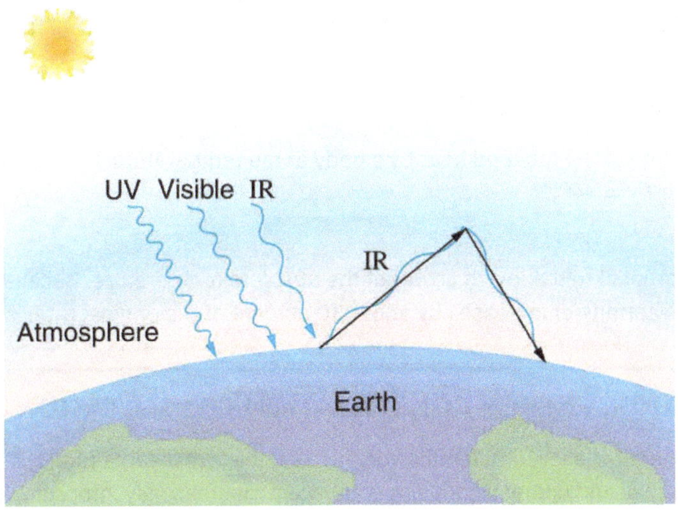

FIGURE 14.28 The greenhouse effect is a name given to the trapping of energy in the Earth's atmosphere by a process similar to that used in greenhouses. The atmosphere, like window glass, is transparent to incoming visible radiation and most of the Sun's infrared. These wavelengths are absorbed by the Earth and re-emitted as infrared. Since Earth's temperature is much lower than that of the Sun, the infrared radiated by the Earth has a much longer wavelength. The atmosphere, like glass, traps these longer infrared rays, keeping the Earth warmer than it would otherwise be. The amount of trapping depends on concentrations of trace gases like carbon dioxide, and a change in the concentration of these gases is believed to affect the Earth's surface temperature.

The greenhouse effect is also central to the discussion of global warming due to emission of carbon dioxide and methane (and other so-called greenhouse gases) into the Earth's atmosphere from industrial production and farming. Changes in global climate could lead to more intense storms, precipitation changes (affecting agriculture), reduction in rain forest biodiversity, and rising sea levels.

Heating and cooling are often significant contributors to energy use in individual homes. Mária Telkes, a Hungarian-born American scientist, was among the foremost developers of solar energy applications in industrial and community use. After inventing a widely deployed solar seawater distiller used on World War II life rafts, she partnered with architect Eleanor Raymond to design the first modern home to be completely heated by solar power. Air warmed on rooftop collectors transferred heat to salts, which stored the heat for later use. Telkes later worked with the Department of Energy to develop the first solar-electrically powered home. Current research efforts into developing environmentally friendly homes quite often focus on reducing conventional heating and cooling through better building materials, strategically positioning windows to optimize radiation gain from the Sun, and opening spaces to allow convection. It is possible to build a zero-energy house that allows for comfortable living in most parts of the United States with hot and humid summers and cold winters.

FIGURE 14.29 This simple but effective solar cooker uses the greenhouse effect and reflective material to trap and retain solar energy. Made of inexpensive, durable materials, it saves money and labor, and is of particular economic value in countries with lower energy availability. Mária Telkes, a pioneering innovator in solar applications, developed some of the earliest models of these cookers in the 1950s. (credit: E.B. Kauai)

Conversely, dark space is very cold, about $3\text{K}\ (-\ 454\text{ºF})$, so that the Earth radiates energy into the dark sky. Owing to the fact that clouds have lower emissivity than either oceans or land masses, they reflect some of the radiation back to the surface, greatly reducing heat transfer into dark space, just as they greatly reduce heat transfer into the atmosphere during the day. The rate of heat transfer from soil and grasses can be so rapid that frost may occur on clear summer evenings, even in warm latitudes.

CHECK YOUR UNDERSTANDING

What is the change in the rate of the radiated heat by a body at the temperature $T_1 = 20\text{ºC}$ compared to when the body is at the temperature $T_2 = 40\text{ºC}$?

Solution

The radiated heat is proportional to the fourth power of the *absolute temperature*. Because $T_1 = 293\text{ K}$ and $T_2 = 313\text{ K}$, the rate of heat transfer increases by about 30 percent of the original rate.

CAREER CONNECTION: ENERGY CONSERVATION CONSULTATION

The cost of energy is generally believed to remain very high for the foreseeable future. Thus, passive control of heat loss in both commercial and domestic housing will become increasingly important. Energy consultants measure and analyze the flow of energy into and out of houses and ensure that a healthy exchange of air is maintained inside the house. The job prospects for an energy consultant are strong.

PROBLEM-SOLVING STRATEGIES FOR THE METHODS OF HEAT TRANSFER

1. *Examine the situation to determine what type of heat transfer is involved.*
2. *Identify the type(s) of heat transfer—conduction, convection, or radiation.*
3. *Identify exactly what needs to be determined in the problem (identify the unknowns). A written list is very useful.*
4. *Make a list of what is given or can be inferred from the problem as stated (identify the knowns).*
5. *Solve the appropriate equation for the quantity to be determined (the unknown).*
6. For conduction, equation $\frac{Q}{t} = \frac{kA(T_2 - T_1)}{d}$ is appropriate. Table 14.3 lists thermal conductivities. For convection, determine the amount of matter moved and use equation $Q = mc\Delta T$, to calculate the heat transfer involved in the temperature change of the fluid. If a phase change accompanies convection, equation $Q = mL_\text{f}$ or $Q = mL_\text{v}$ is appropriate to find the heat transfer involved in the phase change. Table 14.2 lists information relevant to phase change. For radiation, equation $\frac{Q_\text{net}}{t} = \sigma e A\left(T_2^4 - T_1^4\right)$ gives the

net heat transfer rate.

7. *Insert the knowns along with their units into the appropriate equation and obtain numerical solutions complete with units.*
8. *Check the answer to see if it is reasonable. Does it make sense?*

Glossary

conduction heat transfer through stationary matter by physical contact

convection heat transfer by the macroscopic movement of fluid

emissivity measure of how well an object radiates

greenhouse effect warming of the Earth that is due to gases such as carbon dioxide and methane that absorb infrared radiation from the Earth's surface and reradiate it in all directions, thus sending a fraction of it back toward the surface of the Earth

heat the spontaneous transfer of energy due to a temperature difference

heat of sublimation the energy required to change a substance from the solid phase to the vapor phase

kilocalorie $1 \text{ kilocalorie} = 1000 \text{ calories}$

latent heat coefficient a physical constant equal to the amount of heat transferred for every 1 kg of a substance during the change in phase of the substance

mechanical equivalent of heat the work needed to produce the same effects as heat transfer

net rate of heat transfer by radiation is $\frac{Q_{\text{net}}}{t} = \sigma eA\left(T_2^4 - T_1^4\right)$

***R* factor** the ratio of thickness to the conductivity of a material

radiation energy transferred by electromagnetic waves directly as a result of a temperature difference

radiation heat transfer which occurs when microwaves, infrared radiation, visible light, or other electromagnetic radiation is emitted or absorbed

rate of conductive heat transfer rate of heat transfer from one material to another

specific heat the amount of heat necessary to change the temperature of 1.00 kg of a substance by 1.00 ºC

Stefan-Boltzmann law of radiation $\frac{Q}{t} = \sigma eAT^4$, where σ is the Stefan-Boltzmann constant, A is the surface area of the object, T is the absolute temperature, and e is the emissivity

sublimation the transition from the solid phase to the vapor phase

thermal conductivity the property of a material's ability to conduct heat

Section Summary

14.1 Heat

- Heat and work are the two distinct methods of energy transfer.
- Heat is energy transferred solely due to a temperature difference.
- Any energy unit can be used for heat transfer, and the most common are kilocalorie (kcal) and joule (J).
- Kilocalorie is defined to be the energy needed to change the temperature of 1.00 kg of water between 14.5°C and 15.5°C.
- The mechanical equivalent of this heat transfer is $1.00 \text{ kcal} = 4186 \text{ J}$.

14.2 Temperature Change and Heat Capacity

- The transfer of heat Q that leads to a change ΔT in the temperature of a body with mass m is $Q = mc\Delta T$, where c is the specific heat of the material. This relationship can also be considered as the definition of specific heat.

14.3 Phase Change and Latent Heat

- Most substances can exist either in solid, liquid, and gas forms, which are referred to as "phases."
- Phase changes occur at fixed temperatures for a given substance at a given pressure, and these temperatures are called boiling and freezing (or melting) points.
- During phase changes, heat absorbed or released is given by:
  $Q = mL$,
  where L is the latent heat coefficient.

14.4 Heat Transfer Methods

- Heat is transferred by three different methods: conduction, convection, and radiation.

14.5 Conduction

- Heat conduction is the transfer of heat between two objects in direct contact with each other.
- The rate of heat transfer Q/t (energy per unit time) is proportional to the temperature difference $T_2 - T_1$ and the contact area A and inversely proportional to the distance d between the objects:
  $$\frac{Q}{t} = \frac{kA(T_2 - T_1)}{d}.$$

14.6 Convection

- Convection is heat transfer by the macroscopic

movement of mass. Convection can be natural or forced and generally transfers thermal energy faster than conduction. Table 14.4 gives wind-chill factors, indicating that moving air has the same chilling effect of much colder stationary air. *Convection that occurs along with a phase change* can transfer energy from cold regions to warm ones.

14.7 Radiation

- Radiation is the rate of heat transfer through the emission or absorption of electromagnetic waves.
- The rate of heat transfer depends on the surface area and the fourth power of the absolute temperature:

$$\frac{Q}{t} = \sigma e A T^4,$$

where $\sigma = 5.67 \times 10^{-8}\ \text{J/s} \cdot \text{m}^2 \cdot \text{K}^4$ is the Stefan-Boltzmann constant and e is the emissivity of the body. For a black body, $e = 1$ whereas a shiny white or perfect reflector has $e = 0$, with real objects having values of e between 1 and 0. The net rate of heat transfer by radiation is

$$\frac{Q_{\text{net}}}{t} = \sigma e A\left(T_2^4 - T_1^4\right)$$

where T_1 is the temperature of an object surrounded by an environment with uniform temperature T_2 and e is the emissivity of the *object.*

Conceptual Questions

14.1 Heat

1. How is heat transfer related to temperature?

2. Describe a situation in which heat transfer occurs. What are the resulting forms of energy?

3. When heat transfers into a system, is the energy stored as heat? Explain briefly.

14.2 Temperature Change and Heat Capacity

4. What three factors affect the heat transfer that is necessary to change an object's temperature?

5. The brakes in a car increase in temperature by ΔT when bringing the car to rest from a speed v. How much greater would ΔT be if the car initially had twice the speed? You may assume the car to stop sufficiently fast so that no heat transfers out of the brakes.

14.3 Phase Change and Latent Heat

6. Heat transfer can cause temperature and phase changes. What else can cause these changes?

7. How does the latent heat of fusion of water help slow the decrease of air temperatures, perhaps preventing temperatures from falling significantly below $0°\text{C}$, in the vicinity of large bodies of water?

8. What is the temperature of ice right after it is formed by freezing water?

9. If you place $0°\text{C}$ ice into $0°\text{C}$ water in an insulated container, what will happen? Will some ice melt, will more water freeze, or will neither take place?

10. What effect does condensation on a glass of ice water have on the rate at which the ice melts? Will the condensation speed up the melting process or slow it down?

11. In very humid climates where there are numerous bodies of water, such as in Florida, it is unusual for temperatures to rise above about $35°\text{C}(95°\text{F})$. In deserts, however, temperatures can rise far above this. Explain how the evaporation of water helps limit high temperatures in humid climates.

12. In winters, it is often warmer in San Francisco than in nearby Sacramento, 150 km inland. In summers, it is nearly always hotter in Sacramento. Explain how the bodies of water surrounding San Francisco moderate its extreme temperatures.

13. Putting a lid on a boiling pot greatly reduces the heat transfer necessary to keep it boiling. Explain why.

14. Freeze-dried foods have been dehydrated in a vacuum. During the process, the food freezes and must be heated to facilitate dehydration. Explain both how the vacuum speeds up dehydration and why the food freezes as a result.

15. When still air cools by radiating at night, it is unusual for temperatures to fall below the dew point. Explain why.

16. In a physics classroom demonstration, an instructor inflates a balloon by mouth and then cools it in liquid nitrogen. When cold, the shrunken balloon has a small amount of light blue liquid in it, as well as some snow-like crystals. As it warms up, the liquid boils, and part of the crystals sublimate, with some crystals lingering for awhile and then producing a liquid. Identify the blue liquid and the two solids in the cold balloon.

Justify your identifications using data from Table 14.2.

14.4 Heat Transfer Methods

17. What are the main methods of heat transfer from the hot core of Earth to its surface? From Earth's surface to outer space?

18. When our bodies get too warm, they respond by sweating and increasing blood circulation to the surface to transfer thermal energy away from the core. What effect will this have on a person in a $40.0°C$ hot tub?

19. Figure 14.30 shows a cut-away drawing of a thermos bottle (also known as a Dewar flask), which is a device designed specifically to slow down all forms of heat transfer. Explain the functions of the various parts, such as the vacuum, the silvering of the walls, the thin-walled long glass neck, the rubber support, the air layer, and the stopper.

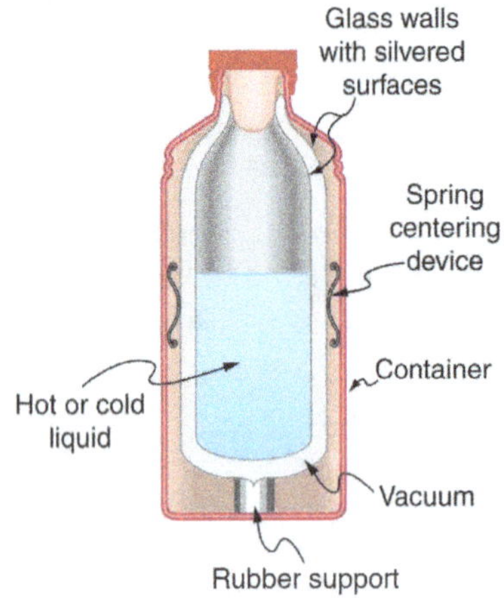

FIGURE 14.30 The construction of a thermos bottle is designed to inhibit all methods of heat transfer.

14.5 Conduction

20. Some electric stoves have a flat ceramic surface with heating elements hidden beneath. A pot placed over a heating element will be heated, while it is safe to touch the surface only a few centimeters away. Why is ceramic, with a conductivity less than that of a metal but greater than that of a good insulator, an ideal choice for the stove top?

21. Loose-fitting white clothing covering most of the body is ideal for desert dwellers, both in the hot Sun and during cold evenings. Explain how such clothing is advantageous during both day and night.

FIGURE 14.31 A jellabiya is worn by many men in Egypt. (credit: Zerida)

14.6 Convection

22. One way to make a fireplace more energy efficient is to have an external air supply for the combustion of its fuel. Another is to have room air circulate around the outside of the fire box and back into the room. Detail the methods of heat transfer involved in each.

23. On cold, clear nights horses will sleep under the cover of large trees. How does this help them keep warm?

14.7 Radiation

24. When watching a daytime circus in a large, dark-colored tent, you sense significant heat transfer from the tent. Explain why this occurs.

25. Satellites designed to observe the radiation from cold (3 K) dark space have sensors that are shaded from the Sun, Earth, and Moon and that are cooled to very low temperatures. Why must the sensors be at low temperature?

26. Why are cloudy nights generally warmer than clear ones?

27. Why are thermometers that are used in weather stations shielded from the sunshine? What does a thermometer measure if it is shielded from the sunshine and also if it is not?

28. On average, would Earth be warmer or cooler

without the atmosphere? Explain your answer.

Problems & Exercises

14.2 Temperature Change and Heat Capacity

1. On a hot day, the temperature of an 80,000-L swimming pool increases by $1.50°C$. What is the net heat transfer during this heating? Ignore any complications, such as loss of water by evaporation.
2. Show that $1 \text{ cal/g} \cdot °C = 1 \text{ kcal/kg} \cdot °C$.
3. To sterilize a 50.0-g glass baby bottle, we must raise its temperature from $22.0°C$ to $95.0°C$. How much heat transfer is required?
4. The same heat transfer into identical masses of different substances produces different temperature changes. Calculate the final temperature when 1.00 kcal of heat transfers into 1.00 kg of the following, originally at $20.0°C$: (a) water; (b) concrete; (c) steel; and (d) mercury.
5. Rubbing your hands together warms them by converting work into thermal energy. If a woman rubs her hands back and forth for a total of 20 rubs, at a distance of 7.50 cm per rub, and with an average frictional force of 40.0 N, what is the temperature increase? The mass of tissues warmed is only 0.100 kg, mostly in the palms and fingers.
6. A 0.250-kg block of a pure material is heated from $20.0°C$ to $65.0°C$ by the addition of 4.35 kJ of energy. Calculate its specific heat and identify the substance of which it is most likely composed.
7. Suppose identical amounts of heat transfer into different masses of copper and water, causing identical changes in temperature. What is the ratio of the mass of copper to water?
8. (a) The number of kilocalories in food is determined by calorimetry techniques in which the food is burned and the amount of heat transfer is measured. How many kilocalories per gram are there in a 5.00-g peanut if the energy from burning it is transferred to 0.500 kg of water held in a 0.100-kg aluminum cup, causing a $54.9°C$ temperature increase? (b) Compare your answer to labeling information found on a package of peanuts and comment on whether the values are consistent.
9. Following vigorous exercise, the body temperature of an 80.0-kg person is $40.0°C$. At what rate in watts must the person transfer thermal energy to reduce the the body temperature to $37.0°C$ in 30.0 min, assuming the body continues to produce energy at the rate of 150 W? $(1 \text{ watt} = 1 \text{ joule/second or } 1 \text{ W} = 1 \text{ J/s})$.
10. Even when shut down after a period of normal use, a large commercial nuclear reactor transfers thermal energy at the rate of 150 MW by the radioactive decay of fission products. This heat transfer causes a rapid increase in temperature if the cooling system fails (1 watt = 1 joule/second or 1 W = 1 J/s and 1 MW = 1 megawatt). (a) Calculate the rate of temperature increase in degrees Celsius per second $(°C/s)$ if the mass of the reactor core is $1.60 \times 10^5 \text{ kg}$ and it has an average specific heat of $0.3349 \text{ kJ/kg}° \cdot \text{C}$. (b) How long would it take to obtain a temperature increase of $2000°C$, which could cause some metals holding the radioactive materials to melt? (The initial rate of temperature increase would be greater than that calculated here because the heat transfer is concentrated in a smaller mass. Later, however, the temperature increase would slow down because the 5×10^5-kg steel containment vessel would also begin to heat up.)

FIGURE 14.32 Radioactive spent-fuel pool at a nuclear power plant. Spent fuel stays hot for a long time. (credit: U.S. Department of Energy)

14.3 Phase Change and Latent Heat

11. How much heat transfer (in kilocalories) is required to thaw a 0.450-kg package of frozen vegetables originally at $0°C$ if their heat of fusion

is the same as that of water?

12. A bag containing $0°C$ ice is much more effective in absorbing energy than one containing the same amount of $0°C$ water.
   a. How much heat transfer is necessary to raise the temperature of 0.800 kg of water from $0°C$ to $30.0°C$?
   b. How much heat transfer is required to first melt 0.800 kg of $0°C$ ice and then raise its temperature?
   c. Explain how your answer supports the contention that the ice is more effective.

13. (a) How much heat transfer is required to raise the temperature of a 0.750-kg aluminum pot containing 2.50 kg of water from $30.0°C$ to the boiling point and then boil away 0.750 kg of water? (b) How long does this take if the rate of heat transfer is 500 W
$1 \text{ watt} = 1 \text{ joule/second } (1 \text{ W} = 1 \text{ J/s})$?

14. The formation of condensation on a glass of ice water causes the ice to melt faster than it would otherwise. If 8.00 g of condensation forms on a glass containing both water and 200 g of ice, how many grams of the ice will melt as a result? Assume no other heat transfer occurs.

15. On a trip, you notice that a 3.50-kg bag of ice lasts an average of one day in your cooler. What is the average power in watts entering the ice if it starts at $0°C$ and completely melts to $0°C$ water in exactly one day
$1 \text{ watt} = 1 \text{ joule/second } (1 \text{ W} = 1 \text{ J/s})$?

16. On a certain dry sunny day, a swimming pool's temperature would rise by $1.50°C$ if not for evaporation. What fraction of the water must evaporate to carry away precisely enough energy to keep the temperature constant?

17. (a) How much heat transfer is necessary to raise the temperature of a 0.200-kg piece of ice from $-20.0°C$ to $130°C$, including the energy needed for phase changes?
(b) How much time is required for each stage, assuming a constant 20.0 kJ/s rate of heat transfer?
(c) Make a graph of temperature versus time for this process.

18. In 1986, a gargantuan iceberg broke away from the Ross Ice Shelf in Antarctica. It was approximately a rectangle 160 km long, 40.0 km wide, and 250 m thick.
(a) What is the mass of this iceberg, given that the density of ice is 917 kg/m^3?
(b) How much heat transfer (in joules) is needed to melt it?
(c) How many years would it take sunlight alone to melt ice this thick, if the ice absorbs an average of 100 W/m^2, 12.00 h per day?

19. How many grams of coffee must evaporate from 350 g of coffee in a 100-g glass cup to cool the coffee from $95.0°C$ to $45.0°C$? You may assume the coffee has the same thermal properties as water and that the average heat of vaporization is 2340 kJ/kg (560 cal/g). (You may neglect the change in mass of the coffee as it cools, which will give you an answer that is slightly larger than correct.)

20. (a) It is difficult to extinguish a fire on a crude oil tanker, because each liter of crude oil releases 2.80×10^7 J of energy when burned. To illustrate this difficulty, calculate the number of liters of water that must be expended to absorb the energy released by burning 1.00 L of crude oil, if the water has its temperature raised from $20.0°C$ to $100°C$, it boils, and the resulting steam is raised to $300°C$. (b) Discuss additional complications caused by the fact that crude oil has a smaller density than water.

21. The energy released from condensation in thunderstorms can be very large. Calculate the energy released into the atmosphere for a small storm of radius 1 km, assuming that 1.0 cm of rain is precipitated uniformly over this area.

22. To help prevent frost damage, 4.00 kg of $0°C$ water is sprayed onto a fruit tree.
(a) How much heat transfer occurs as the water freezes?
(b) How much would the temperature of the 200-kg tree decrease if this amount of heat transferred from the tree? Take the specific heat to be $3.35 \text{ kJ/kg} \cdot {}^\circ\text{C}$, and assume that no phase change occurs.

23. A 0.250-kg aluminum bowl holding 0.800 kg of soup at $25.0°C$ is placed in a freezer. What is the final temperature if 377 kJ of energy is transferred from the bowl and soup, assuming the soup's thermal properties are the same as that of water? Explicitly show how you follow the steps in Problem-Solving Strategies for the Effects of Heat Transfer.

24. A 0.0500-kg ice cube at $-30.0°C$ is placed in

0.400 kg of $35.0°C$ water in a very well-insulated container. What is the final temperature?

25. If you pour 0.0100 kg of $20.0°C$ water onto a 1.20-kg block of ice (which is initially at $-15.0°C$), what is the final temperature? You may assume that the water cools so rapidly that effects of the surroundings are negligible.

26. Indigenous people sometimes cook in watertight baskets by placing hot rocks into water to bring it to a boil. What mass of $500°C$ rock must be placed in 4.00 kg of $15.0°C$ water to bring its temperature to $100°C$, if 0.0250 kg of water escapes as vapor from the initial sizzle? You may neglect the effects of the surroundings and take the average specific heat of the rocks to be that of granite.

27. What would be the final temperature of the pan and water in Calculating the Final Temperature When Heat Is Transferred Between Two Bodies: Pouring Cold Water in a Hot Pan if 0.260 kg of water was placed in the pan and 0.0100 kg of the water evaporated immediately, leaving the remainder to come to a common temperature with the pan?

28. In some countries, liquid nitrogen is used on dairy trucks instead of mechanical refrigerators. A 3.00-hour delivery trip requires 200 L of liquid nitrogen, which has a density of $808\ \text{kg/m}^3$.
(a) Calculate the heat transfer necessary to evaporate this amount of liquid nitrogen and raise its temperature to $3.00°C$. (Use c_p and assume it is constant over the temperature range.) This value is the amount of cooling the liquid nitrogen supplies.
(b) What is this heat transfer rate in kilowatt-hours?
(c) Compare the amount of cooling obtained from melting an identical mass of $0°C$ ice with that from evaporating the liquid nitrogen.

29. Some gun fanciers make their own bullets, which involves melting and casting the lead slugs. How much heat transfer is needed to raise the temperature and melt 0.500 kg of lead, starting from $25.0°C$?

14.5 Conduction

30. (a) Calculate the rate of heat conduction through house walls that are 13.0 cm thick and that have an average thermal conductivity twice that of glass wool. Assume there are no windows or doors. The surface area of the walls is $120\ \text{m}^2$ and their inside surface is at $18.0°C$, while their outside surface is at $5.00°C$. (b) How many 1-kW room heaters would be needed to balance the heat transfer due to conduction?

31. The rate of heat conduction out of a window on a winter day is rapid enough to chill the air next to it. To see just how rapidly the windows transfer heat by conduction, calculate the rate of conduction in watts through a 3.00-m^2 window that is $0.635\ \text{cm}$ thick (1/4 in) if the temperatures of the inner and outer surfaces are $5.00°C$ and $-10.0°C$, respectively. This rapid rate will not be maintained—the inner surface will cool, and even result in frost formation.

32. Calculate the rate of heat conduction out of the human body, assuming that the core internal temperature is $37.0°C$, the skin temperature is $34.0°C$, the thickness of the tissues between averages $1.00\ \text{cm}$, and the surface area is $1.40\ \text{m}^2$.

33. Suppose you stand with one foot on ceramic flooring and one foot on a wool carpet, making contact over an area of $80.0\ \text{cm}^2$ with each foot. Both the ceramic and the carpet are 2.00 cm thick and are $10.0°C$ on their bottom sides. At what rate must heat transfer occur from each foot to keep the top of the ceramic and carpet at $33.0°C$? For ceramic, use the thermal conductivity for glass.

34. A man consumes 3000 kcal of food in one day, converting most of it to maintain body temperature. If he loses half this energy by evaporating water (through breathing and sweating), how many kilograms of water evaporate?

35. (a) A firewalker runs across a bed of hot coals without sustaining burns. Calculate the heat transferred by conduction into the sole of one foot of a firewalker given that the bottom of the foot is a 3.00-mm-thick callus with a conductivity at the low end of the range for wood and its density is $300\ \text{kg/m}^3$. The area of contact is $25.0\ \text{cm}^2$, the temperature of the coals is $700°C$, and the time in contact is 1.00 s.
(b) What temperature increase is produced in the $25.0\ \text{cm}^3$ of tissue affected?
(c) What effect do you think this will have on the tissue, keeping in mind that a callus is made of dead cells?

36. (a) What is the rate of heat conduction through the 3.00-cm-thick fur of a large animal having a

1.40-m^2 surface area? Assume that the animal's skin temperature is $32.0°C$, that the air temperature is $-5.00°C$, and that fur has the same thermal conductivity as air. (b) What food intake will the animal need in one day to replace this heat transfer?

37. A walrus transfers energy by conduction through its blubber at the rate of 150 W when immersed in $-1.00°C$ water. The walrus's internal core temperature is $37.0°C$, and it has a surface area of $2.00\ m^2$. What is the average thickness of its blubber, which has the conductivity of fatty tissues without blood?

FIGURE 14.33 Walrus on ice. (credit: Captain Budd Christman, NOAA Corps)

38. Compare the rate of heat conduction through a 13.0-cm-thick wall that has an area of $10.0\ m^2$ and a thermal conductivity twice that of glass wool with the rate of heat conduction through a window that is 0.750 cm thick and that has an area of $2.00\ m^2$, assuming the same temperature difference across each.

39. Suppose a person is covered head to foot by wool clothing with average thickness of 2.00 cm and is transferring energy by conduction through the clothing at the rate of 50.0 W. What is the temperature difference across the clothing, given the surface area is $1.40\ m^2$?

40. Some stove tops are smooth ceramic for easy cleaning. If the ceramic is 0.600 cm thick and heat conduction occurs through the same area and at the same rate as computed in Example 14.6, what is the temperature difference across it? Ceramic has the same thermal conductivity as glass and brick.

41. One easy way to reduce heating (and cooling) costs is to add extra insulation in the attic of a house. Suppose the house already had 15 cm of fiberglass insulation in the attic and in all the exterior surfaces. If you added an extra 8.0 cm of fiberglass to the attic, then by what percentage would the heating cost of the house drop? Take the single story house to be of dimensions 10 m by 15 m by 3.0 m. Ignore air infiltration and heat loss through windows and doors.

42. (a) Calculate the rate of heat conduction through a double-paned window that has a 1.50-m^2 area and is made of two panes of 0.800-cm-thick glass separated by a 1.00-cm air gap. The inside surface temperature is $15.0°C$, while that on the outside is $-10.0°C$. (Hint: There are identical temperature drops across the two glass panes. First find these and then the temperature drop across the air gap. This problem ignores the increased heat transfer in the air gap due to convection.)
(b) Calculate the rate of heat conduction through a 1.60-cm-thick window of the same area and with the same temperatures. Compare your answer with that for part (a).

43. Many decisions are made on the basis of the payback period: the time it will take through savings to equal the capital cost of an investment. Acceptable payback times depend upon the business or philosophy one has. (For some industries, a payback period is as small as two years.) Suppose you wish to install the extra insulation in Exercise 14.41. If energy cost \$1.00 per million joules and the insulation was \$4.00 per square meter, then calculate the simple payback time. Take the average ΔT for the 120 day heating season to be $15.0°C$.

44. For the human body, what is the rate of heat transfer by conduction through the body's tissue with the following conditions: the tissue thickness is 3.00 cm, the change in temperature is $2.00°C$, and the skin area is $1.50\ m^2$. How does this compare with the average heat transfer rate to the body resulting from an energy intake of about 2400 kcal per day? (No exercise is included.)

14.6 Convection

45. At what wind speed does $-10°C$ air cause the same chill factor as still air at $-29°C$?

46. At what temperature does still air cause the same chill factor as $-5°C$ air moving at 15 m/s?

47. The "steam" above a freshly made cup of instant coffee is really water vapor droplets condensing after evaporating from the hot coffee. What is the final temperature of 250 g of hot coffee initially at $90.0°C$ if 2.00 g evaporates from it? The coffee is in a Styrofoam cup, so other methods of heat transfer can be neglected.

48. (a) How many kilograms of water must evaporate from a 60.0-kg woman to lower her body temperature by $0.750^\circ C$?
(b) Is this a reasonable amount of water to evaporate in the form of perspiration, assuming the relative humidity of the surrounding air is low?

49. On a hot dry day, evaporation from a lake has just enough heat transfer to balance the $1.00\ kW/m^2$ of incoming heat from the Sun. What mass of water evaporates in 1.00 h from each square meter? Explicitly show how you follow the steps in the Problem-Solving Strategies for the Effects of Heat Transfer.

50. One winter day, the climate control system of a large university classroom building malfunctions. As a result, $500\ m^3$ of excess cold air is brought in each minute. At what rate in kilowatts must heat transfer occur to warm this air by $10.0^\circ C$ (that is, to bring the air to room temperature)?

51. The Kilauea volcano in Hawaii is the world's most active, disgorging about $5 \times 10^5\ m^3$ of $1200^\circ C$ lava per day. What is the rate of heat transfer out of Earth by convection if this lava has a density of $2700\ kg/m^3$ and eventually cools to $30^\circ C$? Assume that the specific heat of lava is the same as that of granite.

FIGURE 14.34 Lava flow on Kilauea volcano in Hawaii. (credit: J. P. Eaton, U.S. Geological Survey)

52. During heavy exercise, the body pumps 2.00 L of blood per minute to the surface, where it is cooled by $2.00^\circ C$. What is the rate of heat transfer from this forced convection alone, assuming blood has the same specific heat as water and its density is $1050\ kg/m^3$?

53. A person inhales and exhales 2.00 L of $37.0^\circ C$ air, evaporating 4.00×10^{-2} g of water from the lungs and breathing passages with each breath.
(a) How much heat transfer occurs due to evaporation in each breath?
(b) What is the rate of heat transfer in watts if the person is breathing at a moderate rate of 18.0 breaths per minute?
(c) If the inhaled air had a temperature of $20.0^\circ C$, what is the rate of heat transfer for warming the air?
(d) Discuss the total rate of heat transfer as it relates to typical metabolic rates. Will this breathing be a major form of heat transfer for this person?

54. A glass coffee pot has a circular bottom with a 9.00-cm diameter in contact with a heating element that keeps the coffee warm with a continuous heat transfer rate of 50.0 W
(a) What is the temperature of the bottom of the pot, if it is 3.00 mm thick and the inside temperature is $60.0^\circ C$?
(b) If the temperature of the coffee remains constant and all of the heat transfer is removed by evaporation, how many grams per minute evaporate? Take the heat of vaporization to be 2340 kJ/kg.

14.7 Radiation

55. At what net rate does heat radiate from a $275\text{-}m^2$ black roof on a night when the roof's temperature is $30.0^\circ C$ and the surrounding temperature is $15.0^\circ C$? The emissivity of the roof is 0.900.

56. (a) Cherry-red embers in a fireplace are at $850^\circ C$ and have an exposed area of $0.200\ \ m^2$ and an emissivity of 0.980. The surrounding room has a temperature of $18.0^\circ C$. If 50% of the radiant energy enters the room, what is the net rate of radiant heat transfer in kilowatts? (b) Does your answer support the contention that most of the heat transfer into a room by a fireplace comes from infrared radiation?

57. Radiation makes it impossible to stand close to a hot lava flow. Calculate the rate of heat transfer by radiation from $1.00\ \ m^2$ of $1200^\circ C$ fresh lava into $30.0^\circ C$ surroundings, assuming lava's emissivity is 1.00.

58. (a) Calculate the rate of heat transfer by radiation from a car radiator at $110^\circ C$ into a $50.0^\circ C$ environment, if the radiator has an emissivity of 0.750 and a $1.20\text{-}m^2$ surface area. (b) Is this a significant fraction of the heat transfer by an automobile engine? To answer this, assume a horsepower of $200\ hp\ (1.5\ kW)$ and the efficiency of automobile engines as 25%.

59. Find the net rate of heat transfer by radiation from a skier standing in the shade, given the following. She is completely clothed in white (head to foot, including a ski mask), the clothes have an emissivity of 0.200 and a surface temperature of $10.0^{\circ}C$, the surroundings are at $-15.0^{\circ}C$, and her surface area is $1.60\ m^2$.

60. Suppose you walk into a sauna that has an ambient temperature of $50.0^{\circ}C$. (a) Calculate the rate of heat transfer to you by radiation given your skin temperature is $37.0^{\circ}C$, the emissivity of skin is 0.98, and the surface area of your body is $1.50\ m^2$. (b) If all other forms of heat transfer are balanced (the net heat transfer is zero), at what rate will your body temperature increase if your mass is 75.0 kg?

61. Thermography is a technique for measuring radiant heat and detecting variations in surface temperatures that may be medically, environmentally, or militarily meaningful.(a) What is the percent increase in the rate of heat transfer by radiation from a given area at a temperature of $34.0^{\circ}C$ compared with that at $33.0^{\circ}C$, such as on a person's skin? (b) What is the percent increase in the rate of heat transfer by radiation from a given area at a temperature of $34.0^{\circ}C$ compared with that at $20.0^{\circ}C$, such as for warm and cool automobile hoods?

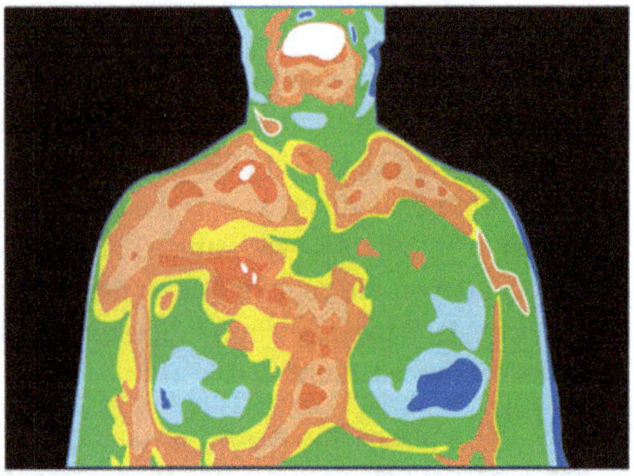

FIGURE 14.35 Artist's rendition of a thermograph of a patient's upper body, showing the distribution of heat represented by different colors.

62. The Sun radiates like a perfect black body with an emissivity of exactly 1. (a) Calculate the surface temperature of the Sun, given that it is a sphere with a 7.00×10^8-m radius that radiates 3.80×10^{26} W into 3-K space. (b) How much power does the Sun radiate per square meter of its surface? (c) How much power in watts per square meter is that value at the distance of Earth, 1.50×10^{11} m away? (This number is called the solar constant.)

63. A large body of lava from a volcano has stopped flowing and is slowly cooling. The interior of the lava is at $1200^{\circ}C$, its surface is at $450^{\circ}C$, and the surroundings are at $27.0^{\circ}C$. (a) Calculate the rate at which energy is transferred by radiation from $1.00\ m^2$ of surface lava into the surroundings, assuming the emissivity is 1.00. (b) Suppose heat conduction to the surface occurs at the same rate. What is the thickness of the lava between the $450^{\circ}C$ surface and the $1200^{\circ}C$ interior, assuming that the lava's conductivity is the same as that of brick?

64. Calculate the temperature the entire sky would have to be in order to transfer energy by radiation at $1000\ W/m^2$ —about the rate at which the Sun radiates when it is directly overhead on a clear day. This value is the effective temperature of the sky, a kind of average that takes account of the fact that the Sun occupies only a small part of the sky but is much hotter than the rest. Assume that the body receiving the energy has a temperature of $27.0^{\circ}C$.

65. (a) A shirtless rider under a circus tent feels the heat radiating from the sunlit portion of the tent. Calculate the temperature of the tent canvas based on the following information: The shirtless rider's skin temperature is $34.0^{\circ}C$ and has an emissivity of 0.970. The exposed area of skin is $0.400\ m^2$. He receives radiation at the rate of 20.0 W—half what you would calculate if the entire region behind him was hot. The rest of the surroundings are at $34.0^{\circ}C$. (b) Discuss how this situation would change if the sunlit side of the tent was nearly pure white and if the rider was covered by a white tunic.

66. Integrated Concepts
One $30.0^{\circ}C$ day the relative humidity is 75.0%, and that evening the temperature drops to $20.0^{\circ}C$, well below the dew point. (a) How many grams of water condense from each cubic meter of air? (b) How much heat transfer occurs by this condensation? (c) What temperature increase could this cause in dry air?

67. Integrated Concepts
Large meteors sometimes strike the Earth, converting most of their kinetic energy into thermal energy. (a) What is the kinetic energy of a 10^9 kg meteor moving at 25.0 km/s? (b) If this meteor lands in a deep ocean and 80% of its kinetic energy goes into heating water, how many

kilograms of water could it raise by $5.0°C$? (c) Discuss how the energy of the meteor is more likely to be deposited in the ocean and the likely effects of that energy.

68. Integrated Concepts
Frozen waste from airplane toilets has sometimes been accidentally ejected at high altitude. Ordinarily it breaks up and disperses over a large area, but sometimes it holds together and strikes the ground. Calculate the mass of $0°C$ ice that can be melted by the conversion of kinetic and gravitational potential energy when a $20.0\ \text{kg}$ piece of frozen waste is released at 12.0 km altitude while moving at 250 m/s and strikes the ground at 100 m/s (since less than 20.0 kg melts, a significant mess results).

69. Integrated Concepts
(a) A large electrical power facility produces 1600 MW of "waste heat," which is dissipated to the environment in cooling towers by warming air flowing through the towers by $5.00°C$. What is the necessary flow rate of air in m^3/s? (b) Is your result consistent with the large cooling towers used by many large electrical power plants?

70. Integrated Concepts
(a) Suppose you start a workout on a Stairmaster, producing power at the same rate as climbing 116 stairs per minute. Assuming your mass is 76.0 kg and your efficiency is 20.0%, how long will it take for your body temperature to rise $1.00°C$ if all other forms of heat transfer in and out of your body are balanced? (b) Is this consistent with your experience in getting warm while exercising?

71. Integrated Concepts
A 76.0-kg person suffering from hypothermia comes indoors and shivers vigorously. How long does it take the heat transfer to increase the person's body temperature by $2.00°C$ if all other forms of heat transfer are balanced?

72. Integrated Concepts
In certain large geographic regions, the underlying rock is hot. Wells can be drilled and water circulated through the rock for heat transfer for the generation of electricity. (a) Calculate the heat transfer that can be extracted by cooling $1.00\ \text{km}^3$ of granite by $100°C$. (b) How long will this take if heat is transferred at a rate of 300 MW, assuming no heat transfers back into the 1.00 km of rock by its surroundings?

73. Integrated Concepts
Heat transfers from your lungs and breathing passages by evaporating water. (a) Calculate the maximum number of grams of water that can be evaporated when you inhale 1.50 L of $37°C$ air with an original relative humidity of 40.0%. (Assume that body temperature is also $37°C$.) (b) How many joules of energy are required to evaporate this amount? (c) What is the rate of heat transfer in watts from this method, if you breathe at a normal resting rate of 10.0 breaths per minute?

74. Integrated Concepts
(a) What is the temperature increase of water falling 55.0 m over Niagara Falls? (b) What fraction must evaporate to keep the temperature constant?

75. Integrated Concepts
Hot air rises because it has expanded. It then displaces a greater volume of cold air, which increases the buoyant force on it. (a) Calculate the ratio of the buoyant force to the weight of $50.0°C$ air surrounded by $20.0°C$ air. (b) What energy is needed to cause $1.00\ m^3$ of air to go from $20.0°C$ to $50.0°C$? (c) What gravitational potential energy is gained by this volume of air if it rises 1.00 m? Will this cause a significant cooling of the air?

76. Unreasonable Results
(a) What is the temperature increase of an 80.0 kg person who consumes 2500 kcal of food in one day with 95.0% of the energy transferred as heat to the body? (b) What is unreasonable about this result? (c) Which premise or assumption is responsible?

77. Unreasonable Results
An Arctic inventor surrounded by ice thinks it would be much less mechanically complex to cool a car engine by melting ice on it than by having a water-cooled system with a radiator, water pump, antifreeze, and so on. (a) If 80.0% of the energy in 1.00 gal of gasoline is converted into "waste heat" in a car engine, how many kilograms of $0°C$ ice could it melt? (b) Is this a reasonable amount of ice to carry around to cool the engine for 1.00 gal of gasoline consumption? (c) What premises or assumptions are unreasonable?

78. Unreasonable Results
(a) Calculate the rate of heat transfer by conduction through a window with an area of $1.00\ m^2$ that is 0.750 cm thick, if its inner surface is at $22.0°C$ and its outer surface is at $35.0°C$. (b) What is unreasonable about this result? (c) Which

premise or assumption is responsible?

79. Unreasonable Results
A meteorite 1.20 cm in diameter is so hot immediately after penetrating the atmosphere that it radiates 20.0 kW of power. (a) What is its temperature, if the surroundings are at 20.0°C and it has an emissivity of 0.800? (b) What is unreasonable about this result? (c) Which premise or assumption is responsible?

80. Construct Your Own Problem
Consider a new model of commercial airplane having its brakes tested as a part of the initial flight permission procedure. The airplane is brought to takeoff speed and then stopped with the brakes alone. Construct a problem in which you calculate the temperature increase of the brakes during this process. You may assume most of the kinetic energy of the airplane is converted to thermal energy in the brakes and surrounding materials, and that little escapes. Note that the brakes are expected to become so hot in this procedure that they ignite and, in order to pass the test, the airplane must be able to withstand the fire for some time without a general conflagration.

81. Construct Your Own Problem
Consider a person outdoors on a cold night. Construct a problem in which you calculate the rate of heat transfer from the person by all three heat transfer methods. Make the initial circumstances such that at rest the person will have a net heat transfer and then decide how much physical activity of a chosen type is necessary to balance the rate of heat transfer. Among the things to consider are the size of the person, type of clothing, initial metabolic rate, sky conditions, amount of water evaporated, and volume of air breathed. Of course, there are many other factors to consider and your instructor may wish to guide you in the assumptions made as well as the detail of analysis and method of presenting your results.

Test Prep for AP® Courses

14.1 Heat

1. An ice cube is placed in a cup of hot water. Which of the following statements correctly describes energy transfer at the molecular level?
   a. Kinetic energy is transferred only from the hot water molecules to the water molecules in the ice.
   b. Kinetic energy is transferred only from the water molecules in the ice to the hot water molecules.
   c. Kinetic energy is transferred mostly from the hot water molecules to the water molecules in the ice.
   d. Kinetic energy is transferred mostly from the water molecules in the ice to the hot water molecules.

2. The molecular description of heat transfer from higher to lower temperatures applies to 'spontaneous' processes, that is, processes in which no energy is added to or removed or from the systems by work or heat. Refrigeration is an example of work being done to remove energy from air within a given space, and thus lower the temperature of the air. Assume a typical kitchen refrigerator, where the air inside the unit forms the system with a temperature of 25°C, and the walls are kept at a constant temperature of 10°C. In terms of molecules and average kinetic energy, describe how the air is made colder.

14.5 Conduction

3. For the experiment that you devised Example 14.1, which variables can be changed, and how should they be changed, so as to shorten the time in which a measurement is made?
   a. Use a smaller quantity of ice (smaller *m*).
   b. Use containers with greater thickness (larger *d*).
   c. Use containers with smaller surface areas (smaller *A*).
   d. Use a lower ambient temperature outside the container (smaller T_2).

4. With reference to Example 14.1, why does the change in the temperature of the ice indicate that it has entirely melted?

5. Which of the following correctly describes the rate of conductive heat transfer for a substance?
   a. The rate decreases with increased surface area and decreased thickness.
   b. The rate increases with increased temperature difference and surface area.
   c. The rate increases with decreased temperature difference and increased thickness.
   d. The rate decreases with decreased temperature difference and increased surface

area.

6. You wish to design a saucepan that has the same rate of thermal conduction as a pan made of silver. You need to use a less costly material, and limit the size of the pan so that the surface area in contact with a range heating element is no more than 50% greater than that of the hypothetical silver pan. Explain what other factor(s) can be adjusted, and by how much, so that your design will be successful. Use Table 14.3 to obtain thermal conductivity values for different substances.

14.6 Convection

7. Under which two conditions would convection in a fluid be greatest?
   a. The gravitational acceleration is large, and the fluid density varies greatly for a given temperature change.
   b. The gravitational acceleration is small, and the fluid density varies greatly for a given temperature change.
   c. The gravitational acceleration is large, and the fluid density varies slightly for a given temperature change.
   d. The gravitational acceleration is small, and the fluid density varies slightly for a given temperature change.

8. Sea breezes occur along coastlines, and consist of cool air moving toward the shore from the ocean. However, this only occurs during the day, and is a stronger effect when the air temperature on the land is greatest and the air temperature above the water is coldest. At night, the breezes are reversed, moving from the land toward the ocean. Taking into consideration the specific heat capacities of water and sand (which is about the same as that of concrete), explain how sea breezes form during the day and change direction at night.

14.7 Radiation

9. Two ideal, black-body radiators have temperatures of 275 K and 1100 K. The rate of heat transfer from the latter radiator is how many times greater than the rate of the former radiator?
   a. 4
   b. 16
   c. 64
   d. 256

10. On a warm, sunny day, a car is parked along a street where there is no shade. The car's windows are closed. The air inside the car becomes noticeably warmer than the air outside. What factors contribute to the higher temperature?

CHAPTER 15
Thermodynamics

FIGURE 15.1 A steam engine uses heat transfer to do work. Tourists regularly ride this narrow-gauge steam engine train near the San Juan Skyway in Durango, Colorado, part of the National Scenic Byways Program. (credit: Dennis Adams)

CHAPTER OUTLINE

CONNECTION FOR AP® COURSES Heat is energy in transit, and it can be used to do work. It can also be converted to any other form of energy. When a car engine burns fuel, for example, heat transfers into a gas. Work is done by the heated gas as it exerts a force through a distance (Essential Knowledge 5.B.5), converting its energy into a variety of other forms—into the car's kinetic or gravitational potential energy; into electrical energy to run the spark plugs, radio, and lights; and into stored energy in the car's battery. But most of the heat produced from burning fuel in the engine does not do work. Rather, the heat is released into the environment, implying that the engine is quite inefficient.

It is often said that modern gasoline engines cannot be made to be significantly more efficient. We hear the same about heat transfer to electrical energy in large power stations, whether they are coal, oil, natural gas, or nuclear powered. Why is that the case? Is the inefficiency caused by design problems that could be solved with better engineering and superior materials? Is it part of some money-making conspiracy by those who sell energy? Actually, the truth is more interesting, and reveals much about the nature of heat transfer. Basic physical laws govern how heat transfer for doing work takes place and place insurmountable limits onto its efficiency. This chapter will explore these laws as well as many applications and concepts associated with them. These topics are part of *thermodynamics*—the study of heat transfer and its relationship to doing work.

This chapter discusses thermodynamics in practical contexts including heat engines, heat pumps, and refrigerators, which support Big Idea 4, and that interactions between systems can result in changes in those systems. As systems either do work or have work done on them, the total energy of a system can change (Enduring Understanding 4.C). These ideas are based on the previous understanding of heat as the process of energy transfer from a higher temperature system to a lower temperature system (Essential Knowledge 4.C.3). You will learn about the first law of thermodynamics, which supports Big Idea 5, that changes that occur as a result of interactions are constrained by conservation laws. The first law of thermodynamics is a special case of energy conservation that explains the relationship between changes in the internal energy of a system (Essential Knowledge 5.B.4) and energy transfer in the form of heat or work (Essential Knowledge 5.B.7). Note that the energy of a system is conserved (Enduring Understanding 5.B). You will also learn about the second law of thermodynamics and entropy. These are applications of Big Idea 7, that the mathematics of probability can be used to describe the behavior of complex systems. For example, an isolated system will reach thermal equilibrium (Enduring Understanding 7.B), a state with higher disorder. This process has a probabilistic nature (Essential Knowledge 7.B.1) and is described by the second law of thermodynamics. The second law of thermodynamics describes the change of entropy for reversible and irreversible processes (Essential Knowledge 7.B.2). Entropy is considered qualitatively at this level.

Big Idea 4 Interactions between systems can result in changes in those systems.

Enduring Understanding 4.C Interactions with other objects or systems can change the total energy of a system.

Essential Knowledge 4.C.3 Energy is transferred spontaneously from a higher temperature system to a lower temperature system. The process through which energy is transferred between systems at different temperatures is called heat.

Big Idea 5 Changes that occur as a result of interactions are constrained by conservation laws.

Enduring Understanding 5.B The energy of a system is conserved.

Essential Knowledge 5.B.4 The internal energy of a system includes the kinetic energy of the objects that make up the system and the potential energy of the configuration of the objects that make up the system.

Essential Knowledge 5.B.5 Energy can be transferred by an external force exerted on an object or system that moves the object or system through a distance; this energy transfer is called work. Energy transfer in mechanical or electrical systems may occur at different rates. Power is defined as the rate of energy transfer into, out of, or within a system. [A piston filled with gas getting compressed or expanded is treated in Physics 2 as a part of thermodynamics.]

Essential Knowledge 5.B.7 The first law of thermodynamics is a specific case of the law of conservation of energy involving the internal energy of a system and the possible transfer of energy through work and/or heat. Examples should include P–V diagrams — isochoric process, isothermal process, isobaric process, adiabatic process. No calculations of heat or internal energy from temperature change; and in this course, examples of these relationships are qualitative and/or semi–quantitative.

Big Idea 7 The mathematics of probability can be used to describe the behavior of complex systems and to interpret the behavior of quantum mechanical systems.

Enduring Understanding 7.B The tendency of isolated systems to move toward states with higher disorder is described by probability.

Essential Knowledge 7.B.1 The approach to thermal equilibrium is a probability process.

Essential Knowledge 7.B.2 The second law of thermodynamics describes the change in entropy for reversible and irreversible processes. Only a qualitative treatment is considered in this course.

15.1 The First Law of Thermodynamics

LEARNING OBJECTIVES

By the end of this section, you will be able to:

- Define the first law of thermodynamics.
- Describe how conservation of energy relates to the first law of thermodynamics.
- Identify instances of the first law of thermodynamics working in everyday situations, including biological metabolism.
- Calculate changes in the internal energy of a system, after accounting for heat transfer and work done.

FIGURE 15.2 This boiling tea kettle represents energy in motion. The water in the kettle is turning to water vapor because heat is being transferred from the stove to the kettle. As the entire system gets hotter, work is done—from the evaporation of the water to the whistling of the kettle. (credit: Gina Hamilton)

If we are interested in how heat transfer is converted into doing work, then the conservation of energy principle is important. The first law of thermodynamics applies the conservation of energy principle to systems where heat transfer and doing work are the methods of transferring energy into and out of the system. The **first law of thermodynamics** states that the change in internal energy of a system equals the net heat transfer *into* the system minus the net work done *by* the system. In equation form, the first law of thermodynamics is

$$\Delta U = Q - W. \tag{15.1}$$

Here ΔU is the *change in internal energy* U of the system. Q is the *net heat transferred into the system*—that is, Q is the sum of all heat transfer into and out of the system. W is the *net work done by the system*—that is, W is the sum of all work done on or by the system. We use the following sign conventions: if Q is positive, then there is a net heat transfer into the system; if W is positive, then there is net work done by the system. So positive Q adds energy to the system and positive W takes energy from the system. Thus $\Delta U = Q - W$. Note also that if more heat transfer into the system occurs than work done, the difference is stored as internal energy. Heat engines are a good example of this—heat transfer into them takes place so that they can do work. (See Figure 15.3.) We will now examine Q, W, and ΔU further.

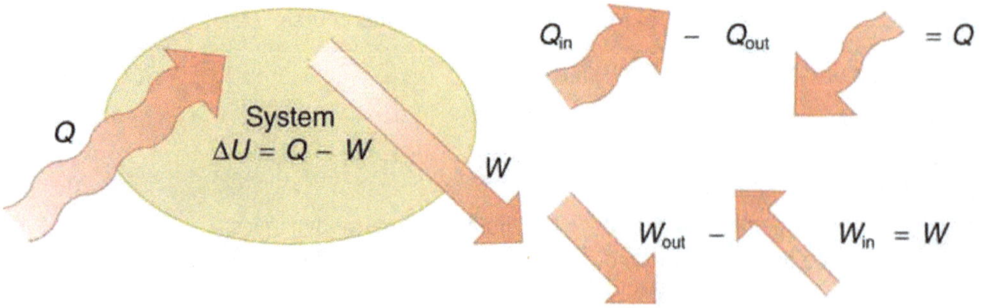

FIGURE 15.3 The first law of thermodynamics is the conservation-of-energy principle stated for a system where heat and work are the methods of transferring energy for a system in thermal equilibrium. Q represents the net heat transfer—it is the sum of all heat transfers into and out of the system. Q is positive for net heat transfer *into* the system. W is the total work done on and by the system. W is positive when more work is done *by* the system than on it. The change in the internal energy of the system, ΔU, is related to heat and work by the first law of thermodynamics, $\Delta U = Q - W$.

MAKING CONNECTIONS: LAW OF THERMODYNAMICS AND LAW OF CONSERVATION OF ENERGY

The first law of thermodynamics is actually the law of conservation of energy stated in a form most useful in thermodynamics. The first law gives the relationship between heat transfer, work done, and the change in internal energy of a system.

Heat *Q* and Work *W*

Heat transfer (Q) and doing work (W) are the two everyday means of bringing energy into or taking energy out of a system. The processes are quite different. Heat transfer, a less organized process, is driven by temperature differences. Work, a quite organized process, involves a macroscopic force exerted through a distance. Nevertheless, heat and work can produce identical results.For example, both can cause a temperature increase. Heat transfer into a system, such as when the Sun warms the air in a bicycle tire, can increase its temperature, and so can work done on the system, as when the bicyclist pumps air into the tire. Once the temperature increase has occurred, it is impossible to tell whether it was caused by heat transfer or by doing work. This uncertainty is an important point. Heat transfer and work are both energy in transit—neither is stored as such in a system. However, both can change the internal energy U of a system. Internal energy is a form of energy completely different from either heat or work.

Internal Energy *U*

We can think about the internal energy of a system in two different but consistent ways. The first is the atomic and molecular view, which examines the system on the atomic and molecular scale. The **internal energy** U of a system is the sum of the kinetic and potential energies of its atoms and molecules. Recall that kinetic plus potential energy is called mechanical energy. Thus internal energy is the sum of atomic and molecular mechanical energy. Because it is impossible to keep track of all individual atoms and molecules, we must deal with averages and distributions. A second way to view the internal energy of a system is in terms of its macroscopic characteristics, which are very similar to atomic and molecular average values.

Macroscopically, we define the change in internal energy ΔU to be that given by the first law of thermodynamics:

$$\Delta U = Q - W. \tag{15.2}$$

Many detailed experiments have verified that $\Delta U = Q - W$, where ΔU is the change in total kinetic and potential energy of all atoms and molecules in a system. It has also been determined experimentally that the internal energy U of a system depends only on the state of the system and *not how it reached that state*. More specifically, U is found to be a function of a few macroscopic quantities (pressure, volume, and temperature, for example), independent of past history such as whether there has been heat transfer or work done. This independence means that if we know the state of a system, we can calculate changes in its internal energy U from a few macroscopic variables.

MAKING CONNECTIONS: MACROSCOPIC AND MICROSCOPIC

In thermodynamics, we often use the macroscopic picture when making calculations of how a system behaves, while the atomic and molecular picture gives underlying explanations in terms of averages and distributions. We shall see this again in later sections of this chapter. For example, in the topic of entropy, calculations will be made using the atomic and molecular view.

To get a better idea of how to think about the internal energy of a system, let us examine a system going from State 1 to State 2. The system has internal energy U_1 in State 1, and it has internal energy U_2 in State 2, no matter how it got to either state. So the change in internal energy $\Delta U = U_2 - U_1$ is independent of what caused the change. In other words, ΔU *is independent of path*. By path, we mean the method of getting from the starting point to the ending point. Why is this independence important? Note that $\Delta U = Q - W$. Both Q and W *depend on path*, but ΔU does not. This path independence means that internal energy U is easier to consider than either heat transfer or work done.

EXAMPLE 15.1

Calculating Change in Internal Energy: The Same Change in U is Produced by Two Different Processes

(a) Suppose there is heat transfer of 40.00 J to a system, while the system does 10.00 J of work. Later, there is heat transfer of 25.00 J out of the system while 4.00 J of work is done on the system. What is the net change in internal energy of the system?

(b) What is the change in internal energy of a system when a total of 150.00 J of heat transfer occurs out of (from) the system and 159.00 J of work is done on the system? (See Figure 15.4).

Strategy

In part (a), we must first find the net heat transfer and net work done from the given information. Then the first law of thermodynamics ($\Delta U = Q - W$) can be used to find the change in internal energy. In part (b), the net heat transfer and work done are given, so the equation can be used directly.

Solution for (a)

The net heat transfer is the heat transfer into the system minus the heat transfer out of the system, or

$$Q = 40.00\,\text{J} - 25.00\,\text{J} = 15.00\ \text{J}. \tag{15.3}$$

Similarly, the total work is the work done by the system minus the work done on the system, or

$$W = 10.00\,\text{J} - 4.00\,\text{J} = 6.00\,\text{J}. \tag{15.4}$$

Thus the change in internal energy is given by the first law of thermodynamics:

$$\Delta U = Q - W = 15.00\,\text{J} - 6.00\,\text{J} = 9.00\,\text{J}. \tag{15.5}$$

We can also find the change in internal energy for each of the two steps. First, consider 40.00 J of heat transfer in and 10.00 J of work out, or

$$\Delta U_1 = Q_1 - W_1 = 40.00\,\text{J} - 10.00\,\text{J} = 30.00\,\text{J}. \tag{15.6}$$

Now consider 25.00 J of heat transfer out and 4.00 J of work in, or

$$\Delta U_2 = Q_2 - W_2 = -25.00\,\text{J} - (-4.00\,\text{J}) = -21.00\,\text{J}. \tag{15.7}$$

The total change is the sum of these two steps, or

$$\Delta U = \Delta U_1 + \Delta U_2 = 30.00\,\text{J} + (-21.00\,\text{J}) = 9.00\,\text{J}. \tag{15.8}$$

Discussion on (a)

No matter whether you look at the overall process or break it into steps, the change in internal energy is the same.

Solution for (b)

Here the net heat transfer and total work are given directly to be $Q = -150.00\text{ J}$ and $W = -159.00\text{ J}$, so that

$$\Delta U = Q - W = -150.00\text{ J} - (-159.00\text{ J}) = 9.00\text{ J}. \tag{15.9}$$

Discussion on (b)

A very different process in part (b) produces the same 9.00-J change in internal energy as in part (a). Note that the change in the system in both parts is related to ΔU and not to the individual Qs or Ws involved. The system ends up in the *same* state in both (a) and (b). Parts (a) and (b) present two different paths for the system to follow between the same starting and ending points, and the change in internal energy for each is the same—it is independent of path.

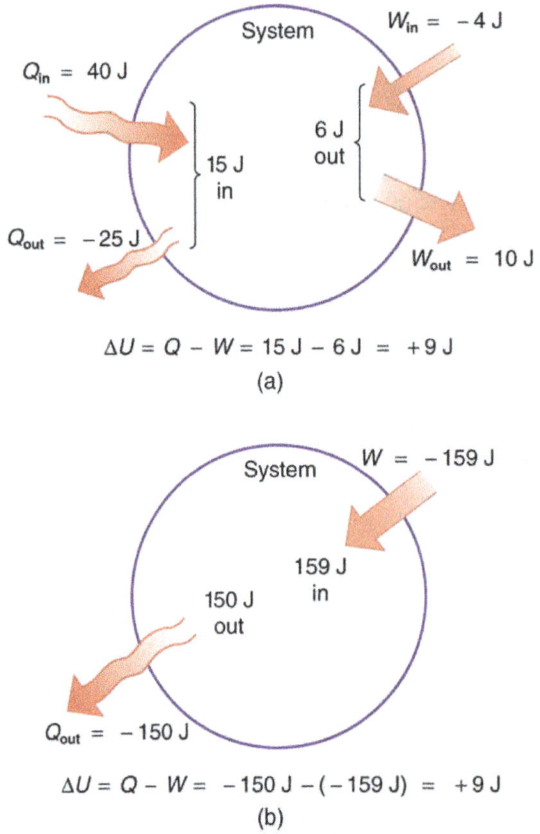

FIGURE 15.4 Two different processes produce the same change in a system. (a) A total of 15.00 J of heat transfer occurs into the system, while work takes out a total of 6.00 J. The change in internal energy is $\Delta U = Q - W = 9.00\text{ J}$. (b) Heat transfer removes 150.00 J from the system while work puts 159.00 J into it, producing an increase of 9.00 J in internal energy. If the system starts out in the same state in (a) and (b), it will end up in the same final state in either case—its final state is related to internal energy, not how that energy was acquired.

Human Metabolism and the First Law of Thermodynamics

Human metabolism is the conversion of food into heat transfer, work, and stored fat. Metabolism is an interesting example of the first law of thermodynamics in action. We now take another look at these topics via the first law of thermodynamics. Considering the body as the system of interest, we can use the first law to examine heat transfer, doing work, and internal energy in activities ranging from sleep to heavy exercise. What are some of the major characteristics of heat transfer, doing work, and energy in the body? For one, body temperature is normally kept constant by heat transfer to the surroundings. This means Q is negative. Another fact is that the body usually does work on the outside world. This means W is positive. In such situations, then, the body loses internal energy, since $\Delta U = Q - W$ is negative.

Now consider the effects of eating. Eating increases the internal energy of the body by adding chemical potential energy (this is an unromantic view of a good steak). The body *metabolizes* all the food we consume. Basically, metabolism is an oxidation process in which the chemical potential energy of food is released. This implies that food input is in the form of work. Food energy is reported in a special unit, known as the Calorie. This energy is measured by burning food in a calorimeter, which is how the units are determined.

In chemistry and biochemistry, one calorie (spelled with a *lowercase* c) is defined as the energy (or heat transfer) required to raise the temperature of one gram of pure water by one degree Celsius. Nutritionists and weight-watchers tend to use the *dietary* calorie, which is frequently called a Calorie (spelled with a *capital* C). One food Calorie is the energy needed to raise the temperature of one *kilogram* of water by one degree Celsius. This means that one dietary Calorie is equal to one kilocalorie for the chemist, and one must be careful to avoid confusion between the two.

Again, consider the internal energy the body has lost. There are three places this internal energy can go—to heat transfer, to doing work, and to stored fat (a tiny fraction also goes to cell repair and growth). Heat transfer and doing work take internal energy out of the body, and food puts it back. If you eat just the right amount of food, then your average internal energy remains constant. Whatever you lose to heat transfer and doing work is replaced by food, so that, in the long run, $\Delta U = 0$. If you overeat repeatedly, then ΔU is always positive, and your body stores this extra internal energy as fat. The reverse is true if you eat too little. If ΔU is negative for a few days, then the body metabolizes its own fat to maintain body temperature and do work that takes energy from the body. This process is how dieting produces weight loss.

Life is not always this simple, as any dieter knows. The body stores fat or metabolizes it only if energy intake changes for a period of several days. Once you have been on a major diet, the next one is less successful because your body alters the way it responds to low energy intake. Your basal metabolic rate (BMR) is the rate at which food is converted into heat transfer and work done while the body is at complete rest. The body adjusts its basal metabolic rate to partially compensate for over-eating or under-eating. The body will decrease the metabolic rate rather than eliminate its own fat to replace lost food intake. You will chill more easily and feel less energetic as a result of the lower metabolic rate, and you will not lose weight as fast as before. Exercise helps to lose weight, because it produces both heat transfer from your body and work, and raises your metabolic rate even when you are at rest. Weight loss is also aided by the quite low efficiency of the body in converting internal energy to work, so that the loss of internal energy resulting from doing work is much greater than the work done.It should be noted, however, that living systems are not in thermalequilibrium.

The body provides us with an excellent indication that many thermodynamic processes are *irreversible*. An irreversible process can go in one direction but not the reverse, under a given set of conditions. For example, although body fat can be converted to do work and produce heat transfer, work done on the body and heat transfer into it cannot be converted to body fat. Otherwise, we could skip lunch by sunning ourselves or by walking down stairs. Another example of an irreversible thermodynamic process is photosynthesis. This process is the intake of one form of energy—light—by plants and its conversion to chemical potential energy. Both applications of the first law of thermodynamics are illustrated in Figure 15.5. One great advantage of conservation laws such as the first law of thermodynamics is that they accurately describe the beginning and ending points of complex processes, such as metabolism and photosynthesis, without regard to the complications in between. Table 15.1 presents a summary of terms relevant to the first law of thermodynamics.

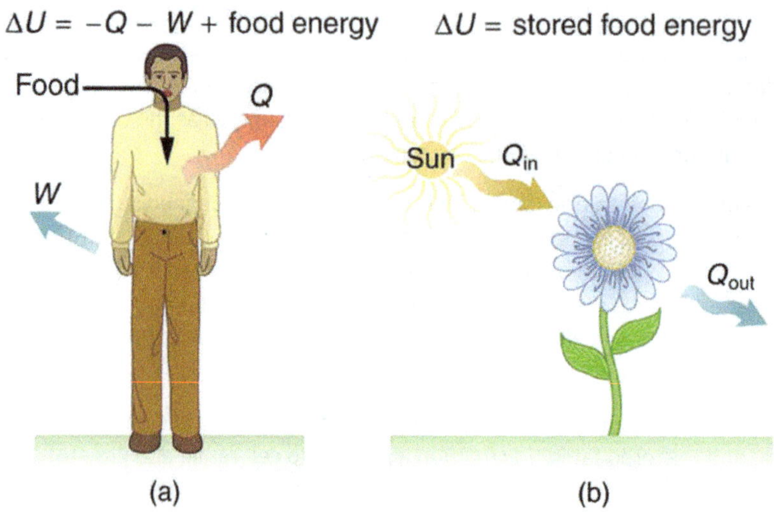

FIGURE 15.5 (a) The first law of thermodynamics applied to metabolism. Heat transferred out of the body (Q) and work done by the body (W) remove internal energy, while food intake replaces it. (Food intake may be considered as work done on the body.) (b) Plants convert part of the radiant heat transfer in sunlight to stored chemical energy, a process called photosynthesis.

Term	Definition
U	Internal energy—the sum of the kinetic and potential energies of a system's atoms and molecules. Can be divided into many subcategories, such as thermal and chemical energy. Depends only on the state of a system (such as its P, V, and T), not on how the energy entered the system. Change in internal energy is path independent.
Q	Heat—energy transferred because of a temperature difference. Characterized by random molecular motion. Highly dependent on path. Q entering a system is positive.
W	Work—energy transferred by a force moving through a distance. An organized, orderly process. Path dependent. W done by a system (either against an external force or to increase the volume of the system) is positive.

TABLE 15.1 Summary of Terms for the First Law of Thermodynamics, $\Delta U=Q-W$

15.2 The First Law of Thermodynamics and Some Simple Processes

LEARNING OBJECTIVES

By the end of this section, you will be able to:

- Describe the processes of a simple heat engine.
- Explain the differences among the simple thermodynamic processes—isobaric, isochoric, isothermal, and adiabatic.
- Calculate total work done in a cyclical thermodynamic process.

FIGURE 15.6 Beginning with the Industrial Revolution, humans have harnessed power through the use of the first law of thermodynamics, before we even understood it completely. This photo, of a steam engine at the Turbinia Works, dates from 1911, a mere 61 years after the first explicit statement of the first law of thermodynamics by Rudolph Clausius. (credit: public domain; author unknown)

One of the most important things we can do with heat transfer is to use it to do work for us. Such a device is called a **heat engine**. Car engines and steam turbines that generate electricity are examples of heat engines. Figure 15.7 shows schematically how the first law of thermodynamics applies to the typical heat engine.

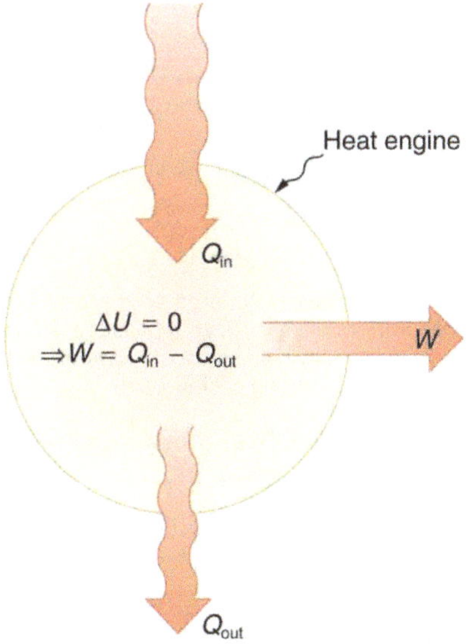

FIGURE 15.7 Schematic representation of a heat engine, governed, of course, by the first law of thermodynamics. It is impossible to devise a system where $Q_{out} = 0$, that is, in which no heat transfer occurs to the environment.

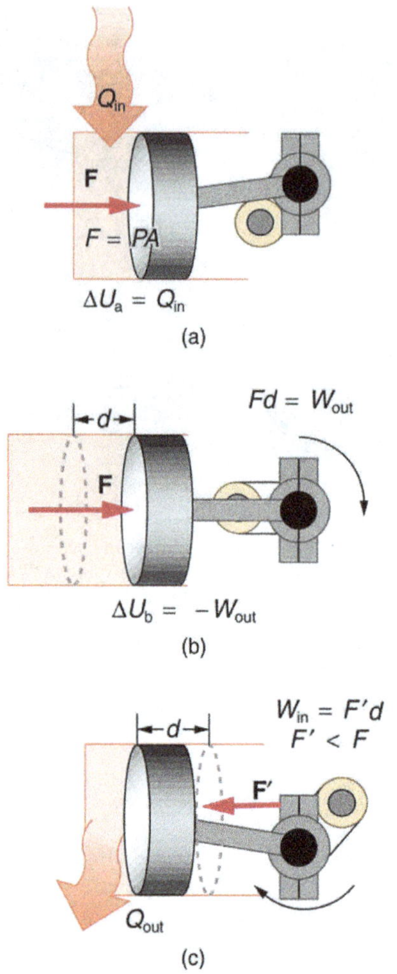

FIGURE 15.8 (a) Heat transfer to the gas in a cylinder increases the internal energy of the gas, creating higher pressure and temperature. (b) The force exerted on the movable cylinder does work as the gas expands. Gas pressure and temperature decrease when it expands, indicating that the gas's internal energy has been decreased by doing work. (c) Heat transfer to the environment further reduces pressure in the gas so that the piston can be more easily returned to its starting position.

The illustrations above show one of the ways in which heat transfer does work. Fuel combustion produces heat transfer to a gas in a cylinder, increasing the pressure of the gas and thereby the force it exerts on a movable piston. The gas does work on the outside world, as this force moves the piston through some distance. Heat transfer to the gas cylinder results in work being done. To repeat this process, the piston needs to be returned to its starting point. Heat transfer now occurs from the gas to the surroundings so that its pressure decreases, and a force is exerted by the surroundings to push the piston back through some distance. Variations of this process are employed daily in hundreds of millions of heat engines. We will examine heat engines in detail in the next section. In this section, we consider some of the simpler underlying processes on which heat engines are based.

PV Diagrams and their Relationship to Work Done on or by a Gas

A process by which a gas does work on a piston at constant pressure is called an **isobaric process**. Since the pressure is constant, the force exerted is constant and the work done is given as

$$P\Delta V. \tag{15.10}$$

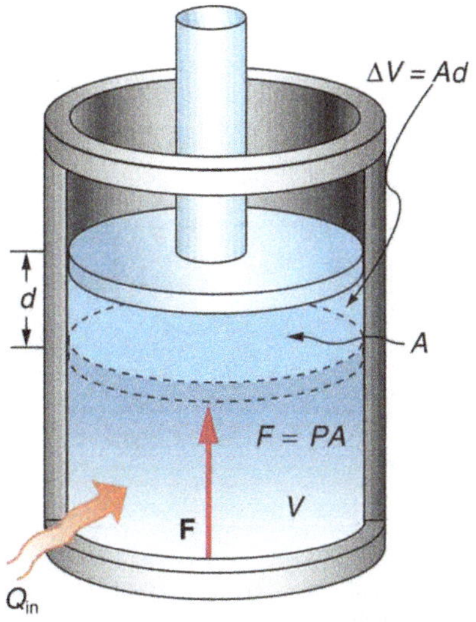

FIGURE 15.9 An isobaric expansion of a gas requires heat transfer to keep the pressure constant. Since pressure is constant, the work done is $P\Delta V$.

$$W = Fd \tag{15.11}$$

See the symbols as shown in Figure 15.9. Now $F = PA$, and so

$$W = PAd. \tag{15.12}$$

Because the volume of a cylinder is its cross-sectional area A times its length d, we see that $Ad = \Delta V$, the change in volume; thus,

$$W = P\Delta V \text{ (isobaric process)}. \tag{15.13}$$

Note that if ΔV is positive, then W is positive, meaning that work is done *by* the gas on the outside world.

(Note that the pressure involved in this work that we've called P is the pressure of the gas *inside* the tank. If we call the pressure outside the tank P_{ext}, an expanding gas would be working *against* the external pressure; the work done would therefore be $W = -P_{ext}\Delta V$ (isobaric process). Many texts use this definition of work, and not the definition based on internal pressure, as the basis of the First Law of Thermodynamics. This definition reverses the sign conventions for work, and results in a statement of the first law that becomes $\Delta U = Q + W$.)

It is not surprising that $W = P\Delta V$, since we have already noted in our treatment of fluids that pressure is a type of potential energy per unit volume and that pressure in fact has units of energy divided by volume. We also noted in our discussion of the ideal gas law that PV has units of energy. In this case, some of the energy associated with pressure becomes work.

Figure 15.10 shows a graph of pressure versus volume (that is, a PV diagram for an isobaric process. You can see in the figure that the work done is the area under the graph. This property of PV diagrams is very useful and broadly applicable: *the work done on or by a system in going from one state to another equals the area under the curve on a PV diagram.*

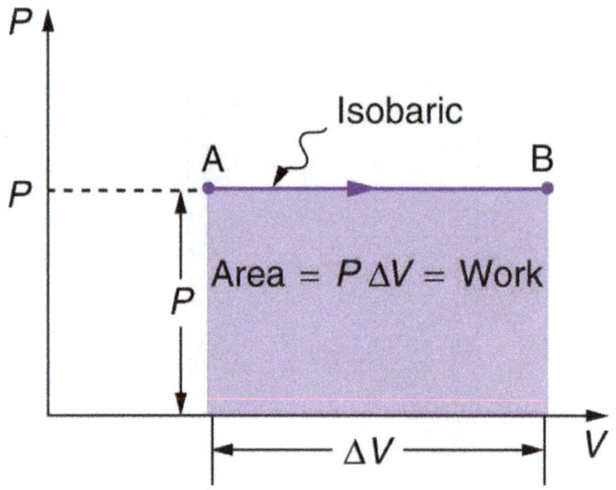

FIGURE 15.10 A graph of pressure versus volume for a constant-pressure, or isobaric, process, such as the one shown in Figure 15.9. The area under the curve equals the work done by the gas, since $W = P\Delta V$.

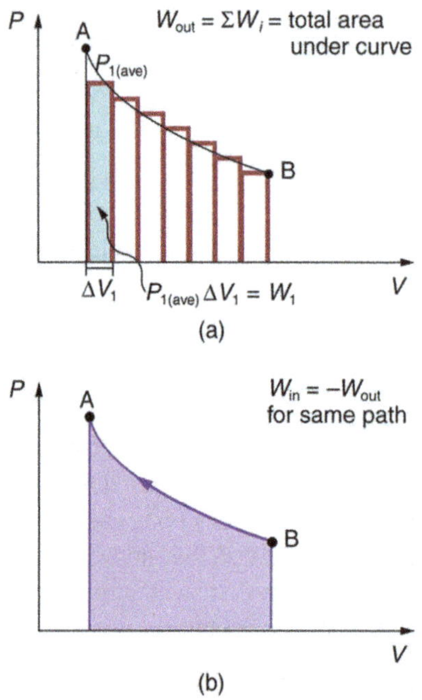

FIGURE 15.11 (a) A *PV* diagram in which pressure varies as well as volume. The work done for each interval is its average pressure times the change in volume, or the area under the curve over that interval. Thus the total area under the curve equals the total work done. (b) Work must be done on the system to follow the reverse path. This is interpreted as a negative area under the curve.

We can see where this leads by considering Figure 15.11(a), which shows a more general process in which both pressure and volume change. The area under the curve is closely approximated by dividing it into strips, each having an average constant pressure $P_{i(\text{ave})}$. The work done is $W_i = P_{i(\text{ave})}\Delta V_i$ for each strip, and the total work done is the sum of the W_i. Thus the total work done is the total area under the curve. If the path is reversed, as in Figure 15.11(b), then work is done on the system. The area under the curve in that case is negative, because ΔV is negative.

PV diagrams clearly illustrate that *the work done depends on the path taken and not just the endpoints*. This path dependence is seen in Figure 15.12(a), where more work is done in going from A to C by the path via point B than by the path via point D. The vertical paths, where volume is constant, are called **isochoric** processes. Since volume is constant, $\Delta V = 0$, and no work is done in an isochoric process. Now, if the system follows the cyclical path ABCDA, as in Figure 15.12(b), then the total work done is the area inside the loop. The negative area below path CD subtracts, leaving only the area inside the rectangle. In fact, the work done in any cyclical process (one that returns to its starting point) is the area inside the loop it forms on a *PV* diagram, as Figure 15.12(c) illustrates for a general cyclical process. Note that the loop must be traversed in the clockwise direction for work to be positive—that is, for there to be a net work output.

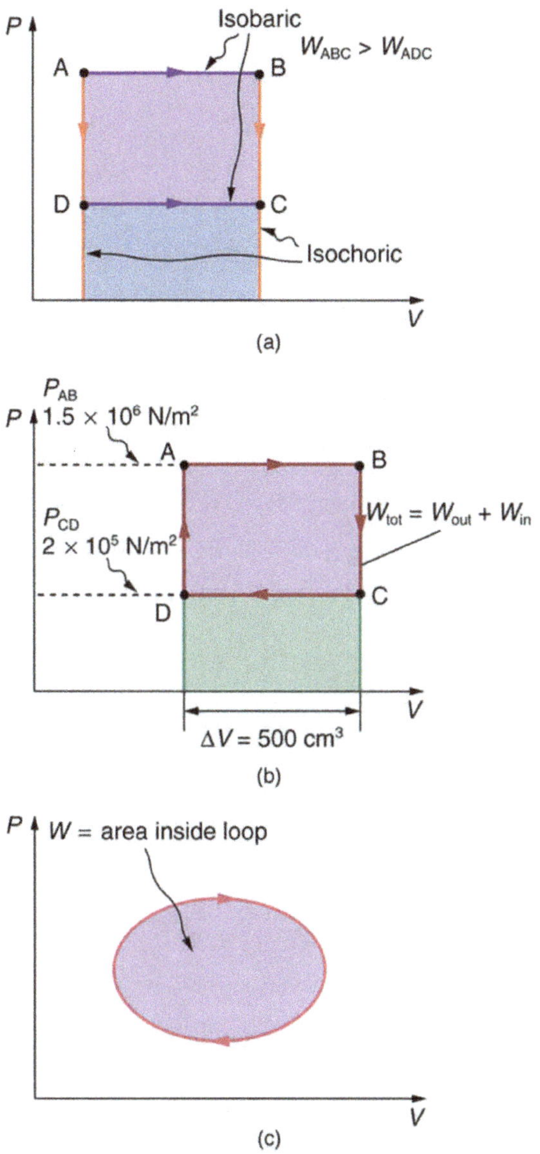

FIGURE 15.12 (a) The work done in going from A to C depends on path. The work is greater for the path ABC than for the path ADC, because the former is at higher pressure. In both cases, the work done is the area under the path. This area is greater for path ABC. (b) The total work done in the cyclical process ABCDA is the area inside the loop, since the negative area below CD subtracts out, leaving just the area inside the rectangle. (The values given for the pressures and the change in volume are intended for use in the example below.) (c) The area inside any closed loop is the work done in the cyclical process. If the loop is traversed in a clockwise direction, W is positive—it is work done on the outside environment. If the loop is traveled in a counter-clockwise direction, W is negative—it is work that is done to the system.

EXAMPLE 15.2

Total Work Done in a Cyclical Process Equals the Area Inside the Closed Loop on a *PV* Diagram

Calculate the total work done in the cyclical process ABCDA shown in Figure 15.12(b) by the following two methods to verify that work equals the area inside the closed loop on the PV diagram. (Take the data in the figure to be precise to three significant figures.) (a) Calculate the work done along each segment of the path and add these values to get the total work. (b) Calculate the area inside the rectangle ABCDA.

Strategy

To find the work along any path on a PV diagram, you use the fact that work is pressure times change in volume, or $W = P\Delta V$. So in part (a), this value is calculated for each leg of the path around the closed loop.

Solution for (a)

The work along path AB is

$$\begin{aligned} W_{AB} &= P_{AB}\Delta V_{AB} \\ &= (1.50\times10^6\ \text{N/m}^2)(5.00\times10^{-4}\ \text{m}^3) = 750\ \text{J}. \end{aligned} \quad (15.14)$$

Since the path BC is isochoric, $\Delta V_{BC} = 0$, and so $W_{BC} = 0$. The work along path CD is negative, since ΔV_{CD} is negative (the volume decreases). The work is

$$\begin{aligned} W_{CD} &= P_{CD}\Delta V_{CD} \\ &= (2.00\times10^5\ \text{N/m}^2)(-5.00\times10^{-4}\ \text{m}^3) = -100\ \text{J}. \end{aligned} \quad (15.15)$$

Again, since the path DA is isochoric, $\Delta V_{DA} = 0$, and so $W_{DA} = 0$. Now the total work is

$$\begin{aligned} W &= W_{AB} + W_{BC} + W_{CD} + W_{DA} \\ &= 750\ \text{J} + 0 + (-100\text{J}) + 0 = 650\ \text{J}. \end{aligned} \quad (15.16)$$

Solution for (b)

The area inside the rectangle is its height times its width, or

$$\begin{aligned} \text{area} &= (P_{AB} - P_{CD})\Delta V \\ &= \left[(1.50\times10^6\ \text{N/m}^2) - (2.00\times10^5\ \text{N/m}^2)\right](5.00\times10^{-4}\ \text{m}^3) \\ &= 650\ \text{J}. \end{aligned} \quad (15.17)$$

Thus,

$$\text{area} = 650\ \text{J} = W. \quad (15.18)$$

Discussion

The result, as anticipated, is that the area inside the closed loop equals the work done. The area is often easier to calculate than is the work done along each path. It is also convenient to visualize the area inside different curves on PV diagrams in order to see which processes might produce the most work. Recall that work can be done to the system, or by the system, depending on the sign of W. A positive W is work that is done by the system on the outside environment; a negative W represents work done by the environment on the system.

Figure 15.13(a) shows two other important processes on a PV diagram. For comparison, both are shown starting from the same point A. The upper curve ending at point B is an **isothermal** process—that is, one in which temperature is kept constant. If the gas behaves like an ideal gas, as is often the case, and if no phase change occurs, then $PV = nRT$. Since T is constant, PV is a constant for an isothermal process. We ordinarily expect the temperature of a gas to decrease as it expands, and so we correctly suspect that heat transfer must occur from the surroundings to the gas to keep the temperature constant during an isothermal expansion. To show this more rigorously for the special case of a monatomic ideal gas, we note that the average kinetic energy of an atom in such a gas is given by

$$\frac{1}{2}m\bar{v}^2 = \frac{3}{2}kT. \quad (15.19)$$

The kinetic energy of the atoms in a monatomic ideal gas is its only form of internal energy, and so its total internal energy U is

$$U = N\frac{1}{2}m\bar{v}^2 = \frac{3}{2}NkT,\ \text{(monatomic ideal gas)}, \quad (15.20)$$

where N is the number of atoms in the gas. This relationship means that the internal energy of an ideal monatomic gas is constant during an isothermal process—that is, $\Delta U = 0$. If the internal energy does not change, then the net heat transfer into the gas must equal the net work done by the gas. That is, because $\Delta U = Q - W = 0$ here, $Q = W$. We must have just enough heat transfer to replace the work done. An isothermal process is inherently slow, because heat transfer occurs continuously to keep the gas temperature constant at all times and must be allowed to spread through the gas so that there are no hot or cold regions.

Note that diatomic gases, such as those in air, have different formulas for average kinetic energy of an atom and total internal energy.

Also shown in Figure 15.13(a) is a curve AC for an **adiabatic** process, defined to be one in which there is no heat transfer—that is, $Q = 0$. Processes that are nearly adiabatic can be achieved either by using very effective insulation or by performing the process so fast that there is little time for heat transfer. Temperature must decrease during an adiabatic expansion process, since work is done at the expense of internal energy:

$$U = \frac{3}{2}NkT. \tag{15.21}$$

(You might have noted that a gas released into atmospheric pressure from a pressurized cylinder is substantially colder than the gas in the cylinder.) In fact, because $Q = 0$, $\Delta U = -W$ for an adiabatic process. Lower temperature results in lower pressure along the way, so that curve AC is lower than curve AB, and less work is done. If the path ABCA could be followed by cooling the gas from B to C at constant volume (isochorically), Figure 15.13(b), there would be a net work output.

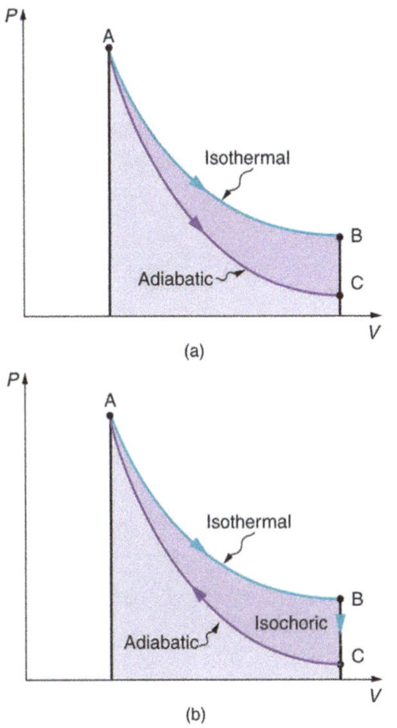

FIGURE 15.13 (a) The upper curve is an isothermal process ($\Delta T = 0$), whereas the lower curve is an adiabatic process ($Q = 0$). Both start from the same point A, but the isothermal process does more work than the adiabatic because heat transfer into the gas takes place to keep its temperature constant. This keeps the pressure higher all along the isothermal path than along the adiabatic path, producing more work. The adiabatic path thus ends up with a lower pressure and temperature at point C, even though the final volume is the same as for the isothermal process. (b) The cycle ABCA produces a net work output.

Reversible Processes

Both isothermal and adiabatic processes such as shown in Figure 15.13 are reversible in principle. A **reversible process** is one in which both the system and its environment can return to exactly the states they were in by following the reverse path. The reverse isothermal and adiabatic paths are BA and CA, respectively. Real macroscopic processes are never exactly reversible. In the previous examples, our system is a gas (like that in Figure 15.9), and its environment is the piston, cylinder, and the rest of the universe. If there are any energy-dissipating mechanisms, such as friction or turbulence, then heat transfer to the environment occurs for either direction of the piston. So, for example, if the path BA is followed and there is friction, then the gas will be returned to its original state but the environment will not—it will have been heated in both directions. Reversibility requires the direction of heat transfer to reverse for the reverse path. Since dissipative mechanisms cannot be completely eliminated, real processes cannot be reversible.

There must be reasons that real macroscopic processes cannot be reversible. We can imagine them going in reverse. For example, heat transfer occurs spontaneously from hot to cold and never spontaneously the reverse. Yet it would not violate the first law of thermodynamics for this to happen. In fact, all spontaneous processes, such as bubbles bursting, never go in reverse. There is a second thermodynamic law that forbids them from going in reverse. When we study this law, we will learn something about nature and also find that such a law limits the efficiency of heat engines. We will find that heat engines with the greatest possible theoretical efficiency would have to use reversible processes, and even they cannot convert all heat transfer into doing work. Table 15.2 summarizes the simpler thermodynamic processes and their definitions.

Isobaric	Constant pressure $W = P\Delta V$
Isochoric	Constant volume $W = 0$
Isothermal	Constant temperature $Q = W$
Adiabatic	No heat transfer $Q = 0$

TABLE 15.2 Summary of Simple Thermodynamic Processes

PHET EXPLORATIONS

States of Matter

Watch different types of molecules form a solid, liquid, or gas. Add or remove heat and watch the phase change. Change the temperature or volume of a container and see a pressure-temperature diagram respond in real time. Relate the interaction potential to the forces between molecules.

Click to view content (https://openstax.org/books/college-physics-ap-courses-2e/pages/15-2-the-first-law-of-thermodynamics-and-some-simple-processes)

15.3 Introduction to the Second Law of Thermodynamics: Heat Engines and Their Efficiency

LEARNING OBJECTIVES

By the end of this section, you will be able to:

- State the expressions of the second law of thermodynamics.
- Calculate the efficiency and carbon dioxide emission of a coal-fired electricity plant, using second law characteristics.
- Describe and define the Otto cycle.

FIGURE 15.14 These ice floes melt during the Arctic summer. Some of them refreeze in the winter, but the second law of thermodynamics predicts that it would be extremely unlikely for the water molecules contained in these particular floes to reform the distinctive alligator-like shape they formed when the picture was taken in the summer of 2009. (credit: Patrick Kelley, U.S. Coast Guard, U.S. Geological Survey)

The second law of thermodynamics deals with the direction taken by spontaneous processes. Many processes occur spontaneously in one direction only—that is, they are irreversible, under a given set of conditions. Although irreversibility is seen in day-to-day life—a broken glass does not resume its original state, for instance—complete irreversibility is a statistical statement that cannot be seen during the lifetime of the universe. More precisely, an **irreversible process** is one that depends on path. If the process can go in only one direction, then the reverse path differs fundamentally and the process cannot be reversible. For example, as noted in the previous section, heat involves the transfer of energy from higher to lower temperature. A cold object in contact with a hot one never gets colder, transferring heat to the hot object and making it hotter. Furthermore, mechanical energy, such as kinetic energy, can be completely converted to thermal energy by friction, but the reverse is impossible. A hot stationary object never spontaneously cools off and starts moving. Yet another example is the expansion of a puff of gas introduced into one corner of a vacuum chamber. The gas expands to fill the chamber, but it never regroups in the corner. The random motion of the gas molecules could take them all back to the corner, but this is never observed to happen. (See Figure 15.15.)

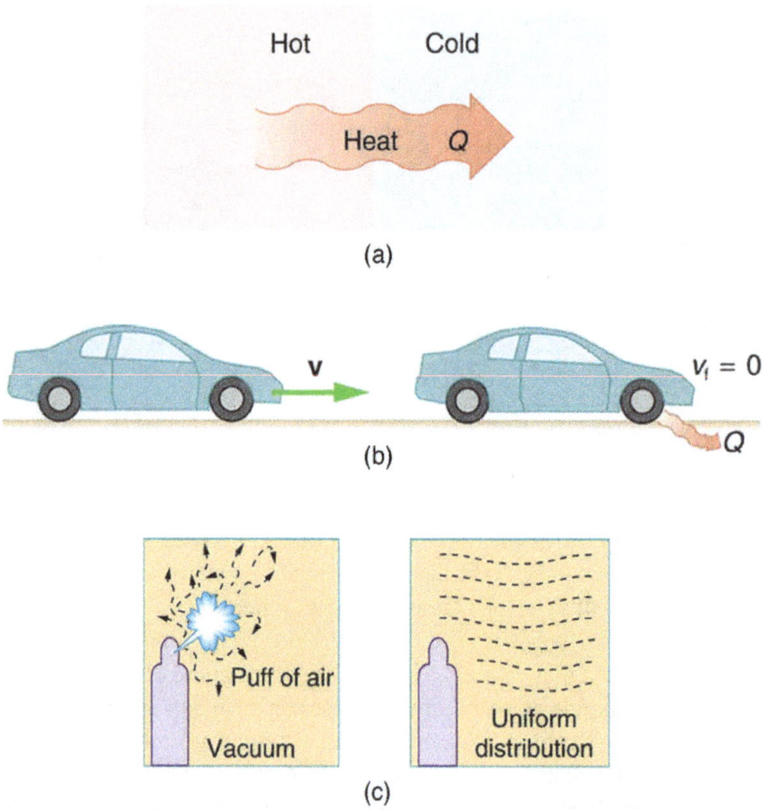

FIGURE 15.15 Examples of one-way processes in nature. (a) Heat transfer occurs spontaneously from hot to cold and not from cold to hot. (b) The brakes of this car convert its kinetic energy to heat transfer to the environment. The reverse process is impossible. (c) The burst of gas let into this vacuum chamber quickly expands to uniformly fill every part of the chamber. The random motions of the gas molecules will never return them to the corner.

The fact that certain processes never occur suggests that there is a law forbidding them to occur. The first law of thermodynamics would allow them to occur—none of those processes violate conservation of energy. The law that forbids these processes is called the second law of thermodynamics. We shall see that the second law can be stated in many ways that may seem different, but which in fact are equivalent. Like all natural laws, the second law of thermodynamics gives insights into nature, and its several statements imply that it is broadly applicable, fundamentally affecting many apparently disparate processes.

The already familiar direction of heat transfer from hot to cold is the basis of our first version of the **second law of thermodynamics**.

THE SECOND LAW OF THERMODYNAMICS (FIRST EXPRESSION)

Heat transfer occurs spontaneously from higher- to lower-temperature bodies but never spontaneously in the reverse direction.

Another way of stating this: It is impossible for any process to have as its sole result heat transfer from a cooler to a hotter object.

Heat Engines

Now let us consider a device that uses heat transfer to do work. As noted in the previous section, such a device is called a heat engine, and one is shown schematically in Figure 15.16(b). Gasoline and diesel engines, jet engines, and steam turbines are all heat engines that do work by using part of the heat transfer from some source. Heat transfer from the hot object (or hot reservoir) is denoted as Q_{h}, while heat transfer into the cold object (or cold reservoir) is Q_{c}, and the work done by the engine is W. The temperatures of the hot and cold reservoirs are T_{h} and T_{c}, respectively.

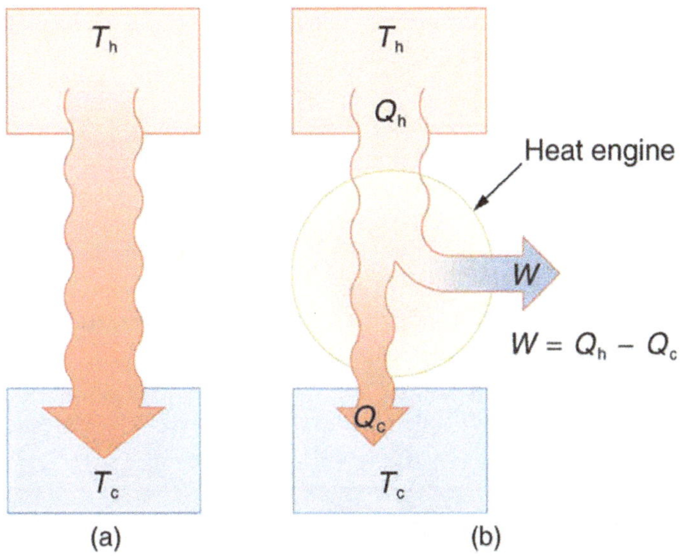

FIGURE 15.16 (a) Heat transfer occurs spontaneously from a hot object to a cold one, consistent with the second law of thermodynamics. (b) A heat engine, represented here by a circle, uses part of the heat transfer to do work. The hot and cold objects are called the hot and cold reservoirs. Q_h is the heat transfer out of the hot reservoir, W is the work output, and Q_c is the heat transfer into the cold reservoir.

Because the hot reservoir is heated externally, which is energy intensive, it is important that the work is done as efficiently as possible. In fact, we would like W to equal Q_h, and for there to be no heat transfer to the environment ($Q_c = 0$). Unfortunately, this is impossible. The **second law of thermodynamics** also states, with regard to using heat transfer to do work (the second expression of the second law):

THE SECOND LAW OF THERMODYNAMICS (SECOND EXPRESSION)

It is impossible in any system for heat transfer from a reservoir to completely convert to work in a cyclical process in which the system returns to its initial state.

A **cyclical process** brings a system, such as the gas in a cylinder, back to its original state at the end of every cycle. Most heat engines, such as reciprocating piston engines and rotating turbines, use cyclical processes. The second law, just stated in its second form, clearly states that such engines cannot have perfect conversion of heat transfer into work done. Before going into the underlying reasons for the limits on converting heat transfer into work, we need to explore the relationships among W, Q_h, and Q_c, and to define the efficiency of a cyclical heat engine. As noted, a cyclical process brings the system back to its original condition at the end of every cycle. Such a system's internal energy U is the same at the beginning and end of every cycle—that is, $\Delta U = 0$. The first law of thermodynamics states that

$$\Delta U = Q - W, \tag{15.22}$$

where Q is the *net* heat transfer during the cycle ($Q = Q_h - Q_c$) and W is the net work done by the system. Since $\Delta U = 0$ for a complete cycle, we have

$$0 = Q - W, \tag{15.23}$$

so that

$$W = Q. \tag{15.24}$$

Thus the net work done by the system equals the net heat transfer into the system, or

$$W = Q_h - Q_c \text{ (cyclical process)}, \tag{15.25}$$

just as shown schematically in Figure 15.16(b). The problem is that in all processes, there is some heat transfer Q_c to the environment—and usually a very significant amount at that.

In the conversion of energy to work, we are always faced with the problem of getting less out than we put in. We define *conversion efficiency* Eff to be the ratio of useful work output to the energy input (or, in other words, the ratio of what we get to what we spend). In that spirit, we define the efficiency of a heat engine to be its net work output W divided by heat transfer to the engine Q_h; that is,

$$Eff = \frac{W}{Q_h}. \tag{15.26}$$

Since $W = Q_h - Q_c$ in a cyclical process, we can also express this as

$$Eff = \frac{Q_h - Q_c}{Q_h} = 1 - \frac{Q_c}{Q_h} \text{ (cyclical process)}, \tag{15.27}$$

making it clear that an efficiency of 1, or 100%, is possible only if there is no heat transfer to the environment ($Q_c = 0$). Note that all Qs are positive. The direction of heat transfer is indicated by a plus or minus sign. For example, Q_c is out of the system and so is preceded by a minus sign.

EXAMPLE 15.3

Daily Work Done by a Coal-Fired Power Station, Its Efficiency and Carbon Dioxide Emissions

A coal-fired power station is a huge heat engine. It uses heat transfer from burning coal to do work to turn turbines, which are used to generate electricity. In a single day, a large coal power station has 2.50×10^{14} J of heat transfer from coal and 1.48×10^{14} J of heat transfer into the environment. (a) What is the work done by the power station? (b) What is the efficiency of the power station? (c) In the combustion process, the following chemical reaction occurs: $C + O_2 \rightarrow CO_2$. This implies that every 12 kg of coal puts 12 kg + 16 kg + 16 kg = 44 kg of carbon dioxide into the atmosphere. Assuming that 1 kg of coal can provide 2.5×10^6 J of heat transfer upon combustion, how much CO_2 is emitted per day by this power plant?

Strategy for (a)

We can use $W = Q_h - Q_c$ to find the work output W, assuming a cyclical process is used in the power station. In this process, water is boiled under pressure to form high-temperature steam, which is used to run steam turbine-generators, and then condensed back to water to start the cycle again.

Solution for (a)

Work output is given by:

$$W = Q_h - Q_c. \tag{15.28}$$

Substituting the given values:

$$\begin{aligned} W &= 2.50 \times 10^{14}\text{ J} - 1.48 \times 10^{14}\text{ J} \\ &= 1.02 \times 10^{14}\text{ J}. \end{aligned} \tag{15.29}$$

Strategy for (b)

The efficiency can be calculated with $Eff = \frac{W}{Q_h}$ since Q_h is given and work W was found in the first part of this example.

Solution for (b)

Efficiency is given by: $Eff = \frac{W}{Q_h}$. The work W was just found to be 1.02×10^{14} J, and Q_h is given, so the efficiency is

$$\begin{aligned} Eff &= \frac{1.02 \times 10^{14}\text{ J}}{2.50 \times 10^{14}\text{ J}} \\ &= 0.408\text{, or }40.8\% \end{aligned} \tag{15.30}$$

Strategy for (c)

The daily consumption of coal is calculated using the information that each day there is 2.50×10^{14} J of heat transfer from coal. In the combustion process, we have $C + O_2 \rightarrow CO_2$. So every 12 kg of coal puts 12 kg + 16 kg + 16 kg = 44 kg of CO_2 into the atmosphere.

Solution for (c)

The daily coal consumption is

$$\frac{2.50\times10^{14}\text{ J}}{2.50\times10^{6}\text{ J/kg}} = 1.0\times10^{8}\text{ kg}. \qquad (15.31)$$

Assuming that the coal is pure and that all the coal goes toward producing carbon dioxide, the carbon dioxide produced per day is

$$1.0\times10^{8}\text{ kg coal}\times\frac{44\text{ kg CO}_2}{12\text{ kg coal}} = 3.7\times10^{8}\text{ kg CO}_2. \qquad (15.32)$$

This is 370,000 metric tons of CO_2 produced every day.

Discussion

If all the work output is converted to electricity in a period of one day, the average power output is 1180 MW (this is left to you as an end-of-chapter problem). This value is about the size of a large-scale conventional power plant. The efficiency found is acceptably close to the value of 42% given for coal power stations. It means that fully 59.2% of the energy is heat transfer to the environment, which usually results in warming lakes, rivers, or the ocean near the power station, and is implicated in a warming planet generally. While the laws of thermodynamics limit the efficiency of such plants—including plants fired by nuclear fuel, oil, and natural gas—the heat transfer to the environment could be, and sometimes is, used for heating homes or for industrial processes. The generally low cost of energy has not made it economical to make better use of the waste heat transfer from most heat engines. Coal-fired power plants produce the greatest amount of CO_2 per unit energy output (compared to natural gas or oil), making coal the least efficient fossil fuel.

With the information given in Example 15.3, we can find characteristics such as the efficiency of a heat engine without any knowledge of how the heat engine operates, but looking further into the mechanism of the engine will give us greater insight. Figure 15.17 illustrates the operation of the common four-stroke gasoline engine. The four steps shown complete this heat engine's cycle, bringing the gasoline-air mixture back to its original condition.

The **Otto cycle** shown in Figure 15.18(a) is used in four-stroke internal combustion engines, although in fact the true Otto cycle paths do not correspond exactly to the strokes of the engine.

The adiabatic process AB corresponds to the nearly adiabatic compression stroke of the gasoline engine. In both cases, work is done on the system (the gas mixture in the cylinder), increasing its temperature and pressure. Along path BC of the Otto cycle, heat transfer Q_h into the gas occurs at constant volume, causing a further increase in pressure and temperature. This process corresponds to burning fuel in an internal combustion engine, and takes place so rapidly that the volume is nearly constant. Path CD in the Otto cycle is an adiabatic expansion that does work on the outside world, just as the power stroke of an internal combustion engine does in its nearly adiabatic expansion. The work done by the system along path CD is greater than the work done on the system along path AB, because the pressure is greater, and so there is a net work output. Along path DA in the Otto cycle, heat transfer Q_c from the gas at constant volume reduces its temperature and pressure, returning it to its original state. In an internal combustion engine, this process corresponds to the exhaust of hot gases and the intake of an air-gasoline mixture at a considerably lower temperature. In both cases, heat transfer into the environment occurs along this final path.

The net work done by a cyclical process is the area inside the closed path on a PV diagram, such as that inside path ABCDA in Figure 15.18. Note that in every imaginable cyclical process, it is absolutely necessary for heat transfer from the system to occur in order to get a net work output. In the Otto cycle, heat transfer occurs along path DA. If no heat transfer occurs, then the return path is the same, and the net work output is zero. The lower the temperature on the path AB, the less work has to be done to compress the gas. The area inside the closed path is then greater, and so the engine does more work and is thus more efficient. Similarly, the higher the temperature along path CD, the more work output there is. (See Figure 15.19.) So efficiency is related to the temperatures of the hot and cold reservoirs. In the next section, we shall see what the absolute limit to the efficiency of a heat engine is, and how it is related to temperature.

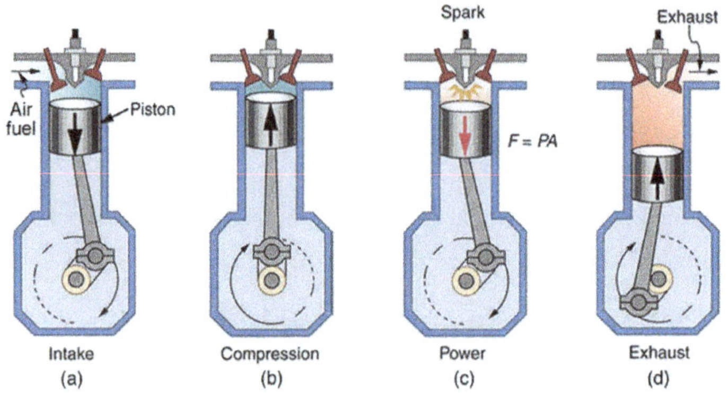

FIGURE 15.17 In the four-stroke internal combustion gasoline engine, heat transfer into work takes place in the cyclical process shown here. The piston is connected to a rotating crankshaft, which both takes work out of and does work on the gas in the cylinder. (a) Air is mixed with fuel during the intake stroke. (b) During the compression stroke, the air-fuel mixture is rapidly compressed in a nearly adiabatic process, as the piston rises with the valves closed. Work is done on the gas. (c) The power stroke has two distinct parts. First, the air-fuel mixture is ignited, converting chemical potential energy into thermal energy almost instantaneously, which leads to a great increase in pressure. Then the piston descends, and the gas does work by exerting a force through a distance in a nearly adiabatic process. (d) The exhaust stroke expels the hot gas to prepare the engine for another cycle, starting again with the intake stroke.

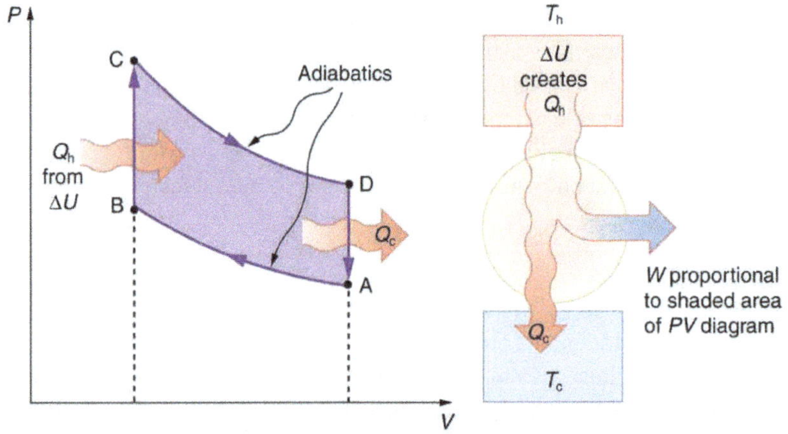

FIGURE 15.18 *PV* diagram for a simplified Otto cycle, analogous to that employed in an internal combustion engine. Point A corresponds to the start of the compression stroke of an internal combustion engine. Paths AB and CD are adiabatic and correspond to the compression and power strokes of an internal combustion engine, respectively. Paths BC and DA are isochoric and accomplish similar results to the ignition and exhaust-intake portions, respectively, of the internal combustion engine's cycle. Work is done on the gas along path AB, but more work is done by the gas along path CD, so that there is a net work output.

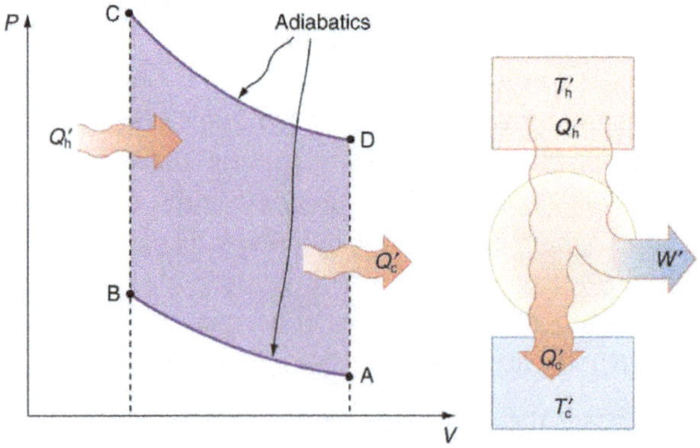

FIGURE 15.19 This Otto cycle produces a greater work output than the one in Figure 15.18, because the starting temperature of path CD is higher and the starting temperature of path AB is lower. The area inside the loop is greater, corresponding to greater net work output.

15.4 Carnot's Perfect Heat Engine: The Second Law of Thermodynamics Restated

LEARNING OBJECTIVES

By the end of this section, you will be able to:

- Identify a Carnot cycle.
- Calculate maximum theoretical efficiency of a nuclear reactor.
- Explain how dissipative processes affect the ideal Carnot engine.

FIGURE 15.20 This novelty toy, known as the drinking bird, is an example of Carnot's engine. It contains methylene chloride (mixed with a dye) in the abdomen, which boils at a very low temperature—about 100°F. To operate, one gets the bird's head wet. As the water evaporates, fluid moves up into the head, causing the bird to become top-heavy and dip forward back into the water. This cools down the methylene chloride in the head, and it moves back into the abdomen, causing the bird to become bottom heavy and tip up. Except for a very small input of energy—the original head-wetting—the bird becomes a perpetual motion machine of sorts. (credit: Arabesk.nl, Wikimedia Commons)

We know from the second law of thermodynamics that a heat engine cannot be 100% efficient, since there must always be some heat transfer Q_c to the environment, which is often called waste heat. How efficient, then, can a heat engine be? This question was answered at a theoretical level in 1824 by a young French engineer, Sadi Carnot (1796–1832), in his study of the then-emerging heat engine technology crucial to the Industrial Revolution. He devised a theoretical cycle, now called the **Carnot cycle**, which is the most efficient cyclical process possible. The second law of thermodynamics can be restated in terms of the Carnot cycle, and so what Carnot actually discovered was this fundamental law. Any heat engine employing the Carnot cycle is called a **Carnot engine**.

What is crucial to the Carnot cycle—and, in fact, defines it—is that only reversible processes are used. Irreversible processes involve dissipative factors, such as friction and turbulence. This increases heat transfer Q_c to the environment and reduces the efficiency of the engine. Obviously, then, reversible processes are superior.

CARNOT ENGINE

Stated in terms of reversible processes, the **second law of thermodynamics** has a third form:

A Carnot engine operating between two given temperatures has the greatest possible efficiency of any heat engine operating between these two temperatures. Furthermore, all engines employing only reversible processes have this same maximum efficiency when operating between the same given temperatures.

Figure 15.21 shows the PV diagram for a Carnot cycle. The cycle comprises two isothermal and two adiabatic processes. Recall that both isothermal and adiabatic processes are, in principle, reversible.

Carnot also determined the efficiency of a perfect heat engine—that is, a Carnot engine. It is always true that the efficiency of a cyclical heat engine is given by:

$$Eff = \frac{Q_h - Q_c}{Q_h} = 1 - \frac{Q_c}{Q_h}. \quad 15.33$$

What Carnot found was that for a perfect heat engine, the ratio Q_c/Q_h equals the ratio of the absolute temperatures of the heat reservoirs. That is, $Q_c/Q_h = T_c/T_h$ for a Carnot engine, so that the maximum or **Carnot efficiency** Eff_C is given by

$$Eff_C = 1 - \frac{T_c}{T_h}, \quad 15.34$$

where T_h and T_c are in kelvins (or any other absolute temperature scale). No real heat engine can do as well as the Carnot efficiency—an actual efficiency of about 0.7 of this maximum is usually the best that can be accomplished. But the ideal Carnot engine, like the drinking bird above, while a fascinating novelty, has zero power. This makes it unrealistic for any applications.

Carnot's interesting result implies that 100% efficiency would be possible only if $T_c = 0\ \text{K}$—that is, only if the cold reservoir were at absolute zero, a practical and theoretical impossibility. But the physical implication is this—the only way to have all heat transfer go into doing work is to remove *all* thermal energy, and this requires a cold reservoir at absolute zero.

It is also apparent that the greatest efficiencies are obtained when the ratio T_c/T_h is as small as possible. Just as discussed for the Otto cycle in the previous section, this means that efficiency is greatest for the highest possible temperature of the hot reservoir and lowest possible temperature of the cold reservoir. (This setup increases the area inside the closed loop on the *PV* diagram; also, it seems reasonable that the greater the temperature difference, the easier it is to divert the heat transfer to work.) The actual reservoir temperatures of a heat engine are usually related to the type of heat source and the temperature of the environment into which heat transfer occurs. Consider the following example.

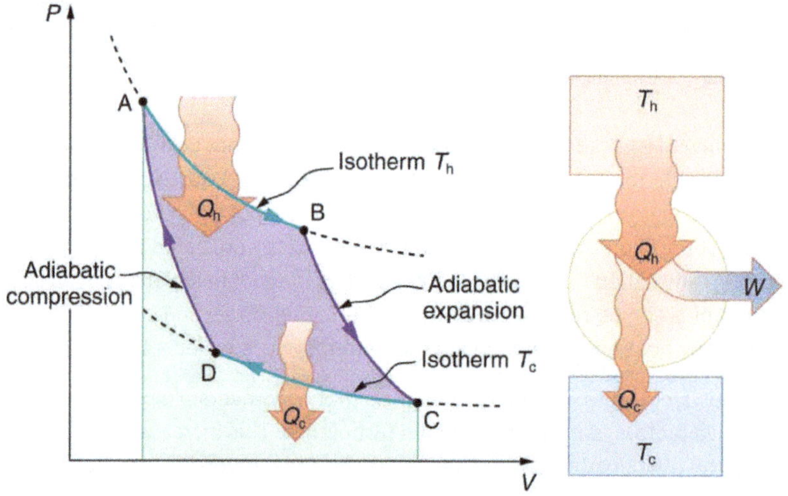

FIGURE 15.21 *PV* diagram for a Carnot cycle, employing only reversible isothermal and adiabatic processes. Heat transfer Q_h occurs into the working substance during the isothermal path AB, which takes place at constant temperature T_h. Heat transfer Q_c occurs out of the working substance during the isothermal path CD, which takes place at constant temperature T_c. The net work output W equals the area inside the path ABCDA. Also shown is a schematic of a Carnot engine operating between hot and cold reservoirs at temperatures T_h and T_c. Any heat engine using reversible processes and operating between these two temperatures will have the same maximum efficiency as the Carnot engine.

EXAMPLE 15.4

Maximum Theoretical Efficiency for a Nuclear Reactor

A nuclear power reactor has pressurized water at 300ºC. (Higher temperatures are theoretically possible but practically not, due to limitations with materials used in the reactor.) Heat transfer from this water is a complex process (see Figure 15.22). Steam, produced in the steam generator, is used to drive the turbine-generators. Eventually the steam is condensed to water at 27ºC and then heated again to start the cycle over. Calculate the maximum theoretical efficiency for a heat engine operating between these two temperatures.

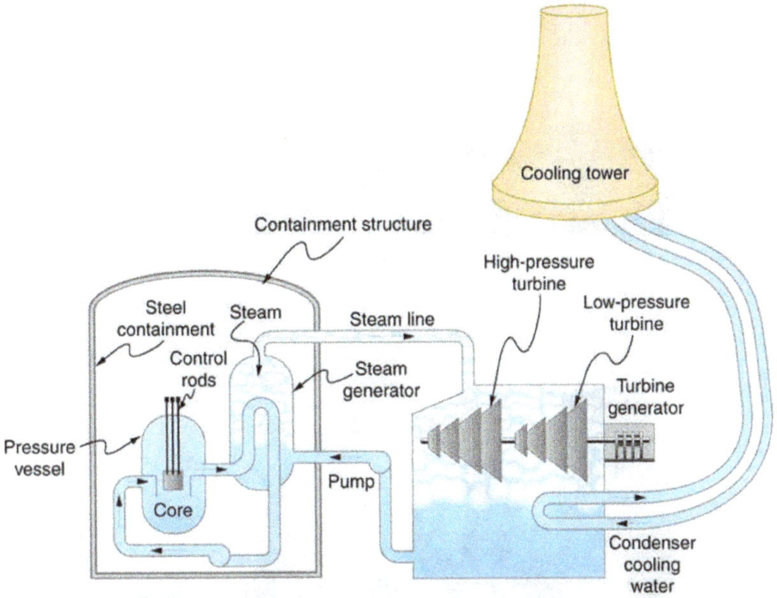

FIGURE 15.22 Schematic diagram of a pressurized water nuclear reactor and the steam turbines that convert work into electrical energy. Heat exchange is used to generate steam, in part to avoid contamination of the generators with radioactivity. Two turbines are used because this is less expensive than operating a single generator that produces the same amount of electrical energy. The steam is condensed to liquid before being returned to the heat exchanger, to keep exit steam pressure low and aid the flow of steam through the turbines (equivalent to using a lower-temperature cold reservoir). The considerable energy associated with condensation must be dissipated into the local environment; in this example, a cooling tower is used so there is no direct heat transfer to an aquatic environment. (Note that the water going to the cooling tower does not come into contact with the steam flowing over the turbines.)

Strategy

Since temperatures are given for the hot and cold reservoirs of this heat engine, $Eff_\text{C} = 1 - \frac{T_\text{c}}{T_\text{h}}$ can be used to calculate the Carnot (maximum theoretical) efficiency. Those temperatures must first be converted to kelvins.

Solution

The hot and cold reservoir temperatures are given as $300ºC$ and $27.0ºC$, respectively. In kelvins, then, $T_\text{h} = 573\text{ K}$ and $T_\text{c} = 300\text{ K}$, so that the maximum efficiency is

$$Eff_\text{C} = 1 - \frac{T_\text{c}}{T_\text{h}}. \quad 15.35$$

Thus,

$$\begin{aligned} Eff_\text{C} &= 1 - \frac{300\text{ K}}{573\text{ K}} \\ &= 0.476, \text{ or } 47.6\%. \end{aligned} \quad 15.36$$

Discussion

A typical nuclear power station's actual efficiency is about 35%, a little better than 0.7 times the maximum possible value, a tribute to superior engineering. Electrical power stations fired by coal, oil, and natural gas have greater actual efficiencies (about 42%), because their boilers can reach higher temperatures and pressures. The cold reservoir temperature in any of these power stations is limited by the local environment. Figure 15.23 shows (a) the exterior of a nuclear power station and (b) the exterior of a coal-fired power station. Both have cooling towers into which water from the condenser enters the tower near the top and is sprayed downward, cooled by evaporation.

(a)

(b)

FIGURE 15.23 (a) A nuclear power station (credit: BlatantWorld.com) and (b) a coal-fired power station. Both have cooling towers in which water evaporates into the environment, representing Q_c. The nuclear reactor, which supplies Q_h, is housed inside the dome-shaped containment buildings. (credit: Robert & Mihaela Vicol, publicphoto.org)

Since all real processes are irreversible, the actual efficiency of a heat engine can never be as great as that of a Carnot engine, as illustrated in Figure 15.24(a). Even with the best heat engine possible, there are always dissipative processes in peripheral equipment, such as electrical transformers or car transmissions. These further reduce the overall efficiency by converting some of the engine's work output back into heat transfer, as shown in Figure 15.24(b).

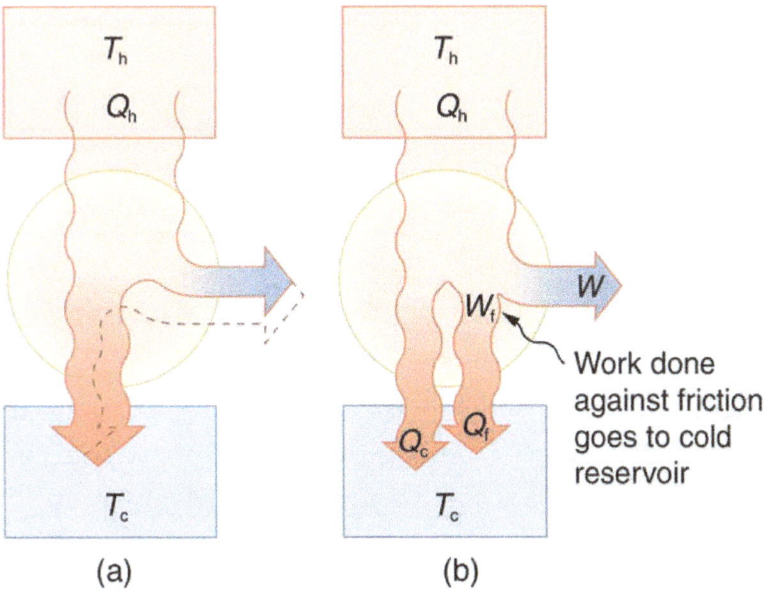

FIGURE 15.24 Real heat engines are less efficient than Carnot engines. (a) Real engines use irreversible processes, reducing the heat transfer to work. Solid lines represent the actual process; the dashed lines are what a Carnot engine would do between the same two reservoirs. (b) Friction and other dissipative processes in the output mechanisms of a heat engine convert some of its work output into heat transfer to the environment.

15.5 Applications of Thermodynamics: Heat Pumps and Refrigerators

LEARNING OBJECTIVES

By the end of this section, you will be able to:

- Describe the use of heat engines in heat pumps and refrigerators.
- Demonstrate how a heat pump works to warm an interior space.
- Explain the differences between heat pumps and refrigerators.
- Calculate a heat pump's coefficient of performance.

FIGURE 15.25 Almost every home contains a refrigerator. Most people don't realize they are also sharing their homes with a heat pump. (credit: Id1337x, Wikimedia Commons)

Heat pumps, air conditioners, and refrigerators utilize heat transfer from cold to hot. They are heat engines run backward. We say backward, rather than reverse, because except for Carnot engines, all heat engines, though they can be run backward, cannot truly be reversed. Heat transfer occurs from a cold reservoir Q_c and into a hot one. This requires work input W, which is also converted to heat transfer. Thus the heat transfer to the hot reservoir is $Q_h = Q_c + W$. (Note that Q_h, Q_c, and W are positive, with their directions indicated on schematics rather than by sign.) A heat pump's mission is for heat transfer Q_h to occur into a warm environment, such as a home in the winter. The mission of air conditioners and refrigerators is for heat transfer Q_c to occur from a cool environment, such as chilling a room or keeping food at lower temperatures than the environment. (Actually, a heat pump can be used both to heat and cool a space. It is essentially an air conditioner and a heating unit all in one. In this section we will concentrate on its heating mode.)

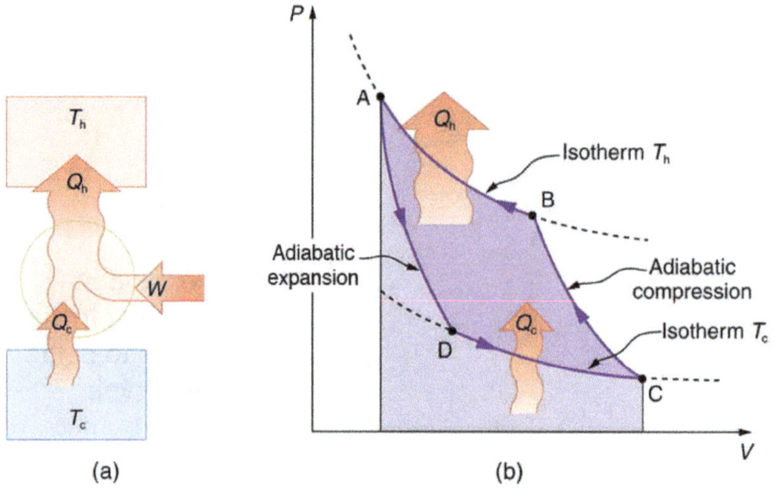

FIGURE 15.26 Heat pumps, air conditioners, and refrigerators are heat engines operated backward. The one shown here is based on a Carnot (reversible) engine. (a) Schematic diagram showing heat transfer from a cold reservoir to a warm reservoir with a heat pump. The directions of W , Q_h, and Q_c are opposite what they would be in a heat engine. (b) PV diagram for a Carnot cycle similar to that in Figure 15.27 but reversed, following path ADCBA. The area inside the loop is negative, meaning there is a net work input. There is heat transfer Q_c into the system from a cold reservoir along path DC, and heat transfer Q_h out of the system into a hot reservoir along path BA.

Heat Pumps

The great advantage of using a heat pump to keep your home warm, rather than just burning fuel, is that a heat pump supplies $Q_h = Q_c + W$. Heat transfer is from the outside air, even at a temperature below freezing, to the indoor space. You only pay for W, and you get an additional heat transfer of Q_c from the outside at no cost; in many cases, at least twice as much energy is transferred to the heated space as is used to run the heat pump. When you burn fuel to keep warm, you pay for all of it. The disadvantage is that the work input (required by the second law of thermodynamics) is sometimes more expensive than simply burning fuel, especially if the work is done by electrical energy.

The basic components of a heat pump in its heating mode are shown in Figure 15.27. A working fluid such as a non-CFC refrigerant is used. In the outdoor coils (the evaporator), heat transfer Q_c occurs to the working fluid from the cold outdoor air, turning it into a gas.

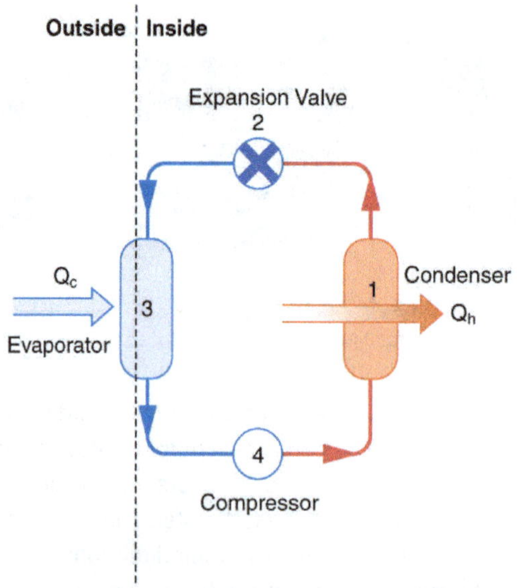

FIGURE 15.27 A simple heat pump has four basic components: (1) condenser, (2) expansion valve, (3) evaporator, and (4) compressor. In the heating mode, heat transfer Q_c occurs to the working fluid in the evaporator (3) from the colder outdoor air, turning it into a gas. The electrically driven compressor (4) increases the temperature and pressure of the gas and forces it into the condenser coils (1) inside the heated space. Because the temperature of the gas is higher than the temperature in the room, heat transfer from the gas to the room

occurs as the gas condenses to a liquid. The working fluid is then cooled as it flows back through an expansion valve (2) to the outdoor evaporator coils.

The electrically driven compressor (work input W) raises the temperature and pressure of the gas and forces it into the condenser coils that are inside the heated space. Because the temperature of the gas is higher than the temperature inside the room, heat transfer to the room occurs and the gas condenses to a liquid. The liquid then flows back through a pressure-reducing valve to the outdoor evaporator coils, being cooled through expansion. (In a cooling cycle, the evaporator and condenser coils exchange roles and the flow direction of the fluid is reversed.)

The quality of a heat pump is judged by how much heat transfer Q_h occurs into the warm space compared with how much work input W is required. In the spirit of taking the ratio of what you get to what you spend, we define a **heat pump's coefficient of performance** (COP_{hp}) to be

$$COP_{hp} = \frac{Q_h}{W}. \qquad 15.37$$

Since the efficiency of a heat engine is $Eff = W/Q_h$, we see that $COP_{hp} = 1/Eff$, an important and interesting fact. First, since the efficiency of any heat engine is less than 1, it means that COP_{hp} is always greater than 1—that is, a heat pump always has more heat transfer Q_h than work put into it. Second, it means that heat pumps work best when temperature differences are small. The efficiency of a perfect, or Carnot, engine is $Eff_C = 1 - (T_c/T_h)$; thus, the smaller the temperature difference, the smaller the efficiency and the greater the COP_{hp} (because $COP_{hp} = 1/Eff$). In other words, heat pumps do not work as well in very cold climates as they do in more moderate climates.

Friction and other irreversible processes reduce heat engine efficiency, but they do *not* benefit the operation of a heat pump—instead, they reduce the work input by converting part of it to heat transfer back into the cold reservoir before it gets into the heat pump.

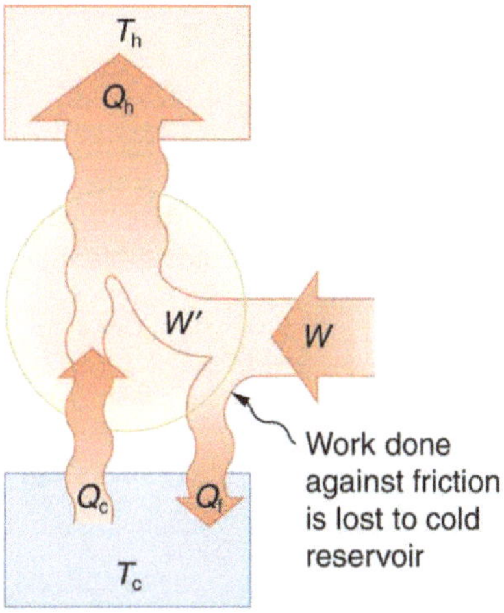

FIGURE 15.28 When a real heat engine is run backward, some of the intended work input (W) goes into heat transfer before it gets into the heat engine, thereby reducing its coefficient of performance COP_{hp}. In this figure, W' represents the portion of W that goes into the heat pump, while the remainder of W is lost in the form of frictional heat (Q_f) to the cold reservoir. If all of W had gone into the heat pump, then Q_h would have been greater. The best heat pump uses adiabatic and isothermal processes, since, in theory, there would be no dissipative processes to reduce the heat transfer to the hot reservoir.

EXAMPLE 15.5

The Best COP_{hp} of a Heat Pump for Home Use

A heat pump used to warm a home must employ a cycle that produces a working fluid at temperatures greater than typical indoor temperature so that heat transfer to the inside can take place. Similarly, it must produce a working fluid at temperatures that are colder than the outdoor temperature so that heat transfer occurs from outside. Its hot and cold reservoir temperatures therefore cannot be too close, placing a limit on its COP_{hp}. (See Figure 15.29.)

What is the best coefficient of performance possible for such a heat pump, if it has a hot reservoir temperature of $45.0°C$ and a cold reservoir temperature of $-15.0°C$?

Strategy

A Carnot engine reversed will give the best possible performance as a heat pump. As noted above, $COP_{hp} = 1/Eff$, so that we need to first calculate the Carnot efficiency to solve this problem.

Solution

Carnot efficiency in terms of absolute temperature is given by:

$$Eff_C = 1 - \frac{T_c}{T_h}. \tag{15.38}$$

The temperatures in kelvins are $T_h = 318 \text{ K}$ and $T_c = 258 \text{ K}$, so that

$$Eff_C = 1 - \frac{258 \text{ K}}{318 \text{ K}} = 0.1887. \tag{15.39}$$

Thus, from the discussion above,

$$COP_{hp} = \frac{1}{Eff} = \frac{1}{0.1887} = 5.30, \tag{15.40}$$

or

$$COP_{hp} = \frac{Q_h}{W} = 5.30, \tag{15.41}$$

so that

$$Q_h = 5.30 \text{ W}. \tag{15.42}$$

Discussion

This result means that the heat transfer by the heat pump is 5.30 times as much as the work put into it. It would cost 5.30 times as much for the same heat transfer by an electric room heater as it does for that produced by this heat pump. This is not a violation of conservation of energy. Cold ambient air provides 4.3 J per 1 J of work from the electrical outlet.

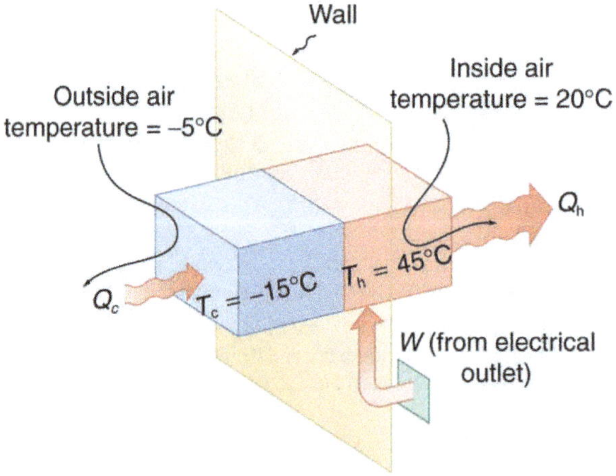

FIGURE 15.29 Heat transfer from the outside to the inside, along with work done to run the pump, takes place in the heat pump of the example above. Note that the cold temperature produced by the heat pump is lower than the outside temperature, so that heat transfer into the working fluid occurs. The pump's compressor produces a temperature greater than the indoor temperature in order for heat transfer into the house to occur.

Real heat pumps do not perform quite as well as the ideal one in the previous example; their values of COP_{hp} range from about 2 to 4. This range means that the heat transfer Q_h from the heat pumps is 2 to 4 times as great as the work W put into them. Their economical feasibility is still limited, however, since W is usually supplied by electrical energy that costs more per joule than heat transfer by burning fuels like natural gas. Furthermore, the initial cost of a heat pump is greater than that of many furnaces, so that a heat pump must last longer for its cost to be recovered. Heat pumps are most likely to be economically superior where winter temperatures are mild, electricity is relatively cheap, and other fuels are relatively expensive. Also, since they can cool as well as heat a space, they have advantages where cooling in summer months is also desired. Thus some of the best locations for heat pumps are in warm summer climates with cool winters. Figure 15.30 shows a heat pump, called a *"reverse cycle"* or *"split-system cooler"* in some countries.

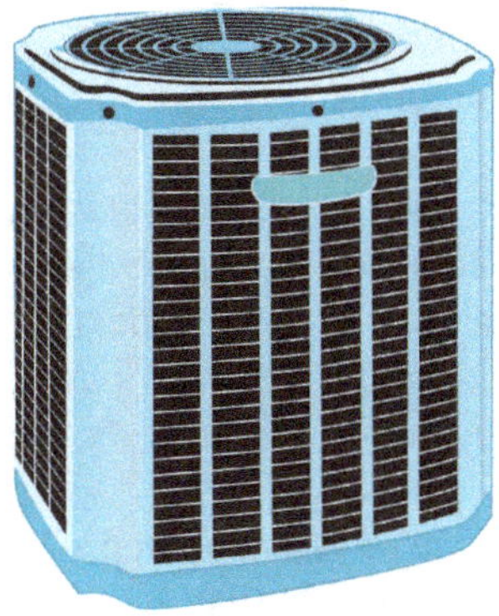

FIGURE 15.30 In hot weather, heat transfer occurs from air inside the room to air outside, cooling the room. In cool weather, heat transfer occurs from air outside to air inside, warming the room. This switching is achieved by reversing the direction of flow of the working fluid.

Air Conditioners and Refrigerators

Air conditioners and refrigerators are designed to cool something down in a warm environment. As with heat pumps, work input is required for heat transfer from cold to hot, and this is expensive. The quality of air conditioners and refrigerators is judged by how much heat transfer Q_c occurs from a cold environment compared with how much work input W is required. What is considered the benefit in a heat pump is considered waste heat in a refrigerator. We thus define the **coefficient of performance** (COP_{ref}) of an air conditioner or refrigerator to be

$$COP_{ref} = \frac{Q_c}{W}. \quad 15.43$$

Noting again that $Q_h = Q_c + W$, we can see that an air conditioner will have a lower coefficient of performance than a heat pump, because $COP_{hp} = Q_h/W$ and Q_h is greater than Q_c. In this module's Problems and Exercises, you will show that

$$COP_{ref} = COP_{hp} - 1 \quad 15.44$$

for a heat engine used as either an air conditioner or a heat pump operating between the same two temperatures. Real air conditioners and refrigerators typically do remarkably well, having values of COP_{ref} ranging from 2 to 6. These numbers are better than the COP_{hp} values for the heat pumps mentioned above, because the temperature differences are smaller, but they are less than those for Carnot engines operating between the same two temperatures.

A type of COP rating system called the "energy efficiency rating" (EER) has been developed. This rating is an example where non-SI units are still used and relevant to consumers. To make it easier for the consumer, Australia, Canada, New Zealand, and the U.S. use an Energy Star Rating out of 5 stars—the more stars, the more energy efficient the appliance. EERs are expressed in mixed units of British thermal units (Btu) per hour of heating or cooling divided by the power input in watts. Room air conditioners are readily available with EERs ranging from 6 to 12. Although not the same as the COPs just described, these EERs are good for comparison purposes—the greater the EER, the cheaper an air conditioner is to operate (but the higher its purchase price is likely to be).

The EER of an air conditioner or refrigerator can be expressed as

$$EER = \frac{Q_c/t_1}{W/t_2}, \quad 15.45$$

where Q_c is the amount of heat transfer from a cold environment in British thermal units, t_1 is time in hours, W is the work input in joules, and t_2 is time in seconds.

PROBLEM-SOLVING STRATEGIES FOR THERMODYNAMICS

1. *Examine the situation to determine whether heat, work, or internal energy are involved.* Look for any system where the primary methods of transferring energy are heat and work. Heat engines, heat pumps, refrigerators, and air conditioners are examples of such systems.
2. *Identify the system of interest and draw a labeled diagram of the system showing energy flow.*
3. *Identify exactly what needs to be determined in the problem (identify the unknowns).* A written list is useful. Maximum efficiency means a Carnot engine is involved. Efficiency is not the same as the coefficient of performance.
4. *Make a list of what is given or can be inferred from the problem as stated (identify the knowns).* Be sure to distinguish heat transfer into a system from heat transfer out of the system, as well as work input from work output. In many situations, it is useful to determine the type of process, such as isothermal or adiabatic.
5. *Solve the appropriate equation for the quantity to be determined (the unknown).*
6. *Substitute the known quantities along with their units into the appropriate equation and obtain numerical solutions complete with units.*
7. *Check the answer to see if it is reasonable: Does it make sense?* For example, efficiency is always less than 1, whereas coefficients of performance are greater than 1.

15.6 Entropy and the Second Law of Thermodynamics: Disorder and the Unavailability of Energy

LEARNING OBJECTIVES

By the end of this section, you will be able to:

- Define entropy and calculate the increase of entropy in a system with reversible and irreversible processes.
- Explain the expected fate of the universe in entropic terms.
- Calculate the increasing disorder of a system.

FIGURE 15.31 The ice in this drink is slowly melting. Eventually the liquid will reach thermal equilibrium, as predicted by the second law of thermodynamics. (credit: Jon Sullivan, PDPhoto.org)

There is yet another way of expressing the second law of thermodynamics. This version relates to a concept called **entropy**. By examining it, we shall see that the directions associated with the second law—heat transfer from hot to cold, for example—are related to the tendency in nature for systems to become disordered and for less energy to be available for use as work. The entropy of a system can in fact be shown to be a measure of its disorder and of the unavailability of energy to do work.

MAKING CONNECTIONS: ENTROPY, ENERGY, AND WORK

Recall that the simple definition of energy is the ability to do work. Entropy is a measure of how much energy is not available to do work. Although all forms of energy are interconvertible, and all can be used to do work, it is not always possible, even in principle, to convert the entire available energy into work. That unavailable energy is of interest in thermodynamics, because the field of thermodynamics arose from efforts to convert heat to work.

We can see how entropy is defined by recalling our discussion of the Carnot engine. We noted that for a Carnot cycle, and hence for any reversible processes, $Q_c/Q_h = T_c/T_h$. Rearranging terms yields

$$\frac{Q_c}{T_c} = \frac{Q_h}{T_h} \qquad (15.46)$$

for any reversible process. Q_c and Q_h are absolute values of the heat transfer at temperatures T_c and T_h, respectively. This ratio of Q/T is defined to be the **change in entropy** ΔS for a reversible process,

$$\Delta S = \left(\frac{Q}{T}\right)_{\text{rev}}, \qquad (15.47)$$

where Q is the heat transfer, which is positive for heat transfer into and negative for heat transfer out of, and T is the absolute temperature at which the reversible process takes place. The SI unit for entropy is joules per kelvin (J/K). If temperature changes during the process, then it is usually a good approximation (for small changes in temperature) to take T to be the average temperature, avoiding the need to use integral calculus to find ΔS.

The definition of ΔS is strictly valid only for reversible processes, such as used in a Carnot engine. However, we can find ΔS precisely even for real, irreversible processes. The reason is that the entropy s of a system, like internal energy U, depends only on the state of the system and not how it reached that condition. Entropy is a property of state. Thus the change in entropy ΔS of a system between state 1 and state 2 is the same no matter how the change occurs. We just need to find or imagine a reversible process that takes us from state 1 to state 2 and calculate ΔS for that process. That will be the change in entropy for any process going from state 1 to state 2. (See Figure 15.32.)

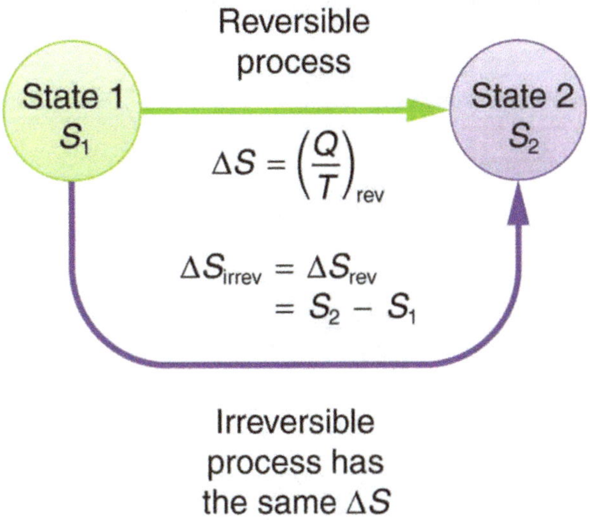

FIGURE 15.32 When a system goes from state 1 to state 2, its entropy changes by the same amount ΔS, whether a hypothetical reversible path is followed or a real irreversible path is taken.

Now let us take a look at the change in entropy of a Carnot engine and its heat reservoirs for one full cycle. The hot reservoir has a loss of entropy $\Delta S_h = -Q_h/T_h$, because heat transfer occurs out of it (remember that when heat transfers out, then Q has a negative sign). The cold reservoir has a gain of entropy $\Delta S_c = Q_c/T_c$, because heat transfer occurs into it. (We assume the reservoirs are sufficiently large that their temperatures are constant.) So the total change in entropy is

$$\Delta S_{\text{tot}} = \Delta S_{\text{h}} + \Delta S_{\text{c}}. \tag{15.48}$$

Thus, since we know that $Q_{\text{h}}/T_{\text{h}} = Q_{\text{c}}/T_{\text{c}}$ for a Carnot engine,

$$\Delta S_{\text{tot}} = -\frac{Q_{\text{h}}}{T_{\text{h}}} + \frac{Q_{\text{c}}}{T_{\text{c}}} = 0. \tag{15.49}$$

This result, which has general validity, means that *the total change in entropy for a system in any reversible process is zero.*

The entropy of various parts of the system may change, but the total change is zero. Furthermore, the system does not affect the entropy of its surroundings, since heat transfer between them does not occur. Thus the reversible process changes neither the total entropy of the system nor the entropy of its surroundings. Sometimes this is stated as follows: *Reversible processes do not affect the total entropy of the universe.* Real processes are not reversible, though, and they do change total entropy. We can, however, use hypothetical reversible processes to determine the value of entropy in real, irreversible processes. The following example illustrates this point.

EXAMPLE 15.6

Entropy Increases in an Irreversible (Real) Process

Spontaneous heat transfer from hot to cold is an irreversible process. Calculate the total change in entropy if 4000 J of heat transfer occurs from a hot reservoir at $T_{\text{h}} = 600\text{ K}(327°\text{ C})$ to a cold reservoir at $T_{\text{c}} = 250\text{ K}(-23°\text{ C})$, assuming there is no temperature change in either reservoir. (See Figure 15.33.)

Strategy

How can we calculate the change in entropy for an irreversible process when $\Delta S_{\text{tot}} = \Delta S_{\text{h}} + \Delta S_{\text{c}}$ is valid only for reversible processes? Remember that the total change in entropy of the hot and cold reservoirs will be the same whether a reversible or irreversible process is involved in heat transfer from hot to cold. So we can calculate the change in entropy of the hot reservoir for a hypothetical reversible process in which 4000 J of heat transfer occurs from it; then we do the same for a hypothetical reversible process in which 4000 J of heat transfer occurs to the cold reservoir. This produces the same changes in the hot and cold reservoirs that would occur if the heat transfer were allowed to occur irreversibly between them, and so it also produces the same changes in entropy.

Solution

We now calculate the two changes in entropy using $\Delta S_{\text{tot}} = \Delta S_{\text{h}} + \Delta S_{\text{c}}$. First, for the heat transfer from the hot reservoir,

$$\Delta S_{\text{h}} = \frac{-Q_{\text{h}}}{T_{\text{h}}} = \frac{-4000\text{ J}}{600\text{ K}} = -6.67\text{ J/K}. \tag{15.50}$$

And for the cold reservoir,

$$\Delta S_{\text{c}} = \frac{Q_{\text{c}}}{T_{\text{c}}} = \frac{4000\text{ J}}{250\text{ K}} = 16.0\text{ J/K}. \tag{15.51}$$

Thus the total is

$$\begin{aligned} \Delta S_{\text{tot}} &= \Delta S_{\text{h}} + \Delta S_{\text{c}} \\ &= (-6.67 + 16.0)\text{ J/K} \\ &= 9.33\text{ J/K}. \end{aligned} \tag{15.52}$$

Discussion

There is an *increase* in entropy for the system of two heat reservoirs undergoing this irreversible heat transfer. We will see that this means there is a loss of ability to do work with this transferred energy. Entropy has increased, and energy has become unavailable to do work.

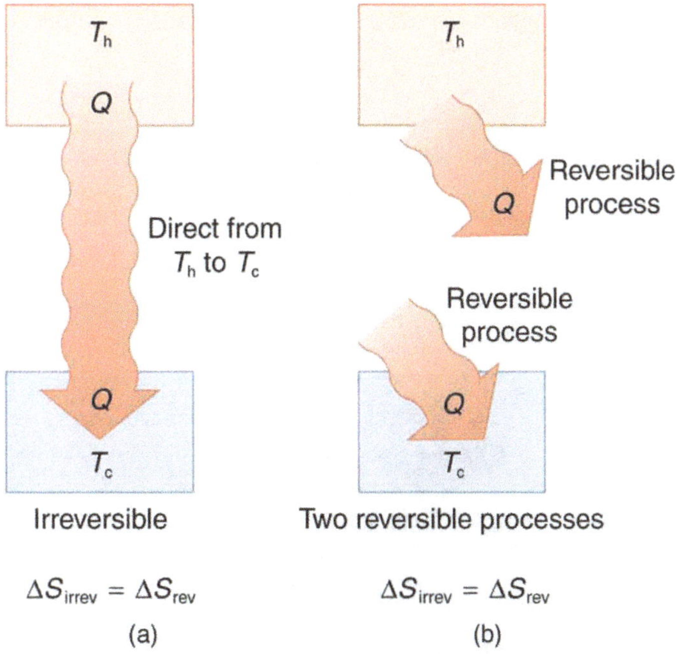

FIGURE 15.33 (a) Heat transfer from a hot object to a cold one is an irreversible process that produces an overall increase in entropy. (b) The same final state and, thus, the same change in entropy is achieved for the objects if reversible heat transfer processes occur between the two objects whose temperatures are the same as the temperatures of the corresponding objects in the irreversible process.

It is reasonable that entropy increases for heat transfer from hot to cold. Since the change in entropy is Q/T, there is a larger change at lower temperatures. The decrease in entropy of the hot object is therefore less than the increase in entropy of the cold object, producing an overall increase, just as in the previous example. This result is very general:

There is an increase in entropy for any system undergoing an irreversible process.

With respect to entropy, there are only two possibilities: entropy is constant for a reversible process, and it increases for an irreversible process. There is a fourth version of **the second law of thermodynamics stated in terms of entropy**:

The total entropy of a system either increases or remains constant in any process; it never decreases.

For example, heat transfer cannot occur spontaneously from cold to hot, because entropy would decrease.

Entropy is very different from energy. Entropy is *not* conserved but increases in all real processes. Reversible processes (such as in Carnot engines) are the processes in which the most heat transfer to work takes place and are also the ones that keep entropy constant. Thus we are led to make a connection between entropy and the availability of energy to do work.

Entropy and the Unavailability of Energy to Do Work

What does a change in entropy mean, and why should we be interested in it? One reason is that entropy is directly related to the fact that not all heat transfer can be converted into work. The next example gives some indication of how an increase in entropy results in less heat transfer into work.

EXAMPLE 15.7

Less Work is Produced by a Given Heat Transfer When Entropy Change is Greater

(a) Calculate the work output of a Carnot engine operating between temperatures of 600 K and 100 K for 4000 J of heat transfer to the engine. (b) Now suppose that the 4000 J of heat transfer occurs first from the 600 K reservoir to a 250 K reservoir (without doing any work, and this produces the increase in entropy calculated above) before transferring into a Carnot engine operating between 250 K and 100 K. What work output is produced? (See Figure 15.34.)

Strategy

In both parts, we must first calculate the Carnot efficiency and then the work output.

Solution (a)

The Carnot efficiency is given by

$$Eff_{\mathrm{C}} = 1 - \frac{T_{\mathrm{c}}}{T_{\mathrm{h}}}. \tag{15.53}$$

Substituting the given temperatures yields

$$Eff_{\mathrm{C}} = 1 - \frac{100\ \mathrm{K}}{600\ \mathrm{K}} = 0.833. \tag{15.54}$$

Now the work output can be calculated using the definition of efficiency for any heat engine as given by

$$Eff = \frac{W}{Q_{\mathrm{h}}}. \tag{15.55}$$

Solving for W and substituting known terms gives

$$\begin{aligned} W &= Eff_{\mathrm{C}} Q_{\mathrm{h}} \\ &= (0.833)(4000\ \mathrm{J}) = 3333\ \mathrm{J}. \end{aligned} \tag{15.56}$$

Solution (b)

Similarly,

$$Eff'_{\mathrm{C}} = 1 - \frac{T_{\mathrm{c}}}{T'_{\mathrm{c}}} = 1 - \frac{100\ \mathrm{K}}{250\ \mathrm{K}} = 0.600, \tag{15.57}$$

so that

$$\begin{aligned} W &= Eff'_{\mathrm{C}} Q_h \\ &= (0.600)(4000\ \mathrm{J}) = 2400\ \mathrm{J}. \end{aligned} \tag{15.58}$$

Discussion

There is 933 J less work from the same heat transfer in the second process. This result is important. The same heat transfer into two perfect engines produces different work outputs, because the entropy change differs in the two cases. In the second case, entropy is greater and less work is produced. Entropy is associated with the *un*availability of energy to do work.

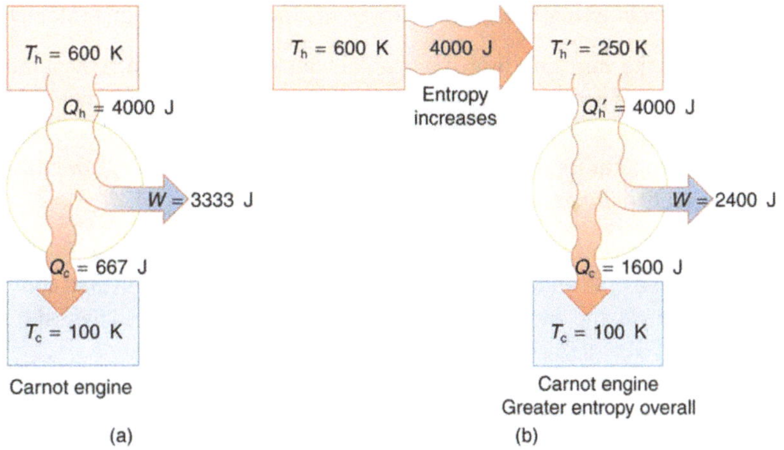

FIGURE 15.34 (a) A Carnot engine working at between 600 K and 100 K has 4000 J of heat transfer and performs 3333 J of work. (b) The 4000 J of heat transfer occurs first irreversibly to a 250 K reservoir and then goes into a Carnot engine. The increase in entropy caused by the heat transfer to a colder reservoir results in a smaller work output of 2400 J. There is a permanent loss of 933 J of energy for the purpose of doing work.

When entropy increases, a certain amount of energy becomes *permanently* unavailable to do work. The energy is not lost, but its character is changed, so that some of it can never be converted to doing work—that is, to an organized force acting through a distance. For instance, in the previous example, 933 J less work was done after an increase in entropy of 9.33 J/K occurred in the 4000 J heat transfer from the 600 K reservoir to the 250 K reservoir. It can be shown that the amount of energy that becomes unavailable for work is

$$W_{\text{unavail}} = \Delta S \cdot T_0, \tag{15.59}$$

where T_0 is the lowest temperature utilized. In the previous example,

$$W_{\text{unavail}} = (9.33\ \text{J/K})(100\ \text{K}) = 933\ \text{J} \tag{15.60}$$

as found.

Heat Death of the Universe: An Overdose of Entropy

In the early, energetic universe, all matter and energy were easily interchangeable and identical in nature. Gravity played a vital role in the young universe. Although it may have *seemed* disorderly, and therefore, superficially entropic, in fact, there was enormous potential energy available to do work—all the future energy in the universe.

As the universe matured, temperature differences arose, which created more opportunity for work. Stars are hotter than planets, for example, which are warmer than icy asteroids, which are warmer still than the vacuum of the space between them.

Most of these are cooling down from their usually violent births, at which time they were provided with energy of their own—nuclear energy in the case of stars, volcanic energy on Earth and other planets, and so on. Without additional energy input, however, their days are numbered.

As entropy increases, less and less energy in the universe is available to do work. On Earth, we still have great stores of energy such as fossil and nuclear fuels; large-scale temperature differences, which can provide wind energy; geothermal energies due to differences in temperature in Earth's layers; and tidal energies owing to our abundance of liquid water. As these are used, a certain fraction of the energy they contain can never be converted into doing work. Eventually, all fuels will be exhausted, all temperatures will equalize, and it will be impossible for heat engines to function, or for work to be done.

Entropy increases in a closed system, such as the universe. But in parts of the universe, for instance, in the Solar system, it is not a locally closed system. Energy flows from the Sun to the planets, replenishing Earth's stores of energy. The Sun will continue to supply us with energy for about another five billion years. We will enjoy direct solar energy, as well as side effects of solar energy, such as wind power and biomass energy from photosynthetic plants. The energy from the Sun will keep our water at the liquid state, and the Moon's gravitational pull will continue to provide tidal energy. But Earth's geothermal energy will slowly run down and won't be replenished.

But in terms of the universe, and the very long-term, very large-scale picture, the entropy of the universe is increasing, and so the availability of energy to do work is constantly decreasing. Eventually, when all stars have died, all forms of potential energy have been utilized, and all temperatures have equalized (depending on the mass of the universe, either at a very high temperature following a universal contraction, or a very low one, just before all activity ceases) there will be no possibility of doing work.

Either way, the universe is destined for thermodynamic equilibrium—maximum entropy. This is often called the *heat death of the universe*, and will mean the end of all activity. However, whether the universe contracts and heats up, or continues to expand and cools down, the end is not near. Calculations of black holes suggest that entropy can easily continue for at least 10^{100} years.

Order to Disorder

Entropy is related not only to the unavailability of energy to do work—it is also a measure of disorder. This notion was initially postulated by Ludwig Boltzmann in the 1800s. For example, melting a block of ice means taking a highly structured and orderly system of water molecules and converting it into a disorderly liquid in which molecules have no fixed positions. (See Figure 15.35.) There is a large increase in entropy in the process, as seen in the following example.

EXAMPLE 15.8

Entropy Associated with Disorder

Find the increase in entropy of 1.00 kg of ice originally at $0^\circ\ \text{C}$ that is melted to form water at $0^\circ\ \text{C}$.

Strategy

As before, the change in entropy can be calculated from the definition of ΔS once we find the energy Q needed to melt the ice.

Solution

The change in entropy is defined as:

$$\Delta S = \frac{Q}{T}. \tag{15.61}$$

Here Q is the heat transfer necessary to melt 1.00 kg of ice and is given by

$$Q = mL_{\text{f}}, \tag{15.62}$$

where m is the mass and L_{f} is the latent heat of fusion. $L_{\text{f}} = 334\ \text{kJ/kg}$ for water, so that

$$Q = (1.00\ \text{kg})(334\ \text{kJ/kg}) = 3.34 \times 10^5\ \text{J}. \tag{15.63}$$

Now the change in entropy is positive, since heat transfer occurs into the ice to cause the phase change; thus,

$$\Delta S = \frac{Q}{T} = \frac{3.34 \times 10^5\ \text{J}}{T}. \tag{15.64}$$

T is the melting temperature of ice. That is, $T = 0^\circ\text{C} = 273\ \text{K}$. So the change in entropy is

$$\begin{aligned} \Delta S &= \frac{3.34 \times 10^5\ \text{J}}{273\ \text{K}} \\ &= 1.22 \times 10^3\ \text{J/K}. \end{aligned} \tag{15.65}$$

Discussion

This is a significant increase in entropy accompanying an increase in disorder.

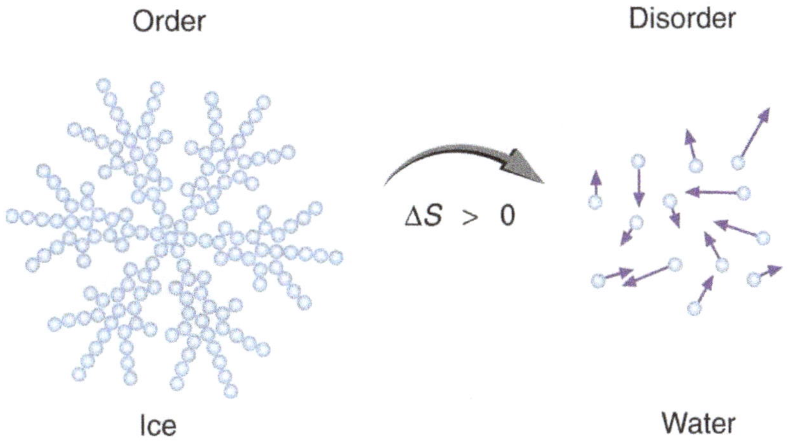

FIGURE 15.35 When ice melts, it becomes more disordered and less structured. The systematic arrangement of molecules in a crystal structure is replaced by a more random and less orderly movement of molecules without fixed locations or orientations. Its entropy increases because heat transfer occurs into it. Entropy is a measure of disorder.

In another easily imagined example, suppose we mix equal masses of water originally at two different temperatures, say 20.0° C and 40.0° C. The result is water at an intermediate temperature of 30.0° C. Three outcomes have resulted: entropy has increased, some energy has become unavailable to do work, and the system has become less orderly. Let us think about each of these results.

First, entropy has increased for the same reason that it did in the example above. Mixing the two bodies of water has the same effect as heat transfer from the hot one and the same heat transfer into the cold one. The mixing decreases the entropy of the hot water but increases the entropy of the cold water by a greater amount, producing an overall increase in entropy.

Second, once the two masses of water are mixed, there is only one temperature—you cannot run a heat engine with them. The energy that could have been used to run a heat engine is now unavailable to do work.

Third, the mixture is less orderly, or to use another term, less structured. Rather than having two masses at different temperatures and with different distributions of molecular speeds, we now have a single mass with a uniform temperature.

These three results—entropy, unavailability of energy, and disorder—are not only related but are in fact essentially equivalent.

Life, Evolution, and the Second Law of Thermodynamics

Some people misunderstand the second law of thermodynamics, stated in terms of entropy, to say that the process of the evolution of life violates this law. Over time, complex organisms evolved from much simpler ancestors, representing a large decrease in entropy of the Earth's biosphere. It is a fact that living organisms have evolved to be highly structured, and much lower in entropy than the substances from which they grow. But it is *always* possible for the entropy of one part of the universe to decrease, provided the total change in entropy of the universe increases. In equation form, we can write this as

$$\Delta S_{\text{tot}} = \Delta S_{\text{syst}} + \Delta S_{\text{envir}} > 0. \qquad 15.66$$

Thus ΔS_{syst} can be negative as long as ΔS_{envir} is positive and greater in magnitude.

How is it possible for a system to decrease its entropy? Energy transfer is necessary. If I pick up marbles that are scattered about the room and put them into a cup, my work has decreased the entropy of that system. If I gather iron ore from the ground and convert it into steel and build a bridge, my work has decreased the entropy of that system. Energy coming from the Sun can decrease the entropy of local systems on Earth—that is, ΔS_{syst} is negative. But the overall entropy of the rest of the universe increases by a greater amount—that is, ΔS_{envir} is positive and greater in magnitude. Thus, $\Delta S_{\text{tot}} = \Delta S_{\text{syst}} + \Delta S_{\text{envir}} > 0$, and the second law of thermodynamics is *not* violated.

Every time a plant stores some solar energy in the form of chemical potential energy, or an updraft of warm air lifts a soaring bird, the Earth can be viewed as a heat engine operating between a hot reservoir supplied by the Sun and a cold reservoir supplied by dark outer space—a heat engine of high complexity, causing local decreases in entropy as it uses part of the heat transfer from the Sun into deep space. There is a large total increase in entropy resulting from this massive heat transfer. A small part of this heat transfer is stored in structured systems on Earth, producing much smaller local decreases in entropy. (See Figure 15.36.)

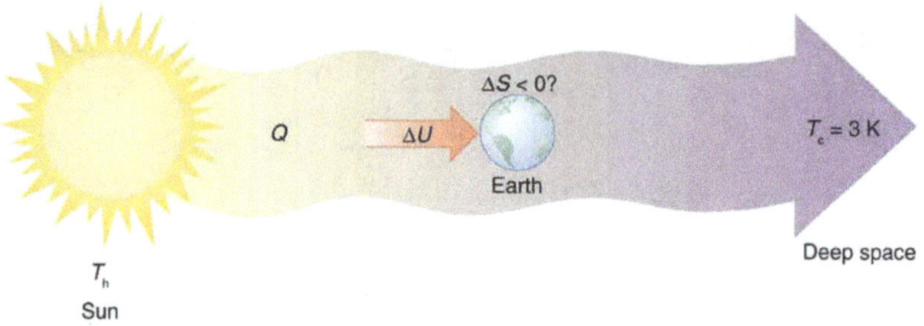

FIGURE 15.36 Earth's entropy may decrease in the process of intercepting a small part of the heat transfer from the Sun into deep space. Entropy for the entire process increases greatly while Earth becomes more structured with living systems and stored energy in various forms.

PHET EXPLORATIONS

Reversible Reactions

Watch a reaction proceed over time. How does total energy affect a reaction rate? Vary temperature, barrier height, and potential energies. Record concentrations and time in order to extract rate coefficients. Do temperature dependent studies to extract Arrhenius parameters. This simulation is best used with teacher guidance because it presents an analogy of chemical reactions.

Click to view content (https://openstax.org/l/21reversereact).

PhET

15.7 Statistical Interpretation of Entropy and the Second Law of Thermodynamics: The Underlying Explanation

LEARNING OBJECTIVES

By the end of this section, you will be able to:

- Identify probabilities in entropy.
- Analyze statistical probabilities in entropic systems.

FIGURE 15.37 When you toss a coin a large number of times, heads and tails tend to come up in roughly equal numbers. Why doesn't heads come up 100, 90, or even 80% of the time? (credit: Jon Sullivan, PDPhoto.org)

The various ways of formulating the second law of thermodynamics tell what happens rather than why it happens.

Why should heat transfer occur only from hot to cold? Why should energy become ever less available to do work? Why should the universe become increasingly disorderly? The answer is that it is a matter of overwhelming probability. Disorder is simply vastly more likely than order.

When you watch an emerging rain storm begin to wet the ground, you will notice that the drops fall in a disorganized manner both in time and in space. Some fall close together, some far apart, but they never fall in straight, orderly rows. It is not impossible for rain to fall in an orderly pattern, just highly unlikely, because there are many more disorderly ways than orderly ones. To illustrate this fact, we will examine some random processes, starting with coin tosses.

Coin Tosses

What are the possible outcomes of tossing 5 coins? Each coin can land either heads or tails. On the large scale, we are concerned only with the total heads and tails and not with the order in which heads and tails appear. The following possibilities exist:

$$\begin{array}{c} 5 \text{ heads, } 0 \text{ tails} \\ 4 \text{ heads, } 1 \text{ tail} \\ 3 \text{ heads, } 2 \text{ tails} \\ 2 \text{ heads, } 3 \text{ tails} \\ 1 \text{ head, } 4 \text{ tails} \\ 0 \text{ head, } 5 \text{ tails} \end{array} \quad (15.67)$$

These are what we call macrostates. A **macrostate** is an overall property of a system. It does not specify the details of the system, such as the order in which heads and tails occur or which coins are heads or tails.

Using this nomenclature, a system of 5 coins has the 6 possible macrostates just listed. Some macrostates are more likely to occur than others. For instance, there is only one way to get 5 heads, but there are several ways to get 3 heads and 2 tails, making the latter macrostate more probable. Table 15.3 lists of all the ways in which 5 coins can be tossed, taking into account the order in which heads and tails occur. Each sequence is called a **microstate**—a detailed description of every element of a system.

	Individual microstates	Number of microstates
5 heads, 0 tails	HHHHH	1
4 heads, 1 tail	HHHHT, HHHTH, HHTHH, HTHHH, THHHH	5
3 heads, 2 tails	HTHTH, THTHH, HTHHT, THHTH, THHHT HTHTH, THTHH, HTHHT, THHTH, THHHT	10
2 heads, 3 tails	TTTHH, TTHHT, THHTT, HHTTT, TTHTH, THTHT, HTHTT, THTTH, HTTHT, HTTTH	10
1 head, 4 tails	TTTTH, TTTHT, TTHTT, THTTT, HTTTT	5

TABLE 15.3 5-Coin Toss

	Individual microstates	Number of microstates
0 heads, 5 tails	TTTTT	1
		Total: 32

TABLE 15.3 5-Coin Toss

The macrostate of 3 heads and 2 tails can be achieved in 10 ways and is thus 10 times more probable than the one having 5 heads. Not surprisingly, it is equally probable to have the reverse, 2 heads and 3 tails. Similarly, it is equally probable to get 5 tails as it is to get 5 heads. Note that all of these conclusions are based on the crucial assumption that each microstate is equally probable. With coin tosses, this requires that the coins not be asymmetric in a way that favors one side over the other, as with loaded dice. With any system, the assumption that all microstates are equally probable must be valid, or the analysis will be erroneous.

The two most orderly possibilities are 5 heads or 5 tails. (They are more structured than the others.) They are also the least likely, only 2 out of 32 possibilities. The most disorderly possibilities are 3 heads and 2 tails and its reverse. (They are the least structured.) The most disorderly possibilities are also the most likely, with 20 out of 32 possibilities for the 3 heads and 2 tails and its reverse. If we start with an orderly array like 5 heads and toss the coins, it is very likely that we will get a less orderly array as a result, since 30 out of the 32 possibilities are less orderly. So even if you start with an orderly state, there is a strong tendency to go from order to disorder, from low entropy to high entropy. The reverse can happen, but it is unlikely.

Macrostate		Number of microstates
Heads	Tails	(W)
100	0	1
99	1	1.0×10^{2}
95	5	7.5×10^{7}
90	10	1.7×10^{13}
75	25	2.4×10^{23}
60	40	1.4×10^{28}
55	45	6.1×10^{28}
51	49	9.9×10^{28}
50	50	1.0×10^{29}

TABLE 15.4 100-Coin Toss

Macrostate		Number of microstates
49	51	9.9×10^{28}
45	55	6.1×10^{28}
40	60	1.4×10^{28}
25	75	2.4×10^{23}
10	90	1.7×10^{13}
5	95	7.5×10^{7}
1	99	1.0×10^{2}
0	100	1
		Total: 1.27×10^{30}

TABLE 15.4 100-Coin Toss

This result becomes dramatic for larger systems. Consider what happens if you have 100 coins instead of just 5. The most orderly arrangements (most structured) are 100 heads or 100 tails. The least orderly (least structured) is that of 50 heads and 50 tails. There is only 1 way (1 microstate) to get the most orderly arrangement of 100 heads. There are 100 ways (100 microstates) to get the next most orderly arrangement of 99 heads and 1 tail (also 100 to get its reverse). And there are 1.0×10^{29} ways to get 50 heads and 50 tails, the least orderly arrangement. Table 15.4 is an abbreviated list of the various macrostates and the number of microstates for each macrostate. The total number of microstates—the total number of different ways 100 coins can be tossed—is an impressively large 1.27×10^{30}. Now, if we start with an orderly macrostate like 100 heads and toss the coins, there is a virtual certainty that we will get a less orderly macrostate. If we keep tossing the coins, it is possible, but exceedingly unlikely, that we will ever get back to the most orderly macrostate. If you tossed the coins once each second, you could expect to get either 100 heads or 100 tails once in 2×10^{22} years! This period is 1 trillion (10^{12}) times longer than the age of the universe, and so the chances are essentially zero. In contrast, there is an 8% chance of getting 50 heads, a 73% chance of getting from 45 to 55 heads, and a 96% chance of getting from 40 to 60 heads. Disorder is highly likely.

Disorder in a Gas

The fantastic growth in the odds favoring disorder that we see in going from 5 to 100 coins continues as the number of entities in the system increases. Let us now imagine applying this approach to perhaps a small sample of gas. Because counting microstates and macrostates involves statistics, this is called **statistical analysis**. The macrostates of a gas correspond to its macroscopic properties, such as volume, temperature, and pressure; and its microstates correspond to the detailed description of the positions and velocities of its atoms. Even a small amount of gas has a huge number of atoms: $1.0\ \text{cm}^3$ of an ideal gas at 1.0 atm and $0^\circ\ \text{C}$ has 2.7×10^{19} atoms. So each macrostate has an immense number of microstates. In plain language, this means that there are an immense number of ways in which the atoms in a gas can be arranged, while still having the same pressure, temperature, and so on.

The most likely conditions (or macrostates) for a gas are those we see all the time—a random distribution of atoms in space with a Maxwell-Boltzmann distribution of speeds in random directions, as predicted by kinetic theory. This is the most disorderly and least structured condition we can imagine. In contrast, one type of very orderly and structured macrostate has all of the atoms in one corner of a container with identical velocities. There are very few ways to accomplish this (very few microstates corresponding to it), and so it is exceedingly unlikely ever to occur. (See Figure 15.38(b).) Indeed, it is so unlikely that we have a law saying that it is impossible, which has never been observed to be violated—the second law of thermodynamics.

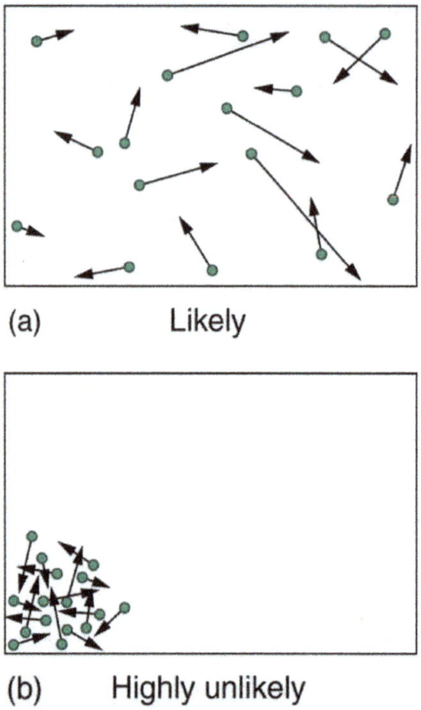

FIGURE 15.38 (a) The ordinary state of gas in a container is a disorderly, random distribution of atoms or molecules with a Maxwell-Boltzmann distribution of speeds. It is so unlikely that these atoms or molecules would ever end up in one corner of the container that it might as well be impossible. (b) With energy transfer, the gas can be forced into one corner and its entropy greatly reduced. But left alone, it will spontaneously increase its entropy and return to the normal conditions, because they are immensely more likely.

The disordered condition is one of high entropy, and the ordered one has low entropy. With a transfer of energy from another system, we could force all of the atoms into one corner and have a local decrease in entropy, but at the cost of an overall increase in entropy of the universe. If the atoms start out in one corner, they will quickly disperse and become uniformly distributed and will never return to the orderly original state (Figure 15.38(b)). Entropy will increase. With such a large sample of atoms, it is possible—but unimaginably unlikely—for entropy to decrease. Disorder is vastly more likely than order.

The arguments that disorder and high entropy are the most probable states are quite convincing. The great Austrian physicist Ludwig Boltzmann (1844–1906)—who, along with Maxwell, made so many contributions to kinetic theory—proved that the entropy of a system in a given state (a macrostate) can be written as

$$S = k \ln W, \tag{15.68}$$

where $k = 1.38 \times 10^{-23}$ J/K is Boltzmann's constant, and $\ln W$ is the natural logarithm of the number of microstates W corresponding to the given macrostate. W is proportional to the probability that the macrostate will occur. Thus entropy is directly related to the probability of a state—the more likely the state, the greater its entropy. Boltzmann proved that this expression for s is equivalent to the definition $\Delta S = Q/T$, which we have used extensively.

Thus the second law of thermodynamics is explained on a very basic level: entropy either remains the same or increases in every process. This phenomenon is due to the extraordinarily small probability of a decrease, based on the extraordinarily larger number of microstates in systems with greater entropy. Entropy *can* decrease, but for any macroscopic system, this outcome is so unlikely that it will never be observed.

EXAMPLE 15.9

Entropy Increases in a Coin Toss

Suppose you toss 100 coins starting with 60 heads and 40 tails, and you get the most likely result, 50 heads and 50 tails. What is the change in entropy?

Strategy

Noting that the number of microstates is labeled W in Table 15.4 for the 100-coin toss, we can use $\Delta S = S_f - S_i = k \ln W_f - k \ln W_i$ to calculate the change in entropy.

Solution

The change in entropy is

$$\Delta S = S_f - S_i = k \ln W_f - k \ln W_i, \quad (15.69)$$

where the subscript i stands for the initial 60 heads and 40 tails state, and the subscript f for the final 50 heads and 50 tails state. Substituting the values for W from Table 15.4 gives

$$\begin{aligned} \Delta S &= (1.38 \times 10^{-23}\ \text{J/K})[\ln(1.0 \times 10^{29}) - \ln(1.4 \times 10^{28})] \\ &= 2.7 \times 10^{-23}\ \text{J/K} \end{aligned} \quad (15.70)$$

Discussion

This increase in entropy means we have moved to a less orderly situation. It is not impossible for further tosses to produce the initial state of 60 heads and 40 tails, but it is less likely. There is about a 1 in 90 chance for that decrease in entropy (-2.7×10^{-23} J/K) to occur. If we calculate the decrease in entropy to move to the most orderly state, we get $\Delta S = -92 \times 10^{-23}$ J/K. There is about a 1 in 10^{30} chance of this change occurring. So while very small decreases in entropy are unlikely, slightly greater decreases are impossibly unlikely. These probabilities imply, again, that for a macroscopic system, a decrease in entropy is impossible. For example, for heat transfer to occur spontaneously from 1.00 kg of 0ºC ice to its 0ºC environment, there would be a decrease in entropy of 1.22×10^3 J/K. Given that a ΔS of 10^{-21} J/K corresponds to about a 1 in 10^{30} chance, a decrease of this size (10^3 J/K) is an *utter* impossibility. Even for a milligram of melted ice to spontaneously refreeze is impossible.

PROBLEM-SOLVING STRATEGIES FOR ENTROPY

1. *Examine the situation to determine if entropy is involved.*
2. *Identify the system of interest and draw a labeled diagram of the system showing energy flow.*
3. *Identify exactly what needs to be determined in the problem (identify the unknowns).* A written list is useful.
4. *Make a list of what is given or can be inferred from the problem as stated (identify the knowns).* You must carefully identify the heat transfer, if any, and the temperature at which the process takes place. It is also important to identify the initial and final states.
5. *Solve the appropriate equation for the quantity to be determined (the unknown).* Note that the change in entropy can be determined between any states by calculating it for a reversible process.
6. *Substitute the known value along with their units into the appropriate equation, and obtain numerical solutions complete with units.*
7. *To see if it is reasonable: Does it make sense?* For example, total entropy should increase for any real process or be constant for a reversible process. Disordered states should be more probable and have greater entropy than ordered states.

Glossary

adiabatic process a process in which no heat transfer takes place

Carnot cycle a cyclical process that uses only reversible processes, the adiabatic and isothermal processes

Carnot efficiency the maximum theoretical efficiency for a heat engine

Carnot engine a heat engine that uses a Carnot cycle

change in entropy the ratio of heat transfer to temperature Q/T

coefficient of performance for a heat pump, it is the ratio of heat transfer at the output (the hot reservoir) to the work supplied; for a refrigerator or air conditioner, it is the ratio of heat transfer from the cold reservoir to the work supplied

cyclical process a process in which the path returns to its original state at the end of every cycle

entropy a measurement of a system's disorder and its inability to do work in a system

first law of thermodynamics states that the change in internal energy of a system equals the net heat transfer *into* the system minus the net work done *by* the system

heat engine a machine that uses heat transfer to do work

heat pump a machine that generates heat transfer from cold to hot

human metabolism conversion of food into heat transfer, work, and stored fat

internal energy the sum of the kinetic and potential energies of a system's atoms and molecules

irreversible process any process that depends on path direction

isobaric process constant-pressure process in which a gas does work

isochoric process a constant-volume process

isothermal process a constant-temperature process

macrostate an overall property of a system

microstate each sequence within a larger macrostate

Otto cycle a thermodynamic cycle, consisting of a pair of adiabatic processes and a pair of isochoric processes, that converts heat into work, e.g., the four-stroke engine cycle of intake, compression, ignition, and exhaust

reversible process a process in which both the heat engine system and the external environment theoretically can be returned to their original states

second law of thermodynamics heat transfer flows from a hotter to a cooler object, never the reverse, and some heat energy in any process is lost to available work in a cyclical process

second law of thermodynamics stated in terms of entropy the total entropy of a system either increases or remains constant; it never decreases

statistical analysis using statistics to examine data, such as counting microstates and macrostates

Section Summary

15.1 The First Law of Thermodynamics

- The first law of thermodynamics is given as $\Delta U = Q - W$, where ΔU is the change in internal energy of a system, Q is the net heat transfer (the sum of all heat transfer into and out of the system), and W is the net work done (the sum of all work done on or by the system).
- Both Q and W are energy in transit; only ΔU represents an independent quantity capable of being stored.
- The internal energy U of a system depends only on the state of the system and not how it reached that state.
- Metabolism of living organisms, and photosynthesis of plants, are specialized types of heat transfer, doing work, and internal energy of systems.

15.2 The First Law of Thermodynamics and Some Simple Processes

- One of the important implications of the first law of thermodynamics is that machines can be harnessed to do work that humans previously did by hand or by external energy supplies such as running water or the heat of the Sun. A machine that uses heat transfer to do work is known as a heat engine.
- There are several simple processes, used by heat engines, that flow from the first law of thermodynamics. Among them are the isobaric, isochoric, isothermal and adiabatic processes.
- These processes differ from one another based on how they affect pressure, volume, temperature, and heat transfer.
- If the work done is performed on the outside environment, work (W) will be a positive value. If the work done is done to the heat engine system, work (W) will be a negative value.
- Some thermodynamic processes, including isothermal and adiabatic processes, are reversible in theory; that is, both the thermodynamic system and the environment can be returned to their initial states. However, because of loss of energy

owing to the second law of thermodynamics, complete reversibility does not work in practice.

15.3 Introduction to the Second Law of Thermodynamics: Heat Engines and Their Efficiency

- The two expressions of the second law of thermodynamics are: (i) Heat transfer occurs spontaneously from higher- to lower-temperature bodies but never spontaneously in the reverse direction; and (ii) It is impossible in any system for heat transfer from a reservoir to completely convert to work in a cyclical process in which the system returns to its initial state.
- Irreversible processes depend on path and do not return to their original state. Cyclical processes are processes that return to their original state at the end of every cycle.
- In a cyclical process, such as a heat engine, the net work done by the system equals the net heat transfer into the system, or $W = Q_h - Q_c$, where Q_h is the heat transfer from the hot object (hot reservoir), and Q_c is the heat transfer into the cold object (cold reservoir).
- Efficiency can be expressed as $Eff = \frac{W}{Q_h}$, the ratio of work output divided by the amount of energy input.
- The four-stroke gasoline engine is often explained in terms of the Otto cycle, which is a repeating sequence of processes that convert heat into work.

15.4 Carnot's Perfect Heat Engine: The Second Law of Thermodynamics Restated

- The Carnot cycle is a theoretical cycle that is the most efficient cyclical process possible. Any engine using the Carnot cycle, which uses only reversible processes (adiabatic and isothermal), is known as a Carnot engine.
- Any engine that uses the Carnot cycle enjoys the maximum theoretical efficiency.
- While Carnot engines are ideal engines, in reality, no engine achieves Carnot's theoretical maximum efficiency, since dissipative processes, such as friction, play a role. Carnot cycles without heat loss may be possible at absolute zero, but this has never been seen in nature.

15.5 Applications of Thermodynamics: Heat Pumps and Refrigerators

- An artifact of the second law of thermodynamics is the ability to heat an interior space using a heat pump. Heat pumps compress cold ambient air and, in so doing, heat it to room temperature without violation of conservation principles.
- To calculate the heat pump's coefficient of performance, use the equation $COP_{hp} = \frac{Q_h}{W}$.
- A refrigerator is a heat pump; it takes warm ambient air and expands it to chill it.

15.6 Entropy and the Second Law of Thermodynamics: Disorder and the Unavailability of Energy

- Entropy is the loss of energy available to do work.
- Another form of the second law of thermodynamics states that the total entropy of a system either increases or remains constant; it never decreases.
- Entropy is zero in a reversible process; it increases in an irreversible process.
- The ultimate fate of the universe is likely to be thermodynamic equilibrium, where the universal temperature is constant and no energy is available to do work.
- Entropy is also associated with the tendency toward disorder in a closed system.

15.7 Statistical Interpretation of Entropy and the Second Law of Thermodynamics: The Underlying Explanation

- Disorder is far more likely than order, which can be seen statistically.
- The entropy of a system in a given state (a macrostate) can be written as
  $S = k \ln W$,
  where $k = 1.38 \times 10^{-23}$ J/K is Boltzmann's constant, and $\ln W$ is the natural logarithm of the number of microstates W corresponding to the given macrostate.

Conceptual Questions

15.1 The First Law of Thermodynamics

1. Describe the photo of the tea kettle at the beginning of this section in terms of heat transfer, work done, and internal energy. How is heat being transferred? What is the work done and what is doing it? How does the kettle maintain its internal energy?

2. The first law of thermodynamics and the conservation of energy, as discussed in Conservation of Energy, are clearly related. How do they differ in the types of energy considered?

3. Heat transfer Q and work done W are always energy in transit, whereas internal energy U is energy stored in a system. Give an example of each type of energy, and state specifically how it is either in transit or resides in a system.

4. How do heat transfer and internal energy differ? In particular, which can be stored as such in a system and which cannot?

5. If you run down some stairs and stop, what happens to your kinetic energy and your initial gravitational potential energy?

6. Give an explanation of how food energy (calories) can be viewed as molecular potential energy (consistent with the atomic and molecular definition of internal energy).

7. Identify the type of energy transferred to your body in each of the following as either internal energy, heat transfer, or doing work: (a) basking in sunlight; (b) eating food; (c) riding an elevator to a higher floor.

15.2 The First Law of Thermodynamics and Some Simple Processes

8. A great deal of effort, time, and money has been spent in the quest for the so-called perpetual-motion machine, which is defined as a hypothetical machine that operates or produces useful work indefinitely and/or a hypothetical machine that produces more work or energy than it consumes. Explain, in terms of heat engines and the first law of thermodynamics, why or why not such a machine is likely to be constructed.

9. One method of converting heat transfer into doing work is for heat transfer into a gas to take place, which expands, doing work on a piston, as shown in the figure below. (a) Is the heat transfer converted directly to work in an isobaric process, or does it go through another form first? Explain your answer. (b) What about in an isothermal process? (c) What about in an adiabatic process (where heat transfer occurred prior to the adiabatic process)?

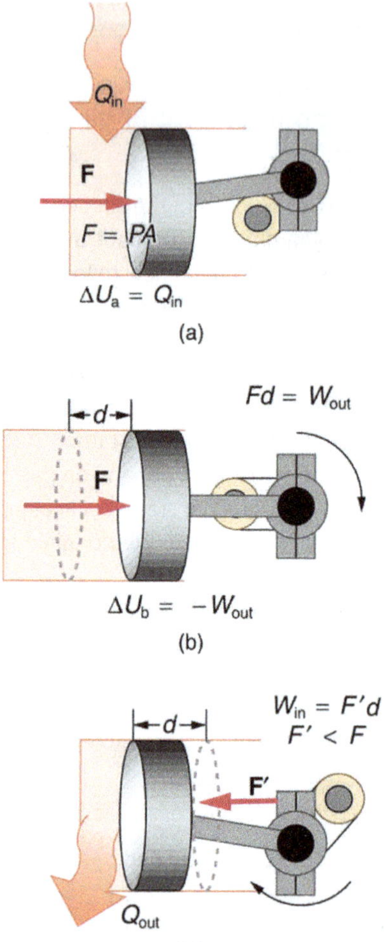

FIGURE 15.39

10. Would the previous question make any sense for an isochoric process? Explain your answer.

11. We ordinarily say that $\Delta U = 0$ for an isothermal process. Does this assume no phase change takes place? Explain your answer.

12. The temperature of a rapidly expanding gas decreases. Explain why in terms of the first law of thermodynamics. (Hint: Consider whether the gas does work and whether heat transfer occurs rapidly into the gas through conduction.)

13. Which cyclical process represented by the two closed loops, ABCFA and ABDEA, on the PV diagram in the figure below produces the greatest *net* work? Is that process also the one with the smallest work input required to return it to point A? Explain your responses.

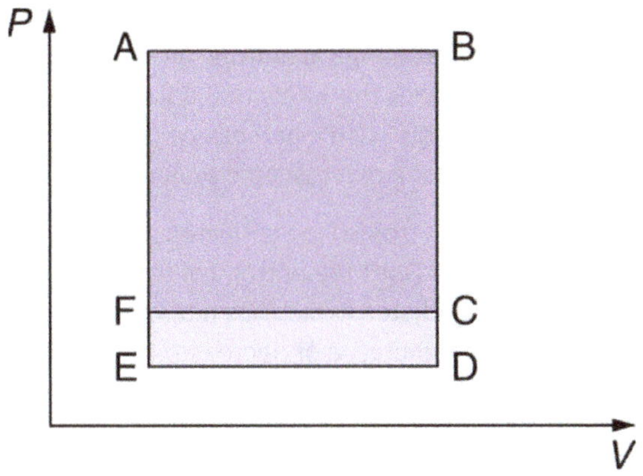

FIGURE 15.40 The two cyclical processes shown on this PV diagram start with and return the system to the conditions at point A, but they follow different paths and produce different amounts of work.

14. A real process may be nearly adiabatic if it occurs over a very short time. How does the short time span help the process to be adiabatic?

15. It is unlikely that a process can be isothermal unless it is a very slow process. Explain why. Is the same true for isobaric and isochoric processes? Explain your answer.

15.3 Introduction to the Second Law of Thermodynamics: Heat Engines and Their Efficiency

16. Imagine you are driving a car up Pike's Peak in Colorado. To raise a car weighing 1000 kilograms a distance of 100 meters would require about a million joules. You could raise a car 12.5 kilometers with the energy in a gallon of gas. Driving up Pike's Peak (a mere 3000-meter climb) should consume a little less than a quart of gas. But other considerations have to be taken into account. Explain, in terms of efficiency, what factors may keep you from realizing your ideal energy use on this trip.

17. Is a temperature difference necessary to operate a heat engine? State why or why not.

18. Definitions of efficiency vary depending on how energy is being converted. Compare the definitions of efficiency for the human body and heat engines. How does the definition of efficiency in each relate to the type of energy being converted into doing work?

19. Why—other than the fact that the second law of thermodynamics says reversible engines are the most efficient—should heat engines employing reversible processes be more efficient than those employing irreversible processes? Consider that dissipative mechanisms are one cause of irreversibility.

15.4 Carnot's Perfect Heat Engine: The Second Law of Thermodynamics Restated

20. Think about the drinking bird at the beginning of this section (Figure 15.20). Although the bird enjoys the theoretical maximum efficiency possible, if left to its own devices over time, the bird will cease "drinking." What are some of the dissipative processes that might cause the bird's motion to cease?

21. Can improved engineering and materials be employed in heat engines to reduce heat transfer into the environment? Can they eliminate heat transfer into the environment entirely?

22. Does the second law of thermodynamics alter the conservation of energy principle?

15.5 Applications of Thermodynamics: Heat Pumps and Refrigerators

23. Explain why heat pumps do not work as well in very cold climates as they do in milder ones. Is the same true of refrigerators?

24. In some Northern European nations, homes are being built without heating systems of any type. They are very well insulated and are kept warm by the body heat of the residents. However, when the residents are not at home, it is still warm in these houses. What is a possible explanation?

25. Why do refrigerators, air conditioners, and heat pumps operate most cost-effectively for cycles with a small difference between T_h and T_c? (Note that the temperatures of the cycle employed are crucial to its COP.)

26. Grocery store managers contend that there is *less* total energy consumption in the summer if the store is kept at a *low* temperature. Make arguments to support or refute this claim, taking into account that there are numerous refrigerators and freezers in the store.

27. Can you cool a kitchen by leaving the refrigerator door open?

15.6 Entropy and the Second Law of Thermodynamics: Disorder and the Unavailability of Energy

28. A woman shuts her summer cottage up in September and returns in June. No one has entered the cottage in the meantime. Explain what she is likely to find, in terms of the second law of thermodynamics.

29. Consider a system with a certain energy content, from which we wish to extract as much work as possible. Should the system's entropy be high or low? Is this orderly or disorderly? Structured or uniform? Explain briefly.

30. Does a gas become more orderly when it liquefies? Does its entropy change? If so, does the entropy increase or decrease? Explain your answer.

31. Explain how water's entropy can decrease when it freezes without violating the second law of thermodynamics. Specifically, explain what happens to the entropy of its surroundings.

32. Is a uniform-temperature gas more or less orderly than one with several different temperatures? Which is more structured? In which can heat transfer result in work done without heat transfer from another system?

33. Give an example of a spontaneous process in which a system becomes less ordered and energy becomes less available to do work. What happens to the system's entropy in this process?

34. What is the change in entropy in an adiabatic process? Does this imply that adiabatic processes are reversible? Can a process be precisely adiabatic for a macroscopic system?

35. Does the entropy of a star increase or decrease as it radiates? Does the entropy of the space into which it radiates (which has a temperature of about 3 K) increase or decrease? What does this do to the entropy of the universe?

36. Explain why a building made of bricks has smaller entropy than the same bricks in a disorganized pile. Do this by considering the number of ways that each could be formed (the number of microstates in each macrostate).

15.7 Statistical Interpretation of Entropy and the Second Law of Thermodynamics: The Underlying Explanation

37. Explain why a building made of bricks has smaller entropy than the same bricks in a disorganized pile. Do this by considering the number of ways that each could be formed (the number of microstates in each macrostate).

Problems & Exercises

15.1 The First Law of Thermodynamics

1. What is the change in internal energy of a car if you put 12.0 gal of gasoline into its tank? The energy content of gasoline is 1.3×10^8 J/gal. All other factors, such as the car's temperature, are constant.

2. How much heat transfer occurs from a system, if its internal energy decreased by 150 J while it was doing 30.0 J of work?

3. A system does 1.80×10^8 J of work while 7.50×10^8 J of heat transfer occurs to the environment. What is the change in internal energy of the system assuming no other changes (such as in temperature or by the addition of fuel)?

4. What is the change in internal energy of a system which does 4.50×10^5 J of work while 3.00×10^6 J of heat transfer occurs into the system, and 8.00×10^6 J of heat transfer occurs to the environment?

5. Suppose a woman does 500 J of work and 9500 J of heat transfer occurs into the environment in the process. (a) What is the decrease in her internal energy, assuming no change in temperature or consumption of food? (That is, there is no other energy transfer.) (b) What is her efficiency?

6. (a) How much food energy will a man metabolize in the process of doing 35.0 kJ of work with an efficiency of 5.00%? (b) How much heat transfer occurs to the environment to keep his temperature constant? Explicitly show how you follow the steps in the Problem-Solving Strategy for thermodynamics found in Problem-Solving Strategies for Thermodynamics.

7. (a) What is the average metabolic rate in watts of a man who metabolizes 10,500 kJ of food energy in one day? (b) What is the maximum amount of work in joules he can do without breaking down fat, assuming a maximum efficiency of 20.0%? (c) Compare his work output with the daily output of a 187-W (0.250-horsepower) motor.

8. (a) How long will the energy in a 1470-kJ (350-kcal) cup of yogurt last in a woman doing work at the rate of 150 W with an efficiency of 20.0% (such as in leisurely climbing stairs)? (b) Does the time found in part (a) imply that it is easy to consume more food energy than you can reasonably expect to work off with exercise?

9. (a) A woman climbing the Washington Monument metabolizes 6.00×10^2 kJ of food energy. If her efficiency is 18.0%, how much heat transfer occurs to the environment to keep her temperature constant? (b) Discuss the amount of heat transfer found in (a). Is it consistent with the fact that you quickly warm up when exercising?

15.2 The First Law of Thermodynamics and Some Simple Processes

10. A car tire contains $0.0380\ \text{m}^3$ of nitrogen at a gauge pressure of $2.20 \times 10^5\ \text{N/m}^2$ (about 32 psi). How much more internal energy does this gas have than the same volume has at zero gauge pressure (which is equivalent to normal atmospheric pressure)? (Use $U = \frac{5}{2}NkT$ for the internal energy of nitrogen, a diatomic gas.)

11. A helium-filled rigid ball has a gauge pressure of 0.200 atm and a volume of 10.0 L. How much greater is the internal energy of the helium in the ball than it would be at zero gauge pressure?

12. Steam to drive an old-fashioned steam locomotive is supplied at a constant gauge pressure of $1.75 \times 10^6\ \text{N/m}^2$ (about 250 psi) to a piston with a 0.200-m radius. (a) By calculating $P\Delta V$, find the work done by the steam when the piston moves 0.800 m. Note that this is the net work output, since gauge pressure is used. (b) Now find the amount of work by calculating the force exerted times the distance traveled. Is the answer the same as in part (a)?

13. A hand-driven tire pump has a piston with a 2.50-cm diameter and a maximum stroke of 30.0 cm. (a) How much work do you do in one stroke if the average gauge pressure is $2.40 \times 10^5\ \text{N/m}^2$ (about 35 psi)? (b) What average force do you exert on the piston, neglecting friction and gravitational force?

14. Calculate the net work output of a heat engine following path ABCDA in the figure below.

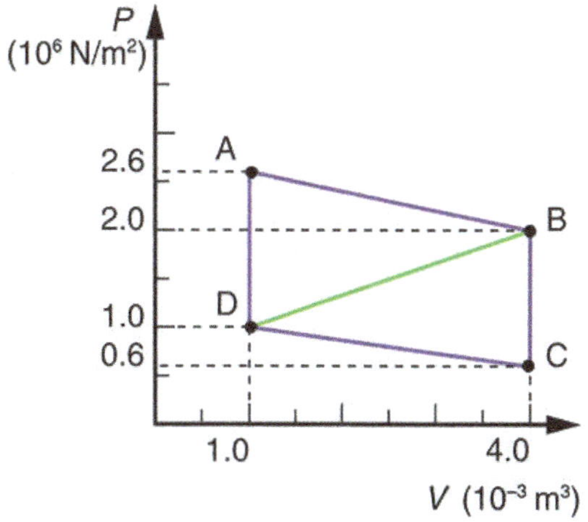

FIGURE 15.41

15. What is the net work output of a heat engine that follows path ABDA in the figure above, with a straight line from B to D? Why is the work output less than for path ABCDA? Explicitly show how you follow the steps in the Problem-Solving Strategies for Thermodynamics.

16. Unreasonable Results
What is wrong with the claim that a cyclical heat engine does 4.00 kJ of work on an input of 24.0 kJ of heat transfer while 16.0 kJ of heat transfers to the environment?

17. (a) A cyclical heat engine, operating between temperatures of 450° C and 150° C produces 4.00 MJ of work on a heat transfer of 5.00 MJ into the engine. How much heat transfer occurs to the environment? (b) What is unreasonable about the engine? (c) Which premise is unreasonable?

18. Construct Your Own Problem
Consider a car's gasoline engine. Construct a problem in which you calculate the maximum efficiency this engine can have. Among the things to consider are the effective hot and cold reservoir temperatures. Compare your calculated efficiency with the actual efficiency of car engines.

19. Construct Your Own Problem
Consider a car trip into the mountains. Construct a problem in which you calculate the overall efficiency of the car for the trip as a ratio of kinetic and potential energy gained to fuel consumed. Compare this efficiency to the thermodynamic efficiency quoted for gasoline engines and discuss why the thermodynamic efficiency is so much greater. Among the factors to be considered are the gain in altitude and speed, the mass of the car, the distance traveled, and typical fuel economy.

15.3 Introduction to the Second Law of Thermodynamics: Heat Engines and Their Efficiency

20. A certain heat engine does 10.0 kJ of work and 8.50 kJ of heat transfer occurs to the environment in a cyclical process. (a) What was the heat transfer into this engine? (b) What was the engine's efficiency?

21. With 2.56×10^6 J of heat transfer into this engine, a given cyclical heat engine can do only 1.50×10^5 J of work. (a) What is the engine's efficiency? (b) How much heat transfer to the environment takes place?

22. (a) What is the work output of a cyclical heat engine having a 22.0% efficiency and 6.00×10^9 J of heat transfer into the engine? (b) How much heat transfer occurs to the environment?

23. (a) What is the efficiency of a cyclical heat engine in which 75.0 kJ of heat transfer occurs to the environment for every 95.0 kJ of heat transfer into the engine? (b) How much work does it produce for 100 kJ of heat transfer into the engine?

24. The engine of a large ship does 2.00×10^8 J of work with an efficiency of 5.00%. (a) How much heat transfer occurs to the environment? (b) How many barrels of fuel are consumed, if each barrel produces 6.00×10^9 J of heat transfer when burned?

25. (a) How much heat transfer occurs to the environment by an electrical power station that uses 1.25×10^{14} J of heat transfer into the engine with an efficiency of 42.0%? (b) What is the ratio of heat transfer to the environment to work output? (c) How much work is done?

26. Assume that the turbines at a coal-powered power plant were upgraded, resulting in an improvement in efficiency of 3.32%. Assume that prior to the upgrade the power station had an efficiency of 36% and that the heat transfer into the engine in one day is still the same at 2.50×10^{14} J. (a) How much more electrical energy is produced due to the upgrade? (b) How much less heat transfer occurs to the environment due to the upgrade?

27. This problem compares the energy output and heat transfer to the environment by two different types of nuclear power stations—one with the normal efficiency of 34.0%, and another with an improved efficiency of 40.0%. Suppose both have the same heat transfer into the engine in one day, 2.50×10^{14} J. (a) How much more electrical energy is produced by the more efficient power station? (b) How much less heat transfer occurs to the environment by the more efficient power station? (One type of more efficient nuclear power station, the gas-cooled reactor, has not been reliable enough to be economically feasible in spite of its greater efficiency.)

15.4 Carnot's Perfect Heat Engine: The Second Law of Thermodynamics Restated

28. A certain gasoline engine has an efficiency of 30.0%. What would the hot reservoir temperature be for a Carnot engine having that efficiency, if it operates with a cold reservoir temperature of $200^\circ C$?

29. A gas-cooled nuclear reactor operates between hot and cold reservoir temperatures of $700^\circ C$ and $27.0^\circ C$. (a) What is the maximum efficiency of a heat engine operating between these temperatures? (b) Find the ratio of this efficiency to the Carnot efficiency of a standard nuclear reactor (found in Example 15.4).

30. (a) What is the hot reservoir temperature of a Carnot engine that has an efficiency of 42.0% and a cold reservoir temperature of $27.0^\circ C$? (b) What must the hot reservoir temperature be for a real heat engine that achieves 0.700 of the maximum efficiency, but still has an efficiency of 42.0% (and a cold reservoir at $27.0^\circ C$)? (c) Does your answer imply practical limits to the efficiency of car gasoline engines?

31. Steam locomotives have an efficiency of 17.0% and operate with a hot steam temperature of $425^\circ C$. (a) What would the cold reservoir temperature be if this were a Carnot engine? (b) What would the maximum efficiency of this steam engine be if its cold reservoir temperature were $150^\circ C$?

32. Practical steam engines utilize $450^\circ C$ steam, which is later exhausted at $270^\circ C$. (a) What is the maximum efficiency that such a heat engine can have? (b) Since $270^\circ C$ steam is still quite hot, a second steam engine is sometimes operated using the exhaust of the first. What is the maximum efficiency of the second engine if its exhaust has a temperature of $150^\circ C$? (c) What is the overall efficiency of the two engines? (d) Show that this is the same efficiency as a single Carnot engine operating between $450^\circ C$ and $150^\circ C$. Explicitly show how you follow the steps in the Problem-Solving Strategies for Thermodynamics.

33. A coal-fired electrical power station has an efficiency of 38%. The temperature of the steam leaving the boiler is $550^\circ C$. What percentage of the maximum efficiency does this station obtain? (Assume the temperature of the environment is $20^\circ C$.)

34. Would you be willing to financially back an inventor who is marketing a device that she claims has 25 kJ of heat transfer at 600 K, has heat transfer to the environment at 300 K, and does 12 kJ of work? Explain your answer.

35. Unreasonable Results
(a) Suppose you want to design a steam engine that has heat transfer to the environment at $270^\circ C$ and has a Carnot efficiency of 0.800. What temperature of hot steam must you use? (b) What is unreasonable about the temperature? (c) Which premise is unreasonable?

36. Unreasonable Results
Calculate the cold reservoir temperature of a steam engine that uses hot steam at $450^\circ C$ and has a Carnot efficiency of 0.700. (b) What is unreasonable about the temperature? (c) Which premise is unreasonable?

15.5 Applications of Thermodynamics: Heat Pumps and Refrigerators

37. What is the coefficient of performance of an ideal heat pump that has heat transfer from a cold temperature of $-25.0^\circ C$ to a hot temperature of $40.0^\circ C$?

38. Suppose you have an ideal refrigerator that cools an environment at $-20.0^\circ C$ and has heat transfer to another environment at $50.0^\circ C$. What is its coefficient of performance?

39. What is the best coefficient of performance possible for a hypothetical refrigerator that could make liquid nitrogen at $-200^\circ C$ and has heat transfer to the environment at $35.0^\circ C$?

40. In a very mild winter climate, a heat pump has heat transfer from an environment at $5.00^\circ C$ to one at $35.0^\circ C$. What is the best possible coefficient of performance for these temperatures? Explicitly show how you follow the steps in the Problem-Solving Strategies for Thermodynamics.

41. (a) What is the best coefficient of performance for a heat pump that has a hot reservoir temperature of $50.0^\circ C$ and a cold reservoir temperature of $-20.0^\circ C$? (b) How much heat transfer occurs into the warm environment if 3.60×10^7 J of work ($10.0 kW \cdot h$) is put into it? (c) If the cost of this work input is 10.0 cents/kW $\cdot$ h, how does its cost compare with the direct heat transfer achieved by burning natural gas at a cost of 85.0 cents per therm. (A therm is a common unit of energy for natural gas and equals 1.055×10^8 J.)

42. (a) What is the best coefficient of performance for a refrigerator that cools an environment at $-30.0^\circ C$ and has heat transfer to another environment at $45.0^\circ C$? (b) How much work in joules must be done for a heat transfer of 4186 kJ from the cold environment? (c) What is the cost of doing this if the work costs 10.0 cents per 3.60×10^6 J (a kilowatt-hour)? (d) How many kJ of heat transfer occurs into the warm environment? (e) Discuss what type of refrigerator might operate between these temperatures.

43. Suppose you want to operate an ideal refrigerator with a cold temperature of $-10.0^\circ C$, and you would like it to have a coefficient of performance of 7.00. What is the hot reservoir temperature for such a refrigerator?

44. An ideal heat pump is being considered for use in heating an environment with a temperature of $22.0^\circ C$. What is the cold reservoir temperature if the pump is to have a coefficient of performance of 12.0?

45. A 4-ton air conditioner removes 5.06×10^7 J (48,000 British thermal units) from a cold environment in 1.00 h. (a) What energy input in joules is necessary to do this if the air conditioner has an energy efficiency rating (EER) of 12.0? (b) What is the cost of doing this if the work costs 10.0 cents per 3.60×10^6 J (one kilowatt-hour)?
(c) Discuss whether this cost seems realistic. Note that the energy efficiency rating (EER) of an air conditioner or refrigerator is defined to be the number of British thermal units of heat transfer from a cold environment per hour divided by the watts of power input.

46. Show that the coefficients of performance of refrigerators and heat pumps are related by $COP_{ref} = COP_{hp} - 1$.

Start with the definitions of the COPs and the conservation of energy relationship between Q_h, Q_c, and W.

15.6 Entropy and the Second Law of Thermodynamics: Disorder and the Unavailability of Energy

47. (a) On a winter day, a certain house loses 5.00×10^8 J of heat to the outside (about 500,000 Btu). What is the total change in entropy due to this heat transfer alone, assuming an average indoor temperature of 21.0° C and an average outdoor temperature of 5.00° C? (b) This large change in entropy implies a large amount of energy has become unavailable to do work. Where do we find more energy when such energy is lost to us?

48. On a hot summer day, 4.00×10^6 J of heat transfer into a parked car takes place, increasing its temperature from 35.0° C to 45.0° C. What is the increase in entropy of the car due to this heat transfer alone?

49. A hot rock ejected from a volcano's lava fountain cools from 1100° C to 40.0° C, and its entropy decreases by 950 J/K. How much heat transfer occurs from the rock?

50. When 1.60×10^5 J of heat transfer occurs into a meat pie initially at 20.0° C, its entropy increases by 480 J/K. What is its final temperature?

51. The Sun radiates energy at the rate of 3.80×10^{26} W from its 5500° C surface into dark empty space (a negligible fraction radiates onto Earth and the other planets). The effective temperature of deep space is -270° C. (a) What is the increase in entropy in one day due to this heat transfer? (b) How much work is made unavailable?

52. (a) In reaching equilibrium, how much heat transfer occurs from 1.00 kg of water at 40.0° C when it is placed in contact with 1.00 kg of 20.0° C water in reaching equilibrium? (b) What is the change in entropy due to this heat transfer? (c) How much work is made unavailable, taking the lowest temperature to be 20.0° C? Explicitly show how you follow the steps in the Problem-Solving Strategies for Entropy.

53. What is the decrease in entropy of 25.0 g of water that condenses on a bathroom mirror at a temperature of 35.0° C, assuming no change in temperature and given the latent heat of vaporization to be 2450 kJ/kg?

54. Find the increase in entropy of 1.00 kg of liquid nitrogen that starts at its boiling temperature, boils, and warms to 20.0° C at constant pressure.

55. A large electrical power station generates 1000 MW of electricity with an efficiency of 35.0%. (a) Calculate the heat transfer to the power station, Q_h, in one day. (b) How much heat transfer Q_c occurs to the environment in one day? (c) If the heat transfer in the cooling towers is from 35.0° C water into the local air mass, which increases in temperature from 18.0° C to 20.0° C, what is the total increase in entropy due to this heat transfer? (d) How much energy becomes unavailable to do work because of this increase in entropy, assuming an 18.0° C lowest temperature? (Part of Q_c could be utilized to operate heat engines or for simply heating the surroundings, but it rarely is.)

56. (a) How much heat transfer occurs from 20.0 kg of 90.0° C water placed in contact with 20.0 kg of 10.0° C water, producing a final temperature of 50.0° C? (b) How much work could a Carnot engine do with this heat transfer, assuming it operates between two reservoirs at constant temperatures of 90.0° C and 10.0° C? (c) What increase in entropy is produced by mixing 20.0 kg of 90.0° C water with 20.0 kg of 10.0° C water? (d) Calculate the amount of work made unavailable by this mixing using a low temperature of 10.0° C, and compare it with the work done by the Carnot engine. Explicitly show how you follow the steps in the Problem-Solving Strategies for Entropy. (e) Discuss how everyday processes make increasingly more energy unavailable to do work, as implied by this problem.

15.7 Statistical Interpretation of Entropy and the Second Law of Thermodynamics: The Underlying Explanation

57. Using Table 15.4, verify the contention that if you toss 100 coins each second, you can expect to get 100 heads or 100 tails once in 2×10^{22} years; calculate the time to two-digit accuracy.

58. What percent of the time will you get something in the range from 60 heads and 40 tails through 40 heads and 60 tails when tossing 100 coins? The total number of microstates in that range is 1.22×10^{30}. (Consult Table 15.4.)

59. (a) If tossing 100 coins, how many ways

(microstates) are there to get the three most likely macrostates of 49 heads and 51 tails, 50 heads and 50 tails, and 51 heads and 49 tails? (b) What percent of the total possibilities is this? (Consult Table 15.4.)

60. (a) What is the change in entropy if you start with 100 coins in the 45 heads and 55 tails macrostate, toss them, and get 51 heads and 49 tails? (b) What if you get 75 heads and 25 tails? (c) How much more likely is 51 heads and 49 tails than 75 heads and 25 tails? (d) Does either outcome violate the second law of thermodynamics?

61. (a) What is the change in entropy if you start with 10 coins in the 5 heads and 5 tails macrostate, toss them, and get 2 heads and 8 tails? (b) How much more likely is 5 heads and 5 tails than 2 heads and 8 tails? (Take the ratio of the number of microstates to find out.) (c) If you were betting on 2 heads and 8 tails would you accept odds of 252 to 45? Explain why or why not.

Macrostate		Number of Microstates (*W*)
Heads	Tails	
10	0	1
9	1	10
8	2	45
7	3	120
6	4	210
5	5	252
4	6	210

TABLE 15.5 10-Coin Toss

Macrostate		Number of Microstates (*W*)
3	7	120
2	8	45
1	9	10
0	10	1
		Total: 1024

TABLE 15.5 10-Coin Toss

62. (a) If you toss 10 coins, what percent of the time will you get the three most likely macrostates (6 heads and 4 tails, 5 heads and 5 tails, 4 heads and 6 tails)? (b) You can realistically toss 10 coins and count the number of heads and tails about twice a minute. At that rate, how long will it take on average to get either 10 heads and 0 tails or 0 heads and 10 tails?

63. (a) Construct a table showing the macrostates and all of the individual microstates for tossing 6 coins. (Use Table 15.5 as a guide.) (b) How many macrostates are there? (c) What is the total number of microstates? (d) What percent chance is there of tossing 5 heads and 1 tail? (e) How much more likely are you to toss 3 heads and 3 tails than 5 heads and 1 tail? (Take the ratio of the number of microstates to find out.)

64. In an air conditioner, 12.65 MJ of heat transfer occurs from a cold environment in 1.00 h. (a) What mass of ice melting would involve the same heat transfer? (b) How many hours of operation would be equivalent to melting 900 kg of ice? (c) If ice costs 20 cents per kg, do you think the air conditioner could be operated more cheaply than by simply using ice? Describe in detail how you evaluate the relative costs.

Test Prep for AP® Courses

15.1 The First Law of Thermodynamics

1. A cylinder is divided in half by a movable disk in the middle. Each half is filled with an equal number of gas molecules, but one half is at a higher temperature than the other. Which choice best describes what happens next?

a. Nothing.
b. The high temperature side expands, compressing the low temperature side.
c. Heat moves from hot to cold, so the low temperature side will gradually increase in temperature and expand
d. (b) happens quickly, but after that (c) happens more slowly.

2. Imagine a solid material at the molecular level as consisting of a bunch of billiard balls connected to each other by springs (this is actually a surprisingly useful approximation). If we have two blocks of the same material, but in one the billiard balls are shaking back and forth on their springs a great deal, and in the other they are barely moving, which block is at the higher temperature? Using what you know about conservation of momentum in collisions, describe which block will transfer energy to the other, and justify your answer.

3. A system has 300 J of work done on it, and has a heat transfer of -320 J. Compared to prior to these processes, the internal energy is:
   a. 20 J less
   b. 20 J more
   c. 620 J more
   d. 620 J less

4. Find a snack or drink item in the classroom, or at your next meal. Find the total Calories (kilocalories) in the item, and calculate how long it would take exercising at 150 W (moderately, climbing stairs) at 20% efficiency to burn off this energy.

5. A potato cannon has the fuel combusted, generating a lot of heat and pressure, which launch a potato. The combustion process _____ the internal energy, while launching the potato _____ the internal energy of the potato cannon.
   a. increases, increases
   b. increases, decreases
   c. decreases, increases
   d. decreases, decreases

6. Describe what happens to the system inside of a refrigerator or freezer in terms of heat transfer, work, and conservation of energy. Confine yourself to time periods in which the door is closed.

15.2 The First Law of Thermodynamics and Some Simple Processes

7. In Figure 15.41, how much work is done by the system in process AB?
   a. 4.5×10^3 J
   b. 6.0×10^3 J
   c. 6.9×10^3 J
   d. 7.8×10^3 J

8. Consider process CD in Figure 15.41. Does this represent work done by or on the system, and how much?

9. A thermodynamic process begins at 1.2×10^6 N/m^2 and 5 L. The state then changes to 1.2×10^6 N/m^2 and 2 L. Next it becomes 2.2×10^6 N/m^2 and 2 L. The next change is 2.2×10^6 N/m^2 and 5 L. Finally, the system ends at 1.0×10^6 N/m^2 and 5 L.

On Figure 15.40, this process is best described by
   a. EFCDB
   b. DEFCD
   c. CFABC
   d. CFABD

10. The first step of a thermodynamic cycle is an isobaric process with increasing volume. The second is an isochoric process, with decreasing pressure. The last step may be either an isothermal or adiabatic process, ending at the starting point of the isobaric process. Sketch a graph of these two possibilities, and comment on which will have greater net work per cycle.

11. In Figure 15.41, which of the following cycles has the greatest net work output?
   a. ABDA
   b. BCDB
   c. (a) and (b) are equal
   d. ADCBA

12. Look at Figure 15.40, and assign values to the three pressures and two volumes given in the graph. Then calculate the net work for the cycle ABCFEDCFA using those values. How does this work compare to the heat output or input of the system? Which value(s) would you change to maximize the net work per cycle?

15.6 Entropy and the Second Law of Thermodynamics: Disorder and the Unavailability of Energy

13. Equal masses of steam (100 degrees C) and ice (0 degrees C) are placed in contact with each other in an otherwise insulated container. They both end up as liquid water at a common temperature. The steam ___ entropy and ___ order, while the ice ___ entropy and ___ order.
   a. gained, gained, lost, lost
   b. gained, lost, lost, gained
   c. lost, gained, gained, lost
   d. lost, lost, gained, gained

14. A high temperature reservoir losing heat and hence entropy is a reversible process. A low temperature reservoir gaining a certain amount of heat and hence entropy is a reversible process. But a high temperature reservoir losing heat to a low temperature reservoir is irreversible. Why?

15.7 Statistical Interpretation of Entropy and the Second Law of Thermodynamics: The Underlying Explanation

15. A piston is resting halfway into a cylinder containing gas in thermal equilibrium. The layer of molecules next to the closed end of the cylinder is suddenly flash-heated to a very high temperature. Which best describes what happens next?

a. The high temperature molecules push out the piston until their energy is reduced enough that the system is in equilibrium.
b. The molecules with the highest temperature bounce off their neighbors, losing energy to them, and so on until the system is at a new equilibrium with the piston moved out.
c. The molecules with the highest temperature bounce off their neighbors, losing energy to them, and so on until the system is at a new equilibrium with the piston where it started.
d. The high temperature molecules push out the piston until their energy is reduced enough that the system is in equilibrium, and then the piston gets sucked back in.

16. Design a macroscopic simulation using reasonably common materials to represent one very high energy particle gradually transferring energy to a bunch of lower energy particles, and determine if you end up with some sort of equilibrium.

CHAPTER 16
Oscillatory Motion and Waves

FIGURE 16.1 There are at least four types of waves in this picture—only the water waves are evident. There are also sound waves, light waves, and waves on the guitar strings. (credit: John Norton)

CHAPTER OUTLINE

CONNECTION FOR AP® COURSES In this chapter, students are introduced to oscillation, the regular variation in the position of a system about a central point accompanied by transfer of energy and momentum, and to **waves**. A child's swing, a pendulum, a spring, and a vibrating string are all examples of oscillations. This chapter will address simple harmonic motion and periods of vibration, aspects of oscillation that produce waves, a common phenomenon in everyday life. Waves carry energy from one place to another." This chapter will show how harmonic oscillations produce waves that transport energy across space and through time. The information and examples presented support Big Ideas 1, 2, and 3 of the AP® Physics Curriculum Framework.

The chapter opens by discussing the forces that govern oscillations and waves. It goes on to discuss important concepts such as **simple harmonic motion**, uniform harmonic motion, and damped harmonic motion. You will also learn about energy in simple harmonic motion and how it changes from kinetic to potential, and how the total sum, which would be the mechanical energy of the oscillator, remains constant or conserved at all times. The chapter also discusses characteristics of waves, such as their frequency, period of oscillation, and the forms in which they can exist, i.e., transverse or longitudinal. The chapter ends by discussing what happens when two or more waves overlap and how the **amplitude** of the resultant wave changes, leading to the phenomena of **superposition** and **interference**.

The concepts in this chapter support:

Big Idea 3 The interactions of an object with other objects can be described by forces.

Enduring Understanding 3.B Classically, the acceleration of an object interacting with other objects can be predicted by using $\vec{a} = \sum \frac{\vec{F}}{m}$.

Essential Knowledge 3.B.3 Restoring forces can result in oscillatory motion. When a linear restoring force is exerted on an object displaced from an equilibrium position, the object will undergo a special type of motion called simple harmonic motion. Examples should include gravitational force exerted by the Earth on a simple pendulum and a mass-spring oscillator.

Big Idea 4 Interactions between systems can result in changes in those systems.

Enduring Understanding 4.C Interactions with other objects or systems can change the total energy of a system.

Essential Knowledge 4.C.1 The energy of a system includes its kinetic energy, potential energy, and microscopic internal energy. Examples should include gravitational potential energy, elastic potential energy, and kinetic energy.

Essential Knowledge 4.C.2 Mechanical energy (the sum of kinetic and potential energy) is transferred into or out of a system when an external force is exerted on a system such that a component of the force is parallel to its displacement. The process through which the energy is transferred is called work.

Big Idea 5 Changes that occur as a result of interactions are constrained by conservation laws.

Enduring Understanding 5.B The energy of a system is conserved.

Essential Knowledge 5.B.2 A system with internal structure can have internal energy, and changes in a system's internal structure can result in changes in internal energy. [Physics 1: includes mass-spring oscillators and simple pendulums. Physics 2: includes charged object in electric fields and examining changes in internal energy with changes in configuration.]

Big Idea 6 Waves can transfer energy and momentum from one location to another without the permanent transfer of mass and serve as a mathematical model for the description of other phenomena.

Enduring Understanding 6.A A wave is a traveling disturbance that transfers energy and momentum.

Essential Knowledge 6.A.1 Waves can propagate via different oscillation modes such as transverse and longitudinal.

Essential Knowledge 6.A.2 For propagation, mechanical waves require a medium, while electromagnetic waves do not require a physical medium. Examples should include light traveling through a vacuum and sound not traveling through a vacuum.

Essential Knowledge 6.A.3 The amplitude is the maximum displacement of a wave from its equilibrium value.

Essential Knowledge 6.A.4 Classically, the energy carried by a wave depends on and increases with amplitude. Examples should include sound waves.

Enduring Understanding 6.B A periodic wave is one that repeats as a function of both time and position and can be described by its amplitude, frequency, wavelength, speed, and energy.

Essential Knowledge 6.B.1 The period is the repeat time of the wave. The frequency is the number of repetitions over a period of time.

Essential Knowledge 6.B.2 The wavelength is the repeat distance of the wave.

Essential Knowledge 6.B.3 A simple wave can be described by an equation involving one sine or cosine function involving the wavelength, amplitude, and frequency of the wave.

Essential Knowledge 6.B.4 The wavelength is the ratio of speed over frequency.

Enduring Understanding 6.C Only waves exhibit interference and diffraction.

Essential Knowledge 6.C.1 When two waves cross, they travel through each other; they do not bounce off each other. Where the waves overlap, the resulting displacement can be determined by adding the displacements of the two waves. This is called superposition.

Enduring Understanding 6.D Interference and superposition lead to standing waves and beats.

Essential Knowledge 6.D.1 Two or more wave pulses can interact in such a way as to produce amplitude variations in the resultant wave. When two pulses cross, they travel through each other; they do not bounce off each other. Where the pulses overlap, the resulting displacement can be determined by adding the displacements of the two pulses. This is called superposition.

Essential Knowledge 6.D.2 Two or more traveling waves can interact in such a way as to produce amplitude variations in the resultant wave.

Essential Knowledge 6.D.3 Standing waves are the result of the addition of incident and reflected waves that are confined to a region and have nodes and antinodes. Examples should include waves on a fixed length of string, and sound waves in both closed and open tubes.

Essential Knowledge 6.D.4 The possible wavelengths of a standing wave are determined by the size of the region to which it is confined.

Essential Knowledge 6.D.5 Beats arise from the addition of waves of slightly different frequency.

Click to view content (https://openstax.org/books/college-physics-ap-courses-2e/pages/16-connection-for-ap-r-courses)

16.1 Hooke's Law: Stress and Strain Revisited

LEARNING OBJECTIVES

By the end of this section, you will be able to:

- Explain Newton's third law of motion with respect to stress and deformation.
- Describe the restoration of force and displacement.
- Calculate the energy in Hooke's Law of deformation, and the stored energy in a spring.

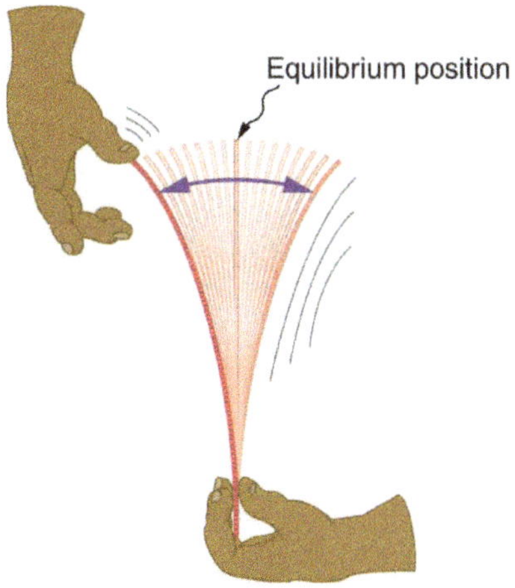

FIGURE 16.2 When displaced from its vertical equilibrium position, this plastic ruler oscillates back and forth because of the restoring force opposing displacement. When the ruler is on the left, there is a force to the right, and vice versa.

Newton's first law implies that an object oscillating back and forth is experiencing forces. Without force, the object would move in a straight line at a constant speed rather than oscillate. Consider, for example, plucking a plastic ruler to the left as shown in Figure 16.2. The deformation of the ruler creates a force in the opposite direction, known as a **restoring force**. Once released, the restoring force causes the ruler to move back toward its stable equilibrium position, where the net force on it is zero. However, by the time the ruler gets there, it gains momentum and continues to move to the right, producing the opposite deformation. It is then forced to the left, back through equilibrium, and the process is repeated until dissipative forces dampen the motion. These forces remove mechanical energy from the system, gradually reducing the motion until the ruler comes to rest.

The simplest oscillations occur when the restoring force is directly proportional to displacement. When stress and strain were covered in Newton's Third Law of Motion, the name was given to this relationship between force and displacement was Hooke's law:

$$F = -kx. \tag{16.1}$$

Here, F is the restoring force, x is the displacement from equilibrium or **deformation**, and k is a constant related to the difficulty in deforming the system. The minus sign indicates the restoring force is in the direction opposite to the displacement.

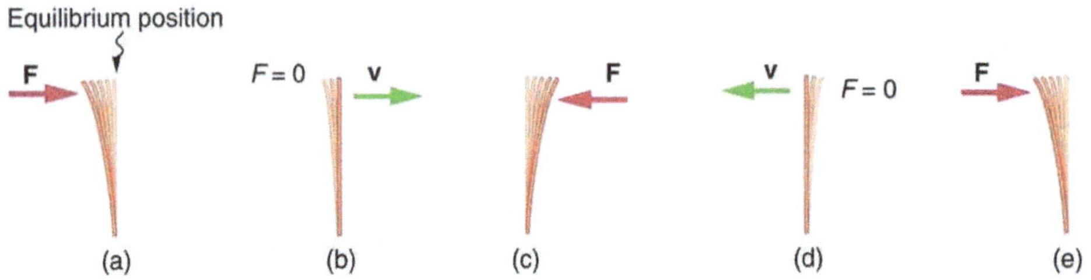

FIGURE 16.3 (a) The plastic ruler has been released, and the restoring force is returning the ruler to its equilibrium position. (b) The net force is zero at the equilibrium position, but the ruler has momentum and continues to move to the right. (c) The restoring force is in the opposite direction. It stops the ruler and moves it back toward equilibrium again. (d) Now the ruler has momentum to the left. (e) In the absence of damping (caused by frictional forces), the ruler reaches its original position. From there, the motion will repeat itself.

The **force constant** k is related to the rigidity (or stiffness) of a system—the larger the force constant, the greater the restoring force, and the stiffer the system. The units of k are newtons per meter (N/m). For example, k is directly related to Young's modulus when we stretch a string. Figure 16.4 shows a graph of the absolute value of the restoring force versus the displacement for a system that can be described by Hooke's law—a simple spring in this case. The slope of the graph equals the force constant k in newtons per meter. A common physics laboratory exercise is to measure restoring forces created by springs, determine if they follow Hooke's law, and calculate their force constants if they do.

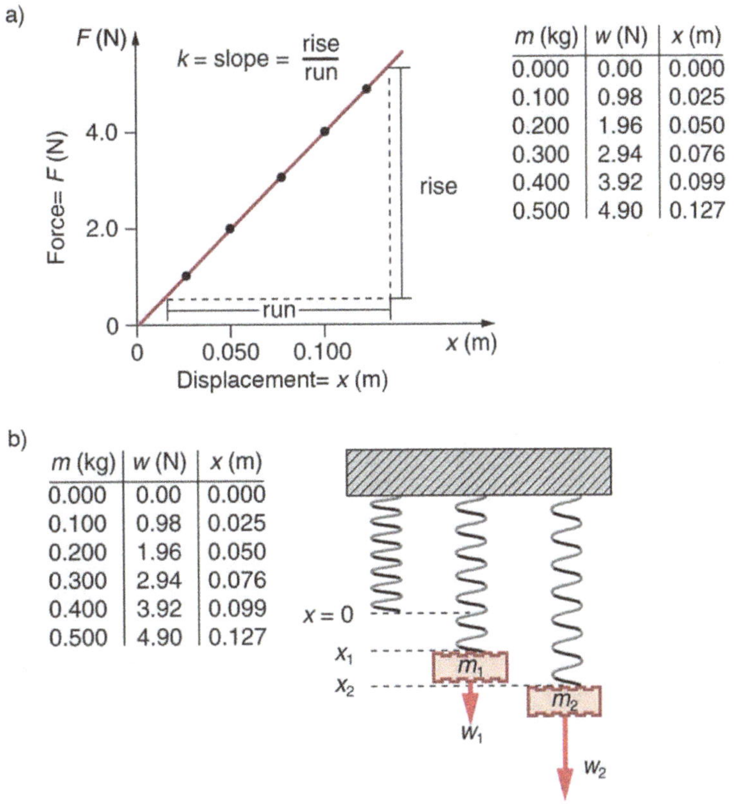

m (kg)	w (N)	x (m)
0.000	0.00	0.000
0.100	0.98	0.025
0.200	1.96	0.050
0.300	2.94	0.076
0.400	3.92	0.099
0.500	4.90	0.127

FIGURE 16.4 (a) A graph of absolute value of the restoring force versus displacement is displayed. The fact that the graph is a straight line means that the system obeys Hooke's law. The slope of the graph is the force constant k. (b) The data in the graph were generated by measuring the displacement of a spring from equilibrium while supporting various weights. The restoring force equals the weight supported, if the mass is stationary.

EXAMPLE 16.1

How Stiff Are Car Springs?

FIGURE 16.5 The mass of a car increases due to the introduction of a passenger. This affects the displacement of the car on its suspension system. (credit: exfordy on Flickr)

What is the force constant for the suspension system of a car that settles 1.20 cm when an 80.0-kg person gets in?

Strategy

Consider the car to be in its equilibrium position $x = 0$ before the person gets in. The car then settles down 1.20 cm, which means it is displaced to a position $x = -1.20 \times 10^{-2}$ m. At that point, the springs supply a restoring force F equal to the person's weight $w = mg = (80.0 \text{ kg})(9.80 \text{ m/s}^2) = 784 \text{ N}$. We take this force to be F in Hooke's law. Knowing F and x, we can then solve the force constant k.

Solution

1. Solve Hooke's law, $F = -kx$, for k:

$$k = -\frac{F}{x}. \quad (16.2)$$

Substitute known values and solve k:

$$\begin{aligned} k &= -\frac{784 \text{ N}}{-1.20 \times 10^{-2} \text{ m}} \\ &= 6.53 \times 10^4 \text{ N/m}. \end{aligned} \quad (16.3)$$

Discussion

Note that F and x have opposite signs because they are in opposite directions—the restoring force is up, and the displacement is down. Also, note that the car would oscillate up and down when the person got in if it were not for damping (due to frictional forces) provided by shock absorbers. Bouncing cars are a sure sign of bad shock absorbers.

Energy in Hooke's Law of Deformation

In order to produce a deformation, work must be done. That is, a force must be exerted through a distance, whether you pluck a guitar string or compress a car spring. If the only result is deformation, and no work goes into thermal, sound, or kinetic energy, then all the work is initially stored in the deformed object as some form of potential energy. The potential energy stored in a spring is $\text{PE}_{\text{el}} = \frac{1}{2}kx^2$. Here, we generalize the idea to elastic potential energy for a deformation of any system that can be described by Hooke's law. Hence,

$$\text{PE}_{\text{el}} = \frac{1}{2}kx^2, \quad (16.4)$$

where PE_{el} is the **elastic potential energy** stored in any deformed system that obeys Hooke's law and has a displacement x from equilibrium and a force constant k.

It is possible to find the work done in deforming a system in order to find the energy stored. This work is performed by an applied force F_{app}. The applied force is exactly opposite to the restoring force (action-reaction), and so $F_{\text{app}} = kx$. Figure 16.6 shows a graph of the applied force versus deformation x for a system that can be described by Hooke's law. Work done on the system is force multiplied by distance, which equals the area under the curve or $(1/2)kx^2$ (Method A in the figure). Another way to determine the work is to note that the force increases linearly from 0 to kx, so that the average force is $(1/2)\,kx$, the distance moved is x, and thus $W = F_{\text{app}}d = [(1/2)kx](x) = (1/2)kx^2$ (Method B in the figure).

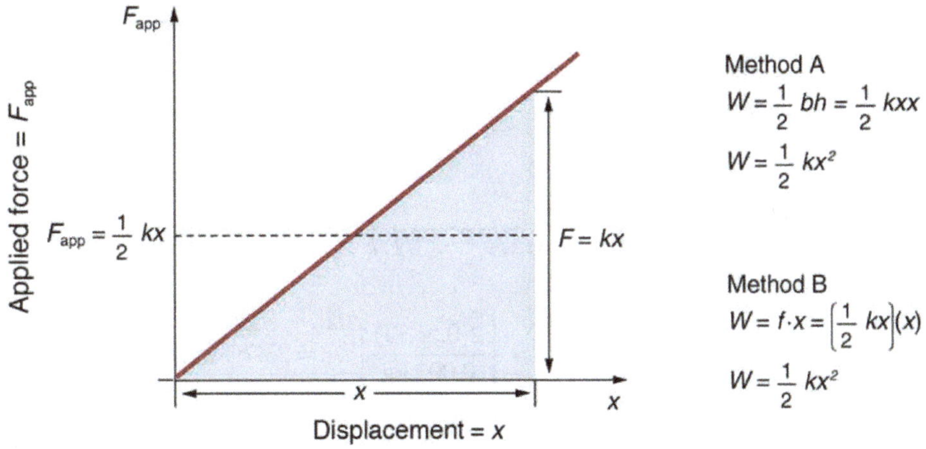

FIGURE 16.6 A graph of applied force versus distance for the deformation of a system that can be described by Hooke's law is displayed. The work done on the system equals the area under the graph or the area of the triangle, which is half its base multiplied by its height, or $W = (1/2)kx^2$.

EXAMPLE 16.2

Calculating Stored Energy: A Toy Gun Spring

We can use a toy gun's spring mechanism to ask and answer two simple questions: (a) How much energy is stored in the spring of a toy gun that has a force constant of 50.0 N/m and is compressed 0.150 m? (b) If you neglect friction and the mass of the spring, at what speed will a 2.00-g projectile be ejected from the gun?

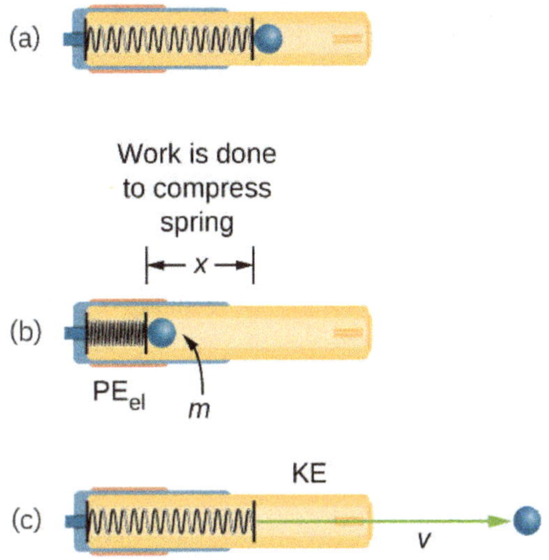

FIGURE 16.7 (a) In this image of the gun, the spring is uncompressed before being cocked. (b) The spring has been compressed a distance x, and the projectile is in place. (c) When released, the spring converts elastic potential energy PE_{el} into kinetic energy.

Strategy for a

(a): The energy stored in the spring can be found directly from elastic potential energy equation, because k and x are given.

Solution for a

Entering the given values for k and x yields

$$\begin{aligned} PE_{el} &= \tfrac{1}{2}kx^2 = \tfrac{1}{2}(50.0\text{ N/m})(0.150\text{ m})^2 = 0.563\text{ N}\cdot\text{m} \\ &= 0.563\text{ J} \end{aligned} \quad (16.5)$$

Strategy for b

Because there is no friction, the potential energy is converted entirely into kinetic energy. The expression for kinetic energy can be solved for the projectile's speed.

Solution for b

1. Identify known quantities:

$$\mathrm{KE_f} = \mathrm{PE_{el}} \text{ or } 1/2\, mv^2 = (1/2)\, kx^2 = \mathrm{PE_{el}} = 0.563 \text{ J} \tag{16.6}$$

2. Solve for v:

$$v = \left[\frac{2\mathrm{PE_{el}}}{m}\right]^{1/2} = \left[\frac{2(0.563 \text{ J})}{0.002 \text{ kg}}\right]^{1/2} = 23.7(\text{J/kg})^{1/2} \tag{16.7}$$

3. Convert units: 23.7 m/s

Discussion

(a) and (b): This projectile speed is impressive for a toy gun (more than 80 km/h). The numbers in this problem seem reasonable. The force needed to compress the spring is small enough for an adult to manage, and the energy imparted to the dart is small enough to limit the damage it might do, especially because the darts in many of these guns are made of soft material with a rubber tip. Yet, the speed of the dart is great enough for it to travel an acceptable distance.

CHECK YOUR UNDERSTANDING

Envision holding the end of a ruler with one hand and deforming it with the other. When you let go, you can see the oscillations of the ruler. In what way could you modify this simple experiment to increase the rigidity of the system?

Solution
You could hold the ruler at its midpoint so that the part of the ruler that oscillates is half as long as in the original experiment.

CHECK YOUR UNDERSTANDING

If you apply a deforming force on an object and let it come to equilibrium, what happened to the work you did on the system?

Solution
It was stored in the object as potential energy.

16.2 Period and Frequency in Oscillations

LEARNING OBJECTIVES

By the end of this section, you will be able to:

- Observe the vibrations of a guitar string.
- Determine the frequency of oscillations.

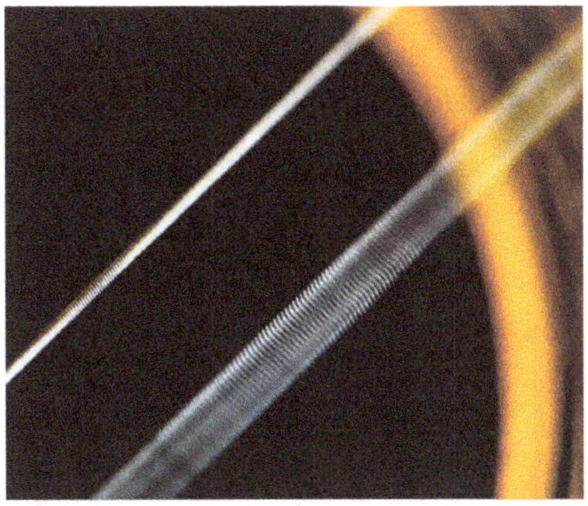

FIGURE 16.8 The strings on this guitar vibrate at regular time intervals. (credit: JAR)

When you pluck a guitar string, the resulting sound has a steady tone and lasts a long time. Each successive vibration of the string takes the same time as the previous one. We define **periodic motion** to be a motion that repeats itself at regular time intervals, such as exhibited by the guitar string or by an object on a spring moving up and down. The time to complete one oscillation remains constant and is called the **period** T. Its units are usually seconds, but may be any convenient unit of time. The word period refers to the time for some event whether repetitive or not; but we shall be primarily interested in periodic motion, which is by definition repetitive. A concept closely related to period is the frequency of an event. For example, if you get a paycheck twice a month, the frequency of payment is two per month and the period between checks is half a month. **Frequency** f is defined to be the number of events per unit time. For periodic motion, frequency is the number of oscillations per unit time. The relationship between frequency and period is

$$f = \frac{1}{T}. \tag{16.8}$$

The SI unit for frequency is the *cycle per second*, which is defined to be a *hertz* (Hz):

$$1 \text{ Hz} = 1 \frac{\text{cycle}}{\text{s}} \text{ or } 1 \text{ Hz} = \frac{1}{\text{s}} \tag{16.9}$$

A cycle is one complete oscillation. Note that a vibration can be a single or multiple event, whereas oscillations are usually repetitive for a significant number of cycles.

EXAMPLE 16.3

Determine the Frequency of Two Oscillations: Medical Ultrasound and the Period of Middle C

We can use the formulas presented in this module to determine both the frequency based on known oscillations and the oscillation based on a known frequency. Let's try one example of each. (a) A medical imaging device produces ultrasound by oscillating with a period of 0.400 µs. What is the frequency of this oscillation? (b) The frequency of middle C on a typical musical instrument is 264 Hz. What is the time for one complete oscillation?

Strategy

Both questions (a) and (b) can be answered using the relationship between period and frequency. In question (a), the period T is given and we are asked to find frequency f. In question (b), the frequency f is given and we are asked to find the period T.

Solution a

1. Substitute $0.400\ \mu\text{s}$ for T in $f = \frac{1}{T}$:

$$f = \frac{1}{T} = \frac{1}{0.400 \times 10^{-6}\ \text{s}}. \tag{16.10}$$

Solve to find

$$f = 2.50 \times 10^{6}\ \text{Hz}. \tag{16.11}$$

Discussion a

The frequency of sound found in (a) is much higher than the highest frequency that humans can hear and, therefore, is called ultrasound. Appropriate oscillations at this frequency generate ultrasound used for noninvasive medical diagnoses, such as observations of a fetus in the womb.

Solution b

1. Identify the known values:
   The time for one complete oscillation is the period T:

$$f = \frac{1}{T}. \quad (16.12)$$

2. Solve for T:

$$T = \frac{1}{f}. \quad (16.13)$$

3. Substitute the given value for the frequency into the resulting expression:

$$T = \frac{1}{f} = \frac{1}{264\text{ Hz}} = \frac{1}{264\text{ cycles/s}} = 3.79 \times 10^{-3}\text{ s} = 3.79\text{ ms}. \quad (16.14)$$

Discussion b

The period found in (b) is the time per cycle, but this value is often quoted as simply the time in convenient units (ms or milliseconds in this case).

CHECK YOUR UNDERSTANDING

Identify an event in your life (such as receiving a paycheck) that occurs regularly. Identify both the period and frequency of this event.

Solution

I visit my parents for dinner every other Sunday. The frequency of my visits is 26 per calendar year. The period is two weeks.

16.3 Simple Harmonic Motion: A Special Periodic Motion

LEARNING OBJECTIVES

By the end of this section, you will be able to:

- Describe a simple harmonic oscillator.
- Explain the link between simple harmonic motion and waves.

The oscillations of a system in which the net force can be described by Hooke's law are of special importance, because they are very common. They are also the simplest oscillatory systems. **Simple Harmonic Motion** (SHM) is the name given to oscillatory motion for a system where the net force can be described by Hooke's law, and such a system is called a **simple harmonic oscillator**. If the net force can be described by Hooke's law and there is no *damping* (by friction or other non-conservative forces), then a simple harmonic oscillator will oscillate with equal displacement on either side of the equilibrium position, as shown for an object on a spring in Figure 16.9. The maximum displacement from equilibrium is called the **amplitude** X. The units for amplitude and displacement are the same, but depend on the type of oscillation. For the object on the spring, the units of amplitude and displacement are meters; whereas for sound oscillations, they have units of pressure (and other types of oscillations have yet other units). Because amplitude is the maximum displacement, it is related to the energy in the oscillation.

TAKE-HOME EXPERIMENT: SHM AND THE MARBLE

Find a bowl or basin that is shaped like a hemisphere on the inside. Place a marble inside the bowl and tilt the bowl periodically so the marble rolls from the bottom of the bowl to equally high points on the sides of the bowl. Get a feel for the force required to maintain this periodic motion. What is the restoring force and what role does the force you apply play in the simple harmonic motion (SHM) of the marble?

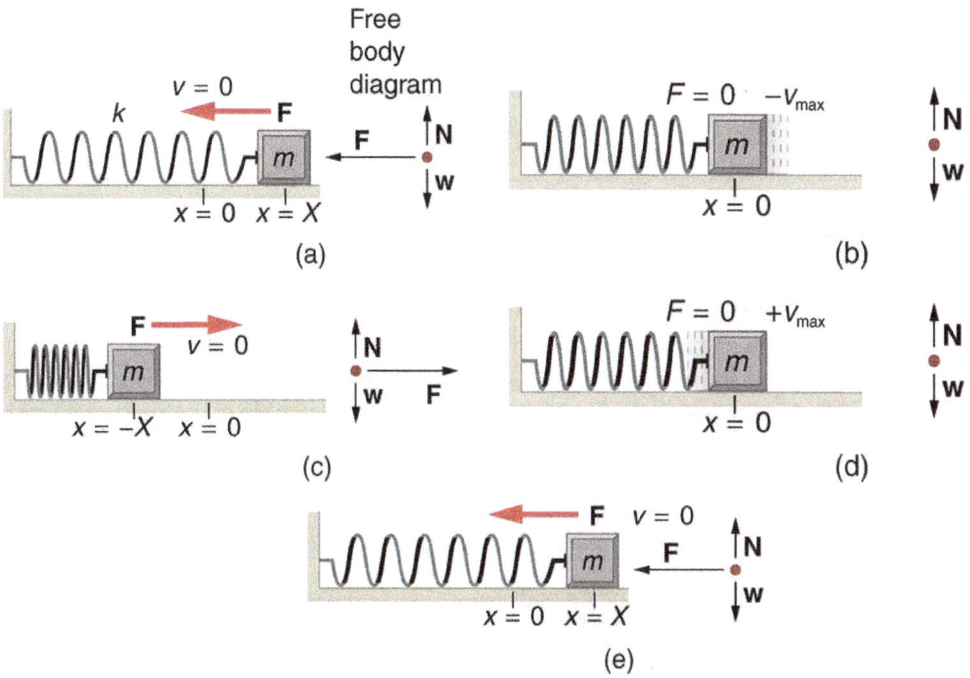

FIGURE 16.9 An object attached to a spring sliding on a frictionless surface is an uncomplicated simple harmonic oscillator. When displaced from equilibrium, the object performs simple harmonic motion that has an amplitude X and a period T. The object's maximum speed occurs as it passes through equilibrium. The stiffer the spring is, the smaller the period T. The greater the mass of the object is, the greater the period T.

What is so significant about simple harmonic motion? One special thing is that the period T and frequency f of a simple harmonic oscillator are independent of amplitude. The string of a guitar, for example, will oscillate with the same frequency whether plucked gently or hard. Because the period is constant, a simple harmonic oscillator can be used as a clock.

Two important factors do affect the period of a simple harmonic oscillator. The period is related to how stiff the system is. A very stiff object has a large force constant k, which causes the system to have a smaller period. For example, you can adjust a diving board's stiffness—the stiffer it is, the faster it vibrates, and the shorter its period. Period also depends on the mass of the oscillating system. The more massive the system is, the longer the period. For example, a heavy person on a diving board bounces up and down more slowly than a light one.

In fact, the mass m and the force constant k are the *only* factors that affect the period and frequency of simple harmonic motion.

PERIOD OF SIMPLE HARMONIC OSCILLATOR

The *period of a simple harmonic oscillator* is given by

$$T = 2\pi\sqrt{\frac{m}{k}} \qquad (16.15)$$

and, because $f = 1/T$, the *frequency of a simple harmonic oscillator* is

$$f = \frac{1}{2\pi}\sqrt{\frac{k}{m}}. \qquad (16.16)$$

Note that neither T nor f has any dependence on amplitude.

TAKE-HOME EXPERIMENT: MASS AND RULER OSCILLATIONS

Find two identical wooden or plastic rulers. Tape one end of each ruler firmly to the edge of a table so that the length of each ruler that protrudes from the table is the same. On the free end of one ruler tape a heavy object such as a few large coins. Pluck the ends of the rulers at the same time and observe which one undergoes more cycles in a time period, and measure the period of oscillation of each of the rulers.

EXAMPLE 16.4

Calculate the Frequency and Period of Oscillations: Bad Shock Absorbers in a Car

If the shock absorbers in a car go bad, then the car will oscillate at the least provocation, such as when going over bumps in the road and after stopping (See Figure 16.10). Calculate the frequency and period of these oscillations for such a car if the car's mass (including its load) is 900 kg and the force constant (k) of the suspension system is 6.53×10^4 N/m.

Strategy

The frequency of the car's oscillations will be that of a simple harmonic oscillator as given in the equation $f = \frac{1}{2\pi}\sqrt{\frac{k}{m}}$. The mass and the force constant are both given.

Solution

1. Enter the known values of k and m:

$$f = \frac{1}{2\pi}\sqrt{\frac{k}{m}} = \frac{1}{2\pi}\sqrt{\frac{6.53 \times 10^4\text{ N/m}}{900\text{ kg}}}. \quad (16.17)$$

2. Calculate the frequency:

$$\frac{1}{2\pi}\sqrt{72.6/\text{s}^2} = 1.3656/\text{s}^1 \approx 1.36/\text{s}^1 = 1.36\text{Hz}. \quad (16.18)$$

3. You could use $T = 2\pi\sqrt{\frac{m}{k}}$ to calculate the period, but it is simpler to use the relationship $T = 1/f$ and substitute the value just found for f:

$$T = \frac{1}{f} = \frac{1}{1.356\text{ Hz}} = 0.738\text{ s}. \quad (16.19)$$

Discussion

The values of T and f both seem about right for a bouncing car. You can observe these oscillations if you push down hard on the end of a car and let go.

The Link between Simple Harmonic Motion and Waves

If a time-exposure photograph of the bouncing car were taken as it drove by, the headlight would make a wavelike streak, as shown in Figure 16.10. Similarly, Figure 16.11 shows an object bouncing on a spring as it leaves a wavelike "trace" of its position on a moving strip of paper. Both waves are sine functions. All simple harmonic motion is intimately related to sine and cosine waves.

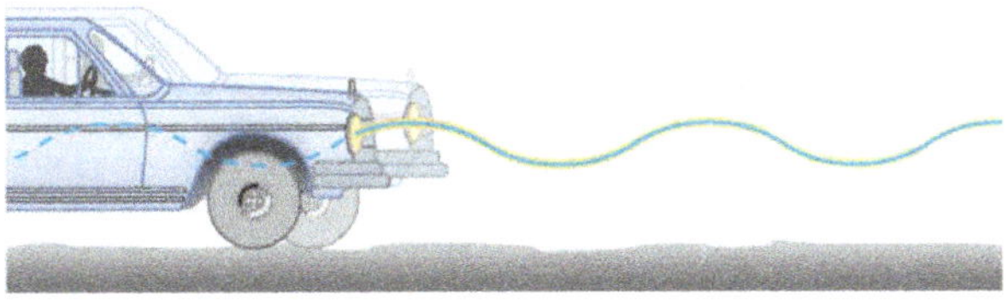

FIGURE 16.10 The bouncing car makes a wavelike motion. If the restoring force in the suspension system can be described only by Hooke's law, then the wave is a sine function. (The wave is the trace produced by the headlight as the car moves to the right.)

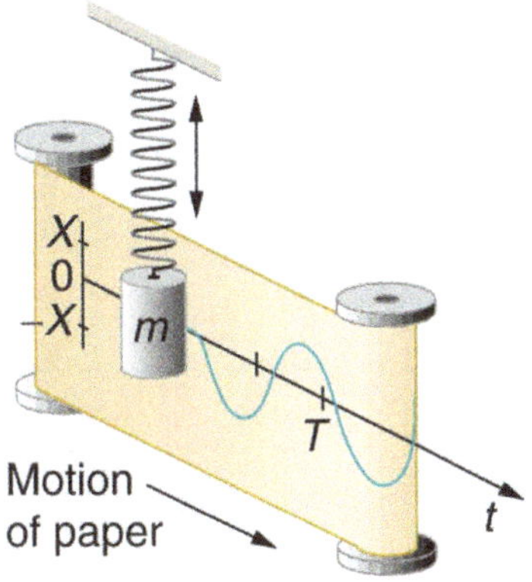

FIGURE 16.11 The vertical position of an object bouncing on a spring is recorded on a strip of moving paper, leaving a sine wave.

The displacement as a function of time t in any simple harmonic motion—that is, one in which the net restoring force can be described by Hooke's law, is given by

$$x(t)= X\cos\frac{2\pi t}{T}, \tag{16.20}$$

where X is amplitude. At $t = 0$, the initial position is $x_0 = X$, and the displacement oscillates back and forth with a period T. (When $t = T$, we get $x = X$ again because $\cos 2\pi = 1$.). Furthermore, from this expression for x, the velocity v as a function of time is given by:

$$v(t)= -v_{\text{max}}\sin\left(\frac{2\pi t}{T}\right), \tag{16.21}$$

where $v_{\text{max}} = 2\pi X/T = X\sqrt{k/m}$. The object has zero velocity at maximum displacement—for example, $v = 0$ when $t = 0$, and at that time $x = X$. The minus sign in the first equation for $v(t)$ gives the correct direction for the velocity. Just after the start of the motion, for instance, the velocity is negative because the system is moving back toward the equilibrium point. Finally, we can get an expression for acceleration using Newton's second law. [Then we have $x(t)$, $v(t)$, t, and $a(t)$, the quantities needed for kinematics and a description of simple harmonic motion.] According to Newton's second law, the acceleration is $a = F/m = kx/m$. So, $a(t)$ is also a cosine function:

$$a(t)= -\frac{kX}{m}\cos\frac{2\pi t}{T}. \tag{16.22}$$

Hence, $a(t)$ is directly proportional to and in the opposite direction to $x(t)$.

Figure 16.12 shows the simple harmonic motion of an object on a spring and presents graphs of $x(t)$, $v(t)$, and $a(t)$ versus time.

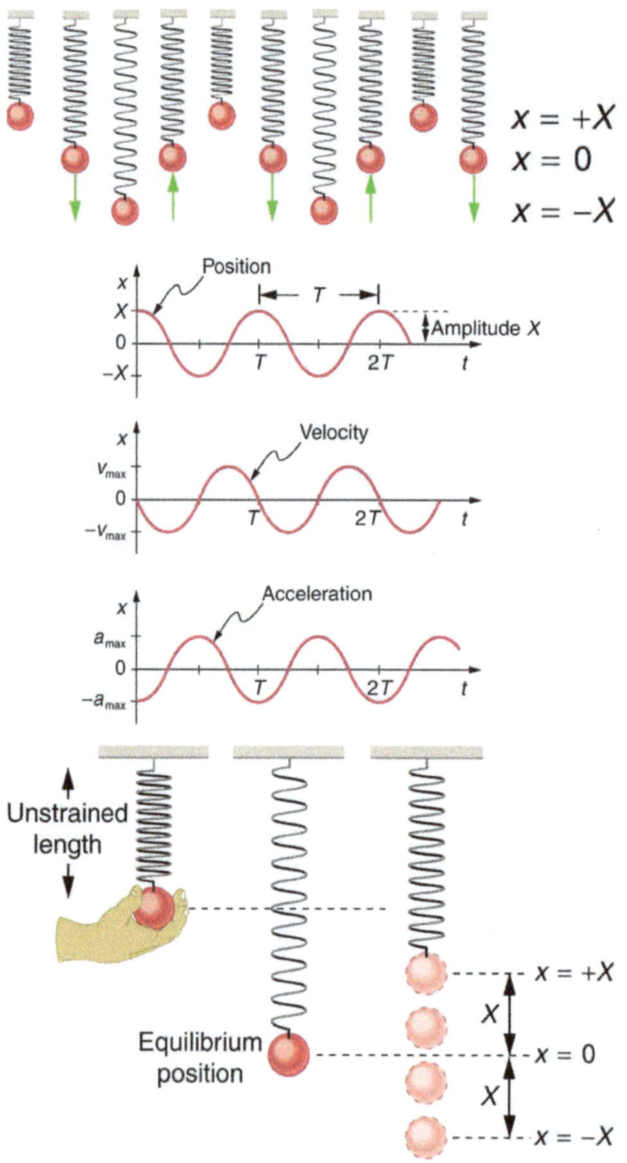

FIGURE 16.12 Graphs of $x(t)$, $v(t)$, and $a(t)$ versus t for the motion of an object on a spring. The net force on the object can be described by Hooke's law, and so the object undergoes simple harmonic motion. Note that the initial position has the vertical displacement at its maximum value X; v is initially zero and then negative as the object moves down; and the initial acceleration is negative, back toward the equilibrium position and becomes zero at that point.

The most important point here is that these equations are mathematically straightforward and are valid for all simple harmonic motion. They are very useful in visualizing waves associated with simple harmonic motion, including visualizing how waves add with one another.

CHECK YOUR UNDERSTANDING

Suppose you pluck a banjo string. You hear a single note that starts out loud and slowly quiets over time. Describe what happens to the sound waves in terms of period, frequency and amplitude as the sound decreases in volume.

Solution

Frequency and period remain essentially unchanged. Only amplitude decreases as volume decreases.

CHECK YOUR UNDERSTANDING

A babysitter is pushing a child on a swing. At the point where the swing reaches X, where would the corresponding point on a wave of this motion be located?

Solution

X is the maximum deformation, which corresponds to the amplitude of the wave. The point on the wave would either be at the very top or the very bottom of the curve.

PHET EXPLORATIONS

Masses and Springs

A realistic mass and spring laboratory. Hang masses from springs and adjust the spring stiffness and damping. You can even slow time. Transport the lab to different planets. A chart shows the kinetic, potential, and thermal energy for each spring.

Click to view content (https://openstax.org/books/college-physics-ap-courses-2e/pages/16-3-simple-harmonic-motion-a-special-periodic-motion)

16.4 The Simple Pendulum

LEARNING OBJECTIVES

By the end of this section, you will be able to:

- Measure acceleration due to gravity.

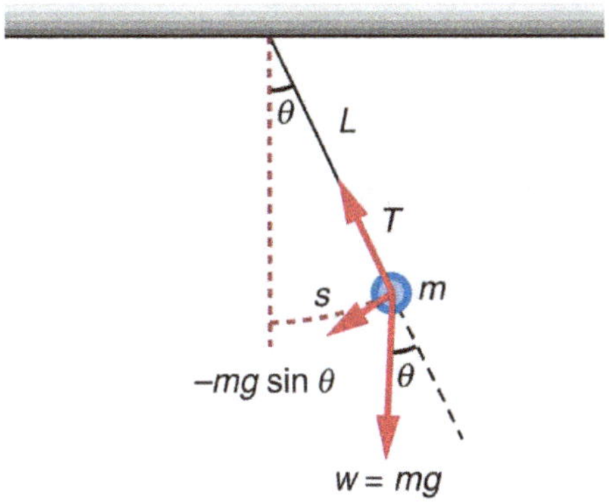

FIGURE 16.13 A simple pendulum has a small-diameter bob and a string that has a very small mass but is strong enough not to stretch appreciably. The linear displacement from equilibrium is s, the length of the arc. Also shown are the forces on the bob, which result in a net force of $-mg\ \sin\theta$ toward the equilibrium position—that is, a restoring force.

Pendulums are in common usage. Some have crucial uses, such as in clocks; some are for fun, such as a child's swing; and some are just there, such as the sinker on a fishing line. For small displacements, a pendulum is a simple harmonic oscillator. A **simple pendulum** is defined to have an object that has a small mass, also known as the pendulum bob, which is suspended from a light wire or string, such as shown in Figure 16.13. Exploring the simple pendulum a bit further, we can discover the conditions under which it performs simple harmonic motion, and we can derive an interesting expression for its period.

We begin by defining the displacement to be the arc length s. We see from Figure 16.13 that the net force on the bob is tangent to the arc and equals $-mg\ \sin\ \theta$. (The weight mg has components $mg\ \cos\ \theta$ along the string and $mg\ \sin\ \theta$ tangent to the arc.) Tension in the string exactly cancels the component $mg\ \cos\ \theta$ parallel to the string. This leaves a *net* restoring force back toward the equilibrium position at $\theta = 0$.

Now, if we can show that the restoring force is directly proportional to the displacement, then we have a simple harmonic oscillator. In trying to determine if we have a simple harmonic oscillator, we should note that for small angles (less than about 15°), $\sin\ \theta \approx\ \theta$ ($\sin\ \theta$ and θ differ by about 1% or less at smaller angles). Thus, for angles less than about 15°, the restoring force F is

$$F \approx -mg\theta. \qquad 16.23$$

The displacement s is directly proportional to θ. When θ is expressed in radians, the arc length in a circle is related to its radius (L in this instance) by:

$$s = L\theta, \tag{16.24}$$

so that

$$\theta = \frac{s}{L}. \tag{16.25}$$

For small angles, then, the expression for the restoring force is:

$$F \approx -\frac{mg}{L}s \tag{16.26}$$

This expression is of the form:

$$F = -kx, \tag{16.27}$$

where the force constant is given by $k = mg/L$ and the displacement is given by $x = s$. For angles less than about $15°$, the restoring force is directly proportional to the displacement, and the simple pendulum is a simple harmonic oscillator.

Using this equation, we can find the period of a pendulum for amplitudes less than about $15°$. For the simple pendulum:

$$T = 2\pi\sqrt{\frac{m}{k}} = 2\pi\sqrt{\frac{m}{mg/L}}. \tag{16.28}$$

Thus,

$$T = 2\pi\sqrt{\frac{L}{g}} \tag{16.29}$$

for the period of a simple pendulum. This result is interesting because of its simplicity. The only things that affect the period of a simple pendulum are its length and the acceleration due to gravity. The period is completely independent of other factors, such as mass. As with simple harmonic oscillators, the period T for a pendulum is nearly independent of amplitude, especially if θ is less than about $15°$. Even simple pendulum clocks can be finely adjusted and accurate.

Note the dependence of T on g. If the length of a pendulum is precisely known, it can actually be used to measure the acceleration due to gravity. Consider the following example.

EXAMPLE 16.5

Measuring Acceleration due to Gravity: The Period of a Pendulum

What is the acceleration due to gravity in a region where a simple pendulum having a length 75.000 cm has a period of 1.7357 s?

Strategy

We are asked to find g given the period T and the length L of a pendulum. We can solve $T = 2\pi\sqrt{\frac{L}{g}}$ for g, assuming only that the angle of deflection is less than $15°$.

Solution

1. Square $T = 2\pi\sqrt{\frac{L}{g}}$ and solve for g:

$$g = 4\pi^2\frac{L}{T^2}. \tag{16.30}$$

2. Substitute known values into the new equation:

$$g = 4\pi^2\frac{0.75000\text{ m}}{(1.7357\text{ s})^2}. \tag{16.31}$$

3. Calculate to find g:

$$g = 9.8281\ \text{m/s}^2. \tag{16.32}$$

Discussion

This method for determining g can be very accurate. This is why length and period are given to five digits in this example. For the precision of the approximation $\sin\theta \approx \theta$ to be better than the precision of the pendulum length and period, the maximum displacement angle should be kept below about $0.5°$.

MAKING CAREER CONNECTIONS

Knowing g can be important in geological exploration; for example, a map of g over large geographical regions aids the study of plate tectonics and helps in the search for oil fields and large mineral deposits.

TAKE HOME EXPERIMENT: DETERMINING g

Use a simple pendulum to determine the acceleration due to gravity g in your own locale. Cut a piece of a string or dental floss so that it is about 1 m long. Attach a small object of high density to the end of the string (for example, a metal nut or a car key). Starting at an angle of less than $10°$, allow the pendulum to swing and measure the pendulum's period for 10 oscillations using a stopwatch. Calculate g. How accurate is this measurement? How might it be improved?

CHECK YOUR UNDERSTANDING

An engineer builds two simple pendula. Both are suspended from small wires secured to the ceiling of a room. Each pendulum hovers 2 cm above the floor. Pendulum 1 has a bob with a mass of $10\ \text{kg}$. Pendulum 2 has a bob with a mass of $100\ \text{kg}$. Describe how the motion of the pendula will differ if the bobs are both displaced by $12°$.

Solution

The movement of the pendula will not differ at all because the mass of the bob has no effect on the motion of a simple pendulum. The pendula are only affected by the period (which is related to the pendulum's length) and by the acceleration due to gravity.

PHET EXPLORATIONS

Pendulum Lab

Play with one or two pendulums and discover how the period of a simple pendulum depends on the length of the string, the mass of the pendulum bob, and the amplitude of the swing. It's easy to measure the period using the photogate timer. You can vary friction and the strength of gravity. Use the pendulum to find the value of g on planet X. Notice the anharmonic behavior at large amplitude.

Click to view content (https://openstax.org/books/college-physics-ap-courses-2e/pages/16-4-the-simple-pendulum)

16.5 Energy and the Simple Harmonic Oscillator

LEARNING OBJECTIVES

By the end of this section, you will be able to:

- Determine the maximum speed of an oscillating system.

To study the energy of a simple harmonic oscillator, we first consider all the forms of energy it can have We know from Hooke's Law: Stress and Strain Revisited that the energy stored in the deformation of a simple harmonic oscillator is a form of potential energy given by:

$$PE_{el} = \frac{1}{2}kx^2. \tag{16.33}$$

Because a simple harmonic oscillator has no dissipative forces, the other important form of energy is kinetic energy KE. Conservation of energy for these two forms is:

$$KE + PE_{el} = \text{constant} \tag{16.34}$$

or

$$\frac{1}{2}mv^2 + \frac{1}{2}kx^2 = \text{constant}. \tag{16.35}$$

This statement of conservation of energy is valid for *all* simple harmonic oscillators, including ones where the gravitational force plays a role

Namely, for a simple pendulum we replace the velocity with $v = L\omega$, the spring constant with $k = mg/L$, and the displacement term with $x = L\theta$. Thus

$$\frac{1}{2}mL^2\omega^2 + \frac{1}{2}mgL\theta^2 = \text{constant}. \tag{16.36}$$

In the case of undamped simple harmonic motion, the energy oscillates back and forth between kinetic and potential, going completely from one to the other as the system oscillates. So for the simple example of an object on a frictionless surface attached to a spring, as shown again in Figure 16.14, the motion starts with all of the energy stored in the spring. As the object starts to move, the elastic potential energy is converted to kinetic energy, becoming entirely kinetic energy at the equilibrium position. It is then converted back into elastic potential energy by the spring, the velocity becomes zero when the kinetic energy is completely converted, and so on. This concept provides extra insight here and in later applications of simple harmonic motion, such as alternating current circuits.

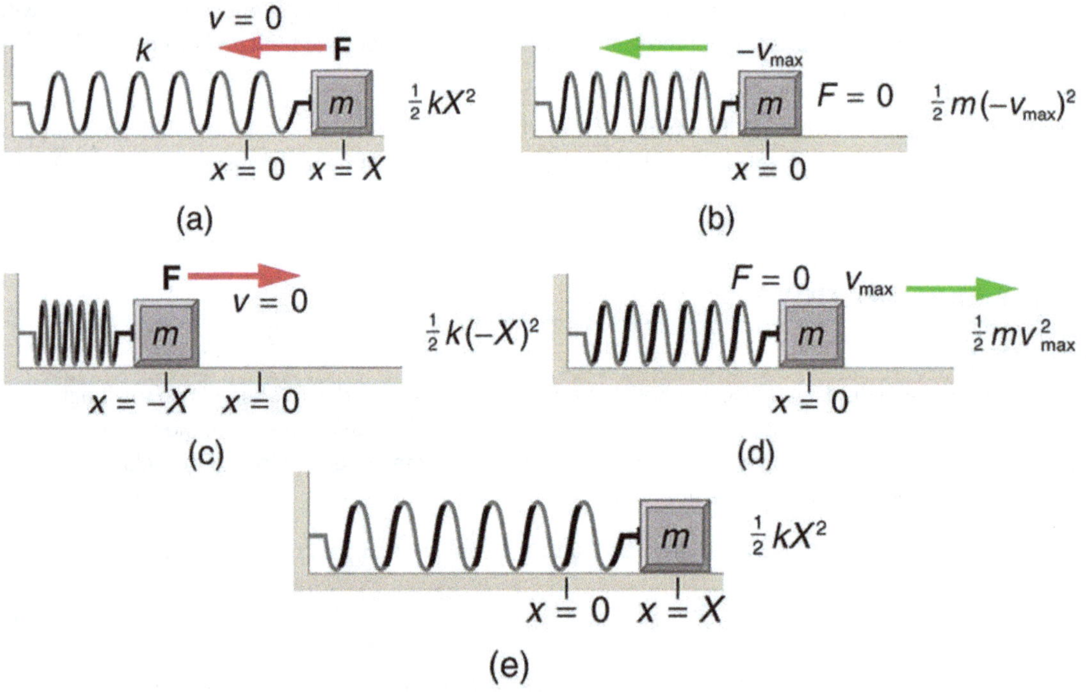

FIGURE 16.14 The transformation of energy in simple harmonic motion is illustrated for an object attached to a spring on a frictionless surface.

The conservation of energy principle can be used to derive an expression for velocity v. If we start our simple harmonic motion with zero velocity and maximum displacement ($x = X$), then the total energy is

$$\frac{1}{2}kX^2. \tag{16.37}$$

This total energy is constant and is shifted back and forth between kinetic energy and potential energy, at most times being shared by each. The conservation of energy for this system in equation form is thus:

$$\frac{1}{2}mv^2 + \frac{1}{2}kx^2 = \frac{1}{2}kX^2. \tag{16.38}$$

Solving this equation for v yields:

$$v = \pm\sqrt{\frac{k}{m}\left(X^2 - x^2\right)}. \tag{16.39}$$

Manipulating this expression algebraically gives:

$$v = \pm\sqrt{\frac{k}{m}}X\sqrt{1 - \frac{x^2}{X^2}} \tag{16.40}$$

and so

$$v = \pm v_{\text{max}}\sqrt{1 - \frac{x^2}{X^2}}, \tag{16.41}$$

where

$$v_{\text{max}} = \sqrt{\frac{k}{m}}X. \tag{16.42}$$

From this expression, we see that the velocity is a maximum (v_{max}) at $x = 0$, as stated earlier in $v(t) = -v_{\text{max}} \sin \frac{2\pi t}{T}$. Notice that the maximum velocity depends on three factors. Maximum velocity is directly proportional to amplitude. As you might guess, the greater the maximum displacement the greater the maximum velocity. Maximum velocity is also greater for stiffer systems, because they exert greater force for the same displacement. This observation is seen in the expression for v_{max}; it is proportional to the square root of the force constant k. Finally, the maximum velocity is smaller for objects that have larger masses, because the maximum velocity is inversely proportional to the square root of m. For a given force, objects that have large masses accelerate more slowly.

A similar calculation for the simple pendulum produces a similar result, namely:

$$\omega_{\text{max}} = \sqrt{\frac{g}{L}}\theta_{\text{max}}. \tag{16.43}$$

EXAMPLE 16.6

Determine the Maximum Speed of an Oscillating System: A Bumpy Road

Suppose that a car is 900 kg and has a suspension system that has a force constant $k = 6.53 \times 10^4$ N/m. The car hits a bump and bounces with an amplitude of 0.100 m. What is its maximum vertical velocity if you assume no damping occurs?

Strategy

We can use the expression for v_{max} given in $v_{\text{max}} = \sqrt{\frac{k}{m}}X$ to determine the maximum vertical velocity. The variables m and k are given in the problem statement, and the maximum displacement X is 0.100 m.

Solution

1. Identify known.
2. Substitute known values into $v_{\text{max}} = \sqrt{\frac{k}{m}}X$:

$$v_{\text{max}} = \sqrt{\frac{6.53 \times 10^4 \text{ N/m}}{900 \text{ kg}}}(0.100 \text{ m}). \quad 16.44$$

3. Calculate to find $v_{\text{max}} = 0.852 \text{ m/s}$.

Discussion

This answer seems reasonable for a bouncing car. There are other ways to use conservation of energy to find v_{max}. We could use it directly, as was done in the example featured in Hooke's Law: Stress and Strain Revisited.

The small vertical displacement y of an oscillating simple pendulum, starting from its equilibrium position, is given as

$$y(t) = a \sin \omega t, \quad 16.45$$

where a is the amplitude, ω is the angular velocity and t is the time taken. Substituting $\omega = \frac{2\pi}{T}$, we have

$$y(t) = a \sin\left(\frac{2\pi t}{T}\right). \quad 16.46$$

Thus, the displacement of pendulum is a function of time as shown above.

Also the velocity of the pendulum is given by

$$v(t) = \frac{2a\pi}{T} \cos\left(\frac{2\pi t}{T}\right), \quad 16.47$$

so the motion of the pendulum is a function of time.

CHECK YOUR UNDERSTANDING

Why does it hurt more if your hand is snapped with a ruler than with a loose spring, even if the displacement of each system is equal?

Solution

The ruler is a stiffer system, which carries greater force for the same amount of displacement. The ruler snaps your hand with greater force, which hurts more.

CHECK YOUR UNDERSTANDING

You are observing a simple harmonic oscillator. Identify one way you could decrease the maximum velocity of the system.

Solution

You could increase the mass of the object that is oscillating.

16.6 Uniform Circular Motion and Simple Harmonic Motion

LEARNING OBJECTIVES

By the end of this section, you will be able to:

- Compare simple harmonic motion with uniform circular motion.

FIGURE 16.15 The horses on this merry-go-round exhibit uniform circular motion. (credit: Wonderlane, Flickr)

There is an easy way to produce simple harmonic motion by using uniform circular motion. Figure 16.16 shows one way of using this method. A ball is attached to a uniformly rotating vertical turntable, and its shadow is projected on the floor as shown. The shadow undergoes simple harmonic motion. Hooke's law usually describes uniform circular motions (ω constant) rather than systems that have large visible displacements. So observing the projection of uniform circular motion, as in Figure 16.16, is often easier than observing a precise large-scale simple harmonic oscillator. If studied in sufficient depth, simple harmonic motion produced in this manner can give considerable insight into many aspects of oscillations and waves and is very useful mathematically. In our brief treatment, we shall indicate some of the major features of this relationship and how they might be useful.

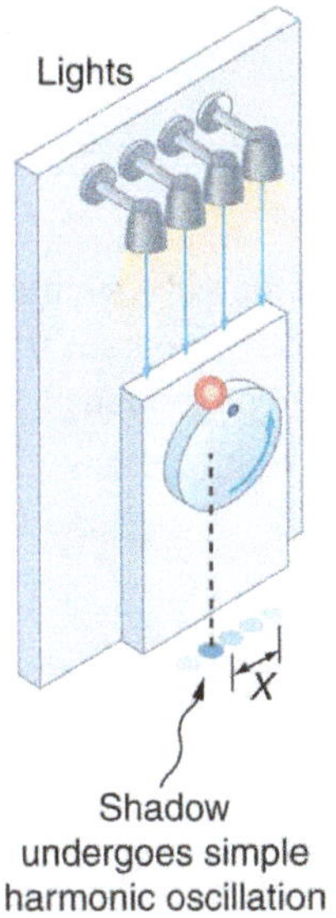

FIGURE 16.16 The shadow of a ball rotating at constant angular velocity ω on a turntable goes back and forth in precise simple harmonic motion.

Figure 16.17 shows the basic relationship between uniform circular motion and simple harmonic motion. The point P travels around the circle at constant angular velocity ω. The point P is analogous to an object on the merry-go-round. The projection of the position of P onto a fixed axis undergoes simple harmonic motion and is analogous to the shadow of the object. At the time shown in the figure, the projection has position x and moves to the left with velocity v. The velocity of the point P around the circle equals $\bar{v}_{\text{max}}$ .The projection of $\bar{v}_{\text{max}}$ on the x-axis is the velocity v of the simple harmonic motion along the x-axis.

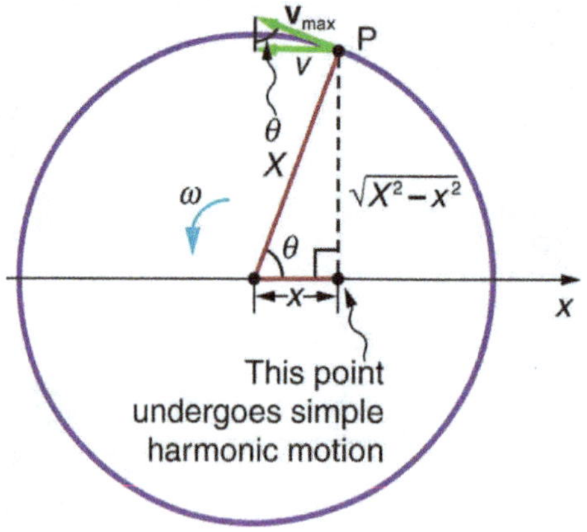

FIGURE 16.17 A point P moving on a circular path with a constant angular velocity ω is undergoing uniform circular motion. Its projection on the x-axis undergoes simple harmonic motion. Also shown is the velocity of this point around the circle, $\bar{v}_{max}$, and its projection, which is v. Note that these velocities form a similar triangle to the displacement triangle.

To see that the projection undergoes simple harmonic motion, note that its position x is given by

$$x = X \cos \theta, \quad 16.48$$

where $\theta = \omega t$, ω is the constant angular velocity, and X is the radius of the circular path. Thus,

$$x = X \cos \omega t. \quad 16.49$$

The angular velocity ω is in radians per unit time; in this case 2π radians is the time for one revolution T. That is, $\omega = 2\pi/T$. Substituting this expression for ω, we see that the position x is given by:

$$x(t)= \cos\left(\frac{2\pi t}{T}\right). \quad 16.50$$

This expression is the same one we had for the position of a simple harmonic oscillator in Simple Harmonic Motion: A Special Periodic Motion. If we make a graph of position versus time as in Figure 16.18, we see again the wavelike character (typical of simple harmonic motion) of the projection of uniform circular motion onto the x-axis.

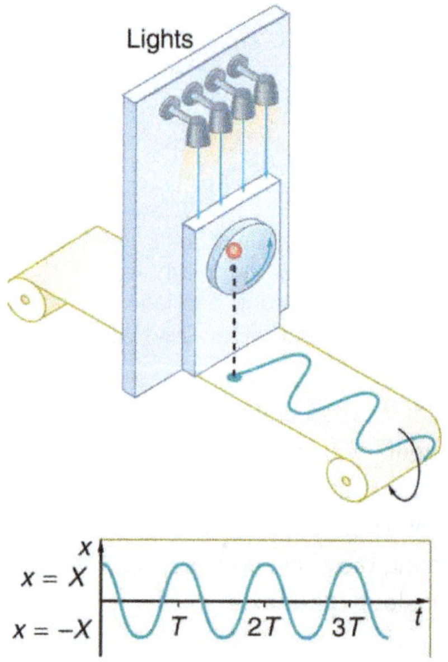

FIGURE 16.18 The position of the projection of uniform circular motion performs simple harmonic motion, as this wavelike graph of x versus t indicates.

Now let us use Figure 16.17 to do some further analysis of uniform circular motion as it relates to simple harmonic motion. The triangle formed by the velocities in the figure and the triangle formed by the displacements (X, x, and $\sqrt{X^2 - x^2}$) are similar right triangles. Taking ratios of similar sides, we see that

$$\frac{v}{v_{\text{max}}} = \frac{\sqrt{X^2 - x^2}}{X} = \sqrt{1 - \frac{x^2}{X^2}}. \quad 16.51$$

We can solve this equation for the speed v or

$$v = v_{\text{max}}\sqrt{1 - \frac{x^2}{X^2}}. \quad 16.52$$

This expression for the speed of a simple harmonic oscillator is exactly the same as the equation obtained from conservation of energy considerations in Energy and the Simple Harmonic Oscillator.You can begin to see that it is possible to get all of the characteristics of simple harmonic motion from an analysis of the projection of uniform circular motion.

Finally, let us consider the period T of the motion of the projection. This period is the time it takes the point P to complete one revolution. That time is the circumference of the circle $2\pi X$ divided by the velocity around the circle, v_{max}. Thus, the period T is

$$T = \frac{2\pi \text{X}}{v_{\text{max}}}. \quad 16.53$$

We know from conservation of energy considerations that

$$v_{\text{max}} = \sqrt{\frac{k}{m}}X. \quad 16.54$$

Solving this equation for X/v_{max} gives

$$\frac{X}{v_{\text{max}}} = \sqrt{\frac{m}{k}}. \quad 16.55$$

Substituting this expression into the equation for T yields

$$T = 2\pi\sqrt{\frac{m}{k}}. \quad 16.56$$

Thus, the period of the motion is the same as for a simple harmonic oscillator. We have determined the period for any simple harmonic oscillator using the relationship between uniform circular motion and simple harmonic motion.

Some modules occasionally refer to the connection between uniform circular motion and simple harmonic motion. Moreover, if you carry your study of physics and its applications to greater depths, you will find this relationship useful. It can, for example, help to analyze how waves add when they are superimposed.

CHECK YOUR UNDERSTANDING

Identify an object that undergoes uniform circular motion. Describe how you could trace the simple harmonic motion of this object as a wave.

Solution

A record player undergoes uniform circular motion. You could attach dowel rod to one point on the outside edge of the turntable and attach a pen to the other end of the dowel. As the record player turns, the pen will move. You can drag a long piece of paper under the pen, capturing its motion as a wave.

16.7 Damped Harmonic Motion

LEARNING OBJECTIVES

By the end of this section, you will be able to:

- Compare and discuss underdamped and overdamped oscillating systems.
- Explain critically damped system.

FIGURE 16.19 In order to counteract dampening forces, this mom needs to keep pushing the swing. (credit: Erik A. Johnson, Flickr)

A guitar string stops oscillating a few seconds after being plucked. To keep a child happy on a swing, you must keep pushing. Although we can often make friction and other non-conservative forces negligibly small, completely undamped motion is rare. In fact, we may even want to damp oscillations, such as with car shock absorbers.

For a system that has a small amount of damping, the period and frequency are nearly the same as for simple harmonic motion, but the amplitude gradually decreases as shown in Figure 16.20. This occurs because the non-conservative damping force removes energy from the system, usually in the form of thermal energy. In general, energy removal by non-conservative forces is described as

$$W_{\text{nc}} = \Delta(\text{KE} + \text{PE}), \tag{16.57}$$

where W_{nc} is work done by a non-conservative force (here the damping force). For a damped harmonic oscillator, W_{nc} is negative because it removes mechanical energy (KE + PE) from the system.

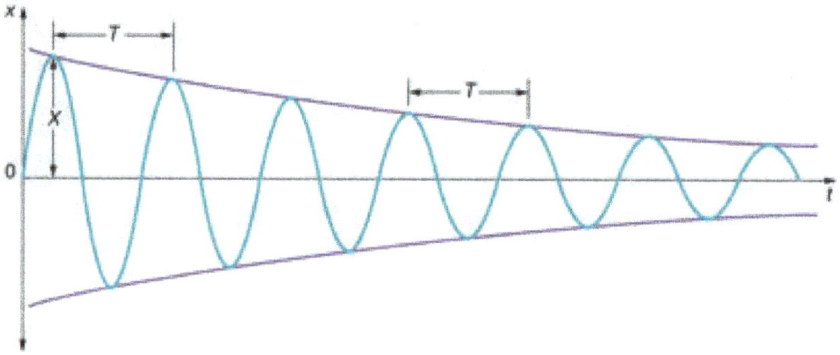

FIGURE 16.20 In this graph of displacement versus time for a harmonic oscillator with a small amount of damping, the amplitude slowly decreases, but the period and frequency are nearly the same as if the system were completely undamped.

If you gradually *increase* the amount of damping in a system, the period and frequency begin to be affected, because damping opposes and hence slows the back and forth motion. (The net force is smaller in both directions.) If there is very large damping, the system does not even oscillate—it slowly moves toward equilibrium. Figure 16.21 shows the displacement of a harmonic oscillator for different amounts of damping. When we want to damp out oscillations, such as in the suspension of a car, we may want the system to return to equilibrium as quickly as possible **Critical damping** is defined as the condition in which the damping of an oscillator results in it returning as quickly as possible to its equilibrium position The critically damped system may overshoot the equilibrium position, but if it does, it will do so only once. Critical damping is represented by Curve A in Figure 16.21. With less-than critical damping, the system will return to equilibrium faster but will overshoot and cross over one or more times. Such a system is **underdamped**; its displacement is represented by the curve in Figure 16.20. Curve B in Figure 16.21 represents an **overdamped** system. As with critical damping, it too may overshoot the equilibrium position, but will reach equilibrium over a longer period of time.

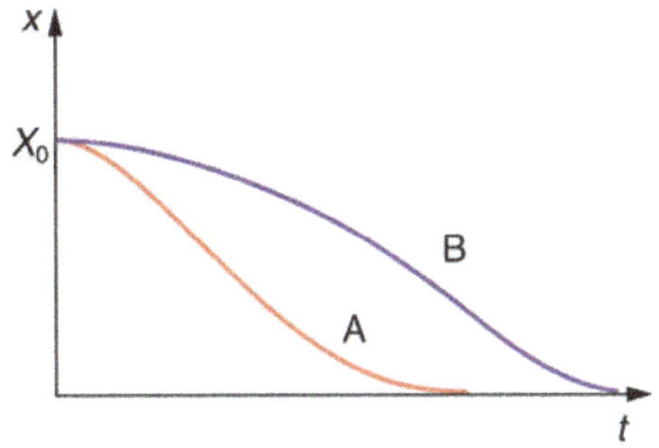

FIGURE 16.21 Displacement versus time for a critically damped harmonic oscillator (A) and an overdamped harmonic oscillator (B). The critically damped oscillator returns to equilibrium at $X = 0$ in the smallest time possible without overshooting.

Critical damping is often desired, because such a system returns to equilibrium rapidly and remains at equilibrium as well. In addition, a constant force applied to a critically damped system moves the system to a new equilibrium position in the shortest time possible without overshooting or oscillating about the new position. For example, when you stand on bathroom scales that have a needle gauge, the needle moves to its equilibrium position without oscillating. It would be quite inconvenient if the needle oscillated about the new equilibrium position for a long time before settling. Damping forces can vary greatly in character. Friction, for example, is sometimes independent of velocity (as assumed in most places in this text). But many damping forces depend on velocity—sometimes in complex ways, sometimes simply being proportional to velocity.

EXAMPLE 16.7

Damping an Oscillatory Motion: Friction on an Object Connected to a Spring

Damping oscillatory motion is important in many systems, and the ability to control the damping is even more so. This is generally attained using non-conservative forces such as the friction between surfaces, and viscosity for objects moving through fluids. The following example considers friction. Suppose a 0.200-kg object is connected to a spring as shown in Figure 16.22, but there is simple friction between the object and the surface, and the coefficient of friction μ_k is equal to 0.0800. (a) What is the frictional force between the surfaces? (b) What total distance does the object travel if it is released 0.100 m from equilibrium, starting at $v = 0$? The force constant of the spring is $k = 50.0 \text{ N/m}$.

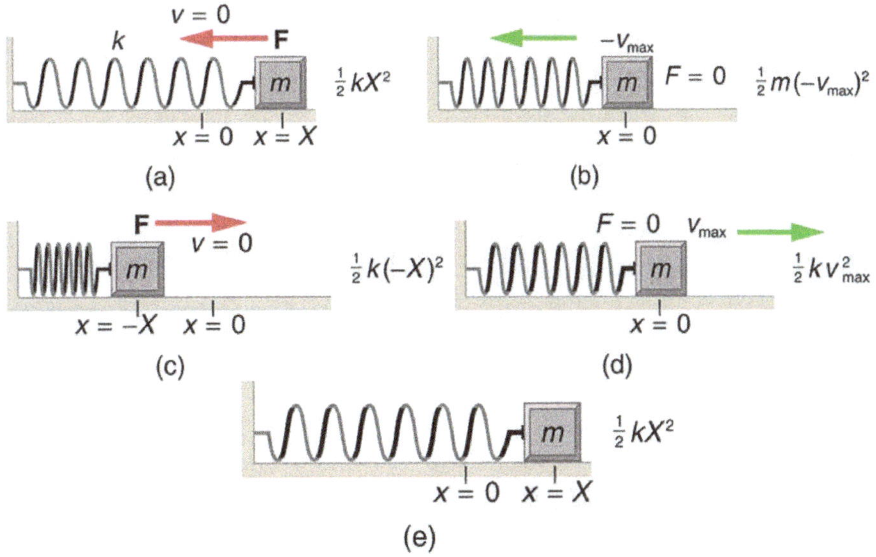

FIGURE 16.22 The transformation of energy in simple harmonic motion is illustrated for an object attached to a spring on a frictionless surface.

Strategy

This problem requires you to integrate your knowledge of various concepts regarding waves, oscillations, and damping. To solve an integrated concept problem, you must first identify the physical principles involved. Part (a) is about the frictional force. This is a topic involving the application of Newton's Laws. Part (b) requires an understanding of work and conservation of energy, as well as some understanding of horizontal oscillatory systems.

Now that we have identified the principles we must apply in order to solve the problems, we need to identify the knowns and unknowns for each part of the question, as well as the quantity that is constant in Part (a) and Part (b) of the question.

Solution a

1. Choose the proper equation: Friction is $f = \mu_k mg$.
2. Identify the known values.
3. Enter the known values into the equation:

$$f = (0.0800)(0.200\text{ kg})(9.80\text{ m/s}^2). \tag{16.58}$$

4. Calculate and convert units: $f = 0.157\text{ N}$.

Discussion a

The force here is small because the system and the coefficients are small.

Solution b

Identify the known:

- The system involves elastic potential energy as the spring compresses and expands, friction that is related to the work done, and the kinetic energy as the body speeds up and slows down.
- Energy is not conserved as the mass oscillates because friction is a non-conservative force.
- The motion is horizontal, so gravitational potential energy does not need to be considered.
- Because the motion starts from rest, the energy in the system is initially $\text{PE}_{\text{el,i}} = (1/2)kX^2$. This energy is removed by work done by friction $W_{\text{nc}} = -fd$, where d is the total distance traveled and $f = \mu_k mg$ is the force of friction. When the system stops moving, the friction force will balance the force exerted by the spring, so $\text{PE}_{\text{e1,f}} = (1/2)kx^2$ where x is the final position and is given by

$$\begin{aligned} F_{\text{el}} &= f \\ kx &= \mu_k mg. \\ x &= \frac{\mu_k mg}{k} \end{aligned} \tag{16.59}$$

1. By equating the work done to the energy removed, solve for the distance d.
2. The work done by the non-conservative forces equals the initial, stored elastic potential energy. Identify the correct equation to use:

$$\text{W}_{\text{nc}} = \Delta(\text{KE} + \text{PE}) = \text{PE}_{\text{el,f}} - \text{PE}_{\text{el,i}} = \frac{1}{2}k\left(\left(\frac{\mu_k mg}{k}\right)^2 - X^2\right). \tag{16.60}$$

3. Recall that $W_{\text{nc}} = -fd$.
4. Enter the friction as $f = \mu_k mg$ into $W_{\text{nc}} = -fd$, thus

$$W_{\text{nc}} = -\mu_k mgd. \tag{16.61}$$

5. Combine these two equations to find

$$\frac{1}{2}k\left(\left(\frac{\mu_k mg}{k}\right)^2 - X^2\right) = -\mu_k mgd. \tag{16.62}$$

6. Solve the equation for d:

$$d = \frac{k}{2\mu_k mg}\left(X^2 - \left(\frac{\mu_k mg}{k}\right)^2\right). \tag{16.63}$$

7. Enter the known values into the resulting equation:

$$d = \frac{50.0 \text{ N/m}}{2(0.0800)(0.200 \text{ kg})(9.80 \text{ m/s}^2)}\left((0.100 \text{ m})^2 - \left(\frac{(0.0800)(0.200 \text{ kg})(9.80 \text{ m/s}^2)}{50.0 \text{ N/m}}\right)^2\right). \quad 16.64$$

8. Calculate d and convert units:

$$d = 1.59 \text{ m}. \quad 16.65$$

Discussion b

This is the total distance traveled back and forth across $x = 0$, which is the undamped equilibrium position. The number of oscillations about the equilibrium position will be more than $d/X = (1.59 \text{ m})/(0.100 \text{ m}) = 15.9$ because the amplitude of the oscillations is decreasing with time. At the end of the motion, this system will not return to $x = 0$ for this type of damping force, because static friction will exceed the restoring force. This system is underdamped. In contrast, an overdamped system with a simple constant damping force would not cross the equilibrium position $x = 0$ a single time. For example, if this system had a damping force 20 times greater, it would only move 0.0484 m toward the equilibrium position from its original 0.100-m position.

This worked example illustrates how to apply problem-solving strategies to situations that integrate the different concepts you have learned. The first step is to identify the physical principles involved in the problem. The second step is to solve for the unknowns using familiar problem-solving strategies. These are found throughout the text, and many worked examples show how to use them for single topics. In this integrated concepts example, you can see how to apply them across several topics. You will find these techniques useful in applications of physics outside a physics course, such as in your profession, in other science disciplines, and in everyday life.

CHECK YOUR UNDERSTANDING

Why are completely undamped harmonic oscillators so rare?

Solution

Friction often comes into play whenever an object is moving. Friction causes damping in a harmonic oscillator.

CHECK YOUR UNDERSTANDING

Describe the difference between overdamping, underdamping, and critical damping.

Solution

An overdamped system moves slowly toward equilibrium. An underdamped system moves quickly to equilibrium, but will oscillate about the equilibrium point as it does so. A critically damped system moves as quickly as possible toward equilibrium without oscillating about the equilibrium.

16.8 Forced Oscillations and Resonance

LEARNING OBJECTIVES

By the end of this section, you will be able to:

- Observe resonance of a paddle ball on a string.
- Observe amplitude of a damped harmonic oscillator.

FIGURE 16.23 You can cause the strings in a piano to vibrate simply by producing sound waves from your voice. (credit: Matt Billings, Flickr)

Sit in front of a piano sometime and sing a loud brief note at it with the dampers off its strings. It will sing the same note back at you—the strings, having the same frequencies as your voice, are resonating in response to the forces from the sound waves that you sent to them. Your voice and a piano's strings is a good example of the fact that objects—in this case, piano strings—can be forced to oscillate but oscillate best at their natural frequency. In this section, we shall briefly explore applying a *periodic driving force* acting on a simple harmonic oscillator. The driving force puts energy into the system at a certain frequency, not necessarily the same as the natural frequency of the system. The **natural frequency** is the frequency at which a system would oscillate if there were no driving and no damping force.

Most of us have played with toys involving an object supported on an elastic band, something like the paddle ball suspended from a finger in Figure 16.24. Imagine the finger in the figure is your finger. At first you hold your finger steady, and the ball bounces up and down with a small amount of damping. If you move your finger up and down slowly, the ball will follow along without bouncing much on its own. As you increase the frequency at which you move your finger up and down, the ball will respond by oscillating with increasing amplitude. When you drive the ball at its natural frequency, the ball's oscillations increase in amplitude with each oscillation for as long as you drive it. The phenomenon of driving a system with a frequency equal to its natural frequency is called **resonance**. A system being driven at its natural frequency is said to **resonate**. As the driving frequency gets progressively higher than the resonant or natural frequency, the amplitude of the oscillations becomes smaller, until the oscillations nearly disappear and your finger simply moves up and down with little effect on the ball.

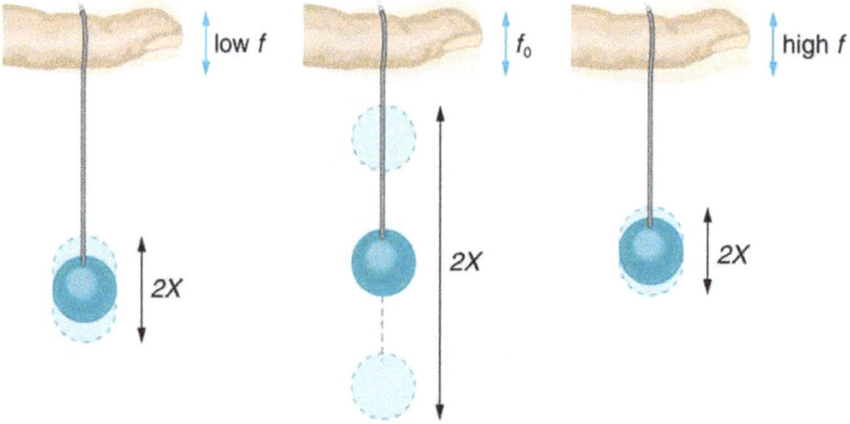

FIGURE 16.24 The paddle ball on its rubber band moves in response to the finger supporting it. If the finger moves with the natural frequency f_0 of the ball on the rubber band, then a resonance is achieved, and the amplitude of the ball's oscillations increases dramatically. At higher and lower driving frequencies, energy is transferred to the ball less efficiently, and it responds with lower-amplitude oscillations.

Figure 16.25 shows a graph of the amplitude of a damped harmonic oscillator as a function of the frequency of the periodic force driving it. There are three curves on the graph, each representing a different amount of damping. All three curves peak at the point where the frequency of the driving force equals the natural frequency of the harmonic oscillator. The highest peak, or greatest response, is for the least amount of damping, because less energy is removed by the damping force.

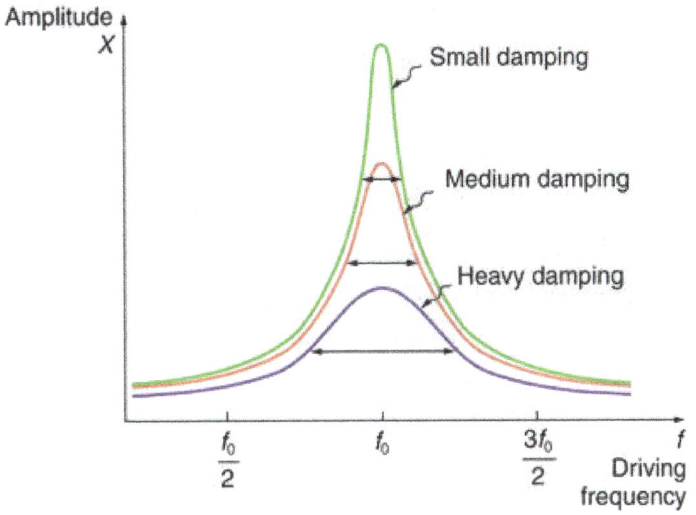

FIGURE 16.25 Amplitude of a harmonic oscillator as a function of the frequency of the driving force. The curves represent the same oscillator with the same natural frequency but with different amounts of damping. Resonance occurs when the driving frequency equals the natural frequency, and the greatest response is for the least amount of damping. The narrowest response is also for the least damping.

It is interesting that the widths of the resonance curves shown in Figure 16.25 depend on damping: the less the damping, the narrower the resonance. The message is that if you want a driven oscillator to resonate at a very specific frequency, you need as little damping as possible. Little damping is the case for piano strings and many other musical instruments. Conversely, if you want small-amplitude oscillations, such as in a car's suspension system, then you want heavy damping. Heavy damping reduces the amplitude, but the tradeoff is that the system responds at more frequencies.

These features of driven harmonic oscillators apply to a huge variety of systems. When you tune a radio, for example, you are adjusting its resonant frequency so that it only oscillates to the desired station's broadcast (driving) frequency. The more selective the radio is in discriminating between stations, the smaller its damping. Magnetic resonance imaging (MRI) is a widely used medical diagnostic tool in which atomic nuclei (mostly hydrogen nuclei) are made to resonate by incoming radio waves (on the order of 100 MHz). A child on a swing is driven by a parent at the swing's natural frequency to achieve maximum amplitude. In all of these cases, the efficiency of energy transfer from the driving force into the oscillator is best at resonance. Speed bumps and gravel roads prove that even a car's suspension system is not immune to resonance. In spite of finely engineered shock absorbers, which ordinarily convert mechanical energy to thermal energy almost as fast as it comes in, speed bumps still cause a large-amplitude oscillation. On gravel roads that are corrugated, you may have noticed that if you travel at the "wrong" speed, the bumps are very noticeable whereas at other speeds you may hardly feel the bumps at all. Figure 16.26 shows a photograph of a famous example (the Tacoma Narrows Bridge) of the destructive effects of a driven harmonic oscillation. The Millennium Bridge in London was closed for a short period of time for the same reason while inspections were carried out.

In our bodies, the chest cavity is a clear example of a system at resonance. The diaphragm and chest wall drive the oscillations of the chest cavity which result in the lungs inflating and deflating. The system is critically damped and the muscular diaphragm oscillates at the resonant value for the system, making it highly efficient.

FIGURE 16.26 In 1940, the Tacoma Narrows Bridge in Washington state collapsed. Heavy cross winds drove the bridge into oscillations at its resonant frequency. Damping decreased when support cables broke loose and started to slip over the towers, allowing increasingly greater amplitudes until the structure failed (credit: PRI's *Studio 360*, via Flickr)

CHECK YOUR UNDERSTANDING

A famous magic trick involves a performer singing a note toward a crystal glass until the glass shatters. Explain why the trick works in terms of resonance and natural frequency.

Solution

The performer must be singing a note that corresponds to the natural frequency of the glass. As the sound wave is directed at the glass, the glass responds by resonating at the same frequency as the sound wave. With enough energy introduced into the system, the glass begins to vibrate and eventually shatters.

16.9 Waves

LEARNING OBJECTIVES

By the end of this section, you will be able to:

- State the characteristics of a wave.
- Calculate the velocity of wave propagation.

FIGURE 16.27 Waves in the ocean behave similarly to all other types of waves. (credit: Steve Jurveston, Flickr)

What do we mean when we say something is a wave? The most intuitive and easiest wave to imagine is the familiar water wave. More precisely, a **wave** is a disturbance that propagates, or moves from the place it was created. For water waves, the disturbance is in the surface of the water, perhaps created by a rock thrown into a pond or by a swimmer splashing the surface repeatedly. For sound waves, the disturbance is a change in air pressure, perhaps created by the oscillating cone inside a speaker. For earthquakes, there are several types of disturbances, including disturbance of Earth's surface and pressure disturbances under the surface. Even radio waves are most easily understood using an analogy with water waves. Visualizing water waves is useful because there is more to it than just a mental image. Water waves exhibit characteristics common to all waves, such as amplitude, period, frequency and energy. All wave characteristics can be described by a small set of underlying principles.

A wave is a disturbance that propagates, or moves from the place it was created. The simplest waves repeat themselves for several cycles and are associated with simple harmonic motion. Let us start by considering the simplified water wave in Figure 16.28. The wave is an up and down disturbance of the water surface. It causes a sea gull to move up and down in simple harmonic motion as the wave crests and troughs (peaks and valleys) pass under the bird. The time for one complete up and down motion is the wave's period T. The wave's frequency is $f = 1/T$, as usual. The wave itself moves to the right in the figure. This movement of the wave is actually the disturbance moving to the right, not the water itself (or the bird would move to the right). We define **wave velocity** v_W to be the speed at which the disturbance moves. Wave velocity is sometimes also called the *propagation velocity or propagation speed,* because the disturbance propagates from one location to another.

MISCONCEPTION ALERT

Many people think that water waves push water from one direction to another. In fact, the particles of water tend to stay in one location, save for moving up and down due to the energy in the wave. The energy moves forward through the water, but the water stays in one place. If you feel yourself pushed in an ocean, what you feel is the energy of the wave, not a rush of water.

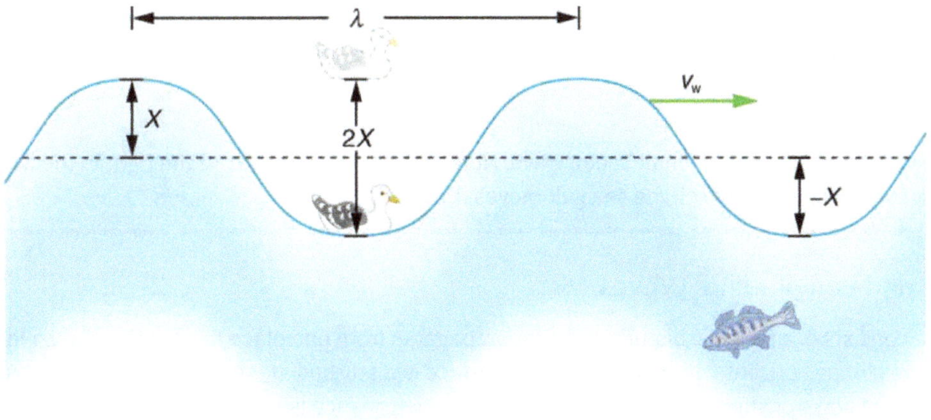

FIGURE 16.28 An idealized ocean wave passes under a sea gull that bobs up and down in simple harmonic motion. The wave has a wavelength λ, which is the distance between adjacent identical parts of the wave. The up and down disturbance of the surface propagates parallel to the surface at a speed v_W.

The water wave in the figure also has a length associated with it, called its **wavelength** λ, the distance between adjacent identical parts of a wave. (λ is the distance parallel to the direction of propagation.) The speed of propagation v_W is the distance the wave travels in a given time, which is one wavelength in the time of one period. In equation form, that is

$$v_W = \frac{\lambda}{T} \quad 16.66$$

or

$$v_W = f\lambda. \quad 16.67$$

This fundamental relationship holds for all types of waves. For water waves, v_W is the speed of a surface wave; for sound, v_W is the speed of sound; and for visible light, v_W is the speed of light, for example.

TAKE-HOME EXPERIMENT: WAVES IN A BOWL

Fill a large bowl or basin with water and wait for the water to settle so there are no ripples. Gently drop a cork into the middle of the bowl. Estimate the wavelength and period of oscillation of the water wave that propagates away from the cork. Remove the cork from the bowl and wait for the water to settle again. Gently drop the cork at a height that is different from the first drop. Does the wavelength depend upon how high above the water the cork is dropped?

EXAMPLE 16.8

Calculate the Velocity of Wave Propagation: Gull in the Ocean

Calculate the wave velocity of the ocean wave in Figure 16.28 if the distance between wave crests is 10.0 m and the time for a sea gull to bob up and down is 5.00 s.

Strategy

We are asked to find v_{w}. The given information tells us that $\lambda = 10.0\text{ m}$ and $T = 5.00\text{ s}$. Therefore, we can use $v_{\text{w}} = \frac{\lambda}{T}$ to find the wave velocity.

Solution

1. Enter the known values into $v_{\text{w}} = \frac{\lambda}{T}$:

$$v_{\text{w}} = \frac{10.0\text{ m}}{5.00\text{ s}}. \quad (16.68)$$

2. Solve for v_{w} to find $v_{\text{w}} = 2.00\text{ m/s}$.

Discussion

This slow speed seems reasonable for an ocean wave. Note that the wave moves to the right in the figure at this speed, not the varying speed at which the sea gull moves up and down.

Transverse and Longitudinal Waves

A simple wave consists of a periodic disturbance that propagates from one place to another. The wave in Figure 16.29 propagates in the horizontal direction while the surface is disturbed in the vertical direction. Such a wave is called a **transverse wave** or shear wave; in such a wave, the disturbance is perpendicular to the direction of propagation. In contrast, in a **longitudinal wave** or compressional wave, the disturbance is parallel to the direction of propagation. Figure 16.30 shows an example of a longitudinal wave. The size of the disturbance is its amplitude X and is completely independent of the speed of propagation v_{w}.

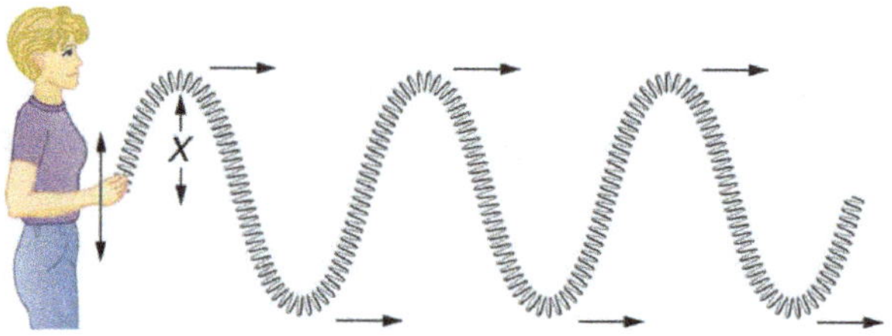

FIGURE 16.29 In this example of a transverse wave, the wave propagates horizontally, and the disturbance in the cord is in the vertical direction.

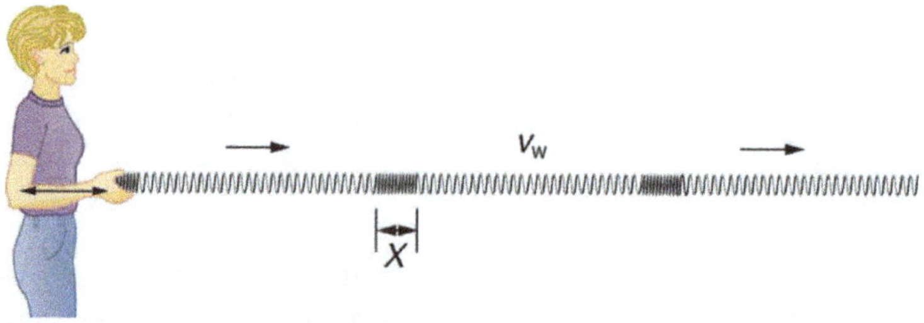

FIGURE 16.30 In this example of a longitudinal wave, the wave propagates horizontally, and the disturbance in the cord is also in the horizontal direction.

Waves may be transverse, longitudinal, or *a combination of the two*. (Water waves are actually a combination of transverse and longitudinal. The simplified water wave illustrated in Figure 16.28 shows no longitudinal motion of the bird.) The waves on the strings of musical instruments are transverse—so are electromagnetic waves, such as visible light.

Sound waves in air and water are longitudinal. Their disturbances are periodic variations in pressure that are transmitted in fluids. Fluids do not have appreciable shear strength, and thus the sound waves in them must be longitudinal or compressional. Sound in solids can be both longitudinal and transverse.

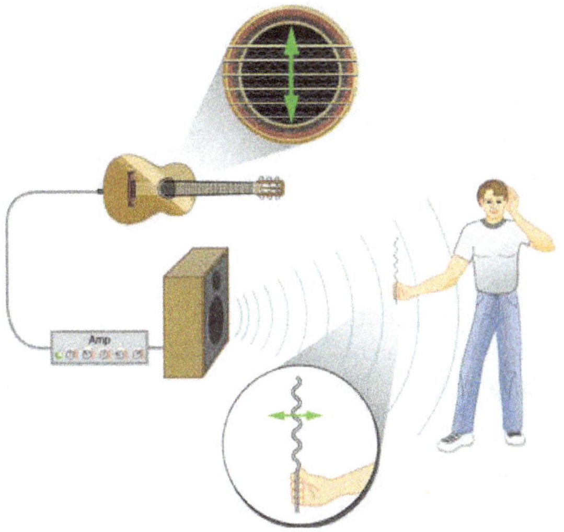

FIGURE 16.31 The wave on a guitar string is transverse. The sound wave rattles a sheet of paper in a direction that shows the sound wave is longitudinal.

Earthquake waves under Earth's surface also have both longitudinal and transverse components (called compressional or P-waves and shear or S-waves, respectively). These components have important individual characteristics—they propagate at different speeds, for example. Earthquakes also have surface waves that are similar to surface waves on water.

CHECK YOUR UNDERSTANDING

Why is it important to differentiate between longitudinal and transverse waves?

Solution

In the different types of waves, energy can propagate in a different direction relative to the motion of the wave. This is important to understand how different types of waves affect the materials around them.

PHET EXPLORATIONS

Wave on a String

Watch a string vibrate in slow motion. Wiggle the end of the string and make waves, or adjust the frequency and amplitude of an oscillator. Adjust the damping and tension. The end can be fixed, loose, or open.

Click to view content (https://openstax.org/books/college-physics-ap-courses-2e/pages/16-9-waves)

16.10 Superposition and Interference

LEARNING OBJECTIVES

By the end of this section, you will be able to:

- Explain standing waves.
- Describe the mathematical representation of overtones and beat frequency.

FIGURE 16.32 These waves result from the superposition of several waves from different sources, producing a complex pattern. (credit: waterborough, Wikimedia Commons)

Most waves do not look very simple. They look more like the waves in Figure 16.32 than like the simple water wave considered in Waves. (Simple waves may be created by a simple harmonic oscillation, and thus have a sinusoidal shape). Complex waves are more interesting, even beautiful, but they look formidable. Most waves appear complex because they result from several simple waves adding together. Luckily, the rules for adding waves are quite simple.

When two or more waves arrive at the same point, they superimpose themselves on one another. More specifically, the disturbances of waves are superimposed when they come together—a phenomenon called **superposition**. Each disturbance corresponds to a force, and forces add. If the disturbances are along the same line, then the resulting wave is a simple addition of the disturbances of the individual waves—that is, their amplitudes add. Figure 16.33 and Figure 16.34 illustrate superposition in two special cases, both of which produce simple results.

Figure 16.33 shows two identical waves that arrive at the same point exactly in phase. The crests of the two waves are precisely aligned, as are the troughs. This superposition produces pure **constructive interference**. Because the disturbances add, pure constructive interference produces a wave that has twice the amplitude of the individual waves, but has the same wavelength.

Figure 16.34 shows two identical waves that arrive exactly out of phase—that is, precisely aligned crest to trough—producing pure **destructive interference**. Because the disturbances are in the opposite direction for this superposition, the resulting amplitude is zero for pure destructive interference—the waves completely cancel.

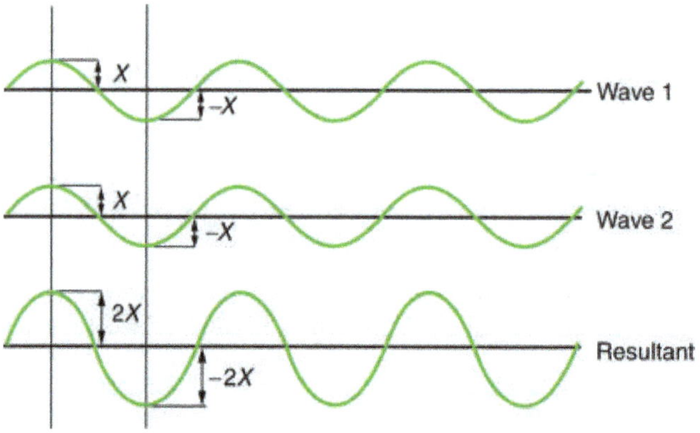

FIGURE 16.33 Pure constructive interference of two identical waves produces one with twice the amplitude, but the same wavelength.

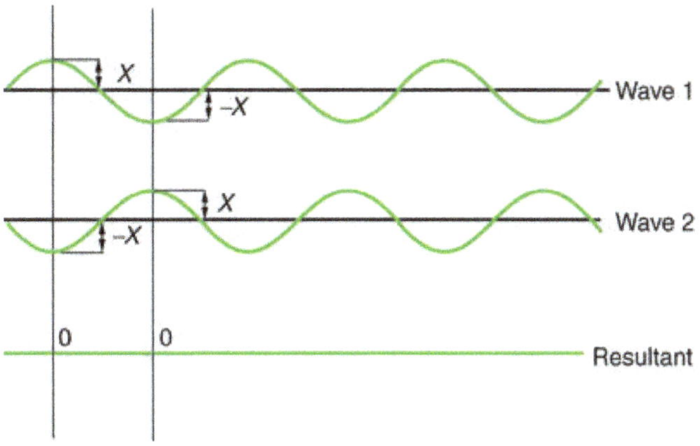

FIGURE 16.34 Pure destructive interference of two identical waves produces zero amplitude, or complete cancellation.

While pure constructive and pure destructive interference do occur, they require precisely aligned identical waves. The superposition of most waves produces a combination of constructive and destructive interference and can vary from place to place and time to time. Sound from a stereo, for example, can be loud in one spot and quiet in another. Varying loudness means the sound waves add partially constructively and partially destructively at different locations. A stereo has at least two speakers creating sound waves, and waves can reflect from walls. All these waves superimpose. An example of sounds that vary over time from constructive to destructive is found in the combined whine of airplane jets heard by a stationary passenger. The combined sound can fluctuate up and down in volume as the sound from the two engines varies in time from constructive to destructive. These examples are of waves that are similar.

An example of the superposition of two dissimilar waves is shown in Figure 16.35. Here again, the disturbances add and subtract, producing a more complicated looking wave.

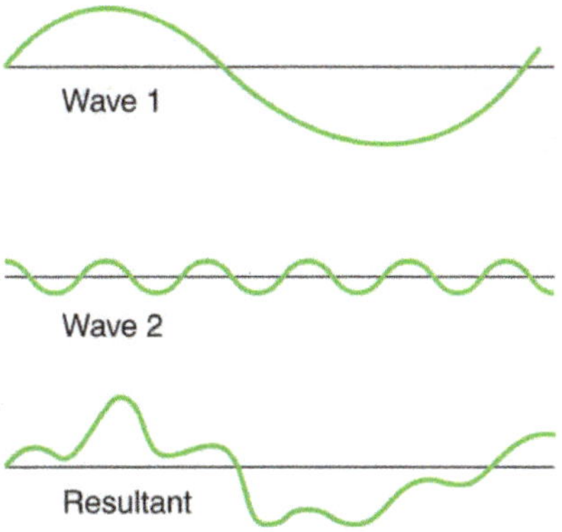

FIGURE 16.35 Superposition of non-identical waves exhibits both constructive and destructive interference.

Standing Waves

Sometimes waves do not seem to move; rather, they just vibrate in place. Unmoving waves can be seen on the surface of a glass of milk in a refrigerator, for example. Vibrations from the refrigerator motor create waves on the milk that oscillate up and down but do not seem to move across the surface. These waves are formed by the superposition of two or more moving waves, such as illustrated in Figure 16.36 for two identical waves moving in opposite directions. The waves move through each other with their disturbances adding as they go by. If the two waves have the same amplitude and wavelength, then they alternate between constructive and destructive interference. The resultant looks like a wave standing in place and, thus, is called a **standing wave**. Waves on the glass of milk are one example of standing waves. There are other standing waves, such as on guitar strings and in organ pipes. With the glass of milk, the two waves that produce standing waves may come from reflections from the side of the glass.

A closer look at earthquakes provides evidence for conditions appropriate for resonance, standing waves, and constructive and destructive interference. A building may be vibrated for several seconds with a driving frequency matching that of the natural frequency of vibration of the building—producing a resonance resulting in one building collapsing while neighboring buildings do not. Often buildings of a certain height are devastated while other taller buildings remain intact. The building height matches the condition for setting up a standing wave for that particular height. As the earthquake waves travel along the surface of Earth and reflect off denser rocks, constructive interference occurs at certain points. Often areas closer to the epicenter are not damaged while areas farther away are damaged.

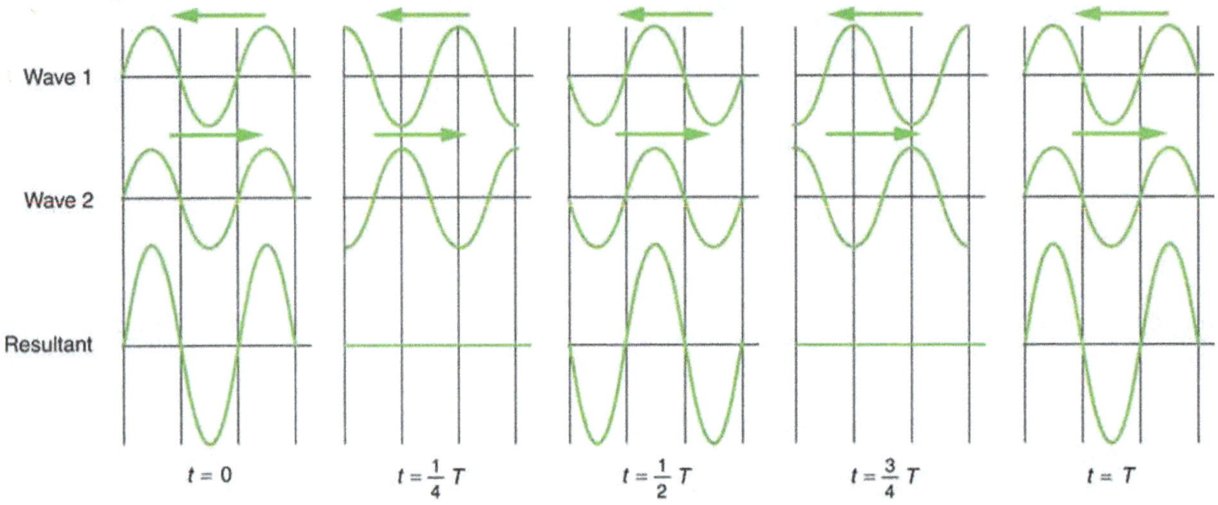

FIGURE 16.36 Standing wave created by the superposition of two identical waves moving in opposite directions. The oscillations are at fixed locations in space and result from alternately constructive and destructive interference.

Standing waves are also found on the strings of musical instruments and are due to reflections of waves from the ends of the string. Figure 16.37 and Figure 16.38 show three standing waves that can be created on a string that is fixed at both ends. **Nodes** are the points where the string does not move; more generally, nodes are where the wave disturbance is zero in a standing wave. The fixed ends of strings must be nodes, too, because the string cannot move there. The word **antinode** is used to denote the location of maximum amplitude in standing waves. Standing waves on strings have a frequency that is related to the propagation speed v_{w} of the disturbance on the string. The wavelength λ is determined by the distance between the points where the string is fixed in place.

The lowest frequency, called the **fundamental frequency**, is thus for the longest wavelength, which is seen to be $\lambda_1 = 2L$. Therefore, the fundamental frequency is $f_1 = v_{\mathrm{w}}/\lambda_1 = v_{\mathrm{w}}/2L$. In this case, the **overtones** or harmonics are multiples of the fundamental frequency. As seen in Figure 16.38, the first harmonic can easily be calculated since $\lambda_2 = L$. Thus, $f_2 = v_{\mathrm{w}}/\lambda_2 = v_{\mathrm{w}}/2L = 2f_1$. Similarly, $f_3 = 3f_1$, and so on. All of these frequencies can be changed by adjusting the tension in the string. The greater the tension, the greater v_{w} is and the higher the frequencies. This observation is familiar to anyone who has ever observed a string instrument being tuned. We will see in later chapters that standing waves are crucial to many resonance phenomena, such as in sounding boxes on string instruments.

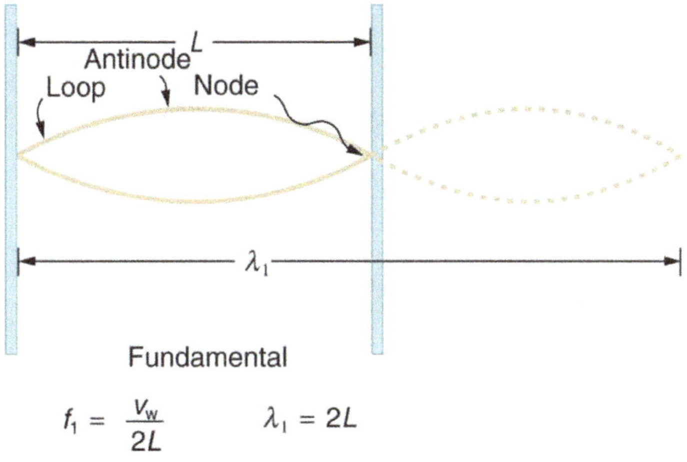

FIGURE 16.37 The figure shows a string oscillating at its fundamental frequency.

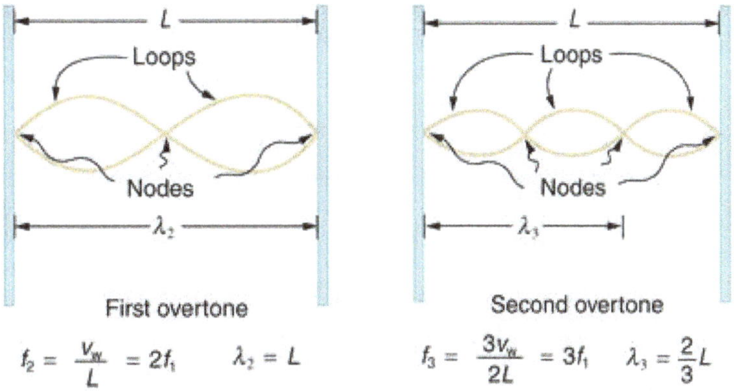

FIGURE 16.38 First and second overtones are shown.

Beats

Striking two adjacent keys on a piano produces a warbling combination usually considered to be unpleasant. The superposition of two waves of similar but not identical frequencies is the culprit. Another example is often noticeable in jet aircraft, particularly the two-engine variety, while taxiing. The combined sound of the engines goes up and down in loudness. This varying loudness happens because the sound waves have similar but not identical frequencies. The discordant warbling of the piano and the fluctuating loudness of the jet engine noise are both due to alternately constructive and destructive interference as the two waves go in and out of phase. Figure 16.39 illustrates this graphically.

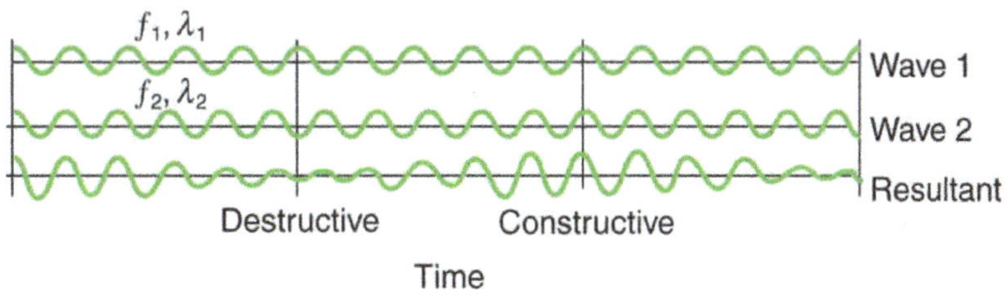

FIGURE 16.39 Beats are produced by the superposition of two waves of slightly different frequencies but identical amplitudes. The waves alternate in time between constructive interference and destructive interference, giving the resulting wave a time-varying amplitude.

The wave resulting from the superposition of two similar-frequency waves has a frequency that is the average of the two. This wave fluctuates in amplitude, or *beats*, with a frequency called the **beat frequency**. We can determine the beat frequency by adding two waves together mathematically. Note that a wave can be represented at one point in space as

$$x = X\cos\left(\frac{2\pi t}{T}\right) = X\cos(2\pi ft), \quad 16.69$$

where $f = 1/T$ is the frequency of the wave. Adding two waves that have different frequencies but identical amplitudes produces a resultant

$$x = x_1 + x_2. \quad 16.70$$

More specifically,

$$x = X\cos(2\pi f_1 t) + X\cos(2\pi f_2 t). \quad 16.71$$

Using a trigonometric identity, it can be shown that

$$x = 2X\cos(\pi f_B t)\cos(2\pi f_{ave} t), \quad 16.72$$

where

$$f_B = |f_1 - f_2| \quad 16.73$$

is the beat frequency, and f_{ave} is the average of f_1 and f_2. These results mean that the resultant wave has twice the amplitude and the average frequency of the two superimposed waves, but it also fluctuates in overall amplitude at the beat frequency f_B. The first cosine term in the expression effectively causes the amplitude to go up and down. The second cosine term is the wave with frequency f_{ave}. This result is valid for all types of waves. However, if it is a sound wave, providing the two frequencies are similar, then what we hear is an average frequency that gets louder and softer (or warbles) at the beat frequency.

MAKING CAREER CONNECTIONS

Piano tuners use beats routinely in their work. When comparing a note with a tuning fork, they listen for beats and adjust the string until the beats go away (to zero frequency). For example, if the tuning fork has a 256 Hz frequency and two beats per second are heard, then the other frequency is either 254 or 258 Hz. Most keys hit multiple strings, and these strings are actually adjusted until they have nearly the same frequency and give a slow beat for richness. Twelve-string guitars and mandolins are also tuned using beats.

While beats may sometimes be annoying in audible sounds, we will find that beats have many applications. Observing beats is a very useful way to compare similar frequencies. There are applications of beats as apparently disparate as in ultrasonic imaging and radar speed traps.

CHECK YOUR UNDERSTANDING

Imagine you are holding one end of a jump rope, and your friend holds the other. If your friend holds her end still, you can move your end up and down, creating a transverse wave. If your friend then begins to move her end up and down, generating a wave in the opposite direction, what resultant wave forms would you expect to see in the jump rope?

Solution

The rope would alternate between having waves with amplitudes two times the original amplitude and reaching equilibrium with no amplitude at all. The wavelengths will result in both constructive and destructive interference

CHECK YOUR UNDERSTANDING

Define nodes and antinodes.

Solution

Nodes are areas of wave interference where there is no motion. Antinodes are areas of wave interference where the motion is at its maximum point.

CHECK YOUR UNDERSTANDING

You hook up a stereo system. When you test the system, you notice that in one corner of the room, the sounds seem dull. In another area, the sounds seem excessively loud. Describe how the sound moving about the room could result in these effects.

Solution

With multiple speakers putting out sounds into the room, and these sounds bouncing off walls, there is bound to be some wave interference. In the dull areas, the interference is probably mostly destructive. In the louder areas, the interference is probably mostly constructive.

PHET EXPLORATIONS

Wave Interference

Make waves with a dripping faucet, audio speaker, or laser! Add a second source or a pair of slits to create an interference pattern.

Click to view content (https://openstax.org/books/college-physics-ap-courses-2e/pages/16-10-superposition-and-interference)

16.11 Energy in Waves: Intensity

LEARNING OBJECTIVES

By the end of this section, you will be able to:

- Calculate the intensity and the power of rays and waves.

FIGURE 16.40 The destructive effect of an earthquake is palpable evidence of the energy carried in these waves. The Richter scale rating of earthquakes is related to both their amplitude and the energy they carry. (credit: Petty Officer 2nd Class Candice Villarreal, U.S. Navy)

All waves carry energy. The energy of some waves can be directly observed. Earthquakes can shake whole cities to the ground, performing the work of thousands of wrecking balls.

Loud sounds pulverize nerve cells in the inner ear, causing permanent hearing loss. Ultrasound is used for deep-heat treatment of muscle strains. A laser beam can burn away a malignancy. Water waves chew up beaches.

The amount of energy in a wave is related to its amplitude. Large-amplitude earthquakes produce large ground displacements. Loud sounds have higher pressure amplitudes and come from larger-amplitude source vibrations than soft sounds. Large ocean breakers churn up the shore more than small ones. More quantitatively, a wave is a displacement that is resisted by a restoring force. The larger the displacement x, the larger the force $F = kx$ needed to create it. Because work W is related to force multiplied by distance (Fx) and energy is put into the wave by the work done to create it, the energy in a wave is related to amplitude. In fact, a wave's energy is directly proportional to its amplitude squared because

$$W \propto Fx = kx^2. \quad (16.74)$$

The energy effects of a wave depend on time as well as amplitude. For example, the longer deep-heat ultrasound is applied, the more energy it transfers. Waves can also be concentrated or spread out. Sunlight, for example, can be focused to burn wood. Earthquakes spread out, so they do less damage the farther they get from the source. In both cases, changing the area the waves cover has important effects. All these pertinent factors are included in the definition of **intensity** I as power per unit area:

$$I = \frac{P}{A} \quad (16.75)$$

where P is the power carried by the wave through area A. The definition of intensity is valid for any energy in transit, including that carried by waves. The SI unit for intensity is watts per square meter (W/m^2). For example, infrared and visible energy from the Sun impinge on Earth at an intensity of $1300\ W/m^2$ just above the atmosphere. There are other intensity-related units in use, too. The most common is the decibel. For example, a 90 decibel sound level corresponds to an intensity of $10^{-3}\ W/m^2$. (This quantity is not much power per unit area considering that 90 decibels is a relatively high sound level. Decibels will be discussed in some detail in a later chapter.

EXAMPLE 16.9

Calculating intensity and power: How much energy is in a ray of sunlight?

The average intensity of sunlight on Earth's surface is about $700\ W/m^2$.

(a) Calculate the amount of energy that falls on a solar collector having an area of $0.500\ m^2$ in $4.00\ h$.

(b) What intensity would such sunlight have if concentrated by a magnifying glass onto an area 200 times smaller than its own?

Strategy a

Because power is energy per unit time or $P = \frac{E}{t}$, the definition of intensity can be written as $I = \frac{P}{A} = \frac{E/t}{A}$, and this equation can be solved for E with the given information.

Solution a

1. Begin with the equation that states the definition of intensity:

$$I = \frac{P}{A}. \quad (16.76)$$

2. Replace P with its equivalent E/t:

$$I = \frac{E/t}{A}. \quad (16.77)$$

3. Solve for E:

$$E = IAt. \quad (16.78)$$

4. Substitute known values into the equation:

$$E = \left(700\ W/m^2\right)\left(0.500\ m^2\right)[(4.00\ h)(3600\ s/h)]. \quad (16.79)$$

5. Calculate to find E and convert units:

$$5.04 \times 10^6\ J, \quad (16.80)$$

Discussion a

The energy falling on the solar collector in 4 h in part is enough to be useful—for example, for heating a significant amount of water.

Strategy b

Taking a ratio of new intensity to old intensity and using primes for the new quantities, we will find that it depends on the ratio of the areas. All other quantities will cancel.

Solution b

1. Take the ratio of intensities, which yields:

$$\frac{I'}{I} = \frac{P'/A'}{P/A} = \frac{A}{A'} \left(\text{The powers cancel because } P' = P\right). \quad 16.81$$

2. Identify the knowns:

$$A = 200A', \quad 16.82$$

$$\frac{I'}{I} = 200. \quad 16.83$$

3. Substitute known quantities:

$$I' = 200I = 200\left(700 \text{ W/m}^2\right). \quad 16.84$$

4. Calculate to find I':

$$I' = 1.40 \times 10^5 \text{ W/m}^2. \quad 16.85$$

Discussion b

Decreasing the area increases the intensity considerably. The intensity of the concentrated sunlight could even start a fire.

EXAMPLE 16.10

Determine the combined intensity of two waves: Perfect constructive interference

If two identical waves are spatially separated, each having an intensity of 1.00 W/m^2, interfere perfectly constructively in a particular location, what is the intensity of the wave at this particular location?

Strategy

We know from Superposition and Interference that when two identical waves, which have equal amplitudes X, interfere perfectly constructively, the resulting wave has an amplitude of $2X$. Because a wave's intensity is proportional to amplitude squared, the intensity of the resulting wave is four times as great as in the individual waves.

Solution

1. Recall that intensity is proportional to amplitude squared.
2. Calculate the new amplitude:

$$I' \propto \left(X'\right)^2 = (2X)^2 = 4X^2. \quad 16.86$$

3. Recall that the intensity of the old amplitude was:

$$I \propto X^2. \quad 16.87$$

4. Take the ratio of new intensity to the old intensity. This gives:

$$\frac{I'}{I} = 4. \quad 16.88$$

5. Calculate to find I':

$$I' = 4I = 4.00 \text{ W/m}^2. \quad 16.89$$

Discussion

The intensity goes up by a factor of 4 when the amplitude doubles. This answer is a little disquieting. The two individual waves each have intensities of 1.00 W/m^2, yet their sum has an intensity of 4.00 W/m^2, which may appear to violate conservation of energy. This violation, of course, cannot happen. What does happen is intriguing.

The area over which the intensity is 4.00 W/m^2 is much less than the area covered by the two waves before they interfered. There are other areas where the intensity is zero. The addition of waves is not as simple as our first look in Superposition and Interference suggested. We actually get a pattern of both constructive interference and destructive interference whenever two waves are added. For example, if we have two stereo speakers putting out 1.00 W/m^2 each, there will be places in the room where the intensity is 4.00 W/m^2, other places where the intensity is zero, and others in between. Figure 16.41 shows what this interference might look like. We will pursue interference patterns elsewhere in this text.

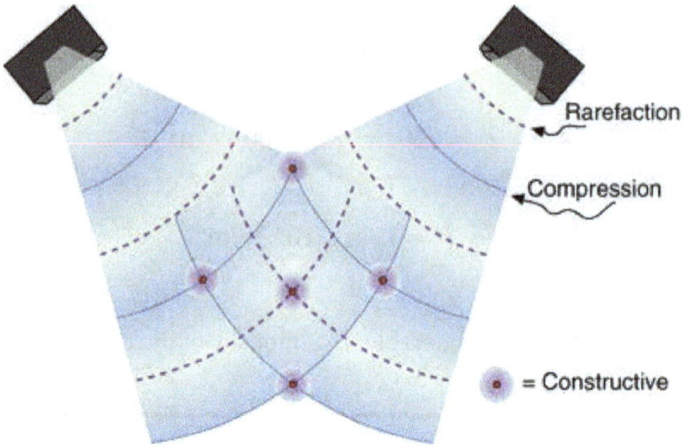

FIGURE 16.41 These stereo speakers produce both constructive interference and destructive interference in the room, a property common to the superposition of all types of waves. The shading is proportional to intensity.

CHECK YOUR UNDERSTANDING

Which measurement of a wave is most important when determining the wave's intensity?

Solution

Amplitude, because a wave’s energy is directly proportional to its amplitude squared.

Glossary

amplitude the maximum displacement from the equilibrium position of an object oscillating around the equilibrium position

antinode the location of maximum amplitude in standing waves

beat frequency the frequency of the amplitude fluctuations of a wave

constructive interference when two waves arrive at the same point exactly in phase; that is, the crests of the two waves are precisely aligned, as are the troughs

critical damping the condition in which the damping of an oscillator causes it to return as quickly as possible to its equilibrium position without oscillating back and forth about this position

deformation displacement from equilibrium

destructive interference when two identical waves arrive at the same point exactly out of phase; that is, precisely aligned crest to trough

elastic potential energy potential energy stored as a result of deformation of an elastic object, such as the stretching of a spring

force constant a constant related to the rigidity of a system: the larger the force constant, the more rigid the system; the force constant is represented by *k*

frequency number of events per unit of time

fundamental frequency the lowest frequency of a periodic waveform

intensity power per unit area

longitudinal wave a wave in which the disturbance is parallel to the direction of propagation

natural frequency the frequency at which a system would oscillate if there were no driving and no damping forces

nodes the points where the string does not move; more generally, nodes are where the wave disturbance is zero in a standing wave

oscillate moving back and forth regularly between two points

over damping the condition in which damping of an oscillator causes it to return to equilibrium without oscillating; oscillator moves more slowly toward equilibrium than in the critically damped system

overtones multiples of the fundamental frequency of a sound

period time it takes to complete one oscillation

periodic motion motion that repeats itself at regular time intervals

resonance the phenomenon of driving a system with a frequency equal to the system's natural frequency

resonate a system being driven at its natural frequency

restoring force force acting in opposition to the force caused by a deformation

simple harmonic motion the oscillatory motion in a system where the net force can be described by Hooke's law

simple harmonic oscillator a device that implements Hooke's law, such as a mass that is attached to a spring, with the other end of the spring being connected to a rigid support such as a wall

simple pendulum an object with a small mass suspended from a light wire or string

superposition the phenomenon that occurs when two or more waves arrive at the same point

transverse wave a wave in which the disturbance is perpendicular to the direction of propagation

under damping the condition in which damping of an oscillator causes it to return to equilibrium with the amplitude gradually decreasing to zero; system returns to equilibrium faster but overshoots and crosses the equilibrium position one or more times

wave a disturbance that moves from its source and carries energy

wave velocity the speed at which the disturbance moves. Also called the propagation velocity or propagation speed

wavelength the distance between adjacent identical parts of a wave

Section Summary

16.1 Hooke's Law: Stress and Strain Revisited

- An oscillation is a back and forth motion of an object between two points of deformation.
- An oscillation may create a wave, which is a disturbance that propagates from where it was created.
- The simplest type of oscillations and waves are related to systems that can be described by Hooke's law:
  $F = -kx,$
  where F is the restoring force, x is the displacement from equilibrium or deformation, and k is the force constant of the system.
- Elastic potential energy PE_{el} stored in the deformation of a system that can be described by Hooke's law is given by
  $PE_{el} = (1/2)kx^2.$

16.2 Period and Frequency in Oscillations

- Periodic motion is a repetitious oscillation.
- The time for one oscillation is the period T.
- The number of oscillations per unit time is the frequency f.
- These quantities are related by
  $f = \frac{1}{T}$.

16.3 Simple Harmonic Motion: A Special Periodic Motion

- Simple harmonic motion is oscillatory motion for a system that can be described only by Hooke's law. Such a system is also called a simple harmonic oscillator.
- Maximum displacement is the amplitude X. The period T and frequency f of a simple harmonic oscillator are given by
  $T = 2\pi\sqrt{\frac{m}{k}}$ and $f = \frac{1}{2\pi}\sqrt{\frac{k}{m}}$, where m is the mass of the system.
- Displacement in simple harmonic motion as a function of time is given by $x(t)= X \cos \frac{2\pi t}{T}$.
- The velocity is given by $v(t) = -v_{\text{max}} \sin \frac{2\pi t}{T}$, where $v_{\text{max}} = \sqrt{k/m}X$.
- The acceleration is found to be
  $a(t)= -\frac{kX}{m} \cos \frac{2\pi t}{T}$.

16.4 The Simple Pendulum

- A mass m suspended by a wire of length L is a simple pendulum and undergoes simple harmonic motion for amplitudes less than about 15°. The period of a simple pendulum is
  $$T = 2\pi\sqrt{\frac{L}{g}},$$
  where L is the length of the string and g is the acceleration due to gravity.

16.5 Energy and the Simple Harmonic Oscillator

- Energy in the simple harmonic oscillator is shared between elastic potential energy and kinetic energy, with the total being constant:
  $$\frac{1}{2}mv^2 + \frac{1}{2}kx^2 = \text{constant}.$$
- Maximum velocity depends on three factors: it is directly proportional to amplitude, it is greater for stiffer systems, and it is smaller for objects that have larger masses:
  $$v_{\text{max}} = \sqrt{\frac{k}{m}}X.$$

16.6 Uniform Circular Motion and Simple Harmonic Motion

A projection of uniform circular motion undergoes simple harmonic oscillation.

16.7 Damped Harmonic Motion

- Damped harmonic oscillators have non-conservative forces that dissipate their energy.
- Critical damping returns the system to equilibrium as fast as possible without overshooting.
- An underdamped system will oscillate through the equilibrium position.
- An overdamped system moves more slowly toward equilibrium than one that is critically damped.

16.8 Forced Oscillations and Resonance

- A system's natural frequency is the frequency at which the system will oscillate if not affected by driving or damping forces.
- A periodic force driving a harmonic oscillator at its natural frequency produces resonance. The system is said to resonate.
- The less damping a system has, the higher the amplitude of the forced oscillations near resonance. The more damping a system has, the broader response it has to varying driving frequencies.

16.9 Waves

- A wave is a disturbance that moves from the point of creation with a wave velocity v_{w}.
- A wave has a wavelength λ, which is the distance between adjacent identical parts of the wave.
- Wave velocity and wavelength are related to the wave's frequency and period by $v_{\text{w}} = \frac{\lambda}{T}$ or $v_{\text{w}} = f\lambda$.
- A transverse wave has a disturbance perpendicular to its direction of propagation, whereas a longitudinal wave has a disturbance parallel to its direction of propagation.

16.10 Superposition and Interference

- Superposition is the combination of two waves at the same location.
- Constructive interference occurs when two identical waves are superimposed in phase.
- Destructive interference occurs when two identical waves are superimposed exactly out of phase.
- A standing wave is one in which two waves superimpose to produce a wave that varies in amplitude but does not propagate.
- Nodes are points of no motion in standing waves.

- An antinode is the location of maximum amplitude of a standing wave.
- Waves on a string are resonant standing waves with a fundamental frequency and can occur at higher multiples of the fundamental, called overtones or harmonics.
- Beats occur when waves of similar frequencies f_1 and f_2 are superimposed. The resulting amplitude oscillates with a beat frequency given by $f_B = |f_1 - f_2|$.

16.11 Energy in Waves: Intensity

Intensity is defined to be the power per unit area: $I = \frac{P}{A}$ and has units of W/m^2.

Conceptual Questions

16.1 Hooke's Law: Stress and Strain Revisited

1. Describe a system in which elastic potential energy is stored.

16.3 Simple Harmonic Motion: A Special Periodic Motion

2. What conditions must be met to produce simple harmonic motion?
3. (a) If frequency is not constant for some oscillation, can the oscillation be simple harmonic motion? (b) Can you think of any examples of harmonic motion where the frequency may depend on the amplitude?
4. Give an example of a simple harmonic oscillator, specifically noting how its frequency is independent of amplitude.
5. Explain why you expect an object made of a stiff material to vibrate at a higher frequency than a similar object made of a spongy material.
6. As you pass a freight truck with a trailer on a highway, you notice that its trailer is bouncing up and down slowly. Is it more likely that the trailer is heavily loaded or nearly empty? Explain your answer.
7. Some people modify cars to be much closer to the ground than when manufactured. Should they install stiffer springs? Explain your answer.

16.4 The Simple Pendulum

8. Pendulum clocks are made to run at the correct rate by adjusting the pendulum's length. Suppose you move from one city to another where the acceleration due to gravity is slightly greater, taking your pendulum clock with you, will you have to lengthen or shorten the pendulum to keep the correct time, other factors remaining constant? Explain your answer.

16.5 Energy and the Simple Harmonic Oscillator

9. Explain in terms of energy how dissipative forces such as friction reduce the amplitude of a harmonic oscillator. Also explain how a driving mechanism can compensate. (A pendulum clock is such a system.)

16.7 Damped Harmonic Motion

10. Give an example of a damped harmonic oscillator. (They are more common than undamped or simple harmonic oscillators.)
11. How would a car bounce after a bump under each of these conditions?
    - overdamping
    - underdamping
    - critical damping
12. Most harmonic oscillators are damped and, if undriven, eventually come to a stop. How is this observation related to the second law of thermodynamics?

16.8 Forced Oscillations and Resonance

13. Why are soldiers in general ordered to "route step" (walk out of step) across a bridge?

16.9 Waves

14. Give one example of a transverse wave and another of a longitudinal wave, being careful to note the relative directions of the disturbance and wave propagation in each.
15. What is the difference between propagation speed and the frequency of a wave? Does one or both affect wavelength? If so, how?

16.10 Superposition and Interference

16. Speakers in stereo systems have two color-coded terminals to indicate how to hook up the wires. If the wires are reversed, the speaker moves in a direction opposite that of a properly connected

speaker. Explain why it is important to have both speakers connected the same way.

16.11 Energy in Waves: Intensity

17. Two identical waves undergo pure constructive interference. Is the resultant intensity twice that of the individual waves? Explain your answer.

18. Circular water waves decrease in amplitude as they move away from where a rock is dropped. Explain why.

Problems & Exercises

16.1 Hooke's Law: Stress and Strain Revisited

1. Fish are hung on a spring scale to determine their mass (most fishermen feel no obligation to truthfully report the mass).
(a) What is the force constant of the spring in such a scale if it the spring stretches 8.00 cm for a 10.0 kg load?
(b) What is the mass of a fish that stretches the spring 5.50 cm?
(c) How far apart are the half-kilogram marks on the scale?

2. It is weigh-in time for the local under-85-kg rugby team. The bathroom scale used to assess eligibility can be described by Hooke's law and is depressed 0.75 cm by its maximum load of 120 kg. (a) What is the spring's effective spring constant? (b) A player stands on the scales and depresses it by 0.48 cm. Is he eligible to play on this under-85 kg team?

3. One type of BB gun uses a spring-driven plunger to blow the BB from its barrel. (a) Calculate the force constant of its plunger's spring if you must compress it 0.150 m to drive the 0.0500-kg plunger to a top speed of 20.0 m/s. (b) What force must be exerted to compress the spring?

4. (a) The springs of a pickup truck act like a single spring with a force constant of 1.30×10^5 N/m. By how much will the truck be depressed by its maximum load of 1000 kg?
(b) If the pickup truck has four identical springs, what is the force constant of each?

5. When an 80.0-kg man stands on a pogo stick, the spring is compressed 0.120 m.
(a) What is the force constant of the spring? (b) Will the spring be compressed more when he hops down the road?

6. A spring has a length of 0.200 m when a 0.300-kg mass hangs from it, and a length of 0.750 m when a 1.95-kg mass hangs from it. (a) What is the force constant of the spring? (b) What is the unloaded length of the spring?

16.2 Period and Frequency in Oscillations

7. What is the period of 60.0 Hz electrical power?

8. If your heart rate is 150 beats per minute during strenuous exercise, what is the time per beat in units of seconds?

9. Find the frequency of a tuning fork that takes 2.50×10^{-3} s to complete one oscillation.

10. A stroboscope is set to flash every 8.00×10^{-5} s. What is the frequency of the flashes?

11. A tire has a tread pattern with a crevice every 2.00 cm. Each crevice makes a single vibration as the tire moves. What is the frequency of these vibrations if the car moves at 30.0 m/s?

12. Engineering Application
Each piston of an engine makes a sharp sound every other revolution of the engine. (a) How fast is a race car going if its eight-cylinder engine emits a sound of frequency 750 Hz, given that the engine makes 2000 revolutions per kilometer? (b) At how many revolutions per minute is the engine rotating?

16.3 Simple Harmonic Motion: A Special Periodic Motion

13. A type of cuckoo clock keeps time by having a mass bouncing on a spring, usually something cute like a cherub in a chair. What force constant is needed to produce a period of 0.500 s for a 0.0150-kg mass?

14. If the spring constant of a simple harmonic oscillator is doubled, by what factor will the mass of the system need to change in order for the frequency of the motion to remain the same?

15. A 0.500-kg mass suspended from a spring oscillates with a period of 1.50 s. How much mass must be added to the object to change the period to 2.00 s?

16. By how much leeway (both percentage and mass) would you have in the selection of the mass of the object in the previous problem if you did not wish the new period to be greater than 2.01 s or less than 1.99 s?

17. Suppose you attach the object with mass m to a vertical spring originally at rest, and let it bounce up and down. You release the object from rest at the spring's original rest length. (a) Show that the spring exerts an upward force of $2.00\ mg$ on the object at its lowest point. (b) If the spring has a force constant of $10.0\ \text{N/m}$ and a 0.25-kg-mass object is set in motion as described, find the amplitude of the oscillations. (c) Find the maximum velocity.

18. A diver on a diving board is undergoing simple harmonic motion. Her mass is 55.0 kg and the period of her motion is 0.800 s. The next diver is a male whose period of simple harmonic oscillation is 1.05 s. What is his mass if the mass of the board is negligible?

19. Suppose a diving board with no one on it bounces up and down in a simple harmonic motion with a frequency of 4.00 Hz. The board has an effective mass of 10.0 kg. What is the frequency of the simple harmonic motion of a 75.0-kg diver on the board?

20.

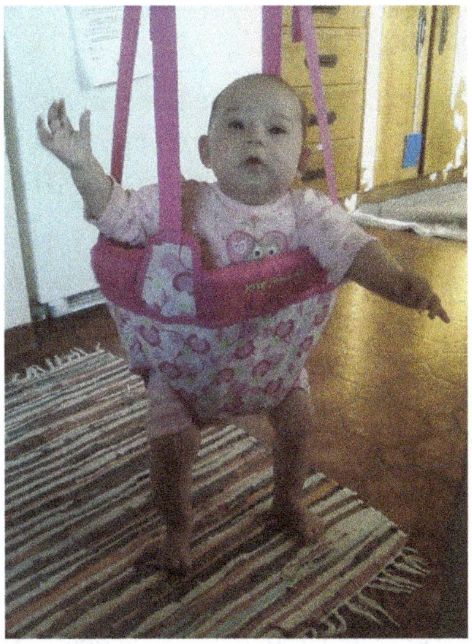

FIGURE 16.42 This child's toy relies on springs to keep infants entertained. (credit: By Humboldthead, Flickr)

The device pictured in Figure 16.42 entertains infants while keeping them from wandering. The child bounces in a harness suspended from a door frame by a spring constant.
(a) If the spring stretches 0.250 m while supporting an 8.0-kg child, what is its spring constant?
(b) What is the time for one complete bounce of this child? (c) What is the child's maximum velocity if the amplitude of her bounce is 0.200 m?

21. A 90.0-kg skydiver hanging from a parachute bounces up and down with a period of 1.50 s. What is the new period of oscillation when a second skydiver, whose mass is 60.0 kg, hangs from the legs of the first, as seen in Figure 16.43.

FIGURE 16.43 The oscillations of one skydiver are about to be affected by a second skydiver. (credit: U.S. Army, www.army.mil)

16.4 The Simple Pendulum

As usual, the acceleration due to gravity in these problems is taken to be $g = 9.80\ \text{m/s}^2$, unless otherwise specified.

22. What is the length of a pendulum that has a period of 0.500 s?

23. Some people think a pendulum with a period of 1.00 s can be driven with "mental energy" or psycho kinetically, because its period is the same as an average heartbeat. True or not, what is the length of such a pendulum?

24. What is the period of a 1.00-m-long pendulum?

25. How long does it take a child on a swing to complete one swing if her center of gravity is 4.00 m below the pivot?

26. The pendulum on a cuckoo clock is 5.00 cm long. What is its frequency?

27. Two parakeets sit on a swing with their combined center of mass 10.0 cm below the pivot. At what frequency do they swing?

28. (a) A pendulum that has a period of 3.00000 s and that is located where the acceleration due to gravity is $9.79\ \text{m/s}^2$ is moved to a location where the acceleration due to gravity is $9.82\ \text{m/s}^2$. What is its new period? (b) Explain why so many digits are needed in the value for the period, based on the relation between the period and the acceleration due to gravity.

29. A pendulum with a period of 2.00000 s in one location $(g = 9.80\ \text{m/s}^2)$ is moved to a new location where the period is now 1.99796 s. What is the acceleration due to gravity at its new location?

30. (a) What is the effect on the period of a pendulum if you double its length?
(b) What is the effect on the period of a pendulum if you decrease its length by 5.00%?

31. Find the ratio of the new/old periods of a pendulum if the pendulum were transported from Earth to the Moon, where the acceleration due to gravity is $1.63\ \text{m/s}^2$.

32. At what rate will a pendulum clock run on the Moon, where the acceleration due to gravity is $1.63\ \text{m/s}^2$, if it keeps time accurately on Earth? That is, find the time (in hours) it takes the clock's hour hand to make one revolution on the Moon.

33. Suppose the length of a clock's pendulum is changed by 1.000%, exactly at noon one day. What time will it read 24.00 hours later, assuming it the pendulum has kept perfect time before the change? Note that there are two answers, and perform the calculation to four-digit precision.

34. If a pendulum-driven clock gains 5.00 s/day, what fractional change in pendulum length must be made for it to keep perfect time?

16.5 Energy and the Simple Harmonic Oscillator

35. The length of nylon rope from which a mountain climber is suspended has a force constant of $1.40 \times 10^4 \text{N/m}$
(a) What is the frequency at which he bounces, given his mass plus and the mass of his equipment are 90.0 kg? Ignore the change in gravitational potential energy after the cord begins to stretch.
(b) How much would this rope stretch to break the climber's fall if he free-falls 2.00 m before the rope runs out of slack? Hint: Use conservation of energy.
(c) Repeat both parts of this problem in the situation where twice this length of nylon rope is used.

36. Engineering Application
Near the top of the Citigroup Center building in New York City, there is an object with mass of $4.00 \times 10^5\ \text{kg}$ on springs that have adjustable force constants. Its function is to dampen wind-driven oscillations of the building by oscillating at the same frequency as the building is being driven—the driving force is transferred to the object, which oscillates instead of the entire building. (a) What effective force constant should the springs have to make the object oscillate with a period of 2.00 s? (b) What energy is stored in the springs for a 2.00-m displacement from equilibrium?

16.6 Uniform Circular Motion and Simple Harmonic Motion

37. (a)What is the maximum velocity of an 85.0-kg person bouncing on a bathroom scale having a force constant of $1.50 \times 10^6\ \text{N/m}$, if the amplitude of the bounce is 0.200 cm? (b)What is the maximum energy stored in the spring?

38. A novelty clock has a 0.0100-kg mass object bouncing on a spring that has a force constant of 1.25 N/m. What is the maximum velocity of the object if the object bounces 3.00 cm above and below its equilibrium position? (b) How many joules of kinetic energy does the object have at its maximum velocity?

39. At what positions is the speed of a simple harmonic oscillator half its maximum? That is, what values of x/X give $v = \pm v_{\text{max}}/2$, where X is the amplitude of the motion?

40. A ladybug sits 12.0 cm from the center of a Beatles music album spinning at 33.33 rpm. What is the maximum velocity of its shadow on the wall behind the turntable, if illuminated parallel to the record by the parallel rays of the setting Sun?

16.7 Damped Harmonic Motion

41. The amplitude of a lightly damped oscillator decreases by 3.0% during each cycle. What percentage of the mechanical energy of the oscillator is lost in each cycle?

16.8 Forced Oscillations and Resonance

42. How much energy must the shock absorbers of a 1200-kg car dissipate in order to damp a bounce that initially has a velocity of 0.800 m/s at the equilibrium position? Assume the car returns to its original vertical position.

43. If a car has a suspension system with a force constant of $5.00 \times 10^4\ \text{N/m}$, how much energy must the car's shocks remove to dampen an oscillation starting with a maximum displacement of 0.0750 m?

44. (a) How much will a spring that has a force constant of 40.0 N/m be stretched by an object with a mass of 0.500 kg when hung motionless from the spring? (b) Calculate the decrease in gravitational potential energy of the 0.500-kg object when it descends this distance. (c) Part of this gravitational energy goes into the spring. Calculate the energy stored in the spring by this stretch, and compare it with the gravitational potential energy. Explain where the rest of the energy might go.

45. Suppose you have a 0.750-kg object on a horizontal surface connected to a spring that has a force constant of 150 N/m. There is simple friction between the object and surface with a static coefficient of friction $\mu_s = 0.100$. (a) How far can the spring be stretched without moving the mass? (b) If the object is set into oscillation with an amplitude twice the distance found in part (a), and the kinetic coefficient of friction is $\mu_k = 0.0850$, what total distance does it travel before stopping? Assume it starts at the maximum amplitude.

46. Engineering Application: A suspension bridge oscillates with an effective force constant of 1.00×10^8 N/m. (a) How much energy is needed to make it oscillate with an amplitude of 0.100 m? (b) If soldiers march across the bridge with a cadence equal to the bridge's natural frequency and impart 1.00×10^4 J of energy each second, how long does it take for the bridge's oscillations to go from 0.100 m to 0.500 m amplitude?

16.9 Waves

47. Storms in the South Pacific can create waves that travel all the way to the California coast, which are 12,000 km away. How long does it take them if they travel at 15.0 m/s?

48. Waves on a swimming pool propagate at 0.750 m/s. You splash the water at one end of the pool and observe the wave go to the opposite end, reflect, and return in 30.0 s. How far away is the other end of the pool?

49. Wind gusts create ripples on the ocean that have a wavelength of 5.00 cm and propagate at 2.00 m/s. What is their frequency?

50. How many times a minute does a boat bob up and down on ocean waves that have a wavelength of 40.0 m and a propagation speed of 5.00 m/s?

51. Scouts at a camp shake the rope bridge they have just crossed and observe the wave crests to be 8.00 m apart. If they shake the bridge twice per second, what is the propagation speed of the waves?

52. What is the wavelength of the waves you create in a swimming pool if you splash your hand at a rate of 2.00 Hz and the waves propagate at 0.800 m/s?

53. What is the wavelength of an earthquake that shakes you with a frequency of 10.0 Hz and gets to another city 84.0 km away in 12.0 s?

54. Radio waves transmitted through space at 3.00×10^8 m/s by the Voyager spacecraft have a wavelength of 0.120 m. What is their frequency?

55. Your ear is capable of differentiating sounds that arrive at the ear just 1.00 ms apart. What is the minimum distance between two speakers that produce sounds that arrive at noticeably different times on a day when the speed of sound is 340 m/s?

56. (a) Seismographs measure the arrival times of earthquakes with a precision of 0.100 s. To get the distance to the epicenter of the quake, they compare the arrival times of S- and P-waves, which travel at different speeds. Figure 16.44) If S- and P-waves travel at 4.00 and 7.20 km/s, respectively, in the region considered, how precisely can the distance to the source of the earthquake be determined? (b) Seismic waves from underground detonations of nuclear bombs can be used to locate the test site and detect violations of test bans. Discuss whether your answer to (a) implies a serious limit to such detection. (Note also that the uncertainty is greater if there is an uncertainty in the propagation speeds of the S- and P-waves.)

FIGURE 16.44 A seismograph as described in above problem.(credit: Oleg Alexandrov)

16.10 Superposition and Interference

57. A car has two horns, one emitting a frequency of 199 Hz and the other emitting a frequency of 203 Hz. What beat frequency do they produce?

58. The middle-C hammer of a piano hits two strings, producing beats of 1.50 Hz. One of the strings is tuned to 260.00 Hz. What frequencies could the other string have?

59. Two tuning forks having frequencies of 460 and 464 Hz are struck simultaneously. What average frequency will you hear, and what will the beat frequency be?

60. Twin jet engines on an airplane are producing an average sound frequency of 4100 Hz with a beat frequency of 0.500 Hz. What are their individual frequencies?

61. A wave traveling on a Slinky® that is stretched to 4 m takes 2.4 s to travel the length of the Slinky and back again. (a) What is the speed of the wave? (b) Using the same Slinky stretched to the same length, a standing wave is created which consists of three antinodes and four nodes. At what frequency must the Slinky be oscillating?

62. Three adjacent keys on a piano (F, F-sharp, and G) are struck simultaneously, producing frequencies of 349, 370, and 392 Hz. What beat frequencies are produced by this discordant combination?

16.11 Energy in Waves: Intensity

63. Medical Application
Ultrasound of intensity $1.50 \times 10^2\ \text{W/m}^2$ is produced by the rectangular head of a medical imaging device measuring 3.00 by 5.00 cm. What is its power output?

64. The low-frequency speaker of a stereo set has a surface area of $0.05\ \text{m}^2$ and produces 1W of acoustical power. What is the intensity at the speaker? If the speaker projects sound uniformly in all directions, at what distance from the speaker is the intensity $0.1\ \text{W/m}^2$?

65. To increase intensity of a wave by a factor of 50, by what factor should the amplitude be increased?

66. Engineering Application
A device called an insolation meter is used to measure the intensity of sunlight has an area of 100 cm^2 and registers 6.50 W. What is the intensity in W/m^2?

67. Astronomy Application
Energy from the Sun arrives at the top of the Earth's atmosphere with an intensity of $1.30\ \text{kW/m}^2$. How long does it take for $1.8 \times 10^9\ \text{J}$ to arrive on an area of $1.00\ \text{m}^2$?

68. Suppose you have a device that extracts energy from ocean breakers in direct proportion to their intensity. If the device produces 10.0 kW of power on a day when the breakers are 1.20 m high, how much will it produce when they are 0.600 m high?

69. Engineering Application
(a) A photovoltaic array of (solar cells) is 10.0% efficient in gathering solar energy and converting it to electricity. If the average intensity of sunlight on one day is $700\ \text{W/m}^2$, what area should your array have to gather energy at the rate of 100 W? (b) What is the maximum cost of the array if it must pay for itself in two years of operation averaging 10.0 hours per day? Assume that it earns money at the rate of 9.00 ¢ per kilowatt-hour.

70. A microphone receiving a pure sound tone feeds an oscilloscope, producing a wave on its screen. If the sound intensity is originally $2.00 \times 10^{-5}\ \text{W/m}^2$, but is turned up until the amplitude increases by 30.0%, what is the new intensity?

71. Medical Application
(a) What is the intensity in W/m^2 of a laser beam used to burn away cancerous tissue that, when 90.0% absorbed, puts 500 J of energy into a circular spot 2.00 mm in diameter in 4.00 s? (b) Discuss how this intensity compares to the average intensity of sunlight (about $700\ \text{W/m}^2$) and the implications that would have if the laser

beam entered your eye. Note how the amount of damage depends on the time duration of the exposure.

Test Prep for AP® Courses

16.1 Hooke's Law: Stress and Strain Revisited

1. Which of the following represents the distance (how much ground the particle covers) moved by a particle in a simple harmonic motion in one time period? (Here, *A* represents the amplitude of the oscillation.)
   a. 0 cm
   b. *A* cm
   c. 2*A* cm
   d. 4*A* cm

2. A spring has a spring constant of 80 $N \cdot m^{-1}$. What is the force required to (a) compress the spring by 5 cm and (b) expand the spring by 15 cm?

3. In the formula $F = -kx$, what does the minus sign indicate?
   a. It indicates that the restoring force is in the direction of the displacement.
   b. It indicates that the restoring force is in the direction opposite the displacement.
   c. It indicates that mechanical energy in the system decreases when a system undergoes oscillation.
   d. None of the above

4. The splashing of a liquid resembles an oscillation. The restoring force in this scenario will be due to which of the following?
   a. Potential energy
   b. Kinetic energy
   c. Gravity
   d. Mechanical energy

16.2 Period and Frequency in Oscillations

5. A mass attached to a spring oscillates and completes 50 full cycles in 30 s. What is the time period and frequency of this system?

16.3 Simple Harmonic Motion: A Special Periodic Motion

6. Use these figures to answer the following questions.

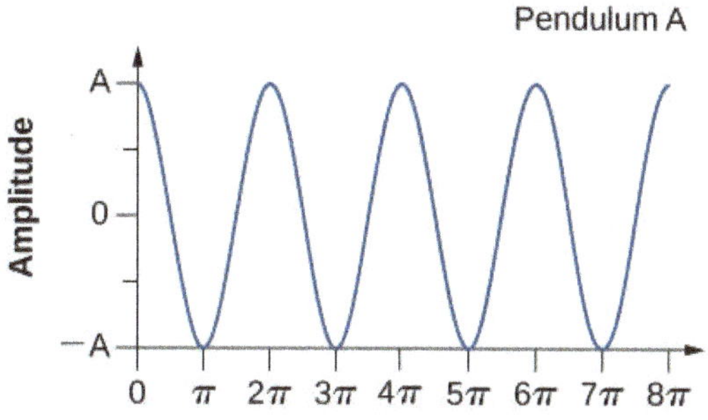

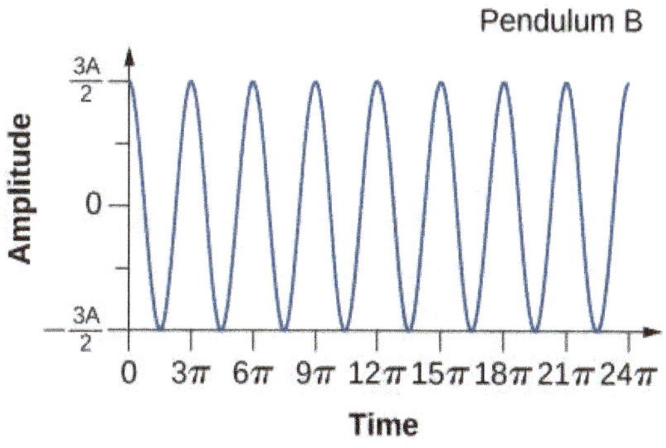

FIGURE 16.45

   a. Which of the two pendulums oscillates with larger amplitude?
   b. Which of the two pendulums oscillates at a higher frequency?

7. A particle of mass 100 g undergoes a simple harmonic motion. The restoring force is provided by a spring with a spring constant of 40 $N \cdot m^{-1}$. What is the period of oscillation?
   a. 10π
   b. 0.5π
   c. 0.1π
   d. 1π

8. The graph shows the simple harmonic motion of a mass *m* attached to a spring with spring constant *k*.

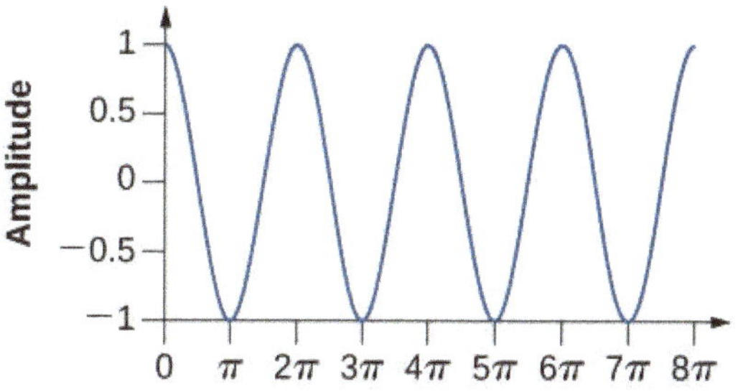

FIGURE 16.46

What is the displacement at time 8π?

a. 1 m
b. 0 m
c. Not defined
d. −1 m

9. A pendulum of mass 200 g undergoes simple harmonic motion when acted upon by a force of 15 N. The pendulum crosses the point of equilibrium at a speed of 5 m•s^{-1}. What is the energy of the pendulum at the center of the oscillation?

16.4 The Simple Pendulum

10. A ball is attached to a string of length 4 m to make a pendulum. The pendulum is placed at a location that is away from the Earth's surface by twice the radius of the Earth. What is the acceleration due to gravity at that height and what is the period of the oscillations?

11. Which of the following gives the correct relation between the acceleration due to gravity and period of a pendulum?
a. $g = \frac{2\pi L}{T^2}$
b. $g = \frac{4\pi^2 L}{T^2}$
c. $g = \frac{2\pi L}{T}$
d. $g = \frac{2\pi^2 L}{T}$

12. Tom has two pendulums with him. Pendulum 1 has a ball of mass 0.1 kg attached to it and has a length of 5 m. Pendulum 2 has a ball of mass 0.5 kg attached to a string of length 1 m. How does mass of the ball affect the frequency of the pendulum? Which pendulum will have a higher frequency and why?

16.5 Energy and the Simple Harmonic Oscillator

13. A mass of 1 kg undergoes simple harmonic motion with amplitude of 1 m. If the period of the oscillation is 1 s, calculate the internal energy of the system.

16.6 Uniform Circular Motion and Simple Harmonic Motion

14. In the equation $x = A \sin \omega t$, what values can the position x take?
a. −1 to +1
b. −*A* to +*A*
c. 0
d. −*t* to *t*

16.7 Damped Harmonic Motion

15. The non-conservative damping force removes energy from a system in which form?
a. Mechanical energy
b. Electrical energy
c. Thermal energy
d. None of the above

16. The time rate of change of mechanical energy for a damped oscillator is always:
a. 0
b. Negative
c. Positive
d. Undefined

17. A 0.5-kg object is connected to a spring that undergoes oscillatory motion. There is friction between the object and the surface it is kept on given by coefficient of friction $\mu_k = 0.06$. If the object is released 0.2 m from equilibrium, what is the distance that the object travels? Given that the force constant of the spring is 50 N m^{-1} and the frictional force between the objects is 0.294 N.

16.8 Forced Oscillations and Resonance

18. How is constant amplitude sustained in forced oscillations?

16.9 Waves

19. What is the difference between the waves coming from a tuning fork and electromagnetic waves?

20. Represent longitudinal and transverse waves in a graphical form.

21. Why is the sound produced by a tambourine different from that produced by drums?

22. A transverse wave is traveling left to right. Which of the following is correct about the motion of particles in the wave?
a. The particles move up and down when the wave travels in a vacuum.
b. The particles move left and right when the wave travels in a medium.
c. The particles move up and down when the wave travels in a medium.
d. The particles move right and left when the wave travels in a vacuum.

23.

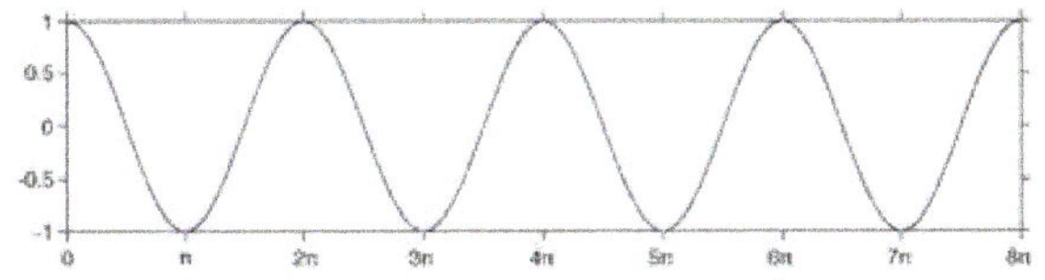

FIGURE 16.47

The graph shows propagation of a mechanical wave. What is the wavelength of this wave?

16.10 Superposition and Interference

24. A guitar string has a number of frequencies at which it vibrates naturally. Which of the following is true in this context?

a. The resonant frequencies of the string are integer multiples of fundamental frequencies.
b. The resonant frequencies of the string are not integer multiples of fundamental frequencies.
c. They have harmonic overtones.
d. None of the above

25. Explain the principle of superposition with figures that show the changes in the wave amplitude.

26. In this figure which points represent the points of constructive interference?

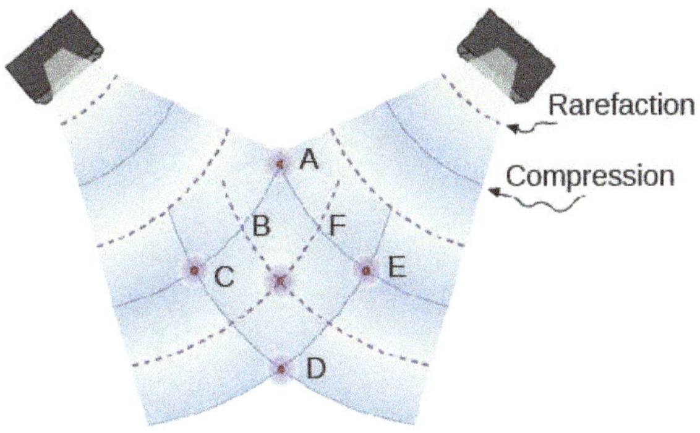

FIGURE 16.48

a. A, B, F
b. A, B, C, D, E, F
c. A, C, D, E
d. A, B, D

27. A string is fixed on both sides. It is snapped from both ends at the same time by applying an equal force. What happens to the shape of the waves generated in the string? Also, will you observe an overlap of waves?

28. In the preceding question, what would happen to the amplitude of the waves generated in this way? Also, consider another scenario where the string is snapped up from one end and down from the other end. What will happen in this situation?

29. Two sine waves travel in the same direction in a medium. The amplitude of each wave is A, and the phase difference between the two is 180°. What is the resultant amplitude?

a. $2A$
b. $3A$
c. 0
d. $9A$

30. Standing wave patterns consist of nodes and antinodes formed by repeated interference between two waves of the same frequency traveling in opposite directions. What are nodes and antinodes and how are they produced?

CHAPTER 17
Physics of Hearing

FIGURE 17.1 This tree fell some time ago. When it fell, atoms in the air were disturbed. Physicists would call this disturbance sound whether someone was around to hear it or not. (credit: B.A. Bowen Photography)

CHAPTER OUTLINE

CONNECTION FOR AP® COURSES In this chapter, the concept of waves is specifically applied to the phenomena of sound. As such, Big Idea 6 continues to be supported, as sound waves carry energy and momentum from one location to another without the permanent transfer of mass. This energy is carried through vibrations caused by disturbances in air pressure (Enduring Understanding 6.A). As air pressure increases, amplitudes of vibration and energy transfer do as well. This idea (Enduring Understanding 6.A.4) explains why a very loud sound can break glass.

The chapter continues the fundamental analysis of waves addressed in Chapter 16. Sound waves are periodic, and can therefore be expressed as a function of position and time. Furthermore, sound waves are described by amplitude, frequency, wavelength, and speed (Enduring Understanding 6.B). The relationship between speed and frequency is analyzed further in Section 17.4, as the frequency of sound depends upon the relative motion between the source and observer. This concept, known as the Doppler effect, supports Essential Knowledge 6.B.5.

Like all other waves, sound waves can overlap. When they do so, their interaction will produce an amplitude variation within the resultant wave. This amplitude can be determined by adding the displacement of the two pulses, through a process called superposition. This process, covered in Section 17.5, reinforces the content in Enduring Understanding 6.D.1.

In situations where the interfering waves are confined, such as on a fixed length of string or in a tube, standing waves can result. These waves are the result of interference between the incident and reflecting wave. Standing waves are described using nodes and antinodes, and their wavelengths are determined by the size of the region to which they are confined. This chapter's description of both standing waves and the concept of beats strongly support Enduring Understanding 6.D, as well as Essential Knowledge 6.D.1, 6.D.3, and 6.D.4.

The concepts in this chapter support:

Big Idea 6 Waves can transfer energy and momentum from one location to another without the permanent transfer of mass and serve as a mathematical model for the description of other phenomena.

Enduring Understanding 6.B A periodic wave is one that repeats as a function of both time and position and can be described by its amplitude, frequency, wavelength, speed, and energy.

Essential Knowledge 6.B.5 The observed frequency of a wave depends on the relative motion of the source and the observer. This is a qualitative measurement only.

Enduring Understanding 6.D Interference and superposition lead to standing waves and beats.

Essential Knowledge 6.D.1 Two or more wave pulses can interact in such a way as to produce amplitude variations in the resultant wave. When two pulses cross, they travel through each other; they do not bounce off each other. Where the pulses overlap, the resulting displacement can be determined by adding the displacements of the two pulses. This is called superposition.

Essential Knowledge 6.D.3 Standing waves are the result of the addition of incident and reflected waves that are confined to a region and have nodes and antinodes. Examples should include waves on a fixed length of string, and sound waves in both closed and open tubes.

Essential Knowledge 6.D.4 The possible wavelengths of a standing wave are determined by the size of the region in which it is confined.

Click to view content (https://openstax.org/books/college-physics-ap-courses-2e/pages/17-connection-for-ap-r-courses)

17.1 Sound

LEARNING OBJECTIVES

By the end of this section, you will be able to:

- Define sound and hearing.
- Describe sound as a longitudinal wave.

FIGURE 17.2 This glass has been shattered by a high-intensity sound wave of the same frequency as the resonant frequency of the glass. While the sound is not visible, the effects of the sound prove its existence. (credit: ||read||, Flickr)

Sound can be used as a familiar illustration of waves. Because hearing is one of our most important senses, it is interesting to see how the physical properties of sound correspond to our perceptions of it. **Hearing** is the perception of sound, just as vision is the perception of visible light. But sound has important applications beyond hearing. Ultrasound, for example, is not heard but can be employed to form medical images and is also used in treatment.

The physical phenomenon of **sound** is defined to be a disturbance of matter that is transmitted from its source outward. Sound is a wave. On the atomic scale, it is a disturbance of atoms that is far more ordered than their thermal motions. In many instances, sound is a periodic wave, and the atoms undergo simple harmonic motion. In this text, we shall explore such periodic sound waves.

A vibrating string produces a sound wave as illustrated in Figure 17.3, Figure 17.4, and Figure 17.5. As the string oscillates back and forth, it transfers energy to the air, mostly as thermal energy created by turbulence. But a small part of the string's energy goes into compressing and expanding the surrounding air, creating slightly higher and lower local pressures. These compressions (high pressure regions) and rarefactions (low pressure regions) move out as longitudinal pressure waves having the same frequency as the string—they are the disturbance that is a sound wave. (Sound waves in air and most fluids are longitudinal, because fluids have almost no shear strength. In solids, sound waves can be both transverse and longitudinal.) Figure 17.5 shows a graph of gauge pressure versus distance from the vibrating string.

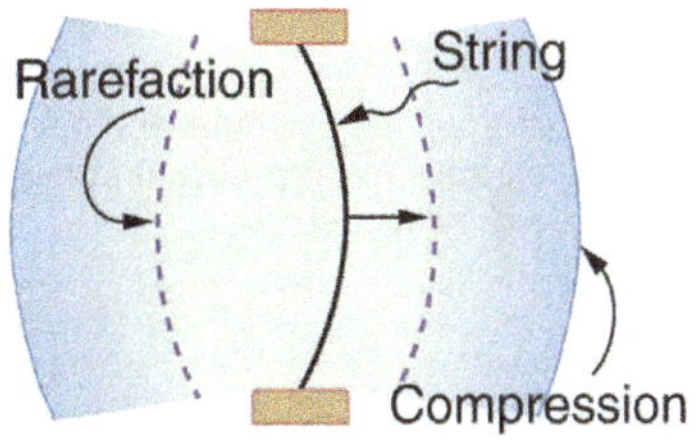

FIGURE 17.3 A vibrating string moving to the right compresses the air in front of it and expands the air behind it.

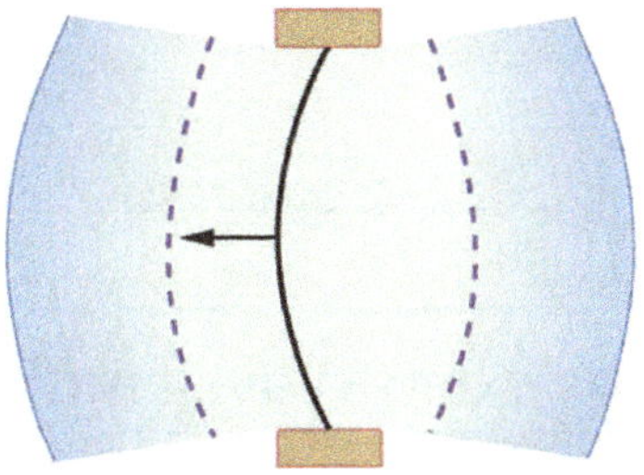

FIGURE 17.4 As the string moves to the left, it creates another compression and rarefaction as the ones on the right move away from the string.

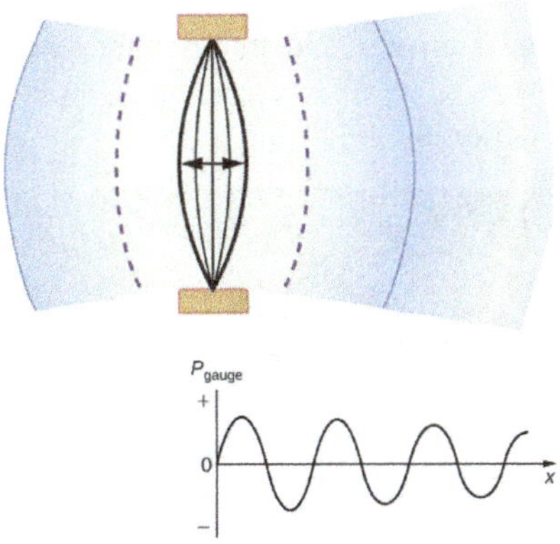

FIGURE 17.5 After many vibrations, there are a series of compressions and rarefactions moving out from the string as a sound wave. The graph shows gauge pressure versus distance from the source. Pressures vary only slightly from atmospheric for ordinary sounds.

The amplitude of a sound wave decreases with distance from its source, because the energy of the wave is spread over a larger and larger area. But it is also absorbed by objects, such as the eardrum in Figure 17.6, and converted to thermal energy by the viscosity of air. In addition, during each compression a little heat transfers to the air and during each rarefaction even less heat transfers from the air, so that the heat transfer reduces the organized disturbance into random thermal motions. (These processes can be viewed as a manifestation of the second law of thermodynamics presented in Introduction to the Second Law of Thermodynamics: Heat Engines and Their Efficiency.) Whether the heat transfer from compression to rarefaction is significant depends on how far apart they are—that is, it depends on wavelength. Wavelength, frequency, amplitude, and speed of propagation are important for sound, as they are for all waves.

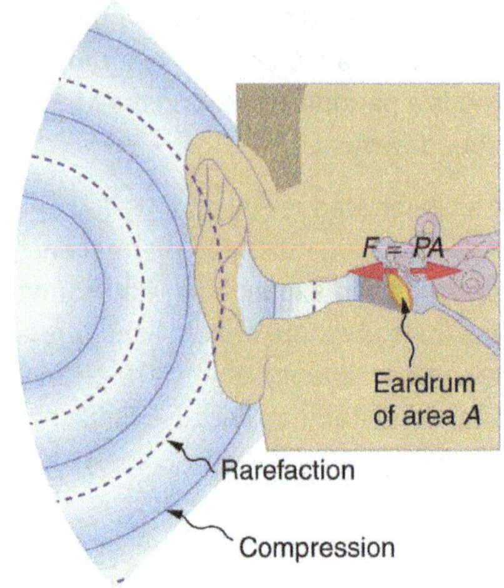

FIGURE 17.6 Sound wave compressions and rarefactions travel up the ear canal and force the eardrum to vibrate. There is a net force on the eardrum, since the sound wave pressures differ from the atmospheric pressure found behind the eardrum. A complicated mechanism converts the vibrations to nerve impulses, which are perceived by the person.

PHET EXPLORATIONS

Wave Interference

Make waves with a dripping faucet, audio speaker, or laser! Add a second source or a pair of slits to create an interference pattern.

Click to view content (https://openstax.org/books/college-physics-ap-courses-2e/pages/17-1-sound)

PhET

17.2 Speed of Sound, Frequency, and Wavelength

LEARNING OBJECTIVES

By the end of this section, you will be able to:

- Define pitch.
- Describe the relationship between the speed of sound, its frequency, and its wavelength.
- Describe the effects on the speed of sound as it travels through various media.
- Describe the effects of temperature on the speed of sound.

FIGURE 17.7 When a firework explodes, the light energy is perceived before the sound energy. Sound travels more slowly than light does. (credit: Dominic Alves, Flickr)

Sound, like all waves, travels at a certain speed and has the properties of frequency and wavelength. You can observe direct evidence of the speed of sound while watching a fireworks display. The flash of an explosion is seen well before its sound is heard, implying both that sound travels at a finite speed and that it is much slower than light. You can also directly sense the frequency of a sound. Perception of frequency is called **pitch**. The wavelength of sound is not directly sensed, but indirect evidence is found in the correlation of the size of musical instruments with their pitch. Small instruments, such as a piccolo, typically make high-pitch sounds, while large instruments, such as a tuba, typically make low-pitch sounds. High pitch means small wavelength, and the size of a musical instrument is directly related to the wavelengths of sound it produces. So a small instrument creates short-wavelength sounds. Similar arguments hold that a large instrument creates long-wavelength sounds.

The relationship of the speed of sound, its frequency, and wavelength is the same as for all waves:

$$v_W = f\lambda, \quad (17.1)$$

where v_W is the speed of sound, f is its frequency, and λ is its wavelength. The wavelength of a sound is the distance between adjacent identical parts of a wave—for example, between adjacent compressions as illustrated in Figure 17.8. The frequency is the same as that of the source and is the number of waves that pass a point per unit time.

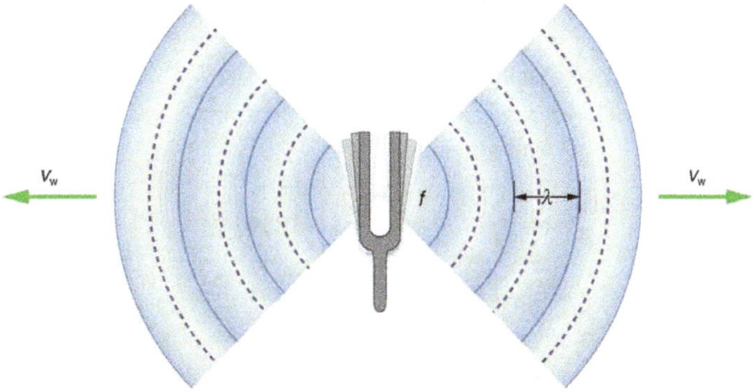

FIGURE 17.8 A sound wave emanates from a source vibrating at a frequency f, propagates at v_W, and has a wavelength λ.

Table 17.1 makes it apparent that the speed of sound varies greatly in different media. The speed of sound in a medium is determined by a combination of the medium's rigidity (or compressibility in gases) and its density. The more rigid (or less compressible) the medium, the faster the speed of sound. For materials that have similar rigidities, sound will travel faster through the one with the lower density because the sound energy is more easily transferred from particle to particle. The speed of sound in air is low, because air is compressible. Because liquids and solids are relatively rigid and very difficult to compress, the speed of sound in such media is generally greater than in gases.

Medium	v_W(m/s)
Gases at $0°C$	
Air	331
Carbon dioxide	259
Oxygen	316
Helium	965
Hydrogen	1290

TABLE 17.1 Speed of Sound in Various Media

Medium	v_w(m/s)
***Liquids at** $20°C$*	
Ethanol	1160
Mercury	1450
Water, fresh	1480
Sea water	1540
Human tissue	1540
Solids (longitudinal or bulk)	
Vulcanized rubber	54
Polyethylene	920
Marble	3810
Glass, Pyrex	5640
Lead	1960
Aluminum	5120
Steel	5960

TABLE 17.1 Speed of Sound in Various Media

Earthquakes, essentially sound waves in Earth's crust, are an interesting example of how the speed of sound depends on the rigidity of the medium. Earthquakes have both longitudinal and transverse components, and these travel at different speeds. The bulk modulus of granite is greater than its shear modulus. For that reason, the speed of longitudinal or pressure waves (P-waves) in earthquakes in granite is significantly higher than the speed of transverse or shear waves (S-waves). Both components of earthquakes travel slower in less rigid material, such as sediments. P-waves have speeds of 4 to 7 km/s, and S-waves correspondingly range in speed from 2 to 5 km/s, both being faster in more rigid material. The P-wave gets progressively farther ahead of the S-wave as they travel through Earth's crust. The time between the P- and S-waves is routinely used to determine the distance to their source, the epicenter of the earthquake. The time and nature of these wave differences also provides the evidence for the nature of Earth's core. Through careful analysis of seismographic records of large earthquakes whose waves could be clearly detected around the world, Richard Dixon Oldham established that waves passing through the center of the Earth behaved as if they were moving through a different medium: a liquid. Later on, Inge Lehmann used more precise observations (partly based on a better coordinated network of seismographs she helped set up) to better define the nature of the core: that it was a solid inner core surrounded by a liquid outer core.

The speed of sound is affected by temperature in a given medium. For air at sea level, the speed of sound is given by

$$v_\mathrm{W} = (331\ \mathrm{m/s})\sqrt{\frac{T}{273\ \mathrm{K}}}, \tag{17.2}$$

where the temperature (denoted as T) is in units of kelvin. The speed of sound in gases is related to the average speed of particles in the gas, v_{rms}, and that

$$v_{\text{rms}} = \sqrt{\frac{3kT}{m}}, \tag{17.3}$$

where k is the Boltzmann constant (1.38×10^{-23} J/K) and m is the mass of each (identical) particle in the gas. So, it is reasonable that the speed of sound in air and other gases should depend on the square root of temperature. While not negligible, this is not a strong dependence. At 0°C, the speed of sound is 331 m/s, whereas at 20.0°C it is 343 m/s, less than a 4% increase. Figure 17.9 shows a use of the speed of sound by a bat to sense distances. Echoes are also used in medical imaging.

FIGURE 17.9 A bat uses sound echoes to find its way about and to catch prey. The time for the echo to return is directly proportional to the distance.

One of the more important properties of sound is that its speed is nearly independent of frequency. This independence is certainly true in open air for sounds in the audible range of 20 to 20,000 Hz. If this independence were not true, you would certainly notice it for music played by a marching band in a football stadium, for example. Suppose that high-frequency sounds traveled faster—then the farther you were from the band, the more the sound from the low-pitch instruments would lag that from the high-pitch ones. But the music from all instruments arrives in cadence independent of distance, and so all frequencies must travel at nearly the same speed. Recall that

$$v_{\text{w}} = f\lambda. \tag{17.4}$$

In a given medium under fixed conditions, v_{w} is constant, so that there is a relationship between f and λ; the higher the frequency, the smaller the wavelength. See Figure 17.10 and consider the following example.

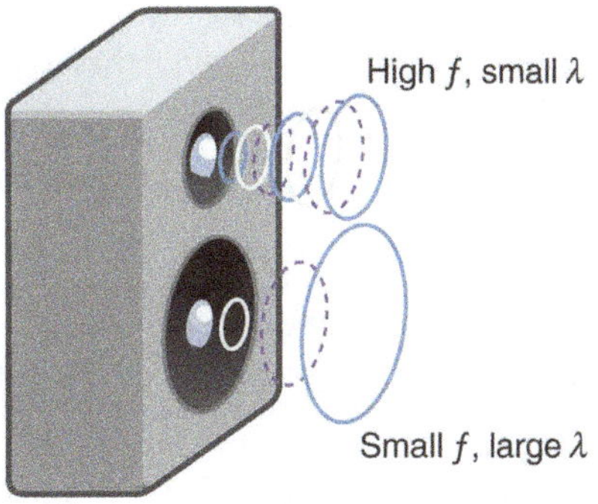

FIGURE 17.10 Because they travel at the same speed in a given medium, low-frequency sounds must have a greater wavelength than high-frequency sounds. Here, the lower-frequency sounds are emitted by the large speaker, called a woofer, while the higher-frequency sounds are emitted by the small speaker, called a tweeter.

EXAMPLE 17.1

Calculating Wavelengths: What Are the Wavelengths of Audible Sounds?

Calculate the wavelengths of sounds at the extremes of the audible range, 20 and 20,000 Hz, in 30.0°C air. (Assume that the frequency values are accurate to two significant figures.)

Strategy

To find wavelength from frequency, we can use $v_{\text{w}} = f\lambda$.

Solution

1. Identify knowns. The value for v_w, is given by

$$v_w = (331\text{ m/s})\sqrt{\frac{T}{273\text{ K}}}. \quad (17.5)$$

2. Convert the temperature into kelvin and then enter the temperature into the equation

$$v_w = (331\text{ m/s})\sqrt{\frac{303\text{ K}}{273\text{ K}}} = 348.7\text{ m/s}. \quad (17.6)$$

3. Solve the relationship between speed and wavelength for λ:

$$\lambda = \frac{v_w}{f}. \quad (17.7)$$

4. Enter the speed and the minimum frequency to give the maximum wavelength:

$$\lambda_{max} = \frac{348.7\text{ m/s}}{20\text{ Hz}} = 17\text{ m}. \quad (17.8)$$

5. Enter the speed and the maximum frequency to give the minimum wavelength:

$$\lambda_{min} = \frac{348.7\text{ m/s}}{20{,}000\text{ Hz}} = 0.017\text{ m} = 1.7\text{ cm}. \quad (17.9)$$

Discussion

Because the product of f multiplied by λ equals a constant, the smaller f is, the larger λ must be, and vice versa.

The speed of sound can change when sound travels from one medium to another. However, the frequency usually remains the same because it is like a driven oscillation and has the frequency of the original source. If v_w changes and f remains the same, then the wavelength λ must change. That is, because $v_w = f\lambda$, the higher the speed of a sound, the greater its wavelength for a given frequency.

MAKING CONNECTIONS: TAKE-HOME INVESTIGATION—VOICE AS A SOUND WAVE

Suspend a sheet of paper so that the top edge of the paper is fixed and the bottom edge is free to move. You could tape the top edge of the paper to the edge of a table. Gently blow near the edge of the bottom of the sheet and note how the sheet moves. Speak softly and then louder such that the sounds hit the edge of the bottom of the paper, and note how the sheet moves. Explain the effects.

CHECK YOUR UNDERSTANDING

Imagine you observe two fireworks explode. You hear the explosion of one as soon as you see it. However, you see the other firework for several milliseconds before you hear the explosion. Explain why this is so.

Solution

Sound and light both travel at definite speeds. The speed of sound is slower than the speed of light. The first firework is probably very close by, so the speed difference is not noticeable. The second firework is farther away, so the light arrives at your eyes noticeably sooner than the sound wave arrives at your ears.

CHECK YOUR UNDERSTANDING

You observe two musical instruments that you cannot identify. One plays high-pitch sounds and the other plays low-pitch sounds. How could you determine which is which without hearing either of them play?

Solution

Compare their sizes. High-pitch instruments are generally smaller than low-pitch instruments because they generate a smaller wavelength.

17.3 Sound Intensity and Sound Level

LEARNING OBJECTIVES

By the end of this section, you will be able to:

- Define intensity, sound intensity, and sound pressure level.
- Calculate sound intensity levels in decibels (dB).

FIGURE 17.11 Noise on crowded roadways like this one in Delhi makes it hard to hear others unless they shout. (credit: Lingaraj G J, Flickr)

In a quiet forest, you can sometimes hear a single leaf fall to the ground. After settling into bed, you may hear your blood pulsing through your ears. But when a passing motorist has his stereo turned up, you cannot even hear what the person next to you in your car is saying. We are all very familiar with the loudness of sounds and aware that they are related to how energetically the source is vibrating. In cartoons depicting a screaming person (or an animal making a loud noise), the cartoonist often shows an open mouth with a vibrating uvula, the hanging tissue at the back of the mouth, to suggest a loud sound coming from the throat Figure 17.12. High noise exposure is hazardous to hearing, and it is common for musicians to have hearing losses that are sufficiently severe that they interfere with the musicians' abilities to perform. The relevant physical quantity is sound intensity, a concept that is valid for all sounds whether or not they are in the audible range.

Intensity is defined to be the power per unit area carried by a wave. Power is the rate at which energy is transferred by the wave. In equation form, **intensity** I is

$$I = \frac{P}{A}, \tag{17.10}$$

where P is the power through an area A. The SI unit for I is $\mathrm{W/m^2}$. The intensity of a sound wave is related to its amplitude squared by the following relationship:

$$I = \frac{(\Delta p)^2}{2\rho v_\mathrm{w}}. \tag{17.11}$$

Here Δp is the pressure variation or pressure amplitude (half the difference between the maximum and minimum pressure in the sound wave) in units of pascals (Pa) or $\mathrm{N/m^2}$. (We are using a lower case p for pressure to distinguish it from power, denoted by P above.) The energy (as kinetic energy $\frac{mv^2}{2}$) of an oscillating element of air due to a traveling sound wave is proportional to its amplitude squared. In this equation, ρ is the density of the material in which the sound wave travels, in units of $\mathrm{kg/m^3}$, and v_w is the speed of sound in the medium, in units of m/s. The pressure variation is proportional to the amplitude of the oscillation, and so I varies as $(\Delta p)^2$ (Figure 17.12). This relationship is consistent with the fact that the sound wave is produced by some vibration; the greater its pressure amplitude, the more the air is compressed in the sound it creates.

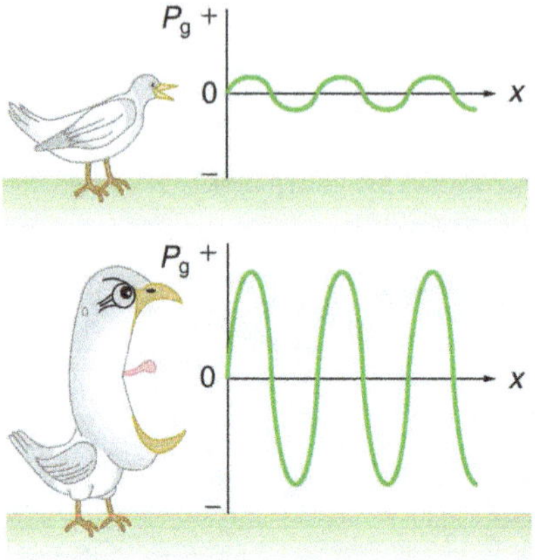

FIGURE 17.12 Graphs of the gauge pressures in two sound waves of different intensities. The more intense sound is produced by a source that has larger-amplitude oscillations and has greater pressure maxima and minima. Because pressures are higher in the greater-intensity sound, it can exert larger forces on the objects it encounters.

Sound intensity levels are quoted in decibels (dB) much more often than sound intensities in watts per meter squared. Decibels are the unit of choice in the scientific literature as well as in the popular media. The reasons for this choice of units are related to how we perceive sounds. How our ears perceive sound can be more accurately described by the logarithm of the intensity rather than directly to the intensity. The **sound intensity level** β in decibels of a sound having an intensity I in watts per meter squared is defined to be

$$\beta\,(\text{dB}) = 10\log_{10}\left(\frac{I}{I_0}\right), \tag{17.12}$$

where $I_0 = 10^{-12}\ \text{W/m}^2$ is a reference intensity. In particular, I_0 is the lowest or threshold intensity of sound a person with normal hearing can perceive at a frequency of 1000 Hz. Sound intensity level is not the same as intensity. Because β is defined in terms of a ratio, it is a unitless quantity telling you the *level* of the sound relative to a fixed standard ($10^{-12}\ \text{W/m}^2$, in this case). The units of decibels (dB) are used to indicate this ratio is multiplied by 10 in its definition. The bel, upon which the decibel is based, is named for Alexander Graham Bell, the inventor of the telephone.

Sound intensity level $\boldsymbol{\beta}$ (dB)	Intensity $I(\text{W/m}^2)$	Example/effect
0	1×10^{-12}	Threshold of hearing at 1000 Hz
10	1×10^{-11}	Rustle of leaves
20	1×10^{-10}	Whisper at 1 m distance
30	1×10^{-9}	Quiet home
40	1×10^{-8}	Average home
50	1×10^{-7}	Average office, soft music
60	1×10^{-6}	Normal conversation
70	1×10^{-5}	Noisy office, busy traffic
80	1×10^{-4}	Loud radio, classroom lecture

TABLE 17.2 Sound Intensity Levels and Intensities

Sound intensity level β (dB)	Intensity I(W/m^2)	Example/effect
90	1×10^{-3}	Inside a heavy truck; damage from prolonged exposure[1]
100	1×10^{-2}	Noisy factory, siren at 30 m; damage from 8 h per day exposure
110	1×10^{-1}	Damage from 30 min per day exposure
120	1	Loud rock concert, pneumatic chipper at 2 m; threshold of pain
140	1×10^{2}	Jet airplane at 30 m; severe pain, damage in seconds
160	1×10^{4}	Bursting of eardrums

TABLE 17.2 Sound Intensity Levels and Intensities

The decibel level of a sound having the threshold intensity of $10^{-12}\ \mathrm{W/m^2}$ is $\beta = 0\ \mathrm{dB}$, because $\log_{10} 1 = 0$. That is, the threshold of hearing is 0 decibels. Table 17.2 gives levels in decibels and intensities in watts per meter squared for some familiar sounds.

One of the more striking things about the intensities in Table 17.2 is that the intensity in watts per meter squared is quite small for most sounds. The ear is sensitive to as little as a trillionth of a watt per meter squared—even more impressive when you realize that the area of the eardrum is only about $1\ \mathrm{cm}^2$, so that only 10^{-16} W falls on it at the threshold of hearing! Air molecules in a sound wave of this intensity vibrate over a distance of less than one molecular diameter, and the gauge pressures involved are less than 10^{-9} atm.

Another impressive feature of the sounds in Table 17.2 is their numerical range. Sound intensity varies by a factor of 10^{12} from threshold to a sound that causes damage in seconds. You are unaware of this tremendous range in sound intensity because how your ears respond can be described approximately as the logarithm of intensity. Thus, sound intensity levels in decibels fit your experience better than intensities in watts per meter squared. The decibel scale is also easier to relate to because most people are more accustomed to dealing with numbers such as 0, 53, or 120 than numbers such as 1.00×10^{-11}.

One more observation readily verified by examining Table 17.2 or using $I = \frac{(\Delta p)^2}{2\rho v_\mathrm{W}}$ is that each factor of 10 in intensity corresponds to 10 dB. For example, a 90 dB sound compared with a 60 dB sound is 30 dB greater, or three factors of 10 (that is, 10^3 times) as intense. Another example is that if one sound is 10^7 as intense as another, it is 70 dB higher. See Table 17.3.

1 Several government agencies and health-related professional associations recommend that 85 dB not be exceeded for 8-hour daily exposures in the absence of hearing protection.

I_2/I_1	$\beta_2 - \beta_1$
2.0	3.0 dB
5.0	7.0 dB
10.0	10.0 dB

TABLE 17.3 Ratios of Intensities and Corresponding Differences in Sound Intensity Levels

EXAMPLE 17.2

Calculating Sound Intensity Levels: Sound Waves

Calculate the sound intensity level in decibels for a sound wave traveling in air at $0°C$ and having a pressure amplitude of 0.656 Pa.

Strategy

We are given Δp, so we can calculate I using the equation $I = (\Delta p)^2/\left(2\rho v_w\right)^2$. Using I, we can calculate β straight from its definition in $\beta\ (\text{dB}) = 10\ \log_{10}\left(I/I_0\right)$.

Solution

(1) Identify knowns:

Sound travels at 331 m/s in air at $0°C$.

Air has a density of $1.29\ \text{kg/m}^3$ at atmospheric pressure and $0°C$.

(2) Enter these values and the pressure amplitude into $I = (\Delta p)^2/\left(2\rho v_w\right)$:

$$I = \frac{(\Delta p)^2}{2\rho v_w} = \frac{(0.656\ \text{Pa})^2}{2\left(1.29\ \text{kg/m}^3\right)(331\ \text{m/s})} = 5.04 \times 10^{-4}\ \text{W/m}^2. \tag{17.13}$$

(3) Enter the value for I and the known value for I_0 into $\beta\ (\text{dB}) = 10\ \log_{10}\left(I/I_0\right)$. Calculate to find the sound intensity level in decibels:

$$10\ \log_{10}\left(5.04 \times 10^8\right) = 10\ \left(8.70\right)\ \text{dB} = 87\ \text{dB}. \tag{17.14}$$

Discussion

This 87 dB sound has an intensity five times as great as an 80 dB sound. So a factor of five in intensity corresponds to a difference of 7 dB in sound intensity level. This value is true for any intensities differing by a factor of five.

EXAMPLE 17.3

Change Intensity Levels of a Sound: What Happens to the Decibel Level?

Show that if one sound is twice as intense as another, it has a sound level about 3 dB higher.

Strategy

You are given that the ratio of two intensities is 2 to 1, and are then asked to find the difference in their sound levels in decibels. You can solve this problem using of the properties of logarithms.

Solution

(1) Identify knowns:

The ratio of the two intensities is 2 to 1, or:

$$\frac{I_2}{I_1} = 2.00. \tag{17.15}$$

We wish to show that the difference in sound levels is about 3 dB. That is, we want to show:

$$\beta_2 - \beta_1 = 3 \text{ dB}. \tag{17.16}$$

Note that:

$$\log_{10} b - \log_{10} a = \log_{10}\left(\frac{b}{a}\right). \tag{17.17}$$

(2) Use the definition of β to get:

$$\beta_2 - \beta_1 = 10 \log_{10}\left(\frac{I_2}{I_1}\right) = 10 \log_{10} 2.00 = 10\ (0.301) \text{ dB}. \tag{17.18}$$

Thus,

$$\beta_2 - \beta_1 = 3.01 \text{ dB}. \tag{17.19}$$

Discussion

This means that the two sound intensity levels differ by 3.01 dB, or about 3 dB, as advertised. Note that because only the ratio I_2/I_1 is given (and not the actual intensities), this result is true for any intensities that differ by a factor of two. For example, a 56.0 dB sound is twice as intense as a 53.0 dB sound, a 97.0 dB sound is half as intense as a 100 dB sound, and so on.

It should be noted at this point that there is another decibel scale in use, called the **sound pressure level**, based on the ratio of the pressure amplitude to a reference pressure. This scale is used particularly in applications where sound travels in water. It is beyond the scope of most introductory texts to treat this scale because it is not commonly used for sounds in air, but it is important to note that very different decibel levels may be encountered when sound pressure levels are quoted. For example, ocean noise pollution produced by ships may be as great as 200 dB expressed in the sound pressure level, where the more familiar sound intensity level we use here would be something under 140 dB for the same sound.

TAKE-HOME INVESTIGATION: FEELING SOUND

Find a CD player and a CD that has rock music. Place the player on a light table, insert the CD into the player, and start playing the CD. Place your hand gently on the table next to the speakers. Increase the volume and note the level when the table just begins to vibrate as the rock music plays. Increase the reading on the volume control until it doubles. What has happened to the vibrations?

CHECK YOUR UNDERSTANDING

Describe how amplitude is related to the loudness of a sound.

Solution

Amplitude is directly proportional to the experience of loudness. As amplitude increases, loudness increases.

CHECK YOUR UNDERSTANDING

Identify common sounds at the levels of 10 dB, 50 dB, and 100 dB.

Solution

10 dB: Running fingers through your hair.

50 dB: Inside a quiet home with no television or radio.

100 dB: Take-off of a jet plane.

17.4 Doppler Effect and Sonic Booms

LEARNING OBJECTIVES

By the end of this section, you will be able to:

- Define Doppler effect, Doppler shift, and sonic boom.
- Calculate the frequency of a sound heard by someone observing Doppler shift.
- Describe the sounds produced by objects moving faster than the speed of sound.

The characteristic sound of a motorcycle buzzing by is an example of the **Doppler effect**. The high-pitch scream shifts dramatically to a lower-pitch roar as the motorcycle passes by a stationary observer. The closer the motorcycle brushes by, the more abrupt the shift. The faster the motorcycle moves, the greater the shift. We also hear this characteristic shift in frequency for passing race cars, airplanes, and trains. It is so familiar that it is used to imply motion and children often mimic it in play.

The Doppler effect is an alteration in the observed frequency of a sound due to motion of either the source or the observer. Although less familiar, this effect is easily noticed for a stationary source and moving observer. For example, if you ride a train past a stationary warning bell, you will hear the bell's frequency shift from high to low as you pass by. The actual change in frequency due to relative motion of source and observer is called a **Doppler shift**. The Doppler effect and Doppler shift are named for the Austrian physicist and mathematician Christian Johann Doppler (1803–1853), who did experiments with both moving sources and moving observers. Doppler, for example, had musicians play on a moving open train car and also play standing next to the train tracks as a train passed by. Their music was observed both on and off the train, and changes in frequency were measured.

What causes the Doppler shift? Figure 17.13, Figure 17.14, and Figure 17.15 compare sound waves emitted by stationary and moving sources in a stationary air mass. Each disturbance spreads out spherically from the point where the sound was emitted. If the source is stationary, then all of the spheres representing the air compressions in the sound wave centered on the same point, and the stationary observers on either side see the same wavelength and frequency as emitted by the source, as in Figure 17.13. If the source is moving, as in Figure 17.14, then the situation is different. Each compression of the air moves out in a sphere from the point where it was emitted, but the point of emission moves. This moving emission point causes the air compressions to be closer together on one side and farther apart on the other. Thus, the wavelength is shorter in the direction the source is moving (on the right in Figure 17.14), and longer in the opposite direction (on the left in Figure 17.14). Finally, if the observers move, as in Figure 17.15, the frequency at which they receive the compressions changes. The observer moving toward the source receives them at a higher frequency, and the person moving away from the source receives them at a lower frequency.

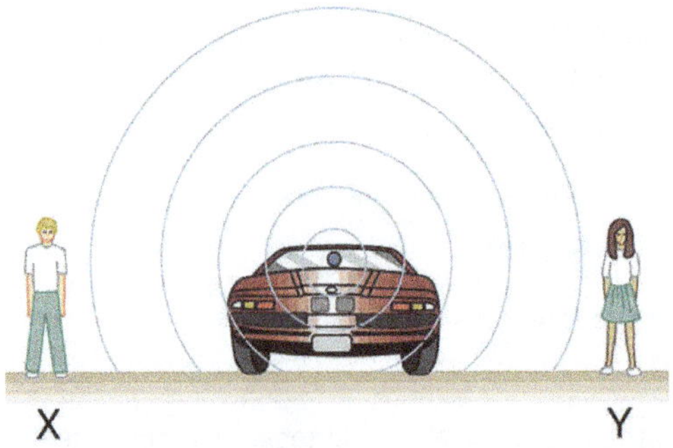

FIGURE 17.13 Sounds emitted by a source spread out in spherical waves. Because the source, observers, and air are stationary, the

wavelength and frequency are the same in all directions and to all observers.

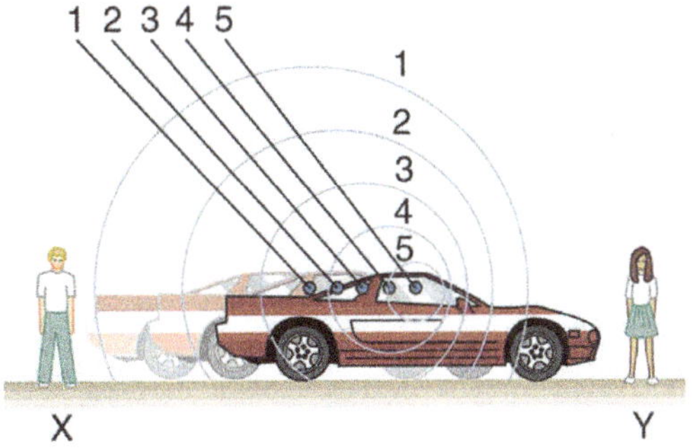

FIGURE 17.14 Sounds emitted by a source moving to the right spread out from the points at which they were emitted. The wavelength is reduced and, consequently, the frequency is increased in the direction of motion, so that the observer on the right hears a higher-pitch sound. The opposite is true for the observer on the left, where the wavelength is increased and the frequency is reduced.

FIGURE 17.15 The same effect is produced when the observers move relative to the source. Motion toward the source increases frequency as the observer on the right passes through more wave crests than she would if stationary. Motion away from the source decreases frequency as the observer on the left passes through fewer wave crests than he would if stationary.

We know that wavelength and frequency are related by $v_W = f\lambda$, where v_W is the fixed speed of sound. The sound moves in a medium and has the same speed v_W in that medium whether the source is moving or not. Thus f multiplied by λ is a constant. Because the observer on the right in Figure 17.14 receives a shorter wavelength, the frequency she receives must be higher. Similarly, the observer on the left receives a longer wavelength, and hence he hears a lower frequency. The same thing happens in Figure 17.15. A higher frequency is received by the observer moving toward the source, and a lower frequency is received by an observer moving away from the source. In general, then, relative motion of source and observer toward one another increases the received frequency. Relative motion apart decreases frequency. The greater the relative speed is, the greater the effect.

THE DOPPLER EFFECT

The Doppler effect occurs not only for sound but for any wave when there is relative motion between the observer and the source. There are Doppler shifts in the frequency of sound, light, and water waves, for example. Doppler shifts can be used to determine velocity, such as when ultrasound is reflected from blood in a medical diagnostic. The recession of galaxies is determined by the shift in the frequencies of light received from them and has implied much about the origins of the universe. Modern physics has been profoundly affected by observations of Doppler shifts.

For a stationary observer and a moving source, the frequency f_{obs} received by the observer can be shown to be

$$f_{obs} = f_s\left(\frac{v_W}{v_W \pm v_s}\right), \quad 17.20$$

where f_s is the frequency of the source, v_s is the speed of the source along a line joining the source and observer, and v_W is the speed of sound. The minus sign is used for motion toward the observer and the plus sign for motion away from the observer, producing the appropriate shifts up and down in frequency. Note that the greater the speed of the source, the greater the effect. Similarly, for a stationary source and moving observer, the frequency received by the observer f_{obs} is given by

$$f_{obs} = f_s \left(\frac{v_w \pm v_{obs}}{v_w} \right), \tag{17.21}$$

where v_{obs} is the speed of the observer along a line joining the source and observer. Here the plus sign is for motion toward the source, and the minus is for motion away from the source.

EXAMPLE 17.4

Calculate Doppler Shift: A Train Horn

Suppose a train that has a 150-Hz horn is moving at 35.0 m/s in still air on a day when the speed of sound is 340 m/s.

(a) What frequencies are observed by a stationary person at the side of the tracks as the train approaches and after it passes?

(b) What frequency is observed by the train's engineer traveling on the train?

Strategy

To find the observed frequency in (a), $f_{obs} = f_s \left(\frac{v_w}{v_w \pm v_s} \right)$, must be used because the source is moving. The minus sign is used for the approaching train, and the plus sign for the receding train. In (b), there are two Doppler shifts—one for a moving source and the other for a moving observer.

Solution for (a)

(1) Enter known values into $f_{obs} = f_s \left(\frac{v_w}{v_w - v_s} \right)$.

$$f_{obs} = f_s \left(\frac{v_w}{v_w - v_s} \right) = (150\text{ Hz}) \left(\frac{340\text{ m/s}}{340\text{ m/s} - 35.0\text{ m/s}} \right) \tag{17.22}$$

(2) Calculate the frequency observed by a stationary person as the train approaches.

$$f_{obs} = (150\text{ Hz})(1.11) = 167\text{ Hz} \tag{17.23}$$

(3) Use the same equation with the plus sign to find the frequency heard by a stationary person as the train recedes.

$$f_{obs} = f_s \left(\frac{v_w}{v_w + v_s} \right) = (150\text{ Hz}) \left(\frac{340\text{ m/s}}{340\text{ m/s} + 35.0\text{ m/s}} \right) \tag{17.24}$$

(4) Calculate the second frequency.

$$f_{obs} = (150\text{ Hz})(0.907) = 136\text{ Hz} \tag{17.25}$$

Discussion on (a)

The numbers calculated are valid when the train is far enough away that the motion is nearly along the line joining train and observer. In both cases, the shift is significant and easily noticed. Note that the shift is 17.0 Hz for motion toward and 14.0 Hz for motion away. The shifts are not symmetric.

Solution for (b)

(1) Identify knowns:

- It seems reasonable that the engineer would receive the same frequency as emitted by the horn, because the relative velocity between them is zero.
- Relative to the medium (air), the speeds are $v_s = v_{obs} = 35.0\text{ m/s}$.
- The first Doppler shift is for the moving observer; the second is for the moving source.

(2) Use the following equation:

$$f_{obs} = \left[f_s \left(\frac{v_w \pm v_{obs}}{v_w} \right) \right] \left(\frac{v_w}{v_w \pm v_s} \right). \tag{17.26}$$

The quantity in the square brackets is the Doppler-shifted frequency due to a moving observer. The factor on the right is the effect of the moving source.

(3) Because the train engineer is moving in the direction toward the horn, we must use the plus sign for v_{obs}; however, because the horn is also moving in the direction away from the engineer, we also use the plus sign for v_s. But the train is carrying both the engineer and the horn at the same velocity, so $v_s = v_{obs}$. As a result, everything but f_s cancels, yielding

$$f_{obs} = f_s. \quad (17.27)$$

Discussion for (b)

We may expect that there is no change in frequency when source and observer move together because it fits your experience. For example, there is no Doppler shift in the frequency of conversations between driver and passenger on a motorcycle. People talking when a wind moves the air between them also observe no Doppler shift in their conversation. The crucial point is that source and observer are not moving relative to each other.

Sonic Booms to Bow Wakes

What happens to the sound produced by a moving source, such as a jet airplane, that approaches or even exceeds the speed of sound? The answer to this question applies not only to sound but to all other waves as well.

Suppose a jet airplane is coming nearly straight at you, emitting a sound of frequency f_s. The greater the plane's speed v_s, the greater the Doppler shift and the greater the value observed for f_{obs}. Now, as v_s approaches the speed of sound, f_{obs} approaches infinity, because the denominator in $f_{obs} = f_s\left(\frac{v_w}{v_w \pm v_s}\right)$ approaches zero. At the speed of sound, this result means that in front of the source, each successive wave is superimposed on the previous one because the source moves forward at the speed of sound. The observer gets them all at the same instant, and so the frequency is infinite. (Before airplanes exceeded the speed of sound, some people argued it would be impossible because such constructive superposition would produce pressures great enough to destroy the airplane.) If the source exceeds the speed of sound, no sound is received by the observer until the source has passed, so that the sounds from the approaching source are mixed with those from it when receding. This mixing appears messy, but something interesting happens—a sonic boom is created. (See Figure 17.16.)

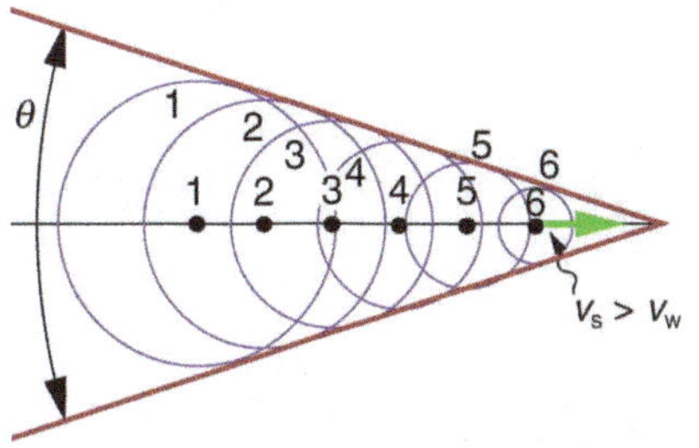

FIGURE 17.16 Sound waves from a source that moves faster than the speed of sound spread spherically from the point where they are emitted, but the source moves ahead of each. Constructive interference along the lines shown (actually a cone in three dimensions) creates a shock wave called a sonic boom. The faster the speed of the source, the smaller the angle θ.

There is constructive interference along the lines shown (a cone in three dimensions) from similar sound waves arriving there simultaneously. This superposition forms a disturbance called a **sonic boom**, a constructive interference of sound created by an object moving faster than sound. Inside the cone, the interference is mostly destructive, and so the sound intensity there is much less than on the shock wave. An aircraft creates two sonic booms, one from its nose and one from its tail. (See Figure 17.17.) During television coverage of space shuttle landings, two distinct booms could often be heard. These were separated by exactly the time it would take the shuttle to pass by a point. Observers on the ground often do not see the aircraft creating the sonic boom, because it has passed by before the shock wave reaches them, as seen in Figure 17.17. If the aircraft flies close by at low altitude, pressures in the sonic boom can be destructive and break windows as well as rattle nerves. Because of how destructive sonic booms can be, supersonic flights are banned over populated areas of the United States.

FIGURE 17.17 Two sonic booms, created by the nose and tail of an aircraft, are observed on the ground after the plane has passed by.

Sonic booms are one example of a broader phenomenon called bow wakes. A **bow wake**, such as the one in Figure 17.18, is created when the wave source moves faster than the wave propagation speed. Water waves spread out in circles from the point where created, and the bow wake is the familiar V-shaped wake trailing the source. A more exotic bow wake is created when a subatomic particle travels through a medium faster than the speed of light travels in that medium. (In a vacuum, the maximum speed of light will be $c = 3.00 \times 10^8\ \text{m/s}$; in the medium of water, the speed of light is closer to $0.75c$. If the particle creates light in its passage, that light spreads on a cone with an angle indicative of the speed of the particle, as illustrated in Figure 17.19. Such a bow wake is called Cerenkov radiation and is commonly observed in particle physics.

FIGURE 17.18 Bow wake created by a duck. Constructive interference produces the rather structured wake, while there is relatively little wave action inside the wake, where interference is mostly destructive. (credit: Horia Varlan, Flickr)

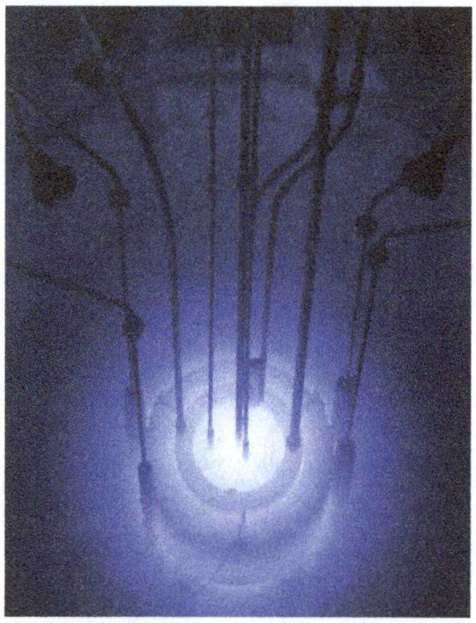

FIGURE 17.19 The blue glow in this research reactor pool is Cerenkov radiation caused by subatomic particles traveling faster than the speed of light in water. (credit: U.S. Nuclear Regulatory Commission)

Doppler shifts and sonic booms are interesting sound phenomena that occur in all types of waves. They can be of considerable use. For example, the Doppler shift in ultrasound can be used to measure blood velocity, while police use the Doppler shift in radar (a microwave) to measure car velocities. In meteorology, the Doppler shift is used to track the motion of storm clouds; such "Doppler Radar" can give velocity and direction and rain or snow potential of imposing weather fronts. In astronomy, we can examine the light emitted from distant galaxies and determine their speed relative to ours. As galaxies move away from us, their light is shifted to a lower frequency, and so to a longer wavelength—the so-called red shift. Such information from galaxies far, far away has allowed us to estimate the age of the universe (from the Big Bang) as about 14 billion years.

CHECK YOUR UNDERSTANDING

Why did scientist Christian Doppler observe musicians both on a moving train and also from a stationary point not on the train?

Solution

Doppler needed to compare the perception of sound when the observer is stationary and the sound source moves, as well as when the sound source and the observer are both in motion.

CHECK YOUR UNDERSTANDING

Describe a situation in your life when you might rely on the Doppler shift to help you either while driving a car or walking near traffic.

Solution

If I am driving and I hear Doppler shift in an ambulance siren, I would be able to tell when it was getting closer and also if it has passed by. This would help me to know whether I needed to pull over and let the ambulance through.

17.5 Sound Interference and Resonance: Standing Waves in Air Columns

LEARNING OBJECTIVES

By the end of this section, you will be able to:

- Define antinode, node, fundamental, overtones, and harmonics.
- Identify instances of sound interference in everyday situations.
- Describe how sound interference occurring inside open and closed tubes changes the characteristics of the sound, and how this applies to sounds produced by musical instruments.
- Calculate the length of a tube using sound wave measurements.

FIGURE 17.20 Some types of headphones use the phenomena of constructive and destructive interference to cancel out outside noises. (credit: JVC America, Flickr)

Interference is the hallmark of waves, all of which exhibit constructive and destructive interference exactly analogous to that seen for water waves. In fact, one way to prove something "is a wave" is to observe interference effects. So, sound being a wave, we expect it to exhibit interference; we have already mentioned a few such effects, such as the beats from two similar notes played simultaneously.

Figure 17.21 shows a clever use of sound interference to cancel noise. Larger-scale applications of active noise reduction by destructive interference are contemplated for entire passenger compartments in commercial aircraft. To obtain destructive interference, a fast electronic analysis is performed, and a second sound is introduced with its maxima and minima exactly reversed from the incoming noise. Sound waves in fluids are pressure waves and consistent with Pascal's principle; pressures from two different sources add and subtract like simple numbers; that is, positive and negative gauge pressures add to a much smaller pressure, producing a lower-intensity sound. Although completely destructive interference is possible only under the simplest conditions, it is possible to reduce noise levels by 30 dB or more using this technique.

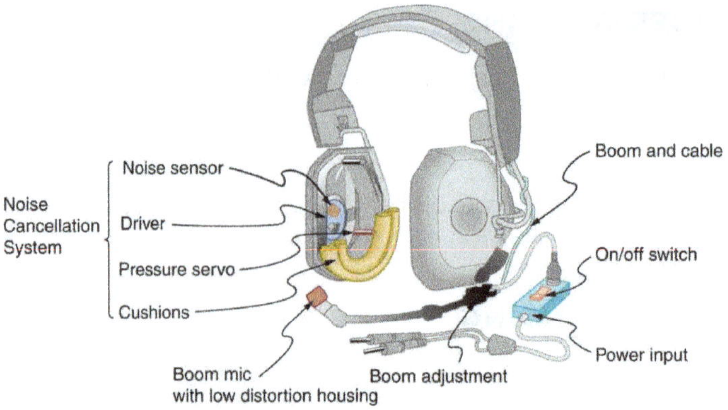

FIGURE 17.21 Headphones designed to cancel noise with destructive interference create a sound wave exactly opposite to the incoming sound. These headphones can be more effective than the simple passive attenuation used in most ear protection. Such headphones were used on the record-setting, around the world nonstop flight of the Voyager aircraft to protect the pilots' hearing from engine noise.

Where else can we observe sound interference? All sound resonances, such as in musical instruments, are due to constructive and destructive interference. Only the resonant frequencies interfere constructively to form standing waves, while others interfere destructively and are absent. From the toot made by blowing over a bottle, to the characteristic flavor of a violin's sounding box, to the recognizability of a great singer's voice, resonance and standing waves play a vital role.

INTERFERENCE

Interference is such a fundamental aspect of waves that observing interference is proof that something is a wave. The wave nature of light was established by experiments showing interference. Similarly, when electrons scattered from crystals exhibited interference, their wave nature was confirmed to be exactly as predicted by symmetry with certain wave characteristics of light.

Suppose we hold a tuning fork near the end of a tube that is closed at the other end, as shown in Figure 17.22, Figure 17.23, Figure 17.24, and Figure 17.25. If the tuning fork has just the right frequency, the air column in the tube resonates loudly, but at most frequencies it vibrates very little. This observation just means that the air column has only certain natural frequencies. The figures show how a resonance at the lowest of these natural frequencies is formed. A disturbance travels down the tube at the speed of sound and bounces off the closed end. If the tube is just the right length, the reflected sound arrives back at the tuning fork exactly half a cycle later, and it interferes constructively with the continuing sound produced by the tuning fork. The incoming and reflected sounds form a standing wave in the tube as shown.

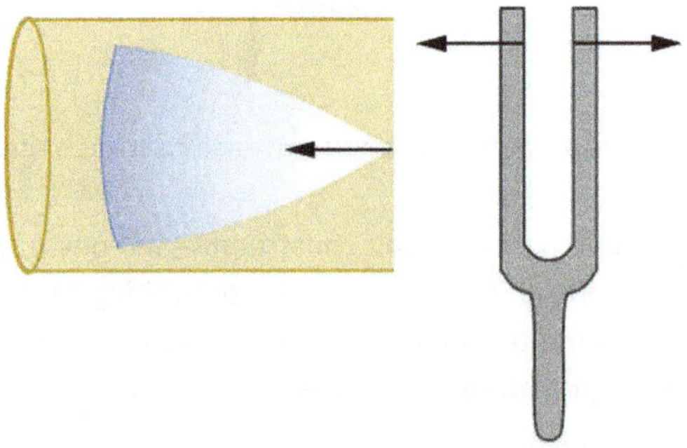

FIGURE 17.22 Resonance of air in a tube closed at one end, caused by a tuning fork. A disturbance moves down the tube.

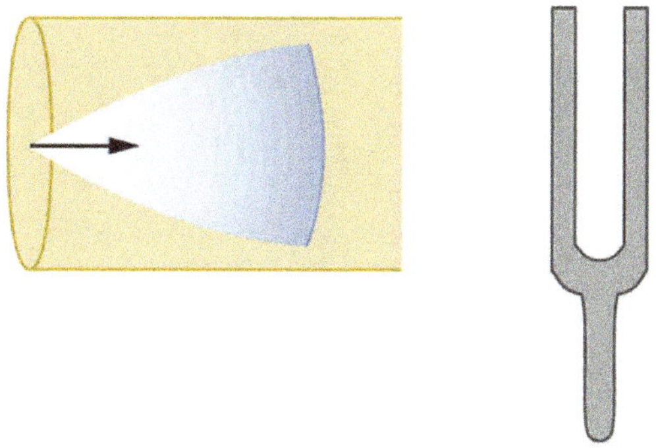

FIGURE 17.23 Resonance of air in a tube closed at one end, caused by a tuning fork. The disturbance reflects from the closed end of the tube.

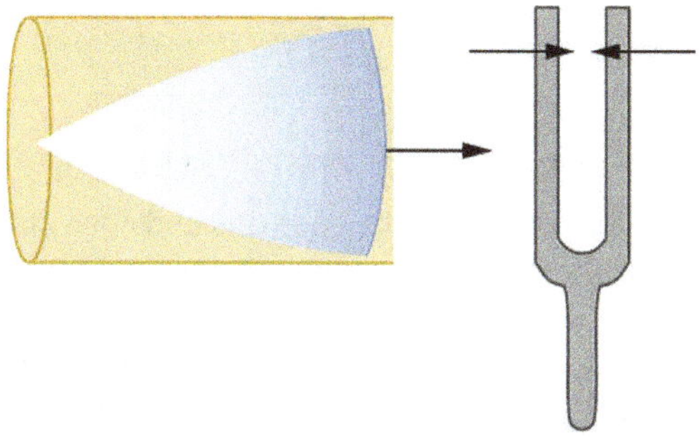

FIGURE 17.24 Resonance of air in a tube closed at one end, caused by a tuning fork. If the length of the tube L is just right, the disturbance gets back to the tuning fork half a cycle later and interferes constructively with the continuing sound from the tuning fork. This interference forms a standing wave, and the air column resonates.

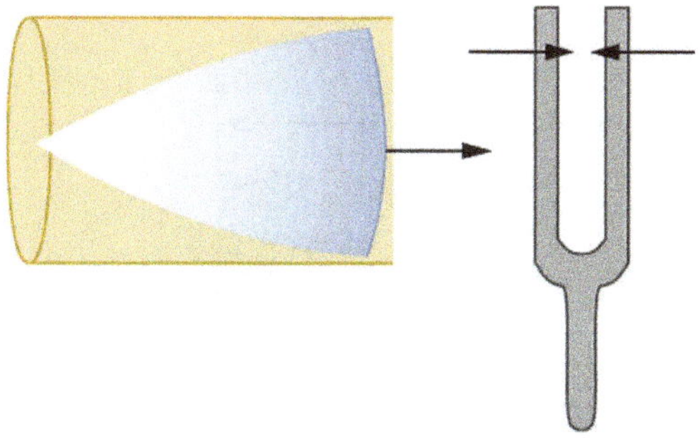

FIGURE 17.25 Resonance of air in a tube closed at one end, caused by a tuning fork. A graph of air displacement along the length of the tube shows none at the closed end, where the motion is constrained, and a maximum at the open end. This standing wave has one-fourth of its wavelength in the tube, so that $\lambda = 4L$.

The standing wave formed in the tube has its maximum air displacement (an **antinode**) at the open end, where motion is unconstrained, and no displacement (a **node**) at the closed end, where air movement is halted. The distance from a node to an antinode is one-fourth of a wavelength, and this equals the length of the tube; thus, $\lambda = 4L$. This same resonance can be produced by a vibration introduced at or near the closed end of the tube, as shown in Figure 17.26. It is best to consider this a natural vibration of the air column independently of how it is induced.

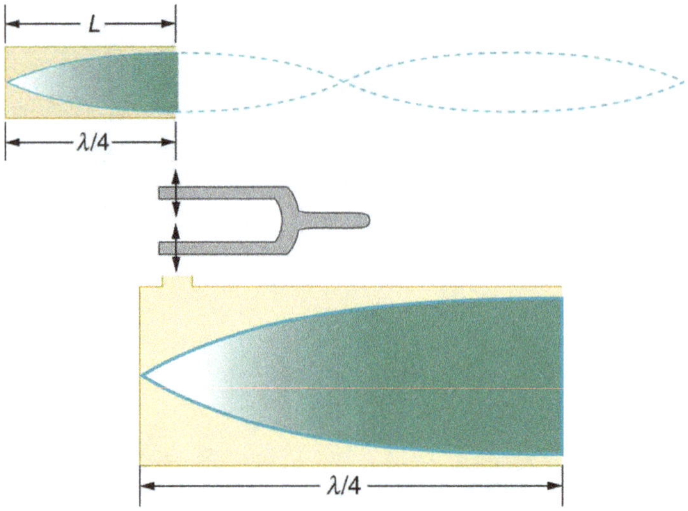

FIGURE 17.26 The same standing wave is created in the tube by a vibration introduced near its closed end.

Given that maximum air displacements are possible at the open end and none at the closed end, there are other, shorter wavelengths that can resonate in the tube, such as the one shown in Figure 17.27. Here the standing wave has three-fourths of its wavelength in the tube, or $L = (3/4)\lambda'$, so that $\lambda' = 4L/3$. Continuing this process reveals a whole series of shorter-wavelength and higher-frequency sounds that resonate in the tube. We use specific terms for the resonances in any system. The lowest resonant frequency is called the **fundamental**, while all higher resonant frequencies are called **overtones**. All resonant frequencies are integral multiples of the fundamental, and they are collectively called **harmonics**. The fundamental is the first harmonic, the first overtone is the second harmonic, and so on. Figure 17.28 shows the fundamental and the first three overtones (the first four harmonics) in a tube closed at one end.

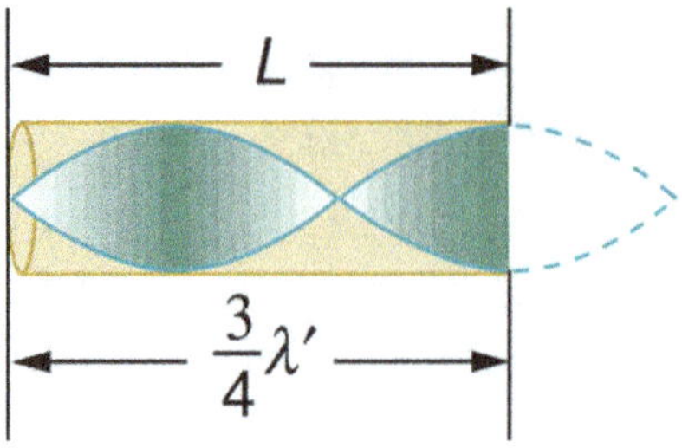

FIGURE 17.27 Another resonance for a tube closed at one end. This has maximum air displacements at the open end, and none at the closed end. The wavelength is shorter, with three-fourths λ' equaling the length of the tube, so that $\lambda' = 4L/3$. This higher-frequency vibration is the first overtone.

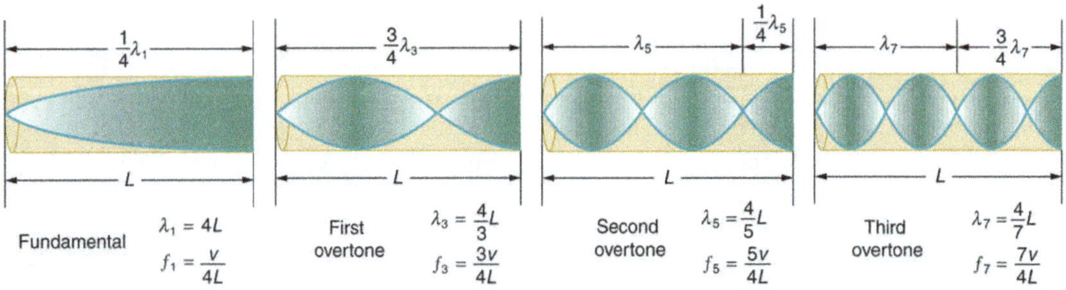

FIGURE 17.28 The fundamental and three lowest overtones for a tube closed at one end. All have maximum air displacements at the open end and none at the closed end.

The fundamental and overtones can be present simultaneously in a variety of combinations. For example, middle C on a trumpet has a sound distinctively different from middle C on a clarinet, both instruments being modified versions of a tube closed at one end. The fundamental frequency is the same (and usually the most intense), but the overtones and their mix of intensities are different and subject to shading by the musician. This mix is what gives various musical instruments (and human voices) their distinctive characteristics, whether they have air columns, strings, sounding boxes, or drumheads. In fact, much of our speech is determined by shaping the cavity formed by the throat and mouth and positioning the tongue to adjust the fundamental and combination of overtones. Simple resonant cavities can be made to resonate with the sound of the vowels, for example. (See Figure 17.29.) In males, at puberty, the larynx grows and the shape of the resonant cavity changes giving rise to the difference in predominant frequencies in speech between different sexes.

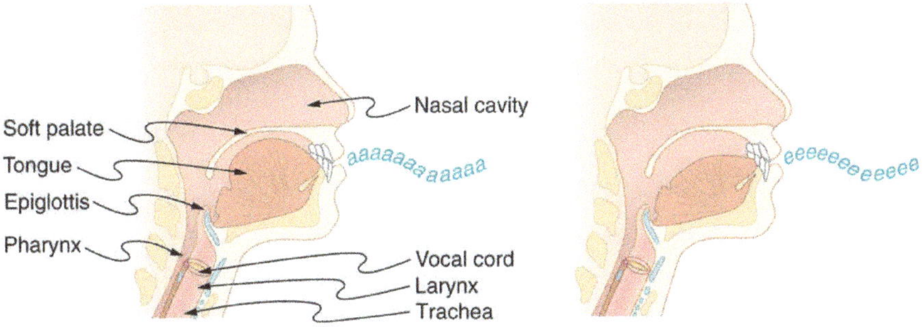

FIGURE 17.29 The throat and mouth form an air column closed at one end that resonates in response to vibrations in the voice box. The spectrum of overtones and their intensities vary with mouth shaping and tongue position to form different sounds. The voice box can be replaced with a mechanical vibrator, and understandable speech is still possible. Variations in basic shapes make different voices recognizable.

Now let us look for a pattern in the resonant frequencies for a simple tube that is closed at one end. The fundamental has $\lambda = 4L$, and frequency is related to wavelength and the speed of sound as given by:

$$v_\text{w} = f\lambda. \tag{17.28}$$

Solving for f in this equation gives

$$f = \frac{v_\text{w}}{\lambda} = \frac{v_\text{w}}{4L}, \tag{17.29}$$

where v_w is the speed of sound in air. Similarly, the first overtone has $\lambda' = 4L/3$ (see Figure 17.28), so that

$$f' = 3\frac{v_\text{w}}{4L} = 3f. \tag{17.30}$$

Because $f' = 3f$, we call the first overtone the third harmonic. Continuing this process, we see a pattern that can be generalized in a single expression. The resonant frequencies of a tube closed at one end are

$$f_n = n\frac{v_\text{w}}{4L}, n = 1,3,5, \tag{17.31}$$

where f_1 is the fundamental, f_3 is the first overtone, and so on. It is interesting that the resonant frequencies depend on the speed of sound and, hence, on temperature. This dependence poses a noticeable problem for organs in old unheated cathedrals, and it is also the reason why musicians commonly bring their wind instruments to room temperature before playing them.

EXAMPLE 17.5

Find the Length of a Tube with a 128 Hz Fundamental

(a) What length should a tube closed at one end have on a day when the air temperature, is 22.0°C, if its fundamental frequency is to be 128 Hz (C below middle C)?

(b) What is the frequency of its fourth overtone?

Strategy

The length L can be found from the relationship in $f_n = n\frac{v_\text{w}}{4L}$, but we will first need to find the speed of sound v_w.

Solution for (a)

(1) Identify knowns:

- the fundamental frequency is 128 Hz

- the air temperature is $22.0°C$

(2) Use $f_n = n\frac{v_W}{4L}$ to find the fundamental frequency ($n = 1$).

$$f_1 = \frac{v_W}{4L} \tag{17.32}$$

(3) Solve this equation for length.

$$L = \frac{v_W}{4f_1} \tag{17.33}$$

(4) Find the speed of sound using $v_W = (331 \text{ m/s})\sqrt{\frac{T}{273 \text{ K}}}$.

$$v_W = (331 \text{ m/s})\sqrt{\frac{295 \text{ K}}{273 \text{ K}}} = 344 \text{ m/s} \tag{17.34}$$

(5) Enter the values of the speed of sound and frequency into the expression for L.

$$L = \frac{v_W}{4f_1} = \frac{344 \text{ m/s}}{4(128 \text{ Hz})} = 0.672 \text{ m} \tag{17.35}$$

Discussion on (a)

Many wind instruments are modified tubes that have finger holes, valves, and other devices for changing the length of the resonating air column and hence, the frequency of the note played. Horns producing very low frequencies, such as tubas, require tubes so long that they are coiled into loops.

Solution for (b)

(1) Identify knowns:

- the first overtone has $n = 3$
- the second overtone has $n = 5$
- the third overtone has $n = 7$
- the fourth overtone has $n = 9$

(2) Enter the value for the fourth overtone into $f_n = n\frac{v_W}{4L}$.

$$f_9 = 9\frac{v_W}{4L} = 9f_1 = 1.15 \text{ kHz} \tag{17.36}$$

Discussion on (b)

Whether this overtone occurs in a simple tube or a musical instrument depends on how it is stimulated to vibrate and the details of its shape. The trombone, for example, does not produce its fundamental frequency and only makes overtones.

Another type of tube is one that is *open* at both ends. Examples are some organ pipes, flutes, and oboes. The resonances of tubes open at both ends can be analyzed in a very similar fashion to those for tubes closed at one end. The air columns in tubes open at both ends have maximum air displacements at both ends, as illustrated in Figure 17.30. Standing waves form as shown.

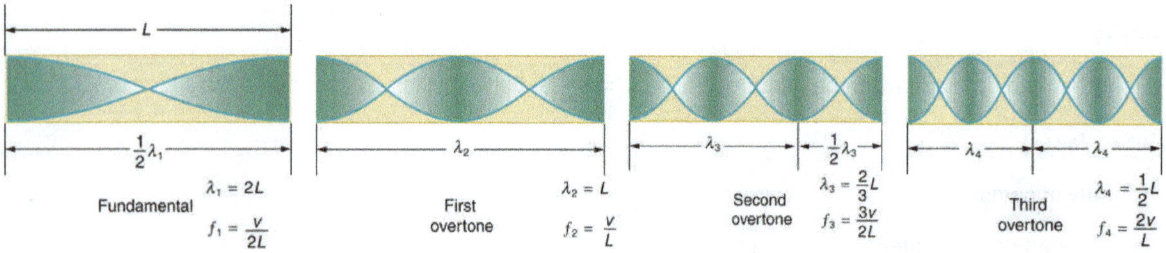

FIGURE 17.30 The resonant frequencies of a tube open at both ends are shown, including the fundamental and the first three overtones. In

all cases the maximum air displacements occur at both ends of the tube, giving it different natural frequencies than a tube closed at one end.

Based on the fact that a tube open at both ends has maximum air displacements at both ends, and using Figure 17.30 as a guide, we can see that the resonant frequencies of a tube open at both ends are:

$$f_n = n\frac{v_\mathrm{w}}{2L},\ n = 1, 2, 3...,\qquad (17.37)$$

where f_1 is the fundamental, f_2 is the first overtone, f_3 is the second overtone, and so on. Note that a tube open at both ends has a fundamental frequency twice what it would have if closed at one end. It also has a different spectrum of overtones than a tube closed at one end. So if you had two tubes with the same fundamental frequency but one was open at both ends and the other was closed at one end, they would sound different when played because they have different overtones. Middle C, for example, would sound richer played on an open tube, because it has even multiples of the fundamental as well as odd. A closed tube has only odd multiples.

REAL-WORLD APPLICATIONS: RESONANCE IN EVERYDAY SYSTEMS

Resonance occurs in many different systems, including strings, air columns, and atoms. Resonance is the driven or forced oscillation of a system at its natural frequency. At resonance, energy is transferred rapidly to the oscillating system, and the amplitude of its oscillations grows until the system can no longer be described by Hooke's law. An example of this is the distorted sound intentionally produced in certain types of rock music.

Wind instruments use resonance in air columns to amplify tones made by lips or vibrating reeds. Other instruments also use air resonance in clever ways to amplify sound. Figure 17.31 shows a violin and a guitar, both of which have sounding boxes but with different shapes, resulting in different overtone structures. The vibrating string creates a sound that resonates in the sounding box, greatly amplifying the sound and creating overtones that give the instrument its characteristic flavor. The more complex the shape of the sounding box, the greater its ability to resonate over a wide range of frequencies. The marimba, like the one shown in Figure 17.32 uses pots or gourds below the wooden slats to amplify their tones. The resonance of the pot can be adjusted by adding water.

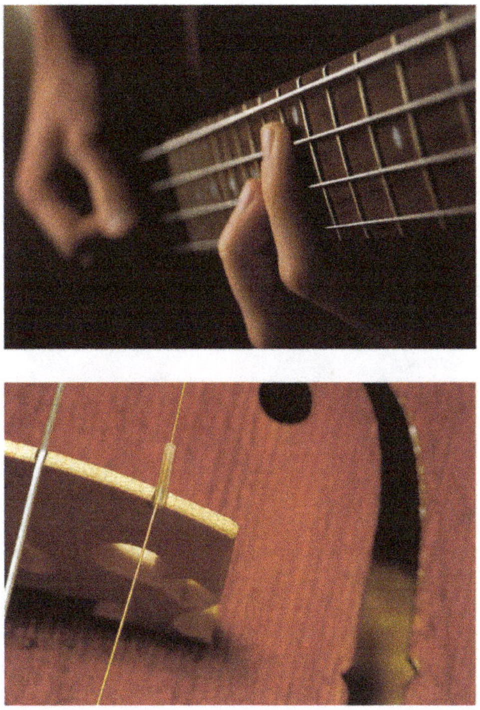

FIGURE 17.31 String instruments such as violins and guitars use resonance in their sounding boxes to amplify and enrich the sound created by their vibrating strings. The bridge and supports couple the string vibrations to the sounding boxes and air within. (credits: guitar, Feliciano Guimares, Fotopedia; violin, Steve Snodgrass, Flickr)

FIGURE 17.32 Resonance has been used in musical instruments since prehistoric times. This marimba uses gourds as resonance chambers to amplify its sound. (credit: APC Events, Flickr)

We have emphasized sound applications in our discussions of resonance and standing waves, but these ideas apply to any system that has wave characteristics. Vibrating strings, for example, are actually resonating and have fundamentals and overtones similar to those for air columns. More subtle are the resonances in atoms due to the wave character of their electrons. Their orbitals can be viewed as standing waves, which have a fundamental (ground state) and overtones (excited states). It is fascinating that wave characteristics apply to such a wide range of physical systems.

CHECK YOUR UNDERSTANDING

Describe how noise-canceling headphones differ from standard headphones used to block outside sounds.

Solution

Regular headphones only block sound waves with a physical barrier. Noise-canceling headphones use destructive interference to reduce the loudness of outside sounds.

CHECK YOUR UNDERSTANDING

How is it possible to use a standing wave's node and antinode to determine the length of a closed-end tube?

Solution

When the tube resonates at its natural frequency, the wave's node is located at the closed end of the tube, and the antinode is located at the open end. The length of the tube is equal to one-fourth of the wavelength of this wave. Thus, if we know the wavelength of the wave, we can determine the length of the tube.

17.6 Hearing

LEARNING OBJECTIVES

By the end of this section, you will be able to:

- Define hearing, pitch, loudness, timbre, note, tone, phon, ultrasound, and infrasound.
- Compare loudness to frequency and intensity of a sound.
- Identify structures of the inner ear and explain how they relate to sound perception.

FIGURE 17.33 Hearing allows these vocalists, the band, and the fans to enjoy music. (credit: Reggie Mathalone, CC BY)

The human ear has a tremendous range and sensitivity. It can give us a wealth of simple information—such as pitch, loudness, and direction. And from its input we can detect musical quality and nuances of voiced emotion. How is our hearing related to the physical qualities of sound, and how does the hearing mechanism work?

Hearing is the perception of sound. (Perception is commonly defined to be awareness through the senses, a typically circular definition of higher-level processes in living organisms.) Normal human hearing encompasses frequencies from 20 to 20,000 Hz, an impressive range. Sounds below 20 Hz are called **infrasound**, whereas those above 20,000 Hz are **ultrasound**. Neither is perceived by the ear, although infrasound can sometimes be felt as vibrations. When we do hear low-frequency vibrations, such as the sounds of a diving board, we hear the individual vibrations only because there are higher-frequency sounds in each. Other animals have hearing ranges different from that of humans. Dogs can hear sounds as high as 30,000 Hz, whereas bats and dolphins can hear up to 100,000-Hz sounds. You may have noticed that dogs respond to the sound of a dog whistle which produces sound out of the range of human hearing. Elephants are known to respond to frequencies below 20 Hz.

The perception of frequency is called **pitch**. Most of us have excellent relative pitch, which means that we can tell whether one sound has a different frequency from another. Typically, we can discriminate between two sounds if their frequencies differ by 0.3% or more. For example, 500.0 and 501.5 Hz are noticeably different. Pitch perception is directly related to frequency and is not greatly affected by other physical quantities such as intensity. Musical **notes** are particular sounds that can be produced by most instruments and in Western music have particular names. Combinations of notes constitute music. Some people can identify musical notes, such as A-sharp, C, or E-flat, just by listening to them. This uncommon ability is called perfect pitch.

The ear is remarkably sensitive to low-intensity sounds. The lowest audible intensity or threshold is about $10^{-12}\ \text{W/m}^2$ or 0 dB. Sounds as much as 10^{12} more intense can be briefly tolerated. Very few measuring devices are capable of observations over a range of a trillion. The perception of intensity is called **loudness**. At a given frequency, it is possible to discern differences of about 1 dB, and a change of 3 dB is easily noticed. But loudness is not related to intensity alone. Frequency has a major effect on how loud a sound seems. The ear has its maximum sensitivity to frequencies in the range of 2000 to 5000 Hz, so that sounds in this range are perceived as being louder than, say, those at 500 or 10,000 Hz, even when they all have the same intensity. Sounds near the high- and low-frequency extremes of the hearing range seem even less loud, because the ear is even less sensitive at those frequencies. Table 17.4 gives the dependence of certain human hearing perceptions on physical quantities.

Perception	Physical quantity
Pitch	Frequency
Loudness	Intensity and Frequency
Timbre	Number and relative intensity of multiple frequencies. Subtle craftsmanship leads to non-linear effects and more detail.

TABLE 17.4 Sound Perceptions

Perception	Physical quantity
Note	Basic unit of music with specific names, combined to generate tunes
Tone	Number and relative intensity of multiple frequencies.

TABLE 17.4 Sound Perceptions

When a violin plays middle C, there is no mistaking it for a piano playing the same note. The reason is that each instrument produces a distinctive set of frequencies and intensities. We call our perception of these combinations of frequencies and intensities **tone** quality, or more commonly the **timbre** of the sound. It is more difficult to correlate timbre perception to physical quantities than it is for loudness or pitch perception. Timbre is more subjective. Terms such as dull, brilliant, warm, cold, pure, and rich are employed to describe the timbre of a sound. So the consideration of timbre takes us into the realm of perceptual psychology, where higher-level processes in the brain are dominant. This is true for other perceptions of sound, such as music and noise. We shall not delve further into them; rather, we will concentrate on the question of loudness perception.

A unit called a **phon** is used to express loudness numerically. Phons differ from decibels because the phon is a unit of loudness perception, whereas the decibel is a unit of physical intensity. Figure 17.34 shows the relationship of loudness to intensity (or intensity level) and frequency for persons with normal hearing. The curved lines are equal-loudness curves. Each curve is labeled with its loudness in phons. Any sound along a given curve will be perceived as equally loud by the average person. The curves were determined by having large numbers of people compare the loudness of sounds at different frequencies and sound intensity levels. At a frequency of 1000 Hz, phons are taken to be numerically equal to decibels. The following example helps illustrate how to use the graph:

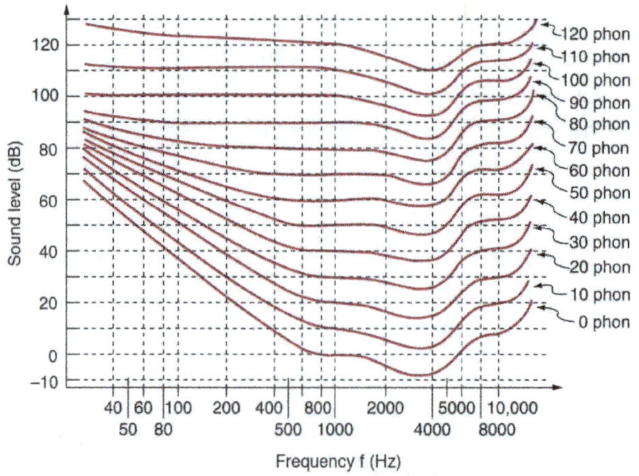

FIGURE 17.34 The relationship of loudness in phons to intensity level (in decibels) and intensity (in watts per meter squared) for persons with normal hearing. The curved lines are equal-loudness curves—all sounds on a given curve are perceived as equally loud. Phons and decibels are defined to be the same at 1000 Hz.

EXAMPLE 17.6

Measuring Loudness: Loudness Versus Intensity Level and Frequency

(a) What is the loudness in phons of a 100-Hz sound that has an intensity level of 80 dB? (b) What is the intensity level in decibels of a 4000-Hz sound having a loudness of 70 phons? (c) At what intensity level will an 8000-Hz sound have the same loudness as a 200-Hz sound at 60 dB?

Strategy for (a)

The graph in Figure 17.34 should be referenced in order to solve this example. To find the loudness of a given sound, you must know its frequency and intensity level and locate that point on the square grid, then interpolate between loudness curves to get the loudness in phons.

Solution for (a)

(1) Identify knowns:

- The square grid of the graph relating phons and decibels is a plot of intensity level versus frequency—both physical quantities.
- 100 Hz at 80 dB lies halfway between the curves marked 70 and 80 phons.

(2) Find the loudness: 75 phons.

Strategy for (b)

The graph in Figure 17.34 should be referenced in order to solve this example. To find the intensity level of a sound, you must have its frequency and loudness. Once that point is located, the intensity level can be determined from the vertical axis.

Solution for (b)

(1) Identify knowns:

- Values are given to be 4000 Hz at 70 phons.

(2) Follow the 70-phon curve until it reaches 4000 Hz. At that point, it is below the 70 dB line at about 67 dB.

(3) Find the intensity level:

67 dB

Strategy for (c)

The graph in Figure 17.34 should be referenced in order to solve this example.

Solution for (c)

(1) Locate the point for a 200 Hz and 60 dB sound.

(2) Find the loudness: This point lies just slightly above the 50-phon curve, and so its loudness is 51 phons.

(3) Look for the 51-phon level is at 8000 Hz: 63 dB.

Discussion

These answers, like all information extracted from Figure 17.34, have uncertainties of several phons or several decibels, partly due to difficulties in interpolation, but mostly related to uncertainties in the equal-loudness curves.

Further examination of the graph in Figure 17.34 reveals some interesting facts about human hearing. First, sounds below the 0-phon curve are not perceived by most people. So, for example, a 60 Hz sound at 40 dB is inaudible. The 0-phon curve represents the threshold of normal hearing. We can hear some sounds at intensity levels below 0 dB. For example, a 3-dB, 5000-Hz sound is audible, because it lies above the 0-phon curve. The loudness curves all have dips in them between about 2000 and 5000 Hz. These dips mean the ear is most sensitive to frequencies in that range. For example, a 15-dB sound at 4000 Hz has a loudness of 20 phons, the same as a 20-dB sound at 1000 Hz. The curves rise at both extremes of the frequency range, indicating that a greater-intensity level sound is needed at those frequencies to be perceived to be as loud as at middle frequencies. For example, a sound at 10,000 Hz must have an intensity level of 30 dB to seem as loud as a 20 dB sound at 1000 Hz. Sounds above 120 phons are painful as well as damaging.

We do not often utilize our full range of hearing. This is particularly true for frequencies above 8000 Hz, which are rare in the environment and are unnecessary for understanding conversation or appreciating music. In fact, people who have lost the ability to hear such high frequencies are usually unaware of their loss until tested. The shaded region in Figure 17.35 is the frequency and intensity region where most conversational sounds fall. The curved lines indicate what effect hearing losses of 40 and 60 phons will have. A 40-phon hearing loss at all frequencies still allows a person to understand conversation, although it will seem very quiet. A person with a 60-phon loss at all frequencies will hear only the lowest frequencies and will not be able to understand speech unless it is much louder than normal. Even so, speech may seem indistinct, because higher frequencies are not as well perceived. The conversational speech region also has a gender component, in that female voices are usually characterized by higher frequencies. So the person with a 60-phon hearing impediment might have difficulty understanding the normal conversation of a woman.

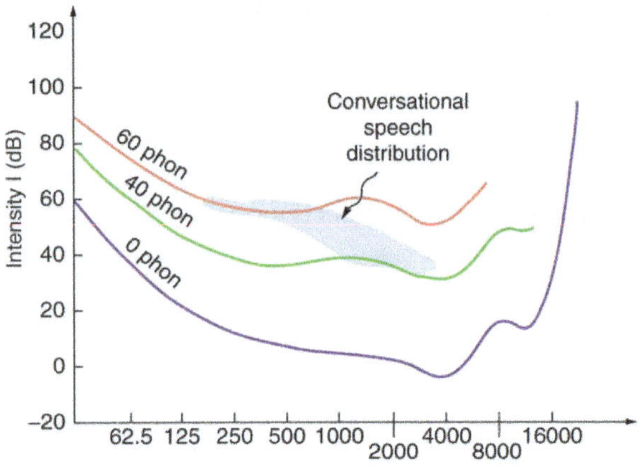

FIGURE 17.35 The shaded region represents frequencies and intensity levels found in normal conversational speech. The 0-phon line represents the normal hearing threshold, while those at 40 and 60 represent thresholds for people with 40- and 60-phon hearing losses, respectively.

Hearing tests are performed over a range of frequencies, usually from 250 to 8000 Hz, and can be displayed graphically in an audiogram like that in Figure 17.36. The hearing threshold is measured in dB *relative to the normal threshold*, so that normal hearing registers as 0 dB at all frequencies. Hearing loss caused by noise typically shows a dip near the 4000 Hz frequency, irrespective of the frequency that caused the loss and often affects both ears. The most common form of hearing loss comes with age and is called *presbycusis*—literally elder ear. Such loss is increasingly severe at higher frequencies, and interferes with music appreciation and speech recognition.

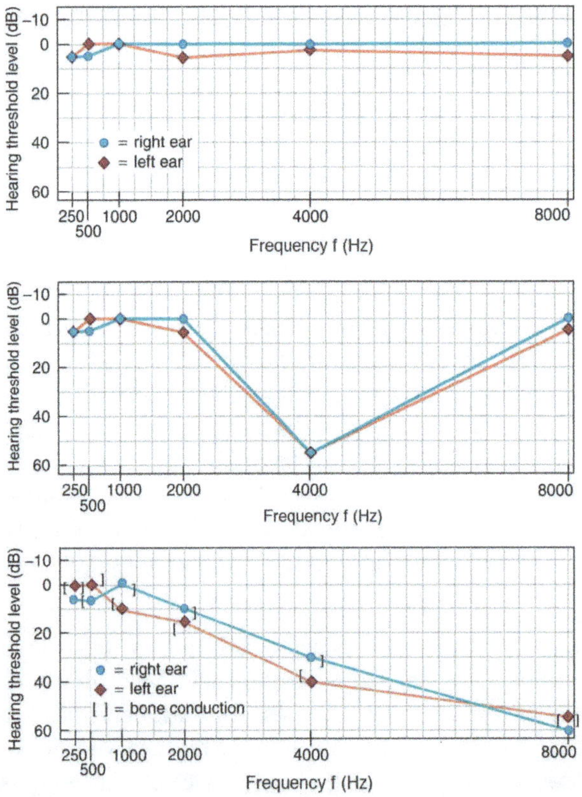

FIGURE 17.36 Audiograms showing the threshold in intensity level versus frequency for three different individuals. Intensity level is measured relative to the normal threshold. The top left graph is that of a person with normal hearing. The graph to its right has a dip at

4000 Hz and is that of a child who suffered hearing loss due to a cap gun. The third graph is typical of presbycusis, the progressive loss of higher frequency hearing with age. Tests performed by bone conduction (brackets) can distinguish nerve damage from middle ear damage.

THE HEARING MECHANISM

The hearing mechanism involves some interesting physics. The sound wave that impinges upon our ear is a pressure wave. The ear is a transducer that converts sound waves into electrical nerve impulses in a manner much more sophisticated than, but analogous to, a microphone. Figure 17.37 shows the gross anatomy of the ear with its division into three parts: the outer ear or ear canal; the middle ear, which runs from the eardrum to the cochlea; and the inner ear, which is the cochlea itself. The body part normally referred to as the ear is technically called the pinna.

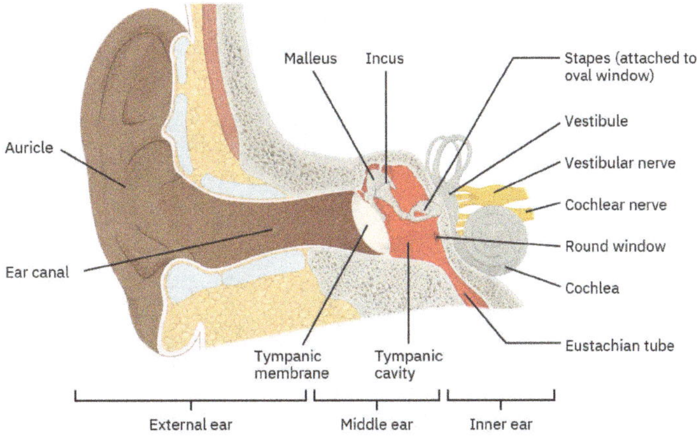

FIGURE 17.37 The illustration shows the gross anatomy of the human ear.

The outer ear, or ear canal, carries sound to the recessed protected eardrum. The air column in the ear canal resonates and is partially responsible for the sensitivity of the ear to sounds in the 2000 to 5000 Hz range. The middle ear converts sound into mechanical vibrations and applies these vibrations to the cochlea. The lever system of the middle ear takes the force exerted on the eardrum by sound pressure variations, amplifies it and transmits it to the inner ear via the oval window, creating pressure waves in the cochlea approximately 40 times greater than those impinging on the eardrum. (See Figure 17.38.) Two muscles in the middle ear (not shown) protect the inner ear from very intense sounds. They react to intense sound in a few milliseconds and reduce the force transmitted to the cochlea. This protective reaction can also be triggered by your own voice, so that humming while shooting a gun, for example, can reduce noise damage.

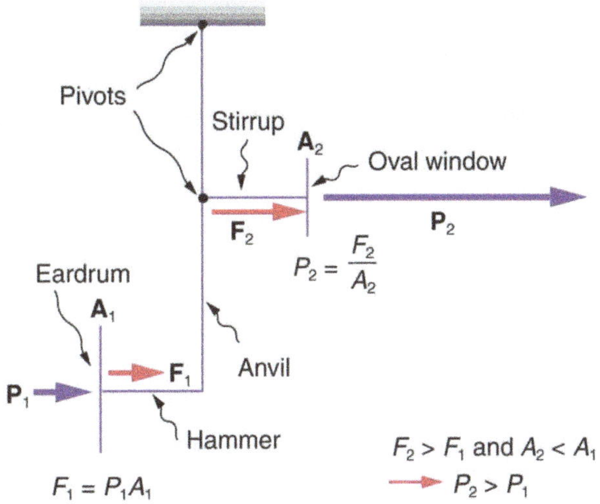

FIGURE 17.38 This schematic shows the middle ear's system for converting sound pressure into force, increasing that force through a lever system, and applying the increased force to a small area of the cochlea, thereby creating a pressure about 40 times that in the original sound wave. A protective muscle reaction to intense sounds greatly reduces the mechanical advantage of the lever system.

Figure 17.39 shows the middle and inner ear in greater detail. Pressure waves moving through the cochlea cause the tectorial membrane to vibrate, rubbing cilia (called hair cells), which stimulate nerves that send electrical signals to the brain. The membrane resonates at different positions for different frequencies, with high frequencies stimulating nerves at the near end and low frequencies at the far end. The complete operation of the cochlea is still not understood, but several mechanisms for sending information to the brain are known to be involved. For sounds below about 1000 Hz, the nerves send signals at the same frequency as the sound. For frequencies greater than about 1000 Hz, the nerves signal frequency by position. There is a structure to the cilia, and there are connections between nerve cells that perform signal processing before information is sent to the brain. Intensity information is partly indicated by the number of nerve signals and by volleys of signals. The brain processes the cochlear nerve signals to provide additional information such as source direction (based on time and intensity comparisons of sounds from both ears). Higher-level processing produces many nuances, such as music appreciation.

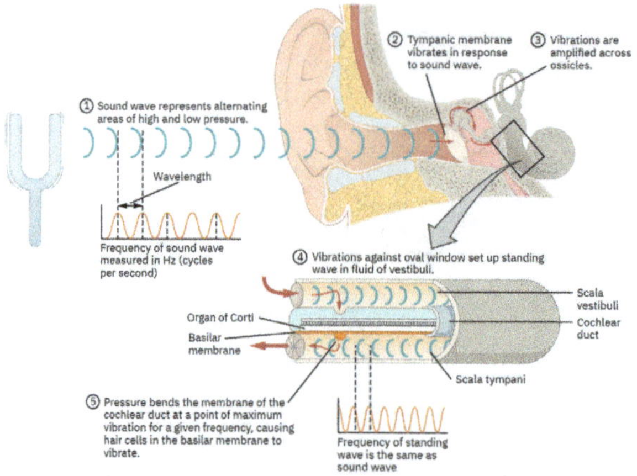

FIGURE 17.39 The inner ear, or cochlea, is a coiled tube about 3 mm in diameter and 3 cm in length if uncoiled. When the oval window is forced inward, as shown, a pressure wave travels through the perilymph in the direction of the arrows, stimulating nerves at the base of cilia in the organ of Corti.

Hearing losses can occur because of problems in the middle or inner ear. Conductive losses in the middle ear can be partially overcome by sending sound vibrations to the cochlea through the skull. Hearing aids for this purpose usually press against the bone behind the ear, rather than simply amplifying the sound sent into the ear canal as many hearing aids do. Damage to the nerves in the cochlea is not repairable, but amplification can partially compensate. There is a risk that amplification will produce further damage. Another common failure in the cochlea is damage or loss of the cilia but with nerves remaining functional. Cochlear implants that stimulate the nerves directly are now available and widely accepted. Over 100,000 implants are in use, in about equal numbers of adults and children.

The cochlear implant was pioneered in Melbourne, Australia, by Graeme Clark in the 1970s for his deaf father. The implant consists of three external components and two internal components. The external components are a microphone for picking up sound and converting it into an electrical signal, a speech processor to select certain frequencies and a transmitter to transfer the signal to the internal components through electromagnetic induction. The internal components consist of a receiver/transmitter secured in the bone beneath the skin, which converts the signals into electric impulses and sends them through an internal cable to the cochlea and an array of about 24 electrodes wound through the cochlea. These electrodes in turn send the impulses directly into the brain. The electrodes basically emulate the cilia.

CHECK YOUR UNDERSTANDING

Are ultrasound and infrasound imperceptible to all hearing organisms? Explain your answer.

Solution

No, the range of perceptible sound is based in the range of human hearing. Many other organisms perceive either infrasound or ultrasound.

17.7 Ultrasound

LEARNING OBJECTIVES

By the end of this section, you will be able to:

- Define acoustic impedance and intensity reflection coefficient.
- Describe medical and other uses of ultrasound technology.
- Calculate acoustic impedance using density values and the speed of ultrasound.
- Calculate the velocity of a moving object using Doppler-shifted ultrasound.

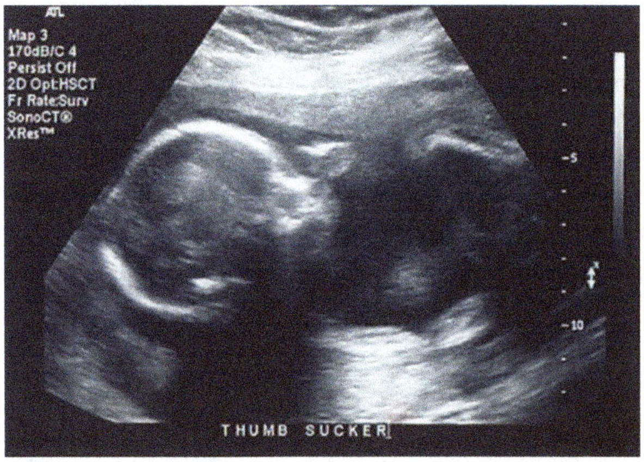

FIGURE 17.40 Ultrasound is used in medicine to painlessly and noninvasively monitor patient health and diagnose a wide range of disorders. (credit: abbybatchelder, Flickr)

Any sound with a frequency above 20,000 Hz (or 20 kHz)—that is, above the highest audible frequency—is defined to be ultrasound. In practice, it is possible to create ultrasound frequencies up to more than a gigahertz. (Higher frequencies are difficult to create; furthermore, they propagate poorly because they are very strongly absorbed.) Ultrasound has a tremendous number of applications, which range from burglar alarms to use in cleaning delicate objects to the guidance systems of bats. We begin our discussion of ultrasound with some of its applications in medicine, in which it is used extensively both for diagnosis and for therapy.

CHARACTERISTICS OF ULTRASOUND

The characteristics of ultrasound, such as frequency and intensity, are wave properties common to all types of waves. Ultrasound also has a wavelength that limits the fineness of detail it can detect. This characteristic is true of all waves. We can never observe details significantly smaller than the wavelength of our probe; for example, we will never see individual atoms with visible light, because the atoms are so small compared with the wavelength of light.

Ultrasound in Medical Therapy

Ultrasound, like any wave, carries energy that can be absorbed by the medium carrying it, producing effects that vary with intensity. When focused to intensities of 10^3 to $10^5\ \mathrm{W/m^2}$, ultrasound can be used to shatter gallstones or pulverize cancerous tissue in surgical procedures. (See Figure 17.41.) Intensities this great can damage individual cells, variously causing their protoplasm to stream inside them, altering their permeability, or rupturing their walls through *cavitation*. Cavitation is the creation of vapor cavities in a fluid—the longitudinal vibrations in ultrasound alternatively compress and expand the medium, and at sufficient amplitudes the expansion separates molecules. Most cavitation damage is done when the cavities collapse, producing even greater shock pressures.

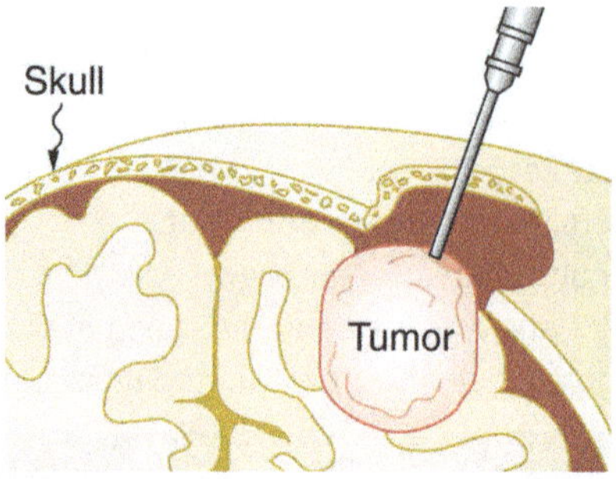

FIGURE 17.41 The tip of this small probe oscillates at 23 kHz with such a large amplitude that it pulverizes tissue on contact. The debris is then aspirated. The speed of the tip may exceed the speed of sound in tissue, thus creating shock waves and cavitation, rather than a smooth simple harmonic oscillator–type wave.

Most of the energy carried by high-intensity ultrasound in tissue is converted to thermal energy. In fact, intensities of 10^3 to $10^4\ \text{W/m}^2$ are commonly used for deep-heat treatments called ultrasound diathermy. Frequencies of 0.8 to 1 MHz are typical. In both athletics and physical therapy, ultrasound diathermy is most often applied to injured or overworked muscles to relieve pain and improve flexibility. Skill is needed by the therapist to avoid "bone burns" and other tissue damage caused by overheating and cavitation, sometimes made worse by reflection and focusing of the ultrasound by joint and bone tissue.

In some instances, you may encounter a different decibel scale, called the sound *pressure* level, when ultrasound travels in water or in human and other biological tissues. We shall not use the scale here, but it is notable that numbers for sound pressure levels range 60 to 70 dB higher than you would quote for β, the sound intensity level used in this text. Should you encounter a sound pressure level of 220 decibels, then, it is not an astronomically high intensity, but equivalent to about 155 dB—high enough to destroy tissue, but not as unreasonably high as it might seem at first.

Ultrasound in Medical Diagnostics

When used for imaging, ultrasonic waves are emitted from a transducer, a crystal exhibiting the piezoelectric effect (the expansion and contraction of a substance when a voltage is applied across it, causing a vibration of the crystal). These high-frequency vibrations are transmitted into any tissue in contact with the transducer. Similarly, if a pressure is applied to the crystal (in the form of a wave reflected off tissue layers), a voltage is produced which can be recorded. The crystal therefore acts as both a transmitter and a receiver of sound. Ultrasound is also partially absorbed by tissue on its path, both on its journey away from the transducer and on its return journey. From the time between when the original signal is sent and when the reflections from various boundaries between media are received, (as well as a measure of the intensity loss of the signal), the nature and position of each boundary between tissues and organs may be deduced.

Reflections at boundaries between two different media occur because of differences in a characteristic known as the **acoustic impedance** Z of each substance. Impedance is defined as

$$Z = \rho v, \tag{17.38}$$

where ρ is the density of the medium (in kg/m^3) and v is the speed of sound through the medium (in m/s). The units for Z are therefore $\text{kg/(m}^2 \cdot \text{s)}$.

Table 17.5 shows the density and speed of sound through various media (including various soft tissues) and the associated acoustic impedances. Note that the acoustic impedances for soft tissue do not vary much but that there is a big difference between the acoustic impedance of soft tissue and air and also between soft tissue and bone.

Medium	Density (kg/m^3)	Speed of Ultrasound (m/s)	Acoustic Impedance $(\text{kg}/(\text{m}^2 \cdot \text{s}))$
Air	1.3	330	429
Water	1000	1500	1.5×10^6
Blood	1060	1570	1.66×10^6
Fat	925	1450	1.34×10^6
Muscle (average)	1075	1590	1.70×10^6
Bone (varies)	1400–1900	4080	5.7×10^6 to 7.8×10^6
Barium titanate (transducer material)	5600	5500	30.8×10^6

TABLE 17.5 The Ultrasound Properties of Various Media, Including Soft Tissue Found in the Body

At the boundary between media of different acoustic impedances, some of the wave energy is reflected and some is transmitted. The greater the *difference* in acoustic impedance between the two media, the greater the reflection and the smaller the transmission.

The **intensity reflection coefficient** a is defined as the ratio of the intensity of the reflected wave relative to the incident (transmitted) wave. This statement can be written mathematically as

$$a = \frac{(Z_2 - Z_1)^2}{(Z_1 + Z_2)^2}, \quad (17.39)$$

where Z_1 and Z_2 are the acoustic impedances of the two media making up the boundary. A reflection coefficient of zero (corresponding to total transmission and no reflection) occurs when the acoustic impedances of the two media are the same. An impedance "match" (no reflection) provides an efficient coupling of sound energy from one medium to another. The image formed in an ultrasound is made by tracking reflections (as shown in Figure 17.42) and mapping the intensity of the reflected sound waves in a two-dimensional plane.

EXAMPLE 17.7

Calculate Acoustic Impedance and Intensity Reflection Coefficient: Ultrasound and Fat Tissue

(a) Using the values for density and the speed of ultrasound given in Table 17.5, show that the acoustic impedance of fat tissue is indeed $1.34 \times 10^6\ \text{kg}/(\text{m}^2{\cdot}\text{s})$.

(b) Calculate the intensity reflection coefficient of ultrasound when going from fat to muscle tissue.

Strategy for (a)

The acoustic impedance can be calculated using $Z = \rho v$ and the values for ρ and v found in Table 17.5.

Solution for (a)

(1) Substitute known values from Table 17.5 into $Z = \rho v$.

$$Z = \rho v = \left(925\ \text{kg/m}^3\right)(1450\ \text{m/s}) \quad (17.40)$$

(2) Calculate to find the acoustic impedance of fat tissue.

$$1.34 \times 10^6 \text{ kg/(m}^2 \cdot \text{s)} \tag{17.41}$$

This value is the same as the value given for the acoustic impedance of fat tissue.

Strategy for (b)

The intensity reflection coefficient for any boundary between two media is given by $a = \frac{(Z_2 - Z_1)^2}{(Z_1 + Z_2)^2}$, and the acoustic impedance of muscle is given in Table 17.5.

Solution for (b)

Substitute known values into $a = \frac{(Z_2 - Z_1)^2}{(Z_1 + Z_2)^2}$ to find the intensity reflection coefficient:

$$a = \frac{(Z_2 - Z_1)^2}{(Z_1 + Z_2)^2} = \frac{\left(1.34 \times 10^6 \text{ kg/(m}^2 \cdot \text{ s)} - 1.70 \times 10^6 \text{ kg/(m}^2 \cdot \text{ s)}\right)^2}{\left(1.70 \times 10^6 \text{ kg/(m}^2 \cdot \text{ s)} + 1.34 \times 10^6 \text{ kg/(m}^2 \cdot \text{ s)}\right)^2} = 0.014 \tag{17.42}$$

Discussion

This result means that only 1.4% of the incident intensity is reflected, with the remaining being transmitted.

The applications of ultrasound in medical diagnostics have produced untold benefits with no known risks. Diagnostic intensities are too low (about 10^{-2} W/m^2) to cause thermal damage. More significantly, ultrasound has been in use for several decades and detailed follow-up studies do not show evidence of ill effects, quite unlike the case for x-rays.

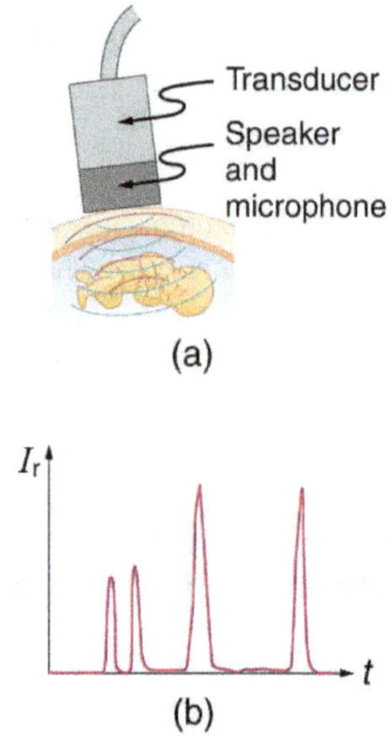

FIGURE 17.42 (a) An ultrasound speaker doubles as a microphone. Brief bleeps are broadcast, and echoes are recorded from various depths. (b) Graph of echo intensity versus time. The time for echoes to return is directly proportional to the distance of the reflector, yielding this information noninvasively.

The most common ultrasound applications produce an image like that shown in Figure 17.43. The speaker-microphone broadcasts a directional beam, sweeping the beam across the area of interest. This is accomplished by having multiple ultrasound sources in the probe's head, which are phased to interfere constructively in a given, adjustable direction. Echoes are measured as a function of position as well as depth. A computer constructs an image that reveals the shape and density of internal structures.

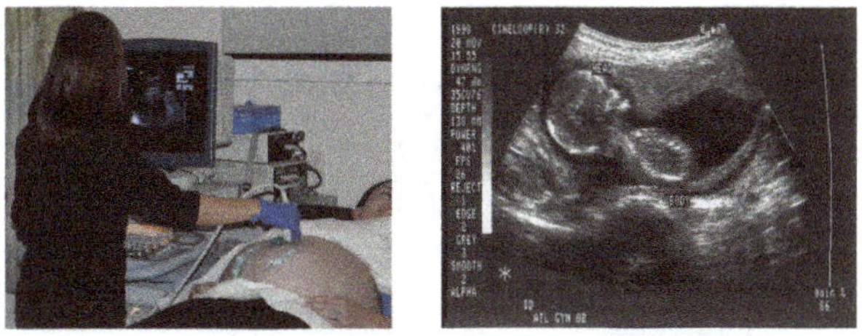

(a) (b)

FIGURE 17.43 (a) An ultrasonic image is produced by sweeping the ultrasonic beam across the area of interest, in this case the person's abdomen. Data are recorded and analyzed in a computer, providing a two-dimensional image (credit: COD Newsroom, Flickr). (b) Ultrasound image of 12-week-old fetus. (credit: Public Health Image Library, CDC)

How much detail can ultrasound reveal? The image in Figure 17.43 is typical of low-cost systems, but that in Figure 17.44 shows the remarkable detail possible with more advanced systems, including 3D imaging. Ultrasound today is commonly used in prenatal care. Such imaging can be used to see if the fetus is developing at a normal rate, and help in the determination of serious problems early in the pregnancy. Ultrasound is also in wide use to image the chambers of the heart and the flow of blood within the beating heart, using the Doppler effect (echocardiology).

Whenever a wave is used as a probe, it is very difficult to detect details smaller than its wavelength λ. Indeed, current technology cannot do quite this well. Abdominal scans may use a 7-MHz frequency, and the speed of sound in tissue is about 1540 m/s—so the wavelength limit to detail would be $\lambda = \frac{v_\text{w}}{f} = \frac{1540\text{ m/s}}{7\times10^6\text{ Hz}} = 0.22\text{ mm}$. In practice, 1-mm detail is attainable, which is sufficient for many purposes. Higher-frequency ultrasound would allow greater detail, but it does not penetrate as well as lower frequencies do. The accepted rule of thumb is that you can effectively scan to a depth of about 500λ into tissue. For 7 MHz, this penetration limit is $500 \times 0.22\text{ mm}$, which is 0.11 m. Higher frequencies may be employed in smaller organs, such as the eye, but are not practical for looking deep into the body.

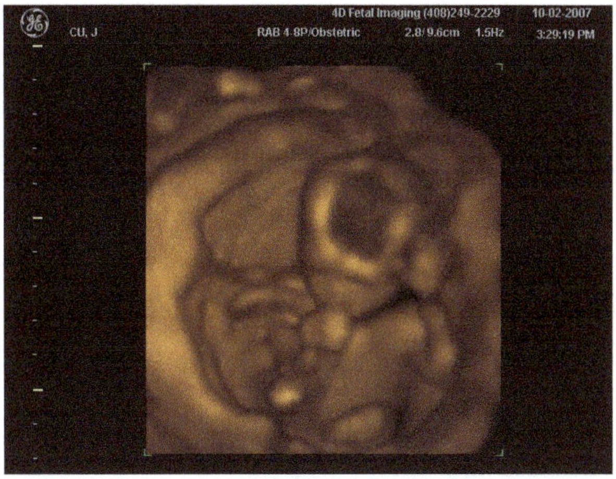

FIGURE 17.44 A 3D ultrasound image of a fetus. (credit: Jennie Cu, Wikimedia Commons)

In addition to shape information, ultrasonic scans can produce density information superior to that found in X-rays, because the intensity of a reflected sound is related to changes in density. Sound is most strongly reflected at places where density changes are greatest.

Another major use of ultrasound in medical diagnostics is to detect motion and determine velocity through the Doppler shift of an echo, known as **Doppler-shifted ultrasound**. This technique is used to monitor fetal heartbeat, measure blood velocity, and detect occlusions in blood vessels, for example. (See Figure 17.45.) The magnitude of the Doppler shift in an echo is directly proportional to the velocity of whatever reflects the sound. Because an echo is involved, there is actually a double shift. The first occurs because the reflector (say a fetal heart) is a moving observer and receives a Doppler-shifted frequency. The reflector then acts as a moving source, producing a second Doppler shift.

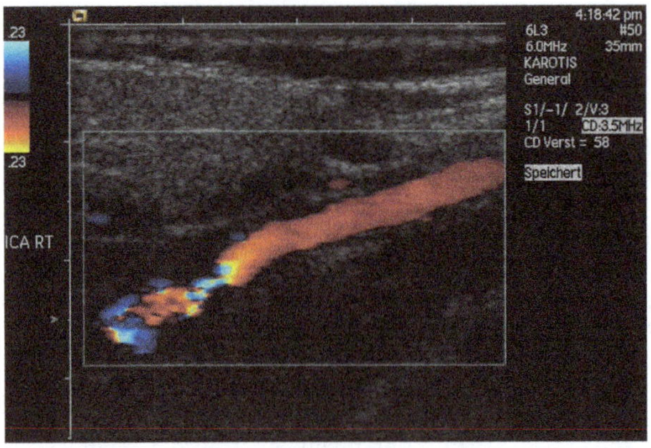

FIGURE 17.45 This Doppler-shifted ultrasonic image of a partially occluded artery uses color to indicate velocity. The highest velocities are in red, while the lowest are blue. The blood must move faster through the constriction to carry the same flow. (credit: Arning C, Grzyska U, Wikimedia Commons)

A clever technique is used to measure the Doppler shift in an echo. The frequency of the echoed sound is superimposed on the broadcast frequency, producing beats. The beat frequency is $F_B = |f_1 - f_2|$, and so it is directly proportional to the Doppler shift $(f_1 - f_2)$ and hence, the reflector's velocity. The advantage in this technique is that the Doppler shift is small (because the reflector's velocity is small), so that great accuracy would be needed to measure the shift directly. But measuring the beat frequency is easy, and it is not affected if the broadcast frequency varies somewhat. Furthermore, the beat frequency is in the audible range and can be amplified for audio feedback to the medical observer.

USES FOR DOPPLER-SHIFTED RADAR

Doppler-shifted radar echoes are used to measure wind velocities in storms as well as aircraft and automobile speeds. The principle is the same as for Doppler-shifted ultrasound. There is evidence that bats and dolphins may also sense the velocity of an object (such as prey) reflecting their ultrasound signals by observing its Doppler shift.

EXAMPLE 17.8

Calculate Velocity of Blood: Doppler-Shifted Ultrasound

Ultrasound that has a frequency of 2.50 MHz is sent toward blood in an artery that is moving toward the source at 20.0 cm/s, as illustrated in Figure 17.46. Use the speed of sound in human tissue as 1540 m/s. (Assume that the frequency of 2.50 MHz is accurate to seven significant figures.)

a. What frequency does the blood receive?
b. What frequency returns to the source?
c. What beat frequency is produced if the source and returning frequencies are mixed?

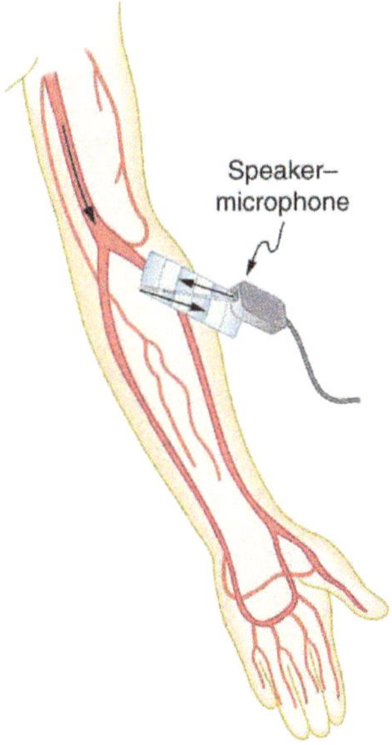

FIGURE 17.46 Ultrasound is partly reflected by blood cells and plasma back toward the speaker-microphone. Because the cells are moving, two Doppler shifts are produced—one for blood as a moving observer, and the other for the reflected sound coming from a moving source. The magnitude of the shift is directly proportional to blood velocity.

Strategy

The first two questions can be answered using $f_{obs} = f_s\left(\frac{v_w}{v_w \pm v_s}\right)$ and $f_{obs} = f_s\left(\frac{v_w \pm v_{obs}}{v_w}\right)$ for the Doppler shift. The last question asks for beat frequency, which is the difference between the original and returning frequencies.

Solution for (a)

(1) Identify knowns:

- The blood is a moving observer, and so the frequency it receives is given by

$$f_{obs} = f_s\left(\frac{v_w \pm v_{obs}}{v_w}\right). \quad 17.43$$

- v_b is the blood velocity (v_{obs} here) and the plus sign is chosen because the motion is toward the source.

(2) Enter the given values into the equation.

$$f_{obs} = (2{,}500{,}000 \text{ Hz})\left(\frac{1540 \text{ m/s} + 0.2 \text{ m/s}}{1540 \text{ m/s}}\right) \quad 17.44$$

(3) Calculate to find the frequency: 2,500,325 Hz.

Solution for (b)

(1) Identify knowns:

- The blood acts as a moving source.
- The microphone acts as a stationary observer.
- The frequency leaving the blood is 2,500,325 Hz, but it is shifted upward as given by

$$f_{obs} = f_s\left(\frac{v_w}{v_w - v_b}\right). \quad 17.45$$

f_{obs} is the frequency received by the speaker-microphone.

- The source velocity is v_b.
- The minus sign is used because the motion is toward the observer.

The minus sign is used because the motion is toward the observer.

(2) Enter the given values into the equation:

$$f_{\text{obs}} = (2{,}500{,}325\ \text{Hz})\left(\frac{1540\ \text{m/s}}{1540\ \text{m/s} - 0.200\ \text{m/s}}\right) \quad 17.46$$

(3) Calculate to find the frequency returning to the source: 2,500,649 Hz.

Solution for (c)

(1) Identify knowns:

- The beat frequency is simply the absolute value of the difference between f_s and f_{obs}, as stated in:

$$f_B = |f_{\text{obs}} - f_s|. \quad 17.47$$

(2) Substitute known values:

$$|2{,}500{,}649\ \text{Hz} - 2{,}500{,}000\ \text{Hz}| \quad 17.48$$

(3) Calculate to find the beat frequency: 649 Hz.

Discussion

The Doppler shifts are quite small compared with the original frequency of 2.50 MHz. It is far easier to measure the beat frequency than it is to measure the echo frequency with an accuracy great enough to see shifts of a few hundred hertz out of a couple of megahertz. Furthermore, variations in the source frequency do not greatly affect the beat frequency, because both f_s and f_{obs} would increase or decrease. Those changes subtract out in $f_B = |f_{\text{obs}} - f_s|$.

INDUSTRIAL AND OTHER APPLICATIONS OF ULTRASOUND

Industrial, retail, and research applications of ultrasound are common. A few are discussed here. Ultrasonic cleaners have many uses. Jewelry, machined parts, and other objects that have odd shapes and crevices are immersed in a cleaning fluid that is agitated with ultrasound typically about 40 kHz in frequency. The intensity is great enough to cause cavitation, which is responsible for most of the cleansing action. Because cavitation-produced shock pressures are large and well transmitted in a fluid, they reach into small crevices where even a low-surface-tension cleaning fluid might not penetrate.

Sonar is a familiar application of ultrasound. Sonar typically employs ultrasonic frequencies in the range from 30.0 to 100 kHz. Bats, dolphins, submarines, and even some birds use ultrasonic sonar. Echoes are analyzed to give distance and size information both for guidance and finding prey. In most sonar applications, the sound reflects quite well because the objects of interest have significantly different density than the medium in which they travel. When the Doppler shift is observed, velocity information can also be obtained. Submarine sonar can be used to obtain such information, and there is evidence that some bats also sense velocity from their echoes.

Similarly, there are a range of relatively inexpensive devices that measure distance by timing ultrasonic echoes. Many cameras, for example, use such information to focus automatically. Some doors open when their ultrasonic ranging devices detect a nearby object, and certain home security lights turn on when their ultrasonic rangers observe motion. Ultrasonic “measuring tapes” also exist to measure such things as room dimensions. Sinks in public restrooms are sometimes automated with ultrasound devices to turn faucets on and off when people wash their hands. These devices reduce the spread of germs and can conserve water.

Ultrasound is used for nondestructive testing in industry and by the military. Because ultrasound reflects well from any large change in density, it can reveal cracks and voids in solids, such as aircraft wings, that are too small to be seen with x-rays. For similar reasons, ultrasound is also good for measuring the thickness of coatings, particularly where there are several layers involved.

Basic research in solid state physics employs ultrasound. Its attenuation is related to a number of physical characteristics, making it a useful probe. Among these characteristics are structural changes such as those found in liquid crystals, the transition of a material to a superconducting phase, as well as density and other properties.

These examples of the uses of ultrasound are meant to whet the appetites of the curious, as well as to illustrate the underlying physics of ultrasound. There are many more applications, as you can easily discover for yourself.

CHECK YOUR UNDERSTANDING

Why is it possible to use ultrasound both to observe a fetus in the womb and also to destroy cancerous tumors in the body?

Solution

Ultrasound can be used medically at different intensities. Lower intensities do not cause damage and are used for medical imaging. Higher intensities can pulverize and destroy targeted substances in the body, such as tumors.

Glossary

acoustic impedance property of medium that makes the propagation of sound waves more difficult
antinode point of maximum displacement
bow wake V-shaped disturbance created when the wave source moves faster than the wave propagation speed
Doppler effect an alteration in the observed frequency of a sound due to motion of either the source or the observer
Doppler shift the actual change in frequency due to relative motion of source and observer
Doppler-shifted ultrasound a medical technique to detect motion and determine velocity through the Doppler shift of an echo
fundamental the lowest-frequency resonance
harmonics the term used to refer collectively to the fundamental and its overtones
hearing the perception of sound
infrasound sounds below 20 Hz
intensity the power per unit area carried by a wave
intensity reflection coefficient a measure of the ratio of the intensity of the wave reflected off a boundary between two media relative to the intensity of the incident wave
loudness the perception of sound intensity
node point of zero displacement
note basic unit of music with specific names, combined to generate tunes
overtones all resonant frequencies higher than the fundamental
phon the numerical unit of loudness
pitch the perception of the frequency of a sound
sonic boom a constructive interference of sound created by an object moving faster than sound
sound a disturbance of matter that is transmitted from its source outward
sound intensity level a unitless quantity telling you the level of the sound relative to a fixed standard
sound pressure level the ratio of the pressure amplitude to a reference pressure
timbre number and relative intensity of multiple sound frequencies
tone number and relative intensity of multiple sound frequencies
ultrasound sounds above 20,000 Hz

Section Summary

17.1 Sound

- Sound is a disturbance of matter that is transmitted from its source outward.
- Sound is one type of wave.
- Hearing is the perception of sound.

17.2 Speed of Sound, Frequency, and Wavelength

The relationship of the speed of sound v_w, its frequency f, and its wavelength λ is given by

$$v_w = f\lambda,$$

which is the same relationship given for all waves.

In air, the speed of sound is related to air temperature T by

$$v_w = (331 \text{ m/s})\sqrt{\frac{T}{273 \text{ K}}}.$$

v_w is the same for all frequencies and wavelengths.

17.3 Sound Intensity and Sound Level

- Intensity is the same for a sound wave as was defined for all waves; it is

  $$I = \frac{P}{A},$$

  where P is the power crossing area A. The SI unit for I is watts per meter squared. The intensity of a sound wave is also related to the pressure amplitude Δp

  $$I = \frac{(\Delta p)^2}{2\rho v_w},$$

  where ρ is the density of the medium in which the sound wave travels and v_w is the speed of sound in the medium.
- Sound intensity level in units of decibels (dB) is

  $$\beta\,(\text{dB}) = 10 \log_{10}\left(\frac{I}{I_0}\right),$$

  where $I_0 = 10^{-12}\ \text{W/m}^2$ is the threshold intensity of hearing.

17.4 Doppler Effect and Sonic Booms

- The Doppler effect is an alteration in the observed frequency of a sound due to motion of either the source or the observer.
- The actual change in frequency is called the Doppler shift.
- A sonic boom is constructive interference of sound created by an object moving faster than sound.
- A sonic boom is a type of bow wake created when any wave source moves faster than the wave propagation speed.

- For a stationary observer and a moving source, the observed frequency f_{obs} is:
$$f_{obs} = f_s\left(\frac{v_w}{v_w \pm v_s}\right),$$
where f_s is the frequency of the source, v_s is the speed of the source, and v_w is the speed of sound. The minus sign is used for motion toward the observer and the plus sign for motion away.
- For a stationary source and moving observer, the observed frequency is:
$$f_{obs} = f_s\left(\frac{v_w \pm v_{obs}}{v_w}\right),$$
where v_{obs} is the speed of the observer.

17.5 Sound Interference and Resonance: Standing Waves in Air Columns

- Sound interference and resonance have the same properties as defined for all waves.
- In air columns, the lowest-frequency resonance is called the fundamental, whereas all higher resonant frequencies are called overtones. Collectively, they are called harmonics.
- The resonant frequencies of a tube closed at one end are:
$$f_n = n\frac{v_w}{4L}, n = 1, 3, 5...,$$
f_1 is the fundamental and L is the length of the tube.
- The resonant frequencies of a tube open at both ends are:
$$f_n = n\frac{v_w}{2L}, n = 1, 2, 3...$$

17.6 Hearing

- The range of audible frequencies is 20 to 20,000 Hz.
- Those sounds above 20,000 Hz are ultrasound, whereas those below 20 Hz are infrasound.
- The perception of frequency is pitch.
- The perception of intensity is loudness.
- Loudness has units of phons.

17.7 Ultrasound

- The acoustic impedance is defined as:
$$Z = \rho v,$$
ρ is the density of a medium through which the sound travels and v is the speed of sound through that medium.
- The intensity reflection coefficient a, a measure of the ratio of the intensity of the wave reflected off a boundary between two media relative to the intensity of the incident wave, is given by
$$a = \frac{(Z_2 - Z_1)^2}{(Z_1 + Z_2)^2}.$$
- The intensity reflection coefficient is a unitless quantity.

Conceptual Questions

17.2 Speed of Sound, Frequency, and Wavelength

1. How do sound vibrations of atoms differ from thermal motion?

2. When sound passes from one medium to another where its propagation speed is different, does its frequency or wavelength change? Explain your answer briefly.

17.3 Sound Intensity and Sound Level

3. Six members of a synchronized swim team wear earplugs to protect themselves against water pressure at depths, but they can still hear the music and perform the combinations in the water perfectly. One day, they were asked to leave the pool so the dive team could practice a few dives, and they tried to practice on a mat, but seemed to have a lot more difficulty. Why might this be?

4. A community is concerned about a plan to bring train service to their downtown from the town's outskirts. The current sound intensity level, even though the rail yard is blocks away, is 70 dB downtown. The mayor assures the public that there will be a difference of only 30 dB in sound in the downtown area. Should the townspeople be concerned? Why?

17.4 Doppler Effect and Sonic Booms

5. Is the Doppler shift real or just a sensory illusion?

6. Due to efficiency considerations related to its bow wake, the supersonic transport aircraft must maintain a cruising speed that is a constant ratio to the speed of sound (a constant Mach number). If the aircraft flies from warm air into colder air, should it increase or decrease its speed? Explain your answer.

7. When you hear a sonic boom, you often cannot see the plane that made it. Why is that?

17.5 Sound Interference and Resonance: Standing Waves in Air Columns

8. How does an unamplified guitar produce sounds so much more intense than those of a plucked string

held taut by a simple stick?

9. You are given two wind instruments of identical length. One is open at both ends, whereas the other is closed at one end. Which is able to produce the lowest frequency?

10. What is the difference between an overtone and a harmonic? Are all harmonics overtones? Are all overtones harmonics?

17.6 Hearing

11. Why can a hearing test show that your threshold of hearing is 0 dB at 250 Hz, when Figure 17.35 implies that no one can hear such a frequency at less than 20 dB?

17.7 Ultrasound

12. If audible sound follows a rule of thumb similar to that for ultrasound, in terms of its absorption, would you expect the high or low frequencies from your neighbor's stereo to penetrate into your house? How does this expectation compare with your experience?

13. Elephants and whales are known to use infrasound to communicate over very large distances. What are the advantages of infrasound for long distance communication?

14. It is more difficult to obtain a high-resolution ultrasound image in the abdominal region of someone who is overweight than for someone who has a slight build. Explain why this statement is accurate.

15. Suppose you read that 210-dB ultrasound is being used to pulverize cancerous tumors. You calculate the intensity in watts per centimeter squared and find it is unreasonably high ($10^5\ \text{W/cm}^2$). What is a possible explanation?

Problems & Exercises

17.2 Speed of Sound, Frequency, and Wavelength

1. When poked by a spear, an operatic soprano lets out a 1200-Hz shriek. What is its wavelength if the speed of sound is 345 m/s?

2. What frequency sound has a 0.10-m wavelength when the speed of sound is 340 m/s?

3. Calculate the speed of sound on a day when a 1500 Hz frequency has a wavelength of 0.221 m.

4. (a) What is the speed of sound in a medium where a 100-kHz frequency produces a 5.96-cm wavelength? (b) Which substance in Table 17.1 is this likely to be?

5. Show that the speed of sound in 20.0°C air is 343 m/s, as claimed in the text.

6. Air temperature in the Sahara Desert can reach 56.0°C (about 134°F). What is the speed of sound in air at that temperature?

7. Dolphins make sounds in air and water. What is the ratio of the wavelength of a sound in air to its wavelength in seawater? Assume air temperature is 20.0°C.

8. A sonar echo returns to a submarine 1.20 s after being emitted. What is the distance to the object creating the echo? (Assume that the submarine is in the ocean, not in fresh water.)

9. (a) If a submarine's sonar can measure echo times with a precision of 0.0100 s, what is the smallest difference in distances it can detect? (Assume that the submarine is in the ocean, not in fresh water.) (b) Discuss the limits this time resolution imposes on the ability of the sonar system to detect the size and shape of the object creating the echo.

10. A physicist at a fireworks display times the lag between seeing an explosion and hearing its sound, and finds it to be 0.400 s. (a) How far away is the explosion if air temperature is 24.0°C and if you neglect the time taken for light to reach the physicist? (b) Calculate the distance to the explosion taking the speed of light into account. Note that this distance is negligibly greater.

11. Suppose a bat uses sound echoes to locate its insect prey, 3.00 m away. (See Figure 17.9.) (a) Calculate the echo times for temperatures of 5.00°C and 35.0°C. (b) What percent uncertainty does this cause for the bat in locating the insect? (c) Discuss the significance of this uncertainty and whether it could cause difficulties for the bat. (In practice, the bat continues to use sound as it closes in, eliminating most of any difficulties imposed by this and other effects, such as motion of the prey.)

17.3 Sound Intensity and Sound Level

12. What is the intensity in watts per meter squared of 85.0-dB sound?

13. The warning tag on a lawn mower states that it produces noise at a level of 91.0 dB. What is this in watts per meter squared?

14. A sound wave traveling in $20°C$ air has a pressure amplitude of 0.5 Pa. What is the intensity of the wave?

15. What intensity level does the sound in the preceding problem correspond to?

16. What sound intensity level in dB is produced by earphones that create an intensity of $4.00 \times 10^{-2}\ W/m^2$?

17. Show that an intensity of $10^{-12}\ W/m^2$ is the same as $10^{-16}\ W/cm^2$.

18. (a) What is the decibel level of a sound that is twice as intense as a 90.0-dB sound? (b) What is the decibel level of a sound that is one-fifth as intense as a 90.0-dB sound?

19. (a) What is the intensity of a sound that has a level 7.00 dB lower than a $4.00 \times 10^{-9}\ W/m^2$ sound? (b) What is the intensity of a sound that is 3.00 dB higher than a $4.00 \times 10^{-9}\ W/m^2$ sound?

20. (a) How much more intense is a sound that has a level 17.0 dB higher than another? (b) If one sound has a level 23.0 dB less than another, what is the ratio of their intensities?

21. People with good hearing can perceive sounds as low in level as $-8.00\ dB$ at a frequency of 3000 Hz. What is the intensity of this sound in watts per meter squared?

22. If a large housefly 3.0 m away from you makes a noise of 40.0 dB, what is the noise level of 1000 flies at that distance, assuming interference has a negligible effect?

23. Ten cars in a circle at a boom box competition produce a 120-dB sound intensity level at the center of the circle. What is the average sound intensity level produced there by each stereo, assuming interference effects can be neglected?

24. The amplitude of a sound wave is measured in terms of its maximum gauge pressure. By what factor does the amplitude of a sound wave increase if the sound intensity level goes up by 40.0 dB?

25. If a sound intensity level of 0 dB at 1000 Hz corresponds to a maximum gauge pressure (sound amplitude) of 10^{-9} atm, what is the maximum gauge pressure in a 60-dB sound? What is the maximum gauge pressure in a 120-dB sound?

26. An 8-hour exposure to a sound intensity level of 90.0 dB may cause hearing damage. What energy in joules falls on a 0.800-cm-diameter eardrum so exposed?

27. (a) Ear trumpets were never very common, but they did aid people with hearing losses by gathering sound over a large area and concentrating it on the smaller area of the eardrum. What decibel increase does an ear trumpet produce if its sound gathering area is $900\ cm^2$ and the area of the eardrum is $0.500\ cm^2$, but the trumpet only has an efficiency of 5.00% in transmitting the sound to the eardrum? (b) Comment on the usefulness of the decibel increase found in part (a).

28. Sound is more effectively transmitted into a stethoscope by direct contact than through the air, and it is further intensified by being concentrated on the smaller area of the eardrum. It is reasonable to assume that sound is transmitted into a stethoscope 100 times as effectively compared with transmission though the air. What, then, is the gain in decibels produced by a stethoscope that has a sound gathering area of $15.0\ cm^2$, and concentrates the sound onto two eardrums with a total area of $0.900\ cm^2$ with an efficiency of 40.0%?

29. Loudspeakers can produce intense sounds with surprisingly small energy input in spite of their low efficiencies. Calculate the power input needed to produce a 90.0-dB sound intensity level for a 12.0-cm-diameter speaker that has an efficiency of 1.00%. (This value is the sound intensity level right at the speaker.)

17.4 Doppler Effect and Sonic Booms

30. (a) What frequency is received by a person watching an oncoming ambulance moving at 110 km/h and emitting a steady 800-Hz sound from its siren? The speed of sound on this day is 345 m/s. (b) What frequency does she receive after the ambulance has passed?

31. (a) At an air show a jet flies directly toward the stands at a speed of 1200 km/h, emitting a frequency of 3500 Hz, on a day when the speed of sound is 342 m/s. What frequency is received by the observers? (b) What frequency do they receive as the plane flies directly away from them?

32. What frequency is received by a mouse just before being dispatched by a hawk flying at it at 25.0 m/s and emitting a screech of frequency 3500 Hz? Take the speed of sound to be 331 m/s.

33. A spectator at a parade receives an 888-Hz tone from an oncoming trumpeter who is playing an 880-Hz note. At what speed is the musician approaching if the speed of sound is 338 m/s?

34. A commuter train blows its 200-Hz horn as it approaches a crossing. The speed of sound is 335 m/s. (a) An observer waiting at the crossing receives a frequency of 208 Hz. What is the speed of the train? (b) What frequency does the observer receive as the train moves away?

35. Can you perceive the shift in frequency produced when you pull a tuning fork toward you at 10.0 m/s on a day when the speed of sound is 344 m/s? To answer this question, calculate the factor by which the frequency shifts and see if it is greater than 0.300%.

36. Two eagles fly directly toward one another, the first at 15.0 m/s and the second at 20.0 m/s. Both screech, the first one emitting a frequency of 3200 Hz and the second one emitting a frequency of 3800 Hz. What frequencies do they receive if the speed of sound is 330 m/s?

37. What is the minimum speed at which a source must travel toward you for you to be able to hear that its frequency is Doppler shifted? That is, what speed produces a shift of 0.300% on a day when the speed of sound is 331 m/s?

17.5 Sound Interference and Resonance: Standing Waves in Air Columns

38. A "showy" custom-built car has two brass horns that are supposed to produce the same frequency but actually emit 263.8 and 264.5 Hz. What beat frequency is produced?

39. What beat frequencies will be present: (a) If the musical notes A and C are played together (frequencies of 220 and 264 Hz)? (b) If D and F are played together (frequencies of 297 and 352 Hz)? (c) If all four are played together?

40. What beat frequencies result if a piano hammer hits three strings that emit frequencies of 127.8, 128.1, and 128.3 Hz?

41. A piano tuner hears a beat every 2.00 s when listening to a 264.0-Hz tuning fork and a single piano string. What are the two possible frequencies of the string?

42. (a) What is the fundamental frequency of a 0.672-m-long tube, open at both ends, on a day when the speed of sound is 344 m/s? (b) What is the frequency of its second harmonic?

43. If a wind instrument, such as a tuba, has a fundamental frequency of 32.0 Hz, what are its first three overtones? It is closed at one end. (The overtones of a real tuba are more complex than this example, because it is a tapered tube.)

44. What are the first three overtones of a bassoon that has a fundamental frequency of 90.0 Hz? It is open at both ends. (The overtones of a real bassoon are more complex than this example, because its double reed makes it act more like a tube closed at one end.)

45. How long must a flute be in order to have a fundamental frequency of 262 Hz (this frequency corresponds to middle C on the evenly tempered chromatic scale) on a day when air temperature is $20.0^\circ C$? It is open at both ends.

46. What length should an oboe have to produce a fundamental frequency of 110 Hz on a day when the speed of sound is 343 m/s? It is open at both ends.

47. What is the length of a tube that has a fundamental frequency of 176 Hz and a first overtone of 352 Hz if the speed of sound is 343 m/s?

48. (a) Find the length of an organ pipe closed at one end that produces a fundamental frequency of 256 Hz when air temperature is $18.0^\circ C$. (b) What is its fundamental frequency at $25.0^\circ C$?

49. By what fraction will the frequencies produced by a wind instrument change when air temperature goes from $10.0^\circ C$ to $30.0^\circ C$? That is, find the ratio of the frequencies at those temperatures.

50. The ear canal resonates like a tube closed at one end. (See Figure 17.37.) If ear canals range in length from 1.80 to 2.60 cm in an average population, what is the range of fundamental resonant frequencies? Take air temperature to be $37.0^\circ C$, which is the same as body temperature. How does this result correlate with the intensity versus frequency graph (Figure 17.35 of the human ear?

51. Calculate the first overtone in an ear canal, which resonates like a 2.40-cm-long tube closed at one end, by taking air temperature to be $37.0^\circ C$. Is the ear particularly sensitive to such a frequency? (The resonances of the ear canal are complicated by its nonuniform shape, which we shall ignore.)

52. A crude approximation of voice production is to consider the breathing passages and mouth to be a resonating tube closed at one end. (See Figure 17.29.) (a) What is the fundamental frequency if the tube is 0.240-m long, by taking air temperature to be $37.0^\circ C$? (b) What would this frequency become if the person replaced the air with helium? Assume the same temperature dependence for helium as for air.

53. (a) Students in a physics lab are asked to find the length of an air column in a tube closed at one end that has a fundamental frequency of 256 Hz. They hold the tube vertically and fill it with water to the top, then lower the water while a 256-Hz tuning fork is rung and listen for the first resonance. What is the air temperature if the resonance occurs for a length of 0.336 m? (b) At what length will they observe the second resonance (first overtone)?

54. What frequencies will a 1.80-m-long tube produce in the audible range at $20.0^\circ C$ if: (a) The tube is closed at one end? (b) It is open at both ends?

17.6 Hearing

55. The factor of 10^{-12} in the range of intensities to which the ear can respond, from threshold to that causing damage after brief exposure, is truly remarkable. If you could measure distances over the same range with a single instrument and the smallest distance you could measure was 1 mm, what would the largest be?

56. The frequencies to which the ear responds vary by a factor of 10^3. Suppose the speedometer on your car measured speeds differing by the same factor of 10^3, and the greatest speed it reads is 90.0 mi/h. What would be the slowest nonzero speed it could read?

57. What are the closest frequencies to 500 Hz that an average person can clearly distinguish as being different in frequency from 500 Hz? The sounds are not present simultaneously.

58. Can the average person tell that a 2002-Hz sound has a different frequency than a 1999-Hz sound without playing them simultaneously?

59. If your radio is producing an average sound intensity level of 85 dB, what is the next lowest sound intensity level that is clearly less intense?

60. Can you tell that your roommate turned up the sound on the TV if its average sound intensity level goes from 70 to 73 dB?

61. Based on the graph in Figure 17.34, what is the threshold of hearing in decibels for frequencies of 60, 400, 1000, 4000, and 15,000 Hz? Note that many AC electrical appliances produce 60 Hz, music is commonly 400 Hz, a reference frequency is 1000 Hz, your maximum sensitivity is near 4000 Hz, and many older TVs produce a 15,750 Hz whine.

62. What sound intensity levels must sounds of frequencies 60, 3000, and 8000 Hz have in order to have the same loudness as a 40-dB sound of frequency 1000 Hz (that is, to have a loudness of 40 phons)?

63. What is the approximate sound intensity level in decibels of a 600-Hz tone if it has a loudness of 20 phons? If it has a loudness of 70 phons?

64. (a) What are the loudnesses in phons of sounds having frequencies of 200, 1000, 5000, and 10,000 Hz, if they are all at the same 60.0-dB sound intensity level? (b) If they are all at 110 dB? (c) If they are all at 20.0 dB?

65. Suppose a person has a 50-dB hearing loss at all frequencies. By how many factors of 10 will low-intensity sounds need to be amplified to seem normal to this person? Note that smaller amplification is appropriate for more intense sounds to avoid further hearing damage.

66. If a woman needs an amplification of 5.0×10^{12} times the threshold intensity to enable her to hear at all frequencies, what is her overall hearing loss in dB? Note that smaller amplification is appropriate for more intense sounds to avoid further damage to her hearing from levels above 90 dB.

67. (a) What is the intensity in watts per meter squared of a just barely audible 200-Hz sound? (b) What is the intensity in watts per meter squared of a barely audible 4000-Hz sound?

68. (a) Find the intensity in watts per meter squared of a 60.0-Hz sound having a loudness of 60 phons. (b) Find the intensity in watts per meter squared of a 10,000-Hz sound having a loudness of 60 phons.

69. A person has a hearing threshold 10 dB above normal at 100 Hz and 50 dB above normal at 4000 Hz. How much more intense must a 100-Hz tone be than a 4000-Hz tone if they are both barely audible to this person?

70. A child has a hearing loss of 60 dB near 5000 Hz, due to noise exposure, and normal hearing elsewhere. How much more intense is a 5000-Hz tone than a 400-Hz tone if they are both barely audible to the child?

71. What is the ratio of intensities of two sounds of identical frequency if the first is just barely discernible as louder to a person than the second?

17.7 Ultrasound

Unless otherwise indicated, for problems in this section, assume that the speed of sound through human tissues is 1540 m/s.

72. What is the sound intensity level in decibels of ultrasound of intensity 10^5 W/m^2, used to pulverize tissue during surgery?

73. Is 155-dB ultrasound in the range of intensities used for deep heating? Calculate the intensity of this ultrasound and compare this intensity with values quoted in the text.

74. Find the sound intensity level in decibels of $2.00 \times 10^{-2} \text{ W/m}^2$ ultrasound used in medical diagnostics.

75. The time delay between transmission and the arrival of the reflected wave of a signal using ultrasound traveling through a piece of fat tissue was 0.13 ms. At what depth did this reflection occur?

76. In the clinical use of ultrasound, transducers are always coupled to the skin by a thin layer of gel or oil, replacing the air that would otherwise exist between the transducer and the skin. (a) Using the values of acoustic impedance given in Table 17.5 calculate the intensity reflection coefficient between transducer material and air. (b) Calculate the intensity reflection coefficient between transducer material and gel (assuming for this problem that its acoustic impedance is identical to that of water). (c) Based on the results of your calculations, explain why the gel is used.

77. (a) Calculate the minimum frequency of ultrasound that will allow you to see details as small as 0.250 mm in human tissue. (b) What is the effective depth to which this sound is effective as a diagnostic probe?

78. (a) Find the size of the smallest detail observable in human tissue with 20.0-MHz ultrasound. (b) Is its effective penetration depth great enough to examine the entire eye (about 3.00 cm is needed)? (c) What is the wavelength of such ultrasound in 0°C air?

79. (a) Echo times are measured by diagnostic ultrasound scanners to determine distances to reflecting surfaces in a patient. What is the difference in echo times for tissues that are 3.50 and 3.60 cm beneath the surface? (This difference is the minimum resolving time for the scanner to see details as small as 0.100 cm, or 1.00 mm. Discrimination of smaller time differences is needed to see smaller details.) (b) Discuss whether the period T of this ultrasound must be smaller than the minimum time resolution. If so, what is the minimum frequency of the ultrasound and is that out of the normal range for diagnostic ultrasound?

80. (a) How far apart are two layers of tissue that produce echoes having round-trip times (used to measure distances) that differ by 0.750 µs ? (b) What minimum frequency must the ultrasound have to see detail this small?

81. (a) A bat uses ultrasound to find its way among trees. If this bat can detect echoes 1.00 ms apart, what minimum distance between objects can it detect? (b) Could this distance explain the difficulty that bats have finding an open door when they accidentally get into a house?

82. A dolphin is able to tell in the dark that the ultrasound echoes received from two sharks come from two different objects only if the sharks are separated by 3.50 m, one being that much farther away than the other. (a) If the ultrasound has a frequency of 100 kHz, show this ability is not limited by its wavelength. (b) If this ability is due to the dolphin's ability to detect the arrival times of echoes, what is the minimum time difference the dolphin can perceive?

83. A diagnostic ultrasound echo is reflected from moving blood and returns with a frequency 500 Hz higher than its original 2.00 MHz. What is the velocity of the blood? (Assume that the frequency of 2.00 MHz is accurate to seven significant figures and 500 Hz is accurate to three significant figures.)

84. Ultrasound reflected from an oncoming bloodstream that is moving at 30.0 cm/s is mixed with the original frequency of 2.50 MHz to produce beats. What is the beat frequency? (Assume that the frequency of 2.50 MHz is accurate to seven significant figures.)

Test Prep for AP® Courses

17.2 Speed of Sound, Frequency, and Wavelength

1. A teacher wants to demonstrate that the speed of sound is not a constant value. Considering her regular classroom voice as the control, which of the following will increase the speed of sound leaving her mouth?

I. Submerge her mouth underwater and speak at the same volume.
II. Increase the temperature of the room and speak at the same volume.
III. Increase the pitch of her voice and speak at the same volume.

a. I only
b. I and II only
c. I, II and III
d. II and III
e. III only

2. All members of an orchestra begin tuning their instruments at the same time. While some woodwind instruments play high frequency notes, other stringed instruments play notes of lower frequency. Yet an audience member will hear all notes simultaneously, in apparent contrast to the equation.
Explain how a student could demonstrate the flaw in the above logic, using a slinky, stopwatch, and meter stick. Make sure to explain what relationship is truly demonstrated in the above equation, in addition to what would be necessary to get the speed of the slinky to actually change. You may include diagrams and equations as part of your explanation.

17.3 Sound Intensity and Sound Level

3. In order to waken a sleeping child, the volume on an alarm clock is tripled. Under this new scenario, how much more energy will be striking the child's ear drums each second?

a. twice as much
b. three times as much
c. approximately 4.8 times as much
d. six times as much
e. nine times as much

4. A musician strikes the strings of a guitar such that they vibrate with twice the amplitude.

a. Explain why this requires an energy input greater than twice the original value.
b. Explain why the sound leaving the string will not result in a decibel level that is twice as great.

17.4 Doppler Effect and Sonic Booms

5. A baggage handler stands on the edge of a runway as a landing plane approaches. Compared to the pitch of the plane as heard by the plane's pilot, which of the following correctly describes the sensation experienced by the handler?

a. The frequency of the plane will be lower pitched according to the baggage handler and will become even lower pitched as the plane slows to a stop.
b. The frequency of the plane will be lower pitched according to the baggage handler but will increase in pitch as the plane slows to a stop.
c. The frequency of the plane will be higher pitched according to the baggage handler but will decrease in pitch as the plane slows to a stop.
d. The frequency of the plane will be higher pitched according to the baggage handler and will further increase in pitch as the plane slows to a stop.

6. The following graph represents the perceived frequency of a car as it passes a student.

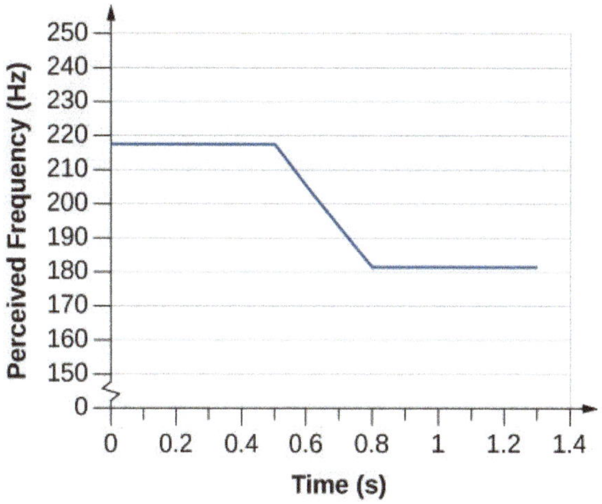

FIGURE 17.47 Plot of time versus perceived frequency to illustrate the Doppler effect.

a. If the true frequency of the car's horn is 200 Hz, how fast was the car traveling?

b. On the graph above, draw a line demonstrating the perceived frequency for a car traveling twice as fast. Label all intercepts, maximums, and minimums on the graph.

17.5 Sound Interference and Resonance: Standing Waves in Air Columns

7. A common misconception is that two wave pulses traveling in opposite directions will reflect off each other. Outline a procedure that you would use to convince someone that the two wave pulses do not reflect off each other, but instead travel through each other. You may use sketches to represent your understanding. Be sure to provide evidence to not only refute the original claim, but to support yours as well.

8. Two wave pulses are traveling toward each other on a string, as shown below. Which of the following representations correctly shows the string as the two pulses overlap?

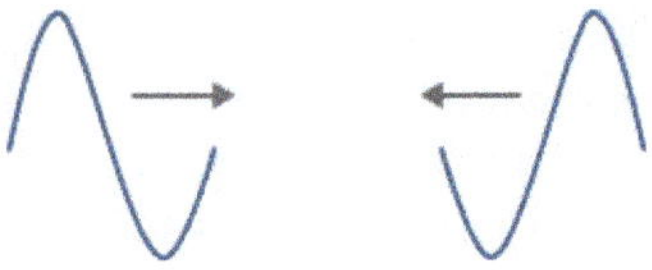
FIGURE 17.48

a.

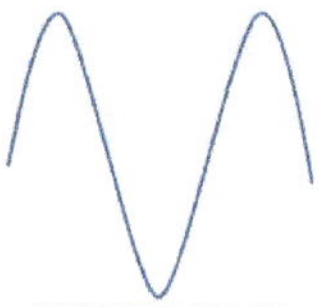
FIGURE 17.49

b.

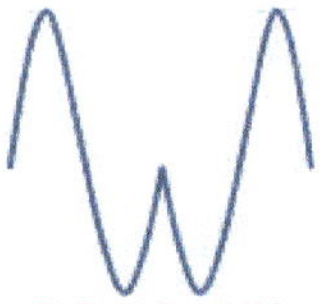
FIGURE 17.50

c.

FIGURE 17.51

d.

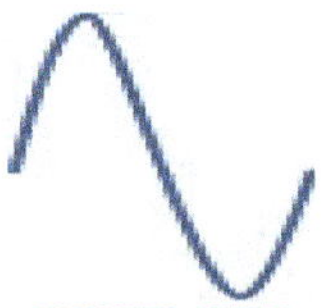
FIGURE 17.52

9. A student sends a transverse wave pulse of amplitude A along a rope attached at one end. As the pulse returns to the student, a second pulse of amplitude $3A$ is sent along the opposite side of the rope. What is the resulting amplitude when the two pulses interact?

a. $4A$
b. A
c. $2A$, on the side of the original wave pulse
d. $2A$, on the side of the second wave pulse

10. A student would like to demonstrate destructive interference using two sound sources. Explain how the student could set up this demonstration and what restrictions they would need to place upon their sources. Be sure to consider both the layout of space and the sounds created in your explanation.

11. A student is shaking a flexible string attached to a wooden board in a rhythmic manner. Which of the following choices will decrease the wavelength within the rope?

I. The student could shake her hand back and forth with greater frequency.
II. The student could shake her hand back in forth with a greater amplitude.
III. The student could increase the tension within the rope by stepping backwards from the board.

a. I only
b. I and II
c. I and III
d. II and III
e. I, II, and III

12. A ripple tank has two locations (L1 and L2) that vibrate in tandem as shown below. Both L1 and L2 vibrate in a plane perpendicular to the page, creating a two-dimensional interference pattern.

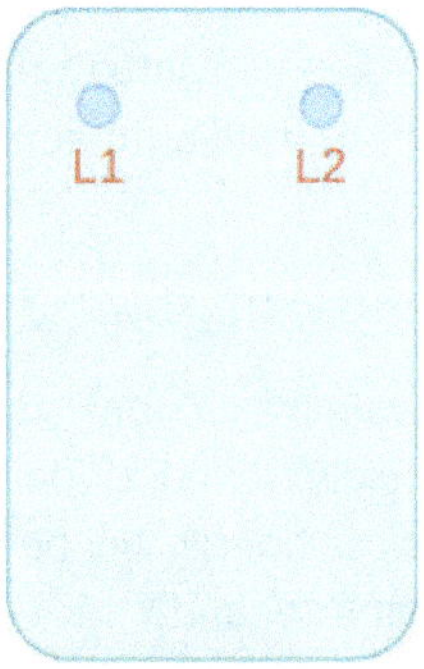

FIGURE 17.53

Describe an experimental procedure to determine the speed of the waves created within the water, including all additional equipment that you would need. You may use the diagram below to help your description, or you may create one of your own. Include enough detail so that another student could carry out your experiment.

13. A string is vibrating between two posts as shown above. Students are to determine the speed of the wave within this string. They have already measured the amount of time necessary for the wave to oscillate up and down. The students must also take what other measurements to determine the speed of the wave?

a. The distance between the two posts.
b. The amplitude of the wave
c. The tension in the string
d. The amplitude of the wave and the tension in the string
e. The distance between the two posts, the amplitude of the wave, and the tension in the string

14. The accepted speed of sound in room temperature air is 346 m/s. Knowing that their school is colder than usual, a group of students is asked to determine the speed of sound in their room. They are permitted to use any materials necessary; however, their lab procedure must utilize standing wave patterns. The students collect the information Table 17.6.

Trial Number	Wavelength (m)	Frequency (Hz)	
1	3.45	95	
2	2.32	135	
3	1.70	190	
4	1.45	240	
5	1.08	305	

TABLE 17.6

a. Describe an experimental procedure the group of students could have used to obtain this data. Include diagrams of the experimental setup and any equipment used in the process.
b. Select a set of data points from the table and plot those points on a graph to determine the speed of sound within the classroom. Fill in the blank column in the table for any quantities you graph other than the given data. Label the axes and indicate the scale for each. Draw a best-fit line or curve through your data points.
c. Using information from the graph, determine the speed of sound within the student's classroom, and explain what characteristic of the graph provides this evidence.
d. Determine the temperature of the classroom.

15. A tube is open at one end. If the fundamental frequency f is created by a wavelength λ, then which of the following describes the frequency and wavelength associated with the tube's fourth overtone?

f λ

(a) $4f\lambda/4$
(b) $4f\lambda$
(c) $9f\lambda/9$
(d) $9f\lambda$

16. A group of students were tasked with collecting information about standing waves. Table 17.7 a series of their data, showing the length of an air column and a resonant frequency present when the column is struck.

Length (m)	Resonant Frequency (Hz)
1	85.75
2	43
3	29
4	21.5

TABLE 17.7

a. From their data, determine whether the air column was open or closed on each end.
b. Predict the resonant frequency of the column at a length of 2.5 meters.

17. When a student blows across a glass half-full of water, a resonant frequency is created within the air column remaining in the glass. Which of the following can the student do to increase this resonant frequency?

I. Add more water to the glass.
II. Replace the water with a more dense fluid.
III. Increase the temperature of the room.

a. I only
b. I and III
c. II and III
d. all of the above

18. A student decides to test the speed of sound through wood using a wooden ruler. The student rests the ruler on a desk with half of its length protruding off the desk edge. The student then holds one end in place and strikes the protruding end with his other hand, creating a musical sound, and counts the number of vibrations of the ruler. Explain why the student would not be able to measure the speed of sound through wood using this method.

19. A musician stands outside in a field and plucks a string on an acoustic guitar. Standing waves will most likely occur in which of the following media? Select two answers.
   a. The guitar string
   b. The air inside the guitar
   c. The air surrounding the guitar
   d. The ground beneath the musician

20.

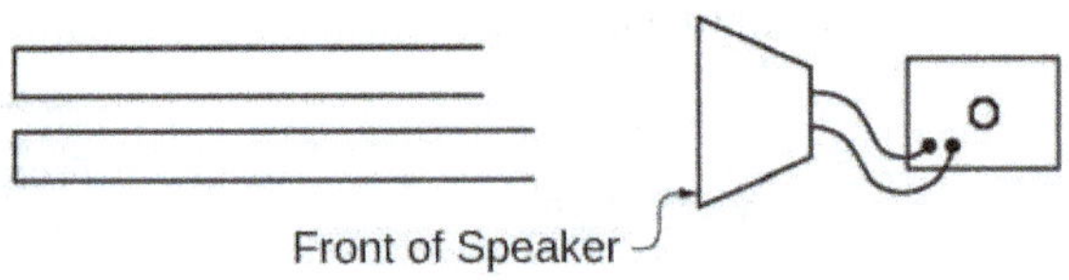

FIGURE 17.54

This figure shows two tubes that are identical except for their slightly different lengths. Both tubes have one open end and one closed end. A speaker connected to a variable frequency generator is placed in front of the tubes, as shown. The speaker is set to produce a note of very low frequency when turned on. The frequency is then slowly increased to produce resonances in the tubes. Students observe that at first only one of the tubes resonates at a time. Later, as the frequency gets very high, there are times when both tubes resonate. In a clear, coherent, paragraph-length answer, explain why there are some high frequencies, but no low frequencies, at which both tubes resonate. You may include diagrams and/or equations as part of your explanation.

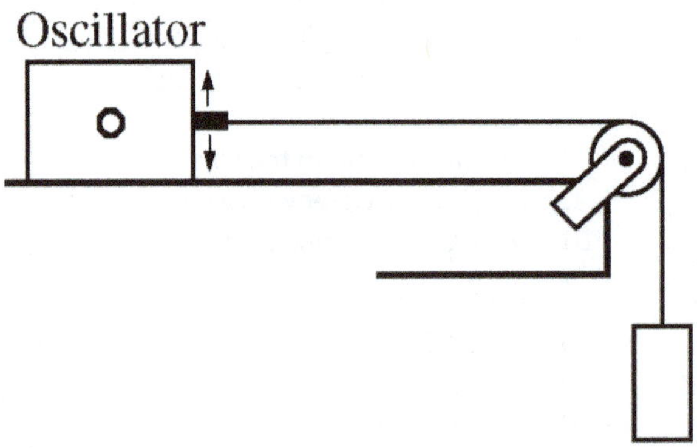

FIGURE 17.55

21. A student connects one end of a string with negligible mass to an oscillator. The other end of the string is passed over a pulley and attached to a suspended weight, as shown above. The student finds that a standing wave with one antinode is formed on the string when the frequency of the oscillator is f_0. The student then moves the oscillator to shorten the horizontal segment of string to half its original length. At what frequency will a standing wave with one antinode now be formed on the string?
   a. $f_0/2$
   b. f_0
   c. $2f_0$
   d. There is no frequency at which a standing wave will be formed.

22. A guitar string of length L is bound at both ends. Table 17.8 shows the string's harmonic frequencies when struck.

Harmonic Number	Frequency
1	$225/L$
2	$450/L$
3	$675/L$
4	$900/L$

TABLE 17.8

   a. Based on the information above, what is the speed of the wave within the string?
   b. The guitarist then slides her finger along the neck of the guitar, changing the string length as a result. Calculate the fundamental frequency of the string and wave speed present if the string length is reduced to 2/3 L.

CHAPTER 18
Electric Charge and Electric Field

FIGURE 18.1 Static electricity from this plastic slide causes the child's hair to stand on end. The sliding motion stripped electrons away from the child's body, leaving an excess of positive charges, which repel each other along each strand of hair. (credit: Ken Bosma/Wikimedia Commons)

CHAPTER OUTLINE

CONNECTION FOR AP® COURSES The image of American politician and scientist Benjamin Franklin (1706–1790) flying a kite in a thunderstorm (shown in Figure 18.2) is familiar to every schoolchild. In this experiment, Franklin demonstrated a connection between lightning and static electricity. Sparks were drawn from a key hung on a kite string during an electrical storm. These sparks were like those produced by static electricity, such as the spark that jumps from your finger to a metal doorknob after you walk across a wool carpet. Much has been written about Franklin. His experiments were only part of the life of a man who was a scientist, inventor, revolutionary, statesman, and writer. Franklin's experiments were not performed in isolation, nor were they the only ones to reveal connections.

FIGURE 18.2 Benjamin Franklin, his kite, and electricity.

When Benjamin Franklin demonstrated that lightning was related to static electricity, he made a connection that is now part of the evidence that all directly experienced forces (except gravitational force) are manifestations of the electromagnetic force. For example, the Italian scientist Luigi Galvani (1737-1798) performed a series of experiments in which static electricity was used to stimulate contractions of leg muscles of dead frogs, an effect already known in humans subjected to static discharges. But Galvani also found that if he joined one end of two metal wires (say copper and zinc) and touched the other ends of the wires to muscles; he produced the same effect in frogs as static discharge. Alessandro Volta (1745-1827), partly inspired by Galvani's work, experimented with various combinations of metals and developed the battery.

During the same era, other scientists made progress in discovering fundamental connections. The periodic table was developed as systematic properties of the elements were discovered. This influenced the development and refinement of the concept of atoms as the basis of matter. Such submicroscopic descriptions of matter also help explain a great deal more. Atomic and molecular interactions, such as the forces of friction, cohesion, and adhesion, are now known to be manifestations of the electromagnetic force.

Static electricity is just one aspect of the electromagnetic force, which also includes moving electricity and magnetism. All the macroscopic forces that we experience directly, such as the sensations of touch and the tension in a rope, are due to the electromagnetic force, one of the four fundamental forces in nature. The gravitational force, another fundamental force, is actually sensed through the electromagnetic interaction of molecules, such as between those in our feet and those on the top of a bathroom scale. (The other two fundamental forces, the strong nuclear force and the weak nuclear force, cannot be sensed on the human scale.)

This chapter begins the study of electromagnetic phenomena at a fundamental level. The next several chapters will cover static electricity, moving electricity, and magnetism – collectively known as electromagnetism. In this chapter, we begin with the study of electric phenomena due to charges that are at least temporarily stationary, called electrostatics, or static electricity.

The chapter introduces several very important concepts of charge, electric force, and electric field, as well as defining the relationships between these concepts. The charge is defined as a property of a system (Big Idea 1) that can affect its interaction with other charged systems (Enduring Understanding 1.B). The law of conservation of electric charge is also discussed (Essential Knowledge 1.B.1). The two kinds of electric charge are defined as positive and negative, providing an explanation for having positively charged, negatively charged, or neutral objects (containing equal quantities of positive and negative charges) (Essential Knowledge 1.B.2). The discrete nature of the electric charge is introduced in this chapter by defining the elementary charge as the smallest observed unit of charge that can be isolated, which is the electron charge (Essential Knowledge 1.B.3). The concepts of a system (having internal structure) and of an object (having no internal structure) are implicitly introduced to explain charges carried by the electron and proton (Enduring Understanding 1.A, Essential Knowledge 1.A.1).

An electric field is caused by the presence of charged objects (Enduring Understanding 2.C) and can be used to explain interactions between electrically charged objects (Big Idea 2). The electric force represents the effect of an electric field on a charge placed in the field. The magnitude and direction of the electric force are defined by the magnitude and direction of the electric field and magnitude and sign of the charge (Essential Knowledge 2.C.1). The magnitude of the electric field is proportional to the net charge of the objects that created that field (Essential Knowledge 2.C.2). For the special case of a spherically symmetric charged object, the electric field outside the object is radial, and its magnitude varies as the inverse square of the radial distance from the center of that object (Essential Knowledge 2.C.3). The chapter provides examples of vector field maps for various charged systems, including point charges, spherically symmetric charge distributions, and uniformly charged parallel plates (Essential Knowledge 2.C.1, Essential Knowledge 2.C.2). For multiple point charges, the chapter explains how to find the vector field map by adding the electric field vectors of each individual object, including the special case of two equal charges having opposite signs, known as an electric dipole (Essential Knowledge 2.C.4). The special case of two oppositely charged parallel plates with uniformly distributed electric charge when the electric field is perpendicular to the plates and is constant in both magnitude and direction is described in detail, providing many opportunities for problem solving and applications (Essential Knowledge 2.C.5).

The idea that interactions can be described by forces is also reinforced in this chapter (Big Idea 3). Like all other forces that you have learned about so far, electric force is a vector that affects the motion according to Newton's laws (Enduring Understanding 3.A). It is clearly stated in the chapter that electric force appears as a result of interactions between two charged objects (Essential Knowledge 3.A.3, Essential Knowledge 3.C.2). At the macroscopic level the electric force is a long-range force (Enduring Understanding 3.C); however, at the microscopic level many contact forces, such as friction, can be explained by interatomic electric forces (Essential Knowledge 3.C.4). This understanding of friction is helpful when considering properties of conductors and insulators and the transfer of charge by conduction.

Interactions between systems can result in changes in those systems (Big Idea 4). In the case of charged systems, such interactions can lead to changes of electric properties (Enduring Understanding 4.E), such as charge distribution (Essential Knowledge 4.E.3). Any changes are governed by conservation laws (Big Idea 5). Depending on whether the system is closed or open, certain quantities of the system remain the same or changes in those quantities are equal to the amount of transfer of this quantity from or to the system (Enduring Understanding 5.A). The electric charge is one of these quantities (Essential Knowledge 5.A.2). Therefore, the electric charge of a system is conserved (Enduring Understanding 5.C) and the exchange of electric charge between objects in a system does not change the total electric charge of the system (Essential Knowledge 5.C.2).

Big Idea 1 Objects and systems have properties such as mass and charge. Systems may have internal structure.

Enduring Understanding 1.A The internal structure of a system determines many properties of the system.

Essential Knowledge 1.A.1 A system is an object or a collection of objects. Objects are treated as having no internal structure.

Enduring Understanding 1.B Electric charge is a property of an object or system that affects its interactions with other objects or systems containing charge.

Essential Knowledge 1.B.1 Electric charge is conserved. The net charge of a system is equal to the sum of the charges of all the objects in the system.

Essential Knowledge 1.B.2 There are only two kinds of electric charge. Neutral objects or systems contain equal quantities of positive and negative charge, with the exception of some fundamental particles that have no electric charge.

Essential Knowledge 1.B.3 The smallest observed unit of charge that can be isolated is the electron charge, also known as the elementary charge.

Big Idea 2 Fields existing in space can be used to explain interactions.

Enduring Understanding 2.C An electric field is caused by an object with electric charge.

Essential Knowledge 2.C.1 The magnitude of the electric force *F* exerted on an object with electric charge *q* by an electric field ($\vec{E}$ is $\vec{F} = q\vec{E}$. The direction of the force is determined by the direction of the field and the sign of the charge, with positively charged objects accelerating in the direction of the field and negatively charged objects accelerating in the direction opposite the field. This should include a vector field map for positive point charges, negative point charges, spherically symmetric charge distribution, and uniformly charged parallel plates.

Essential Knowledge 2.C.2 The magnitude of the electric field vector is proportional to the net electric charge of the object(s) creating that field. This includes positive point charges, negative point charges, spherically symmetric charge distributions, and uniformly charged parallel plates.

Essential Knowledge 2.C.3 The electric field outside a spherically symmetric charged object is radial, and its magnitude varies as the inverse square of the radial distance from the center of that object. Electric field lines are not in the curriculum. Students will be expected to rely only on the rough intuitive sense underlying field lines, wherein the field is viewed as analogous to something emanating uniformly from a source.

Essential Knowledge 2.C.4 The electric field around dipoles and other systems of electrically charged objects (that can be modeled as point objects) is found by vector addition of the field of each individual object. Electric dipoles are treated qualitatively in this course as a teaching analogy to facilitate student understanding of magnetic dipoles.

Essential Knowledge 2.C.5 Between two oppositely charged parallel plates with uniformly distributed electric charge, at points far from the edges of the plates, the electric field is perpendicular to the plates and is constant in both magnitude and direction.

Big Idea 3 The interactions of an object with other objects can be described by forces.

Enduring Understanding 3.A All forces share certain common characteristics when considered by observers in inertial reference frames.

Essential Knowledge 3.A.3 A force exerted on an object is always due to the interaction of that object with another object.

Enduring Understanding 3.C At the macroscopic level, forces can be categorized as either long-range (action-at-a-distance) forces or contact forces.

Essential Knowledge 3.C.2 Electric force results from the interaction of one object that has an electric charge with another object that has an electric charge.

Essential Knowledge 3.C.4 Contact forces result from the interaction of one object touching another object, and they arise from interatomic electric forces. These forces include tension, friction, normal, spring (Physics 1), and buoyant (Physics 2).

Big Idea 4 Interactions between systems can result in changes in those systems.

Enduring Understanding 4.E The electric and magnetic properties of a system can change in response to the presence of, or changes in, other objects or systems.

Essential Knowledge 4.E.3 The charge distribution in a system can be altered by the effects of electric forces produced by a charged object.

Big Idea 5 Changes that occur as a result of interactions are constrained by conservation laws.

Enduring Understanding 5.A Certain quantities are conserved, in the sense that the changes of those quantities in a given system are always equal to the transfer of that quantity to or from the system by all possible interactions with other systems.

Essential Knowledge 5.A.2 For all systems under all circumstances, energy, charge, linear momentum, and angular momentum are conserved.

Enduring Understanding 5.C The electric charge of a system is conserved.

Essential Knowledge 5.C.2 The exchange of electric charges among a set of objects in a system conserves electric charge.

Click to view content (https://openstax.org/books/college-physics-ap-courses-2e/pages/18-connection-for-ap-r-courses)

18.1 Static Electricity and Charge: Conservation of Charge

LEARNING OBJECTIVES

By the end of this section, you will be able to:

- Define electric charge, and describe how the two types of charge interact.
- Describe three common situations that generate static electricity.
- State the law of conservation of charge.

FIGURE 18.3 Borneo amber was mined in Sabah, Malaysia, from shale-sandstone-mudstone veins. When a piece of amber is rubbed with a piece of silk, the amber gains more electrons, giving it a net negative charge. At the same time, the silk, having lost electrons, becomes positively charged. (credit: Sebakoamber, Wikimedia Commons)

What makes plastic wrap cling? Static electricity. Not only are applications of static electricity common these days, its existence has been known since ancient times. The first record of its effects dates to ancient Greeks who noted more than 500 years B.C. that polishing amber temporarily enabled it to attract bits of straw (see Figure 18.3). The very word *electric* derives from the Greek word for amber (*electron*).

Many of the characteristics of static electricity can be explored by rubbing things together. Rubbing creates the spark you get from walking across a wool carpet, for example. Static cling generated in a clothes dryer and the attraction of straw to recently polished amber also result from rubbing. Similarly, lightning results from air movements under certain weather conditions. You can also rub a balloon on your hair, and the static electricity created can then make the balloon cling to a wall. We also have to be cautious of static electricity, especially in dry climates. When we pump gasoline, we are warned to discharge ourselves (after sliding across the seat) on a metal surface before grabbing the gas nozzle. Attendants in hospital operating rooms must wear booties with a conductive strip of aluminum foil on the bottoms to avoid creating sparks which may ignite flammable anesthesia gases combined with the oxygen being used.

Some of the most basic characteristics of static electricity include:

- The effects of static electricity are explained by a physical quantity not previously introduced, called electric charge.
- There are only two types of charge, one called positive and the other called negative.
- Like charges repel, whereas unlike charges attract.
- The force between charges decreases with distance.

How do we know there are two types of **electric charge**? When various materials are rubbed together in controlled ways, certain combinations of materials always produce one type of charge on one material and the opposite type on the other. By convention, we call one type of charge "positive", and the other type "negative." For example, when glass is rubbed with silk, the glass becomes positively charged and the silk negatively charged. Since the glass and silk have opposite charges, they attract one another like clothes that have rubbed together in a dryer. Two glass rods rubbed with silk in this manner will repel one another, since each rod has positive charge on it. Similarly, two silk cloths so rubbed will repel, since both cloths have negative charge. Figure 18.4 shows how these simple materials can be used to explore the nature of the force between charges.

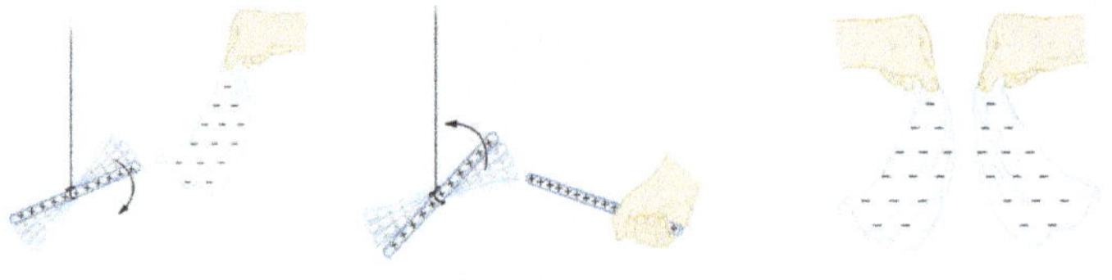

FIGURE 18.4 A glass rod becomes positively charged when rubbed with silk, while the silk becomes negatively charged. (a) The glass rod is attracted to the silk because their charges are opposite. (b) Two similarly charged glass rods repel. (c) Two similarly charged silk cloths repel.

More sophisticated questions arise. Where do these charges come from? Can you create or destroy charge? Is there a smallest unit of charge? Exactly how does the force depend on the amount of charge and the distance between charges? Such questions obviously occurred to Benjamin Franklin and other early researchers, and they interest us even today.

Charge Carried by Electrons and Protons

Franklin wrote in his letters and books that he could see the effects of electric charge but did not understand what caused the phenomenon. Today we have the advantage of knowing that normal matter is made of atoms, and that atoms contain positive and negative charges, usually in equal amounts.

Figure 18.5 shows a simple model of an atom with negative **electrons** orbiting its positive nucleus. The nucleus is positive due to the presence of positively charged **protons**. Nearly all charge in nature is due to electrons and protons, which are two of the three building blocks of most matter. (The third is the neutron, which is neutral, carrying no charge.) Other charge-carrying particles are observed in cosmic rays and nuclear decay, and are created in particle accelerators. All but the electron and proton survive only a short time and are quite rare by comparison.

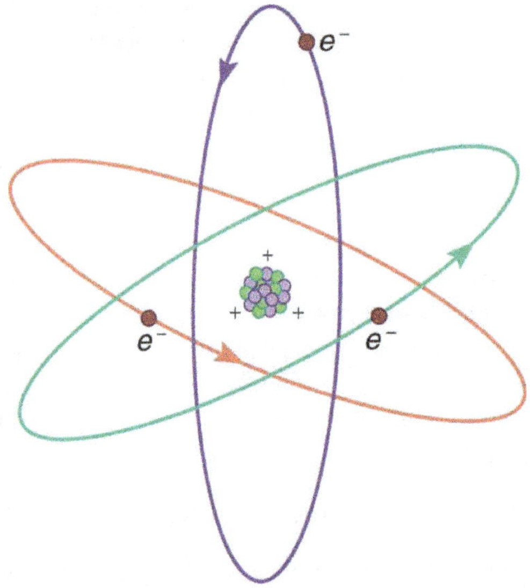

FIGURE 18.5 This simplified (and not to scale) view of an atom is called the planetary model of the atom. Negative electrons orbit a much heavier positive nucleus, as the planets orbit the much heavier sun. There the similarity ends, because forces in the atom are electromagnetic, whereas those in the planetary system are gravitational. Normal macroscopic amounts of matter contain immense numbers of atoms and molecules and, hence, even greater numbers of individual negative and positive charges.

The charges of electrons and protons are identical in magnitude but opposite in sign. Furthermore, all charged objects in nature are integral multiples of this basic quantity of charge, meaning that all charges are made of combinations of a basic unit of charge. Usually, charges are formed by combinations of electrons and protons. The magnitude of this basic charge is

$$|q_e| = 1.60 \times 10^{-19}\ \text{C}. \qquad 18.1$$

The symbol q is commonly used for charge and the subscript e indicates the charge of a single electron (or proton).

The SI unit of charge is the coulomb (C). The number of protons needed to make a charge of 1.00 C is

$$1.00\text{ C} \times \frac{1\text{ proton}}{1.60 \times 10^{-19}\text{ C}} = 6.25 \times 10^{18}\text{ protons.} \tag{18.2}$$

Similarly, 6.25×10^{18} electrons have a combined charge of −1.00 coulomb. Just as there is a smallest bit of an element (an atom), there is a smallest bit of charge. There is no directly observed charge smaller than $|q_e|$ (see Things Great and Small: The Submicroscopic Origin of Charge), and all observed charges are integral multiples of $|q_e|$.

THINGS GREAT AND SMALL: THE SUBMICROSCOPIC ORIGIN OF CHARGE

With the exception of exotic, short-lived particles, all charge in nature is carried by electrons and protons. Electrons carry the charge we have named negative. Protons carry an equal-magnitude charge that we call positive. (See Figure 18.6.) Electron and proton charges are considered fundamental building blocks, since all other charges are integral multiples of those carried by electrons and protons. Electrons and protons are also two of the three fundamental building blocks of ordinary matter. The neutron is the third and has zero total charge.

Figure 18.6 shows a person touching a Van de Graaff generator and receiving excess positive charge. The expanded view of a hair shows the existence of both types of charges but an excess of positive. The repulsion of these positive like charges causes the strands of hair to repel other strands of hair and to stand up. The further blowup shows an artist's conception of an electron and a proton perhaps found in an atom in a strand of hair.

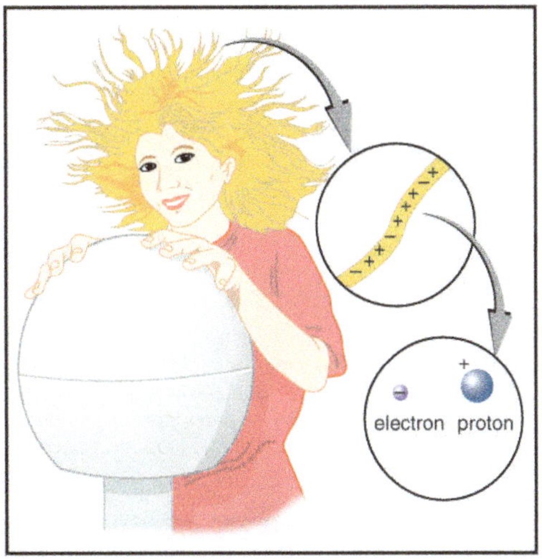

FIGURE 18.6 When this person touches a Van de Graaff generator, some electrons are attracted to the generator, resulting in an excess of positive charge, causing her hair to stand on end. The charges in one hair are shown. An artist's conception of an electron and a proton illustrate the particles carrying the negative and positive charges. We cannot really see these particles with visible light because they are so small (the electron seems to be an infinitesimal point), but we know a great deal about their measurable properties, such as the charges they carry.

The electron seems to have no substructure; in contrast, when the substructure of protons is explored by scattering extremely energetic electrons from them, it appears that there are point-like particles inside the proton. These sub-particles, named quarks, have never been directly observed, but they are believed to carry fractional charges as seen in Figure 18.7. Charges on electrons and protons and all other directly observable particles are unitary, but these quark substructures carry charges of either $-\frac{1}{3}$ or $+\frac{2}{3}$. There are continuing attempts to observe fractional charge directly and to learn of the properties of quarks, which are perhaps the ultimate substructure of matter.

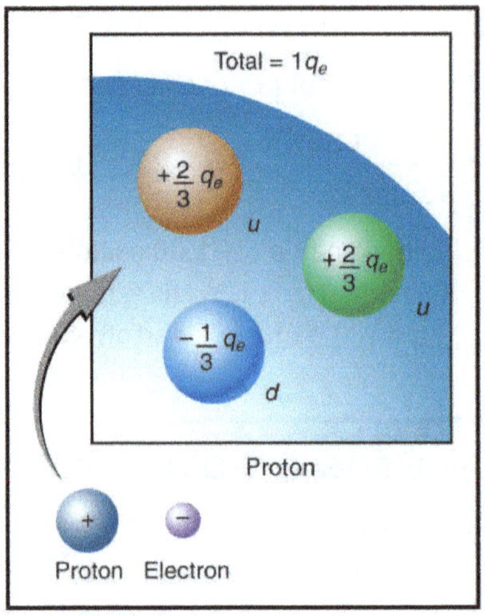

FIGURE 18.7 Artist's conception of fractional quark charges inside a proton. A group of three quark charges add up to the single positive charge on the proton: $-\frac{1}{3}q_e + \frac{2}{3}q_e + \frac{2}{3}q_e = +1q_e$.

Separation of Charge in Atoms

Charges in atoms and molecules can be separated—for example, by rubbing materials together. Some atoms and molecules have a greater affinity for electrons than others and will become negatively charged by close contact in rubbing, leaving the other material positively charged. (See Figure 18.8.) Positive charge can similarly be induced by rubbing. Methods other than rubbing can also separate charges. Batteries, for example, use combinations of substances that interact in such a way as to separate charges. Chemical interactions may transfer negative charge from one substance to the other, making one battery terminal negative and leaving the first one positive.

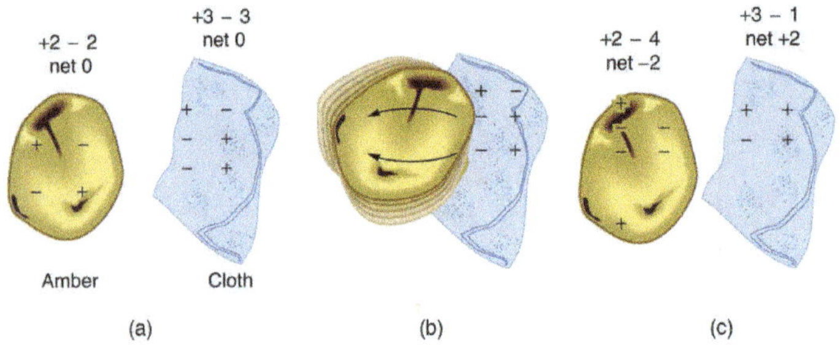

FIGURE 18.8 When materials are rubbed together, charges can be separated, particularly if one material has a greater affinity for electrons than another. (a) Both the amber and cloth are originally neutral, with equal positive and negative charges. Only a tiny fraction of the charges are involved, and only a few of them are shown here. (b) When rubbed together, some negative charge is transferred to the amber, leaving the cloth with a net positive charge. (c) When separated, the amber and cloth now have net charges, but the absolute value of the net positive and negative charges will be equal.

No charge is actually created or destroyed when charges are separated as we have been discussing. Rather, existing charges are moved about. In fact, in all situations the total amount of charge is always constant. This universally obeyed law of nature is called the **law of conservation of charge**.

LAW OF CONSERVATION OF CHARGE

Total charge is constant in any process.

In more exotic situations, such as in particle accelerators, mass, Δm, can be created from energy in the amount $\Delta m = \frac{E}{c^2}$. Sometimes, the created mass is charged, such as when an electron is created. Whenever a charged particle is created, another having an opposite charge is always created along with it, so that the total charge created is zero. Usually, the two particles are "matter-antimatter" counterparts. For example, an antielectron would usually be created at the same time as an electron. The antielectron has a positive charge (it is called a positron), and so the total charge created is zero. (See Figure 18.9.) All particles have antimatter counterparts with opposite signs. When matter and antimatter counterparts are brought together, they completely annihilate one another. By annihilate, we mean that the mass of the two particles is converted to energy E, again obeying the relationship $\Delta m = \frac{E}{c^2}$. Since the two particles have equal and opposite charge, the total charge is zero before and after the annihilation; thus, total charge is conserved.

MAKING CONNECTIONS: CONSERVATION LAWS

Only a limited number of physical quantities are universally conserved. Charge is one—energy, momentum, and angular momentum are others. Because they are conserved, these physical quantities are used to explain more phenomena and form more connections than other, less basic quantities. We find that conserved quantities give us great insight into the rules followed by nature and hints to the organization of nature. Discoveries of conservation laws have led to further discoveries, such as the weak nuclear force and the quark substructure of protons and other particles.

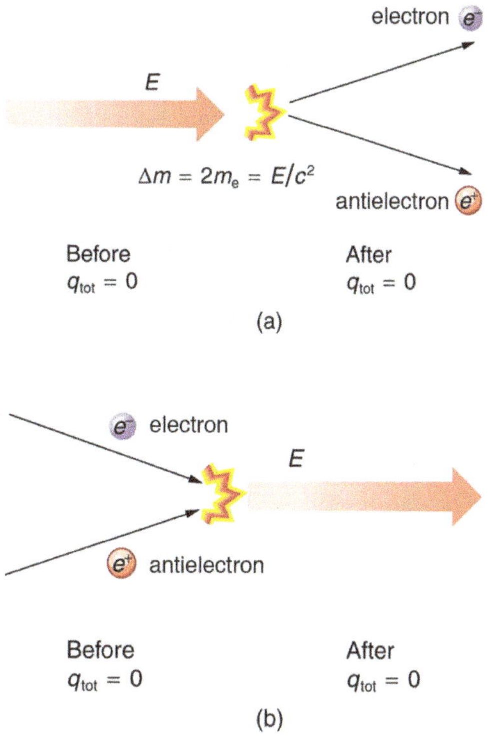

FIGURE 18.9 (a) When enough energy is present, it can be converted into matter. Here the matter created is an electron–antielectron pair. (m_e is the electron's mass.) The total charge before and after this event is zero. (b) When matter and antimatter collide, they annihilate each other; the total charge is conserved at zero before and after the annihilation.

The law of conservation of charge is absolute—it has never been observed to be violated. Charge, then, is a special physical quantity, joining a very short list of other quantities in nature that are always conserved. Other conserved quantities include energy, momentum, and angular momentum.

PHET EXPLORATIONS

Balloons and Static Electricity

Why does a balloon stick to your sweater? Rub a balloon on a sweater, then let go of the balloon and it flies over and sticks to the sweater. View the charges in the sweater, balloons, and the wall.

Click to view content (https://openstax.org/books/college-physics-ap-courses-2e/pages/18-1-static-electricity-and-charge-conservation-of-charge)

PhET

18.2 Conductors and Insulators

LEARNING OBJECTIVES

By the end of this section, you will be able to:

- Define conductor and insulator, explain the difference, and give examples of each.
- Describe three methods for charging an object.
- Explain what happens to an electric force as you move farther from the source.
- Define polarization.

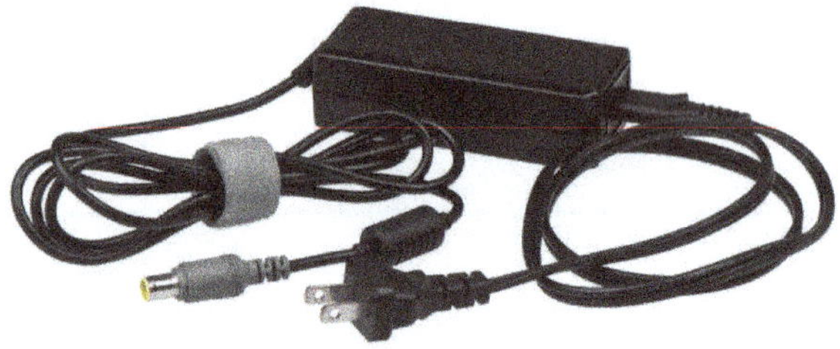

FIGURE 18.10 This power adapter uses metal wires and connectors to conduct electricity from the wall socket to a laptop computer. The conducting wires allow electrons to move freely through the cables, which are shielded by rubber and plastic. These materials act as insulators that don't allow electric charge to escape outward. (credit: Evan-Amos, Wikimedia Commons)

Some substances, such as metals and salty water, allow charges to move through them with relative ease. Some of the electrons in metals and similar conductors are not bound to individual atoms or sites in the material. These **free electrons** can move through the material much as air moves through loose sand. Any substance that has free electrons and allows charge to move relatively freely through it is called a **conductor**. The moving electrons may collide with fixed atoms and molecules, losing some energy, but they can move in a conductor. Superconductors allow the movement of charge without any loss of energy. Salty water and other similar conducting materials contain free ions that can move through them. An ion is an atom or molecule having a positive or negative (nonzero) total charge. In other words, the total number of electrons is not equal to the total number of protons.

Other substances, such as glass, do not allow charges to move through them. These are called **insulators**. Electrons and ions in insulators are bound in the structure and cannot move easily—as much as 10^{23} times more slowly than in conductors. Pure water and dry table salt are insulators, for example, whereas molten salt and salty water are conductors.

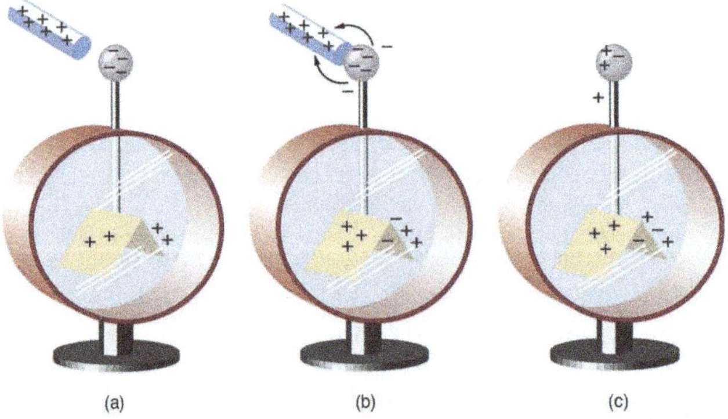

FIGURE 18.11 An electroscope is a favorite instrument in physics demonstrations and student laboratories. It is typically made with gold foil leaves hung from a (conducting) metal stem and is insulated from the room air in a glass-walled container. (a) A positively charged glass rod is brought near the tip of the electroscope, attracting electrons to the top and leaving a net positive charge on the leaves. Like charges in the light flexible gold leaves repel, separating them. (b) When the rod is touched against the ball, electrons are attracted and transferred, reducing the net charge on the glass rod but leaving the electroscope positively charged. (c) The excess charges are evenly distributed in the stem and leaves of the electroscope once the glass rod is removed.

Charging by Contact

Figure 18.11 shows an electroscope being charged by touching it with a positively charged glass rod. Because the glass rod is an insulator, it must actually touch the electroscope to transfer charge to or from it. (Note that the extra positive charges reside on the surface of the glass rod as a result of rubbing it with silk before starting the experiment.) Since only electrons move in metals, we see that they are attracted to the top of the electroscope. There, some are transferred to the positive rod by touch, leaving the electroscope with a net positive charge.

Electrostatic repulsion in the leaves of the charged electroscope separates them. The electrostatic force has a horizontal component that results in the leaves moving apart as well as a vertical component that is balanced by the gravitational force. Similarly, the electroscope can be negatively charged by contact with a negatively charged object.

Charging by Induction

It is not necessary to transfer excess charge directly to an object in order to charge it. Figure 18.12 shows a method of **induction** wherein a charge is created in a nearby object, without direct contact. Here we see two neutral metal spheres in contact with one another but insulated from the rest of the world. A positively charged rod is brought near one of them, attracting negative charge to that side, leaving the other sphere positively charged.

This is an example of induced **polarization** of neutral objects. Polarization is the separation of charges in an object that remains neutral. If the spheres are now separated (before the rod is pulled away), each sphere will have a net charge. Note that the object closest to the charged rod receives an opposite charge when charged by induction. Note also that no charge is removed from the charged rod, so that this process can be repeated without depleting the supply of excess charge.

Another method of charging by induction is shown in Figure 18.13. The neutral metal sphere is polarized when a charged rod is brought near it. The sphere is then grounded, meaning that a conducting wire is run from the sphere to the ground. Since the earth is large and most ground is a good conductor, it can supply or accept excess charge easily. In this case, electrons are attracted to the sphere through a wire called the ground wire, because it supplies a conducting path to the ground. The ground connection is broken before the charged rod is removed, leaving the sphere with an excess charge opposite to that of the rod. Again, an opposite charge is achieved when charging by induction and the charged rod loses none of its excess charge.

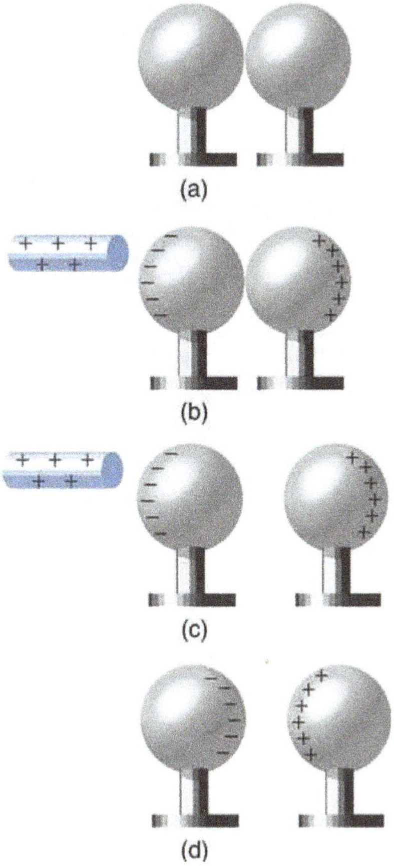

FIGURE 18.12 Charging by induction. (a) Two uncharged or neutral metal spheres are in contact with each other but insulated from the rest of the world. (b) A positively charged glass rod is brought near the sphere on the left, attracting negative charge and leaving the other

sphere positively charged. (c) The spheres are separated before the rod is removed, thus separating negative and positive charge. (d) The spheres retain net charges after the inducing rod is removed—without ever having been touched by a charged object.

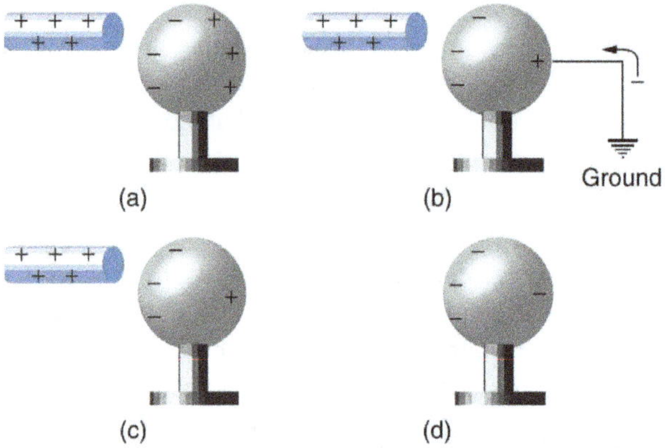

FIGURE 18.13 Charging by induction, using a ground connection. (a) A positively charged rod is brought near a neutral metal sphere, polarizing it. (b) The sphere is grounded, allowing electrons to be attracted from the earth's ample supply. (c) The ground connection is broken. (d) The positive rod is removed, leaving the sphere with an induced negative charge.

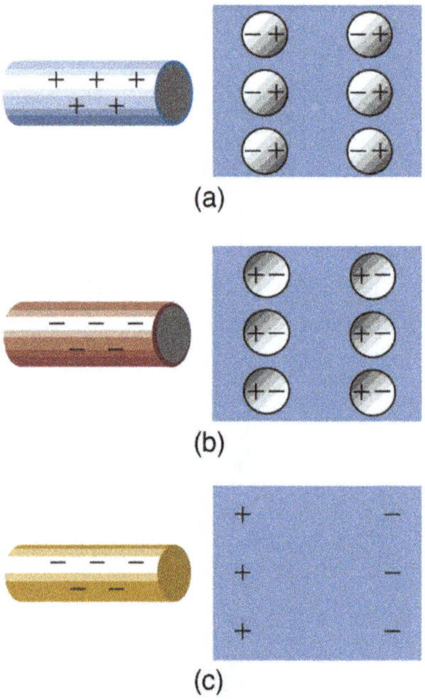

FIGURE 18.14 Both positive and negative objects attract a neutral object by polarizing its molecules. (a) A positive object brought near a neutral insulator polarizes its molecules. There is a slight shift in the distribution of the electrons orbiting the molecule, with unlike charges being brought nearer and like charges moved away. Since the electrostatic force decreases with distance, there is a net attraction. (b) A negative object produces the opposite polarization, but again attracts the neutral object. (c) The same effect occurs for a conductor; since the unlike charges are closer, there is a net attraction.

Neutral objects can be attracted to any charged object. The pieces of straw attracted to polished amber are neutral, for example. If you run a plastic comb through your hair, the charged comb can pick up neutral pieces of paper. Figure 18.14 shows how the polarization of atoms and molecules in neutral objects results in their attraction to a charged object.

When a charged rod is brought near a neutral substance, an insulator in this case, the distribution of charge in atoms and molecules is shifted slightly. Opposite charge is attracted nearer the external charged rod, while like charge is repelled. Since the electrostatic force decreases with distance, the repulsion of like charges is weaker than the attraction of unlike charges, and so there is a net attraction. Thus a positively charged glass rod attracts neutral pieces of paper, as will a negatively charged rubber rod. Some molecules, like water, are polar molecules. Polar molecules have a natural or inherent separation of charge, although they are neutral overall. Polar molecules are particularly affected by other charged objects and show greater polarization effects than molecules with naturally uniform charge distributions.

CHECK YOUR UNDERSTANDING

Can you explain the attraction of water to the charged rod in the figure below?

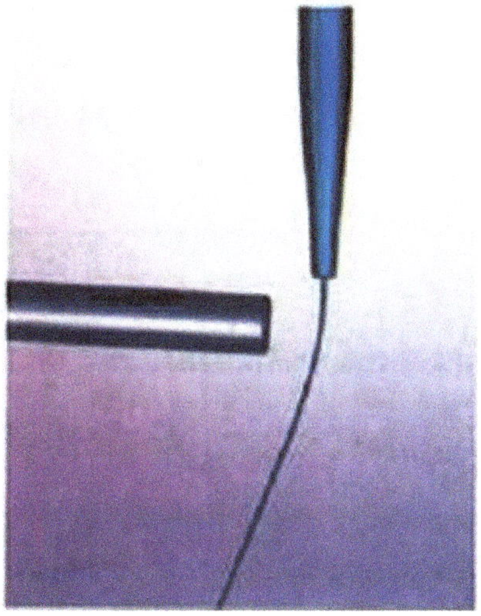

FIGURE 18.15

Solution

Water molecules are polarized, giving them slightly positive and slightly negative sides. This makes water even more susceptible to a charged rod's attraction. In addition, tap water contains dissolved ions (positive and negative charges). As the water flows downward, due to the force of gravity, the charged conductor exerts a net attraction to the opposite charges in the stream of water, pulling it closer.

PHET EXPLORATIONS

John Travoltage

Make sparks fly with John Travoltage. Wiggle Johnnie's foot and he picks up charges from the carpet. Bring his hand close to the door knob and get rid of the excess charge.

Click to view content (https://openstax.org/books/college-physics-ap-courses-2e/pages/18-2-conductors-and-insulators)

18.3 Conductors and Electric Fields in Static Equilibrium

LEARNING OBJECTIVES

By the end of this section, you will be able to:

- List the three properties of a conductor in electrostatic equilibrium.
- Explain the effect of an electric field on free charges in a conductor.
- Explain why no electric field may exist inside a conductor.
- Describe the electric field surrounding Earth.
- Explain what happens to an electric field applied to an irregular conductor.
- Describe how a lightning rod works.
- Explain how a metal car may protect passengers inside from the dangerous electric fields caused by a downed line touching the car.

Conductors contain **free charges** that move easily. When excess charge is placed on a conductor or the conductor is put into a static electric field, charges in the conductor quickly respond to reach a steady state called **electrostatic equilibrium**.

Figure 18.16 shows the effect of an electric field on free charges in a conductor. The free charges move until the field is perpendicular to the conductor's surface. There can be no component of the field parallel to the surface in electrostatic equilibrium, since, if there were, it would produce further movement of charge. A positive free charge is shown, but free charges can be either positive or negative and are, in fact, negative in metals. The motion of a positive charge is equivalent to the motion of a negative charge in the opposite direction.

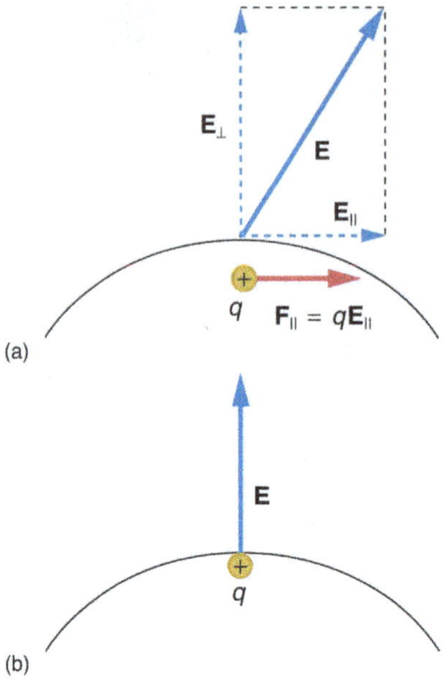

FIGURE 18.16 When an electric field $\mathbf{E}$ is applied to a conductor, free charges inside the conductor move until the field is perpendicular to the surface. (a) The electric field is a vector quantity, with both parallel and perpendicular components. The parallel component $(\mathbf{E}_{\|})$ exerts a force $(\mathbf{F}_{\|})$ on the free charge q, which moves the charge until $\mathbf{F}_{\|} = 0$. (b) The resulting field is perpendicular to the surface. The free charge has been brought to the conductor's surface, leaving electrostatic forces in equilibrium.

A conductor placed in an **electric field** will be **polarized**. Figure 18.17 shows the result of placing a neutral conductor in an originally uniform electric field. The field becomes stronger near the conductor but entirely disappears inside it.

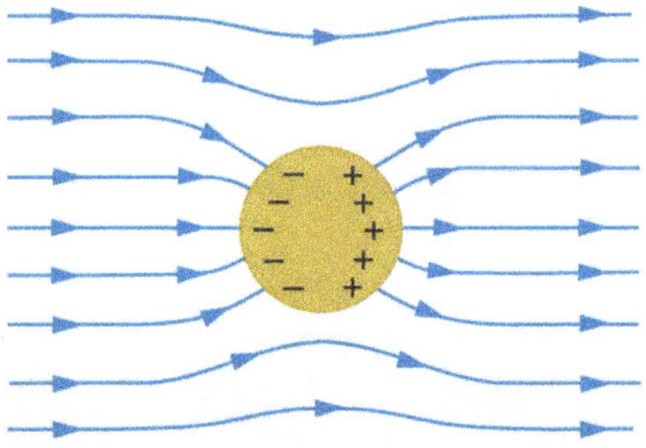

FIGURE 18.17 This illustration shows a spherical conductor in static equilibrium with an originally uniform electric field. Free charges move within the conductor, polarizing it, until the electric field lines are perpendicular to the surface. The field lines end on excess negative charge on one section of the surface and begin again on excess positive charge on the opposite side. No electric field exists inside the conductor, since free charges in the conductor would continue moving in response to any field until it was neutralized.

MISCONCEPTION ALERT: ELECTRIC FIELD INSIDE A CONDUCTOR

Excess charges placed on a spherical conductor repel and move until they are evenly distributed, as shown in Figure 18.18. Excess charge is forced to the surface until the field inside the conductor is zero. Outside the conductor, the field is exactly the same as if the conductor were replaced by a point charge at its center equal to the excess charge.

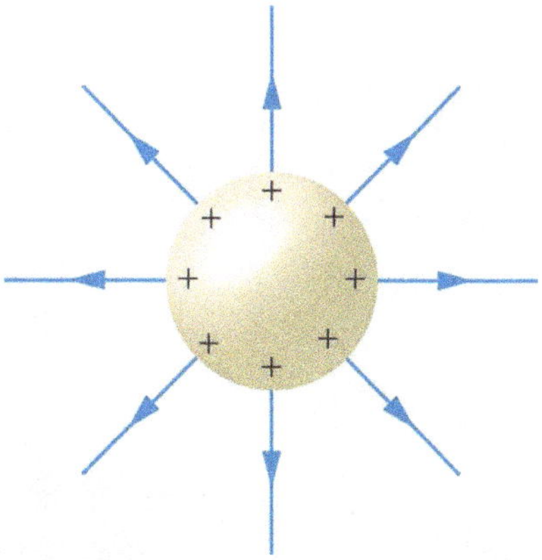

FIGURE 18.18 The mutual repulsion of excess positive charges on a spherical conductor distributes them uniformly on its surface. The resulting electric field is perpendicular to the surface and zero inside. Outside the conductor, the field is identical to that of a point charge at the center equal to the excess charge.

PROPERTIES OF A CONDUCTOR IN ELECTROSTATIC EQUILIBRIUM

1. The electric field is zero inside a conductor.
2. Just outside a conductor, the electric field lines are perpendicular to its surface, ending or beginning on charges on the surface.
3. Any excess charge resides entirely on the surface or surfaces of a conductor.

The properties of a conductor are consistent with the situations already discussed and can be used to analyze any conductor in electrostatic equilibrium. This can lead to some interesting new insights, such as described below.

How can a very uniform electric field be created? Consider a system of two metal plates with opposite charges on them, as shown in Figure 18.19. The properties of conductors in electrostatic equilibrium indicate that the electric field between the plates will be uniform in strength and direction. Except near the edges, the excess charges distribute themselves uniformly, producing field lines that are uniformly spaced (hence uniform in strength) and perpendicular to the surfaces (hence uniform in direction, since the plates are flat). The edge effects are less important when the plates are close together.

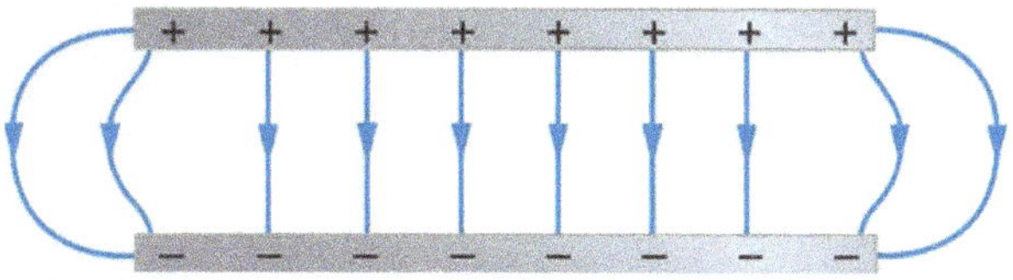

FIGURE 18.19 Two metal plates with equal, but opposite, excess charges. The field between them is uniform in strength and direction except near the edges. One use of such a field is to produce uniform acceleration of charges between the plates, such as in the electron gun of a TV tube.

Earth's Electric Field

A near uniform electric field of approximately 150 N/C, directed downward, surrounds Earth, with the magnitude increasing slightly as we get closer to the surface. What causes the electric field? At around 100 km above the surface of Earth we have a layer of charged particles, called the **ionosphere**. The ionosphere is responsible for a range of phenomena including the electric field surrounding Earth. In fair weather the ionosphere is positive and the Earth largely negative, maintaining the electric field (Figure 18.20(a)).

In storm conditions clouds form and localized electric fields can be larger and reversed in direction (Figure 18.20(b)). The exact charge distributions depend on the local conditions, and variations of Figure 18.20(b) are possible.

If the electric field is sufficiently large, the insulating properties of the surrounding material break down and it becomes conducting. For air this occurs at around 3×10^6 N/C. Air ionizes ions and electrons recombine, and we get discharge in the form of lightning sparks and corona discharge.

FIGURE 18.20 Earth's electric field. (a) Fair weather field. Earth and the ionosphere (a layer of charged particles) are both conductors. They produce a uniform electric field of about 150 N/C. (credit: D. H. Parks) (b) Storm fields. In the presence of storm clouds, the local electric fields can be larger. At very high fields, the insulating properties of the air break down and lightning can occur. (credit: Jan-Joost Verhoef)

Electric Fields on Uneven Surfaces

So far we have considered excess charges on a smooth, symmetrical conductor surface. What happens if a conductor has sharp corners or is pointed? Excess charges on a nonuniform conductor become concentrated at the sharpest points. Additionally, excess charge may move on or off the conductor at the sharpest points.

To see how and why this happens, consider the charged conductor in Figure 18.21. The electrostatic repulsion of like charges is most effective in moving them apart on the flattest surface, and so they become least concentrated there. This is because the forces between identical pairs of charges at either end of the conductor are identical, but the components of the forces parallel to the surfaces are different. The component parallel to the surface is greatest on the flattest surface and, hence, more effective in moving the charge.

The same effect is produced on a conductor by an externally applied electric field, as seen in Figure 18.21 (c). Since the field lines must be perpendicular to the surface, more of them are concentrated on the most curved parts.

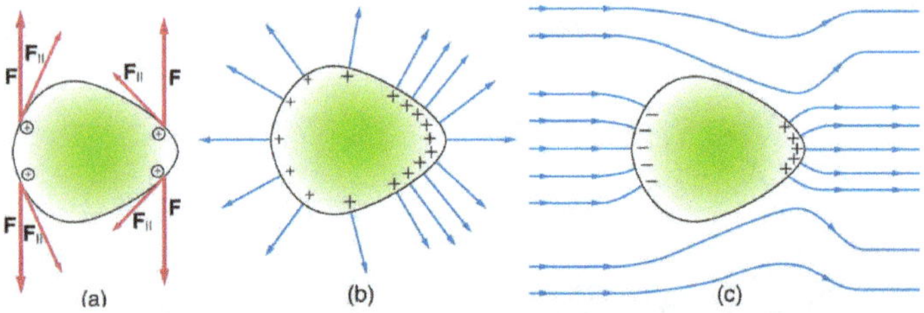

FIGURE 18.21 Excess charge on a nonuniform conductor becomes most concentrated at the location of greatest curvature. (a) The forces between identical pairs of charges at either end of the conductor are identical, but the components of the forces parallel to the surface are different. It is $\mathbf{F}_{||}$ that moves the charges apart once they have reached the surface. (b) $\mathbf{F}_{||}$ is smallest at the more pointed end, the charges are left closer together, producing the electric field shown. (c) An uncharged conductor in an originally uniform electric field is polarized, with the most concentrated charge at its most pointed end.

Applications of Conductors

On a very sharply curved surface, such as shown in Figure 18.22, the charges are so concentrated at the point that the resulting electric field can be great enough to remove them from the surface. This can be useful.

Lightning rods work best when they are most pointed. The large charges created in storm clouds induce an opposite charge on a building that can result in a lightning bolt hitting the building. The induced charge is bled away continually by a lightning rod, preventing the more dramatic lightning strike.

Of course, we sometimes wish to prevent the transfer of charge rather than to facilitate it. In that case, the conductor should be very smooth and have as large a radius of curvature as possible. (See Figure 18.23.) Smooth surfaces are used on high-voltage transmission lines, for example, to avoid leakage of charge into the air.

Another device that makes use of some of these principles is a **Faraday cage**. This is a metal shield that encloses a volume. All electrical charges will reside on the outside surface of this shield, and there will be no electrical field inside. A Faraday cage is used to prohibit stray electrical fields in the environment from interfering with sensitive measurements, such as the electrical signals inside a nerve cell.

During electrical storms if you are driving a car, it is best to stay inside the car as its metal body acts as a Faraday cage with zero electrical field inside. If in the vicinity of a lightning strike, its effect is felt on the outside of the car and the inside is unaffected, provided you remain totally inside. This is also true if an active ("hot") electrical wire was broken (in a storm or an accident) and fell on your car.

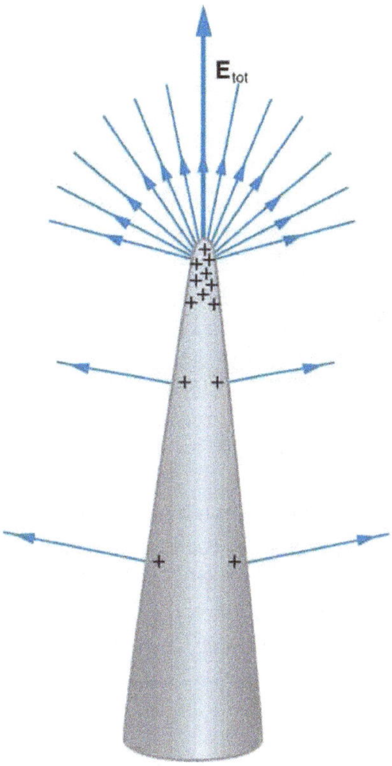

FIGURE 18.22 A very pointed conductor has a large charge concentration at the point. The electric field is very strong at the point and can exert a force large enough to transfer charge on or off the conductor. Lightning rods are used to prevent the buildup of large excess charges on structures and, thus, are pointed.

FIGURE 18.23 (a) A lightning rod is pointed to facilitate the transfer of charge. (credit: Romaine, Wikimedia Commons) (b) This Van de Graaff generator has a smooth surface with a large radius of curvature to prevent the transfer of charge and allow a large voltage to be generated. The mutual repulsion of like charges is evident in the person's hair while touching the metal sphere. (credit: Jon 'ShakataGaNai' Davis/Wikimedia Commons).

18.4 Coulomb's Law

LEARNING OBJECTIVES

By the end of this section, you will be able to:

- State Coulomb's law in terms of how the electrostatic force changes with the distance between two objects.
- Calculate the electrostatic force between two charged point forces, such as electrons or protons.
- Compare the electrostatic force to the gravitational attraction for a proton and an electron; for a human and the Earth.

FIGURE 18.24 This NASA image of Arp 87 shows the result of a strong gravitational attraction between two galaxies. In contrast, at the subatomic level, the electrostatic attraction between two objects, such as an electron and a proton, is far greater than their mutual attraction due to gravity. (credit: NASA/HST)

Through the work of scientists in the late 18th century, the main features of the **electrostatic force**—the existence of two types of charge, the observation that like charges repel, unlike charges attract, and the decrease of force with distance—were eventually refined, and expressed as a mathematical formula. The mathematical formula for the electrostatic force is called **Coulomb's law** after the French physicist Charles Coulomb (1736–1806), who performed experiments and first proposed a formula to calculate it.

COULOMB'S LAW

$$F = k\frac{|q_1 q_2|}{r^2}. \tag{18.3}$$

Coulomb's law calculates the magnitude of the force F between two point charges, q_1 and q_2, separated by a distance r. In SI units, the constant k is equal to

$$k = 8.988 \times 10^9 \frac{\text{N} \cdot \text{m}^2}{\text{C}^2} \approx 8.99 \times 10^9 \frac{\text{N} \cdot \text{m}^2}{\text{C}^2}. \tag{18.4}$$

The electrostatic force is a vector quantity and is expressed in units of newtons. The force is understood to be along the line joining the two charges. (See Figure 18.25.)

Although the formula for Coulomb's law is simple, it was no mean task to prove it. The experiments Coulomb did, with the primitive equipment then available, were difficult. Modern experiments have verified Coulomb's law to great precision. For example, it has been shown that the force is inversely proportional to distance between two objects squared $\left(F \propto 1/r^2\right)$ to an accuracy of 1 part in 10^{16}. No exceptions have ever been found, even at the small distances within the atom.

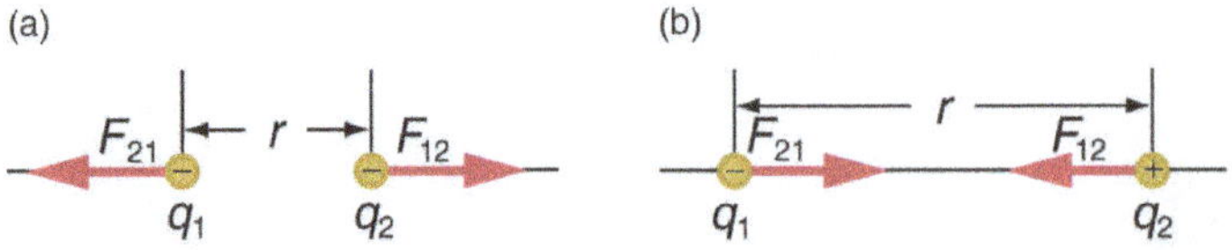

FIGURE 18.25 The magnitude of the electrostatic force F between point charges q_1 and q_2 separated by a distance r is given by Coulomb's law. Note that Newton's third law (every force exerted creates an equal and opposite force) applies as usual—the force on q_1 is equal in

magnitude and opposite in direction to the force it exerts on q_2. (a) Like charges. (b) Unlike charges.

EXAMPLE 18.1

How Strong is the Coulomb Force Relative to the Gravitational Force?

Compare the electrostatic force between an electron and proton separated by 0.530×10^{-10} m with the gravitational force between them. This distance is their average separation in a hydrogen atom.

Strategy

To compare the two forces, we first compute the electrostatic force using Coulomb's law, $F = k\frac{|q_1 q_2|}{r^2}$. We then calculate the gravitational force using Newton's universal law of gravitation. Finally, we take a ratio to see how the forces compare in magnitude.

Solution

Entering the given and known information about the charges and separation of the electron and proton into the expression of Coulomb's law yields

$$F = k\frac{|q_1 q_2|}{r^2} \quad 18.5$$

$$=\left(8.99 \times 10^9 \text{ N} \cdot \text{m}^2/\text{C}^2\right)\times\frac{(1.60\times10^{-19}\text{ C})(1.60\times10^{-19}\text{ C})}{(0.530\times10^{-10}\text{ m})^2} \quad 18.6$$

Thus the Coulomb force is

$$F = 8.19 \times 10^{-8} \text{ N}. \quad 18.7$$

The charges are opposite in sign, so this is an attractive force. This is a very large force for an electron—it would cause an acceleration of 8.99×10^{22} m/s^2 (verification is left as an end-of-section problem).The gravitational force is given by Newton's law of gravitation as:

$$F_G = G\frac{mM}{r^2}, \quad 18.8$$

where $G = 6.67 \times 10^{-11}$ N · m^2/kg^2. Here m and M represent the electron and proton masses, which can be found in the appendices. Entering values for the knowns yields

$$F_G = (6.67 \times 10^{-11}\text{ N} \cdot \text{m}^2/\text{kg}^2) \times \frac{(9.11 \times 10^{-31}\text{ kg})(1.67 \times 10^{-27}\text{ kg})}{(0.530 \times 10^{-10}\text{ m})^2} = 3.61 \times 10^{-47}\text{ N} \quad 18.9$$

This is also an attractive force, although it is traditionally shown as positive since gravitational force is always attractive. The ratio of the magnitude of the electrostatic force to gravitational force in this case is, thus,

$$\frac{F}{F_G} = 2.27 \times 10^{39}. \quad 18.10$$

Discussion

This is a remarkably large ratio! Note that this will be the ratio of electrostatic force to gravitational force for an electron and a proton at any distance (taking the ratio before entering numerical values shows that the distance cancels). This ratio gives some indication of just how much larger the Coulomb force is than the gravitational force between two of the most common particles in nature.

As the example implies, gravitational force is completely negligible on a small scale, where the interactions of individual charged particles are important. On a large scale, such as between the Earth and a person, the reverse is true. Most objects are nearly electrically neutral, and so attractive and repulsive **Coulomb forces** nearly cancel. Gravitational force on a large scale dominates interactions between large objects because it is always attractive, while Coulomb forces tend to cancel.

18.5 Electric Field: Concept of a Field Revisited

LEARNING OBJECTIVES

By the end of this section, you will be able to:

- Describe a force field and calculate the strength of an electric field due to a point charge.
- Calculate the force exerted on a test charge by an electric field.
- Explain the relationship between electrical force (F) on a test charge and electrical field strength (E).

Contact forces, such as between a baseball and a bat, are explained on the small scale by the interaction of the charges in atoms and molecules in close proximity. They interact through forces that include the **Coulomb force**. Action at a distance is a force between objects that are not close enough for their atoms to "touch." That is, they are separated by more than a few atomic diameters.

For example, a charged rubber comb attracts neutral bits of paper from a distance via the Coulomb force. It is very useful to think of an object being surrounded in space by a **force field**. The force field carries the force to another object (called a test object) some distance away.

Concept of a Field

A field is a way of conceptualizing and mapping the force that surrounds any object and acts on another object at a distance without apparent physical connection. For example, the gravitational field surrounding the earth (and all other masses) represents the gravitational force that would be experienced if another mass were placed at a given point within the field.

In the same way, the Coulomb force field surrounding any charge extends throughout space. Using Coulomb's law, $F = k|q_1 q_2|/r^2$, its magnitude is given by the equation $F = k|qQ|/r^2$, for a **point charge** (a particle having a charge Q) acting on a **test charge** q at a distance r (see Figure 18.26). Both the magnitude and direction of the Coulomb force field depend on Q and the test charge q.

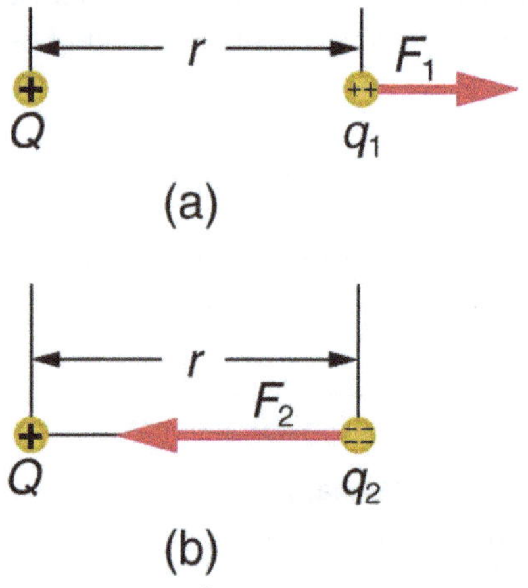

FIGURE 18.26 The Coulomb force field due to a positive charge Q is shown acting on two different charges. Both charges are the same distance from Q. (a) Since q_1 is positive, the force F_1 acting on it is repulsive. (b) The charge q_2 is negative and greater in magnitude than q_1, and so the force F_2 acting on it is attractive and stronger than F_1. The Coulomb force field is thus not unique at any point in space, because it depends on the test charges q_1 and q_2 as well as the charge Q.

To simplify things, we would prefer to have a field that depends only on Q and not on the test charge q. The electric field is defined in such a manner that it represents only the charge creating it and is unique at every point in space. Specifically, the electric field E is defined to be the ratio of the Coulomb force to the test charge:

$$\mathbf{E} = \frac{\mathbf{F}}{q}, \tag{18.11}$$

where $\mathbf{F}$ is the electrostatic force (or Coulomb force) exerted on a positive test charge q. It is understood that $\mathbf{E}$ is in the same direction as $\mathbf{F}$. It is also assumed that q is so small that it does not alter the charge distribution creating the electric field. The units of electric field are newtons per coulomb (N/C). If the electric field is known, then the electrostatic force on any charge q is simply obtained by multiplying charge times electric field, or $\mathbf{F} = q\mathbf{E}$. Consider the electric field due to a point charge Q. According to Coulomb's law, the force it exerts on a test charge q is $F = k|\,qQ\,|/r^2$. Thus the magnitude of the electric field, E, for a point charge is

$$E = \left|\frac{F}{q}\right| = k\left|\frac{qQ}{qr^2}\right| = k\frac{|Q|}{r^2}. \quad (18.12)$$

Since the test charge cancels, we see that

$$E = k\frac{|Q|}{r^2}. \quad (18.13)$$

The electric field is thus seen to depend only on the charge Q and the distance r; it is completely independent of the test charge q.

EXAMPLE 18.2

Calculating the Electric Field of a Point Charge

Calculate the strength and direction of the electric field E due to a point charge of 2.00 nC (nano-Coulombs) at a distance of 5.00 mm from the charge.

Strategy

We can find the electric field created by a point charge by using the equation $E = kQ/r^2$.

Solution

Here $Q = 2.00 \times 10^{-9}$ C and $r = 5.00 \times 10^{-3}$ m. Entering those values into the above equation gives

$$\begin{aligned} E &= k\frac{Q}{r^2} \\ &= (8.99 \times 10^9\ \text{N} \cdot \text{m}^2/\text{C}^2) \times \frac{(2.00 \times 10^{-9}\ \text{C})}{(5.00 \times 10^{-3}\ \text{m})^2} \\ &= 7.19 \times 10^5\ \text{N/C}. \end{aligned} \quad (18.14)$$

Discussion

This **electric field strength** is the same at any point 5.00 mm away from the charge Q that creates the field. It is positive, meaning that it has a direction pointing away from the charge Q.

EXAMPLE 18.3

Calculating the Force Exerted on a Point Charge by an Electric Field

What force does the electric field found in the previous example exert on a point charge of $-0.250\ \mu\text{C}$?

Strategy

Since we know the electric field strength and the charge in the field, the force on that charge can be calculated using the definition of electric field $\mathbf{E} = \mathbf{F}/q$ rearranged to $\mathbf{F} = q\mathbf{E}$.

Solution

The magnitude of the force on a charge $q = -0.250\ \mu\text{C}$ exerted by a field of strength $E = 7.20 \times 10^5$ N/C is thus,

$$\begin{aligned} F &= -qE \\ &= (0.250 \times 10^{-6}\ \text{C})(7.20 \times 10^5\ \text{N/C}) \\ &= 0.180\ \text{N}. \end{aligned} \quad (18.15)$$

Because q is negative, the force is directed opposite to the direction of the field.

Discussion

The force is attractive, as expected for unlike charges. (The field was created by a positive charge and here acts on a negative charge.) The charges in this example are typical of common static electricity, and the modest attractive force obtained is similar to forces experienced in static cling and similar situations.

PHET EXPLORATIONS

Electric Field of Dreams

Play ball! Add charges to the Field of Dreams and see how they react to the electric field. Turn on a background electric field and adjust the direction and magnitude.

Click to view content (https://openstax.org/l/02electric_field_dreams).

18.6 Electric Field Lines: Multiple Charges

LEARNING OBJECTIVES

By the end of this section, you will be able to:

- Calculate the total force (magnitude and direction) exerted on a test charge from more than one charge
- Describe an electric field diagram of a positive point charge; of a negative point charge with twice the magnitude of positive charge
- Draw the electric field lines between two points of the same charge; between two points of opposite charge.

Drawings using lines to represent **electric fields** around charged objects are very useful in visualizing field strength and direction. Since the electric field has both magnitude and direction, it is a vector. Like all **vectors**, the electric field can be represented by an arrow that has length proportional to its magnitude and that points in the correct direction. (We have used arrows extensively to represent force vectors, for example.)

Figure 18.27 shows two pictorial representations of the same electric field created by a positive point charge Q. Figure 18.27 (b) shows the standard representation using continuous lines. Figure 18.27 (a) shows numerous individual arrows with each arrow representing the force on a test charge q. Field lines are essentially a map of infinitesimal force vectors.

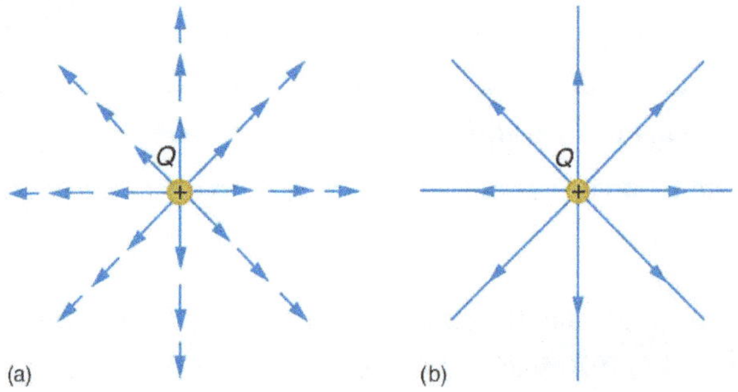

FIGURE 18.27 Two equivalent representations of the electric field due to a positive charge Q. (a) Arrows representing the electric field's magnitude and direction. (b) In the standard representation, the arrows are replaced by continuous field lines having the same direction at any point as the electric field. The closeness of the lines is directly related to the strength of the electric field. A test charge placed anywhere will feel a force in the direction of the field line; this force will have a strength proportional to the density of the lines (being greater near the charge, for example).

Note that the electric field is defined for a positive test charge q, so that the field lines point away from a positive charge and toward a negative charge. (See Figure 18.28.) The electric field strength is exactly proportional to the number of field lines per unit area, since the magnitude of the electric field for a point charge is $E = k|Q|/r^2$ and area is proportional to r^2. This pictorial representation, in which field lines represent the direction and their closeness (that is, their areal density or the number of lines crossing a unit area) represents strength, is used for all fields: electrostatic, gravitational, magnetic, and others.

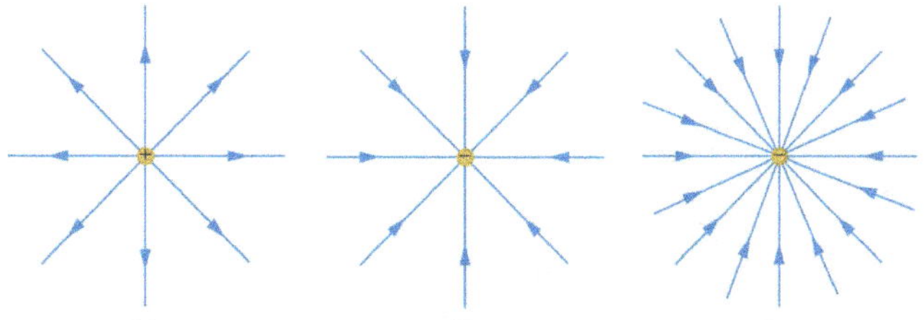

FIGURE 18.28 The electric field surrounding three different point charges. (a) A positive charge. (b) A negative charge of equal magnitude. (c) A larger negative charge.

In many situations, there are multiple charges. The total electric field created by multiple charges is the vector sum of the individual fields created by each charge. The following example shows how to add electric field vectors.

EXAMPLE 18.4

Adding Electric Fields

Find the magnitude and direction of the total electric field due to the two point charges, q_1 and q_2, at the origin of the coordinate system as shown in Figure 18.29.

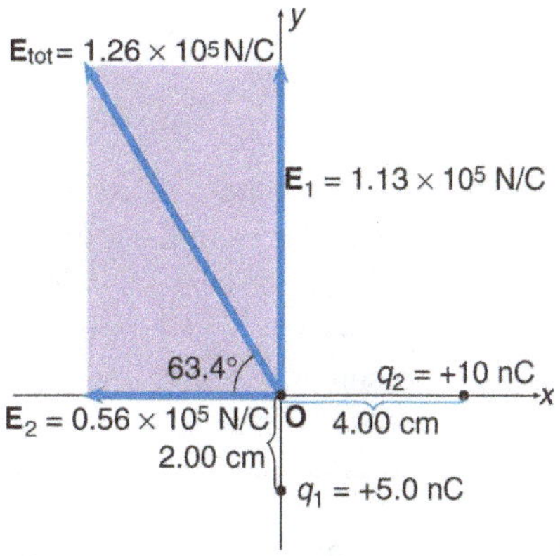

FIGURE 18.29 The electric fields $\mathbf{E}_1$ and $\mathbf{E}_2$ at the origin O add to $\mathbf{E}_{\text{tot}}$.

Strategy

Since the electric field is a vector (having magnitude and direction), we add electric fields with the same vector techniques used for other types of vectors. We first must find the electric field due to each charge at the point of interest, which is the origin of the coordinate system (O) in this instance. We pretend that there is a positive test charge, q, at point O, which allows us to determine the direction of the fields $\mathbf{E}_1$ and $\mathbf{E}_2$. Once those fields are found, the total field can be determined using **vector addition.**

Solution

The electric field strength at the origin due to q_1 is labeled E_1 and is calculated:

$$E_1 = k\frac{q_1}{r_1^2} = \left(8.99\times10^9\ \text{N}\cdot\text{m}^2/\text{C}^2\right)\frac{\left(5.00\times10^{-9}\ \text{C}\right)}{\left(2.00\times10^{-2}\ \text{m}\right)^2} \quad 18.16$$

$$E_1 = 1.124\times10^5\ \text{N/C}.$$

Similarly, E_2 is

$$E_2 = k\frac{q_2}{r_2^2} = \left(8.99 \times 10^9 \text{ N} \cdot \text{m}^2/\text{C}^2\right)\frac{\left(10.0\times10^{-9}\text{ C}\right)}{\left(4.00\times10^{-2}\text{ m}\right)^2}$$
$$E_2 = 0.5619 \times 10^5 \text{ N/C}. \quad (18.17)$$

Four digits have been retained in this solution to illustrate that E_1 is exactly twice the magnitude of E_2. Now arrows are drawn to represent the magnitudes and directions of $\mathbf{E}_1$ and $\mathbf{E}_2$. (See Figure 18.29.) The direction of the electric field is that of the force on a positive charge so both arrows point directly away from the positive charges that create them. The arrow for $\mathbf{E}_1$ is exactly twice the length of that for $\mathbf{E}_2$. The arrows form a right triangle in this case and can be added using the Pythagorean theorem. The magnitude of the total field E_{tot} is

$$\begin{aligned} E_{\text{tot}} &= (E_1^2 + E_2^2)^{1/2} \\ &= \left\{(1.124 \times 10^5 \text{ N/C})^2 + (0.5619 \times 10^5 \text{ N/C})^2\right\}^{1/2} \\ &= 1.26 \times 10^5 \text{ N/C}. \end{aligned} \quad (18.18)$$

The direction is

$$\begin{aligned} \theta &= \tan^{-1}\left(\frac{E_1}{E_2}\right) \\ &= \tan^{-1}\left(\frac{1.124\times10^5 \text{ N/C}}{0.5619\times10^5 \text{ N/C}}\right) \\ &= 63.4^\circ, \end{aligned} \quad (18.19)$$

or 63.4° above the *x*-axis.

Discussion

In cases where the electric field vectors to be added are not perpendicular, vector components or graphical techniques can be used. The total electric field found in this example is the total electric field at only one point in space. To find the total electric field due to these two charges over an entire region, the same technique must be repeated for each point in the region. This impossibly lengthy task (there are an infinite number of points in space) can be avoided by calculating the total field at representative points and using some of the unifying features noted next.

Figure 18.30 shows how the electric field from two point charges can be drawn by finding the total field at representative points and drawing electric field lines consistent with those points. While the electric fields from multiple charges are more complex than those of single charges, some simple features are easily noticed.

For example, the field is weaker between like charges, as shown by the lines being farther apart in that region. (This is because the fields from each charge exert opposing forces on any charge placed between them.) (See Figure 18.30 and Figure 18.31(a).) Furthermore, at a great distance from two like charges, the field becomes identical to the field from a single, larger charge.

Figure 18.31(b) shows the electric field of two unlike charges. The field is stronger between the charges. In that region, the fields from each charge are in the same direction, and so their strengths add. The field of two unlike charges is weak at large distances, because the fields of the individual charges are in opposite directions and so their strengths subtract. At very large distances, the field of two unlike charges looks like that of a smaller single charge.

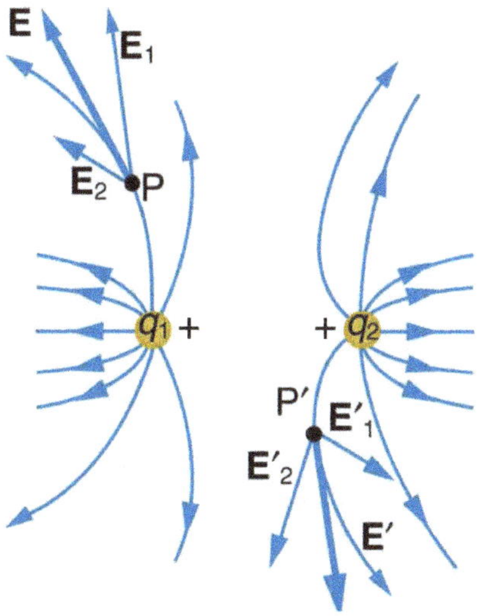

FIGURE 18.30 Two positive point charges q_1 and q_2 produce the resultant electric field shown. The field is calculated at representative points and then smooth field lines drawn following the rules outlined in the text.

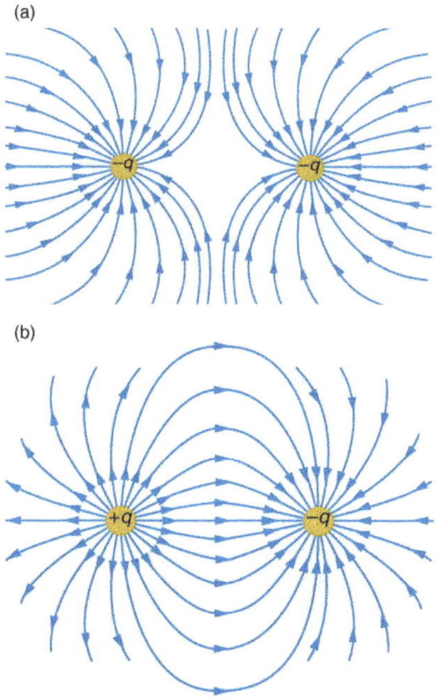

FIGURE 18.31 (a) Two negative charges produce the fields shown. It is very similar to the field produced by two positive charges, except that the directions are reversed. The field is clearly weaker between the charges. The individual forces on a test charge in that region are in opposite directions. (b) Two opposite charges produce the field shown, which is stronger in the region between the charges.

We use electric field lines to visualize and analyze electric fields (the lines are a pictorial tool, not a physical entity in themselves). The properties of electric field lines for any charge distribution can be summarized as follows:

1. Field lines must begin on positive charges and terminate on negative charges, or at infinity in the hypothetical case of isolated charges.
2. The number of field lines leaving a positive charge or entering a negative charge is proportional to the magnitude of the charge.
3. The strength of the field is proportional to the closeness of the field lines—more precisely, it is proportional to the number of lines per unit area perpendicular to the lines.
4. The direction of the electric field is tangent to the field line at any point in space.
5. Field lines can never cross.

The last property means that the field is unique at any point. The field line represents the direction of the field; so if they crossed, the field would have two directions at that location (an impossibility if the field is unique).

PHET EXPLORATIONS

Charges and Fields

Move point charges around on the playing field and then view the electric field, voltages, equipotential lines, and more. It's colorful, it's dynamic, it's free.

Click to view content (https://openstax.org/books/college-physics-ap-courses-2e/pages/18-6-electric-field-lines-multiple-charges)

PhET

18.7 Electric Forces in Biology

LEARNING OBJECTIVES

By the end of this section, you will be able to:

- Describe how a water molecule is polar.
- Explain electrostatic screening by a water molecule within a living cell.

Classical electrostatics has an important role to play in modern molecular biology. Large molecules such as proteins, nucleic acids, and so on—so important to life—are usually electrically charged. DNA itself is highly charged; it is the electrostatic force that not only holds the molecule together but gives the molecule structure and strength. Figure 18.32 is a schematic of the DNA double helix.

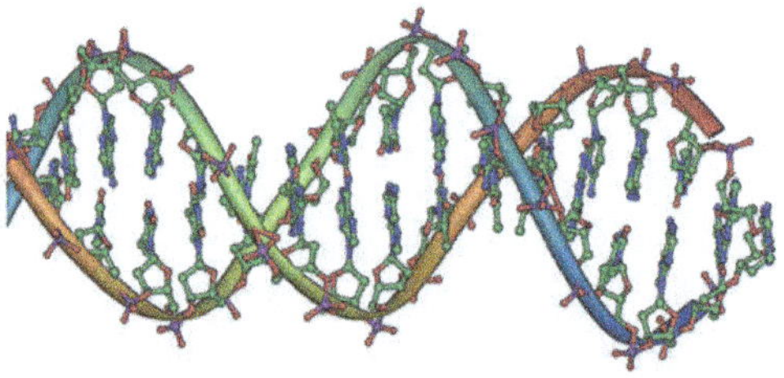

FIGURE 18.32 DNA is a highly charged molecule. The DNA double helix shows the two coiled strands each containing a row of nitrogenous bases, which "code" the genetic information needed by a living organism. The strands are connected by bonds between pairs of bases. While pairing combinations between certain bases are fixed (C-G and A-T), the sequence of nucleotides in the strand varies. (credit: Jerome Walker)

The four nucleotide bases are given the symbols A (adenine), C (cytosine), G (guanine), and T (thymine). The order of the four bases varies in each strand, but the pairing between bases is always the same. C and G are always paired and A and T are always paired, which helps to preserve the order of bases in cell division (mitosis) so as to pass on the correct genetic information. Since the Coulomb force drops with distance ($F \propto 1/r^2$), the distances between the base pairs must be small enough that the electrostatic force is sufficient to hold them together.

DNA is a highly charged molecule, with about $2q_e$ (fundamental charge) per 0.3×10^{-9} m. The distance separating the two strands that make up the DNA structure is about 1 nm, while the distance separating the individual atoms within each base is about 0.3 nm.

One might wonder why electrostatic forces do not play a larger role in biology than they do if we have so many charged molecules. The reason is that the electrostatic force is "diluted" due to **screening** between molecules. This is due to the presence of other charges in the cell.

Polarity of Water Molecules

The best example of this charge screening is the water molecule, represented as H_2O. Water is a strongly **polar molecule**. Its 10 electrons (8 from the oxygen atom and 2 from the two hydrogen atoms) tend to remain closer to the oxygen nucleus than the hydrogen nuclei. This creates two centers of equal and opposite charges—what is called a **dipole**, as illustrated in Figure 18.33. The magnitude of the dipole is called the dipole moment.

These two centers of charge will terminate some of the electric field lines coming from a free charge, as on a DNA molecule. This results in a reduction in the strength of the **Coulomb interaction**. One might say that screening makes the Coulomb force a short range force rather than long range.

Cell Membranes

Other ions of importance in biology that can reduce or screen Coulomb interactions are Na^+, and K^+, and Cl^-. These ions are located both inside and outside of living cells. The movement of these ions through cell membranes is crucial to the motion of nerve impulses through nerve axons.

Recent studies of electrostatics in biology seem to show that electric fields in cells can be extended over larger distances, in spite of screening, by "microtubules" within the cell. These microtubules are hollow tubes composed of proteins that guide the movement of chromosomes when cells divide, the motion of other organisms within the cell, and provide mechanisms for motion of some cells (as motors).

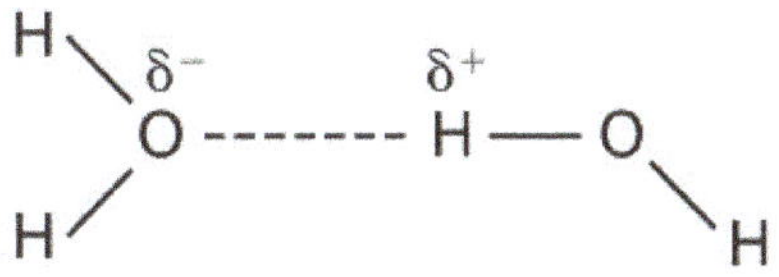

FIGURE 18.33 This schematic shows water (H_2O) as a polar molecule. Unequal sharing of electrons between the oxygen (O) and hydrogen (H) atoms leads to a net separation of positive and negative charge—forming a dipole. The symbols δ^- and δ^+ indicate that the oxygen side of the H_2O molecule tends to be more negative, while the hydrogen ends tend to be more positive. This leads to an attraction of opposite charges between molecules.

You are likely familiar with the role of electrical signals in nerve conduction and the importance of charges in cardiac and related activity. Changes in electrical properties are also essential in core biological processes. Ernest Everett Just, whose expertise in understanding and handling egg cells led to a number of critical experimental discoveries, investigated the role of the cell membrane in reproductive fertilization. In one key experiment, Just established that the egg membrane undergoes a depolarizing "wave of negativity" the moment it fuses with a sperm cell. This change in charge is now known as the "fast block" that ensures that only one sperm cell fuses with an egg cell and is critical for embryonic development.

Bioelectricity and Wound Healing

Just as electrical forces drive activities in healthy cells and systems, they are also critical in damaged ones. Scientists have long known that injuries or infections are managed by the body through various responses, including increased white blood cell concentrations, swelling, and tissue repair. For example, human cells damaged by wounds heal through a complex process. But what triggers it?

Physicists and biologists working together at Vanderbilt University used an ultra-precise laser to uncover the processes organisms use to repair damage. Lead researchers Andrea Page-Degraw and Shane Hutson and study author Erica Shannon discovered that immediately upon damage, cells release calcium ions and eventually other molecules, driving an electrochemical response that initiates the healing process. Shannon notes that different types of damage lead to different chemical releases, demonstrating how organisms may initiate specific responses to best address the injury.

While far more research is required to understand the triggering and response method, other research indicates that bioelectricity is highly involved in wound healing. Several studies have indicated that precise and low-level electrical stimulation of wounds (such as those from surgeries) leads to faster healing. While the mechanisms are not fully understood, electrical stimulation is a growing area of research and practice in medicine.

18.8 Applications of Electrostatics

LEARNING OBJECTIVES

By the end of this section, you will be able to:

The study of **electrostatics** has proven useful in many areas. This module covers just a few of the many applications of electrostatics.

- Name several real-world applications of the study of electrostatics.

The Van de Graaff Generator

Van de Graaff generators (or Van de Graaffs) are not only spectacular devices used to demonstrate high voltage due to static electricity—they are also used for serious research. The first was built by Robert Van de Graaff in 1931 (based on original suggestions by Lord Kelvin) for use in nuclear physics research. Figure 18.34 shows a schematic of a large research version. Van de Graaffs utilize both smooth and pointed surfaces, and conductors and insulators to generate large static charges and, hence, large voltages.

A very large excess charge can be deposited on the sphere, because it moves quickly to the outer surface. Practical limits arise because the large electric fields polarize and eventually ionize surrounding materials, creating free charges that neutralize excess charge or allow it to escape. Nevertheless, voltages of 15 million volts are well within practical limits.

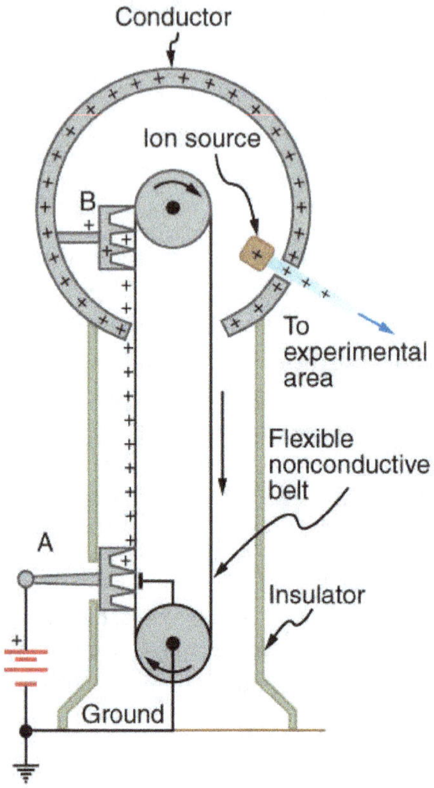

FIGURE 18.34 Schematic of Van de Graaff generator. A battery (A) supplies excess positive charge to a pointed conductor, the points of which spray the charge onto a moving insulating belt near the bottom. The pointed conductor (B) on top in the large sphere picks up the charge. (The induced electric field at the points is so large that it removes the charge from the belt.) This can be done because the charge does not remain inside the conducting sphere but moves to its outside surface. An ion source inside the sphere produces positive ions, which are accelerated away from the positive sphere to high velocities.

TAKE-HOME EXPERIMENT: ELECTROSTATICS AND HUMIDITY

Rub a comb through your hair and use it to lift pieces of paper. It may help to tear the pieces of paper rather than cut them neatly. Repeat the exercise in your bathroom after you have had a long shower and the air in the bathroom is moist. Is it easier to get electrostatic effects in dry or moist air? Why would torn paper be more attractive to the comb than cut paper? Explain your observations.

Xerography

Most copy machines use an electrostatic process called **xerography**—a word coined from the Greek words *xeros* for dry and *graphos* for writing. The heart of the process is shown in simplified form in Figure 18.35.

A selenium-coated aluminum drum is sprayed with positive charge from points on a device called a corotron. Selenium is a substance with an interesting property—it is a **photoconductor**. That is, selenium is an insulator when in the dark and a conductor when exposed to light.

In the first stage of the xerography process, the conducting aluminum drum is **grounded** so that a negative charge is induced under the thin layer of uniformly positively charged selenium. In the second stage, the surface of the drum is exposed to the image of whatever is to be copied. Where the image is light, the selenium becomes conducting, and the positive charge is neutralized. In dark areas, the positive charge remains, and so the image has been transferred to the drum.

The third stage takes a dry black powder, called toner, and sprays it with a negative charge so that it will be attracted to the positive regions of the drum. Next, a blank piece of paper is given a greater positive charge than on the drum so that it will pull the toner from the drum. Finally, the paper and electrostatically held toner are passed through heated pressure rollers, which melt and permanently adhere the toner within the fibers of the paper.

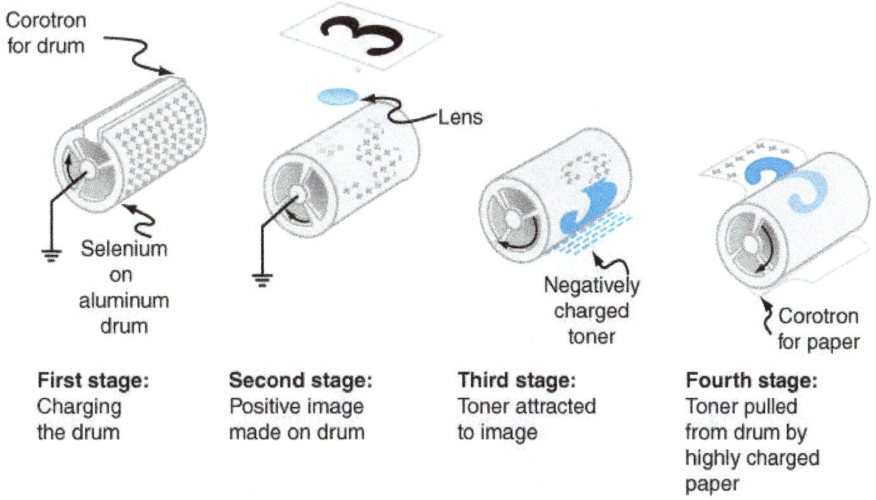

FIGURE 18.35 Xerography is a dry copying process based on electrostatics. The major steps in the process are the charging of the photoconducting drum, transfer of an image creating a positive charge duplicate, attraction of toner to the charged parts of the drum, and transfer of toner to the paper. Not shown are heat treatment of the paper and cleansing of the drum for the next copy.

Laser Printers

Laser printers use the xerographic process to make high-quality images on paper, employing a laser to produce an image on the photoconducting drum as shown in Figure 18.36. In its most common application, the laser printer receives output from a computer, and it can achieve high-quality output because of the precision with which laser light can be controlled. Many laser printers do significant information processing, such as making sophisticated letters or fonts, and may contain a computer more powerful than the one giving them the raw data to be printed.

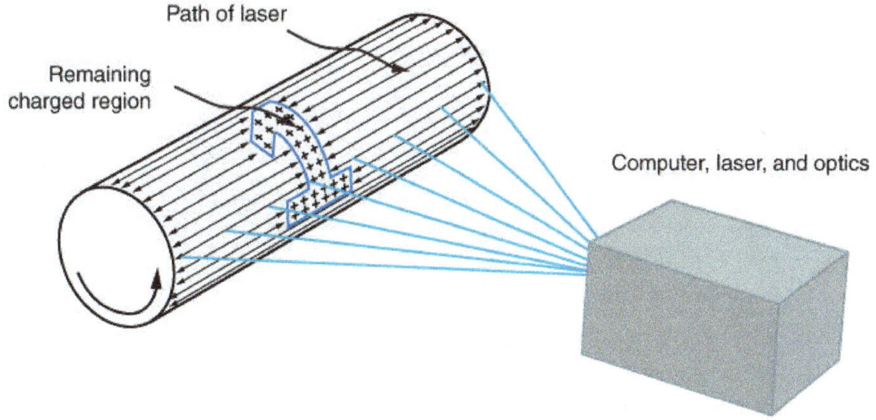

FIGURE 18.36 In a laser printer, a laser beam is scanned across a photoconducting drum, leaving a positive charge image. The other steps for charging the drum and transferring the image to paper are the same as in xerography. Laser light can be very precisely controlled, enabling laser printers to produce high-quality images.

Ink Jet Printers and Electrostatic Painting

The **ink jet printer**, commonly used to print computer-generated text and graphics, also employs electrostatics. A nozzle makes a fine spray of tiny ink droplets, which are then given an electrostatic charge. (See Figure 18.37.)

Once charged, the droplets can be directed, using pairs of charged plates, with great precision to form letters and images on paper. Ink jet printers can produce color images by using a black jet and three other jets with primary colors, usually cyan, magenta, and yellow, much as a color television produces color. (This is more difficult with xerography, requiring multiple drums and toners.)

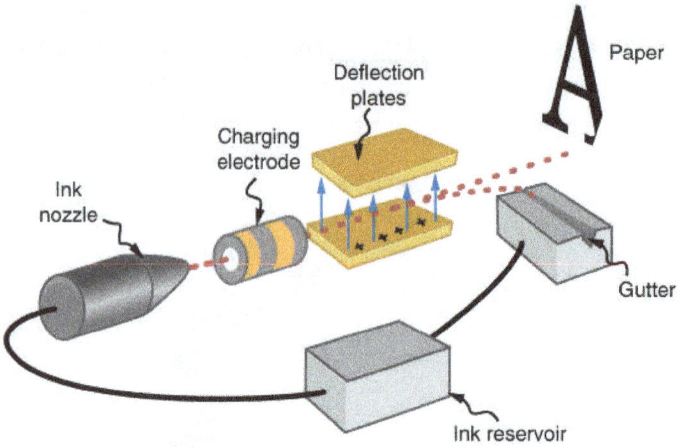

FIGURE 18.37 The nozzle of an ink-jet printer produces small ink droplets, which are sprayed with electrostatic charge. Various computer-driven devices are then used to direct the droplets to the correct positions on a page.

Electrostatic painting employs electrostatic charge to spray paint onto odd-shaped surfaces. Mutual repulsion of like charges causes the paint to fly away from its source. Surface tension forms drops, which are then attracted by unlike charges to the surface to be painted. Electrostatic painting can reach those hard-to-get at places, applying an even coat in a controlled manner. If the object is a conductor, the electric field is perpendicular to the surface, tending to bring the drops in perpendicularly. Corners and points on conductors will receive extra paint. Felt can similarly be applied.

Smoke Precipitators and Electrostatic Air Cleaning

Another important application of electrostatics is found in air cleaners, both large and small. The electrostatic part of the process places excess (usually positive) charge on smoke, dust, pollen, and other particles in the air and then passes the air through an oppositely charged grid that attracts and retains the charged particles. (See Figure 18.38.)

Large **electrostatic precipitators** are used industrially to remove over 99% of the particles from stack gas emissions associated with the burning of coal and oil. Home precipitators, often in conjunction with the home heating and air conditioning system, are very effective in removing polluting particles, irritants, and allergens.

FIGURE 18.38 (a) Schematic of an electrostatic precipitator. Air is passed through grids of opposite charge. The first grid charges airborne

particles, while the second attracts and collects them. (b) The dramatic effect of electrostatic precipitators is seen by the absence of smoke from this power plant. (credit: Cmdalgleish, Wikimedia Commons)

PROBLEM-SOLVING STRATEGIES FOR ELECTROSTATICS

1. Examine the situation to determine if static electricity is involved. This may concern separated stationary charges, the forces among them, and the electric fields they create.
2. Identify the system of interest. This includes noting the number, locations, and types of charges involved.
3. Identify exactly what needs to be determined in the problem (identify the unknowns). A written list is useful. Determine whether the Coulomb force is to be considered directly—if so, it may be useful to draw a free-body diagram, using electric field lines.
4. Make a list of what is given or can be inferred from the problem as stated (identify the knowns). It is important to distinguish the Coulomb force F from the electric field E, for example.
5. Solve the appropriate equation for the quantity to be determined (the unknown) or draw the field lines as requested.
6. Examine the answer to see if it is reasonable: Does it make sense? Are units correct and the numbers involved reasonable?

Integrated Concepts

The Integrated Concepts exercises for this module involve concepts such as electric charges, electric fields, and several other topics. Physics is most interesting when applied to general situations involving more than a narrow set of physical principles. The electric field exerts force on charges, for example, and hence the relevance of Dynamics: Force and Newton's Laws of Motion. The following topics are involved in some or all of the problems labeled "Integrated Concepts":

- Kinematics
- Two-Dimensional Kinematics
- Dynamics: Force and Newton's Laws of Motion
- Uniform Circular Motion and Gravitation
- Statics and Torque
- Fluid Statics

The following worked example illustrates how this strategy is applied to an Integrated Concept problem:

EXAMPLE 18.5

Acceleration of a Charged Drop of Gasoline

If steps are not taken to ground a gasoline pump, static electricity can be placed on gasoline when filling your car's tank. Suppose a tiny drop of gasoline has a mass of 4.00×10^{-15} kg and is given a positive charge of 3.20×10^{-19} C. (a) Find the weight of the drop. (b) Calculate the electric force on the drop if there is an upward electric field of strength 3.00×10^{5} N/C due to other static electricity in the vicinity. (c) Calculate the drop's acceleration.

Strategy

To solve an integrated concept problem, we must first identify the physical principles involved and identify the chapters in which they are found. Part (a) of this example asks for weight. This is a topic of dynamics and is defined in Dynamics: Force and Newton's Laws of Motion. Part (b) deals with electric force on a charge, a topic of Electric Charge and Electric Field. Part (c) asks for acceleration, knowing forces and mass. These are part of Newton's laws, also found in Dynamics: Force and Newton's Laws of Motion.

The following solutions to each part of the example illustrate how the specific problem-solving strategies are applied. These involve identifying knowns and unknowns, checking to see if the answer is reasonable, and so on.

Solution for (a)

Weight is mass times the acceleration due to gravity, as first expressed in

$$w = mg. \tag{18.20}$$

Entering the given mass and the average acceleration due to gravity yields

$$w = (4.00 \times 10^{-15}\ \text{kg})(9.80\ \text{m/s}^2) = 3.92 \times 10^{-14}\ \text{N}. \tag{18.21}$$

Discussion for (a)

This is a small weight, consistent with the small mass of the drop.

Solution for (b)

The force an electric field exerts on a charge is given by rearranging the following equation:

$$F = qE. \tag{18.22}$$

Here we are given the charge (3.20×10^{-19} C is twice the fundamental unit of charge) and the electric field strength, and so the electric force is found to be

$$F = (3.20 \times 10^{-19}\ \text{C})(3.00 \times 10^{5}\ \text{N/C}) = 9.60 \times 10^{-14}\ \text{N}. \tag{18.23}$$

Discussion for (b)

While this is a small force, it is greater than the weight of the drop.

Solution for (c)

The acceleration can be found using Newton's second law, provided we can identify all of the external forces acting on the drop. We assume only the drop's weight and the electric force are significant. Since the drop has a positive charge and the electric field is given to be upward, the electric force is upward. We thus have a one-dimensional (vertical direction) problem, and we can state Newton's second law as

$$a = \frac{F_{\text{net}}}{m}. \tag{18.24}$$

where $F_{\text{net}} = F - w$. Entering this and the known values into the expression for Newton's second law yields

$$\begin{aligned} a &= \frac{F-w}{m} \\ &= \frac{9.60\times10^{-14}\ \text{N} - 3.92\times10^{-14}\ \text{N}}{4.00\times10^{-15}\ \text{kg}} \\ &= 14.2\ \text{m/s}^2. \end{aligned} \tag{18.25}$$

Discussion for (c)

This is an upward acceleration great enough to carry the drop to places where you might not wish to have gasoline.

This worked example illustrates how to apply problem-solving strategies to situations that include topics in different chapters. The first step is to identify the physical principles involved in the problem. The second step is to solve for the unknown using familiar problem-solving strategies. These are found throughout the text, and many worked examples show how to use them for single topics. In this integrated concepts example, you can see how to apply them across several topics. You will find these techniques useful in applications of physics outside a physics course, such as in your profession, in other science disciplines, and in everyday life. The following problems will build your skills in the broad application of physical principles.

UNREASONABLE RESULTS

The Unreasonable Results exercises for this module have results that are unreasonable because some premise is unreasonable or because certain of the premises are inconsistent with one another. Physical principles applied correctly then produce unreasonable results. The purpose of these problems is to give practice in assessing whether nature is being accurately described, and if it is not to trace the source of difficulty.

PROBLEM-SOLVING STRATEGY

To determine if an answer is reasonable, and to determine the cause if it is not, do the following.

1. Solve the problem using strategies as outlined above. Use the format followed in the worked examples in the text to solve the problem as usual.
2. Check to see if the answer is reasonable. Is it too large or too small, or does it have the wrong sign, improper units, and so on?
3. If the answer is unreasonable, look for what specifically could cause the identified difficulty. Usually, the manner in which the answer is unreasonable is an indication of the difficulty. For example, an extremely large Coulomb force could be due to the assumption of an excessively large separated charge.

Glossary

conductor a material that allows electrons to move separately from their atomic orbits
conductor an object with properties that allow charges to move about freely within it
Coulomb force another term for the electrostatic force
Coulomb interaction the interaction between two charged particles generated by the Coulomb forces they exert on one another
Coulomb's law the mathematical equation calculating the electrostatic force vector between two charged particles
dipole a molecule's lack of symmetrical charge distribution, causing one side to be more positive and another to be more negative
electric charge a physical property of an object that causes it to be attracted toward or repelled from another charged object; each charged object generates and is influenced by a force called an electromagnetic force
electric field a three-dimensional map of the electric force extended out into space from a point charge
electric field lines a series of lines drawn from a point charge representing the magnitude and direction of force exerted by that charge
electromagnetic force one of the four fundamental forces of nature; the electromagnetic force consists of static electricity, moving electricity and magnetism
electron a particle orbiting the nucleus of an atom and carrying the smallest unit of negative charge
electrostatic equilibrium an electrostatically balanced state in which all free electrical charges have stopped moving about
electrostatic force the amount and direction of attraction or repulsion between two charged bodies
electrostatic precipitators filters that apply charges to particles in the air, then attract those charges to a filter, removing them from the airstream
electrostatic repulsion the phenomenon of two objects with like charges repelling each other
electrostatics the study of electric forces that are static or slow-moving
Faraday cage a metal shield which prevents electric charge from penetrating its surface
field a map of the amount and direction of a force acting on other objects, extending out into space
free charge an electrical charge (either positive or negative) which can move about separately from its base molecule
free electron an electron that is free to move away from its atomic orbit
grounded connected to the ground with a conductor, so that charge flows freely to and from the Earth to the grounded object
grounded when a conductor is connected to the Earth, allowing charge to freely flow to and from Earth's unlimited reservoir
induction the process by which an electrically charged object brought near a neutral object creates a charge in that object
ink-jet printer small ink droplets sprayed with an electric charge are controlled by electrostatic plates to create images on paper
insulator a material that holds electrons securely within their atomic orbits
ionosphere a layer of charged particles located around 100 km above the surface of Earth, which is responsible for a range of phenomena including the electric field surrounding Earth
laser printer uses a laser to create a photoconductive image on a drum, which attracts dry ink particles that are then rolled onto a sheet of paper to print a high-quality copy of the image
law of conservation of charge states that whenever a charge is created, an equal amount of charge with the opposite sign is created simultaneously
photoconductor a substance that is an insulator until it is exposed to light, when it becomes a conductor
point charge A charged particle, designated Q, generating an electric field
polar molecule a molecule with an asymmetrical distribution of positive and negative charge
polarization slight shifting of positive and negative charges to opposite sides of an atom or molecule
polarized a state in which the positive and negative charges within an object have collected in separate locations
proton a particle in the nucleus of an atom and carrying a positive charge equal in magnitude and opposite in sign to the amount of negative charge carried by an electron
screening the dilution or blocking of an electrostatic force on a charged object by the presence of other charges nearby
static electricity a buildup of electric charge on the surface of an object
test charge A particle (designated q) with either a positive or negative charge set down within an electric field generated by a point charge
Van de Graaff generator a machine that produces a large amount of excess charge, used for experiments with high voltage
vector a quantity with both magnitude and direction

vector addition mathematical combination of two or more vectors, including their magnitudes, directions, and positions

xerography a dry copying process based on electrostatics

Section Summary

18.1 Static Electricity and Charge: Conservation of Charge

- There are only two types of charge, which we call positive and negative.
- Like charges repel, unlike charges attract, and the force between charges decreases with the square of the distance.
- The vast majority of positive charge in nature is carried by protons, while the vast majority of negative charge is carried by electrons.
- The electric charge of one electron is equal in magnitude and opposite in sign to the charge of one proton.
- An ion is an atom or molecule that has nonzero total charge due to having unequal numbers of electrons and protons.
- The SI unit for charge is the coulomb (C), with protons and electrons having charges of opposite sign but equal magnitude; the magnitude of this basic charge $|q_e|$ is $|q_e| = 1.60 \times 10^{-19}$ C.
- Whenever charge is created or destroyed, equal amounts of positive and negative are involved.
- Most often, existing charges are separated from neutral objects to obtain some net charge.
- Both positive and negative charges exist in neutral objects and can be separated by rubbing one object with another. For macroscopic objects, negatively charged means an excess of electrons and positively charged means a depletion of electrons.
- The law of conservation of charge ensures that whenever a charge is created, an equal charge of the opposite sign is created at the same time.

18.2 Conductors and Insulators

- Polarization is the separation of positive and negative charges in a neutral object.
- A conductor is a substance that allows charge to flow freely through its atomic structure.
- An insulator holds charge within its atomic structure.
- Objects with like charges repel each other, while those with unlike charges attract each other.
- A conducting object is said to be grounded if it is connected to the Earth through a conductor. Grounding allows transfer of charge to and from the earth's large reservoir.
- Objects can be charged by contact with another charged object and obtain the same sign charge.
- If an object is temporarily grounded, it can be charged by induction, and obtains the opposite sign charge.
- Polarized objects have their positive and negative charges concentrated in different areas, giving them a non-symmetrical charge.
- Polar molecules have an inherent separation of charge.

18.3 Conductors and Electric Fields in Static Equilibrium

- A conductor allows free charges to move about within it.
- The electrical forces around a conductor will cause free charges to move around inside the conductor until static equilibrium is reached.
- Any excess charge will collect along the surface of a conductor.
- Conductors with sharp corners or points will collect more charge at those points.
- A lightning rod is a conductor with sharply pointed ends that collect excess charge on the building caused by an electrical storm and allow it to dissipate back into the air.
- Electrical storms result when the electrical field of Earth's surface in certain locations becomes more strongly charged, due to changes in the insulating effect of the air.
- A Faraday cage acts like a shield around an object, preventing electric charge from penetrating inside.

18.4 Coulomb's Law

- Frenchman Charles Coulomb was the first to publish the mathematical equation that describes the electrostatic force between two objects.
- Coulomb's law gives the magnitude of the force between point charges. It is
$$F = k\frac{|q_1 q_2|}{r^2},$$
where q_1 and q_2 are two point charges separated by a distance r, and $k \approx 8.99 \times 10^9\ \mathrm{N \cdot m^2/C^2}$
- This Coulomb force is extremely basic, since most charges are due to point-like particles. It is responsible for all electrostatic effects and underlies most macroscopic forces.

- The Coulomb force is extraordinarily strong compared with the gravitational force, another basic force—but unlike gravitational force it can cancel, since it can be either attractive or repulsive.
- The electrostatic force between two subatomic particles is far greater than the gravitational force between the same two particles.

18.5 Electric Field: Concept of a Field Revisited

- The electrostatic force field surrounding a charged object extends out into space in all directions.
- The electrostatic force exerted by a point charge on a test charge at a distance r depends on the charge of both charges, as well as the distance between the two.
- The electric field $\mathbf{E}$ is defined to be
  $$\mathbf{E} = \frac{\mathbf{F}}{q},$$
  where $\mathbf{F}$ is the Coulomb or electrostatic force exerted on a small positive test charge q. $\mathbf{E}$ has units of N/C.
- The magnitude of the electric field $\mathbf{E}$ created by a point charge Q is
  $$\mathbf{E} = k\frac{|Q|}{r^2}.$$
  where r is the distance from Q. The electric field $\mathbf{E}$ is a vector and fields due to multiple charges add like vectors.

18.6 Electric Field Lines: Multiple Charges

- Drawings of electric field lines are useful visual tools. The properties of electric field lines for any charge distribution are that:
- Field lines must begin on positive charges and terminate on negative charges, or at infinity in the hypothetical case of isolated charges.
- The number of field lines leaving a positive charge or entering a negative charge is proportional to the magnitude of the charge.
- The strength of the field is proportional to the closeness of the field lines—more precisely, it is proportional to the number of lines per unit area perpendicular to the lines.
- The direction of the electric field is tangent to the field line at any point in space.
- Field lines can never cross.

18.7 Electric Forces in Biology

- Many molecules in living organisms, such as DNA, carry a charge.
- An uneven distribution of the positive and negative charges within a polar molecule produces a dipole.
- The effect of a Coulomb field generated by a charged object may be reduced or blocked by other nearby charged objects.
- Biological systems contain water, and because water molecules are polar, they have a strong effect on other molecules in living systems.

18.8 Applications of Electrostatics

- Electrostatics is the study of electric fields in static equilibrium.
- In addition to research using equipment such as a Van de Graaff generator, many practical applications of electrostatics exist, including photocopiers, laser printers, ink-jet printers and electrostatic air filters.

Conceptual Questions

18.1 Static Electricity and Charge: Conservation of Charge

1. There are very large numbers of charged particles in most objects. Why, then, don't most objects exhibit static electricity?

2. Why do most objects tend to contain nearly equal numbers of positive and negative charges?

18.2 Conductors and Insulators

3. An eccentric inventor attempts to levitate by first placing a large negative charge on himself and then putting a large positive charge on the ceiling of his workshop. Instead, while attempting to place a large negative charge on himself, his clothes fly off. Explain.

4. If you have charged an electroscope by contact with a positively charged object, describe how you could use it to determine the charge of other objects. Specifically, what would the leaves of the electroscope do if other charged objects were brought near its knob?

5. When a glass rod is rubbed with silk, it becomes positive and the silk becomes negative—yet both attract dust. Does the dust have a third type of charge that is attracted to both positive and negative? Explain.

6. Why does a car always attract dust right after it is polished? (Note that car wax and car tires are insulators.)

7. Describe how a positively charged object can be used to give another object a negative charge. What is the name of this process?

8. What is grounding? What effect does it have on a charged conductor? On a charged insulator?

18.3 Conductors and Electric Fields in Static Equilibrium

9. Is the object in Figure 18.39 a conductor or an insulator? Justify your answer.

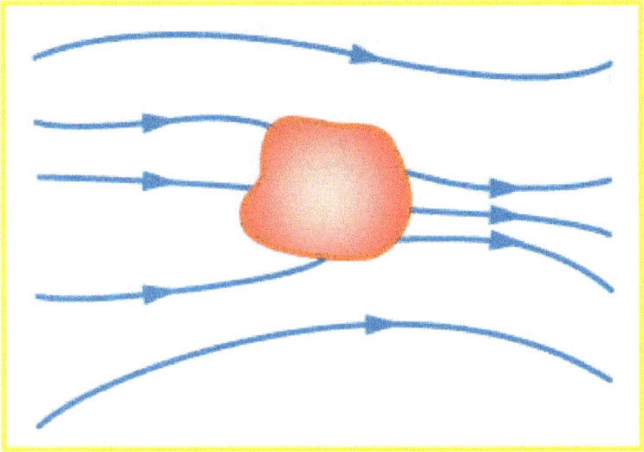

FIGURE 18.39

10. If the electric field lines in the figure above were perpendicular to the object, would it necessarily be a conductor? Explain.

11. The discussion of the electric field between two parallel conducting plates, in this module states that edge effects are less important if the plates are close together. What does close mean? That is, is the actual plate separation crucial, or is the ratio of plate separation to plate area crucial?

12. Would the self-created electric field at the end of a pointed conductor, such as a lightning rod, remove positive or negative charge from the conductor? Would the same sign charge be removed from a neutral pointed conductor by the application of a similar externally created electric field? (The answers to both questions have implications for charge transfer utilizing points.)

13. Why is a golfer with a metal club over her shoulder vulnerable to lightning in an open fairway? Would she be any safer under a tree?

14. Can the belt of a Van de Graaff accelerator be a conductor? Explain.

15. Are you relatively safe from lightning inside an automobile? Give two reasons.

16. Discuss pros and cons of a lightning rod being grounded versus simply being attached to a building.

17. Using the symmetry of the arrangement, show that the net Coulomb force on the charge q at the center of the square below (Figure 18.40) is zero if the charges on the four corners are exactly equal.

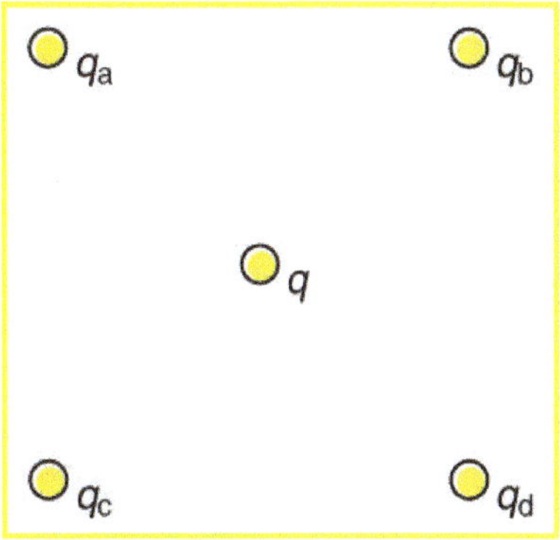

FIGURE 18.40 Four point charges q_a, q_b, q_c, and q_d lie on the corners of a square and q is located at its center.

18. (a) Using the symmetry of the arrangement, show that the electric field at the center of the square in Figure 18.40 is zero if the charges on the four corners are exactly equal. (b) Show that this is also true for any combination of charges in which $q_a = q_d$ and $q_b = q_c$

19. (a) What is the direction of the total Coulomb force on q in Figure 18.40 if q is negative, $q_a = q_c$ and both are negative, and $q_b = q_d$ and both are positive? (b) What is the direction of the electric field at the center of the square in this situation?

20. Considering Figure 18.40, suppose that $q_a = q_d$ and $q_b = q_c$. First show that q is in static equilibrium. (You may neglect the gravitational force.) Then discuss whether the equilibrium is stable or unstable, noting that this may depend on the signs of the charges and the direction of displacement of q from the center of the square.

21. If $q_a = 0$ in Figure 18.40, under what conditions will there be no net Coulomb force on q?

22. In regions of low humidity, one develops a special "grip" when opening car doors, or touching metal door knobs. This involves placing as much of the hand on the device as possible, not just the ends of one's fingers. Discuss the induced charge and explain why this is done.

23. Tollbooth stations on roadways and bridges usually have a piece of wire stuck in the pavement before them that will touch a car as it approaches. Why is this done?

24. Suppose a person carries an excess charge. To maintain their charged status can they be standing on ground wearing just any pair of shoes? How would you discharge them? What are the consequences if they simply walk away?

18.4 Coulomb's Law

25. Figure 18.41 shows the charge distribution in a water molecule, which is called a polar molecule because it has an inherent separation of charge. Given water's polar character, explain what effect humidity has on removing excess charge from objects.

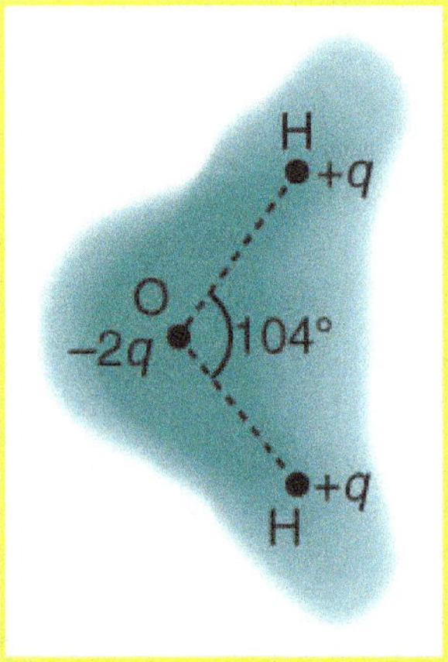

FIGURE 18.41 Schematic representation of the outer electron cloud of a neutral water molecule. The electrons spend more time near the oxygen than the hydrogens, giving a permanent charge separation as shown. Water is thus a *polar molecule*. It is more easily affected by electrostatic forces than molecules with uniform charge distributions.

26. Using Figure 18.41, explain, in terms of Coulomb's law, why a polar molecule (such as in Figure 18.41) is attracted by both positive and negative charges.

27. Given the polar character of water molecules, explain how ions in the air form nucleation centers for rain droplets.

18.5 Electric Field: Concept of a Field Revisited

28. Why must the test charge q in the definition of the electric field be vanishingly small?

29. Are the direction and magnitude of the Coulomb force unique at a given point in space? What about the electric field?

18.6 Electric Field Lines: Multiple Charges

30. Compare and contrast the Coulomb force field and the electric field. To do this, make a list of five properties for the Coulomb force field analogous to the five properties listed for electric field lines. Compare each item in your list of Coulomb force field properties with those of the electric field—are they the same or different? (For example, electric field lines cannot cross. Is the same true for Coulomb field lines?)

31. Figure 18.42 shows an electric field extending over three regions, labeled I, II, and III. Answer the following questions. (a) Are there any isolated charges? If so, in what region and what are their signs? (b) Where is the field strongest? (c) Where is it weakest? (d) Where is the field the most uniform?

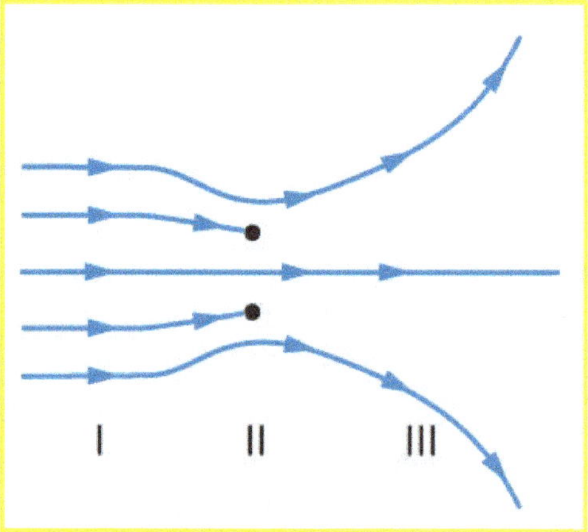

FIGURE 18.42

18.7 Electric Forces in Biology

32. A cell membrane is a thin layer enveloping a cell. The thickness of the membrane is much less than the size of the cell. In a static situation the membrane has a charge distribution of -2.5×10^{-6} C/m ^{2} on its inner surface and $+2.5 \times 10^{-6}$ C/m^2 on its outer surface. Draw a diagram of the cell and the surrounding cell membrane. Include on this diagram the charge distribution and the corresponding electric field. Is there any electric field inside the cell? Is there any electric field outside the cell?

Problems & Exercises

18.1 Static Electricity and Charge: Conservation of Charge

1. Common static electricity involves charges ranging from nanocoulombs to microcoulombs. (a) How many electrons are needed to form a charge of $-2.00\ \text{nC}$ (b) How many electrons must be removed from a neutral object to leave a net charge of $0.500\ \mu\text{C}$?

2. If 1.80×10^{20} electrons move through a pocket calculator during a full day's operation, how many coulombs of charge moved through it?

3. To start a car engine, the car battery moves 3.75×10^{21} electrons through the starter motor. How many coulombs of charge were moved?

4. A certain lightning bolt moves 40.0 C of charge. How many fundamental units of charge $|q_e|$ is this?

18.2 Conductors and Insulators

5. Suppose a speck of dust in an electrostatic precipitator has 1.0000×10^{12} protons in it and has a net charge of –5.00 nC (a very large charge for a small speck). How many electrons does it have?

6. An amoeba has 1.00×10^{16} protons and a net charge of 0.300 pC. (a) How many fewer electrons are there than protons? (b) If you paired them up, what fraction of the protons would have no electrons?

7. A 50.0 g ball of copper has a net charge of $2.00\ \mu\text{C}$. What fraction of the copper's electrons has been removed? (Each copper atom has 29 protons, and copper has an atomic mass of 63.5.)

8. What net charge would you place on a 100 g piece of sulfur if you put an extra electron on 1 in 10^{12} of its atoms? (Sulfur has an atomic mass of 32.1.)

9. How many coulombs of positive charge are there in 4.00 kg of plutonium, given its atomic mass is 244 and that each plutonium atom has 94 protons?

18.3 Conductors and Electric Fields in Static Equilibrium

10. Sketch the electric field lines in the vicinity of the conductor in Figure 18.43 given the field was originally uniform and parallel to the object's long axis. Is the resulting field small near the long side of the object?

FIGURE 18.43

11. Sketch the electric field lines in the vicinity of the conductor in Figure 18.44 given the field was originally uniform and parallel to the object's long axis. Is the resulting field small near the long side of the object?

FIGURE 18.44

12. Sketch the electric field between the two conducting plates shown in Figure 18.45, given the top plate is positive and an equal amount of negative charge is on the bottom plate. Be certain to indicate the distribution of charge on the plates.

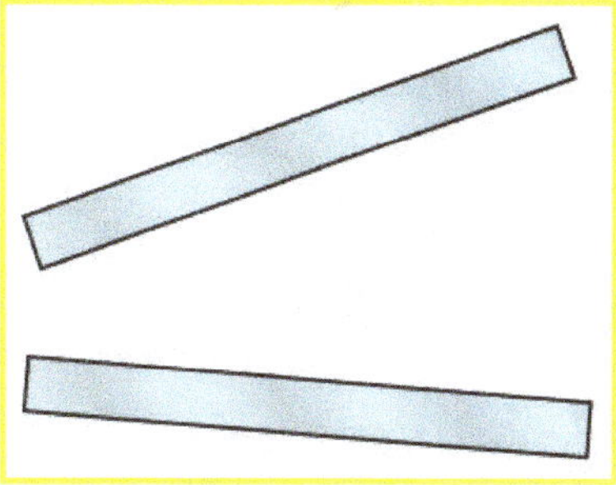

FIGURE 18.45

13. Sketch the electric field lines in the vicinity of the charged insulator in Figure 18.46 noting its nonuniform charge distribution.

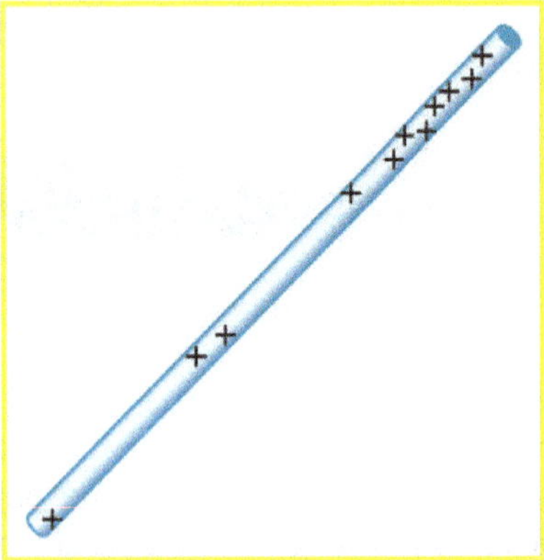

FIGURE 18.46 A charged insulating rod such as might be used in a classroom demonstration.

14. What is the force on the charge located at $x = 8.00\text{ cm}$ in Figure 18.47(a) given that $q = 1.00\ \mu\text{C}$?

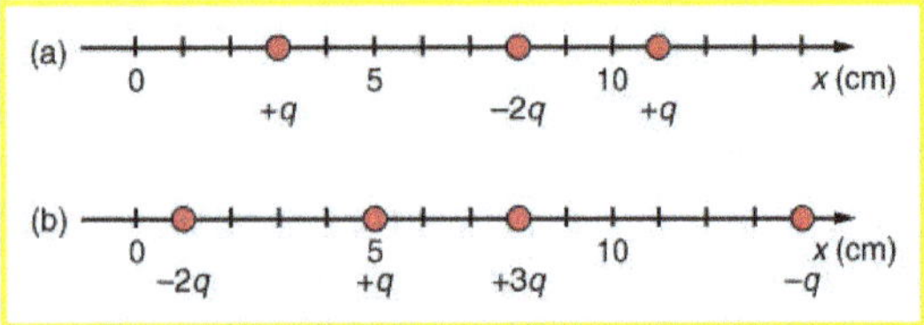

FIGURE 18.47 (a) Point charges located at 3.00, 8.00, and 11.0 cm along the x-axis. (b) Point charges located at 1.00, 5.00, 8.00, and 14.0 cm along the x-axis.

15. (a) Find the total electric field at $x = 11.00\text{ cm}$ in Figure 18.47(b). (b) If the charges are allowed to move and eventually be brought to rest by friction, what will the final charge configuration be? (That is, will there be a single charge, double charge, etc., and what will its value(s) be?)

16. (a) Find the electric field at $x = 5.00\text{ cm}$ in Figure 18.47(a), given that $q = 1.00\ \mu\text{C}$. (b) At what position between 3.00 and 8.00 cm is the total electric field the same as that for $-2q$ alone? (c) Can the electric field be zero anywhere between 0.00 and 8.00 cm? (d) At very large positive or negative values of *x*, the electric field approaches zero in both (a) and (b). In which does it most rapidly approach zero and why? (e) At what position to the right of 11.0 cm is the total electric field zero, other than at infinity? (Hint: A graphing calculator can yield considerable insight in this problem.)

17. (a) Find the total Coulomb force on a charge of 2.00 nC located at $x = 4.00\text{ cm}$ in Figure 18.47 (b), given that $q = 1.00\ \mu\text{C}$. (b) Find the *x*-position at which the electric field is zero in Figure 18.47 (b).

18. Using the symmetry of the arrangement, determine the direction of the force on q in the figure below, given that $q_a = q_b = +7.50\ \mu\text{C}$ and $q_c = q_d = -7.50\ \mu\text{C}$. (b) Calculate the magnitude of the force on the charge q, given that the square is 10.0 cm on a side and $q = 2.00\ \mu\text{C}$.

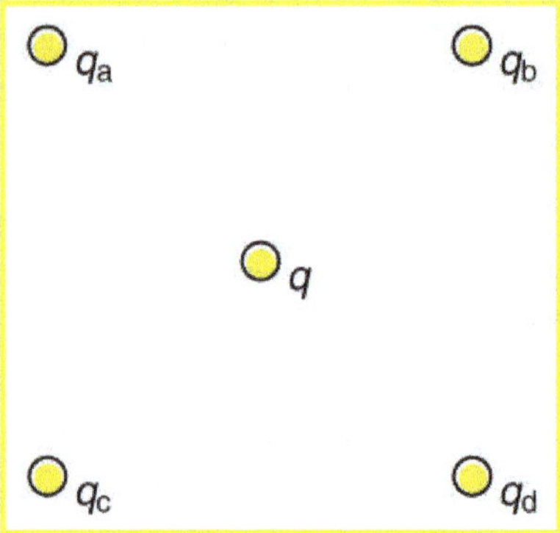

FIGURE 18.48

19. (a) Using the symmetry of the arrangement, determine the direction of the electric field at the center of the square in Figure 18.48, given that $q_a = q_b = -1.00\ \mu\text{C}$ and $q_c = q_d = +1.00\ \mu\text{C}$. (b) Calculate the magnitude of the electric field at the location of q, given that the square is 5.00 cm on a side.

20. Find the electric field at the location of q_a in Figure 18.48 given that $q_b = q_c = q_d = +2.00\text{ nC}$, $q = -1.00\text{ nC}$, and the square is 20.0 cm on a side.

21. Find the total Coulomb force on the charge q in Figure 18.48, given that $q = 1.00\ \mu\text{C}$, $q_a = 2.00\ \mu\text{C}$, $q_b = -3.00\ \mu\text{C}$, $q_c = -4.00\ \mu\text{C}$, and $q_d = +1.00\ \mu\text{C}$. The square is 50.0 cm on a side.

22. (a) Find the electric field at the location of q_a in Figure 18.49, given that $q_b = +10.00\ \mu\text{C}$ and $q_c = -5.00\ \mu\text{C}$. (b) What is the force on q_a, given that $q_a = +1.50\text{ nC}$?

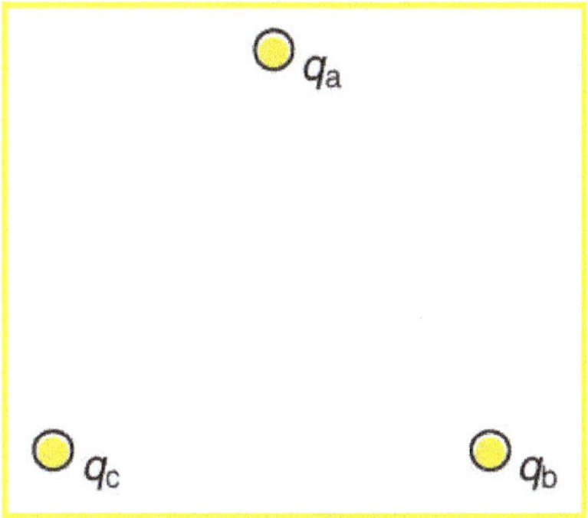

FIGURE 18.49 Point charges located at the corners of an equilateral triangle 25.0 cm on a side.

23. (a) Find the electric field at the center of the triangular configuration of charges in Figure 18.49, given that q_a=+2.50 nC, $q_b = -8.00$ nC, and q_c=+1.50 nC. (b) Is there any combination of charges, other than $q_a = q_b = q_c$, that will produce a zero strength electric field at the center of the triangular configuration?

18.4 Coulomb's Law

24. What is the repulsive force between two pith balls that are 8.00 cm apart and have equal charges of – 30.0 nC?

25. (a) How strong is the attractive force between a glass rod with a $0.700\ \mu$C charge and a silk cloth with a $-0.600\ \mu$C charge, which are 12.0 cm apart, using the approximation that they act like point charges? (b) Discuss how the answer to this problem might be affected if the charges are distributed over some area and do not act like point charges.

26. Two point charges exert a 5.00 N force on each other. What will the force become if the distance between them is increased by a factor of three?

27. Two point charges are brought closer together, increasing the force between them by a factor of 25. By what factor was their separation decreased?

28. How far apart must two point charges of 75.0 nC (typical of static electricity) be to have a force of 1.00 N between them?

29. If two equal charges each of 1 C each are separated in air by a distance of 1 km, what is the magnitude of the force acting between them? You will see that even at a distance as large as 1 km, the repulsive force is substantial because 1 C is a very significant amount of charge.

30. A test charge of $+2\ \mu$C is placed halfway between a charge of $+6\ \mu$C and another of $+4\ \mu$C separated by 10 cm. (a) What is the magnitude of the force on the test charge? (b) What is the direction of this force (away from or toward the $+6\ \mu$C charge)?

31. Bare free charges do not remain stationary when close together. To illustrate this, calculate the acceleration of two isolated protons separated by 2.00 nm (a typical distance between gas atoms). Explicitly show how you follow the steps in the Problem-Solving Strategy for electrostatics.

32. (a) By what factor must you change the distance between two point charges to change the force between them by a factor of 10? (b) Explain how the distance can either increase or decrease by this factor and still cause a factor of 10 change in the force.

33. Suppose you have a total charge q_{tot} that you can split in any manner. Once split, the separation distance is fixed. How do you split the charge to achieve the greatest force?

34. (a) Common transparent tape becomes charged when pulled from a dispenser. If one piece is placed above another, the repulsive force can be great enough to support the top piece's weight. Assuming equal point charges (only an approximation), calculate the magnitude of the charge if electrostatic force is great enough to support the weight of a 10.0 mg piece of tape held 1.00 cm above another. (b) Discuss whether the magnitude of this charge is consistent with what is typical of static electricity.

35. (a) Find the ratio of the electrostatic to gravitational force between two electrons. (b) What is this ratio for two protons? (c) Why is the ratio different for electrons and protons?

36. At what distance is the electrostatic force between two protons equal to the weight of one proton?

37. A certain five cent coin contains 5.00 g of nickel. What fraction of the nickel atoms' electrons, removed and placed 1.00 m above it, would support the weight of this coin? The atomic mass of nickel is 58.7, and each nickel atom contains 28 electrons and 28 protons.

38. (a) Two point charges totaling $8.00\ \mu$C exert a repulsive force of 0.150 N on one another when separated by 0.500 m. What is the charge on

each? (b) What is the charge on each if the force is attractive?

39. Point charges of $5.00\ \mu\text{C}$ and $-3.00\ \mu\text{C}$ are placed 0.250 m apart. (a) Where can a third charge be placed so that the net force on it is zero? (b) What if both charges are positive?

40. Two point charges q_1 and q_2 are $3.00\ \text{m}$ apart, and their total charge is $20\ \mu\text{C}$. (a) If the force of repulsion between them is 0.075N, what are magnitudes of the two charges? (b) If one charge attracts the other with a force of 0.525N, what are the magnitudes of the two charges? Note that you may need to solve a quadratic equation to reach your answer.

18.5 Electric Field: Concept of a Field Revisited

41. What is the magnitude and direction of an electric field that exerts a $2.00 \times 10^{-5}\ \text{N}$ upward force on a $-1.75\ \mu\text{C}$ charge?

42. What is the magnitude and direction of the force exerted on a $3.50\ \mu\text{C}$ charge by a 250 N/C electric field that points due east?

43. Calculate the magnitude of the electric field 2.00 m from a point charge of 5.00 mC (such as found on the terminal of a Van de Graaff).

44. (a) What magnitude point charge creates a 10,000 N/C electric field at a distance of 0.250 m? (b) How large is the field at 10.0 m?

45. Calculate the initial (from rest) acceleration of a proton in a $5.00 \times 10^6\ \text{N/C}$ electric field (such as created by a research Van de Graaff). Explicitly show how you follow the steps in the Problem-Solving Strategy for electrostatics.

46. (a) Find the magnitude and direction of an electric field that exerts a $4.80 \times 10^{-17}\ \text{N}$ westward force on an electron. (b) What magnitude and direction force does this field exert on a proton?

18.6 Electric Field Lines: Multiple Charges

47. (a) Sketch the electric field lines near a point charge $+q$. (b) Do the same for a point charge $-3.00q$.

48. Sketch the electric field lines a long distance from the charge distributions shown in Figure 18.31 (a) and (b)

49. Figure 18.50 shows the electric field lines near two charges q_1 and q_2. What is the ratio of their magnitudes? (b) Sketch the electric field lines a long distance from the charges shown in the figure.

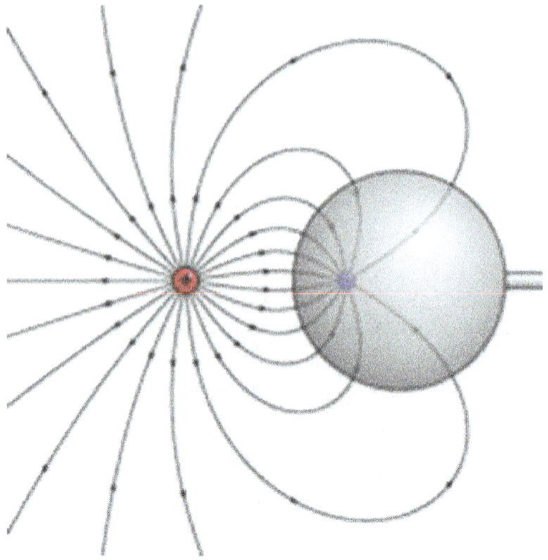

FIGURE 18.50 The electric field near two charges.

50. Sketch the electric field lines in the vicinity of two opposite charges, where the negative charge is three times greater in magnitude than the positive. (See Figure 18.50 for a similar situation).

18.8 Applications of Electrostatics

51. (a) What is the electric field 5.00 m from the center of the terminal of a Van de Graaff with a 3.00 mC charge, noting that the field is equivalent to that of a point charge at the center of the terminal? (b) At this distance, what force does the field exert on a $2.00\ \mu\text{C}$ charge on the Van de Graaff's belt?

52. (a) What is the direction and magnitude of an electric field that supports the weight of a free electron near the surface of Earth? (b) Discuss what the small value for this field implies regarding the relative strength of the gravitational and electrostatic forces.

53. A simple and common technique for accelerating electrons is shown in Figure 18.51, where there is a uniform electric field between two plates. Electrons are released, usually from a hot filament, near the negative plate, and there is a small hole in the positive plate that allows the electrons to continue moving. (a) Calculate the acceleration of the electron if the field strength is $2.50 \times 10^4\ \text{N/C}$. (b) Explain why the electron will not be pulled back to the positive plate once it moves through the hole.

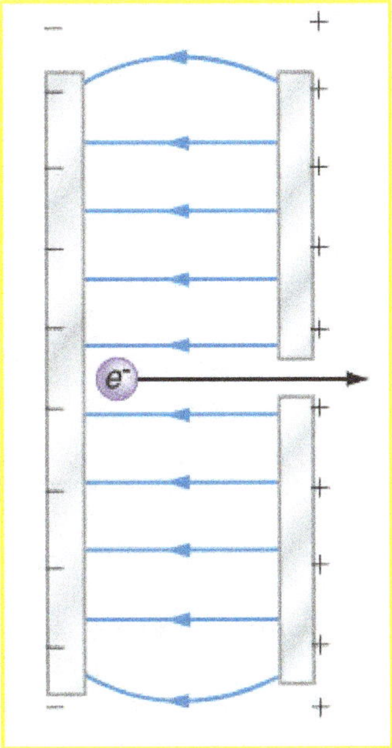

FIGURE 18.51 Parallel conducting plates with opposite charges on them create a relatively uniform electric field used to accelerate electrons to the right. Those that go through the hole can be used to make a TV or computer screen glow or to produce X-rays.

54. Earth has a net charge that produces an electric field of approximately 150 N/C downward at its surface. (a) What is the magnitude and sign of the excess charge, noting the electric field of a conducting sphere is equivalent to a point charge at its center? (b) What acceleration will the field produce on a free electron near Earth's surface? (c) What mass object with a single extra electron will have its weight supported by this field?

55. Point charges of $25.0\ \mu\text{C}$ and $45.0\ \mu\text{C}$ are placed 0.500 m apart. (a) At what point along the line between them is the electric field zero? (b) What is the electric field halfway between them?

56. What can you say about two charges q_1 and q_2, if the electric field one-fourth of the way from q_1 to q_2 is zero?

57. Integrated Concepts
Calculate the angular velocity ω of an electron orbiting a proton in the hydrogen atom, given the radius of the orbit is $0.530 \times 10^{-10}\ \text{m}$. You may assume that the proton is stationary and the centripetal force is supplied by Coulomb attraction.

58. Integrated Concepts
An electron has an initial velocity of $5.00 \times 10^{6}\ \text{m/s}$ in a uniform $2.00 \times 10^{5}\ \text{N/C}$ strength electric field. The field accelerates the electron in the direction opposite to its initial velocity. (a) What is the direction of the electric field? (b) How far does the electron travel before coming to rest? (c) How long does it take the electron to come to rest? (d) What is the electron's velocity when it returns to its starting point?

59. Integrated Concepts
The practical limit to an electric field in air is about $3.00 \times 10^{6}\ \text{N/C}$. Above this strength, sparking takes place because air begins to ionize and charges flow, reducing the field. (a) Calculate the distance a free proton must travel in this field to reach 3.00% of the speed of light, starting from rest. (b) Is this practical in air, or must it occur in a vacuum?

60. Integrated Concepts
A 5.00 g charged insulating ball hangs on a 30.0 cm long string in a uniform horizontal electric field as shown in Figure 18.52. Given the charge on the ball is $1.00\ \mu\text{C}$, find the strength of the field.

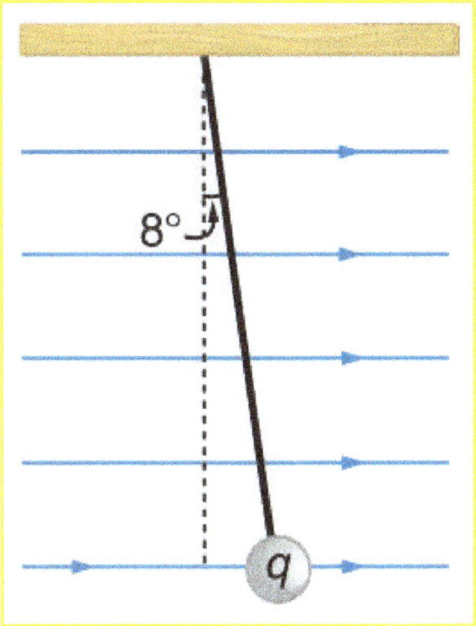

FIGURE 18.52 A horizontal electric field causes the charged ball to hang at an angle of 8.00°.

61. Integrated Concepts
Figure 18.53 shows an electron passing between two charged metal plates that create an 100 N/C vertical electric field perpendicular to the electron's original horizontal velocity. (These can be used to change the electron's direction, such as in an oscilloscope.) The initial speed of the electron is $3.00 \times 10^{6}\ \text{m/s}$, and the horizontal distance it travels in the uniform field is 4.00 cm. (a) What is its vertical deflection? (b) What is the vertical component of its final velocity? (c) At what angle does it exit? Neglect any edge effects.

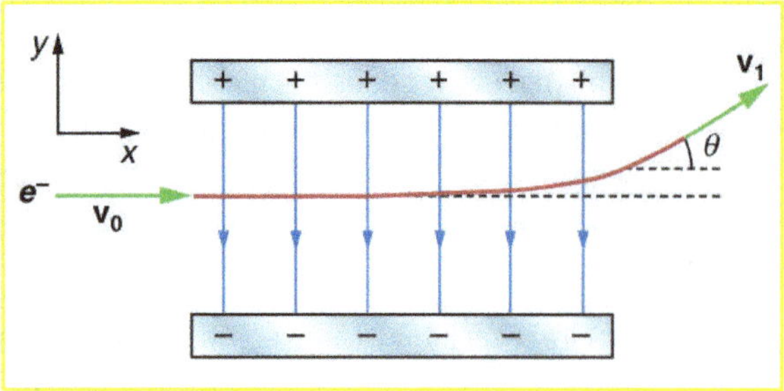

FIGURE 18.53

62. Integrated Concepts
The classic Millikan oil drop experiment was the first to obtain an accurate measurement of the charge on an electron. In it, oil drops were suspended against the gravitational force by a vertical electric field. (See Figure 18.54.) Given the oil drop to be $1.00\ \mu m$ in radius and have a density of $920\ kg/m^3$: (a) Find the weight of the drop. (b) If the drop has a single excess electron, find the electric field strength needed to balance its weight.

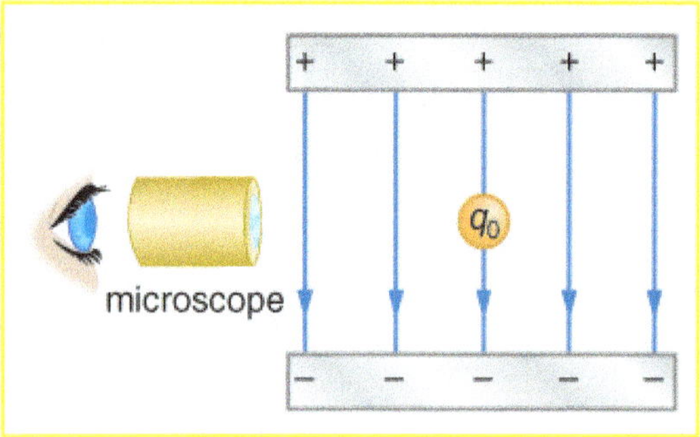

FIGURE 18.54 In the Millikan oil drop experiment, small drops can be suspended in an electric field by the force exerted on a single excess electron. Classically, this experiment was used to determine the electron charge q_e by measuring the electric field and mass of the drop.

63. Integrated Concepts
(a) In Figure 18.55, four equal charges q lie on the corners of a square. A fifth charge Q is on a mass m directly above the center of the square, at a height equal to the length d of one side of the square. Determine the magnitude of q in terms of Q, m, and d, if the Coulomb force is to equal the weight of m. (b) Is this equilibrium stable or unstable? Discuss.

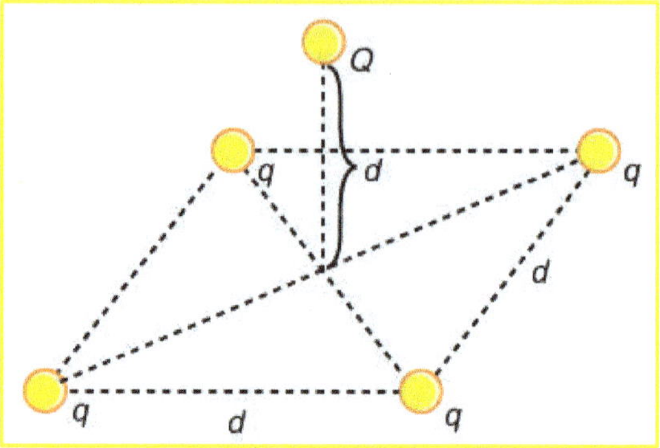

FIGURE 18.55 Four equal charges on the corners of a horizontal square support the weight of a fifth charge located directly above the center of the square.

64. Unreasonable Results
(a) Calculate the electric field strength near a 10.0 cm diameter conducting sphere that has 1.00 C of excess charge on it. (b) What is unreasonable about this result? (c) Which assumptions are responsible?

65. Unreasonable Results
(a) Two 0.500 g raindrops in a thunderhead are 1.00 cm apart when they each acquire 1.00 mC charges. Find their acceleration. (b) What is unreasonable about this result? (c) Which premise or assumption is responsible?

66. Unreasonable Results
A wrecking yard inventor wants to pick up cars by charging a 0.400 m diameter ball and inducing an equal and opposite charge on the car. If a car has a 1000 kg mass and the ball is to be able to lift it from a distance of 1.00 m: (a) What minimum charge must be used? (b) What is the electric field near the surface of the ball? (c) Why are these results unreasonable? (d) Which premise or assumption is responsible?

67. Construct Your Own Problem
Consider two insulating balls with evenly distributed equal and opposite charges on their surfaces, held with a certain distance between the centers of the balls. Construct a problem in which you calculate the electric field (magnitude and direction) due to the balls at various points along a line running through the centers of the balls and extending to infinity on either side. Choose interesting points and comment on the meaning of the field at those points. For example, at what points might the field be just that due to one ball and where does the field become negligibly small? Among the things to be considered are the magnitudes of the charges and the distance

between the centers of the balls. Your instructor may wish for you to consider the electric field off axis or for a more complex array of charges, such as those in a water molecule.

68. Construct Your Own Problem
Consider identical spherical conducting space ships in deep space where gravitational fields from other bodies are negligible compared to the gravitational attraction between the ships. Construct a problem in which you place identical excess charges on the space ships to exactly counter their gravitational attraction. Calculate the amount of excess charge needed. Examine whether that charge depends on the distance between the centers of the ships, the masses of the ships, or any other factors. Discuss whether this would be an easy, difficult, or even impossible thing to do in practice.

69. Critical Thinking A frictionless circular track with a diameter of 4.00 m has two spheres of 10.0 kg each anchored very near it. The track is oriented with a diameter along the *x*-axis. The anchored spheres are just outside the track. One of the anchored spheres is just left of the origin at a distance of $1.00 \times 10^{-15}\,\text{m}$ from it, and the other is on the *x*-axis just right of the track at a distance of $1.00 \times 10^{-15}\,\text{m}$ past $(4, 0)$. Each sphere carries a charge of 2.00×10^{-9} C. (Note: The slight distance from the track is so the particles cannot collide, and does not enter into the calculations for three significant figures.) (a) A third sphere has a mass of 10.00 kg and carries a charge of -1.00×10^{-9} C. It is free to move on the track. It is initially placed an equal length from the two anchored spheres at $(2.00, 2.00)$. What is the total force on the third sphere? (Be certain to include gravity between the spheres.) (b) Will the third sphere move? (c) Label the first two spheres A and B, and the movable sphere C. Now start sphere C at $(1.00, 2.00)$. What are the forces on sphere C? (d) Will sphere C now move? (e) If it does, where will it stop moving and reverse course? If it does not move, you may skip this part. (f) How many equilibrium points are there on the track at which the movable sphere will remain stationary? Where are they?

Test Prep for AP® Courses

18.1 Static Electricity and Charge: Conservation of Charge

1. When a glass rod is rubbed against silk, which of the following statements is true?
a. Electrons are removed from the silk.
b. Electrons are removed from the rod.
c. Protons are removed from the silk.
d. Protons are removed from the rod.

2. In an experiment, three microscopic latex spheres are sprayed into a chamber and become charged with +3*e*, +5*e*, and −3*e*, respectively. Later, all three spheres collide simultaneously and then separate. Which of the following are possible values for the final charges on the spheres? Select *two* answers.

	X	Y	Z
(a)	+4*e*	−4*e*	+5*e*
(b)	−4*e*	+4.5*e*	+5.5*e*
(c)	+5*e*	−8*e*	+7*e*
(d)	+6*e*	+6*e*	−7*e*

3. If objects X and Y attract each other, which of the following will be false?
a. X has positive charge and Y has negative charge.
b. X has negative charge and Y has positive charge.
c. X and Y both have positive charge.
d. X is neutral and Y has a charge.

4. Suppose a positively charged object A is brought in contact with an uncharged object B in a closed system. What type of charge will be left on object B?
a. negative
b. positive
c. neutral
d. cannot be determined

5. What will be the net charge on an object which attracts neutral pieces of paper but repels a negatively charged balloon?
a. negative
b. positive
c. neutral
d. cannot be determined

6. When two neutral objects are rubbed against each other, the first one gains a net charge of 3*e*. Which of the following statements is true?
a. The second object gains 3*e* and is negatively charged.

b. The second object loses $3e$ and is negatively charged.
c. The second object gains $3e$ and is positively charged.
d. The second object loses $3e$ and is positively charged.

7. In an experiment, a student runs a comb through his hair several times and brings it close to small pieces of paper. Which of the following will he observe?
a. Pieces of paper repel the comb.
b. Pieces of paper are attracted to the comb.
c. Some pieces of paper are attracted and some repel the comb.
d. There is no attraction or repulsion between the pieces of paper and the comb.

8. In an experiment a negatively charged balloon (balloon X) is repelled by another charged balloon Y. However, an object Z is attracted to balloon Y. Which of the following can be the charge on Z? Select *two* answers.
a. negative
b. positive
c. neutral
d. cannot be determined

9. Suppose an object has a charge of 1 C and gains 6.88×10^{18} electrons.
a. What will be the net charge of the object?
b. If the object has gained electrons from a neutral object, what will be the charge on the neutral object?
c. Find and explain the relationship between the total charges of the two objects before and after the transfer.
d. When a third object is brought in contact with the first object (after it gains the electrons), the resulting charge on the third object is 0.4 C. What was its initial charge?

10. The charges on two identical metal spheres (placed in a closed system) are -2.4×10^{-17} C and -4.8×10^{-17} C.
a. How many electrons will be equivalent to the charge on each sphere?
b. If the two spheres are brought in contact and then separated, find the charge on each sphere.
c. Calculate the number of electrons that would be equivalent to the resulting charge on each sphere.

11. In an experiment the following observations are made by a student for four charged objects W, X, Y, and Z:
- A glass rod rubbed with silk attracts W.
- W attracts Z but repels X.
- X attracts Z but repels Y.
- Y attracts W and Z.

Estimate whether the charges on each of the four objects are positive, negative, or neutral.

18.2 Conductors and Insulators

12. Some students experimenting with an uncharged metal sphere want to give the sphere a net charge using a charged aluminum pie plate. Which of the following steps would give the sphere a net charge of the same sign as the pie plate?
a. bringing the pie plate close to, but not touching, the metal sphere, then moving the pie plate away.
b. bringing the pie plate close to, but not touching, the metal sphere, then momentarily touching a grounding wire to the metal sphere.
c. bringing the pie plate close to, but not touching, the metal sphere, then momentarily touching a grounding wire to the pie plate.
d. touching the pie plate to the metal sphere.

13.

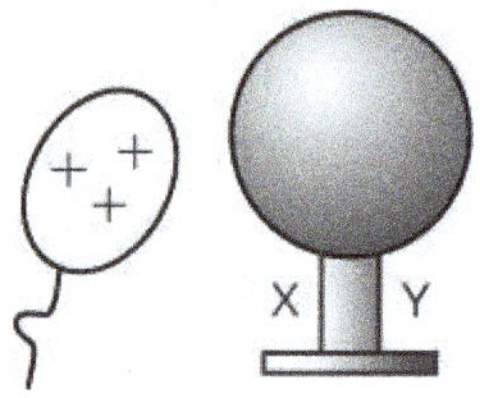

FIGURE 18.56 Balloon and sphere.

When the balloon is brought closer to the sphere, there will be a redistribution of charges. What is this phenomenon called?
a. electrostatic repulsion
b. conduction
c. polarization
d. none of the above

14. What will be the charge at Y (i.e., the part of the sphere furthest from the balloon)?
a. positive
b. negative
c. zero
d. It can be positive or negative depending on the material.

15. What will be the net charge on the sphere?

a. positive
b. negative
c. zero
d. It can be positive or negative depending on the material.

16. If Y is grounded while the balloon is still close to X, which of the following will be true?
a. Electrons will flow from the sphere to the ground.
b. Electrons will flow from the ground to the sphere.
c. Protons will flow from the sphere to the ground.
d. Protons will flow from the ground to the sphere.

17. If the balloon is moved away after grounding, what will be the net charge on the sphere?
a. positive
b. negative
c. zero
d. It can be positive or negative depending on the material.

18. A positively charged rod is used to charge a sphere by induction. Which of the following is true?
a. The sphere must be a conductor.
b. The sphere must be an insulator.
c. The sphere can be a conductor or insulator but must be connected to ground.
d. The sphere can be a conductor or insulator but must be already charged.

19.

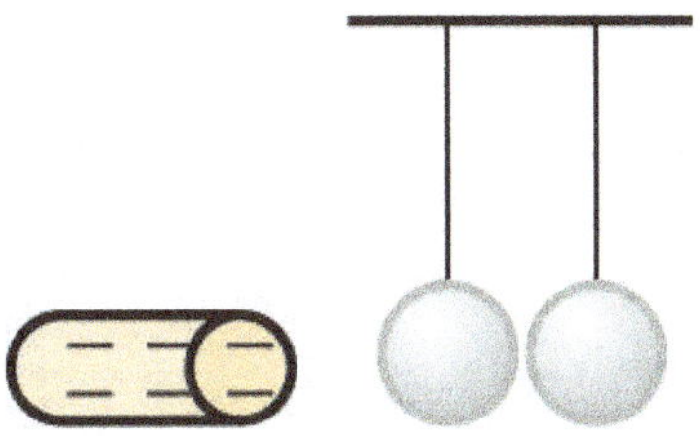

FIGURE 18.57 Rod and metal balls.

As shown in the figure above, two metal balls are suspended and a negatively charged rod is brought close to them.
a. If the two balls are in contact with each other what will be the charges on each ball?
b. Explain how the balls get these charges.
c. What will happen to the charge on the second ball (i.e., the ball further away from the rod) if it is momentarily grounded while the rod is still there?
d. If (instead of grounding) the second ball is moved away and then the rod is removed from the first ball, will the two balls have induced charges? If yes, what will be the charges? If no, why not?

20. Two experiments are performed using positively charged glass rods and neutral electroscopes. In the first experiment the rod is brought in contact with the electroscope. In the second experiment the rod is only brought close to the electroscope but not in contact. However, while the rod is close, the electroscope is momentarily grounded and then the rod is removed. In both experiments the needles of the electroscopes deflect, which indicates the presence of charges.
a. What is the charging method in each of the two experiments?
b. What is the net charge on the electroscope in the first experiment? Explain how the electroscope obtains that charge.
c. Is the net charge on the electroscope in the second experiment different from that of the first experiment? Explain why.

18.3 Conductors and Electric Fields in Static Equilibrium

21.

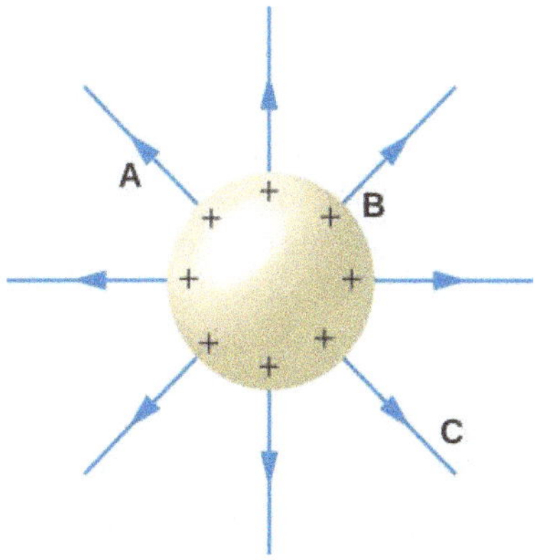

FIGURE 18.58 A sphere conductor.

An electric field due to a positively charged spherical conductor is shown above. Where will the electric field be weakest?
a. Point A
b. Point B
c. Point C
d. Same at all points

22.

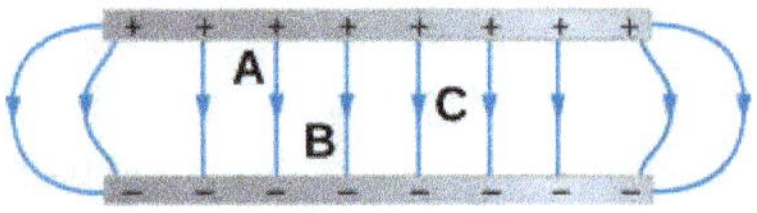

FIGURE 18.59 Electric field between two parallel metal plates.

The electric field created by two parallel metal plates is shown above. Where will the electric field be strongest?

a. Point A
b. Point B
c. Point C
d. Same at all points

23. Suppose that the electric field experienced due to a positively charged small spherical conductor at a certain distance is *E*. What will be the percentage change in electric field experienced at thrice the distance if the charge on the conductor is doubled?

24.

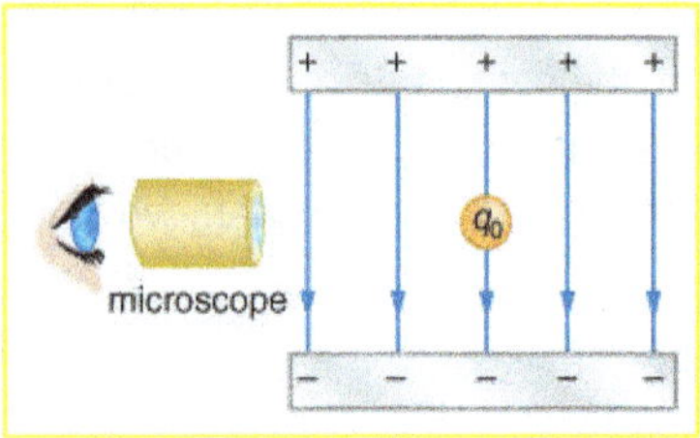

FIGURE 18.60 Millikan oil drop experiment.

The classic Millikan oil drop experiment setup is shown above. In this experiment oil drops are suspended in a vertical electric field against the gravitational force to measure their charge. If the mass of a negatively charged drop suspended in an electric field of 1.18×10^{-4} N/C strength is 3.85×10^{-21} g, find the number of excess electrons in the drop.

18.4 Coulomb's Law

25. For questions 25–27, suppose that the electrostatics force between two charges is *F*. What will be the force if the distance between them is halved?

a. $4F$
b. $2F$
c. $F/4$
d. $F/2$

26. Which of the following is false?

a. If the charge of one of the particles is doubled and that of the second is unchanged, the force will become $2F$.
b. If the charge of one of the particles is doubled and that of the second is halved, the force will remain *F*.
c. If the charge of both the particles is doubled, the force will become $4F$.
d. None of the above.

27. Which of the following is true about the gravitational force between the particles?

a. It will be 3.25×10^{-38} *F*.
b. It will be 3.25×10^{38} *F*.
c. It will be equal to *F*.
d. It is not possible to determine the gravitational force as the masses of the particles are not given.

28. Two massive, positively charged particles are initially held a fixed distance apart. When they are moved farther apart, the magnitude of their mutual gravitational force changes by a factor of *n*. Which of the following indicates the factor by which the magnitude of their mutual electrostatic force changes?

a. $1/n^2$
b. $1/n$
c. n
d. n^2

29. a. What is the electrostatic force between two charges of 1 C each, separated by a distance of 0.5 m?
b. How will this force change if the distance is increased to 1 m?

30. a. Find the ratio of the electrostatic force to the gravitational force between two electrons.
b. Will this ratio change if the two electrons are replaced by protons? If yes, find the new ratio.

18.5 Electric Field: Concept of a Field Revisited

31. Two particles with charges $+2q$ and $+q$ are separated by a distance *r*. The $+2q$ particle has an electric field *E* at distance *r* and exerts a force *F* on the $+q$ particle. Use this information to answer questions 31–32.
What is the electric field of the $+q$ particle at the same distance and what force does it exert on the $+2q$ particle?

a. $E/2$, $F/2$
b. E, $F/2$
c. $E/2$, F

d. E, F

32. When the $+q$ particle is replaced by a $+3q$ particle, what will be the electric field and force from the $+2q$ particle experienced by the $+3q$ particle?

a. $E/3$, $3F$
b. E, $3F$
c. $E/3$, F
d. E, F

33. The direction of the electric field of a negative charge is

a. inward for both positive and negative charges.
b. outward for both positive and negative charges.
c. inward for other positive charges and outward for other negative charges.
d. outward for other positive charges and inward for other negative charges.

34. The force responsible for holding an atom together is

a. frictional
b. electric
c. gravitational
d. magnetic

35. When a positively charged particle exerts an inward force on another particle *P*, what will be the charge of *P*?

a. positive
b. negative
c. neutral
d. cannot be determined

36. Find the force exerted due to a particle having a charge of 3.2×10^{-19} C on another identical particle 5 cm away.

37. Suppose that the force exerted on an electron is 5.6×10^{-17} N, directed to the east.

a. Find the magnitude of the electric field that exerts the force.
b. What will be the direction of the electric field?
c. If the electron is replaced by a proton, what will be the magnitude of force exerted?
d. What will be the direction of force on the proton?

18.6 Electric Field Lines: Multiple Charges

38.

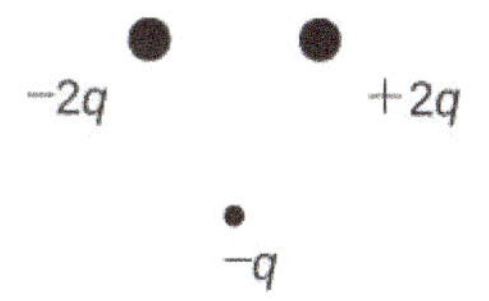

FIGURE 18.61

An electric dipole (with $+2q$ and $-2q$ as the two charges) is shown in the figure above. A third charge, $-q$ is placed equidistant from the dipole charges. What will be the direction of the net force on the third charge?

a. →
b. ←
c. ↓
d. ↑

39.

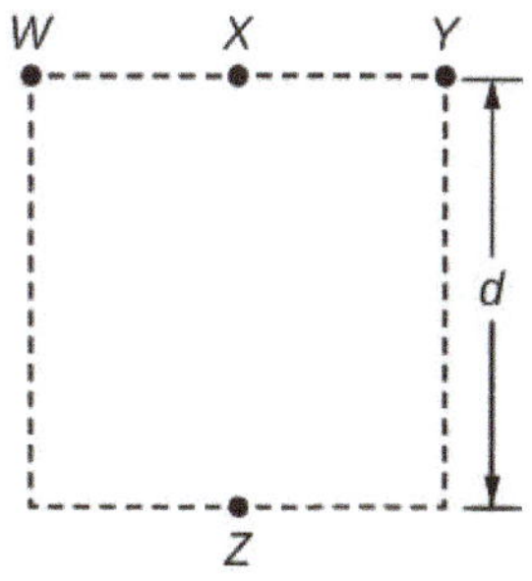

FIGURE 18.62

Four objects, each with charge $+q$, are held fixed on a square with sides of length d, as shown in the figure. Objects X and Z are at the midpoints of the sides of the square. The electrostatic force exerted by object W on object X is F. Use this information to answer questions 39–40.
What is the magnitude of force exerted by object W on Z?

a. $F/7$
b. $F/5$
c. $F/3$
d. $F/2$

40. What is the magnitude of the net force exerted on object X by objects W, Y, and Z?

a. $F/4$
b. $F/2$
c. $9F/4$
d. $3F$

41.

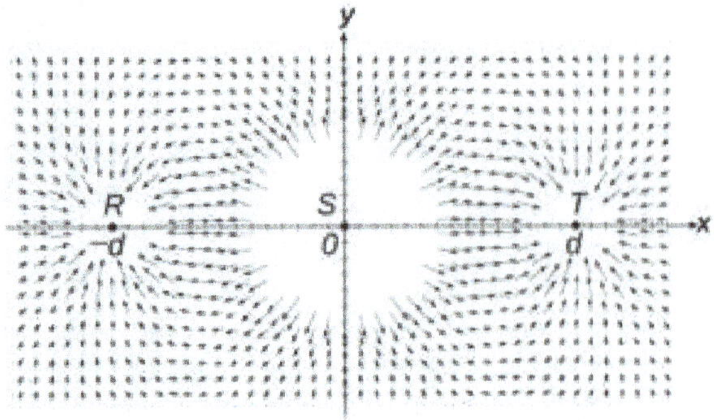

FIGURE 18.63 Electric field with three charged objects.

The figure above represents the electric field in the vicinity of three small charged objects, *R*, *S*, and *T*. The objects have charges $-q$, $+2q$, and $-q$, respectively, and are located on the *x*-axis at $-d$, 0, and *d*. Field vectors of very large magnitude are omitted for clarity.

(a) i) Briefly describe the characteristics of the field diagram that indicate that the sign of the charges of objects *R* and *T* is negative and that the sign of the charge of object *S* is positive.

ii) Briefly describe the characteristics of the field diagram that indicate that the magnitudes of the charges of objects *R* and *T* are equal and that the magnitude of the charge of object *S* is about twice that of objects *R* and *T*.

For the following parts, an electric field directed to the right is defined to be positive.

(b) On the axes below, sketch a graph of the electric field *E* along the *x*-axis as a function of position *x*.

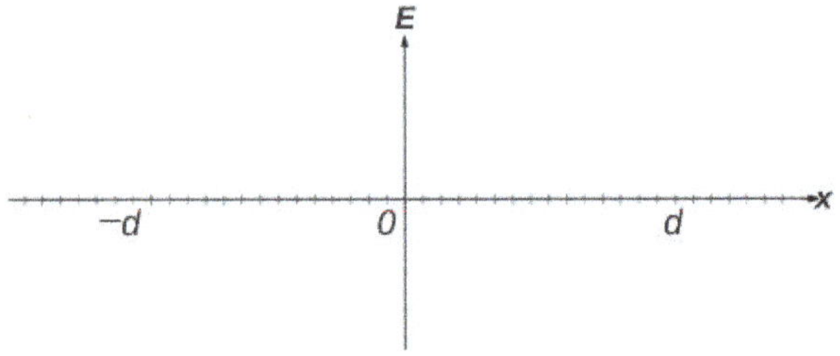

FIGURE 18.64 An Electric field (E) axis and Position (x) axis.

(c) Write an expression for the electric field *E* along the *x*-axis as a function of position *x* in the region between objects *S* and *T* in terms of *q*, *d*, and fundamental constants, as appropriate.

(d) Your classmate tells you there is a point between *S* and *T* where the electric field is zero. Determine whether this statement is true, and explain your reasoning using two of the representations from parts (a), (b), or (c).

CHAPTER 19

Electric Potential and Electric Field

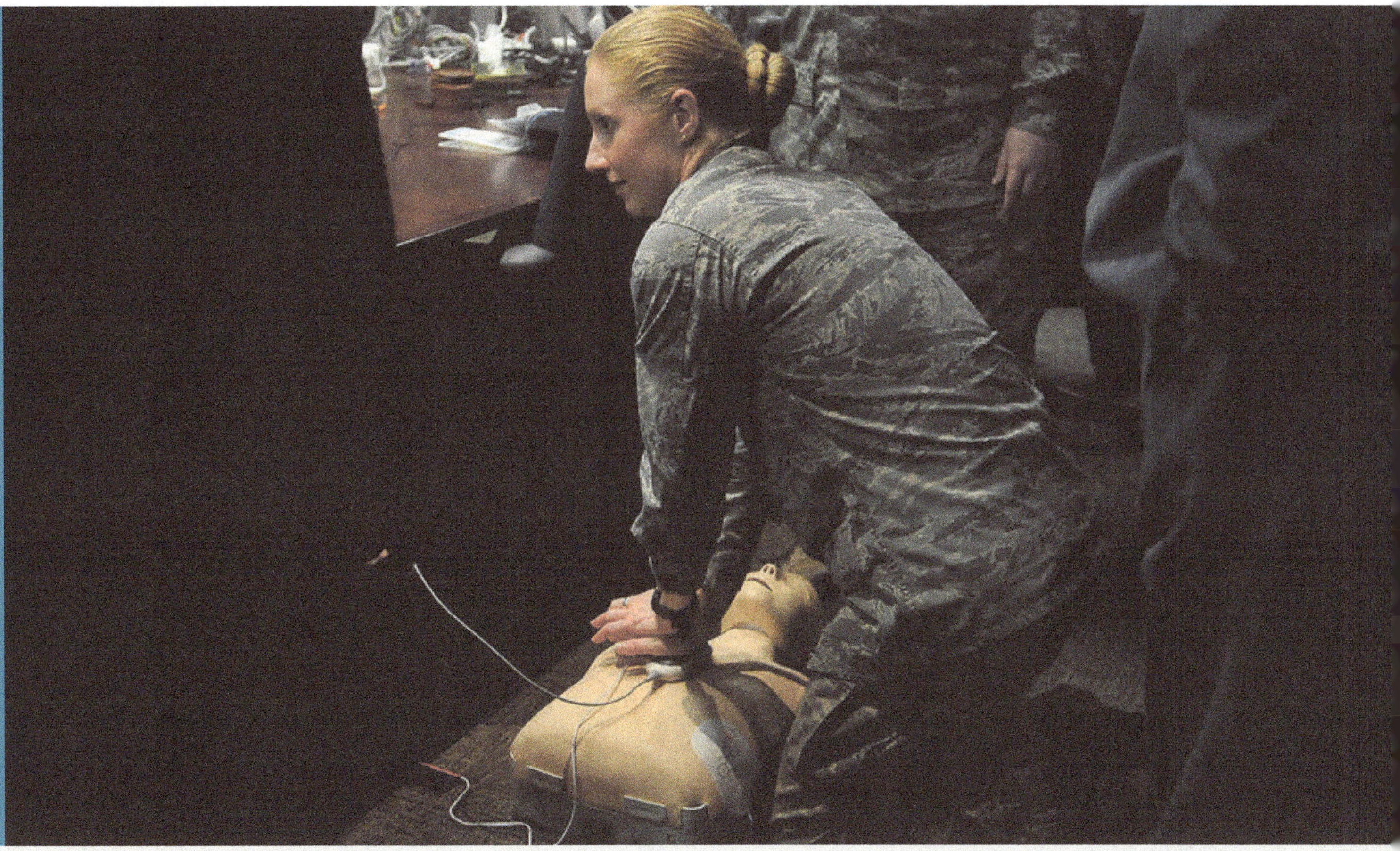

FIGURE 19.1 Automated external defibrillator unit (AED) (credit: U.S. Defense Department photo/Tech. Sgt. Suzanne M. Day)

CHAPTER OUTLINE

CONNECTION FOR AP® COURSES In Electric Charge and Electric Field, we just scratched the surface (or at least rubbed it) of electrical phenomena. Two of the most familiar aspects of electricity are its energy and *voltage*. We know, for example, that great amounts of electrical energy can be stored in batteries, are transmitted cross-country through power lines, and may jump from clouds to explode the sap of trees. In a similar manner, at molecular levels, *ions* cross cell membranes and transfer information. We also know about voltages associated with electricity. Batteries are typically a few volts, the outlets in your home produce 120 volts, and power lines can be as high as hundreds of thousands of volts. But energy and voltage are not the same thing. A motorcycle battery, for example, is small and would not be very successful in replacing the much larger battery in a car, yet each has the same voltage. In this chapter, we shall examine the relationship between voltage and electrical energy and begin to explore some of the many applications of electricity. We do so by introducing the concept of electric potential and describing the relationship between electric field and electric potential.

This chapter presents the concept of equipotential lines (lines of equal potential) as a way to visualize the electric field (Enduring Understanding 2.E, Essential Knowledge 2.E.2). An analogy between the isolines on topographic maps for gravitational field and equipotential lines for the electric field is used to develop a conceptual understanding of equipotential lines (Essential Knowledge 2.E.1). The relationship between the magnitude of an electric field, change in electric potential, and displacement is stated for a uniform field and extended for the more general case using the concept of the “average value” of the electric field (Essential Knowledge 2.E.3).

The concept that an electric field is caused by charged objects (Enduring Understanding 2.C) supports Big Idea 2, that fields exist in space and can be used to explain interactions. The relationship between the electric field, electric charge, and electric force (Essential Knowledge 2.C.1) is used to describe the behavior of charged particles. The uniformity of the electric field between two oppositely charged parallel plates with uniformly distributed electric charge (Essential Knowledge 2.C.5), as well as the properties of materials and their geometry, are used to develop understanding of the capacitance of a capacitor (Essential Knowledge 4.E.4).

This chapter also supports Big Idea 4, that interactions between systems result in changes in those systems. This idea is applied to electric properties of various systems of charged objects, demonstrating the effect of electric interactions on electric properties of systems (Enduring Understanding 4.E). This fact in turn supports Big Idea 5, that changes due to interactions are governed by conservation laws. In particular, the energy of a system is conserved (Enduring Understanding 5.B). Any system that has internal structure can have internal energy. For a system of charged objects, internal energy can change as a result of changes in the arrangement of charges and their geometric configuration as long as work is done on, or by, the system (Essential Knowledge 5.B.2). When objects within the system interact with conservative forces, such as electric forces, the internal energy is defined by the potential energy of that interaction (Essential Knowledge 5.B.3). In general, the internal energy of a system is the sum of the kinetic energies of all its objects and the potential energy of interaction between the objects within the system (Essential Knowledge 5.B.4).

The concepts in this chapter support:

Big Idea 1 Objects and systems have properties such as mass and charge. Systems may have internal structure.

Enduring Understanding 1.E Materials have many macroscopic properties that result from the arrangement and interactions of the atoms and molecules that make up the material.

Essential Knowledge 1.E.4 Matter has a property called electric permittivity.

Big Idea 2 Fields existing in space can be used to explain interactions.

Enduring Understanding 2.C An electric field is caused by an object with electric charge.

Essential Knowledge 2.C.1 The magnitude of the electric force F exerted on an object with electric charge q by an electric field F= qE. The direction of the force is determined by the direction of the field and the sign of the charge, with positively charged objects accelerating in the direction of the field and negatively charged objects accelerating in the direction opposite the field. This should include a vector field map for positive point charges, negative point charges, spherically symmetric charge distribution, and uniformly charged parallel plates.

Essential Knowledge 2.C.5 Between two oppositely charged parallel plates with uniformly distributed electric charge, at points far from the edges of the plates, the electric field is perpendicular to the plates and is constant in both magnitude and direction.

Enduring Understanding 2.E Physicists often construct a map of isolines connecting points of equal value for some quantity related to a field and use these maps to help visualize the field.

Essential Knowledge 2.E.1 Isolines on a topographic (elevation) map describe lines of approximately equal gravitational potential energy per unit mass (gravitational equipotential). As the distance between two different isolines decreases, the steepness of the surface increases. [Contour lines on topographic maps are useful teaching tools for introducing the concept of equipotential lines. Students are encouraged to use the analogy in their answers when explaining gravitational and electrical potential and potential differences.]

Essential Knowledge 2.E.2 Isolines in a region where an electric field exists represent lines of equal electric potential, referred to as equipotential lines.

Essential Knowledge 2.E.3 The average value of the electric field in a region equals the change in electric potential across that region divided by the change in position (displacement) in the relevant direction.

Big Idea 4 Interactions between systems can result in changes in those systems.

Enduring Understanding 4.E The electric and magnetic properties of a system can change in response to the presence of, or changes in, other objects or systems.

Essential Knowledge 4.E.4 The resistance of a resistor, and the capacitance of a capacitor, can be understood from the basic properties of electric fields and forces, as well as the properties of materials and their geometry.

Big Idea 5 Changes that occur as a result of interactions are constrained by conservation laws.

Enduring Understanding 5.B The energy of a system is conserved.

Essential Knowledge 5.B.2 A system with internal structure can have internal energy, and changes in a system's internal structure can result in changes in internal energy. [Physics 1: includes mass–spring oscillators and simple pendulums. Physics 2: charged object in electric fields and examining changes in internal energy with changes in configuration.]

Essential Knowledge 5.B.3 A system with internal structure can have potential energy. Potential energy exists within a system if the objects within that system interact with conservative forces.

Essential Knowledge 5.B.4 The internal energy of a system includes the kinetic energy of the objects that make up the system and the potential energy of the configuration of the objects that make up the system.

Click to view content (https://openstax.org/books/college-physics-ap-courses-2e/pages/19-connection-for-ap-r-courses)

19.1 Electric Potential Energy: Potential Difference

LEARNING OBJECTIVES

By the end of this section, you will be able to:

- Define electric potential and electric potential energy.
- Describe the relationship between potential difference and electrical potential energy.
- Explain electron volt and its usage in submicroscopic process.
- Determine electric potential energy given potential difference and amount of charge.

When a free positive charge q is accelerated by an electric field, such as shown in Figure 19.2, it is given kinetic energy. The process is analogous to an object being accelerated by a gravitational field. It is as if the charge is going down an electrical hill where its electric potential energy is converted to kinetic energy. Let us explore the work done on a charge q by the electric field in this process, so that we may develop a definition of electric potential energy.

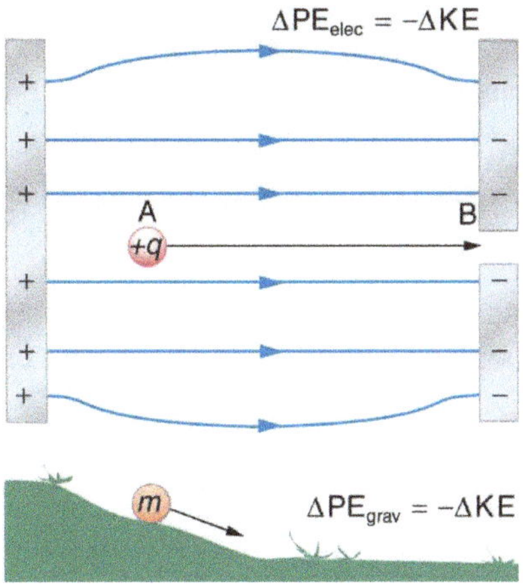

FIGURE 19.2 A charge accelerated by an electric field is analogous to a mass going down a hill. In both cases potential energy is converted to another form. Work is done by a force, but since this force is conservative, we can write $W = -\Delta\text{PE}$.

The electrostatic or Coulomb force is conservative, which means that the work done on q is independent of the path taken. This is exactly analogous to the gravitational force in the absence of dissipative forces such as friction. When a force is conservative, it is possible to define a potential energy associated with the force, and it is usually easier to deal with the potential energy (because it depends only on position) than to calculate the work directly.

We use the letters PE to denote electric potential energy, which has units of joules (J). The change in potential energy, ΔPE, is crucial, since the work done by a conservative force is the negative of the change in potential energy; that is, $W = -\Delta\text{PE}$. For example, work W done to accelerate a positive charge from rest is positive and results from a loss in PE, or a negative ΔPE. There must be a minus sign in front of ΔPE to make W positive. PE can be found at any point by taking one point as a reference and calculating the work needed to move a charge to the other point.

POTENTIAL ENERGY

$W = -\Delta\text{PE}$. For example, work W done to accelerate a positive charge from rest is positive and results from a loss in PE, or a negative ΔPE. There must be a minus sign in front of ΔPE to make W positive. PE can be found at any point by taking one point as a reference and calculating the work needed to move a charge to the other point.

Gravitational potential energy and electric potential energy are quite analogous. Potential energy accounts for work done by a conservative force and gives added insight regarding energy and energy transformation without the necessity of dealing with the force directly. It is much more common, for example, to use the concept of voltage (related to electric potential energy) than to deal with the Coulomb force directly.

Calculating the work directly is generally difficult, since $W = Fd\cos\theta$ and the direction and magnitude of F can be complex for multiple charges, for odd-shaped objects, and along arbitrary paths. But we do know that, since $F = qE$, the work, and hence ΔPE, is proportional to the test charge q. To have a physical quantity that is independent of test charge, we define **electric potential** V (or simply potential, since electric is understood) to be the potential energy per unit charge:

$$V = \frac{\text{PE}}{q}. \tag{19.1}$$

ELECTRIC POTENTIAL

This is the electric potential energy per unit charge.

$$V = \frac{\text{PE}}{q} \tag{19.2}$$

Since PE is proportional to q, the dependence on q cancels. Thus V does not depend on q. The change in potential energy ΔPE is crucial, and so we are concerned with the difference in potential or potential difference ΔV between two points, where

$$\Delta V = V_{\text{B}} - V_{\text{A}} = \frac{\Delta\text{PE}}{q}. \tag{19.3}$$

The **potential difference** between points A and B, $V_{\text{B}} - V_{\text{A}}$, is thus defined to be the change in potential energy of a charge q moved from A to B, divided by the charge. Units of potential difference are joules per coulomb, given the name volt (V) after Alessandro Volta.

$$1\ \text{V} = 1\ \frac{\text{J}}{\text{C}} \tag{19.4}$$

POTENTIAL DIFFERENCE

The potential difference between points A and B, $V_{\text{B}} - V_{\text{A}}$, is defined to be the change in potential energy of a charge q moved from A to B, divided by the charge. Units of potential difference are joules per coulomb, given the name volt (V) after Alessandro Volta.

$$1\text{ V} = 1\ \frac{\text{J}}{\text{C}} \tag{19.5}$$

The familiar term **voltage** is the common name for potential difference. Keep in mind that whenever a voltage is quoted, it is understood to be the potential difference between two points. For example, every battery has two terminals, and its voltage is the potential difference between them. More fundamentally, the point you choose to be zero volts is arbitrary. This is analogous to the fact that gravitational potential energy has an arbitrary zero, such as sea level or perhaps a lecture hall floor.

In summary, the relationship between potential difference (or voltage) and electrical potential energy is given by

$$\Delta V = \frac{\Delta \text{PE}}{q} \text{ and } \Delta \text{PE} = q\Delta V. \tag{19.6}$$

POTENTIAL DIFFERENCE AND ELECTRICAL POTENTIAL ENERGY

The relationship between potential difference (or voltage) and electrical potential energy is given by

$$\Delta V = \frac{\Delta \text{PE}}{q} \text{ and } \Delta \text{PE} = q\Delta V. \tag{19.7}$$

The second equation is equivalent to the first.

Voltage is not the same as energy. Voltage is the energy per unit charge. Thus a motorcycle battery and a car battery can both have the same voltage (more precisely, the same potential difference between battery terminals), yet one stores much more energy than the other since $\Delta \text{PE} = q\Delta V$. The car battery can move more charge than the motorcycle battery, although both are 12 V batteries.

EXAMPLE 19.1

Calculating Energy

Suppose you have a 12.0 V motorcycle battery that can move 5000 C of charge, and a 12.0 V car battery that can move 60,000 C of charge. How much energy does each deliver? (Assume that the numerical value of each charge is accurate to three significant figures.)

Strategy

To say we have a 12.0 V battery means that its terminals have a 12.0 V potential difference. When such a battery moves charge, it puts the charge through a potential difference of 12.0 V, and the charge is given a change in potential energy equal to $\Delta \text{PE} = q\Delta V$.

So to find the energy output, we multiply the charge moved by the potential difference.

Solution

For the motorcycle battery, $q = 5000\text{ C}$ and $\Delta V = 12.0\text{ V}$. The total energy delivered by the motorcycle battery is

$$\begin{aligned} \Delta \text{PE}_{\text{cycle}} &= (5000\text{ C})(12.0\text{ V}) \\ &= (5000\text{ C})(12.0\text{ J/C}) \\ &= 6.00\times10^4\text{ J}. \end{aligned} \tag{19.8}$$

Similarly, for the car battery, $q = 60{,}000\text{ C}$ and

$$\begin{aligned}\Delta PE_{car} &= (60{,}000\ C)(12.0\ V) \\ &= 7.20\times 10^{5}\ J.\end{aligned} \quad (19.9)$$

Discussion

While voltage and energy are related, they are not the same thing. The voltages of the batteries are identical, but the energy supplied by each is quite different. Note also that as a battery is discharged, some of its energy is used internally and its terminal voltage drops, such as when headlights dim because of a low car battery. The energy supplied by the battery is still calculated as in this example, but not all of the energy is available for external use.

Note that the energies calculated in the previous example are absolute values. The change in potential energy for the battery is negative, since it loses energy. These batteries, like many electrical systems, actually move negative charge—electrons in particular. The batteries repel electrons from their negative terminals (A) through whatever circuitry is involved and attract them to their positive terminals (B) as shown in Figure 19.3. The change in potential is $\Delta V = V_B - V_A = +12\ V$ and the charge q is negative, so that $\Delta PE = q\Delta V$ is negative, meaning the potential energy of the battery has decreased when q has moved from A to B.

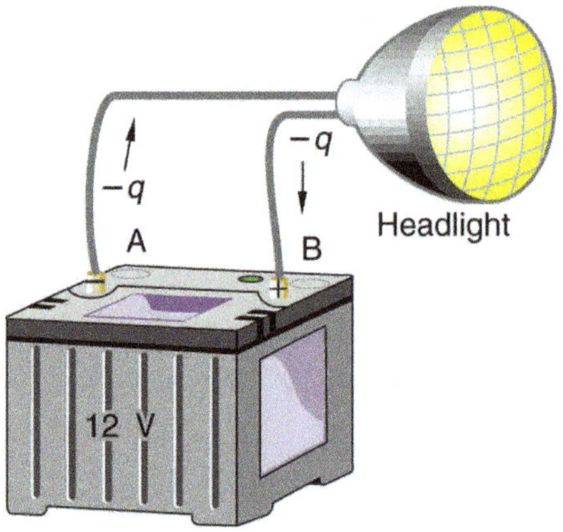

FIGURE 19.3 A battery moves negative charge from its negative terminal through a headlight to its positive terminal. Appropriate combinations of chemicals in the battery separate charges so that the negative terminal has an excess of negative charge, which is repelled by it and attracted to the excess positive charge on the other terminal. In terms of potential, the positive terminal is at a higher voltage than the negative. Inside the battery, both positive and negative charges move.

EXAMPLE 19.2

How Many Electrons Move through a Headlight Each Second?

When a 12.0 V car battery runs a single 30.0 W headlight, how many electrons pass through it each second?

Strategy

To find the number of electrons, we must first find the charge that moved in 1.00 s. The charge moved is related to voltage and energy through the equation $\Delta PE = q\Delta V$. A 30.0 W lamp uses 30.0 joules per second. Since the battery loses energy, we have $\Delta PE = -30.0\ J$ and, since the electrons are going from the negative terminal to the positive, we see that $\Delta V = +12.0\ V$.

Solution

To find the charge q moved, we solve the equation $\Delta PE = q\Delta V$:

$$q = \frac{\Delta PE}{\Delta V}. \quad (19.10)$$

Entering the values for ΔPE and ΔV, we get

$$q = \frac{-30.0\ J}{+12.0\ V} = \frac{-30.0\ J}{+12.0\ J/C} = -2.50\ C. \quad (19.11)$$

The number of electrons n_e is the total charge divided by the charge per electron. That is,

$$n_e = \frac{-2.50\text{ C}}{-1.60\times10^{-19}\text{ C/e}^-} = 1.56\times10^{19}\text{ electrons.} \quad (19.12)$$

Discussion

This is a very large number. It is no wonder that we do not ordinarily observe individual electrons with so many being present in ordinary systems. In fact, electricity had been in use for many decades before it was determined that the moving charges in many circumstances were negative. Positive charge moving in the opposite direction of negative charge often produces identical effects; this makes it difficult to determine which is moving or whether both are moving.

The Electron Volt

The energy per electron is very small in macroscopic situations like that in the previous example—a tiny fraction of a joule. But on a submicroscopic scale, such energy per particle (electron, proton, or ion) can be of great importance. For example, even a tiny fraction of a joule can be great enough for these particles to destroy organic molecules and harm living tissue. The particle may do its damage by direct collision, or it may create harmful x rays, which can also inflict damage. It is useful to have an energy unit related to submicroscopic effects. Figure 19.4 shows a situation related to the definition of such an energy unit. An electron is accelerated between two charged metal plates as it might be in an old-model television tube or oscilloscope. The electron is given kinetic energy that is later converted to another form—light in the television tube, for example. (Note that downhill for the electron is uphill for a positive charge.) Since energy is related to voltage by $\Delta\text{PE} = q\Delta V$, we can think of the joule as a coulomb-volt.

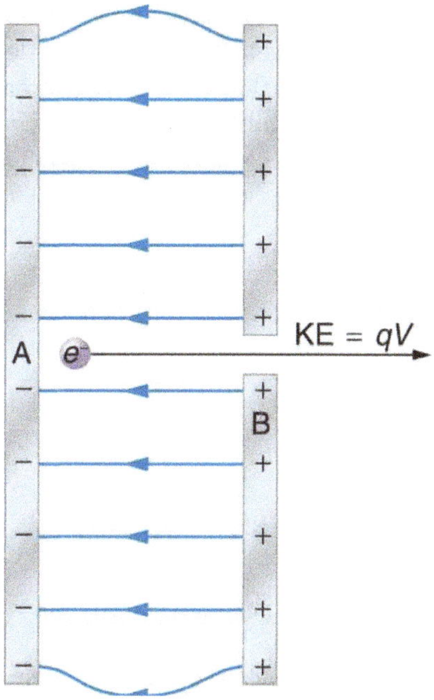

FIGURE 19.4 A typical electron gun accelerates electrons using a potential difference between two metal plates. The energy of the electron in electron volts is numerically the same as the voltage between the plates. For example, a 5000 V potential difference produces 5000 eV electrons.

On the submicroscopic scale, it is more convenient to define an energy unit called the **electron volt** (eV), which is the energy given to a fundamental charge accelerated through a potential difference of 1 V. In equation form,

$$\begin{aligned} 1\text{ eV} &= (1.60\times10^{-19}\text{ C})(1\text{ V})=\left(1.60\times10^{-19}\text{ C}\right)(1\text{ J/C}) \\ &= 1.60\times10^{-19}\text{ J.} \end{aligned} \quad (19.13)$$

ELECTRON VOLT

On the submicroscopic scale, it is more convenient to define an energy unit called the electron volt (eV), which is the energy given to a fundamental charge accelerated through a potential difference of 1 V. In equation form,

$$\begin{aligned} 1\text{ eV} &= \left(1.60 \times 10^{-19}\text{ C}\right)(1\text{ V}) = \left(1.60 \times 10^{-19}\text{ C}\right)(1\text{ J/C}) \\ &= 1.60 \times 10^{-19}\text{ J.} \end{aligned} \tag{19.14}$$

An electron accelerated through a potential difference of 1 V is given an energy of 1 eV. It follows that an electron accelerated through 50 V is given 50 eV. A potential difference of 100,000 V (100 kV) will give an electron an energy of 100,000 eV (100 keV), and so on. Similarly, an ion with a double positive charge accelerated through 100 V will be given 200 eV of energy. These simple relationships between accelerating voltage and particle charges make the electron volt a simple and convenient energy unit in such circumstances.

CONNECTIONS: ENERGY UNITS

The electron volt (eV) is the most common energy unit for submicroscopic processes. This will be particularly noticeable in the chapters on modern physics. Energy is so important to so many subjects that there is a tendency to define a special energy unit for each major topic. There are, for example, calories for food energy, kilowatt-hours for electrical energy, and therms for natural gas energy.

The electron volt is commonly employed in submicroscopic processes—chemical valence energies and molecular and nuclear binding energies are among the quantities often expressed in electron volts. For example, about 5 eV of energy is required to break up certain organic molecules. If a proton is accelerated from rest through a potential difference of 30 kV, it is given an energy of 30 keV (30,000 eV) and it can break up as many as 6000 of these molecules ($30{,}000\text{ eV} \div 5\text{ eV per molecule} = 6000\text{ molecules}$). Nuclear decay energies are on the order of 1 MeV (1,000,000 eV) per event and can, thus, produce significant biological damage.

Conservation of Energy

The total energy of a system is conserved if there is no net addition (or subtraction) of work or heat transfer. For conservative forces, such as the electrostatic force, conservation of energy states that mechanical energy is a constant.

Mechanical energy is the sum of the kinetic energy and potential energy of a system; that is, $\text{KE} + \text{PE} = \text{constant}$. A loss of PE of a charged particle becomes an increase in its KE. Here PE is the electric potential energy. Conservation of energy is stated in equation form as

$$\text{KE} + \text{PE} = \text{constant} \tag{19.15}$$

or

$$\text{KE}_\text{i} + \text{PE}_\text{i} = \text{KE}_\text{f} + \text{PE}_\text{f}, \tag{19.16}$$

where i and f stand for initial and final conditions. As we have found many times before, considering energy can give us insights and facilitate problem solving.

EXAMPLE 19.3

Electrical Potential Energy Converted to Kinetic Energy

Calculate the final speed of a free electron accelerated from rest through a potential difference of 100 V. (Assume that this numerical value is accurate to three significant figures.)

Strategy

We have a system with only conservative forces. Assuming the electron is accelerated in a vacuum, and neglecting the gravitational force (we will check on this assumption later), all of the electrical potential energy is converted into kinetic energy. We can identify the initial and final forms of energy to be
$\text{KE}_\text{i} = 0, \text{KE}_\text{f} = ½mv^2, \text{PE}_\text{i} = qV, \text{and PE}_\text{f} = 0.$

Solution

Conservation of energy states that

$$\text{KE}_\text{i} + \text{PE}_\text{i} = \text{KE}_\text{f} + \text{PE}_\text{f}. \quad (19.17)$$

Entering the forms identified above, we obtain

$$qV = \frac{mv^2}{2}. \quad (19.18)$$

We solve this for v:

$$v = \sqrt{\frac{2qV}{m}}. \quad (19.19)$$

Entering values for q, V, and m gives

$$\begin{aligned} v &= \sqrt{\frac{2\left(-1.60\times10^{-19}\text{ C}\right)(-100\text{ J/C})}{9.11\times10^{-31}\text{ kg}}} \\ &= 5.93\times10^6\text{ m/s}. \end{aligned} \quad (19.20)$$

Discussion

Note that both the charge and the initial voltage are negative, as in Figure 19.4. From the discussions in Electric Charge and Electric Field, we know that electrostatic forces on small particles are generally very large compared with the gravitational force. The large final speed confirms that the gravitational force is indeed negligible here. The large speed also indicates how easy it is to accelerate electrons with small voltages because of their very small mass. Voltages much higher than the 100 V in this problem are typically used in electron guns. Those higher voltages produce electron speeds so great that relativistic effects must be taken into account. That is why a low voltage is considered (accurately) in this example.

19.2 Electric Potential in a Uniform Electric Field

LEARNING OBJECTIVES

By the end of this section, you will be able to:

- Describe the relationship between voltage and electric field.
- Derive an expression for the electric potential and electric field.
- Calculate electric field strength given distance and voltage.

In the previous section, we explored the relationship between voltage and energy. In this section, we will explore the relationship between voltage and electric field. For example, a uniform electric field $\mathbf{E}$ is produced by placing a potential difference (or voltage) ΔV across two parallel metal plates, labeled A and B. (See Figure 19.5.) Examining this will tell us what voltage is needed to produce a certain electric field strength; it will also reveal a more fundamental relationship between electric potential and electric field. From a physicist's point of view, either ΔV or $\mathbf{E}$ can be used to describe any charge distribution. ΔV is most closely tied to energy, whereas $\mathbf{E}$ is most closely related to force. ΔV is a **scalar** quantity and has no direction, while $\mathbf{E}$ is a **vector** quantity, having both magnitude and direction. (Note that the magnitude of the electric field strength, a scalar quantity, is represented by E below.) The relationship between ΔV and $\mathbf{E}$ is revealed by calculating the work done by the force in moving a charge from point A to point B. But, as noted in Electric Potential Energy: Potential Difference, this is complex for arbitrary charge distributions, requiring calculus. We therefore look at a uniform electric field as an interesting special case.

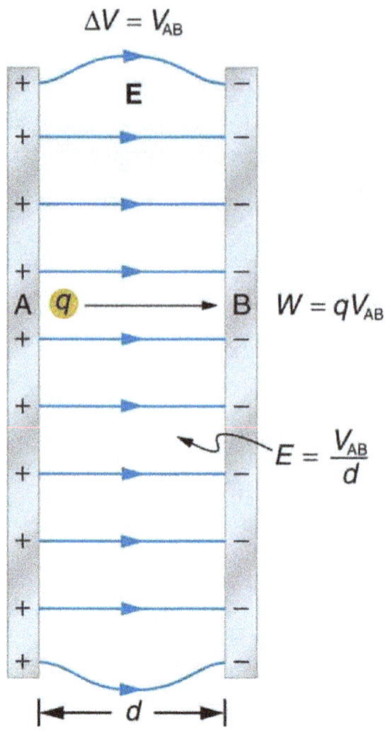

FIGURE 19.5 The relationship between V and E for parallel conducting plates is $E = V/d$. (Note that $\Delta V = V_{\text{AB}}$ in magnitude. For a charge that is moved from plate A at higher potential to plate B at lower potential, a minus sign needs to be included as follows: $-\Delta V = V_{\text{A}} - V_{\text{B}} = V_{\text{AB}}$. See the text for details.)

The work done by the electric field in Figure 19.5 to move a positive charge q from A, the positive plate, higher potential, to B, the negative plate, lower potential, is

$$W = -\Delta\text{PE} = -q\Delta V. \tag{19.21}$$

The potential difference between points A and B is

$$-\Delta V = -(V_{\text{B}} - V_{\text{A}}) = V_{\text{A}} - V_{\text{B}} = V_{\text{AB}}. \tag{19.22}$$

Entering this into the expression for work yields

$$W = qV_{\text{AB}}. \tag{19.23}$$

Work is $W = Fd\cos\theta$; here $\cos\theta = 1$, since the path is parallel to the field, and so $W = Fd$. Since $F = qE$, we see that $W = qEd$. Substituting this expression for work into the previous equation gives

$$qEd = qV_{\text{AB}}. \tag{19.24}$$

The charge cancels, and so the voltage between points A and B is seen to be

$$\left.\begin{aligned} V_{\text{AB}} &= Ed \\ E &= \frac{V_{\text{AB}}}{d} \end{aligned}\right\}\text{(uniform } E\text{ - field only)}, \tag{19.25}$$

where d is the distance from A to B, or the distance between the plates in Figure 19.5. Note that the above equation implies the units for electric field are volts per meter. We already know the units for electric field are newtons per coulomb; thus the following relation among units is valid:

$$1\text{ N/C} = 1\text{ V/m}. \tag{19.26}$$

VOLTAGE BETWEEN POINTS A AND B

$$\left.\begin{aligned} V_{\text{AB}} &= Ed \\ E &= \frac{V_{\text{AB}}}{d} \end{aligned}\right\}\text{(uniform } E\text{ - field only)}, \tag{19.27}$$

where d is the distance from A to B, or the distance between the plates.

EXAMPLE 19.4

What Is the Highest Voltage Possible between Two Plates?

Dry air will support a maximum electric field strength of about 3.0×10^6 V/m. Above that value, the field creates enough ionization in the air to make the air a conductor. This allows a discharge or spark that reduces the field. What, then, is the maximum voltage between two parallel conducting plates separated by 2.5 cm of dry air?

Strategy

We are given the maximum electric field E between the plates and the distance d between them. The equation $V_{AB} = Ed$ can thus be used to calculate the maximum voltage.

Solution

The potential difference or voltage between the plates is

$$V_{AB} = Ed. \quad (19.28)$$

Entering the given values for E and d gives

$$V_{AB} = (3.0 \times 10^6 \text{ V/m})(0.025 \text{ m}) = 7.5 \times 10^4 \text{ V} \quad (19.29)$$

or

$$V_{AB} = 75 \text{ kV}. \quad (19.30)$$

(The answer is quoted to only two digits, since the maximum field strength is approximate.)

Discussion

One of the implications of this result is that it takes about 75 kV to make a spark jump across a 2.5 cm (1 in.) gap, or 150 kV for a 5 cm spark. This limits the voltages that can exist between conductors, perhaps on a power transmission line. A smaller voltage will cause a spark if there are points on the surface, since points create greater fields than smooth surfaces. Humid air breaks down at a lower field strength, meaning that a smaller voltage will make a spark jump through humid air. The largest voltages can be built up, say with static electricity, on dry days.

FIGURE 19.6 A spark chamber is used to trace the paths of high-energy particles. Ionization created by the particles as they pass through the gas between the plates allows a spark to jump. The sparks are perpendicular to the plates, following electric field lines between them. The potential difference between adjacent plates is not high enough to cause sparks without the ionization produced by particles from accelerator experiments (or cosmic rays). (credit: Daderot, Wikimedia Commons)

EXAMPLE 19.5

Field and Force inside an Electron Gun

(a) An electron gun has parallel plates separated by 4.00 cm and gives electrons 25.0 keV of energy. What is the electric field strength between the plates? (b) What force would this field exert on a piece of plastic with a $0.500\ \mu\text{C}$ charge that gets between the plates?

Strategy

Since the voltage and plate separation are given, the electric field strength can be calculated directly from the expression $E = \frac{V_{\text{AB}}}{d}$. Once the electric field strength is known, the force on a charge is found using $\mathbf{F} = q\,\mathbf{E}$. Since the electric field is in only one direction, we can write this equation in terms of the magnitudes, $F = q\,E$.

Solution for (a)

The expression for the magnitude of the electric field between two uniform metal plates is

$$E = \frac{V_{\text{AB}}}{d}. \tag{19.31}$$

Since the electron is a single charge and is given 25.0 keV of energy, the potential difference must be 25.0 kV. Entering this value for V_{AB} and the plate separation of 0.0400 m, we obtain

$$E = \frac{25.0\text{ kV}}{0.0400\text{ m}} = 6.25 \times 10^5\text{ V/m}. \tag{19.32}$$

Solution for (b)

The magnitude of the force on a charge in an electric field is obtained from the equation

$$F = qE. \tag{19.33}$$

Substituting known values gives

$$F = (0.500 \times 10^{-6}\text{ C})(6.25 \times 10^5\text{ V/m}) = 0.313\text{ N}. \tag{19.34}$$

Discussion

Note that the units are newtons, since $1\text{ V/m} = 1\text{ N/C}$. The force on the charge is the same no matter where the charge is located between the plates. This is because the electric field is uniform between the plates.

In more general situations, regardless of whether the electric field is uniform, it points in the direction of decreasing potential, because the force on a positive charge is in the direction of $\mathbf{E}$ and also in the direction of lower potential V. Furthermore, the magnitude of $\mathbf{E}$ equals the rate of decrease of V with distance. The faster V decreases over distance, the greater the electric field. In equation form, the general relationship between voltage and electric field is

$$E = -\frac{\Delta V}{\Delta s}, \tag{19.35}$$

where Δs is the distance over which the change in potential, ΔV, takes place. The minus sign tells us that $\mathbf{E}$ points in the direction of decreasing potential. The electric field is said to be the *gradient* (as in grade or slope) of the electric potential.

RELATIONSHIP BETWEEN VOLTAGE AND ELECTRIC FIELD

In equation form, the general relationship between voltage and electric field is

$$E = -\frac{\Delta V}{\Delta s}, \quad (19.36)$$

where Δs is the distance over which the change in potential, ΔV, takes place. The minus sign tells us that $\mathbf{E}$ points in the direction of decreasing potential. The electric field is said to be the *gradient* (as in grade or slope) of the electric potential.

For continually changing potentials, ΔV and Δs become infinitesimals and differential calculus must be employed to determine the electric field.

19.3 Electrical Potential Due to a Point Charge

LEARNING OBJECTIVES

By the end of this section, you will be able to:

- Explain point charges and express the equation for electric potential of a point charge.
- Distinguish between electric potential and electric field.
- Determine the electric potential of a point charge given charge and distance.

Point charges, such as electrons, are among the fundamental building blocks of matter. Furthermore, spherical charge distributions (like on a metal sphere) create external electric fields exactly like a point charge. The electric potential due to a point charge is, thus, a case we need to consider. Using calculus to find the work needed to move a test charge q from a large distance away to a distance of r from a point charge Q, and noting the connection between work and potential $(W = -q\Delta V)$, it can be shown that the *electric potential V of a point charge* is

$$V = \frac{kQ}{r} \text{ (Point Charge)}, \quad (19.37)$$

where k is a constant equal to $9.0 \times 10^9 \text{ N} \cdot \text{m}^2/\text{C}^2$.

ELECTRIC POTENTIAL V OF A POINT CHARGE

The electric potential V of a point charge is given by

$$V = \frac{kQ}{r} \text{ (Point Charge)}. \quad (19.38)$$

The potential at infinity is chosen to be zero. Thus V for a point charge decreases with distance, whereas $\mathbf{E}$ for a point charge decreases with distance squared:

$$E = \frac{F}{q} = \frac{kQ}{r^2}. \quad (19.39)$$

Recall that the electric potential V is a scalar and has no direction, whereas the electric field $\mathbf{E}$ is a vector. To find the voltage due to a combination of point charges, you add the individual voltages as numbers. To find the total electric field, you must add the individual fields as *vectors*, taking magnitude and direction into account. This is consistent with the fact that V is closely associated with energy, a scalar, whereas $\mathbf{E}$ is closely associated with force, a vector.

EXAMPLE 19.6

What Voltage Is Produced by a Small Charge on a Metal Sphere?

Charges in static electricity are typically in the nanocoulomb (nC) to microcoulomb (μC) range. What is the voltage 5.00 cm away from the center of a 1-cm diameter metal sphere that has a -3.00 nC static charge?

Strategy

As we have discussed in Electric Charge and Electric Field, charge on a metal sphere spreads out uniformly and produces a field like that of a point charge located at its center. Thus we can find the voltage using the equation $V = kQ/r$.

Solution

Entering known values into the expression for the potential of a point charge, we obtain

$$\begin{aligned} V &= k\frac{Q}{r} \\ &= \left(8.99 \times 10^9 \text{ N} \cdot \text{m}^2/\text{C}^2\right)\left(\frac{-3.00\times10^{-9} \text{ C}}{5.00\times10^{-2} \text{ m}}\right) \\ &= -539 \text{ V}. \end{aligned} \quad 19.40$$

Discussion

The negative value for voltage means a positive charge would be attracted from a larger distance, since the potential is lower (more negative) than at larger distances. Conversely, a negative charge would be repelled, as expected.

EXAMPLE 19.7

What Is the Excess Charge on a Van de Graaff Generator

A demonstration Van de Graaff generator has a 25.0 cm diameter metal sphere that produces a voltage of 100 kV near its surface. (See Figure 19.7.) What excess charge resides on the sphere? (Assume that each numerical value here is shown with three significant figures.)

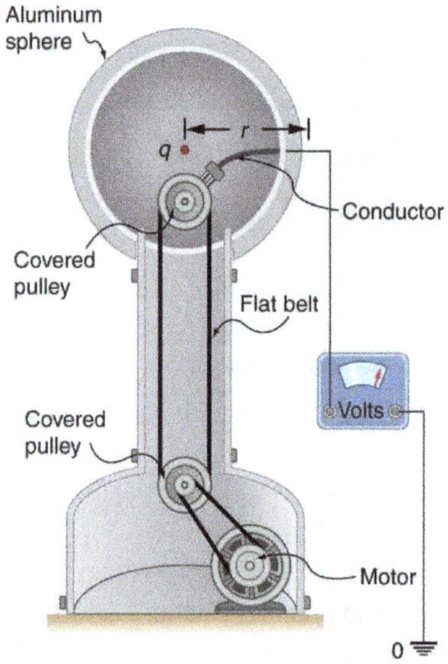

FIGURE 19.7 The voltage of this demonstration Van de Graaff generator is measured between the charged sphere and ground. Earth's potential is taken to be zero as a reference. The potential of the charged conducting sphere is the same as that of an equal point charge at its center.

Strategy

The potential on the surface will be the same as that of a point charge at the center of the sphere, 12.5 cm away. (The radius of the sphere is 12.5 cm.) We can thus determine the excess charge using the equation

$$V = \frac{kQ}{r}. \quad 19.41$$

Solution

Solving for Q and entering known values gives

$$\begin{aligned} Q &= \frac{rV}{k} \\ &= \frac{(0.125\text{ m})\left(100\times 10^3\text{ V}\right)}{8.99\times 10^9\text{ N}\cdot\text{m}^2/\text{C}^2} \\ &= 1.39\times 10^{-6}\text{ C} = 1.39\ \mu\text{C}. \end{aligned} \tag{19.42}$$

Discussion

This is a relatively small charge, but it produces a rather large voltage. We have another indication here that it is difficult to store isolated charges.

The voltages in both of these examples could be measured with a meter that compares the measured potential with ground potential. Ground potential is often taken to be zero (instead of taking the potential at infinity to be zero). It is the potential difference between two points that is of importance, and very often there is a tacit assumption that some reference point, such as Earth or a very distant point, is at zero potential. As noted in Electric Potential Energy: Potential Difference, this is analogous to taking sea level as $h = 0$ when considering gravitational potential energy, $\text{PE}_\text{g} = mgh$.

19.4 Equipotential Lines

LEARNING OBJECTIVES

By the end of this section, you will be able to:

- Explain equipotential lines and equipotential surfaces.
- Describe the action of grounding an electrical appliance.
- Compare electric field and equipotential lines.

We can represent electric potentials (voltages) pictorially, just as we drew pictures to illustrate electric fields. Of course, the two are related. Consider Figure 19.8, which shows an isolated positive point charge and its electric field lines. Electric field lines radiate out from a positive charge and terminate on negative charges. While we use blue arrows to represent the magnitude and direction of the electric field, we use green lines to represent places where the electric potential is constant. These are called **equipotential lines** in two dimensions, or *equipotential surfaces* in three dimensions. The term *equipotential* is also used as a noun, referring to an equipotential line or surface. The potential for a point charge is the same anywhere on an imaginary sphere of radius r surrounding the charge. This is true since the potential for a point charge is given by $V = kQ/r$ and, thus, has the same value at any point that is a given distance r from the charge. An equipotential sphere is a circle in the two-dimensional view of Figure 19.8. Since the electric field lines point radially away from the charge, they are perpendicular to the equipotential lines.

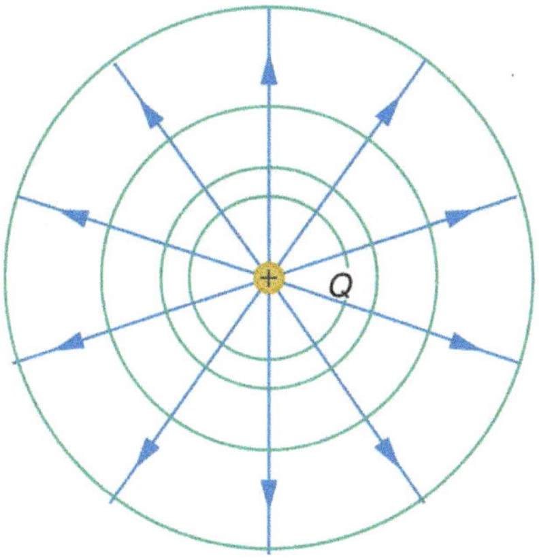

FIGURE 19.8 An isolated point charge Q with its electric field lines in blue and equipotential lines in green. The potential is the same along each equipotential line, meaning that no work is required to move a charge anywhere along one of those lines. Work is needed to move a charge from one equipotential line to another. Equipotential lines are perpendicular to electric field lines in every case.

It is important to note that *equipotential lines are always perpendicular to electric field lines.* No work is required to move a charge along an equipotential, since $\Delta V = 0$. Thus the work is

$$W = -\Delta \text{PE} = -q\Delta V = 0. \quad (19.43)$$

Work is zero if force is perpendicular to motion. Force is in the same direction as $\mathbf{E}$, so that motion along an equipotential must be perpendicular to $\mathbf{E}$. More precisely, work is related to the electric field by

$$W = Fd \cos \theta = qEd \cos \theta = 0. \quad (19.44)$$

Note that in the above equation, E and F symbolize the magnitudes of the electric field strength and force, respectively. Neither q nor $\mathbf{E}$ nor d is zero, and so $\cos \theta$ must be 0, meaning θ must be 90°. In other words, motion along an equipotential is perpendicular to $\mathbf{E}$.

One of the rules for static electric fields and conductors is that the electric field must be perpendicular to the surface of any conductor. This implies that a *conductor is an equipotential surface in static situations*. There can be no voltage difference across the surface of a conductor, or charges will flow. One of the uses of this fact is that a conductor can be fixed at zero volts by connecting it to the earth with a good conductor—a process called **grounding**. Grounding can be a useful safety tool. For example, grounding the metal case of an electrical appliance ensures that it is at zero volts relative to the earth.

GROUNDING

A conductor can be fixed at zero volts by connecting it to the earth with a good conductor—a process called grounding.

Because a conductor is an equipotential, it can replace any equipotential surface. For example, in Figure 19.8 a charged spherical conductor can replace the point charge, and the electric field and potential surfaces outside of it will be unchanged, confirming the contention that a spherical charge distribution is equivalent to a point charge at its center.

Figure 19.9 shows the electric field and equipotential lines for two equal and opposite charges. Given the electric field lines, the equipotential lines can be drawn simply by making them perpendicular to the electric field lines. Conversely, given the equipotential lines, as in Figure 19.10(a), the electric field lines can be drawn by making them perpendicular to the equipotentials, as in Figure 19.10(b).

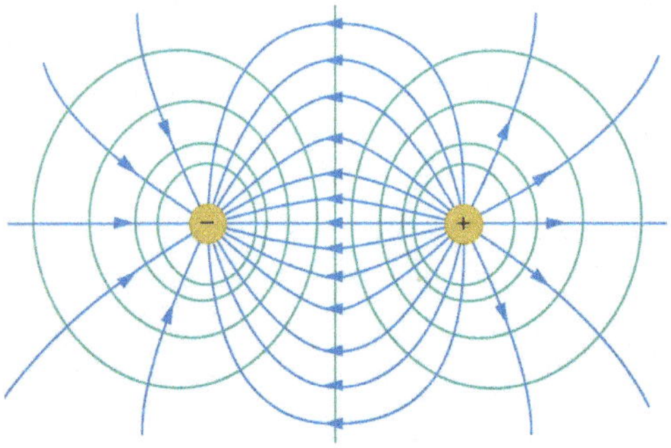

FIGURE 19.9 The electric field lines and equipotential lines for two equal but opposite charges. The equipotential lines can be drawn by making them perpendicular to the electric field lines, if those are known. Note that the potential is greatest (most positive) near the positive charge and least (most negative) near the negative charge.

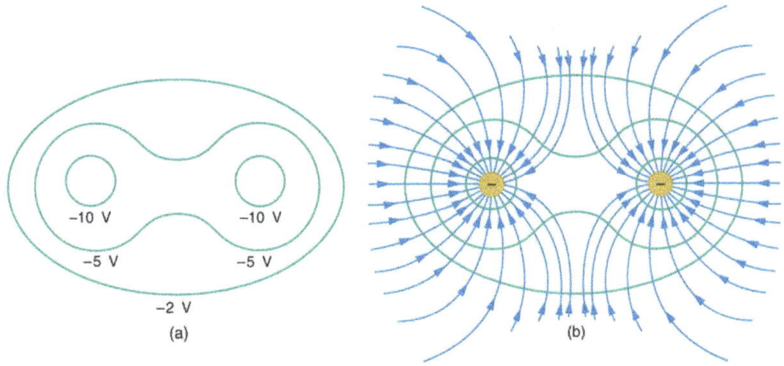

FIGURE 19.10 (a) These equipotential lines might be measured with a voltmeter in a laboratory experiment. (b) The corresponding electric field lines are found by drawing them perpendicular to the equipotentials. Note that these fields are consistent with two equal negative charges.

One of the most important cases is that of the familiar parallel conducting plates shown in Figure 19.11. Between the plates, the equipotentials are evenly spaced and parallel. The same field could be maintained by placing conducting plates at the equipotential lines at the potentials shown.

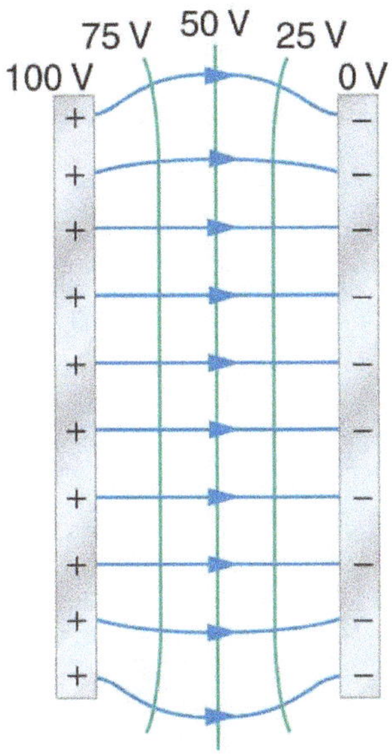

FIGURE 19.11 The electric field and equipotential lines between two metal plates.

An important application of electric fields and equipotential lines involves the heart. The heart relies on electrical signals to maintain its rhythm. The movement of electrical signals causes the chambers of the heart to contract and relax. When a person has a heart attack, the movement of these electrical signals may be disturbed. An artificial pacemaker and a defibrillator can be used to initiate the rhythm of electrical signals. The equipotential lines around the heart, the thoracic region, and the axis of the heart are useful ways of monitoring the structure and functions of the heart. An electrocardiogram (ECG) measures the small electric signals being generated during the activity of the heart. More about the relationship between electric fields and the heart is discussed in Energy Stored in Capacitors.

PHET EXPLORATIONS

Charges and Fields

Move point charges around on the playing field and then view the electric field, voltages, equipotential lines, and more. It's colorful, it's dynamic, it's free.

Click to view content (https://openstax.org/books/college-physics-ap-courses-2e/pages/19-4-equipotential-lines)

19.5 Capacitors and Dielectrics

LEARNING OBJECTIVES

By the end of this section, you will be able to:

- Describe the action of a capacitor and define capacitance.
- Explain parallel plate capacitors and their capacitances.
- Discuss the process of increasing the capacitance of a dielectric.
- Determine capacitance given charge and voltage.

A **capacitor** is a device used to store electric charge. Capacitors have applications ranging from filtering static out of radio reception to energy storage in heart defibrillators. Typically, commercial capacitors have two conducting parts close to one another, but not touching, such as those in Figure 19.12. (Most of the time an insulator is used between the two plates to provide separation—see the discussion on dielectrics below.) When battery terminals are connected to an initially uncharged capacitor, equal amounts of positive and negative charge, $+Q$ and $-Q$, are separated into its two plates. The capacitor remains neutral overall, but we refer to it as storing a charge Q in this circumstance.

CAPACITOR

A capacitor is a device used to store electric charge.

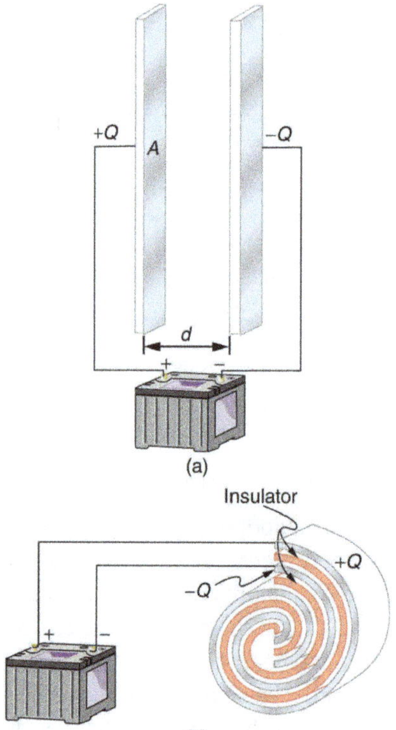

FIGURE 19.12 Both capacitors shown here were initially uncharged before being connected to a battery. They now have separated charges of $+Q$ and $-Q$ on their two halves. (a) A parallel plate capacitor. (b) A rolled capacitor with an insulating material between its two conducting sheets.

The amount of charge Q a *capacitor* can store depends on two major factors—the voltage applied and the capacitor's physical characteristics, such as its size.

THE AMOUNT OF CHARGE Q A CAPACITOR CAN STORE

The amount of charge Q a *capacitor* can store depends on two major factors—the voltage applied and the capacitor's physical characteristics, such as its size.

A system composed of two identical, parallel conducting plates separated by a distance, as in Figure 19.13, is called a **parallel plate capacitor**. It is easy to see the relationship between the voltage and the stored charge for a parallel plate capacitor, as shown in Figure 19.13. Each electric field line starts on an individual positive charge and ends on a negative one, so that there will be more field lines if there is more charge. (Drawing a single field line per charge is a convenience, only. We can draw many field lines for each charge, but the total number is proportional to the number of charges.) The electric field strength is, thus, directly proportional to Q.

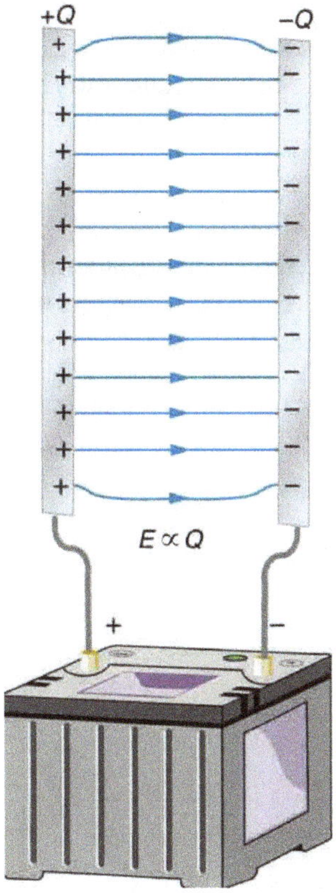

FIGURE 19.13 Electric field lines in this parallel plate capacitor, as always, start on positive charges and end on negative charges. Since the electric field strength is proportional to the density of field lines, it is also proportional to the amount of charge on the capacitor.

The field is proportional to the charge:

$$E \propto Q, \tag{19.45}$$

where the symbol $\propto$ means "proportional to." From the discussion in Electric Potential in a Uniform Electric Field, we know that the voltage across parallel plates is $V = Ed$. Thus,

$$V \propto E. \tag{19.46}$$

It follows, then, that $V \propto Q$, and conversely,

$$Q \propto V. \tag{19.47}$$

This is true in general: The greater the voltage applied to any capacitor, the greater the charge stored in it.

Different capacitors will store different amounts of charge for the same applied voltage, depending on their physical characteristics. We define their **capacitance** C to be such that the charge Q stored in a capacitor is proportional to C. The charge stored in a capacitor is given by

$$Q = CV. \tag{19.48}$$

This equation expresses the two major factors affecting the amount of charge stored. Those factors are the physical characteristics of the capacitor, C, and the voltage, V. Rearranging the equation, we see that *capacitance* C *is the amount of charge stored per volt,* or

$$C = \frac{Q}{V}. \tag{19.49}$$

CAPACITANCE

Capacitance C is the amount of charge stored per volt, or

$$C = \frac{Q}{V}. \tag{19.50}$$

The unit of capacitance is the farad (F), named for Michael Faraday (1791–1867), an English scientist who contributed to the fields of electromagnetism and electrochemistry. Since capacitance is charge per unit voltage, we see that a farad is a coulomb per volt, or

$$1\ \text{F} = \frac{1\ \text{C}}{1\ \text{V}}. \tag{19.51}$$

A 1-farad capacitor would be able to store 1 coulomb (a very large amount of charge) with the application of only 1 volt. One farad is, thus, a very large capacitance. Typical capacitors range from fractions of a picofarad $\left(1\ \text{pF} = 10^{-12}\ \text{F}\right)$ to millifarads $\left(1\ \text{mF} = 10^{-3}\ \text{F}\right)$.

Figure 19.14 shows some common capacitors. Capacitors are primarily made of ceramic, glass, or plastic, depending upon purpose and size. Insulating materials, called dielectrics, are commonly used in their construction, as discussed below.

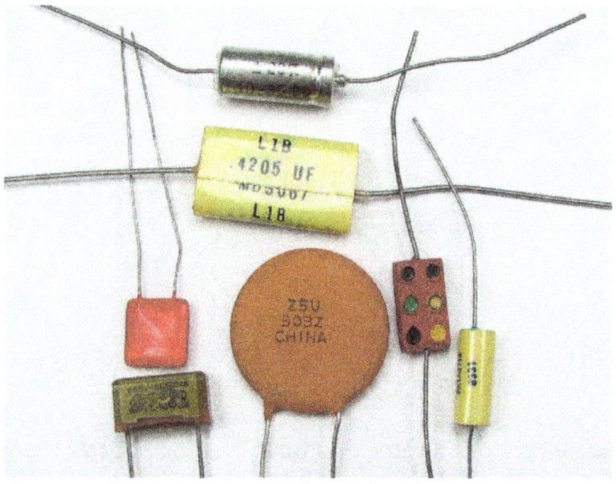

FIGURE 19.14 Some typical capacitors. Size and value of capacitance are not necessarily related. (credit: Windell Oskay)

Parallel Plate Capacitor

The parallel plate capacitor shown in Figure 19.15 has two identical conducting plates, each having a surface area A, separated by a distance d (with no material between the plates). When a voltage V is applied to the capacitor, it stores a charge Q, as shown. We can see how its capacitance depends on A and d by considering the characteristics of the Coulomb force. We know that like charges repel, unlike charges attract, and the force between charges decreases with distance. So it seems quite reasonable that the bigger the plates are, the more charge they can store—because the charges can spread out more. Thus C should be greater for larger A. Similarly, the closer the plates are together, the greater the attraction of the opposite charges on them. So C should be greater for smaller d.

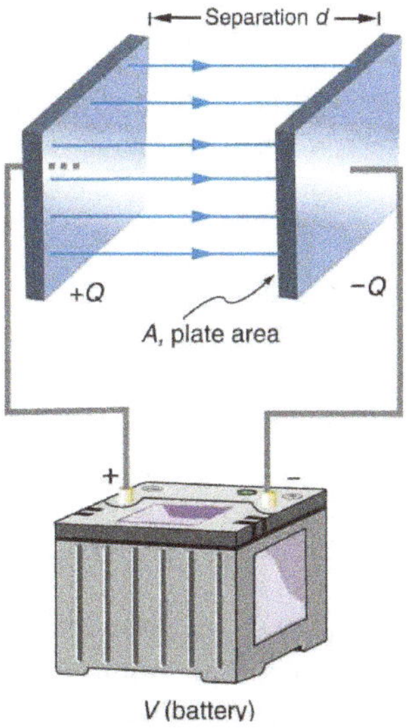

FIGURE 19.15 Parallel plate capacitor with plates separated by a distance d. Each plate has an area A.

It can be shown that for a parallel plate capacitor there are only two factors (A and d) that affect its capacitance C. The capacitance of a parallel plate capacitor in equation form is given by

$$C = \varepsilon_0 \frac{A}{d}. \tag{19.52}$$

CAPACITANCE OF A PARALLEL PLATE CAPACITOR

$$C = \varepsilon_0 \frac{A}{d} \tag{19.53}$$

A is the area of one plate in square meters, and d is the distance between the plates in meters. The constant ε_0 is the permittivity of free space; its numerical value in SI units is $\varepsilon_0 = 8.85 \times 10^{-12}\ \text{F/m}$. The units of F/m are equivalent to $\text{C}^2/\text{N} \cdot \text{m}^2$. The small numerical value of ε_0 is related to the large size of the farad. A parallel plate capacitor must have a large area to have a capacitance approaching a farad. (Note that the above equation is valid when the parallel plates are separated by air or free space. When another material is placed between the plates, the equation is modified, as discussed below.)

EXAMPLE 19.8

Capacitance and Charge Stored in a Parallel Plate Capacitor

(a) What is the capacitance of a parallel plate capacitor with metal plates, each of area $1.00\ \text{m}^2$, separated by 1.00 mm? (b) What charge is stored in this capacitor if a voltage of $3.00 \times 10^3\ \text{V}$ is applied to it?

Strategy

Finding the capacitance C is a straightforward application of the equation $C = \varepsilon_0 A/d$. Once C is found, the charge stored can be found using the equation $Q = CV$.

Solution for (a)

Entering the given values into the equation for the capacitance of a parallel plate capacitor yields

$$\begin{aligned} C &= \varepsilon_0 \frac{A}{d} = \left(8.85 \times 10^{-12}\ \frac{\text{F}}{\text{m}}\right) \frac{1.00\ \text{m}^2}{1.00 \times 10^{-3}\ \text{m}} \\ &= 8.85 \times 10^{-9}\ \text{F} = 8.85\ \text{nF}. \end{aligned} \tag{19.54}$$

Discussion for (a)

This small value for the capacitance indicates how difficult it is to make a device with a large capacitance. Special techniques help, such as using very large area thin foils placed close together.

Solution for (b)

The charge stored in any capacitor is given by the equation $Q = CV$. Entering the known values into this equation gives

$$\begin{aligned} Q &= CV = (8.85 \times 10^{-9}\ \text{F})\left(3.00 \times 10^{3}\ \text{V}\right) \\ &= 26.6\ \mu\text{C}. \end{aligned} \tag{19.55}$$

Discussion for (b)

This charge is only slightly greater than those found in typical static electricity. Since air breaks down at about $3.00 \times 10^6\ \text{V/m}$, more charge cannot be stored on this capacitor by increasing the voltage.

Another interesting biological example dealing with electric potential is found in the cell's plasma membrane. The membrane sets a cell off from its surroundings and also allows ions to selectively pass in and out of the cell. There is a potential difference across the membrane of about $-70\ \text{mV}$. This is due to the mainly negatively charged ions in the cell and the predominance of positively charged sodium (Na^+) ions outside. Things change when a nerve cell is stimulated. Na^+ ions are allowed to pass through the membrane into the cell, producing a positive membrane potential—the nerve signal. The cell membrane is about 7 to 10 nm thick. An approximate value of the electric field across it is given by

$$E = \frac{V}{d} = \frac{-70 \times 10^{-3}\ \text{V}}{8 \times 10^{-9}\ \text{m}} = -9 \times 10^{6}\ \text{V/m}. \tag{19.56}$$

This electric field is enough to cause a breakdown in air.

Dielectric

The previous example highlights the difficulty of storing a large amount of charge in capacitors. If d is made smaller to produce a larger capacitance, then the maximum voltage must be reduced proportionally to avoid breakdown (since $E = V/d$). An important solution to this difficulty is to put an insulating material, called a **dielectric**, between the plates of a capacitor and allow d to be as small as possible. Not only does the smaller d make the capacitance greater, but many insulators can withstand greater electric fields than air before breaking down.

There is another benefit to using a dielectric in a capacitor. Depending on the material used, the capacitance is greater than that given by the equation $C = \varepsilon_0 \frac{A}{d}$ by a factor κ, called the *dielectric constant*. A parallel plate capacitor with a dielectric between its plates has a capacitance given by

$$C = \kappa\varepsilon_0 \frac{A}{d}\ \text{(parallel plate capacitor with dielectric).} \tag{19.57}$$

Values of the dielectric constant κ for various materials are given in Table 19.1. Note that κ for vacuum is exactly 1, and so the above equation is valid in that case, too. If a dielectric is used, perhaps by placing Teflon between the plates of the capacitor in Example 19.8, then the capacitance is greater by the factor κ, which for Teflon is 2.1.

TAKE-HOME EXPERIMENT: BUILDING A CAPACITOR

How large a capacitor can you make using a chewing gum wrapper? The plates will be the aluminum foil, and the separation (dielectric) in between will be the paper.

Material	Dielectric constant κ	Dielectric strength (V/m)
Vacuum	1.00000	–
Air	1.00059	3×10^6
Bakelite	4.9	24×10^6
Fused quartz	3.78	8×10^6
Neoprene rubber	6.7	12×10^6
Nylon	3.4	14×10^6
Paper	3.7	16×10^6
Polystyrene	2.56	24×10^6
Pyrex glass	5.6	14×10^6
Silicon oil	2.5	15×10^6
Strontium titanate	233	8×10^6
Teflon	2.1	60×10^6
Water	80	–

TABLE 19.1 Dielectric Constants and Dielectric Strengths for Various Materials at 20°C

Note also that the dielectric constant for air is very close to 1, so that air-filled capacitors act much like those with vacuum between their plates *except* that the air can become conductive if the electric field strength becomes too great. (Recall that $E = V/d$ for a parallel plate capacitor.) Also shown in Table 19.1 are maximum electric field strengths in V/m, called **dielectric strengths**, for several materials. These are the fields above which the material begins to break down and conduct. The dielectric strength imposes a limit on the voltage that can be applied for a given plate separation. For instance, in Example 19.8, the separation is 1.00 mm, and so the voltage limit for air is

$$\begin{aligned} V &= E \cdot d \\ &= (3 \times 10^6 \text{ V/m})(1.00 \times 10^{-3} \text{ m}) \\ &= 3000 \text{ V}. \end{aligned} \tag{19.58}$$

However, the limit for a 1.00 mm separation filled with Teflon is 60,000 V, since the dielectric strength of Teflon is 60×10^6 V/m. So the same capacitor filled with Teflon has a greater capacitance and can be subjected to a much greater voltage. Using the capacitance we calculated in the above example for the air-filled parallel plate capacitor, we find that the Teflon-filled capacitor can store a maximum charge of

$$\begin{aligned} Q &= CV \\ &= \kappa C_{\text{air}} V \\ &= (2.1)(8.85 \text{ nF})(6.0 \times 10^4 \text{ V}) \\ &= 1.1 \text{ mC}. \end{aligned} \tag{19.59}$$

This is 42 times the charge of the same air-filled capacitor.

DIELECTRIC STRENGTH

The maximum electric field strength above which an insulating material begins to break down and conduct is called its dielectric strength.

Microscopically, how does a dielectric increase capacitance? Polarization of the insulator is responsible. The more easily it is polarized, the greater its dielectric constant κ. Water, for example, is a **polar molecule** because one end of the molecule has a slight positive charge and the other end has a slight negative charge. The polarity of water causes it to have a relatively large dielectric constant of 80. The effect of polarization can be best explained in terms of the characteristics of the Coulomb force. Figure 19.16 shows the separation of charge schematically in the molecules of a dielectric material placed between the charged plates of a capacitor. The Coulomb force between the closest ends of the molecules and the charge on the plates is attractive and very strong, since they are very close together. This attracts more charge onto the plates than if the space were empty and the opposite charges were a distance d away.

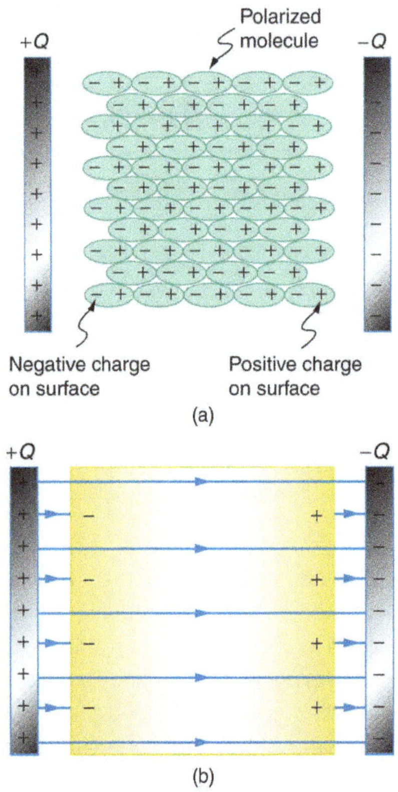

FIGURE 19.16 (a) The molecules in the insulating material between the plates of a capacitor are polarized by the charged plates. This produces a layer of opposite charge on the surface of the dielectric that attracts more charge onto the plate, increasing its capacitance. (b) The dielectric reduces the electric field strength inside the capacitor, resulting in a smaller voltage between the plates for the same charge. The capacitor stores the same charge for a smaller voltage, implying that it has a larger capacitance because of the dielectric.

Another way to understand how a dielectric increases capacitance is to consider its effect on the electric field inside the capacitor. Figure 19.16(b) shows the electric field lines with a dielectric in place. Since the field lines end on charges in the dielectric, there are fewer of them going from one side of the capacitor to the other. So the electric field strength is less than if there were a vacuum between the plates, even though the same charge is on the plates. The voltage between the plates is $V = Ed$, so it too is reduced by the dielectric. Thus there is a smaller voltage V for the same charge Q; since $C = Q/V$, the capacitance C is greater.

The dielectric constant is generally defined to be $\kappa = E_0/E$, or the ratio of the electric field in a vacuum to that in the dielectric material, and is intimately related to the polarizability of the material.

THINGS GREAT AND SMALL

The Submicroscopic Origin of Polarization

Polarization is a separation of charge within an atom or molecule. As has been noted, the planetary model of the atom pictures it as having a positive nucleus orbited by negative electrons, analogous to the planets orbiting the Sun. Although this model is not completely accurate, it is very helpful in explaining a vast range of phenomena and will be refined elsewhere, such as in Atomic Physics. The submicroscopic origin of polarization can be modeled as shown in Figure 19.17.

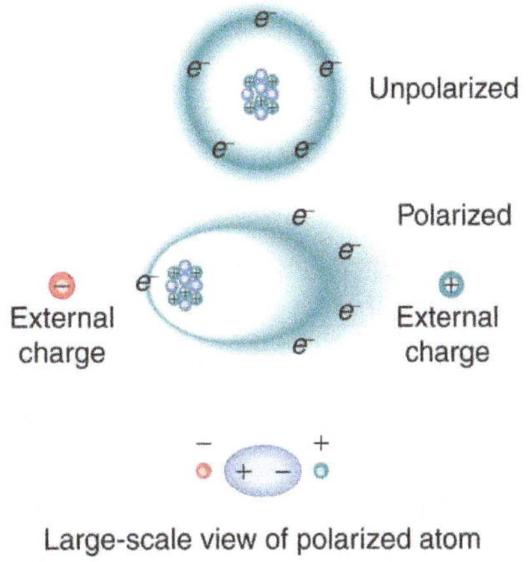

FIGURE 19.17 Artist's conception of a polarized atom. The orbits of electrons around the nucleus are shifted slightly by the external charges (shown exaggerated). The resulting separation of charge within the atom means that it is polarized. Note that the unlike charge is now closer to the external charges, causing the polarization.

We will find in Atomic Physics that the orbits of electrons are more properly viewed as electron clouds with the density of the cloud related to the probability of finding an electron in that location (as opposed to the definite locations and paths of planets in their orbits around the Sun). This cloud is shifted by the Coulomb force so that the atom on average has a separation of charge. Although the atom remains neutral, it can now be the source of a Coulomb force, since a charge brought near the atom will be closer to one type of charge than the other.

Some molecules, such as those of water, have an inherent separation of charge and are thus called polar molecules. Figure 19.18 illustrates the separation of charge in a water molecule, which has two hydrogen atoms and one oxygen atom (H_2O). The water molecule is not symmetric—the hydrogen atoms are repelled to one side, giving the molecule a boomerang shape. The electrons in a water molecule are more concentrated around the more highly charged oxygen nucleus than around the hydrogen nuclei. This makes the oxygen end of the molecule slightly negative and leaves the hydrogen ends slightly positive. The inherent separation of charge in polar molecules makes it easier to align them with external fields and charges. Polar molecules therefore exhibit greater polarization effects and have greater dielectric constants. Those who study chemistry will find that the polar nature of water has many effects. For example, water molecules gather ions much more effectively because they have an electric field and a separation of charge to attract charges of both signs. Also, as brought out in the previous chapter, polar water provides a shield or screening of the electric fields in the highly charged molecules of interest in biological systems.

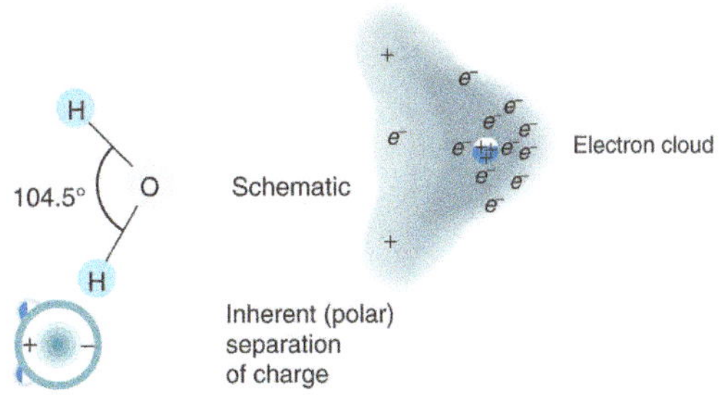

FIGURE 19.18 Artist's conception of a water molecule. There is an inherent separation of charge, and so water is a polar molecule. Electrons in the molecule are attracted to the oxygen nucleus and leave an excess of positive charge near the two hydrogen nuclei. (Note that the schematic on the right is a rough illustration of the distribution of electrons in the water molecule. It does not show the actual

numbers of protons and electrons involved in the structure.)

PHET EXPLORATIONS

Capacitor Lab

Explore how a capacitor works! Change the size of the plates and add a dielectric to see the effect on capacitance. Change the voltage and see charges built up on the plates. Observe the electric field in the capacitor. Measure the voltage and the electric field.

Click to view content (https://openstax.org/books/college-physics-ap-courses-2e/pages/19-5-capacitors-and-dielectrics)

PhET

19.6 Capacitors in Series and Parallel

LEARNING OBJECTIVES

By the end of this section, you will be able to:

- Derive expressions for total capacitance in series and in parallel.
- Identify series and parallel parts in the combination of connection of capacitors.
- Calculate the effective capacitance in series and parallel given individual capacitances.

Several capacitors may be connected together in a variety of applications. Multiple connections of capacitors act like a single equivalent capacitor. The total capacitance of this equivalent single capacitor depends both on the individual capacitors and how they are connected. There are two simple and common types of connections, called *series* and *parallel*, for which we can easily calculate the total capacitance. Certain more complicated connections can also be related to combinations of series and parallel.

Capacitance in Series

Figure 19.19(a) shows a series connection of three capacitors with a voltage applied. As for any capacitor, the capacitance of the combination is related to charge and voltage by $C = \frac{Q}{V}$.

Note in Figure 19.19 that opposite charges of magnitude Q flow to either side of the originally uncharged combination of capacitors when the voltage V is applied. Conservation of charge requires that equal-magnitude charges be created on the plates of the individual capacitors, since charge is only being separated in these originally neutral devices. The end result is that the combination resembles a single capacitor with an effective plate separation greater than that of the individual capacitors alone. (See Figure 19.19(b).) Larger plate separation means smaller capacitance. It is a general feature of series connections of capacitors that the total capacitance is less than any of the individual capacitances.

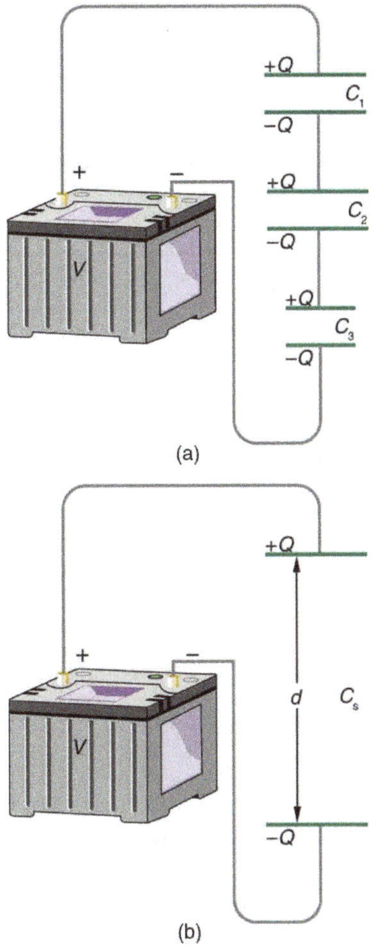

FIGURE 19.19 (a) Capacitors connected in series. The magnitude of the charge on each plate is Q. (b) An equivalent capacitor has a larger plate separation d. Series connections produce a total capacitance that is less than that of any of the individual capacitors.

We can find an expression for the total capacitance by considering the voltage across the individual capacitors shown in Figure 19.19. Solving $C = \frac{Q}{V}$ for V gives $V = \frac{Q}{C}$. The voltages across the individual capacitors are thus $V_1 = \frac{Q}{C_1}$, $V_2 = \frac{Q}{C_2}$, and $V_3 = \frac{Q}{C_3}$. The total voltage is the sum of the individual voltages:

$$V = V_1 + V_2 + V_3. \quad (19.60)$$

Now, calling the total capacitance C_S for series capacitance, consider that

$$V = \frac{Q}{C_S} = V_1 + V_2 + V_3. \quad (19.61)$$

Entering the expressions for V_1, V_2, and V_3, we get

$$\frac{Q}{C_S} = \frac{Q}{C_1} + \frac{Q}{C_2} + \frac{Q}{C_3}. \quad (19.62)$$

Canceling the Qs, we obtain the equation for the total capacitance in series C_S to be

$$\frac{1}{C_S} = \frac{1}{C_1} + \frac{1}{C_2} + \frac{1}{C_3} + ..., \quad (19.63)$$

where "..." indicates that the expression is valid for any number of capacitors connected in series. An expression of this form always results in a total capacitance C_S that is less than any of the individual capacitances $C_1, C_2, ...$, as the next example illustrates.

TOTAL CAPACITANCE IN SERIES, C_S

Total capacitance in series: $\frac{1}{C_S} = \frac{1}{C_1} + \frac{1}{C_2} + \frac{1}{C_3} + \ldots$

EXAMPLE 19.9

What Is the Series Capacitance?

Find the total capacitance for three capacitors connected in series, given their individual capacitances are 1.000, 5.000, and 8.000 μF.

Strategy

With the given information, the total capacitance can be found using the equation for capacitance in series.

Solution

Entering the given capacitances into the expression for $\frac{1}{C_S}$ gives $\frac{1}{C_S} = \frac{1}{C_1} + \frac{1}{C_2} + \frac{1}{C_3}$.

$$\frac{1}{C_S} = \frac{1}{1.000\ \mu\text{F}} + \frac{1}{5.000\ \mu\text{F}} + \frac{1}{8.000\ \mu\text{F}} = \frac{1.325}{\mu\text{F}} \quad 19.64$$

Inverting to find C_S yields $C_S = \frac{\mu\text{F}}{1.325} = 0.755\ \mu\text{F}$.

Discussion

The total series capacitance C_s is less than the smallest individual capacitance, as promised. In series connections of capacitors, the sum is less than the parts. In fact, it is less than any individual. Note that it is sometimes possible, and more convenient, to solve an equation like the above by finding the least common denominator, which in this case (showing only whole-number calculations) is 40. Thus,

$$\frac{1}{C_S} = \frac{40}{40\ \mu\text{F}} + \frac{8}{40\ \mu\text{F}} + \frac{5}{40\ \mu\text{F}} = \frac{53}{40\ \mu\text{F}}, \quad 19.65$$

so that

$$C_S = \frac{40\ \mu\text{F}}{53} = 0.755\ \mu\text{F}. \quad 19.66$$

Capacitors in Parallel

Figure 19.20(a) shows a parallel connection of three capacitors with a voltage applied. Here the total capacitance is easier to find than in the series case. To find the equivalent total capacitance C_p, we first note that the voltage across each capacitor is V, the same as that of the source, since they are connected directly to it through a conductor. (Conductors are equipotentials, and so the voltage across the capacitors is the same as that across the voltage source.) Thus the capacitors have the same charges on them as they would have if connected individually to the voltage source. The total charge Q is the sum of the individual charges:

$$Q = Q_1 + Q_2 + Q_3. \quad 19.67$$

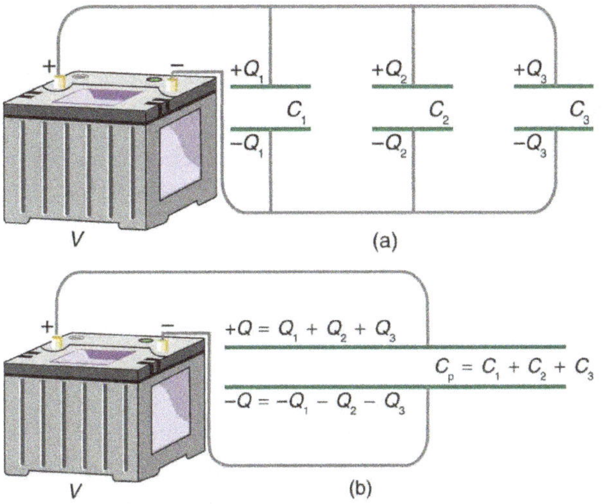

FIGURE 19.20 (a) Capacitors in parallel. Each is connected directly to the voltage source just as if it were all alone, and so the total capacitance in parallel is just the sum of the individual capacitances. (b) The equivalent capacitor has a larger plate area and can therefore hold more charge than the individual capacitors.

Using the relationship $Q = CV$, we see that the total charge is $Q = C_p V$, and the individual charges are $Q_1 = C_1 V$, $Q_2 = C_2 V$, and $Q_3 = C_3 V$. Entering these into the previous equation gives

$$C_p V = C_1 V + C_2 V + C_3 V. \tag{19.68}$$

Canceling V from the equation, we obtain the equation for the total capacitance in parallel C_p:

$$C_p = C_1 + C_2 + C_3 + ... \tag{19.69}$$

Total capacitance in parallel is simply the sum of the individual capacitances. (Again the "..." indicates the expression is valid for any number of capacitors connected in parallel.) So, for example, if the capacitors in the example above were connected in parallel, their capacitance would be

$$C_p = 1.000\ \mu F + 5.000\ \mu F + 8.000\ \mu F = 14.000\ \mu F. \tag{19.70}$$

The equivalent capacitor for a parallel connection has an effectively larger plate area and, thus, a larger capacitance, as illustrated in Figure 19.20(b).

TOTAL CAPACITANCE IN PARALLEL, C_p

Total capacitance in parallel $C_p = C_1 + C_2 + C_3 + ...$

More complicated connections of capacitors can sometimes be combinations of series and parallel. (See Figure 19.21.) To find the total capacitance of such combinations, we identify series and parallel parts, compute their capacitances, and then find the total.

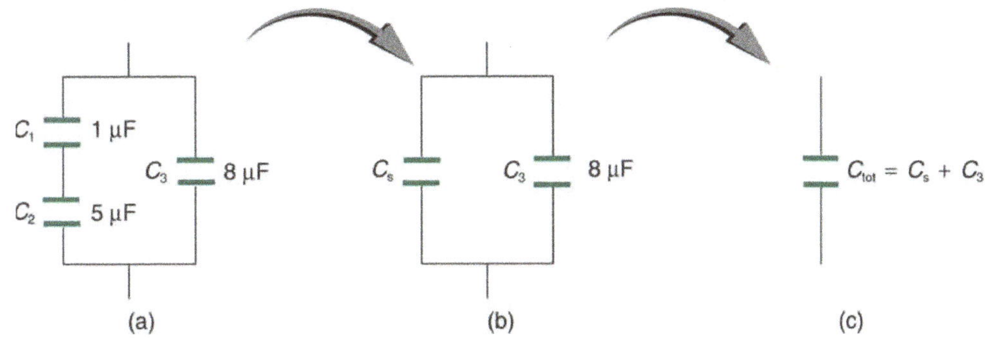

FIGURE 19.21 (a) This circuit contains both series and parallel connections of capacitors. See Example 19.10 for the calculation of the overall capacitance of the circuit. (b) C_1 and C_2 are in series; their equivalent capacitance C_S is less than either of them. (c) Note that C_S is in parallel with C_3. The total capacitance is, thus, the sum of C_S and C_3.

EXAMPLE 19.10

A Mixture of Series and Parallel Capacitance

Find the total capacitance of the combination of capacitors shown in Figure 19.21. Assume the capacitances in Figure 19.21 are known to three decimal places ($C_1 = 1.000\ \mu\text{F}$, $C_2 = 5.000\ \mu\text{F}$, and $C_3 = 8.000\ \mu\text{F}$), and round your answer to three decimal places.

Strategy

To find the total capacitance, we first identify which capacitors are in series and which are in parallel. Capacitors C_1 and C_2 are in series. Their combination, labeled C_S in the figure, is in parallel with C_3.

Solution

Since C_1 and C_2 are in series, their total capacitance is given by $\frac{1}{C_S} = \frac{1}{C_1} + \frac{1}{C_2} + \frac{1}{C_3}$. Entering their values into the equation gives

$$\frac{1}{C_S} = \frac{1}{C_1} + \frac{1}{C_2} = \frac{1}{1.000\ \mu\text{F}} + \frac{1}{5.000\ \mu\text{F}} = \frac{1.200}{\mu\text{F}}. \quad 19.71$$

Inverting gives

$$C_S = 0.833\ \mu\text{F}. \quad 19.72$$

This equivalent series capacitance is in parallel with the third capacitor; thus, the total is the sum

$$\begin{aligned} C_{\text{tot}} &= C_S + C_S \\ &= 0.833\ \mu\text{F} + 8.000\ \mu\text{F} \\ &= 8.833\ \mu\text{F}. \end{aligned} \quad 19.73$$

Discussion

This technique of analyzing the combinations of capacitors piece by piece until a total is obtained can be applied to larger combinations of capacitors.

19.7 Energy Stored in Capacitors

LEARNING OBJECTIVES

By the end of this section, you will be able to:

- List some uses of capacitors.
- Express in equation form the energy stored in a capacitor.
- Explain the function of a defibrillator.

Most of us have seen dramatizations in which medical personnel use a **defibrillator** to pass an electric current through a patient's heart to get it to beat normally. (Review Figure 19.22.) Often realistic in detail, the person applying the shock directs another person to “make it 400 joules this time.” The energy delivered by the defibrillator is stored in a capacitor and can be adjusted to fit the situation. SI units of joules are often employed. Less dramatic is the use of capacitors in microelectronics, such as certain handheld calculators, to supply energy when batteries are charged. (See Figure 19.22.) Capacitors are also used to supply energy for flash lamps on cameras.

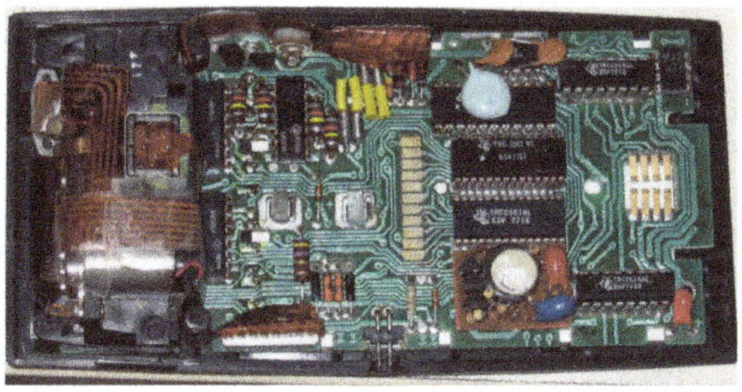

FIGURE 19.22 Energy stored in the large capacitor is used to preserve the memory of an electronic calculator when its batteries are charged. (credit: Kucharek, Wikimedia Commons)

Energy stored in a capacitor is electrical potential energy, and it is thus related to the charge Q and voltage V on the capacitor. We must be careful when applying the equation for electrical potential energy $\Delta \text{PE} = q\Delta V$ to a capacitor. Remember that ΔPE is the potential energy of a charge q going through a voltage ΔV. But the capacitor starts with zero voltage and gradually comes up to its full voltage as it is charged. The first charge placed on a capacitor experiences a change in voltage $\Delta V = 0$, since the capacitor has zero voltage when uncharged. The final charge placed on a capacitor experiences $\Delta V = V$, since the capacitor now has its full voltage V on it. The average voltage on the capacitor during the charging process is $V/2$, and so the average voltage experienced by the full charge q is $V/2$. Thus the energy stored in a capacitor, E_{cap}, is

$$E_{\text{cap}} = \frac{QV}{2}, \tag{19.74}$$

where Q is the charge on a capacitor with a voltage V applied. (Note that the energy is not QV, but $QV/2$.) Charge and voltage are related to the capacitance C of a capacitor by $Q = CV$, and so the expression for E_{cap} can be algebraically manipulated into three equivalent expressions:

$$E_{\text{cap}} = \frac{QV}{2} = \frac{CV^2}{2} = \frac{Q^2}{2C}, \tag{19.75}$$

where Q is the charge and V the voltage on a capacitor C. The energy is in joules for a charge in coulombs, voltage in volts, and capacitance in farads.

ENERGY STORED IN CAPACITORS

The energy stored in a capacitor can be expressed in three ways:

$$E_{\text{cap}} = \frac{QV}{2} = \frac{CV^2}{2} = \frac{Q^2}{2C}, \tag{19.76}$$

where Q is the charge, V is the voltage, and C is the capacitance of the capacitor. The energy is in joules for a charge in coulombs, voltage in volts, and capacitance in farads.

In a defibrillator, the delivery of a large charge in a short burst to a set of paddles across a person's chest can be a lifesaver. The person's heart attack might have arisen from the onset of fast, irregular beating of the heart—cardiac or ventricular fibrillation. The application of a large shock of electrical energy can terminate the arrhythmia and allow the body's pacemaker to resume normal patterns. Today it is common for ambulances to carry a defibrillator, which also uses an electrocardiogram to analyze the patient's heartbeat pattern. Automated external defibrillators (AED) are found in many public places (Figure 19.23). These are designed to be used by lay persons. The device automatically diagnoses the patient's heart condition and then applies the shock with appropriate energy and waveform. CPR is recommended in many cases before use of an AED.

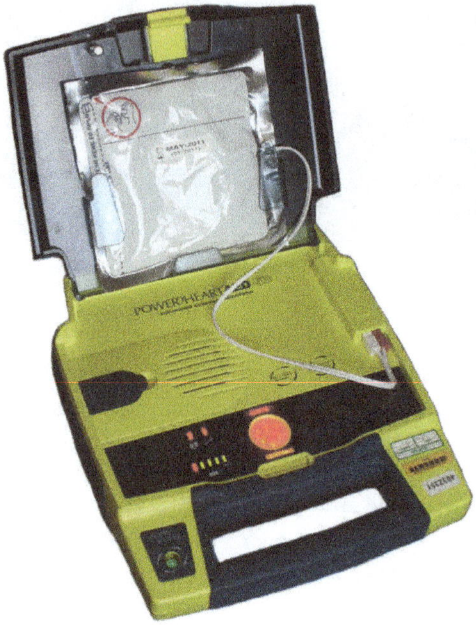

FIGURE 19.23 Automated external defibrillators are found in many public places. These portable units provide verbal instructions for use in the important first few minutes for a person suffering a cardiac attack. (credit: Owain Davies, Wikimedia Commons)

EXAMPLE 19.11

Capacitance in a Heart Defibrillator

A heart defibrillator delivers 4.00×10^2 J of energy by discharging a capacitor initially at 1.00×10^4 V. What is its capacitance?

Strategy

We are given E_{cap} and V, and we are asked to find the capacitance C. Of the three expressions in the equation for E_{cap}, the most convenient relationship is

$$E_{\text{cap}} = \frac{CV^2}{2}. \quad (19.77)$$

Solution

Solving this expression for C and entering the given values yields

$$\begin{aligned} C &= \frac{2E_{\text{cap}}}{V^2} = \frac{2(4.00 \times 10^2\ \text{J})}{(1.00 \times 10^4\ \text{V})^2} = 8.00 \times 10^{-6}\ \text{F} \\ &= 8.00\ \mu\text{F}. \end{aligned} \quad (19.78)$$

Discussion

This is a fairly large, but manageable, capacitance at 1.00×10^4 V.

Glossary

capacitance amount of charge stored per unit volt
capacitor a device that stores electric charge
defibrillator a machine used to provide an electrical shock to a heart attack victim's heart in order to restore the heart's normal rhythmic pattern
dielectric an insulating material
dielectric strength the maximum electric field above which an insulating material begins to break down and conduct
electric potential potential energy per unit charge
electron volt the energy given to a fundamental charge accelerated through a potential difference of one volt
equipotential line a line along which the electric potential is constant
grounding fixing a conductor at zero volts by connecting it to the earth or ground
mechanical energy sum of the kinetic energy and potential energy of a system; this sum is a constant
parallel plate capacitor two identical conducting plates separated by a distance
polar molecule a molecule with inherent separation of charge
potential difference (or voltage) change in potential energy of a charge moved from one point to another, divided by the charge; units of potential difference are joules per coulomb, known as volt
scalar physical quantity with magnitude but no direction
vector physical quantity with both magnitude and direction

Section Summary

19.1 Electric Potential Energy: Potential Difference

- Electric potential is potential energy per unit charge.
- The potential difference between points A and B, $V_B - V_A$, defined to be the change in potential energy of a charge q moved from A to B, is equal to the change in potential energy divided by the charge, Potential difference is commonly called voltage, represented by the symbol ΔV.

$$\Delta V = \frac{\Delta \text{PE}}{q} \text{ and } \Delta\text{PE} = q\Delta V.$$

- An electron volt is the energy given to a fundamental charge accelerated through a potential difference of 1 V. In equation form,

$$\begin{aligned} 1 \text{ eV} &= (1.60 \times 10^{-19} \text{ C})(1 \text{ V}) = \left(1.60 \times 10^{-19} \text{ C}\right)(1 \text{ J/C}) \\ &= 1.60 \times 10^{-19} \text{ J.} \end{aligned}$$

- Mechanical energy is the sum of the kinetic energy and potential energy of a system, that is, $\text{KE} + \text{PE}$. This sum is a constant.

19.2 Electric Potential in a Uniform Electric Field

- The voltage between points A and B is

$$\left.\begin{aligned} V_{AB} &= Ed \\ E &= \frac{V_{AB}}{d} \end{aligned}\right\} (\text{uniform } E \text{ - field only}),$$

where d is the distance from A to B, or the distance between the plates.
- In equation form, the general relationship between voltage and electric field is

$$E = -\frac{\Delta V}{\Delta s},$$

where Δs is the distance over which the change in potential, ΔV, takes place. The minus sign tells us that $\mathbf{E}$ points in the direction of decreasing potential.) The electric field is said to be the *gradient* (as in grade or slope) of the electric potential.

19.3 Electrical Potential Due to a Point Charge

- Electric potential of a point charge is $V = kQ/r$.
- Electric potential is a scalar, and electric field is a vector. Addition of voltages as numbers gives the voltage due to a combination of point charges, whereas addition of individual fields as vectors gives the total electric field.

19.4 Equipotential Lines

- An equipotential line is a line along which the electric potential is constant.
- An equipotential surface is a three-dimensional version of equipotential lines.
- Equipotential lines are always perpendicular to electric field lines.
- The process by which a conductor can be fixed at zero volts by connecting it to the earth with a good conductor is called grounding.

19.5 Capacitors and Dielectrics

- A capacitor is a device used to store charge.
- The amount of charge Q a capacitor can store depends on two major factors—the voltage applied

and the capacitor's physical characteristics, such as its size.

- The capacitance C is the amount of charge stored per volt, or
  $C = \frac{Q}{V}$.
- The capacitance of a parallel plate capacitor is $C = \varepsilon_0 \frac{A}{d}$, when the plates are separated by air or free space. ε_0 is called the permittivity of free space.
- A parallel plate capacitor with a dielectric between its plates has a capacitance given by
  $C = \kappa\varepsilon_0 \frac{A}{d}$,
  where κ is the dielectric constant of the material.
- The maximum electric field strength above which an insulating material begins to break down and conduct is called dielectric strength.

19.6 Capacitors in Series and Parallel

- Total capacitance in series
  $\frac{1}{C_S} = \frac{1}{C_1} + \frac{1}{C_2} + \frac{1}{C_3} + ...$
- Total capacitance in parallel
  $C_p = C_1 + C_2 + C_3 + ...$
- If a circuit contains a combination of capacitors in series and parallel, identify series and parallel parts, compute their capacitances, and then find the total.

19.7 Energy Stored in Capacitors

- Capacitors are used in a variety of devices, including defibrillators, microelectronics such as calculators, and flash lamps, to supply energy.
- The energy stored in a capacitor can be expressed in three ways:
  $E_{cap} = \frac{QV}{2} = \frac{CV^2}{2} = \frac{Q^2}{2C}$,
  where Q is the charge, V is the voltage, and C is the capacitance of the capacitor. The energy is in joules when the charge is in coulombs, voltage is in volts, and capacitance is in farads.

Conceptual Questions

19.1 Electric Potential Energy: Potential Difference

1. Voltage is the common word for potential difference. Which term is more descriptive, voltage or potential difference?

2. If the voltage between two points is zero, can a test charge be moved between them with zero net work being done? Can this necessarily be done without exerting a force? Explain.

3. What is the relationship between voltage and energy? More precisely, what is the relationship between potential difference and electric potential energy?

4. Voltages are always measured between two points. Why?

5. How are units of volts and electron volts related? How do they differ?

19.2 Electric Potential in a Uniform Electric Field

6. Discuss how potential difference and electric field strength are related. Give an example.

7. What is the strength of the electric field in a region where the electric potential is constant?

8. Will a negative charge, initially at rest, move toward higher or lower potential? Explain why.

19.3 Electrical Potential Due to a Point Charge

9. In what region of space is the potential due to a uniformly charged sphere the same as that of a point charge? In what region does it differ from that of a point charge?

10. Can the potential of a non-uniformly charged sphere be the same as that of a point charge? Explain.

19.4 Equipotential Lines

11. What is an equipotential line? What is an equipotential surface?

12. Explain in your own words why equipotential lines and surfaces must be perpendicular to electric field lines.

13. Can different equipotential lines cross? Explain.

19.5 Capacitors and Dielectrics

14. Does the capacitance of a device depend on the applied voltage? What about the charge stored in it?

15. Use the characteristics of the Coulomb force to explain why capacitance should be proportional to the plate area of a capacitor. Similarly, explain why capacitance should be inversely proportional to the separation between plates.

16. Give the reason why a dielectric material increases capacitance compared with what it would be with air between the plates of a capacitor. What is the independent reason that a dielectric material also allows a greater voltage to be applied to a capacitor? (The dielectric thus increases C and permits a greater V.)

17. How does the polar character of water molecules help to explain water's relatively large dielectric constant? (Figure 19.18)

18. Sparks will occur between the plates of an air-filled capacitor at lower voltage when the air is humid than when dry. Explain why, considering the polar character of water molecules.

19. Water has a large dielectric constant, but it is rarely used in capacitors. Explain why.

20. Membranes in living cells, including those in humans, are characterized by a separation of charge across the membrane. Effectively, the membranes are thus charged capacitors with important functions related to the potential difference across the membrane. Is energy required to separate these charges in living membranes and, if so, is its source the metabolization of food energy or some other source?

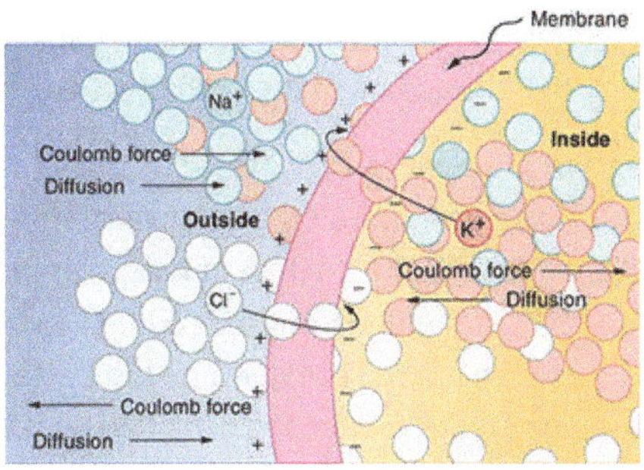

FIGURE 19.24 The semipermeable membrane of a cell has different concentrations of ions inside and out. Diffusion moves the K^+ (potassium) and Cl^- (chloride) ions in the directions shown, until the Coulomb force halts further transfer. This results in a layer of positive charge on the outside, a layer of negative charge on the inside, and thus a voltage across the cell membrane. The membrane is normally impermeable to Na^+ (sodium ions).

19.6 Capacitors in Series and Parallel

21. If you wish to store a large amount of energy in a capacitor bank, would you connect capacitors in series or parallel? Explain.

19.7 Energy Stored in Capacitors

22. How does the energy contained in a charged capacitor change when a dielectric is inserted, assuming the capacitor is isolated and its charge is constant? Does this imply that work was done?

23. What happens to the energy stored in a capacitor connected to a battery when a dielectric is inserted? Was work done in the process?

Problems & Exercises

19.1 Electric Potential Energy: Potential Difference

1. Find the ratio of speeds of an electron and a negative hydrogen ion (one having an extra electron) accelerated through the same voltage, assuming non-relativistic final speeds. Take the mass of the hydrogen ion to be 1.67×10^{-27} kg.

2. An evacuated tube uses an accelerating voltage of 40 kV to accelerate electrons to hit a copper plate and produce x rays. Non-relativistically, what would be the maximum speed of these electrons?

3. A bare helium nucleus has two positive charges and a mass of 6.64×10^{-27} kg. (a) Calculate its kinetic energy in joules at 2.00% of the speed of light. (b) What is this in electron volts? (c) What voltage would be needed to obtain this energy?

4. Integrated Concepts
Singly charged gas ions are accelerated from rest through a voltage of 13.0 V. At what temperature will the average kinetic energy of gas molecules be the same as that given these ions?

5. Integrated Concepts
The temperature near the center of the Sun is thought to be 15 million degrees Celsius $\left(1.5\times10^{7}\ ^\circ\text{C}\right)$. Through what voltage must a singly charged ion be accelerated to have the same energy as the average kinetic energy of ions at this temperature?

6. Integrated Concepts
(a) What is the average power output of a heart defibrillator that dissipates 400 J of energy in 10.0 ms? (b) Considering the high-power output, why doesn't the defibrillator produce serious burns?

7. Integrated Concepts
A lightning bolt strikes a tree, moving 20.0 C of charge through a potential difference of 1.00×10^{2} MV. (a) What energy was dissipated? (b) What mass of water could be raised from 15°C to the boiling point and then boiled by this energy?

(c) Discuss the damage that could be caused to the tree by the expansion of the boiling steam.

8. Integrated Concepts
A 12.0 V battery-operated bottle warmer heats 50.0 g of glass, 2.50×10^2 g of baby formula, and 2.00×10^2 g of aluminum from $20.0°C$ to $90.0°C$. (a) How much charge is moved by the battery? (b) How many electrons per second flow if it takes 5.00 min to warm the formula? (Hint: Assume that the specific heat of baby formula is about the same as the specific heat of water.)

9. Integrated Concepts
A battery-operated car utilizes a 12.0 V system. Find the charge the batteries must be able to move in order to accelerate the 750 kg car from rest to 25.0 m/s, make it climb a 2.00×10^2 m high hill, and then cause it to travel at a constant 25.0 m/s by exerting a 5.00×10^2 N force for an hour.

10. Integrated Concepts
Fusion probability is greatly enhanced when appropriate nuclei are brought close together, but mutual Coulomb repulsion must be overcome. This can be done using the kinetic energy of high-temperature gas ions or by accelerating the nuclei toward one another. (a) Calculate the potential energy of two singly charged nuclei separated by 1.00×10^{-12} m by finding the voltage of one at that distance and multiplying by the charge of the other. (b) At what temperature will atoms of a gas have an average kinetic energy equal to this needed electrical potential energy?

11. Unreasonable Results
(a) Find the voltage near a 10.0 cm diameter metal sphere that has 8.00 C of excess positive charge on it. (b) What is unreasonable about this result? (c) Which assumptions are responsible?

12. Construct Your Own Problem
Consider a battery used to supply energy to a cellular phone. Construct a problem in which you determine the energy that must be supplied by the battery, and then calculate the amount of charge it must be able to move in order to supply this energy. Among the things to be considered are the energy needs and battery voltage. You may need to look ahead to interpret manufacturer's battery ratings in ampere-hours as energy in joules.

19.2 Electric Potential in a Uniform Electric Field

13. Show that units of V/m and N/C for electric field strength are indeed equivalent.

14. What is the strength of the electric field between two parallel conducting plates separated by 1.00 cm and having a potential difference (voltage) between them of 1.50×10^4 V?

15. The electric field strength between two parallel conducting plates separated by 4.00 cm is 7.50×10^4 V/m. (a) What is the potential difference between the plates? (b) The plate with the lowest potential is taken to be at zero volts. What is the potential 1.00 cm from that plate (and 3.00 cm from the other)?

16. How far apart are two conducting plates that have an electric field strength of 4.50×10^3 V/m between them, if their potential difference is 15.0 kV?

17. (a) Will the electric field strength between two parallel conducting plates exceed the breakdown strength for air (3.0×10^6 V/m) if the plates are separated by 2.00 mm and a potential difference of 5.0×10^3 V is applied? (b) How close together can the plates be with this applied voltage?

18. The voltage across a membrane forming a cell wall is 80.0 mV and the membrane is 9.00 nm thick. What is the electric field strength? (The value is surprisingly large, but correct. Membranes are discussed in Capacitors and Dielectrics and Nerve Conduction—Electrocardiograms.) You may assume a uniform electric field.

19. Membrane walls of living cells have surprisingly large electric fields across them due to separation of ions. (Membranes are discussed in some detail in Nerve Conduction—Electrocardiograms.) What is the voltage across an 8.00 nm–thick membrane if the electric field strength across it is 5.50 MV/m? You may assume a uniform electric field.

20. Two parallel conducting plates are separated by 10.0 cm, and one of them is taken to be at zero volts. (a) What is the electric field strength between them, if the potential 8.00 cm from the zero volt plate (and 2.00 cm from the other) is 450 V? (b) What is the voltage between the plates?

21. Find the maximum potential difference between two parallel conducting plates separated by 0.500 cm of air, given the maximum sustainable electric field strength in air to be 3.0×10^6 V/m.

22. A doubly charged ion is accelerated to an energy of 32.0 keV by the electric field between two parallel conducting plates separated by 2.00 cm. What is the electric field strength between the plates?

23. An electron is to be accelerated in a uniform electric field having a strength of 2.00×10^6 V/m. (a) What energy in keV is given to the electron if it is accelerated through 0.400 m? (b) Over what distance would it have to be accelerated to increase its energy by 50.0 GeV?

19.3 Electrical Potential Due to a Point Charge

24. A 0.500 cm diameter plastic sphere, used in a static electricity demonstration, has a uniformly distributed 40.0 pC charge on its surface. What is the potential near its surface?

25. What is the potential 0.530×10^{-10} m from a proton (the average distance between the proton and electron in a hydrogen atom)?

26. (a) A sphere has a surface uniformly charged with 1.00 C. At what distance from its center is the potential 5.00 MV? (b) What does your answer imply about the practical aspect of isolating such a large charge?

27. How far from a $1.00\ \mu C$ point charge will the potential be 100 V? At what distance will it be 2.00×10^2 V?

28. What are the sign and magnitude of a point charge that produces a potential of -2.00 V at a distance of 1.00 mm?

29. If the potential due to a point charge is 5.00×10^2 V at a distance of 15.0 m, what are the sign and magnitude of the charge?

30. In nuclear fission, a nucleus splits roughly in half. (a) What is the potential 2.00×10^{-14} m from a fragment that has 46 protons in it? (b) What is the potential energy in MeV of a similarly charged fragment at this distance?

31. A research Van de Graaff generator has a 2.00-m-diameter metal sphere with a charge of 5.00 mC on it. (a) What is the potential near its surface? (b) At what distance from its center is the potential 1.00 MV? (c) An oxygen atom with three missing electrons is released near the Van de Graaff generator. What is its energy in MeV at this distance?

32. An electrostatic paint sprayer has a 0.200-m-diameter metal sphere at a potential of 25.0 kV that repels paint droplets onto a grounded object. (a) What charge is on the sphere? (b) What charge must a 0.100-mg drop of paint have to arrive at the object with a speed of 10.0 m/s?

33. In one of the classic nuclear physics experiments at the beginning of the 20th century, an alpha particle was accelerated toward a gold nucleus, and its path was substantially deflected by the Coulomb interaction. If the energy of the doubly charged alpha nucleus was 5.00 MeV, how close to the gold nucleus (79 protons) could it come before being deflected?

34. (a) What is the potential between two points situated 10 cm and 20 cm from a $3.0\ \mu C$ point charge? (b) To what location should the point at 20 cm be moved to increase this potential difference by a factor of two?

35. Unreasonable Results
(a) What is the final speed of an electron accelerated from rest through a voltage of 25.0 MV by a negatively charged Van de Graaff terminal?
(b) What is unreasonable about this result?
(c) Which assumptions are responsible?

19.4 Equipotential Lines

36. (a) Sketch the equipotential lines near a point charge $+q$. Indicate the direction of increasing potential. (b) Do the same for a point charge $-3q$.

37. Sketch the equipotential lines for the two equal positive charges shown in Figure 19.25. Indicate the direction of increasing potential.

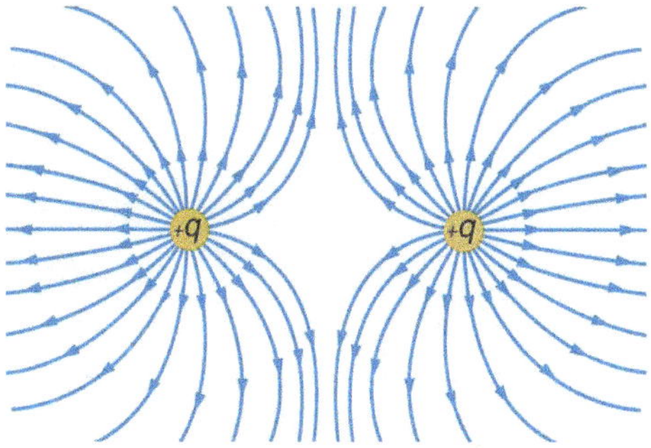

FIGURE 19.25 The electric field near two equal positive charges is directed away from each of the charges.

38. Figure 19.26 shows the electric field lines near two charges q_1 and q_2, the first having a magnitude four times that of the second. Sketch the equipotential lines for these two charges, and indicate the direction of increasing potential.

39. Sketch the equipotential lines a long distance from

the charges shown in Figure 19.26. Indicate the direction of increasing potential.

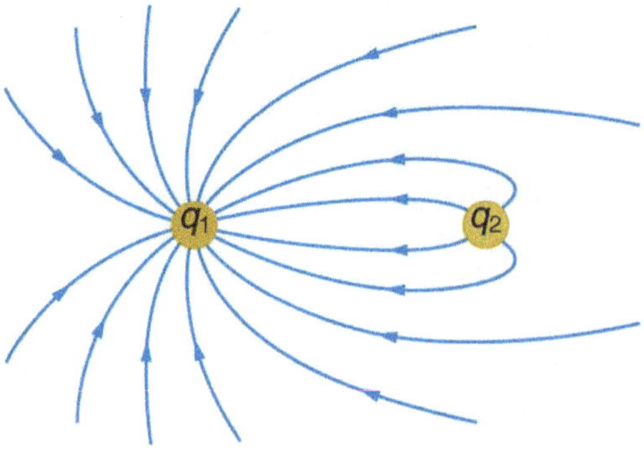

FIGURE 19.26 The electric field near two charges.

40. Sketch the equipotential lines in the vicinity of two opposite charges, where the negative charge is three times as great in magnitude as the positive. See Figure 19.26 for a similar situation. Indicate the direction of increasing potential.

41. Sketch the equipotential lines in the vicinity of the negatively charged conductor in Figure 19.27. How will these equipotentials look a long distance from the object?

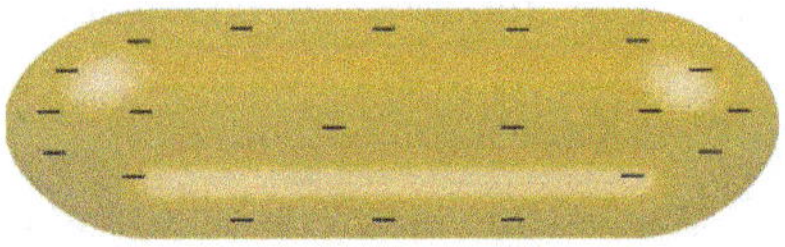

FIGURE 19.27 A negatively charged conductor.

42. Sketch the equipotential lines surrounding the two conducting plates shown in Figure 19.28, given the top plate is positive and the bottom plate has an equal amount of negative charge. Be certain to indicate the distribution of charge on the plates. Is the field strongest where the plates are closest? Why should it be?

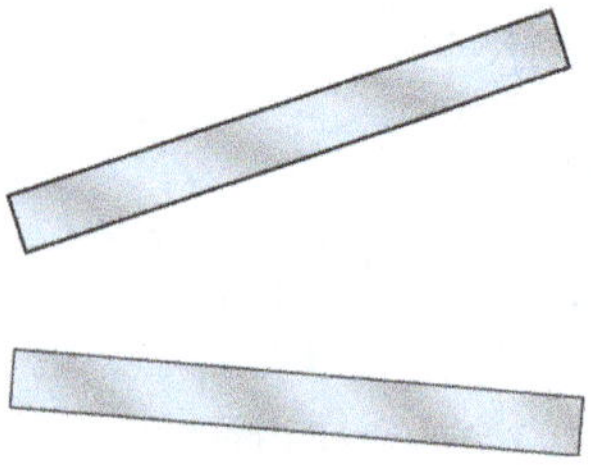

FIGURE 19.28

43. (a) Sketch the electric field lines in the vicinity of the charged insulator in Figure 19.29. Note its non-uniform charge distribution. (b) Sketch equipotential lines surrounding the insulator. Indicate the direction of increasing potential.

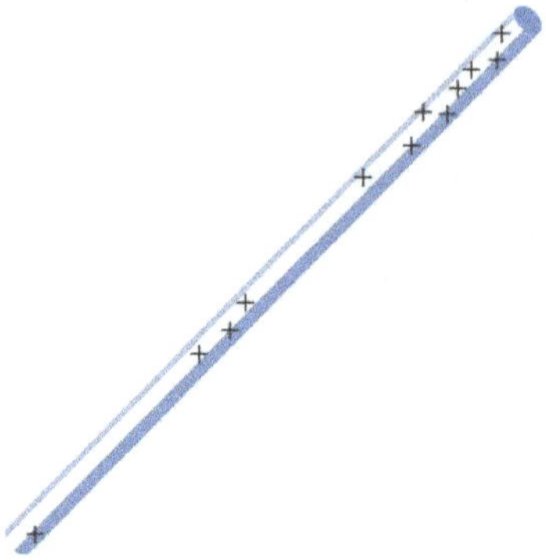

FIGURE 19.29 A charged insulating rod such as might be used in a classroom demonstration.

44. The naturally occurring electrical field on the ground to an open sky point 3.00 m above is 1.13 × 10^2 N/C. This open point in the sky is at a greater electric potential than the ground. (a) Calculate the electric potential at this height. (b) Sketch electric field and equipotential lines for this scenario. Calculate the electric potential at this height. (c) Sketch electric field and equipotential lines for this scenario.

45. The lesser electric ray (*Narcine bancroftii*) maintains an incredible charge on its head and a charge equal in magnitude but opposite in sign on its tail (Figure 19.30). (a) Sketch the equipotential lines surrounding the ray. (b) Sketch the equipotentials when the ray is near a ship with a conducting surface. (c) How could this charge distribution be of use to the ray?

FIGURE 19.30 Lesser electric ray (*Narcine bancroftii*) (credit: National Oceanic and Atmospheric Administration, NOAA's Fisheries Collection).

19.5 Capacitors and Dielectrics

46. What charge is stored in a $180\ \mu\text{F}$ capacitor when 120 V is applied to it?

47. Find the charge stored when 5.50 V is applied to an 8.00 pF capacitor.

48. What charge is stored in the capacitor in Example

19.8?

49. Calculate the voltage applied to a $2.00\ \mu\text{F}$ capacitor when it holds $3.10\ \mu\text{C}$ of charge.

50. What voltage must be applied to an 8.00 nF capacitor to store 0.160 mC of charge?

51. What capacitance is needed to store $3.00\ \mu\text{C}$ of charge at a voltage of 120 V?

52. What is the capacitance of a large Van de Graaff generator's terminal, given that it stores 8.00 mC of charge at a voltage of 12.0 MV?

53. Find the capacitance of a parallel plate capacitor having plates of area $5.00\ \text{m}^2$ that are separated by 0.100 mm of Teflon.

54. (a)What is the capacitance of a parallel plate capacitor having plates of area $1.50\ \text{m}^2$ that are separated by 0.0200 mm of neoprene rubber? (b) What charge does it hold when 9.00 V is applied to it?

55. Integrated Concepts
A prankster applies 450 V to an $80.0\ \mu\text{F}$ capacitor and then tosses it to an unsuspecting victim. The victim's finger is burned by the discharge of the capacitor through 0.200 g of flesh. What is the temperature increase of the flesh? Is it reasonable to assume no phase change?

56. Unreasonable Results
(a) A certain parallel plate capacitor has plates of area $4.00\ \text{m}^2$, separated by 0.0100 mm of nylon, and stores 0.170 C of charge. What is the applied voltage? (b) What is unreasonable about this result? (c) Which assumptions are responsible or inconsistent?

19.6 Capacitors in Series and Parallel

57. Find the total capacitance of the combination of capacitors in Figure 19.31.

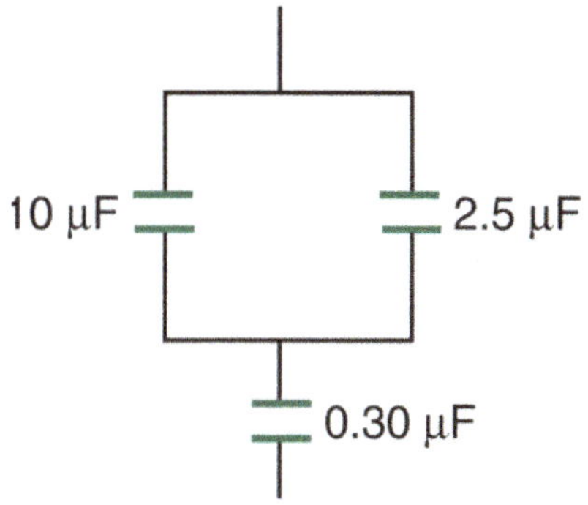

FIGURE 19.31 A combination of series and parallel connections of capacitors.

58. Suppose you want a capacitor bank with a total capacitance of 0.750 F and you possess numerous 1.50 mF capacitors. What is the smallest number you could hook together to achieve your goal, and how would you connect them?

59. What total capacitances can you make by connecting a $5.00\ \mu\text{F}$ and an $8.00\ \mu\text{F}$ capacitor together?

60. Find the total capacitance of the combination of capacitors shown in Figure 19.32.

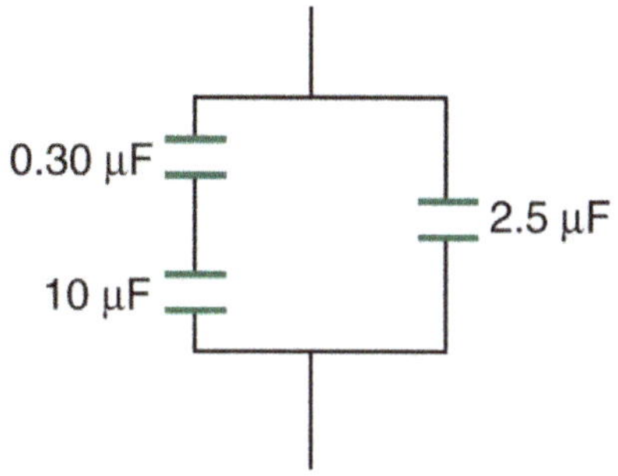

FIGURE 19.32 A combination of series and parallel connections of capacitors.

61. Find the total capacitance of the combination of capacitors shown in Figure 19.33.

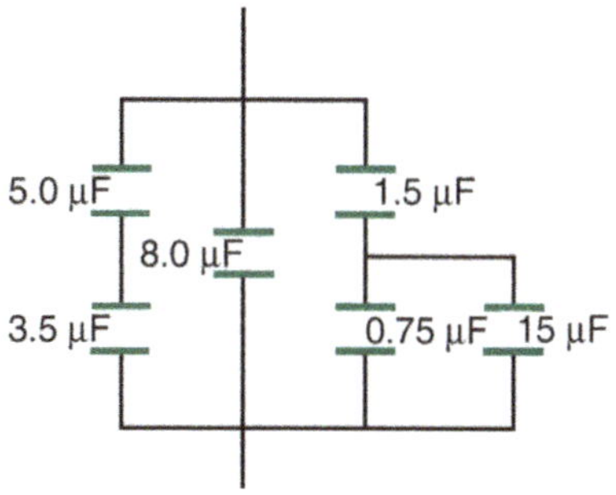

FIGURE 19.33 A combination of series and parallel connections of capacitors.

62. Unreasonable Results
(a) An $8.00\ \mu\text{F}$ capacitor is connected in parallel to another capacitor, producing a total capacitance of $5.00\ \mu\text{F}$. What is the capacitance of the second capacitor? (b) What is unreasonable about this result? (c) Which assumptions are unreasonable or inconsistent?

19.7 Energy Stored in Capacitors

63. (a) What is the energy stored in the $10.0\ \mu\text{F}$ capacitor of a heart defibrillator charged to $9.00 \times 10^3\ \text{V}$? (b) Find the amount of stored charge.

64. In open heart surgery, a much smaller amount of energy will defibrillate the heart. (a) What voltage is applied to the $8.00\ \mu F$ capacitor of a heart defibrillator that stores 40.0 J of energy? (b) Find the amount of stored charge.

65. A $165\ \mu F$ capacitor is used in conjunction with a motor. How much energy is stored in it when 119 V is applied?

66. Suppose you have a 9.00 V battery, a $2.00\ \mu F$ capacitor, and a $7.40\ \mu F$ capacitor. (a) Find the charge and energy stored if the capacitors are connected to the battery in series. (b) Do the same for a parallel connection.

67. A nervous physicist worries that the two metal shelves of his wood frame bookcase might obtain a high voltage if charged by static electricity, perhaps produced by friction. (a) What is the capacitance of the empty shelves if they have area $1.00 \times 10^2\ m^2$ and are 0.200 m apart? (b) What is the voltage between them if opposite charges of magnitude 2.00 nC are placed on them? (c) To show that this voltage poses a small hazard, calculate the energy stored.

68. Show that for a given dielectric material the maximum energy a parallel plate capacitor can store is directly proportional to the volume of dielectric ($\text{Volume} = A \cdot d$). Note that the applied voltage is limited by the dielectric strength.

69. Construct Your Own Problem
Consider a heart defibrillator similar to that discussed in Example 19.11. Construct a problem in which you examine the charge stored in the capacitor of a defibrillator as a function of stored energy. Among the things to be considered are the applied voltage and whether it should vary with energy to be delivered, the range of energies involved, and the capacitance of the defibrillator. You may also wish to consider the much smaller energy needed for defibrillation during open-heart surgery as a variation on this problem.

70. Unreasonable Results
(a) On a particular day, it takes 9.60×10^3 J of electric energy to start a truck's engine. Calculate the capacitance of a capacitor that could store that amount of energy at 12.0 V. (b) What is unreasonable about this result? (c) Which assumptions are responsible?

Test Prep for AP® Courses

19.1 Electric Potential Energy: Potential Difference

1. An electron is placed in an electric field of 12.0 N/C to the right. What is the resulting force on the electron?
a. 1.33×10^{-20} N right
b. 1.33×10^{-20} N left
c. 1.92×10^{-18} N right
d. 1.92×10^{-18} N left

2. A positively charged object in a certain electric field is currently being pushed west by the resulting force. How will the force change if the charge grows? What if it becomes negative?

3. A −5.0 C charge is being forced south by a 60 N force. What are the magnitude and direction of the local electric field?
a. 12 N/C south
b. 12 N/C north
c. 300 N/C south
d. 300 N/C north

4. A charged object has a net force of 100 N east acting on it due to an electric field of 50 N/C pointing north. How is this possible? If not, why not?

5. How many electrons have to be moved by a car battery containing 7.20×10^5 J at 12 V to reduce the energy by 1%?
a. 4.80×10^{27}
b. 4.00×10^{26}
c. 3.75×10^{21}
d. 3.13×10^{20}

6. Most of the electricity in the power grid is generated by powerful turbines spinning around. Why don't these turbines slow down from the work they do moving electrons?

7. A typical AAA battery can move 2000 C of charge at 1.5 V. How long will this run a 50 mW LED?
a. 1000 minutes
b. 120,000 seconds
c. 15 hours
d. 250 minutes

8. Find an example car (or other vehicle) battery, and compute how many of the AAA batteries in the previous problem it would take to equal the energy stored in it. Which is more compact?

9. What is the internal energy of a system consisting of two point charges, one 2.0 μC, and the other −3.0 μC, placed 1.2 m away from each other?

a. -3.8×10^{-2} J
b. -4.5×10^{-2} J
c. 4.5×10^{-2} J
d. 3.8×10^{-2} J

10. A system of three point charges has a 1.00 μC charge at the origin, a −2.00 μC charge at x=30 cm, and a 3.00 μC charge at x=70 cm. What is the total stored potential energy of this configuration?

11. A system has 2.00 μC charges at (50 cm, 0) and (−50 cm, 0) and a −1.00 μC charge at (0, 70 cm). As the y-coordinate of the −1.00 μC charge increases, the potential energy ___. As the y-coordinate of the −1.00 μC charge decreases, the potential energy ___.
a. increases, increases
b. increases, decreases
c. decreases, increases
d. decreases, decreases

12. A system of three point charges has a 1.00 μC charge at the origin, a −2.00 μC charge at x=30 cm, and a 3.00 μC charge at x=70 cm. What happens to the total potential energy of this system if the −2.00 μC charge and the 3.00 μC charge trade places?

13. Take a square configuration of point charges, two positive and two negative, all of the same magnitude, with like charges sharing diagonals. What will happen to the internal energy of this system if one of the negative charges becomes a positive charge of the same magnitude?
a. increase
b. decrease
c. no change
d. not enough information

14. Take a square configuration of point charges, two positive and two negative, all of the same magnitude, with like charges sharing diagonals. What will happen to the internal energy of this system if the sides of the square decrease in length?

15. A system has 2.00 μC charges at (50 cm, 0) and (−50 cm, 0) and a −1.00 μC charge at (0, 70 cm), with a velocity in the $-y$-direction. When the −1.00 μC charge is at (0, 0) the potential energy is at a ___ and the kinetic energy is ___.
a. maximum, maximum
b. maximum, minimum
c. minimum, maximum
d. minimum, minimum

16. What is the velocity of an electron that goes through a 10 V potential after initially being at rest?

19.2 Electric Potential in a Uniform Electric Field

17. A negatively charged massive particle is dropped from above the two plates in Figure 19.5 into the space between them. Which best describes the trajectory it takes?
a. A rightward-curving parabola
b. A leftward-curving parabola
c. A rightward-curving section of a circle
d. A leftward-curving section of a circle

18. Two massive particles with identical charge are launched into the uniform field between two plates from the same launch point with the same velocity. They both impact the positively charged plate, but the second one does so four times as far as the first. What sign is the charge? What physical difference would give them different impact points (quantify as a relative percent)? How does this compare to the gravitational projectile motion case?

19. Two plates are lying horizontally, but stacked with one 10.0 cm above the other. If the upper plate is held at +100 V, what is the magnitude and direction of the electric field between the plates if the lower is held at +50.0 V? -50.0 V?
a. 500 V/m, 1500 V/m, down
b. 500 V/m, 1500 V/m, up
c. 1500 V/m, 500 V/m, down
d. 1500 V/m, 500 V/m, up

20. Two parallel conducting plates are 15 cm apart, each with an area of 0.75 m^2. The left one has a charge of -0.225 C placed on it, while the right has a charge of 0.225 C. What is the magnitude and direction of the electric field between the two?

21. Consider three parallel conducting plates, with a space of 3.0 cm between them. The leftmost one is at a potential of +45 V, the middle one is held at ground, and the rightmost is at a potential of -75 V. What is the magnitude of the average electric field on an electron traveling between the plates? (Assume that the middle one has holes for the electron to go through.)
a. 1500 V/m
b. 2500 V/m

c. 4000 V/m
d. 2000 V/m

22. A new kind of electron gun has a rear plate at −25.0 kV, a grounded plate 2.00 cm in front of that, and a +25.0 kV plate 4.00 cm in front of that. What is the magnitude of the average electric field?

23. A certain electric potential isoline graph has isolines every 5.0 V. If six of these lines cross a 40 cm path drawn between two points of interest, what is the (magnitude of the average) electric field along this path?

a. 750 V/m
b. 150 V/m
c. 38 V/m
d. 75 V/m

24. Given a system of two parallel conducting plates held at a fixed potential difference, describe what happens to the isolines of the electric potential between them as the distance between them is changed. How does this relate to the electric field strength?

19.4 Equipotential Lines

25. How would Figure 19.10 be different with two positive charges replacing the two negative charges?

a. The equipotential lines would have positive values.
b. It would actually resemble Figure 19.9.
c. no change
d. not enough information

26. Consider two conducting plates, placed on adjacent sides of a square, but with a 1-m space between the corner of the square and the plate. These plates are not touching, not centered on each other, but are at right angles. Each plate is 1 m wide. If the plates are held at a fixed potential difference ΔV, draw the equipotential lines for this system.

27. As isolines of electric potential get closer together, the electric field gets stronger. What shape would a hill have as the isolines of gravitational potential get closer together?

a. constant slope
b. steeper slope
c. shallower slope
d. a U-shape

28. Between Figure 19.9 and Figure 19.10, which more closely resembles the gravitational field between two equal masses, and why?

29. How much work is necessary to keep a positive point charge in orbit around a negative point charge?

a. A lot; this system is unstable.
b. Just a little; the isolines are far enough apart that crossing them doesn't take much work.
c. None; we're traveling along an isoline, which requires no work.
d. There's not enough information to tell.

30. Consider two conducting plates, placed on adjacent sides of a square, but with a 1-m space between the corner of the square and the plate. These plates are not touching, not centered on each other, but are at right angles. Each plate is 1 m wide. If the plates are held at a fixed potential difference ΔV, sketch the path of both a positively charged object placed between the near ends, and a negatively charged object placed near the open ends.

19.5 Capacitors and Dielectrics

31. Two parallel plate capacitors are otherwise identical, except the second one has twice the distance between the plates of the first. If placed in otherwise identical circuits, how much charge will the second plate have on it compared to the first?

a. four times as much
b. twice as much
c. the same
d. half as much

32. In a very simple circuit consisting of a battery and a capacitor with an adjustable distance between the plates, how does the voltage vary as the distance is altered?

33. A parallel plate capacitor with adjustable-size square plates is placed in a circuit. How does the charge on the capacitor change as the length of the sides of the plates is increased?

a. it grows proportional to length^2
b. it grows proportional to length
c. it shrinks proportional to length
d. it shrinks proportional to length^2

34. Design an experiment to test the relative permittivities of various materials, and briefly describe some basic features of the results.

35. A student was changing one of the dimensions of a square parallel plate capacitor and measuring the resultant charge in a circuit with a battery. However, the student forgot which dimension was being varied, and didn't write it or any units down. Given the table, which dimension was it?

Dimension	Charge(μC)
1.00	0.50
1.10	0.61
1.20	0.71
1.30	0.86

TABLE 19.2

a. The distance between the plates
b. The area
c. The length of a side
d. Both the area and the length of a side

36. In an experiment in which a circular parallel plate capacitor in a circuit with a battery has the radius and plate separation grow at the same relative rate, what will happen to the total charge on the capacitor?

19.7 Energy Stored in Capacitors

37. Consider a parallel plate capacitor, with no dielectric material, attached to a battery with a fixed voltage. What happens when a dielectric is inserted into the capacitor?
a. Nothing changes, except now there is a dielectric in the capacitor.
b. The energy in the system decreases, making it very easy to move the dielectric in.
c. You have to do work to move the dielectric, increasing the energy in the system.
d. The reversed polarity destroys the battery.

38. Consider a parallel plate capacitor with no dielectric material. It was attached to a battery with a fixed voltage to charge up, but now the battery has been disconnected. What happens to the energy of the system and the dielectric material when a dielectric is inserted into the capacitor?

39. What happens to the energy stored in a circuit as you increase the number of capacitors connected in parallel? Series?
a. increases, increases
b. increases, decreases
c. decreases, increases
d. decreases, decreases

40. What would the capacitance of a capacitor with the same total internal energy as the car battery in Example 19.1 have to be? Can you explain why we use batteries instead of capacitors for this application?

41. Consider a parallel plate capacitor with metal plates, each of square shape of 1.00 m on a side, separated by 1.00 mm. What is the energy of this capacitor with 3.00×10^{3} V applied to it?
a. 3.98×10^{-2} J
b. 5.08×10^{14} J
c. 1.33×10^{-5} J
d. 1.69×10^{11} J

42. Consider a parallel plate capacitor with metal plates, each of square shape of 1.00 m on a side, separated by 1.00 mm. What is the internal energy stored in this system if the charge on the capacitor is 30.0 μC?

43. Consider a parallel plate capacitor with metal plates, each of square shape of 1.00 m on a side, separated by 1.00 mm. If the plates grow in area while the voltage is held fixed, the capacitance ___ and the stored energy ___.
a. decreases, decreases
b. decreases, increases
c. increases, decreases
d. increases, increases

44. Consider a parallel plate capacitor with metal plates, each of square shape of 1.00 m on a side, separated by 1.00 mm. What happens to the energy of this system if the area of the plates increases while the charge remains fixed?

APPENDIX A

Atomic Masses

Atomic Number, Z	Name	Atomic Mass Number, A	Symbol	Atomic Mass (u)	Percent Abundance or Decay Mode	Half-life, $t_{1/2}$
0	neutron	1	n	1.008 665	β^-	10.37 min
1	Hydrogen	1	^1H	1.007 825	99.985%	
	Deuterium	2	^2H or D	2.014 102	0.015%	
	Tritium	3	^3H or T	3.016 050	β^-	12.33 y
2	Helium	3	^3He	3.016 030	$1.38 \times 10^{-4}\%$	
		4	^4He	4.002 603	$\approx 100\%$	
3	Lithium	6	^6Li	6.015 121	7.5%	
		7	^7Li	7.016 003	92.5%	
4	Beryllium	7	^7Be	7.016 928	EC	53.29 d
		9	^9Be	9.012 182	100%	
5	Boron	10	^{10}B	10.012 937	19.9%	
		11	^{11}B	11.009 305	80.1%	
6	Carbon	11	^{11}C	11.011 432	EC, β^+	

TABLE A1 Atomic Masses

Atomic Number, Z	Name	Atomic Mass Number, A	Symbol	Atomic Mass (u)	Percent Abundance or Decay Mode	Half-life, $t_{1/2}$
		12	^{12}C	12.000 000	98.90%	
		13	^{13}C	13.003 355	1.10%	
		14	^{14}C	14.003 241	β^-	5730 y
7	Nitrogen	13	^{13}N	13.005 738	β^+	9.96 min
		14	^{14}N	14.003 074	99.63%	
		15	^{15}N	15.000 108	0.37%	
8	Oxygen	15	^{15}O	15.003 065	EC, β^+	122 s
		16	^{16}O	15.994 915	99.76%	
		18	^{18}O	17.999 160	0.200%	
9	Fluorine	18	^{18}F	18.000 937	EC, β^+	1.83 h
		19	^{19}F	18.998 403	100%	
10	Neon	20	^{20}Ne	19.992 435	90.51%	
		22	^{22}Ne	21.991 383	9.22%	
11	Sodium	22	^{22}Na	21.994 434	β^+	2.602 y
		23	^{23}Na	22.989 767	100%	

TABLE A1 Atomic Masses

Atomic Number, Z	Name	Atomic Mass Number, A	Symbol	Atomic Mass (u)	Percent Abundance or Decay Mode	Half-life, $t_{1/2}$
		24	^{24}Na	23.990 961	β^-	14.96 h
12	Magnesium	24	^{24}Mg	23.985 042	78.99%	
13	Aluminum	27	^{27}Al	26.981 539	100%	
14	Silicon	28	^{28}Si	27.976 927	92.23%	2.62h
		31	^{31}Si	30.975 362	β^-	
15	Phosphorus	31	^{31}P	30.973 762	100%	
		32	^{32}P	31.973 907	β^-	14.28 d
16	Sulfur	32	^{32}S	31.972 070	95.02%	
		35	^{35}S	34.969 031	β^-	87.4 d
17	Chlorine	35	^{35}Cl	34.968 852	75.77%	
		37	^{37}Cl	36.965 903	24.23%	
18	Argon	40	^{40}Ar	39.962 384	99.60%	
19	Potassium	39	^{39}K	38.963 707	93.26%	
		40	^{40}K	39.963 999	0.0117%, EC, β^-	1.28×10^9 y
20	Calcium	40	^{40}Ca	39.962 591	96.94%	

TABLE A1 Atomic Masses

Atomic Number, *Z*	Name	Atomic Mass Number, *A*	Symbol	Atomic Mass (u)	Percent Abundance or Decay Mode	Half-life, $t_{1/2}$
21	Scandium	45	^{45}Sc	44.955 910	100%	
22	Titanium	48	^{48}Ti	47.947 947	73.8%	
23	Vanadium	51	^{51}V	50.943 962	99.75%	
24	Chromium	52	^{52}Cr	51.940 509	83.79%	
25	Manganese	55	^{55}Mn	54.938 047	100%	
26	Iron	56	^{56}Fe	55.934 939	91.72%	
27	Cobalt	59	^{59}Co	58.933 198	100%	
		60	^{60}Co	59.933 819	β^-	5.271 y
28	Nickel	58	^{58}Ni	57.935 346	68.27%	
		60	^{60}Ni	59.930 788	26.10%	
29	Copper	63	^{63}Cu	62.939 598	69.17%	
		65	^{65}Cu	64.927 793	30.83%	
30	Zinc	64	^{64}Zn	63.929 145	48.6%	
		66	^{66}Zn	65.926 034	27.9%	
31	Gallium	69	^{69}Ga	68.925 580	60.1%	

TABLE A1 Atomic Masses

Atomic Number, Z	Name	Atomic Mass Number, A	Symbol	Atomic Mass (u)	Percent Abundance or Decay Mode	Half-life, $t_{1/2}$
32	Germanium	72	^{72}Ge	71.922 079	27.4%	
		74	^{74}Ge	73.921 177	36.5%	
33	Arsenic	75	^{75}As	74.921 594	100%	
34	Selenium	80	^{80}Se	79.916 520	49.7%	
35	Bromine	79	^{79}Br	78.918 336	50.69%	
36	Krypton	84	^{84}Kr	83.911 507	57.0%	
37	Rubidium	85	^{85}Rb	84.911 794	72.17%	
38	Strontium	86	^{86}Sr	85.909 267	9.86%	
		88	^{88}Sr	87.905 619	82.58%	
		90	^{90}Sr	89.907 738	β^-	28.8 y
39	Yttrium	89	^{89}Y	88.905 849	100%	
		90	^{90}Y	89.907 152	β^-	64.1 h
40	Zirconium	90	^{90}Zr	89.904 703	51.45%	
41	Niobium	93	^{93}Nb	92.906 377	100%	
42	Molybdenum	98	^{98}Mo	97.905 406	24.13%	

TABLE A1 Atomic Masses

Atomic Number, Z	Name	Atomic Mass Number, A	Symbol	Atomic Mass (u)	Percent Abundance or Decay Mode	Half-life, $t_{1/2}$
43	Technetium	98	^{98}Tc	97.907 215	β^-	$4.2 \times 10^6 y$
44	Ruthenium	102	^{102}Ru	101.904 348	31.6%	
45	Rhodium	103	^{103}Rh	102.905 500	100%	
46	Palladium	106	^{106}Pd	105.903 478	27.33%	
47	Silver	107	^{107}Ag	106.905 092	51.84%	
		109	^{109}Ag	108.904 757	48.16%	
48	Cadmium	114	^{114}Cd	113.903 357	28.73%	
49	Indium	115	^{115}In	114.903 880	95.7%, β^-	$4.4 \times 10^{14} y$
50	Tin	120	^{120}Sn	119.902 200	32.59%	
51	Antimony	121	^{121}Sb	120.903 821	57.3%	
52	Tellurium	130	^{130}Te	129.906 229	33.8%, β^-	$2.5 \times 10^{21} y$
53	Iodine	127	^{127}I	126.904 473	100%	
		131	^{131}I	130.906 114	β^-	8.040 d
54	Xenon	132	^{132}Xe	131.904 144	26.9%	
		136	^{136}Xe	135.907 214	8.9%	

TABLE A1 Atomic Masses

Atomic Number, Z	Name	Atomic Mass Number, A	Symbol	Atomic Mass (u)	Percent Abundance or Decay Mode	Half-life, $t_{1/2}$
55	Cesium	133	^{133}Cs	132.905 429	100%	
		134	^{134}Cs	133.906 696	EC, β^-	2.06 y
56	Barium	137	^{137}Ba	136.905 812	11.23%	
		138	^{138}Ba	137.905 232	71.70%	
57	Lanthanum	139	^{139}La	138.906 346	99.91%	
58	Cerium	140	^{140}Ce	139.905 433	88.48%	
59	Praseodymium	141	^{141}Pr	140.907 647	100%	
60	Neodymium	142	^{142}Nd	141.907 719	27.13%	
61	Promethium	145	^{145}Pm	144.912 743	EC, α	17.7 y
62	Samarium	152	^{152}Sm	151.919 729	26.7%	
63	Europium	153	^{153}Eu	152.921 225	52.2%	
64	Gadolinium	158	^{158}Gd	157.924 099	24.84%	
65	Terbium	159	^{159}Tb	158.925 342	100%	
66	Dysprosium	164	^{164}Dy	163.929 171	28.2%	
67	Holmium	165	^{165}Ho	164.930 319	100%	

TABLE A1 Atomic Masses

Atomic Number, Z	Name	Atomic Mass Number, A	Symbol	Atomic Mass (u)	Percent Abundance or Decay Mode	Half-life, $t_{1/2}$
68	Erbium	166	^{166}Er	165.930 290	33.6%	
69	Thulium	169	^{169}Tm	168.934 212	100%	
70	Ytterbium	174	^{174}Yb	173.938 859	31.8%	
71	Lutecium	175	^{175}Lu	174.940 770	97.41%	
72	Hafnium	180	^{180}Hf	179.946 545	35.10%	
73	Tantalum	181	^{181}Ta	180.947 992	99.98%	
74	Tungsten	184	^{184}W	183.950 928	30.67%	
75	Rhenium	187	^{187}Re	186.955 744	62.6%, β^-	4.6×10^{10} y
76	Osmium	191	^{191}Os	190.960 920	β^-	15.4 d
		192	^{192}Os	191.961 467	41.0%	
77	Iridium	191	^{191}Ir	190.960 584	37.3%	
		193	^{193}Ir	192.962 917	62.7%	
78	Platinum	195	^{195}Pt	194.964 766	33.8%	
79	Gold	197	^{197}Au	196.966 543	100%	
		198	^{198}Au	197.968 217	β^-	2.696 d

TABLE A1 Atomic Masses

Atomic Number, Z	Name	Atomic Mass Number, A	Symbol	Atomic Mass (u)	Percent Abundance or Decay Mode	Half-life, $t_{1/2}$
80	Mercury	199	^{199}Hg	198.968 253	16.87%	
		202	^{202}Hg	201.970 617	29.86%	
81	Thallium	205	^{205}Tl	204.974 401	70.48%	
82	Lead	206	^{206}Pb	205.974 440	24.1%	
		207	^{207}Pb	206.975 872	22.1%	
		208	^{208}Pb	207.976 627	52.4%	
		210	^{210}Pb	209.984 163	α, β^-	22.3 y
		211	^{211}Pb	210.988 735	β^-	36.1 min
		212	^{212}Pb	211.991 871	β^-	10.64 h
83	Bismuth	209	^{209}Bi	208.980 374	100%	
		211	^{211}Bi	210.987 255	α, β^-	2.14 min
84	Polonium	210	^{210}Po	209.982 848	α	138.38 d
85	Astatine	218	^{218}At	218.008 684	α, β^-	1.6 s
86	Radon	222	^{222}Rn	222.017 570	α	3.82 d
87	Francium	223	^{223}Fr	223.019 733	α, β^-	21.8 min

TABLE A1 Atomic Masses

Atomic Number, *Z*	Name	Atomic Mass Number, *A*	Symbol	Atomic Mass (u)	Percent Abundance or Decay Mode	Half-life, $t_{1/2}$
88	Radium	226	^{226}Ra	226.025 402	α	1.60×10^3 y
89	Actinium	227	^{227}Ac	227.027 750	α, β^-	21.8 y
90	Thorium	228	^{228}Th	228.028 715	α	1.91 y
		232	^{232}Th	232.038 054	100%, α	1.41×10^{10} y
91	Protactinium	231	^{231}Pa	231.035 880	α	3.28×10^4 y
92	Uranium	233	^{233}U	233.039 628	α	1.59×10^3 y
		235	^{235}U	235.043 924	0.720%, α	7.04×10^8 y
		236	^{236}U	236.045 562	α	2.34×10^7 y
		238	^{238}U	238.050 784	99.2745%, α	4.47×10^9 y
		239	^{239}U	239.054 289	β^-	23.5 min
93	Neptunium	239	^{239}Np	239.052 933	β^-	2.355 d
94	Plutonium	239	^{239}Pu	239.052 157	α	2.41×10^4 y
95	Americium	243	^{243}Am	243.061 375	α, fission	7.37×10^3 y
96	Curium	245	^{245}Cm	245.065 483	α	8.50×10^3 y
97	Berkelium	247	^{247}Bk	247.070 300	α	1.38×10^3 y

TABLE A1 Atomic Masses

Atomic Number, Z	Name	Atomic Mass Number, A	Symbol	Atomic Mass (u)	Percent Abundance or Decay Mode	Half-life, $t_{1/2}$
98	Californium	249	^{249}Cf	249.074 844	α	351 y
99	Einsteinium	254	^{254}Es	254.088 019	α, β^-	276 d
100	Fermium	253	^{253}Fm	253.085 173	EC, α	3.00 d
101	Mendelevium	255	^{255}Md	255.091 081	EC, α	27 min
102	Nobelium	255	^{255}No	255.093 260	EC, α	3.1 min
103	Lawrencium	257	^{257}Lr	257.099 480	EC, α	0.646 s
104	Rutherfordium	261	^{261}Rf	261.108 690	α	1.08 min
105	Dubnium	262	^{262}Db	262.113 760	α, fission	34 s
106	Seaborgium	263	^{263}Sg	263.11 86	α, fission	0.8 s
107	Bohrium	262	^{262}Bh	262.123 1	α	0.102 s
108	Hassium	264	^{264}Hs	264.128 5	α	0.08 ms
109	Meitnerium	266	^{266}Mt	266.137 8	α	3.4 ms

TABLE A1 Atomic Masses

APPENDIX B

Selected Radioactive Isotopes

Decay modes are α, β^-, β^+, electron capture (EC) and isomeric transition (IT). EC results in the same daughter nucleus as would β^+ decay. IT is a transition from a metastable excited state. Energies for $\beta^\pm$ decays are the maxima; average energies are roughly one-half the maxima.

Isotope	$t_{1/2}$	DecayMode(s)	Energy(MeV)	Percent		γ-Ray Energy(MeV)	Percent
^{3}H	12.33 y	β^-	0.0186	100%			
^{14}C	5730 y	β^-	0.156	100%			
^{13}N	9.96 min	β^+	1.20	100%			
^{22}Na	2.602 y	β^+	0.55	90%	γ	1.27	100%
^{32}P	14.28 d	β^-	1.71	100%			
^{35}S	87.4 d	β^-	0.167	100%			
^{36}Cl	3.00×10^5 y	β^-	0.710	100%			
^{40}K	1.28×10^9 y	β^-	1.31	89%			
^{43}K	22.3 h	β^-	0.827	87%	γs	0.373	87%
						0.618	87%
^{45}Ca	165 d	β^-	0.257	100%			
^{51}Cr	27.70 d	EC			γ	0.320	10%
^{52}Mn	5.59d	β^+	3.69	28%	γs	1.33	28%
						1.43	28%
^{52}Fe	8.27 h	β^+	1.80	43%		0.169	43%
						0.378	43%
^{59}Fe	44.6 d	β^-s	0.273	45%	γs	1.10	57%
			0.466	55%		1.29	43%

TABLE B1 Selected Radioactive Isotopes

Isotope	$t_{1/2}$	DecayMode(s)	Energy(MeV)	Percent		γ-Ray Energy(MeV)	Percent
^{60}Co	5.271 y	β^-	0.318	100%	γs	1.17	100%
						1.33	100%
^{65}Zn	244.1 d	EC			γ	1.12	51%
^{67}Ga	78.3 h	EC			γs	0.0933	70%
						0.185	35%
						0.300	19%
						others	
^{75}Se	118.5 d	EC			γs	0.121	20%
						0.136	65%
						0.265	68%
						0.280	20%
						others	
^{86}Rb	18.8 d	β^-s	0.69	9%	γ	1.08	9%
			1.77	91%			
^{85}Sr	64.8 d	EC			γ	0.514	100%
^{90}Sr	28.8 y	β^-	0.546	100%			
^{90}Y	64.1 h	β^-	2.28	100%			
^{99m}Tc	6.02 h	IT			γ	0.142	100%
^{113m}In	99.5 min	IT			γ	0.392	100%
^{123}I	13.0 h	EC			γ	0.159	$\approx$100%
^{131}I	8.040 d	β^-s	0.248	7%	γs	0.364	85%
			0.607	93%		others	
			others				
^{129}Cs	32.3 h	EC			γs	0.0400	35%

TABLE B1 Selected Radioactive Isotopes

Isotope	$t_{1/2}$	DecayMode(s)	Energy(MeV)	Percent		γ-Ray Energy(MeV)	Percent
						0.372	32%
						0.411	25%
						others	
^{137}Cs	30.17 y	β^-s	0.511	95%	γ	0.662	95%
			1.17	5%			
^{140}Ba	12.79 d	β^-	1.035	$\approx 100\%$	γs	0.030	25%
						0.044	65%
						0.537	24%
						others	
^{198}Au	2.696 d	β^-	1.161	$\approx 100\%$	γ	0.412	$\approx 100\%$
^{197}Hg	64.1 h	EC			γ	0.0733	100%
^{210}Po	138.38 d	α	5.41	100%			
^{226}Ra	1.60×10^3 y	αs	4.68	5%	γ	0.186	100%
			4.87	95%			
^{235}U	7.038×10^8 y	α	4.68	$\approx 100\%$	γs	numerous	<0.400%
^{238}U	4.468×10^9 y	αs	4.22	23%	γ	0.050	23%
			4.27	77%			
^{237}Np	2.14×10^6 y	αs	numerous		γs	numerous	<0.250%
			4.96 (max.)				
^{239}Pu	2.41×10^4 y	αs	5.19	11%	γs	7.5×10^{-5}	73%
			5.23	15%		0.013	15%
			5.24	73%		0.052	10%
						others	
^{243}Am	7.37×10^3 y	αs	Max. 5.44		γs	0.075	

TABLE B1 Selected Radioactive Isotopes

Isotope	$t_{1/2}$	DecayMode(s)	Energy(MeV)	Percent		γ-Ray Energy(MeV)	Percent
			5.37	88%		others	
			5.32	11%			
			others				

TABLE B1 Selected Radioactive Isotopes

APPENDIX C

Useful Information

This appendix is broken into several tables.

- Table C1, Important Constants
- Table C2, Submicroscopic Masses
- Table C3, Solar System Data
- Table C4, Metric Prefixes for Powers of Ten and Their Symbols
- Table C5, The Greek Alphabet
- Table C6, SI units
- Table C7, Selected British Units
- Table C8, Other Units
- Table C9, Useful Formulae

Symbol	Meaning	Best Value	Approximate Value
c	Speed of light in vacuum	2.99792458×10^8 m/s	3.00×10^8 m/s
G	Gravitational constant	$6.67408(31) \times 10^{-11}\ \text{N} \cdot \text{m}^2/\text{kg}^2$	$6.67 \times 10^{-11}\ \text{N} \cdot \text{m}^2/\text{kg}^2$
N_A	Avogadro's number	$6.02214076 \times 10^{23}$	6.02×10^{23}
k	Boltzmann's constant	1.380649×10^{-23} J/K	1.38×10^{-23} J/K
R	Gas constant	$8.3144621(75)\ \text{J/mol} \cdot \text{K}$	$8.31\ \text{J/mol} \cdot \text{K} = 1.99\ \text{cal/mol} \cdot \text{K} = 0.0821\ \text{atm} \cdot \text{L/mol} \cdot \text{K}$
σ	Stefan-Boltzmann constant	$5.670373(21) \times 10^{-8}\ \text{W/m}^2 \cdot \text{K}$	$5.67 \times 10^{-8}\ \text{W/m}^2 \cdot \text{K}$
k	Coulomb force constant	$8.987551788... \times 10^9\ \text{N} \cdot \text{m}^2/\text{C}^2$	$8.99 \times 10^9\ \text{N} \cdot \text{m}^2/\text{C}^2$
q_e	Charge on electron	$-1.602176634 \times 10^{-19}$ C	-1.60×10^{-19} C
ε_0	Permittivity of free space	$8.854187817... \times 10^{-12}\ \text{C}^2/\text{N} \cdot \text{m}^2$	$8.85 \times 10^{-12}\ \text{C}^2/\text{N} \cdot \text{m}^2$
μ_0	Permeability of free space	$4\pi \times 10^{-7}\ \text{T} \cdot \text{m/A}$	$1.26 \times 10^{-6}\ \text{T} \cdot \text{m/A}$
h	Planck's constant	$6.62607015 \times 10^{-34}\ \text{J} \cdot \text{s}$	$6.63 \times 10^{-34}\ \text{J} \cdot \text{s}$

TABLE C1 Important Constants [1]

1 Stated values are according to the National Institute of Standards and Technology Reference on Constants, Units, and Uncertainty, www.physics.nist.gov/cuu (http://www.physics.nist.gov/cuu) (accessed May 18, 2012). Values in parentheses are the uncertainties in the last digits. Numbers without uncertainties are exact as defined.

Symbol	Meaning	Best Value	Approximate Value
m_e	Electron mass	$9.10938291(40) \times 10^{-31}$ kg	9.11×10^{-31} kg
m_p	Proton mass	$1.672621777(74) \times 10^{-27}$ kg	1.6726×10^{-27} kg
m_n	Neutron mass	$1.674927351(74) \times 10^{-27}$ kg	1.6749×10^{-27} kg
u	Atomic mass unit	$1.660538921(73) \times 10^{-27}$ kg	1.6605×10^{-27} kg

TABLE C2 Submicroscopic Masses [2]

Sun	mass	1.99×10^{30} kg
	average radius	6.96×10^{8} m
	Earth-sun distance (average)	1.496×10^{11} m
Earth	mass	5.9736×10^{24} kg
	average radius	6.376×10^{6} m
	orbital period	3.16×10^{7} s
Moon	mass	7.35×10^{22} kg
	average radius	1.74×10^{6} m
	orbital period (average)	2.36×10^{6} s
	Earth-moon distance (average)	3.84×10^{8} m

TABLE C3 Solar System Data

Prefix	Symbol	Value	Prefix	Symbol	Value
tera	T	10^{12}	deci	d	10^{-1}
giga	G	10^{9}	centi	c	10^{-2}
mega	M	10^{6}	milli	m	10^{-3}
kilo	k	10^{3}	micro	μ	10^{-6}
hecto	h	10^{2}	nano	n	10^{-9}

TABLE C4 Metric Prefixes for Powers of Ten and Their Symbols

2 Stated values are according to the National Institute of Standards and Technology Reference on Constants, Units, and Uncertainty, www.physics.nist.gov/cuu (http://www.physics.nist.gov/cuu) (accessed May 18, 2012). Values in parentheses are the uncertainties in the last digits. Numbers without uncertainties are exact as defined.

Prefix	Symbol	Value	Prefix	Symbol	Value
deka	da	10^1	pico	p	10^{-12}
–	–	$10^0 (= 1)$	femto	f	10^{-15}

TABLE C4 Metric Prefixes for Powers of Ten and Their Symbols

Alpha	A	α	Eta	H	η	Nu	N	ν	Tau	T	τ
Beta	B	β	Theta	Θ	θ	Xi	Ξ	ξ	Upsilon	Υ	υ
Gamma	Γ	γ	Iota	I	ι	Omicron	O	o	Phi	Φ	ϕ
Delta	Δ	δ	Kappa	K	κ	Pi	Π	π	Chi	X	χ
Epsilon	E	ε	Lambda	Λ	λ	Rho	P	ρ	Psi	Ψ	ψ
Zeta	Z	ζ	Mu	M	μ	Sigma	Σ	σ	Omega	Ω	ω

TABLE C5 The Greek Alphabet

	Entity	Abbreviation	Name
Fundamental units	Length	m	meter
	Mass	kg	kilogram
	Time	s	second
	Current	A	ampere
Supplementary unit	Angle	rad	radian
Derived units	Force	$\mathrm{N = kg \cdot m/s^2}$	newton
	Energy	$\mathrm{J = kg \cdot m^2/s^2}$	joule
	Power	$\mathrm{W = J/s}$	watt
	Pressure	$\mathrm{Pa = N/m^2}$	pascal
	Frequency	$\mathrm{Hz = 1/s}$	hertz
	Electronic potential	$\mathrm{V = J/C}$	volt
	Capacitance	$\mathrm{F = C/V}$	farad
	Charge	$\mathrm{C = s \cdot A}$	coulomb

TABLE C6 SI Units

	Entity	Abbreviation	Name
	Resistance	$\Omega = \text{V/A}$	ohm
	Magnetic field	$\text{T} = \text{N/(A} \cdot \text{m)}$	tesla
	Nuclear decay rate	$\text{Bq} = 1/\text{s}$	becquerel

TABLE C6 SI Units

Length	1 inch (in.)= 2.54 cm (exactly)
	1 foot (ft)= 0.3048 m
	1 mile (mi)= 1.609 km
Force	1 pound (lb)= 4.448 N
Energy	1 British thermal unit (Btu)= 1.055×10^3 J
Power	1 horsepower (hp)= 746 W
Pressure	$1\ \text{lb/in}^2 = 6.895 \times 10^3$ Pa

TABLE C7 Selected British Units

Length	1 light year (ly) = 9.46×10^{15} m
	1 astronomical unit (au) = 1.50×10^{11} m
	1 nautical mile = 1.852 km
	1 angstrom(Å) = 10^{-10} m
Area	1 acre (ac) = $4.05 \times 10^3\ \text{m}^2$
	1 square foot (ft^2) = $9.29 \times 10^{-2}\ \text{m}^2$
	1 barn (b) = $10^{-28}\ \text{m}^2$
Volume	1 liter (L) = $10^{-3}\ \text{m}^3$
	1 U.S. gallon (gal) = $3.785 \times 10^{-3}\ \text{m}^3$
Mass	1 solar mass = 1.99×10^{30} kg
	1 metric ton = 10^3 kg
	1 atomic mass unit (u) = 1.6605×10^{-27} kg

TABLE C8 Other Units

Time	1 year (y) $= 3.16 \times 10^7$ s
	1 day (d) $= 86{,}400$ s
Speed	1 mile per hour (mph) $= 1.609$ km/h
	1 nautical mile per hour (naut) $= 1.852$ km/h
Angle	1 degree (°) $= 1.745 \times 10^{-2}$ rad
	1 minute of arc (′) = 1/60 degree
	1 second of arc (″) = 1/60 minute of arc
	1 grad $= 1.571 \times 10^{-2}$ rad
Energy	1 kiloton TNT (kT) $= 4.2 \times 10^{12}$ J
	1 kilowatt hour ($kW \cdot h$) $= 3.60 \times 10^6$ J
	1 food calorie (kcal) = 4186 J
	1 calorie (cal) = 4.186 J
	1 electron volt (eV) $= 1.60 \times 10^{-19}$ J
Pressure	1 atmosphere (atm) $= 1.013 \times 10^5$ Pa
	1 millimeter of mercury (mm Hg) = 133.3 Pa
	1 torricelli (torr) = 1 mm Hg = 133.3 Pa
Nuclear decay rate	1 curie (Ci) $= 3.70 \times 10^{10}$ Bq

TABLE C8 Other Units

Circumference of a circle with radius r or diameter d	$C = 2\pi r = \pi d$
Area of a circle with radius r or diameter d	$A = \pi r^2 = \pi d^2/4$
Area of a sphere with radius r	$A = 4\pi r^2$
Volume of a sphere with radius r	$V = (4/3)\left(\pi r^3\right)$

TABLE C9 Useful Formulae

APPENDIX D

Glossary of Key Symbols and Notation

In this glossary, key symbols and notation are briefly defined.

Symbol	Definition
$\overline{\text{any symbol}}$	average (indicated by a bar over a symbol—e.g., $\bar{v}$ is average velocity)
°C	Celsius degree
°F	Fahrenheit degree
//	parallel
$\perp$	perpendicular
$\propto$	proportional to
$\pm$	plus or minus
$_0$	zero as a subscript denotes an initial value
α	alpha rays
α	angular acceleration
α	temperature coefficient(s) of resistivity
β	beta rays
β	sound level
β	volume coefficient of expansion
β^-	electron emitted in nuclear beta decay
β^+	positron decay
γ	gamma rays
γ	surface tension
$\gamma = 1/\sqrt{1 - v^2/c^2}$	a constant used in relativity
Δ	change in whatever quantity follows

TABLE D1

Symbol	Definition
δ	uncertainty in whatever quantity follows
ΔE	change in energy between the initial and final orbits of an electron in an atom
ΔE	uncertainty in energy
Δm	difference in mass between initial and final products
ΔN	number of decays that occur
Δp	change in momentum
Δp	uncertainty in momentum
$\Delta \mathrm{PE}_{\mathrm{g}}$	change in gravitational potential energy
$\Delta \theta$	rotation angle
Δs	distance traveled along a circular path
Δt	uncertainty in time
Δt_0	proper time as measured by an observer at rest relative to the process
ΔV	potential difference
Δx	uncertainty in position
ε_0	permittivity of free space
η	viscosity
θ	angle between the force vector and the displacement vector
θ	angle between two lines
θ	contact angle
θ	direction of the resultant
θ_b	Brewster's angle
θ_c	critical angle
κ	dielectric constant
λ	decay constant of a nuclide

TABLE D1

Symbol	Definition
λ	wavelength
λ_n	wavelength in a medium
μ_0	permeability of free space
μ_k	coefficient of kinetic friction
μ_s	coefficient of static friction
v_e	electron neutrino
π^+	positive pion
π^-	negative pion
π^0	neutral pion
ρ	density
ρ_c	critical density, the density needed to just halt universal expansion
ρ_fl	fluid density
$\bar{\rho}_\mathrm{obj}$	average density of an object
ρ/ρ_w	specific gravity
τ	characteristic time constant for a resistance and inductance (RL) or resistance and capacitance (RC) circuit
τ	characteristic time for a resistor and capacitor (RC) circuit
τ	torque
Υ	upsilon meson
Φ	magnetic flux
ϕ	phase angle
Ω	ohm (unit)
ω	angular velocity
A	ampere (current unit)
A	area

TABLE D1

Symbol	Definition
A	cross-sectional area
A	total number of nucleons
a	acceleration
a_B	Bohr radius
a_c	centripetal acceleration
a_t	tangential acceleration
AC	alternating current
AM	amplitude modulation
atm	atmosphere
B	baryon number
B	blue quark color
$\overline{B}$	antiblue (yellow) antiquark color
b	quark flavor bottom or beauty
B	bulk modulus
B	magnetic field strength
B_{int}	electron's intrinsic magnetic field
B_{orb}	orbital magnetic field
BE	binding energy of a nucleus—it is the energy required to completely disassemble it into separate protons and neutrons
BE/A	binding energy per nucleon
Bq	becquerel—one decay per second
C	capacitance (amount of charge stored per volt)
C	coulomb (a fundamental SI unit of charge)
C_p	total capacitance in parallel
C_s	total capacitance in series

TABLE D1

Symbol	Definition
CG	center of gravity
CM	center of mass
c	quark flavor charm
c	specific heat
c	speed of light
Cal	kilocalorie
cal	calorie
COP_{hp}	heat pump's coefficient of performance
COP_{ref}	coefficient of performance for refrigerators and air conditioners
$\cos\theta$	cosine
$\cot\theta$	cotangent
$\csc\theta$	cosecant
D	diffusion constant
d	displacement
d	quark flavor down
dB	decibel
d_{i}	distance of an image from the center of a lens
d_{o}	distance of an object from the center of a lens
DC	direct current
E	electric field strength
ε	emf (voltage) or Hall electromotive force
emf	electromotive force
E	energy of a single photon
E	nuclear reaction energy

TABLE D1

Symbol	Definition
E	relativistic total energy
E	total energy
E_0	ground state energy for hydrogen
E_0	rest energy
EC	electron capture
E_{cap}	energy stored in a capacitor
Eff	efficiency—the useful work output divided by the energy input
Eff_C	Carnot efficiency
E_{in}	energy consumed (food digested in humans)
E_{ind}	energy stored in an inductor
E_{out}	energy output
e	emissivity of an object
e^+	antielectron or positron
eV	electron volt
F	farad (unit of capacitance, a coulomb per volt)
F	focal point of a lens
$\mathbf{F}$	force
F	magnitude of a force
F	restoring force
F_{B}	buoyant force
F_{c}	centripetal force
F_{i}	force input
$\mathbf{F}_{\text{net}}$	net force
F_{o}	force output

TABLE D1

Symbol	Definition
FM	frequency modulation
f	focal length
f	frequency
f_0	resonant frequency of a resistance, inductance, and capacitance (RLC) series circuit
f_0	threshold frequency for a particular material (photoelectric effect)
f_1	fundamental
f_2	first overtone
f_3	second overtone
f_B	beat frequency
f_k	magnitude of kinetic friction
f_s	magnitude of static friction
G	gravitational constant
G	green quark color
$\overline{G}$	antigreen (magenta) antiquark color
g	acceleration due to gravity
g	gluons (carrier particles for strong nuclear force)
h	change in vertical position
h	height above some reference point
h	maximum height of a projectile
h	Planck's constant
hf	photon energy
h_i	height of the image
h_o	height of the object
I	electric current

TABLE D1

Symbol	Definition
I	intensity
I	intensity of a transmitted wave
I	moment of inertia (also called rotational inertia)
I_0	intensity of a polarized wave before passing through a filter
I_{ave}	average intensity for a continuous sinusoidal electromagnetic wave
I_{rms}	average current
J	joule
J/Ψ	Joules/psi meson
K	kelvin
k	Boltzmann constant
k	force constant of a spring
K_α	x rays created when an electron falls into an $n = 1$ shell vacancy from the $n = 3$ shell
K_β	x rays created when an electron falls into an $n = 2$ shell vacancy from the $n = 3$ shell
kcal	kilocalorie
KE	translational kinetic energy
KE + PE	mechanical energy
KE_e	kinetic energy of an ejected electron
KE_{rel}	relativistic kinetic energy
KE_{rot}	rotational kinetic energy
$\overline{\text{KE}}$	thermal energy
kg	kilogram (a fundamental SI unit of mass)
L	angular momentum
L	liter
L	magnitude of angular momentum

TABLE D1

Symbol	Definition
L	self-inductance
ℓ	angular momentum quantum number
L_α	x rays created when an electron falls into an $n = 2$ shell
L_e	electron total family number
L_μ	muon family total number
L_τ	tau family total number
L_{f}	heat of fusion
L_{f} and L_{v}	latent heat coefficients
L_{orb}	orbital angular momentum
L_{s}	heat of sublimation
L_{v}	heat of vaporization
L_z	z - component of the angular momentum
M	angular magnification
M	mutual inductance
m	indicates metastable state
m	magnification
m	mass
m	mass of an object as measured by a person at rest relative to the object
m	meter (a fundamental SI unit of length)
m	order of interference
m	overall magnification (product of the individual magnifications)
$m\left({}^{A}\text{X}\right)$	atomic mass of a nuclide
MA	mechanical advantage
m_{e}	magnification of the eyepiece

TABLE D1

Symbol	Definition
m_e	mass of the electron
m_ℓ	angular momentum projection quantum number
m_n	mass of a neutron
m_{o}	magnification of the objective lens
mol	mole
m_p	mass of a proton
m_{s}	spin projection quantum number
N	magnitude of the normal force
N	newton
$\mathbf{N}$	normal force
N	number of neutrons
n	index of refraction
n	number of free charges per unit volume
N_{A}	Avogadro's number
N_{r}	Reynolds number
$\mathrm{N \cdot m}$	newton-meter (work-energy unit)
$\mathrm{N \cdot m}$	newtons times meters (SI unit of torque)
OE	other energy
P	power
P	power of a lens
P	pressure
$\mathbf{p}$	momentum
p	momentum magnitude
p	relativistic momentum

TABLE D1

Symbol	Definition
$\mathbf{p}_{tot}$	total momentum
$\mathbf{p}'_{tot}$	total momentum some time later
P_{abs}	absolute pressure
P_{atm}	atmospheric pressure
P_{atm}	standard atmospheric pressure
PE	potential energy
PE_{el}	elastic potential energy
PE_{elec}	electric potential energy
PE_s	potential energy of a spring
P_g	gauge pressure
P_{in}	power consumption or input
P_{out}	useful power output going into useful work or a desired, form of energy
Q	latent heat
Q	net heat transferred into a system
Q	flow rate—volume per unit time flowing past a point
$+Q$	positive charge
$-Q$	negative charge
q	electron charge
q_p	charge of a proton
q	test charge
QF	quality factor
R	activity, the rate of decay
R	radius of curvature of a spherical mirror
R	red quark color

TABLE D1

Symbol	Definition
$\overline{R}$	antired (cyan) quark color
R	resistance
$\mathbf{R}$	resultant or total displacement
R	Rydberg constant
R	universal gas constant
r	distance from pivot point to the point where a force is applied
r	internal resistance
$r_{\perp}$	perpendicular lever arm
r	radius of a nucleus
r	radius of curvature
r	resistivity
r or rad	radiation dose unit
rem	roentgen equivalent man
rad	radian
RBE	relative biological effectiveness
RC	resistor and capacitor circuit
rms	root mean square
r_n	radius of the *n*th H-atom orbit
R_{p}	total resistance of a parallel connection
R_{s}	total resistance of a series connection
R_{s}	Schwarzschild radius
S	entropy
$\mathbf{S}$	intrinsic spin (intrinsic angular momentum)
S	magnitude of the intrinsic (internal) spin angular momentum

TABLE D1

Symbol	Definition
S	shear modulus
S	strangeness quantum number
s	quark flavor strange
s	second (fundamental SI unit of time)
s	spin quantum number
s	total displacement
$\sec\theta$	secant
$\sin\theta$	sine
s_z	z-component of spin angular momentum
T	period—time to complete one oscillation
T	temperature
T_c	critical temperature—temperature below which a material becomes a superconductor
T	tension
T	tesla (magnetic field strength B)
t	quark flavor top or truth
t	time
$t_{1/2}$	half-life—the time in which half of the original nuclei decay
$\tan\theta$	tangent
U	internal energy
u	quark flavor up
u	unified atomic mass unit
u	velocity of an object relative to an observer
u'	velocity relative to another observer
V	electric potential

TABLE D1

Symbol	Definition
V	terminal voltage
V	volt (unit)
V	volume
$\mathbf{v}$	relative velocity between two observers
v	speed of light in a material
$\mathbf{v}$	velocity
$\bar{\mathbf{v}}$	average fluid velocity
$V_B - V_A$	change in potential
$\mathbf{v}_d$	drift velocity
V_p	transformer input voltage
V_{rms}	rms voltage
V_s	transformer output voltage
$\mathbf{v}_{tot}$	total velocity
v_w	propagation speed of sound or other wave
$\mathbf{v}_w$	wave velocity
W	work
W	net work done by a system
W	watt
w	weight
w_{fl}	weight of the fluid displaced by an object
W_c	total work done by all conservative forces
W_{nc}	total work done by all nonconservative forces
W_{out}	useful work output
X	amplitude

TABLE D1

Symbol	Definition
X	symbol for an element
${}^{Z}_{A}X_{N}$	notation for a particular nuclide
x	deformation or displacement from equilibrium
x	displacement of a spring from its undeformed position
x	horizontal axis
X_{C}	capacitive reactance
X_{L}	inductive reactance
x_{rms}	root mean square diffusion distance
y	vertical axis
Y	elastic modulus or Young's modulus
Z	atomic number (number of protons in a nucleus)
Z	impedance

TABLE D1

ANSWER KEY

Chapter 1

Problems & Exercises

1.
(a) 27.8 m/s

(b) 62.1 mph

3.
$$\frac{1.0\text{ m}}{\text{s}} = \frac{1.0\text{ m}}{\text{s}} \times \frac{3600\text{ s}}{1\text{ hr}} \times \frac{1\text{ km}}{1000\text{ m}}$$

$= 3.6\text{ km/h}$.

5.
length: $377\text{ ft}; 4.53 \times 10^3\text{ in.}$ width: $280\text{ ft}; 3.3 \times 10^3\text{ in.}$

7.
8.847 km

9.
(a) $1.3 \times 10^{-9}\text{ m}$

(b) 40 km/My

11.
2 kg

13.
(a) $85.5\text{ to }94.5\text{ km/h}$

(b) $53.1\text{ to }58.7\text{ mi/h}$

15.
(a) $7.6 \times 10^7\text{ beats}$

(b) $7.57 \times 10^7\text{ beats}$

(c) $7.57 \times 10^7\text{ beats}$

17.
(a) 3

(b) 3

(c) 3

19.
(a) 2.2%

(b) $59\text{ to }61\text{ km/h}$

21.
$80 \pm 3\text{ beats/min}$

23.
2.8 h

25.

$11 \pm 1 \text{ cm}^3$

27.
$12.06 \pm 0.04 \text{ m}^2$

29.
Sample answer: 2×10^9 heartbeats

31.
Sample answer: 2×10^{31} if an average human lifetime is taken to be about 70 years.

33.
Sample answer: 50 atoms

35.
Sample answers:

(a) 10^{12} cells/hummingbird

(b) 10^{16} cells/human

Chapter 2

Problems & Exercises

1.
(a) 7 m

(b) 7 m

(c) $+7 \text{ m}$

3.
a. $8 \text{ m} + 2 \text{ m} + 3 \text{ m} = \underline{13 \text{ m}}$

b. $\underline{9 \text{ m}}$

c. $\Delta x = 11 \text{ m} - 2 \text{ m} = \underline{9 \text{ m}}$

5.
(a) $3.0 \times 10^4 \text{ m/s}$

(b) 0 m/s

7.
2×10^7 years

9.
$34.689 \text{ m/s} = 124.88 \text{ km/h}$

11.
(a) 40.0 km/h

(b) 34.3 km/h, 25° S of E.

(c) average speed $= 3.20 \text{ km/h}$, $\bar{v} = 0$.

13.
384,000 km

15.
(a) $6.61 \times 10^{15} \text{ rev/s}$

(b) 0 m/s

16.

4.29 m/s^2

18.
(a) 1.43 s

(b) $-2.50\ m/s^2$

20.
(a) 10.8 m/s

(b)

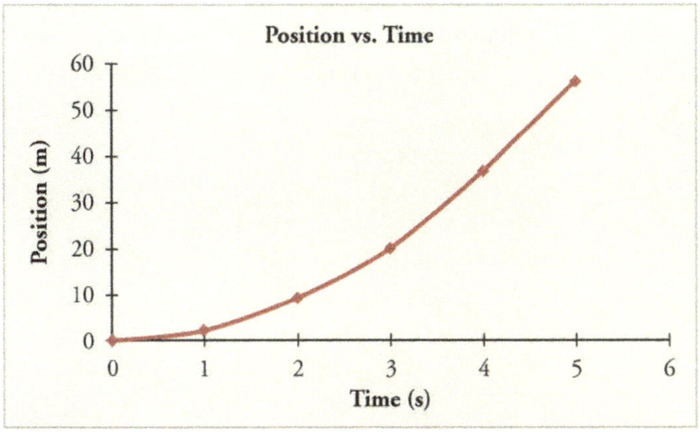

21.
38.9 m/s (about 87 miles per hour)

23.
(a) 16.5 s

(b) 13.5 s

(c) $-2.68\ m/s^2$

25.
(a) 20.0 m

(b) -1.00 m/s

(c) This result does not really make sense. If the runner starts at 9.00 m/s and decelerates at $2.00\ m/s^2$, then she will have stopped after 4.50 s. If she continues to decelerate, she will be running backwards.

27.
0.799 m

29.
(a) 28.0 m/s

(b) 50.9 s

(c) 7.68 km to accelerate and 713 m to decelerate

31.
(a) 51.4 m

(b) 17.1 s

33.
(a) $-80.4\ m/s^2$

(b) 9.33×10^{-2} s

35.
(a) $7.7\ \text{m/s}$

(b) $-15 \times 10^2\ \text{m/s}^2$. This is about 3 times the deceleration of the pilots, who were falling from thousands of meters high!

37.
(a) $32.6\ \text{m/s}^2$

(b) $162\ \text{m/s}$

(c) $v > v_{\text{max}}$, because the assumption of constant acceleration is not valid for a dragster. A dragster changes gears, and would have a greater acceleration in first gear than second gear than third gear, etc. The acceleration would be greatest at the beginning, so it would not be accelerating at $32.6\ \text{m/s}^2$ during the last few meters, but substantially less, and the final velocity would be less than 162 m/s.

39.
104 s

40.
(a) $v = 12.2\ \text{m/s};\ a = 4.07\ \text{m/s}^2$

(b) $v = 11.2\ \text{m/s}$

41.
(a) $y_1 = 6.28\ \text{m};\ v_1 = 10.1\ \text{m/s}$

(b) $y_2 = 10.1\ \text{m};\ v_2 = 5.20\ \text{m/s}$

(c) $y_3 = 11.5\ \text{m};\ v_3 = 0.300\ \text{m/s}$

(d) $y_4 = 10.4\ \text{m};\ v_4 = -4.60\ \text{m/s}$

43.
$v_0 = 4.95\ \text{m/s}$

45.
(a) $a = -9.80\ \text{m/s}^2;\ v_0 = 13.0\ \text{m/s};\ y_0 = 0\ \text{m}$

(b) $v = 0\text{m/s}$. Unknown is distance y to top of trajectory, where velocity is zero. Use equation $v^2 = v_0^2 + 2a(y - y_0)$ because it contains all known values except for y, so we can solve for y. Solving for y gives

$$\begin{aligned} v^2 - v_0^2 &= 2a(y - y_0) \\ \frac{v^2 - v_0^2}{2a} &= y - y_0 \\ y &= y_0 + \frac{v^2 - v_0^2}{2a} = 0\ \text{m} + \frac{(0\ \text{m/s})^2 - (13.0\ \text{m/s})^2}{2\left(-9.80\ \text{m/s}^2\right)} = 8.62\ \text{m} \end{aligned}$$

Dolphins measure about 2 meters long and can jump several times their length out of the water, so this is a reasonable result.

(c) $2.65\ \text{s}$

47.

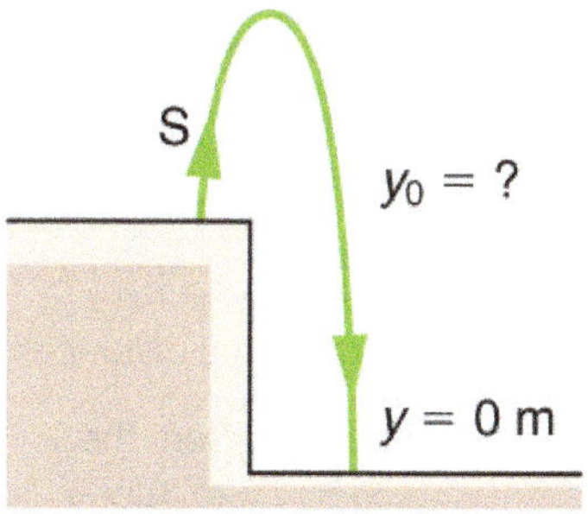

(a) 8.26 m

(b) 0.717 s

49.
1.91 s

51.
(a) 94.0 m

(b) 3.13 s

53.
(a) -70.0 m/s (downward)

(b) 6.10 s

55.
(a) 19.6 m

(b) 18.5 m

57.
(a) 305 m

(b) 262 m, -29.2 m/s

(c) 8.91 s

59.
(a) 115 m/s

(b) 5.0 m/s^2

61.
$$v = \frac{(11.7 - 6.95) \times 10^3 \text{ m}}{(40.0 - 20.0) \text{ s}} = 238 \text{ m/s}$$

63.

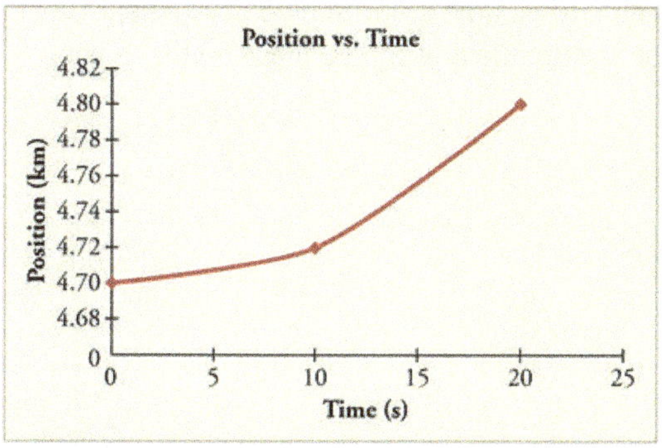

65.
(a) 6 m/s

(b) 12 m/s

(c) $3\ \text{m/s}^2$

(d) 10 s

67.
(a) Car A is traveling faster at the checkpoint because it must go past the speed of car B to reach the same distance.

(b) i. Yes, the equation is consistent with the answer because the speed of car A is only a constant away from the correct answer. ii. Yes, the equation makes sense because $V = 2V_0$.

(c)

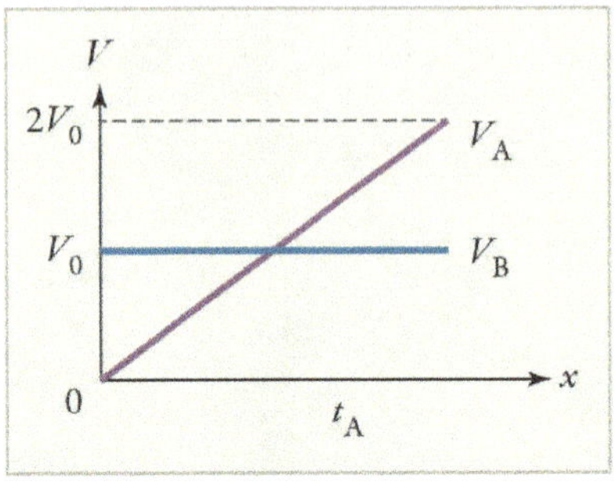

FIGURE 2.67

Test Prep for AP® Courses

1.
(a)

3.
(a) Use tape to mark off two distances on the track — one for cart *A* before the collision and one for the combined carts after the collision. Push cart *A* to give it an initial speed. Use a stopwatch to measure the time it takes for the cart(s) to cross the marked distances. The speeds are the distances divided by the times.

(b) If the measurement errors are of the same magnitude, they will have a greater effect after the collision. The speed of the combined carts will be less than the initial speed of cart *A*. As a result, these errors will be a greater percentage of the actual velocity value after the collision occurs. (Note: Other arguments could properly be made for 'more error before the collision' and error that 'equally affects both sets of measurement.')

5.
The position vs. time graph should be represented with a positively sloped line whose slope steadily decreases to zero. The *y*-intercept of the graph may be any value. The line on the velocity vs. time graph should have a positive *y*-intercept and a negative slope. Because the final velocity of the book is zero, the line should finish on the *x*-axis.

The position vs. time graph should be represented with a negatively sloped line whose slope steadily decreases to zero. The *y*-intercept of the graph may be any value. The line on the velocity vs. time graph should have a negative *y*-intercept and a positive slope. Because the final velocity of the book is zero, the line should finish on the *x*-axis.]

7.
(c)

Chapter 3

Problems & Exercises

1.
(a) 480 m

(b) 379 m, 18.4° east of north

3.

north component 3.21 km, east component 3.83 km

5.
19.5 m, 4.65° south of west

7.
(a) 26.6 m, 65.1° north of east

(b) 26.6 m, 65.1° south of west

9.
52.9 m, 90.1° with respect to the *x*-axis.

11.
x-component 4.41 m/s

y-component 5.07 m/s

13.
(a) 1.56 km

(b) 120 m east

15.
North-component 87.0 km, east-component 87.0 km

17.
30.8 m, 35.8 west of north

19.
(a) 30.8 m, 54.2° south of west

(b) 30.8 m, 54.2° north of east

21.
18.4 km south, then 26.2 km west(b) 31.5 km at 45.0° south of west, then 5.56 km at 45.0° west of north

23.
7.34 km, 63.5° south of east

25.
$$x = 1.30\ \text{m} \times 10^2$$
$$y = 30.9\ \text{m}.$$

27.
(a) 3.50 s

(b) 28.6 m/s (c) 34.3 m/s

(d) 44.7 m/s, 50.2° below horizontal

29.
(a) 18.4°

(b) The arrow will go over the branch.

31.
$$R = \frac{v_0^2}{\sin 2\theta_0 g}$$

For $\theta = 45°$, $R = \frac{v_0^2}{g}$

$R = 91.8$ m for $v_0 = 30$ m/s; $R = 163$ m for $v_0 = 40$ m/s; $R = 255$ m for $v_0 = 50$ m/s.

33.
(a) 560 m/s

(b) 8.00×10^3 m

(c) 80.0 m. This error is not significant because it is only 1% of the answer in part (b).

35.
1.50 m, assuming launch angle of $45°$

37.
$\theta = 6.1°$

yes, the ball lands at 5.3 m from the net

39.
(a) −0.486 m

(b) The larger the muzzle velocity, the smaller the deviation in the vertical direction, because the time of flight would be smaller. Air resistance would have the effect of decreasing the time of flight, therefore increasing the vertical deviation.

41.
4.23 m. No, the owl is not lucky; he misses the nest.

43.
No, the maximum range (neglecting air resistance) is about 92 m.

45.
15.0 m/s

47.
(a) 24.2 m/s

(b) The ball travels a total of 57.4 m with the brief gust of wind.

49.
$y - y_0 = 0 = v_{0y}t - \frac{1}{2}gt^2 = (v_0 \sin\theta)t - \frac{1}{2}gt^2,$

so that $t = \frac{2(v_0 \sin\theta)}{g}$

$x - x_0 = v_{0x}t = (v_0 \cos\theta)t = R,$ and substituting for t gives:

$$R = v_0 \cos\theta\left(\frac{2v_0 \sin\theta}{g}\right) = \frac{2v_0^2 \sin\theta \cos\theta}{g}$$

since $2 \sin\theta \cos\theta = \sin 2\theta,$ the range is:

$$R = \frac{v_0{}^2 \sin 2\theta}{g}.$$

52.
(a) 35.8 km, $45°$ south of east

(b) 5.53 m/s, $45°$ south of east

(c) 56.1 km, $45°$ south of east

54.
(a) 0.70 m/s faster

(b) Second runner wins

(c) 4.17 m

56.
$17.0 \text{ m/s}, 22.1°$

58.
(a) $230 \text{ m/s}, 8.0°$ south of west

(b) The wind should make the plane travel slower and more to the south, which is what was calculated.

60.
(a) 63.5 m/s

(b) 29.6 m/s

62.
$6.68 \text{ m/s}, 53.3°$ south of west

64.
(a) $H_{\text{average}} = 14.9 \frac{\text{km/s}}{\text{Mly}}$

(b) 20.2 billion years

66.
$1.72 \text{ m/s}, 42.3°$ north of east

71.
(a) Since $\sin^2 50 > \sin^2 40$, then B reaches the greatest height.

(b) i. Yes, it is consistent because $\sin 50 > \sin 40$. ii. No, it does not make sense because *y* is proportional to $\sin^2 \theta$.

(c)

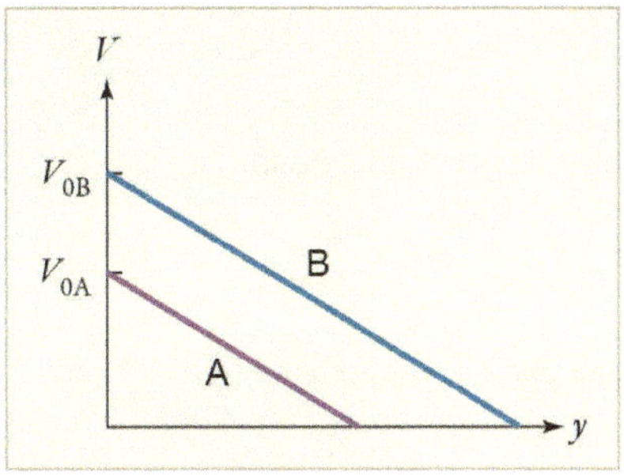

FIGURE 3.61

Test Prep for AP® Courses

1.
(d)

3.
We would need to know the horizontal and vertical positions of each ball at several times. From that data, we could deduce the velocities over several time intervals and also the accelerations (both horizontal and vertical) for each ball over several time intervals.

5.
The graph of the ball's vertical velocity over time should begin at 4.90 m/s during the time interval 0 - 0.1 sec (there should be a data point at t = 0.05 sec, v = 4.90 m/s). It should then have a slope of -9.8 m/s^2, crossing through v = 0 at t = 0.55 sec and ending at v = -0.98 m/s at t = 0.65 sec.

The graph of the ball's horizontal velocity would be a constant positive value, a flat horizontal line at some positive velocity from t = 0 until t = 0.7 sec.

Chapter 4

Problems & Exercises

1.
265 N

3.
13.3 m/s^2

7.
(a) 12 m/s^2.

(b) The acceleration is not one-fourth of what it was with all rockets burning because the frictional force is still as large as it was with all rockets burning.

9.
(a) The system is the child in the wagon plus the wagon.

(b)

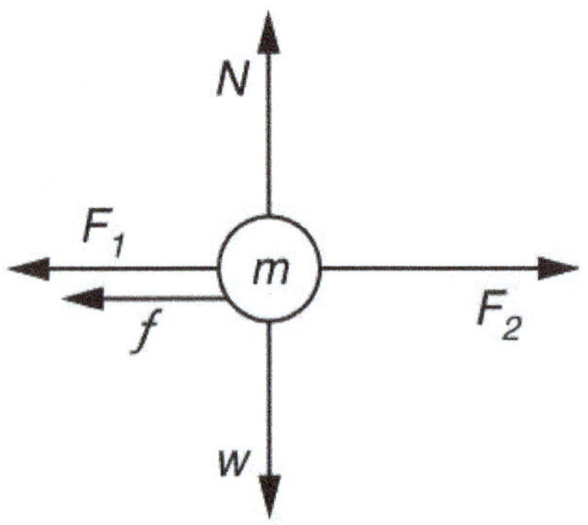

(c) $a = 0.130 \text{ m/s}^2$ in the direction of the second child's push.

(d) $a = 0.00 \text{ m/s}^2$

11.
(a) $3.68 \times 10^3 \text{ N}$. This force is 5.00 times greater than his weight.

(b) 3750 N; 11.3° above horizontal

13.
1.5×10^3 N, 150 kg, 150 kg

15.
Force on shell: 2.64×10^7 N

Force exerted on ship = -2.64×10^7 N, by Newton's third law

17.
a. 0.11 m/s^2
b. 1.2×10^4 N

19.
(a) 7.84×10^{-4} N

(b) 1.89×10^{-3} N. This is 2.41 times the tension in the vertical strand.

21.
Newton's second law applied in vertical direction gives

$$F_y = F - 2T \sin\theta = 0$$
$$F = 2T \sin\theta$$

$$T = \frac{F}{2\sin\theta}.$$

23.

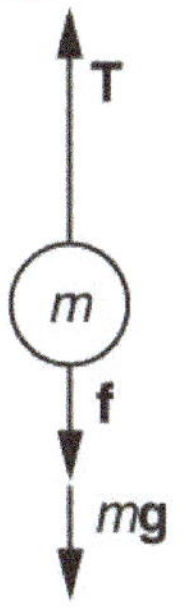

Using the free-body diagram:

$F_{\text{net}} = T - f - mg = ma,$

so that

$$a = \frac{T-f-mg}{m} = \frac{1.250\times10^{7}\ \text{N}-4.50\times10^{6}\ N-(5.00\times10^{5}\ \text{kg})(9.80\ \text{m/s}^2)}{5.00\times10^{5}\ \text{kg}} = 6.20\ \text{m/s}^2.$$

25.

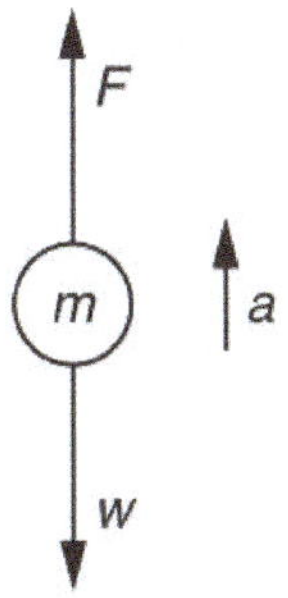

1. Use Newton's laws of motion.
2. Given : $a = 4.00g = (4.00)(9.80\ \text{m/s}^2) = 39.2\ \text{m/s}^2$; $m = 70.0\ \text{kg}$,
   Find: F.
3. $\sum F = +F - w = ma$, so that $F = ma + w = ma + mg = m(a+g)$.
   $F = (70.0\ \text{kg})[(39.2\ \text{m/s}^2) + (9.80\ \text{m/s}^2)] = 3.43\times10^3\,\text{N}$. The force exerted by the high-jumper is actually down on the ground, but F is up from the ground and makes him jump.
4. This result is reasonable, since it is quite possible for a person to exert a force of the magnitude of 10^3 N.

27.
(a) 4.41×10^5 N

(b) 1.50×10^5 N

29.
(a) 910 N

(b) 1.11×10^3 N

31.
$a = 0.139$ m/s, $\theta = 12.4°$ north of east

33.
1. Use Newton's laws since we are looking for forces.

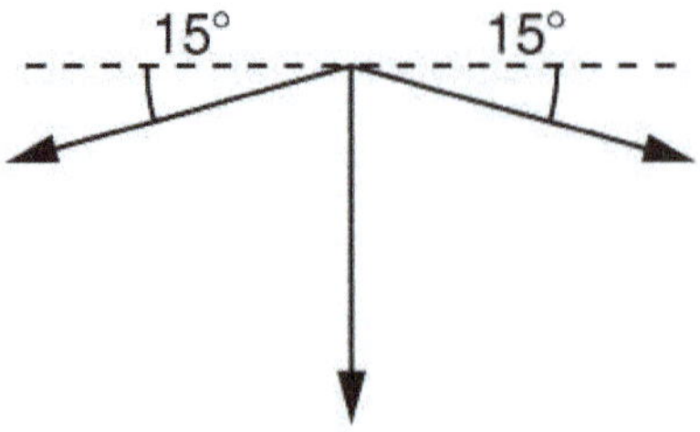

2. Draw a free-body diagram:
3. The tension is given as $T = 25.0\text{ N}$. Find F_{app}. Using Newton's laws gives: $\Sigma F_y = 0$, so that applied force is due to the y-components of the two tensions: $F_{app} = 2\,T\,\sin\theta = 2(25.0\text{ N})\sin(15°) = 12.9\text{ N}$
   The x-components of the tension cancel. $\sum F_x = 0$.
4. This seems reasonable, since the applied tensions should be greater than the force applied to the tooth.

40.
10.2 m/s^2, $4.67°$ from vertical

42.

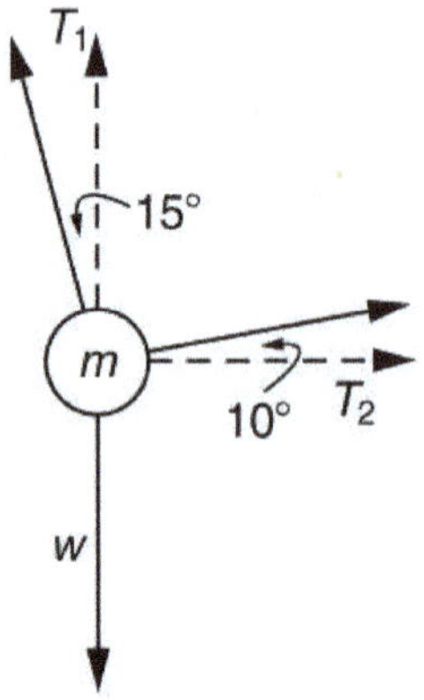

$T_1 = 736\text{ N}$

$T_2 = 194\text{ N}$

44.
(a) 7.43 m/s

(b) 2.97 m

46.
(a) 4.20 m/s

(b) 29.4 m/s^2

(c) $4.31 \times 10^3\text{ N}$

48.
(a) 47.1 m/s

(b) $2.47 \times 10^3\text{ m/s}^2$

(c) $6.18 \times 10^3\text{ N}$. The average force is 252 times the shell's weight.

52.
(a) 1×10^{-13}

(b) 1×10^{-11}

54.
10^2

55.
(a) Box A travels faster at the finishing distance since a greater force with equal mass results in a greater acceleration. Also, a greater acceleration over the same distance results in a greater final speed.

(b) i. Yes, it is consistent because a greater force results in a greater final speed. ii. It does not make sense because $V = \sqrt{2(f/m)x} = \mathrm{K}\sqrt{(F)}$.

(c)

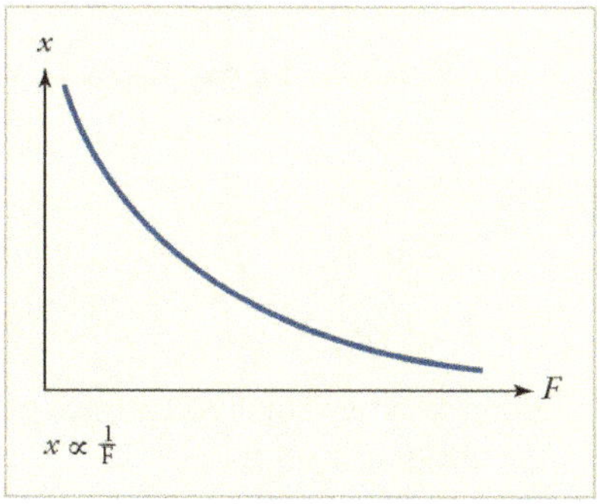

FIGURE 4.41

Test Prep for AP® Courses

1.

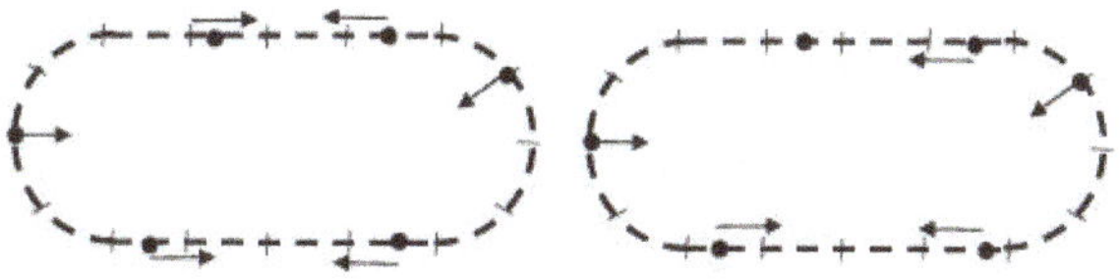

FIGURE 4.44

Car X is shown on the left, and Car Y is shown on the right.

i.

Car X takes longer to accelerate and does not spend any time traveling at top speed. Car Y accelerates over a shorter time and spends time going at top speed. So Car Y must cover the straightaways in a shorter time. Curves take the same time, so Car Y must overall take a shorter time.

ii.

The only difference in the calculations for the time of one segment of linear acceleration is the difference in distances. That shows that Car X takes longer to accelerate. The equation $\frac{d}{4v_c} = t_c$ corresponds to Car Y traveling for a time at top speed.

Substituting $a = \frac{v_c}{t_1}$ into the displacement equation in part (b) ii gives $D = \frac{3}{2}v_c t_1$. This shows that a car takes less time to reach its maximum speed when it accelerates over a shorter distance. Therefore, Car Y reaches its maximum speed more quickly, and spends more time at its maximum speed than Car X does, as argued in part (b) i.

3.
A body cannot exert a force on itself. The hawk may accelerate as a result of several forces. The hawk may accelerate toward Earth as a result of the force due to gravity. The hawk may accelerate as a result of the additional force exerted on it by wind. The hawk may accelerate as a result of orienting its body to create less air resistance, thus increasing the net force forward.

5.
(a) A soccer player, gravity, air, and friction commonly exert forces on a soccer ball being kicked.

(b) Gravity and the surrounding water commonly exert forces on a dolphin jumping. (The dolphin moves its muscles to exert a force on the water. The water exerts an equal force on the dolphin, resulting in the dolphin's motion.)

(c) Gravity and air exert forces on a parachutist drifting to Earth.

7.
(c)

9.

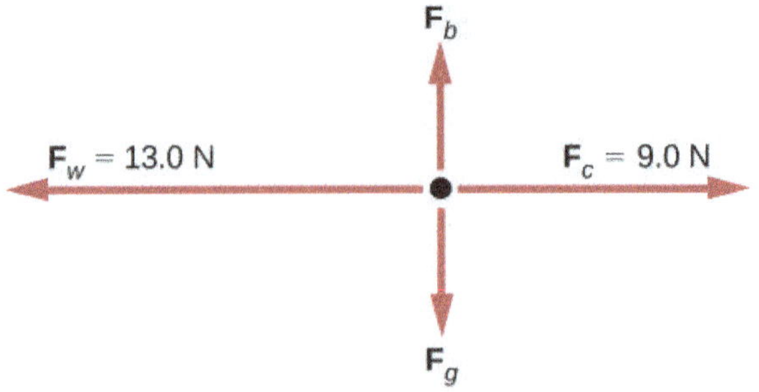

FIGURE 4.45

The diagram consists of a black dot in the center and two small red arrows pointing up (Fb) and down (Fg) and two long red arrows pointing right (Fc = 9.0 N) and left (Fw=13.0 N).

In the diagram, F_g represents the force due to gravity on the balloon, and F_b represents the buoyant force. These two forces are equal in magnitude and opposite in direction. F_c represents the force of the current. F_w represents the force of the wind. The net force on the balloon will be $F_w - F_c = 4.0$ N and the balloon will accelerate in the direction the wind is blowing.

11.
Since $m = F/a$, the parachutist has a mass of $539 \ \text{N}/9.8 \ \text{km/s}^2 = 55 \ \text{kg}$.

For the first 2 s, the parachutist accelerates at 9.8 m/s^2.

$$\begin{aligned} v &= at \\ &= 9.8\frac{\text{m}}{\text{s}^2} \bullet 2\text{s} \\ &= 19.6 \ \frac{\text{m}}{\text{s}} \end{aligned}$$

Her speed after 2 s is 19.6 m/s.

From 2 s to 10 s, the net force on the parachutist is 539 N – 615 N, or 76 N upward.

$$\begin{aligned} a &= \frac{F}{m} \\ &= \frac{-76 \ \text{N}}{55 \ \text{kg}} \\ &= -1.4 \ \frac{\text{m}}{\text{s}^2} \end{aligned}$$

Since $v = v_0 + at$, $v = 19.6 \ \text{m/s}^2 + (-1.4 \ \text{m/s}^2)(8\text{s}) \ = 8.4 \ \text{m/s}^2$.

At 10 s, the parachutist is falling to Earth at 8.4 m/s.

13.
The system includes the gardener and the wheelbarrow with its contents. The following forces are important to include: the weight of the wheelbarrow, the weight of the gardener, the normal force for the wheelbarrow and the gardener, the force of the gardener pushing against the ground and the equal force of the ground pushing back against the gardener, and any friction in the wheelbarrow's wheels.

15.
The system undergoing acceleration is the two figure skaters together.

Net force = $120 \ \text{N} - 5.0 \ \text{N} = 115 \ \text{N}$.

Total mass = $40\ \text{kg} + 50\ \text{kg} = 90\ \text{kg}.$

Using Newton's second law, we have that

$$\begin{aligned} a &= \frac{F}{m} \\ &= \frac{115\ \text{N}}{90\ \text{kg}} \\ &= 1.28\ \frac{\text{m}}{\text{s}^2} \end{aligned}$$

The pair accelerates forward at 1.28 m/s^2.

17.
The force of tension must equal the force of gravity plus the force necessary to accelerate the mass. $F = mg$ can be used to calculate the first, and $F = ma$ can be used to calculate the second.

For gravity:

$$F = mg$$
$$= (120.0\ \text{kg})(9.8\ \text{m/s}^2)$$
$$= 1205.4\ \text{N}$$

For acceleration:

$$F = ma$$
$$= (120.0\ \text{kg})(1.3\ \text{m/s}^2)$$
$$= 159.9\ \text{N}$$

The total force of tension in the cable is 1176 N + 156 N = 1332 N.

19.
(b)

21.

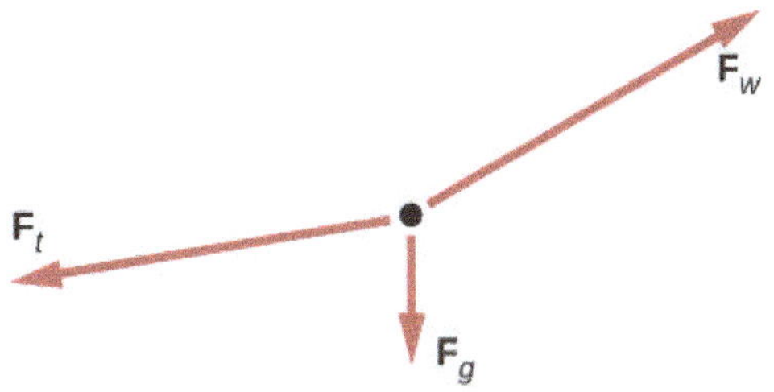

FIGURE 4.47

The diagram has a black dot and three solid red arrows pointing away from the dot. Arrow Ft is long and pointing to the left and slightly down. Arrow Fw is also long and is a bit below a diagonal line halfway between pointing up and pointing to the right. A short arrow Fg is pointing down.

$\mathbf{F}_g$ is the force on the kite due to gravity.

$\mathbf{F}_w$ is the force exerted on the kite by the wind.

$\mathbf{F}_t$ is the force of tension in the string holding the kite. It must balance the vector sum of the other two forces for the kite to float stationary in the air.

23.
(b)

25.

(d)

27.
A free-body diagram would show a northward force of 64 N and a westward force of 38 N. The net force is equal to the sum of the two applied forces. It can be found using the Pythagorean theorem:

$$F_{\text{net}} = \sqrt{F_x{}^2 + F_y{}^w}$$
$$= \sqrt{(38\ \text{N})^2 + (64\ \text{N})^2}$$
$$= 74.4\ \text{N}$$

Since $a = \frac{F}{m}$,

$$a = \frac{74.4\ \text{N}}{825\ \text{kg}}$$
$$= 0.09\ \text{m/s}^2$$

The boulder will accelerate at 0.09 m/s^2.

29.
(b)

31.
(b)

33.
(d)

Chapter 5

Problems & Exercises

1.
5.00 N

4.
(a) 588 N

(b) 1.96 m/s^2

6.
(a) 3.29 m/s^2

(b) 3.52 m/s^2

(c) 980 N; 945 N

10.
1.83 m/s^2

14.
(a) 4.20 m/s^2

(b) 2.74 m/s^2

(c) –0.195 m/s^2

16.
(a) 1.03×10^6 N

(b) 3.48×10^5 N

18.
(a) 51.0 N

(b) 0.720 m/s^2

20.
$115 \text{ m/s}; 414 \text{ km/hr}$

22.
$25.1 \text{ m/s}; 9.90 \text{ m/s}$

24.
2.9

26.
$$[\eta] = \frac{[F_s]}{[r][v]} = \frac{\text{kg} \cdot \text{m/s}^2}{\text{m} \cdot \text{m/s}} = \frac{\text{kg}}{\text{m} \cdot \text{s}}$$

28.
$0.76 \text{ kg/m} \cdot \text{s}$

29.
$1.90 \times 10^{-3} \text{ cm}$

31.
(a)1 mm
(b) This does seem reasonable, since the lead does seem to shrink a little when you push on it.

33.
(a)9 cm
(b)This seems reasonable for nylon climbing rope, since it is not supposed to stretch that much.

35.
8.59 mm

37.
$1.49 \times 10^{-7} \text{ m}$

39.
(a) $3.99 \times 10^{-7} \text{ m}$

(b) $9.67 \times 10^{-8} \text{ m}$

41.
$4 \times 10^6 \text{ N/m}^2$. This is about 36 atm, greater than a typical jar can withstand.

43.
1.4 cm

45.
(a) Bead A has the larger radius because both have the same weight and drag force. Since A takes longer to fall, its speed is less and, therefore, it must have larger area or radius.

(b) i. This equation is not consistent because it shows that the bead that took longer to fall has a smaller radius. ii. It does not make sense because *r* is proportional to *t*.

(c)

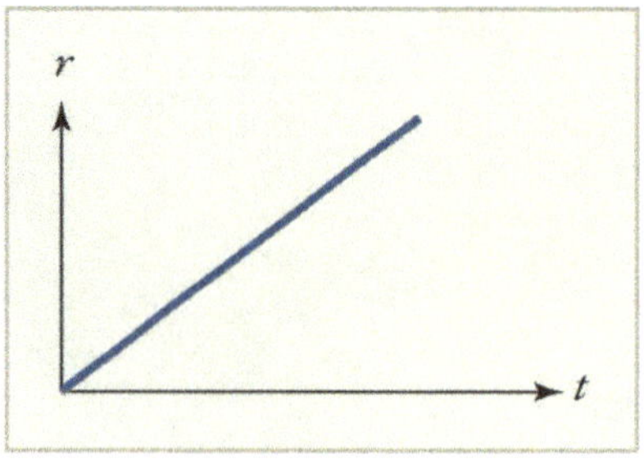

FIGURE 5.23

Test Prep for AP® Courses

1.
(b)

3.
(c)

Chapter 6

Problems & Exercises

1.
723 km

3.
5×10^7 rotations

5.
117 rad/s

7.
76.2 rad/s

728 rpm

8.
(a) 33.3 rad/s

(b) 500 N

(c) 40.8 m

10.
12.9 rev/min

12.
4×10^{21} m

14.
a) $3.47 \times 10^4 \text{ m/s}^2, 3.55 \times 10^3\ g$

b) 51.1 m/s

16.
a) 31.4 rad/s

b) 118 m/s

c) 384 m/s

d)The centripetal acceleration felt by Olympic skaters is 12 times larger than the acceleration due to gravity. That's quite a lot of acceleration in itself. The centripetal acceleration felt by Button's nose was 39.2 times larger than the acceleration due to gravity. It is no wonder that he ruptured small blood vessels in his spins.

18.
a) 0.524 km/s

b) 29.7 km/s

20.
(a) 1.35×10^3 rpm

(b) 8.47×10^3 m/s^2

(c) 8.47×10^{-12} N

(d) 865

21.
(a) 16.6 m/s

(b) 19.6 m/s^2

(c)

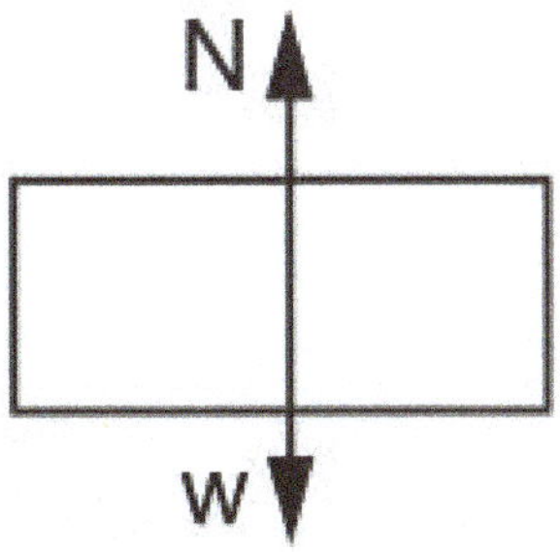

(d) 1.76×10^3 N or $3.00\ w$, that is, the normal force (upward) is three times her weight.

(e) This answer seems reasonable, since she feels like she's being forced into the chair MUCH stronger than just by gravity.

22.
a) 40.5 m/s^2

b) 905 N

c) The force in part (b) is very large. The acceleration in part (a) is too much, about 4 g.

d) The speed of the swing is too large. At the given velocity at the bottom of the swing, there is enough kinetic energy to send the child all the way over the top, ignoring friction.

23.
a) 483 N

b) 17.4 N

c) 2.24 times her weight, 0.0807 times her weight

25.
4.14°

27.
a) 24.6 m

b) 36.6 m/s^2

c) $a_c = 3.73\ g$. This does not seem too large, but it is clear that bobsledders feel a lot of force on them going through sharply banked turns.

29.
a) 2.56 rad/s

b) $5.71°$

30.
a) 16.2 m/s

b) 0.234

32.
a) 1.84

b) A coefficient of friction this much greater than 1 is unreasonable .

c) The assumed speed is too great for the tight curve.

33.
a) 5.979×10^{24} kg

b) This is identical to the best value to three significant figures.

35.
a) $1.62\ \text{m/s}^2$

b) $3.75\ \text{m/s}^2$

37.
a) $3.42 \times 10^{-5}\ \text{m/s}^2$

b) $3.34 \times 10^{-5}\ \text{m/s}^2$

The values are nearly identical. One would expect the gravitational force to be the same as the centripetal force at the core of the system.

39.
a) 7.01×10^{-7} N

b) 1.35×10^{-6} N, 0.521

41.
a) $1.66 \times 10^{-10}\ \text{m/s}^2$

b) 2.17×10^{5} m/s

42.
a) 2.937×10^{17} kg

b) 4.91×10^{-8}

of the Earth's mass.

c) The mass of the mountain and its fraction of the Earth's mass are too great.

d) The gravitational force assumed to be exerted by the mountain is too great.

44.
1.98×10^{30} kg

46.
$\frac{M_J}{M_E} = 316$

48.
a) 2.11×10^{4} m/s

b) 1.05×10^4 m/s

c) 2.86×10^{-7} s

d) 1.83×10^8 N

e) 2.22×10^5 J

49.
a) 5.08×10^3 km

b) This radius is unreasonable because it is less than the radius of earth.

c) The premise of a one-hour orbit is inconsistent with the known radius of the earth.

51.
(a) The normal force is greatest at point B. At point A, the normal force and the weight are the net force; at point B, only the normal force points in the same direction as the net force.

(b) i. This is not consistent because a larger radius should decease the net force and tension, not increase it. ii. This does not make sense because $F_c = mv^2/r$.

(c)

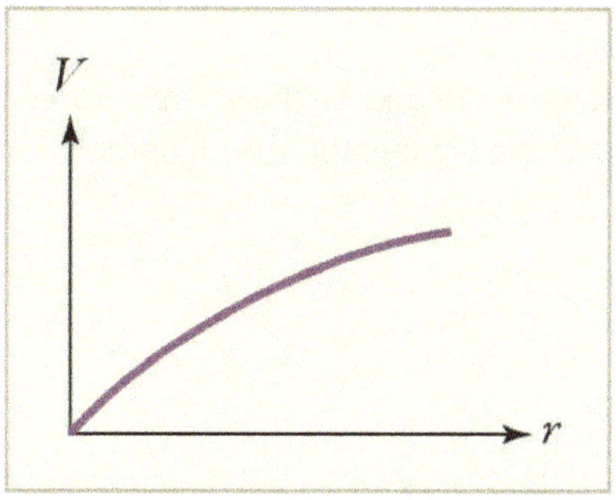

FIGURE 6.36

Test Prep for AP® Courses

1.
(a)

3.
(b)

5.
(b)

Chapter 7

Problems & Exercises

1.
$3.00 \text{ J} = 7.17 \times 10^{-4}$ kcal

3.
(a) 5.92×10^5 J

(b) -5.88×10^5 J

(c) The net force is zero.

5.
3.14×10^3 J

7.

(a) -700 J

(b) 0

(c) 700 J

(d) 38.6 N

(e) 0

9.
$1/250$

11.
$1.1 \times 10^{10}\text{ J}$

13.
$2.8 \times 10^{3}\text{ N}$

15.
102 N

16.
(a) $1.96{\times}10^{16}\text{ J}$

(b) The ratio of gravitational potential energy in the lake to the energy stored in the bomb is 0.52. That is, the energy stored in the lake is approximately half that in a 9-megaton fusion bomb.

18.
(a) 1.8 J

(b) 8.6 J

20.
$$v_f = \sqrt{2gh + {v_0}^2} = \sqrt{2(9.80\text{ m/s}^2)(-0.180\text{ m}) + (2.00\text{ m/s})^2} = 0.687\text{ m/s}$$

22.
$7.81{\times}10^{5}\text{ N/m}$

24.
9.46 m/s

26.
$4{\times}10^{4}$ molecules

27.
Equating ΔPE_g and ΔKE, we obtain $v = \sqrt{2gh + {v_0}^2} = \sqrt{2(9.80\text{ m/s}^2)(20.0\text{ m}) + (15.0\text{ m/s})^2} = 24.8\text{ m/s}$

29.
(a) 25×10^{6} years

(b) This is much, much longer than human time scales.

30.
$2{\times}10^{-10}$

32.
(a) 40

(b) 8 million

34.
$149

36.
(a) 208 W

(b) 141 s

38.
(a) 3.20 s

(b) 4.04 s

40.
(a) 9.46×10^7 J

(b) 2.54 y

42.
Identify knowns: $m = 950$ kg, slope angle $\theta = 2.00°$, $v = 3.00$ m/s, $f = 600$ N

Identify unknowns: power P of the car, force F that car applies to road

Solve for unknown:

$$P = \frac{W}{t} = \frac{Fd}{t} = F\left(\frac{d}{t}\right) = Fv,$$

where F is parallel to the incline and must oppose the resistive forces and the force of gravity:

$$F = f + w = 600\text{ N} + mg \sin\theta$$

Insert this into the expression for power and solve:

$$\begin{aligned} P &= (f + mg \sin\theta)v \\ &= \left[600\text{ N} + (950\text{ kg})\left(9.80\text{ m/s}^2\right)\sin 2°\right](30.0\text{ m/s}) \\ &= 2.77 \times 10^4\text{ W} \end{aligned}$$

About 28 kW (or about 37 hp) is reasonable for a car to climb a gentle incline.

44.
(a) 9.5 min

(b) 69 flights of stairs

46.
641 W, 0.860 hp

48.
31 g

50.
14.3%

52.
(a) 3.21×10^4 N

(b) 2.35×10^3 N

(c) Ratio of net force to weight of person is 41.0 in part (a); 3.00 in part (b)

54.
(a) 108 kJ

(b) 599 W

56.
(a) 144 J

(b) 288 W

58.
(a) 2.50×10^{12} J

(b) 2.52%

(c) 1.4×10^{4} kg (14 metric tons)

60.
(a) 294 N

(b) 118 J

(c) 49.0 W

62.
(a) $0.500\ \text{m/s}^2$

(b) 62.5 N

(c) Assuming the acceleration of the swimmer decreases linearly with time over the 5.00 s interval, the frictional force must therefore be increasing linearly with time, since $f = F - ma$. If the acceleration decreases linearly with time, the velocity will contain a term dependent on time squared (t^2). Therefore, the water resistance will not depend linearly on the velocity.

64.
(a) 16.1×10^{3} N

(b) 3.22×10^{5} J

(c) 5.66 m/s

(d) 4.00 kJ

66.
(a) 4.65×10^{3} kcal

(b) 38.8 kcal/min

(c) This power output is higher than the highest value on Table 7.5, which is about 35 kcal/min (corresponding to 2415 watts) for sprinting.

(d) It would be impossible to maintain this power output for 2 hours (imagine sprinting for 2 hours!).

69.
(a) 4.32 m/s

(b) 3.47×10^{3} N

(c) 8.93 kW

70.
(a) Box A has the greatest speed since it has the greatest work done; work equals change in kinetic energy and thus fastest speed.

(b) i. Yes, this equation is consistent. An increased force or distance increases the work done, and thus increases the change in kinesthetic energy. ii. No, this equation does not make sense.

(c)

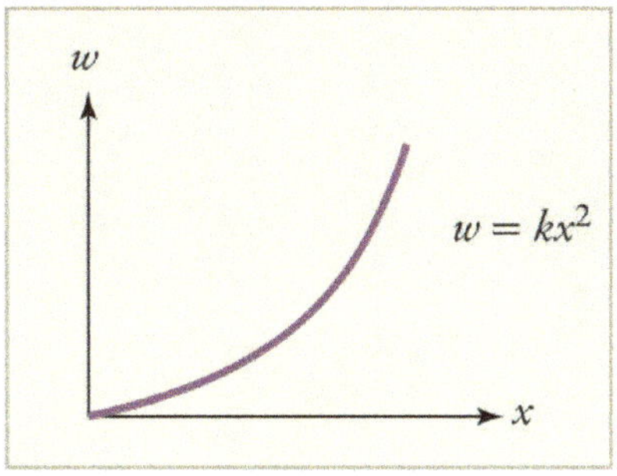

FIGURE 7.44

Test Prep for AP® Courses

1.
(b)

3.
(d)

5.
(a)

7.
The kinetic energy should change in the form of −cos, with an initial value of 0 or slightly above, and ending at the same level.

9.
Any force acting perpendicular will have no effect on kinetic energy. Obvious examples are gravity and the normal force, but others include wind directly from the side and rain or other precipitation falling straight down.

11.
Note that the wind is pushing from behind and one side, so your KE will increase. The net force has components of 1400 N in the direction of travel and 212 N perpendicular to the direction of travel. So the net force is 1420 N at 8.5 degrees from the direction of travel.

13.
Gravity has a component perpendicular to the cannon (and to displacement, so it is irrelevant) and has a component parallel to the cannon. The latter is equal to 9.8 N. Thus the net force in the direction of the displacement is 45 N – 9.8 N, and the kinetic energy is 53 J.

15.
The potato cannon (and many other projectile launchers) above is an option, with a force launching the projectile, friction, potentially gravity depending on the direction it is pointed, etc. A drag (or other) car accelerating is another possibility.

17.
The kinetic energy of the rear wagon increases. The front wagon does not, until the rear wagon collides with it. The total system may be treated by its center of mass, halfway between the wagons, and its energy increases by the same amount as the sum of the two individual wagons.

19.
(d)

21.
0.049 J; 0.041 m, 0.25 m

23.
20 m high, 20 m/s.

25.

(a)

27.
(d)

29.
(c)

31.
(b)

33.
(c)

35.
(c)

37.
(c), (d)

39.
(a)

41.
(b)

Chapter 8

Problems & Exercises

1.
(a) $1.50 \times 10^4\ \text{kg} \cdot \text{m/s}$

(b) 625 to 1

(c) $6.66 \times 10^2\ \text{kg} \cdot \text{m/s}$

3.
(a) $8.00 \times 10^4\ \text{m/s}$

(b) $1.20 \times 10^6\ \text{kg} \cdot \text{m/s}$

(c) Because the momentum of the airplane is 3 orders of magnitude smaller than of the ship, the ship will not recoil very much. The recoil would be $-0.0100\ \text{m/s}$, which is probably not noticeable.

5.
54 s

7.
$9.00 \times 10^3\ \text{N}$

9.
a) $2.40 \times 10^3\ \text{N}$ toward the leg

b) The force on each hand would have the same magnitude as that found in part (a) (but in opposite directions by Newton's third law) because the change in momentum and the time interval are the same.

11.
a) $800\ \text{kg} \cdot \text{m/s}$ away from the wall

b) $1.20\ \text{m/s}$ away from the wall

13.
(a) $1.50 \times 10^6\ \text{N}$ away from the dashboard

(b) 1.00×10^5 N away from the dashboard

15.
4.69×10^5 N in the boat's original direction of motion

17.
2.10×10^3 N away from the wall

19.
$$\mathbf{p} = m\mathbf{v} \Rightarrow p^2 = m^2 v^2 \Rightarrow \frac{p^2}{m} = mv^2$$
$$\Rightarrow \frac{p^2}{2m} = \frac{1}{2}mv^2 = KE$$
$$KE = \frac{p^2}{2m}$$

21.
60.0 g

23.
0.122 m/s

25.
In a collision with an identical car, momentum is conserved. Afterwards $v_\text{f} = 0$ for both cars. The change in momentum will be the same as in the crash with the tree. However, the force on the body is not determined since the time is not known. A padded stop will reduce injurious force on body.

27.
22.4 m/s in the same direction as the original motion

29.
0.250 m/s

31.
(a) 86.4 N perpendicularly away from the bumper

(b) 0.389 J

(c) 64.0%

33.
(a) 8.06 m/s

(b) -56.0 J

(c)(i) 7.88 m/s; (ii) -223 J

35.
(a) 0.163 m/s in the direction of motion of the more massive satellite

(b) 81.6 J

(c) 8.70×10^{-2} m/s in the direction of motion of the less massive satellite, 81.5 J. Because there are no external forces, the velocity of the center of mass of the two-satellite system is unchanged by the collision. The two velocities calculated above are the velocity of the center of mass in each of the two different individual reference frames. The loss in KE is the same in both reference frames because the KE lost to internal forces (heat, friction, etc.) is the same regardless of the coordinate system chosen.

37.
0.704 m/s

−2.25 m/s

38.

(a) 4.58 m/s away from the bullet

(b) 31.5 J

(c) −0.491 m/s

(d) 3.38 J

40.
(a) 1.02×10^{-6} m/s

(b) 5.63×10^{20} J (almost all KE lost)

(c) Recoil speed is 6.79×10^{-17} m/s, energy lost is 6.25×10^{9} J. The plume will not affect the momentum result because the plume is still part of the Moon system. The plume may affect the kinetic energy result because a significant part of the initial kinetic energy may be transferred to the kinetic energy of the plume particles.

42.
24.8 m/s

44.
(a) 4.00 kg

(b) 210 J

(c) The clown does work to throw the barbell, so the kinetic energy comes from the muscles of the clown. The muscles convert the chemical potential energy of ATP into kinetic energy.

45.
(a) 3.00 m/s, $60°$ below x-axis

(b) Find speed of first puck after collision: $0 = mv'_1 \sin 30° - mv'_2 \sin 60° \Rightarrow v'_1 = v_2 \frac{\sin 60°}{\sin 30°} = 5.196 \text{ m/s}$

Verify that ratio of initial to final KE equals one: $\left.\begin{array}{l} \text{KE} = \frac{1}{2}mv_1{}^2 = 18m \text{ J} \\ \text{KE} = \frac{1}{2}mv'_1{}^2 + \frac{1}{2}mv'_2{}^2 = 18m \text{ J} \end{array}\right\} \frac{\text{KE}}{\text{KE}'} = 1.00$

47.
(a) -2.26 m/s

(b) 7.63×10^{3} J

(c) The ground will exert a normal force to oppose recoil of the cannon in the vertical direction. The momentum in the vertical direction is transferred to the earth. The energy is transferred into the ground, making a dent where the cannon is. After long barrages, cannon have erratic aim because the ground is full of divots.

49.
(a) 5.36×10^{5} m/s at $-29.5°$

(b) 7.52×10^{-13} J

51.
We are given that $m_1 = m_2 \equiv m$. The given equations then become:

$v_1 = v_1 \cos \theta_1 + v_2 \cos \theta_2$
and

$0 = v'_1 \sin \theta_1 + v'_2 \sin \theta_2$.
Square each equation to get

$$\begin{aligned} v_1{}^2 &= v'_1{}^2 \cos^2 \theta_1 + v'_2{}^2 \cos^2 \theta_2 + 2v'_1 v'_2 \cos \theta_1 \cos \theta_2 \\ 0 &= v'_1{}^2 \sin^2 \theta_1 + v'_2{}^2 \sin^2 \theta_2 + 2v'_1 v'_2 \sin \theta_1 \sin \theta_2. \end{aligned}$$
Add these two equations and simplify:

$$\begin{aligned} v_1^2 &= {v'_1}^2 + {v'_2}^2 + 2v'_1 v'_2(\cos\theta_1 \cos\theta_2 + \sin\theta_1 \sin\theta_2) \\ &= {v'_1}^2 + {v'_2}^2 + 2v'_1 v'_2\left[\tfrac{1}{2}\cos(\theta_1 - \theta_2) + \tfrac{1}{2}\cos(\theta_1 + \theta_2) + \tfrac{1}{2}\cos(\theta_1 - \theta_2) - \tfrac{1}{2}\cos(\theta_1 + \theta_2)\right] \\ &= {v'_1}^2 + {v'_2}^2 + 2v'_1 v'_2 \cos(\theta_1 - \theta_2). \end{aligned}$$

Multiply the entire equation by $\frac{1}{2}m$ to recover the kinetic energy:

$$\frac{1}{2}m{v_1}^2 = \frac{1}{2}m{v'_1}^2 + \frac{1}{2}m{v'_2}^2 + mv'_1 v'_2 \cos(\theta_1 - \theta_2)$$

53.
39.2 m/s^2

55.
4.16×10^3 m/s

57.
The force needed to give a small mass Δm an acceleration $a_{\Delta m}$ is $F = \Delta m a_{\Delta m}$. To accelerate this mass in the small time interval Δt requires $v_e = a_{\Delta m}\Delta t$, so $F = v_e \frac{\Delta m}{\Delta t}$. By Newton's third law, this force is equal in magnitude to the thrust force acting on the rocket, so $F_{\text{thrust}} = v_e \frac{\Delta m}{\Delta t}$, where all quantities are positive. Applying Newton's second law to the rocket gives $F_{\text{thrust}} - mg = ma \Rightarrow a = \frac{v_e}{m}\frac{\Delta m}{\Delta t} - g$, where m is the mass of the rocket and unburnt fuel.

60.
2.63×10^3 kg

61.
(a) 0.421 m/s away from the ejected fluid.

(b) 0.237 J.

Test Prep for AP® Courses

1.
(b)

3.
(b)

5.
(a)

7.
(c) (based on calculation of $F = \frac{m\Delta v}{\Delta t}$)

9.
(c)

11.
(d)

13.
(b)

15.
(d)

17.
(b)

19.
(c)

21.

(b)

23.
(c)

25.
(b)

27.
(a)

29.
(c)

31.
(b)

33.
(a)

35.
(b)

37.
(a)

39.
(a)

41.
(d)

43.
(c). Because of conservation of momentum, the final velocity of the combined mass must be 4.286 m/s. The initial kinetic energy is $(0.5)(2.0)(15)^2 = 225\text{ J}$. The final kinetic energy is $(0.5)(7.0)(4.286)^2 = 64\text{ J}$, so the difference is −161 J.

45.
(a)

47.
(d)

49.
(c)

51.
(b)

Chapter 9

Problems & Exercises

1.
a) $46.8\text{ N}\cdot\text{m}$

b) It does not matter at what height you push. The torque depends on only the magnitude of the force applied and the perpendicular distance of the force's application from the hinges. (Children don't have a tougher time opening a door because they push lower than adults, they have a tougher time because they don't push far enough from the hinges.)

3.
23.3 N

5.
Given:

$$m_1 = 26.0\text{ kg}, m_2 = 32.0\text{ kg}, m_s = 12.0\text{ kg},$$
$$r_1 = 1.60\text{ m}, r_s = 0.160\text{ m, find (a) } r_2, \text{ (b) } F_p$$

a) Since children are balancing:

$$\text{net } \tau_{cw} = -\text{net } \tau_{ccw}$$
$$\Rightarrow w_1 r_1 + m_s g r_s = w_2 r_2$$

So, solving for r_2 gives:

$$r_2 = \frac{w_1 r_1 + m_s g r_s}{w_2} = \frac{m_1 g r_1 + m_s g r_s}{m_2 g} = \frac{m_1 r_1 + m_s r_s}{m_2}$$
$$= \frac{(26.0\text{ kg})(1.60\text{ m}) + (12.0\text{ kg})(0.160\text{ m})}{32.0\text{ kg}}$$
$$= 1.36\text{ m}$$

b) Since the children are not moving:

$$\text{net } F = 0 = F_p - w_1 - w_2 - w_s$$
$$\Rightarrow F_p = w_1 + w_2 + w_s$$

So that

$$F_p = (26.0\text{ kg} + 32.0\text{ kg} + 12.0\text{ kg})(9.80\text{ m/s}^2)$$
$$= 686\text{ N}$$

6.
$F_{wall} = 1.43 \times 10^3$ N

8.
a) 2.55×10^3 N, 16.3° to the left of vertical (i.e., toward the wall)

b) 0.292

10.
$F_B = 2.12 \times 10^4$ N

12.
a) 0.167, or about one-sixth of the weight is supported by the opposite shore.

b) $F = 2.0 \times 10^4$ N, straight up.

14.
a) 21.6 N

b) 21.6 N

16.
350 N directly upwards

19.
25

50 N

21.
a) MA = 18.5

b) $F_i = 29.1$ N

c) 510 N downward

23.

1.3×10^3 N

25.
a) $T = 299$ N

b) 897 N upward

26.
$$\begin{aligned} F_B &= 470 \text{ N}; r_1 = 4.00 \text{ cm}; w_a = 2.50 \text{ kg}; r_2 = 16.0 \text{ cm}; w_b = 4.00 \text{ kg}; r_3 = 38.0 \text{ cm} \\ F_E &= w_a\left(\frac{r_2}{r_1} - 1\right) + w_b\left(\frac{r_3}{r_1} - 1\right) \\ &= (2.50 \text{ kg})(9.80 \text{ m/s}^2)\left(\frac{16.0 \text{ cm}}{4.0 \text{ cm}} - 1\right) \\ &\quad + (4.00 \text{ kg})(9.80 \text{ m/s}^2)\left(\frac{38.0 \text{ cm}}{4.00 \text{ cm}} - 1\right) \\ &= 407 \text{ N} \end{aligned}$$

28.
$$1.1 \times 10^3 \text{ N}$$
$\theta = 190°$ ccw from positive x axis

30.
$F_V = 97$ N, $\theta = 59°$

32.
(a) 25 N downward

(b) 75 N upward

33.
(a) $F_A = 2.21 \times 10^3$ N upward

(b) $F_B = 2.94 \times 10^3$ N downward

35.
(a) $F_{\text{teeth on bullet}} = 1.2 \times 10^2$ N upward

(b) $F_J = 84$ N downward

37.
(a) 147 N downward

(b) 1680 N, 3.4 times her weight

(c) 118 J

(d) 49.0 W

39.
a) $\bar{x}_2 = 2.33$ m

b) The seesaw is 3.0 m long, and hence, there is only 1.50 m of board on the other side of the pivot. The second child is off the board.

c) The position of the first child must be shortened, i.e. brought closer to the pivot.

Test Prep for AP® Courses

1.
(a)

3.
Both objects are in equilibrium. However, they will respond differently if a force is applied to their sides. If the cone placed on its base is displaced to the side, its center of gravity will remain over its base and it will return to its

original position. When the traffic cone placed on its tip is displaced to the side, its center of gravity will drift from its base, causing a torque that will accelerate it to the ground.

5.
(d)

7.

a. $\mathbf{F}_L = 7350$ N, $\mathbf{F}_R = 2450$ N
b. As the car moves to the right side of the bridge, $\mathbf{F}_L$ will decrease and $\mathbf{F}_R$ will increase. (At exactly halfway across the bridge, $\mathbf{F}_L$ and $\mathbf{F}_R$ will both be 4900 N.)

9.
The student should mention that the guiding principle behind simple machines is the second condition of equilibrium. Though the torque leaving a machine must be equivalent to torque entering a machine, the same requirement does not exist for forces. As a result, by decreasing the lever arm to the existing force, the size of the existing force will be increased. The mechanical advantage will be equivalent to the ratio of the forces exiting and entering the machine.

11.

a. The force placed on your bicep muscle will be greater than the force placed on the dumbbell. The bicep muscle is closer to your elbow than the downward force placed on your hand from the dumbbell. Because the elbow is the pivot point of the system, this results in a decreased lever arm for the bicep. As a result, the force on the bicep must be greater than that placed on the dumbbell. (How much greater? The ratio between the bicep and dumbbell forces is equal to the inverted ratio of their distances from the elbow. If the dumbbell is ten times further from the elbow than the bicep, the force on the bicep will be 200 pounds!)
b. The force placed on your bicep muscle will decrease. As the forearm lifts the dumbbell, it will get closer to the elbow. As a result, the torque placed on the arm from the weight will decrease and the countering torque created by the bicep muscle will do so as well.

Chapter 10

Problems & Exercises

1.
$\omega = 0.737 \text{ rev/s}$

3.
(a) -0.26 rad/s^2

(b) 27 rev

5.
(a) 80 rad/s^2

(b) 1.0 rev

7.
(a) 45.7 s

(b) 116 rev

9.
a) 600 rad/s^2

b) 450 rad/s

c) 21.0 m/s

10.
(a) 0.338 s

(b) 0.0403 rev

(c) 0.313 s

12.
$0.50\ \text{kg} \cdot \text{m}^2$

14.
(a) $50.4\ \text{N} \cdot \text{m}$

(b) $17.1\ \text{rad/s}^2$

(c) $17.0\ \text{rad/s}^2$

16.
$3.96 \times 10^{18}\ \text{s}$

or $1.26 \times 10^{11}\ \text{y}$

18.
$$I_{end} = I_{center} + m\left(\frac{l}{2}\right)^2$$
Thus, $I_{center} = I_{end} - \frac{1}{4}ml^2 = \frac{1}{3}ml^2 - \frac{1}{4}ml^2 = \frac{1}{12}ml^2$

19.
(a) 2.0 ms

(b) The time interval is too short.

(c) The moment of inertia is much too small, by one to two orders of magnitude. A torque of $500\ \text{N} \cdot \text{m}$ is reasonable.

20.
(a) 17,500 rpm

(b) This angular velocity is very high for a disk of this size and mass. The radial acceleration at the edge of the disk is > 50,000 gs.

(c) Flywheel mass and radius should both be much greater, allowing for a lower spin rate (angular velocity).

21.
(a) 185 J

(b) 0.0785 rev

(c) $W = 9.81\ \text{N}$

23.
(a) $2.57 \times 10^{29}\ \text{J}$

(b) $\text{KE}_{\text{rot}} = 2.65 \times 10^{33}\ \text{J}$

25.
$\text{KE}_{\text{rot}} = 434\ \text{J}$

27.
(a) $128\ \text{rad/s}$

(b) $19.9\ \text{m}$

29.
(a) $10.4\ \text{rad/s}^2$

(b) net $W = 6.11\ \text{J}$

34.
(a) 1.49 kJ

(b) 2.52×10^4 N

36.
(a) 2.66×10^{40} kg · m²/s

(b) 7.07×10^{33} kg · m²/s

The angular momentum of the Earth in its orbit around the Sun is 3.77×10^6 times larger than the angular momentum of the Earth around its axis.

38.
$22.5 \text{ kg} \cdot \text{m}^2/\text{s}$

40.
25.3 rpm

43.
(a) 0.156 rad/s

(b) 1.17×10^{-2} J

(c) $0.188 \text{ kg} \cdot \text{m/s}$

45.
(a) 3.13 rad/s

(b) Initial KE = 438 J, final KE = 438 J

47.
(a) 1.70 rad/s

(b) Initial KE = 22.5 J, final KE = 2.04 J

(c) $1.50 \text{ kg} \cdot \text{m/s}$

48.
(a) $5.64 \times 10^{33} \text{ kg} \cdot \text{m}^2/\text{s}$

(b) $1.39 \times 10^{22} \text{ N} \cdot \text{m}$

(c) 2.17×10^{15} N

Test Prep for AP® Courses

1.
(b)

3.
(d)

5.
(d)

You are given a thin rod of length 1.0 m and mass 2.0 kg, a small lead weight of 0.50 kg, and a not-so-small lead weight of 1.0 kg. The rod has three holes, one in each end and one through the middle, which may either hold a pivot point or one of the small lead weights.

7.
(a)

9.
(c)

11.
(a)

13.
(a)

15.
(b)

17.
(c)

19.
(b)

21.
(b)

23.
(c)

25.
(d)

27.
A door on hinges is a rotational system. When you push or pull on the door handle, the angular momentum of the system changes. If a weight is hung on the door handle, then pushing on the door with the same force will cause a different increase in angular momentum. If you push or pull near the hinges with the same force, the resulting angular momentum of the system will also be different.

29.
Since the globe is stationary to start with,

$$\tau = \frac{\Delta L}{\Delta t}$$

$$\tau \cdot \Delta t = \Delta L$$

By substituting,

120 N•m • 1.2 s = 144 N•m•s.

The angular momentum of the globe after 1.2 s is 144 N•m•s.

Chapter 11

Problems & Exercises

1.
$1.610\ \text{cm}^3$

3.
(a) 2.58 g

(b) The volume of your body increases by the volume of air you inhale. The average density of your body decreases when you take a deep breath, because the density of air is substantially smaller than the average density of the body before you took the deep breath.

4.
$2.70\ \text{g/cm}^3$

6.
(a) 0.163 m

(b) Equivalent to 19.4 gallons, which is reasonable

8.

7.9×10^2 kg/m^3

9.
15.8 g/cm^3

10.
(a) 10^{18} kg/m^3

(b) 2×10^4 m

11.
3.59×10^6 Pa; or 521 lb/in^2

13.
2.36×10^3 N

14.
0.760 m

16.
$$\begin{aligned}(h\rho g)_{\text{units}} &= (\text{m})(\text{kg/m}^3)(\text{m/s}^2)=(\text{kg}\cdot\text{m}^2)/(\text{m}^3\cdot\text{s}^2)\\ &= (\text{kg}\cdot\text{m/s}^2)(1/\text{m}^2)\\ &= \text{N/m}^2\end{aligned}$$

18.
(a) 20.5 mm Hg

(b) The range of pressures in the eye is 12–24 mm Hg, so the result in part (a) is within that range

20.
1.09×10^3 N/m^2

22.
24.0 N

24.
2.55×10^7 Pa; or 251 atm

26.
5.76×10^3 N extra force

28.
(a) $V = d_i A_i = d_o A_o \Rightarrow d_o = d_i\left(\frac{A_i}{A_o}\right)$.

Now, using equation:

$$\frac{F_1}{A_1} = \frac{F_2}{A_2} \Rightarrow F_o = F_i\left(\frac{A_o}{A_i}\right).$$

Finally,

$$W_o = F_o d_o = \left(\frac{F_i A_o}{A_i}\right)\left(\frac{d_i A_i}{A_o}\right) = F_i d_i = W_i.$$

In other words, the work output equals the work input.

(b) If the system is not moving, friction would not play a role. With friction, we know there are losses, so that $W_{\text{out}} = W_{\text{in}} - W_{\text{f}}$; therefore, the work output is less than the work input. In other words, with friction, you need to push harder on the input piston than was calculated for the nonfriction case.

29.
Balloon:

$$P_g = 5.00 \text{ cm } H_2O,$$
$$P_{abs} = 1.035 \times 10^3 \text{ cm } H_2O.$$

Jar:

$$P_g = -50.0 \text{ mm Hg},$$
$$P_{abs} = 710 \text{ mm Hg}.$$

31.
4.08 m

33.
$$\Delta P = 38.7 \text{ mm Hg},$$
$$\text{Leg blood pressure} = \frac{159}{119}.$$

35.
22.4 cm^2

36.
91.7%

38.
815 kg/m^3

40.
(a) 41.4 g

(b) 41.4 cm^3

(c) 1.09 g/cm^3

42.
(a) 39.5 g

(b) 50 cm^3

(c) 0.79 g/cm^3

It is ethyl alcohol.

44.
8.21 N

46.
(a) 960 kg/m^3

(b) 6.34%

She indeed floats more in seawater.

48.
(a) 0.24

(b) 0.68

(c) Yes, the cork will float because $\rho_{obj} < \rho_{\text{ethyl alcohol}} (0.678 \text{ g/cm}^3 < 0.79 \text{ g/cm}^3)$

50.
The difference is 0.006%.

52.
$$F_{net} = F_2 - F_1 = P_2 A - P_1 A = (P_2 - P_1)A$$
$$= (h_2 \rho_{fl} g - h_1 \rho_{fl} g)A$$

$=(h_2 - h_1)\rho_{fl} g A$

where ρ_{fl} = density of fluid. Therefore,

$F_{net} = (h_2 - h_1)A\rho_{fl} g = V_{fl}\rho_{fl} g = m_{fl} g = w_{fl}$

where is w_{fl} the weight of the fluid displaced.

54.
592 N/m^2

56.
2.23×10^{-2} mm Hg

58.
(a) 1.65×10^{-3} m

(b) 3.71×10^{-4} m

60.
6.32×10^{-2} N/m

Based on the values in table, the fluid is probably glycerin.

62.

$$\begin{aligned} P_w &= 14.6 \text{ N/m}^2, \\ P_a &= 4.46 \text{ N/m}^2, \\ P_{sw} &= 7.40 \text{ N/m}^2. \end{aligned}$$

Alcohol forms the most stable bubble, since the absolute pressure inside is closest to atmospheric pressure.

64.
5.1°

This is near the value of $\theta = 0^\circ$ for most organic liquids.

66.
-2.78

The ratio is negative because water is raised whereas mercury is lowered.

68.
479 N

70.
1.96 N

71.
-63.0 cm H_2O

73.
(a) $3.81 \times 10^3 \text{ N/m}^2$

(b) 28.7 mm Hg, which is sufficient to trigger micturition reflex

75.
(a) 13.6 m water

(b) 76.5 cm water

77.
(a) 3.98×10^6 Pa

(b) 2.1×10^{-3} cm

79.
(a) 2.97 cm

(b) 3.39×10^{-6} J

(c) Work is done by the surface tension force through an effective distance $h/2$ to raise the column of water.

81.
(a) 2.01×10^4 N

(b) 1.17×10^{-3} m

(c) 2.56×10^{10} N/m^2

83.
(a) 1.38×10^4 N

(b) 2.81×10^7 N/m^2

(c) 283 N

85.
(a) 867 N

(b) This is too much force to exert with a hand pump.

(c) The assumed radius of the pump is too large; it would be nearly two inches in diameter—too large for a pump or even a master cylinder. The pressure is reasonable for bicycle tires.

Test Prep for AP® Courses

1.
(e)

3.
(a) 100 kg/m^3 (b) 60% (c) yes; yes (76% will be submerged) (d) answers vary

Chapter 12

Problems & Exercises

1.
2.78 cm^3/s

3.
27 cm/s

5.
(a) 0.75 m/s

(b) 0.13 m/s

7.
(a) 40.0 cm^2

(b) 5.09×10^7

9.
(a) 22 h

(b) 0.016 s

11.
(a) 12.6 m/s

(b) 0.0800 m^3/s

(c) No, independent of density.

13.
(a) 0.402 L/s

(b) 0.584 cm

15.
(a) $127\ \text{cm}^3/\text{s}$

(b) 0.890 cm

17.
$$\begin{aligned} P &= \frac{\text{Force}}{\text{Area}}, \\ (P)_{\text{units}} &= \text{N/m}^2 = \text{N} \cdot \text{m/m}^3 = \text{J/m}^3 \\ &= \text{energy/volume} \end{aligned}$$

19.
184 mm Hg

21.
$2.54 \times 10^5\ \text{N}$

23.
(a) $1.58 \times 10^6\ \text{N/m}^2$

(b) 163 m

25.
(a) $9.56 \times 10^8\ \text{W}$

(b) 1.4

27.
1.26 W

29.
(a) $3.02 \times 10^{-3}\ \text{N}$

(b) 1.03×10^{-3}

31.
$1.60\ \text{cm}^3/\text{min}$

33.
$8.7 \times 10^{-11}\ \text{m}^3/\text{s}$

35.
0.316

37.
(a) 1.52

(b) Turbulence will decrease the flow rate of the blood, which would require an even larger increase in the pressure difference, leading to higher blood pressure.

39.
$225\ \text{mPa} \cdot \text{s}$
41.
$0.138\ \text{Pa} \cdot \text{s},$
or

Olive oil.

43.
(a) $1.62 \times 10^4\ \text{N/m}^2$

(b) $0.111\ \text{cm}^3/\text{s}$

(c)10.6 cm

45.
1.59

47.
$2.95 \times 10^6\ \text{N/m}^2$(gauge pressure)

51.
$N_\text{R} = 1.99 \times 10^2 < 2000$

53.
(a) nozzle: 1.27×10^5 , not laminar

(b) hose: 3.51×10^4, not laminar.

55.
2.54 << 2000, laminar.

57.
1.02 m/s

$1.28 \times 10^{-2}\ \text{L/s}$

59.
(a)$\geq 13.0\ \text{m}$

(b) $2.68 \times 10^{-6}\ \text{N/m}^2$

61.
(a) 23.7 atm or $344\ \text{lb/in}^2$

(b) The pressure is much too high.

(c) The assumed flow rate is very high for a garden hose.

(d) 5.27×10^6 > > 3000, turbulent, contrary to the assumption of laminar flow when using this equation.

62.
$1.41 \times 10^{-3}\ \text{m}$

64.
$1.3 \times 10^2\ \text{s}$

66.
0.391 s

Test Prep for AP® Courses

1.
(c)

3.
(a)

5.
(a)

7.
(a)

9.
(d)

Chapter 13

Problems & Exercises

1.
$102°F$

3.
$20.0°C$ and $25.6°C$

5.
$9890°F$

7.
(a) $22.2°C$

(b)
$$\begin{aligned}\Delta T(°F) &= T_2(°F)-T_1(°F)\\ &= \tfrac{9}{5}T_2(°C)+32.0° - \left(\tfrac{9}{5}T_1(°C)+32.0°\right)\\ &= \tfrac{9}{5}(T_2(°C)-T_1(°C)) = \tfrac{9}{5}\Delta T(°C)\end{aligned}$$

9.
169.98 m

11.
5.4×10^{-6} m

13.
Because the area gets smaller, the price of the land DECREASES by ~$17,000.

15.
$$\begin{aligned}V &= V_0 + \Delta V = V_0(1+\beta\Delta T)\\ &= (60.00\text{ L})\left[1+\left(950\times10^{-6}/°C\right)(35.0°C - 15.0°C)\right]\\ &= 61.1\text{ L}\end{aligned}$$

17.
(a) 9.35 mL

(b) 7.56 mL

19.
0.832 mm

21.
We know how the length changes with temperature: $\Delta L = \alpha L_0 \Delta T$. Also we know that the volume of a cube is related to its length by $V = L^3$, so the final volume is then $V = V_0 + \Delta V = (L_0 + \Delta L)^3$. Substituting for ΔL gives

$$V = (L_0 + \alpha L_0 \Delta T)^3 = L_0^3(1+\alpha\Delta T)^3.$$

Now, because $\alpha\Delta T$ is small, we can use the binomial expansion:

$$V \approx L_0^3(1+3\alpha\Delta T) = L_0^3 + 3\alpha L_0^3\Delta T.$$

So writing the length terms in terms of volumes gives $V = V_0 + \Delta V \approx V_0 + 3\alpha V_0 \Delta T$, and so

$$\Delta V = \beta V_0 \Delta T \approx 3\alpha V_0 \Delta T, \text{ or } \beta \approx 3\alpha.$$

22.
1.62 atm

24.

(a) 0.136 atm

(b) 0.135 atm. The difference between this value and the value from part (a) is negligible.

26.
(a) $nRT = \text{(mol)(J/mol} \cdot \text{K)(K)} = \text{J}$

(b) $nRT = \text{(mol)(cal/mol} \cdot \text{K)(K)} = \text{cal}$

(c)
$$\begin{aligned} nRT &= \text{(mol)(L} \cdot \text{atm/mol} \cdot \text{K)(K)} \\ &= \text{L} \cdot \text{atm} = (\text{m}^3)(\text{N/m}^2) \\ &= \text{N} \cdot \text{m} = \text{J} \end{aligned}$$

28.
7.86×10^{-2} mol

30.
(a) $6.02 \times 10^5\ \text{km}^3$

(b) 6.02×10^8 km

32.
$-73.9°\text{C}$

34.
(a) $9.14 \times 10^6\ \text{N/m}^2$

(b) $8.23 \times 10^6\ \text{N/m}^2$

(c) 2.16 K

(d) No. The final temperature needed is much too low to be easily achieved for a large object.

36.
41 km

38.
(a) 3.7×10^{-17} Pa

(b) $6.0 \times 10^{17}\ \text{m}^3$

(c) 8.4×10^2 km

39.
1.25×10^3 m/s

41.
(a) 1.20×10^{-19} J

(b) 1.24×10^{-17} J

43.
458 K

45.
1.95×10^7 K

47.
6.09×10^5 m/s

49.
7.89×10^4 Pa

51.

(a) 1.99×10^5 Pa

(b) 0.97 atm

53.
3.12×10^4 Pa

55.
78.3%

57.
(a) 2.12×10^4 Pa

(b) $1.06\ \%$

59.
(a) 8.80×10^{-2} g

(b) 6.30×10^3 Pa; the two values are nearly identical.

61.
82.3%

63.
4.77°C

65.
38.3 m

67.
$\frac{(F_B/w_{Cu})}{(F_B/w_{Cu})'} = 1.02$. The buoyant force supports nearly the exact same amount of force on the copper block in both circumstances.

69.
(a) 4.41×10^{10} mol/m^3

(b) It's unreasonably large.

(c) At high pressures such as these, the ideal gas law can no longer be applied. As a result, unreasonable answers come up when it is used.

71.
(a) 7.03×10^8 m/s

(b) The velocity is too high—it's greater than the speed of light.

(c) The assumption that hydrogen inside a supernova behaves as an idea gas is responsible, because of the great temperature and density in the core of a star. Furthermore, when a velocity greater than the speed of light is obtained, classical physics must be replaced by relativity, a subject not yet covered.

Test Prep for AP® Courses

1.
(a), (c)

3.
(d)

5.
(b)

7.

(a) 7.29 × 10^{-21} J; (b) 352K or 79ºC

Chapter 14

Problems & Exercises

1.
5.02×10^8 J

3.
3.07×10^3 J

5.
0.171ºC

7.
10.8

9.
617 W

11.
35.9 kcal

13.
(a) 591 kcal

(b) 4.94×10^3 s

15.
13.5 W

17.
(a) 148 kcal

(b) 0.418 s, 3.34 s, 4.19 s, 22.6 s, 0.456 s

19.
33.0 g

20.
(a) 9.67 L

(b) Crude oil is less dense than water, so it floats on top of the water, thereby exposing it to the oxygen in the air, which it uses to burn. Also, if the water is under the oil, it is less efficient in absorbing the heat generated by the oil.

22.
a) 319 kcal

b) 2.00ºC

24.
20.6ºC

26.
4.38 kg

28.
(a) 1.57×10^4 kcal

(b) 18.3 kW · h

(c) 1.29×10^4 kcal

30.
(a) 1.01×10^3 W

(b) One

32.
84.0 W

34.
2.59 kg

36.
(a) 39.7 W

(b) 820 kcal

38.
35 to 1, window to wall

40.
1.05×10^3 K

42.
(a) 83 W

(b) 24 times that of a double pane window.

44.
20.0 W, 17.2% of 2400 kcal per day

45.
10 m/s

47.
85.7°C

49.
1.48 kg

51.
2×10^4 MW

53.
(a) 97.2 J

(b) 29.2 W

(c) 9.49 W

(d) The total rate of heat loss would be $29.2 \text{ W} + 9.49 \text{ W} = 38.7 \text{ W}$. While sleeping, our body consumes 83 W of power, while sitting it consumes 120 to 210 W. Therefore, the total rate of heat loss from breathing will not be a major form of heat loss for this person.

55.
-21.7 kW
Note that the negative answer implies heat loss to the surroundings.

57.
-266 kW

59.
-36.0 W

61.
(a) 1.31%

(b) 20.5%

63.
(a) $-15.0\ \text{kW}$

(b) 4.2 cm

65.
(a) $48.5°C$

(b) A pure white object reflects more of the radiant energy that hits it, so a white tent would prevent more of the sunlight from heating up the inside of the tent, and the white tunic would prevent that heat which entered the tent from heating the rider. Therefore, with a white tent, the temperature would be lower than $48.5°C$, and the rate of radiant heat transferred to the rider would be less than 20.0 W.

67.
(a) $3 \times 10^{17}\ \text{J}$

(b) $1 \times 10^{13}\ \text{kg}$

(c) When a large meteor hits the ocean, it causes great tidal waves, dissipating large amount of its energy in the form of kinetic energy of the water.

69.
(a) $3.44 \times 10^{5}\ \text{m}^3/\text{s}$

(b) This is equivalent to 12 million cubic feet of air per second. That is tremendous. This is too large to be dissipated by heating the air by only $5°C$. Many of these cooling towers use the circulation of cooler air over warmer water to increase the rate of evaporation. This would allow much smaller amounts of air necessary to remove such a large amount of heat because evaporation removes larger quantities of heat than was considered in part (a).

71.
20.9 min

73.
(a) 3.96×10^{-2} g

(b) 96.2 J

(c) 16.0 W

75.
(a) 1.102

(b) $2.79 \times 10^{4}\ \text{J}$

(c) 12.6 J. This will not cause a significant cooling of the air because it is much less than the energy found in part (b), which is the energy required to warm the air from $20.0°C$ to $50.0°C$.

76.
(a) $36°C$

(b) Any temperature increase greater than about $3°C$ would be unreasonably large. In this case the final temperature of the person would rise to $73°C\ (163°F)$.

(c) The assumption of 95% heat retention is unreasonable.

78.
(a) 1.46 kW

(b) Very high power loss through a window. An electric heater of this power can keep an entire room warm.

(c) The surface temperatures of the window do not differ by as great an amount as assumed. The inner surface will be warmer, and the outer surface will be cooler.

Test Prep for AP® Courses

1.
(c)

3.
(a)

5.
(b)

7.
(a)

9.
(d)

Chapter 15

Problems & Exercises

1.
$1.6 \times 10^9\ \text{J}$

3.
$-9.30 \times 10^8\ \text{J}$

5.
(a) $-1.0 \times 10^4\ \text{J}$, or $-2.39\ \text{kcal}$

(b) 5.00%

7.
(a) 122 W

(b) $2.10 \times 10^6\ \text{J}$

(c) Work done by the motor is $1.61 \times 10^7\ \text{J}$;thus the motor produces 7.67 times the work done by the man

9.
(a) 492 kJ

(b) This amount of heat is consistent with the fact that you warm quickly when exercising. Since the body is inefficient, the excess heat produced must be dissipated through sweating, breathing, etc.

10.
$2.09 \times 10^4\ \text{J}$

12.
(a) $W = P\Delta V = 1.76 \times 10^5\ \text{J}$

(b) $W = Fd = 1.76 \times 10^5\ \text{J}$. Yes, the answer is the same.

14.
$W = 4.5 \times 10^3\ \text{J}$

16.
W is not equal to the difference between the heat input and the heat output.

20.
(a) $18.5\ \text{kJ}$

(b) 54.1%

22.

(a) 1.32×10^9 J

(b) 4.68×10^9 J

24.

(a) 3.80×10^9 J

(b) 0.667 barrels

26.

(a) 8.30×10^{12} J, which is 3.32% of 2.50×10^{14} J.

(b) -8.30×10^{12} J, where the negative sign indicates a reduction in heat transfer to the environment.

28.

403ºC

30.

(a) 244ºC

(b) 477ºC

(c)Yes, since automobiles engines cannot get too hot without overheating, their efficiency is limited.

32.

(a) $Eff_1 = 1 - \frac{T_{c,1}}{T_{h,1}} = 1 - \frac{543\text{ K}}{723\text{ K}} = 0.249 \text{ or } 24.9\%$

(b) $Eff_2 = 1 - \frac{423\text{ K}}{543\text{ K}} = 0.221 \text{ or } 22.1\%$

(c) $Eff_1 = 1 - \frac{T_{c,1}}{T_{h,1}} \Rightarrow T_{c,1} = T_{h,1}(1,-,eff_1)$ similarly, $T_{c,2} = T_{h,2}(1 - Eff_2)$

$$T_{c,2} = T_{h,1}(1 - Eff_1)(1 - Eff_2) \equiv T_{h,1}\left(1 - Eff_{\text{overall}}\right)$$

using $T_{h,2} = T_{c,1}$ in above equation gives $\therefore \left(1 - Eff_{\text{overall}}\right) = (1 - Eff_1)(1 - Eff_2)$

$$Eff_{\text{overall}} = 1 - (1 - 0.249)(1 - 0.221) = 41.5\%$$

(d) $Eff_{\text{overall}} = 1 - \frac{423\text{ K}}{723\text{ K}} = 0.415 \text{ or } 41.5\%$

34.

The heat transfer to the cold reservoir is $Q_c = Q_h - W = 25\text{ kJ} - 12\text{ kJ} = 13\text{ kJ}$, so the efficiency is $Eff = 1 - \frac{Q_c}{Q_h} = 1 - \frac{13\text{ kJ}}{25\text{ kJ}} = 0.48$. The Carnot efficiency is $Eff_C = 1 - \frac{T_c}{T_h} = 1 - \frac{300\text{ K}}{600\text{ K}} = 0.50$. The actual efficiency is 96% of the Carnot efficiency, which is much higher than the best-ever achieved of about 70%, so her scheme is likely to be fraudulent.

36.

(a) –56.3ºC

(b) The temperature is too cold for the output of a steam engine (the local environment). It is below the freezing point of water.

(c) The assumed efficiency is too high.

37.

4.82

39.

0.311

41.

(a) 4.61

(b) 1.66×10^8 J or 3.97×10^4 kcal

(c) To transfer 1.66×10^8 J, heat pump costs $1.00, natural gas costs $1.34.

43.
27.6ºC

45.
(a) 1.44×10^7 J

(b) 40 cents

(c) This cost seems quite realistic; it says that running an air conditioner all day would cost $9.59 (if it ran continuously).

47.
(a) 9.78×10^4 J/K

(b) In order to gain more energy, we must generate it from things within the house, like a heat pump, human bodies, and other appliances. As you know, we use a lot of energy to keep our houses warm in the winter because of the loss of heat to the outside.

49.
8.01×10^5 J

51.
(a) 1.04×10^{31} J/K

(b) 3.28×10^{31} J

53.
199 J/K

55.
(a) 2.47×10^{14} J

(b) 1.60×10^{14} J

(c) 2.85×10^{10} J/K

(d) 8.29×10^{12} J

57.
It should happen twice in every 1.27×10^{30} s or once in every 6.35×10^{29} s

$$\left(6.35 \times 10^{29}\ \text{s}\right)\left(\frac{1\ \text{h}}{3600\ \text{s}}\right)\left(\frac{1\ \text{d}}{24\ \text{h}}\right)\left(\frac{1\ \text{y}}{365.25\ \text{d}}\right) = 2.0 \times 10^{22}\ \text{y}$$

59.
(a) 3.0×10^{29}

(b) 24%

61.
(a) -2.38×10^{-23} J/K

(b) 5.6 times more likely

(c) If you were betting on two heads and 8 tails, the odds of breaking even are 252 to 45, so on average you would break even. So, no, you wouldn't bet on odds of 252 to 45.

63.
(b) 7

(c) 64

(d) 9.38%

(e) 3.33 times more likely (20 to 6)

Test Prep for AP® Courses

1.
(d)

3.
(a)

5.
(b)

7.
(c)

9.
(d)

11.
(a)

13.
(c)

15.
(b)

Chapter 16

Problems & Exercises

1.
(a) $1.23 \times 10^3\ \text{N/m}$

(b) $6.88\ \text{kg}$

(c) $4.00\ \text{mm}$

3.
(a) 889 N/m

(b) 133 N

5.
(a) $6.53 \times 10^3\ \text{N/m}$

(b) Yes

7.
16.7 ms

8.
$0.400\ \text{s/beats}$

9.
400 Hz

10.
12,500 Hz

11.
1.50 kHz

12.
(a) 93.8 m/s

(b) 11.3×10^3 rev/min

13.
2.37 N/m

15.
0.389 kg

18.
94.7 kg

21.
1.94 s

22.
6.21 cm

24.
2.01 s

26.
2.23 Hz

28.
(a) 2.99541 s

(b) Since the period is related to the square root of the acceleration of gravity, when the acceleration changes by 1% the period changes by $(0.01)^2 = 0.01\%$ so it is necessary to have at least 4 digits after the decimal to see the changes.

30.
(a) Period increases by a factor of 1.41 ($\sqrt{2}$)

(b) Period decreases to 97.5% of old period

32.
Slow by a factor of 2.45

34.
length must increase by 0.0116%.

35.
(a) 1.99 Hz

(b) 50.2 cm

(c) 1.40 Hz, 71.0 cm

36.
(a) 3.95×10^6 N/m

(b) 7.90×10^6 J

37.
a). 0.266 m/s

b). 3.00 J

39.
$\pm\frac{\sqrt{3}}{2}$

42.
384 J

44.
(a). 0.123 m

(b). −0.600 J

(c). 0.300 J. The rest of the energy may go into heat caused by friction and other damping forces.

46.
(a) 5.00×10^5 J

(b) 1.20×10^3 s

47.
$t = 9.26$ d

49.
$f = 40.0$ Hz

51.
$v_\text{w} = 16.0$ m/s

53.
$\lambda = 700$ m

55.
$d = 34.0$ cm

57.
$f = 4$ Hz

59.
462 Hz,

4 Hz

61.
(a) 3.33 m/s

(b) 1.25 Hz

63.
0.225 W

65.
7.07

67.
16.0 d

68.
2.50 kW

70.
3.38×10^{-5} W/m^2

Test Prep for AP® Courses

1.
(d)

3.

(b)

5.
The frequency is given by

$$f = \frac{1}{T} = \frac{50 \quad cycles}{30s} = 1.66 \quad Hz$$

Time period is:

$$T = \frac{1}{f} = \frac{1}{1.66} = 0.6 \quad \text{s}$$

7.
(c)

9.
The energy of the particle at the center of the oscillation is given by

$$E = \frac{1}{2}mv^2 = \frac{1}{2} \times 0.2 \quad \text{kg} \times (5 \text{ m·s}^{-1})^2 = 2.5 \quad \text{J}$$

11.
(b)

13.
19.7 J

15.
(c)

17.

$$d = \frac{k}{2\mu_K mg}\left(X^2 - \frac{\mu_K mg}{k}\right)^2 \; where \;\; k = 50 \;\; \text{N} \cdot \text{m}^{-1} \; \mu_k = 0.06 \, m = 0.5\text{kg}$$

$$d = \frac{50\text{N} \cdot \text{m}^{-1}}{2 \times 0.06 \times 9.8\text{m} \cdot \text{s}^{-2}}\left((0.2)^2 - \left(\frac{(0.06 \times 0.5\text{kg} \times 9.8\text{m} \cdot \text{s}^{-2})^2}{(50\text{N} \cdot \text{m}^{-1})^2}\right)\right) = 1.698 \quad \text{m}$$

19.
The waves coming from a tuning fork are mechanical waves that are longitudinal in nature, whereas electromagnetic waves are transverse in nature.

21.
The sound energy coming out of an instrument depends on its size. The sound waves produced are relative to the size of the musical instrument. A smaller instrument such as a tambourine will produce a high-pitched sound (higher frequency, shorter wavelength), whereas a larger instrument such as a drum will produce a deeper sound (lower frequency, longer wavelength).

23.
$2\pi \quad \text{m}$

25.
The student explains the principle of superposition and then shows two waves adding up to form a bigger wave when a crest adds with a crest and a trough with another trough. Also the student shows a wave getting cancelled out when a crest meets a trough and vice versa.

27.
The student must note that the shape of the wave remains the same and there is first an overlap and then receding of the waves.

29.

(c)

Chapter 17

Problems & Exercises

1.
0.288 m

3.
332 m/s

5.

$$\begin{aligned} v_{\text{w}} &= (331\text{ m/s})\sqrt{\frac{T}{273\text{ K}}} = (331\text{ m/s})\sqrt{\frac{293\text{ K}}{273\text{ K}}} \\ &= 343\text{ m/s} \end{aligned}$$

7.
0.223

9.
(a) 7.70 m

(b) This means that sonar is good for spotting and locating large objects, but it isn't able to resolve smaller objects, or detect the detailed shapes of objects. Objects like ships or large pieces of airplanes can be found by sonar, while smaller pieces must be found by other means.

11.
(a) 18.0 ms, 17.1 ms

(b) 5.00%

(c) This uncertainty could definitely cause difficulties for the bat, if it didn't continue to use sound as it closed in on its prey. A 5% uncertainty could be the difference between catching the prey around the neck or around the chest, which means that it could miss grabbing its prey.

12.
$3.16 \times 10^{-4}\text{ W/m}^2$

14.
$3.04 \times 10^{-4}\text{ W/m}^2$

16.
106 dB

18.
(a) 93 dB

(b) 83 dB

20.
(a) 50.1

(b) 5.01×10^{-3} or $\frac{1}{200}$

22.
70.0 dB

24.
100

26.
$1.45 \times 10^{-3}\text{ J}$

28.
28.2 dB

30.
(a) 878 Hz

(b) 735 Hz

32.
$3.79 \times 10^3\ \text{Hz}$

34.
(a) 12.9 m/s

(b) 193 Hz

36.
First eagle hears $4.23 \times 10^3\ \text{Hz}$

Second eagle hears $3.56 \times 10^3\ \text{Hz}$

38.
0.7 Hz

40.
0.3 Hz, 0.2 Hz, 0.5 Hz

42.
(a) 256 Hz

(b) 512 Hz

44.
180 Hz, 270 Hz, 360 Hz

46.
1.56 m

48.
(a) 0.334 m

(b) 259 Hz

50.
3.39 to 4.90 kHz

52.
(a) 367 Hz

(b) 1.07 kHz

54.
(a) $f_n = n(47.6\ \text{Hz}),\ \ n = 1, 3, 5,..., 419$

(b) $f_n = n(95.3\ \text{Hz}),\ \ n = 1, 2, 3,..., 210$

55.
$1 \times 10^6\ \text{km}$

57.
498.5 or 501.5 Hz

59.
82 dB

61.
approximately 48, 9, 0, −7, and 20 dB, respectively

63.

(a) 23 dB

(b) 70 dB

65.
Five factors of 10

67.
(a) $2 \times 10^{-10}\ \text{W/m}^2$

(b) $2 \times 10^{-13}\ \text{W/m}^2$

69.
2.5

71.
1.26

72.
170 dB

74.
103 dB

76.
(a) 1.00

(b) 0.823

(c) Gel is used to facilitate the transmission of the ultrasound between the transducer and the patient's body.

78.
(a) $77.0\ \mu\text{m}$

(b) Effective penetration depth = 3.85 cm, which is enough to examine the eye.

(c) $16.6\ \mu\text{m}$

80.
(a) $5.78 \times 10^{-4}\ \text{m}$

(b) $2.67 \times 10^{6}\ \text{Hz}$

82.
(a) $v_\text{w} = 1540\ \text{m/s} = f\lambda \Rightarrow \lambda = \frac{1540\ \text{m/s}}{100{\times}10^3\ \text{Hz}} = 0.0154\ \text{m} < 3.50\ \text{m}$. Because the wavelength is much shorter than the distance in question, the wavelength is not the limiting factor.

(b) 4.55 ms

84.
974 Hz

(Note: extra digits were retained in order to show the difference.)

Test Prep for AP® Courses

1.
(b)

3.
(e)

5.
(c)

7.
Answers vary. Students could include a sketch showing an increased amplitude when two waves occupy the same location. Students could also cite conceptual evidence such as sound waves passing through each other.

9.
(d)

11.
(c)

13.
(a)

15.
(c)

17.
(b)

18.
Striking the end of a protruding ruler would create transverse waves, not sound waves. Any measurable, audible sound would come from the repetitive striking of the ruler against the desk. The student is confused about the speed of sound through solids versus the speed of sound in air.

19.
(a), (b)

21.
(c)

Chapter 18

Problems & Exercises

1.
(a) 1.25×10^{10}

(b) 3.13×10^{12}

3.
-600 C

5.
1.03×10^{12}

7.
9.09×10^{-13}

9.
1.48×10^{8} C

15.
(a) 2.12×10^{5} N/C

(b) one charge of $+q$

17.
(a) 0.252 N to the left

(b) $x = 6.07$ cm

19.
(a)The electric field at the center of the square will be straight up, since q_a and q_b are positive and q_c and q_d are

negative and all have the same magnitude.

(b) 2.04×10^7 N/C (upward)

21.
0.102 N, in the $-y$ direction

23.
(a) $\vec{E} = 4.36 \times 10^3$ N/C, 35.0°, below the horizontal.

(b) No

25.
(a) 0.263 N

(b) If the charges are distributed over some area, there will be a concentration of charge along the side closest to the oppositely charged object. This effect will increase the net force.

27.
The separation decreased by a factor of 5.

31.
$$\begin{aligned} F &= k\frac{|q_1 q_2|}{r^2} = ma \Rightarrow a = \frac{kq^2}{mr^2} \\ &= \frac{\left(9.00\times10^9 \text{ N}\cdot\text{m}^2/\text{C}^2\right)\left(1.60\times10^{-19} \text{ m}\right)^2}{\left(1.67\times10^{-27} \text{ kg}\right)\left(2.00\times10^{-9} \text{ m}\right)^2} \\ &= 3.45 \times 10^{16} \text{ m/s}^2 \end{aligned}$$

32.
(a) 3.2

(b) If the distance increases by 3.2, then the force will decrease by a factor of 10 ; if the distance decreases by 3.2, then the force will increase by a factor of 10. Either way, the force changes by a factor of 10.

34.
(a) 1.04×10^{-9} C

(b) This charge is approximately 1 nC, which is consistent with the magnitude of charge typical for static electricity

37.
1.02×10^{-11}

39.
a. 0.859 m beyond negative charge on line connecting two charges
b. 0.109 m from lesser charge on line connecting two charges

42.
8.75×10^{-4} N

44.
(a) 6.94×10^{-8} C

(b) 6.25 N/C

46.
(a) 300 N/C (east)

(b) 4.80×10^{-17} N (east)

52.
(a) 5.58×10^{-11} N/C

(b)the coulomb force is extraordinarily stronger than gravity

54.
(a) -6.76×10^5 C

(b) 2.63×10^{13} m/s^2 (upward)

(c) 2.45×10^{-18} kg

56.
The charge q_2 is 9 times greater than q_1.

69.
(a) The forces are balanced in the *x*-direction, so the net force is vertical. It is composed of the sum of the vertical components of the Coulomb force and the gravitational force.

$$\mathbf{F}_y = -2\left(\frac{kq_1q_2}{r^2} + G\frac{m_1m_2}{r^2}\right)\cos 45° =$$

$$-2\left(\frac{8.99\times10^9(1.00\times10^{-9})(2.00\times10^{-9})}{8} + 6.67 \times 10^{-11}\frac{(10.0)(10.0)}{8}\right)$$

$$\cos 45° = -4.36 \times 10^{-9}\text{ N}$$

(b) No, it is in a metastable position. Since it cannot move horizontally, it cannot traverse any part of the track.

$$\mathbf{F}_x = -\left(\frac{kq_1q_2}{4} + G\frac{m_1m_2}{4}\right)\frac{1}{2} + \left(\frac{kq_1q_2}{12} + G\frac{m_1m_2}{12}\right)\frac{\sqrt{3}}{2} =$$

(c) $-\left(\frac{8.99\times10^9(-1.00\times10^{-9})(2.00\times10^{-9})}{4}\frac{1}{2} - 6.67 \times 10^{-11}\frac{(10.0)(10.0)}{4}\frac{1}{2}\right)$

$$+\left(\frac{8.99\times10^9(-1.00\times10^{-9})(2.00\times10^{-9})}{12}\frac{\sqrt{3}}{2} - 6.67 \times 10^{-11}\frac{(10.0)(10.0)}{12}\frac{\sqrt{3}}{2}\right)\text{N} = 2.60 \times 10^{-9}\text{ N}$$

$$\mathbf{F}_y = -\left(\frac{kq_1q_2}{4} + G\frac{m_1m_2}{4}\right)\frac{\sqrt{3}}{2} - \left(\frac{kq_1q_2}{12} + G\frac{m_1m_2}{12}\right)\frac{1}{2} = -2.08 \times 10^{-9}\text{ N}$$

$$-\left(\frac{8.99\times10^9(1.00\times10^{-9})(2.00\times10^{-9})}{4}\frac{\sqrt{3}}{2} - 6.67 \times 10^{-11}\frac{(10.0)(10.0)}{4}\frac{\sqrt{3}}{2}\right)$$

$$-\left(\frac{8.99\times10^9(1.00\times10^{-9})(2.00\times10^{-9})}{12}\frac{1}{2} + 6.67 \times 10^{-11}\frac{(10.0)(10.0)}{12}\frac{1}{2}\right)\text{N} = -6.36 \times 10^{-9}\text{ N}$$

(d) Yes.

(e) It will reach $(1, -\sqrt{3})$ before it will change direction.

(f) The metastable positions where there is no component in one direction are $(0, 0)$, $(4, 0)$, $(2, 2)$, and $(2, -2)$. They number 4.

Test Prep for AP® Courses

1.
(b)

3.
(c)

5.
(a)

7.
(b)

9.
(a) -0.1 C, (b) 1.1 C, (c) Both charges will be equal to 1 C, law of conservation of charge, (d) 0.9 C

11.
W is negative, X is positive, Y is negative, Z is neutral.

13.
(c)

15.
(c)

17.
(b)

19.
a) Ball 1 will have positive charge and Ball 2 will have negative charge. b) The negatively charged rod attracts positive charge of Ball 1. The electrons of Ball 1 are transferred to Ball 2, making it negatively charged. c) If Ball 2 is grounded while the rod is still there, it will lose its negative charge to the ground. d) Yes, Ball 1 will be positively charged and Ball 2 will be negatively charge.

21.
(c)

23.
decrease by 77.78%.

25.
(a)

27.
(d)

29.
(a) 3.60×10^{10} N, (b) It will become 1/4 of the original value; hence it will be equal to 8.99×10^{9} N

31.
(c)

33.
(a)

35.
(b)

37.
(a) 350 N/C, (b) west, (c) 5.6×10−17 N, (d) west.

39.
(b)

41.
(a) i) Field vectors near objects point toward negatively charged objects and away from positively charged objects.

(a) ii) The vectors closest to *R* and *T* are about the same length and start at about the same distance. We have that $q_R/d^2 = q_T/d^2$, so the charge on *R* is about the same as the charge on *T*. The closest vectors around *S* are about the same length as those around *R* and *T*. The vectors near *S* start at about 6 units away, while vectors near *R* and *T* start at about 4 units. We have that $q_R/d^2 = q_S/D^2$, so $q_S/q_R = D^2/d^2 = 36/16 = 2.25$, and so the charge on *S* is about twice that on *R* and *T*.

(b)

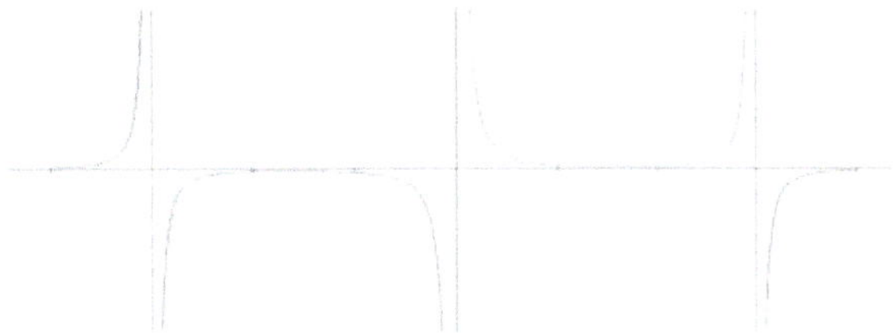

FIGURE 18.65 A vector diagram.

(c)

$$E = k\left[-\frac{q}{(d+x)^2} + \frac{2q}{(x)^2} + \frac{q}{(d-x)^2}\right]$$

(d) The statement is not true. The vector diagram shows field vectors in this region with nonzero length, and the vectors not shown have even greater lengths. The equation in part (c) shows that, when $0 < x < d$, the denominator of the negative term is always greater than the denominator of the third term, but the numerator is the same. So the negative term always has a smaller magnitude than the third term and since the second term is positive the sum of the terms is always positive.

Chapter 19

Problems & Exercises

1.
42.8

4.
1.00×10^5 K

6.
(a) 4×10^4 W

(b) A defibrillator does not cause serious burns because the skin conducts electricity well at high voltages, like those used in defibrillators. The gel used aids in the transfer of energy to the body, and the skin doesn't absorb the energy, but rather lets it pass through to the heart.

8.
(a) 7.40×10^3 C

(b) 1.54×10^{20} electrons per second

9.
3.89×10^6 C

11.
(a) 1.44×10^{12} V

(b) This voltage is very high. A 10.0 cm diameter sphere could never maintain this voltage; it would discharge.

(c) An 8.00 C charge is more charge than can reasonably be accumulated on a sphere of that size.

15.
(a) 3.00 kV

(b) 750 V

17.
(a) No. The electric field strength between the plates is 2.5×10^6 V/m, which is lower than the breakdown strength for air (3.0×10^6 V/m).

(b) 1.7 mm

19.
44.0 mV

21.
15 kV

23.
(a) 800 KeV

(b) 25.0 km

24.
144 V

26.
(a) 1.80 km

(b) A charge of 1 C is a very large amount of charge; a sphere of radius 1.80 km is not practical.

28.
-2.22×10^{-13} C

30.
(a) 3.31×10^{6} V

(b) 152 MeV

32.
(a) 2.78×10^{-7} C

(b) 2.00×10^{-10} C

35.
(a) 2.96×10^{9} m/s

(b) This velocity is far too great. It is faster than the speed of light.

(c) The assumption that the speed of the electron is far less than that of light and that the problem does not require a relativistic treatment produces an answer greater than the speed of light.

46.
21.6 mC

48.
80.0 mC

50.
20.0 kV

52.
667 pF

54.
(a) 4.4 μF

(b) 4.0×10^{-5} C

56.
(a) 14.2 kV

(b) The voltage is unreasonably large, more than 100 times the breakdown voltage of nylon.

(c) The assumed charge is unreasonably large and cannot be stored in a capacitor of these dimensions.

57.
$0.293\ \mu F$

59.
$3.08\ \mu F$ in series combination, $13.0\ \mu F$ in parallel combination

60.
$2.79\ \mu F$

62.
(a) $-3.00\ \mu F$

(b) You cannot have a negative value of capacitance.

(c) The assumption that the capacitors were hooked up in parallel, rather than in series, was incorrect. A parallel connection always produces a greater capacitance, while here a smaller capacitance was assumed. This could happen only if the capacitors are connected in series.

63.
(a) $405\ J$

(b) $90.0\ mC$

64.
(a) 3.16 kV

(b) 25.3 mC

66.
(a) $1.42 \times 10^{-5}\ C, 6.38 \times 10^{-5}\ J$

(b) $8.46 \times 10^{-5}\ C, 3.81 \times 10^{-4}\ J$

67.
(a) $4.43 \times 10^{-12}\ F$

(b) $0.452\ V$

(c) $4.52 \times 10^{-10}\ J$

70.
(a) $133\ F$

(b) Such a capacitor would be too large to carry with a truck. The size of the capacitor would be enormous.

(c) It is unreasonable to assume that a capacitor can store the amount of energy needed.

Test Prep for AP® Courses

1.
(d)

3.
(b)

5.
(c)

7.
(a)

9.
(b)

11.

(b)

13.
(a)

15.
(c)

17.
(b)

19.
(a)

21.
(d)

23.
(d)

25.
(a)

27.
(b)

29.
(c)

31.
(d)

33.
(a)

35.
(c)

37.
(c)

39.
(b)

41.
(a)

43.
(d)

Chapter 20

Problems & Exercises

1.
0.278 mA

3.
0.250 A

5.
1.50ms

7.

INDEX

Symbols

A

B

C

S

College Physics for AP® Courses 2e

Volume 2: Chapters 20-34

SENIOR CONTRIBUTING AUTHORS
IRINA LYUBLINSKAYA, CUNY COLLEGE OF STATEN ISLAND
GREGG WOLFE, AVONWORTH HIGH SCHOOL
DOUGLAS INGRAM, TEXAS CHRISTIAN UNIVERSITY
LIZA PUJJI, MANUKAU INSTITUTE OF TECHNOLOGY
SUDHI OBEROI, RAMAN RESEARCH INSTITUTE
NATHAN CZUBA, SABIO ACADEMY

openstax™

ISBN: 978-1-711470-84-9

OpenStax
Rice University
6100 Main Street MS-375
Houston, Texas 77005

To learn more about OpenStax, visit https://openstax.org.
Individual print copies and bulk orders can be purchased through our website.

COLOR PAPERBACK BOOK ISBN-13	978-1-711470-84-9
DIGITAL VERSION ISBN-13	978-1-951693-61-9
ORIGINAL PUBLICATION YEAR	**2022**

1 2 3 4 5 6 7 8 9 10 RS 22

OpenStax

OpenStax provides free, peer-reviewed, openly licensed textbooks for introductory college and Advanced Placement® courses and low-cost, personalized courseware that helps students learn. A nonprofit ed tech initiative based at Rice University, we're committed to helping students access the tools they need to complete their courses and meet their educational goals.

Rice University

OpenStax, OpenStax CNX, and OpenStax Tutor are initiatives of Rice University. As a leading research university with a distinctive commitment to undergraduate education, Rice University aspires to path-breaking research, unsurpassed teaching, and contributions to the betterment of our world. It seeks to fulfill this mission by cultivating a diverse community of learning and discovery that produces leaders across the spectrum of human endeavor.

RICE

Philanthropic Support

OpenStax is grateful for the generous philanthropic partners who advance our mission to improve educational access and learning for everyone. To see the impact of our supporter community and our most updated list of partners, please visit openstax.org/impact.

Arnold Ventures
Chan Zuckerberg Initiative
Chegg, Inc.
Arthur and Carlyse Ciocca Charitable Foundation
Digital Promise
Ann and John Doerr
Bill & Melinda Gates Foundation
Girard Foundation
Google Inc.
The William and Flora Hewlett Foundation
The Hewlett-Packard Company
Intel Inc.
Rusty and John Jaggers
The Calvin K. Kazanjian Economics Foundation
Charles Koch Foundation
Leon Lowenstein Foundation, Inc.
The Maxfield Foundation
Burt and Deedee McMurtry
Michelson 20MM Foundation
National Science Foundation
The Open Society Foundations
Jumee Yhu and David E. Park III
Brian D. Patterson USA-International Foundation
The Bill and Stephanie Sick Fund
Steven L. Smith & Diana T. Go
Stand Together
Robin and Sandy Stuart Foundation
The Stuart Family Foundation
Tammy and Guillermo Treviño
Valhalla Charitable Foundation
White Star Education Foundation
Schmidt Futures
William Marsh Rice University

Contents

CHAPTER 13
Temperature, Kinetic Theory, and the Gas Laws 561

CHAPTER 14
Heat and Heat Transfer Methods 613

CHAPTER 15
Thermodynamics 661

CHAPTER 22
Magnetism 1023

CHAPTER 23
Electromagnetic Induction, AC Circuits, and Electrical Technologies 1075

CHAPTER 24
Electromagnetic Waves 1135

CHAPTER 20
Electric Current, Resistance, and Ohm's Law

FIGURE 20.1 Electric energy in massive quantities is transmitted from this hydroelectric facility, the Srisailam power station located along the Krishna River in India (http://en.wikipedia.org/wiki/Srisailam_Dam), by the movement of charge—that is, by electric current. (credit: Chintohere, Wikimedia Commons)

CHAPTER OUTLINE

CONNECTION FOR AP® COURSES In our daily lives, we see and experience many examples of electricity which involve electric current, the movement of charge. These include the flicker of numbers on a handheld calculator, nerve impulses carrying signals of vision to the brain, an ultrasound device sending a signal to a computer screen, the brain sending a message for a baby to twitch its toes, an electric train pulling its load over a mountain pass, and a hydroelectric plant sending energy to metropolitan and rural users.

Humankind has indeed harnessed electricity, the basis of technology, to improve the quality of life. While the previous two chapters concentrated on static electricity and the fundamental force underlying its behavior, the next few chapters will be devoted to electric and magnetic phenomena involving electric current. In addition to exploring applications of electricity, we shall gain new insights into its nature – in particular, the fact that all magnetism results from electric current.

This chapter supports learning objectives covered under Big Ideas 1, 4, and 5 of the AP Physics Curriculum Framework. Electric charge is a property of a system (Big Idea 1) that affects its interaction with other charged systems (Enduring Understanding 1.B), whereas electric current is fundamentally the movement of charge through a conductor and is based on the fact that electric charge is conserved within a system (Essential Knowledge 1.B.1). The conservation of charge also leads to the concept of an electric circuit as a closed loop of electrical current. In addition, this chapter discusses examples showing that the current in a circuit is resisted by the elements of the circuit and the strength of the resistance depends on the material of the elements. The macroscopic properties of materials, including resistivity, depend on their molecular and atomic structure (Enduring Understanding 1.E). In addition, resistivity depends on the temperature of the material (Essential Knowledge 1.E.2).

The chapter also describes how the interaction of systems of objects can result in changes in those systems (Big Idea 4). For example, electric properties of a system of charged objects can change in response to the presence of, or changes in, other charged objects or systems (Enduring Understanding 4.E). A simple circuit with a resistor and an energy source is an example of such a system. The current through the resistor in the circuit is equal to the difference of potentials across the resistor divided by its resistance (Essential Knowledge 4.E.4).

The unifying theme of the physics curriculum is that any changes in the systems due to interactions are governed by laws of conservation (Big Idea 5). This chapter applies the idea of energy conservation (Enduring Understanding 5.B) to electric circuits and connects concepts of electric energy and electric power as rates of energy use (Essential Knowledge 5.B.5). While the laws of conservation of energy in electric circuits are fully described by Kirchoff's rules, which are introduced in the next chapter (Essential Knowledge 5.B.9), the specific definition of power (based on Essential Knowledge 5.B.9) is that it is the rate at which energy is transferred from a resistor as the product of the electric potential difference across the resistor and the current through the resistor.

Big Idea 1 Objects and systems have properties such as mass and charge. Systems may have internal structure.

Enduring Understanding 1.B Electric charge is a property of an object or system that affects its interactions with other objects or systems containing charge.

Essential Knowledge 1.B.1 Electric charge is conserved. The net charge of a system is equal to the sum of the charges of all the objects in the system.

Enduring Understanding 1.E Materials have many macroscopic properties that result from the arrangement and interactions of the atoms and molecules that make up the material.

Essential Knowledge 1.E.2 Matter has a property called resistivity.

Big Idea 4 Interactions between systems can result in changes in those systems.

Enduring Understanding 4.E The electric and magnetic properties of a system can change in response to the presence of, or changes in, other objects or systems.

Essential Knowledge 4.E.4 The resistance of a resistor, and the capacitance of a capacitor, can be understood from the basic properties of electric fields and forces, as well as the properties of materials and their geometry.

Big Idea 5: Changes that occur as a result of interactions are constrained by conservation laws.

Enduring Understanding 5.B The energy of a system is conserved.

Essential Knowledge 5.B.5 Energy can be transferred by an external force exerted on an object or system that moves the object or system through a distance; this energy transfer is called work. Energy transfer in mechanical or electrical systems may occur at different rates. Power is defined as the rate of energy transfer into, out of, or within a system. [A piston filled with gas getting compressed or expanded is treated in Physics 2 as a part of thermodynamics.]

Essential Knowledge 5.B.9 Kirchhoff's loop rule describes conservation of energy in electrical circuits. [The application of Kirchhoff's laws to circuits is introduced in Physics 1 and further developed in Physics 2 in the context of more complex circuits, including those with capacitors.]

Click to view content (https://openstax.org/books/college-physics-ap-courses-2e/pages/20-connection-for-ap-r-courses)

20.1 Current

LEARNING OBJECTIVES

By the end of this section, you will be able to:

- Define electric current, ampere, and drift velocity
- Describe the direction of charge flow in conventional current.
- Use drift velocity to calculate current and vice versa.

Electric Current

Electric current is defined to be the rate at which charge flows. A large current, such as that used to start a truck engine, moves a large amount of charge in a small time, whereas a small current, such as that used to operate a hand-held calculator, moves a small amount of charge over a long period of time. In equation form, **electric current** I is defined to be

$$I = \frac{\Delta Q}{\Delta t}, \quad 20.1$$

where ΔQ is the amount of charge passing through a given area in time Δt. (As in previous chapters, initial time is often taken to be zero, in which case $\Delta t = t$.) (See Figure 20.2.) The SI unit for current is the **ampere** (A), named for the French physicist André-Marie Ampère (1775–1836). Since $I = \Delta Q/\Delta t$, we see that an ampere is one coulomb per second:

$$1\text{ A} = 1\text{ C/s} \quad 20.2$$

Not only are fuses and circuit breakers rated in amperes (or amps), so are many electrical appliances.

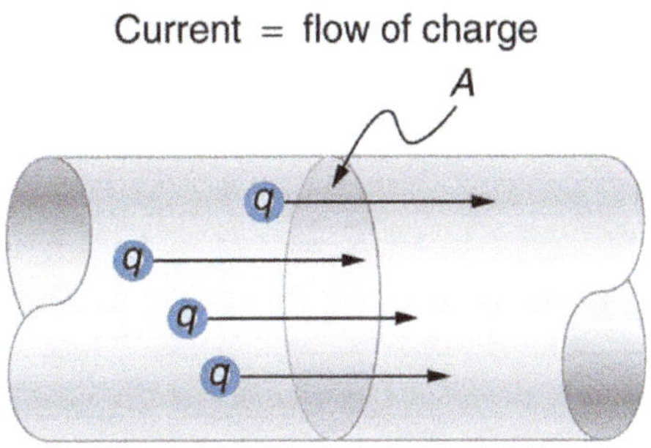

FIGURE 20.2 The rate of flow of charge is current. An ampere is the flow of one coulomb through an area in one second.

EXAMPLE 20.1

Calculating Currents: Current in a Truck Battery and a Handheld Calculator

(a) What is the current involved when a truck battery sets in motion 720 C of charge in 4.00 s while starting an engine? (b) How long does it take 1.00 C of charge to flow through a handheld calculator if a 0.300-mA current is flowing?

Strategy

We can use the definition of current in the equation $I = \Delta Q/\Delta t$ to find the current in part (a), since charge and time are given. In part (b), we rearrange the definition of current and use the given values of charge and current to find the time required.

Solution for (a)

Entering the given values for charge and time into the definition of current gives

$$\begin{aligned} I &= \frac{\Delta Q}{\Delta t} = \frac{720\text{ C}}{4.00\text{ s}} = 180\text{ C/s} \\ &= 180\text{ A}. \end{aligned} \tag{20.3}$$

Discussion for (a)

This large value for current illustrates the fact that a large charge is moved in a small amount of time. The currents in these "starter motors" are fairly large because large frictional forces need to be overcome when setting something in motion.

Solution for (b)

Solving the relationship $I = \Delta Q/\Delta t$ for time Δt, and entering the known values for charge and current gives

$$\begin{aligned} \Delta t &= \frac{\Delta Q}{I} = \frac{1.00\text{ C}}{0.300\times10^{-3}\text{ C/s}} \\ &= 3.33\times10^{3}\text{ s}. \end{aligned} \tag{20.4}$$

Discussion for (b)

This time is slightly less than an hour. The small current used by the hand-held calculator takes a much longer time to move a smaller charge than the large current of the truck starter. So why can we operate our calculators only seconds after turning them on? It's because calculators require very little energy. Such small current and energy demands allow handheld calculators to operate from solar cells or to get many hours of use out of small batteries. Remember, calculators do not have moving parts in the same way that a truck engine has with cylinders and pistons, so the technology requires smaller currents.

Figure 20.3 shows a simple circuit and the standard schematic representation of a battery, conducting path, and load (a resistor). Schematics are very useful in visualizing the main features of a circuit. A single schematic can represent a wide variety of situations. The schematic in Figure 20.3 (b), for example, can represent anything from a truck battery connected to a headlight lighting the street in front of the truck to a small battery connected to a penlight lighting a keyhole in a door. Such schematics are useful because the analysis is the same for a wide variety of situations. We need to understand a few schematics to apply the concepts and analysis to many more situations.

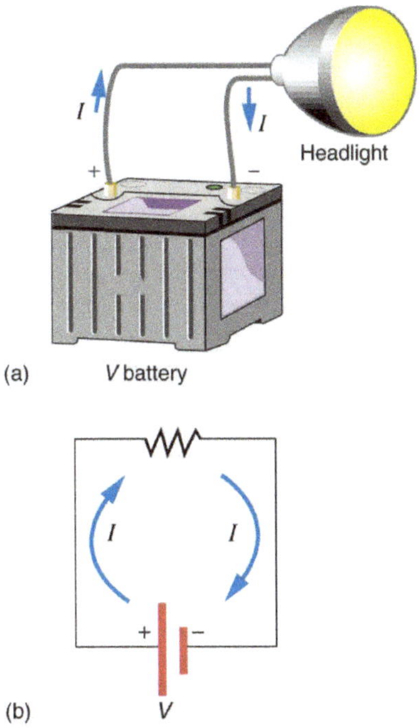

FIGURE 20.3 (a) A simple electric circuit. A closed path for current to flow through is supplied by conducting wires connecting a load to the terminals of a battery. (b) In this schematic, the battery is represented by the two parallel red lines, conducting wires are shown as straight lines, and the zigzag represents the load. The schematic represents a wide variety of similar circuits.

Note that the direction of current flow in Figure 20.3 is from positive to negative. *The direction of conventional current is the direction that positive charge would flow.* Depending on the situation, positive charges, negative charges, or both may move. In metal wires, for example, current is carried by electrons—that is, negative charges move. In ionic solutions, such as salt water, both positive and negative charges move. This is also true in nerve cells. A Van de Graaff generator used for nuclear research can produce a current of pure positive charges, such as protons. Figure 20.4 illustrates the movement of charged particles that compose a current. The fact that conventional current is taken to be in the direction that positive charge would flow can be traced back to American politician and scientist Benjamin Franklin in the 1700s. He named the type of charge associated with electrons negative, long before they were known to carry current in so many situations. Franklin, in fact, was totally unaware of the small-scale structure of electricity.

It is important to realize that there is an electric field in conductors responsible for producing the current, as illustrated in Figure 20.4. Unlike static electricity, where a conductor in equilibrium cannot have an electric field in it, conductors carrying a current have an electric field and are not in static equilibrium. An electric field is needed to supply energy to move the charges.

MAKING CONNECTIONS: TAKE-HOME INVESTIGATION—ELECTRIC CURRENT ILLUSTRATION

Find a straw and little peas that can move freely in the straw. Place the straw flat on a table and fill the straw with peas. When you pop one pea in at one end, a different pea should pop out the other end. This demonstration is an analogy for an electric current. Identify what compares to the electrons and what compares to the supply of energy. What other analogies can you find for an electric current?

Note that the flow of peas is based on the peas physically bumping into each other; electrons flow due to mutually repulsive electrostatic forces.

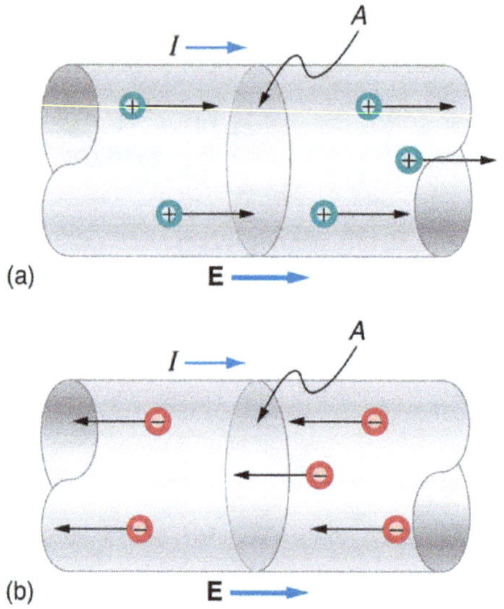

FIGURE 20.4 Current I is the rate at which charge moves through an area A, such as the cross-section of a wire. Conventional current is defined to move in the direction of the electric field. (a) Positive charges move in the direction of the electric field and the same direction as conventional current. (b) Negative charges move in the direction opposite to the electric field. Conventional current is in the direction opposite to the movement of negative charge. The flow of electrons is sometimes referred to as electronic flow.

EXAMPLE 20.2

Calculating the Number of Electrons that Move through a Calculator

If the 0.300-mA current through the calculator mentioned in the Example 20.1 example is carried by electrons, how many electrons per second pass through it?

Strategy

The current calculated in the previous example was defined for the flow of positive charge. For electrons, the magnitude is the same, but the sign is opposite, $I_{\text{electrons}} = -0.300 \times 10^{-3}$ C/s .Since each electron (e^-) has a charge of -1.60×10^{-19} C, we can convert the current in coulombs per second to electrons per second.

Solution

Starting with the definition of current, we have

$$I_{\text{electrons}} = \frac{\Delta Q_{\text{electrons}}}{\Delta t} = \frac{-0.300 \times 10^{-3}\ \text{C}}{\text{s}}. \tag{20.5}$$

We divide this by the charge per electron, so that

$$\begin{aligned} \frac{e^-}{\text{s}} &= \frac{-0.300 \times 10^{-3}\ \text{C}}{\text{s}} \times \frac{1\ e^-}{-1.60 \times 10^{-19}\ \text{C}} \\ &= 1.88 \times 10^{15}\ \frac{e^-}{\text{s}}. \end{aligned} \tag{20.6}$$

Discussion

There are so many charged particles moving, even in small currents, that individual charges are not noticed, just as individual water molecules are not noticed in water flow. Even more amazing is that they do not always keep moving forward like soldiers in a parade. Rather they are like a crowd of people with movement in different directions but a general trend to move forward. There are lots of collisions with atoms in the metal wire and, of course, with other electrons.

Drift Velocity

Electrical signals are known to move very rapidly. Telephone conversations carried by currents in wires cover large distances without noticeable delays. Lights come on as soon as a switch is flicked. Most electrical signals carried by currents travel at speeds on the order of 10^8 m/s, a significant fraction of the speed of light. Interestingly, the individual charges that make up the current move *much* more slowly on average, typically drifting at speeds on the order of 10^{-4} m/s. How do we reconcile these two speeds, and what does it tell us about standard conductors?

The high speed of electrical signals results from the fact that the force between charges acts rapidly at a distance. Thus, when a free charge is forced into a wire, as in Figure 20.5, the incoming charge pushes other charges ahead of it, which in turn push on charges farther down the line. The density of charge in a system cannot easily be increased, and so the signal is passed on rapidly. The resulting electrical shock wave moves through the system at nearly the speed of light. To be precise, this rapidly moving signal or shock wave is a rapidly propagating change in electric field.

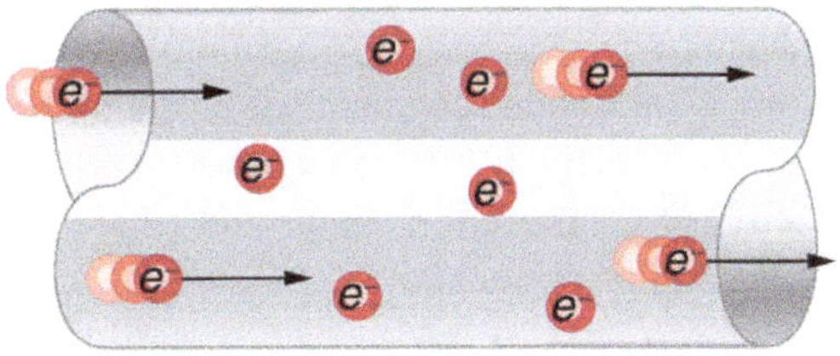

FIGURE 20.5 When charged particles are forced into this volume of a conductor, an equal number are quickly forced to leave. The repulsion between like charges makes it difficult to increase the number of charges in a volume. Thus, as one charge enters, another leaves almost immediately, carrying the signal rapidly forward.

Good conductors have large numbers of free charges in them. In metals, the free charges are free electrons. Figure 20.6 shows how free electrons move through an ordinary conductor. The distance that an individual electron can move between collisions with atoms or other electrons is quite small. The electron paths thus appear nearly random, like the motion of atoms in a gas. But there is an electric field in the conductor that causes the electrons to drift in the direction shown (opposite to the field, since they are negative). The **drift velocity** v_d is the average velocity of the free charges. Drift velocity is quite small, since there are so many free charges. If we have an estimate of the density of free electrons in a conductor, we can calculate the drift velocity for a given current. The larger the density, the lower the velocity required for a given current.

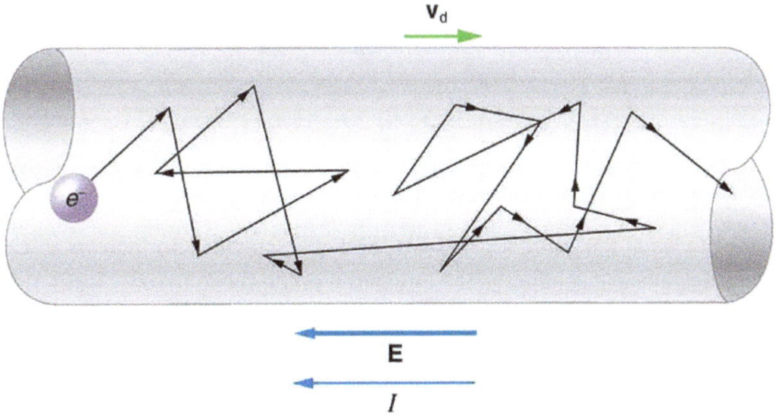

FIGURE 20.6 Free electrons moving in a conductor make many collisions with other electrons and atoms. The path of one electron is shown. The average velocity of the free charges is called the drift velocity, v_d, and it is in the direction opposite to the electric field for electrons. The collisions normally transfer energy to the conductor, requiring a constant supply of energy to maintain a steady current.

CONDUCTION OF ELECTRICITY AND HEAT

Good electrical conductors are often good heat conductors, too. This is because large numbers of free electrons can carry electrical current and can transport thermal energy.

The free-electron collisions transfer energy to the atoms of the conductor. The electric field does work in moving the electrons through a distance, but that work does not increase the kinetic energy (nor speed, therefore) of the electrons. The work is transferred to the conductor's atoms, possibly increasing temperature. Thus a continuous power input is required to keep a current flowing. An exception, of course, is found in superconductors, for reasons we shall explore in a later chapter. Superconductors can have a steady current without a continual supply of energy—a great energy savings. In contrast, the supply of energy can be useful, such as in a lightbulb filament. The supply of energy is necessary to increase the temperature of the tungsten filament, so that the filament glows.

MAKING CONNECTIONS: TAKE-HOME INVESTIGATION—FILAMENT OBSERVATIONS

Find a lightbulb with a filament. Look carefully at the filament and describe its structure. To what points is the filament connected?

We can obtain an expression for the relationship between current and drift velocity by considering the number of free charges in a segment of wire, as illustrated in Figure 20.7. *The number of free charges per unit volume* is given the symbol n and depends on the material. The shaded segment has a volume Ax, so that the number of free charges in it is nAx. The charge ΔQ in this segment is thus $qnAx$, where q is the amount of charge on each carrier. (Recall that for electrons, q is -1.60×10^{-19} C.) Current is charge moved per unit time; thus, if all the original charges move out of this segment in time Δt, the current is

$$I = \frac{\Delta Q}{\Delta t} = \frac{qnAx}{\Delta t}. \tag{20.7}$$

Note that $x/\Delta t$ is the magnitude of the drift velocity, v_d, since the charges move an average distance x in a time Δt. Rearranging terms gives

$$I = nqAv_d, \tag{20.8}$$

where I is the current through a wire of cross-sectional area A made of a material with a free charge density n. The carriers of the current each have charge q and move with a drift velocity of magnitude v_d.

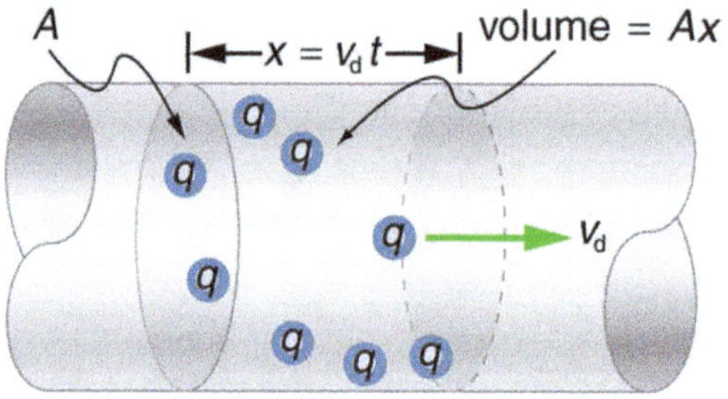

FIGURE 20.7 All the charges in the shaded volume of this wire move out in a time t, having a drift velocity of magnitude $v_d = x/t$. See text for further discussion.

Note that simple drift velocity is not the entire story. The speed of an electron is much greater than its drift velocity. In addition, not all of the electrons in a conductor can move freely, and those that do might move somewhat faster or slower than the drift velocity. So what do we mean by free electrons? Atoms in a metallic conductor are packed in the form of a lattice structure. Some electrons are far enough away from the atomic nuclei that they do not experience the attraction of the nuclei as much as the inner electrons do. These are the free electrons. They are not bound to a single atom but can instead move freely among the atoms in a "sea" of electrons. These free electrons respond by accelerating when an electric field is applied. Of course as they move they collide with the atoms in the lattice and other electrons, generating thermal energy, and the conductor gets warmer. In an insulator, the organization of the atoms and the structure do not allow for such free electrons.

EXAMPLE 20.3

Calculating Drift Velocity in a Common Wire

Calculate the drift velocity of electrons in a 12-gauge copper wire (which has a diameter of 2.053 mm) carrying a 20.0-A current, given that there is one free electron per copper atom. (Household wiring often contains 12-gauge copper wire, and the maximum current allowed in such wire is usually 20 A.) The density of copper is $8.80 \times 10^3\ \text{kg/m}^3$.

Strategy

We can calculate the drift velocity using the equation $I = nqAv_\text{d}$. The current $I = 20.0\text{ A}$ is given, and $q = -1.60 \times 10^{-19}\text{C}$ is the charge of an electron. We can calculate the area of a cross-section of the wire using the formula $A = \pi r^2$, where *r* is one-half the given diameter, 2.053 mm. We are given the density of copper, $8.80 \times 10^3\text{ kg/m}^3$, and the periodic table shows that the atomic mass of copper is 63.54 g/mol. We can use these two quantities along with Avogadro's number, $6.02 \times 10^{23}\text{ atoms/mol}$, to determine n, the number of free electrons per cubic meter.

Solution

First, calculate the density of free electrons in copper. There is one free electron per copper atom. Therefore, is the same as the number of copper atoms per m^3. We can now find n as follows:

$$\begin{aligned} n &= \frac{1\ e^-}{\text{atom}} \times \frac{6.02 \times 10^{23}\text{ atoms}}{\text{mol}} \times \frac{1\text{ mol}}{63.54\text{ g}} \times \frac{1000\text{ g}}{\text{kg}} \times \frac{8.80 \times 10^3\text{ kg}}{1\text{ m}^3} \\ &= 8.342 \times 10^{28}\ e^-/\text{m}^3. \end{aligned} \tag{20.9}$$

The cross-sectional area of the wire is

$$\begin{aligned} A &= \pi r^2 \\ &= \pi\left(\frac{2.053 \times 10^{-3}\text{ m}}{2}\right)^2 \\ &= 3.310 \times 10^{-6}\text{ m}^2. \end{aligned} \tag{20.10}$$

Rearranging $I = nqAv_\text{d}$ to isolate drift velocity gives

$$\begin{aligned} v_\text{d} &= \frac{I}{nqA} \\ &= \frac{20.0\text{ A}}{(8.342 \times 10^{28}/\text{m}^3)(-1.60 \times 10^{-19}\text{ C})(3.310 \times 10^{-6}\text{ m}^2)} \\ &= -4.53 \times 10^{-4}\text{ m/s}. \end{aligned} \tag{20.11}$$

Discussion

The minus sign indicates that the negative charges are moving in the direction opposite to conventional current. The small value for drift velocity (on the order of 10^{-4} m/s) confirms that the signal moves on the order of 10^{12} times faster (about 10^8 m/s) than the charges that carry it.

20.2 Ohm's Law: Resistance and Simple Circuits

LEARNING OBJECTIVES

By the end of this section, you will be able to:

- Explain the origin of Ohm's law.
- Calculate voltages, currents, or resistances with Ohm's law.
- Explain what an ohmic material is.
- Describe a simple circuit.

What drives current? We can think of various devices—such as batteries, generators, wall outlets, and so on—which are necessary to maintain a current. All such devices create a potential difference and are loosely referred to as voltage sources. When a voltage source is connected to a conductor, it applies a potential difference V that creates an electric field. The electric field in turn exerts force on charges, causing current.

Ohm's Law

The current that flows through most substances is directly proportional to the voltage V applied to it. The German physicist Georg Simon Ohm (1787–1854) was the first to demonstrate experimentally that the current in a metal wire is *directly proportional to the voltage applied*:

$$I \propto V. \tag{20.12}$$

This important relationship is known as **Ohm's law**. It can be viewed as a cause-and-effect relationship, with voltage the cause and current the effect. This is an empirical law like that for friction—an experimentally observed phenomenon. Such a linear relationship doesn't always occur.

Resistance and Simple Circuits

If voltage drives current, what impedes it? The electric property that impedes current (crudely similar to friction and air resistance) is called **resistance** R. Collisions of moving charges with atoms and molecules in a substance transfer energy to the substance and limit current. Resistance is defined as inversely proportional to current, or

$$I \propto \frac{1}{R}. \qquad 20.13$$

Thus, for example, current is cut in half if resistance doubles. Combining the relationships of current to voltage and current to resistance gives

$$I = \frac{V}{R}. \qquad 20.14$$

This relationship is also called Ohm's law. Ohm's law in this form really defines resistance for certain materials. Ohm's law (like Hooke's law) is not universally valid. The many substances for which Ohm's law holds are called **ohmic**. These include good conductors like copper and aluminum, and some poor conductors under certain circumstances. Ohmic materials have a resistance R that is independent of voltage V and current I. An object that has simple resistance is called a *resistor*, even if its resistance is small. The unit for resistance is an **ohm** and is given the symbol **Ω** (upper case Greek omega). Rearranging $I = V/R$ gives $R = V/I$, and so the units of resistance are 1 ohm = 1 volt per ampere:

$$1\ \Omega = 1\frac{V}{A}. \qquad 20.15$$

Figure 20.8 shows the schematic for a simple circuit. A **simple circuit** has a single voltage source and a single resistor. The wires connecting the voltage source to the resistor can be assumed to have negligible resistance, or their resistance can be included in R.

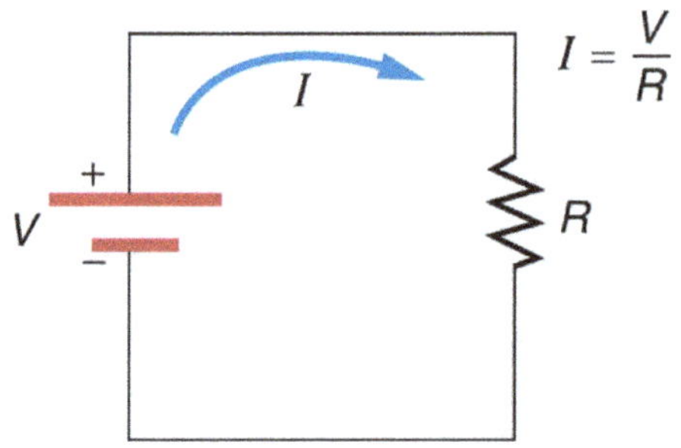

FIGURE 20.8 A simple electric circuit in which a closed path for current to flow is supplied by conductors (usually metal wires) connecting a load to the terminals of a battery, represented by the red parallel lines. The zigzag symbol represents the single resistor and includes any resistance in the connections to the voltage source.

EXAMPLE 20.4

Calculating Resistance: An Automobile Headlight

What is the resistance of an automobile headlight through which 2.50 A flows when 12.0 V is applied to it?

Strategy

We can rearrange Ohm's law as stated by $I = V/R$ and use it to find the resistance.

Solution

Rearranging $I = V/R$ and substituting known values gives

$$R = \frac{V}{I} = \frac{12.0 \text{ V}}{2.50 \text{ A}} = 4.80 \ \Omega. \quad (20.16)$$

Discussion

This is a relatively small resistance, but it is larger than the cold resistance of the headlight. As we shall see in Resistance and Resistivity, resistance usually increases with temperature, and so the bulb has a lower resistance when it is first switched on and will draw considerably more current during its brief warm-up period.

Resistances range over many orders of magnitude. Some ceramic insulators, such as those used to support power lines, have resistances of $10^{12}\ \Omega$ or more. A dry person may have a hand-to-foot resistance of $10^5\ \Omega$, whereas the resistance of the human heart is about $10^3\ \Omega$. A meter-long piece of large-diameter copper wire may have a resistance of $10^{-5}\ \Omega$, and superconductors have no resistance at all (they are non-ohmic). Resistance is related to the shape of an object and the material of which it is composed, as will be seen in Resistance and Resistivity.

Additional insight is gained by solving $I = V/R$ for V, yielding

$$V = IR. \quad (20.17)$$

This expression for V can be interpreted as the *voltage drop across a resistor produced by the flow of current* I. The phrase IR *drop* is often used for this voltage. For instance, the headlight in Example 20.4 has an IR drop of 12.0 V. If voltage is measured at various points in a circuit, it will be seen to increase at the voltage source and decrease at the resistor. Voltage is similar to fluid pressure. The voltage source is like a pump, creating a pressure difference, causing current—the flow of charge. The resistor is like a pipe that reduces pressure and limits flow because of its resistance. Conservation of energy has important consequences here. The voltage source supplies energy (causing an electric field and a current), and the resistor converts it to another form (such as thermal energy). In a simple circuit (one with a single simple resistor), the voltage supplied by the source equals the voltage drop across the resistor, since $\text{PE} = q\Delta V$, and the same q flows through each. Thus the energy supplied by the voltage source and the energy converted by the resistor are equal. (See Figure 20.9.)

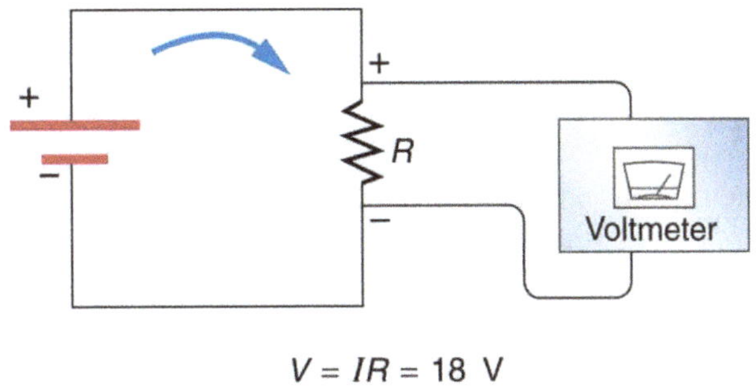

FIGURE 20.9 The voltage drop across a resistor in a simple circuit equals the voltage output of the battery.

PHET EXPLORATIONS

Making Connections: Conservation of Energy

In a simple electrical circuit, the sole resistor converts energy supplied by the source into another form. Conservation of energy is evidenced here by the fact that all of the energy supplied by the source is converted to another form by the resistor alone. We will find that conservation of energy has other important applications in circuits and is a powerful tool in circuit analysis.

PHET EXPLORATIONS

Ohm's Law

See how the equation form of Ohm's law relates to a simple circuit. Adjust the voltage and resistance, and see the current change according to Ohm's law. The sizes of the symbols in the equation change to match the circuit diagram.

Click to view content (https://openstax.org/books/college-physics-ap-courses-2e/pages/20-2-ohms-law-resistance-and-simple-circuits)

20.3 Resistance and Resistivity

LEARNING OBJECTIVES

By the end of this section, you will be able to:

- Explain the concept of resistivity.
- Use resistivity to calculate the resistance of specified configurations of material.
- Use the thermal coefficient of resistivity to calculate the change of resistance with temperature.

Material and Shape Dependence of Resistance

The resistance of an object depends on its shape and the material of which it is composed. The cylindrical resistor in Figure 20.10 is easy to analyze, and, by so doing, we can gain insight into the resistance of more complicated shapes. As you might expect, the cylinder's electric resistance R is directly proportional to its length L, similar to the resistance of a pipe to fluid flow. The longer the cylinder, the more collisions charges will make with its atoms. The greater the diameter of the cylinder, the more current it can carry (again similar to the flow of fluid through a pipe). In fact, R is inversely proportional to the cylinder's cross-sectional area A.

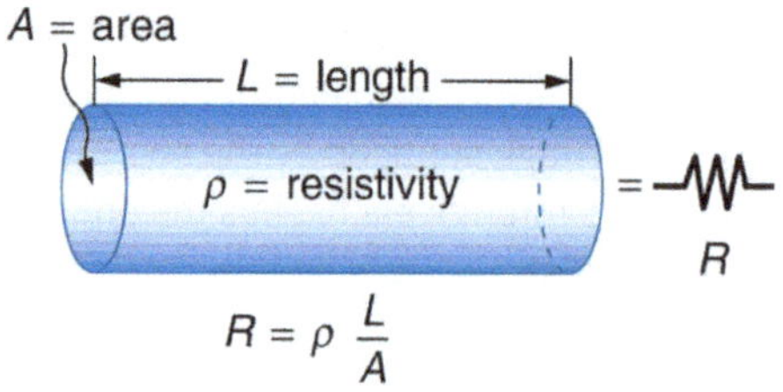

FIGURE 20.10 A uniform cylinder of length L and cross-sectional area A. Its resistance to the flow of current is similar to the resistance posed by a pipe to fluid flow. The longer the cylinder, the greater its resistance. The larger its cross-sectional area A, the smaller its resistance.

For a given shape, the resistance depends on the material of which the object is composed. Different materials offer different resistance to the flow of charge. We define the **resistivity** ρ of a substance so that the **resistance** R of an object is directly proportional to ρ. Resistivity ρ is an *intrinsic* property of a material, independent of its shape or size. The resistance R of a uniform cylinder of length L, of cross-sectional area A, and made of a material with resistivity ρ, is

$$R = \frac{\rho L}{A}. \quad 20.18$$

Table 20.1 gives representative values of ρ. The materials listed in the table are separated into categories of conductors, semiconductors, and insulators, based on broad groupings of resistivities. Conductors have the smallest resistivities, and insulators have the largest; semiconductors have intermediate resistivities. Conductors have varying but large free charge densities, whereas most charges in insulators are bound to atoms and are not free to move. Semiconductors are intermediate, having far fewer free charges than conductors, but having properties that make the number of free charges depend strongly on the type and amount of impurities in the semiconductor. These unique properties of semiconductors are put to use in modern electronics, as will be explored in later chapters.

Material	Resistivity ρ ($\Omega \cdot \text{m}$)
Conductors	
Silver	1.59×10^{-8}
Copper	1.72×10^{-8}
Gold	2.44×10^{-8}
Aluminum	2.65×10^{-8}
Tungsten	5.6×10^{-8}
Iron	9.71×10^{-8}
Platinum	10.6×10^{-8}
Steel	20×10^{-8}
Lead	22×10^{-8}
Manganin (Cu, Mn, Ni alloy)	44×10^{-8}
Constantan (Cu, Ni alloy)	49×10^{-8}
Mercury	96×10^{-8}
Nichrome (Ni, Fe, Cr alloy)	100×10^{-8}
Semiconductors[1]	
Carbon (pure)	3.5×10^{-5}
Carbon	$(3.5 - 60) \times 10^{-5}$
Germanium (pure)	600×10^{-3}
Germanium	$(1 - 600) \times 10^{-3}$
Silicon (pure)	2300
Silicon	0.1–2300
Insulators	
Amber	5×10^{14}

TABLE 20.1 Resistivities ρ of Various materials at $20°\text{C}$

1 Values depend strongly on amounts and types of impurities

Material	Resistivity ρ ($\Omega \cdot \mathrm{m}$)
Glass	$10^9 - 10^{14}$
Lucite	$>10^{13}$
Mica	$10^{11} - 10^{15}$
Quartz (fused)	75×10^{16}
Rubber (hard)	$10^{13} - 10^{16}$
Sulfur	10^{15}
Teflon	$>10^{13}$
Wood	$10^8 - 10^{11}$

TABLE 20.1 Resistivities ρ of Various materials at $20°\mathrm{C}$

EXAMPLE 20.5

Calculating Resistor Diameter: A Headlight Filament

A car headlight filament is made of tungsten and has a cold resistance of $0.350\ \Omega$. If the filament is a cylinder 4.00 cm long (it may be coiled to save space), what is its diameter?

Strategy

We can rearrange the equation $R = \frac{\rho L}{A}$ to find the cross-sectional area A of the filament from the given information. Then its diameter can be found by assuming it has a circular cross-section.

Solution

The cross-sectional area, found by rearranging the expression for the resistance of a cylinder given in $R = \frac{\rho L}{A}$, is

$$A = \frac{\rho L}{R}. \tag{20.19}$$

Substituting the given values, and taking ρ from Table 20.1, yields

$$\begin{aligned} A &= \frac{(5.6\times10^{-8}\ \Omega\cdot\mathrm{m})(4.00\times10^{-2}\ \mathrm{m})}{0.350\ \Omega} \\ &= 6.40\times10^{-9}\ \mathrm{m}^2. \end{aligned} \tag{20.20}$$

The area of a circle is related to its diameter D by

$$A = \frac{\pi D^2}{4}. \tag{20.21}$$

Solving for the diameter D, and substituting the value found for A, gives

$$D = 2\left(\frac{A}{p}\right)^{\frac{1}{2}} = 2\left(\frac{6.40\times10^{-9}\ \text{m}^2}{3.14}\right)^{\frac{1}{2}} = 9.0\times10^{-5}\ \text{m}. \quad (20.22)$$

Discussion

The diameter is just under a tenth of a millimeter. It is quoted to only two digits, because ρ is known to only two digits.

Temperature Variation of Resistance

The resistivity of all materials depends on temperature. Some even become superconductors (zero resistivity) at very low temperatures. (See Figure 20.11.) Conversely, the resistivity of conductors increases with increasing temperature. Since the atoms vibrate more rapidly and over larger distances at higher temperatures, the electrons moving through a metal make more collisions, effectively making the resistivity higher. Over relatively small temperature changes (about $100°\text{C}$ or less), resistivity ρ varies with temperature change ΔT as expressed in the following equation

$$\rho = \rho_0(1 + \alpha\Delta T), \quad (20.23)$$

where ρ_0 is the original resistivity and α is the **temperature coefficient of resistivity**. (See the values of α in Table 20.2 below.) For larger temperature changes, α may vary or a nonlinear equation may be needed to find ρ. Note that α is positive for metals, meaning their resistivity increases with temperature. Some alloys have been developed specifically to have a small temperature dependence. Manganin (which is made of copper, manganese and nickel), for example, has α close to zero (to three digits on the scale in Table 20.2), and so its resistivity varies only slightly with temperature. This is useful for making a temperature-independent resistance standard, for example.

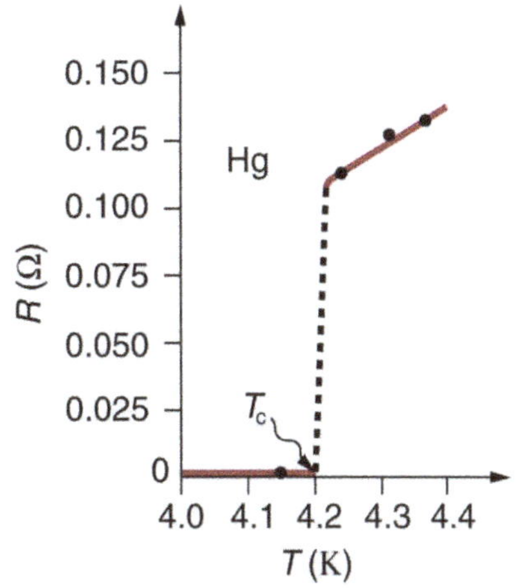

FIGURE 20.11 The resistance of a sample of mercury is zero at very low temperatures—it is a superconductor up to about 4.2 K. Above that critical temperature, its resistance makes a sudden jump and then increases nearly linearly with temperature.

Material	Coefficient α(1/°C)[2]
Conductors	
Silver	3.8×10^{-3}
Copper	3.9×10^{-3}

TABLE 20.2 Tempature Coefficients of Resistivity α

2 Values at 20°C.

Material	Coefficient α(1/°C)[2]
Gold	3.4×10^{-3}
Aluminum	3.9×10^{-3}
Tungsten	4.5×10^{-3}
Iron	5.0×10^{-3}
Platinum	3.93×10^{-3}
Lead	3.9×10^{-3}
Manganin (Cu, Mn, Ni alloy)	0.000×10^{-3}
Constantan (Cu, Ni alloy)	0.002×10^{-3}
Mercury	0.89×10^{-3}
Nichrome (Ni, Fe, Cr alloy)	0.4×10^{-3}
Semiconductors	
Carbon (pure)	-0.5×10^{-3}
Germanium (pure)	-50×10^{-3}
Silicon (pure)	-70×10^{-3}

TABLE 20.2 Tempature Coefficients of Resistivity α

Note also that α is negative for the semiconductors listed in Table 20.2, meaning that their resistivity decreases with increasing temperature. They become better conductors at higher temperature, because increased thermal agitation increases the number of free charges available to carry current. This property of decreasing ρ with temperature is also related to the type and amount of impurities present in the semiconductors.

The resistance of an object also depends on temperature, since R_0 is directly proportional to ρ. For a cylinder we know $R = \rho L/A$, and so, if L and A do not change greatly with temperature, R will have the same temperature dependence as ρ. (Examination of the coefficients of linear expansion shows them to be about two orders of magnitude less than typical temperature coefficients of resistivity, and so the effect of temperature on L and A is about two orders of magnitude less than on ρ.) Thus,

$$R = R_0(1 + \alpha \Delta T) \tag{20.24}$$

is the temperature dependence of the resistance of an object, where R_0 is the original resistance and R is the resistance after a temperature change ΔT. Numerous thermometers are based on the effect of temperature on resistance. (See Figure 20.12.) One of the most common is the thermistor, a semiconductor crystal with a strong temperature dependence, the resistance of which is measured to obtain its temperature. The device is small, so that it quickly comes into thermal equilibrium with the part of a person it touches.

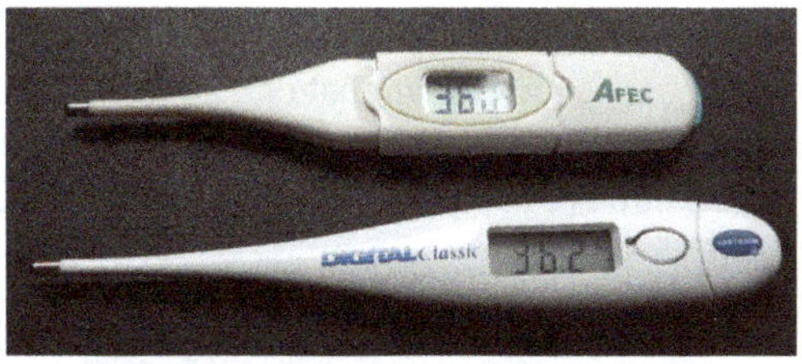

FIGURE 20.12 These familiar thermometers are based on the automated measurement of a thermistor's temperature-dependent resistance. (credit: Biol, Wikimedia Commons)

EXAMPLE 20.6

Calculating Resistance: Hot-Filament Resistance

Although caution must be used in applying $\rho = \rho_0(1 + \alpha\Delta T)$ and $R = R_0(1 + \alpha\Delta T)$ for temperature changes greater than 100°C, for tungsten the equations work reasonably well for very large temperature changes. What, then, is the resistance of the tungsten filament in the previous example if its temperature is increased from room temperature (20°C) to a typical operating temperature of 2850°C?

Strategy

This is a straightforward application of $R = R_0(1 + \alpha\Delta T)$, since the original resistance of the filament was given to be $R_0 = 0.350\ \Omega$, and the temperature change is $\Delta T = 2830^\circ\text{C}$.

Solution

The hot resistance R is obtained by entering known values into the above equation:

$$\begin{aligned} R &= R_0(1 + \alpha\Delta T) \\ &= (0.350\ \Omega)[1+(4.5\times10^{-3}/^\circ\text{C})(2830^\circ\text{C})] \\ &= 4.8\ \Omega. \end{aligned} \tag{20.25}$$

Discussion

This value is consistent with the headlight resistance example in Ohm's Law: Resistance and Simple Circuits.

PHET EXPLORATIONS

Resistance in a Wire

Learn about the physics of resistance in a wire. Change its resistivity, length, and area to see how they affect the wire's resistance. The sizes of the symbols in the equation change along with the diagram of a wire.

Click to view content (https://openstax.org/books/college-physics-ap-courses-2e/pages/20-3-resistance-and-resistivity)

PhET

20.4 Electric Power and Energy

LEARNING OBJECTIVES

By the end of this section, you will be able to:

- Calculate the power dissipated by a resistor and power supplied by a power supply.
- Calculate the cost of electricity under various circumstances.

Power in Electric Circuits

Power is associated by many people with electricity. Knowing that power is the rate of energy use or energy conversion, what is the expression for **electric power**? Power transmission lines might come to mind. We also think of lightbulbs in terms of their power ratings in watts. Let us compare a 25-W bulb with a 60-W bulb. (See Figure

20.13(a).) Since both operate on the same voltage, the 60-W bulb must draw more current to have a greater power rating. Thus the 60-W bulb's resistance must be lower than that of a 25-W bulb. If we increase voltage, we also increase power. For example, when a 25-W bulb that is designed to operate on 120 V is connected to 240 V, it briefly glows very brightly and then burns out. Precisely how are voltage, current, and resistance related to electric power?

(a)

(b)

FIGURE 20.13 (a) Which of these lightbulbs, the 25-W bulb (upper left) or the 60-W bulb (upper right), has the higher resistance? Which draws more current? Which uses the most energy? Can you tell from the color that the 25-W filament is cooler? Is the brighter bulb a different color and if so why? (credits: Dickbauch, Wikimedia Commons; Greg Westfall, Flickr) (b) This compact fluorescent light (CFL) puts out the same intensity of light as the 60-W bulb, but at 1/4 to 1/10 the input power. (credit: dbgg1979, Flickr)

Electric energy depends on both the voltage involved and the charge moved. This is expressed most simply as $\text{PE} = qV$, where q is the charge moved and V is the voltage (or more precisely, the potential difference the charge moves through). Power is the rate at which energy is moved, and so electric power is

$$P = \frac{PE}{t} = \frac{qV}{t}. \quad (20.26)$$

Recognizing that current is $I = q/t$ (note that $\Delta t = t$ here), the expression for power becomes

$$P = IV. \quad (20.27)$$

Electric power (P) is simply the product of current times voltage. Power has familiar units of watts. Since the SI unit for potential energy (PE) is the joule, power has units of joules per second, or watts. Thus, $1 \text{ A} \cdot \text{V} = 1 \text{ W}$. For example, cars often have one or more auxiliary power outlets with which you can charge a cell phone or other electronic devices. These outlets may be rated at 20 A, so that the circuit can deliver a maximum power $P = IV = (20 \text{ A})(12 \text{ V}) = 240 \text{ W}$. In some applications, electric power may be expressed as volt-amperes or even kilovolt-amperes ($1 \text{ kA} \cdot \text{V} = 1 \text{ kW}$).

To see the relationship of power to resistance, we combine Ohm's law with $P = IV$. Substituting $I = V/R$ gives $P = (V/R)V = V^2/R$. Similarly, substituting $V = IR$ gives $P = I(IR) = I^2R$. Three expressions for electric power are listed together here for convenience:

$$P = IV \quad (20.28)$$

$$P = \frac{V^2}{R} \quad (20.29)$$

$$P = I^2R. \quad (20.30)$$

Note that the first equation is always valid, whereas the other two can be used only for resistors. In a simple circuit, with one voltage source and a single resistor, the power supplied by the voltage source and that dissipated by the resistor are identical. (In more complicated circuits, P can be the power dissipated by a single device and not the total power in the circuit.)

Different insights can be gained from the three different expressions for electric power. For example, $P = V^2/R$ implies that the lower the resistance connected to a given voltage source, the greater the power delivered. Furthermore, since voltage is squared in $P = V^2/R$, the effect of applying a higher voltage is perhaps greater than expected. Thus, when the voltage is doubled to a 25-W bulb, its power nearly quadruples to about 100 W, burning it out. If the bulb's resistance remained constant, its power would be exactly 100 W, but at the higher temperature its resistance is higher, too.

EXAMPLE 20.7

Calculating Power Dissipation and Current: Hot and Cold Power

(a) Consider the examples given in Ohm's Law: Resistance and Simple Circuits and Resistance and Resistivity. Then find the power dissipated by the car headlight in these examples, both when it is hot and when it is cold. (b) What current does it draw when cold?

Strategy for (a)

For the hot headlight, we know voltage and current, so we can use $P = IV$ to find the power. For the cold headlight, we know the voltage and resistance, so we can use $P = V^2/R$ to find the power.

Solution for (a)

Entering the known values of current and voltage for the hot headlight, we obtain

$$P = IV = (2.50\text{ A})(12.0\text{ V}) = 30.0\text{ W}. \tag{20.31}$$

The cold resistance was $0.350\ \Omega$, and so the power it uses when first switched on is

$$P = \frac{V^2}{R} = \frac{(12.0\text{ V})^2}{0.350\ \Omega} = 411\text{ W}. \tag{20.32}$$

Discussion for (a)

The 30 W dissipated by the hot headlight is typical. But the 411 W when cold is surprisingly higher. The initial power quickly decreases as the bulb's temperature increases and its resistance increases.

Strategy and Solution for (b)

The current when the bulb is cold can be found several different ways. We rearrange one of the power equations, $P = I^2R$, and enter known values, obtaining

$$I = \sqrt{\frac{P}{R}} = \sqrt{\frac{411\text{ W}}{0.350\ \Omega}} = 34.3\text{ A}. \tag{20.33}$$

Discussion for (b)

The cold current is remarkably higher than the steady-state value of 2.50 A, but the current will quickly decline to that value as the bulb's temperature increases. Most fuses and circuit breakers (used to limit the current in a circuit) are designed to tolerate very high currents briefly as a device comes on. In some cases, such as with electric motors, the current remains high for several seconds, necessitating special "slow blow" fuses.

The Cost of Electricity

The more electric appliances you use and the longer they are left on, the higher your electric bill. This familiar fact is based on the relationship between energy and power. You pay for the energy used. Since $P = E/t$, we see that

$$E = Pt \tag{20.34}$$

is the energy used by a device using power P for a time interval t. For example, the more lightbulbs burning, the greater P used; the longer they are on, the greater t is. The energy unit on electric bills is the kilowatt-hour ($\text{kW} \cdot \text{h}$), consistent with the relationship $E = Pt$. It is easy to estimate the cost of operating electric appliances if you have some idea of their power consumption rate in watts or kilowatts, the time they are on in hours, and the cost per kilowatt-hour for your electric utility. Kilowatt-hours, like all other specialized energy units such as food calories, can be converted to joules. You can prove to yourself that $1\ \text{kW} \cdot \text{h} = 3.6 \times 10^6\ \text{J}$.

The electrical energy (E) used can be reduced either by reducing the time of use or by reducing the power consumption of that appliance or fixture. This will not only reduce the cost, but it will also result in a reduced impact on the environment. Improvements to lighting are some of the fastest ways to reduce the electrical energy used in a home or business. About 20% of a home's use of energy goes to lighting, while the number for commercial establishments is closer to 40%. Fluorescent lights are about four times more efficient than incandescent lights—this is true for both the long tubes and the compact fluorescent lights (CFL). (See Figure 20.13(b).) Thus, a 60-W incandescent bulb can be replaced by a 15-W CFL, which has the same brightness and color. CFLs have a bent tube inside a globe or a spiral-shaped tube, all connected to a standard screw-in base that fits standard incandescent light sockets. (Original problems with color, flicker, shape, and high initial investment for CFLs have been addressed in recent years.) The heat transfer from these CFLs is less, and they last up to 10 times longer. The significance of an investment in such bulbs is addressed in the next example. New white LED lights (which are clusters of small LED bulbs) are even more efficient (twice that of CFLs) and last 5 times longer than CFLs. However, their cost is still high.

MAKING CONNECTIONS: ENERGY, POWER, AND TIME

The relationship $E = Pt$ is one that you will find useful in many different contexts. The energy your body uses in exercise is related to the power level and duration of your activity, for example. The amount of heating by a power source is related to the power level and time it is applied. Even the radiation dose of an X-ray image is related to the power and time of exposure.

EXAMPLE 20.8

Calculating the Cost Effectiveness of Compact Fluorescent Lights (CFL)

If the cost of electricity in your area is 12 cents per kWh, what is the total cost (capital plus operation) of using a 60-W incandescent bulb for 1000 hours (the lifetime of that bulb) if the bulb cost 25 cents? (b) If we replace this bulb with a compact fluorescent light that provides the same light output, but at one-quarter the wattage, and which costs $1.50 but lasts 10 times longer (10,000 hours), what will that total cost be?

Strategy

To find the operating cost, we first find the energy used in kilowatt-hours and then multiply by the cost per kilowatt-hour.

Solution for (a)

The energy used in kilowatt-hours is found by entering the power and time into the expression for energy:

$$E = Pt = (60\ \text{W})(1000\ \text{h}) = 60{,}000\ \text{W} \cdot \text{h}. \qquad 20.35$$

In kilowatt-hours, this is

$$E = 60.0\ \text{kW} \cdot \text{h}. \qquad 20.36$$

Now the electricity cost is

$$\text{cost} = (60.0\ \text{kW} \cdot \text{h})(\$0.12/\text{kW} \cdot \text{h}) = \$7.20. \qquad 20.37$$

The total cost, including the cost of the bulb, will be $7.45 for 1000 hours (about one-half year at 5 hours per day).

Solution for (b)

Since the CFL uses only 15 W and not 60 W, the electricity cost will be $7.20/4 = $1.80. The CFL will last 10 times longer than the incandescent, so that the investment cost will be 1/10 of the bulb cost for that time period of use, or 0.1($1.50) = $0.15. Therefore, the total cost will be $1.95 for 1000 hours.

Discussion

Therefore, it is much cheaper to use the CFLs, even though the initial investment is higher. The increased cost of labor that a business must include for replacing the incandescent bulbs more often has not been figured in here.

MAKING CONNECTIONS: TAKE-HOME EXPERIMENT—ELECTRICAL ENERGY USE INVENTORY

1) Make a list of the power ratings on a range of appliances in your home or room. Explain why something like a toaster has a higher rating than a digital clock. Estimate the energy consumed by these appliances in an average day (by estimating their time of use). Some appliances might only state the operating current. If the household voltage is 120 V, then use $P = IV$. 2) Check out the total wattage used in the rest rooms of your school's floor or building. (You might need to assume the long fluorescent lights in use are rated at 32 W.) Suppose that the building was closed all weekend and that these lights were left on from 6 p.m. Friday until 8 a.m. Monday. What would this oversight cost? How about for an entire year of weekends?

20.5 Alternating Current versus Direct Current

LEARNING OBJECTIVES

By the end of this section, you will be able to:

- Explain the differences and similarities between AC and DC current.
- Calculate rms voltage, current, and average power.
- Explain why AC current is used for power transmission.

Alternating Current

Most of the examples dealt with so far, and particularly those utilizing batteries, have constant voltage sources. Once the current is established, it is thus also a constant. **Direct current** (DC) is the flow of electric charge in only one direction. It is the steady state of a constant-voltage circuit. Most well-known applications, however, use a time-varying voltage source. **Alternating current** (AC) is the flow of electric charge that periodically reverses direction. If the source varies periodically, particularly sinusoidally, the circuit is known as an alternating current circuit. Examples include the commercial and residential power that serves so many of our needs. Figure 20.14 shows graphs of voltage and current versus time for typical DC and AC power. The AC voltages and frequencies commonly used in homes and businesses vary around the world.

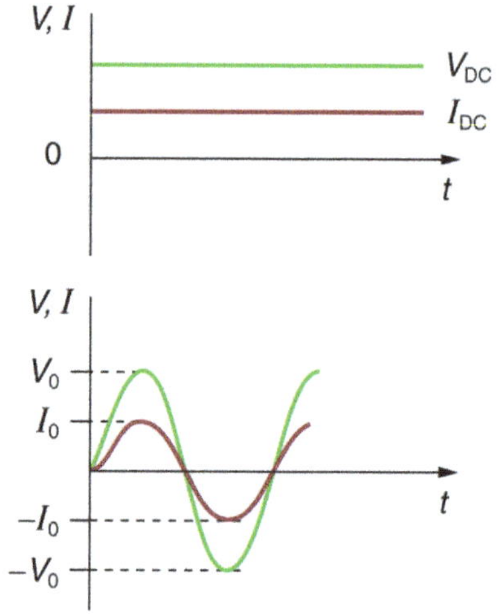

FIGURE 20.14 (a) DC voltage and current are constant in time, once the current is established. (b) A graph of voltage and current versus time for 60-Hz AC power. The voltage and current are sinusoidal and are in phase for a simple resistance circuit. The frequencies and peak voltages of AC sources differ greatly.

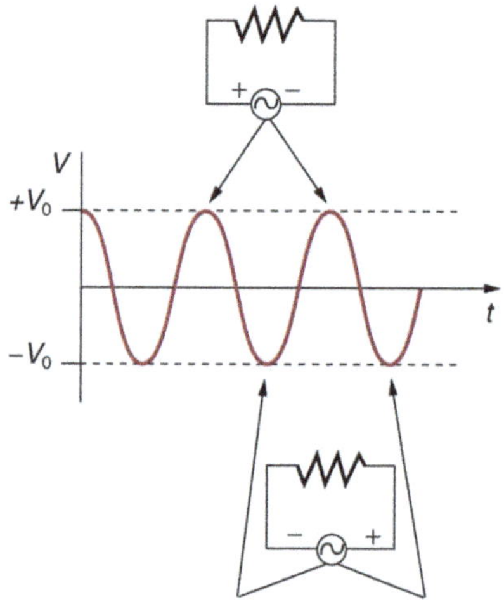

FIGURE 20.15 The potential difference V between the terminals of an AC voltage source fluctuates as shown. The mathematical expression for V is given by $V = V_0 \sin 2\pi ft$.

Figure 20.15 shows a schematic of a simple circuit with an AC voltage source. The voltage between the terminals fluctuates as shown, with the **AC voltage** given by

$$V = V_0 \sin 2\pi ft, \tag{20.38}$$

where V is the voltage at time t, V_0 is the peak voltage, and f is the frequency in hertz. For this simple resistance circuit, $I = V/R$, and so the **AC current** is

$$I = I_0 \sin 2\pi ft, \tag{20.39}$$

where I is the current at time t, and $I_0 = V_0/R$ is the peak current. For this example, the voltage and current are said to be in phase, as seen in Figure 20.14(b).

Current in the resistor alternates back and forth just like the driving voltage, since $I = V/R$. If the resistor is a fluorescent light bulb, for example, it brightens and dims 120 times per second as the current repeatedly goes through zero. A 120-Hz flicker is too rapid for your eyes to detect, but if you wave your hand back and forth between your face and a fluorescent light, you will see a stroboscopic effect evidencing AC. The fact that the light output fluctuates means that the power is fluctuating. The power supplied is $P = IV$. Using the expressions for I and V above, we see that the time dependence of power is $P = I_0 V_0 \sin^2 2\pi ft$, as shown in Figure 20.16.

MAKING CONNECTIONS: TAKE-HOME EXPERIMENT—AC/DC LIGHTS

Wave your hand back and forth between your face and a fluorescent light bulb. Do you observe the same thing with the headlights on your car? Explain what you observe. *Warning: Do not look directly at very bright light.*

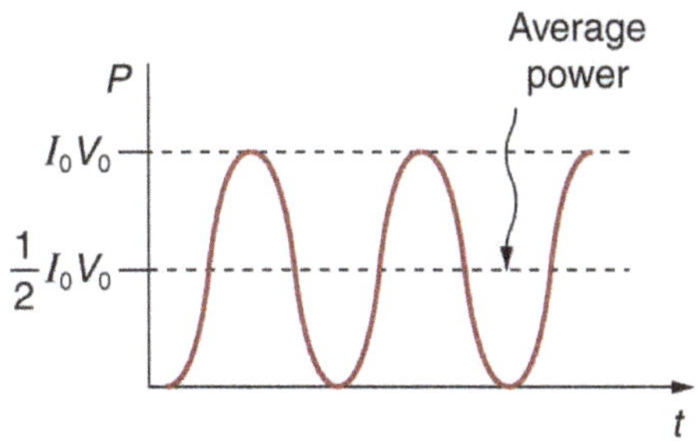

FIGURE 20.16 AC power as a function of time. Since the voltage and current are in phase here, their product is non-negative and fluctuates between zero and I_0V_0. Average power is $(1/2)I_0V_0$.

We are most often concerned with average power rather than its fluctuations—that 60-W light bulb in your desk lamp has an average power consumption of 60 W, for example. As illustrated in Figure 20.16, the average power P_{ave} is

$$P_{ave} = \frac{1}{2}I_0V_0. \tag{20.40}$$

This is evident from the graph, since the areas above and below the $(1/2)I_0V_0$ line are equal, but it can also be proven using trigonometric identities. Similarly, we define an average or **rms current** I_{rms} and average or **rms voltage** V_{rms} to be, respectively,

$$I_{rms} = \frac{I_0}{\sqrt{2}} \tag{20.41}$$

and

$$V_{rms} = \frac{V_0}{\sqrt{2}}. \tag{20.42}$$

where rms stands for root mean square, a particular kind of average. In general, to obtain a root mean square, the particular quantity is squared, its mean (or average) is found, and the square root is taken. This is useful for AC, since the average value is zero. Now,

$$P_{ave} = I_{rms}V_{rms}, \tag{20.43}$$

which gives

$$P_{ave} = \frac{I_0}{\sqrt{2}} \cdot \frac{V_0}{\sqrt{2}} = \frac{1}{2}I_0V_0, \tag{20.44}$$

as stated above. It is standard practice to quote I_{rms}, V_{rms}, and P_{ave} rather than the peak values. For example, most household electricity is 120 V AC, which means that V_{rms} is 120 V. The common 10-A circuit breaker will interrupt a sustained I_{rms} greater than 10 A. Your 1.0-kW microwave oven consumes $P_{ave} = 1.0\text{ kW}$, and so on. You can think of these rms and average values as the equivalent DC values for a simple resistive circuit.

To summarize, when dealing with AC, Ohm's law and the equations for power are completely analogous to those for DC, but rms and average values are used for AC. Thus, for AC, Ohm's law is written

$$I_{rms} = \frac{V_{rms}}{R}. \tag{20.45}$$

The various expressions for AC power P_{ave} are

$$P_{ave} = I_{rms}V_{rms}, \tag{20.46}$$

$$P_{\text{ave}} = \frac{V_{\text{rms}}^2}{R}, \tag{20.47}$$

and

$$P_{\text{ave}} = I_{\text{rms}}^2 R. \tag{20.48}$$

EXAMPLE 20.9

Peak Voltage and Power for AC

(a) What is the value of the peak voltage for 120-V AC power? (b) What is the peak power consumption rate of a 60.0-W AC light bulb?

Strategy

We are told that V_{rms} is 120 V and P_{ave} is 60.0 W. We can use $V_{\text{rms}} = \frac{V_0}{\sqrt{2}}$ to find the peak voltage, and we can manipulate the definition of power to find the peak power from the given average power.

Solution for (a)

Solving the equation $V_{\text{rms}} = \frac{V_0}{\sqrt{2}}$ for the peak voltage V_0 and substituting the known value for V_{rms} gives

$$V_0 = \sqrt{2}V_{\text{rms}} = 1.414(120\text{ V}) = 170\text{ V}. \tag{20.49}$$

Discussion for (a)

This means that the AC voltage swings from 170 V to -170 V and back 60 times every second. An equivalent DC voltage is a constant 120 V.

Solution for (b)

Peak power is peak current times peak voltage. Thus,

$$P_0 = I_0 V_0 = 2\left(\frac{1}{2} I_0 V_0\right) = 2P_{\text{ave}}. \tag{20.50}$$

We know the average power is 60.0 W, and so

$$P_0 = 2(60.0\text{ W}) = 120\text{ W}. \tag{20.51}$$

Discussion

So the power swings from zero to 120 W one hundred twenty times per second (twice each cycle), and the power averages 60 W.

Why Use AC for Power Distribution?

Most large power-distribution systems are AC. Moreover, the power is transmitted at much higher voltages than the 120-V AC (240 V in most parts of the world) we use in homes and on the job. Economies of scale make it cheaper to build a few very large electric power-generation plants than to build numerous small ones. This necessitates sending power long distances, and it is obviously important that energy losses en route be minimized. High voltages can be transmitted with much smaller power losses than low voltages, as we shall see. (See Figure 20.17.) For safety reasons, the voltage at the user is reduced to familiar values. The crucial factor is that it is much easier to increase and decrease AC voltages than DC, so AC is used in most large power distribution systems.

FIGURE 20.17 Power is distributed over large distances at high voltage to reduce power loss in the transmission lines. The voltages generated at the power plant are stepped up by passive devices called transformers (see Transformers) to 330,000 volts (or more in some places worldwide). At the point of use, the transformers reduce the voltage transmitted for safe residential and commercial use. (Credit: GeorgHH, Wikimedia Commons)

EXAMPLE 20.10

Power Losses Are Less for High-Voltage Transmission

(a) What current is needed to transmit 100 MW of power at 200 kV? (b) What is the power dissipated by the transmission lines if they have a resistance of $1.00\ \Omega$? (c) What percentage of the power is lost in the transmission lines?

Strategy

We are given $P_{ave} = 100\ \text{MW}$, $V_{rms} = 200\ \text{kV}$, and the resistance of the lines is $R = 1.00\ \Omega$. Using these givens, we can find the current flowing (from $P = IV$) and then the power dissipated in the lines ($P = I^2 R$), and we take the ratio to the total power transmitted.

Solution

To find the current, we rearrange the relationship $P_{ave} = I_{rms} V_{rms}$ and substitute known values. This gives

$$I_{rms} = \frac{P_{ave}}{V_{rms}} = \frac{100 \times 10^6\ \text{W}}{200 \times 10^3\ \text{V}} = 500\ \text{A}. \quad 20.52$$

Solution

Knowing the current and given the resistance of the lines, the power dissipated in them is found from $P_{ave} = I_{rms}^2 R$. Substituting the known values gives

$$P_{ave} = I_{rms}^2 R = (500\ \text{A})^2 (1.00\ \Omega) = 250\ \text{kW}. \quad 20.53$$

Solution

The percent loss is the ratio of this lost power to the total or input power, multiplied by 100:

$$\%\ \text{loss} = \frac{250\ \text{kW}}{100\ \text{MW}} \times 100 = 0.250\ \%. \quad 20.54$$

Discussion

One-fourth of a percent is an acceptable loss. Note that if 100 MW of power had been transmitted at 25 kV, then a current of 4000 A would have been needed. This would result in a power loss in the lines of 16.0 MW, or 16.0% rather than 0.250%. The lower the voltage, the more current is needed, and the greater the power loss in the fixed-resistance transmission lines. Of course, lower-resistance lines can be built, but this requires larger and more expensive wires. If superconducting lines could be economically produced, there would be no loss in the transmission lines at all. But, as we shall see in a later chapter, there is a limit to current in superconductors, too. In short, high voltages are more economical for transmitting power, and AC voltage is much easier to raise and lower, so that AC is used in most large-scale power distribution systems.

It is widely recognized that high voltages pose greater hazards than low voltages. But, in fact, some high voltages, such as those associated with common static electricity, can be harmless. So it is not voltage alone that determines a hazard. It is not so widely recognized that AC shocks are often more harmful than similar DC shocks. Thomas Edison thought that AC shocks were more harmful and set up a DC power-distribution system in New York City in the late 1800s. There were bitter fights, in particular between Edison and George Westinghouse and Nikola Tesla, who were advocating the use of AC in early power-distribution systems. AC has prevailed largely due to transformers and lower power losses with high-voltage transmission.

PHET EXPLORATIONS

Generator

Generate electricity with a bar magnet! Discover the physics behind the phenomena by exploring magnets and how you can use them to make a bulb light.

Click to view content (https://openstax.org/l/28gen).

PhET

20.6 Electric Hazards and the Human Body

LEARNING OBJECTIVES

By the end of this section, you will be able to:

- Define thermal hazard, shock hazard, and short circuit.
- Explain what effects various levels of current have on the human body.

There are two known hazards of electricity—thermal and shock. A **thermal hazard** is one where excessive electric power causes undesired thermal effects, such as starting a fire in the wall of a house. A **shock hazard** occurs when electric current passes through a person. Shocks range in severity from painful, but otherwise harmless, to heart-stopping lethality. This section considers these hazards and the various factors affecting them in a quantitative manner. Electrical Safety: Systems and Devices will consider systems and devices for preventing electrical hazards.

Thermal Hazards

Electric power causes undesired heating effects whenever electric energy is converted to thermal energy at a rate faster than it can be safely dissipated. A classic example of this is the **short circuit**, a low-resistance path between terminals of a voltage source. An example of a short circuit is shown in Figure 20.18. Insulation on wires leading to an appliance has worn through, allowing the two wires to come into contact. Such an undesired contact with a high voltage is called a *short*. Since the resistance of the short, r, is very small, the power dissipated in the short, $P = V^2/r$, is very large. For example, if V is 120 V and r is $0.100\ \Omega$, then the power is 144 kW, *much* greater than that used by a typical household appliance. Thermal energy delivered at this rate will very quickly raise the temperature of surrounding materials, melting or perhaps igniting them.

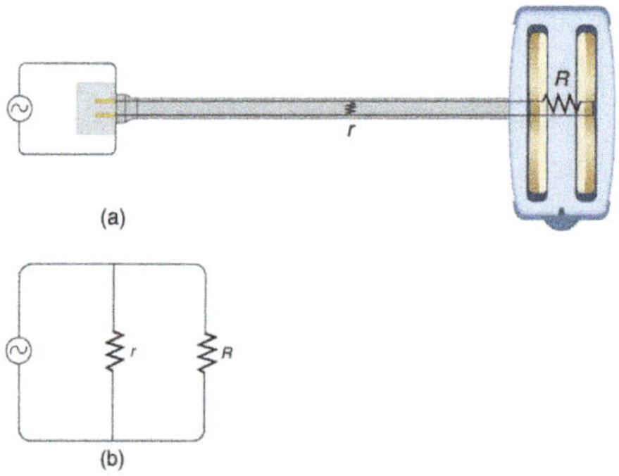

FIGURE 20.18 A short circuit is an undesired low-resistance path across a voltage source. (a) Worn insulation on the wires of a toaster allow them to come into contact with a low resistance r. Since $P = V^2/r$, thermal power is created so rapidly that the cord melts or burns. (b) A schematic of the short circuit.

One particularly insidious aspect of a short circuit is that its resistance may actually be decreased due to the increase in temperature. This can happen if the short creates ionization. These charged atoms and molecules are free to move and, thus, lower the resistance r. Since $P = V^2/r$, the power dissipated in the short rises, possibly causing more ionization, more power, and so on. High voltages, such as the 480-V AC used in some industrial applications, lend themselves to this hazard, because higher voltages create higher initial power production in a short.

Another serious, but less dramatic, thermal hazard occurs when wires supplying power to a user are overloaded with too great a current. As discussed in the previous section, the power dissipated in the supply wires is $P = I^2 R_\text{w}$, where R_w is the resistance of the wires and I the current flowing through them. If either I or R_w is too large, the wires overheat. For example, a worn appliance cord (with some of its braided wires broken) may have $R_\text{w} = 2.00\ \Omega$ rather than the $0.100\ \Omega$ it should be. If 10.0 A of current passes through the cord, then $P = I^2 R_\text{w} = 200\ \text{W}$ is dissipated in the cord—much more than is safe. Similarly, if a wire with a 0.100 - Ω resistance is meant to carry a few amps, but is instead carrying 100 A, it will severely overheat. The power dissipated in the wire will in that case be $P = 1000\ \text{W}$. Fuses and circuit breakers are used to limit excessive currents. (See Figure 20.19 and Figure 20.20.) Each device opens the circuit automatically when a sustained current exceeds safe limits.

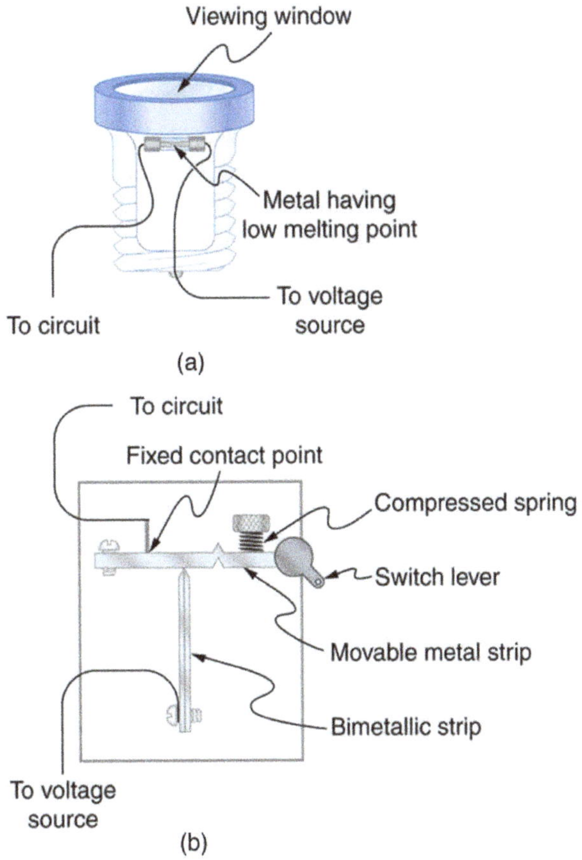

FIGURE 20.19 (a) A fuse has a metal strip with a low melting point that, when overheated by an excessive current, permanently breaks the connection of a circuit to a voltage source. (b) A circuit breaker is an automatic but restorable electric switch. The one shown here has a bimetallic strip that bends to the right and into the notch if overheated. The spring then forces the metal strip downward, breaking the electrical connection at the points.

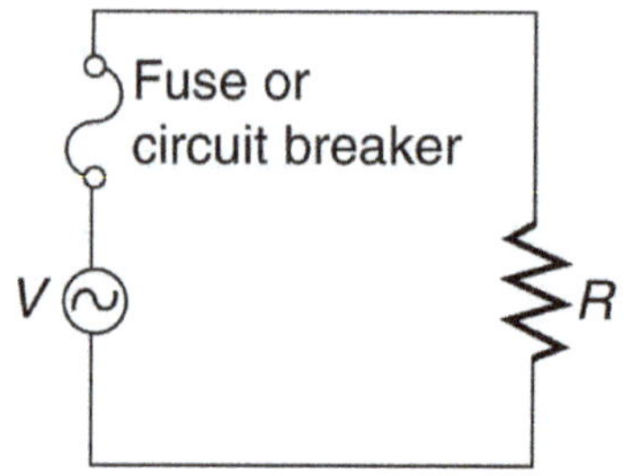

FIGURE 20.20 Schematic of a circuit with a fuse or circuit breaker in it. Fuses and circuit breakers act like automatic switches that open when sustained current exceeds desired limits.

Fuses and circuit breakers for typical household voltages and currents are relatively simple to produce, but those for large voltages and currents experience special problems. For example, when a circuit breaker tries to interrupt the flow of high-voltage electricity, a spark can jump across its points that ionizes the air in the gap and allows the current to continue flowing. Large circuit breakers found in power-distribution systems employ insulating gas and even use jets of gas to blow out such sparks. Here AC is safer than DC, since AC current goes through zero 120 times per second, giving a quick opportunity to extinguish these arcs.

Shock Hazards

Electrical currents through people produce tremendously varied effects. An electrical current can be used to block back pain. The possibility of using electrical current to stimulate muscle action in paralyzed limbs, perhaps allowing paraplegics to walk, is under study. TV dramatizations in which electrical shocks are used to bring a heart attack victim out of ventricular fibrillation (a massively irregular, often fatal, beating of the heart) are more than common. Yet most electrical shock fatalities occur because a current put the heart into fibrillation. A pacemaker uses electrical shocks to stimulate the heart to beat properly. Some fatal shocks do not produce burns, but warts can be safely burned off with electric current (though freezing using liquid nitrogen is now more common). Of course, there are consistent explanations for these disparate effects. The major factors upon which the effects of electrical shock depend are

1. The amount of current I
2. The path taken by the current
3. The duration of the shock
4. The frequency f of the current ($f = 0$ for DC)

Table 20.3 gives the effects of electrical shocks as a function of current for a typical accidental shock. The effects are for a shock that passes through the trunk of the body, has a duration of 1 s, and is caused by 60-Hz power.

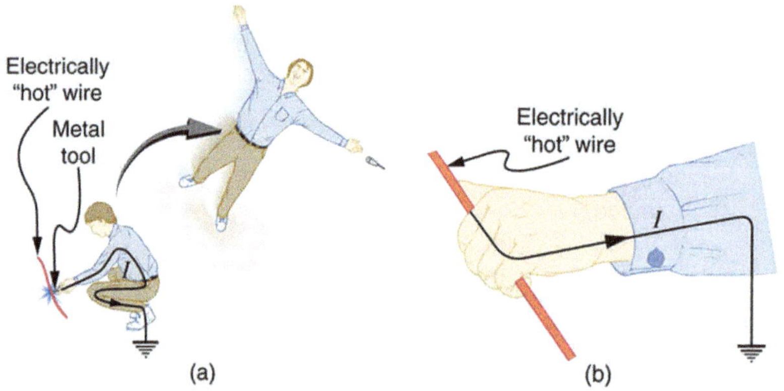

FIGURE 20.21 An electric current can cause muscular contractions with varying effects. (a) The victim is "thrown" backward by involuntary muscle contractions that extend the legs and torso. (b) The victim can't let go of the wire that is stimulating all the muscles in the hand. Those that close the fingers are stronger than those that open them.

Current (mA)	Effect
1	Threshold of sensation
5	Maximum harmless current
10–20	Onset of sustained muscular contraction; cannot let go for duration of shock; contraction of chest muscles may stop breathing during shock
50	Onset of pain
100–300+	Ventricular fibrillation possible; often fatal
300	Onset of burns depending on concentration of current
6000 (6 A)	Onset of sustained ventricular contraction and respiratory paralysis; both cease when shock ends; heartbeat may return to normal; used to defibrillate the heart

TABLE 20.3 Effects of Electrical Shock as a Function of Current[3]

Our bodies are relatively good conductors due to the water in our bodies. Given that larger currents will flow through sections with lower resistance (to be further discussed in the next chapter), electric currents preferentially flow through paths in the human body that have a minimum resistance in a direct path to earth. The earth is a natural electron sink. Wearing insulating shoes, a requirement in many professions, prohibits a pathway for electrons by providing a large resistance in that path. Whenever working with high-power tools (drills), or in risky situations, ensure that you do not provide a pathway for current flow (especially through the heart).

Very small currents pass harmlessly and unfelt through the body. This happens to you regularly without your knowledge. The threshold of sensation is only 1 mA and, although unpleasant, shocks are apparently harmless for currents less than 5 mA. A great number of safety rules take the 5-mA value for the maximum allowed shock. At 10 to 20 mA and above, the current can stimulate sustained muscular contractions much as regular nerve impulses do. People sometimes say they were knocked across the room by a shock, but what really happened was that certain muscles contracted, propelling them in a manner not of their own choosing. (See Figure 20.21(a).) More frightening, and potentially more dangerous, is the "can't let go" effect illustrated in Figure 20.21(b). The muscles that close the fingers are stronger than those that open them, so the hand closes involuntarily on the wire shocking it. This can prolong the shock indefinitely. It can also be a danger to a person trying to rescue the victim, because the rescuer's hand may close about the victim's wrist. Usually the best way to help the victim is to give the fist a hard knock/blow/jar with an insulator or to throw an insulator at the fist. Modern electric fences, used in animal enclosures, are now pulsed on and off to allow people who touch them to get free, rendering them less lethal than in the past.

Greater currents may affect the heart. Its electrical patterns can be disrupted, so that it beats irregularly and ineffectively in a condition called "ventricular fibrillation." This condition often lingers after the shock and is fatal due to a lack of blood circulation. The threshold for ventricular fibrillation is between 100 and 300 mA. At about 300 mA and above, the shock can cause burns, depending on the concentration of current—the more concentrated, the greater the likelihood of burns.

Very large currents cause the heart and diaphragm to contract for the duration of the shock. Both the heart and breathing stop. Interestingly, both often return to normal following the shock. The electrical patterns on the heart are completely erased in a manner that the heart can start afresh with normal beating, as opposed to the permanent disruption caused by smaller currents that can put the heart into ventricular fibrillation. The latter is something like scribbling on a blackboard, whereas the former completely erases it. TV dramatizations of electric shock used to bring a heart attack victim out of ventricular fibrillation also show large paddles. These are used to spread out

3 For an average male shocked through trunk of body for 1 s by 60-Hz AC. Values for females are 60–80% of those listed.

current passed through the victim to reduce the likelihood of burns.

Current is the major factor determining shock severity (given that other conditions such as path, duration, and frequency are fixed, such as in the table and preceding discussion). A larger voltage is more hazardous, but since $I = V/R$, the severity of the shock depends on the combination of voltage and resistance. For example, a person with dry skin has a resistance of about $200\ \text{k}\Omega$. If he comes into contact with 120-V AC, a current $I = (120\ \text{V})/(200\ \text{k}\Omega) = 0.6\ \text{mA}$ passes harmlessly through him. The same person soaking wet may have a resistance of $10.0\ \text{k}\Omega$ and the same 120 V will produce a current of 12 mA—above the “can't let go” threshold and potentially dangerous.

Most of the body's resistance is in its dry skin. When wet, salts go into ion form, lowering the resistance significantly. The interior of the body has a much lower resistance than dry skin because of all the ionic solutions and fluids it contains. If skin resistance is bypassed, such as by an intravenous infusion, a catheter, or exposed pacemaker leads, a person is rendered **microshock sensitive**. In this condition, currents about 1/1000 those listed in Table 20.3 produce similar effects. During open-heart surgery, currents as small as $20\ \mu\text{A}$ can be used to still the heart. Stringent electrical safety requirements in hospitals, particularly in surgery and intensive care, are related to the doubly disadvantaged microshock-sensitive patient. The break in the skin has reduced his resistance, and so the same voltage causes a greater current, and a much smaller current has a greater effect.

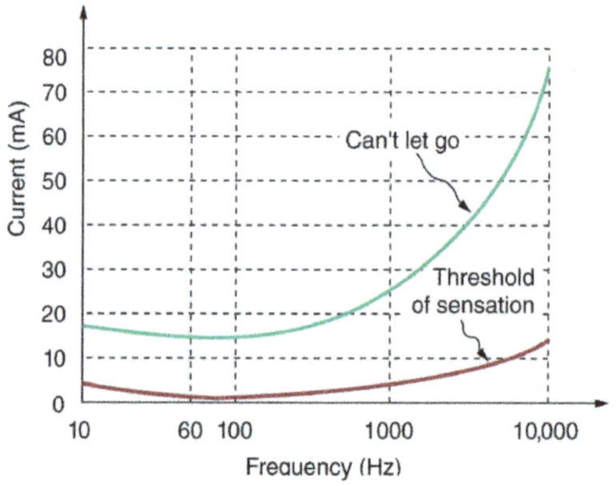

FIGURE 20.22 Graph of average values for the threshold of sensation and the “can't let go” current as a function of frequency. The lower the value, the more sensitive the body is at that frequency.

Factors other than current that affect the severity of a shock are its path, duration, and AC frequency. Path has obvious consequences. For example, the heart is unaffected by an electric shock through the brain, such as may be used to treat manic depression. And it is a general truth that the longer the duration of a shock, the greater its effects. Figure 20.22 presents a graph that illustrates the effects of frequency on a shock. The curves show the minimum current for two different effects, as a function of frequency. The lower the current needed, the more sensitive the body is at that frequency. Ironically, the body is most sensitive to frequencies near the 50- or 60-Hz frequencies in common use. The body is slightly less sensitive for DC ($f = 0$), mildly confirming Edison's claims that AC presents a greater hazard. At higher and higher frequencies, the body becomes progressively less sensitive to any effects that involve nerves. This is related to the maximum rates at which nerves can fire or be stimulated. At very high frequencies, electrical current travels only on the surface of a person. Thus a wart can be burned off with very high frequency current without causing the heart to stop. (Do not try this at home with 60-Hz AC!) Some of the spectacular demonstrations of electricity, in which high-voltage arcs are passed through the air and over people's bodies, employ high frequencies and low currents. (See Figure 20.23.) Electrical safety devices and techniques are discussed in detail in Electrical Safety: Systems and Devices.

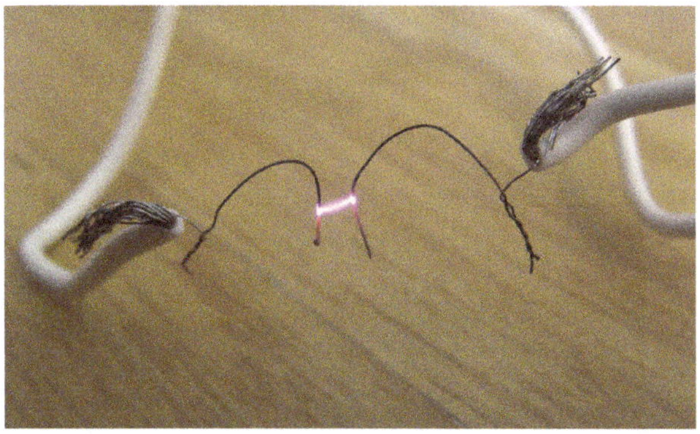

FIGURE 20.23 Is this electric arc dangerous? The answer depends on the AC frequency and the power involved. (credit: Khimich Alex, Wikimedia Commons)

20.7 Nerve Conduction–Electrocardiograms

LEARNING OBJECTIVES

By the end of this section, you will be able to:

- Explain the process by which electric signals are transmitted along a neuron.
- Explain the effects myelin sheaths have on signal propagation.
- Explain what the features of an ECG signal indicate.

Nerve Conduction

Electric currents in the vastly complex system of billions of nerves in our body allow us to sense the world, control parts of our body, and think. These are representative of the three major functions of nerves. First, nerves carry messages from our sensory organs and others to the central nervous system, consisting of the brain and spinal cord. Second, nerves carry messages from the central nervous system to muscles and other organs. Third, nerves transmit and process signals within the central nervous system. The sheer number of nerve cells and the incredibly greater number of connections between them makes this system the subtle wonder that it is. **Nerve conduction** is a general term for electrical signals carried by nerve cells. It is one aspect of **bioelectricity**, or electrical effects in and created by biological systems.

Nerve cells, properly called *neurons*, look different from other cells—they have tendrils, some of them many centimeters long, connecting them with other cells. (See Figure 20.24.) Signals arrive at the cell body across *synapses* or through *dendrites*, stimulating the neuron to generate its own signal, sent along its long *axon* to other nerve or muscle cells. Signals may arrive from many other locations and be transmitted to yet others, conditioning the synapses by use, giving the system its complexity and its ability to learn.

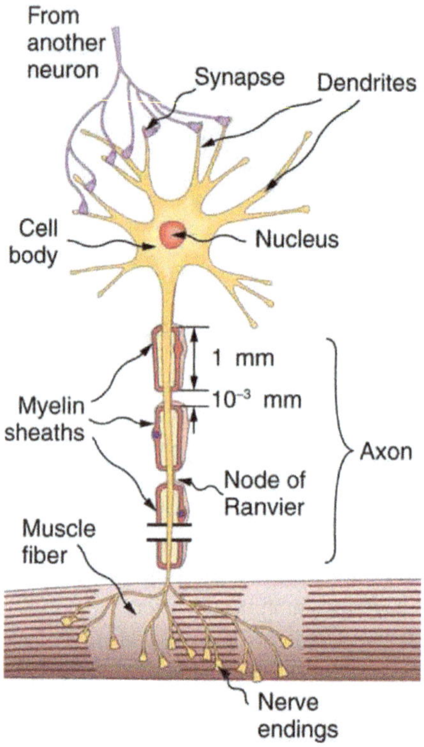

FIGURE 20.24 A neuron with its dendrites and long axon. Signals in the form of electric currents reach the cell body through dendrites and across synapses, stimulating the neuron to generate its own signal sent down the axon. The number of interconnections can be far greater than shown here.

The method by which these electric currents are generated and transmitted is more complex than the simple movement of free charges in a conductor, but it can be understood with principles already discussed in this text. The most important of these are the Coulomb force and diffusion.

Figure 20.25 illustrates how a voltage (potential difference) is created across the cell membrane of a neuron in its resting state. This thin membrane separates electrically neutral fluids having differing concentrations of ions, the most important varieties being Na^+, K^+, and Cl^- (these are sodium, potassium, and chlorine ions with single plus or minus charges as indicated). As discussed in Molecular Transport Phenomena: Diffusion, Osmosis, and Related Processes, free ions will diffuse from a region of high concentration to one of low concentration. But the cell membrane is **semipermeable**, meaning that some ions may cross it while others cannot. In its resting state, the cell membrane is permeable to K^+ and Cl^-, and impermeable to Na^+. Diffusion of K^+ and Cl^- thus creates the layers of positive and negative charge on the outside and inside of the membrane. The Coulomb force prevents the ions from diffusing across in their entirety. Once the charge layer has built up, the repulsion of like charges prevents more from moving across, and the attraction of unlike charges prevents more from leaving either side. The result is two layers of charge right on the membrane, with diffusion being balanced by the Coulomb force. A tiny fraction of the charges move across and the fluids remain neutral (other ions are present), while a separation of charge and a voltage have been created across the membrane.

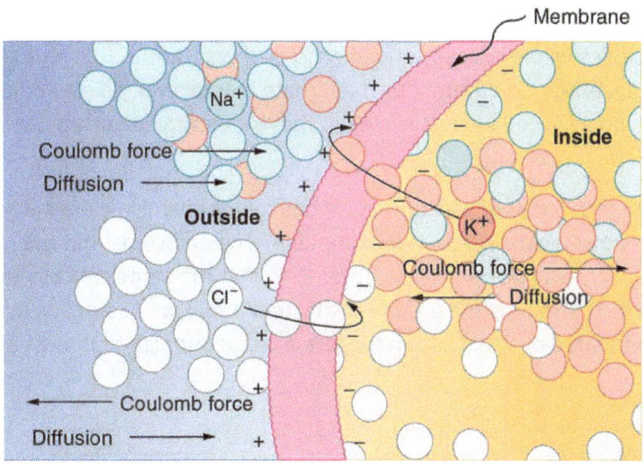

FIGURE 20.25 The semipermeable membrane of a cell has different concentrations of ions inside and out. Diffusion moves the K^+ and Cl^- ions in the direction shown, until the Coulomb force halts further transfer. This results in a layer of positive charge on the outside, a layer of negative charge on the inside, and thus a voltage across the cell membrane. The membrane is normally impermeable to Na^+.

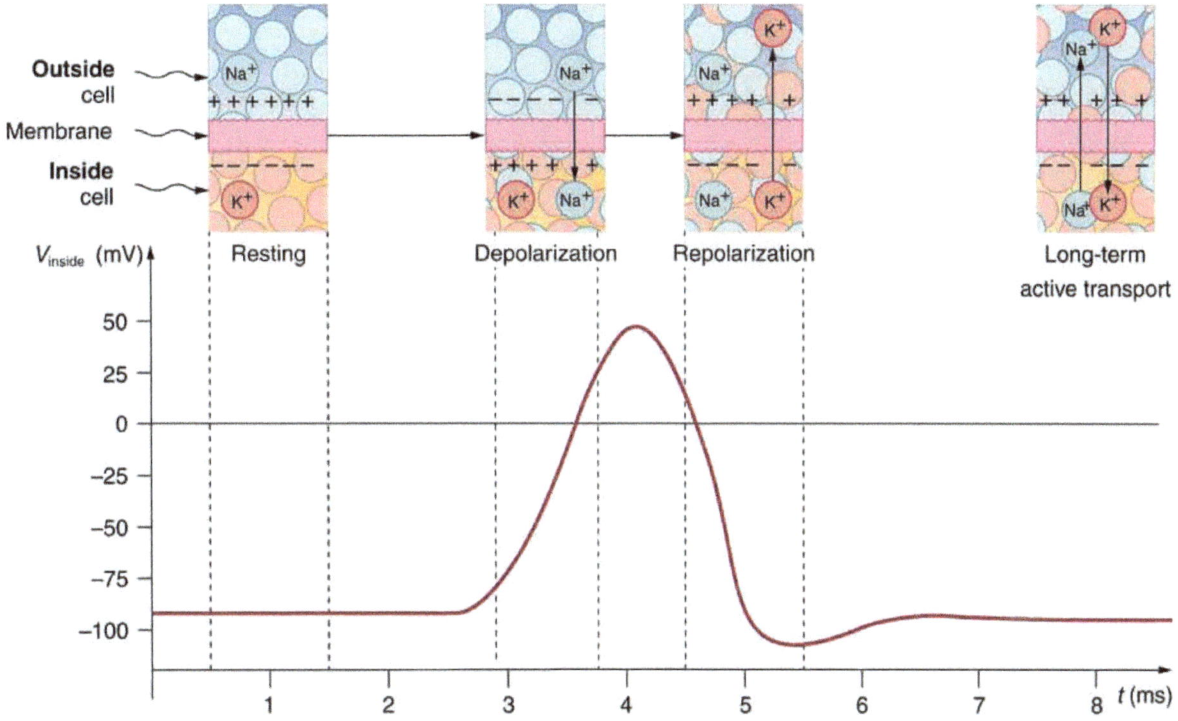

FIGURE 20.26 An action potential is the pulse of voltage inside a nerve cell graphed here. It is caused by movements of ions across the cell membrane as shown. Depolarization occurs when a stimulus makes the membrane permeable to Na^+ ions. Repolarization follows as the membrane again becomes impermeable to Na^+, and K^+ moves from high to low concentration. In the long term, active transport slowly maintains the concentration differences, but the cell may fire hundreds of times in rapid succession without seriously depleting them.

The separation of charge creates a potential difference of 70 to 90 mV across the cell membrane. While this is a small voltage, the resulting electric field ($E = V/d$) across the only 8-nm-thick membrane is immense (on the order of 11 MV/m!) and has fundamental effects on its structure and permeability. Now, if the exterior of a neuron is taken to be at 0 V, then the interior has a *resting potential* of about −90 mV. Such voltages are created across the membranes of almost all types of animal cells but are largest in nerve and muscle cells. In fact, fully 25% of the energy used by cells goes toward creating and maintaining these potentials.

Electric currents along the cell membrane are created by any stimulus that changes the membrane's permeability. The membrane thus temporarily becomes permeable to Na^+, which then rushes in, driven both by diffusion and the Coulomb force. This inrush of Na^+ first neutralizes the inside membrane, or *depolarizes* it, and then makes it slightly positive. The depolarization causes the membrane to again become impermeable to Na^+, and the movement of K^+ quickly returns the cell to its resting potential, or *repolarizes* it. This sequence of events results in a voltage pulse, called the *action potential*. (See Figure 20.26.) Only small fractions of the ions move, so that the cell can fire many hundreds of times without depleting the excess concentrations of Na^+ and K^+. Eventually, the cell must replenish these ions to maintain the concentration differences that create bioelectricity. This sodium-potassium pump is an example of *active transport*, wherein cell energy is used to move ions across membranes against diffusion gradients and the Coulomb force.

The action potential is a voltage pulse at one location on a cell membrane. How does it get transmitted along the cell membrane, and in particular down an axon, as a nerve impulse? The answer is that the changing voltage and electric fields affect the permeability of the adjacent cell membrane, so that the same process takes place there. The adjacent membrane depolarizes, affecting the membrane further down, and so on, as illustrated in Figure 20.27. Thus the action potential stimulated at one location triggers a *nerve impulse* that moves slowly (about 1 m/s) along the cell membrane.

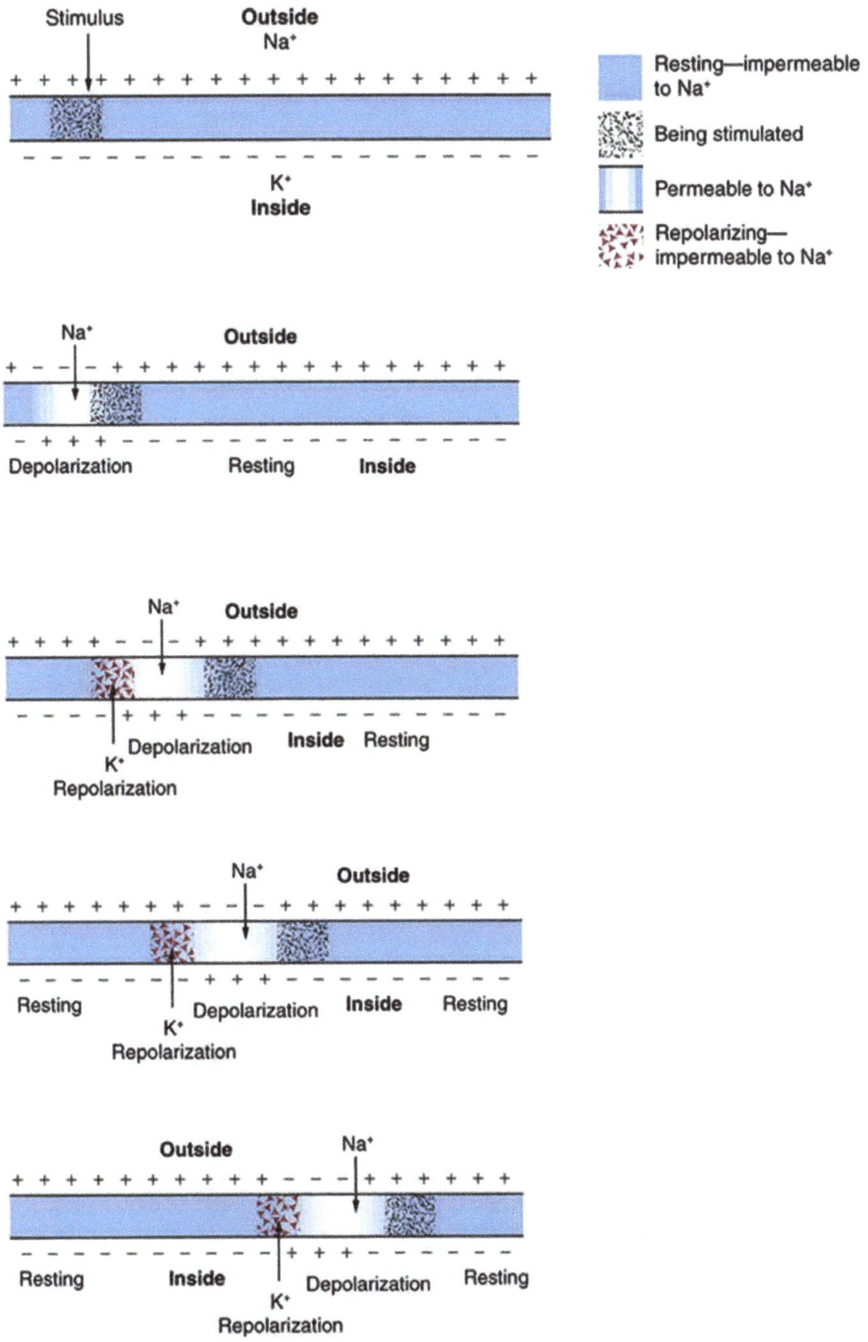

FIGURE 20.27 A nerve impulse is the propagation of an action potential along a cell membrane. A stimulus causes an action potential at one location, which changes the permeability of the adjacent membrane, causing an action potential there. This in turn affects the membrane further down, so that the action potential moves slowly (in electrical terms) along the cell membrane. Although the impulse is due to Na^+ and K^+ going across the membrane, it is equivalent to a wave of charge moving along the outside and inside of the membrane.

Some axons, like that in Figure 20.24, are sheathed with *myelin*, consisting of fat-containing cells. Figure 20.28 shows an enlarged view of an axon having myelin sheaths characteristically separated by unmyelinated gaps (called nodes of Ranvier). This arrangement gives the axon a number of interesting properties. Since myelin is an insulator, it prevents signals from jumping between adjacent nerves (cross talk). Additionally, the myelinated regions transmit electrical signals at a very high speed, as an ordinary conductor or resistor would. There is no action potential in the myelinated regions, so that no cell energy is used in them. There is an IR signal loss in the myelin, but the signal is regenerated in the gaps, where the voltage pulse triggers the action potential at full voltage. So a myelinated axon transmits a nerve impulse faster, with less energy consumption, and is better protected from cross talk than an unmyelinated one. Not all axons are myelinated, so that cross talk and slow signal transmission are a characteristic of the normal operation of these axons, another variable in the nervous system.

The degeneration or destruction of the myelin sheaths that surround the nerve fibers impairs signal transmission and can lead to numerous neurological effects. One of the most prominent of these diseases comes from the body's own immune system attacking the myelin in the central nervous system—multiple sclerosis. MS symptoms include fatigue, vision problems, weakness of arms and legs, loss of balance, and tingling or numbness in one's extremities (neuropathy). It is more apt to strike younger adults, especially females. Causes might come from infection, environmental or geographic affects, or genetics. At the moment there is no known cure for MS.

Most animal cells can fire or create their own action potential. Muscle cells contract when they fire and are often induced to do so by a nerve impulse. In fact, nerve and muscle cells are physiologically similar, and there are even hybrid cells, such as in the heart, that have characteristics of both nerves and muscles. Some animals, like the infamous electric eel (see Figure 20.29), use muscles ganged so that their voltages add in order to create a shock great enough to stun prey.

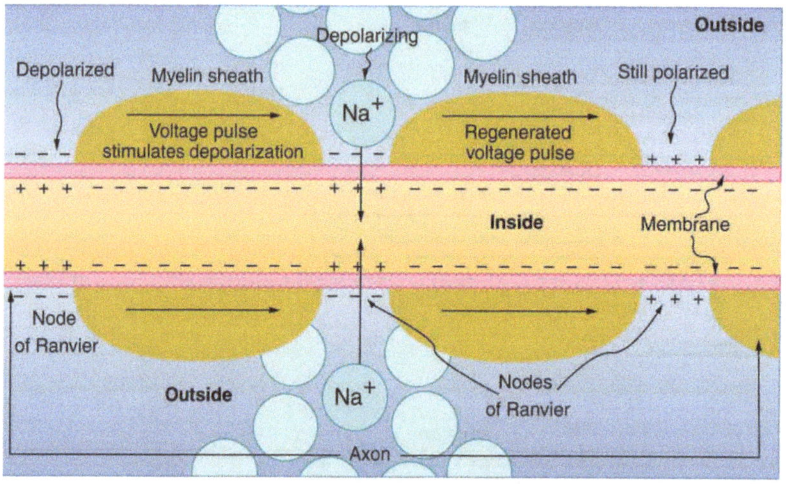

FIGURE 20.28 Propagation of a nerve impulse down a myelinated axon, from left to right. The signal travels very fast and without energy input in the myelinated regions, but it loses voltage. It is regenerated in the gaps. The signal moves faster than in unmyelinated axons and is insulated from signals in other nerves, limiting cross talk.

FIGURE 20.29 An electric eel flexes its muscles to create a voltage that stuns prey. (credit: chrisbb, Flickr)

Electrocardiograms

Just as nerve impulses are transmitted by depolarization and repolarization of adjacent membrane, the depolarization that causes muscle contraction can also stimulate adjacent muscle cells to depolarize (fire) and contract. Thus, a depolarization wave can be sent across the heart, coordinating its rhythmic contractions and enabling it to perform its vital function of propelling blood through the circulatory system. Figure 20.30 is a simplified graphic of a depolarization wave spreading across the heart from the *sinoarterial (SA) node*, the heart's natural pacemaker.

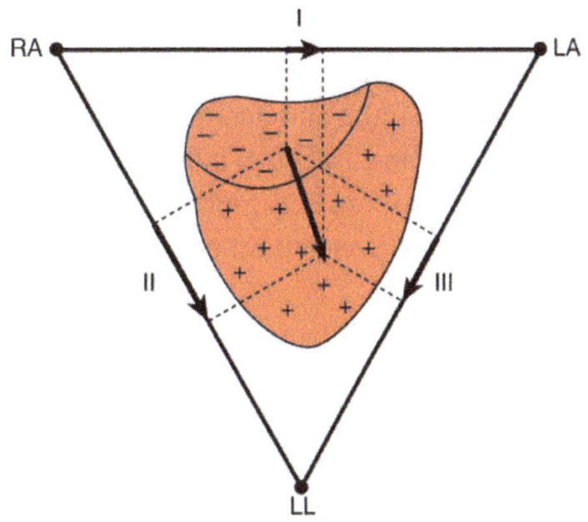

FIGURE 20.30 The outer surface of the heart changes from positive to negative during depolarization. This wave of depolarization is spreading from the top of the heart and is represented by a vector pointing in the direction of the wave. This vector is a voltage (potential difference) vector. Three electrodes, labeled RA, LA, and LL, are placed on the patient. Each pair (called leads I, II, and III) measures a component of the depolarization vector and is graphed in an ECG.

An **electrocardiogram (ECG)** is a record of the voltages created by the wave of depolarization and subsequent repolarization in the heart. (They are also abbreviated EKG.) Voltages between pairs of electrodes placed on the chest are vector components of the voltage wave on the heart. Standard ECGs have 12 or more electrodes, but only three are shown in Figure 20.30 for clarity. Decades ago, three-electrode ECGs were performed by placing electrodes on the left and right arms and the left leg. The voltage between the right arm and the left leg is called the *lead II potential* and is the most often graphed. We shall examine the lead II potential as an indicator of heart-muscle function and see that it is coordinated with arterial blood pressure as well.

Heart function and its four-chamber action are explored in Viscosity and Laminar Flow; Poiseuille's Law. Basically, the right and left atria receive blood from the body and lungs, respectively, and pump the blood into the ventricles. The right and left ventricles, in turn, pump blood through the lungs and the rest of the body, respectively. Depolarization of the heart muscle causes it to contract. After contraction it is repolarized to ready it for the next beat. The ECG measures components of depolarization and repolarization of the heart muscle and can yield significant information on the functioning and malfunctioning of the heart.

Figure 20.31 shows an ECG of the lead II potential and a graph of the corresponding arterial blood pressure. The major features are labeled P, Q, R, S, and T. The *P wave* is generated by the depolarization and contraction of the atria as they pump blood into the ventricles. The *QRS complex* is created by the depolarization of the ventricles as they pump blood to the lungs and body. Since the shape of the heart and the path of the depolarization wave are not simple, the QRS complex has this typical shape and time span. The lead II QRS signal also masks the repolarization of the atria, which occur at the same time. Finally, the *T wave* is generated by the repolarization of the ventricles and is followed by the next P wave in the next heartbeat. Arterial blood pressure varies with each part of the heartbeat, with systolic (maximum) pressure occurring closely after the QRS complex, which signals contraction of the ventricles.

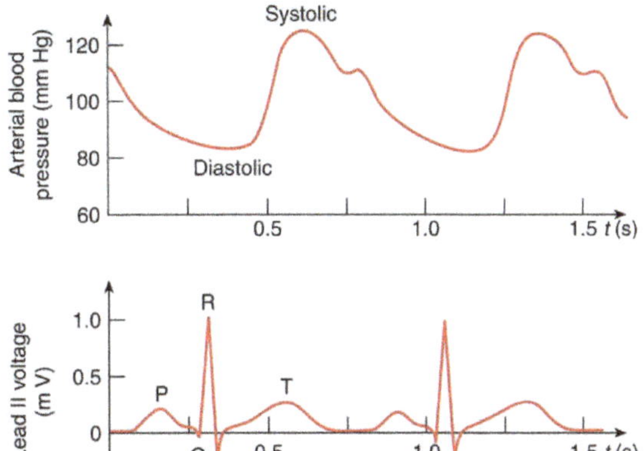

FIGURE 20.31 A lead II ECG with corresponding arterial blood pressure. The QRS complex is created by the depolarization and contraction of the ventricles and is followed shortly by the maximum or systolic blood pressure. See text for further description.

Taken together, the 12 leads of a state-of-the-art ECG can yield a wealth of information about the heart. For example, regions of damaged heart tissue, called infarcts, reflect electrical waves and are apparent in one or more lead potentials. Subtle changes due to slight or gradual damage to the heart are most readily detected by comparing a recent ECG to an older one. This is particularly the case since individual heart shape, size, and orientation can cause variations in ECGs from one individual to another. ECG technology has advanced to the point where a portable ECG monitor can be incorporated into wearable devices and other small objects. See Figure 20.32.

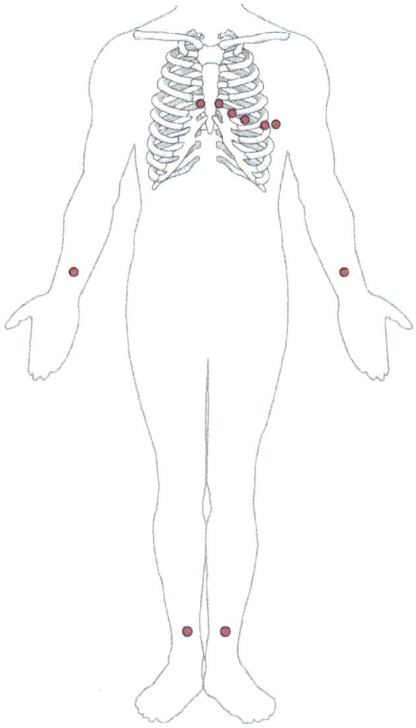

FIGURE 20.32 In a 12-lead ECG, six electrodes are placed on the chest, and four electrodes are placed on the limbs.

PHET EXPLORATIONS

Neuron

Stimulate a neuron and monitor what happens. Pause, rewind, and move forward in time in order to observe the ions as they move across the neuron membrane.

Click to view content (https://openstax.org/books/college-physics-ap-courses-2e/pages/20-7-nerve-conductionelectrocardiograms)

PhET

Glossary

AC current current that fluctuates sinusoidally with time, expressed as $I = I_0 \sin 2\pi ft$, where I is the current at time t, I_0 is the peak current, and f is the frequency in hertz

AC voltage voltage that fluctuates sinusoidally with time, expressed as $V = V_0 \sin 2\pi ft$, where V is the voltage at time t, V_0 is the peak voltage, and f is the frequency in hertz

alternating current (AC) the flow of electric charge that periodically reverses direction

ampere (amp) the SI unit for current; 1 A = 1 C/s

bioelectricity electrical effects in and created by biological systems

direct current (DC) the flow of electric charge in only one direction

drift velocity the average velocity at which free charges flow in response to an electric field

electric current the rate at which charge flows, $I = \Delta Q/\Delta t$

electric power the rate at which electrical energy is supplied by a source or dissipated by a device; it is the product of current times voltage

electrocardiogram (ECG) usually abbreviated ECG, a record of voltages created by depolarization and repolarization, especially in the heart

microshock sensitive a condition in which a person's skin resistance is bypassed, possibly by a medical procedure, rendering the person vulnerable to electrical shock at currents about 1/1000 the normally required level

nerve conduction the transport of electrical signals by nerve cells

ohm the unit of resistance, given by 1Ω = 1 V/A

Ohm's law an empirical relation stating that the current I is proportional to the potential difference V, $\propto V$; it is often written as $I = V/R$, where R is the resistance

ohmic a type of a material for which Ohm's law is valid

resistance the electric property that impedes current; for ohmic materials, it is the ratio of voltage to current, $R = V/I$

resistivity an intrinsic property of a material, independent of its shape or size, directly proportional to the resistance, denoted by ρ

rms current the root mean square of the current, $I_{\text{rms}} = I_0/\sqrt{2}$, where I_0 is the peak current, in an AC system

rms voltage the root mean square of the voltage, $V_{\text{rms}} = V_0/\sqrt{2}$, where V_0 is the peak voltage, in an AC system

semipermeable property of a membrane that allows only certain types of ions to cross it

shock hazard when electric current passes through a person

short circuit also known as a "short," a low-resistance path between terminals of a voltage source

simple circuit a circuit with a single voltage source and a single resistor

temperature coefficient of resistivity an empirical quantity, denoted by α, which describes the change in resistance or resistivity of a material with temperature

thermal hazard a hazard in which electric current causes undesired thermal effects

Section Summary

20.1 Current

- Electric current I is the rate at which charge flows, given by
$$I = \frac{\Delta Q}{\Delta t},$$
where ΔQ is the amount of charge passing through an area in time Δt.
- The direction of conventional current is taken as the direction in which positive charge moves.
- The SI unit for current is the ampere (A), where $1\text{ A} = 1\text{ C/s}$.
- Current is the flow of free charges, such as electrons and ions.
- Drift velocity v_d is the average speed at which these charges move.
- Current I is proportional to drift velocity v_d, as expressed in the relationship $I = nqAv_\text{d}$. Here, I is the current through a wire of cross-sectional area A. The wire's material has a free-charge density n, and each carrier has charge q and a drift velocity v_d.
- Electrical signals travel at speeds about 10^{12} times greater than the drift velocity of free electrons.

20.2 Ohm's Law: Resistance and Simple Circuits

- A simple circuit *is* one in which there is a single voltage source and a single resistance.
- One statement of Ohm's law gives the relationship

between current I, voltage V, and resistance R in a simple circuit to be $I = \frac{V}{R}$.

- Resistance has units of ohms (Ω), related to volts and amperes by $1\ \Omega = 1\ \text{V/A}$.
- There is a voltage or IR drop across a resistor, caused by the current flowing through it, given by $V = IR$.

20.3 Resistance and Resistivity

- The resistance R of a cylinder of length L and cross-sectional area A is $R = \frac{\rho L}{A}$, where ρ is the resistivity of the material.
- Values of ρ in Table 20.1 show that materials fall into three groups—*conductors, semiconductors, and insulators*.
- Temperature affects resistivity; for relatively small temperature changes ΔT, resistivity is $\rho = \rho_0(1 + \alpha\Delta T)$, where ρ_0 is the original resistivity and α is the temperature coefficient of resistivity.
- Table 20.2 gives values for α, the temperature coefficient of resistivity.
- The resistance R of an object also varies with temperature: $R = R_0(1 + \alpha\Delta T)$, where R_0 is the original resistance, and R is the resistance after the temperature change.

20.4 Electric Power and Energy

- Electric power P is the rate (in watts) that energy is supplied by a source or dissipated by a device.
- Three expressions for electrical power are
  $P = IV$,
  $$P = \frac{V^2}{R},$$
  and
  $$P = I^2 R.$$
- The energy used by a device with a power P over a time t is $E = Pt$.

20.5 Alternating Current versus Direct Current

- Direct current (DC) is the flow of electric current in only one direction. It refers to systems where the source voltage is constant.
- The voltage source of an alternating current (AC) system puts out $V = V_0 \sin 2\pi ft$, where V is the voltage at time t, V_0 is the peak voltage, and f is the frequency in hertz.
- In a simple circuit, $I = V/R$ and AC current is $I = I_0 \sin 2\pi ft$, where I is the current at time t, and $I_0 = V_0/R$ is the peak current.
- The average AC power is $P_{\text{ave}} = \frac{1}{2} I_0 V_0$.
- Average (rms) current I_{rms} and average (rms) voltage V_{rms} are $I_{\text{rms}} = \frac{I_0}{\sqrt{2}}$ and $V_{\text{rms}} = \frac{V_0}{\sqrt{2}}$, where rms stands for root mean square.
- Thus, $P_{\text{ave}} = I_{\text{rms}} V_{\text{rms}}$.
- Ohm's law for AC is $I_{\text{rms}} = \frac{V_{\text{rms}}}{R}$.
- Expressions for the average power of an AC circuit are $P_{\text{ave}} = I_{\text{rms}} V_{\text{rms}}$, $P_{\text{ave}} = \frac{V_{\text{rms}}^2}{R}$, and $P_{\text{ave}} = I_{\text{rms}}^2 R$, analogous to the expressions for DC circuits.

20.6 Electric Hazards and the Human Body

- The two types of electric hazards are thermal (excessive power) and shock (current through a person).
- Shock severity is determined by current, path, duration, and AC frequency.
- Table 20.3 lists shock hazards as a function of current.
- Figure 20.22 graphs the threshold current for two hazards as a function of frequency.

20.7 Nerve Conduction–Electrocardiograms

- Electric potentials in neurons and other cells are created by ionic concentration differences across semipermeable membranes.
- Stimuli change the permeability and create action potentials that propagate along neurons.
- Myelin sheaths speed this process and reduce the needed energy input.
- This process in the heart can be measured with an electrocardiogram (ECG).

Conceptual Questions

20.1 Current

1. Can a wire carry a current and still be neutral—that is, have a total charge of zero? Explain.

2. Car batteries are rated in ampere-hours ($\text{A} \cdot \text{h}$). To what physical quantity do ampere-hours correspond (voltage, charge, . . .), and what relationship do ampere-hours have to energy content?

3. If two different wires having identical cross-sectional areas carry the same current, will the drift velocity be higher or lower in the better conductor? Explain in terms of the equation $v_d = \frac{I}{nqA}$, by considering how the density of charge carriers n relates to whether or not a material is a good conductor.

4. Why are two conducting paths from a voltage source to an electrical device needed to operate the device?

5. In cars, one battery terminal is connected to the metal body. How does this allow a single wire to supply current to electrical devices rather than two wires?

6. Why isn't a bird sitting on a high-voltage power line electrocuted? Contrast this with the situation in which a large bird hits two wires simultaneously with its wings.

20.2 Ohm's Law: Resistance and Simple Circuits

7. The IR drop across a resistor means that there is a change in potential or voltage across the resistor. Is there any change in current as it passes through a resistor? Explain.

8. How is the IR drop in a resistor similar to the pressure drop in a fluid flowing through a pipe?

20.3 Resistance and Resistivity

9. In which of the three semiconducting materials listed in Table 20.1 do impurities supply free charges? (Hint: Examine the range of resistivity for each and determine whether the pure semiconductor has the higher or lower conductivity.)

10. Does the resistance of an object depend on the path current takes through it? Consider, for example, a rectangular bar—is its resistance the same along its length as across its width? (See Figure 20.33.)

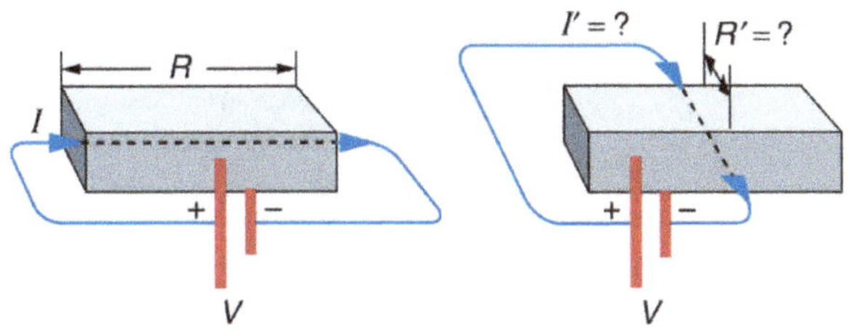

FIGURE 20.33 Does current taking two different paths through the same object encounter different resistance?

11. If aluminum and copper wires of the same length have the same resistance, which has the larger diameter? Why?

12. Explain why $R = R_0(1 + \alpha\Delta T)$ for the temperature variation of the resistance R of an object is not as accurate as $\rho = \rho_0(1 + \alpha\Delta T)$, which gives the temperature variation of resistivity ρ.

20.4 Electric Power and Energy

13. Why do incandescent lightbulbs grow dim late in their lives, particularly just before their filaments break?

14. The power dissipated in a resistor is given by $P = V^2/R$, which means power decreases if resistance increases. Yet this power is also given by $P = I^2R$, which means power increases if resistance increases. Explain why there is no contradiction here.

20.5 Alternating Current versus Direct Current

15. Give an example of a use of AC power other than in the household. Similarly, give an example of a use of DC power other than that supplied by batteries.

16. Why do voltage, current, and power go through zero 120 times per second for 60-Hz AC electricity?

17. You are riding in a train, gazing into the distance through its window. As close objects streak by, you notice that the nearby fluorescent lights make *dashed* streaks. Explain.

20.6 Electric Hazards and the Human Body

18. Using an ohmmeter, a student measures the resistance between various points on his body. They find that the resistance between two points on the same finger is about the same as the resistance between two points on opposite hands—both are several hundred thousand ohms. Furthermore, the resistance decreases when more skin is brought into contact with the probes of the ohmmeter. Finally, there is a dramatic drop in resistance (to a few thousand ohms) when the skin is wet. Explain these observations and their implications regarding skin and internal resistance of the human body.

19. What are the two major hazards of electricity?

20. Why isn't a short circuit a shock hazard?

21. What determines the severity of a shock? Can you say that a certain voltage is hazardous without further information?

22. An electrified needle is used to burn off warts, with the circuit being completed by having the patient sit on a large butt plate. Why is this plate

large?

23. Some surgery is performed with high-voltage electricity passing from a metal scalpel through the tissue being cut. Considering the nature of electric fields at the surface of conductors, why would you expect most of the current to flow from the sharp edge of the scalpel? Do you think high- or low-frequency AC is used?

24. Some devices often used in bathrooms, such as hairdryers, often have safety messages saying "Do not use when the bathtub or basin is full of water." Why is this so?

25. We are often advised to not flick electric switches with wet hands, dry your hand first. We are also advised to never throw water on an electric fire. Why is this so?

26. Before working on a power transmission line, experts will touch the line with the back of the hand as a final check that the voltage is zero. Why the back of the hand?

27. Why is the resistance of wet skin so much smaller than dry, and why do blood and other bodily fluids have low resistances?

28. Could a person on intravenous infusion (an IV) be microshock sensitive?

29. In view of the small currents that cause shock hazards and the larger currents that circuit breakers and fuses interrupt, how do they play a role in preventing shock hazards?

20.7 Nerve Conduction–Electrocardiograms

30. Note that in Figure 20.25, both the concentration gradient and the Coulomb force tend to move Na^+ ions into the cell. What prevents this?

31. Define depolarization, repolarization, and the action potential.

32. Explain the properties of myelinated nerves in terms of the insulating properties of myelin.

Problems & Exercises

20.1 Current

1. What is the current in milliamperes produced by the solar cells of a pocket calculator through which 4.00 C of charge passes in 4.00 h?

2. A total of 600 C of charge passes through a flashlight in 0.500 h. What is the average current?

3. What is the current when a typical static charge of $0.250\ \mu C$ moves from your finger to a metal doorknob in $1.00\ \mu s$?

4. Find the current when 2.00 nC jumps between your comb and hair over a $0.500\text{ - }\mu s$ time interval.

5. A large lightning bolt had a 20,000-A current and moved 30.0 C of charge. What was its duration?

6. The 200-A current through a spark plug moves 0.300 mC of charge. How long does the spark last?

7. (a) A defibrillator sends a 6.00-A current through the chest of a patient by applying a 10,000-V potential as in the figure below. What is the resistance of the path? (b) The defibrillator paddles make contact with the patient through a conducting gel that greatly reduces the path resistance. Discuss the difficulties that would ensue if a larger voltage were used to produce the same current through the patient, but with the path having perhaps 50 times the resistance. (Hint: The current must be about the same, so a higher voltage would imply greater power. Use this equation for power: $P = I^2 R$.)

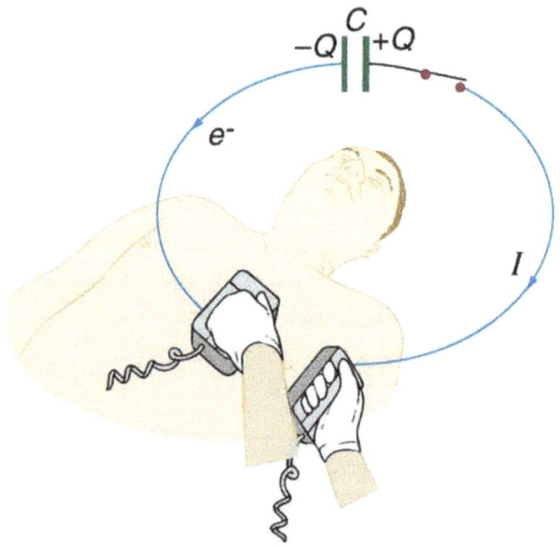

FIGURE 20.34 The capacitor in a defibrillation unit drives a current through the heart of a patient.

8. During open-heart surgery, a defibrillator can be used to bring a patient out of cardiac arrest. The resistance of the path is $500\ \Omega$ and a 10.0-mA current is needed. What voltage should be applied?

9. (a) A defibrillator passes 12.0 A of current through the torso of a person for 0.0100 s. How much charge moves? (b) How many electrons pass through the wires connected to the patient? (See figure two problems earlier.)

10. A clock battery wears out after moving 10,000 C of charge through the clock at a rate of 0.500 mA. (a) How long did the clock run? (b) How many electrons per second flowed?

11. The batteries of a submerged non-nuclear submarine supply 1000 A at full speed ahead. How long does it take to move Avogadro's number (6.02×10^{23}) of electrons at this rate?

12. Electron guns are used in X-ray tubes. The electrons are accelerated through a relatively large voltage and directed onto a metal target, producing X-rays. (a) How many electrons per second strike the target if the current is 0.500 mA? (b) What charge strikes the target in 0.750 s?

13. A large cyclotron directs a beam of He^{++} nuclei onto a target with a beam current of 0.250 mA. (a) How many He^{++} nuclei per second is this? (b) How long does it take for 1.00 C to strike the target? (c) How long before 1.00 mol of He^{++} nuclei strike the target?

14. Repeat the above example on Example 20.3, but for a wire made of silver and given there is one free electron per silver atom.

15. Using the results of the above example on Example 20.3, find the drift velocity in a copper wire of twice the diameter and carrying 20.0 A.

16. A 14-gauge copper wire has a diameter of 1.628 mm. What magnitude current flows when the drift velocity is 1.00 mm/s? (See above example on Example 20.3 for useful information.)

17. SPEAR, a storage ring about 72.0 m in diameter at the Stanford Linear Accelerator (closed in 2009), has a 20.0-A circulating beam of electrons that are moving at nearly the speed of light. (See Figure 20.35.) How many electrons are in the beam?

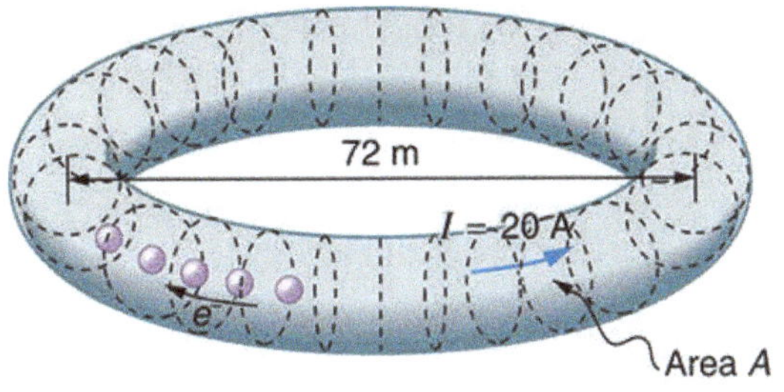

FIGURE 20.35 Electrons circulating in the storage ring called SPEAR constitute a 20.0-A current. Because they travel close to the speed of light, each electron completes many orbits in each second.

20.2 Ohm's Law: Resistance and Simple Circuits

18. What current flows through the bulb of a 3.00-V flashlight when its hot resistance is $3.60\ \Omega$?

19. Calculate the effective resistance of a pocket calculator that has a 1.35-V battery and through which 0.200 mA flows.

20. What is the effective resistance of a car's starter motor when 150 A flows through it as the car battery applies 11.0 V to the motor?

21. How many volts are supplied to operate an indicator light on a DVD player that has a resistance of $140\ \Omega$, given that 25.0 mA passes through it?

22. (a) Find the voltage drop in an extension cord having a $0.0600\text{-}\Omega$ resistance and through which 5.00 A is flowing. (b) A cheaper cord utilizes thinner wire and has a resistance of $0.300\ \Omega$. What is the voltage drop in it when 5.00 A flows? (c) Why is the voltage to whatever appliance is being used reduced by this amount? What is the effect on the appliance?

23. A power transmission line is hung from metal towers with glass insulators having a resistance of $1.00 \times 10^{9}\ \Omega$. What current flows through the insulator if the voltage is 200 kV? (Some high-voltage lines are DC.)

20.3 Resistance and Resistivity

24. What is the resistance of a 20.0-m-long piece of 12-gauge copper wire having a 2.053-mm diameter?

25. The diameter of 0-gauge copper wire is 8.252 mm. Find the resistance of a 1.00-km length of such wire used for power transmission.

26. If the 0.010-mm diameter tungsten filament in a light bulb is to have a resistance of $0.200\ \Omega$ at $20.0^{\circ}C$, how long should it be?

27. Find the ratio of the diameter of aluminum to copper wire, if they have the same resistance per unit length (as they might in household wiring).

28. What current flows through a 2.54-cm-diameter rod of pure silicon that is 20.0 cm long, when 1.00×10^{3} V is applied to it? (Such a rod may be used to make nuclear-particle detectors, for example.)

29. (a) To what temperature must you raise a copper

wire, originally at $20.0°C$, to double its resistance, neglecting any changes in dimensions? (b) Does this happen in household wiring under ordinary circumstances?

30. A resistor made of Nichrome wire is used in an application where its resistance cannot change more than 1.00% from its value at $20.0°C$. Over what temperature range can it be used?

31. Of what material is a resistor made if its resistance is 40.0% greater at $100°C$ than at $20.0°C$?

32. An electronic device designed to operate at any temperature in the range from $-10.0°C$ to $55.0°C$ contains pure carbon resistors. By what factor does their resistance increase over this range?

33. (a) Of what material is a wire made, if it is 25.0 m long with a 0.100 mm diameter and has a resistance of $77.7\ \Omega$ at $20.0°C$? (b) What is its resistance at $150°C$?

34. Assuming a constant temperature coefficient of resistivity, what is the maximum percent decrease in the resistance of a constantan wire starting at $20.0°C$?

35. A wire is drawn through a die, stretching it to four times its original length. By what factor does its resistance increase?

36. A copper wire has a resistance of $0.500\ \Omega$ at $20.0°C$, and an iron wire has a resistance of $0.525\ \Omega$ at the same temperature. At what temperature are their resistances equal?

37. (a) Digital medical thermometers determine temperature by measuring the resistance of a semiconductor device called a thermistor (which has $\alpha = -0.0600/°C$) when it is at the same temperature as the patient. What is a patient's temperature if the thermistor's resistance at that temperature is 82.0% of its value at $37.0°C$ (normal body temperature)? (b) The negative value for α may not be maintained for very low temperatures. Discuss why and whether this is the case here. (Hint: Resistance can't become negative.)

38. Integrated Concepts
(a) Redo Exercise 20.25 taking into account the thermal expansion of the tungsten filament. You may assume a thermal expansion coefficient of $12\times10^{-6}/°C$. (b) By what percentage does your answer differ from that in the example?

39. Unreasonable Results
(a) To what temperature must you raise a resistor made of constantan to double its resistance, assuming a constant temperature coefficient of resistivity? (b) To cut it in half? (c) What is unreasonable about these results? (d) Which assumptions are unreasonable, or which premises are inconsistent?

20.4 Electric Power and Energy

40. What is the power of a 1.00×10^2 MV lightning bolt having a current of 2.00×10^4 A?

41. What power is supplied to the starter motor of a large truck that draws 250 A of current from a 24.0-V battery hookup?

42. A charge of 4.00 C of charge passes through a pocket calculator's solar cells in 4.00 h. What is the power output, given the calculator's voltage output is 3.00 V? (See Figure 20.36.)

FIGURE 20.36 The strip of solar cells just above the keys of this calculator convert light to electricity to supply its energy needs. (credit: Evan-Amos, Wikimedia Commons)

43. How many watts does a flashlight that has 6.00×10^2 C pass through it in 0.500 h use if its voltage is 3.00 V?

44. Find the power dissipated in each of these extension cords: (a) an extension cord having a $0.0600 - \Omega$ resistance and through which 5.00 A is flowing; (b) a cheaper cord utilizing thinner wire and with a resistance of $0.300\ \Omega$.

45. Verify that the units of a volt-ampere are watts, as implied by the equation $P = IV$.

46. Show that the units $1\ V^2/\Omega = 1W$, as implied by the equation $P = V^2/R$.

47. Show that the units $1\ A^2 \cdot \Omega = 1\ W$, as implied by the equation $P = I^2 R$.

48. Verify the energy unit equivalence that $1\ kW \cdot h = 3.60\times10^6\ J$.

49. Electrons in an X-ray tube are accelerated through 1.00×10^2 kV and directed toward a target to produce X-rays. Calculate the power of the electron beam in this tube if it has a current of 15.0 mA.

50. An electric water heater consumes 5.00 kW for 2.00 h per day. What is the cost of running it for one year if electricity costs $12.0\ \text{cents/kW} \cdot \text{h}$? See Figure 20.37.

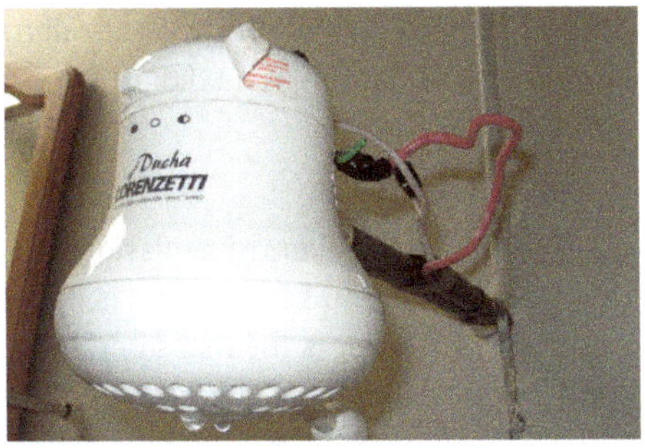

FIGURE 20.37 On-demand electric hot water heater. Heat is supplied to water only when needed. (credit: aviddavid, Flickr)

51. With a 1200-W toaster, how much electrical energy is needed to make a slice of toast (cooking time = 1 minute)? At $9.0\ \text{cents/kW} \cdot \text{h}$, how much does this cost?

52. What would be the maximum cost of a CFL such that the total cost (investment plus operating) would be the same for both CFL and incandescent 60-W bulbs? Assume the cost of the incandescent bulb is 25 cents and that electricity costs $10\ \text{cents/kWh}$. Calculate the cost for 1000 hours, as in the cost effectiveness of CFL example.

53. Some makes of older cars have 6.00-V electrical systems. (a) What is the hot resistance of a 30.0-W headlight in such a car? (b) What current flows through it?

54. Alkaline batteries have the advantage of putting out constant voltage until very nearly the end of their life. How long will an alkaline battery rated at $1.00\ \text{A} \cdot \text{h}$ and 1.58 V keep a 1.00-W flashlight bulb burning?

55. A cauterizer, used to stop bleeding in surgery, puts out 2.00 mA at 15.0 kV. (a) What is its power output? (b) What is the resistance of the path?

56. The average television is said to be on 6 hours per day. Estimate the yearly cost of electricity to operate 100 million TVs, assuming their power consumption averages 150 W and the cost of electricity averages $12.0\ \text{cents/kW} \cdot \text{h}$.

57. An old lightbulb draws only 50.0 W, rather than its original 60.0 W, due to evaporative thinning of its filament. By what factor is its diameter reduced, assuming uniform thinning along its length? Neglect any effects caused by temperature differences.

58. 00-gauge copper wire has a diameter of 9.266 mm. Calculate the power loss in a kilometer of such wire when it carries 1.00×10^2 A.

59. Integrated Concepts
Cold vaporizers pass a current through water, evaporating it with only a small increase in temperature. One such home device is rated at 3.50 A and utilizes 120 V AC with 95.0% efficiency. (a) What is the vaporization rate in grams per minute? (b) How much water must you put into the vaporizer for 8.00 h of overnight operation? (See Figure 20.38.)

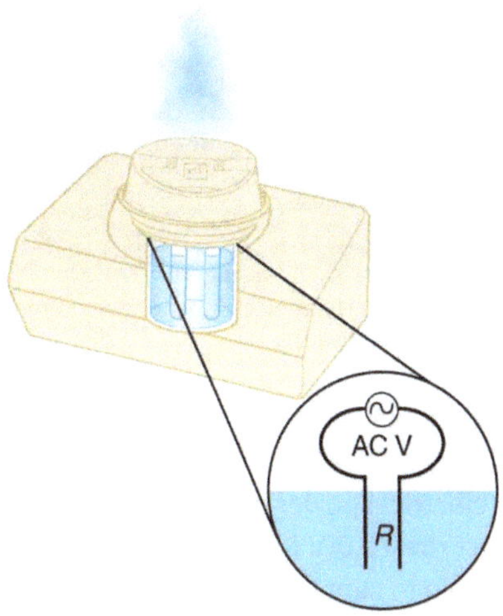

FIGURE 20.38 This cold vaporizer passes current directly through water, vaporizing it directly with relatively little temperature increase.

60. Integrated Concepts
(a) What energy is dissipated by a lightning bolt having a 20,000-A current, a voltage of 1.00×10^2 MV, and a length of 1.00 ms? (b) What mass of tree sap could be raised from 18.0°C to its boiling point and then evaporated by this energy, assuming sap has the same thermal characteristics as water?

61. Integrated Concepts
What current must be produced by a 12.0-V battery-operated bottle warmer in order to heat 75.0 g of glass, 250 g of baby formula, and 3.00×10^2 g of aluminum from 20.0°C to 90.0°C in 5.00 min?

62. Integrated Concepts

How much time is needed for a surgical cauterizer to raise the temperature of 1.00 g of tissue from $37.0°C$ to $100°C$ and then boil away 0.500 g of water, if it puts out 2.00 mA at 15.0 kV? Ignore heat transfer to the surroundings.

63. Integrated Concepts
Hydroelectric generators (see Figure 20.39) at Hoover Dam produce a maximum current of 8.00×10^3 A at 250 kV. (a) What is the power output? (b) The water that powers the generators enters and leaves the system at low speed (thus its kinetic energy does not change) but loses 160 m in altitude. How many cubic meters per second are needed, assuming 85.0% efficiency?

FIGURE 20.39 Hydroelectric generators at the Hoover dam. (credit: Jon Sullivan)

64. Integrated Concepts
(a) Assuming 95.0% efficiency for the conversion of electrical power by the motor, what current must the 12.0-V batteries of a 750-kg electric car be able to supply: (a) To accelerate from rest to 25.0 m/s in 1.00 min? (b) To climb a 2.00×10^2-m-high hill in 2.00 min at a constant 25.0-m/s speed while exerting 5.00×10^2 N of force to overcome air resistance and friction? (c) To travel at a constant 25.0-m/s speed, exerting a 5.00×10^2 N force to overcome air resistance and friction? See Figure 20.40.

FIGURE 20.40 This REVAi, an electric car, gets recharged on a street in London. (credit: Frank Hebbert)

65. Integrated Concepts
A light-rail commuter train draws 630 A of 650-V DC electricity when accelerating. (a) What is its power consumption rate in kilowatts? (b) How long does it take to reach 20.0 m/s starting from rest if its loaded mass is 5.30×10^4 kg, assuming 95.0% efficiency and constant power? (c) Find its average acceleration. (d) Discuss how the acceleration you found for the light-rail train compares to what might be typical for an automobile.

66. Integrated Concepts
(a) An aluminum power transmission line has a resistance of $0.0580\ \Omega/\text{km}$. What is its mass per kilometer? (b) What is the mass per kilometer of a copper line having the same resistance? A lower resistance would shorten the heating time. Discuss the practical limits to speeding the heating by lowering the resistance.

67. Integrated Concepts
(a) An immersion heater utilizing 120 V can raise the temperature of a 1.00×10^2-g aluminum cup containing 350 g of water from $20.0°C$ to $95.0°C$ in 2.00 min. Find its resistance, assuming it is constant during the process. (b) A lower resistance would shorten the heating time. Discuss the practical limits to speeding the heating by lowering the resistance.

68. Integrated Concepts
(a) What is the cost of heating a hot tub containing 1500 kg of water from $10.0°C$ to $40.0°C$, assuming 75.0% efficiency to account for heat transfer to the surroundings? The cost of electricity is $9\ \text{cents/kW} \cdot \text{h}$. (b) What current was used by the 220-V AC electric heater, if this took 4.00 h?

69. Unreasonable Results
(a) What current is needed to transmit 1.00×10^2 MW of power at 480 V? (b) What power is dissipated by the transmission lines if they have a $1.00\text{-}\Omega$ resistance? (c) What is unreasonable about this result? (d) Which assumptions are unreasonable, or which premises are inconsistent?

70. Unreasonable Results
(a) What current is needed to transmit 1.00×10^2 MW of power at 10.0 kV? (b) Find the resistance of 1.00 km of wire that would cause a

0.0100% power loss. (c) What is the diameter of a 1.00-km-long copper wire having this resistance? (d) What is unreasonable about these results? (e) Which assumptions are unreasonable, or which premises are inconsistent?

71. Construct Your Own Problem
Consider an electric immersion heater used to heat a cup of water to make tea. Construct a problem in which you calculate the needed resistance of the heater so that it increases the temperature of the water and cup in a reasonable amount of time. Also calculate the cost of the electrical energy used in your process. Among the things to be considered are the voltage used, the masses and heat capacities involved, heat losses, and the time over which the heating takes place. Your instructor may wish for you to consider a thermal safety switch (perhaps bimetallic) that will halt the process before damaging temperatures are reached in the immersion unit.

20.5 Alternating Current versus Direct Current

72. (a) What is the hot resistance of a 25-W light bulb that runs on 120-V AC? (b) If the bulb's operating temperature is $2700^{\circ}\mathrm{C}$, what is its resistance at $2600^{\circ}\mathrm{C}$?

73. Certain heavy industrial equipment uses AC power that has a peak voltage of 679 V. What is the rms voltage?

74. A certain circuit breaker trips when the rms current is 15.0 A. What is the corresponding peak current?

75. Military aircraft use 400-Hz AC power, because it is possible to design lighter-weight equipment at this higher frequency. What is the time for one complete cycle of this power?

76. A North American tourist takes his 25.0-W, 120-V AC razor to Europe, finds a special adapter, and plugs it into 240 V AC. Assuming constant resistance, what power does the razor consume as it is ruined?

77. In this problem, you will verify statements made at the end of the power losses for Example 20.10. (a) What current is needed to transmit 100 MW of power at a voltage of 25.0 kV? (b) Find the power loss in a $1.00\text{ - }\Omega$ transmission line. (c) What percent loss does this represent?

78. A small office-building air conditioner operates on 408-V AC and consumes 50.0 kW. (a) What is its effective resistance? (b) What is the cost of running the air conditioner during a hot summer month when it is on 8.00 h per day for 30 days and electricity costs $9.00\ \mathrm{cents/kW \cdot h}$?

79. What is the peak power consumption of a 120-V AC microwave oven that draws 10.0 A?

80. What is the peak current through a 500-W room heater that operates on 120-V AC power?

81. Two different electrical devices have the same power consumption, but one is meant to be operated on 120-V AC and the other on 240-V AC. (a) What is the ratio of their resistances? (b) What is the ratio of their currents? (c) Assuming its resistance is unaffected, by what factor will the power increase if a 120-V AC device is connected to 240-V AC?

82. Nichrome wire is used in some radiative heaters. (a) Find the resistance needed if the average power output is to be 1.00 kW utilizing 120-V AC. (b) What length of Nichrome wire, having a cross-sectional area of $5.00\mathrm{mm}^2$, is needed if the operating temperature is $500^{\circ}\ \mathrm{C}$? (c) What power will it draw when first switched on?

83. Find the time after $t = 0$ when the instantaneous voltage of 60-Hz AC first reaches the following values: (a) $V_0/2$ (b) V_0 (c) 0.

84. (a) At what two times in the first period following $t = 0$ does the instantaneous voltage in 60-Hz AC equal V_{rms}? (b) $-V_{\mathrm{rms}}$?

20.6 Electric Hazards and the Human Body

85. (a) How much power is dissipated in a short circuit of 220-V AC through a resistance of $0.250\ \Omega$? (b) What current flows?

86. What voltage is involved in a 1.44-kW short circuit through a $0.100\text{ - }\Omega$ resistance?

87. Find the current through a person and identify the likely effect on her if she touches a 120-V AC source: (a) if she is standing on a rubber mat and offers a total resistance of $300\ \mathrm{k}\Omega$; (b) if she is standing barefoot on wet grass and has a resistance of only $4500\ \Omega$.

88. While taking a bath, a person touches the metal case of a radio. The path through the person to the drainpipe and ground has a resistance of $4000\ \Omega$. What is the smallest voltage on the case of the radio that could cause ventricular fibrillation?

89. Foolishly trying to fish a burning piece of bread

from a toaster with a metal butter knife, a man comes into contact with 120-V AC. He does not even feel it since, luckily, he is wearing rubber-soled shoes. What is the minimum resistance of the path the current follows through the person?

90. (a) During surgery, a current as small as $20.0\ \mu A$ applied directly to the heart may cause ventricular fibrillation. If the resistance of the exposed heart is $300\ \Omega$, what is the smallest voltage that poses this danger? (b) Does your answer imply that special electrical safety precautions are needed?

91. (a) What is the resistance of a 220-V AC short circuit that generates a peak power of 96.8 kW? (b) What would the average power be if the voltage was 120 V AC?

92. A heart defibrillator passes 10.0 A through a patient's torso for 5.00 ms in an attempt to restore normal beating. (a) How much charge passed? (b) What voltage was applied if 500 J of energy was dissipated? (c) What was the path's resistance? (d) Find the temperature increase caused in the 8.00 kg of affected tissue.

93. Integrated Concepts
A short circuit in a 120-V appliance cord has a $0.500\text{-}\Omega$ resistance. Calculate the temperature rise of the 2.00 g of surrounding materials, assuming their specific heat capacity is $0.200\ \text{cal/g}\cdot\text{°C}$ and that it takes 0.0500 s for a circuit breaker to interrupt the current. Is this likely to be damaging?

94. Construct Your Own Problem
Consider a person working in an environment where electric currents might pass through their body. Construct a problem in which you calculate the resistance of insulation needed to protect the person from harm. Among the things to be considered are the voltage to which the person might be exposed, likely body resistance (dry, wet, ...), and acceptable currents (safe but sensed, safe and unfelt, ...).

20.7 Nerve Conduction–Electrocardiograms

95. Integrated Concepts
Use the ECG in Figure 20.31 to determine the heart rate in beats per minute assuming a constant time between beats.

96. Integrated Concepts
(a) Referring to Figure 20.31, find the time systolic pressure lags behind the middle of the QRS complex. (b) Discuss the reasons for the time lag.

97. Critical Thinking A copper wire of length 1.25 m is in a circuit. A current of 2.50 A flows through the wire. (a) Initially, the circuit is at 20.0°C. If there is an energy loss of 3.25 MJ in the first second caused by the wire as soon as the circuit is turned on, what is the radius of the wire? (b) After the wire heats 3.000°C, how much energy is being dissipated by the circuit per second? Neglect the effects of thermal expansion since the wire is considered to be physically constrained from expanding. Assume the current is maintained. (c) At what temperature will the energy dissipation be 1.00% higher than it was at the beginning of the experiment?

Test Prep for AP® Courses

20.1 Current

1. Which of the following can be explained on the basis of conservation of charge in a closed circuit consisting of a battery, resistor, and metal wires?
   a. The number of electrons leaving the battery will be equal to the number of electrons entering the battery.
   b. The number of electrons leaving the battery will be less than the number of electrons entering the battery.
   c. The number of protons leaving the battery will be equal to the number of protons entering the battery.
   d. The number of protons leaving the battery will be less than the number of protons entering the battery.

2. When a battery is connected to a bulb, there is 2.5 A of current in the circuit. What amount of charge will flow though the circuit in a time of 0.5 s?
   a. 0.5 C
   b. 1 C
   c. 1.25 C
   d. 1.5 C

3. If 0.625×10^{20} electrons flow through a circuit each second, what is the current in the circuit?

4. Two students calculate the charge flowing through a circuit. The first student concludes that 300 C of charge flows in 1 minute. The second student concludes that 3.125×10^{19} electrons flow per second. If the current measured in the circuit is 5 A, which of the two students (if any) have performed the calculations correctly?

20.2 Ohm's Law: Resistance and Simple Circuits

5. If the voltage across a fixed resistance is doubled, what happens to the current?
   a. It doubles.
   b. It halves.
   c. It stays the same.
   d. The current cannot be determined.

6. The table below gives the voltages and currents recorded across a resistor.

Voltage (V)	2.50	5.00	7.50	10.00	12.50
Current (A)	0.69	1.38	2.09	2.76	3.49

TABLE 20.4

   a. Plot the graph and comment on the shape.
   b. Calculate the value of the resistor.

7. What is the resistance of a bulb if the current in it is 1.25 A when a 4 V voltage supply is connected to it? If the voltage supply is increased to 7 V, what will be the current in the bulb?

20.3 Resistance and Resistivity

8. Which of the following affect the resistivity of a wire?
   a. length
   b. area of cross section
   c. material
   d. all of the above

9. The lengths and diameters of four wires are given as shown.

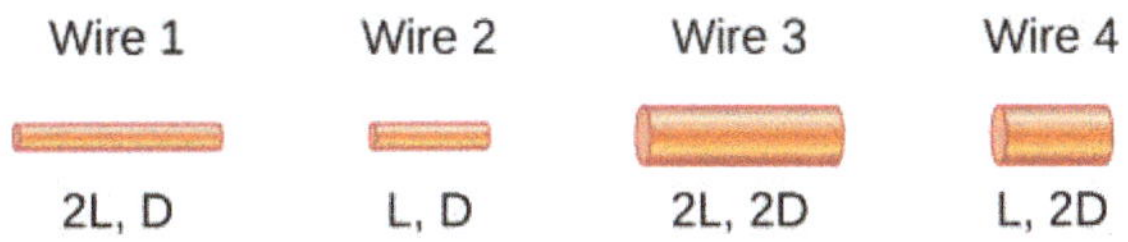

FIGURE 20.41

If the four wires are made from the same material, which of the following is true? Select *two* answers.
   a. Resistance of Wire 3 > Resistance of Wire 2
   b. Resistance of Wire 1 > Resistance of Wire 2
   c. Resistance of Wire 1 < Resistance of Wire 4
   d. Resistance of Wire 4 < Resistance of Wire 3

10. Suppose the resistance of a wire is $R\ \Omega$. What will be the resistance of another wire of the same material having the same length but double the diameter?
   a. $R/2$
   b. $2R$
   c. $R/4$
   d. $4R$

11. The resistances of two wires having the same lengths and cross section areas are 3 Ω and 11 Ω. If the resistivity of the 3 Ω wire is 2.65×10^{-8} Ω•m, find the resistivity of the 1 Ω wire.

12. The lengths and diameters of three wires are given below. If they all have the same resistance, find the ratio of their resistivities.

Wire	*Length*	*Diameter*
Wire 1	2 m	1 cm
Wire 2	1 m	0.5 cm
Wire 3	1 m	1 cm

TABLE 20.5

13. Suppose the resistance of a wire is 2 Ω. If the wire is stretched to three times its length, what will be its resistance? Assume that the volume does not change.

20.4 Electric Power and Energy

14.

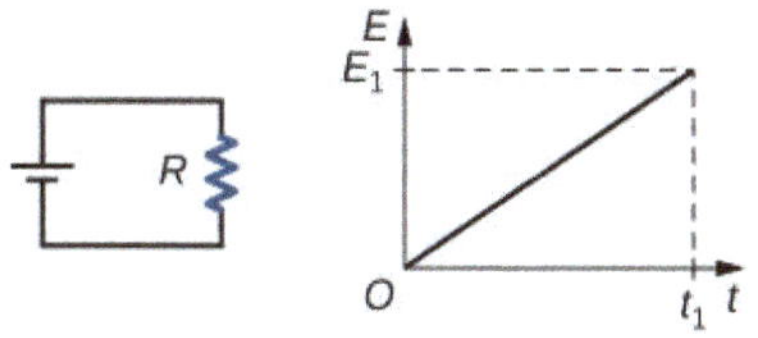

FIGURE 20.42

The circuit shown contains a resistor R connected to a voltage supply. The graph shows the total energy E dissipated by the resistance as a function of time. Which of the following shows the corresponding graph for double resistance, i.e., if R is replaced by $2R$?

a.

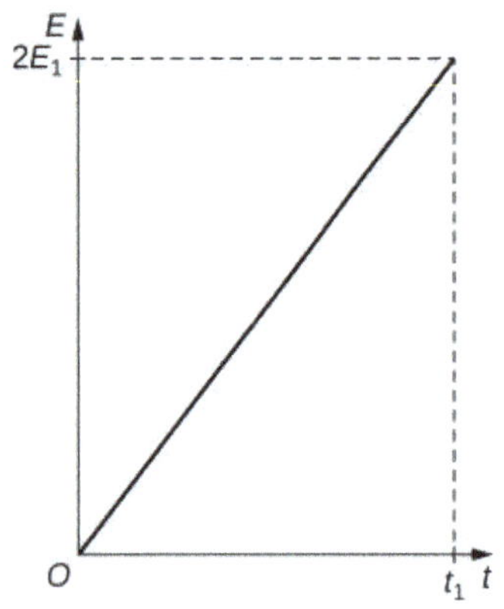

FIGURE 20.43

b.

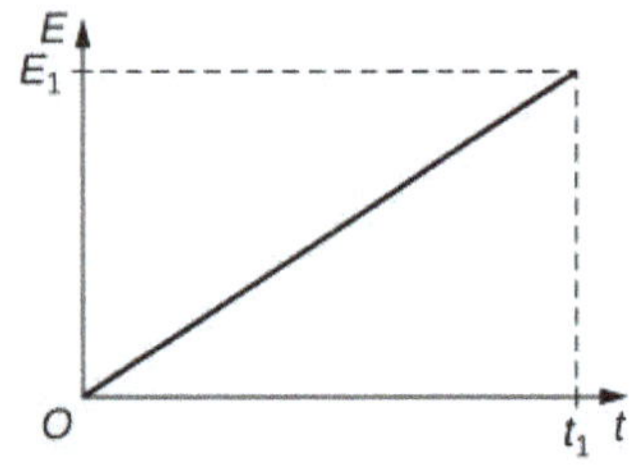

FIGURE 20.44

c.

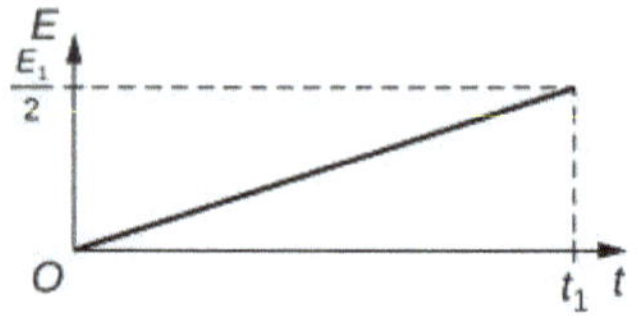

FIGURE 20.45

d.

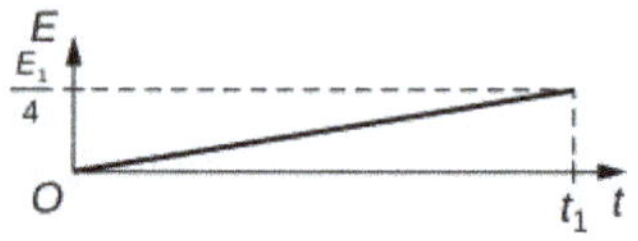

FIGURE 20.46

15. What will be the ratio of the resistance of a 120 W, 220 V lamp to that of a 100 W, 110 V lamp?

CHAPTER 21
Circuits and DC Instruments

FIGURE 21.1 Electric circuits in computers and servers allow large amounts of data to be quickly and accurately analyzed. (credit: WOCinTech Chat/Flickr)

CHAPTER OUTLINE

CONNECTION FOR AP® COURSES Electric circuits are commonplace in our everyday lives. Some circuits are simple, such as those in flashlights while others are extremely complex, such as those used in supercomputers. This chapter takes the topic of electric circuits a step beyond simple circuits by addressing both changes that result from interactions between systems (Big Idea 4) and constraints on such changes due to laws of conservation (Big Idea 5). When the circuit is purely resistive, everything in this chapter applies to both DC and AC. However, matters become more complex when capacitance is involved. We do consider what happens when capacitors are connected to DC voltage sources, but the interaction of capacitors (and other nonresistive devices) with AC sources is left for a later chapter. In addition, a number of important DC instruments, such as meters that measure voltage and current, are covered in this chapter.

Information and examples presented in the chapter examine cause-effect relationships inherent in interactions involving electrical systems. The electrical properties of an electric circuit can change due to other systems (Enduring Understanding 4.E). More specifically, values of currents and potential differences in electric circuits depend on arrangements of individual circuit components (Essential Knowledge 4.E.5). In this chapter several series and parallel combinations of resistors are discussed and their effects on currents and potential differences are analyzed.

In electric circuits the total energy (Enduring Understanding 5.B) and the total electric charge (Enduring Understanding 5.C) are conserved. Kirchoff's rules describe both, energy conservation (Essential Knowledge 5.B.9) and charge conservation (Essential Knowledge 5.C.3). Energy conservation is discussed in terms of the loop rule which specifies that the potential around any closed circuit path must be zero. Charge conservation is applied as conservation of current by equating the sum of all currents entering a junction to the sum of all currents leaving the junction (also known as the junction rule). Kirchoff's rules are used to calculate currents and potential differences in circuits that combine resistors in series and parallel, and resistors and capacitors.

The concepts in this chapter support:

Big Idea 4 Interactions between systems can result in changes in those systems.

Enduring Understanding 4.E The electric and magnetic properties of a system can change in response to the presence of, or changes in, other objects or systems.

Essential Knowledge 4.E.5 The values of currents and electric potential differences in an electric circuit are determined by the properties and arrangement of the individual circuit elements such as sources of emf, resistors, and capacitors.

Big Idea 5 Changes that occur as a result of interactions are constrained by conservation laws.

Enduring Understanding 5.B The energy of a system is conserved.

Essential Knowledge 5.B.9 Kirchhoff's loop rule describes conservation of energy in electrical circuits.

Enduring Understanding 5.C The electric charge of a system is conserved.

Essential Knowledge 5.C.3 Kirchhoff's junction rule describes the conservation of electric charge in electrical circuits. Since charge is conserved, current must be conserved at each junction in the circuit. Examples should include circuits that combine resistors in series and parallel.

21.1 Resistors in Series and Parallel

LEARNING OBJECTIVES

By the end of this section, you will be able to:

- Draw a circuit with resistors in parallel and in series.
- Calculate the voltage drop of a current across a resistor using Ohm's law.
- Contrast the way total resistance is calculated for resistors in series and in parallel.
- Explain why total resistance of a parallel circuit is less than the smallest resistance of any of the resistors in that circuit.
- Calculate total resistance of a circuit that contains a mixture of resistors connected in series and in parallel.

Most circuits have more than one component, called a **resistor** that limits the flow of charge in the circuit. A measure of this limit on charge flow is called **resistance**. The simplest combinations of resistors are the series and parallel connections illustrated in Figure 21.2. The total resistance of a combination of resistors depends on both their individual values and how they are connected.

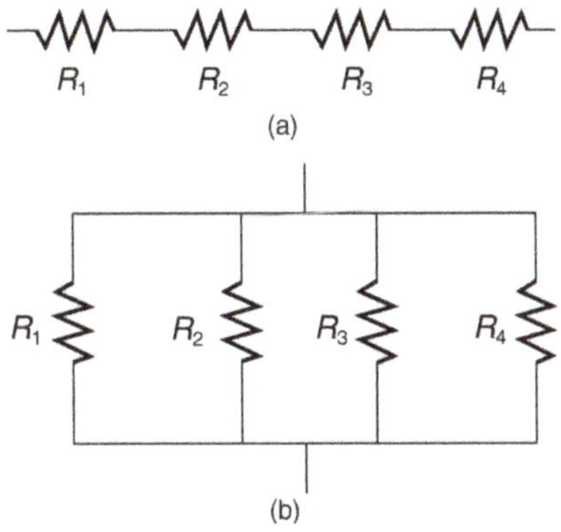

FIGURE 21.2 (a) A series connection of resistors. (b) A parallel connection of resistors.

Resistors in Series

When are resistors in **series**? Resistors are in series whenever the flow of charge, called the **current**, must flow through devices sequentially. For example, if current flows through a person holding a screwdriver and into the Earth, then R_1 in Figure 21.2(a) could be the resistance of the screwdriver's shaft, R_2 the resistance of its handle, R_3 the person's body resistance, and R_4 the resistance of her shoes.

Figure 21.3 shows resistors in series connected to a **voltage** source. It seems reasonable that the total resistance is the sum of the individual resistances, considering that the current has to pass through each resistor in sequence. (This fact would be an advantage to a person wishing to avoid an electrical shock, who could reduce the current by wearing high-resistance rubber-soled shoes. It could be a disadvantage if one of the resistances were a faulty high-resistance cord to an appliance that would reduce the operating current.)

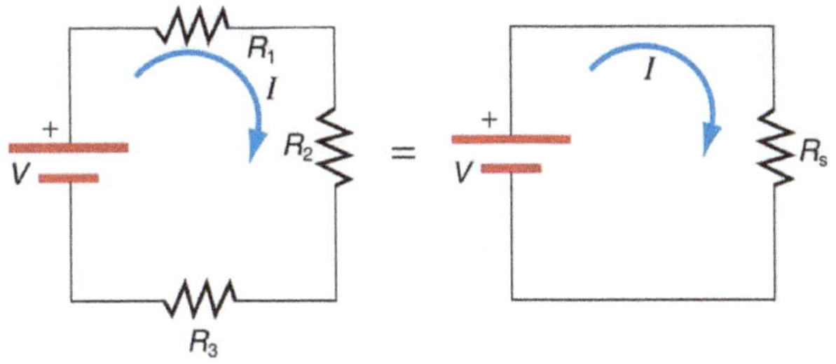

FIGURE 21.3 Three resistors connected in series to a battery (left) and the equivalent single or series resistance (right).

To verify that resistances in series do indeed add, let us consider the loss of electrical power, called a **voltage drop**, in each resistor in Figure 21.3.

According to **Ohm's law**, the voltage drop, V, across a resistor when a current flows through it is calculated using the equation $V = IR$, where I equals the current in amps (A) and R is the resistance in ohms (Ω). Another way to think of this is that V is the voltage necessary to make a current I flow through a resistance R.

So the voltage drop across R_1 is $V_1 = IR_1$, that across R_2 is $V_2 = IR_2$, and that across R_3 is $V_3 = IR_3$. The sum of these voltages equals the voltage output of the source; that is,

$$V = V_1 + V_2 + V_3. \tag{21.1}$$

This equation is based on the conservation of energy and conservation of charge. Electrical potential energy can be described by the equation $PE = qV$, where q is the electric charge and V is the voltage. Thus the energy supplied by the source is qV, while that dissipated by the resistors is

$$qV_1 + qV_2 + qV_3. \tag{21.2}$$

CONNECTIONS: CONSERVATION LAWS

The derivations of the expressions for series and parallel resistance are based on the laws of conservation of energy and conservation of charge, which state that total charge and total energy are constant in any process.

These two laws are directly involved in all electrical phenomena and will be invoked repeatedly to explain both specific effects and the general behavior of electricity.

These energies must be equal, because there is no other source and no other destination for energy in the circuit. Thus, $qV = qV_1 + qV_2 + qV_3$. The charge q cancels, yielding $V = V_1 + V_2 + V_3$, as stated. (Note that the same amount of charge passes through the battery and each resistor in a given amount of time, since there is no capacitance to store charge, there is no place for charge to leak, and charge is conserved.)

Now substituting the values for the individual voltages gives

$$V = IR_1 + IR_2 + IR_3 = I(R_1 + R_2 + R_3). \tag{21.3}$$

Note that for the equivalent single series resistance R_s, we have

$$V = IR_s. \tag{21.4}$$

This implies that the total or equivalent series resistance R_s of three resistors is $R_s = R_1 + R_2 + R_3$.

This logic is valid in general for any number of resistors in series; thus, the total resistance R_s of a series connection is

$$R_s = R_1 + R_2 + R_3 + ..., \tag{21.5}$$

as proposed. Since all of the current must pass through each resistor, it experiences the resistance of each, and resistances in series simply add up.

EXAMPLE 21.1

Calculating Resistance, Current, Voltage Drop, and Power Dissipation: Analysis of a Series Circuit

Suppose the voltage output of the battery in Figure 21.3 is 12.0 V, and the resistances are $R_1 = 1.00\ \Omega$, $R_2 = 6.00\ \Omega$, and $R_3 = 13.0\ \Omega$. (a) What is the total resistance? (b) Find the current. (c) Calculate the voltage drop in each resistor, and show these add to equal the voltage output of the source. (d) Calculate the power dissipated by each resistor. (e) Find the power output of the source, and show that it equals the total power dissipated by the resistors.

Strategy and Solution for (a)

The total resistance is simply the sum of the individual resistances, as given by this equation:

$$\begin{aligned} R_s &= R_1 + R_2 + R_3 \\ &= 1.00\ \Omega + 6.00\ \Omega + 13.0\ \Omega \\ &= 20.0\ \Omega. \end{aligned} \tag{21.6}$$

Strategy and Solution for (b)

The current is found using Ohm's law, $V = IR$. Entering the value of the applied voltage and the total resistance yields the current for the circuit:

$$I = \frac{V}{R_s} = \frac{12.0\text{ V}}{20.0\ \Omega} = 0.600\text{ A}. \tag{21.7}$$

Strategy and Solution for (c)

The voltage—or IR drop—in a resistor is given by Ohm's law. Entering the current and the value of the first resistance yields

$$V_1 = IR_1 = (0.600\text{ A})(1.0\ \Omega) = 0.600\text{ V}. \tag{21.8}$$

Similarly,

$$V_2 = IR_2 = (0.600\text{ A})(6.0\ \Omega) = 3.60\text{ V} \tag{21.9}$$

and

$$V_3 = IR_3 = (0.600\ \text{A})(13.0\ \Omega) = 7.80\ \text{V}. \tag{21.10}$$

Discussion for (c)

The three IR drops add to $12.0\ \text{V}$, as predicted:

$$V_1 + V_2 + V_3 = (0.600 + 3.60 + 7.80)\ \text{V} = 12.0\ \text{V}. \tag{21.11}$$

Strategy and Solution for (d)

The easiest way to calculate power in watts (W) dissipated by a resistor in a DC circuit is to use **Joule's law**, $P = IV$, where P is electric power. In this case, each resistor has the same full current flowing through it. By substituting Ohm's law $V = IR$ into Joule's law, we get the power dissipated by the first resistor as

$$P_1 = I^2 R_1 = (0.600\ \text{A})^2 (1.00\ \Omega) = 0.360\ \text{W}. \tag{21.12}$$

Similarly,

$$P_2 = I^2 R_2 = (0.600\ \text{A})^2 (6.00\ \Omega) = 2.16\ \text{W} \tag{21.13}$$

and

$$P_3 = I^2 R_3 = (0.600\ \text{A})^2 (13.0\ \Omega) = 4.68\ \text{W}. \tag{21.14}$$

Discussion for (d)

Power can also be calculated using either $P = IV$ or $P = \frac{V^2}{R}$, where V is the voltage drop across the resistor (not the full voltage of the source). The same values will be obtained.

Strategy and Solution for (e)

The easiest way to calculate power output of the source is to use $P = IV$, where V is the source voltage. This gives

$$P = (0.600\ \text{A})(12.0\ \text{V}) = 7.20\ \text{W}. \tag{21.15}$$

Discussion for (e)

Note, coincidentally, that the total power dissipated by the resistors is also 7.20 W, the same as the power put out by the source. That is,

$$P_1 + P_2 + P_3 = (0.360 + 2.16 + 4.68)\ \text{W} = 7.20\ \text{W}. \tag{21.16}$$

Power is energy per unit time (watts), and so conservation of energy requires the power output of the source to be equal to the total power dissipated by the resistors.

MAJOR FEATURES OF RESISTORS IN SERIES

1. Series resistances add: $R_s = R_1 + R_2 + R_3 + \ldots.$
2. The same current flows through each resistor in series.
3. Individual resistors in series do not get the total source voltage, but divide it.

Resistors in Parallel

Figure 21.4 shows resistors in **parallel**, wired to a voltage source. Resistors are in parallel when each resistor is connected directly to the voltage source by connecting wires having negligible resistance. Each resistor thus has the full voltage of the source applied to it.

Each resistor draws the same current it would if it alone were connected to the voltage source (provided the voltage source is not overloaded). For example, an automobile's headlights, radio, and so on, are wired in parallel, so that they utilize the full voltage of the source and can operate completely independently. The same is true in your house, or any building. (See Figure 21.4(b).)

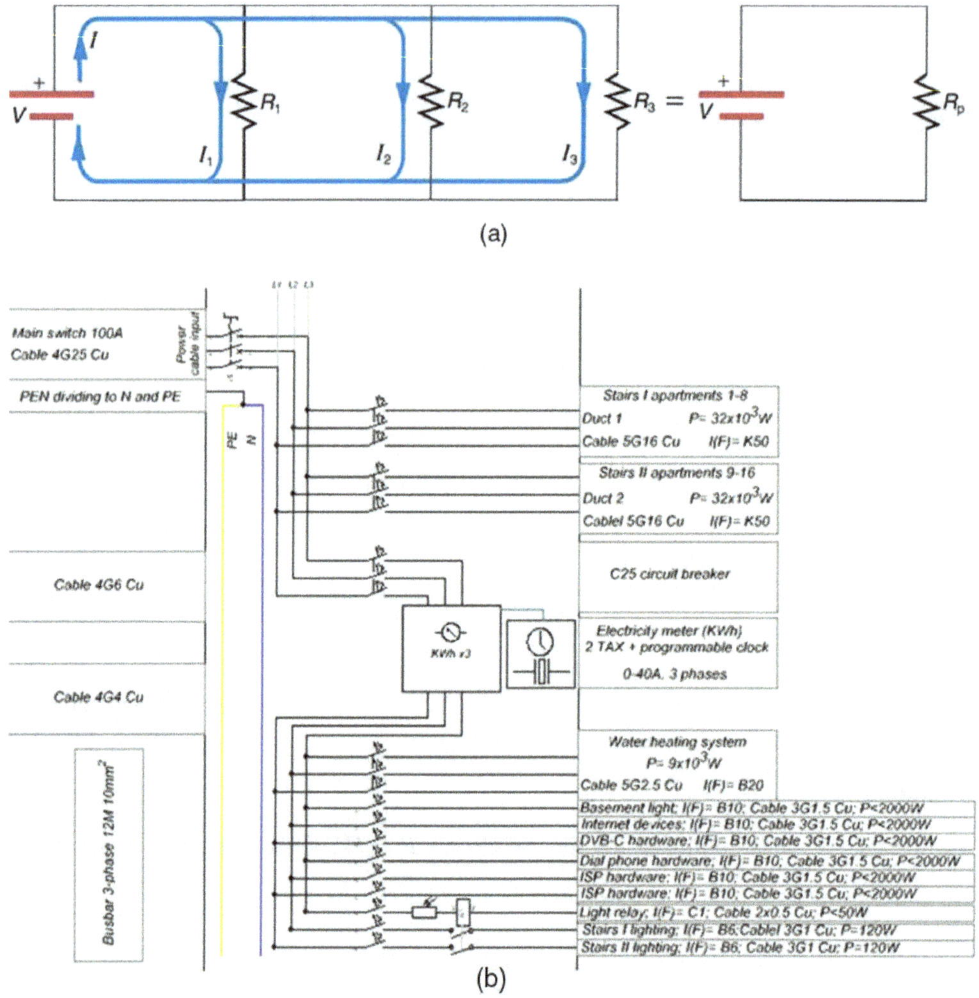

FIGURE 21.4 (a) Three resistors connected in parallel to a battery and the equivalent single or parallel resistance. (b) Electrical power setup in a house. (credit: Dmitry G, Wikimedia Commons)

To find an expression for the equivalent parallel resistance R_p, let us consider the currents that flow and how they are related to resistance. Since each resistor in the circuit has the full voltage, the currents flowing through the individual resistors are $I_1 = \frac{V}{R_1}$, $I_2 = \frac{V}{R_2}$, and $I_3 = \frac{V}{R_3}$. Conservation of charge implies that the total current I produced by the source is the sum of these currents:

$$I = I_1 + I_2 + I_3. \tag{21.17}$$

Substituting the expressions for the individual currents gives

$$I = \frac{V}{R_1} + \frac{V}{R_2} + \frac{V}{R_3} = V\left(\frac{1}{R_1} + \frac{1}{R_2} + \frac{1}{R_3}\right). \tag{21.18}$$

Note that Ohm's law for the equivalent single resistance gives

$$I = \frac{V}{R_p} = V\left(\frac{1}{R_p}\right). \tag{21.19}$$

The terms inside the parentheses in the last two equations must be equal. Generalizing to any number of resistors, the total resistance R_p of a parallel connection is related to the individual resistances by

$$\frac{1}{R_p} = \frac{1}{R_1} + \frac{1}{R_2} + \frac{1}{R_{.3}} + ... \tag{21.20}$$

This relationship results in a total resistance R_p that is less than the smallest of the individual resistances. (This is seen in the next example.) When resistors are connected in parallel, more current flows from the source than would flow for any of them individually, and so the total resistance is lower.

EXAMPLE 21.2

Calculating Resistance, Current, Power Dissipation, and Power Output: Analysis of a Parallel Circuit

Let the voltage output of the battery and resistances in the parallel connection in Figure 21.4 be the same as the previously considered series connection: $V = 12.0\text{ V}$, $R_1 = 1.00\ \Omega$, $R_2 = 6.00\ \Omega$, and $R_3 = 13.0\ \Omega$. (a) What is the total resistance? (b) Find the total current. (c) Calculate the currents in each resistor, and show these add to equal the total current output of the source. (d) Calculate the power dissipated by each resistor. (e) Find the power output of the source, and show that it equals the total power dissipated by the resistors.

Strategy and Solution for (a)

The total resistance for a parallel combination of resistors is found using the equation below. Entering known values gives

$$\frac{1}{R_p} = \frac{1}{R_1} + \frac{1}{R_2} + \frac{1}{R_3} = \frac{1}{1.00\ \Omega} + \frac{1}{6.00\ \Omega} + \frac{1}{13.0\ \Omega}. \tag{21.21}$$

Thus,

$$\frac{1}{R_p} = \frac{1.00}{\Omega} + \frac{0.1667}{\Omega} + \frac{0.07692}{\Omega} = \frac{1.2436}{\Omega}. \tag{21.22}$$

(Note that in these calculations, each intermediate answer is shown with an extra digit.)

We must invert this to find the total resistance R_p. This yields

$$R_p = \frac{1}{1.2436}\Omega = 0.8041\ \Omega. \tag{21.23}$$

The total resistance with the correct number of significant digits is $R_p = 0.804\ \Omega$.

Discussion for (a)

R_p is, as predicted, less than the smallest individual resistance.

Strategy and Solution for (b)

The total current can be found from Ohm's law, substituting R_p for the total resistance. This gives

$$I = \frac{V}{R_p} = \frac{12.0\text{ V}}{0.8041\ \Omega} = 14.92\text{ A}. \tag{21.24}$$

Discussion for (b)

Current I for each device is much larger than for the same devices connected in series (see the previous example). A circuit with parallel connections has a smaller total resistance than the resistors connected in series.

Strategy and Solution for (c)

The individual currents are easily calculated from Ohm's law, since each resistor gets the full voltage. Thus,

$$I_1 = \frac{V}{R_1} = \frac{12.0\text{ V}}{1.00\ \Omega} = 12.0\text{ A}. \tag{21.25}$$

Similarly,

$$I_2 = \frac{V}{R_2} = \frac{12.0\text{ V}}{6.00\,\Omega} = 2.00\text{ A} \tag{21.26}$$

and

$$I_3 = \frac{V}{R_3} = \frac{12.0\text{ V}}{13.0\,\Omega} = 0.92\text{ A.} \tag{21.27}$$

Discussion for (c)

The total current is the sum of the individual currents:

$$I_1 + I_2 + I_3 = 14.92\text{ A.} \tag{21.28}$$

This is consistent with conservation of charge.

Strategy and Solution for (d)

The power dissipated by each resistor can be found using any of the equations relating power to current, voltage, and resistance, since all three are known. Let us use $P = \frac{V^2}{R}$, since each resistor gets full voltage. Thus,

$$P_1 = \frac{V^2}{R_1} = \frac{(12.0\text{ V})^2}{1.00\,\Omega} = 144\text{ W.} \tag{21.29}$$

Similarly,

$$P_2 = \frac{V^2}{R_2} = \frac{(12.0\text{ V})^2}{6.00\,\Omega} = 24.0\text{ W} \tag{21.30}$$

and

$$P_3 = \frac{V^2}{R_3} = \frac{(12.0\text{ V})^2}{13.0\,\Omega} = 11.1\text{ W.} \tag{21.31}$$

Discussion for (d)

The power dissipated by each resistor is considerably higher in parallel than when connected in series to the same voltage source.

Strategy and Solution for (e)

The total power can also be calculated in several ways. Choosing $P = IV$, and entering the total current, yields

$$P = IV = (14.92\text{ A})(12.0\text{ V}) = 179\text{ W.} \tag{21.32}$$

Discussion for (e)

Total power dissipated by the resistors is also 179 W:

$$P_1 + P_2 + P_3 = 144\text{ W} + 24.0\text{ W} + 11.1\text{ W} = 179\text{ W.} \tag{21.33}$$

This is consistent with the law of conservation of energy.

Overall Discussion

Note that both the currents and powers in parallel connections are greater than for the same devices in series.

MAJOR FEATURES OF RESISTORS IN PARALLEL

1. Parallel resistance is found from $\frac{1}{R_\text{p}} = \frac{1}{R_1} + \frac{1}{R_2} + \frac{1}{R_3} + ...$, and it is smaller than any individual resistance in the combination.
2. Each resistor in parallel has the same full voltage of the source applied to it. (Power distribution systems

most often use parallel connections to supply the myriad devices served with the same voltage and to allow them to operate independently.)

3. Parallel resistors do not each get the total current; they divide it.

Combinations of Series and Parallel

More complex connections of resistors are sometimes just combinations of series and parallel. These are commonly encountered, especially when wire resistance is considered. In that case, wire resistance is in series with other resistances that are in parallel.

Combinations of series and parallel can be reduced to a single equivalent resistance using the technique illustrated in Figure 21.5. Various parts are identified as either series or parallel, reduced to their equivalents, and further reduced until a single resistance is left. The process is more time consuming than difficult.

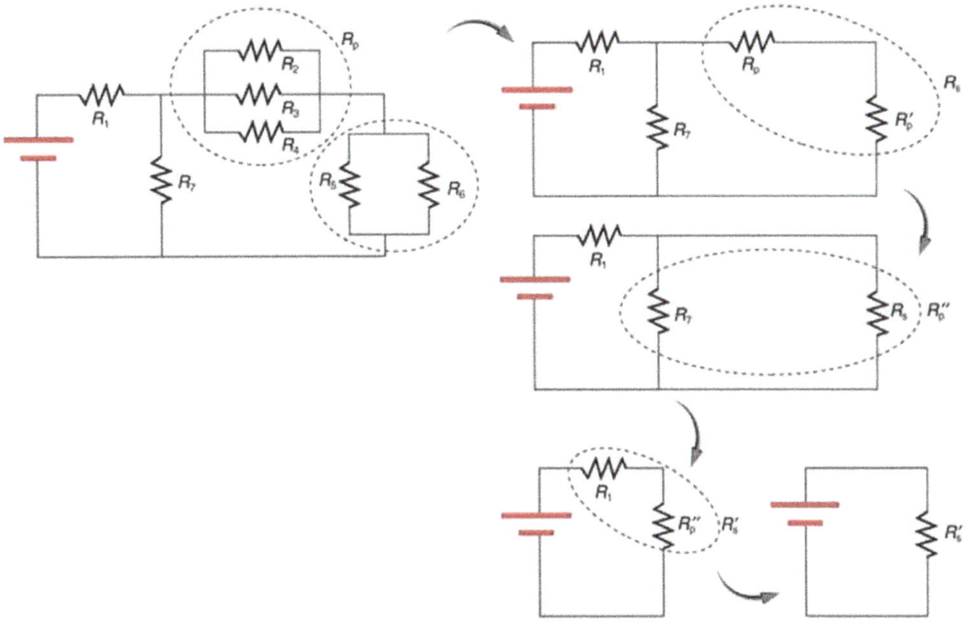

FIGURE 21.5 This combination of seven resistors has both series and parallel parts. Each is identified and reduced to an equivalent resistance, and these are further reduced until a single equivalent resistance is reached.

The simplest combination of series and parallel resistance, shown in Figure 21.6, is also the most instructive, since it is found in many applications. For example, R_1 could be the resistance of wires from a car battery to its electrical devices, which are in parallel. R_2 and R_3 could be the starter motor and a passenger compartment light. We have previously assumed that wire resistance is negligible, but, when it is not, it has important effects, as the next example indicates.

EXAMPLE 21.3

Calculating Resistance, IR Drop, Current, and Power Dissipation: Combining Series and Parallel Circuits

Figure 21.6 shows the resistors from the previous two examples wired in a different way—a combination of series and parallel. We can consider R_1 to be the resistance of wires leading to R_2 and R_3. (a) Find the total resistance. (b) What is the IR drop in R_1? (c) Find the current I_2 through R_2. (d) What power is dissipated by R_2?

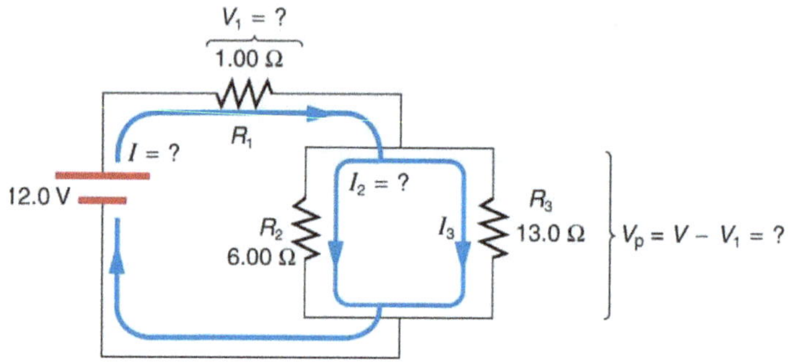

FIGURE 21.6 These three resistors are connected to a voltage source so that R_2 and R_3 are in parallel with one another and that combination is in series with R_1.

Strategy and Solution for (a)

To find the total resistance, we note that R_2 and R_3 are in parallel and their combination R_p is in series with R_1. Thus the total (equivalent) resistance of this combination is

$$R_{tot} = R_1 + R_p. \quad (21.34)$$

First, we find R_p using the equation for resistors in parallel and entering known values:

$$\frac{1}{R_p} = \frac{1}{R_2} + \frac{1}{R_3} = \frac{1}{6.00\ \Omega} + \frac{1}{13.0\ \Omega} = \frac{0.2436}{\Omega}. \quad (21.35)$$

Inverting gives

$$R_p = \frac{1}{0.2436}\Omega = 4.11\ \Omega. \quad (21.36)$$

So the total resistance is

$$R_{tot} = R_1 + R_p = 1.00\ \Omega + 4.11\ \Omega = 5.11\ \Omega. \quad (21.37)$$

Discussion for (a)

The total resistance of this combination is intermediate between the pure series and pure parallel values ($20.0\ \Omega$ and $0.804\ \Omega$, respectively) found for the same resistors in the two previous examples.

Strategy and Solution for (b)

To find the IR drop in R_1, we note that the full current I flows through R_1. Thus its IR drop is

$$V_1 = IR_1. \quad (21.38)$$

We must find I before we can calculate V_1. The total current I is found using Ohm's law for the circuit. That is,

$$I = \frac{V}{R_{tot}} = \frac{12.0\ \text{V}}{5.11\ \Omega} = 2.35\ \text{A}. \quad (21.39)$$

Entering this into the expression above, we get

$$V_1 = IR_1 = (2.35\ \text{A})(1.00\ \Omega) = 2.35\ \text{V}. \quad (21.40)$$

Discussion for (b)

The voltage applied to R_2 and R_3 is less than the total voltage by an amount V_1. When wire resistance is large, it can significantly affect the operation of the devices represented by R_2 and R_3.

Strategy and Solution for (c)

To find the current through R_2, we must first find the voltage applied to it. We call this voltage V_p, because it is applied to a parallel combination of resistors. The voltage applied to both R_2 and R_3 is reduced by the amount V_1, and so it is

$$V_p = V - V_1 = 12.0\text{ V} - 2.35\text{ V} = 9.65\text{ V}. \tag{21.41}$$

Now the current I_2 through resistance R_2 is found using Ohm's law:

$$I_2 = \frac{V_p}{R_2} = \frac{9.65\text{ V}}{6.00\ \Omega} = 1.61\text{ A}. \tag{21.42}$$

Discussion for (c)

The current is less than the 2.00 A that flowed through R_2 when it was connected in parallel to the battery in the previous parallel circuit example.

Strategy and Solution for (d)

The power dissipated by R_2 is given by

$$P_2 = (I_2)^2 R_2 = (1.61\text{ A})^2 (6.00\ \Omega) = 15.5\text{ W}. \tag{21.43}$$

Discussion for (d)

The power is less than the 24.0 W this resistor dissipated when connected in parallel to the 12.0-V source.

Practical Implications

One implication of this last example is that resistance in wires reduces the current and power delivered to a resistor. If wire resistance is relatively large, as in a worn (or a very long) extension cord, then this loss can be significant. If a large current is drawn, the IR drop in the wires can also be significant.

For example, when you are rummaging in the refrigerator and the motor comes on, the refrigerator light dims momentarily. Similarly, you can see the passenger compartment light dim when you start the engine of your car (although this may be due to resistance inside the battery itself).

What is happening in these high-current situations is illustrated in Figure 21.7. The device represented by R_3 has a very low resistance, and so when it is switched on, a large current flows. This increased current causes a larger IR drop in the wires represented by R_1, reducing the voltage across the light bulb (which is R_2), which then dims noticeably.

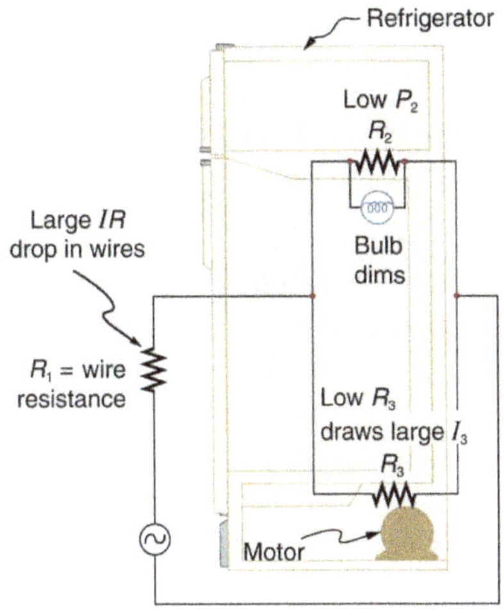

FIGURE 21.7 Why do lights dim when a large appliance is switched on? The answer is that the large current the appliance motor draws causes a significant IR drop in the wires and reduces the voltage across the light.

CHECK YOUR UNDERSTANDING

Can any arbitrary combination of resistors be broken down into series and parallel combinations? See if you can draw a circuit diagram of resistors that cannot be broken down into combinations of series and parallel.

Solution

No, there are many ways to connect resistors that are not combinations of series and parallel, including loops and junctions. In such cases Kirchhoff's rules, to be introduced in Kirchhoff's Rules, will allow you to analyze the circuit.

PROBLEM-SOLVING STRATEGIES FOR SERIES AND PARALLEL RESISTORS

1. Draw a clear circuit diagram, labeling all resistors and voltage sources. This step includes a list of the knowns for the problem, since they are labeled in your circuit diagram.
2. Identify exactly what needs to be determined in the problem (identify the unknowns). A written list is useful.
3. Determine whether resistors are in series, parallel, or a combination of both series and parallel. Examine the circuit diagram to make this assessment. Resistors are in series if the same current must pass sequentially through them.
4. Use the appropriate list of major features for series or parallel connections to solve for the unknowns. There is one list for series and another for parallel. If your problem has a combination of series and parallel, reduce it in steps by considering individual groups of series or parallel connections, as done in this module and the examples. Special note: When finding R_{p}, the reciprocal must be taken with care.
5. Check to see whether the answers are reasonable and consistent. Units and numerical results must be reasonable. Total series resistance should be greater, whereas total parallel resistance should be smaller, for example. Power should be greater for the same devices in parallel compared with series, and so on.

21.2 Electromotive Force: Terminal Voltage

LEARNING OBJECTIVES

By the end of this section, you will be able to:

- Compare and contrast the voltage and the electromagnetic force of an electric power source.
- Describe what happens to the terminal voltage, current, and power delivered to a load as internal resistance of the voltage source increases (due to aging of batteries, for example).
- Explain why it is beneficial to use more than one voltage source connected in parallel.

When you forget to turn off your car lights, they slowly dim as the battery runs down. Why don't they simply blink off when the battery's energy is gone? Their gradual dimming implies that battery output voltage decreases as the battery is depleted.

Furthermore, if you connect an excessive number of 12-V lights in parallel to a car battery, they will be dim even when the battery is fresh and even if the wires to the lights have very low resistance. This implies that the battery's output voltage is reduced by the overload.

The reason for the decrease in output voltage for depleted or overloaded batteries is that all voltage sources have two fundamental parts—a source of electrical energy and an **internal resistance**. Let us examine both.

Electromotive Force

You can think of many different types of voltage sources. Batteries themselves come in many varieties. There are many types of mechanical/electrical generators, driven by many different energy sources, ranging from nuclear to wind. Solar cells create voltages directly from light, while thermoelectric devices create voltage from temperature differences.

A few voltage sources are shown in Figure 21.8. All such devices create a **potential difference** and can supply current if connected to a resistance. On the small scale, the potential difference creates an electric field that exerts force on charges, causing current. We thus use the name **electromotive force**, abbreviated emf.

Emf is not a force at all; it is a special type of potential difference. To be precise, the electromotive force (emf) is the potential difference of a source when no current is flowing. Units of emf are volts.

FIGURE 21.8 A variety of voltage sources (clockwise from top left): the Brazos Wind Farm in Fluvanna, Texas (credit: Leaflet, Wikimedia Commons); the Krasnoyarsk Dam in Russia (credit: Alex Polezhaev); a solar farm (credit: U.S. Department of Energy); and a group of nickel metal hydride batteries (credit: Tiaa Monto). The voltage output of each depends on its construction and load, and equals emf only if there is no load.

Electromotive force is directly related to the source of potential difference, such as the particular combination of chemicals in a battery. However, emf differs from the voltage output of the device when current flows. The voltage across the terminals of a battery, for example, is less than the emf when the battery supplies current, and it declines further as the battery is depleted or loaded down. However, if the device's output voltage can be measured without drawing current, then output voltage will equal emf (even for a very depleted battery).

Internal Resistance

As noted before, a 12-V truck battery is physically larger, contains more charge and energy, and can deliver a larger current than a 12-V motorcycle battery. Both are lead-acid batteries with identical emf, but, because of its size, the truck battery has a smaller internal resistance r. Internal resistance is the inherent resistance to the flow of current within the source itself.

Figure 21.9 is a schematic representation of the two fundamental parts of any voltage source. The emf (represented by a script E in the figure) and internal resistance r are in series. The smaller the internal resistance for a given emf, the more current and the more power the source can supply.

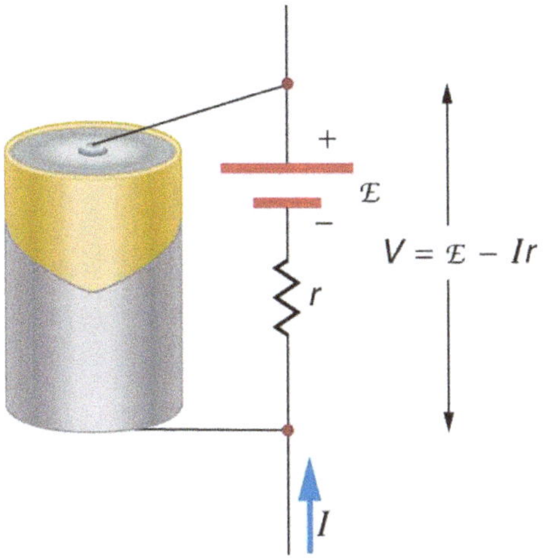

FIGURE 21.9 Any voltage source (in this case, a carbon-zinc dry cell) has an emf related to its source of potential difference, and an internal resistance r related to its construction. (Note that the script E stands for emf.). Also shown are the output terminals across which the terminal voltage V is measured. Since $V = \text{emf} - Ir$, terminal voltage equals emf only if there is no current flowing.

The internal resistance r can behave in complex ways. As noted, r increases as a battery is depleted. But internal resistance may also depend on the magnitude and direction of the current through a voltage source, its temperature, and even its history. The internal resistance of rechargeable nickel-cadmium cells, for example, depends on how many times and how deeply they have been depleted.

THINGS GREAT AND SMALL: THE SUBMICROSCOPIC ORIGIN OF BATTERY POTENTIAL

Various types of batteries are available, with emfs determined by the combination of chemicals involved. We can view this as a molecular reaction (what much of chemistry is about) that separates charge.

The lead-acid battery used in cars and other vehicles is one of the most common types. A single cell (one of six) of this battery is seen in Figure 21.10. The cathode (positive) terminal of the cell is connected to a lead oxide plate, while the anode (negative) terminal is connected to a lead plate. Both plates are immersed in sulfuric acid, the electrolyte for the system.

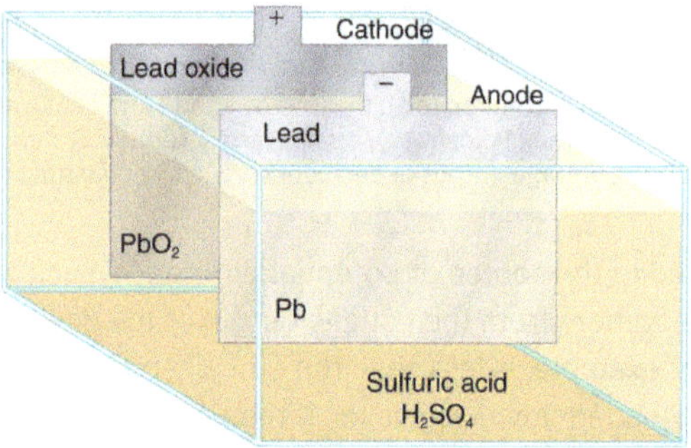

FIGURE 21.10 Artist's conception of a lead-acid cell. Chemical reactions in a lead-acid cell separate charge, sending negative charge to the anode, which is connected to the lead plates. The lead oxide plates are connected to the positive or cathode terminal of the cell. Sulfuric acid conducts the charge as well as participating in the chemical reaction.

The details of the chemical reaction are left to the reader to pursue in a chemistry text, but their results at the molecular level help explain the potential created by the battery. Figure 21.11 shows the result of a single chemical reaction. Two electrons are placed on the anode, making it negative, provided that the cathode supplied two electrons. This leaves the cathode positively charged, because it has lost two electrons. In short, a separation of charge has been driven by a chemical reaction.

Note that the reaction will not take place unless there is a complete circuit to allow two electrons to be supplied to the cathode. Under many circumstances, these electrons come from the anode, flow through a resistance, and return to the cathode. Note also that since the chemical reactions involve substances with resistance, it is not possible to create the emf without an internal resistance.

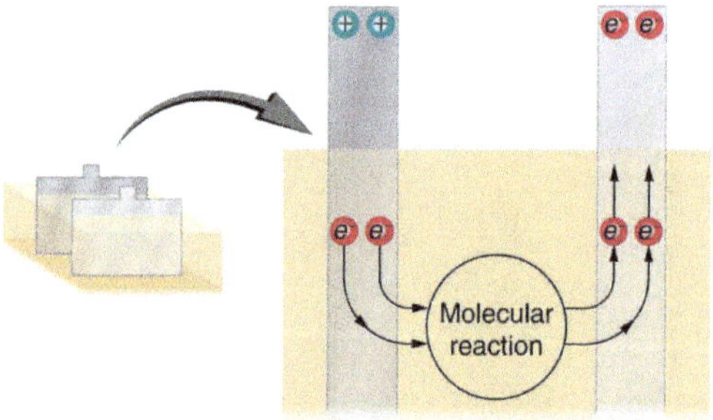

FIGURE 21.11 Artist's conception of two electrons being forced onto the anode of a cell and two electrons being removed from the cathode of the cell. The chemical reaction in a lead-acid battery places two electrons on the anode and removes two from the cathode. It requires a closed circuit to proceed, since the two electrons must be supplied to the cathode.

Why are the chemicals able to produce a unique potential difference? Quantum mechanical descriptions of molecules, which take into account the types of atoms and numbers of electrons in them, are able to predict the energy states they can have and the energies of reactions between them.

In the case of a lead-acid battery, an energy of 2 eV is given to each electron sent to the anode. Voltage is defined as the electrical potential energy divided by charge: $V = \frac{P_{\text{E}}}{q}$. An electron volt is the energy given to a single electron by a voltage of 1 V. So the voltage here is 2 V, since 2 eV is given to each electron. It is the energy produced in each molecular reaction that produces the voltage. A different reaction produces a different energy and, hence, a different voltage.

Terminal Voltage

The voltage output of a device is measured across its terminals and, thus, is called its **terminal voltage** V. Terminal voltage is given by

$$V = \text{emf} - Ir, \tag{21.44}$$

where r is the internal resistance and I is the current flowing at the time of the measurement.

I is positive if current flows away from the positive terminal, as shown in Figure 21.9. You can see that the larger the current, the smaller the terminal voltage. And it is likewise true that the larger the internal resistance, the smaller the terminal voltage.

Suppose a load resistance R_{load} is connected to a voltage source, as in Figure 21.12. Since the resistances are in series, the total resistance in the circuit is $R_{\text{load}} + r$. Thus the current is given by Ohm's law to be

$$I = \frac{\text{emf}}{R_{\text{load}} + r}. \tag{21.45}$$

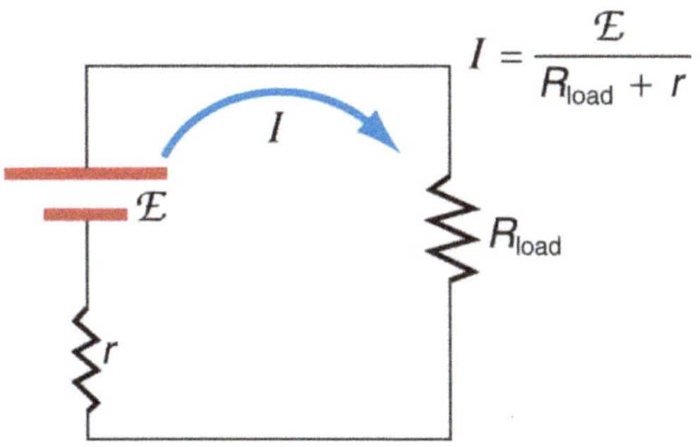

FIGURE 21.12 Schematic of a voltage source and its load R_{load}. Since the internal resistance r is in series with the load, it can significantly affect the terminal voltage and current delivered to the load. (Note that the script E stands for emf.)

We see from this expression that the smaller the internal resistance r, the greater the current the voltage source supplies to its load R_{load}. As batteries are depleted, r increases. If r becomes a significant fraction of the load resistance, then the current is significantly reduced, as the following example illustrates.

EXAMPLE 21.4

Calculating Terminal Voltage, Power Dissipation, Current, and Resistance: Terminal Voltage and Load

A certain battery has a 12.0-V emf and an internal resistance of $0.100\ \Omega$. (a) Calculate its terminal voltage when connected to a $10.0\text{-}\Omega$ load. (b) What is the terminal voltage when connected to a $0.500\text{-}\Omega$ load? (c) What power does the $0.500\text{-}\Omega$ load dissipate? (d) If the internal resistance grows to $0.500\ \Omega$, find the current, terminal voltage, and power dissipated by a $0.500\text{-}\Omega$ load.

Strategy

The analysis above gave an expression for current when internal resistance is taken into account. Once the current is found, the terminal voltage can be calculated using the equation $V = \text{emf} - Ir$. Once current is found, the power dissipated by a resistor can also be found.

Solution for (a)

Entering the given values for the emf, load resistance, and internal resistance into the expression above yields

$$I = \frac{\text{emf}}{R_{\text{load}} + r} = \frac{12.0\ \text{V}}{10.1\ \Omega} = 1.188\ \text{A}. \tag{21.46}$$

Enter the known values into the equation $V = \text{emf} - Ir$ to get the terminal voltage:

$$\begin{aligned} V &= \text{emf} - Ir = 12.0\text{ V} - (1.188\text{ A})(0.100\ \Omega) \\ &= 11.9\text{ V}. \end{aligned} \quad 21.47$$

Discussion for (a)

The terminal voltage here is only slightly lower than the emf, implying that $10.0\ \Omega$ is a light load for this particular battery.

Solution for (b)

Similarly, with $R_{\text{load}} = 0.500\,\Omega$, the current is

$$I = \frac{\text{emf}}{R_{\text{load}} + r} = \frac{12.0\text{ V}}{0.600\,\Omega} = 20.0\text{ A}. \quad 21.48$$

The terminal voltage is now

$$\begin{aligned} V &= \text{emf} - Ir = 12.0\text{ V} - (20.0\text{ A})(0.100\ \Omega) \\ &= 10.0\text{ V}. \end{aligned} \quad 21.49$$

Discussion for (b)

This terminal voltage exhibits a more significant reduction compared with emf, implying $0.500\,\Omega$ is a heavy load for this battery.

Solution for (c)

The power dissipated by the 0.500 - Ω load can be found using the formula $P = I^2 R$. Entering the known values gives

$$P_{\text{load}} = I^2 R_{\text{load}} = (20.0\text{ A})^2 (0.500\ \Omega) = 2.00 \times 10^2\text{ W}. \quad 21.50$$

Discussion for (c)

Note that this power can also be obtained using the expressions $\frac{V^2}{R}$ or IV, where V is the terminal voltage (10.0 V in this case).

Solution for (d)

Here the internal resistance has increased, perhaps due to the depletion of the battery, to the point where it is as great as the load resistance. As before, we first find the current by entering the known values into the expression, yielding

$$I = \frac{\text{emf}}{R_{\text{load}} + r} = \frac{12.0\text{ V}}{1.00\ \Omega} = 12.0\text{ A}. \quad 21.51$$

Now the terminal voltage is

$$\begin{aligned} V &= \text{emf} - Ir = 12.0\text{ V}-(12.0\text{ A})(0.500\ \Omega) \\ &= 6.00\text{ V}, \end{aligned} \quad 21.52$$

and the power dissipated by the load is

$$P_{\text{load}} = I^2 R_{\text{load}} = (12.0\text{ A})^2 (0.500\ \Omega)= 72.0\text{ W}. \quad 21.53$$

Discussion for (d)

We see that the increased internal resistance has significantly decreased terminal voltage, current, and power delivered to a load.

Battery testers, such as those in Figure 21.13, use small load resistors to intentionally draw current to determine whether the terminal voltage drops below an acceptable level. They really test the internal resistance of the battery. If internal resistance is high, the battery is weak, as evidenced by its low terminal voltage.

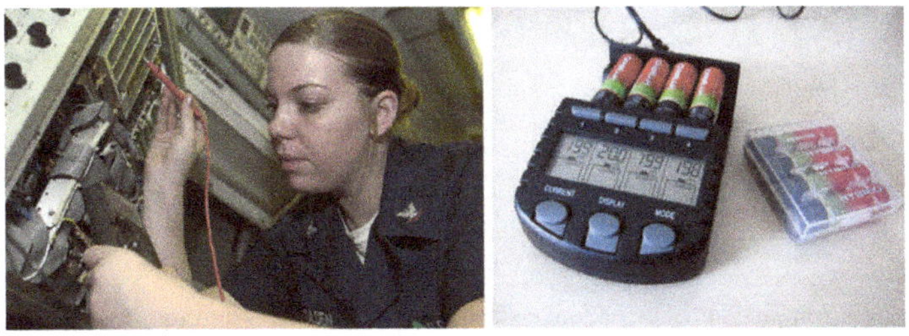

FIGURE 21.13 These two battery testers measure terminal voltage under a load to determine the condition of a battery. The large device is being used by a U.S. Navy electronics technician to test large batteries aboard the aircraft carrier USS *Nimitz* and has a small resistance that can dissipate large amounts of power. (credit: U.S. Navy photo by Photographer's Mate Airman Jason A. Johnston) The small device is used on small batteries and has a digital display to indicate the acceptability of their terminal voltage. (credit: Keith Williamson)

Some batteries can be recharged by passing a current through them in the direction opposite to the current they supply to a resistance. This is done routinely in cars and batteries for small electrical appliances and electronic devices, and is represented pictorially in Figure 21.14. The voltage output of the battery charger must be greater than the emf of the battery to reverse current through it. This will cause the terminal voltage of the battery to be greater than the emf, since $V = \text{emf} - Ir$, and I is now negative.

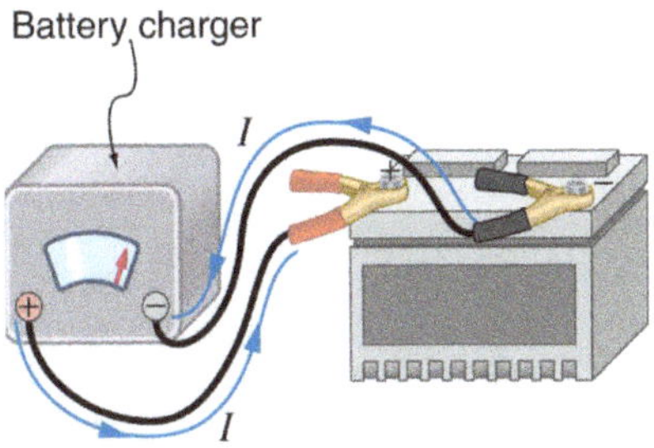

FIGURE 21.14 A car battery charger reverses the normal direction of current through a battery, reversing its chemical reaction and replenishing its chemical potential.

Multiple Voltage Sources

There are two voltage sources when a battery charger is used. Voltage sources connected in series are relatively simple. When voltage sources are in series, their internal resistances add and their emfs add algebraically. (See Figure 21.15.) Series connections of voltage sources are common—for example, in flashlights, toys, and other appliances. Usually, the cells are in series in order to produce a larger total emf.

But if the cells oppose one another, such as when one is put into an appliance backward, the total emf is less, since it is the algebraic sum of the individual emfs.

A battery is a multiple connection of voltaic cells, as shown in Figure 21.16. The disadvantage of series connections of cells is that their internal resistances add. One of the authors once owned a 1957 MGA that had two 6-V batteries in series, rather than a single 12-V battery. This arrangement produced a large internal resistance that caused him many problems in starting the engine.

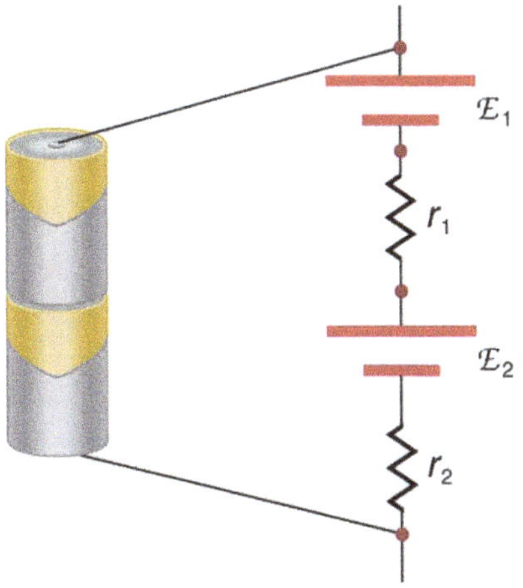

FIGURE 21.15 A series connection of two voltage sources. The emfs (each labeled with a script E) and internal resistances add, giving a

total emf of $\text{emf}_1 + \text{emf}_2$ and a total internal resistance of $r_1 + r_2$.

FIGURE 21.16 Batteries are multiple connections of individual cells, as shown in this modern rendition of an old print. Single cells, such as AA or C cells, are commonly called batteries, although this is technically incorrect.

If the *series* connection of two voltage sources is made into a complete circuit with the emfs in opposition, then a current of magnitude $I = \frac{(\text{emf}_1 - \text{emf}_2)}{r_1 + r_2}$ flows. See Figure 21.17, for example, which shows a circuit exactly analogous to the battery charger discussed above. If two voltage sources in series with emfs in the same sense are connected to a load R_{load}, as in Figure 21.18, then $I = \frac{(\text{emf}_1 + \text{emf}_2)}{r_1 + r_2 + R_{\text{load}}}$ flows.

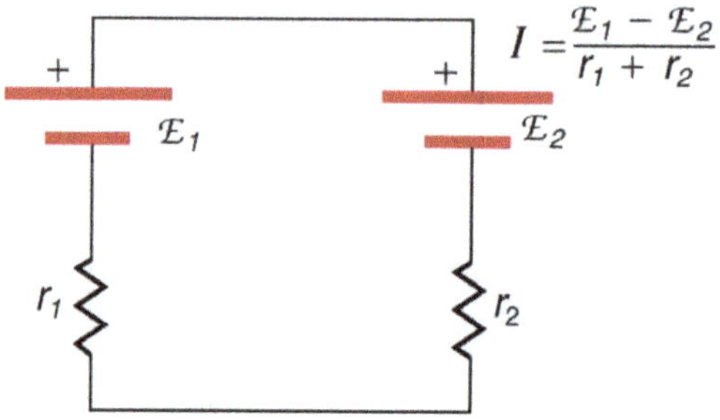

FIGURE 21.17 These two voltage sources are connected in series with their emfs in opposition. Current flows in the direction of the greater emf and is limited to $I = \frac{(\text{emf}_1 - \text{emf}_2)}{r_1 + r_2}$ by the sum of the internal resistances. (Note that each emf is represented by script E in the figure.) A battery charger connected to a battery is an example of such a connection. The charger must have a larger emf than the battery to reverse current through it.

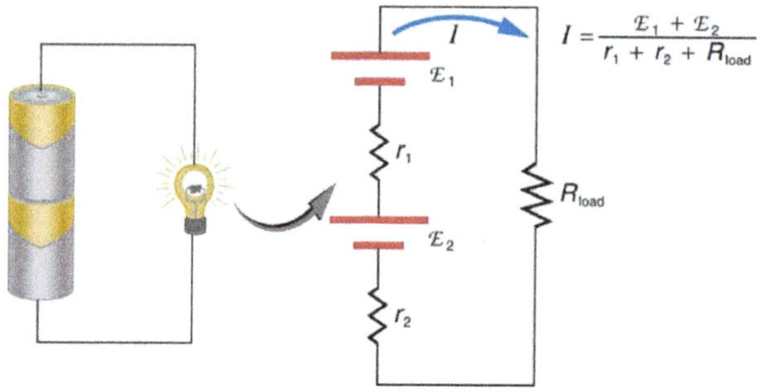

FIGURE 21.18 This schematic represents a flashlight with two cells (voltage sources) and a single bulb (load resistance) in series. The current that flows is $I = \frac{(\text{emf}_1 + \text{emf}_2)}{r_1 + r_2 + R_{\text{load}}}$. (Note that each emf is represented by script E in the figure.)

TAKE-HOME EXPERIMENT: FLASHLIGHT BATTERIES

Find a flashlight that uses several batteries and find new and old batteries. Based on the discussions in this module, predict the brightness of the flashlight when different combinations of batteries are used. Do your predictions match what you observe? Now place new batteries in the flashlight and leave the flashlight switched on for several hours. Is the flashlight still quite bright? Do the same with the old batteries. Is the flashlight as bright when left on for the same length of time with old and new batteries? What does this say for the case when you are limited in the number of available new batteries?

Figure 21.19 shows two voltage sources with identical emfs in parallel and connected to a load resistance. In this simple case, the total emf is the same as the individual emfs. But the total internal resistance is reduced, since the internal resistances are in parallel. The parallel connection thus can produce a larger current.

Here, $I = \frac{\text{emf}}{(r_{\text{tot}} + R_{\text{load}})}$ flows through the load, and r_{tot} is less than those of the individual batteries. For example, some diesel-powered cars use two 12-V batteries in parallel; they produce a total emf of 12 V but can deliver the larger current needed to start a diesel engine.

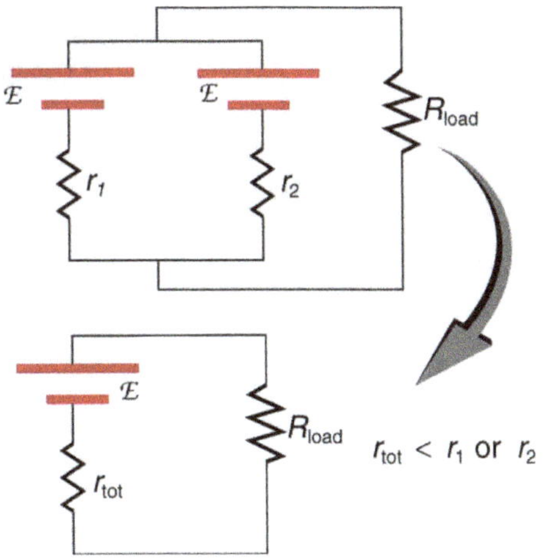

FIGURE 21.19 Two voltage sources with identical emfs (each labeled by script E) connected in parallel produce the same emf but have a smaller total internal resistance than the individual sources. Parallel combinations are often used to deliver more current. Here $I = \frac{\text{emf}}{(r_{\text{tot}} + R_{\text{load}})}$ flows through the load.

Animals as Electrical Detectors

A number of animals both produce and detect electrical signals. Fish, sharks, platypuses, and echidnas (spiny anteaters) all detect electric fields generated by nerve activity in prey. Electric eels produce their own emf through biological cells (electric organs) called electroplaques, which are arranged in both series and parallel as a set of batteries.

Electroplaques are flat, disk-like cells; those of the electric eel have a voltage of 0.15 V across each one. These cells are usually located toward the head or tail of the animal, although in the case of the electric eel, they are found along the entire body. The electroplaques in the South American eel are arranged in 140 rows, with each row stretching horizontally along the body and containing 5,000 electroplaques. This can yield an emf of approximately 600 V, and a current of 1 A—deadly.

The mechanism for detection of external electric fields is similar to that for producing nerve signals in the cell through depolarization and repolarization—the movement of ions across the cell membrane. Within the fish, weak electric fields in the water produce a current in a gel-filled canal that runs from the skin to sensing cells, producing a nerve signal. The Australian platypus, one of the very few mammals that lay eggs, can detect fields of 30 $\frac{\text{mV}}{\text{m}}$, while sharks have been found to be able to sense a field in their snouts as small as 100 $\frac{\text{mV}}{\text{m}}$ (Figure 21.20). Electric eels use their own electric fields produced by the electroplaques to stun their prey or enemies.

FIGURE 21.20 Sand tiger sharks (*Carcharias taurus*), like this one at the Minnesota Zoo, use electroreceptors in their snouts to locate prey. (credit: Jim Winstead, Flickr)

Solar Cell Arrays

Another example dealing with multiple voltage sources is that of combinations of solar cells—wired in both series and parallel combinations to yield a desired voltage and current. Photovoltaic generation (PV), the conversion of sunlight directly into electricity, is based upon the photoelectric effect, in which photons hitting the surface of a solar cell create an electric current in the cell.

Most solar cells are made from pure silicon—either as single-crystal silicon, or as a thin film of silicon deposited upon a glass or metal backing. Most single cells have a voltage output of about 0.5 V, while the current output is a function of the amount of sunlight upon the cell (the incident solar radiation—the insolation). Under bright noon sunlight, a current of about $100\ \text{mA/cm}^2$ of cell surface area is produced by typical single-crystal cells.

Individual solar cells are connected electrically in modules to meet electrical-energy needs. They can be wired together in series or in parallel—connected like the batteries discussed earlier. A solar-cell array or module usually consists of between 36 and 72 cells, with a power output of 50 W to 140 W.

The output of the solar cells is direct current. For most uses in a home, AC is required, so a device called an inverter must be used to convert the DC to AC. Any extra output can then be passed on to the outside electrical grid for sale to the utility.

TAKE-HOME EXPERIMENT: VIRTUAL SOLAR CELLS

One can assemble a “virtual” solar cell array by using playing cards, or business or index cards, to represent a solar cell. Combinations of these cards in series and/or parallel can model the required array output. Assume each card has an output of 0.5 V and a current (under bright light) of 2 A. Using your cards, how would you arrange them to produce an output of 6 A at 3 V (18 W)?

Suppose you were told that you needed only 18 W (but no required voltage). Would you need more cards to make this arrangement?

21.3 Kirchhoff’s Rules

LEARNING OBJECTIVES

By the end of this section, you will be able to:

- Analyze a complex circuit using Kirchhoff’s rules, using the conventions for determining the correct signs of various terms.

Many complex circuits, such as the one in Figure 21.21, cannot be analyzed with the series-parallel techniques developed in Resistors in Series and Parallel and Electromotive Force: Terminal Voltage. There are, however, two circuit analysis rules that can be used to analyze any circuit, simple or complex. These rules are special cases of the laws of conservation of charge and conservation of energy. The rules are known as **Kirchhoff's rules**, after their inventor Gustav Kirchhoff (1824–1887).

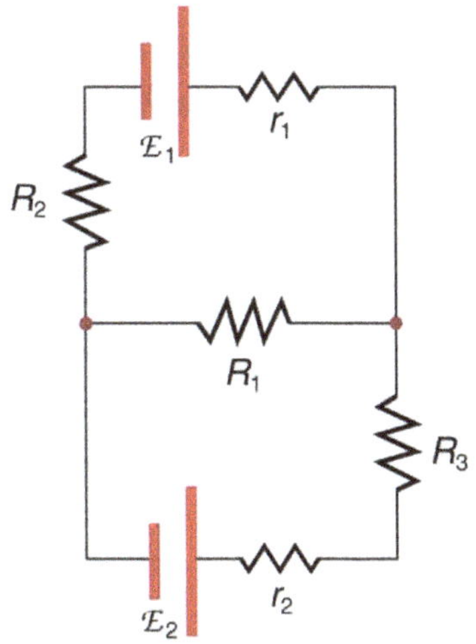

FIGURE 21.21 This circuit cannot be reduced to a combination of series and parallel connections. Kirchhoff's rules, special applications of the laws of conservation of charge and energy, can be used to analyze it. (Note: The script E in the figure represents electromotive force, emf.)

KIRCHHOFF'S RULES

- Kirchhoff's first rule—the junction rule. The sum of all currents entering a junction must equal the sum of all currents leaving the junction.
- Kirchhoff's second rule—the loop rule. The algebraic sum of changes in potential around any closed circuit path (loop) must be zero.

Explanations of the two rules will now be given, followed by problem-solving hints for applying Kirchhoff's rules, and a worked example that uses them.

Kirchhoff's First Rule

Kirchhoff's first rule (the **junction rule**) is an application of the conservation of charge to a junction; it is illustrated in Figure 21.22. Current is the flow of charge, and charge is conserved; thus, whatever charge flows into the junction must flow out. Kirchhoff's first rule requires that $I_1 = I_2 + I_3$ (see figure). Equations like this can and will be used to analyze circuits and to solve circuit problems.

MAKING CONNECTIONS: CONSERVATION LAWS

Kirchhoff's rules for circuit analysis are applications of **conservation laws** to circuits. The first rule is the application of conservation of charge, while the second rule is the application of conservation of energy. Conservation laws, even used in a specific application, such as circuit analysis, are so basic as to form the foundation of that application.

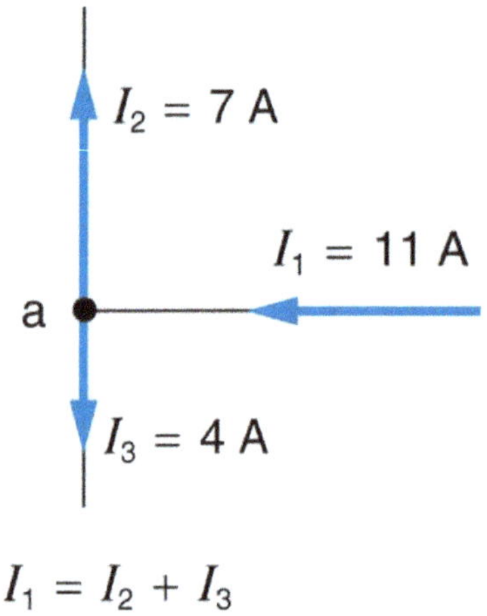

FIGURE 21.22 The junction rule. The diagram shows an example of Kirchhoff's first rule where the sum of the currents into a junction equals the sum of the currents out of a junction. In this case, the current going into the junction splits and comes out as two currents, so that $I_1 = I_2 + I_3$. Here I_1 must be 11 A, since I_2 is 7 A and I_3 is 4 A.

Kirchhoff's Second Rule

Kirchhoff's second rule (the **loop rule**) is an application of conservation of energy. The loop rule is stated in terms of potential, V, rather than potential energy, but the two are related since $\text{PE}_{\text{elec}} = qV$. Recall that **emf** is the potential difference of a source when no current is flowing. In a closed loop, whatever energy is supplied by emf must be transferred into other forms by devices in the loop, since there are no other ways in which energy can be transferred into or out of the circuit. Figure 21.23 illustrates the changes in potential in a simple series circuit loop.

Kirchhoff's second rule requires $\text{emf} - Ir - IR_1 - IR_2 = 0$. Rearranged, this is $\text{emf} = Ir + IR_1 + IR_2$, which means the emf equals the sum of the IR (voltage) drops in the loop.

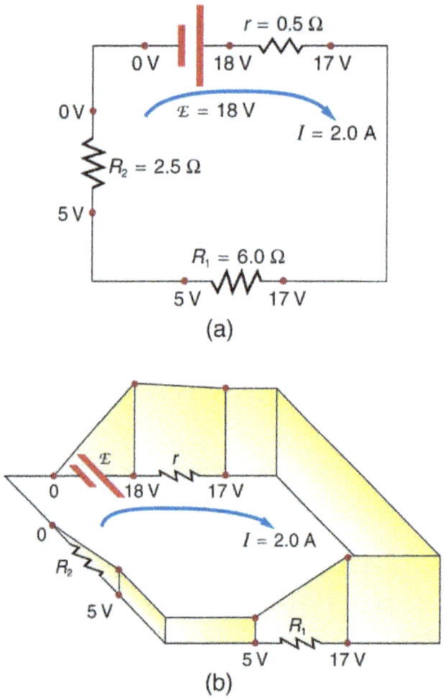

FIGURE 21.23 The loop rule. An example of Kirchhoff's second rule where the sum of the changes in potential around a closed loop must be zero. (a) In this standard schematic of a simple series circuit, the emf supplies 18 V, which is reduced to zero by the resistances, with 1 V across the internal resistance, and 12 V and 5 V across the two load resistances, for a total of 18 V. (b) This perspective view represents the potential as something like a roller coaster, where charge is raised in potential by the emf and lowered by the resistances. (Note that the script E stands for emf.)

Applying Kirchhoff's Rules

By applying Kirchhoff's rules, we generate equations that allow us to find the unknowns in circuits. The unknowns may be currents, emfs, or resistances. Each time a rule is applied, an equation is produced. If there are as many independent equations as unknowns, then the problem can be solved. There are two decisions you must make when applying Kirchhoff's rules. These decisions determine the signs of various quantities in the equations you obtain from applying the rules.

1. When applying Kirchhoff's first rule, the junction rule, you must label the current in each branch and decide in what direction it is going. For example, in Figure 21.21, Figure 21.22, and Figure 21.23, currents are labeled I_1, I_2, I_3, and I, and arrows indicate their directions. There is no risk here, for if you choose the wrong direction, the current will be of the correct magnitude but negative.
2. When applying Kirchhoff's second rule, the loop rule, you must identify a closed loop and decide in which direction to go around it, clockwise or counterclockwise. For example, in Figure 21.23 the loop was traversed in the same direction as the current (clockwise). Again, there is no risk; going around the circuit in the opposite direction reverses the sign of every term in the equation, which is like multiplying both sides of the equation by -1.

Figure 21.24 and the following points will help you get the plus or minus signs right when applying the loop rule. Note that the resistors and emfs are traversed by going from a to b. In many circuits, it will be necessary to construct more than one loop. In traversing each loop, one needs to be consistent for the sign of the change in potential. (See Example 21.5.)

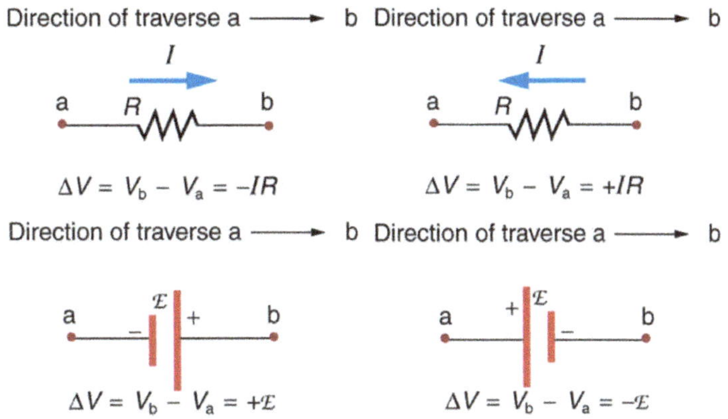

FIGURE 21.24 Each of these resistors and voltage sources is traversed from a to b. The potential changes are shown beneath each element and are explained in the text. (Note that the script E stands for emf.)

- When a resistor is traversed in the same direction as the current, the change in potential is $-IR$. (See Figure 21.24.)
- When a resistor is traversed in the direction opposite to the current, the change in potential is $+IR$. (See Figure 21.24.)
- When an emf is traversed from – to + (the same direction it moves positive charge), the change in potential is +emf. (See Figure 21.24.)
- When an emf is traversed from + to – (opposite to the direction it moves positive charge), the change in potential is –emf. (See Figure 21.24.)

EXAMPLE 21.5

Calculating Current: Using Kirchhoff's Rules

Find the currents flowing in the circuit in Figure 21.25.

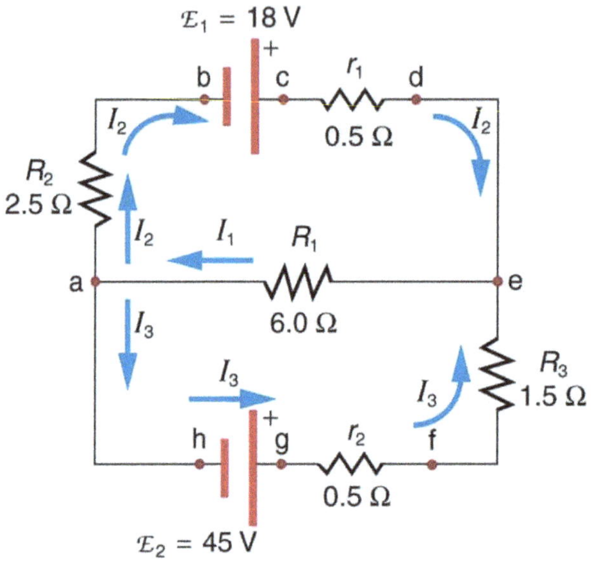

FIGURE 21.25 This circuit is similar to that in Figure 21.21, but the resistances and emfs are specified. (Each emf is denoted by script E.) The currents in each branch are labeled and assumed to move in the directions shown. This example uses Kirchhoff's rules to find the currents.

Strategy

This circuit is sufficiently complex that the currents cannot be found using Ohm's law and the series-parallel techniques—it is necessary to use Kirchhoff's rules. Currents have been labeled I_1, I_2, and I_3 in the figure and assumptions have been made about their directions. Locations on the diagram have been labeled with letters a through h. In the solution we will apply the junction and loop rules, seeking three independent equations to allow us to solve for the three unknown currents.

Solution

We begin by applying Kirchhoff's first or junction rule at point a. This gives

$$I_1 = I_2 + I_3, \tag{21.54}$$

since I_1 flows into the junction, while I_2 and I_3 flow out. Applying the junction rule at e produces exactly the same equation, so that no new information is obtained. This is a single equation with three unknowns—three independent equations are needed, and so the loop rule must be applied.

Now we consider the loop abcdea. Going from a to b, we traverse R_2 in the same (assumed) direction of the current I_2, and so the change in potential is $-I_2R_2$. Then going from b to c, we go from – to +, so that the change in potential is $+\text{emf}_1$. Traversing the internal resistance r_1 from c to d gives $-I_2r_1$. Completing the loop by going from d to a again traverses a resistor in the same direction as its current, giving a change in potential of $-I_1R_1$.

The loop rule states that the changes in potential sum to zero. Thus,

$$-I_2R_2 + \text{emf}_1 - I_2r_1 - I_1R_1 = -I_2(R_2 + r_1) + \text{emf}_1 - I_1R_1 = 0. \tag{21.55}$$

Substituting values from the circuit diagram for the resistances and emf, and canceling the ampere unit gives

$$-3I_2 + 18 - 6I_1 = 0. \tag{21.56}$$

Now applying the loop rule to aefgha (we could have chosen abcdefgha as well) similarly gives

$$+I_1R_1 + I_3R_3 + I_3r_2 - \text{emf}_2 = +I_1R_1 + I_3(R_3 + r_2) - \text{emf}_2 = 0. \tag{21.57}$$

Note that the signs are reversed compared with the other loop, because elements are traversed in the opposite direction. With values entered, this becomes

$$+6I_1 + 2I_3 - 45 = 0. \tag{21.58}$$

These three equations are sufficient to solve for the three unknown currents. First, solve the second equation for I_2:

$$I_2 = 6 - 2I_1. \tag{21.59}$$

Now solve the third equation for I_3:

$$I_3 = 22.5 - 3I_1. \tag{21.60}$$

Substituting these two new equations into the first one allows us to find a value for I_1:

$$I_1 = I_2 + I_3 = (6 - 2I_1) + (22.5 - 3I_1) = 28.5 - 5I_1. \tag{21.61}$$

Combining terms gives

$$6I_1 = 28.5, \text{ and} \tag{21.62}$$

$$I_1 = 4.75 \text{ A}. \tag{21.63}$$

Substituting this value for I_1 back into the fourth equation gives

$$I_2 = 6 - 2I_1 = 6 - 9.50 \tag{21.64}$$

$$I_2 = -3.50 \text{ A}. \tag{21.65}$$

The minus sign means I_2 flows in the direction opposite to that assumed in Figure 21.25.

Finally, substituting the value for I_1 into the fifth equation gives

$$I_3 = 22.5 - 3I_1 = 22.5 - 14.25 \tag{21.66}$$

$$I_3 = 8.25 \text{ A}. \tag{21.67}$$

Discussion

Just as a check, we note that indeed $I_1 = I_2 + I_3$. The results could also have been checked by entering all of the values into the equation for the abcdefgha loop.

PROBLEM-SOLVING STRATEGIES FOR KIRCHHOFF'S RULES

1. Make certain there is a clear circuit diagram on which you can label all known and unknown resistances, emfs, and currents. If a current is unknown, you must assign it a direction. This is necessary for determining the signs of potential changes. If you assign the direction incorrectly, the current will be found to have a negative value—no harm done.
2. Apply the junction rule to any junction in the circuit. Each time the junction rule is applied, you should get an equation with a current that does not appear in a previous application—if not, then the equation is redundant.
3. Apply the loop rule to as many loops as needed to solve for the unknowns in the problem. (There must be as many independent equations as unknowns.) To apply the loop rule, you must choose a direction to go around the loop. Then carefully and consistently determine the signs of the potential changes for each element using the four bulleted points discussed above in conjunction with Figure 21.24.
4. Solve the simultaneous equations for the unknowns. This may involve many algebraic steps, requiring careful checking and rechecking.
5. Check to see whether the answers are reasonable and consistent. The numbers should be of the correct order of magnitude, neither exceedingly large nor vanishingly small. The signs should be reasonable—for example, no resistance should be negative. Check to see that the values obtained satisfy the various equations obtained from applying the rules. The currents should satisfy the junction rule, for example.

The material in this section is correct in theory. We should be able to verify it by making measurements of current and voltage. In fact, some of the devices used to make such measurements are straightforward applications of the principles covered so far and are explored in the next modules. As we shall see, a very basic, even profound, fact results—making a measurement alters the quantity being measured.

CHECK YOUR UNDERSTANDING

Can Kirchhoff's rules be applied to simple series and parallel circuits or are they restricted for use in more complicated circuits that are not combinations of series and parallel?

Solution

Kirchhoff's rules can be applied to any circuit since they are applications to circuits of two conservation laws. Conservation laws are the most broadly applicable principles in physics. It is usually mathematically simpler to use the rules for series and parallel in simpler circuits so we emphasize Kirchhoff's rules for use in more complicated situations. But the rules for series and parallel can be derived from Kirchhoff's rules. Moreover, Kirchhoff's rules can be expanded to devices other than resistors and emfs, such as capacitors, and are one of the basic analysis devices in circuit analysis.

21.4 DC Voltmeters and Ammeters

LEARNING OBJECTIVES

By the end of this section, you will be able to:

- Explain why a voltmeter must be connected in parallel with the circuit.
- Draw a diagram showing an ammeter correctly connected in a circuit.
- Describe how a galvanometer can be used as either a voltmeter or an ammeter.
- Find the resistance that must be placed in series with a galvanometer to allow it to be used as a voltmeter with a given reading.
- Explain why measuring the voltage or current in a circuit can never be exact.

Voltmeters measure voltage, whereas **ammeters** measure current. Some of the meters in automobile dashboards, digital cameras, cell phones, and tuner-amplifiers are voltmeters or ammeters. (See Figure 21.26.) The internal construction of the simplest of these meters and how they are connected to the system they monitor give further insight into applications of series and parallel connections.

FIGURE 21.26 The fuel and temperature gauges (far right and far left, respectively) in this 1996 Volkswagen are voltmeters that register the voltage output of "sender" units, which are hopefully proportional to the amount of gasoline in the tank and the engine temperature. (credit: Christian Giersing)

Voltmeters are connected in parallel with whatever device's voltage is to be measured. A parallel connection is used because objects in parallel experience the same potential difference. (See Figure 21.27, where the voltmeter is represented by the symbol V.)

Ammeters are connected in series with whatever device's current is to be measured. A series connection is used because objects in series have the same current passing through them. (See Figure 21.28, where the ammeter is represented by the symbol A.)

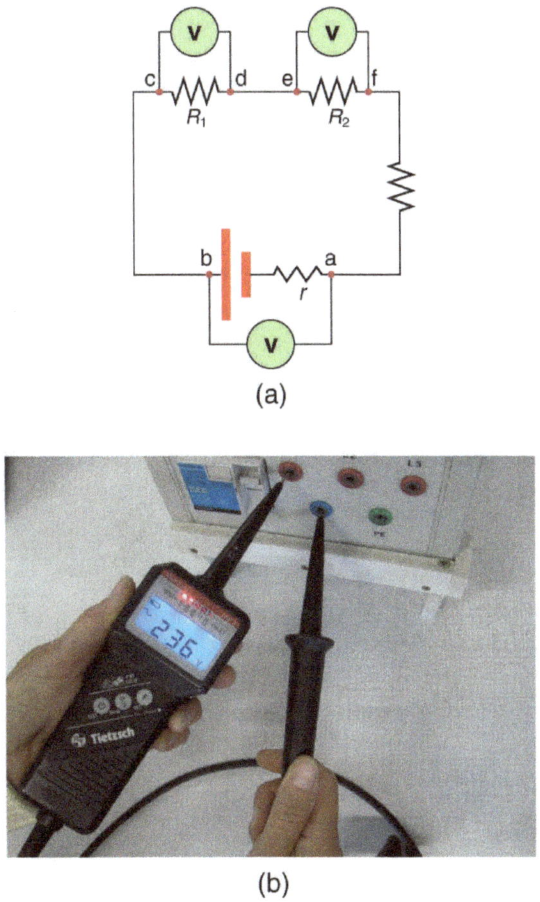

FIGURE 21.27 (a) To measure potential differences in this series circuit, the voltmeter (V) is placed in parallel with the voltage source or either of the resistors. Note that terminal voltage is measured between points a and b. It is not possible to connect the voltmeter directly across the emf without including its internal resistance, r. (b) A digital voltmeter in use. (credit: Messtechniker, Wikimedia Commons)

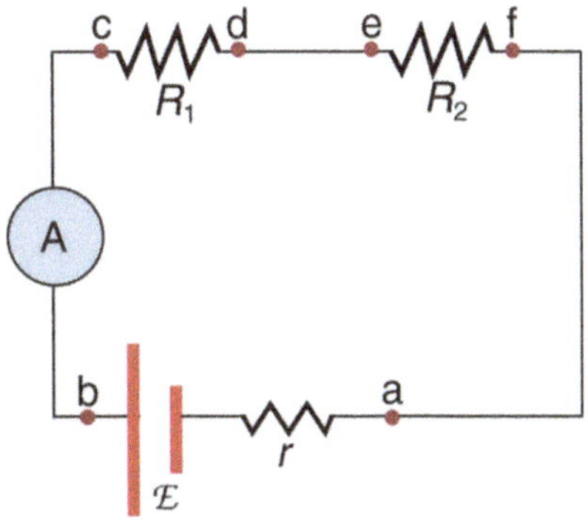

FIGURE 21.28 An ammeter (A) is placed in series to measure current. All of the current in this circuit flows through the meter. The ammeter would have the same reading if located between points d and e or between points f and a as it does in the position shown. (Note that the script capital E stands for emf, and r stands for the internal resistance of the source of potential difference.)

Analog Meters: Galvanometers

Analog meters have a needle that swivels to point at numbers on a scale, as opposed to **digital meters**, which have numerical readouts similar to a hand-held calculator. The heart of most analog meters is a device called a **galvanometer**, denoted by G. Current flow through a galvanometer, I_{G}, produces a proportional needle deflection. (This deflection is due to the force of a magnetic field upon a current-carrying wire.)

The two crucial characteristics of a given galvanometer are its resistance and current sensitivity. **Current sensitivity** is the current that gives a **full-scale deflection** of the galvanometer's needle, the maximum current that the instrument can measure. For example, a galvanometer with a current sensitivity of $50\ \mu\text{A}$ has a maximum deflection of its needle when $50\ \mu\text{A}$ flows through it, reads half-scale when $25\ \mu\text{A}$ flows through it, and so on.

If such a galvanometer has a $25\text{-}\Omega$ resistance, then a voltage of only $V = IR = (50\ \mu\text{A})(25\ \Omega) = 1.25\ \text{mV}$ produces a full-scale reading. By connecting resistors to this galvanometer in different ways, you can use it as either a voltmeter or ammeter that can measure a broad range of voltages or currents.

Galvanometer as Voltmeter

Figure 21.29 shows how a galvanometer can be used as a voltmeter by connecting it in series with a large resistance, R. The value of the resistance R is determined by the maximum voltage to be measured. Suppose you want 10 V to produce a full-scale deflection of a voltmeter containing a $25\text{-}\Omega$ galvanometer with a $50\text{-}\mu\text{A}$ sensitivity. Then 10 V applied to the meter must produce a current of $50\ \mu\text{A}$. The total resistance must be

$$R_{\text{tot}} = R + r = \frac{V}{I} = \frac{10\ \text{V}}{50\ \mu\text{A}} = 200\ \text{k}\Omega\text{, or} \quad (21.68)$$

$$R = R_{\text{tot}} - r = 200\ \text{k}\Omega - 25\ \Omega \approx 200\ \text{k}\Omega. \quad (21.69)$$

(R is so large that the galvanometer resistance, r, is nearly negligible.) Note that 5 V applied to this voltmeter produces a half-scale deflection by producing a $25\text{-}\mu\text{A}$ current through the meter, and so the voltmeter's reading is proportional to voltage as desired.

This voltmeter would not be useful for voltages less than about half a volt, because the meter deflection would be small and difficult to read accurately. For other voltage ranges, other resistances are placed in series with the galvanometer. Many meters have a choice of scales. That choice involves switching an appropriate resistance into series with the galvanometer.

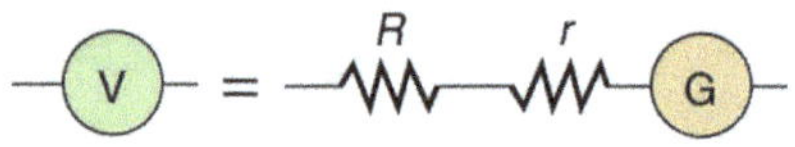

FIGURE 21.29 A large resistance R placed in series with a galvanometer G produces a voltmeter, the full-scale deflection of which depends on the choice of R. The larger the voltage to be measured, the larger R must be. (Note that r represents the internal resistance of the galvanometer.)

Galvanometer as Ammeter

The same galvanometer can also be made into an ammeter by placing it in parallel with a small resistance R, often called the **shunt resistance**, as shown in Figure 21.30. Since the shunt resistance is small, most of the current passes through it, allowing an ammeter to measure currents much greater than those producing a full-scale deflection of the galvanometer.

Suppose, for example, an ammeter is needed that gives a full-scale deflection for 1.0 A, and contains the same $25\text{-}\Omega$ galvanometer with its $50\text{-}\mu\text{A}$ sensitivity. Since R and r are in parallel, the voltage across them is the same.

These IR drops are $IR = I_{\text{G}}r$ so that $IR = \frac{I_{\text{G}}}{I} = \frac{R}{r}$. Solving for R, and noting that I_{G} is $50\ \mu\text{A}$ and I is 0.999950 A, we have

$$R = r\frac{I_{\text{G}}}{I} = (25\ \Omega)\frac{50\ \mu\text{A}}{0.999950\ \text{A}} = 1.25 \times 10^{-3}\ \Omega. \quad (21.70)$$

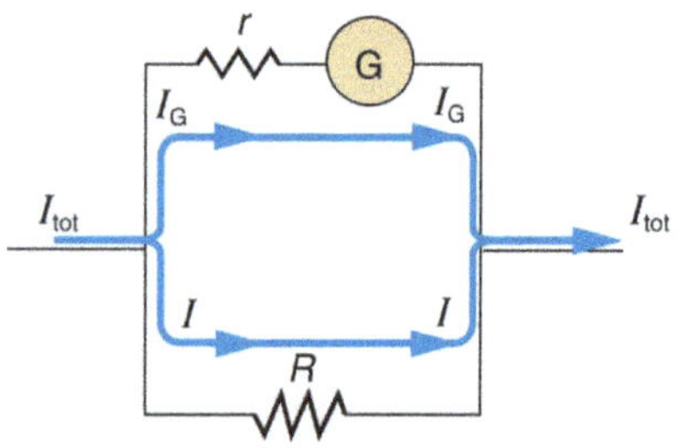

FIGURE 21.30 A small shunt resistance R placed in parallel with a galvanometer G produces an ammeter, the full-scale deflection of which depends on the choice of R. The larger the current to be measured, the smaller R must be. Most of the current (I) flowing through the meter is shunted through R to protect the galvanometer. (Note that r represents the internal resistance of the galvanometer.) Ammeters may also have multiple scales for greater flexibility in application. The various scales are achieved by switching various shunt resistances in parallel with the galvanometer—the greater the maximum current to be measured, the smaller the shunt resistance must be.

Taking Measurements Alters the Circuit

When you use a voltmeter or ammeter, you are connecting another resistor to an existing circuit and, thus, altering the circuit. Ideally, voltmeters and ammeters do not appreciably affect the circuit, but it is instructive to examine the circumstances under which they do or do not interfere.

First, consider the voltmeter, which is always placed in parallel with the device being measured. Very little current flows through the voltmeter if its resistance is a few orders of magnitude greater than the device, and so the circuit is not appreciably affected. (See Figure 21.31(a).) (A large resistance in parallel with a small one has a combined resistance essentially equal to the small one.) If, however, the voltmeter's resistance is comparable to that of the device being measured, then the two in parallel have a smaller resistance, appreciably affecting the circuit. (See Figure 21.31(b).) The voltage across the device is not the same as when the voltmeter is out of the circuit.

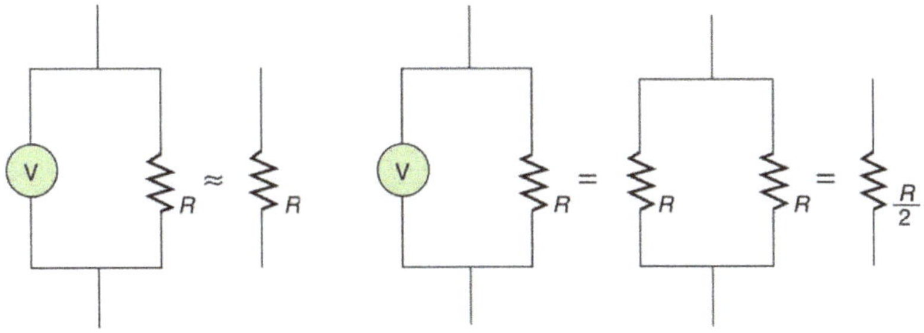

FIGURE 21.31 (a) A voltmeter having a resistance much larger than the device ($R_{\text{Voltmeter}} >> R$) with which it is in parallel produces a parallel resistance essentially the same as the device and does not appreciably affect the circuit being measured. (b) Here the voltmeter has the same resistance as the device ($R_{\text{Voltmeter}} \cong R$), so that the parallel resistance is half of what it is when the voltmeter is not connected. This is an example of a significant alteration of the circuit and is to be avoided.

An ammeter is placed in series in the branch of the circuit being measured, so that its resistance adds to that branch. Normally, the ammeter's resistance is very small compared with the resistances of the devices in the circuit, and so the extra resistance is negligible. (See Figure 21.32(a).) However, if very small load resistances are involved, or if the ammeter is not as low in resistance as it should be, then the total series resistance is significantly greater, and the current in the branch being measured is reduced. (See Figure 21.32(b).)

A practical problem can occur if the ammeter is connected incorrectly. If it was put in parallel with the resistor to measure the current in it, you could possibly damage the meter; the low resistance of the ammeter would allow most of the current in the circuit to go through the galvanometer, and this current would be larger since the effective resistance is smaller.

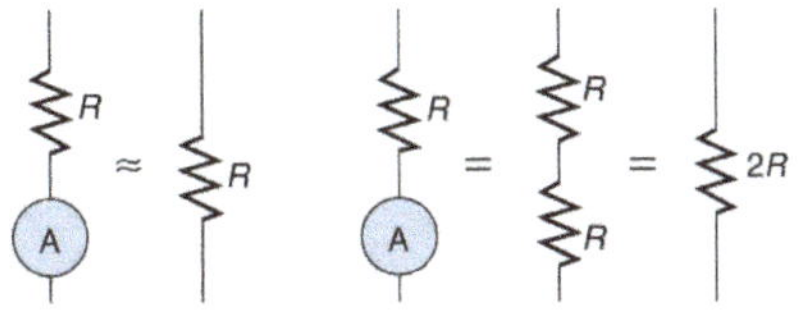

FIGURE 21.32 (a) An ammeter normally has such a small resistance that the total series resistance in the branch being measured is not appreciably increased. The circuit is essentially unaltered compared with when the ammeter is absent. (b) Here the ammeter's resistance is the same as that of the branch, so that the total resistance is doubled and the current is half what it is without the ammeter. This significant alteration of the circuit is to be avoided.

One solution to the problem of voltmeters and ammeters interfering with the circuits being measured is to use galvanometers with greater sensitivity. This allows construction of voltmeters with greater resistance and ammeters with smaller resistance than when less sensitive galvanometers are used.

There are practical limits to galvanometer sensitivity, but it is possible to get analog meters that make measurements accurate to a few percent. Note that the inaccuracy comes from altering the circuit, not from a fault in the meter.

CONNECTIONS: LIMITS TO KNOWLEDGE

Making a measurement alters the system being measured in a manner that produces uncertainty in the measurement. For macroscopic systems, such as the circuits discussed in this module, the alteration can usually be made negligibly small, but it cannot be eliminated entirely. For submicroscopic systems, such as atoms, nuclei, and smaller particles, measurement alters the system in a manner that cannot be made arbitrarily small. This actually limits knowledge of the system—even limiting what nature can know about itself. We shall see profound implications of this when the Heisenberg uncertainty principle is discussed in the modules on quantum mechanics.

There is another measurement technique based on drawing no current at all and, hence, not altering the circuit at all. These are called null measurements and are the topic of Null Measurements. Digital meters that employ solid-state electronics and null measurements can attain accuracies of one part in 10^6.

CHECK YOUR UNDERSTANDING

Digital meters are able to detect smaller currents than analog meters employing galvanometers. How does this explain their ability to measure voltage and current more accurately than analog meters?

Solution

Since digital meters require less current than analog meters, they alter the circuit less than analog meters. Their resistance as a voltmeter can be far greater than an analog meter, and their resistance as an ammeter can be far less than an analog meter. Consult Figure 21.27 and Figure 21.28 and their discussion in the text.

PHET EXPLORATIONS

Circuit Construction Kit (DC Only), Virtual Lab

Stimulate a neuron and monitor what happens. Pause, rewind, and move forward in time in order to observe the ions as they move across the neuron membrane.

Click to view content (https://openstax.org/books/college-physics-ap-courses-2e/pages/21-4-dc-voltmeters-and-ammeters)

21.5 Null Measurements

LEARNING OBJECTIVES

By the end of this section, you will be able to:

- Explain why a null measurement device is more accurate than a standard voltmeter or ammeter.
- Demonstrate how a Wheatstone bridge can be used to accurately calculate the resistance in a circuit.

Standard measurements of voltage and current alter the circuit being measured, introducing uncertainties in the measurements. Voltmeters draw some extra current, whereas ammeters reduce current flow. **Null measurements** balance voltages so that there is no current flowing through the measuring device and, therefore, no alteration of the circuit being measured.

Null measurements are generally more accurate but are also more complex than the use of standard voltmeters and ammeters, and they still have limits to their precision. In this module, we shall consider a few specific types of null measurements, because they are common and interesting, and they further illuminate principles of electric circuits.

The Potentiometer

Suppose you wish to measure the emf of a battery. Consider what happens if you connect the battery directly to a standard voltmeter as shown in Figure 21.33. (Once we note the problems with this measurement, we will examine a null measurement that improves accuracy.) As discussed before, the actual quantity measured is the terminal voltage V, which is related to the emf of the battery by $V = \text{emf} - Ir$, where I is the current that flows and r is the internal resistance of the battery.

The emf could be accurately calculated if r were very accurately known, but it is usually not. If the current I could be made zero, then $V = \text{emf}$, and so emf could be directly measured. However, standard voltmeters need a current to operate; thus, another technique is needed.

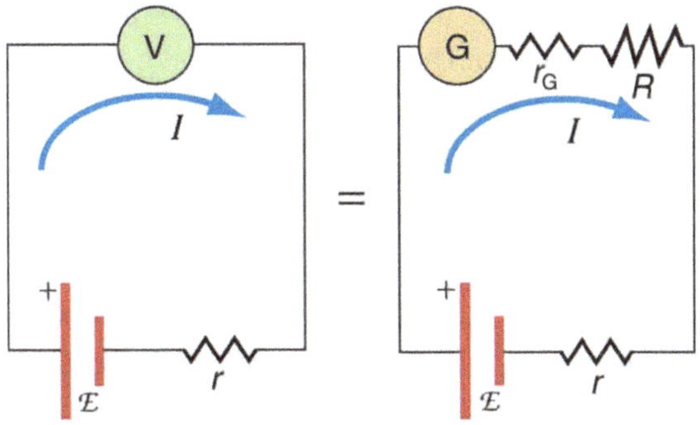

FIGURE 21.33 An analog voltmeter attached to a battery draws a small but nonzero current and measures a terminal voltage that differs from the emf of the battery. (Note that the script capital E symbolizes electromotive force, or emf.) Since the internal resistance of the battery is not known precisely, it is not possible to calculate the emf precisely.

A **potentiometer** is a null measurement device for measuring potentials (voltages). (See Figure 21.34.) A voltage source is connected to a resistor R, say, a long wire, and passes a constant current through it. There is a steady drop in potential (an IR drop) along the wire, so that a variable potential can be obtained by making contact at varying locations along the wire.

Figure 21.34(b) shows an unknown emf_x (represented by script E_x in the figure) connected in series with a galvanometer. Note that emf_x opposes the other voltage source. The location of the contact point (see the arrow on the drawing) is adjusted until the galvanometer reads zero. When the galvanometer reads zero, $\text{emf}_\text{x} = IR_\text{x}$, where R_x is the resistance of the section of wire up to the contact point. Since no current flows through the galvanometer, none flows through the unknown emf, and so emf_x is directly sensed.

Now, a very precisely known standard emf_s is substituted for emf_x, and the contact point is adjusted until the galvanometer again reads zero, so that $\text{emf}_\text{s} = IR_\text{s}$. In both cases, no current passes through the galvanometer, and so the current I through the long wire is the same. Upon taking the ratio $\frac{\text{emf}_\text{x}}{\text{emf}_\text{s}}$, I cancels, giving

$$\frac{\text{emf}_\text{x}}{\text{emf}_\text{s}} = \frac{IR_\text{x}}{IR_\text{s}} = \frac{R_\text{x}}{R_\text{s}}. \qquad 21.71$$

Solving for emf_x gives

$$\text{emf}_\text{x} = \text{emf}_\text{s}\frac{R_\text{x}}{R_\text{s}}. \qquad 21.72$$

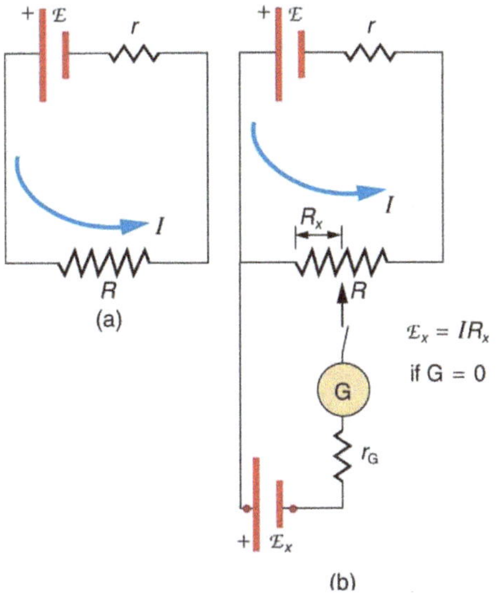

FIGURE 21.34 The potentiometer, a null measurement device. (a) A voltage source connected to a long wire resistor passes a constant current I through it. (b) An unknown emf (labeled script E_x in the figure) is connected as shown, and the point of contact along R is adjusted until the galvanometer reads zero. The segment of wire has a resistance R_x and script $E_\text{x} = IR_\text{x}$, where I is unaffected by the

connection since no current flows through the galvanometer. The unknown emf is thus proportional to the resistance of the wire segment.

Because a long uniform wire is used for R, the ratio of resistances R_x/R_s is the same as the ratio of the lengths of wire that zero the galvanometer for each emf. The three quantities on the right-hand side of the equation are now known or measured, and emf_x can be calculated. The uncertainty in this calculation can be considerably smaller than when using a voltmeter directly, but it is not zero. There is always some uncertainty in the ratio of resistances R_x/R_s and in the standard emf_s. Furthermore, it is not possible to tell when the galvanometer reads exactly zero, which introduces error into both R_x and R_s, and may also affect the current I.

Resistance Measurements and the Wheatstone Bridge

There is a variety of so-called **ohmmeters** that purport to measure resistance. What the most common ohmmeters actually do is to apply a voltage to a resistance, measure the current, and calculate the resistance using Ohm's law. Their readout is this calculated resistance. Two configurations for ohmmeters using standard voltmeters and ammeters are shown in Figure 21.35. Such configurations are limited in accuracy, because the meters alter both the voltage applied to the resistor and the current that flows through it.

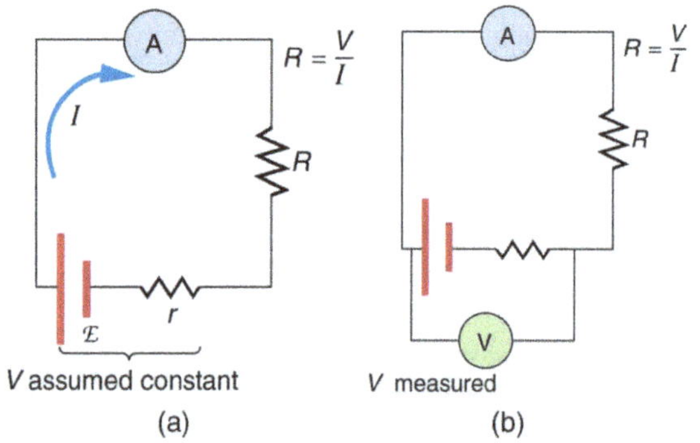

FIGURE 21.35 Two methods for measuring resistance with standard meters. (a) Assuming a known voltage for the source, an ammeter measures current, and resistance is calculated as $R = \frac{V}{I}$. (b) Since the terminal voltage V varies with current, it is better to measure it. V is most accurately known when I is small, but I itself is most accurately known when it is large.

The **Wheatstone bridge** is a null measurement device for calculating resistance by balancing potential drops in a circuit. (See Figure 21.36.) The device is called a bridge because the galvanometer forms a bridge between two branches. A variety of **bridge devices** are used to make null measurements in circuits.

Resistors R_1 and R_2 are precisely known, while the arrow through R_3 indicates that it is a variable resistance. The value of R_3 can be precisely read. With the unknown resistance R_x in the circuit, R_3 is adjusted until the galvanometer reads zero. The potential difference between points b and d is then zero, meaning that b and d are at the same potential. With no current running through the galvanometer, it has no effect on the rest of the circuit. So the branches abc and adc are in parallel, and each branch has the full voltage of the source. That is, the IR drops along abc and adc are the same. Since b and d are at the same potential, the IR drop along ad must equal the IR drop along ab. Thus,

$$I_1 R_1 = I_2 R_3. \tag{21.73}$$

Again, since b and d are at the same potential, the IR drop along dc must equal the IR drop along bc. Thus,

$$I_1 R_2 = I_2 R_x. \tag{21.74}$$

Taking the ratio of these last two expressions gives

$$\frac{I_1 R_1}{I_1 R_2} = \frac{I_2 R_3}{I_2 R_x}. \tag{21.75}$$

Canceling the currents and solving for R_x yields

$$R_x = R_3 \frac{R_2}{R_1}. \tag{21.76}$$

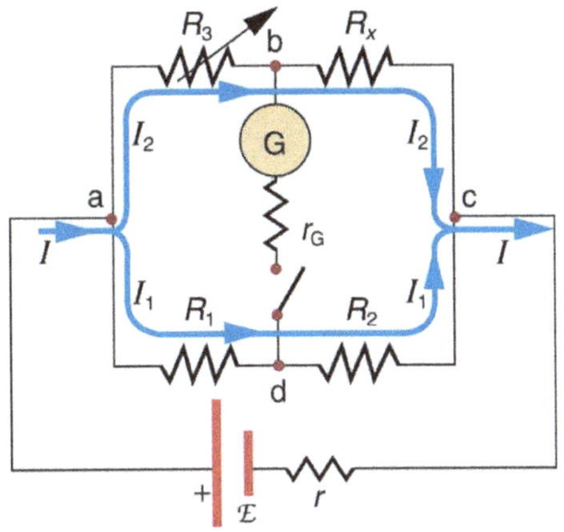

FIGURE 21.36 The Wheatstone bridge is used to calculate unknown resistances. The variable resistance R_3 is adjusted until the galvanometer reads zero with the switch closed. This simplifies the circuit, allowing R_x to be calculated based on the IR drops as discussed in the text.

This equation is used to calculate the unknown resistance when current through the galvanometer is zero. This method can be very accurate (often to four significant digits), but it is limited by two factors. First, it is not possible to get the current through the galvanometer to be exactly zero. Second, there are always uncertainties in R_1, R_2, and R_3, which contribute to the uncertainty in R_x.

CHECK YOUR UNDERSTANDING

Identify other factors that might limit the accuracy of null measurements. Would the use of a digital device that is more sensitive than a galvanometer improve the accuracy of null measurements?

Solution
One factor would be resistance in the wires and connections in a null measurement. These are impossible to make zero, and they can change over time. Another factor would be temperature variations in resistance, which can be reduced but not completely eliminated by choice of material. Digital devices sensitive to smaller currents than analog devices do improve the accuracy of null measurements because they allow you to get the current closer to zero.

21.6 DC Circuits Containing Resistors and Capacitors

- Explain the importance of the time constant, τ, and calculate the time constant for a given resistance and capacitance.
- Explain why batteries in a flashlight gradually lose power and the light dims over time.
- Describe what happens to a graph of the voltage across a capacitor over time as it charges.
- Explain how a timing circuit works and list some applications.
- Calculate the necessary speed of a strobe flash needed to “stop” the movement of an object over a particular length.

When you use a flash camera, it takes a few seconds to charge the capacitor that powers the flash. The light flash discharges the capacitor in a tiny fraction of a second. Why does charging take longer than discharging? This question and a number of other phenomena that involve charging and discharging capacitors are discussed in this module.

RC Circuits

An ***RC* circuit** is one containing a **resistor** *R* and a **capacitor** *C*. The capacitor is an electrical component that stores electric charge.

Figure 21.37 shows a simple *RC* circuit that employs a DC (direct current) voltage source. The capacitor is initially uncharged. As soon as the switch is closed, current flows to and from the initially uncharged capacitor. As charge increases on the capacitor plates, there is increasing opposition to the flow of charge by the repulsion of like charges on each plate.

In terms of voltage, this is because voltage across the capacitor is given by $V_c = Q/C$, where Q is the amount of charge stored on each plate and C is the **capacitance**. This voltage opposes the battery, growing from zero to the maximum emf when fully charged. The current thus decreases from its initial value of $I_0 = \frac{\text{emf}}{R}$ to zero as the voltage on the capacitor reaches the same value as the emf. When there is no current, there is no IR drop, and so the voltage on the capacitor must then equal the emf of the voltage source. This can also be explained with Kirchhoff's second rule (the loop rule), discussed in Kirchhoff's Rules, which says that the algebraic sum of changes in potential around any closed loop must be zero.

The initial current is $I_0 = \frac{\text{emf}}{R}$, because all of the IR drop is in the resistance. Therefore, the smaller the resistance, the faster a given capacitor will be charged. Note that the internal resistance of the voltage source is included in R, as are the resistances of the capacitor and the connecting wires. In the flash camera scenario above, when the batteries powering the camera begin to wear out, their internal resistance rises, reducing the current and lengthening the time it takes to get ready for the next flash.

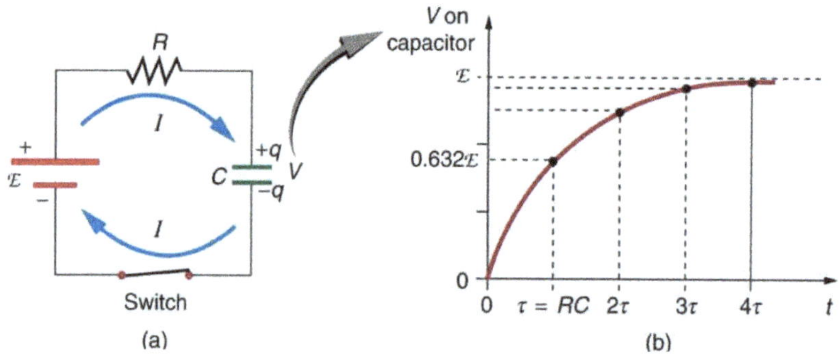

FIGURE 21.37 (a) An RC circuit with an initially uncharged capacitor. Current flows in the direction shown (opposite of electron flow) as soon as the switch is closed. Mutual repulsion of like charges in the capacitor progressively slows the flow as the capacitor is charged, stopping the current when the capacitor is fully charged and $Q = C \cdot \text{emf}$. (b) A graph of voltage across the capacitor versus time, with the switch closing at time $t = 0$. (Note that in the two parts of the figure, the capital script E stands for emf, q stands for the charge stored on the capacitor, and τ is the RC time constant.)

Voltage on the capacitor is initially zero and rises rapidly at first, since the initial current is a maximum. Figure 21.37(b) shows a graph of capacitor voltage versus time (t) starting when the switch is closed at $t = 0$. The voltage approaches emf asymptotically, since the closer it gets to emf the less current flows. The equation for voltage versus time when charging a capacitor C through a resistor R, derived using calculus, is

$$V = \text{emf}(1 - e^{-t/RC}) \text{ (charging)}, \quad 21.77$$

where V is the voltage across the capacitor, emf is equal to the emf of the DC voltage source, and the exponential e = 2.718 ... is the base of the natural logarithm. Note that the units of RC are seconds. We define

$$\tau = RC, \quad 21.78$$

where τ (the Greek letter tau) is called the time constant for an RC circuit. As noted before, a small resistance R allows the capacitor to charge faster. This is reasonable, since a larger current flows through a smaller resistance. It is also reasonable that the smaller the capacitor C, the less time needed to charge it. Both factors are contained in $\tau = RC$.

More quantitatively, consider what happens when $t = \tau = RC$. Then the voltage on the capacitor is

$$V = \text{emf}\left(1 - e^{-1}\right) = \text{emf}(1 - 0.368) = 0.632 \cdot \text{emf}. \quad 21.79$$

This means that in the time $\tau = RC$, the voltage rises to 0.632 of its final value. The voltage will rise 0.632 of the remainder in the next time τ. It is a characteristic of the exponential function that the final value is never reached, but 0.632 of the remainder to that value is achieved in every time, τ. In just a few multiples of the time constant τ, then, the final value is very nearly achieved, as the graph in Figure 21.37(b) illustrates.

Discharging a Capacitor

Discharging a capacitor through a resistor proceeds in a similar fashion, as Figure 21.38 illustrates. Initially, the current is $I_0 = \frac{V_0}{R}$, driven by the initial voltage V_0 on the capacitor. As the voltage decreases, the current and hence the rate of discharge decreases, implying another exponential formula for V. Using calculus, the voltage V on a capacitor C being discharged through a resistor R is found to be

$$V = V_0 \, e^{-t/RC} (\text{discharging}). \quad 21.80$$

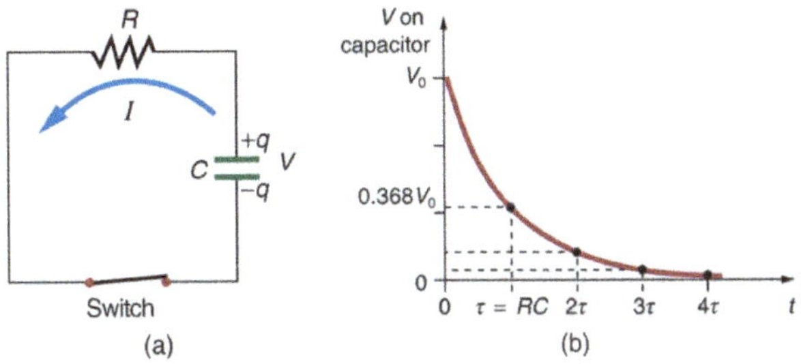

FIGURE 21.38 (a) Closing the switch discharges the capacitor C through the resistor R. Mutual repulsion of like charges on each plate drives the current. (b) A graph of voltage across the capacitor versus time, with $V = V_0$ at $t = 0$. The voltage decreases exponentially, falling a fixed fraction of the way to zero in each subsequent time constant τ.

The graph in Figure 21.38(b) is an example of this exponential decay. Again, the time constant is $\tau = RC$. A small resistance R allows the capacitor to discharge in a small time, since the current is larger. Similarly, a small capacitance requires less time to discharge, since less charge is stored. In the first time interval $\tau = RC$ after the switch is closed, the voltage falls to 0.368 of its initial value, since $V = V_0 \cdot e^{-1} = 0.368V_0$.

During each successive time τ, the voltage falls to 0.368 of its preceding value. In a few multiples of τ, the voltage becomes very close to zero, as indicated by the graph in Figure 21.38(b).

Now we can explain why the flash camera in our scenario takes so much longer to charge than discharge; the resistance while charging is significantly greater than while discharging. The internal resistance of the battery accounts for most of the resistance while charging. As the battery ages, the increasing internal resistance makes the charging process even slower. (You may have noticed this.)

The flash discharge is through a low-resistance ionized gas in the flash tube and proceeds very rapidly. Flash photographs, such as in Figure 21.39, can capture a brief instant of a rapid motion because the flash can be less than a microsecond in duration. Such flashes can be made extremely intense.

During World War II, nighttime reconnaissance photographs were made from the air with a single flash illuminating more than a square kilometer of enemy territory. The brevity of the flash eliminated blurring due to the surveillance aircraft's motion. Today, an important use of intense flash lamps is to pump energy into a laser. The short intense flash can rapidly energize a laser and allow it to reemit the energy in another form.

FIGURE 21.39 This stop-motion photograph of a rufous hummingbird (*Selasphorus rufus*) feeding on a flower was obtained with an extremely brief and intense flash of light powered by the discharge of a capacitor through a gas. (credit: Dean E. Biggins, U.S. Fish and Wildlife Service)

EXAMPLE 21.6

Integrated Concept Problem: Calculating Capacitor Size—Strobe Lights

High-speed flash photography was pioneered by Doc Edgerton in the 1930s, while he was a professor of electrical engineering at MIT. You might have seen examples of his work in the amazing shots of hummingbirds in motion, a drop of milk splattering on a table, or a bullet penetrating an apple (see Figure 21.39). To stop the motion and capture these pictures, one needs a high-intensity, very short pulsed flash, as mentioned earlier in this module.

Suppose one wished to capture the picture of a bullet (moving at 5.0×10^2 m/s) that was passing through an apple. The duration of the flash is related to the RC time constant, τ. What size capacitor would one need in the RC circuit to succeed, if the resistance of the flash tube was $10.0\ \Omega$? Assume the apple is a sphere with a diameter of 8.0×10^{-2} m.

Strategy

We begin by identifying the physical principles involved. This example deals with the strobe light, as discussed above. Figure 21.38 shows the circuit for this probe. The characteristic time τ of the strobe is given as $\tau = RC$.

Solution

We wish to find C, but we don't know τ. We want the flash to be on only while the bullet traverses the apple. So we need to use the kinematic equations that describe the relationship between distance x, velocity v, and time t:

$$x = vt \text{ or } t = \frac{x}{v}. \quad (21.81)$$

The bullet's velocity is given as 5.0×10^2 m/s, and the distance x is 8.0×10^{-2} m. The traverse time, then, is

$$t = \frac{x}{v} = \frac{8.0 \times 10^{-2}\ \text{m}}{5.0 \times 10^2\ \text{m/s}} = 1.6 \times 10^{-4}\ \text{s}. \quad (21.82)$$

We set this value for the crossing time t equal to τ. Therefore,

$$C = \frac{t}{R} = \frac{1.6{\times}10^{-4}\ \text{s}}{10.0\ \Omega} = 16\ \mu\text{F}. \quad (21.83)$$

(Note: Capacitance C is typically measured in farads, F, defined as Coulombs per volt. From the equation, we see that C can also be stated in units of seconds per ohm.)

Discussion

The flash interval of $160\ \mu\text{s}$ (the traverse time of the bullet) is relatively easy to obtain today. Strobe lights have opened up new worlds from science to entertainment. The information from the picture of the apple and bullet was used in the Warren Commission Report on the assassination of President John F. Kennedy in 1963 to confirm that only one bullet was fired.

RC Circuits for Timing

RC circuits are commonly used for timing purposes. A mundane example of this is found in the ubiquitous intermittent wiper systems of modern cars. The time between wipes is varied by adjusting the resistance in an RC circuit. Another example of an RC circuit is found in novelty jewelry, Halloween costumes, and various toys that have battery-powered flashing lights. (See Figure 21.40 for a timing circuit.)

A more crucial use of RC circuits for timing purposes is in the artificial pacemaker, used to control heart rate. The heart rate is normally controlled by electrical signals generated by the sino-atrial (SA) node, which is on the wall of the right atrium chamber. This causes the muscles to contract and pump blood. Sometimes the heart rhythm is abnormal and the heartbeat is too high or too low.

The artificial pacemaker is inserted near the heart to provide electrical signals to the heart when needed with the appropriate time constant. Pacemakers have sensors that detect body motion and breathing to increase the heart rate during exercise to meet the body's increased needs for blood and oxygen.

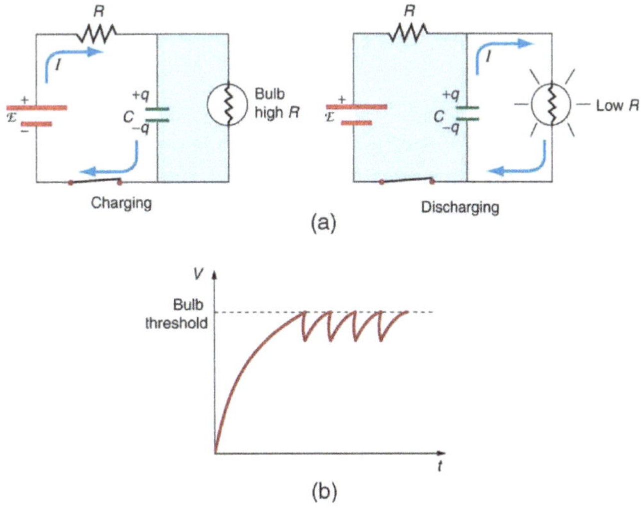

FIGURE 21.40 (a) The lamp in this RC circuit ordinarily has a very high resistance, so that the battery charges the capacitor as if the lamp were not there. When the voltage reaches a threshold value, a current flows through the lamp that dramatically reduces its resistance, and the capacitor discharges through the lamp as if the battery and charging resistor were not there. Once discharged, the process starts again, with the flash period determined by the RC constant τ. (b) A graph of voltage versus time for this circuit.

EXAMPLE 21.7

Calculating Time: *RC* Circuit in a Heart Defibrillator

A heart defibrillator is used to resuscitate an accident victim by discharging a capacitor through the trunk of her body. A simplified version of the circuit is seen in Figure 21.38. (a) What is the time constant if an $8.00\text{-}\mu\text{F}$ capacitor is used and the path resistance through her body is $1.00 \times 10^3\ \Omega$? (b) If the initial voltage is 10.0 kV, how long does it take to decline to $5.00 \times 10^2\ \text{V}$?

Strategy

Since the resistance and capacitance are given, it is straightforward to multiply them to give the time constant asked for in part (a). To find the time for the voltage to decline to $5.00 \times 10^2\ \text{V}$, we repeatedly multiply the initial voltage by 0.368 until a voltage less than or equal to $5.00 \times 10^2\ \text{V}$ is obtained. Each multiplication corresponds to a time of τ seconds.

Solution for (a)

The time constant τ is given by the equation $\tau = RC$. Entering the given values for resistance and capacitance (and remembering that units for a farad can be expressed as s/Ω) gives

$$\tau = RC = (1.00 \times 10^3\ \Omega)(8.00\ \mu F) = 8.00\ \text{ms}. \tag{21.84}$$

Solution for (b)

In the first 8.00 ms, the voltage (10.0 kV) declines to 0.368 of its initial value. That is:

$$V = 0.368V_0 = 3.680 \times 10^3\ \text{V at } t = 8.00\ \text{ms}. \tag{21.85}$$

(Notice that we carry an extra digit for each intermediate calculation.) After another 8.00 ms, we multiply by 0.368 again, and the voltage is

$$\begin{aligned} V' &= 0.368V \\ &= (0.368)\left(3.680 \times 10^3\ \text{V}\right) \\ &= 1.354 \times 10^3\ \text{V at } t = 16.0\ \text{ms}. \end{aligned} \tag{21.86}$$

Similarly, after another 8.00 ms, the voltage is

$$\begin{aligned} V'' &= 0.368V' = (0.368)(1.354 \times 10^3 \text{ V}) \\ &= 498 \text{ V at } t = 24.0 \text{ ms.} \end{aligned} \quad (21.87)$$

Discussion

So after only 24.0 ms, the voltage is down to 498 V, or 4.98% of its original value.Such brief times are useful in heart defibrillation, because the brief but intense current causes a brief but effective contraction of the heart. The actual circuit in a heart defibrillator is slightly more complex than the one in Figure 21.38, to compensate for magnetic and AC effects that will be covered in Magnetism.

CHECK YOUR UNDERSTANDING

When is the potential difference across a capacitor an emf?

Solution

Only when the current being drawn from or put into the capacitor is zero. Capacitors, like batteries, have internal resistance, so their output voltage is not an emf unless current is zero. This is difficult to measure in practice so we refer to a capacitor's voltage rather than its emf. But the source of potential difference in a capacitor is fundamental and it is an emf.

PHET EXPLORATIONS

Circuit Construction Kit (DC only)

An electronics kit in your computer! Build circuits with resistors, light bulbs, batteries, and switches. Take measurements with the realistic ammeter and voltmeter. View the circuit as a schematic diagram, or switch to a life-like view.

Click to view content (https://openstax.org/books/college-physics-ap-courses-2e/pages/21-6-dc-circuits-containing-resistors-and-capacitors)

Glossary

ammeter an instrument that measures current

analog meter a measuring instrument that gives a readout in the form of a needle movement over a marked gauge

bridge device a device that forms a bridge between two branches of a circuit; some bridge devices are used to make null measurements in circuits

capacitance the maximum amount of electric potential energy that can be stored (or separated) for a given electric potential

capacitor an electrical component used to store energy by separating electric charge on two opposing plates

conservation laws require that energy and charge be conserved in a system

current the flow of charge through an electric circuit past a given point of measurement

current sensitivity the maximum current that a galvanometer can read

digital meter a measuring instrument that gives a readout in a digital form

electromotive force (emf) the potential difference of a source of electricity when no current is flowing; measured in volts

full-scale deflection the maximum deflection of a galvanometer needle, also known as current sensitivity; a galvanometer with a full-scale deflection of $50\ \mu A$ has a maximum deflection of its needle when $50\ \mu A$ flows through it

galvanometer an analog measuring device, denoted by G, that measures current flow using a needle deflection caused by a magnetic field force acting upon a current-carrying wire

internal resistance the amount of resistance within the voltage source

Joule's law the relationship between potential electrical power, voltage, and resistance in an electrical circuit, given by: $P_e = IV$

junction rule Kirchhoff's first rule, which applies the conservation of charge to a junction; current is the flow of charge; thus, whatever charge flows into the junction must flow out; the rule can be stated $I_1 = I_2 + I_3$

Kirchhoff's rules a set of two rules, based on conservation of charge and energy, governing current and changes in potential in an electric circuit

loop rule Kirchhoff's second rule, which states that in a closed loop, whatever energy is supplied by emf must be transferred into other forms by devices in the loop, since there are no other ways in which energy can be transferred into or out of the circuit. Thus, the emf equals the sum of the IR (voltage) drops in the loop and can be stated: $\text{emf} = Ir + IR_1 + IR_2$

null measurements methods of measuring current and voltage more accurately by balancing the circuit so that no current flows through the measurement device

Ohm's law the relationship between current, voltage, and resistance within an electrical circuit: $V = IR$

ohmmeter an instrument that applies a voltage to a resistance, measures the current, calculates the resistance using Ohm's law, and provides a readout of this calculated resistance

parallel the wiring of resistors or other components in an electrical circuit such that each component receives an equal voltage from the power source; often pictured in a ladder-shaped diagram, with each component on a rung of the ladder

potential difference the difference in electric potential between two points in an electric circuit, measured in volts

potentiometer a null measurement device for measuring potentials (voltages)

RC circuit a circuit that contains both a resistor and a capacitor

resistance causing a loss of electrical power in a circuit

resistor a component that provides resistance to the current flowing through an electrical circuit

series a sequence of resistors or other components wired into a circuit one after the other

shunt resistance a small resistance R placed in parallel with a galvanometer G to produce an ammeter; the larger the current to be measured, the smaller R must be; most of the current flowing through the meter is shunted through R to protect the galvanometer

terminal voltage the voltage measured across the terminals of a source of potential difference

voltage the electrical potential energy per unit charge; electric pressure created by a power source, such as a battery

voltage drop the loss of electrical power as a current travels through a resistor, wire or other component

voltmeter an instrument that measures voltage

Wheatstone bridge a null measurement device for calculating resistance by balancing potential drops in a circuit

Section Summary

21.1 Resistors in Series and Parallel

- The total resistance of an electrical circuit with resistors wired in a series is the sum of the individual resistances: $R_s = R_1 + R_2 + R_3 + ...$
- Each resistor in a series circuit has the same amount of current flowing through it.
- The voltage drop, or power dissipation, across each individual resistor in a series is different, and their combined total adds up to the power source input.
- The total resistance of an electrical circuit with resistors wired in parallel is less than the lowest resistance of any of the components and can be determined using the formula: $\frac{1}{R_p} = \frac{1}{R_1} + \frac{1}{R_2} + \frac{1}{R_3} + ...$
- Each resistor in a parallel circuit has the same full voltage of the source applied to it.
- The current flowing through each resistor in a parallel circuit is different, depending on the resistance.
- If a more complex connection of resistors is a combination of series and parallel, it can be reduced to a single equivalent resistance by identifying its various parts as series or parallel, reducing each to its equivalent, and continuing until a single resistance is eventually reached.

21.2 Electromotive Force: Terminal Voltage

- All voltage sources have two fundamental parts—a source of electrical energy that has a characteristic electromotive force (emf), and an internal resistance r.
- The emf is the potential difference of a source when no current is flowing.
- The numerical value of the emf depends on the source of potential difference.
- The internal resistance r of a voltage source affects the output voltage when a current flows.
- The voltage output of a device is called its terminal voltage V and is given by $V = \text{emf} - Ir$, where I is the electric current and is positive when flowing away from the positive terminal of the voltage source.
- When multiple voltage sources are in series, their internal resistances add and their emfs add algebraically.
- Solar cells can be wired in series or parallel to provide increased voltage or current, respectively.

21.3 Kirchhoff's Rules

- Kirchhoff's rules can be used to analyze any circuit, simple or complex.
- Kirchhoff's first rule—the junction rule: The sum of all currents entering a junction must equal the sum of all currents leaving the junction.
- Kirchhoff's second rule—the loop rule: The algebraic sum of changes in potential around any closed circuit path (loop) must be zero.
- The two rules are based, respectively, on the laws of conservation of charge and energy.
- When calculating potential and current using Kirchhoff's rules, a set of conventions must be followed for determining the correct signs of various terms.
- The simpler series and parallel rules are special cases of Kirchhoff's rules.

21.4 DC Voltmeters and Ammeters

- Voltmeters measure voltage, and ammeters measure current.
- A voltmeter is placed in parallel with the voltage source to receive full voltage and must have a large resistance to limit its effect on the circuit.
- An ammeter is placed in series to get the full current flowing through a branch and must have a small resistance to limit its effect on the circuit.
- Both can be based on the combination of a resistor and a galvanometer, a device that gives an analog reading of current.
- Standard voltmeters and ammeters alter the circuit being measured and are thus limited in accuracy.

21.5 Null Measurements

- Null measurement techniques achieve greater accuracy by balancing a circuit so that no current flows through the measuring device.
- One such device, for determining voltage, is a potentiometer.
- Another null measurement device, for determining resistance, is the Wheatstone bridge.
- Other physical quantities can also be measured with null measurement techniques.

21.6 DC Circuits Containing Resistors and Capacitors

- An RC circuit is one that has both a resistor and a capacitor.
- The time constant τ for an RC circuit is $\tau = RC$.
- When an initially uncharged ($V_0 = 0$ at $t = 0$)

capacitor in series with a resistor is charged by a DC voltage source, the voltage rises, asymptotically approaching the emf of the voltage source; as a function of time, $V = \text{emf}(1 - e^{-t/RC})(\text{charging})$.

- Within the span of each time constant τ, the voltage rises by 0.632 of the remaining value, approaching the final voltage asymptotically.
- If a capacitor with an initial voltage V_0 is discharged through a resistor starting at $t = 0$, then its voltage decreases exponentially as given by $V = V_0 e^{-t/RC}(\text{discharging})$.
- In each time constant τ, the voltage falls by 0.368 of its remaining initial value, approaching zero asymptotically.

Conceptual Questions

21.1 Resistors in Series and Parallel

1. A switch has a variable resistance that is nearly zero when closed and extremely large when open, and it is placed in series with the device it controls. Explain the effect the switch in Figure 21.41 has on current when open and when closed.

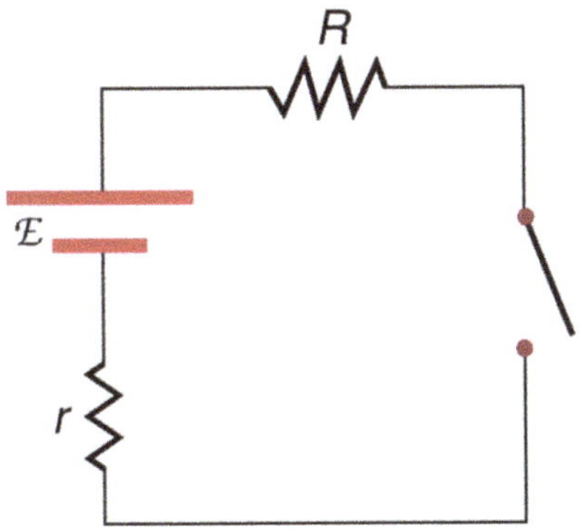

FIGURE 21.41 A switch is ordinarily in series with a resistance and voltage source. Ideally, the switch has nearly zero resistance when closed but has an extremely large resistance when open. (Note that in this diagram, the script E represents the voltage (or electromotive force) of the battery.)

2. What is the voltage across the open switch in Figure 21.41?

3. There is a voltage across an open switch, such as in Figure 21.41. Why, then, is the power dissipated by the open switch small?

4. Why is the power dissipated by a closed switch, such as in Figure 21.41, small?

5. A student in a physics lab mistakenly wired a light bulb, battery, and switch as shown in Figure 21.42. Explain why the bulb is on when the switch is open, and off when the switch is closed. (Do not try this—it is hard on the battery!)

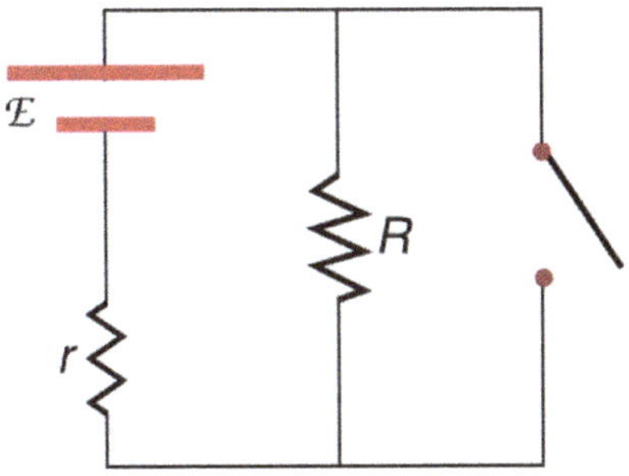

FIGURE 21.42 A wiring mistake put this switch in parallel with the device represented by R. (Note that in this diagram, the script E represents the voltage (or electromotive force) of the battery.)

6. Knowing that the severity of a shock depends on the magnitude of the current through your body, would you prefer to be in series or parallel with a resistance, such as the heating element of a toaster, if shocked by it? Explain.

7. Would your headlights dim when you start your car's engine if the wires in your automobile were superconductors? (Do not neglect the battery's internal resistance.) Explain.

8. Some strings of holiday lights are wired in series to save wiring costs. An old version utilized bulbs that break the electrical connection, like an open switch, when they burn out. If one such bulb burns out, what happens to the others? If such a string operates on 120 V and has 40 identical bulbs, what is the normal operating voltage of each? Newer versions use bulbs that short circuit, like a closed switch, when they burn out. If one such bulb burns out, what happens to the others? If such a string operates on 120 V and has 39 remaining identical bulbs, what is then the operating voltage of each?

9. If two household lightbulbs rated 60 W and 100 W are connected in series to household power, which will be brighter? Explain.

10. Suppose you are doing a physics lab that asks you to put a resistor into a circuit, but all the resistors supplied have a larger resistance than the requested value. How would you connect the

available resistances to attempt to get the smaller value asked for?

11. Before World War II, some radios got power through a “resistance cord” that had a significant resistance. Such a resistance cord reduces the voltage to a desired level for the radio’s tubes and the like, and it saves the expense of a transformer. Explain why resistance cords become warm and waste energy when the radio is on.

12. Some light bulbs have three power settings (not including zero), obtained from multiple filaments that are individually switched and wired in parallel. What is the minimum number of filaments needed for three power settings?

21.2 Electromotive Force: Terminal Voltage

13. Is every emf a potential difference? Is every potential difference an emf? Explain.

14. Explain which battery is doing the charging and which is being charged in Figure 21.43.

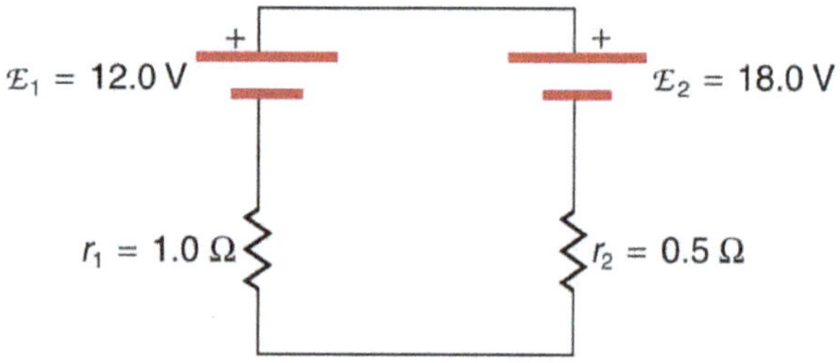

FIGURE 21.43

15. Given a battery, an assortment of resistors, and a variety of voltage and current measuring devices, describe how you would determine the internal resistance of the battery.

16. Two different 12-V automobile batteries on a store shelf are rated at 600 and 850 “cold cranking amps.” Which has the smallest internal resistance?

17. What are the advantages and disadvantages of connecting batteries in series? In parallel?

18. Semitractor trucks use four large 12-V batteries. The starter system requires 24 V, while normal operation of the truck’s other electrical components utilizes 12 V. How could the four batteries be connected to produce 24 V? To produce 12 V? Why is 24 V better than 12 V for starting the truck’s engine (a very heavy load)?

21.3 Kirchhoff’s Rules

19. Can all of the currents going into the junction in Figure 21.44 be positive? Explain.

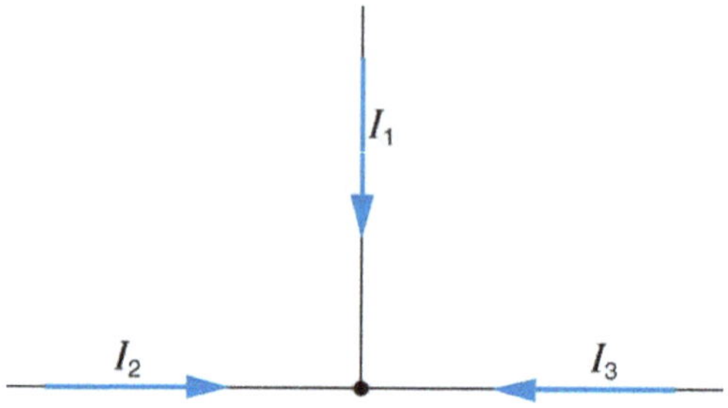

FIGURE 21.44

20. Apply the junction rule to junction b in Figure 21.45. Is any new information gained by applying the junction rule at e? (In the figure, each emf is represented by script E.)

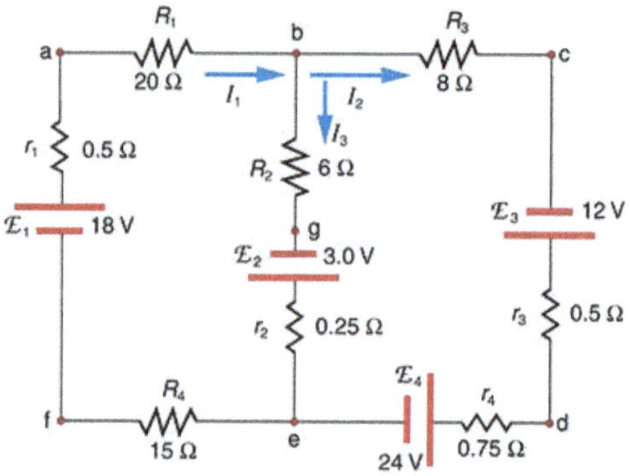

FIGURE 21.45

21. (a) What is the potential difference going from point a to point b in Figure 21.45? (b) What is the potential difference going from c to b? (c) From e to g? (d) From e to d?

22. Apply the loop rule to loop afedcba in Figure 21.45.

23. Apply the loop rule to loops abgefa and cbgedc in Figure 21.45.

21.4 DC Voltmeters and Ammeters

24. Why should you not connect an ammeter directly across a voltage source as shown in Figure 21.46? (Note that script E in the figure stands for emf.)

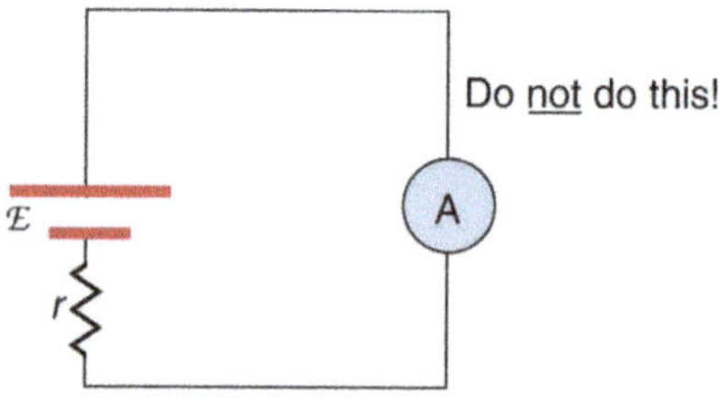

FIGURE 21.46

25. Suppose you are using a multimeter (one designed to measure a range of voltages, currents, and resistances) to measure current in a circuit and you inadvertently leave it in a voltmeter mode.

What effect will the meter have on the circuit? What would happen if you were measuring voltage but accidentally put the meter in the ammeter mode?

26. Specify the points to which you could connect a voltmeter to measure the following potential differences in Figure 21.47: (a) the potential difference of the voltage source; (b) the potential difference across R_1; (c) across R_2; (d) across R_3; (e) across R_2 and R_3. Note that there may be more than one answer to each part.

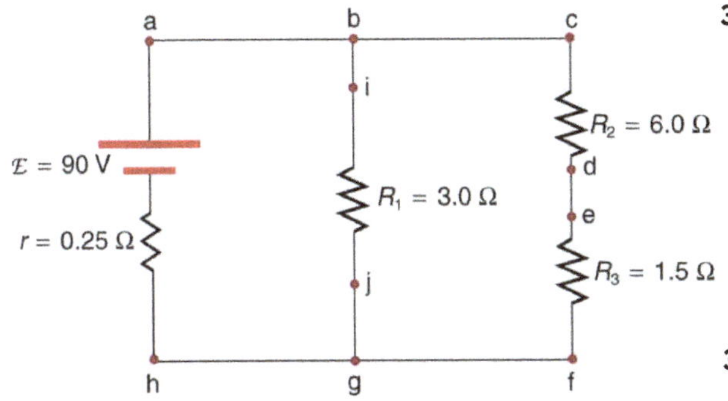

FIGURE 21.47

27. To measure currents in Figure 21.47, you would replace a wire between two points with an ammeter. Specify the points between which you would place an ammeter to measure the following: (a) the total current; (b) the current flowing through R_1; (c) through R_2; (d) through R_3. Note that there may be more than one answer to each part.

21.5 Null Measurements

28. Why can a null measurement be more accurate than one using standard voltmeters and ammeters? What factors limit the accuracy of null measurements?

29. If a potentiometer is used to measure cell emfs on the order of a few volts, why is it most accurate for the standard emf_s to be the same order of magnitude and the resistances to be in the range of a few ohms?

21.6 DC Circuits Containing Resistors and Capacitors

30. Regarding the units involved in the relationship $\tau = RC$, verify that the units of resistance times capacitance are time, that is, $\Omega \cdot \text{F} = \text{s}$.

31. The RC time constant in heart defibrillation is crucial to limiting the time the current flows. If the capacitance in the defibrillation unit is fixed, how would you manipulate resistance in the circuit to adjust the RC constant τ? Would an adjustment of the applied voltage also be needed to ensure that the current delivered has an appropriate value?

32. When making an ECG measurement, it is important to measure voltage variations over small time intervals. The time is limited by the RC constant of the circuit—it is not possible to measure time variations shorter than RC. How would you manipulate R and C in the circuit to allow the necessary measurements?

33. Draw two graphs of charge versus time on a capacitor. Draw one for charging an initially uncharged capacitor in series with a resistor, as in the circuit in Figure 21.37, starting from $t = 0$. Draw the other for discharging a capacitor through a resistor, as in the circuit in Figure 21.38, starting at $t = 0$, with an initial charge Q_0. Show at least two intervals of τ.

34. When charging a capacitor, as discussed in conjunction with Figure 21.37, how long does it take for the voltage on the capacitor to reach emf? Is this a problem?

35. When discharging a capacitor, as discussed in conjunction with Figure 21.38, how long does it take for the voltage on the capacitor to reach zero? Is this a problem?

36. Referring to Figure 21.37, draw a graph of potential difference across the resistor versus time, showing at least two intervals of τ. Also draw a graph of current versus time for this situation.

37. A long, inexpensive extension cord is connected from inside the house to a refrigerator outside. The refrigerator doesn't run as it should. What might be the problem?

38. In Figure 21.40, does the graph indicate the time constant is shorter for discharging than for charging? Would you expect ionized gas to have low resistance? How would you adjust R to get a longer time between flashes? Would adjusting R affect the discharge time?

39. An electronic apparatus may have large capacitors at high voltage in the power supply section, presenting a shock hazard even when the apparatus is switched off. A "bleeder resistor" is therefore placed across such a capacitor, as shown schematically in Figure 21.48, to bleed the charge from it after the apparatus is off. Why must the bleeder resistance be much greater than the effective resistance of the rest of the circuit? How does this affect the time constant for discharging the capacitor?

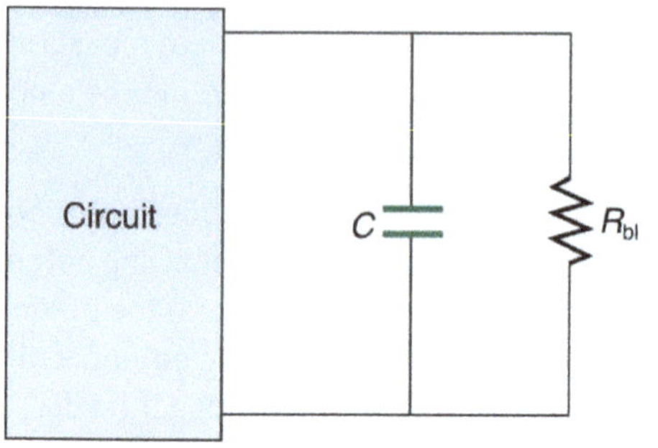

FIGURE 21.48 A bleeder resistor R_{bl} discharges the capacitor in this electronic device once it is switched off.

Problems & Exercises

21.1 Resistors in Series and Parallel

Note: Data taken from figures can be assumed to be accurate to three significant digits.

1. (a) What is the resistance of ten $275\text{-}\Omega$ resistors connected in series? (b) In parallel?

2. (a) What is the resistance of a $1.00 \times 10^2 \ -\Omega$, a $2.50\text{-k}\Omega$, and a $4.00\text{-k}\Omega$ resistor connected in series? (b) In parallel?

3. What are the largest and smallest resistances you can obtain by connecting a $36.0\text{-}\Omega$, a $50.0\text{-}\Omega$, and a $700\text{-}\Omega$ resistor together?

4. An 1800-W toaster, a 1400-W electric frying pan, and a 75-W lamp are plugged into the same outlet in a 15-A, 120-V circuit. (The three devices are in parallel when plugged into the same socket.). (a) What current is drawn by each device? (b) Will this combination blow the 15-A fuse?

5. Your car's 30.0-W headlight and 2.40-kW starter are ordinarily connected in parallel in a 12.0-V system. What power would one headlight and the starter consume if connected in series to a 12.0-V battery? (Neglect any other resistance in the circuit and any change in resistance in the two devices.)

6. (a) Given a 48.0-V battery and $24.0\text{-}\Omega$ and $96.0\text{-}\Omega$ resistors, find the current and power for each when connected in series. (b) Repeat when the resistances are in parallel.

7. Referring to the example combining series and parallel circuits and Figure 21.6, calculate I_3 in the following two different ways: (a) from the known values of I and I_2; (b) using Ohm's law for R_3. In both parts explicitly show how you follow the steps in the Problem-Solving Strategies for Series and Parallel Resistors.

8. Referring to Figure 21.6: (a) Calculate P_3 and note how it compares with P_3 found in the first two example problems in this module. (b) Find the total power supplied by the source and compare it with the sum of the powers dissipated by the resistors.

9. Refer to Figure 21.7 and the discussion of lights dimming when a heavy appliance comes on. (a) Given the voltage source is 120 V, the wire resistance is $0.400\ \Omega$, and the bulb is nominally 75.0 W, what power will the bulb dissipate if a total of 15.0 A passes through the wires when the motor comes on? Assume negligible change in bulb resistance. (b) What power is consumed by the motor?

10. A 240-kV power transmission line carrying $5.00 \times 10^2\ \text{A}$ is hung from grounded metal towers by ceramic insulators, each having a $1.00\times10^9 \ -\Omega$ resistance. Figure 21.49. (a) What is the resistance to ground of 100 of these insulators? (b) Calculate the power dissipated by 100 of them. (c) What fraction of the power carried by the line is this? Explicitly show how you follow the steps in the Problem-Solving Strategies for Series and Parallel Resistors.

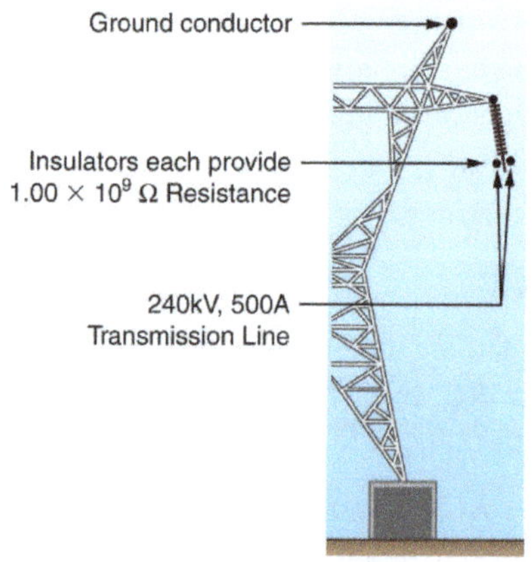

FIGURE 21.49 High-voltage (240-kV) transmission line

carrying 5.00×10^2 A is hung from a grounded metal transmission tower. The row of ceramic insulators provide $1.00 \times 10^9\,\Omega$ of resistance each.

11. Show that if two resistors R_1 and R_2 are combined and one is much greater than the other ($R_1 >> R_2$): (a) Their series resistance is very nearly equal to the greater resistance R_1. (b) Their parallel resistance is very nearly equal to smaller resistance R_2.

12. Unreasonable Results
Two resistors, one having a resistance of $145\ \Omega$, are connected in parallel to produce a total resistance of $150\ \Omega$. (a) What is the value of the second resistance? (b) What is unreasonable about this result? (c) Which assumptions are unreasonable or inconsistent?

13. Unreasonable Results
Two resistors, one having a resistance of $900\ \text{k}\Omega$, are connected in series to produce a total resistance of $0.500\ \text{M}\Omega$. (a) What is the value of the second resistance? (b) What is unreasonable about this result? (c) Which assumptions are unreasonable or inconsistent?

21.2 Electromotive Force: Terminal Voltage

14. Standard automobile batteries have six lead-acid cells in series, creating a total emf of 12.0 V. What is the emf of an individual lead-acid cell?

15. Carbon-zinc dry cells (sometimes referred to as non-alkaline cells) have an emf of 1.54 V, and they are produced as single cells or in various combinations to form other voltages. (a) How many 1.54-V cells are needed to make the common 9-V battery used in many small electronic devices? (b) What is the actual emf of the approximately 9-V battery? (c) Discuss how internal resistance in the series connection of cells will affect the terminal voltage of this approximately 9-V battery.

16. What is the output voltage of a 3.0000-V lithium cell in a digital wristwatch that draws 0.300 mA, if the cell's internal resistance is $2.00\ \Omega$?

17. (a) What is the terminal voltage of a large 1.54-V carbon-zinc dry cell used in a physics lab to supply 2.00 A to a circuit, if the cell's internal resistance is $0.100\ \Omega$? (b) How much electrical power does the cell produce? (c) What power goes to its load?

18. What is the internal resistance of an automobile battery that has an emf of 12.0 V and a terminal voltage of 15.0 V while a current of 8.00 A is charging it?

19. (a) Find the terminal voltage of a 12.0-V motorcycle battery having a $0.600\text{-}\Omega$ internal resistance, if it is being charged by a current of 10.0 A. (b) What is the output voltage of the battery charger?

20. A car battery with a 12-V emf and an internal resistance of $0.050\,\Omega$ is being charged with a current of 60 A. Note that in this process the battery is being charged. (a) What is the potential difference across its terminals? (b) At what rate is thermal energy being dissipated in the battery? (c) At what rate is electric energy being converted to chemical energy? (d) What are the answers to (a) and (b) when the battery is used to supply 60 A to the starter motor?

21. The hot resistance of a flashlight bulb is $2.30\,\Omega$, and it is run by a 1.58-V alkaline cell having a $0.100\text{-}\Omega$ internal resistance. (a) What current flows? (b) Calculate the power supplied to the bulb using $I^2 R_{\text{bulb}}$. (c) Is this power the same as calculated using $\frac{V^2}{R_{\text{bulb}}}$?

22. The label on a portable radio recommends the use of rechargeable nickel-cadmium cells (nicads), although they have a 1.25-V emf while alkaline cells have a 1.58-V emf. The radio has a $3.20\text{-}\Omega$ resistance. (a) Draw a circuit diagram of the radio and its batteries. Now, calculate the power delivered to the radio. (b) When using Nicad cells each having an internal resistance of $0.0400\ \Omega$. (c) When using alkaline cells each having an internal resistance of $0.200\ \Omega$. (d) Does this difference seem significant, considering that the radio's effective resistance is lowered when its volume is turned up?

23. An automobile starter motor has an equivalent resistance of $0.0500\,\Omega$ and is supplied by a 12.0-V battery with a $0.0100\text{-}\Omega$ internal resistance. (a) What is the current to the motor? (b) What voltage is applied to it? (c) What power is supplied to the motor? (d) Repeat these calculations for when the battery connections are corroded and add $0.0900\,\Omega$ to the circuit. (Significant problems are caused by even small amounts of unwanted resistance in low-voltage, high-current applications.)

24. A child's electronic toy is supplied by three 1.58-V alkaline cells having internal resistances of $0.0200\,\Omega$ in series with a 1.53-V carbon-zinc dry cell having a $0.100\text{-}\Omega$ internal resistance. The load resistance is $10.0\,\Omega$. (a) Draw a circuit diagram of the toy and its batteries. (b) What current flows? (c) How much power is supplied to the load? (d) What is the internal resistance of the dry cell if it goes bad, resulting in only 0.500 W being supplied to the load?

25. (a) What is the internal resistance of a voltage source if its terminal voltage drops by 2.00 V when the current supplied increases by 5.00 A? (b) Can the emf of the voltage source be found with the information supplied?

26. A person with body resistance between his hands of $10.0\text{ k}\Omega$ accidentally grasps the terminals of a 20.0-kV power supply. (Do NOT do this!) (a) Draw a circuit diagram to represent the situation. (b) If the internal resistance of the power supply is $2000\,\Omega$, what is the current through his body? (c) What is the power dissipated in his body? (d) If the power supply is to be made safe by increasing its internal resistance, what should the internal resistance be for the maximum current in this situation to be 1.00 mA or less? (e) Will this modification compromise the effectiveness of the power supply for driving low-resistance devices? Explain your reasoning.

27. Electric fish generate current with biological cells called electroplaques, which are physiological emf devices. The electroplaques in the South American eel are arranged in 140 rows, each row stretching horizontally along the body and each containing 5000 electroplaques. Each electroplaque has an emf of 0.15 V and internal resistance of $0.25\,\Omega$. If the water surrounding the fish has resistance of $800\,\Omega$, how much current can the eel produce in water from near its head to near its tail?

28. Integrated Concepts
A 12.0-V emf automobile battery has a terminal voltage of 16.0 V when being charged by a current of 10.0 A. (a) What is the battery's internal resistance? (b) What power is dissipated inside the battery? (c) At what rate (in $^\circ\text{C/min}$) will its temperature increase if its mass is 20.0 kg and it has a specific heat of $0.300\text{ kcal/kg}\cdot{}^\circ\text{C}$, assuming no heat escapes?

29. Unreasonable Results
A 1.58-V alkaline cell with a $0.200\text{-}\Omega$ internal resistance is supplying 8.50 A to a load. (a) What is its terminal voltage? (b) What is the value of the load resistance? (c) What is unreasonable about these results? (d) Which assumptions are unreasonable or inconsistent?

30. Unreasonable Results
(a) What is the internal resistance of a 1.54-V dry cell that supplies 1.00 W of power to a $15.0\text{-}\Omega$ bulb? (b) What is unreasonable about this result? (c) Which assumptions are unreasonable or inconsistent?

21.3 Kirchhoff's Rules

31. Apply the loop rule to loop abcdefgha in Figure 21.25.

32. Apply the loop rule to loop aedcba in Figure 21.25.

33. Verify the second equation in Example 21.5 by substituting the values found for the currents I_1 and I_2.

34. Verify the third equation in Example 21.5 by substituting the values found for the currents I_1 and I_3.

35. Apply the junction rule at point a in Figure 21.50.

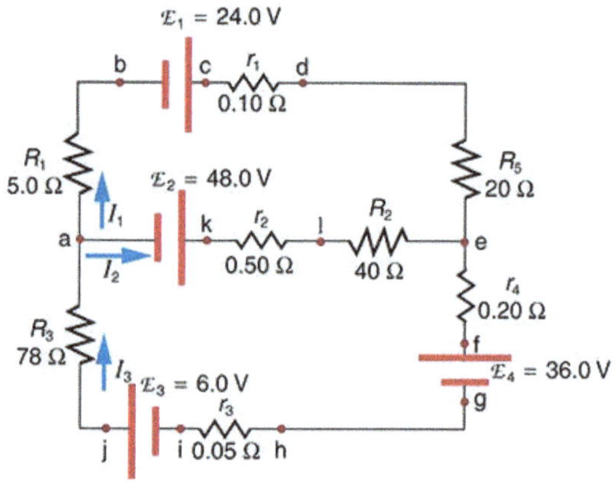

FIGURE 21.50

36. Apply the loop rule to loop abcdefghija in Figure 21.50.

37. Apply the loop rule to loop akledcba in Figure 21.50.

38. Find the currents flowing in the circuit in Figure 21.50. Explicitly show how you follow the steps in the Problem-Solving Strategies for Series and Parallel Resistors.

39. Solve Example 21.5, but use loop abcdefgha instead of loop akledcba. Explicitly show how you follow the steps in the Problem-Solving Strategies for Series and Parallel Resistors.

40. Find the currents flowing in the circuit in Figure 21.45.

41. Unreasonable Results
Consider the circuit in Figure 21.51, and suppose that the emfs are unknown and the currents are given to be $I_1 = 5.00\text{ A}$, $I_2 = 3.0\text{ A}$, and $I_3 = -2.00\text{ A}$. (a) Could you find the emfs? (b) What is wrong with the assumptions?

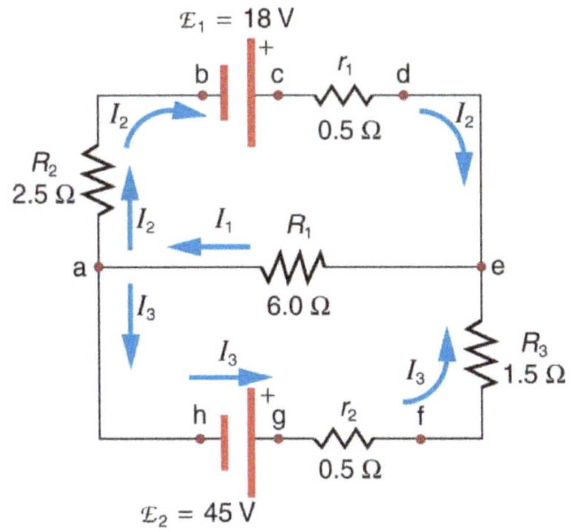

FIGURE 21.51

21.4 DC Voltmeters and Ammeters

42. What is the sensitivity of the galvanometer (that is, what current gives a full-scale deflection) inside a voltmeter that has a $1.00\text{-M}\Omega$ resistance on its 30.0-V scale?

43. What is the sensitivity of the galvanometer (that is, what current gives a full-scale deflection) inside a voltmeter that has a $25.0\text{-k}\Omega$ resistance on its 100-V scale?

44. Find the resistance that must be placed in series with a $25.0\text{-}\Omega$ galvanometer having a $50.0\text{–}\mu\text{A}$ sensitivity (the same as the one discussed in the text) to allow it to be used as a voltmeter with a 0.100-V full-scale reading.

45. Find the resistance that must be placed in series with a $25.0\text{-}\Omega$ galvanometer having a $50.0\text{-}\mu\text{A}$ sensitivity (the same as the one discussed in the text) to allow it to be used as a voltmeter with a 3000-V full-scale reading. Include a circuit diagram with your solution.

46. Find the resistance that must be placed in parallel with a $25.0\text{-}\Omega$ galvanometer having a $50.0\text{-}\mu\text{A}$ sensitivity (the same as the one discussed in the text) to allow it to be used as an ammeter with a 10.0-A full-scale reading. Include a circuit diagram with your solution.

47. Find the resistance that must be placed in parallel with a $25.0\text{-}\Omega$ galvanometer having a $50.0\text{-}\mu\text{A}$ sensitivity (the same as the one discussed in the text) to allow it to be used as an ammeter with a 300-mA full-scale reading.

48. Find the resistance that must be placed in series with a $10.0\text{-}\Omega$ galvanometer having a $100\text{-}\mu\text{A}$ sensitivity to allow it to be used as a voltmeter with: (a) a 300-V full-scale reading, and (b) a 0.300-V full-scale reading.

49. Find the resistance that must be placed in parallel with a $10.0\text{-}\Omega$ galvanometer having a $100\text{-}\mu\text{A}$ sensitivity to allow it to be used as an ammeter with: (a) a 20.0-A full-scale reading, and (b) a 100-mA full-scale reading.

50. Suppose you measure the terminal voltage of a 1.585-V alkaline cell having an internal resistance of $0.100\,\Omega$ by placing a $1.00\text{-k}\Omega$ voltmeter across its terminals. (See Figure 21.52.) (a) What current flows? (b) Find the terminal voltage. (c) To see how close the measured terminal voltage is to the emf, calculate their ratio.

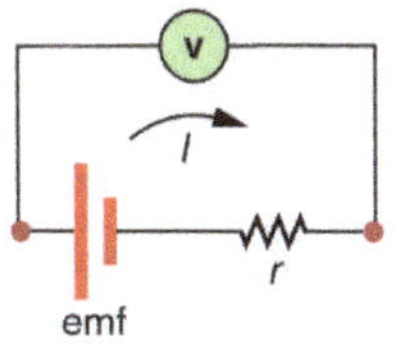

FIGURE 21.52

51. Suppose you measure the terminal voltage of a 3.200-V lithium cell having an internal resistance of $5.00\,\Omega$ by placing a $1.00\text{-k}\Omega$ voltmeter across its terminals. (a) What current flows? (b) Find the terminal voltage. (c) To see how close the measured terminal voltage is to the emf, calculate their ratio.

52. A certain ammeter has a resistance of $5.00\times10^{-5}\ \Omega$ on its 3.00-A scale and contains a $10.0\text{-}\Omega$ galvanometer. What is the sensitivity of the galvanometer?

53. A $1.00\text{-M}\Omega$ voltmeter is placed in parallel with a $75.0\text{-k}\Omega$ resistor in a circuit. (a) Draw a circuit diagram of the connection. (b) What is the resistance of the combination? (c) If the voltage across the combination is kept the same as it was across the $75.0\text{-k}\Omega$ resistor alone, what is the percent increase in current? (d) If the current through the combination is kept the same as it was through the $75.0\text{-k}\Omega$ resistor alone, what is the percentage decrease in voltage? (e) Are the changes found in parts (c) and (d) significant? Discuss.

54. A $0.0200\text{-}\Omega$ ammeter is placed in series with a $10.00\text{-}\Omega$ resistor in a circuit. (a) Draw a circuit diagram of the connection. (b) Calculate the resistance of the combination. (c) If the voltage is kept the same across the combination as it was through the $10.00\text{-}\Omega$ resistor alone, what is the percent decrease in current? (d) If the current is kept the same through the combination as it was through the $10.00\text{-}\Omega$ resistor alone, what is the percent increase in voltage? (e) Are the changes found in parts (c) and (d) significant? Discuss.

55. Unreasonable Results
Suppose you have a $40.0\text{-}\Omega$ galvanometer with a $25.0\text{-}\mu A$ sensitivity. (a) What resistance would you put in series with it to allow it to be used as a voltmeter that has a full-scale deflection for 0.500 mV? (b) What is unreasonable about this result? (c) Which assumptions are responsible?

56. Unreasonable Results
(a) What resistance would you put in parallel with a $40.0\text{-}\Omega$ galvanometer having a $25.0\text{-}\mu A$ sensitivity to allow it to be used as an ammeter that has a full-scale deflection for $10.0\text{-}\mu A$? (b) What is unreasonable about this result? (c) Which assumptions are responsible?

21.5 Null Measurements

57. What is the emf_x of a cell being measured in a potentiometer, if the standard cell's emf is 12.0 V and the potentiometer balances for $R_x = 5.000\,\Omega$ and $R_s = 2.500\,\Omega$?

58. Calculate the emf_x of a dry cell for which a potentiometer is balanced when $R_x = 1.200\ \Omega$, while an alkaline standard cell with an emf of 1.600 V requires $R_s = 1.247\ \Omega$ to balance the potentiometer.

59. When an unknown resistance R_x is placed in a Wheatstone bridge, it is possible to balance the bridge by adjusting R_3 to be $2500\ \Omega$. What is R_x if $\frac{R_2}{R_1} = 0.625$?

60. To what value must you adjust R_3 to balance a Wheatstone bridge, if the unknown resistance R_x is $100\,\Omega$, R_1 is $50.0\,\Omega$, and R_2 is $175\,\Omega$?

61. (a) What is the unknown emf_x in a potentiometer that balances when R_x is $10.0\,\Omega$, and balances when R_s is $15.0\,\Omega$ for a standard 3.000-V emf? (b) The same emf_x is placed in the same potentiometer, which now balances when R_s is $15.0\,\Omega$ for a standard emf of 3.100 V. At what resistance R_x will the potentiometer balance?

62. Suppose you want to measure resistances in the range from $10.0\ \Omega$ to $10.0\ k\Omega$ using a Wheatstone bridge that has $\frac{R_2}{R_1} = 2.000$. Over what range should R_3 be adjustable?

21.6 DC Circuits Containing Resistors and Capacitors

63. The timing device in an automobile's intermittent wiper system is based on an RC time constant and utilizes a $0.500\text{-}\mu F$ capacitor and a variable resistor. Over what range must R be made to vary to achieve time constants from 2.00 to 15.0 s?

64. A heart pacemaker fires 72 times a minute, each time a 25.0-nF capacitor is charged (by a battery in series with a resistor) to 0.632 of its full voltage. What is the value of the resistance?

65. The duration of a photographic flash is related to an RC time constant, which is $0.100\ \mu s$ for a certain camera. (a) If the resistance of the flash lamp is $0.0400\,\Omega$ during discharge, what is the size of the capacitor supplying its energy? (b) What is the time constant for charging the capacitor, if the charging resistance is $800\ k\Omega$?

66. A 2.00- and a $7.50\text{-}\mu F$ capacitor can be connected in series or parallel, as can a 25.0- and a $100\text{-}k\Omega$ resistor. Calculate the four RC time constants possible from connecting the resulting capacitance and resistance in series.

67. After two time constants, what percentage of the final voltage, emf, is on an initially uncharged capacitor C, charged through a resistance R?

68. A $500\text{-}\Omega$ resistor, an uncharged $1.50\text{-}\mu F$ capacitor, and a 6.16-V emf are connected in series. (a) What is the initial current? (b) What is the RC time constant? (c) What is the current after one time constant? (d) What is the voltage on the capacitor after one time constant?

69. A heart defibrillator being used on a patient has an RC time constant of 10.0 ms due to the resistance of the patient and the capacitance of the defibrillator. (a) If the defibrillator has an $8.00\text{-}\mu F$ capacitance, what is the resistance of the path through the patient? (You may neglect the capacitance of the patient and the resistance of the defibrillator.) (b) If the initial voltage is 12.0 kV, how long does it take to decline to

6.00×10^2 V?

70. An ECG monitor must have an RC time constant less than 1.00×10^2 μs to be able to measure variations in voltage over small time intervals. (a) If the resistance of the circuit (due mostly to that of the patient's chest) is 1.00 kΩ, what is the maximum capacitance of the circuit? (b) Would it be difficult in practice to limit the capacitance to less than the value found in (a)?

71. Figure 21.53 shows how a bleeder resistor is used to discharge a capacitor after an electronic device is shut off, allowing a person to work on the electronics with less risk of shock. (a) What is the time constant? (b) How long will it take to reduce the voltage on the capacitor to 0.250% (5% of 5%) of its full value once discharge begins? (c) If the capacitor is charged to a voltage V_0 through a 100-Ω resistance, calculate the time it takes to rise to $0.865V_0$ (This is about two time constants.)

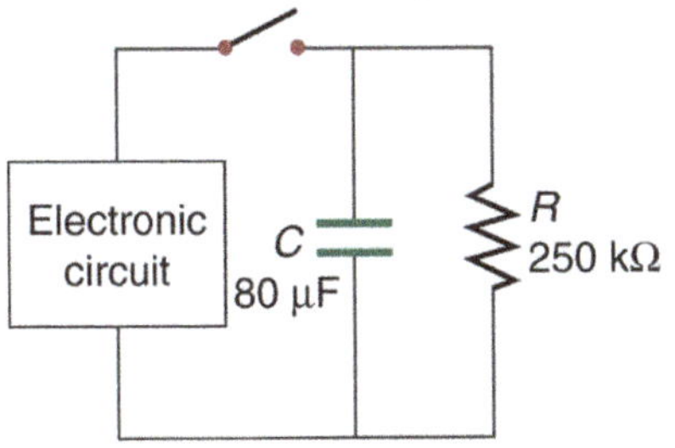

FIGURE 21.53

72. Using the exact exponential treatment, find how much time is required to discharge a 250-μF capacitor through a 500-Ω resistor down to 1.00% of its original voltage.

73. Using the exact exponential treatment, find how much time is required to charge an initially uncharged 100-pF capacitor through a 75.0-MΩ resistor to 90.0% of its final voltage.

74. Integrated Concepts
If you wish to take a picture of a bullet traveling at 500 m/s, then a very brief flash of light produced by an RC discharge through a flash tube can limit blurring. Assuming 1.00 mm of motion during one RC constant is acceptable, and given that the flash is driven by a 600-μF capacitor, what is the resistance in the flash tube?

75. Integrated Concepts
A flashing lamp in a Christmas earring is based on an RC discharge of a capacitor through its resistance. The effective duration of the flash is 0.250 s, during which it produces an average 0.500 W from an average 3.00 V. (a) What energy does it dissipate? (b) How much charge moves through the lamp? (c) Find the capacitance. (d) What is the resistance of the lamp?

76. Integrated Concepts
A 160-μF capacitor charged to 450 V is discharged through a 31.2-kΩ resistor. (a) Find the time constant. (b) Calculate the temperature increase of the resistor, given that its mass is 2.50 g and its specific heat is $1.67 \frac{\text{kJ}}{\text{kg} \cdot {}^\circ\text{C}}$, noting that most of the thermal energy is retained in the short time of the discharge. (c) Calculate the new resistance, assuming it is pure carbon. (d) Does this change in resistance seem significant?

77. Unreasonable Results
(a) Calculate the capacitance needed to get an RC time constant of 1.00×10^3 s with a 0.100-Ω resistor. (b) What is unreasonable about this result? (c) Which assumptions are responsible?

78. Construct Your Own Problem
Consider a camera's flash unit. Construct a problem in which you calculate the size of the capacitor that stores energy for the flash lamp. Among the things to be considered are the voltage applied to the capacitor, the energy needed in the flash and the associated charge needed on the capacitor, the resistance of the flash lamp during discharge, and the desired RC time constant.

79. Construct Your Own Problem
Consider a rechargeable lithium cell that is to be used to power a camcorder. Construct a problem in which you calculate the internal resistance of the cell during normal operation. Also, calculate the minimum voltage output of a battery charger to be used to recharge your lithium cell. Among the things to be considered are the emf and useful terminal voltage of a lithium cell and the current it should be able to supply to a camcorder.

80. Critical Thinking A circuit has a voltage source producing 1.00×10^2 V and a $2.50 \times 10^3 \Omega$ resistor. (a) If the circuit contains nothing else, how much power is dissipated by the resistor? (b) A second $2.50 \times 10^3 \Omega$ resistor is added in parallel to the first resistor. Now how much power is dissipated by the resistors? (c) Now place the two resistors in series. How much power is dissipated by the resistors? (d) Why would a parallel arrangement of resistors dissipate more power than a series arrangement of resistors of the same value? (e) Which delivers more energy in a given time period, the parallel combination of resistors, the series combination of resistors, or is the energy delivered in a given time period the same?

Test Prep for AP® Courses

21.1 Resistors in Series and Parallel

1.

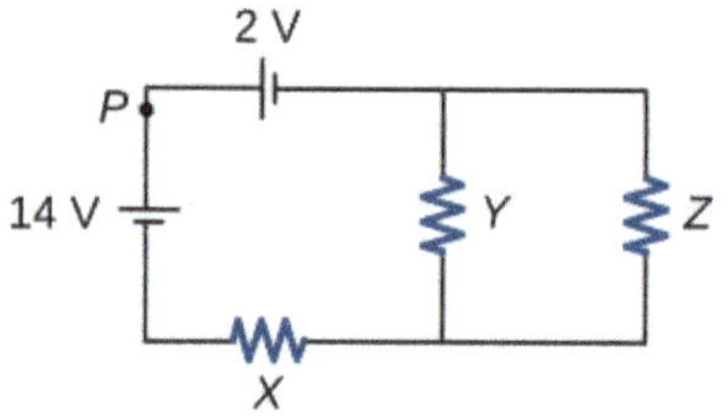

FIGURE 21.54

The figure above shows a circuit containing two batteries and three identical resistors with resistance R. Which of the following changes to the circuit will result in an increase in the current at point P? Select *two* answers.

a. Reversing the connections to the 14 V battery.
b. Removing the 2 V battery and connecting the wires to close the left loop.
c. Rearranging the resistors so all three are in series.
d. Removing the branch containing resistor Z.

2. In a circuit, a parallel combination of six 1.6-kΩ resistors is connected in series with a parallel combination of four 2.4-kΩ resistors. If the source voltage is 24 V, what will be the percentage of total current in one of the 2.4-kΩ resistors?

a. 10%
b. 12%
c. 20%
d. 25%

3. If the circuit in the previous question is modified by removing some of the 1.6 kΩ resistors, the total current in the circuit is 24 mA. How many resistors were removed?

a. 1
b. 2
c. 3
d. 4

4.

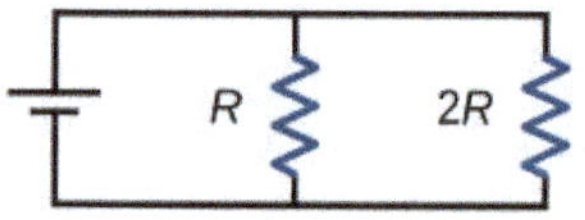

FIGURE 21.55

Two resistors, with resistances R and $2R$ are connected to a voltage source as shown in this figure. If the power dissipated in R is 10 W, what is the power dissipated in $2R$?

a. 1 W
b. 2.5 W
c. 5 W
d. 10 W

5. In a circuit, a parallel combination of two 20-Ω and one 10-Ω resistors is connected in series with a 4-Ω resistor. The source voltage is 36 V.

a. Find the resistor(s) with the maximum current.
b. Find the resistor(s) with the maximum voltage drop.
c. Find the power dissipated in each resistor and hence the total power dissipated in all the resistors. Also find the power output of the source. Are they equal or not? Justify your answer.
d. Will the answers for questions (a) and (b) differ if a 3 Ω resistor is added in series to the 4 Ω resistor? If yes, repeat the question(s) for the new resistor combination.
e. If the values of all the resistors and the source voltage are doubled, what will be the effect on the current?

21.2 Electromotive Force: Terminal Voltage

6. Suppose there are two voltage sources – Sources A and B – with the same emfs but different internal resistances, i.e., the internal resistance of Source A is lower than Source B. If they both supply the same current in their circuits, which of the following statements is true?

a. External resistance in Source A's circuit is more than Source B's circuit.
b. External resistance in Source A's circuit is less than Source B's circuit.
c. External resistance in Source A's circuit is the same as Source B's circuit.
d. The relationship between external resistances in the two circuits can't be determined.

7. Calculate the internal resistance of a voltage source if the terminal voltage of the source increases by 1 V when the current supplied decreases by 4 A? Suppose this source is connected in series (in the same direction) to another source with a different voltage but same internal resistance. What will be the total internal resistance? How will the total internal resistance change if the sources are connected in the opposite direction?

21.3 Kirchhoff's Rules

8. An experiment was set up with the circuit diagram shown. Assume $R_1 = 10\ \Omega$, $R_2 = R_3 = 5\ \Omega$, $r = 0\ \Omega$ and $E = 6$ V.

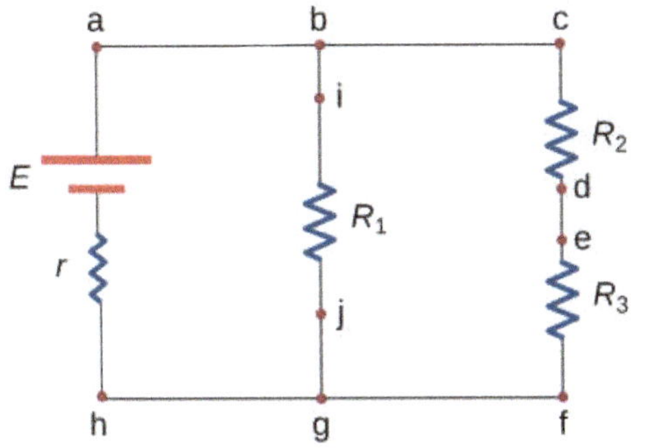

FIGURE 21.56

a. One of the steps to examine the set-up is to test points with the same potential. Which of the following points can be tested?

  a. Points *b*, *c* and *d*.
  b. Points *d*, *e* and *f*.
  c. Points *f*, *h* and *j*.
  d. Points *a*, *h* and *i*.

b. At which three points should the currents be measured so that Kirchhoff's junction rule can be directly confirmed?

  a. Points *b*, *c* and *d*.
  b. Points *d*, *e* and *f*.
  c. Points *f*, *h* and *j*.
  d. Points *a*, *h* and *i*.

c. If the current in the branch with the voltage source is upward and currents in the other two branches are downward, i.e. $I_a = I_i + I_c$, identify which of the following can be true? Select *two* answers.

  a. $I_i = I_j - I_f$
  b. $I_e = I_h - I_i$
  c. $I_c = I_j - I_a$
  d. $I_d = I_h - I_j$

d. The measurements reveal that the current through R_1 is 0.5 A and R_3 is 0.6 A. Based on your knowledge of Kirchoff's laws, confirm which of the following statements are true.

  a. The measured current for R_1 is correct but for R_3 is incorrect.
  b. The measured current for R_3 is correct but for R_1 is incorrect.
  c. Both the measured currents are correct.
  d. Both the measured currents are incorrect.

e. The graph shown in the following figure is the energy dissipated at R_1 as a function of time.

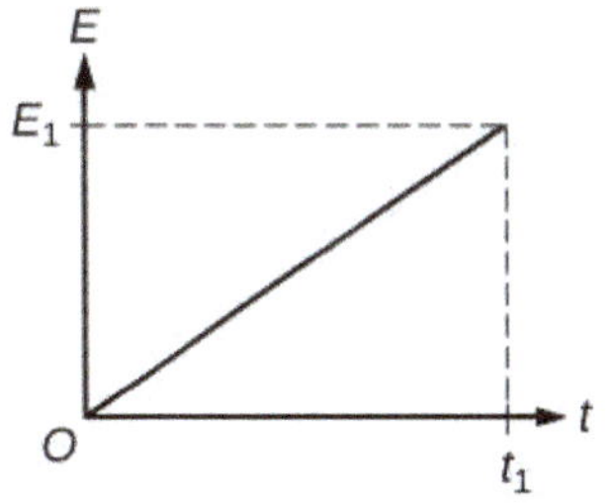

FIGURE 21.57

Which of the following shows the graph for energy dissipated at R_2 as a function of time?

a.

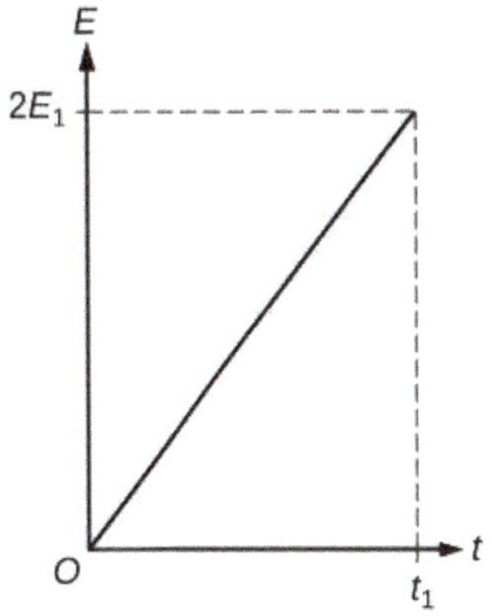

FIGURE 21.58

b.

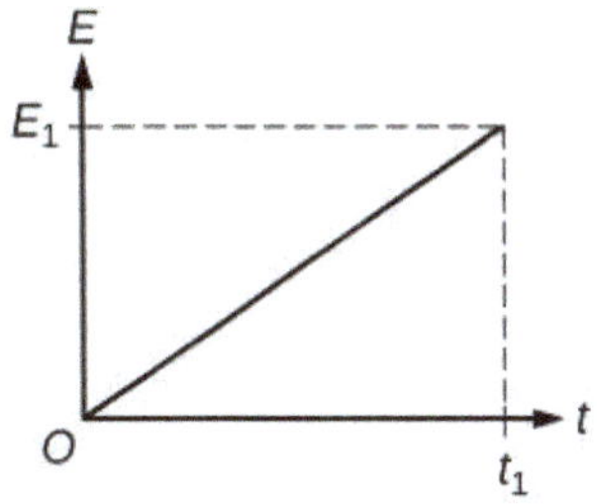

FIGURE 21.59

c.

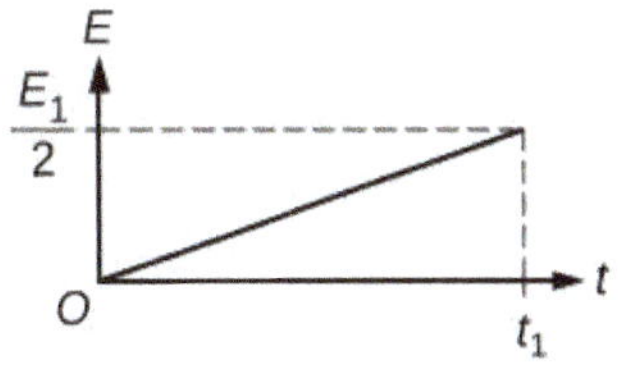

FIGURE 21.60

d.

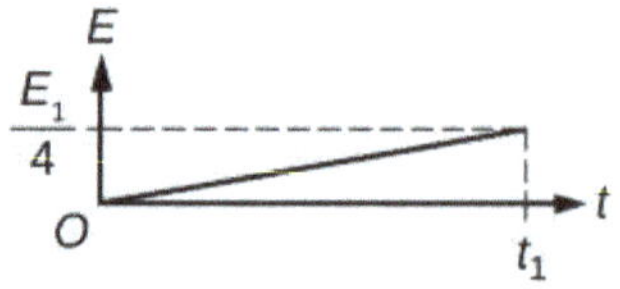

FIGURE 21.61

9. For this question, consider the circuit shown in the following figure.

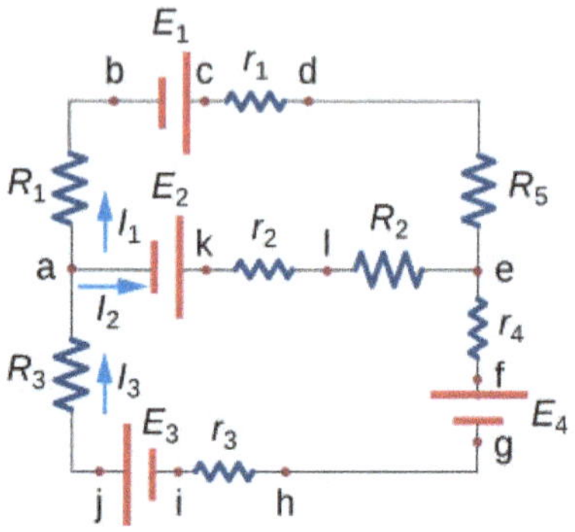

FIGURE 21.62

a. Assuming that none of the three currents (I_1, I_2, and I_3) are equal to zero, which of the following statements is false?

   a. $I_3 = I_1 + I_2$ at point *a*.
   b. $I_2 = I_3 - I_1$ at point *e*.
   c. The current through R_3 is equal to the current through R_5.
   d. The current through R_1 is equal to the current through R_5.

b. Which of the following statements is true?

   a. $E_1 + E_2 + I_1R_1 - I_2R_2 + I_1r_1 - I_2r_2 + I_1R_5 = 0$
   b. $-E_1 + E_2 + I_1R_1 - I_2R_2 + I_1r_1 - I_2r_2 - I_1R_5 = 0$
   c. $E_1 - E_2 - I_1R_1 + I_2R_2 - I_1r_1 + I_2r_2 - I_1R_5 = 0$
   d. $E_1 + E_2 - I_1R_1 + I_2R_2 - I_1r_1 + I_2r_2 + I_1R_5 = 0$

c. If I_1 = 5 A and I_3 = -2 A, which of the following statements is false?

   a. The current through R_1 will flow from *a* to *b* and will be equal to 5 A.
   b. The current through R_3 will flow from *a* to *j* and will be equal to 2 A.
   c. The current through R_5 will flow from *d* to *e* and will be equal to 5 A.
   d. None of the above.

d. If I_1 = 5 A and I_3 = -2 A, I_2 will be equal to

   a. 3 A
   b. -3 A
   c. 7 A
   d. -7 A

10.

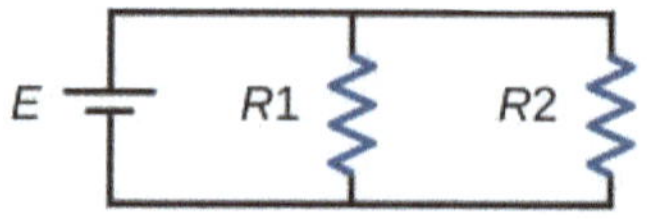

FIGURE 21.63

In an experiment this circuit is set up. Three ammeters are used to record the currents in the three vertical branches (with R_1, R_2, and *E*). The readings of the ammeters in the resistor branches (i.e. currents in R_1 and R_2) are 2 A and 3 A respectively.

a. Find the equation obtained by applying Kirchhoff's loop rule in the loop involving R_1 and R_2.
b. What will be the reading of the third ammeter (i.e. the branch with *E*)? If *E* were replaced by 3*E*, how would this reading change?
c. If the original circuit is modified by adding another voltage source (as shown in the following circuit), find the readings of the three ammeters.

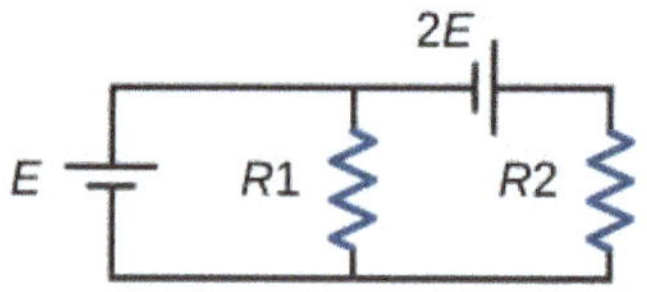

FIGURE 21.64

11.

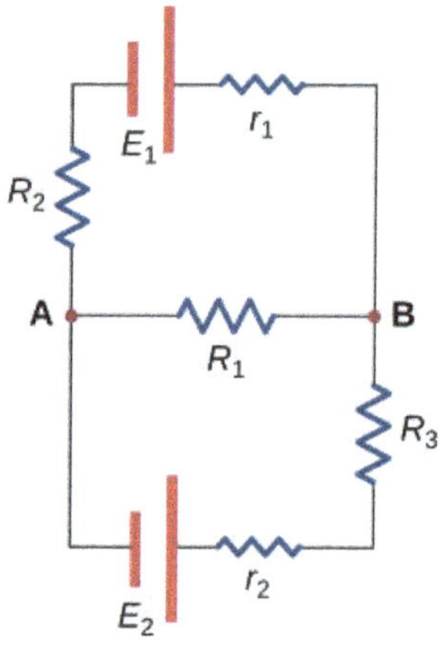

FIGURE 21.65

In this circuit, assume the currents through R_1, R_2 and R_3 are I_1, I_2 and I_3 respectively and all are flowing in the clockwise direction.

a. Find the equation obtained by applying Kirchhoff's junction rule at point A.
b. Find the equations obtained by applying Kirchhoff's loop rule in the upper and lower loops.
c. Assume $R_1 = R_2 = 6\ \Omega$, $R_3 = 12\ \Omega$, $r_1 = r_2 = 0\ \Omega$, E_1 = 6 V and E_2 = 4 V. Calculate I_1, I_2 and I_3.

d. For the situation in which E_2 is replaced by a closed switch, repeat parts (a) and (b). Using the values for R_1, R_2, R_3, r_1 and E_1 from part (c) calculate the currents through the three resistors.
e. For the circuit in part (d) calculate the output power of the voltage source and across all the resistors. Examine if energy is conserved in the circuit.
f. A student implemented the circuit of part (d) in the lab and measured the current though one of the resistors as 0.19 A. According to the results calculated in part (d) identify the resistor(s). Justify any difference in measured and calculated value.

21.6 DC Circuits Containing Resistors and Capacitors

12. A battery is connected to a resistor and an uncharged capacitor. The switch for the circuit is closed at $t = 0$ s.

a. While the capacitor is being charged, which of the following is true?

    a. Current through and voltage across the resistor increase.
    b. Current through and voltage across the resistor decrease.
    c. Current through and voltage across the resistor first increase and then decrease.
    d. Current through and voltage across the resistor first decrease and then increase.

b. When the capacitor is fully charged, which of the following is NOT zero?

    a. Current in the resistor.
    b. Voltage across the resistor.
    c. Current in the capacitor.
    d. None of the above.

13. An uncharged capacitor C is connected in series (with a switch) to a resistor R_1 and a voltage source E. Assume $E = 24$ V, $R_1 = 1.2$ kΩ and $C = 1$ mF.

a. What will be the current through the circuit as the switch is closed? Draw a circuit diagram and show the direction of current after the switch is closed. How long will it take for the capacitor to be 99% charged?
b. After full charging, this capacitor is connected in series to another resistor, $R_2 = 1$ kΩ. What will be the current in the circuit as soon as it's connected? Draw a circuit diagram and show the direction of current. How long will it take for the capacitor voltage to reach 3.24 V?

CHAPTER 22 Magnetism

FIGURE 22.1 The magnificent spectacle of the Aurora Borealis, or northern lights, glows in the northern sky above Bear Lake near Eielson Air Force Base, Alaska. Shaped by the Earth's magnetic field, this light is produced by radiation spewed from solar storms. (credit: Senior Airman Joshua Strang, via Flickr)

CHAPTER OUTLINE

CONNECTION FOR AP® COURSES Magnetism plays a major role in your everyday life. All electric motors, with uses as diverse as powering refrigerators, starting cars, and moving elevators, contain magnets. Magnetic resonance imaging (MRI) has become an important diagnostic tool in the field of medicine, and the use of magnetism to explore brain activity is a subject of contemporary research and development. Other applications of magnetism include computer memory, levitation of high-speed trains, the aurora borealis, and, of course, the first important historical use of magnetism: navigation. You will find all of these applications of magnetism linked by a small number of underlying principles.

In this chapter, you will learn that both the internal properties of an object and the movement of charged particles can generate a magnetic field, and you will learn why all magnetic fields have a north and south pole. You will also learn how magnetic fields exert forces on objects, resulting in the magnetic alignment that makes a compass work.

You will learn how we use this principle to weigh the smallest of subatomic particles with precision and contain superheated plasma to facilitate nuclear fusion.

Big Idea 1 Objects and systems have properties such as mass and charge. Systems may have internal structure.

Enduring Understanding 1.E Materials have many macroscopic properties that result from the arrangement and interactions of the atoms and molecules that make up the material.

Essential Knowledge 1.E.5 Matter has a property called magnetic permeability.

Essential Knowledge 1.E.6 Matter has a property called magnetic dipole moment.

Big Idea 2 Fields existing in space can be used to explain interactions.

Enduring Understanding 2.D A magnetic field is caused by a magnet or a moving electrically charged object. Magnetic fields observed in nature always seem to be produced either by moving charged objects or by magnetic dipoles or combinations of dipoles and never by single poles.

Essential Knowledge 2.D.1 The magnetic field exerts a force on a moving electrically charged object. That magnetic force is perpendicular to the direction of the velocity of the object and to the magnetic field and is proportional to the magnitude of the charge, the magnitude of the velocity, and the magnitude of the magnetic field. It also depends on the angle between the velocity and the magnetic field vectors. Treatment is quantitative for angles of 0°, 90°, or 180° and qualitative for other angles.

Essential Knowledge 2.D.2 The magnetic field vectors around a straight wire that carries electric current are tangent to concentric circles centered on that wire. The field has no component toward the current-carrying wire.

Essential Knowledge 2.D.3 A magnetic dipole placed in a magnetic field, such as the ones created by a magnet or the Earth, will tend to align with the magnetic field vector.

Essential Knowledge 2.D.4 Ferromagnetic materials contain magnetic domains that are themselves magnets.

Big Idea 3 The interactions of an object with other objects can be described by forces.

Enduring Understanding 3.C At the macroscopic level, forces can be categorized as either long-range (action-at-a-distance) forces or contact forces.

Essential Knowledge 3.C.3 A magnetic force results from the interaction of a moving charged object or a magnet with other moving charged objects or another magnet.

Big Idea 4 Interactions between systems can result in changes in those systems.

Enduring Understanding 4.E The electric and magnetic properties of a system can change in response to the presence of, or changes in, other objects or systems.

Essential Knowledge 4.E.1 The magnetic properties of some materials can be affected by magnetic fields at the system. Students should focus on the underlying concepts and not the use of the vocabulary.

FIGURE 22.2 Engineering of technology like iPods would not be possible without a deep understanding of magnetism. (credit: Jesse! S?, Flickr)

Click to view content (https://openstax.org/books/college-physics-ap-courses-2e/pages/22-connection-for-ap-r-courses)

22.1 Magnets

LEARNING OBJECTIVES

By the end of this section, you will be able to:

- Describe the difference between the north and south poles of a magnet.
- Describe how magnetic poles interact with each other.

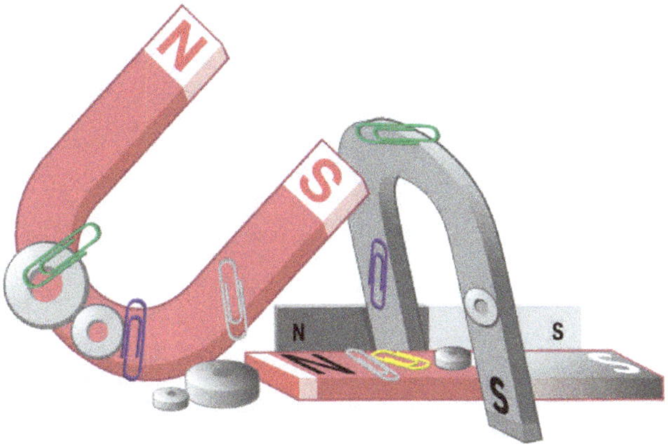

FIGURE 22.3 Magnets come in various shapes, sizes, and strengths. All have both a north pole and a south pole. There is never an isolated pole (a monopole).

All magnets attract iron, such as that in a refrigerator door. However, magnets may attract or repel other magnets. Experimentation shows that all magnets have two poles. If freely suspended, one pole will point toward the north. The two poles are thus named the **north magnetic pole** and the **south magnetic pole** (or more properly, north-seeking and south-seeking poles, for the attractions in those directions).

UNIVERSAL CHARACTERISTICS OF MAGNETS AND MAGNETIC POLES

It is a universal characteristic of all magnets that *like poles repel and unlike poles attract.* (Note the similarity with electrostatics: unlike charges attract and like charges repel.)

Further experimentation shows that it is *impossible to separate north and south poles* in the manner that + and – charges can be separated.

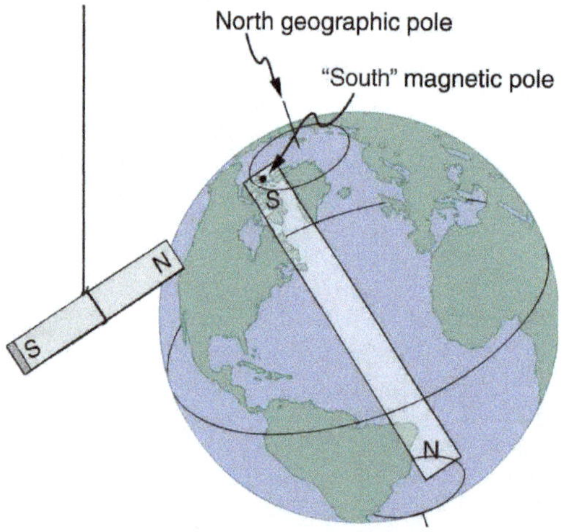

FIGURE 22.4 One end of a bar magnet is suspended from a thread that points toward north. The magnet's two poles are labeled N and S for north-seeking and south-seeking poles, respectively.

MISCONCEPTION ALERT: EARTH'S MAGNETIC POLES

Earth acts like a very large bar magnet with its south-seeking pole near the geographic North Pole. That is why the north pole of your compass is attracted toward the geographic north pole of Earth—because the magnetic pole that is near the geographic North Pole is actually a south magnetic pole! Confusion arises because the geographic term "North Pole" has come to be used (incorrectly) for the magnetic pole that is near the North Pole. Thus, "north magnetic pole" is actually a misnomer—it should be called the south magnetic pole.

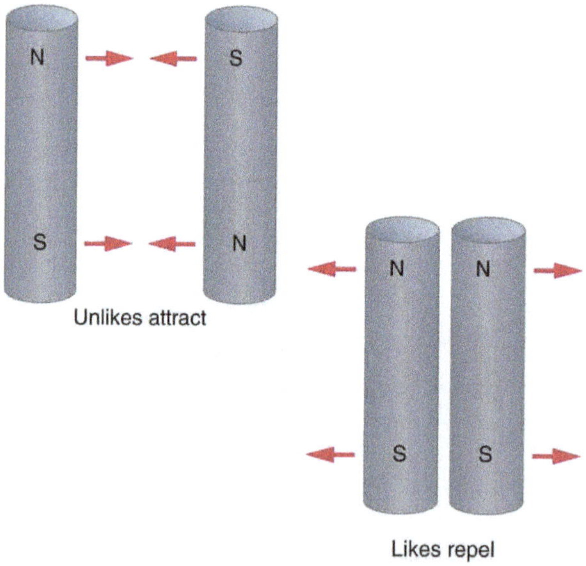

FIGURE 22.5 Unlike poles attract, whereas like poles repel.

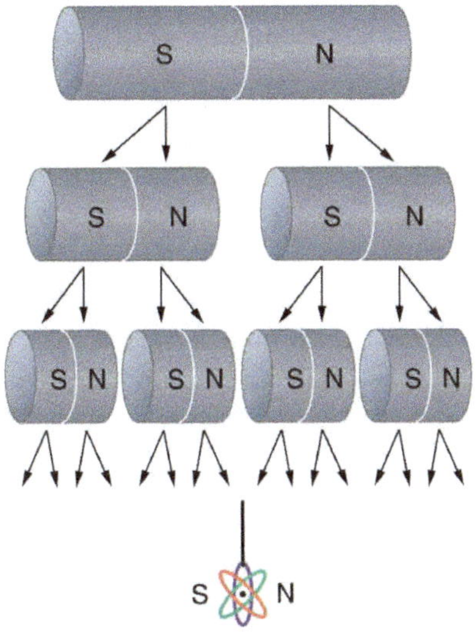

FIGURE 22.6 North and south poles always occur in pairs. Attempts to separate them result in more pairs of poles. If we continue to split the magnet, we will eventually get down to an iron atom with a north pole and a south pole—these, too, cannot be separated.

The fact that magnetic poles always occur in pairs of north and south is true from the very large scale—for example, sunspots always occur in pairs that are north and south magnetic poles—all the way down to the very small scale. Magnetic atoms have both a north pole and a south pole, as do many types of subatomic particles, such as electrons, protons, and neutrons.

MAKING CONNECTIONS: TAKE-HOME EXPERIMENT—REFRIGERATOR MAGNETS

We know that like magnetic poles repel and unlike poles attract. See if you can show this for two refrigerator magnets. Will the magnets stick if you turn them over? Why do they stick to the door anyway? What can you say about the magnetic properties of the door next to the magnet? Do refrigerator magnets stick to metal or plastic spoons? Do they stick to all types of metal?

22.2 Ferromagnets and Electromagnets

LEARNING OBJECTIVES

By the end of this section, you will be able to:

- Define ferromagnet.
- Describe the role of magnetic domains in magnetization.
- Explain the significance of the Curie temperature.
- Describe the relationship between electricity and magnetism.

Ferromagnets

Only certain materials, such as iron, cobalt, nickel, and gadolinium, exhibit strong magnetic effects. Such materials are called **ferromagnetic**, after the Latin word for iron, *ferrum*. A group of materials made from the alloys of the rare earth elements are also used as strong and permanent magnets; a popular one is neodymium. Other materials exhibit weak magnetic effects, which are detectable only with sensitive instruments. Not only do ferromagnetic materials respond strongly to magnets (the way iron is attracted to magnets), they can also be **magnetized** themselves—that is, they can be induced to be magnetic or made into permanent magnets.

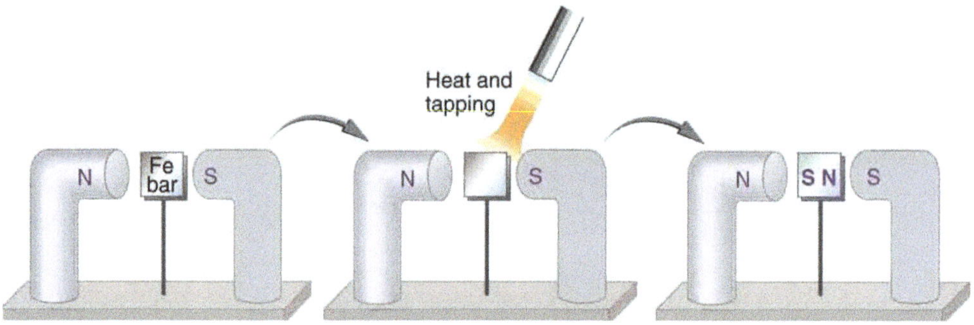

FIGURE 22.7 An unmagnetized piece of iron is placed between two magnets, heated, and then cooled, or simply tapped when cold. The iron becomes a permanent magnet with the poles aligned as shown: its south pole is adjacent to the north pole of the original magnet, and its north pole is adjacent to the south pole of the original magnet. Note that there are attractive forces between the magnets.

When a magnet is brought near a previously unmagnetized ferromagnetic material, it causes local magnetization of the material with unlike poles closest, as in Figure 22.7. (This results in the attraction of the previously unmagnetized material to the magnet.) What happens on a microscopic scale is illustrated in Figure 22.8. The regions within the material called **domains** act like small bar magnets. Within domains, the poles of individual atoms are aligned. Each atom acts like a tiny bar magnet. Domains are small and randomly oriented in an unmagnetized ferromagnetic object. In response to an external magnetic field, the domains may grow to millimeter size, aligning themselves as shown in Figure 22.8(b). This induced magnetization can be made permanent if the material is heated and then cooled, or simply tapped in the presence of other magnets.

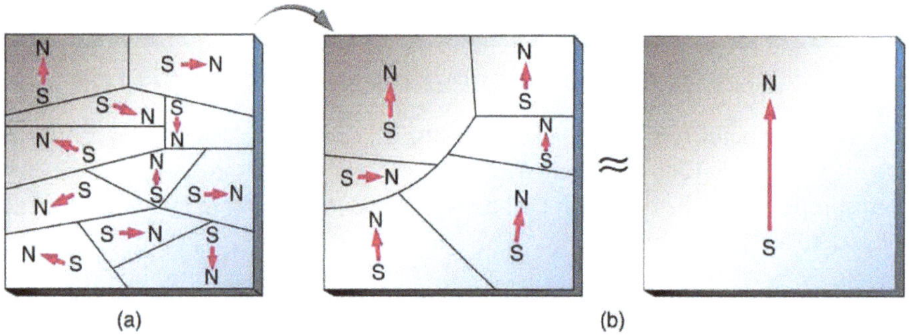

FIGURE 22.8 (a) An unmagnetized piece of iron (or other ferromagnetic material) has randomly oriented domains. (b) When magnetized by an external field, the domains show greater alignment, and some grow at the expense of others. Individual atoms are aligned within domains; each atom acts like a tiny bar magnet.

Conversely, a permanent magnet can be demagnetized by hard blows or by heating it in the absence of another magnet. Increased thermal motion at higher temperature can disrupt and randomize the orientation and the size of the domains. There is a well-defined temperature for ferromagnetic materials, which is called the **Curie temperature**, above which they cannot be magnetized. The Curie temperature for iron is 1043 K $(770^{\circ}\mathrm{C})$, which is well above room temperature. There are several elements and alloys that have Curie temperatures much lower than room temperature and are ferromagnetic only below those temperatures.

Electromagnets

Early in the 19th century, it was discovered that electrical currents cause magnetic effects. The first significant observation was by the Danish scientist Hans Christian Oersted (1777–1851), who found that a compass needle was deflected by a current-carrying wire. This was the first significant evidence that the movement of charges had any connection with magnets. **Electromagnetism** is the use of electric current to make magnets. These temporarily induced magnets are called **electromagnets**. Electromagnets are employed for everything from a wrecking yard crane that lifts scrapped cars to controlling the beam of a 90-km-circumference particle accelerator to the magnets in medical imaging machines (See Figure 22.9).

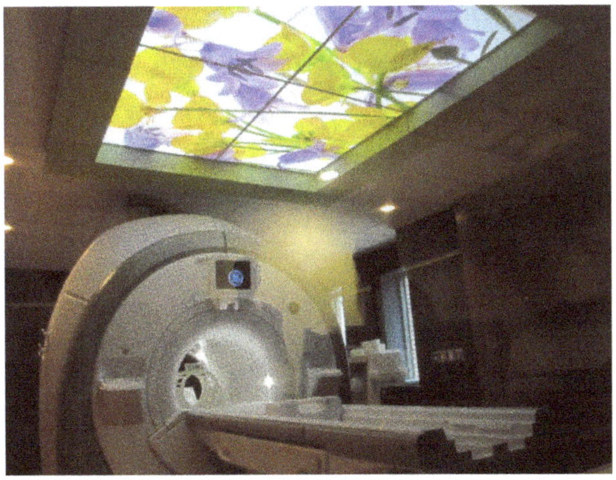

FIGURE 22.9 Instrument for magnetic resonance imaging (MRI). The device uses a superconducting cylindrical coil for the main magnetic field. The patient goes into this "tunnel" on the gurney. (credit: Bill McChesney, Flickr)

Figure 22.10 shows that the response of iron filings to a current-carrying coil and to a permanent bar magnet. The patterns are similar. In fact, electromagnets and ferromagnets have the same basic characteristics—for example, they have north and south poles that cannot be separated and for which like poles repel and unlike poles attract.

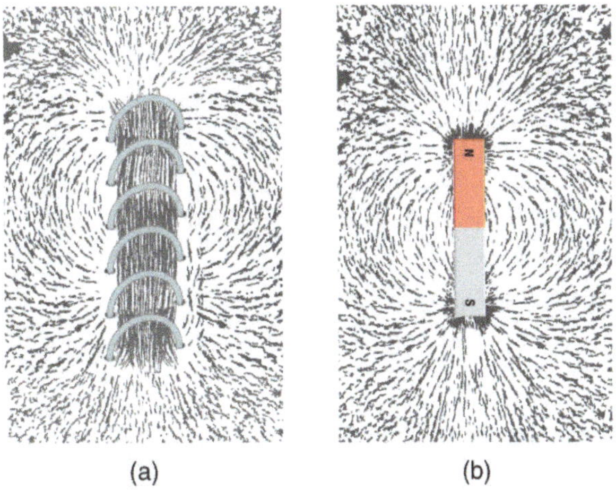

FIGURE 22.10 Iron filings near (a) a current-carrying coil and (b) a magnet act like tiny compass needles, showing the shape of their fields. Their response to a current-carrying coil and a permanent magnet is seen to be very similar, especially near the ends of the coil and the magnet.

Combining a ferromagnet with an electromagnet can produce particularly strong magnetic effects. (See Figure 22.11.) Whenever strong magnetic effects are needed, such as lifting scrap metal, or in particle accelerators, electromagnets are enhanced by ferromagnetic materials. Limits to how strong the magnets can be made are imposed by coil resistance (it will overheat and melt at sufficiently high current), and so superconducting magnets may be employed. These are still limited, because superconducting properties are destroyed by too great a magnetic field.

FIGURE 22.11 An electromagnet with a ferromagnetic core can produce very strong magnetic effects. Alignment of domains in the core produces a magnet, the poles of which are aligned with the electromagnet.

Figure 22.12 shows a few uses of combinations of electromagnets and ferromagnets. Ferromagnetic materials can act as memory devices, because the orientation of the magnetic fields of small domains can be reversed or erased. Magnetic information storage on videotapes and computer hard drives are among the most common applications. This property is vital in our digital world.

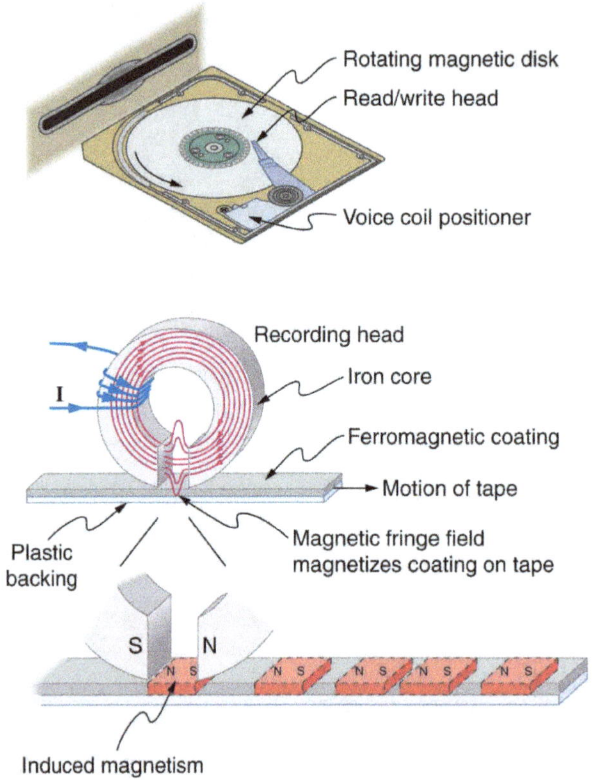

FIGURE 22.12 An electromagnet induces regions of permanent magnetism on a floppy disk coated with a ferromagnetic material. The information stored here is digital (a region is either magnetic or not); in other applications, it can be analog (with a varying strength), such as on audiotapes.

Current: The Source of All Magnetism

An electromagnet creates magnetism with an electric current. In later sections we explore this more quantitatively, finding the strength and direction of magnetic fields created by various currents. But what about ferromagnets? Figure 22.13 shows models of how electric currents create magnetism at the submicroscopic level. (Note that we cannot directly observe the paths of individual electrons about atoms, and so a model or visual image, consistent with all direct observations, is made. We can directly observe the electron's orbital angular momentum, its spin momentum, and subsequent magnetic moments, all of which are explained with electric-current-creating subatomic magnetism.) Currents, including those associated with other submicroscopic particles like protons, allow us to explain ferromagnetism and all other magnetic effects. Ferromagnetism, for example, results from an internal cooperative alignment of electron spins, possible in some materials but not in others.

Crucial to the statement that electric current is the source of all magnetism is the fact that it is impossible to separate north and south magnetic poles. (This is far different from the case of positive and negative charges, which are easily separated.) A current loop always produces a magnetic dipole—that is, a magnetic field that acts like a north pole and south pole pair. Since isolated north and south magnetic poles, called **magnetic monopoles**, are not observed, currents are used to explain all magnetic effects. If magnetic monopoles did exist, then we would have to modify this underlying connection that all magnetism is due to electrical current. There is no known reason that magnetic monopoles should not exist—they are simply never observed—and so searches at the subnuclear level continue. If they do *not* exist, we would like to find out why not. If they *do* exist, we would like to see evidence of them.

ELECTRIC CURRENTS AND MAGNETISM

Electric current is the source of all magnetism.

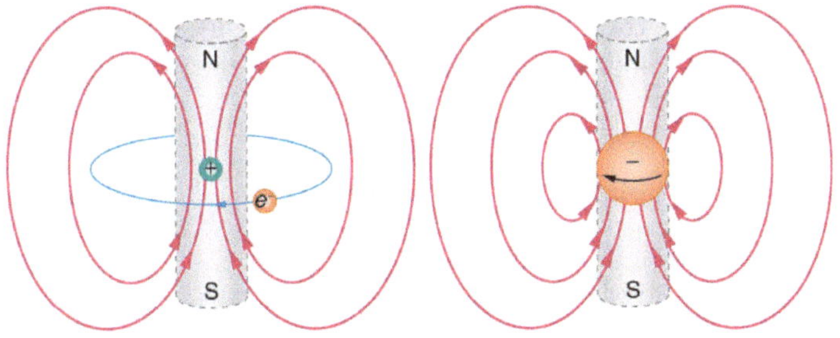

FIGURE 22.13 (a) In the planetary model of the atom, an electron orbits a nucleus, forming a closed-current loop and producing a magnetic field with a north pole and a south pole. (b) Electrons have spin and can be crudely pictured as rotating charge, forming a current that produces a magnetic field with a north pole and a south pole. Neither the planetary model nor the image of a spinning electron is completely consistent with modern physics. However, they do provide a useful way of understanding phenomena.

PHET EXPLORATIONS

Magnets and Electromagnets

Explore the interactions between a compass and bar magnet. Discover how you can use a battery and wire to make a magnet! Can you make it a stronger magnet? Can you make the magnetic field reverse?

Click to view content (https://openstax.org/l/28elec_magnet).

PhET

22.3 Magnetic Fields and Magnetic Field Lines

LEARNING OBJECTIVES

By the end of this section, you will be able to:

- Define magnetic field and describe the magnetic field lines of various magnetic fields.

Einstein is said to have been fascinated by a compass as a child, perhaps musing on how the needle felt a force without direct physical contact. His ability to think deeply and clearly about action at a distance, particularly for gravitational, electric, and magnetic forces, later enabled him to create his revolutionary theory of relativity. Since magnetic forces act at a distance, we define a **magnetic field** to represent magnetic forces. The pictorial representation of **magnetic field lines** is very useful in visualizing the strength and direction of the magnetic field. As shown in Figure 22.14, the **direction of magnetic field lines** is defined to be the direction in which the north end of a compass needle points. The magnetic field is traditionally called the ***B*-field**.

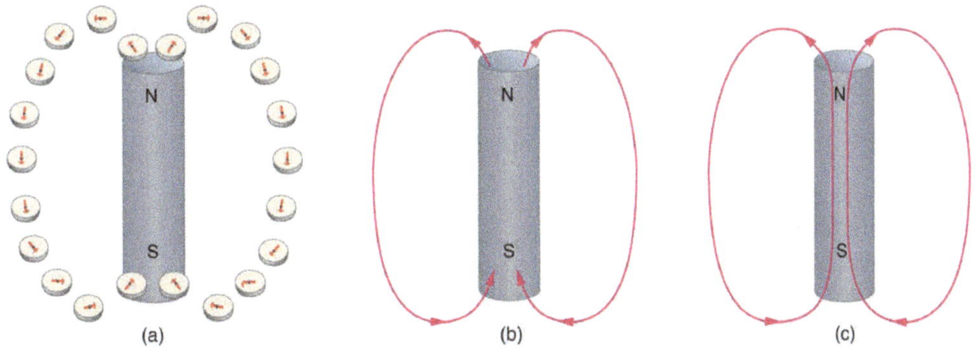

FIGURE 22.14 Magnetic field lines are defined to have the direction that a small compass points when placed at a location. (a) If small compasses are used to map the magnetic field around a bar magnet, they will point in the directions shown: away from the north pole of the magnet, toward the south pole of the magnet. (Recall that the Earth's north magnetic pole is really a south pole in terms of definitions of poles on a bar magnet.) (b) Connecting the arrows gives continuous magnetic field lines. The strength of the field is proportional to the

closeness (or density) of the lines. (c) If the interior of the magnet could be probed, the field lines would be found to form continuous closed loops.

Small compasses used to test a magnetic field will not disturb it. (This is analogous to the way we tested electric fields with a small test charge. In both cases, the fields represent only the object creating them and not the probe testing them.) Figure 22.15 shows how the magnetic field appears for a current loop and a long straight wire, as could be explored with small compasses. A small compass placed in these fields will align itself parallel to the field line at its location, with its north pole pointing in the direction of *B*. Note the symbols used for field into and out of the paper.

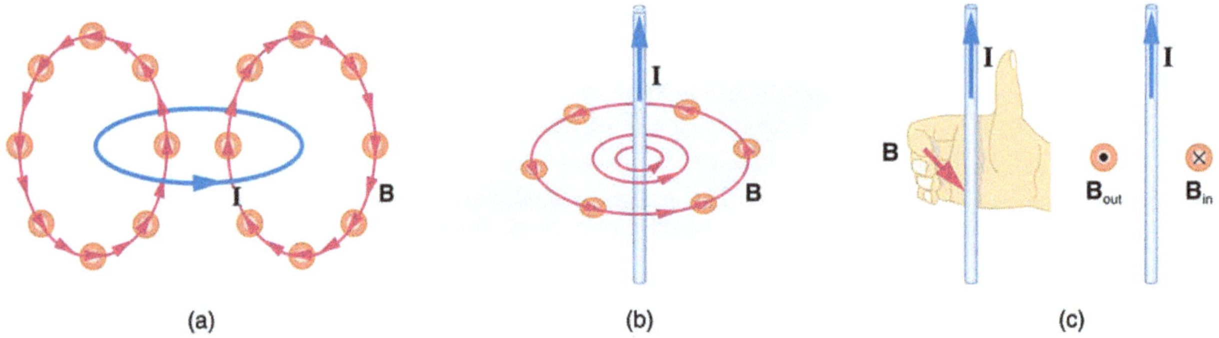

FIGURE 22.15 Small compasses could be used to map the fields shown here. (a) The magnetic field of a circular current loop is similar to that of a bar magnet. (b) A long and straight wire creates a field with magnetic field lines forming circular loops. (c) When the wire is in the plane of the paper, the field is perpendicular to the paper. Note that the symbols used for the field pointing inward (like the tail of an arrow) and the field pointing outward (like the tip of an arrow).

MAKING CONNECTIONS: CONCEPT OF A FIELD

A field is a way of mapping forces surrounding any object that can act on another object at a distance without apparent physical connection. The field represents the object generating it. Gravitational fields map gravitational forces, electric fields map electrical forces, and magnetic fields map magnetic forces.

Extensive exploration of magnetic fields has revealed a number of hard-and-fast rules. We use magnetic field lines to represent the field (the lines are a pictorial tool, not a physical entity in and of themselves). The properties of magnetic field lines can be summarized by these rules:

1. The direction of the magnetic field is tangent to the field line at any point in space. A small compass will point in the direction of the field line.
2. The strength of the field is proportional to the closeness of the lines. It is exactly proportional to the number of lines per unit area perpendicular to the lines (called the areal density).
3. Magnetic field lines can never cross, meaning that the field is unique at any point in space.
4. Magnetic field lines are continuous, forming closed loops without beginning or end. They go from the north pole to the south pole.

The last property is related to the fact that the north and south poles cannot be separated. It is a distinct difference from electric field lines, which begin and end on the positive and negative charges. If magnetic monopoles existed, then magnetic field lines would begin and end on them.

22.4 Magnetic Field Strength: Force on a Moving Charge in a Magnetic Field

LEARNING OBJECTIVES

By the end of this section, you will be able to:

- Describe the effects of magnetic fields on moving charges.
- Use the right hand rule 1 to determine the velocity of a charge, the direction of the magnetic field, and the direction of the magnetic force on a moving charge.
- Calculate the magnetic force on a moving charge.

What is the mechanism by which one magnet exerts a force on another? The answer is related to the fact that all magnetism is caused by current, the flow of charge. *Magnetic fields exert forces on moving charges*, and so they exert forces on other magnets, all of which have moving charges.

Right Hand Rule 1

The magnetic force on a moving charge is one of the most fundamental known. Magnetic force is as important as the electrostatic or Coulomb force. Yet the magnetic force is more complex, in both the number of factors that affects it and in its direction, than the relatively simple Coulomb force. The magnitude of the **magnetic force** F on a charge q moving at a speed v in a magnetic field of strength B is given by

$$F = qvB \sin \theta, \tag{22.1}$$

where θ is the angle between the directions of $\mathbf{v}$ and $\mathbf{B}$. This force is often called the **Lorentz force**. In fact, this is how we define the magnetic field strength B—in terms of the force on a charged particle moving in a magnetic field. The SI unit for magnetic field strength B is called the **tesla** (T) after the eccentric but brilliant inventor Nikola Tesla (1856–1943). To determine how the tesla relates to other SI units, we solve $F = qvB \sin \theta$ for B.

$$B = \frac{F}{qv \sin \theta} \tag{22.2}$$

Because $\sin \theta$ is unitless, the tesla is

$$1\ \text{T} = \frac{1\ \text{N}}{\text{C} \cdot \text{m/s}} = \frac{1\ \text{N}}{\text{A} \cdot \text{m}} \tag{22.3}$$

(note that C/s = A).

Another smaller unit, called the **gauss** (G), where $1\ \text{G} = 10^{-4}\ \text{T}$, is sometimes used. The strongest permanent magnets have fields near 2 T; superconducting electromagnets may attain 10 T or more. The Earth's magnetic field on its surface is only about $5 \times 10^{-5}\ \text{T}$, or 0.5 G.

The *direction* of the magnetic force $\mathbf{F}$ is perpendicular to the plane formed by $\mathbf{v}$ and $\mathbf{B}$, as determined by the **right hand rule 1** (or RHR-1), which is illustrated in Figure 22.16. RHR-1 states that, to determine the direction of the magnetic force on a positive moving charge, you point the thumb of the right hand in the direction of $\mathbf{v}$, the fingers in the direction of $\mathbf{B}$, and a perpendicular to the palm points in the direction of $\mathbf{F}$. One way to remember this is that there is one velocity, and so the thumb represents it. There are many field lines, and so the fingers represent them. The force is in the direction you would push with your palm. The force on a negative charge is in exactly the opposite direction to that on a positive charge.

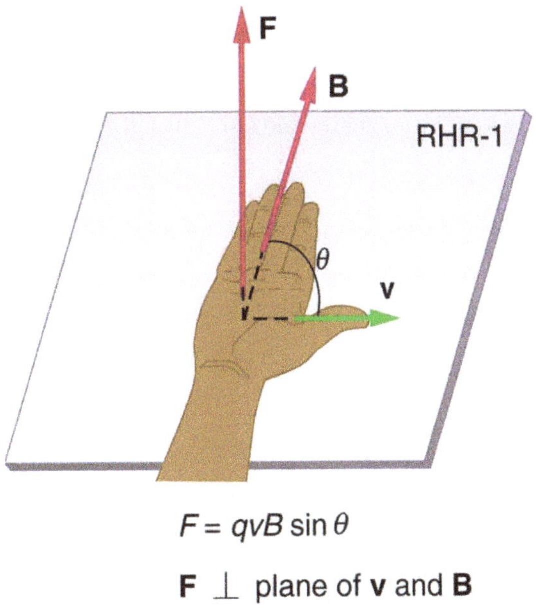

FIGURE 22.16 Magnetic fields exert forces on moving charges. This force is one of the most basic known. The direction of the magnetic force on a moving charge is perpendicular to the plane formed by $\mathbf{v}$ and $\mathbf{B}$ and follows right hand rule–1 (RHR-1) as shown. The magnitude of the force is proportional to q, v, B, and the sine of the angle between $\mathbf{v}$ and $\mathbf{B}$.

MAKING CONNECTIONS: CHARGES AND MAGNETS

There is no magnetic force on static charges. However, there is a magnetic force on moving charges. When charges are stationary, their electric fields do not affect magnets. But, when charges move, they produce magnetic fields that exert forces on other magnets. When there is relative motion, a connection between electric and magnetic fields emerges—each affects the other.

EXAMPLE 22.1

Calculating Magnetic Force: Earth's Magnetic Field on a Charged Glass Rod

With the exception of compasses, you seldom see or personally experience forces due to the Earth's small magnetic field. To illustrate this, suppose that in a physics lab you rub a glass rod with silk, placing a 20-nC positive charge on it. Calculate the force on the rod due to the Earth's magnetic field, if you throw it with a horizontal velocity of 10 m/s due west in a place where the Earth's field is due north parallel to the ground. (The direction of the force is determined with right hand rule 1 as shown in Figure 22.17.)

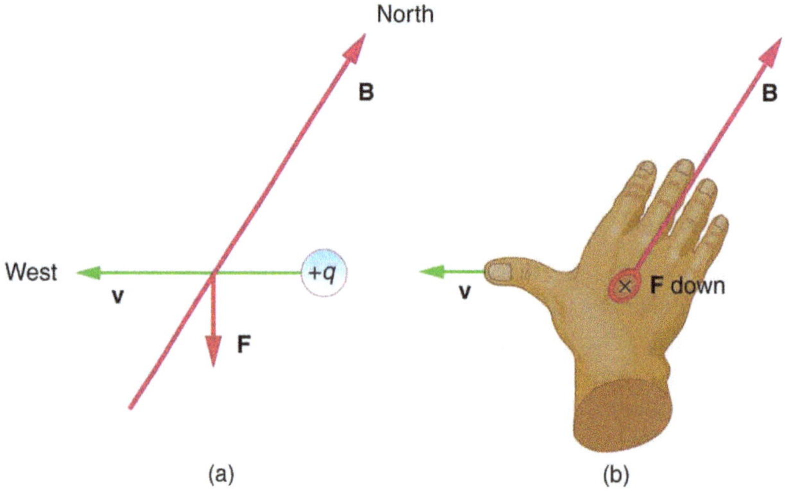

FIGURE 22.17 A positively charged object moving due west in a region where the Earth's magnetic field is due north experiences a force that is straight down as shown. A negative charge moving in the same direction would feel a force straight up.

Strategy

We are given the charge, its velocity, and the magnetic field strength and direction. We can thus use the equation $F = qvB \sin \theta$ to find the force.

Solution

The magnetic force is

$$F = qvB \sin \theta. \tag{22.4}$$

We see that $\sin \theta = 1$, since the angle between the velocity and the direction of the field is 90°. Entering the other given quantities yields

$$\begin{aligned} F &= \left(20 \times 10^{-9}\ \text{C}\right)(10\ \text{m/s})\left(5 \times 10^{-5}\ \text{T}\right) \\ &= 1 \times 10^{-11}\ (\text{C} \cdot \text{m/s})\left(\frac{\text{N}}{\text{C}\cdot\text{m/s}}\right) = 1 \times 10^{-11}\ \text{N}. \end{aligned} \tag{22.5}$$

Discussion

This force is completely negligible on any macroscopic object, consistent with experience. (It is calculated to only one digit, since the Earth's field varies with location and is given to only one digit.) The Earth's magnetic field, however, does produce very important effects, particularly on submicroscopic particles. Some of these are explored in Force on a Moving Charge in a Magnetic Field: Examples and Applications.

22.5 Force on a Moving Charge in a Magnetic Field: Examples and Applications

LEARNING OBJECTIVES

By the end of this section, you will be able to:

- Describe the effects of a magnetic field on a moving charge.
- Calculate the radius of curvature of the path of a charge that is moving in a magnetic field.

Magnetic force can cause a charged particle to move in a circular or spiral path. Cosmic rays are energetic charged particles in outer space, some of which approach the Earth. They can be forced into spiral paths by the Earth's magnetic field. Protons in giant accelerators are kept in a circular path by magnetic force. The bubble chamber photograph in Figure 22.18 shows charged particles moving in such curved paths. The curved paths of charged particles in magnetic fields are the basis of a number of phenomena and can even be used analytically, such as in a mass spectrometer.

FIGURE 22.18 Trails of bubbles are produced by high-energy charged particles moving through the superheated liquid hydrogen in this artist's rendition of a bubble chamber. There is a strong magnetic field perpendicular to the page that causes the curved paths of the particles. The radius of the path can be used to find the mass, charge, and energy of the particle.

So does the magnetic force cause circular motion? Magnetic force is always perpendicular to velocity, so that it does no work on the charged particle. The particle's kinetic energy and speed thus remain constant. The direction of motion is affected, but not the speed. This is typical of uniform circular motion. The simplest case occurs when a charged particle moves perpendicular to a uniform $\boldsymbol{B}$-field, such as shown in Figure 22.19. (If this takes place in a vacuum, the magnetic field is the dominant factor determining the motion.) Here, the magnetic force supplies the centripetal force $F_c = mv^2/r$. Noting that $\sin\theta = 1$, we see that $F = qvB$.

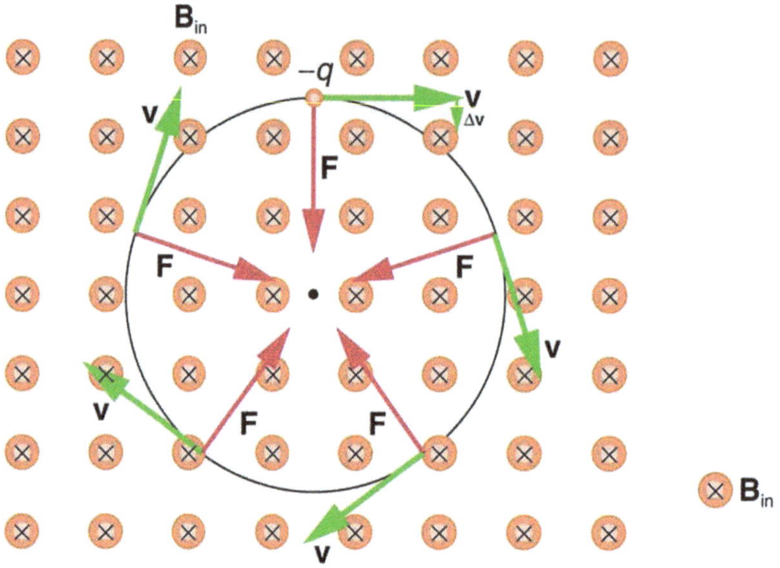

FIGURE 22.19 A negatively charged particle moves in the plane of the page in a region where the magnetic field is perpendicular into the page (represented by the small circles with x's—like the tails of arrows). The magnetic force is perpendicular to the velocity, and so velocity changes in direction but not magnitude. Uniform circular motion results.

Because the magnetic force F supplies the centripetal force F_c, we have

$$qvB = \frac{mv^2}{r}. \quad 22.6$$

Solving for r yields

$$r = \frac{mv}{qB}. \quad 22.7$$

Here, r is the radius of curvature of the path of a charged particle with mass m and charge q, moving at a speed v perpendicular to a magnetic field of strength B. If the velocity is not perpendicular to the magnetic field, then v is the component of the velocity perpendicular to the field. The component of the velocity parallel to the field is unaffected, since the magnetic force is zero for motion parallel to the field. This produces a spiral motion rather than a circular one.

EXAMPLE 22.2

Calculating the Curvature of the Path of an Electron Moving in a Magnetic Field: A Magnet on a TV Screen

A magnet brought near an old-fashioned TV screen such as in Figure 22.20 (TV sets with cathode ray tubes instead of LCD screens) severely distorts its picture by altering the path of the electrons that make its phosphors glow. ***(Don't try this at home, as it will permanently magnetize and ruin the TV.)*** To illustrate this, calculate the radius of curvature of the path of an electron having a velocity of 6.00×10^7 m/s (corresponding to the accelerating voltage of about 10.0 kV used in some TVs) perpendicular to a magnetic field of strength $B = 0.500$ T (obtainable with permanent magnets).

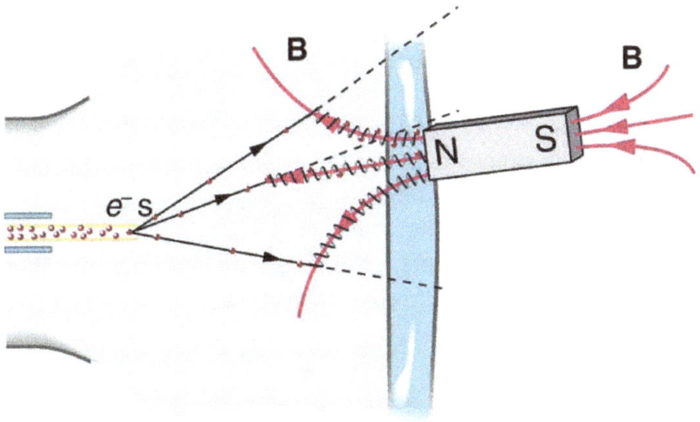

FIGURE 22.20 Side view showing what happens when a magnet comes in contact with a computer monitor or TV screen. Electrons moving toward the screen spiral about magnetic field lines, maintaining the component of their velocity parallel to the field lines. This distorts the image on the screen.

Strategy

We can find the radius of curvature r directly from the equation $r = \frac{mv}{qB}$, since all other quantities in it are given or known.

Solution

Using known values for the mass and charge of an electron, along with the given values of v and B gives us

$$r = \frac{mv}{qB} = \frac{\left(9.11\times10^{-31}\text{ kg}\right)\left(6.00\times10^{7}\text{ m/s}\right)}{\left(1.60\times10^{-19}\text{ C}\right)(0.500\text{ T})} = 6.83\times10^{-4}\text{ m} \quad 22.8$$

or

$$r = 0.683\text{ mm}. \quad 22.9$$

Discussion

The small radius indicates a large effect. The electrons in the TV picture tube are made to move in very tight circles, greatly altering their paths and distorting the image.

Figure 22.21 shows how electrons not moving perpendicular to magnetic field lines follow the field lines. The component of velocity parallel to the lines is unaffected, and so the charges spiral along the field lines. If field strength increases in the direction of motion, the field will exert a force to slow the charges, forming a kind of magnetic mirror, as shown below.

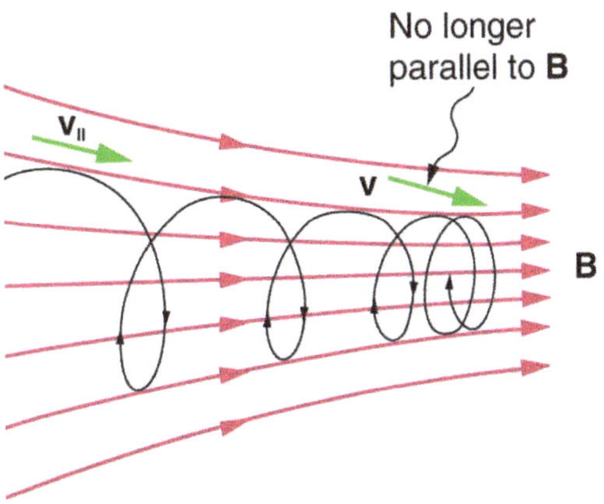

FIGURE 22.21 When a charged particle moves along a magnetic field line into a region where the field becomes stronger, the particle experiences a force that reduces the component of velocity parallel to the field. This force slows the motion along the field line and here

reverses it, forming a “magnetic mirror.”

The properties of charged particles in magnetic fields are related to such different things as the Aurora Australis or Aurora Borealis and particle accelerators. *Charged particles approaching magnetic field lines may get trapped in spiral orbits about the lines rather than crossing them*, as seen above. Some cosmic rays, for example, follow the Earth’s magnetic field lines, entering the atmosphere near the magnetic poles and causing the southern or northern lights through their ionization of molecules in the atmosphere. This glow of energized atoms and molecules is seen in Introduction to Magnetism. Those particles that approach middle latitudes must cross magnetic field lines, and many are prevented from penetrating the atmosphere. Cosmic rays are a component of background radiation; consequently, they give a higher radiation dose at the poles than at the equator.

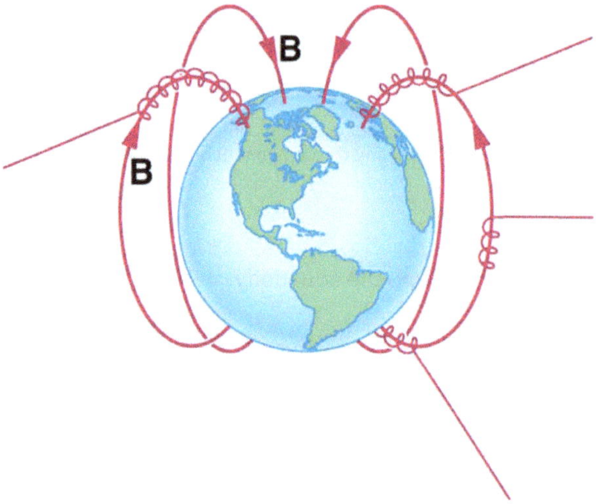

FIGURE 22.22 Energetic electrons and protons, components of cosmic rays, from the Sun and deep outer space often follow the Earth’s magnetic field lines rather than cross them. (Recall that the Earth’s north magnetic pole is really a south pole in terms of a bar magnet.)

Some incoming charged particles become trapped in the Earth’s magnetic field, forming two belts above the atmosphere known as the Van Allen radiation belts after the discoverer James A. Van Allen, an American astrophysicist. (See Figure 22.23.) Particles trapped in these belts form radiation fields (similar to nuclear radiation) so intense that piloted space flights avoid them and satellites with sensitive electronics are kept out of them. In the few minutes it took lunar missions to cross the Van Allen radiation belts, astronauts received radiation doses more than twice the allowed annual exposure for radiation workers. Other planets have similar belts, especially those having strong magnetic fields like Jupiter.

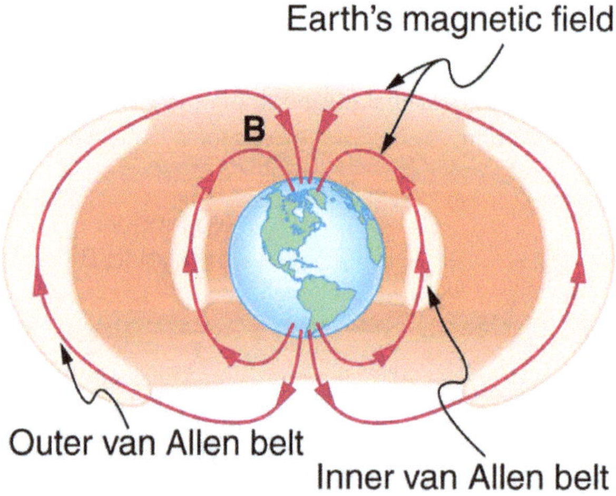

FIGURE 22.23 The Van Allen radiation belts are two regions in which energetic charged particles are trapped in the Earth’s magnetic field. One belt lies about 300 km above the Earth’s surface, the other about 16,000 km. Charged particles in these belts migrate along magnetic field lines and are partially reflected away from the poles by the stronger fields there. The charged particles that enter the atmosphere are replenished by the Sun and sources in deep outer space.

Back on Earth, we have devices that employ magnetic fields to contain charged particles. Among them are the giant particle accelerators that have been used to explore the substructure of matter. (See Figure 22.24.) Magnetic fields not only control the direction of the charged particles, they also are used to focus particles into beams and overcome the repulsion of like charges in these beams.

FIGURE 22.24 The Fermilab facility in Illinois has a large particle accelerator (the most powerful in the world until 2008) that employs magnetic fields (magnets seen here in orange) to contain and direct its beam. This and other accelerators have been in use for several decades and have allowed us to discover some of the laws underlying all matter. (credit: ammcrim, Flickr)

Thermonuclear fusion (like that occurring in the Sun) is a hope for a future clean energy source. One of the most promising devices is the *tokamak*, which uses magnetic fields to contain (or trap) and direct the reactive charged particles. (See Figure 22.25.) Less exotic, but more immediately practical, amplifiers in microwave ovens use a magnetic field to contain oscillating electrons. These oscillating electrons generate the microwaves sent into the oven.

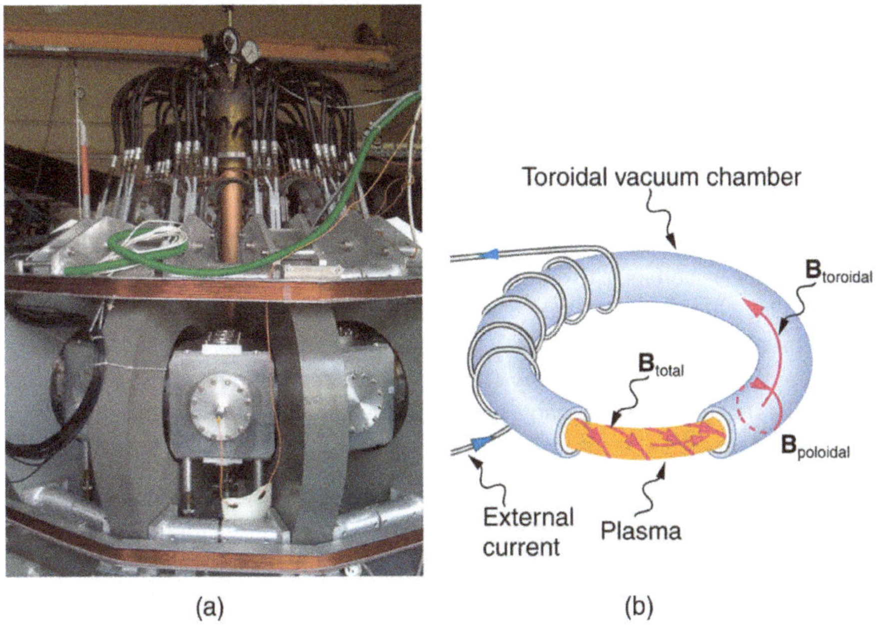

FIGURE 22.25 Tokamaks such as the one shown in the figure are being studied with the goal of economical production of energy by nuclear fusion. Magnetic fields in the doughnut-shaped device contain and direct the reactive charged particles. (credit: David Mellis, Flickr)

Mass spectrometers have a variety of designs, and many use magnetic fields to measure mass. The curvature of a charged particle's path in the field is related to its mass and is measured to obtain mass information. (See More Applications of Magnetism.) Historically, such techniques were employed in the first direct observations of electron charge and mass. Today, mass spectrometers (sometimes coupled with gas chromatographs) are used to determine the make-up and sequencing of large biological molecules.

22.6 The Hall Effect

LEARNING OBJECTIVES

By the end of this section, you will be able to:

- Describe the Hall effect.
- Calculate the Hall emf across a current-carrying conductor.

We have seen effects of a magnetic field on free-moving charges. The magnetic field also affects charges moving in a conductor. One result is the Hall effect, which has important implications and applications.

Figure 22.26 shows what happens to charges moving through a conductor in a magnetic field. The field is perpendicular to the electron drift velocity and to the width of the conductor. Note that conventional current is to the right in both parts of the figure. In part (a), electrons carry the current and move to the left. In part (b), positive charges carry the current and move to the right. Moving electrons feel a magnetic force toward one side of the conductor, leaving a net positive charge on the other side. This separation of charge *creates a voltage* ε, known as the **Hall emf**, *across* the conductor. The creation of a voltage *across* a current-carrying conductor by a magnetic field is known as the **Hall effect**, after Edwin Hall, the American physicist who discovered it in 1879.

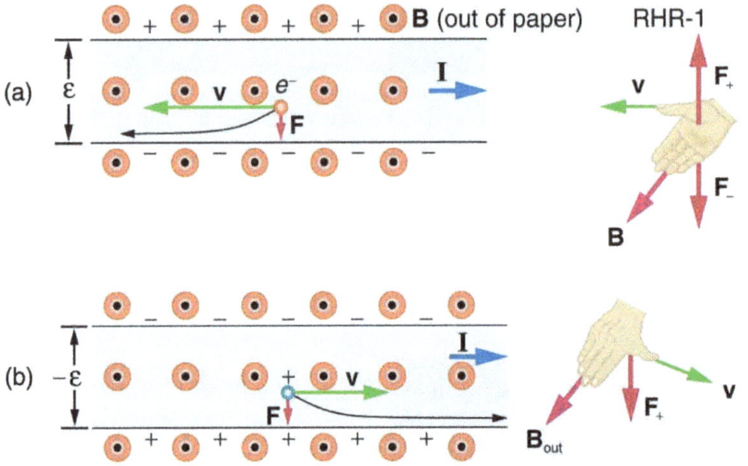

FIGURE 22.26 The Hall effect. (a) Electrons move to the left in this flat conductor (conventional current to the right). The magnetic field is directly out of the page, represented by circled dots; it exerts a force on the moving charges, causing a voltage ε, the Hall emf, across the conductor. (b) Positive charges moving to the right (conventional current also to the right) are moved to the side, producing a Hall emf of the opposite sign, $-\varepsilon$. Thus, if the direction of the field and current are known, the sign of the charge carriers can be determined from the Hall effect.

One very important use of the Hall effect is to determine whether positive or negative charges carries the current. Note that in Figure 22.26(b), where positive charges carry the current, the Hall emf has the sign opposite to when negative charges carry the current. Historically, the Hall effect was used to show that electrons carry current in metals and it also shows that positive charges carry current in some semiconductors. The Hall effect is used today as a research tool to probe the movement of charges, their drift velocities and densities, and so on, in materials. In 1980, it was discovered that the Hall effect is quantized, an example of quantum behavior in a macroscopic object.

The Hall effect has other uses that range from the determination of blood flow rate to precision measurement of magnetic field strength. To examine these quantitatively, we need an expression for the Hall emf, ε, across a conductor. Consider the balance of forces on a moving charge in a situation where B, v, and l are mutually perpendicular, such as shown in Figure 22.27. Although the magnetic force moves negative charges to one side, they cannot build up without limit. The electric field caused by their separation opposes the magnetic force, $F = qvB$, and the electric force, $F_e = qE$, eventually grows to equal it. That is,

$$qE = qvB \tag{22.10}$$

or

$$E = vB. \tag{22.11}$$

Note that the electric field E is uniform across the conductor because the magnetic field B is uniform, as is the conductor. For a uniform electric field, the relationship between electric field and voltage is $E = \varepsilon / l$, where l is the width of the conductor and ε is the Hall emf. Entering this into the last expression gives

$$\frac{\varepsilon}{l} = vB. \tag{22.12}$$

Solving this for the Hall emf yields

$$\varepsilon = Blv \text{ } (B,\, v,\text{ and } l,\text{ mutually perpendicular}), \tag{22.13}$$

where ε is the Hall effect voltage across a conductor of width l through which charges move at a speed v.

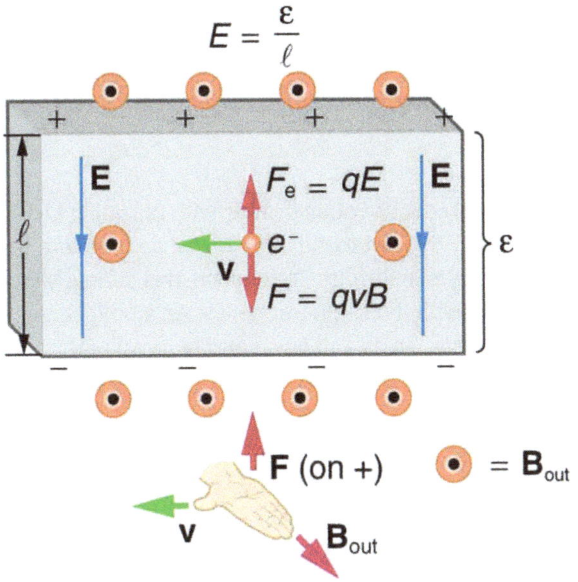

FIGURE 22.27 The Hall emf ε produces an electric force that balances the magnetic force on the moving charges. The magnetic force produces charge separation, which builds up until it is balanced by the electric force, an equilibrium that is quickly reached.

One of the most common uses of the Hall effect is in the measurement of magnetic field strength B. Such devices, called *Hall probes*, can be made very small, allowing fine position mapping. Hall probes can also be made very accurate, usually accomplished by careful calibration. Another application of the Hall effect is to measure fluid flow in any fluid that has free charges (most do). (See Figure 22.28.) A magnetic field applied perpendicular to the flow direction produces a Hall emf ε as shown. Note that the sign of ε depends not on the sign of the charges, but only on the directions of B and v. The magnitude of the Hall emf is $\varepsilon = Blv$, where l is the pipe diameter, so that the average velocity v can be determined from ε providing the other factors are known.

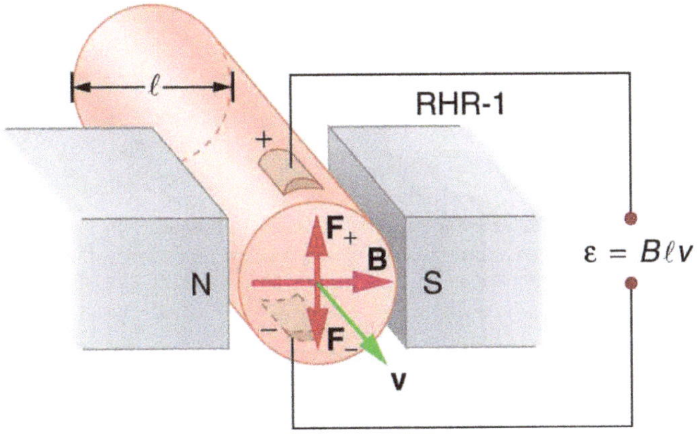

FIGURE 22.28 The Hall effect can be used to measure fluid flow in any fluid having free charges, such as blood. The Hall emf ε is measured across the tube perpendicular to the applied magnetic field and is proportional to the average velocity v.

EXAMPLE 22.3

Calculating the Hall emf: Hall Effect for Blood Flow

A Hall effect flow probe is placed on an artery, applying a 0.100-T magnetic field across it, in a setup similar to that in Figure 22.28. What is the Hall emf, given the vessel's inside diameter is 4.00 mm and the average blood velocity is 20.0 cm/s?

Strategy

Because B, v, and l are mutually perpendicular, the equation $\varepsilon = Blv$ can be used to find ε.

Solution

Entering the given values for B, v, and l gives

$$\begin{aligned} \varepsilon &= Blv = (0.100\ \text{T})\left(4.00 \times 10^{-3}\ \text{m}\right)(0.200\ \text{m/s}) \\ &= 80.0\ \mu\text{V} \end{aligned} \tag{22.14}$$

Discussion

This is the average voltage output. Instantaneous voltage varies with pulsating blood flow. The voltage is small in this type of measurement. ε is particularly difficult to measure, because there are voltages associated with heart action (ECG voltages) that are on the order of millivolts. In practice, this difficulty is overcome by applying an AC magnetic field, so that the Hall emf is AC with the same frequency. An amplifier can be very selective in picking out only the appropriate frequency, eliminating signals and noise at other frequencies.

22.7 Magnetic Force on a Current-Carrying Conductor

LEARNING OBJECTIVES

By the end of this section, you will be able to:

- Describe the effects of a magnetic force on a current-carrying conductor.
- Calculate the magnetic force on a current-carrying conductor.

Because charges ordinarily cannot escape a conductor, the magnetic force on charges moving in a conductor is transmitted to the conductor itself.

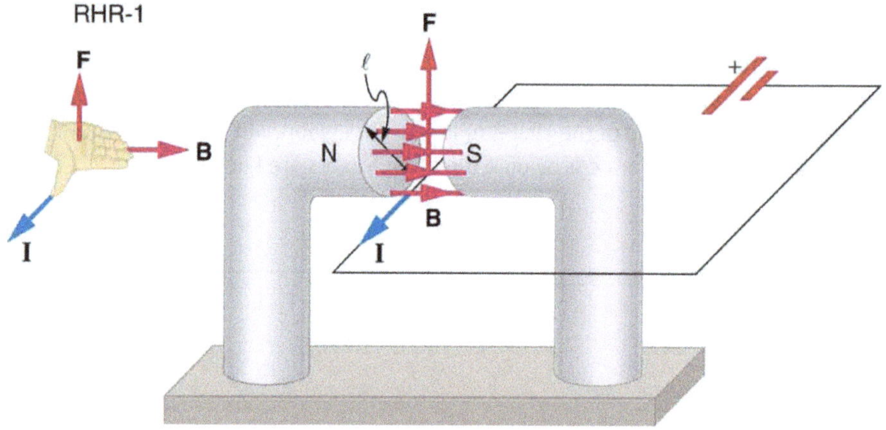

FIGURE 22.29 The magnetic field exerts a force on a current-carrying wire in a direction given by the right hand rule 1 (the same direction as that on the individual moving charges). This force can easily be large enough to move the wire, since typical currents consist of very large numbers of moving charges.

We can derive an expression for the magnetic force on a current by taking a sum of the magnetic forces on individual charges. (The forces add because they are in the same direction.) The force on an individual charge moving at the drift velocity v_d is given by $F = qv_d B \sin\theta$. Taking B to be uniform over a length of wire l and zero elsewhere, the total magnetic force on the wire is then $F = (qv_d B \sin\theta)(N)$, where N is the number of charge carriers in the section of wire of length l. Now, $N = nV$, where n is the number of charge carriers per unit volume and V is the volume of wire in the field. Noting that $V = Al$, where A is the cross-sectional area of the wire, then the force on the wire is $F = (qv_d B \sin\theta)(nAl)$. Gathering terms,

$$F = (nqAv_d)lB \sin\theta. \tag{22.15}$$

Because $nqAv_d = I$ (see Current),

$$F = IlB \sin\theta \tag{22.16}$$

is the equation for *magnetic force on a length l of wire carrying a current I in a uniform magnetic field B*, as shown in Figure 22.30. If we divide both sides of this expression by l, we find that the magnetic force per unit length of wire in a uniform field is $\frac{F}{l} = IB \sin\theta$. The direction of this force is given by RHR-1, with the thumb in the direction of the current I. Then, with the fingers in the direction of B, a perpendicular to the palm points in the direction of F, as in Figure 22.30.

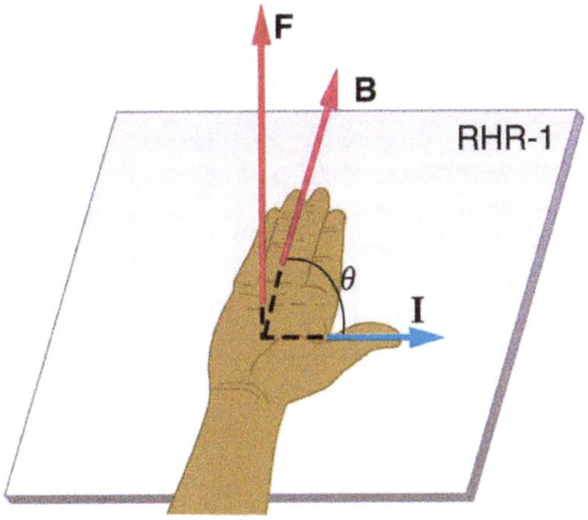

FIGURE 22.30 The force on a current-carrying wire in a magnetic field is $F = IlB \sin \theta$. Its direction is given by RHR-1.

EXAMPLE 22.4

Calculating Magnetic Force on a Current-Carrying Wire: A Strong Magnetic Field

Calculate the force on the wire shown in Figure 22.29, given $B = 1.50 \text{ T}$, $l = 5.00 \text{ cm}$, and $I = 20.0 \text{ A}$.

Strategy

The force can be found with the given information by using $F = IlB \sin \theta$ and noting that the angle θ between I and B is $90°$, so that $\sin \theta = 1$.

Solution

Entering the given values into $F = IlB \sin \theta$ yields

$$F = IlB \sin \theta = (20.0 \text{ A})(0.0500 \text{ m})(1.50 \text{ T})(1). \tag{22.17}$$

The units for tesla are $1 \text{ T} = \frac{\text{N}}{\text{A·m}}$; thus,

$$F = 1.50 \text{ N}. \tag{22.18}$$

Discussion

This large magnetic field creates a significant force on a small length of wire.

Magnetic force on current-carrying conductors is used to convert electric energy to work. (Motors are a prime example—they employ loops of wire and are considered in the next section.) Magnetohydrodynamics (MHD) is the technical name given to a clever application where magnetic force pumps fluids without moving mechanical parts. (See Figure 22.31.)

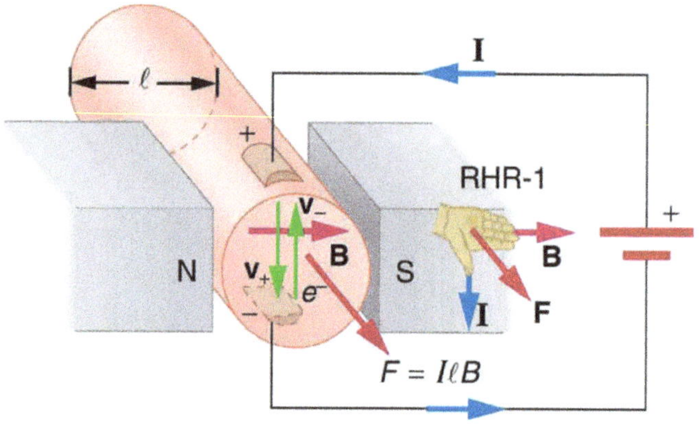

FIGURE 22.31 Magnetohydrodynamics. The magnetic force on the current passed through this fluid can be used as a nonmechanical pump.

A strong magnetic field is applied across a tube and a current is passed through the fluid at right angles to the field, resulting in a force on the fluid parallel to the tube axis as shown. The absence of moving parts makes this attractive for moving a hot, chemically active substance, such as the liquid sodium employed in some nuclear reactors. Experimental artificial hearts are testing with this technique for pumping blood, perhaps circumventing the adverse effects of mechanical pumps. (Cell membranes, however, are affected by the large fields needed in MHD, delaying its practical application in humans.) MHD propulsion for nuclear submarines has been proposed, because it could be considerably quieter than conventional propeller drives. The deterrent value of nuclear submarines is based on their ability to hide and survive a first or second nuclear strike. As we slowly disassemble our nuclear weapons arsenals, the submarine branch will be the last to be decommissioned because of this ability (See Figure 22.32.) Existing MHD drives are heavy and inefficient—much development work is needed.

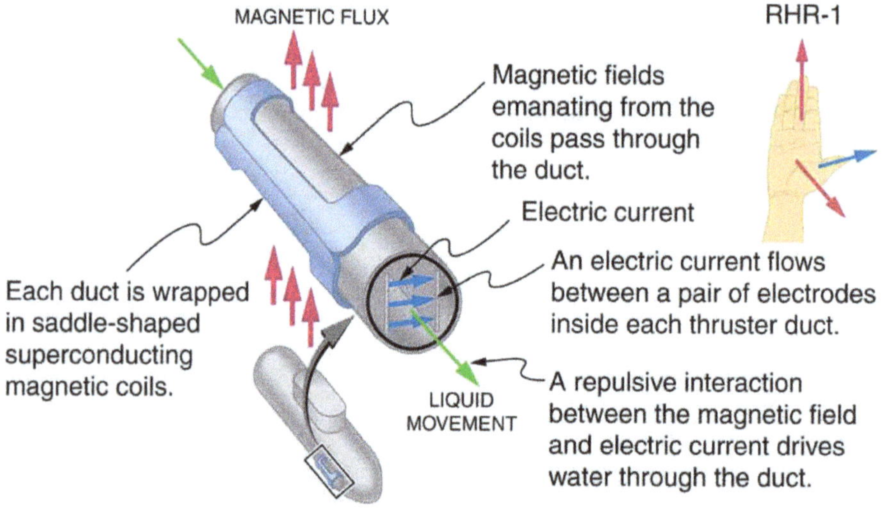

FIGURE 22.32 An MHD propulsion system in a nuclear submarine could produce significantly less turbulence than propellers and allow it to run more silently. The development of a silent drive submarine was dramatized in the book and the film *The Hunt for Red October*.

22.8 Torque on a Current Loop: Motors and Meters

LEARNING OBJECTIVES

By the end of this section, you will be able to:

- Describe how motors and meters work in terms of torque on a current loop.
- Calculate the torque on a current-carrying loop in a magnetic field.

Motors are the most common application of magnetic force on current-carrying wires. Motors have loops of wire in a magnetic field. When current is passed through the loops, the magnetic field exerts torque on the loops, which rotates a shaft. Electrical energy is converted to mechanical work in the process. (See Figure 22.33.)

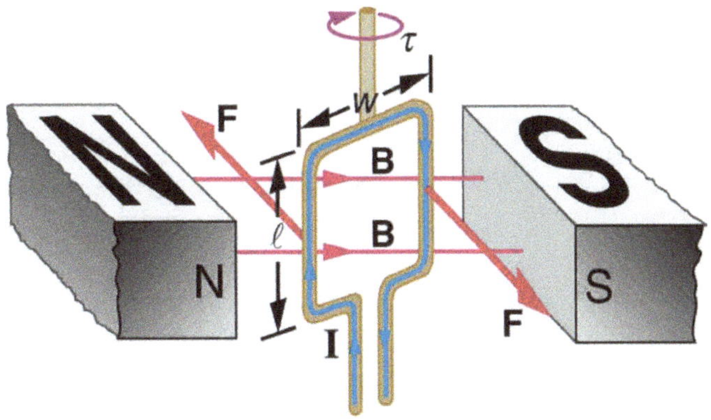

FIGURE 22.33 Torque on a current loop. A current-carrying loop of wire attached to a vertically rotating shaft feels magnetic forces that produce a clockwise torque as viewed from above.

Let us examine the force on each segment of the loop in Figure 22.33 to find the torques produced about the axis of the vertical shaft. (This will lead to a useful equation for the torque on the loop.) We take the magnetic field to be uniform over the rectangular loop, which has width w and height l. First, we note that the forces on the top and bottom segments are vertical and, therefore, parallel to the shaft, producing no torque. Those vertical forces are equal in magnitude and opposite in direction, so that they also produce no net force on the loop. Figure 22.34 shows views of the loop from above. Torque is defined as $\tau = rF \sin \theta$, where F is the force, r is the distance from the pivot that the force is applied, and θ is the angle between r and F. As seen in Figure 22.34(a), right hand rule 1 gives the forces on the sides to be equal in magnitude and opposite in direction, so that the net force is again zero. However, each force produces a clockwise torque. Since $r = w/2$, the torque on each vertical segment is $(w/2)F \sin \theta$, and the two add to give a total torque.

$$\tau = \frac{w}{2}F \sin \theta + \frac{w}{2}F \sin \theta = wF \sin \theta \qquad 22.19$$

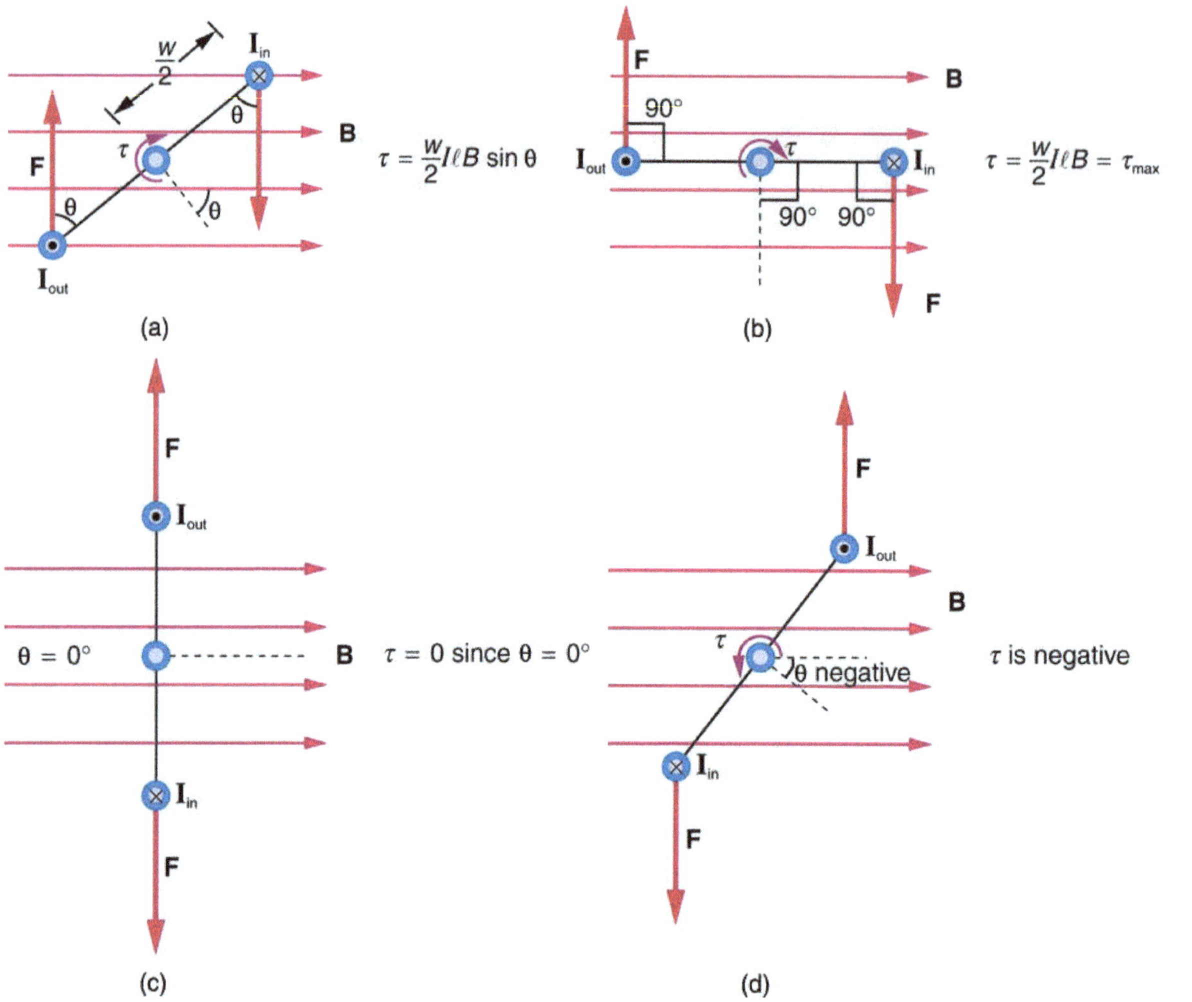

FIGURE 22.34 Top views of a current-carrying loop in a magnetic field. (a) The equation for torque is derived using this view. Note that the perpendicular to the loop makes an angle θ with the field that is the same as the angle between $w/2$ and $\mathbf{F}$. (b) The maximum torque occurs when θ is a right angle and $\sin\theta = 1$. (c) Zero (minimum) torque occurs when θ is zero and $\sin\theta = 0$. (d) The torque reverses once the loop rotates past $\theta = 0$.

Now, each vertical segment has a length l that is perpendicular to B, so that the force on each is $F = IlB$. Entering F into the expression for torque yields

$$\tau = wIlB\sin\theta. \tag{22.20}$$

If we have a multiple loop of N turns, we get N times the torque of one loop. Finally, note that the area of the loop is $A = wl$; the expression for the torque becomes

$$\tau = NIAB\sin\theta. \tag{22.21}$$

This is the torque on a current-carrying loop in a uniform magnetic field. This equation can be shown to be valid for a loop of any shape. The loop carries a current I, has N turns, each of area A, and the perpendicular to the loop makes an angle θ with the field B. The net force on the loop is zero.

EXAMPLE 22.5

Calculating Torque on a Current-Carrying Loop in a Strong Magnetic Field

Find the maximum torque on a 100-turn square loop of a wire of 10.0 cm on a side that carries 15.0 A of current in a 2.00-T field.

Strategy

Torque on the loop can be found using $\tau = NIAB \sin\theta$. Maximum torque occurs when $\theta = 90°$ and $\sin\theta = 1$.

Solution

For $\sin\theta = 1$, the maximum torque is

$$\tau_{\text{max}} = NIAB. \tag{22.22}$$

Entering known values yields

$$\begin{aligned} \tau_{\text{max}} &= (100)(15.0\text{ A})\left(0.100\text{ m}^2\right)(2.00\text{ T}) \\ &= 30.0\text{ N}\cdot\text{m}. \end{aligned} \tag{22.23}$$

Discussion

This torque is large enough to be useful in a motor.

The torque found in the preceding example is the maximum. As the coil rotates, the torque decreases to zero at $\theta = 0$. The torque then *reverses* its direction once the coil rotates past $\theta = 0$. (See Figure 22.34(d).) This means that, unless we do something, the coil will oscillate back and forth about equilibrium at $\theta = 0$. To get the coil to continue rotating in the same direction, we can reverse the current as it passes through $\theta = 0$ with automatic switches called *brushes*. (See Figure 22.35.)

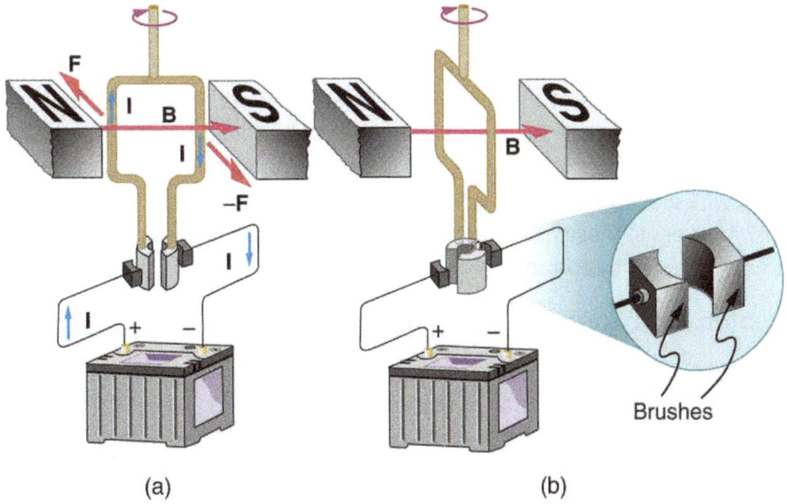

FIGURE 22.35 (a) As the angular momentum of the coil carries it through $\theta = 0$, the brushes reverse the current to keep the torque clockwise. (b) The coil will rotate continuously in the clockwise direction, with the current reversing each half revolution to maintain the clockwise torque.

Meters, such as those in analog fuel gauges on a car, are another common application of magnetic torque on a current-carrying loop. Figure 22.36 shows that a meter is very similar in construction to a motor. The meter in the figure has its magnets shaped to limit the effect of θ by making B perpendicular to the loop over a large angular range. Thus the torque is proportional to I and not θ. A linear spring exerts a counter-torque that balances the current-produced torque. This makes the needle deflection proportional to I. If an exact proportionality cannot be achieved, the gauge reading can be calibrated. To produce a galvanometer for use in analog voltmeters and ammeters that have a low resistance and respond to small currents, we use a large loop area A, high magnetic field B, and low-resistance coils.

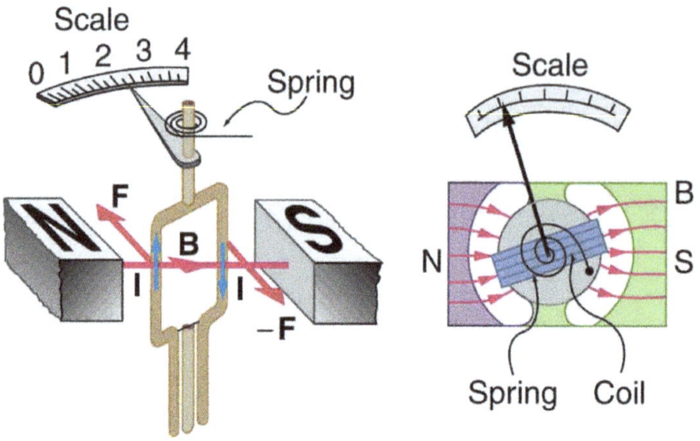

FIGURE 22.36 Meters are very similar to motors but only rotate through a part of a revolution. The magnetic poles of this meter are shaped to keep the component of B perpendicular to the loop constant, so that the torque does not depend on θ and the deflection against the return spring is proportional only to the current I.

22.9 Magnetic Fields Produced by Currents: Ampere's Law

LEARNING OBJECTIVES

By the end of this section, you will be able to:

- Calculate current that produces a magnetic field.
- Use the right hand rule 2 to determine the direction of current or the direction of magnetic field loops.

How much current is needed to produce a significant magnetic field, perhaps as strong as the Earth's field? Surveyors will tell you that overhead electric power lines create magnetic fields that interfere with their compass readings. Indeed, when Oersted discovered in 1820 that a current in a wire affected a compass needle, he was not dealing with extremely large currents. How does the shape of wires carrying current affect the shape of the magnetic field created? We noted earlier that a current loop created a magnetic field similar to that of a bar magnet, but what about a straight wire or a toroid (doughnut)? How is the direction of a current-created field related to the direction of the current? Answers to these questions are explored in this section, together with a brief discussion of the law governing the fields created by currents.

Magnetic Field Created by a Long Straight Current-Carrying Wire: Right Hand Rule 2

Magnetic fields have both direction and magnitude. As noted before, one way to explore the direction of a magnetic field is with compasses, as shown for a long straight current-carrying wire in Figure 22.37. Hall probes can determine the magnitude of the field. The field around a long straight wire is found to be in circular loops. The **right hand rule 2** (RHR-2) emerges from this exploration and is valid for any current segment—*point the thumb in the direction of the current, and the fingers curl in the direction of the magnetic field loops* created by it.

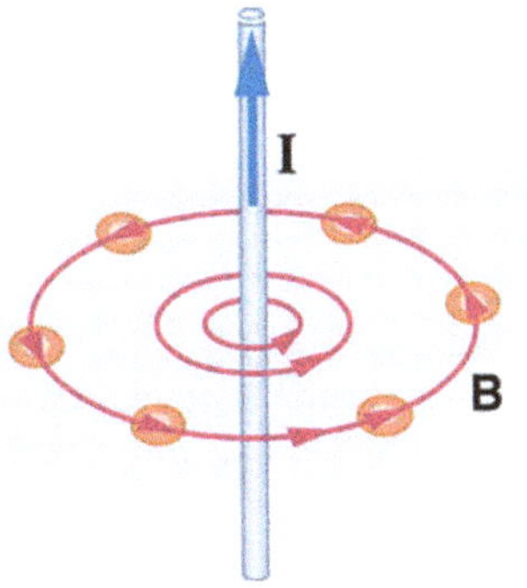

(a)

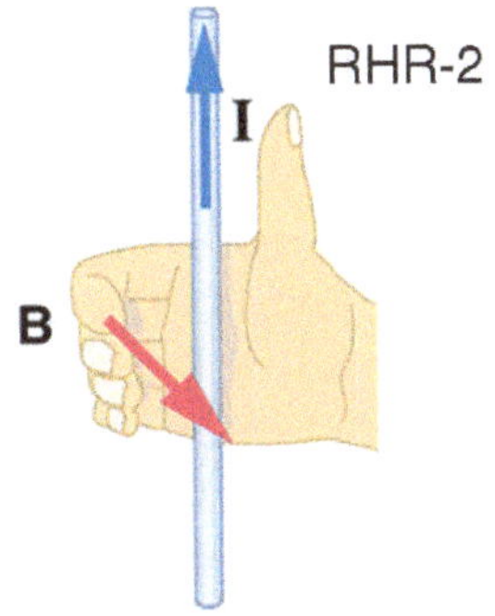

(b)

FIGURE 22.37 (a) Compasses placed near a long straight current-carrying wire indicate that field lines form circular loops centered on the wire. (b) Right hand rule 2 states that, if the right hand thumb points in the direction of the current, the fingers curl in the direction of the field. This rule is consistent with the field mapped for the long straight wire and is valid for any current segment.

The **magnetic field strength (magnitude) produced by a long straight current-carrying wire** is found by experiment to be

$$B = \frac{\mu_0 I}{2\pi r} \text{ (long straight wire)}, \qquad 22.24$$

where I is the current, r is the shortest distance to the wire, and the constant $\mu_0 = 4\pi \times 10^{-7}\ \mathrm{T \cdot m/A}$ is the **permeability of free space**. (μ_0 is one of the basic constants in nature. We will see later that μ_0 is related to the speed of light.) Since the wire is very long, the magnitude of the field depends only on distance from the wire r, not on position along the wire.

EXAMPLE 22.6

Calculating Current that Produces a Magnetic Field

Find the current in a long straight wire that would produce a magnetic field twice the strength of the Earth's at a distance of 5.0 cm from the wire.

Strategy

The Earth's field is about $5.0 \times 10^{-5}\ \mathrm{T}$, and so here B due to the wire is taken to be $1.0 \times 10^{-4}\ \mathrm{T}$. The equation $B = \frac{\mu_0 I}{2\pi r}$ can be used to find I, since all other quantities are known.

Solution

Solving for I and entering known values gives

$$I = \frac{2\pi rB}{\mu_0} = \frac{2\pi\left(5.0\times10^{-2}\text{ m}\right)\left(1.0\times10^{-4}\text{ T}\right)}{4\pi\times10^{-7}\text{ T}\cdot\text{m/A}} = 25\text{ A}. \quad (22.25)$$

Discussion

So a moderately large current produces a significant magnetic field at a distance of 5.0 cm from a long straight wire. Note that the answer is stated to only two digits, since the Earth's field is specified to only two digits in this example.

Ampere's Law and Others

The magnetic field of a long straight wire has more implications than you might at first suspect. *Each segment of current produces a magnetic field like that of a long straight wire, and the total field of any shape current is the vector sum of the fields due to each segment.* The formal statement of the direction and magnitude of the field due to each segment is called the **Biot-Savart law**. Integral calculus is needed to sum the field for an arbitrary shape current. This results in a more complete law, called **Ampere's law**, which relates magnetic field and current in a general way. Ampere's law in turn is a part of **Maxwell's equations**, which give a complete theory of all electromagnetic phenomena. Considerations of how Maxwell's equations appear to different observers led to the modern theory of relativity, and the realization that electric and magnetic fields are different manifestations of the same thing. Most of this is beyond the scope of this text in both mathematical level, requiring calculus, and in the amount of space that can be devoted to it. But for the interested student, and particularly for those who continue in physics, engineering, or similar pursuits, delving into these matters further will reveal descriptions of nature that are elegant as well as profound. In this text, we shall keep the general features in mind, such as RHR-2 and the rules for magnetic field lines listed in Magnetic Fields and Magnetic Field Lines, while concentrating on the fields created in certain important situations.

MAKING CONNECTIONS: RELATIVITY

Hearing all we do about Einstein, we sometimes get the impression that he invented relativity out of nothing. On the contrary, one of Einstein's motivations was to solve difficulties in knowing how different observers see magnetic and electric fields.

Magnetic Field Produced by a Current-Carrying Circular Loop

The magnetic field near a current-carrying loop of wire is shown in Figure 22.38. Both the direction and the magnitude of the magnetic field produced by a current-carrying loop are complex. RHR-2 can be used to give the direction of the field near the loop, but mapping with compasses and the rules about field lines given in Magnetic Fields and Magnetic Field Lines are needed for more detail. There is a simple formula for the **magnetic field strength at the center of a circular loop**. It is

$$B = \frac{\mu_0 I}{2R}\ \text{(at center of loop)}, \quad (22.26)$$

where R is the radius of the loop. This equation is very similar to that for a straight wire, but it is valid *only* at the center of a circular loop of wire. The similarity of the equations does indicate that similar field strength can be obtained at the center of a loop. One way to get a larger field is to have N loops; then, the field is $B = N\mu_0 I/(2R)$. Note that the larger the loop, the smaller the field at its center, because the current is farther away.

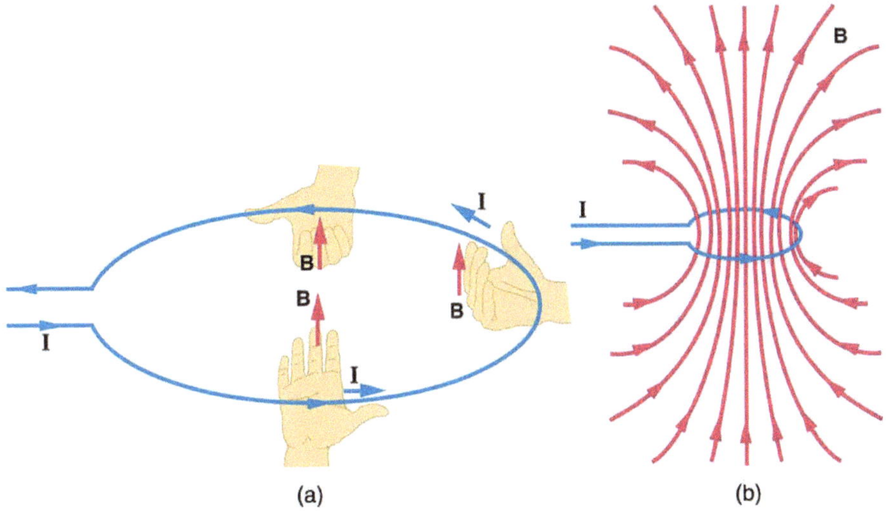

FIGURE 22.38 (a) RHR-2 gives the direction of the magnetic field inside and outside a current-carrying loop. (b) More detailed mapping with compasses or with a Hall probe completes the picture. The field is similar to that of a bar magnet.

Magnetic Field Produced by a Current-Carrying Solenoid

A **solenoid** is a long coil of wire (with many turns or loops, as opposed to a flat loop). Because of its shape, the field inside a solenoid can be very uniform, and also very strong. The field just outside the coils is nearly zero. Figure 22.39 shows how the field looks and how its direction is given by RHR-2.

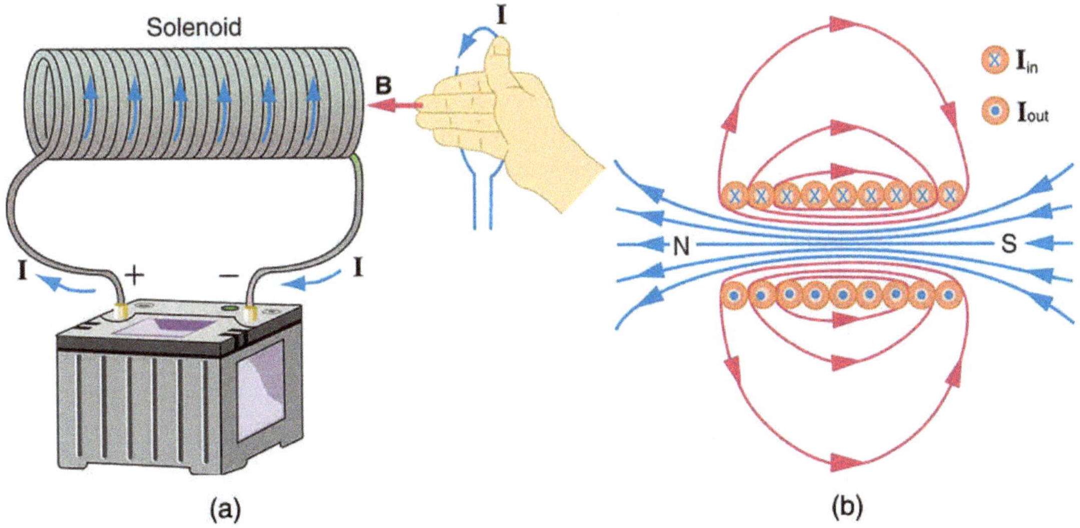

FIGURE 22.39 (a) Because of its shape, the field inside a solenoid of length l is remarkably uniform in magnitude and direction, as indicated by the straight and uniformly spaced field lines. The field outside the coils is nearly zero. (b) This cutaway shows the magnetic field generated by the current in the solenoid.

The magnetic field inside of a current-carrying solenoid is very uniform in direction and magnitude. Only near the ends does it begin to weaken and change direction. The field outside has similar complexities to flat loops and bar magnets, but the **magnetic field strength inside a solenoid** is simply

$$B = \mu_0 nI \quad \text{(inside a solenoid)}, \tag{22.27}$$

where n is the number of loops per unit length of the solenoid ($n = N/l$, with N being the number of loops and l the length). Note that B is the field strength anywhere in the uniform region of the interior and not just at the center. Large uniform fields spread over a large volume are possible with solenoids, as Example 22.7 implies.

EXAMPLE 22.7

Calculating Field Strength inside a Solenoid

What is the field inside a 2.00-m-long solenoid that has 2000 loops and carries a 1600-A current?

Strategy

To find the field strength inside a solenoid, we use $B = \mu_0 nI$. First, we note the number of loops per unit length is

$$n = \frac{N}{l} = \frac{2000}{2.00\text{ m}} = 1000\text{ m}^{-1} = 10\text{ cm}^{-1}. \tag{22.28}$$

Solution

Substituting known values gives

$$\begin{aligned} B &= \mu_0 nI = \left(4\pi \times 10^{-7}\text{ T}\cdot\text{m/A}\right)\left(1000\text{ m}^{-1}\right)(1600\text{ A}) \\ &= 2.01\text{ T}. \end{aligned} \tag{22.29}$$

Discussion

This is a large field strength that could be established over a large-diameter solenoid, such as in medical uses of magnetic resonance imaging (MRI). The very large current is an indication that the fields of this strength are not easily achieved, however. Such a large current through 1000 loops squeezed into a meter's length would produce significant heating. Higher currents can be achieved by using superconducting wires, although this is expensive. There is an upper limit to the current, since the superconducting state is disrupted by very large magnetic fields.

There are interesting variations of the flat coil and solenoid. For example, the toroidal coil used to confine the reactive particles in tokamaks is much like a solenoid bent into a circle. The field inside a toroid is very strong but circular. Charged particles travel in circles, following the field lines, and collide with one another, perhaps inducing fusion. But the charged particles do not cross field lines and escape the toroid. A whole range of coil shapes are used to produce all sorts of magnetic field shapes. Adding ferromagnetic materials produces greater field strengths and can have a significant effect on the shape of the field. Ferromagnetic materials tend to trap magnetic fields (the field lines bend into the ferromagnetic material, leaving weaker fields outside it) and are used as shields for devices that are adversely affected by magnetic fields, including the Earth's magnetic field.

PHET EXPLORATIONS

Generator

Generate electricity with a bar magnet! Discover the physics behind the phenomena by exploring magnets and how you can use them to make a bulb light.

Click to view content (https://openstax.org/l/28gen).

PhET

22.10 Magnetic Force between Two Parallel Conductors

LEARNING OBJECTIVES

By the end of this section, you will be able to:

- Describe the effects of the magnetic force between two conductors.
- Calculate the force between two parallel conductors.

You might expect that there are significant forces between current-carrying wires, since ordinary currents produce significant magnetic fields and these fields exert significant forces on ordinary currents. But you might not expect that the force between wires is used to *define* the ampere. It might also surprise you to learn that this force has something to do with why large circuit breakers burn up when they attempt to interrupt large currents.

The force between two long straight and parallel conductors separated by a distance *r* can be found by applying what we have developed in preceding sections. Figure 22.40 shows the wires, their currents, the fields they create, and the subsequent forces they exert on one another. Let us consider the field produced by wire 1 and the force it exerts on wire 2 (call the force F_2). The field due to I_1 at a distance *r* is given to be

$$B_1 = \frac{\mu_0 I_1}{2\pi r}. \qquad 22.30$$

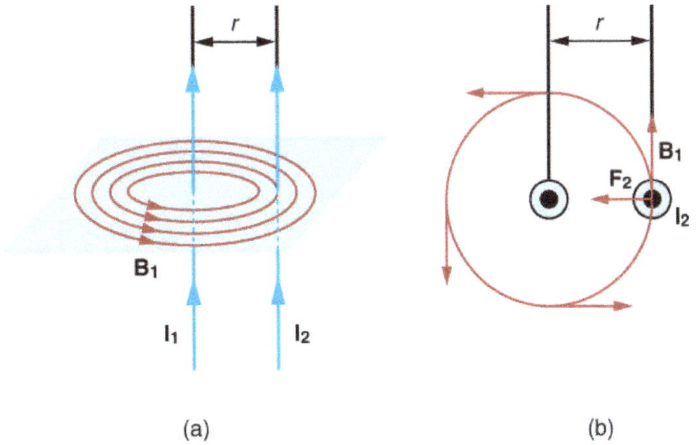

FIGURE 22.40 (a) The magnetic field produced by a long straight conductor is perpendicular to a parallel conductor, as indicated by RHR-2. (b) A view from above of the two wires shown in (a), with one magnetic field line shown for each wire. RHR-1 shows that the force between the parallel conductors is attractive when the currents are in the same direction. A similar analysis shows that the force is repulsive between currents in opposite directions.

This field is uniform along wire 2 and perpendicular to it, and so the force F_2 it exerts on wire 2 is given by $F = IlB \sin\theta$ with $\sin\theta = 1$:

$$F_2 = I_2 l B_1. \qquad 22.31$$

By Newton's third law, the forces on the wires are equal in magnitude, and so we just write F for the magnitude of F_2. (Note that $F_1 = -F_2$.) Since the wires are very long, it is convenient to think in terms of F/l, the force per unit length. Substituting the expression for B_1 into the last equation and rearranging terms gives

$$\frac{F}{l} = \frac{\mu_0 I_1 I_2}{2\pi r}. \qquad 22.32$$

F/l is the force per unit length between two parallel currents I_1 and I_2 separated by a distance *r*. The force is attractive if the currents are in the same direction and repulsive if they are in opposite directions.

This force is responsible for the *pinch effect* in electric arcs and plasmas. The force exists whether the currents are in wires or not. In an electric arc, where currents are moving parallel to one another, there is an attraction that squeezes currents into a smaller tube. In large circuit breakers, like those used in neighborhood power distribution systems, the pinch effect can concentrate an arc between plates of a switch trying to break a large current, burn holes, and even ignite the equipment. Another example of the pinch effect is found in the solar plasma, where jets of ionized material, such as solar flares, are shaped by magnetic forces.

The *operational definition of the ampere* is based on the force between current-carrying wires. Note that for parallel wires separated by 1 meter with each carrying 1 ampere, the force per meter is

$$\frac{F}{l} = \frac{(4\pi \times 10^{-7}\ \mathrm{T \cdot m/A})(1\ \mathrm{A})^2}{(2\pi)(1\ \mathrm{m})} = 2 \times 10^{-7}\ \mathrm{N/m}. \qquad 22.33$$

Since μ_0 is exactly $4\pi \times 10^{-7}\ \mathrm{T \cdot m/A}$ by definition, and because $1\ \mathrm{T} = 1\ \mathrm{N/(A \cdot m)}$, the force per meter is exactly $2 \times 10^{-7}\ \mathrm{N/m}$. This is the basis of the operational definition of the ampere.

THE AMPERE

The official definition of the ampere is:

One ampere of current through each of two parallel conductors of infinite length, separated by one meter in empty space free of other magnetic fields, causes a force of exactly 2×10^{-7} N/m on each conductor.

Infinite-length straight wires are impractical and so, in practice, a current balance is constructed with coils of wire separated by a few centimeters. Force is measured to determine current. This also provides us with a method for measuring the coulomb. We measure the charge that flows for a current of one ampere in one second. That is, $1\ \text{C} = 1\ \text{A} \cdot \text{s}$. For both the ampere and the coulomb, the method of measuring force between conductors is the most accurate in practice.

22.11 More Applications of Magnetism

LEARNING OBJECTIVES

By the end of this section, you will be able to:

- Describe some applications of magnetism.

Mass Spectrometry

The curved paths followed by charged particles in magnetic fields can be put to use. A charged particle moving perpendicular to a magnetic field travels in a circular path having a radius $\boldsymbol{r}$.

$$r = \frac{mv}{qB} \tag{22.34}$$

It was noted that this relationship could be used to measure the mass of charged particles such as ions. A mass spectrometer is a device that measures such masses. Most mass spectrometers use magnetic fields for this purpose, although some of them have extremely sophisticated designs. Since there are five variables in the relationship, there are many possibilities. However, if v, q, and $\boldsymbol{B}$ can be fixed, then the radius of the path $\boldsymbol{r}$ is simply proportional to the mass $\boldsymbol{m}$ of the charged particle. Let us examine one such mass spectrometer that has a relatively simple design. (See Figure 22.41.) The process begins with an ion source, a device like an electron gun. The ion source gives ions their charge, accelerates them to some velocity v, and directs a beam of them into the next stage of the spectrometer. This next region is a *velocity selector* that only allows particles with a particular value of v to get through.

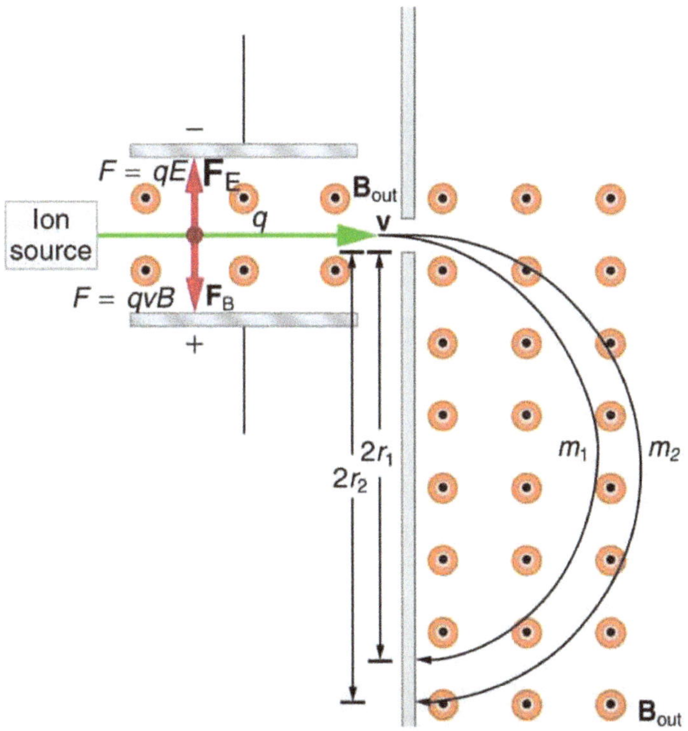

FIGURE 22.41 This mass spectrometer uses a velocity selector to fix v so that the radius of the path is proportional to mass.

The velocity selector has both an electric field and a magnetic field, perpendicular to one another, producing forces in opposite directions on the ions. Only those ions for which the forces balance travel in a straight line into the next region. If the forces balance, then the electric force $F = qE$ equals the magnetic force $F = qvB$, so that $qE = qvB$. Noting that q cancels, we see that

$$v = \frac{E}{B} \tag{22.35}$$

is the velocity particles must have to make it through the velocity selector, and further, that v can be selected by varying E and B. In the final region, there is only a uniform magnetic field, and so the charged particles move in circular arcs with radii proportional to particle mass. The paths also depend on charge q, but since q is in multiples of electron charges, it is easy to determine and to discriminate between ions in different charge states.

Mass spectrometry today is used extensively in chemistry and biology laboratories to identify chemical and biological substances according to their mass-to-charge ratios. In medicine, mass spectrometers are used to measure the concentration of isotopes used as tracers. Usually, biological molecules such as proteins are very large, so they are broken down into smaller fragments before analyzing. Recently, large virus particles have been analyzed as a whole on mass spectrometers. Sometimes a gas chromatograph or high-performance liquid chromatograph provides an initial separation of the large molecules, which are then input into the mass spectrometer.

Cathode Ray Tubes—CRTs—and the Like

What do non-flat-screen TVs, old computer monitors, x-ray machines, and the 2-mile-long Stanford Linear Accelerator have in common? All of them accelerate electrons, making them different versions of the electron gun. Many of these devices use magnetic fields to steer the accelerated electrons. Figure 22.42 shows the construction of the type of cathode ray tube (CRT) found in some TVs, oscilloscopes, and old computer monitors. Two pairs of coils are used to steer the electrons, one vertically and the other horizontally, to their desired destination.

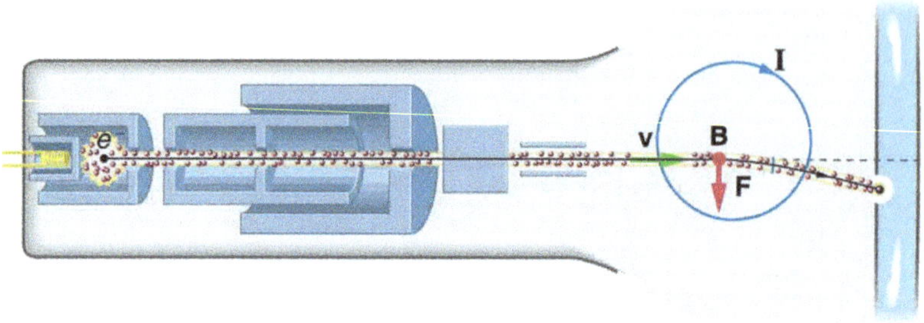

FIGURE 22.42 The cathode ray tube (CRT) is so named because rays of electrons originate at the cathode in the electron gun. Magnetic coils are used to steer the beam in many CRTs. In this case, the beam is moved down. Another pair of horizontal coils would steer the beam horizontally.

Magnetic Resonance Imaging

Magnetic resonance imaging (MRI) is one of the most useful and rapidly growing medical imaging tools. It non-invasively produces two-dimensional and three-dimensional images of the body that provide important medical information with none of the hazards of x-rays. MRI is based on an effect called **nuclear magnetic resonance (NMR)** in which an externally applied magnetic field interacts with the nuclei of certain atoms, particularly those of hydrogen (protons). These nuclei possess their own small magnetic fields, similar to those of electrons and the current loops discussed earlier in this chapter.

When placed in an external magnetic field, such nuclei experience a torque that pushes or aligns the nuclei into one of two new energy states—depending on the orientation of its spin (analogous to the N pole and S pole in a bar magnet). Transitions from the lower to higher energy state can be achieved by using an external radio frequency signal to "flip" the orientation of the small magnets. (This is actually a quantum mechanical process. The direction of the nuclear magnetic field is quantized as is energy in the radio waves. We will return to these topics in later chapters.) The specific frequency of the radio waves that are absorbed and reemitted depends sensitively on the type of nucleus, the chemical environment, and the external magnetic field strength. Therefore, this is a *resonance* phenomenon in which *nuclei* in a *magnetic* field act like resonators (analogous to those discussed in the treatment of sound in Oscillatory Motion and Waves) that absorb and reemit only certain frequencies. Hence, the phenomenon is named *nuclear magnetic resonance (NMR).*

NMR has been used for more than 50 years as an analytical tool. It was formulated in 1946 by F. Bloch and E. Purcell, with the 1952 Nobel Prize in Physics going to them for their work. Over the past two decades, NMR has been developed to produce detailed images in a process now called magnetic resonance imaging (MRI), a name coined to avoid the use of the word "nuclear" and the concomitant implication that nuclear radiation is involved. (It is not.) The 2003 Nobel Prize in Medicine went to P. Lauterbur and P. Mansfield for their work with MRI applications.

The largest part of the MRI unit is a superconducting magnet that creates a magnetic field, typically between 1 and 2 T in strength, over a relatively large volume. MRI images can be both highly detailed and informative about structures and organ functions. It is helpful that normal and non-normal tissues respond differently for slight changes in the magnetic field. In most medical images, the protons that are hydrogen nuclei are imaged. (About 2/3 of the atoms in the body are hydrogen.) Their location and density give a variety of medically useful information, such as organ function, the condition of tissue (as in the brain), and the shape of structures, such as vertebral disks and knee-joint surfaces. MRI can also be used to follow the movement of certain ions across membranes, yielding information on active transport, osmosis, dialysis, and other phenomena. With excellent spatial resolution, MRI can provide information about tumors, strokes, shoulder injuries, infections, etc.

An image requires position information as well as the density of a nuclear type (usually protons). By varying the magnetic field slightly over the volume to be imaged, the resonant frequency of the protons is made to vary with position. Broadcast radio frequencies are swept over an appropriate range and nuclei absorb and reemit them only if the nuclei are in a magnetic field with the correct strength. The imaging receiver gathers information through the body almost point by point, building up a tissue map. The reception of reemitted radio waves as a function of frequency thus gives position information. These "slices" or cross sections through the body are only several mm thick. The intensity of the reemitted radio waves is proportional to the concentration of the nuclear type being flipped, as well as information on the chemical environment in that area of the body. Various techniques are available for enhancing contrast in images and for obtaining more information. Scans called T1, T2, or proton density scans rely on different relaxation mechanisms of nuclei. Relaxation refers to the time it takes for the protons to return to equilibrium after the external field is turned off. This time depends upon tissue type and status (such as inflammation).

While MRI images are superior to x rays for certain types of tissue and have none of the hazards of x rays, they do not completely supplant x-ray images. MRI is less effective than x rays for detecting breaks in bone, for example, and in imaging breast tissue, so the two diagnostic tools complement each other. MRI images are also expensive compared to simple x-ray images and tend to be used most often where they supply information not readily obtained from x rays. Another disadvantage of MRI is that the patient is totally enclosed with detectors close to the body for about 30 minutes or more, leading to claustrophobia. It is also difficult for the obese patient to be in the magnet tunnel. New "open-MRI" machines are now available in which the magnet does not completely surround the patient.

Over the last decade, the development of much faster scans, called "functional MRI" (fMRI), has allowed us to map the functioning of various regions in the brain responsible for thought and motor control. This technique measures the change in blood flow for activities (thought, experiences, action) in the brain. The nerve cells increase their consumption of oxygen when active. Blood hemoglobin releases oxygen to active nerve cells and has somewhat different magnetic properties when oxygenated than when deoxygenated. With MRI, we can measure this and detect a blood oxygen-dependent signal. Most of the brain scans today use fMRI.

Other Medical Uses of Magnetic Fields

Currents in nerve cells and the heart create magnetic fields like any other currents. These can be measured but with some difficulty since their strengths are about 10^{-6} to 10^{-8} *less* than the Earth's magnetic field. Recording of the heart's magnetic field as it beats is called a **magnetocardiogram (MCG)**, while measurements of the brain's magnetic field is called a **magnetoencephalogram (MEG)**. Both give information that differs from that obtained by measuring the electric fields of these organs (ECGs and EEGs), but they are not yet of sufficient importance to make these difficult measurements common.

In both of these techniques, the sensors do not touch the body. MCG can be used in fetal studies, and is probably more sensitive than echocardiography. MCG also looks at the heart's electrical activity whose voltage output is too small to be recorded by surface electrodes as in EKG. It has the potential of being a rapid scan for early diagnosis of cardiac ischemia (obstruction of blood flow to the heart) or problems with the fetus.

MEG can be used to identify abnormal electrical discharges in the brain that produce weak magnetic signals. Therefore, it looks at brain activity, not just brain structure. It has been used for studies of Alzheimer's disease and epilepsy. Advances in instrumentation to measure very small magnetic fields have allowed these two techniques to be used more in recent years. What is used is a sensor called a SQUID, for superconducting quantum interference device. This operates at liquid helium temperatures and can measure magnetic fields thousands of times smaller than the Earth's.

Finally, there is a burgeoning market for magnetic cures in which magnets are applied in a variety of ways to the body, from magnetic bracelets to magnetic mattresses. The best that can be said for such practices is that they are apparently harmless, unless the magnets get close to the patient's computer or magnetic storage disks. Claims are made for a broad spectrum of benefits from cleansing the blood to giving the patient more energy, but clinical studies have not verified these claims, nor is there an identifiable mechanism by which such benefits might occur.

PHET EXPLORATIONS

Magnet and Compass

Ever wonder how a compass worked to point you to the Arctic? Explore the interactions between a compass and bar magnet, and then add the Earth and find the surprising answer! Vary the magnet's strength, and see how things change both inside and outside. Use the field meter to measure how the magnetic field changes.

Click to view content (https://openstax.org/l/28magcomp).

Glossary

Ampere's law the physical law that states that the magnetic field around an electric current is proportional to the current; each segment of current produces a magnetic field like that of a long straight wire, and the total field of any shape current is the vector sum of the fields due to each segment

***B*-field** another term for magnetic field

Biot-Savart law a physical law that describes the magnetic field generated by an electric current in terms of a specific equation

Curie temperature the temperature above which a ferromagnetic material cannot be magnetized

direction of magnetic field lines the direction that the north end of a compass needle points

domains regions within a material that behave like small bar magnets

electromagnet an object that is temporarily magnetic when an electrical current is passed through it

electromagnetism the use of electrical currents to induce magnetism

ferromagnetic materials, such as iron, cobalt, nickel, and gadolinium, that exhibit strong magnetic effects

gauss G, the unit of the magnetic field strength; $1\text{ G} = 10^{-4}\text{ T}$

Hall effect the creation of voltage across a current-carrying conductor by a magnetic field

Hall emf the electromotive force created by a current-carrying conductor by a magnetic field, $\varepsilon = Blv$

Lorentz force the force on a charge moving in a magnetic field

magnetic field the representation of magnetic forces

magnetic field lines the pictorial representation of the strength and the direction of a magnetic field

magnetic field strength (magnitude) produced by a long straight current-carrying wire defined as $B = \frac{\mu_0 I}{2\pi r}$, where I is the current, r is the shortest distance to the wire, and μ_0 is the permeability of free space

magnetic field strength at the center of a circular loop defined as $B = \frac{\mu_0 I}{2R}$ where R is the radius of the loop

magnetic field strength inside a solenoid defined as $B = \mu_0 nI$ where n is the number of loops per unit length of the solenoid ($n = N/l$, with N being the number of loops and l the length)

magnetic force the force on a charge produced by its motion through a magnetic field; the Lorentz force

magnetic monopoles an isolated magnetic pole; a south pole without a north pole, or vice versa (no magnetic monopole has ever been observed)

magnetic resonance imaging (MRI) a medical imaging technique that uses magnetic fields create detailed images of internal tissues and organs

magnetized to be turned into a magnet; to be induced to be magnetic

magnetocardiogram (MCG) a recording of the heart's magnetic field as it beats

magnetoencephalogram (MEG) a measurement of the brain's magnetic field

Maxwell's equations a set of four equations that describe electromagnetic phenomena

meter common application of magnetic torque on a current-carrying loop that is very similar in construction to a motor; by design, the torque is proportional to I and not θ, so the needle deflection is proportional to the current

motor loop of wire in a magnetic field; when current is passed through the loops, the magnetic field exerts torque on the loops, which rotates a shaft; electrical energy is converted to mechanical work in the process

north magnetic pole the end or the side of a magnet that is attracted toward Earth's geographic north pole

nuclear magnetic resonance (NMR) a phenomenon in which an externally applied magnetic field interacts with the nuclei of certain atoms

permeability of free space the measure of the ability of a material, in this case free space, to support a magnetic field; the constant $\mu_0 = 4\pi \times 10^{-7}\text{ T} \cdot \text{m/A}$

right hand rule 1 (RHR-1) the rule to determine the direction of the magnetic force on a positive moving charge: when the thumb of the right hand points in the direction of the charge's velocity $\mathbf{v}$ and the fingers point in the direction of the magnetic field $\mathbf{B}$, then the force on the charge is perpendicular and away from the palm; the force on a negative charge is perpendicular and into the palm

right hand rule 2 (RHR-2) a rule to determine the direction of the magnetic field induced by a current-carrying wire: Point the thumb of the right hand in the direction of current, and the fingers curl in the direction of the magnetic field loops

solenoid a thin wire wound into a coil that produces a magnetic field when an electric current is passed through it

south magnetic pole the end or the side of a magnet that is attracted toward Earth's geographic south pole

tesla T, the SI unit of the magnetic field strength;

$$1\ \text{T} = \frac{1\ \text{N}}{\text{A}\cdot\text{m}}$$

Section Summary

22.1 Magnets

- Magnetism is a subject that includes the properties of magnets, the effect of the magnetic force on moving charges and currents, and the creation of magnetic fields by currents.
- There are two types of magnetic poles, called the north magnetic pole and south magnetic pole.
- North magnetic poles are those that are attracted toward the Earth's geographic north pole.
- Like poles repel and unlike poles attract.
- Magnetic poles always occur in pairs of north and south—it is not possible to isolate north and south poles.

22.2 Ferromagnets and Electromagnets

- Magnetic poles always occur in pairs of north and south—it is not possible to isolate north and south poles.
- All magnetism is created by electric current.
- Ferromagnetic materials, such as iron, are those that exhibit strong magnetic effects.
- The atoms in ferromagnetic materials act like small magnets (due to currents within the atoms) and can be aligned, usually in millimeter-sized regions called domains.
- Domains can grow and align on a larger scale, producing permanent magnets. Such a material is magnetized, or induced to be magnetic.
- Above a material's Curie temperature, thermal agitation destroys the alignment of atoms, and ferromagnetism disappears.
- Electromagnets employ electric currents to make magnetic fields, often aided by induced fields in ferromagnetic materials.

22.3 Magnetic Fields and Magnetic Field Lines

- Magnetic fields can be pictorially represented by magnetic field lines, the properties of which are as follows:

1. The field is tangent to the magnetic field line.
2. Field strength is proportional to the line density.
3. Field lines cannot cross.
4. Field lines are continuous loops.

22.4 Magnetic Field Strength: Force on a Moving Charge in a Magnetic Field

- Magnetic fields exert a force on a moving charge q, the magnitude of which is
  $F = qvB\sin\theta$,
  where θ is the angle between the directions of v and B.
- The SI unit for magnetic field strength B is the tesla (T), which is related to other units by
  $1\ \text{T} = \dfrac{1\ \text{N}}{\text{C}\cdot\text{m/s}} = \dfrac{1\ \text{N}}{\text{A}\cdot\text{m}}$.
- The *direction* of the force on a moving charge is given by right hand rule 1 (RHR-1): Point the thumb of the right hand in the direction of v, the fingers in the direction of B, and a perpendicular to the palm points in the direction of F.
- The force is perpendicular to the plane formed by $\mathbf{v}$ and $\mathbf{B}$. Since the force is zero if $\mathbf{v}$ is parallel to $\mathbf{B}$, charged particles often follow magnetic field lines rather than cross them.

22.5 Force on a Moving Charge in a Magnetic Field: Examples and Applications

- Magnetic force can supply centripetal force and cause a charged particle to move in a circular path of radius
  $r = \dfrac{mv}{qB}$,
  where v is the component of the velocity perpendicular to B for a charged particle with mass m and charge q.

22.6 The Hall Effect

- The Hall effect is the creation of voltage ε, known as the Hall emf, across a current-carrying conductor by a magnetic field.
- The Hall emf is given by
  $\varepsilon = Blv$ (B, v, and l, mutually perpendicular)
  for a conductor of width l through which charges move at a speed v.

22.7 Magnetic Force on a Current-Carrying Conductor

- The magnetic force on current-carrying conductors is given by
  $F = IlB\sin\theta$,
  where I is the current, l is the length of a straight conductor in a uniform magnetic field B, and θ is the angle between I and B. The force follows RHR-1 with the thumb in the direction of I.

22.8 Torque on a Current Loop: Motors and Meters

- The torque τ on a current-carrying loop of any shape in a uniform magnetic field. is
 $\tau = NIAB \sin \theta,$
 where N is the number of turns, I is the current, A is the area of the loop, B is the magnetic field strength, and θ is the angle between the perpendicular to the loop and the magnetic field.

22.9 Magnetic Fields Produced by Currents: Ampere's Law

- The strength of the magnetic field created by current in a long straight wire is given by
 $B = \frac{\mu_0 I}{2\pi r}\text{(long straight wire)},$
 where I is the current, r is the shortest distance to the wire, and the constant
 $\mu_0 = 4\pi \times 10^{-7}\ \text{T} \cdot \text{m/A}$ is the permeability of free space.
- The direction of the magnetic field created by a long straight wire is given by right hand rule 2 (RHR-2): *Point the thumb of the right hand in the direction of current, and the fingers curl in the direction of the magnetic field loops* created by it.
- The magnetic field created by current following any path is the sum (or integral) of the fields due to segments along the path (magnitude and direction as for a straight wire), resulting in a general relationship between current and field known as Ampere's law.
- The magnetic field strength at the center of a circular loop is given by
 $B = \frac{\mu_0 I}{2R}\text{(at center of loop)},$
 where R is the radius of the loop. This equation becomes $B = \mu_0 nI/(2R)$ for a flat coil of N loops. RHR-2 gives the direction of the field about the loop. A long coil is called a solenoid.
- The magnetic field strength inside a solenoid is
 $B = \mu_0 nI\ \text{(inside a solenoid)},$
 where n is the number of loops per unit length of the solenoid. The field inside is very uniform in magnitude and direction.

22.10 Magnetic Force between Two Parallel Conductors

- The force between two parallel currents I_1 and I_2, separated by a distance r, has a magnitude per unit length given by
 $\frac{F}{l} = \frac{\mu_0 I_1 I_2}{2\pi r}.$
- The force is attractive if the currents are in the same direction, repulsive if they are in opposite directions.

22.11 More Applications of Magnetism

- Crossed (perpendicular) electric and magnetic fields act as a velocity filter, giving equal and opposite forces on any charge with velocity perpendicular to the fields and of magnitude
 $v = \frac{E}{B}.$

Conceptual Questions

22.1 Magnets

1. Volcanic and other such activity at the mid-Atlantic ridge extrudes material to fill the gap between separating tectonic plates associated with continental drift. The magnetization of rocks is found to reverse in a coordinated manner with distance from the ridge. What does this imply about the Earth's magnetic field and how could the knowledge of the spreading rate be used to give its historical record?

22.3 Magnetic Fields and Magnetic Field Lines

2. Explain why the magnetic field would not be unique (that is, not have a single value) at a point in space where magnetic field lines might cross. (Consider the direction of the field at such a point.)

3. List the ways in which magnetic field lines and electric field lines are similar. For example, the field direction is tangent to the line at any point in space. Also list the ways in which they differ. For example, electric force is parallel to electric field lines, whereas magnetic force on moving charges is perpendicular to magnetic field lines.

4. Noting that the magnetic field lines of a bar magnet resemble the electric field lines of a pair of equal and opposite charges, do you expect the magnetic field to rapidly decrease in strength with distance from the magnet? Is this consistent with your experience with magnets?

5. Is the Earth's magnetic field parallel to the ground at all locations? If not, where is it parallel to the surface? Is its strength the same at all locations? If not, where is it greatest?

22.4 Magnetic Field Strength: Force on a Moving Charge in a Magnetic Field

6. If a charged particle moves in a straight line through some region of space, can you say that the magnetic field in that region is necessarily zero?

22.5 Force on a Moving Charge in a Magnetic Field: Examples and Applications

7. How can the motion of a charged particle be used to distinguish between a magnetic and an electric field?
8. High-velocity charged particles can damage biological cells and are a component of radiation exposure in a variety of locations ranging from research facilities to natural background. Describe how you could use a magnetic field to shield yourself.
9. If a cosmic ray proton approaches the Earth from outer space along a line toward the center of the Earth that lies in the plane of the equator, in what direction will it be deflected by the Earth's magnetic field? What about an electron? A neutron?
10. What are the signs of the charges on the particles in Figure 22.43?

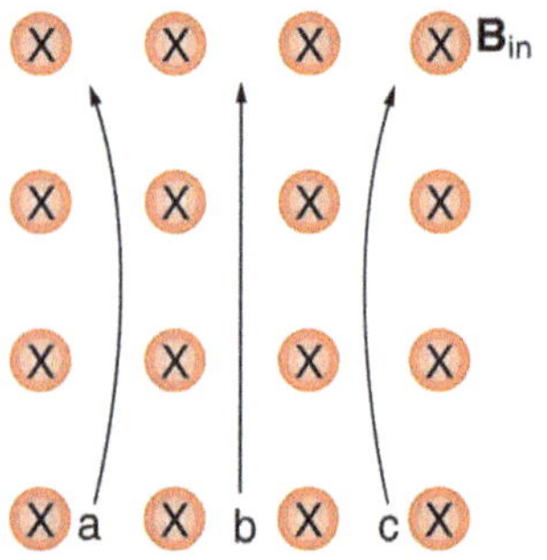

FIGURE 22.43

11. Which of the particles in Figure 22.44 has the greatest velocity, assuming they have identical charges and masses?

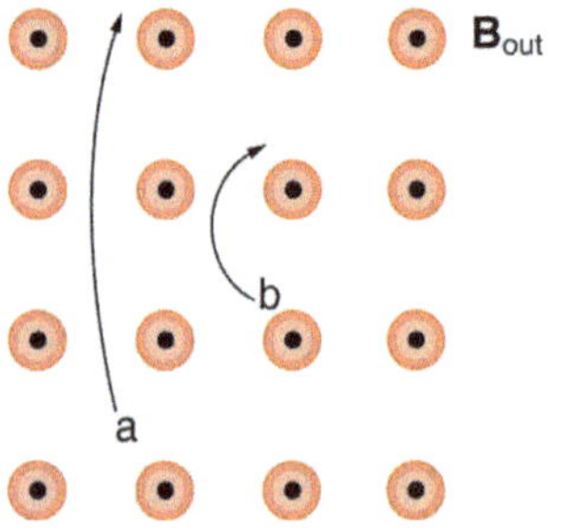

FIGURE 22.44

12. Which of the particles in Figure 22.44 has the greatest mass, assuming all have identical charges and velocities?
13. While operating, a high-precision TV monitor is placed on its side during maintenance. The image on the monitor changes color and blurs slightly. Discuss the possible relation of these effects to the Earth's magnetic field.

22.6 The Hall Effect

14. Discuss how the Hall effect could be used to obtain information on free charge density in a conductor. (Hint: Consider how drift velocity and current are related.)

22.7 Magnetic Force on a Current-Carrying Conductor

15. Draw a sketch of the situation in Figure 22.29 showing the direction of electrons carrying the current, and use RHR-1 to verify the direction of the force on the wire.
16. Verify that the direction of the force in an MHD drive, such as that in Figure 22.31, does not depend on the sign of the charges carrying the current across the fluid.
17. Why would a magnetohydrodynamic drive work better in ocean water than in fresh water? Also, why would superconducting magnets be desirable?
18. Which is more likely to interfere with compass readings, AC current in your refrigerator or DC current when you start your car? Explain.

22.8 Torque on a Current Loop: Motors and Meters

19. Draw a diagram and use RHR-1 to show that the forces on the top and bottom segments of the motor's current loop in Figure 22.33 are vertical and produce no torque about the axis of rotation.

22.9 Magnetic Fields Produced by Currents: Ampere's Law

20. Make a drawing and use RHR-2 to find the direction of the magnetic field of a current loop in a motor (such as in Figure 22.33). Then show that the direction of the torque on the loop is the same as produced by like poles repelling and unlike poles attracting.

22.10 Magnetic Force between Two Parallel Conductors

21. Is the force attractive or repulsive between the

hot and neutral lines hung from power poles? Why?

22. If you have three parallel wires in the same plane, as in Figure 22.45, with currents in the outer two running in opposite directions, is it possible for the middle wire to be repelled by both? Attracted by both? Explain.

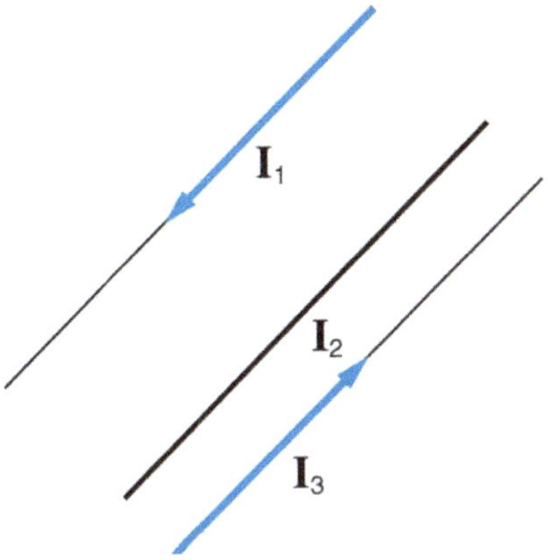

FIGURE 22.45 Three parallel coplanar wires with currents in the outer two in opposite directions.

23. Suppose two long straight wires run perpendicular to one another without touching. Does one exert a net force on the other? If so, what is its direction? Does one exert a net torque on the other? If so, what is its direction? Justify your responses by using the right hand rules.

24. Use the right hand rules to show that the force between the two loops in Figure 22.46 is attractive if the currents are in the same direction and repulsive if they are in opposite directions. Is this consistent with like poles of the loops repelling and unlike poles of the loops attracting? Draw sketches to justify your answers.

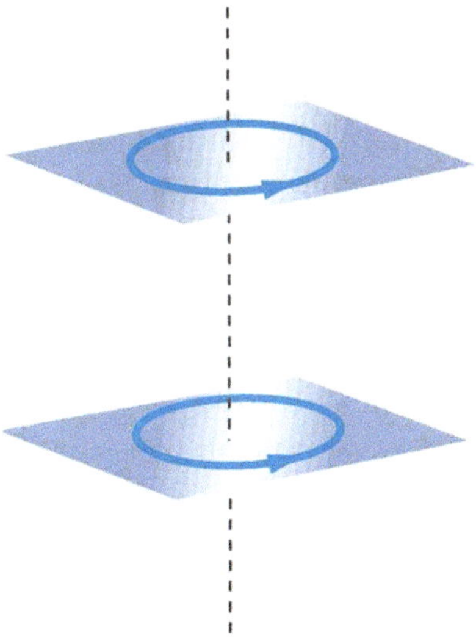

FIGURE 22.46 Two loops of wire carrying currents can exert forces and torques on one another.

25. If one of the loops in Figure 22.46 is tilted slightly relative to the other and their currents are in the same direction, what are the directions of the torques they exert on each other? Does this imply that the poles of the bar magnet-like fields they create will line up with each other if the loops are allowed to rotate?

26. Electric field lines can be shielded by the Faraday cage effect. Can we have magnetic shielding? Can we have gravitational shielding?

22.11 More Applications of Magnetism

27. Measurements of the weak and fluctuating magnetic fields associated with brain activity are called magnetoencephalograms (MEGs). Do the brain's magnetic fields imply coordinated or uncoordinated nerve impulses? Explain.

28. Discuss the possibility that a Hall voltage would be generated on the moving heart of a patient during MRI imaging. Also discuss the same effect on the wires of a pacemaker. (The fact that patients with pacemakers are not given MRIs is significant.)

29. A patient in an MRI unit turns his head quickly to one side and experiences momentary dizziness and a strange taste in his mouth. Discuss the possible causes.

30. You are told that in a certain region there is either a uniform electric or magnetic field. What measurement or observation could you make to determine the type? (Ignore the Earth's magnetic field.)

31. An example of magnetohydrodynamics (MHD) comes from the flow of a river (salty water). This fluid interacts with the Earth's magnetic field to produce a potential difference between the two river banks. How would you go about calculating the potential difference?

32. Draw gravitational field lines between 2 masses, electric field lines between a positive and a negative charge, electric field lines between 2 positive charges and magnetic field lines around a magnet. Qualitatively describe the differences between the fields and the entities responsible for the field lines.

Problems & Exercises

22.4 Magnetic Field Strength: Force on a Moving Charge in a Magnetic Field

1. What is the direction of the magnetic force on a positive charge that moves as shown in each of the six cases shown in Figure 22.47?

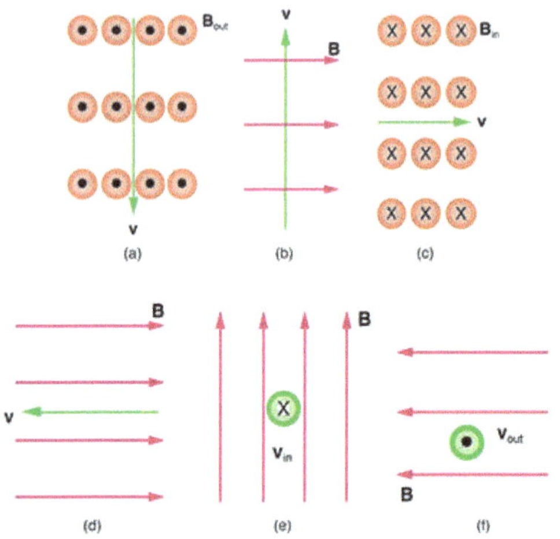

FIGURE 22.47

2. Repeat Exercise 22.1 for a negative charge.

3. What is the direction of the velocity of a negative charge that experiences the magnetic force shown in each of the three cases in Figure 22.48, assuming it moves perpendicular to $\mathbf{B}$?

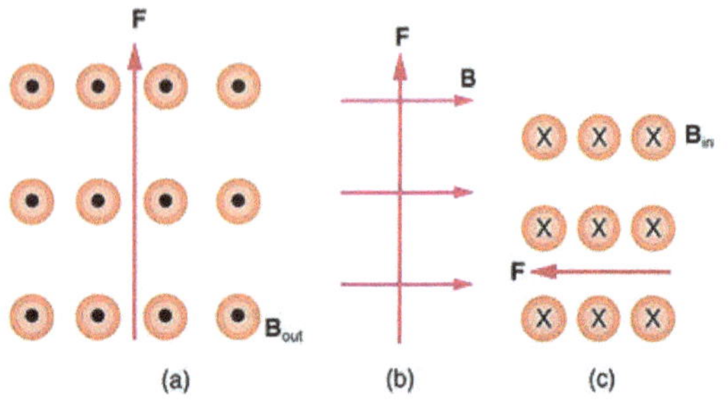

FIGURE 22.48

4. Repeat Exercise 22.3 for a positive charge.

5. What is the direction of the magnetic field that produces the magnetic force on a positive charge as shown in each of the three cases in the figure below, assuming $\mathbf{B}$ is perpendicular to $\mathbf{v}$?

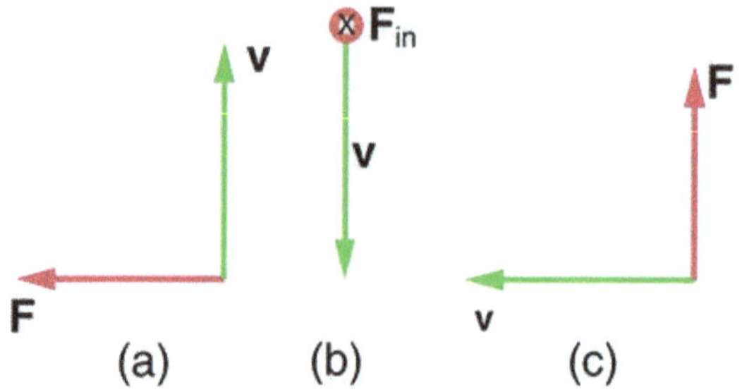

FIGURE 22.49

6. Repeat Exercise 22.5 for a negative charge.

7. What is the maximum magnitude of the force on an aluminum rod with a $0.100\text{-}\mu\text{C}$ charge that you pass between the poles of a 1.50-T permanent magnet at a speed of 5.00 m/s? In what direction is the force?

8. (a) Aircraft sometimes acquire small static charges. Suppose a supersonic jet has a $0.500\text{-}\mu\text{C}$ charge and flies due west at a speed of 660 m/s over the Earth's magnetic south pole (near Earth's geographic north pole), where the $8.00 \times 10^{-5}\text{-T}$ magnetic field points straight down. What are the direction and the magnitude of the magnetic force on the plane? (b) Discuss whether the value obtained in part (a) implies this is a significant or negligible effect.

9. (a) A cosmic ray proton moving toward the Earth at 5.00×10^{7} m/s experiences a magnetic force of 1.70×10^{-16} N. What is the strength of the magnetic field if there is a 45° angle between it and the proton's velocity? (b) Is the value obtained in part (a) consistent with the known strength of the Earth's magnetic field on its surface? Discuss.

10. An electron moving at 4.00×10^{3} m/s in a 1.25-T magnetic field experiences a magnetic force of 1.40×10^{-16} N. What angle does the velocity of the electron make with the magnetic field? There are two answers.

11. (a) A physicist performing a sensitive measurement wants to limit the magnetic force on a moving charge in her equipment to less than 1.00×10^{-12} N. What is the greatest the charge can be if it moves at a maximum speed of 30.0 m/s in the Earth's field? (b) Discuss whether it would be difficult to limit the charge to less than the value found in (a) by comparing it with typical static electricity and noting that static is often absent.

22.5 Force on a Moving Charge in a Magnetic Field: Examples and Applications

If you need additional support for these problems, see More Applications of Magnetism.

12. A cosmic ray electron moves at 7.50×10^6 m/s perpendicular to the Earth's magnetic field at an altitude where field strength is 1.00×10^{-5} T. What is the radius of the circular path the electron follows?

13. A proton moves at 7.50×10^7 m/s perpendicular to a magnetic field. The field causes the proton to travel in a circular path of radius 0.800 m. What is the field strength?

14. (a) Viewers of *Star Trek* hear of an antimatter drive on the Starship *Enterprise*. One possibility for such a futuristic energy source is to store antimatter charged particles in a vacuum chamber, circulating in a magnetic field, and then extract them as needed. Antimatter annihilates with normal matter, producing pure energy. What strength magnetic field is needed to hold antiprotons, moving at 5.00×10^7 m/s in a circular path 2.00 m in radius? Antiprotons have the same mass as protons but the opposite (negative) charge. (b) Is this field strength obtainable with today's technology or is it a futuristic possibility?

15. (a) An oxygen-16 ion with a mass of 2.66×10^{-26} kg travels at 5.00×10^6 m/s perpendicular to a 1.20-T magnetic field, which makes it move in a circular arc with a 0.231-m radius. What positive charge is on the ion? (b) What is the ratio of this charge to the charge of an electron? (c) Discuss why the ratio found in (b) should be an integer.

16. What radius circular path does an electron travel if it moves at the same speed and in the same magnetic field as the proton in Exercise 22.13?

17. A velocity selector in a mass spectrometer uses a 0.100-T magnetic field. (a) What electric field strength is needed to select a speed of 4.00×10^6 m/s? (b) What is the voltage between the plates if they are separated by 1.00 cm?

18. An electron in a TV CRT moves with a speed of 6.00×10^7 m/s, in a direction perpendicular to the Earth's field, which has a strength of 5.00×10^{-5} T. (a) What strength electric field must be applied perpendicular to the Earth's field to make the electron moves in a straight line? (b) If this is done between plates separated by 1.00 cm, what is the voltage applied? (Note that TVs are usually surrounded by a ferromagnetic material to shield against external magnetic fields and avoid the need for such a correction.)

19. (a) At what speed will a proton move in a circular path of the same radius as the electron in Exercise 22.12? (b) What would the radius of the path be if the proton had the same speed as the electron? (c) What would the radius be if the proton had the same kinetic energy as the electron? (d) The same momentum?

20. A mass spectrometer is being used to separate common oxygen-16 from the much rarer oxygen-18, taken from a sample of old glacial ice. (The relative abundance of these oxygen isotopes is related to climatic temperature at the time the ice was deposited.) The ratio of the masses of these two ions is 16 to 18, the mass of oxygen-16 is 2.66×10^{-26} kg, and they are singly charged and travel at 5.00×10^6 m/s in a 1.20-T magnetic field. What is the separation between their paths when they hit a target after traversing a semicircle?

21. (a) Triply charged uranium-235 and uranium-238 ions are being separated in a mass spectrometer. (The much rarer uranium-235 is used as reactor fuel.) The masses of the ions are 3.90×10^{-25} kg and 3.95×10^{-25} kg, respectively, and they travel at 3.00×10^5 m/s in a 0.250-T field. What is the separation between their paths when they hit a target after traversing a semicircle? (b) Discuss whether this distance between their paths seems to be big enough to be practical in the separation of uranium-235 from uranium-238.

22.6 The Hall Effect

22. A large water main is 2.50 m in diameter and the average water velocity is 6.00 m/s. Find the Hall voltage produced if the pipe runs perpendicular to the Earth's 5.00×10^{-5}-T field.

23. What Hall voltage is produced by a 0.200-T field applied across a 2.60-cm-diameter aorta when blood velocity is 60.0 cm/s?

24. (a) What is the speed of a supersonic aircraft with a 17.0-m wingspan, if it experiences a 1.60-V Hall voltage between its wing tips when in level flight over the north magnetic pole, where the Earth's field strength is 8.00×10^{-5} T? (b) Explain why very little current flows as a result of this Hall voltage.

25. A nonmechanical water meter could utilize the Hall effect by applying a magnetic field across a metal pipe and measuring the Hall voltage produced. What is the average fluid velocity in a 3.00-cm-diameter pipe, if a 0.500-T field across it creates a 60.0-mV Hall voltage?

26. Calculate the Hall voltage induced on a patient's heart while being scanned by an MRI unit. Approximate the conducting path on the heart wall by a wire 7.50 cm long that moves at 10.0 cm/s perpendicular to a 1.50-T magnetic field.

27. A Hall probe calibrated to read $1.00\ \mu\text{V}$ when placed in a 2.00-T field is placed in a 0.150-T field. What is its output voltage?

28. Using information in Example 20.6, what would the Hall voltage be if a 2.00-T field is applied across a 10-gauge copper wire (2.588 mm in diameter) carrying a 20.0-A current?

29. Show that the Hall voltage across wires made of the same material, carrying identical currents, and subjected to the same magnetic field is inversely proportional to their diameters. (Hint: Consider how drift velocity depends on wire diameter.)

30. A patient with a pacemaker is mistakenly being scanned for an MRI image. A 10.0-cm-long section of pacemaker wire moves at a speed of 10.0 cm/s perpendicular to the MRI unit's magnetic field and a 20.0-mV Hall voltage is induced. What is the magnetic field strength?

22.7 Magnetic Force on a Current-Carrying Conductor

31. What is the direction of the magnetic force on the current in each of the six cases in Figure 22.50?

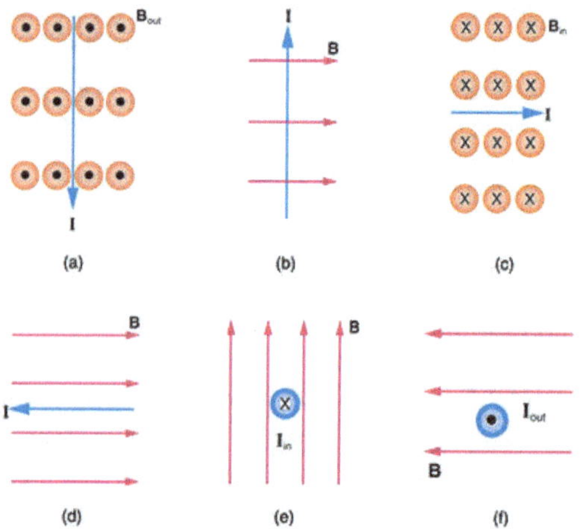

FIGURE 22.50

32. What is the direction of a current that experiences the magnetic force shown in each of the three cases in Figure 22.51, assuming the current runs perpendicular to $\boldsymbol{B}$?

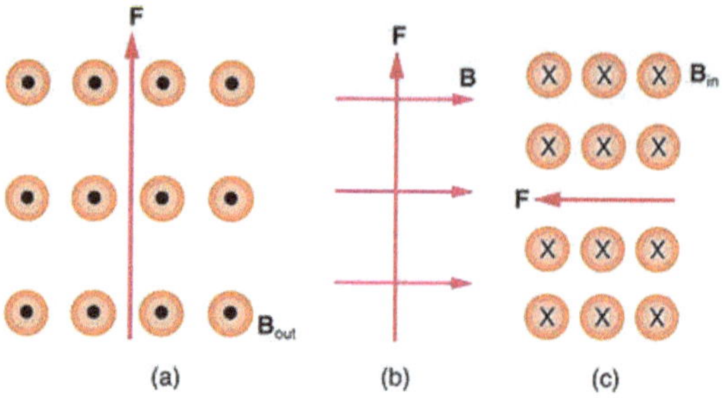

FIGURE 22.51

33. What is the direction of the magnetic field that produces the magnetic force shown on the currents in each of the three cases in Figure 22.52, assuming $\mathbf{B}$ is perpendicular to $\mathbf{I}$?

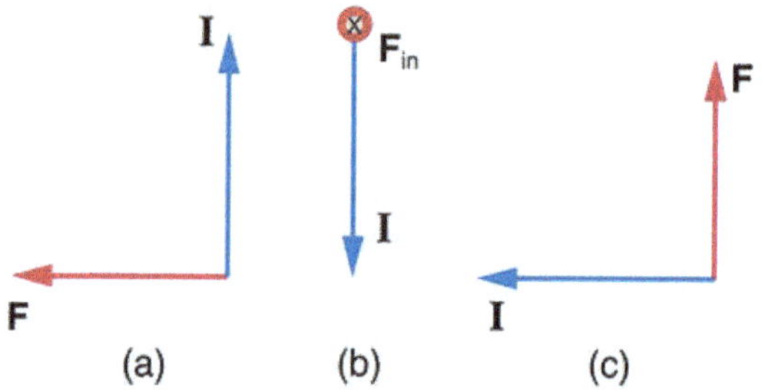

FIGURE 22.52

34. (a) What is the force per meter on a lightning bolt at the equator that carries 20,000 A perpendicular to the Earth's $3.00 \times 10^{-5}\text{-T}$ field? (b) What is the direction of the force if the current is straight up and the Earth's field direction is due north, parallel to the ground?

35. (a) A DC power line for a light-rail system carries 1000 A at an angle of 30.0° to the Earth's $5.00 \times 10^{-5}\ \text{-T}$ field. What is the force on a 100-m section of this line? (b) Discuss practical concerns this presents, if any.

36. What force is exerted on the water in an MHD drive utilizing a 25.0-cm-diameter tube, if 100-A current is passed across the tube that is perpendicular to a 2.00-T magnetic field? (The relatively small size of this force indicates the need for very large currents and magnetic fields to make practical MHD drives.)

37. A wire carrying a 30.0-A current passes between the poles of a strong magnet that is perpendicular to its field and experiences a 2.16-N force on the 4.00 cm of wire in the field. What is the average

field strength?

38. (a) A 0.750-m-long section of cable carrying current to a car starter motor makes an angle of 60° with the Earth's 5.50×10^{-5} T field. What is the current when the wire experiences a force of 7.00×10^{-3} N? (b) If you run the wire between the poles of a strong horseshoe magnet, subjecting 5.00 cm of it to a 1.75-T field, what force is exerted on this segment of wire?

39. (a) What is the angle between a wire carrying an 8.00-A current and the 1.20-T field it is in if 50.0 cm of the wire experiences a magnetic force of 2.40 N? (b) What is the force on the wire if it is rotated to make an angle of 90° with the field?

40. The force on the rectangular loop of wire in the magnetic field in Figure 22.53 can be used to measure field strength. The field is uniform, and the plane of the loop is perpendicular to the field. (a) What is the direction of the magnetic force on the loop? Justify the claim that the forces on the sides of the loop are equal and opposite, independent of how much of the loop is in the field and do not affect the net force on the loop. (b) If a current of 5.00 A is used, what is the force per tesla on the 20.0-cm-wide loop?

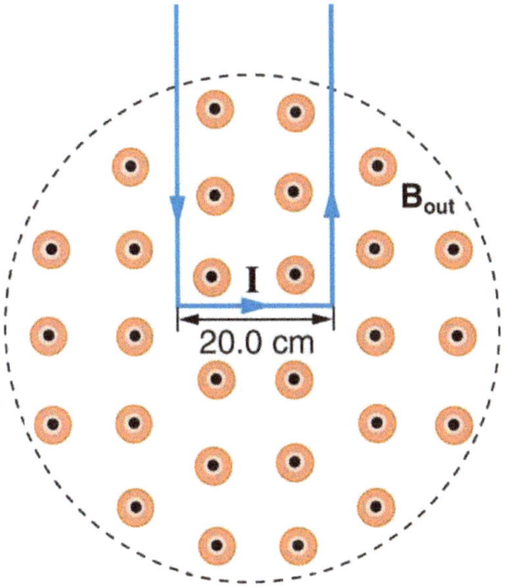

FIGURE 22.53 A rectangular loop of wire carrying a current is perpendicular to a magnetic field. The field is uniform in the region shown and is zero outside that region.

22.8 Torque on a Current Loop: Motors and Meters

41. (a) By how many percent is the torque of a motor decreased if its permanent magnets lose 5.0% of their strength? (b) How many percent would the current need to be increased to return the torque to original values?

42. (a) What is the maximum torque on a 150-turn square loop of wire 18.0 cm on a side that carries a 50.0-A current in a 1.60-T field? (b) What is the torque when θ is 10.9°?

43. Find the current through a loop needed to create a maximum torque of $9.00 \text{ N} \cdot \text{m}$. The loop has 50 square turns that are 15.0 cm on a side and is in a uniform 0.800-T magnetic field.

44. Calculate the magnetic field strength needed on a 200-turn square loop 20.0 cm on a side to create a maximum torque of $300 \text{ N} \cdot \text{m}$ if the loop is carrying 25.0 A.

45. Since the equation for torque on a current-carrying loop is $\tau = NIAB \sin \theta$, the units of $\text{N} \cdot \text{m}$ must equal units of $\text{A} \cdot \text{m}^2 \text{ T}$. Verify this.

46. (a) At what angle θ is the torque on a current loop 90.0% of maximum? (b) 50.0% of maximum? (c) 10.0% of maximum?

47. A proton has a magnetic field due to its spin on its axis. The field is similar to that created by a circular current loop 0.650×10^{-15} m in radius with a current of 1.05×10^{4} A (no kidding). Find the maximum torque on a proton in a 2.50-T field. (This is a significant torque on a small particle.)

48. (a) A 200-turn circular loop of radius 50.0 cm is vertical, with its axis on an east-west line. A current of 100 A circulates clockwise in the loop when viewed from the east. The Earth's field here is due north, parallel to the ground, with a strength of 3.00×10^{-5} T. What are the direction and magnitude of the torque on the loop? (b) Does this device have any practical applications as a motor?

49. Repeat Exercise 22.41, but with the loop lying flat on the ground with its current circulating counterclockwise (when viewed from above) in a location where the Earth's field is north, but at an angle 45.0° below the horizontal and with a strength of 6.00×10^{-5} T.

22.10 Magnetic Force between Two Parallel Conductors

50. (a) The hot and neutral wires supplying DC power to a light-rail commuter train carry 800 A and are separated by 75.0 cm. What is the magnitude and direction of the force between 50.0 m of these wires? (b) Discuss the practical consequences of this force, if any.

51. The force per meter between the two wires of a jumper cable being used to start a stalled car is 0.225 N/m. (a) What is the current in the wires, given they are separated by 2.00 cm? (b) Is the force attractive or repulsive?

52. A 2.50-m segment of wire supplying current to the motor of a submerged submarine carries 1000 A and feels a 4.00-N repulsive force from a parallel wire 5.00 cm away. What is the direction and magnitude of the current in the other wire?

53. The wire carrying 400 A to the motor of a commuter train feels an attractive force of 4.00×10^{-3} N/m due to a parallel wire carrying 5.00 A to a headlight. (a) How far apart are the wires? (b) Are the currents in the same direction?

54. An AC appliance cord has its hot and neutral wires separated by 3.00 mm and carries a 5.00-A current. (a) What is the average force per meter between the wires in the cord? (b) What is the maximum force per meter between the wires? (c) Are the forces attractive or repulsive? (d) Do appliance cords need any special design features to compensate for these forces?

55. Figure 22.54 shows a long straight wire near a rectangular current loop. What is the direction and magnitude of the total force on the loop?

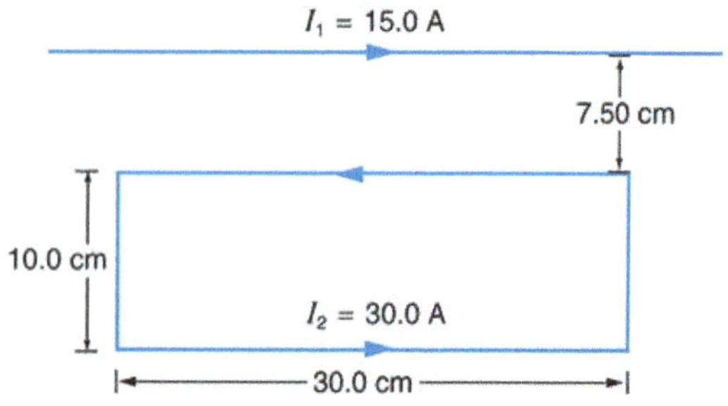

FIGURE 22.54

56. Find the direction and magnitude of the force that each wire experiences in Figure 22.55(a) by, using vector addition.

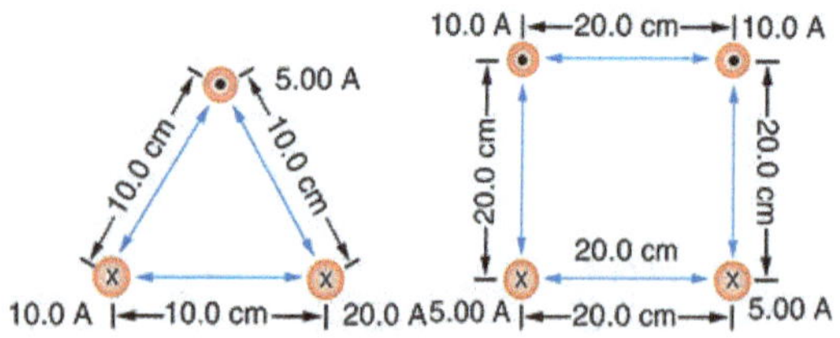

FIGURE 22.55

57. Find the direction and magnitude of the force that each wire experiences in Figure 22.55(b), using vector addition.

22.11 More Applications of Magnetism

58. Indicate whether the magnetic field created in each of the three situations shown in Figure 22.56 is into or out of the page on the left and right of the current.

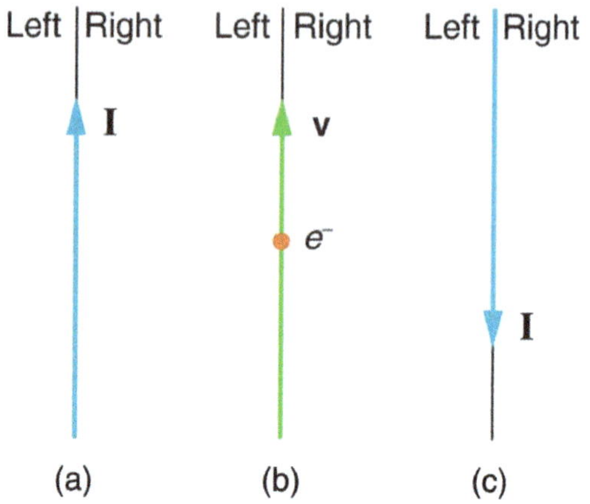

FIGURE 22.56

59. What are the directions of the fields in the center of the loop and coils shown in Figure 22.57?

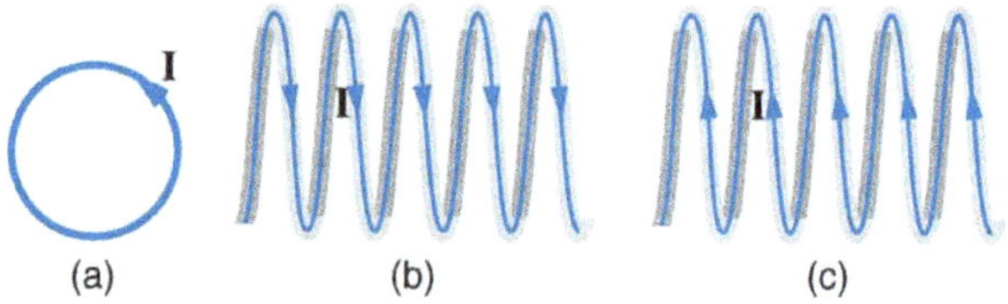

FIGURE 22.57

60. What are the directions of the currents in the loop and coils shown in Figure 22.58?

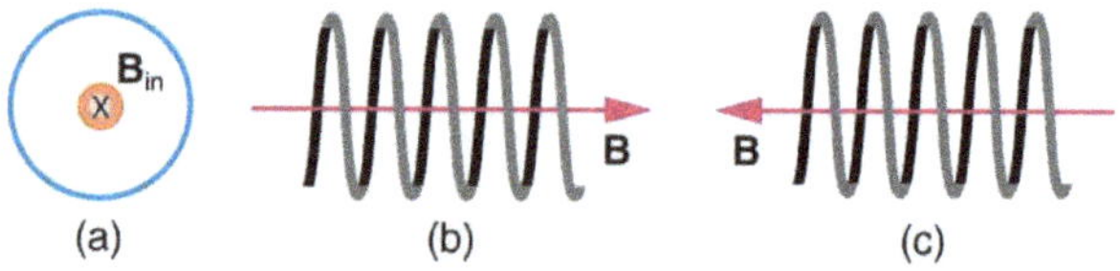

FIGURE 22.58

61. To see why an MRI utilizes iron to increase the magnetic field created by a coil, calculate the current needed in a 400-loop-per-meter circular coil 0.660 m in radius to create a 1.20-T field (typical of an MRI instrument) at its center with no iron present. The magnetic field of a proton is approximately like that of a circular current loop 0.650×10^{-15} m in radius carrying 1.05×10^{4} A. What is the field at the center of such a loop?

62. Inside a motor, 30.0 A passes through a 250-turn circular loop that is 10.0 cm in radius. What is the magnetic field strength created at its center?

63. Nonnuclear submarines use batteries for power when submerged. (a) Find the magnetic field 50.0 cm from a straight wire carrying 1200 A from the batteries to the drive mechanism of a submarine. (b) What is the field if the wires to and from the drive mechanism are side by side? (c) Discuss the effects this could have for a compass on the submarine that is not shielded.

64. How strong is the magnetic field inside a solenoid with 10,000 turns per meter that carries 20.0 A?

65. What current is needed in the solenoid described in Exercise 22.58 to produce a magnetic field 10^4 times the Earth's magnetic field of 5.00×10^{-5} T?

66. How far from the starter cable of a car, carrying 150 A, must you be to experience a field less than the Earth's (5.00×10^{-5} T)? Assume a long straight wire carries the current. (In practice, the body of your car shields the dashboard compass.)

67. Measurements affect the system being measured, such as the current loop in Figure 22.53. (a) Estimate the field the loop creates by calculating the field at the center of a circular loop 20.0 cm in diameter carrying 5.00 A. (b) What is the smallest field strength this loop can be used to measure, if its field must alter the measured field by less than 0.0100%?

68. Figure 22.59 shows a long straight wire just touching a loop carrying a current I_1. Both lie in the same plane. (a) What direction must the current I_2 in the straight wire have to create a field at the center of the loop in the direction opposite to that created by the loop? (b) What is the ratio of I_1/I_2 that gives zero field strength at the center of the loop? (c) What is the direction of the field directly above the loop under this circumstance?

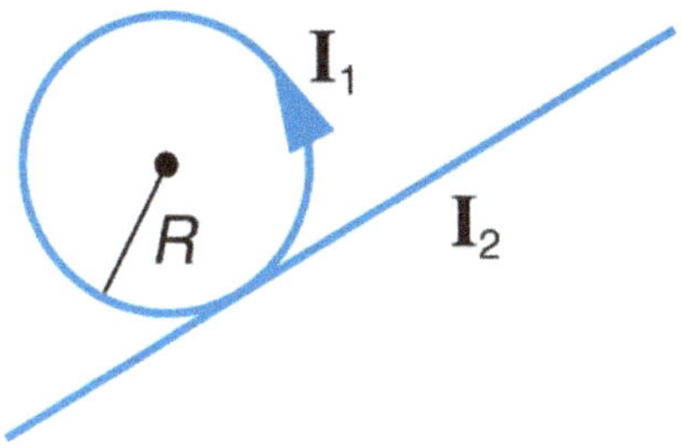

FIGURE 22.59

69. Find the magnitude and direction of the magnetic field at the point equidistant from the wires in Figure 22.55(a), using the rules of vector addition to sum the contributions from each wire.

70. Find the magnitude and direction of the magnetic field at the point equidistant from the wires in Figure 22.55(b), using the rules of vector addition to sum the contributions from each wire.

71. What current is needed in the top wire in Figure 22.55(a) to produce a field of zero at the point equidistant from the wires, if the currents in the bottom two wires are both 10.0 A into the page?

72. Calculate the size of the magnetic field 20 m below a high voltage power line. The line carries 450 MW at a voltage of 300,000 V.

73. Integrated Concepts
(a) A pendulum is set up so that its bob (a thin copper disk) swings between the poles of a permanent magnet as shown in Figure 22.60. What is the magnitude and direction of the magnetic force on the bob at the lowest point in its path, if it has a positive $0.250\ \mu\text{C}$ charge and is released from a height of 30.0 cm above its lowest point? The magnetic field strength is 1.50 T. (b) What is the acceleration of the bob at the bottom of its swing if its mass is 30.0 grams and it is hung from a flexible string? Be certain to include a free-body diagram as part of your analysis.

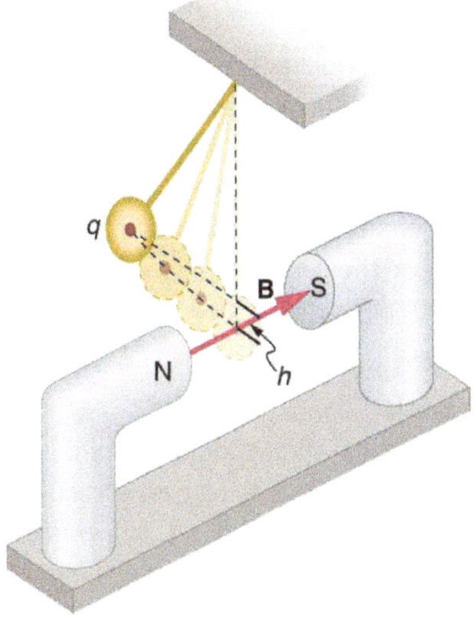

FIGURE 22.60

74. Integrated Concepts
(a) What voltage will accelerate electrons to a speed of 6.00×10^6 m/s? (b) Find the radius of curvature of the path of a *proton* accelerated through this potential in a 0.500-T field and compare this with the radius of curvature of an electron accelerated through the same potential.

75. Integrated Concepts
Find the radius of curvature of the path of a

25.0-MeV proton moving perpendicularly to the 1.20-T field of a cyclotron.

76. Integrated Concepts
To construct a nonmechanical water meter, a 0.500-T magnetic field is placed across the supply water pipe to a home and the Hall voltage is recorded. (a) Find the flow rate in liters per second through a 3.00-cm-diameter pipe if the Hall voltage is 60.0 mV. (b) What would the Hall voltage be for the same flow rate through a 10.0-cm-diameter pipe with the same field applied?

77. Integrated Concepts
(a) Using the values given for an MHD drive in Exercise 22.59, and assuming the force is uniformly applied to the fluid, calculate the pressure created in $\mathrm{N/m^2}$. (b) Is this a significant fraction of an atmosphere?

78. Integrated Concepts
(a) Calculate the maximum torque on a 50-turn, 1.50 cm radius circular current loop carrying $50\ \mu\mathrm{A}$ in a 0.500-T field. (b) If this coil is to be used in a galvanometer that reads $50\ \mu\mathrm{A}$ full scale, what force constant spring must be used, if it is attached 1.00 cm from the axis of rotation and is stretched by the 60° arc moved?

79. Integrated Concepts
A current balance used to define the ampere is designed so that the current through it is constant, as is the distance between wires. Even so, if the wires change length with temperature, the force between them will change. What percent change in force per degree will occur if the wires are copper?

80. Integrated Concepts
(a) Show that the period of the circular orbit of a charged particle moving perpendicularly to a uniform magnetic field is $T = 2\pi m/(qB)$. (b) What is the frequency f? (c) What is the angular velocity ω? Note that these results are independent of the velocity and radius of the orbit and, hence, of the energy of the particle. (Figure 22.61.)

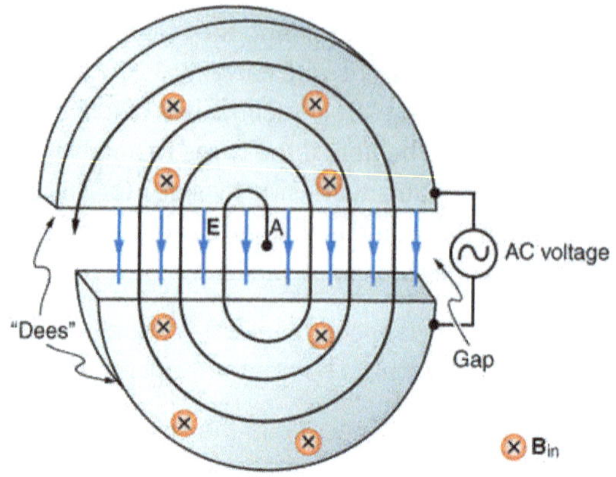

FIGURE 22.61 Cyclotrons accelerate charged particles orbiting in a magnetic field by placing an AC voltage on the metal Dees, between which the particles move, so that energy is added twice each orbit. The frequency is constant, since it is independent of the particle energy—the radius of the orbit simply increases with energy until the particles approach the edge and are extracted for various experiments and applications.

81. Integrated Concepts
A cyclotron accelerates charged particles as shown in Figure 22.61. Using the results of the previous problem, calculate the frequency of the accelerating voltage needed for a proton in a 1.20-T field.

82. Integrated Concepts
(a) A 0.140-kg baseball, pitched at 40.0 m/s horizontally and perpendicular to the Earth's horizontal 5.00×10^{-5} T field, has a 100-nC charge on it. What distance is it deflected from its path by the magnetic force, after traveling 30.0 m horizontally? (b) Would you suggest this as a secret technique for a pitcher to throw curve balls?

83. Integrated Concepts
(a) What is the direction of the force on a wire carrying a current due east in a location where the Earth's field is due north? Both are parallel to the ground. (b) Calculate the force per meter if the wire carries 20.0 A and the field strength is 3.00×10^{-5} T. (c) What diameter copper wire would have its weight supported by this force? (d) Calculate the resistance per meter and the voltage per meter needed.

84. Integrated Concepts
One long straight wire is to be held directly above another by repulsion between their currents. The lower wire carries 100 A and the wire 7.50 cm above it is 10-gauge (2.588 mm diameter) copper wire. (a) What current must flow in the upper wire, neglecting the Earth's field? (b) What is the

smallest current if the Earth's 3.00×10^{-5} T field is parallel to the ground and is not neglected? (c) Is the supported wire in a stable or unstable equilibrium if displaced vertically? If displaced horizontally?

85. Unreasonable Results
(a) Find the charge on a baseball, thrown at 35.0 m/s perpendicular to the Earth's 5.00×10^{-5} T field, that experiences a 1.00-N magnetic force. (b) What is unreasonable about this result? (c) Which assumption or premise is responsible?

86. Unreasonable Results
A charged particle having mass 6.64×10^{-27} kg (that of a helium atom) moving at 8.70×10^{5} m/s perpendicular to a 1.50-T magnetic field travels in a circular path of radius 16.0 mm. (a) What is the charge of the particle? (b) What is unreasonable about this result? (c) Which assumptions are responsible?

87. Unreasonable Results
An inventor wants to generate 120-V power by moving a 1.00-m-long wire perpendicular to the Earth's 5.00×10^{-5} T field. (a) Find the speed with which the wire must move. (b) What is unreasonable about this result? (c) Which assumption is responsible?

88. Unreasonable Results
Frustrated by the small Hall voltage obtained in blood flow measurements, a medical physicist decides to increase the applied magnetic field strength to get a 0.500-V output for blood moving at 30.0 cm/s in a 1.50-cm-diameter vessel. (a) What magnetic field strength is needed? (b) What is unreasonable about this result? (c) Which premise is responsible?

89. Unreasonable Results
A surveyor 100 m from a long straight 200-kV DC power line suspects that its magnetic field may equal that of the Earth and affect compass readings. (a) Calculate the current in the wire needed to create a 5.00×10^{-5} T field at this distance. (b) What is unreasonable about this result? (c) Which assumption or premise is responsible?

90. Construct Your Own Problem
Consider a mass separator that applies a magnetic field perpendicular to the velocity of ions and separates the ions based on the radius of curvature of their paths in the field. Construct a problem in which you calculate the magnetic field strength needed to separate two ions that differ in mass, but not charge, and have the same initial velocity. Among the things to consider are the types of ions, the velocities they can be given before entering the magnetic field, and a reasonable value for the radius of curvature of the paths they follow. In addition, calculate the separation distance between the ions at the point where they are detected.

91. Construct Your Own Problem
Consider using the torque on a current-carrying coil in a magnetic field to detect relatively small magnetic fields (less than the field of the Earth, for example). Construct a problem in which you calculate the maximum torque on a current-carrying loop in a magnetic field. Among the things to be considered are the size of the coil, the number of loops it has, the current you pass through the coil, and the size of the field you wish to detect. Discuss whether the torque produced is large enough to be effectively measured. Your instructor may also wish for you to consider the effects, if any, of the field produced by the coil on the surroundings that could affect detection of the small field.

92. Critical Thinking A magnetic field of 2.00×10^{-7} T in the positive *x*-direction exists. Three electrons pass through the origin, one at a time, each with a velocity of 5.00×10^{7} m/s. The first electron passes the origin along the *x*-axis, the second electron along the *y*-axis, and the third at an angle of $45°$ with respect to both the *y*- and *z*-axes in the *yz*-plane. (a) What is the force acting on each electron? (b) What is the shape of the path of each electron? (c) When, if ever, will each electron return to the origin?

Test Prep for AP® Courses

22.2 Ferromagnets and Electromagnets

1. A bar magnet is oriented so that the north pole of the bar magnet points north. A compass needle is placed to the north of the bar magnet. In which direction does the north pole of the compass needle point?

a. North
b. East
c. South
d. West

2. Assume for simplicity that the Earth's magnetic north pole is at the same location as its geographic north pole. If you are in an airplane flying due west along the equator, as you cross the prime meridian (0° longitude) facing west and look down at a compass you are carrying, you see that the compass needle is perpendicular to your direction of motion, and the north pole of the needle dipole points to your right. As you continue flying due west, describe how and why the orientation of the needle will (or will not) change.

3. Describe how the magnetic domains in an unmagnetized iron rod will respond to the presence of a strong external magnetic field.
   a. The domains will split into monopoles.
   b. The domains will tend to align with the external field.
   c. The domains will tend to orient themselves perpendicular to the external field.
   d. The domains will tend to align so as to cancel out the external field.

4. Describe what steps must be undertaken in order to convert an unmagnetized iron rod into a permanently magnetized state. As part of your answer, explain what a magnetic domain is and how it responds to the steps described.

5. Iron is ferromagnetic and lead is diamagnetic, which means its magnetic domains respond in the opposite direction of ferromagnets but many orders of magnitude more weakly. The two blocks are placed in a magnetic field that points to the right. Which of the following best represents the orientations of the dipoles when the field is present?

	Iron	Lead
(a)	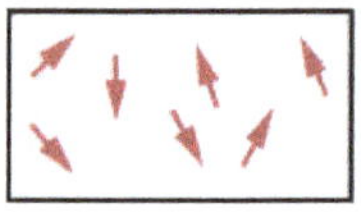 FIGURE 22.62	 FIGURE 22.63
(b)	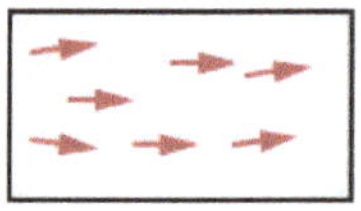 FIGURE 22.64	 FIGURE 22.65
(c)	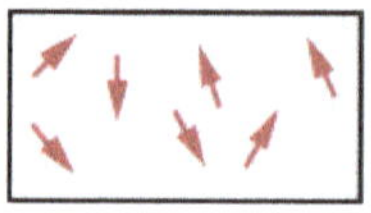 FIGURE 22.66	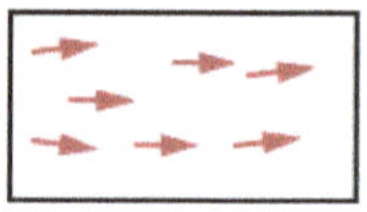 FIGURE 22.67
(d)	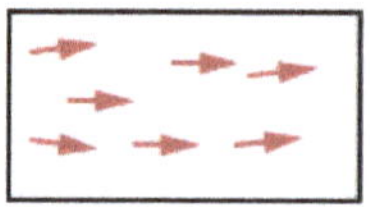 FIGURE 22.68	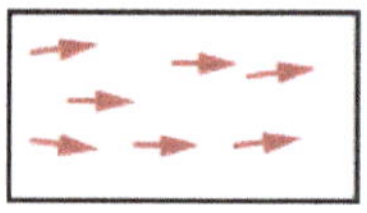 FIGURE 22.69

TABLE 22.1

6. A weather vane is some sort of directional arrow parallel to the ground that may rotate freely in a horizontal plane. A typical weather vane has a large cross-sectional area perpendicular to the direction the arrow is pointing, like a "One Way" street sign. The purpose of the weather vane is to indicate the direction of the wind. As wind blows past the weather vane, it tends to orient the arrow in the same direction as the wind. Consider a weather vane's response to a strong wind. Explain how this is both similar to and different from a magnetic domain's response to an external magnetic field. How does each affect its surroundings?

22.4 Magnetic Field Strength: Force on a Moving Charge in a Magnetic Field

7. A proton moves in the $-x$-direction and encounters a uniform magnetic field pointing in the $+x$-direction. In what direction is the resulting magnetic force on the proton?
   a. The proton experiences no magnetic force.
   b. $+x$-direction
   c. $-y$-direction
   d. $+y$-direction

8. A proton moves with a speed of 240 m/s in the $+x$-direction into a region of a 4.5-T uniform magnetic field directed 62° above the $+x$-direction in the x,y-plane. Calculate the magnitude of the magnetic force on the proton.

22.5 Force on a Moving Charge in a Magnetic Field: Examples and Applications

9. A wire oriented north-south carries current south. The wire is immersed in the Earth's magnetic field, which is also oriented north-south (with a horizontal component pointing north). The Earth's magnetic field also has a vertical component pointing down. What is the direction of the magnetic force felt by the wire?

a. West
b. East
c. Up
d. North

22.6 The Hall Effect

10. An airplane wingspan can be approximated as a conducting rod of length 35 m. As the airplane flies due north, it is flying at a rate of 82 m/s through the Earth's magnetic field, which has a magnitude of 45 μT toward the north in a direction 57° below the horizontal plane. (a) Which end of the wingspan is positively charged, the east or west end? Explain. (b) What is the Hall emf along the wingspan?

22.9 Magnetic Fields Produced by Currents: Ampere's Law

11. An experimentalist fires a beam of electrons, creating a visible path in the air that can be measured. The beam is fired along a direction parallel to a current-carrying wire, and the electrons travel in a circular path in response to the wire's magnetic field. Assuming the mass and charge of the electrons is known, what quantities would you need to measure in order to deduce the current in the wire?

a. the radius of the circular path
b. the average distance between the electrons and the wire
c. the velocity of the electrons
d. two of the above
e. all of the above

12. Electrons starting from rest are accelerated through a potential difference of 240 V and fired into a region of uniform 3.5-mT magnetic field generated by a large solenoid. The electrons are initially moving in the +*x*-direction upon entering the field, and the field is directed into the page. Determine (a) the radius of the circle in which the electrons will move in this uniform magnetic field and (b) the initial direction of the magnetic force the electrons feel upon entering the uniform field of the solenoid.

13. In terms of the direction of force, we use the left-hand rule. Pointing your thumb in the +*x*-direction with the velocity and fingers of the left hand into the page reveals that the magnetic force points down toward the bottom of the page in the −*y*-direction.
A wire along the *y*-axis carries current in the +*y*-direction. In what direction is the magnetic field at a point on the +*x*-axis near the wire?

a. away from the wire
b. vertically upward
c. into the page
d. out of the page

14. Imagine the *xy* coordinate plane is the plane of the page. A wire along the *z*-axis carries current in the +*z*-direction (out of the page, or ⊙). Draw a diagram of the magnetic field in the vicinity of this wire indicating the direction of the field. Also, describe how the strength of the magnetic field varies according to the distance from the *z*-axis.

22.10 Magnetic Force between Two Parallel Conductors

15. Two parallel wires carry equal currents in the same direction and are separated by a small distance. What is the direction of the magnetic force exerted by the two wires on each other?

a. No force since the wires are parallel.
b. No force since the currents are in the same direction.
c. The force is attractive.
d. The force is repulsive.

16. A wire along the *y*-axis carries current in the +*y*-direction. An experimenter would like to arrange a second wire parallel to the first wire and crossing the *x*-axis at the coordinate $x = 2.0\text{ m}$ so that the total magnetic field at the coordinate $x = 1.0\text{ m}$ is zero. In what direction must the current flow in the second wire, assuming it is equal in magnitude to the current in the first wire? Explain.

CHAPTER 23
Electromagnetic Induction, AC Circuits, and Electrical Technologies

FIGURE 23.1 This wind turbine in the Thames Estuary in the UK is an example of induction at work. Wind pushes the blades of the turbine, spinning a shaft attached to magnets. The magnets spin around a conductive coil, inducing an electric current in the coil, and eventually feeding the electrical grid. (credit: phault, Flickr)

CHAPTER OUTLINE

CONNECTION FOR AP® COURSES Nature's displays of symmetry are beautiful and alluring. As shown in Figure 23.2, a butterfly's wings exhibit an appealing symmetry in a complex system. The laws of physics display symmetries at the most basic level – these symmetries are a source of wonder and imply deeper meaning. Since we place a high value on symmetry, we look for it when we explore nature. The remarkable thing is that we find it.

FIGURE 23.2 A butterfly with symmetrically patterned wings is resting on a flower. Physics, like this butterfly, has inherent symmetries. (credit: Thomas Bresson).

This chapter supports Big Idea 4, illustrating how electric and magnetic changes can take place in a system due to interactions with other systems. The hint of symmetry between electricity and magnetism found in the preceding chapter will be elaborated upon in this chapter. Specifically, we know that a current creates a magnetic field. If nature is symmetric in this case, then perhaps a magnetic field can create a current. Historically, it was very shortly after Oersted discovered that currents cause magnetic fields that other scientists asked the following question: Can magnetic fields cause currents? The answer was soon found by experiment to be yes. In 1831, some 12 years after Oersted's discovery, the English scientist Michael Faraday (1791–1862) and the American scientist Joseph Henry (1797–1878) independently demonstrated that magnetic fields can produce currents. The basic process of generating emfs (electromotive forces), and hence currents, with magnetic fields is known as induction; this process is also called "magnetic induction" to distinguish it from charging by induction, which utilizes the Coulomb force.

Today, currents induced by magnetic fields are essential to our technological society. The ubiquitous generator – found in automobiles, on bicycles, in nuclear power plants, and so on – uses magnetism to generate current. Other devices that use magnetism to induce currents include pickup coils in electric guitars, transformers of every size, certain microphones, airport security gates, and damping mechanisms on sensitive chemical balances. Explanations and examples in this chapter will help you understand current induction via magnetic interactions in mechanical systems (Enduring Understanding 4.E, Essential Knowledge 4.E.2). You will also learn how the behavior of AC circuits depends strongly on the effect of magnetic fields on currents.

The content of this chapter supports:

Big Idea 4 Interactions between systems can result in changes in those systems.

Enduring Understanding 4.E The electric and magnetic properties of a system can change in response to the presence of, or changes in, other objects or systems.

Essential Knowledge 4.E.2 Changing magnetic flux induces an electric field that can establish an induced emf in a system.

Click to view content (https://openstax.org/books/college-physics-ap-courses-2e/pages/23-connection-for-ap-r-courses)

23.1 Induced Emf and Magnetic Flux

LEARNING OBJECTIVES

By the end of this section, you will be able to:

- Calculate the flux of a uniform magnetic field through a loop of arbitrary orientation.
- Describe methods to produce an electromotive force (emf) with a magnetic field or magnet and a loop of wire.

The apparatus used by Faraday to demonstrate that magnetic fields can create currents is illustrated in Figure 23.3. When the switch is closed, a magnetic field is produced in the coil on the top part of the iron ring and transmitted to the coil on the bottom part of the ring. The galvanometer is used to detect any current induced in the coil on the bottom. It was found that each time the switch is closed, the galvanometer detects a current in one direction in the coil on the bottom. (You can also observe this in a physics lab.) Each time the switch is opened, the galvanometer detects a current in the opposite direction. Interestingly, if the switch remains closed or open for any length of time, there is no current through the galvanometer. *Closing and opening the switch* induces the current. It is the *change* in magnetic field that creates the current. More basic than the current that flows is the *emf* that causes it. The current is a result of an *emf induced by a changing magnetic field*, whether or not there is a path for current to flow.

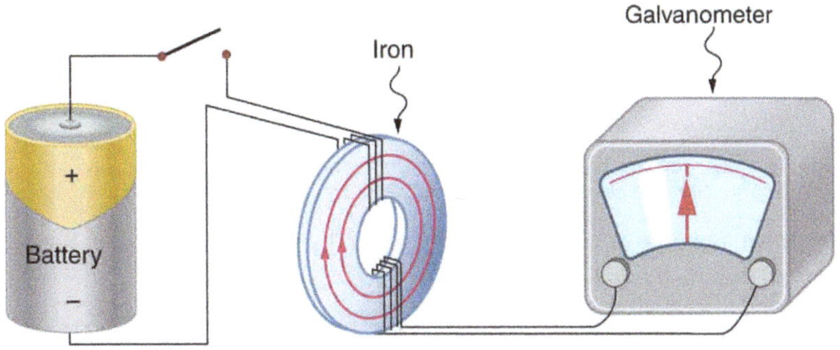

FIGURE 23.3 Faraday's apparatus for demonstrating that a magnetic field can produce a current. A change in the field produced by the top coil induces an emf and, hence, a current in the bottom coil. When the switch is opened and closed, the galvanometer registers currents in opposite directions. No current flows through the galvanometer when the switch remains closed or open.

An experiment easily performed and often done in physics labs is illustrated in Figure 23.4. An emf is induced in the coil when a bar magnet is pushed in and out of it. Emfs of opposite signs are produced by motion in opposite directions, and the emfs are also reversed by reversing poles. The same results are produced if the coil is moved rather than the magnet—it is the relative motion that is important. The faster the motion, the greater the emf, and there is no emf when the magnet is stationary relative to the coil.

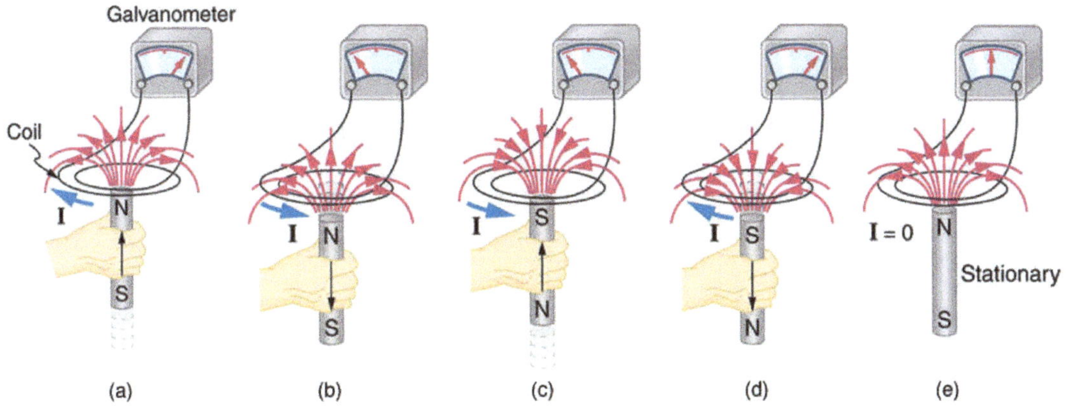

FIGURE 23.4 Movement of a magnet relative to a coil produces emfs as shown. The same emfs are produced if the coil is moved relative to the magnet. The greater the speed, the greater the magnitude of the emf, and the emf is zero when there is no motion.

The method of inducing an emf used in most electric generators is shown in Figure 23.5. A coil is rotated in a magnetic field, producing an alternating current emf, which depends on rotation rate and other factors that will be explored in later sections. Note that the generator is remarkably similar in construction to a motor (another symmetry).

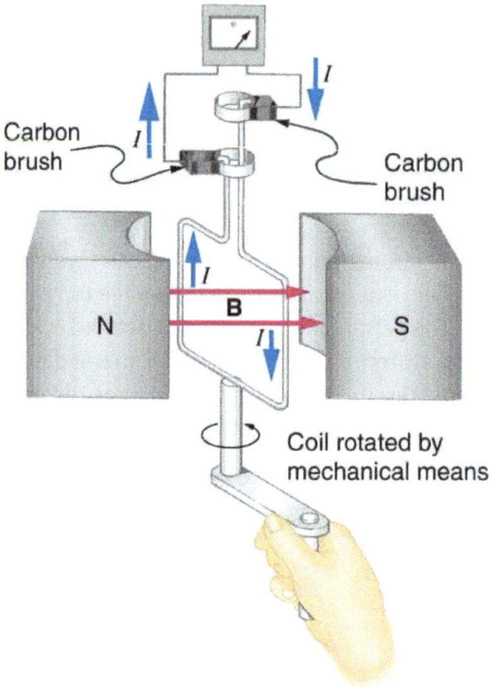

FIGURE 23.5 Rotation of a coil in a magnetic field produces an emf. This is the basic construction of a generator, where work done to turn the coil is converted to electric energy. Note the generator is very similar in construction to a motor.

So we see that changing the magnitude or direction of a magnetic field produces an emf. Experiments revealed that there is a crucial quantity called the **magnetic flux, Φ**, given by

$$\Phi = BA\cos\theta, \tag{23.1}$$

where B is the magnetic field strength over an area A, at an angle θ with the perpendicular to the area as shown in Figure 23.6. **Any change in magnetic flux Φ induces an emf.** This process is defined to be **electromagnetic induction**. Units of magnetic flux Φ are $\mathrm{T \cdot m^2}$. As seen in Figure 23.6, $B\cos\theta = B_\perp$, which is the component of B perpendicular to the area A. Thus magnetic flux is $\Phi = B_\perp A$, the product of the area and the component of the magnetic field perpendicular to it.

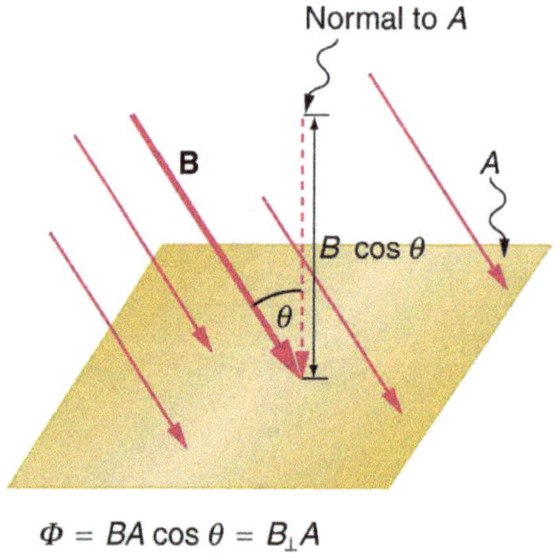

FIGURE 23.6 Magnetic flux Φ is related to the magnetic field and the area over which it exists. The flux $\Phi = BA\cos\theta$ is related to induction; any change in Φ induces an emf.

All induction, including the examples given so far, arises from some change in magnetic flux Φ. For example, Faraday changed B and hence Φ when opening and closing the switch in his apparatus (shown in Figure 23.3). This is also true for the bar magnet and coil shown in Figure 23.4. When rotating the coil of a generator, the angle θ and, hence, Φ is changed. Just how great an emf and what direction it takes depend on the change in Φ and how rapidly the change is made, as examined in the next section.

23.2 Faraday's Law of Induction: Lenz's Law

LEARNING OBJECTIVES

By the end of this section, you will be able to:

- Calculate emf, current, and magnetic fields using Faraday's Law.
- Explain the physical results of Lenz's Law

Faraday's and Lenz's Law

Faraday's experiments showed that the emf induced by a change in magnetic flux depends on only a few factors. First, emf is directly proportional to the change in flux $\Delta\Phi$. Second, emf is greatest when the change in time Δt is smallest—that is, emf is inversely proportional to Δt. Finally, if a coil has N turns, an emf will be produced that is N times greater than for a single coil, so that emf is directly proportional to N. The equation for the emf induced by a change in magnetic flux is

$$\text{emf} = -N\frac{\Delta\Phi}{\Delta t}. \quad 23.2$$

This relationship is known as **Faraday's law of induction**. The units for emf are volts, as is usual.

The minus sign in Faraday's law of induction is very important. The minus means that *the emf creates a current I and magnetic field B that oppose the change in flux $\Delta\Phi$—this is known as Lenz's law*. The direction (given by the minus sign) of the emfis so important that it is called **Lenz's law** after the Russian Heinrich Lenz (1804–1865), who, like Faraday and Henry,independently investigated aspects of induction. Faraday was aware of the direction, but Lenz stated it so clearly that he is credited for its discovery. (See Figure 23.7.)

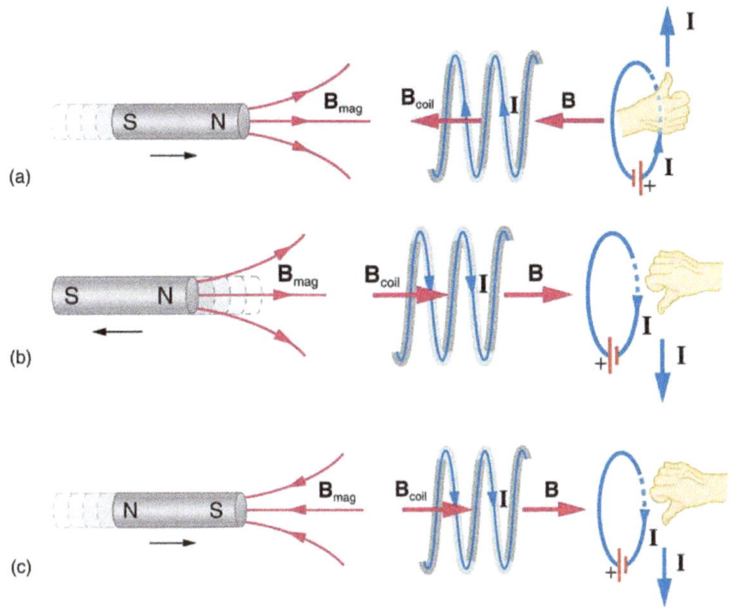

FIGURE 23.7 (a) When this bar magnet is thrust into the coil, the strength of the magnetic field increases in the coil. The current induced in the coil creates another field, in the opposite direction of the bar magnet's to oppose the increase. This is one aspect of *Lenz's law—induction opposes any change in flux*. (b) and (c) are two other situations. Verify for yourself that the direction of the induced B_{coil} shown indeed opposes the change in flux and that the current direction shown is consistent with RHR-2.

PROBLEM-SOLVING STRATEGY FOR LENZ'S LAW

To use Lenz's law to determine the directions of the induced magnetic fields, currents, and emfs:

1. Make a sketch of the situation for use in visualizing and recording directions.
2. Determine the direction of the magnetic field B.
3. Determine whether the flux is increasing or decreasing.
4. Now determine the direction of the induced magnetic field B. It opposes the *change* in flux by adding or

subtracting from the original field.

5. Use RHR-2 to determine the direction of the induced current I that is responsible for the induced magnetic field B.
6. The direction (or polarity) of the induced emf will now drive a current in this direction and can be represented as current emerging from the positive terminal of the emf and returning to its negative terminal.

For practice, apply these steps to the situations shown in Figure 23.7 and to others that are part of the following text material.

Applications of Electromagnetic Induction

There are many applications of Faraday's Law of induction, as we will explore in this chapter and others. At this juncture, let us mention several that have to do with data storage and magnetic fields. A very important application has to do with audio and video *recording tapes*. A plastic tape, coated with iron oxide, moves past a recording head. This recording head is basically a round iron ring about which is wrapped a coil of wire—an electromagnet (Figure 23.8). A signal in the form of a varying input current from a microphone or camera goes to the recording head. These signals (which are a function of the signal amplitude and frequency) produce varying magnetic fields at the recording head. As the tape moves past the recording head, the magnetic field orientations of the iron oxide molecules on the tape are changed thus recording the signal. In the playback mode, the magnetized tape is run past another head, similar in structure to the recording head. The different magnetic field orientations of the iron oxide molecules on the tape induces an emf in the coil of wire in the playback head. This signal then is sent to a loudspeaker or video player.

FIGURE 23.8 Recording and playback heads used with audio and video magnetic tapes. (credit: Steve Jurvetson)

Similar principles apply to computer hard drives, except at a much faster rate. Here recordings are on a coated, spinning disk. Read heads historically were made to work on the principle of induction. However, the input information is carried in digital rather than analog form – a series of 0's or 1's are written upon the spinning hard drive. Today, most hard drive readout devices do not work on the principle of induction, but use a technique known as *giant magnetoresistance*. (The discovery that weak changes in a magnetic field in a thin film of iron and chromium could bring about much larger changes in electrical resistance was one of the first large successes of nanotechnology.) Another application of induction is found on the magnetic stripe on the back of your personal credit card as used at the grocery store or the ATM machine. This works on the same principle as the audio or video tape mentioned in the last paragraph in which a head reads personal information from your card.

Another application of electromagnetic induction is when electrical signals need to be transmitted across a barrier. Consider the *cochlear implant* shown below. Sound is picked up by a microphone on the outside of the skull and is used to set up a varying magnetic field. A current is induced in a receiver secured in the bone beneath the skin and transmitted to electrodes in the inner ear. Electromagnetic induction can be used in other instances where electric signals need to be conveyed across various media.

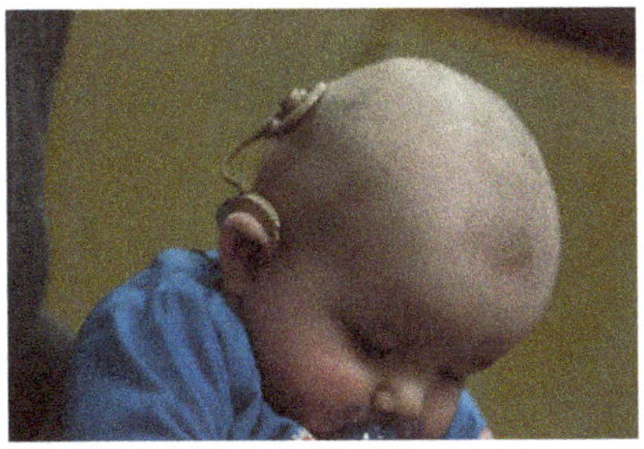

FIGURE 23.9 Electromagnetic induction used in transmitting electric currents across mediums. The device on the baby's head induces an electrical current in a receiver secured in the bone beneath the skin. (credit: Bjorn Knetsch)

Another contemporary area of research in which electromagnetic induction is being successfully implemented (and with substantial potential) is transcranial magnetic simulation. A host of disorders, including depression and hallucinations can be traced to irregular localized electrical activity in the brain. In *transcranial magnetic stimulation*, a rapidly varying and very localized magnetic field is placed close to certain sites identified in the brain. Weak electric currents are induced in the identified sites and can result in recovery of electrical functioning in the brain tissue.

Sleep apnea ("the cessation of breath") affects both adults and infants (especially premature babies and it may be a cause of sudden infant deaths [SID]). In such individuals, breath can stop repeatedly during their sleep. A cessation of more than 20 seconds can be very dangerous. Stroke, heart failure, and tiredness are just some of the possible consequences for a person having sleep apnea. The concern in infants is the stopping of breath for these longer times. One type of monitor to alert parents when a child is not breathing uses electromagnetic induction. A wire wrapped around the infant's chest has an alternating current running through it. The expansion and contraction of the infant's chest as the infant breathes changes the area through the coil. A pickup coil located nearby has an alternating current induced in it due to the changing magnetic field of the initial wire. If the child stops breathing, there will be a change in the induced current, and so a parent can be alerted.

MAKING CONNECTIONS: CONSERVATION OF ENERGY

Lenz's law is a manifestation of the conservation of energy. The induced emf produces a current that opposes the change in flux, because a change in flux means a change in energy. Energy can enter or leave, but not instantaneously. Lenz's law is a consequence. As the change begins, the law says induction opposes and, thus, slows the change. In fact, if the induced emf were in the same direction as the change in flux, there would be a positive feedback that would give us free energy from no apparent source—conservation of energy would be violated.

EXAMPLE 23.1

Calculating Emf: How Great Is the Induced Emf?

Calculate the magnitude of the induced emf when the magnet in Figure 23.7(a) is thrust into the coil, given the following information: the single loop coil has a radius of 6.00 cm and the average value of $B \cos \theta$ (this is given, since the bar magnet's field is complex) increases from 0.0500 T to 0.250 T in 0.100 s.

Strategy

To find the *magnitude* of emf, we use Faraday's law of induction as stated by $\text{emf} = -N\frac{\Delta\Phi}{\Delta t}$, but without the minus sign that indicates direction:

$$\text{emf} = N\frac{\Delta\Phi}{\Delta t}. \quad (23.3)$$

Solution

We are given that $N = 1$ and $\Delta t = 0.100\ \text{s}$, but we must determine the change in flux $\Delta\Phi$ before we can find emf.

Since the area of the loop is fixed, we see that

$$\Delta\Phi = \Delta(BA\ \cos\theta) = A\Delta(B\cos\theta\ ). \tag{23.4}$$

Now $\Delta(B\cos\theta) = 0.200\ \text{T}$, since it was given that $B\cos\theta$ changes from 0.0500 to 0.250 T. The area of the loop is $A = \pi r^2 = (3.14...)(0.060\ \text{m})^2 = 1.13\times10^{-2}\ \text{m}^2$. Thus,

$$\Delta\Phi = (1.13\times10^{-2}\ \text{m}^2)(0.200\ \text{T}\ ). \tag{23.5}$$

Entering the determined values into the expression for emf gives

$$\text{Emf} = N\frac{\Delta\Phi}{\Delta t} = \frac{(1.13\times10^{-2}\ \text{m}^2)(0.200\ \text{T})}{0.100\ \text{s}} = 22.6\ \text{mV}. \tag{23.6}$$

Discussion

While this is an easily measured voltage, it is certainly not large enough for most practical applications. More loops in the coil, a stronger magnet, and faster movement make induction the practical source of voltages that it is.

PHET EXPLORATIONS

Faraday's Electromagnetic Lab

Play with a bar magnet and coils to learn about Faraday's law. Move a bar magnet near one or two coils to make a light bulb glow. View the magnetic field lines. A meter shows the direction and magnitude of the current. View the magnetic field lines or use a meter to show the direction and magnitude of the current. You can also play with electromagnets, generators and transformers!

Click to view content (https://openstax.org/l/Faraday-EM-lab).

23.3 Motional Emf

LEARNING OBJECTIVES

By the end of this section, you will be able to:

- Calculate emf, force, magnetic field, and work due to the motion of an object in a magnetic field.

As we have seen, any change in magnetic flux induces an emf opposing that change—a process known as induction. Motion is one of the major causes of induction. For example, a magnet moved toward a coil induces an emf, and a coil moved toward a magnet produces a similar emf. In this section, we concentrate on motion in a magnetic field that is stationary relative to the Earth, producing what is loosely called *motional emf*.

One situation where motional emf occurs is known as the Hall effect and has already been examined. Charges moving in a magnetic field experience the magnetic force $F = qvB\sin\theta$, which moves opposite charges in opposite directions and produces an $\text{emf} = B\ell v$. We saw that the Hall effect has applications, including measurements of B and v. We will now see that the Hall effect is one aspect of the broader phenomenon of induction, and we will find that motional emf can be used as a power source.

Consider the situation shown in Figure 23.10. A rod is moved at a speed v along a pair of conducting rails separated by a distance ℓ in a uniform magnetic field B. The rails are stationary relative to B and are connected to a stationary resistor R. The resistor could be anything from a light bulb to a voltmeter. Consider the area enclosed by the moving rod, rails, and resistor. B is perpendicular to this area, and the area is increasing as the rod moves. Thus the magnetic flux enclosed by the rails, rod, and resistor is increasing. When flux changes, an emf is induced according to Faraday's law of induction.

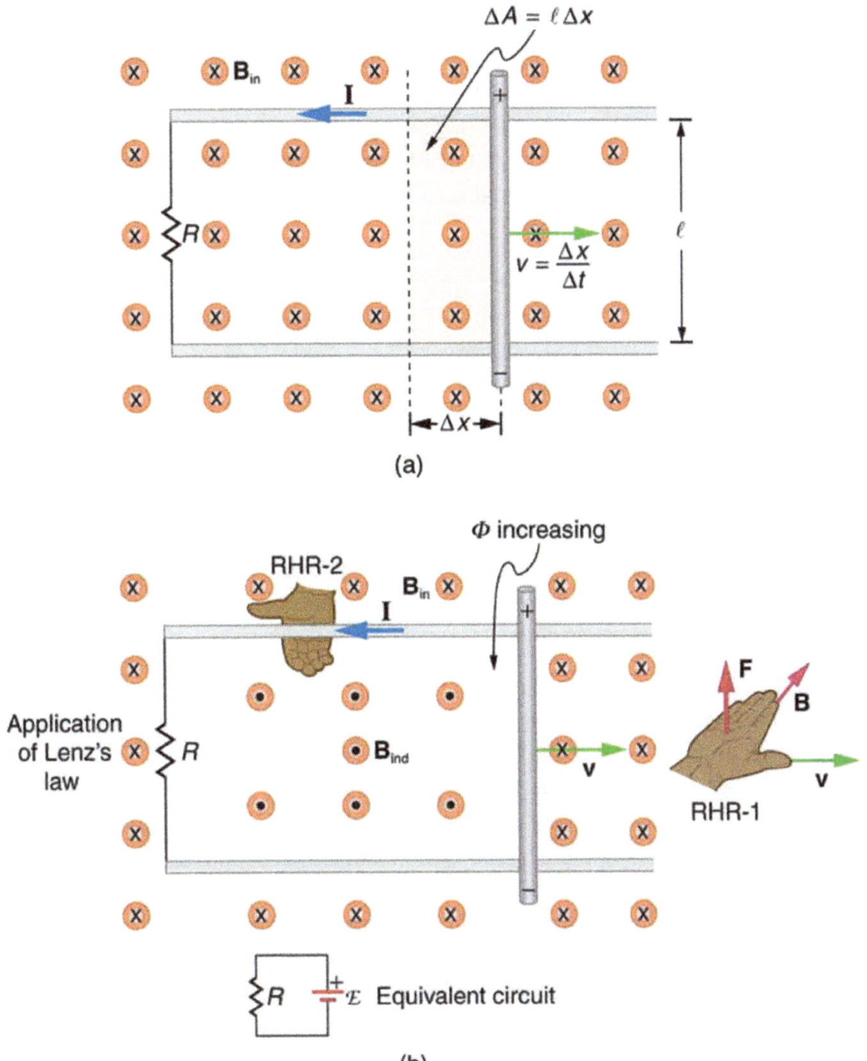

FIGURE 23.10 (a) A motional $\text{emf} = B\ell v$ is induced between the rails when this rod moves to the right in the uniform magnetic field. The magnetic field B is into the page, perpendicular to the moving rod and rails and, hence, to the area enclosed by them. (b) Lenz's law gives the directions of the induced field and current, and the polarity of the induced emf. Since the flux is increasing, the induced field is in the opposite direction, or out of the page. RHR-2 gives the current direction shown, and the polarity of the rod will drive such a current. RHR-1 also indicates the same polarity for the rod. (Note that the script E symbol used in the equivalent circuit at the bottom of part (b) represents emf.)

To find the magnitude of emf induced along the moving rod, we use Faraday's law of induction without the sign:

$$\text{emf} = N\frac{\Delta\Phi}{\Delta t}. \quad 23.7$$

Here and below, "emf" implies the magnitude of the emf. In this equation, $N = 1$ and the flux $\Phi = BA\cos\theta$. We have $\theta = 0°$ and $\cos\theta = 1$, since B is perpendicular to A. Now $\Delta\Phi = \Delta(BA) = B\Delta A$, since B is uniform. Note that the area swept out by the rod is $\Delta A = \ell\Delta x$. Entering these quantities into the expression for emf yields

$$\text{emf} = \frac{B\Delta A}{\Delta t} = B\frac{\ell\Delta x}{\Delta t}. \quad 23.8$$

Finally, note that $\Delta x/\Delta t = v$, the velocity of the rod. Entering this into the last expression shows that

$$\text{emf} = B\ell v \qquad (B,\ \ell,\ \text{and } v \text{ perpendicular}) \quad 23.9$$

is the motional emf. This is the same expression given for the Hall effect previously.

MAKING CONNECTIONS: UNIFICATION OF FORCES

There are many connections between the electric force and the magnetic force. The fact that a moving electric field produces a magnetic field and, conversely, a moving magnetic field produces an electric field is part of why electric and magnetic forces are now considered to be different manifestations of the same force. This classic unification of electric and magnetic forces into what is called the electromagnetic force is the inspiration for contemporary efforts to unify other basic forces.

To find the direction of the induced field, the direction of the current, and the polarity of the induced emf, we apply Lenz's law as explained in Faraday's Law of Induction: Lenz's Law. (See Figure 23.10(b).) Flux is increasing, since the area enclosed is increasing. Thus the induced field must oppose the existing one and be out of the page. And so the RHR-2 requires that I be counterclockwise, which in turn means the top of the rod is positive as shown.

Motional emf also occurs if the magnetic field moves and the rod (or other object) is stationary relative to the Earth (or some observer). We have seen an example of this in the situation where a moving magnet induces an emf in a stationary coil. It is the relative motion that is important. What is emerging in these observations is a connection between magnetic and electric fields. A moving magnetic field produces an electric field through its induced emf. We already have seen that a moving electric field produces a magnetic field—moving charge implies moving electric field and moving charge produces a magnetic field.

Motional emfs in the Earth's weak magnetic field are not ordinarily very large, or we would notice voltage along metal rods, such as a screwdriver, during ordinary motions. For example, a simple calculation of the motional emf of a 1 m rod moving at 3.0 m/s perpendicular to the Earth's field gives $\text{emf} = B\ell v = (5.0 \times 10^{-5}\ \text{T})(1.0\ \text{m})(3.0\ \text{m/s}) = 150\ \mu\text{V}$. This small value is consistent with experience. There is a spectacular exception, however. In 1992 and 1996, attempts were made with the space shuttle to create large motional emfs. The Tethered Satellite was to be let out on a 20 km length of wire as shown in Figure 23.11, to create a 5 kV emf by moving at orbital speed through the Earth's field. This emf could be used to convert some of the shuttle's kinetic and potential energy into electrical energy if a complete circuit could be made. To complete the circuit, the stationary ionosphere was to supply a return path for the current to flow. (The ionosphere is the rarefied and partially ionized atmosphere at orbital altitudes. It conducts because of the ionization. The ionosphere serves the same function as the stationary rails and connecting resistor in Figure 23.10, without which there would not be a complete circuit.) Drag on the current in the cable due to the magnetic force $F = I\ell B \sin\theta$ does the work that reduces the shuttle's kinetic and potential energy and allows it to be converted to electrical energy. The tests were both unsuccessful. In the first, the cable hung up and could only be extended a couple of hundred meters; in the second, the cable broke when almost fully extended. Example 23.2 indicates feasibility in principle.

EXAMPLE 23.2

Calculating the Large Motional Emf of an Object in Orbit

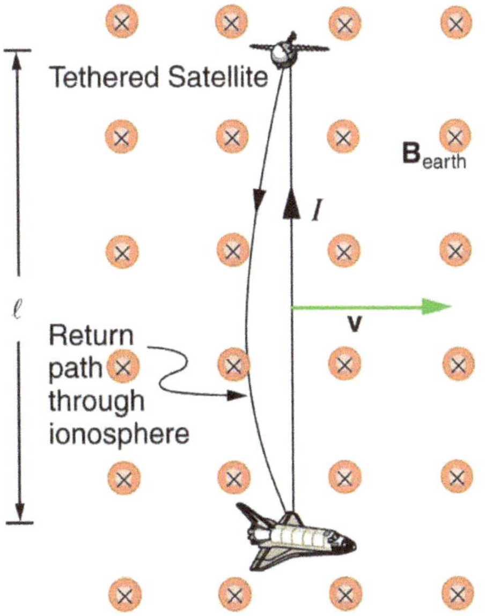

FIGURE 23.11 Motional emf as electrical power conversion for the space shuttle is the motivation for the Tethered Satellite experiment. A 5 kV emf was predicted to be induced in the 20 km long tether while moving at orbital speed in the Earth's magnetic field. The circuit is completed by a return path through the stationary ionosphere.

Calculate the motional emf induced along a 20.0 km long conductor moving at an orbital speed of 7.80 km/s perpendicular to the Earth's 5.00×10^{-5} T magnetic field.

Strategy

This is a straightforward application of the expression for motional emf— $\text{emf} = B\ell v$.

Solution

Entering the given values into $\text{emf} = B\ell v$ gives

$$\begin{aligned} \text{emf} &= B\ell v \\ &= (5.00 \times 10^{-5}\ \text{T})(2.0 \times 10^{4}\ \text{m})(7.80 \times 10^{3}\ \text{m/s}) \\ &= 7.80 \times 10^{3}\ \text{V}. \end{aligned} \tag{23.10}$$

Discussion

The value obtained is greater than the 5 kV measured voltage for the shuttle experiment, since the actual orbital motion of the tether is not perpendicular to the Earth's field. The 7.80 kV value is the maximum emf obtained when $\theta = 90°$ and $\sin\theta = 1$.

23.4 Eddy Currents and Magnetic Damping

LEARNING OBJECTIVES

By the end of this section, you will be able to:

- Explain the magnitude and direction of an induced eddy current, and the effect this will have on the object it is induced in.
- Describe several applications of magnetic damping.

Eddy Currents and Magnetic Damping

As discussed in Motional Emf, motional emf is induced when a conductor moves in a magnetic field or when a magnetic field moves relative to a conductor. If motional emf can cause a current loop in the conductor, we refer to that current as an **eddy current**. Eddy currents can produce significant drag, called **magnetic damping**, on the motion involved. Consider the apparatus shown in Figure 23.12, which swings a pendulum bob between the poles of a strong magnet. (This is another favorite physics lab activity.) If the bob is metal, there is significant drag on the bob as it enters and leaves the field, quickly damping the motion. If, however, the bob is a slotted metal plate, as shown in Figure 23.12(b), there is a much smaller effect due to the magnet. There is no discernible effect on a bob made of an insulator. Why is there drag in both directions, and are there any uses for magnetic drag?

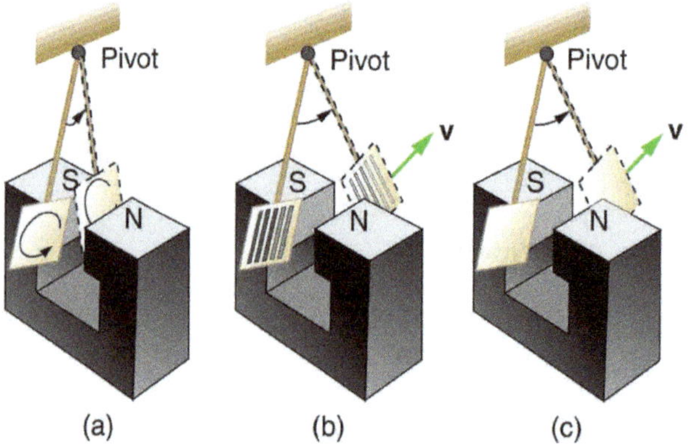

FIGURE 23.12 A common physics demonstration device for exploring eddy currents and magnetic damping. (a) The motion of a metal pendulum bob swinging between the poles of a magnet is quickly damped by the action of eddy currents. (b) There is little effect on the motion of a slotted metal bob, implying that eddy currents are made less effective. (c) There is also no magnetic damping on a nonconducting bob, since the eddy currents are extremely small.

Figure 23.13 shows what happens to the metal plate as it enters and leaves the magnetic field. In both cases, it experiences a force opposing its motion. As it enters from the left, flux increases, and so an eddy current is set up (Faraday's law) in the counterclockwise direction (Lenz's law), as shown. Only the right-hand side of the current loop is in the field, so that there is an unopposed force on it to the left (RHR-1). When the metal plate is completely inside the field, there is no eddy current if the field is uniform, since the flux remains constant in this region. But when the plate leaves the field on the right, flux decreases, causing an eddy current in the clockwise direction that, again, experiences a force to the left, further slowing the motion. A similar analysis of what happens when the plate swings from the right toward the left shows that its motion is also damped when entering and leaving the field.

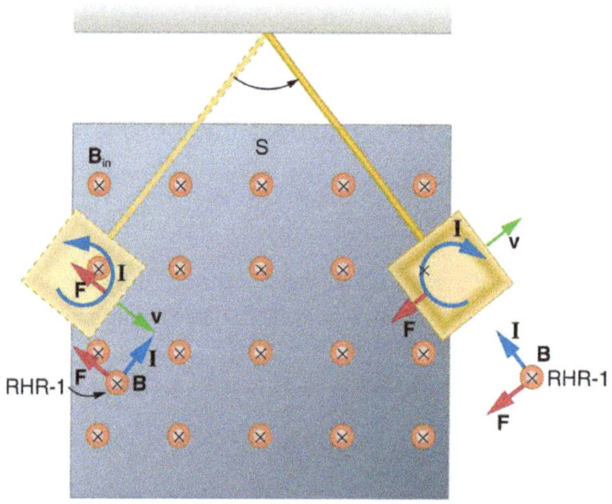

FIGURE 23.13 A more detailed look at the conducting plate passing between the poles of a magnet. As it enters and leaves the field, the change in flux produces an eddy current. Magnetic force on the current loop opposes the motion. There is no current and no magnetic drag when the plate is completely inside the uniform field.

When a slotted metal plate enters the field, as shown in Figure 23.14, an emf is induced by the change in flux, but it is less effective because the slots limit the size of the current loops. Moreover, adjacent loops have currents in opposite directions, and their effects cancel. When an insulating material is used, the eddy current is extremely small, and so magnetic damping on insulators is negligible. If eddy currents are to be avoided in conductors, then they can be slotted or constructed of thin layers of conducting material separated by insulating sheets.

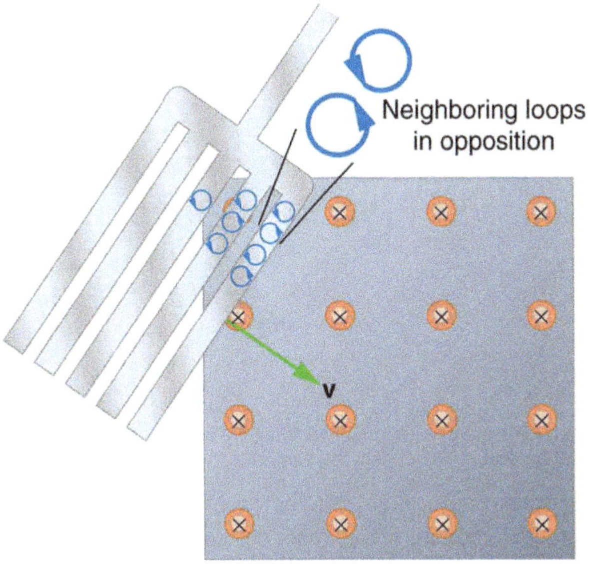

FIGURE 23.14 Eddy currents induced in a slotted metal plate entering a magnetic field form small loops, and the forces on them tend to cancel, thereby making magnetic drag almost zero.

Applications of Magnetic Damping

One use of magnetic damping is found in sensitive laboratory balances. To have maximum sensitivity and accuracy, the balance must be as friction-free as possible. But if it is friction-free, then it will oscillate for a very long time. Magnetic damping is a simple and ideal solution. With magnetic damping, drag is proportional to speed and becomes zero at zero velocity. Thus the oscillations are quickly damped, after which the damping force disappears, allowing the balance to be very sensitive. (See Figure 23.15.) In most balances, magnetic damping is accomplished with a conducting disc that rotates in a fixed field.

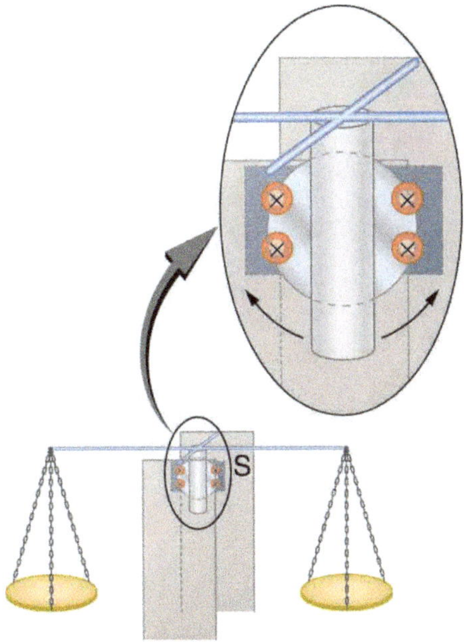

FIGURE 23.15 Magnetic damping of this sensitive balance slows its oscillations. Since Faraday's law of induction gives the greatest effect for the most rapid change, damping is greatest for large oscillations and goes to zero as the motion stops.

Since eddy currents and magnetic damping occur only in conductors, recycling centers can use magnets to separate metals from other materials. Trash is dumped in batches down a ramp, beneath which lies a powerful magnet. Conductors in the trash are slowed by magnetic damping while nonmetals in the trash move on, separating from the metals. (See Figure 23.16.) This works for all metals, not just ferromagnetic ones. A magnet can separate out the ferromagnetic materials alone by acting on stationary trash.

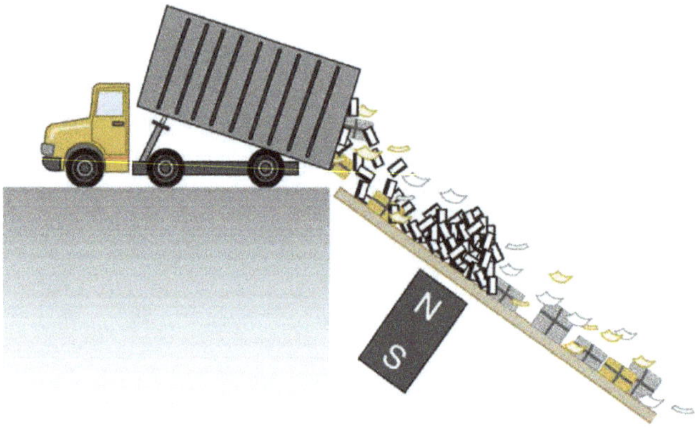

FIGURE 23.16 Metals can be separated from other trash by magnetic drag. Eddy currents and magnetic drag are created in the metals sent down this ramp by the powerful magnet beneath it. Nonmetals move on.

Other major applications of eddy currents are in metal detectors and braking systems in trains and roller coasters. Portable metal detectors (Figure 23.17) consist of a primary coil carrying an alternating current and a secondary coil in which a current is induced. An eddy current will be induced in a piece of metal close to the detector which will cause a change in the induced current within the secondary coil, leading to some sort of signal like a shrill noise. Braking using eddy currents is safer because factors such as rain do not affect the braking and the braking is smoother. However, eddy currents cannot bring the motion to a complete stop, since the force produced decreases with speed. Thus, speed can be reduced from say 20 m/s to 5 m/s, but another form of braking is needed to completely stop the vehicle. Generally, powerful rare earth magnets such as neodymium magnets are used in roller coasters. Figure 23.18 shows rows of magnets in such an application. The vehicle has metal fins (normally containing copper) which pass through the magnetic field slowing the vehicle down in much the same way as with the pendulum bob shown in Figure 23.12.

FIGURE 23.17 A soldier uses a metal detector to search for explosives and weapons. (credit: U.S. Army)

FIGURE 23.18 The rows of rare earth magnets (protruding horizontally) are used for magnetic braking in roller coasters. (credit: Stefan Scheer, Wikimedia Commons)

Induction cooktops have electromagnets under their surface. The magnetic field is varied rapidly producing eddy currents in the base of the pot, causing the pot and its contents to increase in temperature. Induction cooktops have high efficiencies and good response times but the base of the pot needs to be ferromagnetic, iron or steel for induction to work.

23.5 Electric Generators

LEARNING OBJECTIVES

By the end of this section, you will be able to:

- Calculate the emf induced in a generator.
- Calculate the peak emf which can be induced in a particular generator system.

Electric generators induce an emf by rotating a coil in a magnetic field, as briefly discussed in Induced Emf and Magnetic Flux. We will now explore generators in more detail. Consider the following example.

EXAMPLE 23.3

Calculating the Emf Induced in a Generator Coil

The generator coil shown in Figure 23.19 is rotated through one-fourth of a revolution (from $\theta = 0°$ to $\theta = 90°$) in 15.0 ms. The 200-turn circular coil has a 5.00 cm radius and is in a uniform 1.25 T magnetic field. What is the average emf induced?

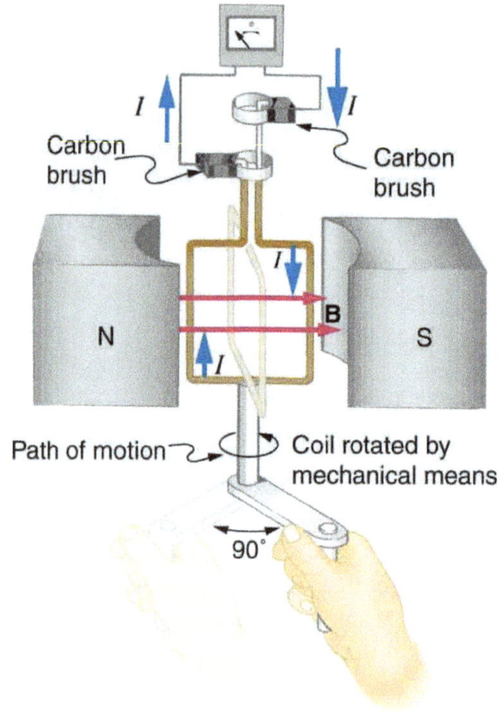

FIGURE 23.19 When this generator coil is rotated through one-fourth of a revolution, the magnetic flux Φ changes from its maximum to zero, inducing an emf.

Strategy

We use Faraday's law of induction to find the average emf induced over a time Δt:

$$\text{emf} = -N\frac{\Delta\Phi}{\Delta t}. \tag{23.11}$$

We know that $N = 200$ and $\Delta t = 15.0 \text{ ms}$, and so we must determine the change in flux $\Delta\Phi$ to find emf.

Solution

Since the area of the loop and the magnetic field strength are constant, we see that

$$\Delta\Phi = \Delta(BA\cos\theta) = AB\Delta(\cos\theta). \tag{23.12}$$

Now, $\Delta(\cos\theta) = -1.0$, since it was given that θ goes from $0°$ to $90°$. Thus $\Delta\Phi = -AB$, and

$$\text{emf} = N\frac{AB}{\Delta t}. \tag{23.13}$$

The area of the loop is $A = \pi r^2 = (3.14...)(0.0500 \text{ m})^2 = 7.85 \times 10^{-3} \text{ m}^2$. Entering this value gives

$$\text{emf} = 200\frac{(7.85 \times 10^{-3} \text{ m}^2)(1.25 \text{ T})}{15.0 \times 10^{-3} \text{ s}} = 131 \text{ V}. \tag{23.14}$$

Discussion

This is a practical average value, similar to the 120 V used in household power.

The emf calculated in Example 23.3 is the average over one-fourth of a revolution. What is the emf at any given instant? It varies with the angle between the magnetic field and a perpendicular to the coil. We can get an expression for emf as a function of time by considering the motional emf on a rotating rectangular coil of width w and height ℓ in a uniform magnetic field, as illustrated in Figure 23.20.

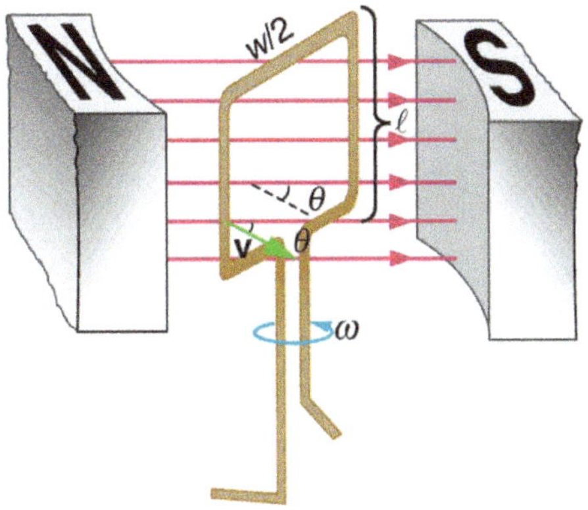

FIGURE 23.20 A generator with a single rectangular coil rotated at constant angular velocity in a uniform magnetic field produces an emf that varies sinusoidally in time. Note the generator is similar to a motor, except the shaft is rotated to produce a current rather than the other way around.

Charges in the wires of the loop experience the magnetic force, because they are moving in a magnetic field. Charges in the vertical wires experience forces parallel to the wire, causing currents. But those in the top and bottom segments feel a force perpendicular to the wire, which does not cause a current. We can thus find the induced emf by considering only the side wires. Motional emf is given to be $\text{emf} = B\ell v$, where the velocity v is perpendicular to the magnetic field $\mathbf{B}$. Here the velocity is at an angle θ with $\mathbf{B}$, so that its component perpendicular to $\mathbf{B}$ is $v\sin\theta$ (see Figure 23.20). Thus in this case the emf induced on each side is $\text{emf} = B\ell v \sin\theta$, and they are in the same direction. The total emf around the loop is then

$$\text{emf} = 2B\ell v \sin\theta. \qquad 23.15$$

This expression is valid, but it does not give emf as a function of time. To find the time dependence of emf, we assume the coil rotates at a constant angular velocity ω. The angle θ is related to angular velocity by $\theta = \omega t$, so that

$$\text{emf} = 2B\ell v \sin\omega t. \qquad 23.16$$

Now, linear velocity v is related to angular velocity ω by $v = r\omega$. Here $r = w/2$, so that $v = (w/2)\omega$, and

$$\text{emf} = 2B\ell\frac{w}{2}\omega \sin\omega t = (\ell w)B\omega \sin\omega t. \qquad 23.17$$

Noting that the area of the loop is $A = \ell w$, and allowing for N loops, we find that

$$\text{emf} = NAB\omega \sin\omega t \qquad 23.18$$

is the **emf induced in a generator coil** of N turns and area A rotating at a constant angular velocity ω in a uniform magnetic field $\mathbf{B}$. This can also be expressed as

$$\text{emf} = \text{emf}_0 \sin\omega t, \qquad 23.19$$

where

$$\text{emf}_0 = NAB\omega \qquad 23.20$$

is the maximum **(peak) emf**. Note that the frequency of the oscillation is $f = \omega/2\pi$, and the period is $T = 1/f = 2\pi/\omega$. Figure 23.21 shows a graph of emf as a function of time, and it now seems reasonable that AC voltage is sinusoidal.

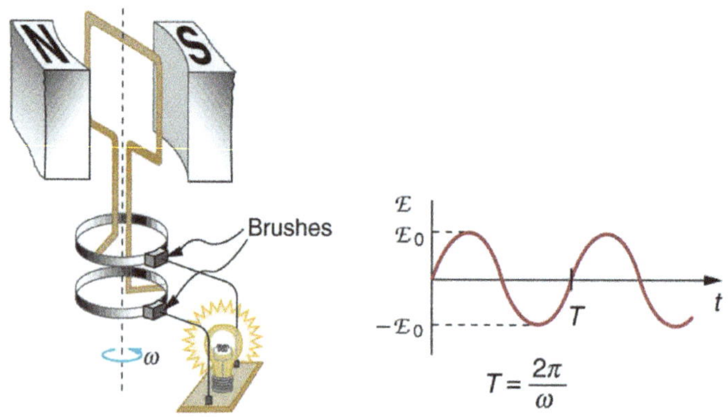

FIGURE 23.21 The emf of a generator is sent to a light bulb with the system of rings and brushes shown. The graph gives the emf of the generator as a function of time. emf_0 is the peak emf. The period is $T = 1/f = 2\pi/\omega$, where f is the frequency. Note that the script E stands for emf.

The fact that the peak emf, $\text{emf}_0 = NAB\omega$, makes good sense. The greater the number of coils, the larger their area, and the stronger the field, the greater the output voltage. It is interesting that the faster the generator is spun (greater ω), the greater the emf. This is noticeable on bicycle generators—at least the cheaper varieties. One of the authors as a juvenile found it amusing to ride his bicycle fast enough to burn out his lights, until he had to ride home lightless one dark night.

Figure 23.22 shows a scheme by which a generator can be made to produce pulsed DC. More elaborate arrangements of multiple coils and split rings can produce smoother DC, although electronic rather than mechanical means are usually used to make ripple-free DC.

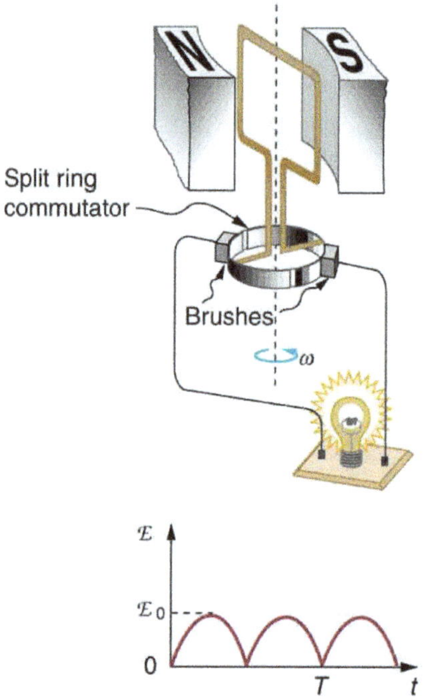

FIGURE 23.22 Split rings, called commutators, produce a pulsed DC emf output in this configuration.

EXAMPLE 23.4

Calculating the Maximum Emf of a Generator

Calculate the maximum emf, emf_0, of the generator that was the subject of Example 23.3.

Strategy

Once ω, the angular velocity, is determined, $\text{emf}_0 = NAB\omega$ can be used to find emf_0. All other quantities are known.

Solution

Angular velocity is defined to be the change in angle per unit time:

$$\omega = \frac{\Delta\theta}{\Delta t}. \tag{23.21}$$

One-fourth of a revolution is $\pi/2$ radians, and the time is 0.0150 s; thus,

$$\begin{aligned}\omega &= \frac{\pi/2 \text{ rad}}{0.0150 \text{ s}} \\ &= 104.7 \text{ rad/s}.\end{aligned} \tag{23.22}$$

104.7 rad/s is exactly 1000 rpm. We substitute this value for ω and the information from the previous example into $\text{emf}_0 = NAB\omega$, yielding

$$\begin{aligned}\text{emf}_0 &= NAB\omega \\ &= 200(7.85 \times 10^{-3} \text{ m}^2)(1.25 \text{ T})(104.7 \text{ rad/s}). \\ &= 206 \text{ V}\end{aligned} \tag{23.23}$$

Discussion

The maximum emf is greater than the average emf of 131 V found in the previous example, as it should be.

In real life, electric generators look a lot different than the figures in this section, but the principles are the same. The source of mechanical energy that turns the coil can be falling water (hydropower), steam produced by the burning of fossil fuels, or the kinetic energy of wind. Figure 23.23 shows a cutaway view of a steam turbine; steam moves over the blades connected to the shaft, which rotates the coil within the generator.

FIGURE 23.23 Steam turbine/generator. The steam produced by burning coal impacts the turbine blades, turning the shaft which is connected to the generator. (credit: Nabonaco, Wikimedia Commons)

Generators illustrated in this section look very much like the motors illustrated previously. This is not coincidental. In fact, a motor becomes a generator when its shaft rotates. Certain early automobiles used their starter motor as a generator. In Back Emf, we shall further explore the action of a motor as a generator.

23.6 Back Emf

LEARNING OBJECTIVES

By the end of this section, you will be able to:

- Explain what back emf is and how it is induced.

It has been noted that motors and generators are very similar. Generators convert mechanical energy into electrical energy, whereas motors convert electrical energy into mechanical energy. Furthermore, motors and generators have the same construction. When the coil of a motor is turned, magnetic flux changes, and an emf (consistent with Faraday's law of induction) is induced. The motor thus acts as a generator whenever its coil rotates. This will happen whether the shaft is turned by an external input, like a belt drive, or by the action of the motor itself. That is, when a motor is doing work and its shaft is turning, an emf is generated. Lenz's law tells us the emf opposes any change, so that the input emf that powers the motor will be opposed by the motor's self-generated emf, called the **back emf** of the motor. (See Figure 23.24.)

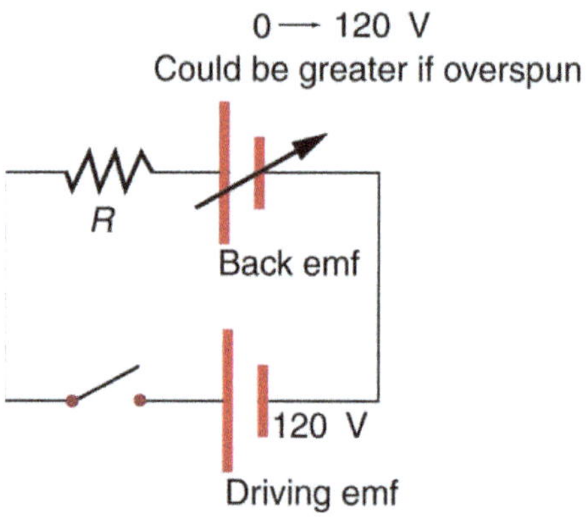

FIGURE 23.24 The coil of a DC motor is represented as a resistor in this schematic. The back emf is represented as a variable emf that opposes the one driving the motor. Back emf is zero when the motor is not turning, and it increases proportionally to the motor's angular velocity.

Back emf is the generator output of a motor, and so it is proportional to the motor's angular velocity ω. It is zero when the motor is first turned on, meaning that the coil receives the full driving voltage and the motor draws maximum current when it is on but not turning. As the motor turns faster and faster, the back emf grows, always opposing the driving emf, and reduces the voltage across the coil and the amount of current it draws. This effect is noticeable in a number of situations. When a vacuum cleaner, refrigerator, or washing machine is first turned on, lights in the same circuit dim briefly due to the IR drop produced in feeder lines by the large current drawn by the motor. When a motor first comes on, it draws more current than when it runs at its normal operating speed. When a mechanical load is placed on the motor, like an electric wheelchair going up a hill, the motor slows, the back emf drops, more current flows, and more work can be done. If the motor runs at too low a speed, the larger current can overheat it (via resistive power in the coil, $P = I^2 R$), perhaps even burning it out. On the other hand, if there is no mechanical load on the motor, it will increase its angular velocity ω until the back emf is nearly equal to the driving emf. Then the motor uses only enough energy to overcome friction.

Consider, for example, the motor coils represented in Figure 23.24. The coils have a $0.400\ \Omega$ equivalent resistance and are driven by a 48.0 V emf. Shortly after being turned on, they draw a current $I = V/R = (48.0\text{ V})/(0.400\ \Omega) = 120\text{ A}$ and, thus, dissipate $P = I^2 R = 5.76\text{ kW}$ of energy as heat transfer. Under normal operating conditions for this motor, suppose the back emf is 40.0 V. Then at operating speed, the total voltage across the coils is 8.0 V (48.0 V minus the 40.0 V back emf), and the current drawn is $I = V/R = (8.0\text{ V})/(0.400\ \Omega) = 20\text{ A}$. Under normal load, then, the power dissipated is $P = IV = (20\text{ A})/(8.0\text{ V}) = 160\text{ W}$. The latter will not cause a problem for this motor, whereas the former 5.76 kW would burn out the coils if sustained.

23.7 Transformers

LEARNING OBJECTIVES

By the end of this section, you will be able to:

- Explain how a transformer works.
- Calculate voltage, current, and/or number of turns given the other quantities.

Transformers do what their name implies—they transform voltages from one value to another (The term voltage is used rather than emf, because transformers have internal resistance). For example, many cell phones, laptops, video games, and power tools and small appliances have a transformer built into their plug-in unit (like that in Figure 23.25) that changes 120 V or 240 V AC into whatever voltage the device uses. Transformers are also used at several points in the power distribution systems, such as illustrated in Figure 23.26. Power is sent long distances at high voltages, because less current is required for a given amount of power, and this means less line loss, as was discussed previously. But high voltages pose greater hazards, so that transformers are employed to produce lower voltage at the user's location.

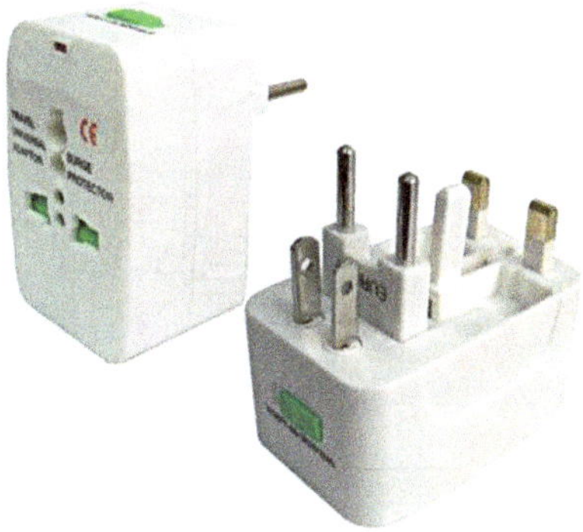

FIGURE 23.25 The plug-in transformer has become increasingly familiar with the proliferation of electronic devices that operate on voltages other than common 120 V AC. Most are in the 3 to 12 V range. (credit: Shop Xtreme)

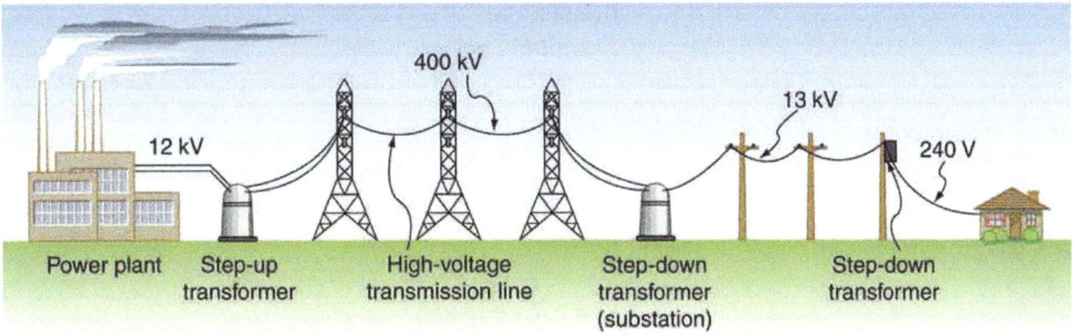

FIGURE 23.26 Transformers change voltages at several points in a power distribution system. Electric power is usually generated at greater than 10 kV, and transmitted long distances at voltages over 200 kV—sometimes as great as 700 kV—to limit energy losses. Local power distribution to neighborhoods or industries goes through a substation and is sent short distances at voltages ranging from 5 to 13 kV. This is reduced to 120, 240, or 480 V for safety at the individual user site.

The type of transformer considered in this text—see Figure 23.27—is based on Faraday's law of induction and is very similar in construction to the apparatus Faraday used to demonstrate magnetic fields could cause currents. The two coils are called the *primary* and *secondary coils.* In normal use, the input voltage is placed on the primary, and the secondary produces the transformed output voltage. Not only does the iron core trap the magnetic field created by the primary coil, its magnetization increases the field strength. Since the input voltage is AC, a time-varying magnetic flux is sent to the secondary, inducing its AC output voltage.

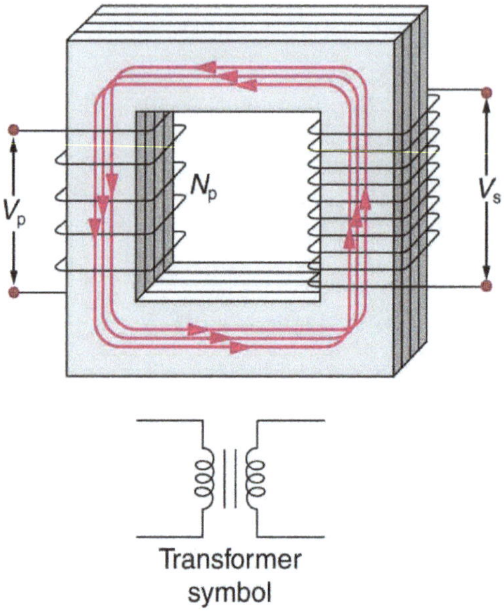

FIGURE 23.27 A typical construction of a simple transformer has two coils wound on a ferromagnetic core that is laminated to minimize eddy currents. The magnetic field created by the primary is mostly confined to and increased by the core, which transmits it to the secondary coil. Any change in current in the primary induces a current in the secondary.

For the simple transformer shown in Figure 23.27, the output voltage V_s depends almost entirely on the input voltage V_p and the ratio of the number of loops in the primary and secondary coils. Faraday's law of induction for the secondary coil gives its induced output voltage V_s to be

$$V_s = -N_s \frac{\Delta \Phi}{\Delta t}, \tag{23.24}$$

where N_s is the number of loops in the secondary coil and $\Delta\Phi/\ \Delta t$ is the rate of change of magnetic flux. Note that the output voltage equals the induced emf ($V_s = \text{emf}_s$), provided coil resistance is small (a reasonable assumption for transformers). The cross-sectional area of the coils is the same on either side, as is the magnetic field strength, and so $\Delta\Phi/\Delta t$ is the same on either side. The input primary voltage V_p is also related to changing flux by

$$V_p = -N_p \frac{\Delta \Phi}{\Delta t}. \tag{23.25}$$

The reason for this is a little more subtle. Lenz's law tells us that the primary coil opposes the change in flux caused by the input voltage V_p, hence the minus sign (This is an example of *self-inductance,* a topic to be explored in some detail in later sections). Assuming negligible coil resistance, Kirchhoff's loop rule tells us that the induced emf exactly equals the input voltage. Taking the ratio of these last two equations yields a useful relationship:

$$\frac{V_s}{V_p} = \frac{N_s}{N_p}. \tag{23.26}$$

This is known as the **transformer equation**, and it simply states that the ratio of the secondary to primary voltages in a transformer equals the ratio of the number of loops in their coils.

The output voltage of a transformer can be less than, greater than, or equal to the input voltage, depending on the ratio of the number of loops in their coils. Some transformers even provide a variable output by allowing connection to be made at different points on the secondary coil. A **step-up transformer** is one that increases voltage, whereas a **step-down transformer** decreases voltage. Assuming, as we have, that resistance is negligible, the electrical power output of a transformer equals its input. This is nearly true in practice—transformer efficiency often exceeds 99%. Equating the power input and output,

$$P_p = I_p V_p = I_s V_s = P_s. \tag{23.27}$$

Rearranging terms gives

$$\frac{V_s}{V_p} = \frac{I_p}{I_s}. \quad 23.28$$

Combining this with $\frac{V_s}{V_p} = \frac{N_s}{N_p}$, we find that

$$\frac{I_s}{I_p} = \frac{N_p}{N_s} \quad 23.29$$

is the relationship between the output and input currents of a transformer. So if voltage increases, current decreases. Conversely, if voltage decreases, current increases.

EXAMPLE 23.5

Calculating Characteristics of a Step-Up Transformer

A portable x-ray unit has a step-up transformer, the 120 V input of which is transformed to the 100 kV output needed by the x-ray tube. The primary has 50 loops and draws a current of 10.00 A when in use. (a) What is the number of loops in the secondary? (b) Find the current output of the secondary.

Strategy and Solution for (a)

We solve $\frac{V_s}{V_p} = \frac{N_s}{N_p}$ for N_s, the number of loops in the secondary, and enter the known values. This gives

$$\begin{aligned} N_s &= N_p \frac{V_s}{V_p} \\ &= (50)\frac{100{,}000 \text{ V}}{120 \text{ V}} = 4.17 \times 10^4. \end{aligned} \quad 23.30$$

Discussion for (a)

A large number of loops in the secondary (compared with the primary) is required to produce such a large voltage. This would be true for neon sign transformers and those supplying high voltage inside TVs and CRTs.

Strategy and Solution for (b)

We can similarly find the output current of the secondary by solving $\frac{I_s}{I_p} = \frac{N_p}{N_s}$ for I_s and entering known values. This gives

$$\begin{aligned} I_s &= I_p \frac{N_p}{N_s} \\ &= (10.00 \text{ A})\frac{50}{4.17\times10^4} = 12.0 \text{ mA}. \end{aligned} \quad 23.31$$

Discussion for (b)

As expected, the current output is significantly less than the input. In certain spectacular demonstrations, very large voltages are used to produce long arcs, but they are relatively safe because the transformer output does not supply a large current. Note that the power input here is $P_p = I_p V_p = (10.00 \text{ A})(120 \text{ V}) = 1.20 \text{ kW}$. This equals the power output $P_p = I_s V_s = (12.0 \text{ mA})(100 \text{ kV}) = 1.20 \text{ kW}$, as we assumed in the derivation of the equations used.

The fact that transformers are based on Faraday's law of induction makes it clear why we cannot use transformers to change DC voltages. If there is no change in primary voltage, there is no voltage induced in the secondary. One possibility is to connect DC to the primary coil through a switch. As the switch is opened and closed, the secondary produces a voltage like that in Figure 23.28. This is not really a practical alternative, and AC is in common use wherever it is necessary to increase or decrease voltages.

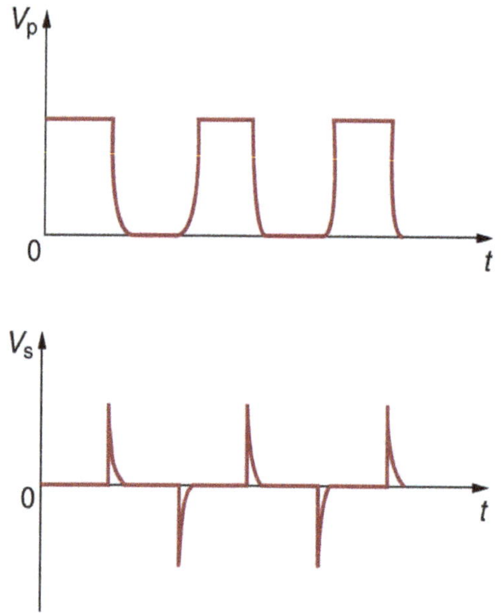

FIGURE 23.28 Transformers do not work for pure DC voltage input, but if it is switched on and off as on the top graph, the output will look something like that on the bottom graph. This is not the sinusoidal AC most AC appliances need.

EXAMPLE 23.6

Calculating Characteristics of a Step-Down Transformer

A battery charger meant for a series connection of ten nickel-cadmium batteries (total emf of 12.5 V DC) needs to have a 15.0 V output to charge the batteries. It uses a step-down transformer with a 200-loop primary and a 120 V input. (a) How many loops should there be in the secondary coil? (b) If the charging current is 16.0 A, what is the input current?

Strategy and Solution for (a)

You would expect the secondary to have a small number of loops. Solving $\frac{V_s}{V_p} = \frac{N_s}{N_p}$ for N_s and entering known values gives

$$\begin{aligned} N_s &= N_p \frac{V_s}{V_p} \\ &= (200)\frac{15.0\text{ V}}{120\text{ V}} = 25. \end{aligned} \tag{23.32}$$

Strategy and Solution for (b)

The current input can be obtained by solving $\frac{I_s}{I_p} = \frac{N_p}{N_s}$ for I_p and entering known values. This gives

$$\begin{aligned} I_p &= I_s \frac{N_s}{N_p} \\ &= (16.0\text{ A})\frac{25}{200} = 2.00\text{ A}. \end{aligned} \tag{23.33}$$

Discussion

The number of loops in the secondary is small, as expected for a step-down transformer. We also see that a small input current produces a larger output current in a step-down transformer. When transformers are used to operate large magnets, they sometimes have a small number of very heavy loops in the secondary. This allows the secondary to have low internal resistance and produce large currents. Note again that this solution is based on the assumption of 100% efficiency—or power out equals power in ($P_p = P_s$)—reasonable for good transformers. In this case the primary and secondary power is 240 W. (Verify this for yourself as a consistency check.) Note that the Ni-Cd batteries need to be charged from a DC power source (as would a 12 V battery). So the AC output of the secondary coil needs to be converted into DC. This is done using something called a rectifier, which uses devices called diodes that allow only a one-way flow of current.

Transformers have many applications in electrical safety systems, which are discussed in Electrical Safety: Systems and Devices.

PHET EXPLORATIONS

Generator

Generate electricity with a bar magnet! Discover the physics behind the phenomena by exploring magnets and how you can use them to make a bulb light.

Click to view content (https://openstax.org/l/28gen).

23.8 Electrical Safety: Systems and Devices

LEARNING OBJECTIVES

By the end of this section, you will be able to:

- Explain how various modern safety features in electric circuits work, with an emphasis on how induction is employed.

Electricity has two hazards. A **thermal hazard** occurs when there is electrical overheating. A **shock hazard** occurs when electric current passes through a person. Both hazards have already been discussed. Here we will concentrate on systems and devices that prevent electrical hazards.

Figure 23.29 shows the schematic for a simple AC circuit with no safety features. This is not how power is distributed in practice. Modern household and industrial wiring requires the **three-wire system**, shown schematically in Figure 23.30, which has several safety features. First is the familiar *circuit breaker* (or *fuse*) to prevent thermal overload. Second, there is a protective *case* around the appliance, such as a toaster or refrigerator. The case's safety feature is that it prevents a person from touching exposed wires and coming into electrical contact with the circuit, helping prevent shocks.

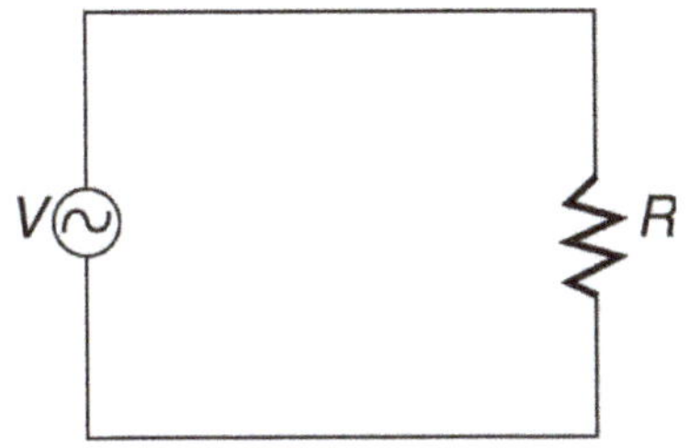

FIGURE 23.29 Schematic of a simple AC circuit with a voltage source and a single appliance represented by the resistance R. There are no safety features in this circuit.

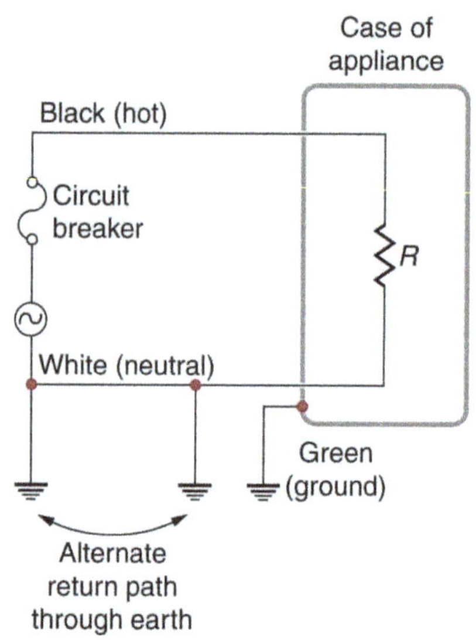

FIGURE 23.30 The three-wire system connects the neutral wire to the earth at the voltage source and user location, forcing it to be at zero volts and supplying an alternative return path for the current through the earth. Also grounded to zero volts is the case of the appliance. A circuit breaker or fuse protects against thermal overload and is in series on the active (live/hot) wire. Note that wire insulation colors vary with region and it is essential to check locally to determine which color codes are in use (and even if they were followed in the particular installation).

There are *three connections to earth or ground* (hereafter referred to as "earth/ground") shown in Figure 23.30. Recall that an earth/ground connection is a low-resistance path directly to the earth. The two earth/ground connections on the *neutral wire* force it to be at zero volts relative to the earth, giving the wire its name. This wire is therefore safe to touch even if its insulation, usually white, is missing. The neutral wire is the return path for the current to follow to complete the circuit. Furthermore, the two earth/ground connections supply an alternative path through the earth, a good conductor, to complete the circuit. The earth/ground connection closest to the power source could be at the generating plant, while the other is at the user's location. The third earth/ground is to the case of the appliance, through the green *earth/ground wire*, forcing the case, too, to be at zero volts. The *live* or *hot wire* (hereafter referred to as "live/hot") supplies voltage and current to operate the appliance. Figure 23.31 shows a more pictorial version of how the three-wire system is connected through a three-prong plug to an appliance.

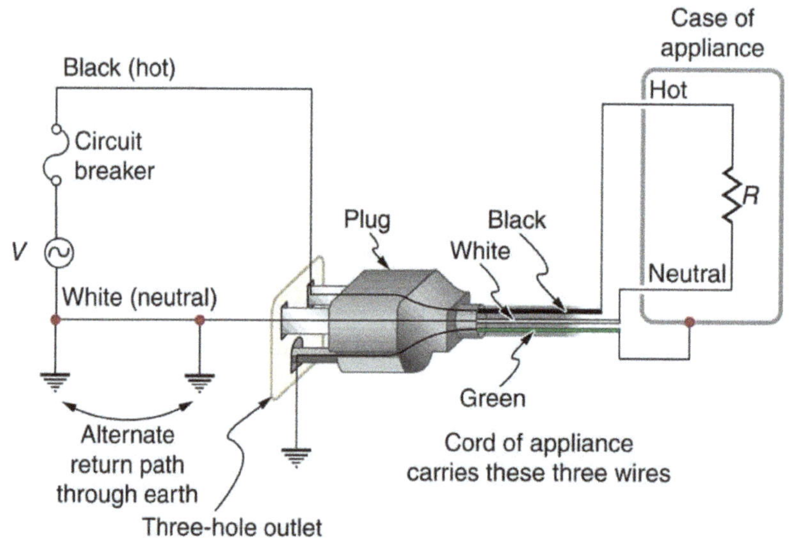

FIGURE 23.31 The standard three-prong plug can only be inserted in one way, to assure proper function of the three-wire system.

A note on insulation color-coding: Insulating plastic is color-coded to identify live/hot, neutral and ground wires but these codes vary around the world. Live/hot wires may be brown, red, black, blue or grey. Neutral wire may be blue, black or white. Since the same color may be used for live/hot or neutral in different parts of the world, it is essential to determine the color code in your region. The only exception is the earth/ground wire which is often green but may be yellow or just bare wire. Striped coatings are sometimes used for the benefit of those who are colorblind.

The three-wire system replaced the older two-wire system, which lacks an earth/ground wire. Under ordinary circumstances, insulation on the live/hot and neutral wires prevents the case from being directly in the circuit, so that the earth/ground wire may seem like double protection. Grounding the case solves more than one problem, however. The simplest problem is worn insulation on the live/hot wire that allows it to contact the case, as shown in Figure 23.32. Lacking an earth/ground connection (some people cut the third prong off the plug because they only have outdated two hole receptacles), a severe shock is possible. This is particularly dangerous in the kitchen, where a good connection to earth/ground is available through water on the floor or a water faucet. With the earth/ground connection intact, the circuit breaker will trip, forcing repair of the appliance. Why are some appliances still sold with two-prong plugs? These have nonconducting cases, such as power tools with impact resistant plastic cases, and are called *doubly insulated*. Modern two-prong plugs can be inserted into the asymmetric standard outlet in only one way, to ensure proper connection of live/hot and neutral wires.

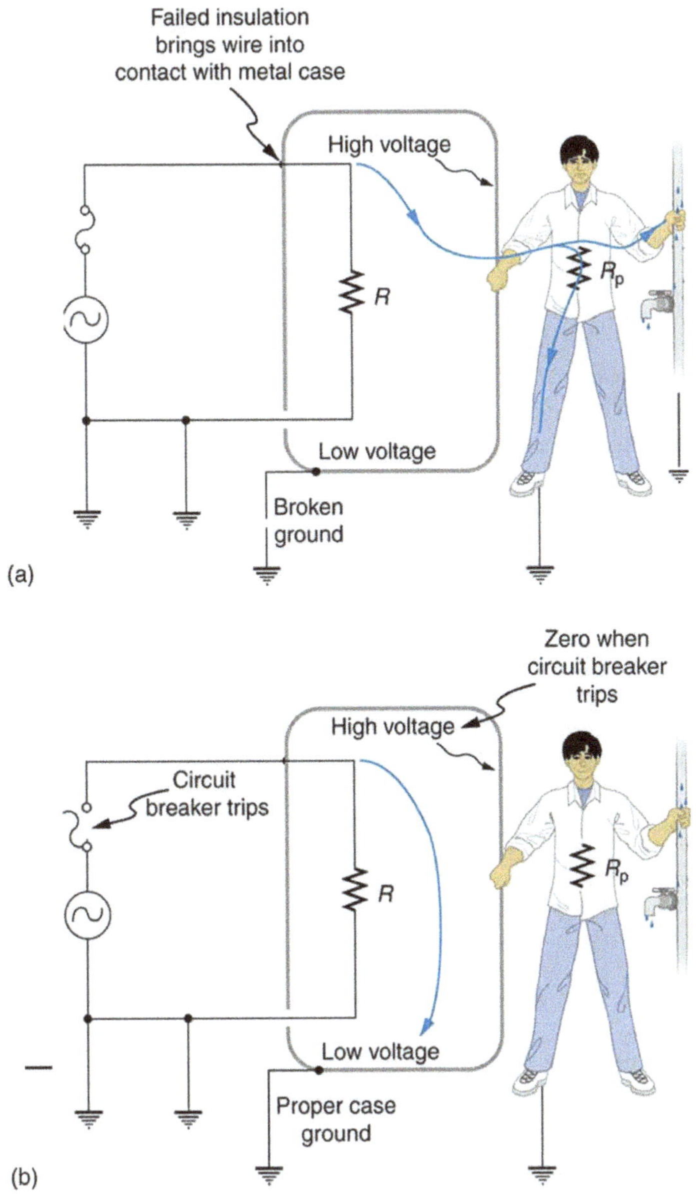

FIGURE 23.32 Worn insulation allows the live/hot wire to come into direct contact with the metal case of this appliance. (a) The earth/ground connection being broken, the person is severely shocked. The appliance may operate normally in this situation. (b) With a proper earth/ground, the circuit breaker trips, forcing repair of the appliance.

Electromagnetic induction causes a more subtle problem that is solved by grounding the case. The AC current in appliances can induce an emf on the case. If grounded, the case voltage is kept near zero, but if the case is not grounded, a shock can occur as pictured in Figure 23.33. Current driven by the induced case emf is called a *leakage current,* although current does not necessarily pass from the resistor to the case.

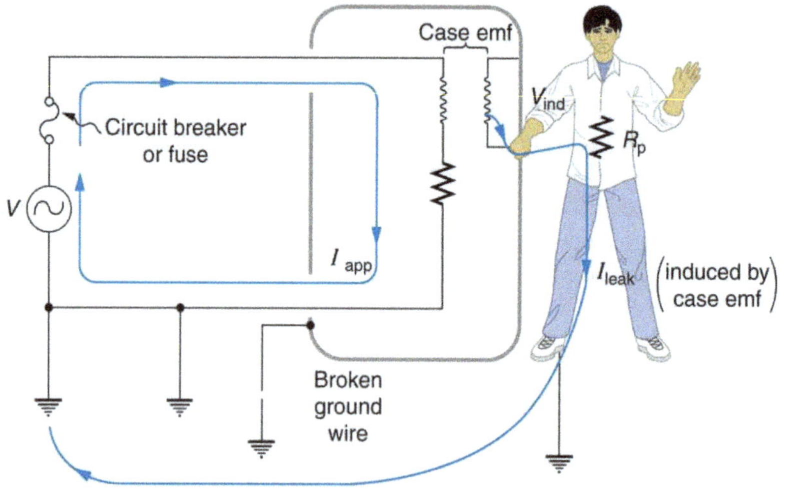

FIGURE 23.33 AC currents can induce an emf on the case of an appliance. The voltage can be large enough to cause a shock. If the case is grounded, the induced emf is kept near zero.

A *ground fault interrupter* (GFI) is a safety device found in updated kitchen and bathroom wiring that works based on electromagnetic induction. GFIs compare the currents in the live/hot and neutral wires. When live/hot and neutral currents are not equal, it is almost always because current in the neutral is less than in the live/hot wire. Then some of the current, again called a leakage current, is returning to the voltage source by a path other than through the neutral wire. It is assumed that this path presents a hazard, such as shown in Figure 23.34. GFIs are usually set to interrupt the circuit if the leakage current is greater than 5 mA, the accepted maximum harmless shock. Even if the leakage current goes safely to earth/ground through an intact earth/ground wire, the GFI will trip, forcing repair of the leakage.

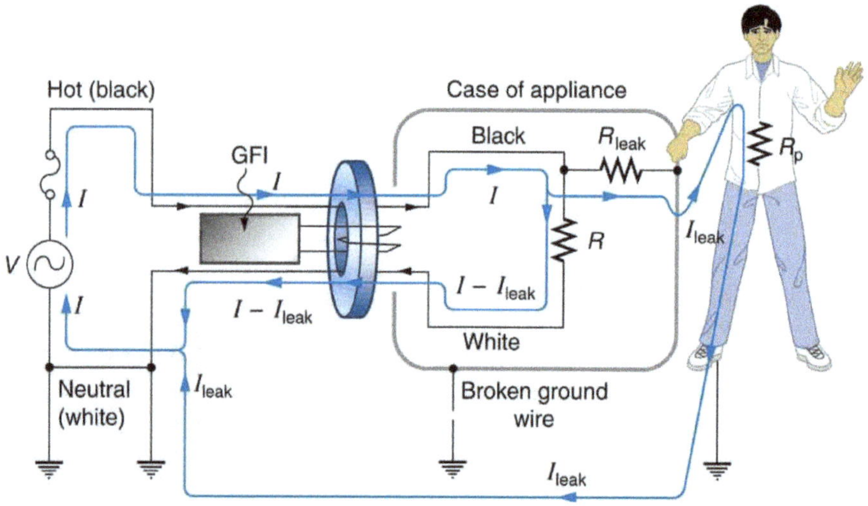

FIGURE 23.34 A ground fault interrupter (GFI) compares the currents in the live/hot and neutral wires and will trip if their difference exceeds a safe value. The leakage current here follows a hazardous path that could have been prevented by an intact earth/ground wire.

Figure 23.35 shows how a GFI works. If the currents in the live/hot and neutral wires are equal, then they induce equal and opposite emfs in the coil. If not, then the circuit breaker will trip.

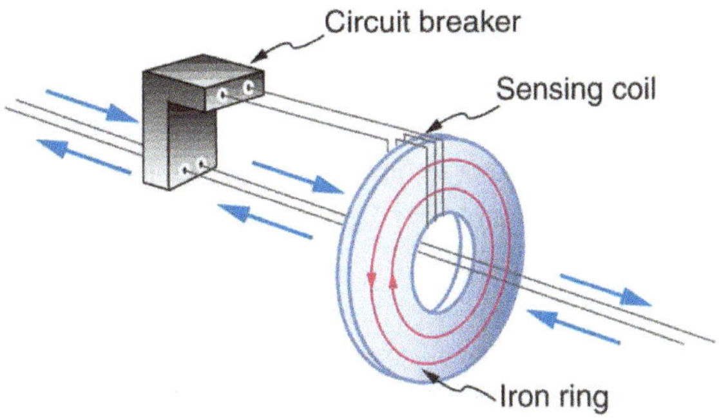

FIGURE 23.35 A GFI compares currents by using both to induce an emf in the same coil. If the currents are equal, they will induce equal but opposite emfs.

Another induction-based safety device is the *isolation transformer*, shown in Figure 23.36. Most isolation transformers have equal input and output voltages. Their function is to put a large resistance between the original voltage source and the device being operated. This prevents a complete circuit between them, even in the circumstance shown. There is a complete circuit through the appliance. But there is not a complete circuit for current to flow through the person in the figure, who is touching only one of the transformer's output wires, and neither output wire is grounded. The appliance is isolated from the original voltage source by the high resistance of the material between the transformer coils, hence the name isolation transformer. For current to flow through the person, it must pass through the high-resistance material between the coils, through the wire, the person, and back through the earth—a path with such a large resistance that the current is negligible.

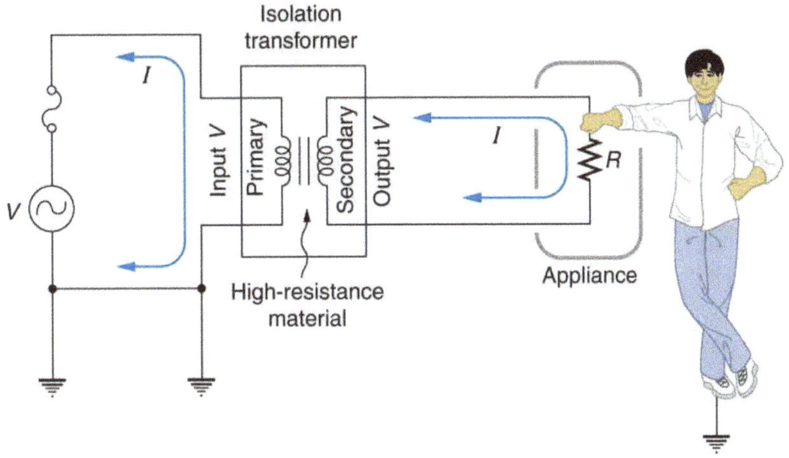

FIGURE 23.36 An isolation transformer puts a large resistance between the original voltage source and the device, preventing a complete circuit between them.

The basics of electrical safety presented here help prevent many electrical hazards. Electrical safety can be pursued to greater depths. There are, for example, problems related to different earth/ground connections for appliances in close proximity. Many other examples are found in hospitals. Microshock-sensitive patients, for instance, require special protection. For these people, currents as low as 0.1 mA may cause ventricular fibrillation. The interested reader can use the material presented here as a basis for further study.

23.9 Inductance

LEARNING OBJECTIVES

By the end of this section, you will be able to:

- Calculate the inductance of an inductor.
- Calculate the energy stored in an inductor.
- Calculate the emf generated in an inductor.

Inductors

Induction is the process in which an emf is induced by changing magnetic flux. Many examples have been discussed so far, some more effective than others. Transformers, for example, are designed to be particularly effective at inducing a desired voltage and current with very little loss of energy to other forms. Is there a useful physical quantity related to how "effective" a given device is? The answer is yes, and that physical quantity is called **inductance**.

Mutual inductance is the effect of Faraday's law of induction for one device upon another, such as the primary coil in transmitting energy to the secondary in a transformer. See Figure 23.37, where simple coils induce emfs in one another.

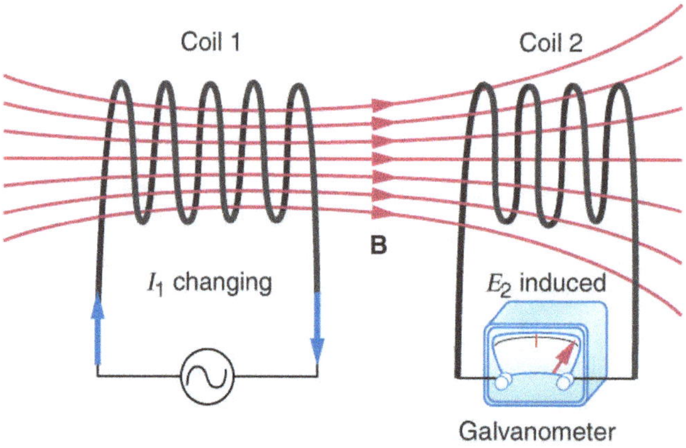

FIGURE 23.37 These coils can induce emfs in one another like an inefficient transformer. Their mutual inductance M indicates the effectiveness of the coupling between them. Here a change in current in coil 1 is seen to induce an emf in coil 2. (Note that "E_2 induced" represents the induced emf in coil 2.)

In the many cases where the geometry of the devices is fixed, flux is changed by varying current. We therefore concentrate on the rate of change of current, $\Delta I/\Delta t$, as the cause of induction. A change in the current I_1 in one device, coil 1 in the figure, induces an emf_2 in the other. We express this in equation form as

$$\text{emf}_2 = -M\frac{\Delta I_1}{\Delta t}, \qquad 23.34$$

where M is defined to be the mutual inductance between the two devices. The minus sign is an expression of Lenz's law. The larger the mutual inductance M, the more effective the coupling. For example, the coils in Figure 23.37 have a small M compared with the transformer coils in Figure 23.27. Units for M are $(\text{V}\cdot\text{s})/\text{A} = \Omega\cdot\text{s}$, which is named a **henry** (H), after Joseph Henry. That is, $1\ \text{H} = 1\ \Omega\cdot\text{s}$.

Nature is symmetric here. If we change the current I_2 in coil 2, we induce an emf_1 in coil 1, which is given by

$$\text{emf}_1 = -M\frac{\Delta I_2}{\Delta t}, \qquad 23.35$$

where M is the same as for the reverse process. Transformers run backward with the same effectiveness, or mutual inductance M.

A large mutual inductance M may or may not be desirable. We want a transformer to have a large mutual inductance. But an appliance, such as an electric clothes dryer, can induce a dangerous emf on its case if the mutual inductance between its coils and the case is large. One way to reduce mutual inductance M is to counterwind coils to cancel the magnetic field produced. (See Figure 23.38.)

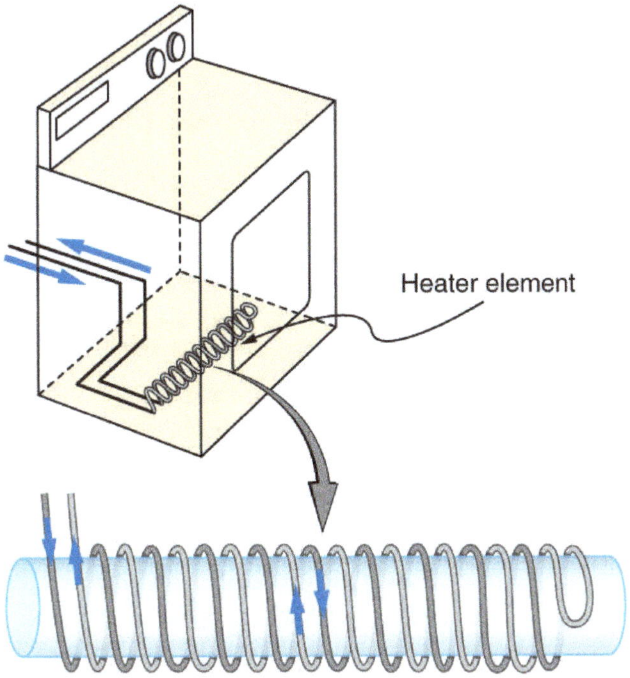

FIGURE 23.38 The heating coils of an electric clothes dryer can be counter-wound so that their magnetic fields cancel one another, greatly reducing the mutual inductance with the case of the dryer.

Self-inductance, the effect of Faraday's law of induction of a device on itself, also exists. When, for example, current through a coil is increased, the magnetic field and flux also increase, inducing a counter emf, as required by Lenz's law. Conversely, if the current is decreased, an emf is induced that opposes the decrease. Most devices have a fixed geometry, and so the change in flux is due entirely to the change in current ΔI through the device. The induced emf is related to the physical geometry of the device and the rate of change of current. It is given by

$$\text{emf} = -L\frac{\Delta I}{\Delta t}, \qquad 23.36$$

where L is the self-inductance of the device. A device that exhibits significant self-inductance is called an **inductor**, and given the symbol in Figure 23.39.

FIGURE 23.39

The minus sign is an expression of Lenz's law, indicating that emf opposes the change in current. Units of self-inductance are henries (H) just as for mutual inductance. The larger the self-inductance L of a device, the greater its opposition to any change in current through it. For example, a large coil with many turns and an iron core has a large L and will not allow current to change quickly. To avoid this effect, a small L must be achieved, such as by counterwinding coils as in Figure 23.38.

A 1 H inductor is a large inductor. To illustrate this, consider a device with $L = 1.0\text{ H}$ that has a 10 A current flowing through it. What happens if we try to shut off the current rapidly, perhaps in only 1.0 ms? An emf, given by $\text{emf} = -L(\Delta I/\Delta t)$, will oppose the change. Thus an emf will be induced given by $\text{emf} = -L(\Delta I/\Delta t)=(1.0\text{ H})[(10\text{ A})/(1.0\text{ ms})]= 10{,}000\text{ V}$. The positive sign means this large voltage is in the same direction as the current, opposing its decrease. Such large emfs can cause arcs, damaging switching equipment, and so it may be necessary to change current more slowly.

There are uses for such a large induced voltage. Camera flashes use a battery, two inductors that function as a transformer, and a switching system or oscillator to induce large voltages. (Remember that we need a changing magnetic field, brought about by a changing current, to induce a voltage in another coil.) The oscillator system will do this many times as the battery voltage is boosted to over one thousand volts. (You may hear the high pitched whine from the transformer as the capacitor is being charged.) A capacitor stores the high voltage for later use in powering the flash. (See Figure 23.40.)

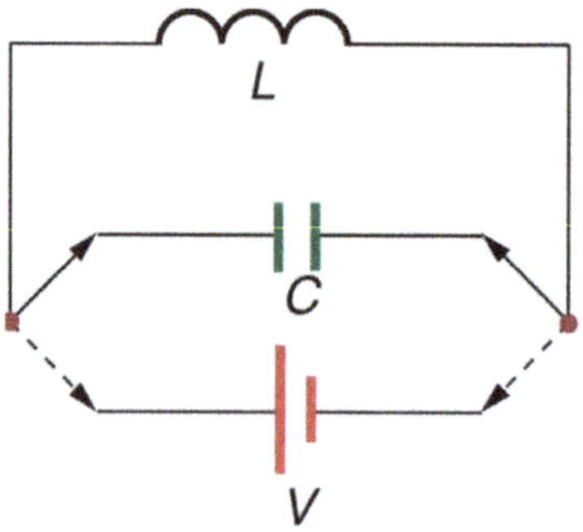

FIGURE 23.40 Through rapid switching of an inductor, 1.5 V batteries can be used to induce emfs of several thousand volts. This voltage can be used to store charge in a capacitor for later use, such as in a camera flash attachment.

It is possible to calculate L for an inductor given its geometry (size and shape) and knowing the magnetic field that it produces. This is difficult in most cases, because of the complexity of the field created. So in this text the inductance L is usually a given quantity. One exception is the solenoid, because it has a very uniform field inside, a nearly zero field outside, and a simple shape. It is instructive to derive an equation for its inductance. We start by noting that the induced emf is given by Faraday's law of induction as $\text{emf} = -N(\Delta\Phi/\Delta t)$ and, by the definition of self-inductance, as $\text{emf} = -L(\Delta I/\Delta t)$. Equating these yields

$$\text{emf} = -N\frac{\Delta\Phi}{\Delta t} = -L\frac{\Delta I}{\Delta t}. \quad 23.37$$

Solving for L gives

$$L = N\frac{\Delta\Phi}{\Delta I}. \quad 23.38$$

This equation for the self-inductance L of a device is always valid. It means that self-inductance L depends on how effective the current is in creating flux; the more effective, the greater $\Delta\Phi/\ \Delta I$ is.

Let us use this last equation to find an expression for the inductance of a solenoid. Since the area A of a solenoid is fixed, the change in flux is $\Delta\Phi = \Delta(BA) = A\Delta B$. To find ΔB, we note that the magnetic field of a solenoid is given by $B = \mu_0 nI = \mu_0\frac{NI}{\ell}$. (Here $n = N/\ell$, where N is the number of coils and ℓ is the solenoid's length.) Only the current changes, so that $\Delta\Phi = A\Delta B = \mu_0 NA\frac{\Delta I}{\ell}$. Substituting $\Delta\Phi$ into $L = N\frac{\Delta\Phi}{\Delta I}$ gives

$$L = N\frac{\Delta\Phi}{\Delta I} = N\frac{\mu_0 NA\frac{\Delta I}{\ell}}{\Delta I}. \quad 23.39$$

This simplifies to

$$L = \frac{\mu_0 N^2 A}{\ell}(\text{solenoid}). \quad 23.40$$

This is the self-inductance of a solenoid of cross-sectional area A and length ℓ. Note that the inductance depends only on the physical characteristics of the solenoid, consistent with its definition.

EXAMPLE 23.7

Calculating the Self-inductance of a Moderate Size Solenoid

Calculate the self-inductance of a 10.0 cm long, 4.00 cm diameter solenoid that has 200 coils.

Strategy

This is a straightforward application of $L = \frac{\mu_0 N^2 A}{\ell}$, since all quantities in the equation except L are known.

Solution

Use the following expression for the self-inductance of a solenoid:

$$L = \frac{\mu_0 N^2 A}{\ell}. \tag{23.41}$$

The cross-sectional area in this example is $A = \pi r^2 = (3.14...)(0.0200 \text{ m})^2 = 1.26 \times 10^{-3} \text{ m}^2$, N is given to be 200, and the length ℓ is 0.100 m. We know the permeability of free space is $\mu_0 = 4\pi \times 10^{-7} \text{ T} \cdot \text{m/A}$. Substituting these into the expression for L gives

$$\begin{aligned} L &= \frac{(4\pi\times10^{-7} \text{ T}\cdot\text{m/A})(200)^2(1.26\times10^{-3} \text{ m}^2)}{0.100 \text{ m}} \\ &= 0.632 \text{ mH}. \end{aligned} \tag{23.42}$$

Discussion

This solenoid is moderate in size. Its inductance of nearly a millihenry is also considered moderate.

One common application of inductance is used in traffic lights that can tell when vehicles are waiting at the intersection. An electrical circuit with an inductor is placed in the road under the place a waiting car will stop over. The body of the car increases the inductance and the circuit changes sending a signal to the traffic lights to change colors. Similarly, metal detectors used for airport security employ the same technique. A coil or inductor in the metal detector frame acts as both a transmitter and a receiver. The pulsed signal in the transmitter coil induces a signal in the receiver. The self-inductance of the circuit is affected by any metal object in the path. Such detectors can be adjusted for sensitivity and also can indicate the approximate location of metal found on a person. See Figure 23.41.

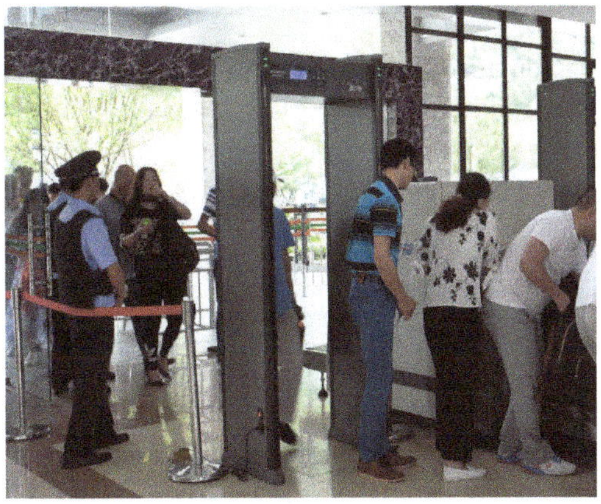

FIGURE 23.41 The familiar security gate at an airport can not only detect metals but also indicate their approximate height above the floor. (credit: shankar s/Flickr)

Energy Stored in an Inductor

We know from Lenz's law that inductances oppose changes in current. There is an alternative way to look at this opposition that is based on energy. Energy is stored in a magnetic field. It takes time to build up energy, and it also takes time to deplete energy; hence, there is an opposition to rapid change. In an inductor, the magnetic field is directly proportional to current and to the inductance of the device. It can be shown that the **energy stored in an inductor** E_{ind} is given by

$$E_{\text{ind}} = \frac{1}{2}LI^2. \tag{23.43}$$

This expression is similar to that for the energy stored in a capacitor.

EXAMPLE 23.8

Calculating the Energy Stored in the Field of a Solenoid

How much energy is stored in the 0.632 mH inductor of the preceding example when a 30.0 A current flows through it?

Strategy

The energy is given by the equation $E_{\text{ind}} = \frac{1}{2}LI^2$, and all quantities except E_{ind} are known.

Solution

Substituting the value for L found in the previous example and the given current into $E_{\text{ind}} = \frac{1}{2}LI^2$ gives

$$\begin{aligned} E_{\text{ind}} &= \frac{1}{2}LI^2 \\ &= 0.5(0.632 \times 10^{-3}\ \text{H})(30.0\ \text{A})^2 = 0.284\ \text{J}. \end{aligned} \qquad 23.44$$

Discussion

This amount of energy is certainly enough to cause a spark if the current is suddenly switched off. It cannot be built up instantaneously unless the power input is infinite.

23.10 RL Circuits

LEARNING OBJECTIVES

By the end of this section, you will be able to:

- Calculate the current in an RL circuit after a specified number of characteristic time steps.
- Calculate the characteristic time of an RL circuit.
- Sketch the current in an RL circuit over time.

We know that the current through an inductor L cannot be turned on or off instantaneously. The change in current changes flux, inducing an emf opposing the change (Lenz's law). How long does the opposition last? Current *will* flow and *can* be turned off, but how long does it take? Figure 23.42 shows a switching circuit that can be used to examine current through an inductor as a function of time.

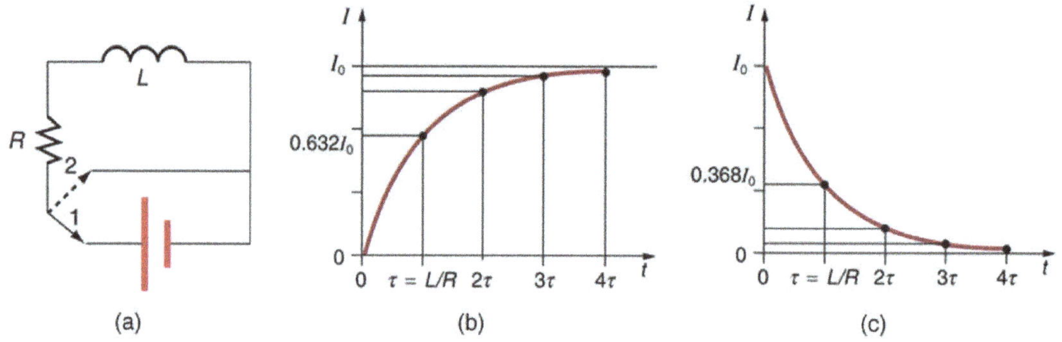

FIGURE 23.42 (a) An *RL* circuit with a switch to turn current on and off. When in position 1, the battery, resistor, and inductor are in series and a current is established. In position 2, the battery is removed and the current eventually stops because of energy loss in the resistor. (b) A graph of current growth versus time when the switch is moved to position 1. (c) A graph of current decay when the switch is moved to position 2.

When the switch is first moved to position 1 (at $t = 0$), the current is zero and it eventually rises to $I_0 = V/R$, where R is the total resistance of the circuit. The opposition of the inductor L is greatest at the beginning, because the amount of change is greatest. The opposition it poses is in the form of an induced emf, which decreases to zero as the current approaches its final value. The opposing emf is proportional to the amount of change left. This is the hallmark of an exponential behavior, and it can be shown with calculus that

$$I = I_0(1 - e^{-t/\tau}) \quad \text{(turning on)}, \qquad 23.45$$

is the current in an *RL* circuit when switched on (Note the similarity to the exponential behavior of the voltage on a charging capacitor). The initial current is zero and approaches $I_0 = V/R$ with a **characteristic time constant** τ for an *RL* circuit, given by

$$\tau = \frac{L}{R}, \qquad 23.46$$

where τ has units of seconds, since $1\ \text{H}{=}1\ \Omega{\cdot}\text{s}$. In the first period of time τ, the current rises from zero to $0.632I_0$, since $I = I_0(1 - e^{-1}) = I_0(1 - 0.368) = 0.632I_0$. The current will go 0.632 of the remainder in the next time τ. A well-known property of the exponential is that the final value is never exactly reached, but 0.632 of the remainder to that value is achieved in every characteristic time τ. In just a few multiples of the time τ, the final value is very nearly achieved, as the graph in Figure 23.42(b) illustrates.

The characteristic time τ depends on only two factors, the inductance L and the resistance R. The greater the inductance L, the greater τ is, which makes sense since a large inductance is very effective in opposing change. The smaller the resistance R, the greater τ is. Again this makes sense, since a small resistance means a large final current and a greater change to get there. In both cases—large L and small R—more energy is stored in the inductor and more time is required to get it in and out.

When the switch in Figure 23.42(a) is moved to position 2 and cuts the battery out of the circuit, the current drops because of energy dissipation by the resistor. But this is also not instantaneous, since the inductor opposes the decrease in current by inducing an emf in the same direction as the battery that drove the current. Furthermore, there is a certain amount of energy, $(1/2)LI_0^2$, stored in the inductor, and it is dissipated at a finite rate. As the current approaches zero, the rate of decrease slows, since the energy dissipation rate is I^2R. Once again the behavior is exponential, and I is found to be

$$I = I_0 e^{-t/\tau} \quad \text{(turning off)}. \tag{23.47}$$

(See Figure 23.42(c).) In the first period of time $\tau = L/R$ after the switch is closed, the current falls to 0.368 of its initial value, since $I = I_0 e^{-1} = 0.368I_0$. In each successive time τ, the current falls to 0.368 of the preceding value, and in a few multiples of τ, the current becomes very close to zero, as seen in the graph in Figure 23.42(c).

EXAMPLE 23.9

Calculating Characteristic Time and Current in an *RL* Circuit

(a) What is the characteristic time constant for a 7.50 mH inductor in series with a $3.00\ \Omega$ resistor? (b) Find the current 5.00 ms after the switch is moved to position 2 to disconnect the battery, if it is initially 10.0 A.

Strategy for (a)

The time constant for an *RL* circuit is defined by $\tau = L/R$.

Solution for (a)

Entering known values into the expression for τ given in $\tau = L/R$ yields

$$\tau = \frac{L}{R} = \frac{7.50\ \text{mH}}{3.00\ \Omega} = 2.50\ \text{ms}. \tag{23.48}$$

Discussion for (a)

This is a small but definitely finite time. The coil will be very close to its full current in about ten time constants, or about 25 ms.

Strategy for (b)

We can find the current by using $I = I_0 e^{-t/\tau}$, or by considering the decline in steps. Since the time is twice the characteristic time, we consider the process in steps.

Solution for (b)

In the first 2.50 ms, the current declines to 0.368 of its initial value, which is

$$\begin{aligned} I &= 0.368 I_0 = (0.368)(10.0\ \text{A}) \\ &= 3.68\ \text{A at } t = 2.50\ \text{ms}. \end{aligned} \tag{23.49}$$

After another 2.50 ms, or a total of 5.00 ms, the current declines to 0.368 of the value just found. That is,

$$\begin{aligned} I' &= 0.368I = (0.368)(3.68\text{ A}) \\ &= 1.35\text{ A at } t = 5.00\text{ ms.} \end{aligned} \quad (23.50)$$

Discussion for (b)

After another 5.00 ms has passed, the current will be 0.183 A (see Exercise 23.69); so, although it does die out, the current certainly does not go to zero instantaneously.

In summary, when the voltage applied to an inductor is changed, the current also changes, *but the change in current lags the change in voltage in an RL circuit*. In Reactance, Inductive and Capacitive, we explore how an *RL* circuit behaves when a sinusoidal AC voltage is applied.

23.11 Reactance, Inductive and Capacitive

LEARNING OBJECTIVES

By the end of this section, you will be able to:

- Sketch voltage and current versus time in simple inductive, capacitive, and resistive circuits.
- Calculate inductive and capacitive reactance.
- Calculate current and/or voltage in simple inductive, capacitive, and resistive circuits.

Many circuits also contain capacitors and inductors, in addition to resistors and an AC voltage source. We have seen how capacitors and inductors respond to DC voltage when it is switched on and off. We will now explore how inductors and capacitors react to sinusoidal AC voltage.

Inductors and Inductive Reactance

Suppose an inductor is connected directly to an AC voltage source, as shown in Figure 23.43. It is reasonable to assume negligible resistance, since in practice we can make the resistance of an inductor so small that it has a negligible effect on the circuit. Also shown is a graph of voltage and current as functions of time.

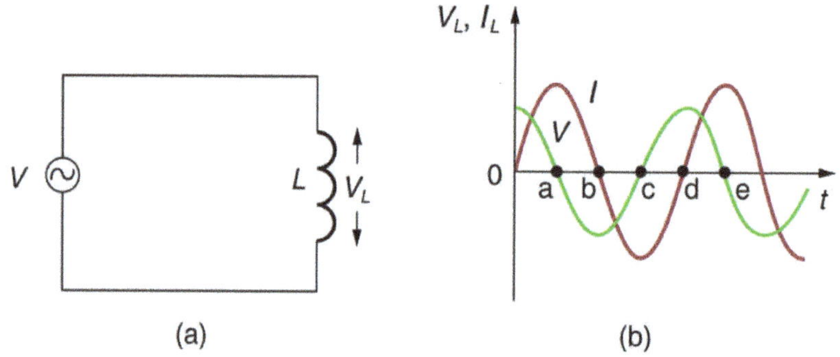

FIGURE 23.43 (a) An AC voltage source in series with an inductor having negligible resistance. (b) Graph of current and voltage across the inductor as functions of time.

The graph in Figure 23.43(b) starts with voltage at a maximum. Note that the current starts at zero and rises to its peak *after* the voltage that drives it, just as was the case when DC voltage was switched on in the preceding section. When the voltage becomes negative at point a, the current begins to decrease; it becomes zero at point b, where voltage is its most negative. The current then becomes negative, again following the voltage. The voltage becomes positive at point c and begins to make the current less negative. At point d, the current goes through zero just as the voltage reaches its positive peak to start another cycle. This behavior is summarized as follows:

> **AC VOLTAGE IN AN INDUCTOR**
>
> When a sinusoidal voltage is applied to an inductor, the voltage leads the current by one-fourth of a cycle, or by a 90º phase angle.

Current lags behind voltage, since inductors oppose change in current. Changing current induces a back emf $V = -L(\Delta I/\Delta t)$. This is considered to be an effective resistance of the inductor to AC. The rms current I through an inductor L is given by a version of Ohm's law:

$$I = \frac{V}{X_L}, \tag{23.51}$$

where V is the rms voltage across the inductor and X_L is defined to be

$$X_L = 2\pi f L, \tag{23.52}$$

with f the frequency of the AC voltage source in hertz (An analysis of the circuit using Kirchhoff's loop rule and calculus actually produces this expression). X_L is called the **inductive reactance**, because the inductor reacts to impede the current. X_L has units of ohms ($1\text{ H} = 1\ \Omega \cdot \text{s}$, so that frequency times inductance has units of $(\text{cycles/s})(\Omega \cdot \text{s}) = \Omega$), consistent with its role as an effective resistance. It makes sense that X_L is proportional to L, since the greater the induction the greater its resistance to change. It is also reasonable that X_L is proportional to frequency f, since greater frequency means greater change in current. That is, $\Delta I/\Delta t$ is large for large frequencies (large f, small Δt). The greater the change, the greater the opposition of an inductor.

EXAMPLE 23.10

Calculating Inductive Reactance and then Current

(a) Calculate the inductive reactance of a 3.00 mH inductor when 60.0 Hz and 10.0 kHz AC voltages are applied. (b) What is the rms current at each frequency if the applied rms voltage is 120 V?

Strategy

The inductive reactance is found directly from the expression $X_L = 2\pi f L$. Once X_L has been found at each frequency, Ohm's law as stated in the Equation $I = V/X_L$ can be used to find the current at each frequency.

Solution for (a)

Entering the frequency and inductance into Equation $X_L = 2\pi f L$ gives

$$X_L = 2\pi f L = 6.28(60.0/\text{s})(3.00\text{ mH}) = 1.13\ \Omega \text{ at } 60\text{ Hz}. \tag{23.53}$$

Similarly, at 10 kHz,

$$X_L = 2\pi f L = 6.28(1.00 \times 10^4/\text{s})(3.00\text{ mH}) = 188\ \Omega \text{ at } 10\text{ kHz}. \tag{23.54}$$

Solution for (b)

The rms current is now found using the version of Ohm's law in Equation $I = V/X_L$, given the applied rms voltage is 120 V. For the first frequency, this yields

$$I = \frac{V}{X_L} = \frac{120\text{ V}}{1.13\ \Omega} = 106\text{ A at } 60\text{ Hz}. \tag{23.55}$$

Similarly, at 10 kHz,

$$I = \frac{V}{X_L} = \frac{120\text{ V}}{188\ \Omega} = 0.637\text{ A at } 10\text{ kHz}. \tag{23.56}$$

Discussion

The inductor reacts very differently at the two different frequencies. At the higher frequency, its reactance is large and the current is small, consistent with how an inductor impedes rapid change. Thus high frequencies are impeded the most. Inductors can be used to filter out high frequencies; for example, a large inductor can be put in series with a sound reproduction system or in series with your home computer to reduce high-frequency sound output from your speakers or high-frequency power spikes into your computer.

Note that although the resistance in the circuit considered is negligible, the AC current is not extremely large because inductive reactance impedes its flow. With AC, there is no time for the current to become extremely large.

Capacitors and Capacitive Reactance

Consider the capacitor connected directly to an AC voltage source as shown in Figure 23.44. The resistance of a circuit like this can be made so small that it has a negligible effect compared with the capacitor, and so we can assume negligible resistance. Voltage across the capacitor and current are graphed as functions of time in the figure.

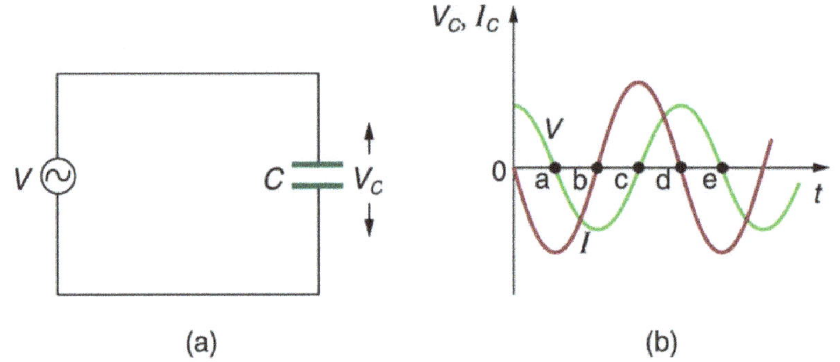

FIGURE 23.44 (a) An AC voltage source in series with a capacitor *C* having negligible resistance. (b) Graph of current and voltage across the capacitor as functions of time.

The graph in Figure 23.44 starts with voltage across the capacitor at a maximum. The current is zero at this point, because the capacitor is fully charged and halts the flow. Then voltage drops and the current becomes negative as the capacitor discharges. At point a, the capacitor has fully discharged ($Q = 0$ on it) and the voltage across it is zero. The current remains negative between points a and b, causing the voltage on the capacitor to reverse. This is complete at point b, where the current is zero and the voltage has its most negative value. The current becomes positive after point b, neutralizing the charge on the capacitor and bringing the voltage to zero at point c, which allows the current to reach its maximum. Between points c and d, the current drops to zero as the voltage rises to its peak, and the process starts to repeat. Throughout the cycle, the voltage follows what the current is doing by one-fourth of a cycle:

AC VOLTAGE IN A CAPACITOR

When a sinusoidal voltage is applied to a capacitor, the voltage follows the current by one-fourth of a cycle, or by a 90° phase angle.

The capacitor is affecting the current, having the ability to stop it altogether when fully charged. Since an AC voltage is applied, there is an rms current, but it is limited by the capacitor. This is considered to be an effective resistance of the capacitor to AC, and so the rms current I in the circuit containing only a capacitor C is given by another version of Ohm's law to be

$$I = \frac{V}{X_C}, \tag{23.57}$$

where V is the rms voltage and X_C is defined (As with X_L, this expression for X_C results from an analysis of the circuit using Kirchhoff's rules and calculus) to be

$$X_C = \frac{1}{2\pi f C}, \tag{23.58}$$

where X_C is called the **capacitive reactance**, because the capacitor reacts to impede the current. X_C has units of ohms (verification left as an exercise for the reader). X_C is inversely proportional to the capacitance C; the larger the capacitor, the greater the charge it can store and the greater the current that can flow. It is also inversely proportional to the frequency f; the greater the frequency, the less time there is to fully charge the capacitor, and so it impedes current less.

EXAMPLE 23.11

Calculating Capacitive Reactance and then Current

(a) Calculate the capacitive reactance of a 5.00 μF capacitor when 60.0 Hz and 10.0 kHz AC voltages are applied. (b) What is the rms current if the applied rms voltage is 120 V?

Strategy

The capacitive reactance is found directly from the expression in $X_C = \frac{1}{2\pi fC}$. Once X_C has been found at each frequency, Ohm's law stated as $I = V/X_C$ can be used to find the current at each frequency.

Solution for (a)

Entering the frequency and capacitance into $X_C = \frac{1}{2\pi fC}$ gives

$$\begin{aligned} X_C &= \frac{1}{2\pi fC} \\ &= \frac{1}{6.28(60.0/\text{s})(5.00\ \mu\text{F})} = 531\ \Omega \text{ at } 60\text{ Hz}. \end{aligned} \qquad 23.59$$

Similarly, at 10 kHz,

$$\begin{aligned} X_C &= \frac{1}{2\pi fC} = \frac{1}{6.28(1.00\times 10^4/\text{s})(5.00\ \mu\text{F})}. \\ &= 3.18\ \Omega \text{ at } 10\text{ kHz} \end{aligned} \qquad 23.60$$

Solution for (b)

The rms current is now found using the version of Ohm's law in $I = V/X_C$, given the applied rms voltage is 120 V. For the first frequency, this yields

$$I = \frac{V}{X_C} = \frac{120\text{ V}}{531\ \Omega} = 0.226\text{ A at } 60\text{ Hz}. \qquad 23.61$$

Similarly, at 10 kHz,

$$I = \frac{V}{X_C} = \frac{120\text{ V}}{3.18\ \Omega} = 37.7\text{ A at } 10\text{ kHz}. \qquad 23.62$$

Discussion

The capacitor reacts very differently at the two different frequencies, and in exactly the opposite way an inductor reacts. At the higher frequency, its reactance is small and the current is large. Capacitors favor change, whereas inductors oppose change. Capacitors impede low frequencies the most, since low frequency allows them time to become charged and stop the current. Capacitors can be used to filter out low frequencies. For example, a capacitor in series with a sound reproduction system rids it of the 60 Hz hum.

Although a capacitor is basically an open circuit, there is an rms current in a circuit with an AC voltage applied to a capacitor. This is because the voltage is continually reversing, charging and discharging the capacitor. If the frequency goes to zero (DC), X_C tends to infinity, and the current is zero once the capacitor is charged. At very high frequencies, the capacitor's reactance tends to zero—it has a negligible reactance and does not impede the current (it acts like a simple wire). *Capacitors have the opposite effect on AC circuits that inductors have.*

Resistors in an AC Circuit

Just as a reminder, consider Figure 23.45, which shows an AC voltage applied to a resistor and a graph of voltage and current versus time. The voltage and current are exactly *in phase* in a resistor. There is no frequency dependence to the behavior of plain resistance in a circuit:

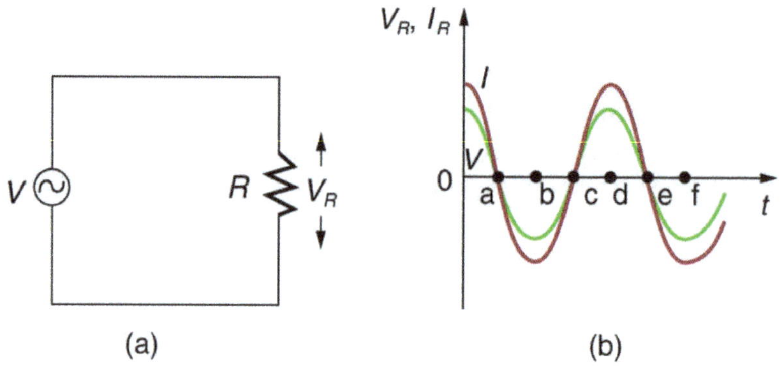

FIGURE 23.45 (a) An AC voltage source in series with a resistor. (b) Graph of current and voltage across the resistor as functions of time, showing them to be exactly in phase.

> **AC VOLTAGE IN A RESISTOR**
>
> When a sinusoidal voltage is applied to a resistor, the voltage is exactly in phase with the current—they have a $0°$ phase angle.

23.12 RLC Series AC Circuits

LEARNING OBJECTIVES

By the end of this section, you will be able to:

- Calculate the impedance, phase angle, resonant frequency, power, power factor, voltage, and/or current in a RLC series circuit.
- Draw the circuit diagram for an RLC series circuit.
- Explain the significance of the resonant frequency.

Impedance

When alone in an AC circuit, inductors, capacitors, and resistors all impede current. How do they behave when all three occur together? Interestingly, their individual resistances in ohms do not simply add. Because inductors and capacitors behave in opposite ways, they partially to totally cancel each other's effect. Figure 23.46 shows an *RLC* series circuit with an AC voltage source, the behavior of which is the subject of this section. The crux of the analysis of an *RLC* circuit is the frequency dependence of X_L and X_C, and the effect they have on the phase of voltage versus current (established in the preceding section). These give rise to the frequency dependence of the circuit, with important "resonance" features that are the basis of many applications, such as radio tuners.

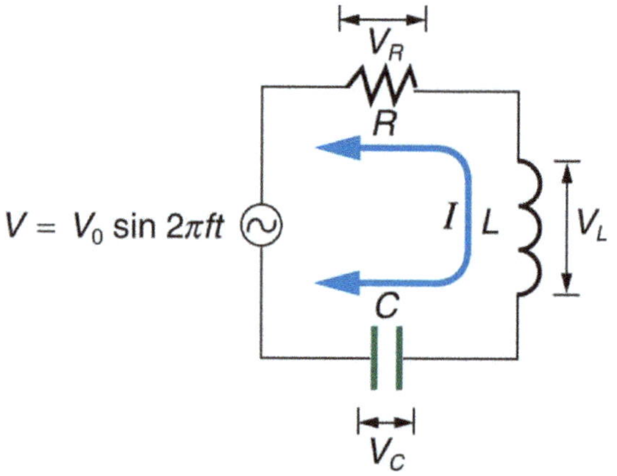

FIGURE 23.46 An *RLC* series circuit with an AC voltage source.

The combined effect of resistance R, inductive reactance X_L, and capacitive reactance X_C is defined to be **impedance**, an AC analogue to resistance in a DC circuit. Current, voltage, and impedance in an *RLC* circuit are related by an AC version of Ohm's law:

$$I_0 = \frac{V_0}{Z} \text{ or } I_{rms} = \frac{V_{rms}}{Z}. \tag{23.63}$$

Here I_0 is the peak current, V_0 the peak source voltage, and Z is the impedance of the circuit. The units of impedance are ohms, and its effect on the circuit is as you might expect: the greater the impedance, the smaller the current. To get an expression for Z in terms of R, X_L, and X_C, we will now examine how the voltages across the various components are related to the source voltage. Those voltages are labeled V_R, V_L, and V_C in Figure 23.46.

Conservation of charge requires current to be the same in each part of the circuit at all times, so that we can say the currents in R, L, and C are equal and in phase. But we know from the preceding section that the voltage across the inductor V_L leads the current by one-fourth of a cycle, the voltage across the capacitor V_C follows the current by one-fourth of a cycle, and the voltage across the resistor V_R is exactly in phase with the current. Figure 23.47 shows these relationships in one graph, as well as showing the total voltage around the circuit $V = V_R + V_L + V_C$, where all four voltages are the instantaneous values. According to Kirchhoff's loop rule, the total voltage around the circuit V is also the voltage of the source.

You can see from Figure 23.47 that while V_R is in phase with the current, V_L leads by $90°$, and V_C follows by $90°$. Thus V_L and V_C are $180°$ out of phase (crest to trough) and tend to cancel, although not completely unless they have the same magnitude. Since the peak voltages are not aligned (not in phase), the peak voltage V_0 of the source does *not* equal the sum of the peak voltages across R, L, and C. The actual relationship is

$$V_0 = \sqrt{{V_{0R}}^2 + (V_{0L} - V_{0C})^2}, \tag{23.64}$$

where V_{0R}, V_{0L}, and V_{0C} are the peak voltages across R, L, and C, respectively. Now, using Ohm's law and definitions from Reactance, Inductive and Capacitive, we substitute $V_0 = I_0 Z$ into the above, as well as $V_{0R} = I_0 R$, $V_{0L} = I_0 X_L$, and $V_{0C} = I_0 X_C$, yielding

$$I_0 Z = \sqrt{{I_0}^2 R^2 + (I_0 X_L - I_0 X_C)^2} = I_0 \sqrt{R^2 + (X_L - X_C)^2}. \tag{23.65}$$

I_0 cancels to yield an expression for Z:

$$Z = \sqrt{R^2 + (X_L - X_C)^2}, \tag{23.66}$$

which is the impedance of an *RLC* series AC circuit. For circuits without a resistor, take $R = 0$; for those without an inductor, take $X_L = 0$; and for those without a capacitor, take $X_C = 0$.

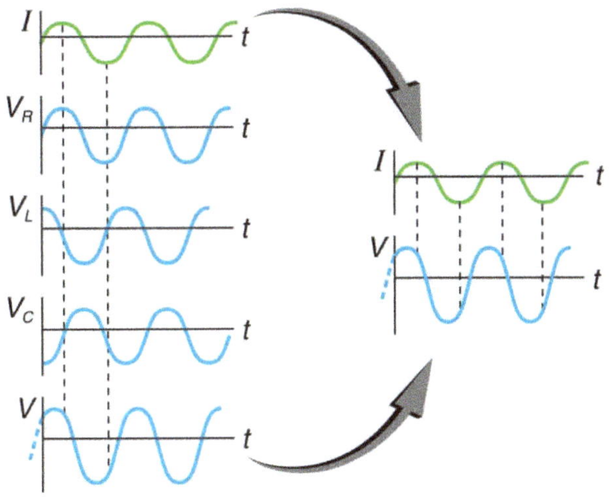

FIGURE 23.47 This graph shows the relationships of the voltages in an *RLC* circuit to the current. The voltages across the circuit elements add to equal the voltage of the source, which is seen to be out of phase with the current.

EXAMPLE 23.12

Calculating Impedance and Current

An *RLC* series circuit has a $40.0\ \Omega$ resistor, a 3.00 mH inductor, and a $5.00\ \mu\text{F}$ capacitor. (a) Find the circuit's impedance at 60.0 Hz and 10.0 kHz, noting that these frequencies and the values for L and C are the same as in Example 23.10 and Example 23.11. (b) If the voltage source has $V_{\text{rms}} = 120\ \text{V}$, what is I_{rms} at each frequency?

Strategy

For each frequency, we use $Z = \sqrt{R^2 + (X_L - X_C)^2}$ to find the impedance and then Ohm's law to find current. We can take advantage of the results of the previous two examples rather than calculate the reactances again.

Solution for (a)

At 60.0 Hz, the values of the reactances were found in Example 23.10 to be $X_L = 1.13\ \Omega$ and in Example 23.11 to be $X_C = 531\ \Omega$. Entering these and the given $40.0\ \Omega$ for resistance into $Z = \sqrt{R^2 + (X_L - X_C)^2}$ yields

$$\begin{aligned} Z &= \sqrt{R^2 + (X_L - X_C)^2} \\ &= \sqrt{(40.0\ \Omega)^2 + (1.13\ \Omega - 531\ \Omega)^2} \\ &= 531\ \Omega \text{ at } 60.0\ \text{Hz}. \end{aligned} \qquad 23.67$$

Similarly, at 10.0 kHz, $X_L = 188\ \Omega$ and $X_C = 3.18\ \Omega$, so that

$$\begin{aligned} Z &= \sqrt{(40.0\ \Omega)^2 + (188\ \Omega - 3.18\ \Omega)^2} \\ &= 190\ \Omega \text{ at } 10.0\ \text{kHz}. \end{aligned} \qquad 23.68$$

Discussion for (a)

In both cases, the result is nearly the same as the largest value, and the impedance is definitely not the sum of the individual values. It is clear that X_L dominates at high frequency and X_C dominates at low frequency.

Solution for (b)

The current I_{rms} can be found using the AC version of Ohm's law in Equation $I_{\text{rms}} = V_{\text{rms}}/Z$:

$I_{\text{rms}} = \frac{V_{\text{rms}}}{Z} = \frac{120\ \text{V}}{531\ \Omega} = 0.226\ \text{A}$ at 60.0 Hz

Finally, at 10.0 kHz, we find

$I_{\text{rms}} = \frac{V_{\text{rms}}}{Z} = \frac{120\ \text{V}}{190\ \Omega} = 0.633\ \text{A}$ at 10.0 kHz

Discussion for (a)

The current at 60.0 Hz is the same (to three digits) as found for the capacitor alone in Example 23.11. The capacitor dominates at low frequency. The current at 10.0 kHz is only slightly different from that found for the inductor alone in Example 23.10. The inductor dominates at high frequency.

Resonance in *RLC* Series AC Circuits

How does an *RLC* circuit behave as a function of the frequency of the driving voltage source? Combining Ohm's law, $I_{\text{rms}} = V_{\text{rms}}/Z$, and the expression for impedance Z from $Z = \sqrt{R^2 + (X_L - X_C)^2}$ gives

$$I_{\text{rms}} = \frac{V_{\text{rms}}}{\sqrt{R^2 + (X_L - X_C)^2}}. \qquad 23.69$$

The reactances vary with frequency, with X_L large at high frequencies and X_C large at low frequencies, as we have seen in three previous examples. At some intermediate frequency f_0, the reactances will be equal and cancel, giving $Z = R$—this is a minimum value for impedance, and a maximum value for I_{rms} results. We can get an expression for f_0 by taking

$$X_L = X_C. \tag{23.70}$$

Substituting the definitions of X_L and X_C,

$$2\pi f_0 L = \frac{1}{2\pi f_0 C}. \tag{23.71}$$

Solving this expression for f_0 yields

$$f_0 = \frac{1}{2\pi\sqrt{LC}}, \tag{23.72}$$

where f_0 is the **resonant frequency** of an *RLC* series circuit. This is also the *natural frequency* at which the circuit would oscillate if not driven by the voltage source. At f_0, the effects of the inductor and capacitor cancel, so that $Z = R$, and I_{rms} is a maximum.

Resonance in AC circuits is analogous to mechanical resonance, where resonance is defined to be a forced oscillation—in this case, forced by the voltage source—at the natural frequency of the system. The receiver in a radio is an *RLC* circuit that oscillates best at its f_0. A variable capacitor is often used to adjust f_0 to receive a desired frequency and to reject others. Figure 23.48 is a graph of current as a function of frequency, illustrating a resonant peak in I_{rms} at f_0. The two curves are for two different circuits, which differ only in the amount of resistance in them. The peak is lower and broader for the higher-resistance circuit. Thus the higher-resistance circuit does not resonate as strongly and would not be as selective in a radio receiver, for example.

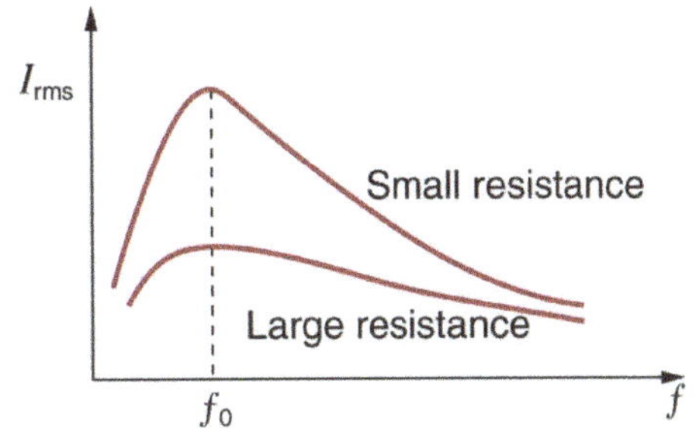

FIGURE 23.48 A graph of current versus frequency for two *RLC* series circuits differing only in the amount of resistance. Both have a resonance at f_0, but that for the higher resistance is lower and broader. The driving AC voltage source has a fixed amplitude V_0.

EXAMPLE 23.13

Calculating Resonant Frequency and Current

For the same *RLC* series circuit having a $40.0\ \Omega$ resistor, a 3.00 mH inductor, and a $5.00\ \mu F$ capacitor: (a) Find the resonant frequency. (b) Calculate I_{rms} at resonance if V_{rms} is 120 V.

Strategy

The resonant frequency is found by using the expression in $f_0 = \frac{1}{2\pi\sqrt{LC}}$. The current at that frequency is the same as if the resistor alone were in the circuit.

Solution for (a)

Entering the given values for L and C into the expression given for f_0 in $f_0 = \frac{1}{2\pi\sqrt{LC}}$ yields

$$\begin{aligned} f_0 &= \frac{1}{2\pi\sqrt{LC}} \\ &= \frac{1}{2\pi\sqrt{(3.00\times10^{-3}\ \text{H})(5.00\times10^{-6}\ \text{F})}} = 1.30\ \text{kHz}. \end{aligned} \tag{23.73}$$

Discussion for (a)

We see that the resonant frequency is between 60.0 Hz and 10.0 kHz, the two frequencies chosen in earlier examples. This was to be expected, since the capacitor dominated at the low frequency and the inductor dominated at the high frequency. Their effects are the same at this intermediate frequency.

Solution for (b)

The current is given by Ohm's law. At resonance, the two reactances are equal and cancel, so that the impedance equals the resistance alone. Thus,

$$I_{\text{rms}} = \frac{V_{\text{rms}}}{Z} = \frac{120\text{ V}}{40.0\ \Omega} = 3.00\text{ A}. \tag{23.74}$$

Discussion for (b)

At resonance, the current is greater than at the higher and lower frequencies considered for the same circuit in the preceding example.

Power in *RLC* Series AC Circuits

If current varies with frequency in an *RLC* circuit, then the power delivered to it also varies with frequency. But the average power is not simply current times voltage, as it is in purely resistive circuits. As was seen in Figure 23.47, voltage and current are out of phase in an *RLC* circuit. There is a **phase angle** ϕ between the source voltage V and the current I, which can be found from

$$\cos\phi = \frac{R}{Z}. \tag{23.75}$$

For example, at the resonant frequency or in a purely resistive circuit $Z = R$, so that $\cos\phi = 1$. This implies that $\phi = 0^\circ$ and that voltage and current are in phase, as expected for resistors. At other frequencies, average power is less than at resonance. This is both because voltage and current are out of phase and because I_{rms} is lower. The fact that source voltage and current are out of phase affects the power delivered to the circuit. It can be shown that the *average power* is

$$P_{\text{ave}} = I_{\text{rms}}V_{\text{rms}}\cos\phi, \tag{23.76}$$

Thus $\cos\phi$ is called the **power factor**, which can range from 0 to 1. Power factors near 1 are desirable when designing an efficient motor, for example. At the resonant frequency, $\cos\phi = 1$.

EXAMPLE 23.14

Calculating the Power Factor and Power

For the same *RLC* series circuit having a $40.0\ \Omega$ resistor, a 3.00 mH inductor, a $5.00\ \mu\text{F}$ capacitor, and a voltage source with a V_{rms} of 120 V: (a) Calculate the power factor and phase angle for $f = 60.0\text{Hz}$. (b) What is the average power at 50.0 Hz? (c) Find the average power at the circuit's resonant frequency.

Strategy and Solution for (a)

The power factor at 60.0 Hz is found from

$$\cos\phi = \frac{R}{Z}. \tag{23.77}$$

We know $Z = 531\ \Omega$ from Example 23.12, so that

$$\cos\phi = \frac{40.0\ \Omega}{531\ \Omega} = 0.0753\text{ at }60.0\text{ Hz}. \tag{23.78}$$

This small value indicates the voltage and current are significantly out of phase. In fact, the phase angle is

$$\phi = \cos^{-1} 0.0753 = 85.7° \text{ at } 60.0 \text{ Hz.} \tag{23.79}$$

Discussion for (a)

The phase angle is close to $90°$, consistent with the fact that the capacitor dominates the circuit at this low frequency (a pure *RC* circuit has its voltage and current $90°$ out of phase).

Strategy and Solution for (b)

The average power at 60.0 Hz is

$$P_{\text{ave}} = I_{\text{rms}} V_{\text{rms}} \cos \phi. \tag{23.80}$$

I_{rms} was found to be 0.226 A in Example 23.12. Entering the known values gives

$$P_{\text{ave}} = (0.226 \text{ A})(120 \text{ V})(0.0753) = 2.04 \text{ W at } 60.0 \text{ Hz.} \tag{23.81}$$

Strategy and Solution for (c)

At the resonant frequency, we know $\cos \phi = 1$, and I_{rms} was found to be 6.00 A in Example 23.13. Thus,

$P_{\text{ave}} = (3.00 \text{ A})(120 \text{ V})(1) = 360 \text{ W}$ at resonance (1.30 kHz)

Discussion

Both the current and the power factor are greater at resonance, producing significantly greater power than at higher and lower frequencies.

Power delivered to an *RLC* series AC circuit is dissipated by the resistance alone. The inductor and capacitor have energy input and output but do not dissipate it out of the circuit. Rather they transfer energy back and forth to one another, with the resistor dissipating exactly what the voltage source puts into the circuit. This assumes no significant electromagnetic radiation from the inductor and capacitor, such as radio waves. Such radiation can happen and may even be desired, as we will see in the next chapter on electromagnetic radiation, but it can also be suppressed as is the case in this chapter. The circuit is analogous to the wheel of a car driven over a corrugated road as shown in Figure 23.49. The regularly spaced bumps in the road are analogous to the voltage source, driving the wheel up and down. The shock absorber is analogous to the resistance damping and limiting the amplitude of the oscillation. Energy within the system goes back and forth between kinetic (analogous to maximum current, and energy stored in an inductor) and potential energy stored in the car spring (analogous to no current, and energy stored in the electric field of a capacitor). The amplitude of the wheels' motion is a maximum if the bumps in the road are hit at the resonant frequency.

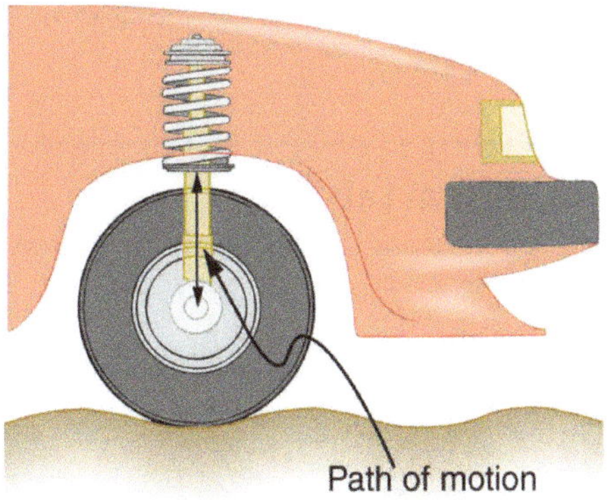

FIGURE 23.49 The forced but damped motion of the wheel on the car spring is analogous to an *RLC* series AC circuit. The shock absorber damps the motion and dissipates energy, analogous to the resistance in an *RLC* circuit. The mass and spring determine the resonant frequency.

A pure *LC* circuit with negligible resistance oscillates at f_0, the same resonant frequency as an *RLC* circuit. It can serve as a frequency standard or clock circuit—for example, in a digital wristwatch. With a very small resistance, only a very small energy input is necessary to maintain the oscillations. The circuit is analogous to a car with no shock absorbers. Once it starts oscillating, it continues at its natural frequency for some time. Figure 23.50 shows the analogy between an *LC* circuit and a mass on a spring.

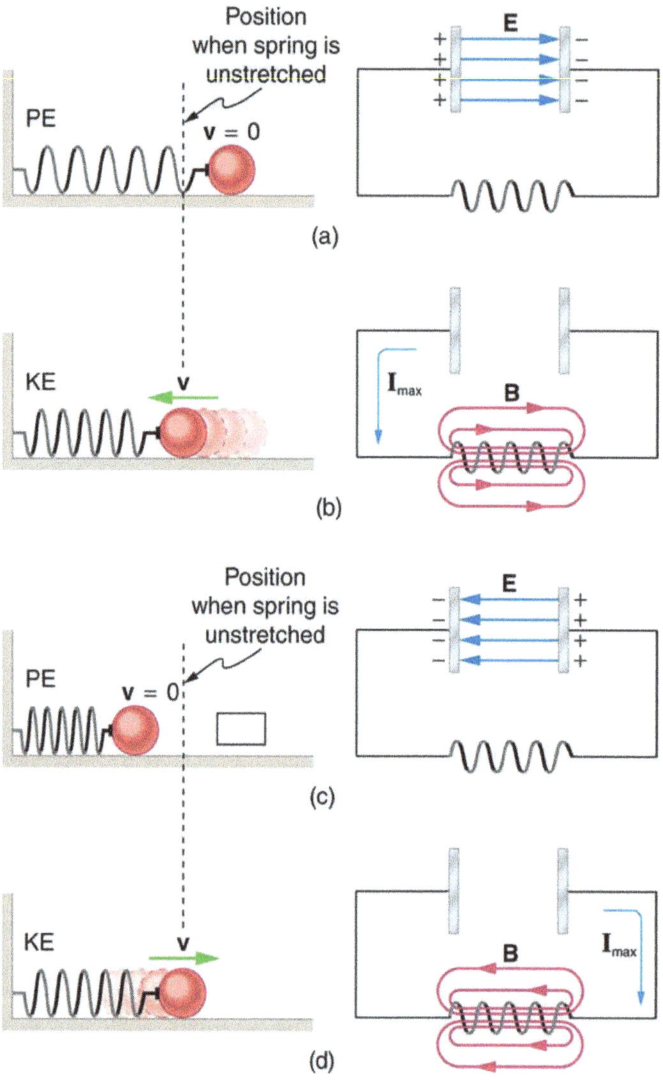

FIGURE 23.50 An *LC* circuit is analogous to a mass oscillating on a spring with no friction and no driving force. Energy moves back and forth between the inductor and capacitor, just as it moves from kinetic to potential in the mass-spring system.

PHET EXPLORATIONS

Circuit Construction Kit (AC+DC), Virtual Lab

Build circuits with capacitors, inductors, resistors and AC or DC voltage sources, and inspect them using lab instruments such as voltmeters and ammeters.

[Click to view content (https://openstax.org/books/college-physics-ap-courses-2e/pages/23-12-rlc-series-ac-circuits)](https://openstax.org/books/college-physics-ap-courses-2e/pages/23-12-rlc-series-ac-circuits)

Glossary

back emf the emf generated by a running motor, because it consists of a coil turning in a magnetic field; it opposes the voltage powering the motor

capacitive reactance the opposition of a capacitor to a change in current; calculated by $X_C = \frac{1}{2\pi fC}$

characteristic time constant denoted by τ, of a particular series *RL* circuit is calculated by $\tau = \frac{L}{R}$, where L is the inductance and R is the resistance

eddy current a current loop in a conductor caused by motional emf

electric generator a device for converting mechanical work into electric energy; it induces an emf by rotating a coil in a magnetic field

electromagnetic induction the process of inducing an emf (voltage) with a change in magnetic flux

emf induced in a generator coil $\text{emf} = NAB\omega \sin \omega t$, where A is the area of an N -turn coil rotated at a constant angular velocity ω in a uniform magnetic field B, over a period of time t

energy stored in an inductor self-explanatory; calculated by $E_{\text{ind}} = \frac{1}{2}LI^2$

Faraday's law of induction the means of calculating the emf in a coil due to changing magnetic flux, given by $\text{emf} = -N\frac{\Delta\Phi}{\Delta t}$

henry the unit of inductance; $1\ \text{H} = 1\ \Omega \cdot \text{s}$

impedance the AC analogue to resistance in a DC circuit; it is the combined effect of resistance, inductive reactance, and capacitive reactance in the form $Z = \sqrt{R^2 + (X_L - X_C)^2}$

inductance a property of a device describing how efficient it is at inducing emf in another device

induction (magnetic induction) the creation of emfs and hence currents by magnetic fields

inductive reactance the opposition of an inductor to a change in current; calculated by $X_L = 2\pi fL$

inductor a device that exhibits significant self-inductance

Lenz's law the minus sign in Faraday's law, signifying that the emf induced in a coil opposes the change in magnetic flux

magnetic damping the drag produced by eddy currents

magnetic flux the amount of magnetic field going through a particular area, calculated with $\Phi = BA \cos \theta$ where B is the magnetic field strength over an area A at an angle θ with the perpendicular to the area

mutual inductance how effective a pair of devices are at inducing emfs in each other

peak emf $\text{emf}_0 = NAB\omega$

phase angle denoted by ϕ, the amount by which the voltage and current are out of phase with each other in a circuit

power factor the amount by which the power delivered in the circuit is less than the theoretical maximum of the circuit due to voltage and current being out of phase; calculated by $\cos \phi$

resonant frequency the frequency at which the impedance in a circuit is at a minimum, and also the frequency at which the circuit would oscillate if not driven by a voltage source; calculated by $f_0 = \frac{1}{2\pi\sqrt{LC}}$

self-inductance how effective a device is at inducing emf in itself

shock hazard the term for electrical hazards due to current passing through a human

step-down transformer a transformer that decreases voltage

step-up transformer a transformer that increases voltage

thermal hazard the term for electrical hazards due to overheating

three-wire system the wiring system used at present for safety reasons, with live, neutral, and ground wires

transformer a device that transforms voltages from one value to another using induction

transformer equation the equation showing that the ratio of the secondary to primary voltages in a transformer equals the ratio of the number of loops in their coils; $\frac{V_\text{s}}{V_\text{p}} = \frac{N_\text{s}}{N_\text{p}}$

Section Summary

23.1 Induced Emf and Magnetic Flux

- The crucial quantity in induction is magnetic flux Φ , defined to be $\Phi = BA \cos \theta$, where B is the magnetic field strength over an area A at an angle θ with the perpendicular to the area.
- Units of magnetic flux Φ are $\text{T} \cdot \text{m}^2$.
- Any change in magnetic flux Φ induces an emf—the process is defined to be electromagnetic induction.

23.2 Faraday's Law of Induction: Lenz's Law

- Faraday's law of induction states that the emfinduced by a change in magnetic flux is

$$\text{emf} = -N\frac{\Delta\Phi}{\Delta t}$$

when flux changes by $\Delta\Phi$ in a time Δt.

- If emf is induced in a coil, N is its number of turns.
- The minus sign means that the emf creates a current I and magnetic field B that *oppose the change in flux* $\Delta\Phi$ —this opposition is known as Lenz's law.

23.3 Motional Emf

- An emf induced by motion relative to a magnetic field B is called a *motional emf* and is given by
$$\text{emf} = B\ell v \qquad (B, \ell, \text{and } v \text{ perpendicular}),$$
where ℓ is the length of the object moving at speed v relative to the field.

23.4 Eddy Currents and Magnetic Damping

- Current loops induced in moving conductors are called eddy currents.
- They can create significant drag, called magnetic damping.

23.5 Electric Generators

- An electric generator rotates a coil in a magnetic field, inducing an emfgiven as a function of time by
$$\text{emf} = NAB\omega \sin \omega t,$$
where A is the area of an N-turn coil rotated at a constant angular velocity ω in a uniform magnetic field B.
- The peak emf emf_0 of a generator is
$$\text{emf}_0 = NAB\omega.$$

23.6 Back Emf

- Any rotating coil will have an induced emf—in motors, this is called back emf, since it opposes the emf input to the motor.

23.7 Transformers

- Transformers use induction to transform voltages from one value to another.
- For a transformer, the voltages across the primary and secondary coils are related by
$$\frac{V_s}{V_p} = \frac{N_s}{N_p},$$
where V_p and V_s are the voltages across primary and secondary coils having N_p and N_s turns.
- The currents I_p and I_s in the primary and secondary coils are related by $\frac{I_s}{I_p} = \frac{N_p}{N_s}$.
- A step-up transformer increases voltage and decreases current, whereas a step-down transformer decreases voltage and increases current.

23.8 Electrical Safety: Systems and Devices

- Electrical safety systems and devices are employed to prevent thermal and shock hazards.
- Circuit breakers and fuses interrupt excessive currents to prevent thermal hazards.
- The three-wire system guards against thermal and shock hazards, utilizing live/hot, neutral, and earth/ground wires, and grounding the neutral wire and case of the appliance.
- A ground fault interrupter (GFI) prevents shock by detecting the loss of current to unintentional paths.
- An isolation transformer insulates the device being powered from the original source, also to prevent shock.
- Many of these devices use induction to perform their basic function.

23.9 Inductance

- Inductance is the property of a device that tells how effectively it induces an emf in another device.
- Mutual inductance is the effect of two devices in inducing emfs in each other.
- A change in current $\Delta I_1/\Delta t$ in one induces an emf emf_2 in the second:
$$\text{emf}_2 = -M\frac{\Delta I_1}{\Delta t},$$
where M is defined to be the mutual inductance between the two devices, and the minus sign is due to Lenz's law.
- Symmetrically, a change in current $\Delta I_2/\Delta t$ through the second device induces an emf emf_1 in the first:
$$\text{emf}_1 = -M\frac{\Delta I_2}{\Delta t},$$
where M is the same mutual inductance as in the reverse process.
- Current changes in a device induce an emf in the device itself.
- Self-inductance is the effect of the device inducing emf in itself.
- The device is called an inductor, and the emf induced in it by a change in current through it is
$$\text{emf} = -L\frac{\Delta I}{\Delta t},$$
where L is the self-inductance of the inductor, and $\Delta I/\Delta t$ is the rate of change of current through it. The minus sign indicates that emf opposes the change in current, as required by Lenz's law.
- The unit of self- and mutual inductance is the henry (H), where $1\text{ H} = 1\ \Omega\cdot\text{s}$.
- The self-inductance L of an inductor is

proportional to how much flux changes with current. For an N-turn inductor,

$$L = N\frac{\Delta\Phi}{\Delta I}.$$

- The self-inductance of a solenoid is

  $$L = \frac{\mu_0 N^2 A}{\ell}\text{(solenoid)},$$

  where N is its number of turns in the solenoid, A is its cross-sectional area, ℓ is its length, and $\mu_0 = 4\pi \times 10^{-7}\ \text{T} \cdot \text{m/A}$ is the permeability of free space.
- The energy stored in an inductor E_{ind} is

  $$E_{\text{ind}} = \frac{1}{2}LI^2.$$

23.10 RL Circuits

- When a series connection of a resistor and an inductor—an *RL* circuit—is connected to a voltage source, the time variation of the current is

  $$I = I_0(1 - e^{-t/\tau}) \quad \text{(turning on)}.$$

  where $I_0 = V/R$ is the final current.
- The characteristic time constant τ is $\tau = \frac{L}{R}$, where L is the inductance and R is the resistance.
- In the first time constant τ, the current rises from zero to $0.632I_0$, and 0.632 of the remainder in every subsequent time interval τ.
- When the inductor is shorted through a resistor, current decreases as

  $$I = I_0 e^{-t/\tau} \quad \text{(turning off)}.$$

  Here I_0 is the initial current.
- Current falls to $0.368I_0$ in the first time interval τ, and 0.368 of the remainder toward zero in each subsequent time τ.

23.11 Reactance, Inductive and Capacitive

- For inductors in AC circuits, we find that when a sinusoidal voltage is applied to an inductor, the voltage leads the current by one-fourth of a cycle, or by a 90° phase angle.
- The opposition of an inductor to a change in current is expressed as a type of AC resistance.
- Ohm's law for an inductor is

  $$I = \frac{V}{X_L},$$

  where V is the rms voltage across the inductor.
- X_L is defined to be the inductive reactance, given by

  $$X_L = 2\pi f L,$$

  with f the frequency of the AC voltage source in hertz.
- Inductive reactance X_L has units of ohms and is greatest at high frequencies.
- For capacitors, we find that when a sinusoidal voltage is applied to a capacitor, the voltage follows the current by one-fourth of a cycle, or by a 90° phase angle.
- Since a capacitor can stop current when fully charged, it limits current and offers another form of AC resistance; Ohm's law for a capacitor is

  $$I = \frac{V}{X_C},$$

  where V is the rms voltage across the capacitor.
- X_C is defined to be the capacitive reactance, given by

  $$X_C = \frac{1}{2\pi f C}.$$

- X_C has units of ohms and is greatest at low frequencies.

23.12 RLC Series AC Circuits

- The AC analogy to resistance is impedance Z, the combined effect of resistors, inductors, and capacitors, defined by the AC version of Ohm's law:

  $$I_0 = \frac{V_0}{Z} \text{ or } I_{\text{rms}} = \frac{V_{\text{rms}}}{Z},$$

  where I_0 is the peak current and V_0 is the peak source voltage.
- Impedance has units of ohms and is given by

  $$Z = \sqrt{R^2 + (X_L - X_C)^2}.$$

- The resonant frequency f_0, at which $X_L = X_C$, is

  $$f_0 = \frac{1}{2\pi\sqrt{LC}}.$$

- In an AC circuit, there is a phase angle ϕ between source voltage V and the current I, which can be found from

  $$\cos\phi = \frac{R}{Z},$$

- $\phi = 0^\circ$ for a purely resistive circuit or an *RLC* circuit at resonance.
- The average power delivered to an *RLC* circuit is affected by the phase angle and is given by

  $$P_{\text{ave}} = I_{\text{rms}} V_{\text{rms}} \cos\phi,$$

  $\cos\phi$ is called the power factor, which ranges from 0 to 1.

Conceptual Questions

23.1 Induced Emf and Magnetic Flux

1. How do the multiple-loop coils and iron ring in the version of Faraday's apparatus shown in Figure 23.3 enhance the observation of induced emf?

2. When a magnet is thrust into a coil as in Figure 23.4(a), what is the direction of the force exerted by

the coil on the magnet? Draw a diagram showing the direction of the current induced in the coil and the magnetic field it produces, to justify your response. How does the magnitude of the force depend on the resistance of the galvanometer?

3. Explain how magnetic flux can be zero when the magnetic field is not zero.

4. Is an emf induced in the coil in Figure 23.51 when it is stretched? If so, state why and give the direction of the induced current.

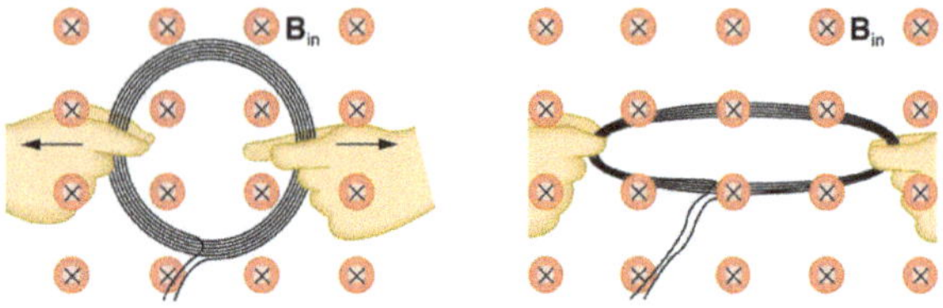

FIGURE 23.51 A circular coil of wire is stretched in a magnetic field.

23.2 Faraday's Law of Induction: Lenz's Law

5. A person who works with large magnets sometimes places her head inside a strong field. She reports feeling dizzy as she quickly turns her head. How might this be associated with induction?

6. A particle accelerator sends high-velocity charged particles down an evacuated pipe. Explain how a coil of wire wrapped around the pipe could detect the passage of individual particles. Sketch a graph of the voltage output of the coil as a single particle passes through it.

23.3 Motional Emf

7. Why must part of the circuit be moving relative to other parts, to have usable motional emf? Consider, for example, that the rails in Figure 23.10 are stationary relative to the magnetic field, while the rod moves.

8. A powerful induction cannon can be made by placing a metal cylinder inside a solenoid coil. The cylinder is forcefully expelled when solenoid current is turned on rapidly. Use Faraday's and Lenz's laws to explain how this works. Why might the cylinder get live/hot when the cannon is fired?

9. An induction stove heats a pot with a coil carrying an alternating current located beneath the pot (and without a hot surface). Can the stove surface be a conductor? Why won't a coil carrying a direct current work?

10. Explain how you could thaw out a frozen water pipe by wrapping a coil carrying an alternating current around it. Does it matter whether or not the pipe is a conductor? Explain.

23.4 Eddy Currents and Magnetic Damping

11. Explain why magnetic damping might not be effective on an object made of several thin conducting layers separated by insulation.

12. Explain how electromagnetic induction can be used to detect metals? This technique is particularly important in detecting buried landmines for disposal, geophysical prospecting and at airports.

23.5 Electric Generators

13. Using RHR-1, show that the emfs in the sides of the generator loop in Figure 23.22 are in the same sense and thus add.

14. The source of a generator's electrical energy output is the work done to turn its coils. How is the work needed to turn the generator related to Lenz's law?

23.6 Back Emf

15. Suppose you find that the belt drive connecting a powerful motor to an air conditioning unit is broken and the motor is running freely. Should you be worried that the motor is consuming a great deal of energy for no useful purpose? Explain why or why not.

23.7 Transformers

16. Explain what causes physical vibrations in transformers at twice the frequency of the AC power involved.

23.8 Electrical Safety: Systems and Devices

17. Does plastic insulation on live/hot wires prevent shock hazards, thermal hazards, or both?

18. Why are ordinary circuit breakers and fuses ineffective in preventing shocks?

19. A GFI may trip just because the live/hot and neutral wires connected to it are significantly different in length. Explain why.

23.9 Inductance

20. How would you place two identical flat coils in contact so that they had the greatest mutual inductance? The least?

21. How would you shape a given length of wire to

give it the greatest self-inductance? The least?

22. Verify, as was concluded without proof in Example 23.7, that units of $\mathrm{T} \cdot \mathrm{m}^2/A = \Omega \cdot \mathrm{s} = \mathrm{H}$.

23.11 Reactance, Inductive and Capacitive

23. Presbycusis is a hearing loss due to age that progressively affects higher frequencies. A hearing aid amplifier is designed to amplify all frequencies equally. To adjust its output for presbycusis, would you put a capacitor in series or parallel with the hearing aid's speaker? Explain.

24. Would you use a large inductance or a large capacitance in series with a system to filter out low frequencies, such as the 100 Hz hum in a sound system? Explain.

25. High-frequency noise in AC power can damage computers. Does the plug-in unit designed to prevent this damage use a large inductance or a large capacitance (in series with the computer) to filter out such high frequencies? Explain.

26. Does inductance depend on current, frequency, or both? What about inductive reactance?

27. Explain why the capacitor in Figure 23.52(a) acts as a low-frequency filter between the two circuits, whereas that in Figure 23.52(b) acts as a high-frequency filter.

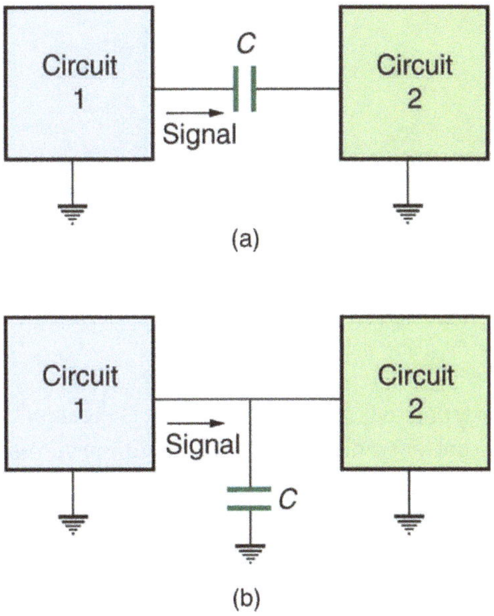

FIGURE 23.52 Capacitors and inductors. Capacitor with high frequency and low frequency.

28. If the capacitors in Figure 23.52 are replaced by inductors, which acts as a low-frequency filter and which as a high-frequency filter?

23.12 RLC Series AC Circuits

29. Does the resonant frequency of an AC circuit depend on the peak voltage of the AC source? Explain why or why not.

30. Suppose you have a motor with a power factor significantly less than 1. Explain why it would be better to improve the power factor as a method of improving the motor's output, rather than to increase the voltage input.

Problems & Exercises

23.1 Induced Emf and Magnetic Flux

1. What is the value of the magnetic flux at coil 2 in Figure 23.53 due to coil 1?

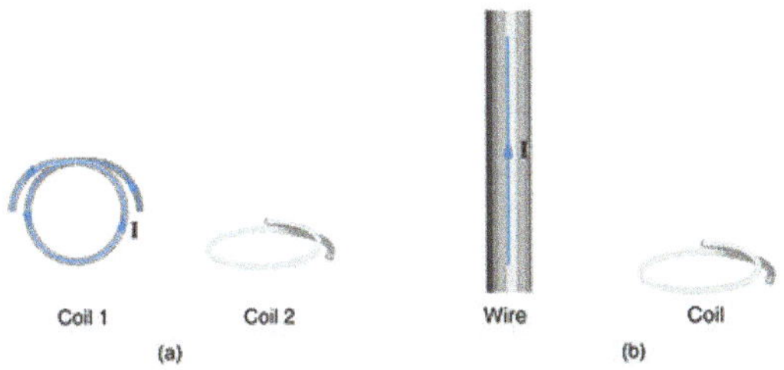

FIGURE 23.53 (a) The planes of the two coils are perpendicular. (b) The wire is perpendicular to the plane of the coil.

2. What is the value of the magnetic flux through the coil in Figure 23.53(b) due to the wire?

23.2 Faraday's Law of Induction: Lenz's Law

3. Referring to Figure 23.54(a), what is the direction of the current induced in coil 2: (a) If the current in coil 1 increases? (b) If the current in coil 1 decreases? (c) If the current in coil 1 is constant? Explicitly show how you follow the steps in the Problem-Solving Strategy for Lenz's Law.

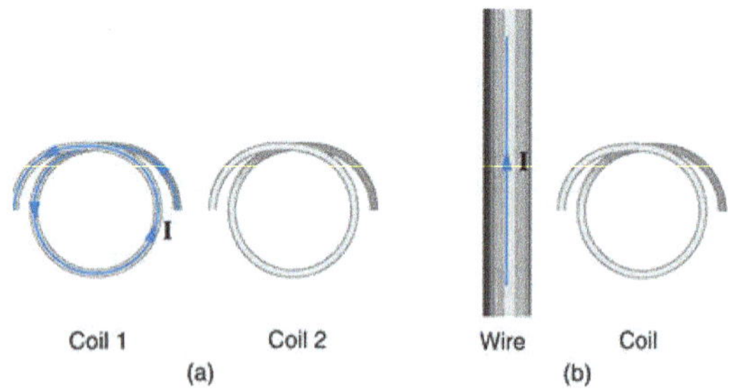

FIGURE 23.54 (a) The coils lie in the same plane. (b) The wire is in the plane of the coil

4. Referring to Figure 23.54(b), what is the direction of the current induced in the coil: (a) If the current in the wire increases? (b) If the current in the wire decreases? (c) If the current in the wire suddenly changes direction? Explicitly show how you follow the steps in the Problem-Solving Strategy for Lenz's Law.

5. Referring to Figure 23.55, what are the directions of the currents in coils 1, 2, and 3 (assume that the coils are lying in the plane of the circuit): (a) When the switch is first closed? (b) When the switch has been closed for a long time? (c) Just after the switch is opened?

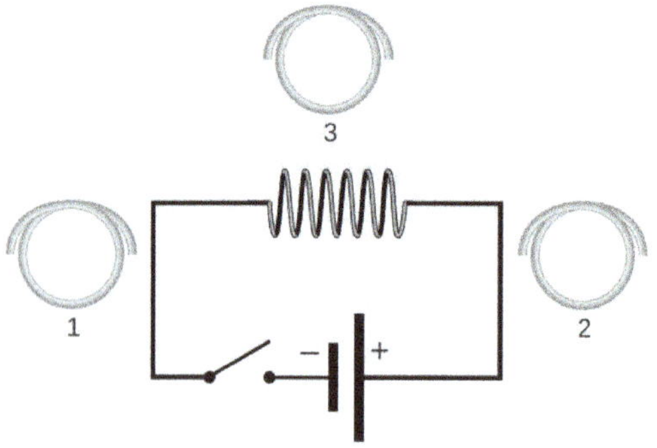

FIGURE 23.55

6. Repeat the previous problem with the battery reversed.

7. Verify that the units of $\Delta\Phi/\ \Delta t$ are volts. That is, show that $1\ \text{T}\cdot\text{m}^2/\text{s} = 1\ \text{V}$.

8. Suppose a 50-turn coil lies in the plane of the page in a uniform magnetic field that is directed into the page. The coil originally has an area of $0.250\ \text{m}^2$. It is stretched to have no area in 0.100 s. What is the direction and magnitude of the induced emf if the uniform magnetic field has a strength of 1.50 T?

9. (a) An MRI technician moves his hand from a region of very low magnetic field strength into an MRI scanner's 2.00 T field with his fingers pointing in the direction of the field. Find the average emf induced in his wedding ring, given its diameter is 2.20 cm and assuming it takes 0.250 s to move it into the field. (b) Discuss whether this current would significantly change the temperature of the ring.

10. Integrated Concepts
Referring to the situation in the previous problem: (a) What current is induced in the ring if its resistance is 0.0100 Ω? (b) What average power is dissipated? (c) What magnetic field is induced at the center of the ring? (d) What is the direction of the induced magnetic field relative to the MRI's field?

11. An emf is induced by rotating a 1000-turn, 20.0 cm diameter coil in the Earth's $5.00 \times 10^{-5}\ \text{T}$ magnetic field. What average emf is induced, given the plane of the coil is originally perpendicular to the Earth's field and is rotated to be parallel to the field in 10.0 ms?

12. A 0.250 m radius, 500-turn coil is rotated one-fourth of a revolution in 4.17 ms, originally having its plane perpendicular to a uniform magnetic field. (This is 60 rev/s.) Find the magnetic field strength needed to induce an average emf of 10,000 V.

13. Integrated Concepts
Approximately how does the emf induced in the loop in Figure 23.54(b) depend on the distance of the center of the loop from the wire?

14. Integrated Concepts
(a) A lightning bolt produces a rapidly varying magnetic field. If the bolt strikes the earth vertically and acts like a current in a long straight wire, it will induce a voltage in a loop aligned like that in Figure 23.54(b). What voltage is induced in a 1.00 m diameter loop 50.0 m from a $2.00 \times 10^6\ \text{A}$ lightning strike, if the current falls to zero in $25.0\ \mu\text{s}$? (b) Discuss circumstances under which such a voltage would produce noticeable consequences.

23.3 Motional Emf

15. Use Faraday's law, Lenz's law, and RHR-1 to show that the magnetic force on the current in the moving rod in Figure 23.10 is in the opposite direction of its velocity.

16. If a current flows in the Satellite Tether shown in Figure 23.11, use Faraday's law, Lenz's law, and RHR-1 to show that there is a magnetic force on the tether in the direction opposite to its velocity.

17. (a) A jet airplane with a 75.0 m wingspan is flying at 280 m/s. What emf is induced between wing tips if the vertical component of the Earth's field is 3.00×10^{-5} T? (b) Is an emf of this magnitude likely to have any consequences? Explain.

18. (a) A nonferrous screwdriver is being used in a 2.00 T magnetic field. What maximum emf can be induced along its 12.0 cm length when it moves at 6.00 m/s? (b) Is it likely that this emf will have any consequences or even be noticed?

19. At what speed must the sliding rod in Figure 23.10 move to produce an emf of 1.00 V in a 1.50 T field, given the rod's length is 30.0 cm?

20. The 12.0 cm long rod in Figure 23.10 moves at 4.00 m/s. What is the strength of the magnetic field if a 95.0 V emf is induced?

21. Prove that when $\mathbf{B}$, ℓ, and v are not mutually perpendicular, motional emf is given by $\text{emf} = B\ell v \sin\theta$. If v is perpendicular to $\mathbf{B}$, then θ is the angle between ℓ and $\mathbf{B}$. If ℓ is perpendicular to $\mathbf{B}$, then θ is the angle between v and $\mathbf{B}$.

22. In the August 1992 space shuttle flight, only 250 m of the conducting tether considered in Example 23.2 could be let out. A 40.0 V motional emf was generated in the Earth's 5.00×10^{-5} T field, while moving at 7.80×10^{3} m/s. What was the angle between the shuttle's velocity and the Earth's field, assuming the conductor was perpendicular to the field?

23. Integrated Concepts
Derive an expression for the current in a system like that in Figure 23.10, under the following conditions. The resistance between the rails is R, the rails and the moving rod are identical in cross section A and have the same resistivity ρ. The distance between the rails is l, and the rod moves at constant speed v perpendicular to the uniform field $\mathbf{B}$. At time zero, the moving rod is next to the resistance R.

24. Integrated Concepts
The Tethered Satellite in Figure 23.11 has a mass of 525 kg and is at the end of a 20.0 km long, 2.50 mm diameter cable with the tensile strength of steel. (a) How much does the cable stretch if a 100 N force is exerted to pull the satellite in? (Assume the satellite and shuttle are at the same altitude above the Earth.) (b) What is the effective force constant of the cable? (c) How much energy is stored in it when stretched by the 100 N force?

25. Integrated Concepts
The Tethered Satellite discussed in this module is producing 5.00 kV, and a current of 10.0 A flows. (a) What magnetic drag force does this produce if the system is moving at 7.80 km/s? (b) How much kinetic energy is removed from the system in 1.00 h, neglecting any change in altitude or velocity during that time? (c) What is the change in velocity if the mass of the system is 100,000 kg? (d) Discuss the long term consequences (say, a week-long mission) on the space shuttle's orbit, noting what effect a decrease in velocity has and assessing the magnitude of the effect.

23.4 Eddy Currents and Magnetic Damping

26. Make a drawing similar to Figure 23.13, but with the pendulum moving in the opposite direction. Then use Faraday's law, Lenz's law, and RHR-1 to show that magnetic force opposes motion.

27.

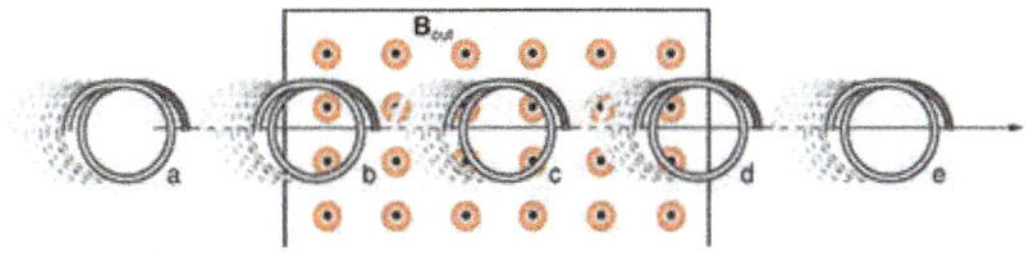

FIGURE 23.56 A coil is moved into and out of a region of uniform magnetic field.

A coil is moved through a magnetic field as shown in Figure 23.56. The field is uniform inside the rectangle and zero outside. What is the direction of the induced current and what is the direction of the magnetic force on the coil at each position shown?

23.5 Electric Generators

28. Calculate the peak voltage of a generator that rotates its 200-turn, 0.100 m diameter coil at 3600 rpm in a 0.800 T field.

29. At what angular velocity in rpm will the peak voltage of a generator be 480 V, if its 500-turn, 8.00 cm diameter coil rotates in a 0.250 T field?

30. What is the peak emf generated by rotating a 1000-turn, 20.0 cm diameter coil in the Earth's 5.00×10^{-5} T magnetic field, given the plane of the coil is originally perpendicular to the Earth's field and is rotated to be parallel to the field in 10.0 ms?

31. What is the peak emf generated by a 0.250 m radius, 500-turn coil is rotated one-fourth of a revolution in 4.17 ms, originally having its plane perpendicular to a uniform magnetic field. (This is 60 rev/s.)

32. (a) A bicycle generator rotates at 1875 rad/s, producing an 18.0 V peak emf. It has a 1.00 by 3.00 cm rectangular coil in a 0.640 T field. How many turns are in the coil? (b) Is this number of turns of wire practical for a 1.00 by 3.00 cm coil?

33. Integrated Concepts
This problem refers to the bicycle generator considered in the previous problem. It is driven by a 1.60 cm diameter wheel that rolls on the outside rim of the bicycle tire. (a) What is the velocity of the bicycle if the generator's angular velocity is 1875 rad/s? (b) What is the maximum emf of the generator when the bicycle moves at 10.0 m/s, noting that it was 18.0 V under the original conditions? (c) If the sophisticated generator can vary its own magnetic field, what field strength will it need at 5.00 m/s to produce a 9.00 V maximum emf?

34. (a) A car generator turns at 400 rpm when the engine is idling. Its 300-turn, 5.00 by 8.00 cm rectangular coil rotates in an adjustable magnetic field so that it can produce sufficient voltage even at low rpms. What is the field strength needed to produce a 24.0 V peak emf? (b) Discuss how this required field strength compares to those available in permanent and electromagnets.

35. Show that if a coil rotates at an angular velocity ω, the period of its AC output is $2\pi/\omega$.

36. A 75-turn, 10.0 cm diameter coil rotates at an angular velocity of 8.00 rad/s in a 1.25 T field, starting with the plane of the coil parallel to the field. (a) What is the peak emf? (b) At what time is the peak emf first reached? (c) At what time is the emf first at its most negative? (d) What is the period of the AC voltage output?

37. (a) If the emf of a coil rotating in a magnetic field is zero at $t = 0$, and increases to its first peak at $t = 0.100\text{ ms}$, what is the angular velocity of the coil? (b) At what time will its next maximum occur? (c) What is the period of the output? (d) When is the output first one-fourth of its maximum? (e) When is it next one-fourth of its maximum?

38. Unreasonable Results
A 500-turn coil with a 0.250 m^2 area is spun in the Earth's $5.00\times10^{-5}\text{ T}$ field, producing a 12.0 kV maximum emf. (a) At what angular velocity must the coil be spun? (b) What is unreasonable about this result? (c) Which assumption or premise is responsible?

23.6 Back Emf

39. Suppose a motor connected to a 120 V source draws 10.0 A when it first starts. (a) What is its resistance? (b) What current does it draw at its normal operating speed when it develops a 100 V back emf?

40. A motor operating on 240 V electricity has a 180 V back emf at operating speed and draws a 12.0 A current. (a) What is its resistance? (b) What current does it draw when it is first started?

41. What is the back emf of a 120 V motor that draws 8.00 A at its normal speed and 20.0 A when first starting?

42. The motor in a toy car operates on 6.00 V, developing a 4.50 V back emf at normal speed. If it draws 3.00 A at normal speed, what current does it draw when starting?

43. Integrated Concepts
The motor in a toy car is powered by four batteries in series, which produce a total emf of 6.00 V. The motor draws 3.00 A and develops a 4.50 V back emf at normal speed. Each battery has a $0.100\ \Omega$ internal resistance. What is the resistance of the motor?

23.7 Transformers

44. A plug-in transformer, like that in Figure 23.25, supplies 9.00 V to a video game system. (a) How many turns are in its secondary coil, if its input voltage is 120 V and the primary coil has 400 turns? (b) What is its input current when its output is 1.30 A?

45. An American traveler in New Zealand carries a transformer to convert New Zealand's standard 240 V to 120 V so that she can use some small appliances on her trip. (a) What is the ratio of turns in the primary and secondary coils of her transformer? (b) What is the ratio of input to output current? (c) How could a New Zealander traveling in the United States use this same transformer to power her 240 V appliances from 120 V?

46. A cassette recorder uses a plug-in transformer to convert 120 V to 12.0 V, with a maximum current output of 200 mA. (a) What is the current input? (b) What is the power input? (c) Is this amount of power reasonable for a small appliance?

47. (a) What is the voltage output of a transformer used for rechargeable flashlight batteries, if its primary has 500 turns, its secondary 4 turns, and the input voltage is 120 V? (b) What input current is required to produce a 4.00 A output? (c) What is the power input?

48. (a) The plug-in transformer for a laptop computer puts out 7.50 V and can supply a maximum current of 2.00 A. What is the maximum input current if the input voltage is 240 V? Assume 100% efficiency. (b) If the actual efficiency is less than 100%, would the input current need to be greater or smaller? Explain.

49. A multipurpose transformer has a secondary coil with several points at which a voltage can be extracted, giving outputs of 5.60, 12.0, and 480 V. (a) The input voltage is 240 V to a primary coil of 280 turns. What are the numbers of turns in the parts of the secondary used to produce the output voltages? (b) If the maximum input current is 5.00 A, what are the maximum output currents (each used alone)?

50. A large power plant generates electricity at 12.0 kV. Its old transformer once converted the voltage to 335 kV. The secondary of this transformer is being replaced so that its output can be 750 kV for more efficient cross-country transmission on upgraded transmission lines. (a) What is the ratio of turns in the new secondary compared with the old secondary? (b) What is the ratio of new current output to old output (at 335 kV) for the same power? (c) If the upgraded transmission lines have the same resistance, what is the ratio of new line power loss to old?

51. If the power output in the previous problem is 1000 MW and line resistance is $2.00\ \Omega$, what were the old and new line losses?

52. Unreasonable Results
The 335 kV AC electricity from a power transmission line is fed into the primary coil of a transformer. The ratio of the number of turns in the secondary to the number in the primary is $N_s/N_p = 1000$. (a) What voltage is induced in the secondary? (b) What is unreasonable about this result? (c) Which assumption or premise is responsible?

53. Construct Your Own Problem
Consider a double transformer to be used to create very large voltages. The device consists of two stages. The first is a transformer that produces a much larger output voltage than its input. The output of the first transformer is used as input to a second transformer that further increases the voltage. Construct a problem in which you calculate the output voltage of the final stage based on the input voltage of the first stage and the number of turns or loops in both parts of both transformers (four coils in all). Also calculate the maximum output current of the final stage based on the input current. Discuss the possibility of power losses in the devices and the effect on the output current and power.

23.8 Electrical Safety: Systems and Devices

54. Integrated Concepts
A short circuit to the grounded metal case of an appliance occurs as shown in Figure 23.57. The person touching the case is wet and only has a $3.00\ \text{k}\Omega$ resistance to earth/ground. (a) What is the voltage on the case if 5.00 mA flows through the person? (b) What is the current in the short circuit if the resistance of the earth/ground wire is $0.200\ \Omega$? (c) Will this trigger the 20.0 A circuit breaker supplying the appliance?

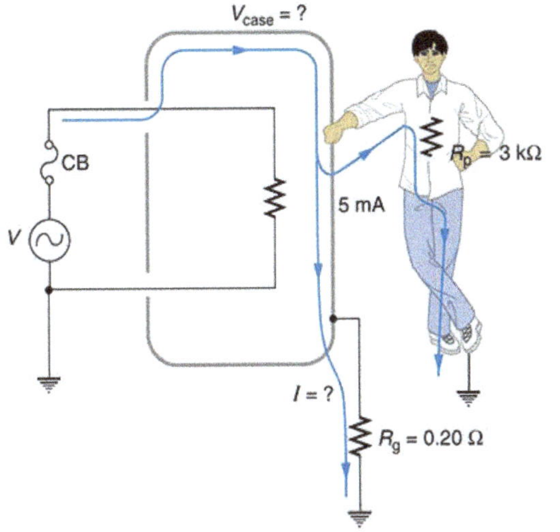

FIGURE 23.57 A person can be shocked even when the case of an appliance is grounded. The large short circuit current produces a voltage on the case of the appliance, since the resistance of the earth/ground wire is not zero.

23.9 Inductance

55. Two coils are placed close together in a physics lab to demonstrate Faraday's law of induction. A current of 5.00 A in one is switched off in 1.00 ms, inducing a 9.00 V emf in the other. What is their mutual inductance?

56. If two coils placed next to one another have a mutual inductance of 5.00 mH, what voltage is induced in one when the 2.00 A current in the other is switched off in 30.0 ms?

57. The 4.00 A current through a 7.50 mH inductor is switched off in 8.33 ms. What is the emf induced opposing this?

58. A device is turned on and 3.00 A flows through it 0.100 ms later. What is the self-inductance of the device if an induced 150 V emf opposes this?

59. Starting with $\text{emf}_2 = -M\frac{\Delta I_1}{\Delta t}$, show that the units of inductance are $(\text{V}\cdot\text{s})/\text{A} = \Omega\cdot\text{s}$.

60. Camera flashes charge a capacitor to high voltage by switching the current through an inductor on and off rapidly. In what time must the 0.100 A current through a 2.00 mH inductor be switched on or off to induce a 500 V emf?

61. A large research solenoid has a self-inductance of 25.0 H. (a) What induced emf opposes shutting it off when 100 A of current through it is switched off in 80.0 ms? (b) How much energy is stored in the inductor at full current? (c) At what rate in watts must energy be dissipated to switch the current off in 80.0 ms? (d) In view of the answer to the last part, is it surprising that shutting it down this quickly is difficult?

62. (a) Calculate the self-inductance of a 50.0 cm long, 10.0 cm diameter solenoid having 1000 loops. (b) How much energy is stored in this inductor when 20.0 A of current flows through it? (c) How fast can it be turned off if the induced emf cannot exceed 3.00 V?

63. A precision laboratory resistor is made of a coil of wire 1.50 cm in diameter and 4.00 cm long, and it has 500 turns. (a) What is its self-inductance? (b) What average emf is induced if the 12.0 A current through it is turned on in 5.00 ms (one-fourth of a cycle for 50 Hz AC)? (c) What is its inductance if it is shortened to half its length and counter-wound (two layers of 250 turns in opposite directions)?

64. The heating coils in a hair dryer are 0.800 cm in diameter, have a combined length of 1.00 m, and a total of 400 turns. (a) What is their total self-inductance assuming they act like a single solenoid? (b) How much energy is stored in them when 6.00 A flows? (c) What average emf opposes shutting them off if this is done in 5.00 ms (one-fourth of a cycle for 50 Hz AC)?

65. When the 20.0 A current through an inductor is turned off in 1.50 ms, an 800 V emf is induced, opposing the change. What is the value of the self-inductance?

66. How fast can the 150 A current through a 0.250 H inductor be shut off if the induced emf cannot exceed 75.0 V?

67. Integrated Concepts
A very large, superconducting solenoid such as one used in MRI scans, stores 1.00 MJ of energy in its magnetic field when 100 A flows. (a) Find its self-inductance. (b) If the coils "go normal," they gain resistance and start to dissipate thermal energy. What temperature increase is produced if all the stored energy goes into heating the 1000 kg magnet, given its average specific heat is $200\ \text{J/kg}\cdot\text{°C}$?

68. Unreasonable Results
A 25.0 H inductor has 100 A of current turned off in 1.00 ms. (a) What voltage is induced to oppose this? (b) What is unreasonable about this result? (c) Which assumption or premise is responsible?

23.10 RL Circuits

69. If you want a characteristic *RL* time constant of 1.00 s, and you have a $500\ \Omega$ resistor, what value of self-inductance is needed?

70. Your *RL* circuit has a characteristic time constant of 20.0 ns, and a resistance of $5.00\ \text{M}\Omega$. (a) What is the inductance of the circuit? (b) What resistance would give you a 1.00 ns time constant, perhaps needed for quick response in an oscilloscope?

71. A large superconducting magnet, used for magnetic resonance imaging, has a 50.0 H inductance. If you want current through it to be adjustable with a 1.00 s characteristic time constant, what is the minimum resistance of system?

72. Verify that after a time of 10.0 ms, the current for the situation considered in Example 23.9 will be 0.183 A as stated.

73. Suppose you have a supply of inductors ranging from 1.00 nH to 10.0 H, and resistors ranging from $0.100\ \Omega$ to $1.00\ \text{M}\Omega$. What is the range of characteristic *RL* time constants you can produce by connecting a single resistor to a single inductor?

74. (a) What is the characteristic time constant of a 25.0 mH inductor that has a resistance of $4.00\ \Omega$? (b) If it is connected to a 12.0 V battery, what is the current after 12.5 ms?

75. What percentage of the final current I_0 flows

through an inductor L in series with a resistor R, three time constants after the circuit is completed?

76. The 5.00 A current through a 1.50 H inductor is dissipated by a $2.00\ \Omega$ resistor in a circuit like that in Figure 23.42 with the switch in position 2. (a) What is the initial energy in the inductor? (b) How long will it take the current to decline to 5.00% of its initial value? (c) Calculate the average power dissipated, and compare it with the initial power dissipated by the resistor.

77. (a) Use the exact exponential treatment to find how much time is required to bring the current through an 80.0 mH inductor in series with a $15.0\ \Omega$ resistor to 99.0% of its final value, starting from zero. (b) Compare your answer to the approximate treatment using integral numbers of τ. (c) Discuss how significant the difference is.

78. (a) Using the exact exponential treatment, find the time required for the current through a 2.00 H inductor in series with a $0.500\ \Omega$ resistor to be reduced to 0.100% of its original value. (b) Compare your answer to the approximate treatment using integral numbers of τ. (c) Discuss how significant the difference is.

23.11 Reactance, Inductive and Capacitive

79. At what frequency will a 30.0 mH inductor have a reactance of $100\ \Omega$?

80. What value of inductance should be used if a $20.0\ \text{k}\Omega$ reactance is needed at a frequency of 500 Hz?

81. What capacitance should be used to produce a $2.00\ \text{M}\Omega$ reactance at 60.0 Hz?

82. At what frequency will an 80.0 mF capacitor have a reactance of $0.250\ \Omega$?

83. (a) Find the current through a 0.500 H inductor connected to a 60.0 Hz, 480 V AC source. (b) What would the current be at 100 kHz?

84. (a) What current flows when a 60.0 Hz, 480 V AC source is connected to a $0.250\ \mu\text{F}$ capacitor? (b) What would the current be at 25.0 kHz?

85. A 20.0 kHz, 16.0 V source connected to an inductor produces a 2.00 A current. What is the inductance?

86. A 20.0 Hz, 16.0 V source produces a 2.00 mA current when connected to a capacitor. What is the capacitance?

87. (a) An inductor designed to filter high-frequency noise from power supplied to a personal computer is placed in series with the computer. What minimum inductance should it have to produce a $2.00\ \text{k}\Omega$ reactance for 15.0 kHz noise? (b) What is its reactance at 60.0 Hz?

88. The capacitor in Figure 23.52(a) is designed to filter low-frequency signals, impeding their transmission between circuits. (a) What capacitance is needed to produce a $100\ \text{k}\Omega$ reactance at a frequency of 120 Hz? (b) What would its reactance be at 1.00 MHz? (c) Discuss the implications of your answers to (a) and (b).

89. The capacitor in Figure 23.52(b) will filter high-frequency signals by shorting them to earth/ground. (a) What capacitance is needed to produce a reactance of $10.0\ \text{m}\Omega$ for a 5.00 kHz signal? (b) What would its reactance be at 3.00 Hz? (c) Discuss the implications of your answers to (a) and (b).

90. Unreasonable Results
In a recording of voltages due to brain activity (an EEG), a 10.0 mV signal with a 0.500 Hz frequency is applied to a capacitor, producing a current of 100 mA. Resistance is negligible. (a) What is the capacitance? (b) What is unreasonable about this result? (c) Which assumption or premise is responsible?

91. Construct Your Own Problem
Consider the use of an inductor in series with a computer operating on 60 Hz electricity. Construct a problem in which you calculate the relative reduction in voltage of incoming high frequency noise compared to 60 Hz voltage. Among the things to consider are the acceptable series reactance of the inductor for 60 Hz power and the likely frequencies of noise coming through the power lines.

23.12 RLC Series AC Circuits

92. An *RL* circuit consists of a $40.0\ \Omega$ resistor and a 3.00 mH inductor. (a) Find its impedance Z at 60.0 Hz and 10.0 kHz. (b) Compare these values of Z with those found in Example 23.12 in which there was also a capacitor.

93. An *RC* circuit consists of a $40.0\ \Omega$ resistor and a $5.00\ \mu\text{F}$ capacitor. (a) Find its impedance at 60.0 Hz and 10.0 kHz. (b) Compare these values of Z with those found in Example 23.12, in which there was also an inductor.

94. An *LC* circuit consists of a $3.00\ \text{mH}$ inductor and a $5.00\ \mu F$ capacitor. (a) Find its impedance at 60.0 Hz and 10.0 kHz. (b) Compare these values of Z with those found in Example 23.12 in which there was also a resistor.

95. What is the resonant frequency of a 0.500 mH inductor connected to a $40.0\ \mu\text{F}$ capacitor?

96. To receive AM radio, you want an *RLC* circuit that can be made to resonate at any frequency between 500 and 1650 kHz. This is accomplished with a fixed $1.00\ \mu\text{H}$ inductor connected to a variable capacitor. What range of capacitance is needed?

97. Suppose you have a supply of inductors ranging from 1.00 nH to 10.0 H, and capacitors ranging from 1.00 pF to 0.100 F. What is the range of resonant frequencies that can be achieved from combinations of a single inductor and a single capacitor?

98. What capacitance do you need to produce a resonant frequency of 1.00 GHz, when using an 8.00 nH inductor?

99. What inductance do you need to produce a resonant frequency of 60.0 Hz, when using a $2.00\ \mu\text{F}$ capacitor?

100. The lowest frequency in the FM radio band is 88.0 MHz. (a) What inductance is needed to produce this resonant frequency if it is connected to a 2.50 pF capacitor? (b) The capacitor is variable, to allow the resonant frequency to be adjusted to as high as 108 MHz. What must the capacitance be at this frequency?

101. An *RLC* series circuit has a $2.50\ \Omega$ resistor, a $100\ \mu\text{H}$ inductor, and an $80.0\ \mu\text{F}$ capacitor.(a) Find the circuit's impedance at 120 Hz. (b) Find the circuit's impedance at 5.00 kHz. (c) If the voltage source has $V_{\text{rms}} = 5.60\ \text{V}$, what is I_{rms} at each frequency? (d) What is the resonant frequency of the circuit? (e) What is I_{rms} at resonance?

102. An *RLC* series circuit has a $1.00\ \text{k}\Omega$ resistor, a $150\ \mu\text{H}$ inductor, and a 25.0 nF capacitor. (a) Find the circuit's impedance at 500 Hz. (b) Find the circuit's impedance at 7.50 kHz. (c) If the voltage source has $V_{\text{rms}} = 408\ \text{V}$, what is I_{rms} at each frequency? (d) What is the resonant frequency of the circuit? (e) What is I_{rms} at resonance?

103. An *RLC* series circuit has a $2.50\ \Omega$ resistor, a $100\ \mu\text{H}$ inductor, and an $80.0\ \mu\text{F}$ capacitor. (a) Find the power factor at $f = 120\ \text{Hz}$. (b) What is the phase angle at 120 Hz? (c) What is the average power at 120 Hz? (d) Find the average power at the circuit's resonant frequency.

104. An *RLC* series circuit has a $1.00\ \text{k}\Omega$ resistor, a $150\ \mu\text{H}$ inductor, and a 25.0 nF capacitor. (a) Find the power factor at $f = 7.50\ \text{Hz}$. (b) What is the phase angle at this frequency? (c) What is the average power at this frequency? (d) Find the average power at the circuit's resonant frequency.

105. An *RLC* series circuit has a $200\ \Omega$ resistor and a 25.0 mH inductor. At 8000 Hz, the phase angle is $45.0°$. (a) What is the impedance? (b) Find the circuit's capacitance. (c) If $V_{\text{rms}} = 408\ \text{V}$ is applied, what is the average power supplied?

106. Referring to Example 23.14, find the average power at 10.0 kHz.

107. Critical Thinking A length of 4.000 m of wire is to be used to detect a magnetic field. The wire is made into a single square loop and rotated at a rate of 400 cycles per second. (a) If the magnetic field is 0.02000 T, what is the magnitude of the average emf that can be generated in the first quarter cycle, provided the loop is initially oriented in a plane perpendicular to the magnetic field? (b) Is there a difference in the magnitude of the average emf generated if the wire is made into two square loops and rotated at the same rate, starting with the same orientation of the loops as that of the loop in part a? If so, what is the average emf possible for the first quarter cycle for two loops being rotated at 400 cycles per second in the magnetic field? (c) If the wire is made into a figure eight, what is the average emf for the first quarter cycle that can be generated by rotating it at 400 cycles per second in the magnetic field, again starting with the same orientation of the oops with respect to the magnetic field? The wire crosses itself in this arrangement. (d) Does the shape of the loop matter?

Test Prep for AP® Courses

23.1 Induced Emf and Magnetic Flux

1. To produce current with a coil and bar magnet you can:

a. move the coil but not the magnet.
b. move the magnet but not the coil.
c. move either the coil or the magnet.
d. It is not possible to produce current.

2. Calculate the magnetic flux for a coil of area 0.2 m^2 placed at an angle of θ=60° (as shown in the figure above) to a magnetic field of strength 1.5×10^{-3} T. At what angle will the flux be at its maximum?

23.5 Electric Generators

3. The emf induced in a coil that is rotating in a magnetic field will be at a maximum when

a. the magnetic flux is at a maximum.
b. the magnetic flux is at a minimum.
c. the change in magnetic flux is at a maximum.
d. the change in magnetic flux is at a minimum.

4. A coil with circular cross section and 20 turns is rotating at a rate of 400 rpm between the poles of a magnet. If the magnetic field strength is 0.6 T and peak voltage is 0.2 V, what is the radius of the coil? If the emf of the coil is zero at t = 0 s, when will it reach its peak emf?

23.7 Transformers

5. Which of the following statements is true for a step-down transformer? Select *two* answers.

a. Primary voltage is higher than secondary voltage.
b. Primary voltage is lower than secondary voltage.
c. Primary current is higher than secondary current.
d. Primary current is lower than secondary current.

6. An ideal step-up transformer with turn ratio 1:30 is supplied with an input power of 120 W. If the output voltage is 210 V, calculate the output power and input current.

23.8 Electrical Safety: Systems and Devices

7. Which of the following statements is true for an isolation transformer?

a. It has more primary turns than secondary turns.
b. It has fewer primary turns than secondary turns.
c. It has an equal number of primary and secondary turns.
d. It can have more, fewer, or an equal number of primary and secondary turns.

8. Explain the working of a ground fault interrupter (GFI).

CHAPTER 24
Electromagnetic Waves

FIGURE 24.1 Human eyes detect these orange "sea goldie" fish swimming over a coral reef in the blue waters of the Gulf of Eilat (Red Sea) using visible light. (credit: Daviddarom, Wikimedia Commons)

CHAPTER OUTLINE

CONNECTION FOR AP® COURSES Electromagnetic waves are all around us. The beauty of a coral reef, the warmth of sunshine, sunburn, an X-ray image revealing a broken bone, even microwave popcorn—all involve **electromagnetic waves**. The list of the various types of electromagnetic waves, ranging from radio transmission waves to nuclear gamma-rays (γ-rays), is interesting in itself. Even more intriguing is that all of these widely varied phenomena are different manifestations of the same thing—electromagnetic waves. (See Figure 24.2.)

What are electromagnetic waves? How are they created, and how do they travel? How can we understand and conceptualize their widely varying properties? What is their relationship to electric and magnetic effects? These and other questions will be explored in this chapter.

Electromagnetic waves support Big Idea 6 that waves can transport energy and momentum. In general, electromagnetic waves behave like any other wave, as they are traveling disturbances (Enduring Understanding 6.A). They consist of oscillating electric and magnetic fields, which can be conceived of as transverse waves (Essential Knowledge 6.A.1). They are periodic and can be described by their amplitude, frequency, wavelength, speed, and energy (Enduring Understanding 6.B).

Simple waves can be modeled mathematically using sine or cosine functions involving the wavelength, amplitude, and frequency of the wave. (Essential Knowledge 6.B.3). However, electromagnetic waves also have some unique properties compared to other waves. They can travel through both matter and a vacuum (Essential Knowledge 6.F.2), unlike mechanical waves, including sound, that require a medium (Essential Knowledge 6.A.2).

Maxwell's equations define the relationship between electric permittivity, the magnetic permeability of free space (vacuum), and the speed of light, which is the speed of propagation of all electromagnetic waves in a vacuum. This chapter uses the properties electric permittivity (Essential Knowledge 1.E.4) and magnetic permeability (Essential Knowledge 1.E.5) to support Big Idea 1 that objects and systems have certain properties and may have internal structure.

The particular properties mentioned are the macroscopic results of the atomic and molecular structure of materials (Enduring Understanding 1.E). Electromagnetic radiation can be modeled as a wave or as fundamental particles (Enduring Understanding 6.F). This chapter also introduces different types of electromagnetic radiation that are characterized by their wavelengths (Essential Knowledge 6.F.1) and have been given specific names (see Figure 24.2).

Big Idea 1 Objects and systems have properties such as mass and charge. Systems may have internal structure.

Enduring Understanding 1.E Materials have many macroscopic properties that result from the arrangement and interactions of the atoms and molecules that make up the material.

Essential Knowledge 1.E.4 Matter has a property called electric permittivity.

Essential Knowledge 1.E.5 Matter has a property called magnetic permeability.

Big Idea 6. Waves can transfer energy and momentum from one location to another without the permanent transfer of mass and serve as a mathematical model for the description of other phenomena.

Enduring Understanding 6.A A wave is a traveling disturbance that transfers energy and momentum.

Essential Knowledge 6.A.1 Waves can propagate via different oscillation modes such as transverse and longitudinal.

Essential Knowledge 6.A.2 For propagation, mechanical waves require a medium, while electromagnetic waves do not require a physical medium. Examples include light traveling through a vacuum and sound not traveling through a vacuum.

Enduring Understanding 6.B A periodic wave is one that repeats as a function of both time and position and can be described by its amplitude, frequency, wavelength, speed, and energy.

Essential Knowledge 6.B.3 A simple wave can be described by an equation involving one sine or cosine function involving the wavelength, amplitude, and frequency of the wave.

Enduring Understanding 6.F Electromagnetic radiation can be modeled as waves or as fundamental particles.

Essential Knowledge 6.F.1 Types of electromagnetic radiation are characterized by their wavelengths, and certain ranges of wavelength have been given specific names. These include (in order of increasing wavelength spanning a range from picometers to kilometers) gamma rays, x-rays, ultraviolet, visible light, infrared, microwaves, and radio waves.

Essential Knowledge 6.F.2 Electromagnetic waves can transmit energy through a medium and through a vacuum.

MISCONCEPTION ALERT: SOUND WAVES VS. RADIO WAVES

Many people confuse sound waves with **radio waves**, one type of electromagnetic (EM) wave. However, sound and radio waves are completely different phenomena. Sound creates pressure variations (waves) in matter, such as air or water, or your eardrum. Conversely, radio waves are *electromagnetic waves*, like visible light, infrared, ultraviolet, X-rays, and gamma rays. EM waves don't need a medium in which to propagate; they can travel through a vacuum, such as outer space.

A radio works because sound waves played by the D.J. at the radio station are converted into electromagnetic waves, then encoded and transmitted in the radio-frequency range. The radio in your car receives the radio waves, decodes the information, and uses a speaker to change it back into a sound wave, bringing sweet music to your ears.

Discovering a New Phenomenon

It is worth noting at the outset that the general phenomenon of electromagnetic waves was predicted by theory before it was realized that light is a form of electromagnetic wave. The prediction was made by James Clerk Maxwell in the mid-19th century when he formulated a single theory combining all the electric and magnetic effects known by scientists at that time. "Electromagnetic waves" was the name he gave to the phenomena his theory predicted.

Such a theoretical prediction followed by experimental verification is an indication of the power of science in general, and physics in particular. The underlying connections and unity of physics allow certain great minds to solve puzzles without having all the pieces. The prediction of electromagnetic waves is one of the most spectacular examples of this power. Certain others, such as the prediction of antimatter, will be discussed in later modules.

FIGURE 24.2 The electromagnetic waves sent and received by this 50-foot radar dish antenna at Kennedy Space Center in Florida are not visible, but help track expendable launch vehicles with high-definition imagery. The first use of this C-band radar dish was for the launch of the Atlas V rocket sending the New Horizons probe toward Pluto. (credit: NASA)

24.1 Maxwell's Equations: Electromagnetic Waves Predicted and Observed

LEARNING OBJECTIVES

By the end of this section, you will be able to:

- Restate Maxwell's equations.

The Scotsman James Clerk Maxwell (1831–1879) is regarded as the greatest theoretical physicist of the 19th century. (See Figure 24.3.) Although he died young, Maxwell not only formulated a complete electromagnetic theory, represented by **Maxwell's equations**, he also developed the kinetic theory of gases and made significant contributions to the understanding of color vision and the nature of Saturn's rings.

FIGURE 24.3 James Clerk Maxwell, a 19th-century physicist, developed a theory that explained the relationship between electricity and magnetism and correctly predicted that visible light is caused by electromagnetic waves. (credit: G. J. Stodart)

Maxwell brought together all the work that had been done by brilliant physicists such as Oersted, Coulomb, Gauss, and Faraday, and added his own insights to develop the overarching theory of electromagnetism. Maxwell's equations are paraphrased here in words because their mathematical statement is beyond the level of this text. However, the equations illustrate how apparently simple mathematical statements can elegantly unite and express a multitude of concepts—why mathematics is the language of science.

MAXWELL'S EQUATIONS

1. **Electric field lines** originate on positive charges and terminate on negative charges. The electric field is defined as the force per unit charge on a test charge, and the strength of the force is related to the electric constant ε_0, also known as the permittivity of free space. From Maxwell's first equation we obtain a special form of Coulomb's law known as Gauss's law for electricity.
2. **Magnetic field lines** are continuous, having no beginning or end. No magnetic monopoles are known to exist. The strength of the magnetic force is related to the magnetic constant μ_0, also known as the permeability of free space. This second of Maxwell's equations is known as Gauss's law for magnetism.
3. A changing magnetic field induces an electromotive force (emf) and, hence, an electric field. The direction of the emf opposes the change. This third of Maxwell's equations is Faraday's law of induction, and includes Lenz's law.
4. Magnetic fields are generated by moving charges or by changing electric fields. This fourth of Maxwell's equations encompasses Ampere's law and adds another source of magnetism—changing electric fields.

Maxwell's equations encompass the major laws of electricity and magnetism. What is not so apparent is the symmetry that Maxwell introduced in his mathematical framework. Especially important is his addition of the hypothesis that changing electric fields create magnetic fields. This is exactly analogous (and symmetric) to Faraday's law of induction and had been suspected for some time, but fits beautifully into Maxwell's equations.

Symmetry is apparent in nature in a wide range of situations. In contemporary research, symmetry plays a major part in the search for sub-atomic particles using massive multinational particle accelerators such as the new Large Hadron Collider at CERN.

MAKING CONNECTIONS: UNIFICATION OF FORCES

Maxwell's complete and symmetric theory showed that electric and magnetic forces are not separate, but different manifestations of the same thing—the electromagnetic force. This classical unification of forces is one motivation for current attempts to unify the four basic forces in nature—the gravitational, electrical, strong, and weak nuclear forces.

Since changing electric fields create relatively weak magnetic fields, they could not be easily detected at the time of

Maxwell's hypothesis. Maxwell realized, however, that oscillating charges, like those in AC circuits, produce changing electric fields. He predicted that these changing fields would propagate from the source like waves generated on a lake by a jumping fish.

The waves predicted by Maxwell would consist of oscillating electric and magnetic fields—defined to be an electromagnetic wave (EM wave). Electromagnetic waves would be capable of exerting forces on charges great distances from their source, and they might thus be detectable. Maxwell calculated that electromagnetic waves would propagate at a speed given by the equation

$$c = \frac{1}{\sqrt{\mu_0 \varepsilon_0}}. \qquad 24.1$$

When the values for μ_0 and ε_0 are entered into the equation for c, we find that

$$c = \frac{1}{\sqrt{(8.85 \times 10^{-12} \frac{\text{C}^2}{\text{N}\cdot\text{m}^2})(4\pi \times 10^{-7} \frac{\text{T}\cdot\text{m}}{\text{A}})}} = 3.00 \times 10^8 \text{ m/s}, \qquad 24.2$$

which is the speed of light. In fact, Maxwell concluded that light is an electromagnetic wave having such wavelengths that it can be detected by the eye.

Other wavelengths should exist—it remained to be seen if they did. If so, Maxwell's theory and remarkable predictions would be verified, the greatest triumph of physics since Newton. Experimental verification came within a few years, but not before Maxwell's death.

Hertz's Observations

The German physicist Heinrich Hertz (1857–1894) was the first to generate and detect certain types of electromagnetic waves in the laboratory. Starting in 1887, he performed a series of experiments that not only confirmed the existence of electromagnetic waves, but also verified that they travel at the speed of light.

Hertz used an AC RLC (resistor-inductor-capacitor) circuit that resonates at a known frequency $f_0 = \frac{1}{2\pi\sqrt{LC}}$ and connected it to a loop of wire as shown in Figure 24.4. High voltages induced across the gap in the loop produced sparks that were visible evidence of the current in the circuit and that helped generate electromagnetic waves.

Across the laboratory, Hertz had another loop attached to another RLC circuit, which could be tuned (as the dial on a radio) to the same resonant frequency as the first and could, thus, be made to receive electromagnetic waves. This loop also had a gap across which sparks were generated, giving solid evidence that electromagnetic waves had been received.

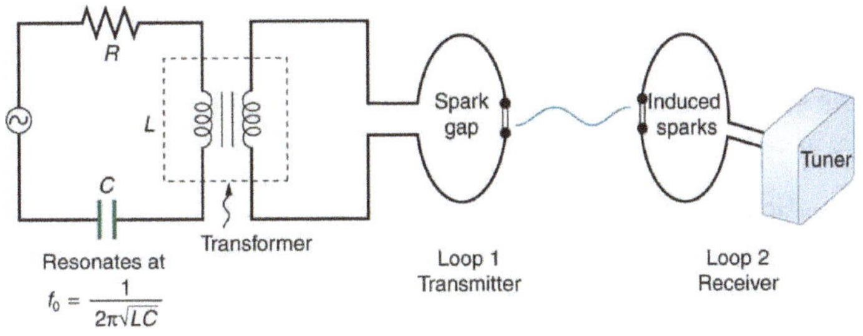

FIGURE 24.4 The apparatus used by Hertz in 1887 to generate and detect electromagnetic waves. An RLC circuit connected to the first loop caused sparks across a gap in the wire loop and generated electromagnetic waves. Sparks across a gap in the second loop located across the laboratory gave evidence that the waves had been received.

Hertz also studied the reflection, refraction, and interference patterns of the electromagnetic waves he generated, verifying their wave character. He was able to determine wavelength from the interference patterns, and knowing their frequency, he could calculate the propagation speed using the equation $v = f\lambda$ (velocity—or speed—equals frequency times wavelength). Hertz was thus able to prove that electromagnetic waves travel at the speed of light. The SI unit for frequency, the hertz ($1 \text{ Hz} = 1 \text{ cycle/s}$), is named in his honor.

24.2 Production of Electromagnetic Waves

LEARNING OBJECTIVES

By the end of this section, you will be able to:

- Describe the electric and magnetic waves as they move out from a source, such as an AC generator.
- Explain the mathematical relationship between the magnetic field strength and the electrical field strength.
- Calculate the maximum strength of the magnetic field in an electromagnetic wave, given the maximum electric field strength.

We can get a good understanding of **electromagnetic waves** (EM) by considering how they are produced. Whenever a current varies, associated electric and magnetic fields vary, moving out from the source like waves. Perhaps the easiest situation to visualize is a varying current in a long straight wire, produced by an AC generator at its center, as illustrated in Figure 24.5.

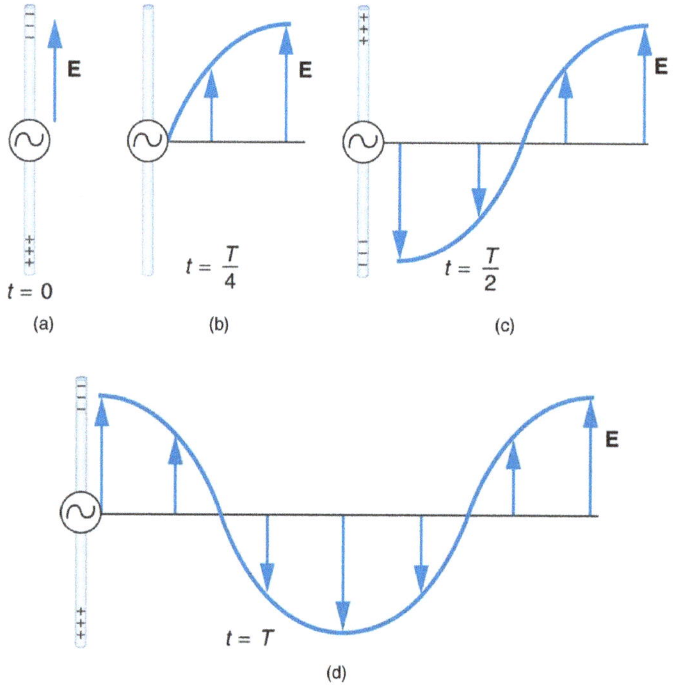

FIGURE 24.5 This long straight gray wire with an AC generator at its center becomes a broadcast antenna for electromagnetic waves. Shown here are the charge distributions at four different times. The electric field ($\mathbf{E}$) propagates away from the antenna at the speed of light, forming part of an electromagnetic wave.

The **electric field** ($\mathbf{E}$) shown surrounding the wire is produced by the charge distribution on the wire. Both the $\mathbf{E}$ and the charge distribution vary as the current changes. The changing field propagates outward at the speed of light.

There is an associated **magnetic field** ($\mathbf{B}$) which propagates outward as well (see Figure 24.6). The electric and magnetic fields are closely related and propagate as an electromagnetic wave. This is what happens in broadcast antennae such as those in radio and TV stations.

Closer examination of the one complete cycle shown in Figure 24.5 reveals the periodic nature of the generator-driven charges oscillating up and down in the antenna and the electric field produced. At time $t = 0$, there is the maximum separation of charge, with negative charges at the top and positive charges at the bottom, producing the maximum magnitude of the electric field (or E-field) in the upward direction. One-fourth of a cycle later, there is no charge separation and the field next to the antenna is zero, while the maximum E-field has moved away at speed c.

As the process continues, the charge separation reverses and the field reaches its maximum downward value, returns to zero, and rises to its maximum upward value at the end of one complete cycle. The outgoing wave has an **amplitude** proportional to the maximum separation of charge. Its **wavelength**(λ) is proportional to the period of the oscillation and, hence, is smaller for short periods or high frequencies. (As usual, wavelength and **frequency**(f) are inversely proportional.)

Electric and Magnetic Waves: Moving Together

Following Ampere's law, current in the antenna produces a magnetic field, as shown in Figure 24.6. The relationship between $\mathbf{E}$ and $\mathbf{B}$ is shown at one instant in Figure 24.6 (a). As the current varies, the magnetic field varies in magnitude and direction.

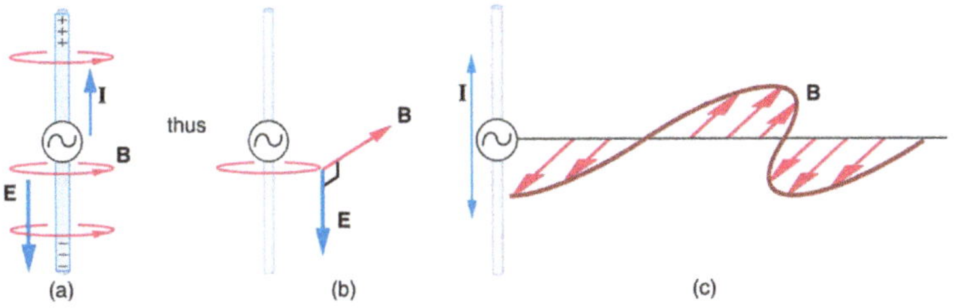

FIGURE 24.6 (a) The current in the antenna produces the circular magnetic field lines. The current ($\mathbf{I}$) produces the separation of charge along the wire, which in turn creates the electric field as shown. (b) The electric and magnetic fields ($\mathbf{E}$ and $\mathbf{B}$) near the wire are perpendicular; they are shown here for one point in space. (c) The magnetic field varies with current and propagates away from the antenna at the speed of light.

The magnetic field lines also propagate away from the antenna at the speed of light, forming the other part of the electromagnetic wave, as seen in Figure 24.6 (b). The magnetic part of the wave has the same period and wavelength as the electric part, since they are both produced by the same movement and separation of charges in the antenna.

The electric and magnetic waves are shown together at one instant in time in Figure 24.7. The electric and magnetic fields produced by a long straight wire antenna are exactly in phase. Note that they are perpendicular to one another and to the direction of propagation, making this a **transverse wave**.

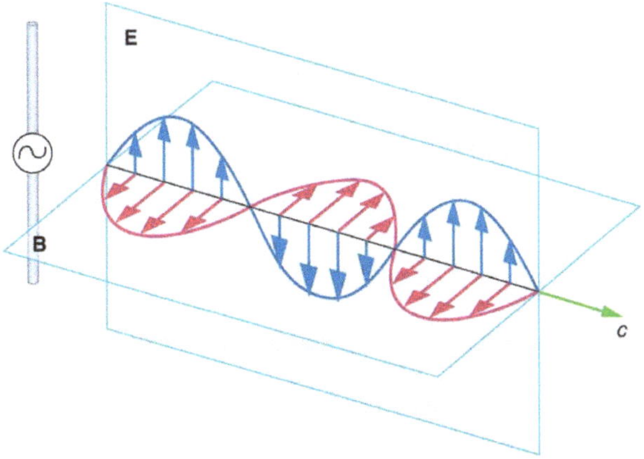

FIGURE 24.7 A part of the electromagnetic wave sent out from the antenna at one instant in time. The electric and magnetic fields ($\mathbf{E}$ and $\mathbf{B}$) are in phase, and they are perpendicular to one another and the direction of propagation. For clarity, the waves are shown only along one direction, but they propagate out in other directions too.

Electromagnetic waves generally propagate out from a source in all directions, sometimes forming a complex radiation pattern. A linear antenna like this one will not radiate parallel to its length, for example. The wave is shown in one direction from the antenna in Figure 24.7 to illustrate its basic characteristics.

Instead of the AC generator, the antenna can also be driven by an AC circuit. In fact, charges radiate whenever they are accelerated. But while a current in a circuit needs a complete path, an antenna has a varying charge distribution forming a **standing wave**, driven by the AC. The dimensions of the antenna are critical for determining the frequency of the radiated electromagnetic waves. This is a **resonant** phenomenon and when we tune radios or TV, we vary electrical properties to achieve appropriate resonant conditions in the antenna.

Receiving Electromagnetic Waves

Electromagnetic waves carry energy away from their source, similar to a sound wave carrying energy away from a standing wave on a guitar string. An antenna for receiving EM signals works in reverse. And like antennas that produce EM waves, receiver antennas are specially designed to resonate at particular frequencies.

An incoming electromagnetic wave accelerates electrons in the antenna, setting up a standing wave. If the radio or TV is switched on, electrical components pick up and amplify the signal formed by the accelerating electrons. The signal is then converted to audio and/or video format. Sometimes big receiver dishes are used to focus the signal onto an antenna.

In fact, charges radiate whenever they are accelerated. When designing circuits, we often assume that energy does not quickly escape AC circuits, and mostly this is true. A broadcast antenna is specially designed to enhance the rate of electromagnetic radiation, and shielding is necessary to keep the radiation close to zero. Some familiar phenomena are based on the production of electromagnetic waves by varying currents. Your microwave oven, for example, sends electromagnetic waves, called microwaves, from a concealed antenna that has an oscillating current imposed on it.

Relating E-Field and B-Field Strengths

There is a relationship between the E- and B-field strengths in an electromagnetic wave. This can be understood by again considering the antenna just described. The stronger the E-field created by a separation of charge, the greater the current and, hence, the greater the B-field created.

Since current is directly proportional to voltage (Ohm's law) and voltage is directly proportional to E-field strength, the two should be directly proportional. It can be shown that the magnitudes of the fields do have a constant ratio, equal to the speed of light. That is,

$$\frac{E}{B} = c \tag{24.3}$$

is the ratio of E-field strength to B-field strength in any electromagnetic wave. This is true at all times and at all locations in space. A simple and elegant result.

EXAMPLE 24.1

Calculating B-Field Strength in an Electromagnetic Wave

What is the maximum strength of the B-field in an electromagnetic wave that has a maximum E-field strength of 1000 V/m?

Strategy

To find the B-field strength, we rearrange the above equation to solve for B, yielding

$$B = \frac{E}{c}. \tag{24.4}$$

Solution

We are given E, and c is the speed of light. Entering these into the expression for B yields

$$B = \frac{1000 \text{ V/m}}{3.00 \times 10^8 \text{ m/s}} = 3.33 \times 10^{-6} \text{ T}, \tag{24.5}$$

Where T stands for Tesla, a measure of magnetic field strength.

Discussion

The B-field strength is less than a tenth of the Earth's admittedly weak magnetic field. This means that a relatively strong electric field of 1000 V/m is accompanied by a relatively weak magnetic field. Note that as this wave spreads out, say with distance from an antenna, its field strengths become progressively weaker.

The result of this example is consistent with the statement made in the module Maxwell's Equations: Electromagnetic Waves Predicted and Observed that changing electric fields create relatively weak magnetic fields.

They can be detected in electromagnetic waves, however, by taking advantage of the phenomenon of resonance, as Hertz did. A system with the same natural frequency as the electromagnetic wave can be made to oscillate. All radio and TV receivers use this principle to pick up and then amplify weak electromagnetic waves, while rejecting all others not at their resonant frequency.

TAKE-HOME EXPERIMENT: ANTENNAS

If you own a cell phone or a laptop, use a search engine or the product documentation to identify the type of antenna it contains. (If you search online, try adding the words "tear down" to the search.) Do the same for a friend's phone or your previous model. What are the differences in reception power or other features?

If you have a radio, try tuning a station to the "edge" of its discernible range, to the point where static interferes with the sound. Touch the antenna with your hand. Does the reception improve? If so, what is likely happening?

PHET EXPLORATIONS

Radio Waves and Electromagnetic Fields

Broadcast radio waves from KPhET. Wiggle the transmitter electron manually or have it oscillate automatically. Display the field as a curve or vectors. The strip chart shows the electron positions at the transmitter and at the receiver.

Click to view content (https://openstax.org/l/28Radiowaves).

PhET

24.3 The Electromagnetic Spectrum

LEARNING OBJECTIVES

By the end of this section, you will be able to:

- List three "rules of thumb" that apply to the different frequencies along the electromagnetic spectrum.
- Explain why the higher the frequency, the shorter the wavelength of an electromagnetic wave.
- Draw a simplified electromagnetic spectrum, indicating the relative positions, frequencies, and spacing of the different types of radiation bands.
- List and explain the different methods by which electromagnetic waves are produced across the spectrum.

In this module we examine how electromagnetic waves are classified into categories such as radio, infrared, ultraviolet, and so on, so that we can understand some of their similarities as well as some of their differences. We will also find that there are many connections with previously discussed topics, such as wavelength and resonance. A brief overview of the production and utilization of electromagnetic waves is found in Table 24.1.

Type of EM wave	Production	Applications	Life sciences aspect	Issues
Radio & TV	Accelerating charges	Communications Remote controls	MRI	Requires controls for band use
Microwaves	Accelerating charges & thermal agitation	Communications Ovens Radar	Deep heating	Cell phone use
Infrared	Thermal agitations & electronic transitions	Thermal imaging Heating	Absorbed by atmosphere	Greenhouse effect

TABLE 24.1 Electromagnetic Waves

Type of EM wave	Production	Applications	Life sciences aspect	Issues
Visible light	Thermal agitations & electronic transitions	All pervasive	Photosynthesis Human vision	
Ultraviolet	Thermal agitations & electronic transitions	Sterilization Cancer control	Vitamin D production	Ozone depletion Cancer causing
X-rays	Inner electronic transitions and fast collisions	Medical Security	Medical diagnosis Cancer therapy	Cancer causing
Gamma rays	Nuclear decay	Nuclear medicineSecurity	Medical diagnosis Cancer therapy	Cancer causing Radiation damage

TABLE 24.1 Electromagnetic Waves

CONNECTIONS: WAVES

There are many types of waves, such as water waves and even earthquakes. Among the many shared attributes of waves are propagation speed, frequency, and wavelength. These are always related by the expression $v_W = f\lambda$. This module concentrates on EM waves, but other modules contain examples of all of these characteristics for sound waves and submicroscopic particles.

As noted before, an electromagnetic wave has a frequency and a wavelength associated with it and travels at the speed of light, or c. The relationship among these wave characteristics can be described by $v_W = f\lambda$, where v_W is the propagation speed of the wave, f is the frequency, and λ is the wavelength. Here $v_W = c$, so that for all electromagnetic waves,

$$c = f\lambda. \tag{24.6}$$

Thus, for all electromagnetic waves, the greater the frequency, the smaller the wavelength.

Figure 24.8 shows how the various types of electromagnetic waves are categorized according to their wavelengths and frequencies—that is, it shows the electromagnetic spectrum. Many of the characteristics of the various types of electromagnetic waves are related to their frequencies and wavelengths, as we shall see.

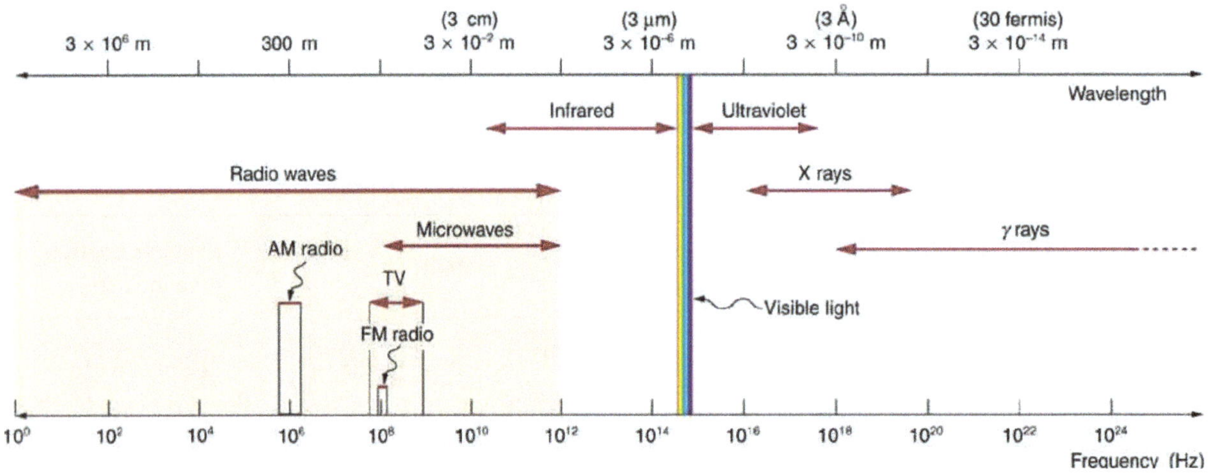

FIGURE 24.8 The electromagnetic spectrum, showing the major categories of electromagnetic waves. The range of frequencies and wavelengths is remarkable. The dividing line between some categories is distinct, whereas other categories overlap.

ELECTROMAGNETIC SPECTRUM: RULES OF THUMB

Three rules that apply to electromagnetic waves in general are as follows:

- High-frequency electromagnetic waves are more energetic and are more able to penetrate than low-frequency waves.
- High-frequency electromagnetic waves can carry more information per unit time than low-frequency waves.
- The shorter the wavelength of any electromagnetic wave probing a material, the smaller the detail it is possible to resolve.

Note that there are exceptions to these rules of thumb.

Transmission, Reflection, and Absorption

What happens when an electromagnetic wave impinges on a material? If the material is transparent to the particular frequency, then the wave can largely be transmitted. If the material is opaque to the frequency, then the wave can be totally reflected. The wave can also be absorbed by the material, indicating that there is some interaction between the wave and the material, such as the thermal agitation of molecules.

Of course it is possible to have partial transmission, reflection, and absorption. We normally associate these properties with visible light, but they do apply to all electromagnetic waves. What is not obvious is that something that is transparent to light may be opaque at other frequencies. For example, ordinary glass is transparent to visible light but largely opaque to ultraviolet radiation. Human skin is opaque to visible light—we cannot see through people—but transparent to X-rays.

Radio and TV Waves

The broad category of **radio waves** is defined to contain any electromagnetic wave produced by currents in wires and circuits. Its name derives from their most common use as a carrier of audio information (i.e., radio). The name is applied to electromagnetic waves of similar frequencies regardless of source. Radio waves from outer space, for example, do not come from alien radio stations. They are created by many astronomical phenomena, and their study has revealed much about nature on the largest scales.

There are many uses for radio waves, and so the category is divided into many subcategories, including microwaves and those electromagnetic waves used for AM and FM radio, cellular telephones, and TV.

The lowest commonly encountered radio frequencies are produced by high-voltage AC power transmission lines at frequencies of 50 or 60 Hz. (See Figure 24.9.) These extremely long wavelength electromagnetic waves (about 6000 km!) are one means of energy loss in long-distance power transmission.

FIGURE 24.9 This high-voltage traction power line running to Eutingen Railway Substation in Germany radiates electromagnetic waves with very long wavelengths. (credit: Zonk43, Wikimedia Commons)

There was a concern regarding potential health hazards associated with exposure to these electromagnetic fields (E-fields). Some people suspect that living near such transmission lines may cause a variety of illnesses, including cancer. But these power lines produce non-ionizing radiation, which government environmental organizations, medical researchers, and cancer organizations indicate are not risk factors for illness. Recent reports that have looked at many European and American epidemiological studies have found no increase in risk for cancer due to exposure to E-fields.

Extremely low frequency (ELF) radio waves of about 1 kHz are used to communicate with submerged submarines. The ability of radio waves to penetrate salt water is related to their wavelength (much like ultrasound penetrating tissue)—the longer the wavelength, the farther they penetrate. Since salt water is a good conductor, radio waves are strongly absorbed by it, and very long wavelengths are needed to reach a submarine under the surface. (See Figure 24.10.)

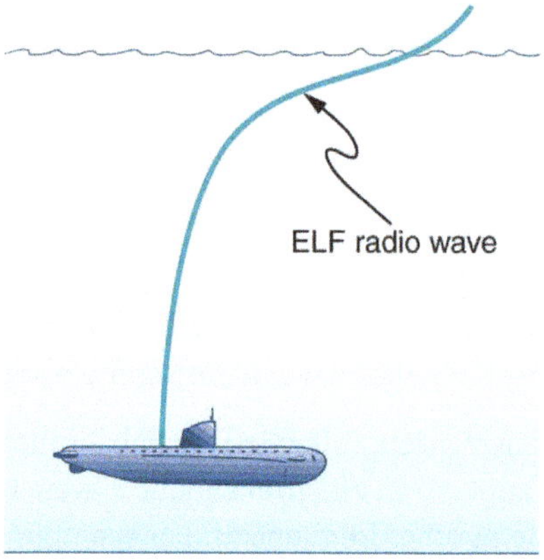

FIGURE 24.10 Very long wavelength radio waves are needed to reach this submarine, requiring extremely low frequency signals (ELF). Shorter wavelengths do not penetrate to any significant depth.

AM radio waves are used to carry commercial radio signals in the frequency range from 540 to 1600 kHz. The abbreviation AM stands for **amplitude modulation**, which is the method for placing information on these waves. (See Figure 24.11.) A **carrier wave** having the basic frequency of the radio station, say 1530 kHz, is varied or modulated in amplitude by an audio signal. The resulting wave has a constant frequency, but a varying amplitude.

A radio receiver tuned to have the same resonant frequency as the carrier wave can pick up the signal, while rejecting the many other frequencies impinging on its antenna. The receiver's circuitry is designed to respond to variations in amplitude of the carrier wave to replicate the original audio signal. That audio signal is amplified to drive a speaker or perhaps to be recorded.

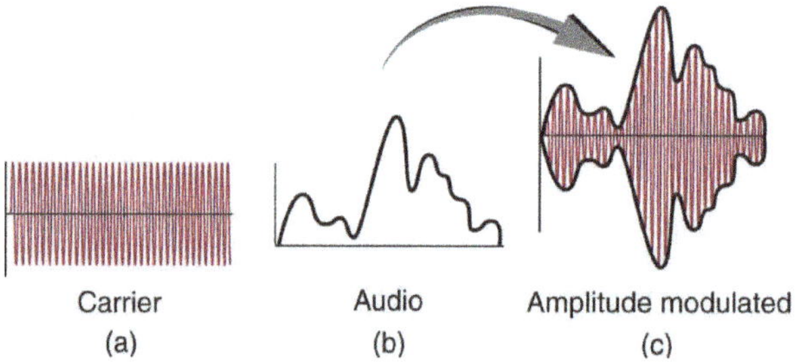

FIGURE 24.11 Amplitude modulation for AM radio. (a) A carrier wave at the station's basic frequency. (b) An audio signal at much lower audible frequencies. (c) The amplitude of the carrier is modulated by the audio signal without changing its basic frequency.

FM Radio Waves

FM radio waves are also used for commercial radio transmission, but in the frequency range of 88 to 108 MHz. FM stands for **frequency modulation**, another method of carrying information. (See Figure 24.12.) Here a carrier wave having the basic frequency of the radio station, perhaps 105.1 MHz, is modulated in frequency by the audio signal, producing a wave of constant amplitude but varying frequency.

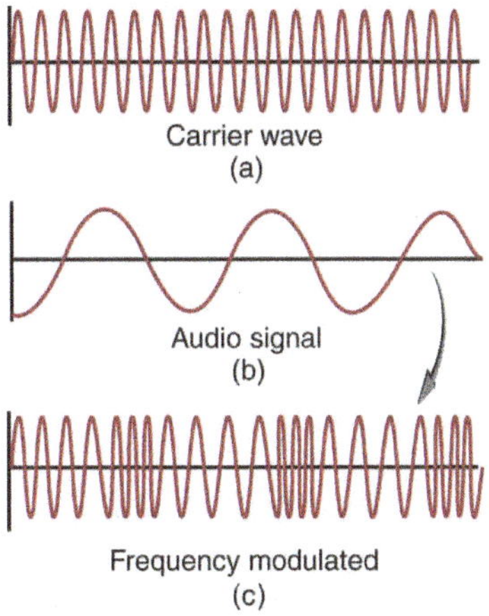

FIGURE 24.12 Frequency modulation for FM radio. (a) A carrier wave at the station's basic frequency. (b) An audio signal at much lower audible frequencies. (c) The frequency of the carrier is modulated by the audio signal without changing its amplitude.

Since audible frequencies range up to 20 kHz (or 0.020 MHz) at most, the frequency of the FM radio wave can vary from the carrier by as much as 0.020 MHz. Thus the carrier frequencies of two different radio stations cannot be closer than 0.020 MHz. An FM receiver is tuned to resonate at the carrier frequency and has circuitry that responds to variations in frequency, reproducing the audio information.

FM radio is inherently less subject to noise from stray radio sources than AM radio. The reason is that amplitudes of waves add. So an AM receiver would interpret noise added onto the amplitude of its carrier wave as part of the information. An FM receiver can be made to reject amplitudes other than that of the basic carrier wave and only look for variations in frequency. It is thus easier to reject noise from FM, since noise produces a variation in amplitude.

Television is also broadcast on electromagnetic waves. Since the waves must carry a great deal of visual as well as audio information, each channel requires a larger range of frequencies than simple radio transmission. TV channels utilize frequencies in the range of 54 to 88 MHz and 174 to 222 MHz. (The entire FM radio band lies between channels 88 MHz and 174 MHz.) These TV channels are called VHF (for **very high frequency**). Other channels called UHF (for **ultra high frequency**) utilize an even higher frequency range of 470 to 1000 MHz.

The TV video signal is AM, while the TV audio is FM. Note that these frequencies are those of free transmission with the user utilizing an old-fashioned roof antenna. Satellite dishes and cable transmission of TV occurs at significantly higher frequencies and is rapidly evolving with the use of the high-definition or HD format.

EXAMPLE 24.2

Calculating Wavelengths of Radio Waves

Calculate the wavelengths of a 1530-kHz AM radio signal, a 105.1-MHz FM radio signal, and a 1.90-GHz cell phone signal.

Strategy

The relationship between wavelength and frequency is $c = f\lambda$, where $c = 3.00 \times 10^8 \text{ m/s}$ is the speed of light (the speed of light is only very slightly smaller in air than it is in a vacuum). We can rearrange this equation to find the wavelength for all three frequencies.

Solution

Rearranging gives

$$\lambda = \frac{c}{f}. \tag{24.7}$$

(a) For the $f = 1530 \text{ kHz}$ AM radio signal, then,

$$\begin{aligned} \lambda &= \frac{3.00\times10^{8}\ \text{m/s}}{1530\times10^{3}\ \text{cycles/s}} \\ &= 196\ \text{m.} \end{aligned} \tag{24.8}$$

(b) For the $f = 105.1\ \text{MHz}$ FM radio signal,

$$\begin{aligned} \lambda &= \frac{3.00\times10^{8}\ \text{m/s}}{105.1\times10^{6}\ \text{cycles/s}} \\ &= 2.85\ \text{m.} \end{aligned} \tag{24.9}$$

(c) And for the $f = 1.90\ \text{GHz}$ cell phone,

$$\begin{aligned} \lambda &= \frac{3.00\times10^{8}\ \text{m/s}}{1.90\times10^{9}\ \text{cycles/s}} \\ &= 0.158\ \text{m.} \end{aligned} \tag{24.10}$$

Discussion

These wavelengths are consistent with the spectrum in Figure 24.8. The wavelengths are also related to other properties of these electromagnetic waves, as we shall see.

The wavelengths found in the preceding example are representative of AM, FM, and cell phones, and account for some of the differences in how they are broadcast and how well they travel. The most efficient length for a linear antenna, such as discussed in Production of Electromagnetic Waves, is $\lambda/2$, half the wavelength of the electromagnetic wave. Thus a very large antenna is needed to efficiently broadcast typical AM radio with its carrier wavelengths on the order of hundreds of meters.

One benefit to these long AM wavelengths is that they can go over and around rather large obstacles (like buildings and hills), just as ocean waves can go around large rocks. FM and TV are best received when there is a line of sight between the broadcast antenna and receiver, and they are often sent from very tall structures. FM, TV, and mobile phone antennas themselves are much smaller than those used for AM, but they are elevated to achieve an unobstructed line of sight. (See Figure 24.13.)

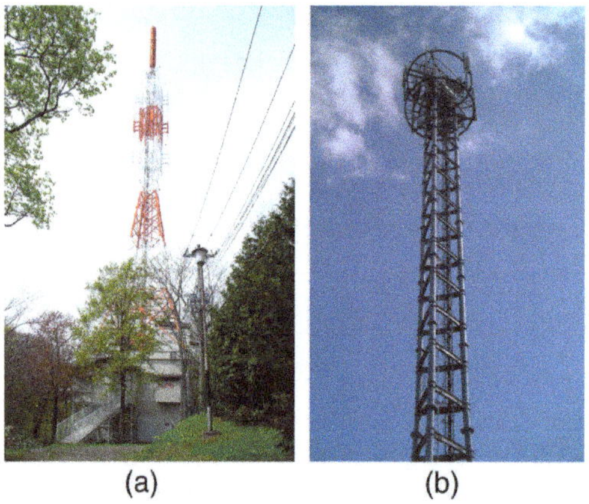

FIGURE 24.13 (a) A large tower is used to broadcast TV signals. The actual antennas are small structures on top of the tower—they are placed at great heights to have a clear line of sight over a large broadcast area. (credit: Ozizo, Wikimedia Commons) (b) The NTT Dokomo mobile phone tower at Tokorozawa City, Japan. (credit: tokoroten, Wikimedia Commons)

Radio Wave Interference

Astronomers and astrophysicists collect signals from outer space using electromagnetic waves. A common problem for astrophysicists is the "pollution" from electromagnetic radiation pervading our surroundings from communication systems in general. Even everyday gadgets like our car keyless entry devices and remote starters and being able to turn TVs on and off using remotes involve radio-wave frequencies. In order to prevent interference between all these electromagnetic signals, strict regulations are drawn up for different organizations to utilize different radio frequency bands.

One reason why we are sometimes asked to switch off our mobile phones (operating in the range of 1.9 GHz) or put them into a noncommunicative mode on airplanes and in hospitals is that important communications or medical equipment often uses similar radio frequencies and their operation can be affected by frequencies used in the communication devices.

For example, radio waves used in magnetic resonance imaging (MRI) have frequencies on the order of 100 MHz, although this varies significantly depending on the strength of the magnetic field used and the nuclear type being scanned. MRI is an important medical imaging and research tool, producing highly detailed two- and three-dimensional images. Radio waves are broadcast, absorbed, and reemitted in a resonance process that is sensitive to the density of nuclei (usually protons or hydrogen nuclei).

The wavelength of 100-MHz radio waves is 3 m, yet using the sensitivity of the resonant frequency to the magnetic field strength, details smaller than a millimeter can be imaged. This is a good example of an exception to a rule of thumb (in this case, the rubric that details much smaller than the probe's wavelength cannot be detected). The intensity of the radio waves used in MRI presents little or no hazard to human health.

Microwaves

Microwaves are the highest-frequency electromagnetic waves that can be produced by currents in macroscopic circuits and devices. Microwave frequencies range from about 10^9 Hz to the highest practical LC resonance at nearly 10^{12} Hz. Since they have high frequencies, their wavelengths are short compared with those of other radio waves—hence the name "microwave."

Microwaves can also be produced by atoms and molecules. They are, for example, a component of electromagnetic radiation generated by **thermal agitation**. The thermal motion of atoms and molecules in any object at a temperature above absolute zero causes them to emit and absorb radiation.

Since it is possible to carry more information per unit time on high frequencies, microwaves are quite suitable for communications. Most satellite-transmitted information is carried on microwaves, as are land-based long-distance transmissions. A clear line of sight between transmitter and receiver is needed because of the short wavelengths involved.

Radar is a common application of microwaves that was first developed in World War II. By detecting and timing microwave echoes, radar systems can determine the distance to objects as diverse as clouds and aircraft. A Doppler shift in the radar echo can be used to determine the speed of a car or the intensity of a rainstorm. Sophisticated radar systems are used to map the Earth and other planets, with a resolution limited by wavelength. (See Figure 24.14.) The shorter the wavelength of any probe, the smaller the detail it is possible to observe.

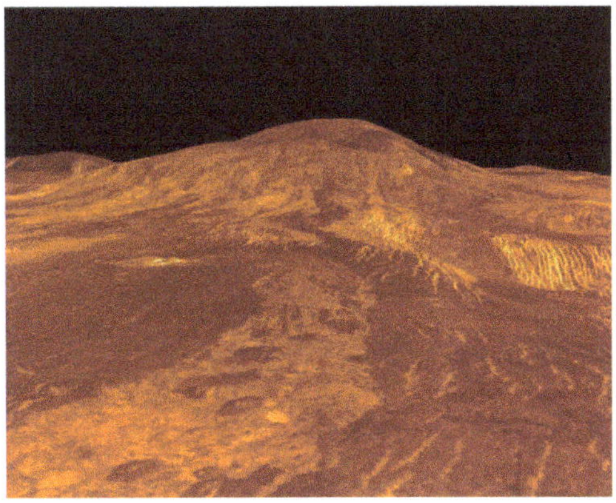

FIGURE 24.14 An image of Sif Mons with lava flows on Venus, based on Magellan synthetic aperture radar data combined with radar altimetry to produce a three-dimensional map of the surface. The Venusian atmosphere is opaque to visible light, but not to the microwaves that were used to create this image. (credit: NSSDC, NASA/JPL)

Heating with Microwaves

How does the ubiquitous microwave oven produce microwaves electronically, and why does food absorb them preferentially? Microwaves at a frequency of 2.45 GHz are produced by accelerating electrons. The microwaves are then used to induce an alternating electric field in the oven.

Water and some other constituents of food have a slightly negative charge at one end and a slightly positive charge at one end (called polar molecules). The range of microwave frequencies is specially selected so that the polar molecules, in trying to keep orienting themselves with the electric field, absorb these energies and increase their temperatures—called dielectric heating.

The energy thereby absorbed results in thermal agitation heating food and not the plate, which does not contain water. Hot spots in the food are related to constructive and destructive interference patterns. Rotating antennas and food turntables help spread out the hot spots.

Another use of microwaves for heating is within the human body. Microwaves will penetrate more than shorter wavelengths into tissue and so can accomplish "deep heating" (called microwave diathermy). This is used for treating muscular pains, spasms, tendonitis, and rheumatoid arthritis.

MAKING CONNECTIONS: TAKE-HOME EXPERIMENT—MICROWAVE OVENS

1. Look at the door of a microwave oven. Describe the structure of the door. Why is there a metal grid on the door? How does the size of the holes in the grid compare with the wavelengths of microwaves used in microwave ovens? What is this wavelength?
2. Place a glass of water (about 250 ml) in the microwave and heat it for 30 seconds. Measure the temperature gain (the ΔT). Assuming that the power output of the oven is 1000 W, calculate the efficiency of the heat-transfer process.
3. Remove the rotating turntable or moving plate and place a cup of water in several places along a line parallel with the opening. Heat for 30 seconds and measure the ΔT for each position. Do you see cases of destructive interference?

Microwaves generated by atoms and molecules far away in time and space can be received and detected by electronic circuits. Deep space acts like a blackbody with a 2.7 K temperature, radiating most of its energy in the microwave frequency range. In 1964, Penzias and Wilson detected this radiation and eventually recognized that it was the radiation of the Big Bang's cooled remnants.

Infrared Radiation

The microwave and infrared regions of the electromagnetic spectrum overlap (see Figure 24.8). **Infrared radiation** is generally produced by thermal motion and the vibration and rotation of atoms and molecules. Electronic transitions in atoms and molecules can also produce infrared radiation.

The range of infrared frequencies extends up to the lower limit of visible light, just below red. In fact, infrared means "below red." Frequencies at its upper limit are too high to be produced by accelerating electrons in circuits, but small systems, such as atoms and molecules, can vibrate fast enough to produce these waves.

Water molecules rotate and vibrate particularly well at infrared frequencies, emitting and absorbing them so efficiently that the emissivity for skin is $e = 0.97$ in the infrared. Night-vision scopes can detect the infrared emitted by various warm objects, including humans, and convert it to visible light.

We can examine radiant heat transfer from a house by using a camera capable of detecting infrared radiation. Reconnaissance satellites can detect buildings, vehicles, and even individual humans by their infrared emissions, whose power radiation is proportional to the fourth power of the absolute temperature. More mundanely, we use infrared lamps, some of which are called quartz heaters, to preferentially warm us because we absorb infrared better than our surroundings.

The Sun radiates like a nearly perfect blackbody (that is, it has $e = 1$), with a 6000 K surface temperature. About half of the solar energy arriving at the Earth is in the infrared region, with most of the rest in the visible part of the spectrum, and a relatively small amount in the ultraviolet. On average, 50 percent of the incident solar energy is absorbed by the Earth.

The relatively constant temperature of the Earth is a result of the energy balance between the incoming solar radiation and the energy radiated from the Earth. Most of the infrared radiation emitted from the Earth is absorbed by CO_2 and H_2O in the atmosphere and then radiated back to Earth or into outer space. This radiation back to Earth is known as the greenhouse effect, and it maintains the surface temperature of the Earth about $40°C$ higher than it would be if there is no absorption. Some scientists think that the increased concentration of CO_2 and other greenhouse gases in the atmosphere, resulting from increases in fossil fuel burning, has increased global average temperatures.

Visible Light

Visible light is the narrow segment of the electromagnetic spectrum to which the normal human eye responds. Visible light is produced by vibrations and rotations of atoms and molecules, as well as by electronic transitions within atoms and molecules. The receivers or detectors of light largely utilize electronic transitions. We say the atoms and molecules are excited when they absorb and relax when they emit through electronic transitions.

Figure 24.15 shows this part of the spectrum, together with the colors associated with particular pure wavelengths. We usually refer to visible light as having wavelengths of between 400 nm and 750 nm. (The retina of the eye actually responds to the lowest ultraviolet frequencies, but these do not normally reach the retina because they are absorbed by the cornea and lens of the eye.)

Red light has the lowest frequencies and longest wavelengths, while violet has the highest frequencies and shortest wavelengths. Blackbody radiation from the Sun peaks in the visible part of the spectrum but is more intense in the red than in the violet, making the Sun yellowish in appearance.

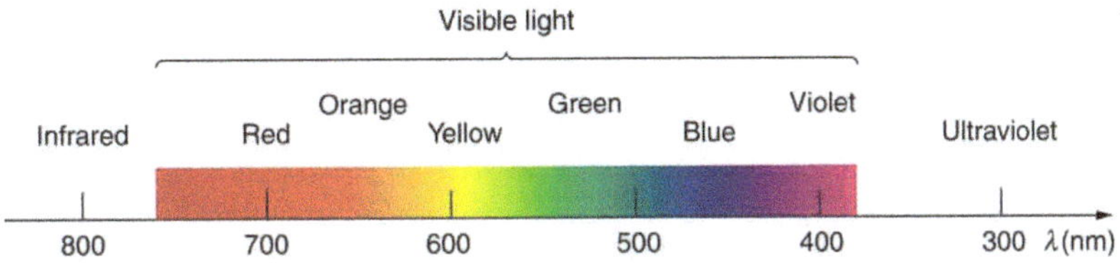

FIGURE 24.15 A small part of the electromagnetic spectrum that includes its visible components. The divisions between infrared, visible, and ultraviolet are not perfectly distinct, nor are those between the seven rainbow colors.

Living things—plants and animals—have evolved to utilize and respond to parts of the electromagnetic spectrum they are embedded in. Visible light is the most predominant and we enjoy the beauty of nature through visible light. Plants are more selective. Photosynthesis makes use of parts of the visible spectrum to make sugars.

EXAMPLE 24.3

Integrated Concept Problem: Correcting Vision with Lasers

During laser vision correction, a brief burst of 193-nm ultraviolet light is projected onto the cornea of a patient. It makes a spot 0.80 mm in diameter and evaporates a layer of cornea $0.30\ \mu m$ thick. Calculate the energy absorbed, assuming the corneal tissue has the same properties as water; it is initially at $34°C$. Assume the evaporated tissue leaves at a temperature of $100°C$.

Strategy

The energy from the laser light goes toward raising the temperature of the tissue and also toward evaporating it. Thus we have two amounts of heat to add together. Also, we need to find the mass of corneal tissue involved.

Solution

To figure out the heat required to raise the temperature of the tissue to $100°C$, we can apply concepts of thermal energy. We know that

$$Q = mc\Delta T, \tag{24.11}$$

where Q is the heat required to raise the temperature, ΔT is the desired change in temperature, m is the mass of tissue to be heated, and c is the specific heat of water equal to 4186 J/kg/K.

Without knowing the mass m at this point, we have

$$Q = m(4186\ \text{J/kg/K})(100°\text{C}-34°\text{C}) = m(276{,}276\ \text{J/kg}) = m(276\ \text{kJ/kg}). \tag{24.12}$$

The latent heat of vaporization of water is 2256 kJ/kg, so that the energy needed to evaporate mass m is

$$Q_\text{v} = mL_\text{v} = m(2256\ \text{kJ/kg}). \tag{24.13}$$

To find the mass m, we use the equation $\rho = m/\text{V}$, where ρ is the density of the tissue and V is its volume. For this case,

$$\begin{aligned} m &= \rho \text{V} \\ &= (1000\ \text{kg/m}^3)(\text{area} \times \text{thickness}(\text{m}^3)) \\ &= (1000\ \text{kg/m}^3)(\pi(0.80\times10^{-3}\ \text{m})^2/4)(0.30\times10^{-6}\ \text{m}) \\ &= 0.151\times10^{-9}\ \text{kg}. \end{aligned} \tag{24.14}$$

Therefore, the total energy absorbed by the tissue in the eye is the sum of Q and Q_v:

$$\text{Q}_\text{tot} = m(c\Delta\text{T} + \text{L}_\text{v}) = (0.151\times10^{-9}\ \text{kg})(276\ \text{kJ/kg} + 2256\ \text{kJ/kg}) = 382\times10^{-9}\ \text{kJ}. \tag{24.15}$$

Discussion

The lasers used for this eye surgery are excimer lasers, whose light is well absorbed by biological tissue. They evaporate rather than burn the tissue, and can be used for precision work. Most lasers used for this type of eye surgery have an average power rating of about one watt. For our example, if we assume that each laser burst from this pulsed laser lasts for 10 ns, and there are 400 bursts per second, then the average power is $\text{Q}_\text{tot} \times 400 = 150\ \text{mW}$.

Optics is the study of the behavior of visible light and other forms of electromagnetic waves. Optics falls into two distinct categories. When electromagnetic radiation, such as visible light, interacts with objects that are large compared with its wavelength, its motion can be represented by straight lines like rays. Ray optics is the study of such situations and includes lenses and mirrors.

When electromagnetic radiation interacts with objects about the same size as the wavelength or smaller, its wave nature becomes apparent. For example, observable detail is limited by the wavelength, and so visible light can never detect individual atoms, because they are so much smaller than its wavelength. Physical or wave optics is the study of such situations and includes all wave characteristics.

TAKE-HOME EXPERIMENT: COLORS THAT MATCH

When you light a match you see largely orange light; when you light a gas stove you see blue light. Why are the colors different? What other colors are present in these?

Ultraviolet Radiation

Ultraviolet means "above violet." The electromagnetic frequencies of **ultraviolet radiation (UV)** extend upward from violet, the highest-frequency visible light. Ultraviolet is also produced by atomic and molecular motions and electronic transitions. The wavelengths of ultraviolet extend from 400 nm down to about 10 nm at its highest frequencies, which overlap with the lowest X-ray frequencies. It was recognized as early as 1801 by Johann Ritter that the solar spectrum had an invisible component beyond the violet range.

Solar UV radiation is broadly subdivided into three regions: UV-A (320–400 nm), UV-B (290–320 nm), and UV-C (220–290 nm), ranked from long to shorter wavelengths (from smaller to larger energies). Most UV-B and all UV-C is absorbed by ozone (O_3) molecules in the upper atmosphere. Consequently, 99% of the solar UV radiation reaching the Earth's surface is UV-A.

One of the first illustrations of UV light's impact on Earth occurred during the Apollo 16 mission in 1972. The mission included the first astronomical images taken from the moon, using a compact and resilient Far Ultraviolet Camera/

Spectrograph designed for moon use by scientist and inventor George Robert Carruthers. Designed to capture UV images without the obscuring effects of the Earth's atmosphere, its most famous image was of the planet itself. Carruthers, who also trained the astronauts on the device's use, mentioned afterward that "the most immediately obvious and spectacular results were really for the Earth observations, because this was the first time that the Earth had been photographed from a distance in ultraviolet (UV) light, so that you could see the full extent of the hydrogen atmosphere, the polar auroris and what we call the tropical airglow belt."

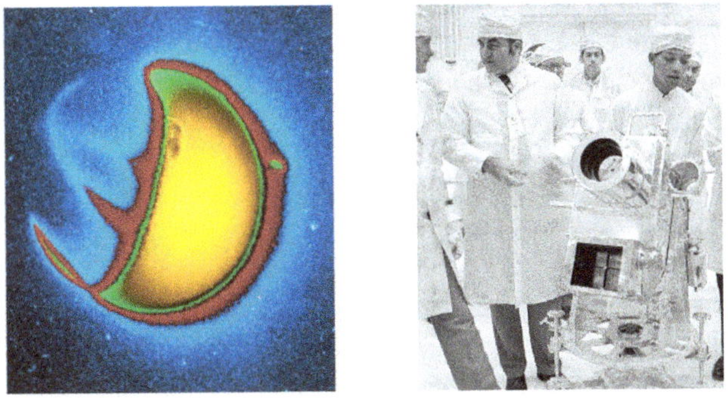

(a) (b)

FIGURE 24.16 An image of Earth captured with the Far UV Camera/Spectrograph on the Moon. The part of the Earth facing the Sun reflects much UV light and bands of UV emission are also apparent on the side facing away from the Sun. These bands are the result of aurora caused by charged particles given off by the Sun. They spiral toward the Earth along Earth's magnetic field lines. George Robert Carruthers of the Naval Research Laboratory designed the device specifically for transport and usage on the moon. In the image on the right, Carruthers explains the operating procedure to the Apollo 16 astronauts. (credit, both images: NASA.)

Human Exposure to UV Radiation

It is largely exposure to UV-B that causes skin cancer. It is estimated that as many as 20% of adults will develop skin cancer over the course of their lifetime. Again, treatment is often successful if caught early. Despite very little UV-B reaching the Earth's surface, there are substantial increases in skin-cancer rates in countries such as Australia, indicating how important it is that UV-B and UV-C continue to be absorbed by the upper atmosphere.

All UV radiation can damage collagen fibers, resulting in an acceleration of the aging process of skin and the formation of wrinkles. Because there is so little UV-B and UV-C reaching the Earth's surface, sunburn is caused by large exposures, and skin cancer from repeated exposure. Some studies indicate a link between overexposure to the Sun when young and melanoma later in life.

The tanning response is a defense mechanism in which the body produces pigments to absorb future exposures in inert skin layers above living cells. Basically UV-B radiation excites DNA molecules, distorting the DNA helix, leading to mutations and the possible formation of cancerous cells.

Repeated exposure to UV-B may also lead to the formation of cataracts in the eyes—a cause of blindness among people living in the equatorial belt where medical treatment is limited. Cataracts, clouding in the eye's lens and a loss of vision, are age related; 60% of those between the ages of 65 and 74 will develop cataracts. However, treatment is easy and successful, as one replaces the lens of the eye with a plastic lens. Prevention is important. Eye protection from UV is more effective with plastic sunglasses than those made of glass.

A major acute effect of extreme UV exposure is the suppression of the immune system, both locally and throughout the body.

Low-intensity ultraviolet is used to sterilize haircutting implements, implying that the energy associated with ultraviolet is deposited in a manner different from lower-frequency electromagnetic waves. (Actually this is true for all electromagnetic waves with frequencies greater than visible light.)

Flash photography is generally not allowed of precious artworks and colored prints because the UV radiation from the flash can cause photo-degradation in the artworks. Often artworks will have an extra-thick layer of glass in front of them, which is especially designed to absorb UV radiation.

UV Light and the Ozone Layer

If all of the Sun's ultraviolet radiation reached the Earth's surface, there would be extremely grave effects on the biosphere from the severe cell damage it causes. However, the layer of ozone (O_3) in our upper atmosphere (10 to 50 km above the Earth) protects life by absorbing most of the dangerous UV radiation.

Unfortunately, today we are observing a depletion in ozone concentrations in the upper atmosphere. This depletion has led to the formation of an "ozone hole" in the upper atmosphere. The hole is more centered over the southern hemisphere, and changes with the seasons, being largest in the spring. This depletion is attributed to the breakdown of ozone molecules by refrigerant gases called chlorofluorocarbons (CFCs).

The UV radiation helps dissociate the CFC's, releasing highly reactive chlorine (Cl) atoms, which catalyze the destruction of the ozone layer. For example, the reaction of $CFCl_3$ with a photon of light (hv) can be written as:

$$CFCl_3 + hv \rightarrow CFCl_2 + Cl. \tag{24.16}$$

The Cl atom then catalyzes the breakdown of ozone as follows:

$$Cl + O_3 \rightarrow ClO + O_2 \text{ and } ClO + O_3 \rightarrow Cl + 2O_2. \tag{24.17}$$

A single chlorine atom could destroy ozone molecules for up to two years before being transported down to the surface. The CFCs are relatively stable and will contribute to ozone depletion for years to come. CFCs are found in refrigerants, air conditioning systems, foams, and aerosols.

International concern over this problem led to the establishment of the "Montreal Protocol" agreement (1987) to phase out CFC production in most countries. However, developing-country participation is needed if worldwide production and elimination of CFCs is to be achieved. Probably the largest contributor to CFC emissions today is China. And while there are indicators that the Protocol has been a success, there is still substantial risk and variability in the ozone layer. The 2019 Antarctic ozone hole was small and short-lived, continuing the general trend toward recovery. But the 2020 Antarctic ozone hole was the largest and longest-lasting on record, partially due to atmospheric conditions. Furthermore, emissions are not the only concern. Susan Solomon and her colleagues at MIT have uncovered the substantial impact of CFC "banks," in certain regions, where outdated and deteriorating equipment (such as air conditioners) or materials can release enough CFCs to be detectable in the atmosphere and deplete the ozone layer. (See Figure 24.17.)

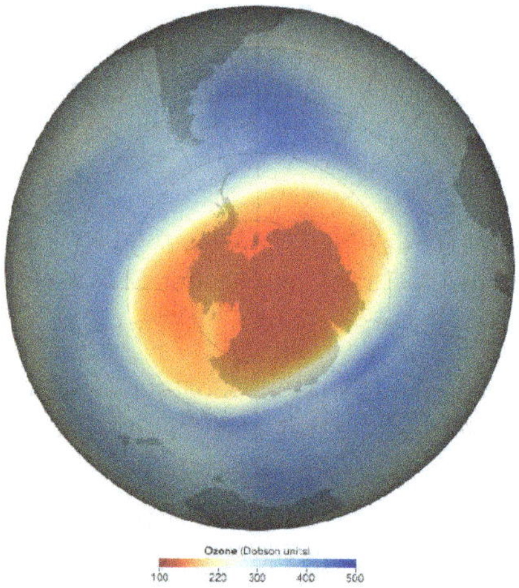

FIGURE 24.17 This map of ozone concentration over Antarctica in September 2020 shows severe depletion suspected to be caused by CFCs. In 2020, ozone depletion was significantly worse than in 2019, but better than in the early 2000s. With less ozone, more ultraviolet radiation from the Sun reaches the surface, causing more damage. (credit: NASA Earth Observatory)

Benefits of UV Light

Besides the adverse effects of ultraviolet radiation, there are also benefits of exposure in nature and uses in technology. Vitamin D production in the skin (epidermis) results from exposure to UVB radiation, generally from sunlight. A number of studies indicate lack of vitamin D can result in the development of a range of cancers (prostate, breast, colon), so a certain amount of UV exposure is helpful. Lack of vitamin D is also linked to osteoporosis. Exposures (with no sunscreen) of 10 minutes a day to arms, face, and legs might be sufficient to provide the accepted dietary level. However, in the winter time north of about 37° latitude, most UVB gets blocked by the atmosphere.

UV radiation is used in the treatment of infantile jaundice and in some skin conditions. It is also used in sterilizing workspaces and tools, and killing germs in a wide range of applications. It is also used as an analytical tool to identify substances.

When exposed to ultraviolet, some substances, such as minerals, glow in characteristic visible wavelengths, a process called fluorescence. So-called black lights emit ultraviolet to cause posters and clothing to fluoresce in the visible. Ultraviolet is also used in special microscopes to detect details smaller than those observable with longer-wavelength visible-light microscopes.

THINGS GREAT AND SMALL: A SUBMICROSCOPIC VIEW OF X-RAY PRODUCTION

X-rays can be created in a high-voltage discharge. They are emitted in the material struck by electrons in the discharge current. There are two mechanisms by which the electrons create X-rays.

The first method is illustrated in Figure 24.18. An electron is accelerated in an evacuated tube by a high positive voltage. The electron strikes a metal plate (e.g., copper) and produces X-rays. Since this is a high-voltage discharge, the electron gains sufficient energy to ionize the atom.

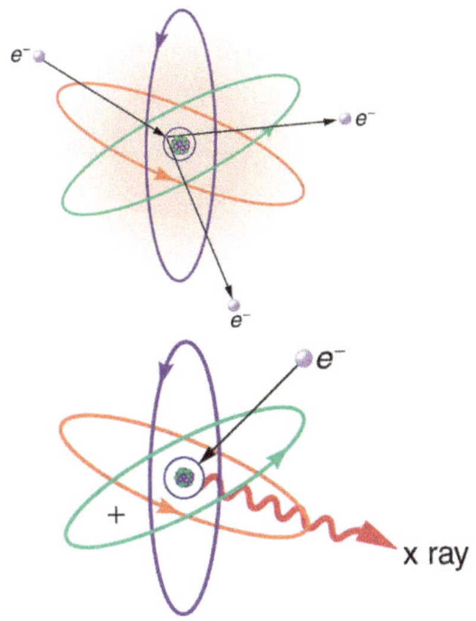

FIGURE 24.18 Artist's conception of an electron ionizing an atom followed by the recapture of an electron and emission of an X-ray. An energetic electron strikes an atom and knocks an electron out of one of the orbits closest to the nucleus. Later, the atom captures another electron, and the energy released by its fall into a low orbit generates a high-energy EM wave called an X-ray.

In the case shown, an inner-shell electron (one in an orbit relatively close to and tightly bound to the nucleus) is ejected. A short time later, another electron is captured and falls into the orbit in a single great plunge. The energy released by this fall is given to an EM wave known as an X-ray. Since the orbits of the atom are unique to the type of atom, the energy of the X-ray is characteristic of the atom, hence the name characteristic X-ray.

The second method by which an energetic electron creates an X-ray when it strikes a material is illustrated in Figure 24.19. The electron interacts with charges in the material as it penetrates. These collisions transfer kinetic energy from the electron to the electrons and atoms in the material.

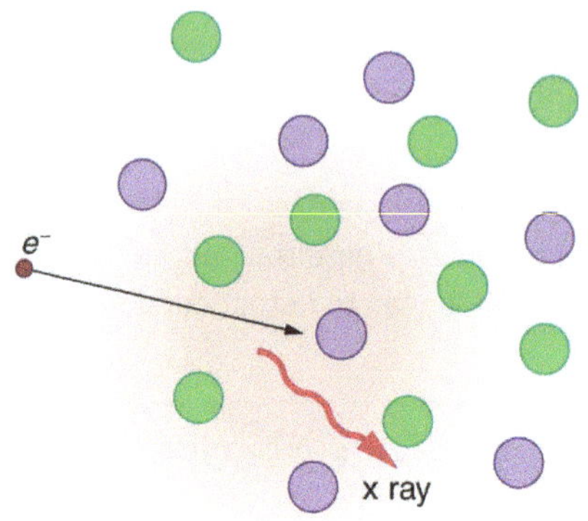

FIGURE 24.19 Artist's conception of an electron being slowed by collisions in a material and emitting X-ray radiation. This energetic electron makes numerous collisions with electrons and atoms in a material it penetrates. An accelerated charge radiates EM waves, a second method by which X-rays are created.

A loss of kinetic energy implies an acceleration, in this case decreasing the electron's velocity. Whenever a charge is accelerated, it radiates EM waves. Given the high energy of the electron, these EM waves can have high energy. We call them X-rays. Since the process is random, a broad spectrum of X-ray energy is emitted that is more characteristic of the electron energy than the type of material the electron encounters. Such EM radiation is called "bremsstrahlung" (German for "braking radiation").

X-Rays

In the 1850s, scientists (such as Faraday) began experimenting with high-voltage electrical discharges in tubes filled with rarefied gases. It was later found that these discharges created an invisible, penetrating form of very high frequency electromagnetic radiation. This radiation was called an **X-ray**, because its identity and nature were unknown.

As described in Things Great and Small, there are two methods by which X-rays are created—both are submicroscopic processes and can be caused by high-voltage discharges. While the low-frequency end of the X-ray range overlaps with the ultraviolet, X-rays extend to much higher frequencies (and energies).

X-rays have adverse effects on living cells similar to those of ultraviolet radiation, and they have the additional liability of being more penetrating, affecting more than the surface layers of cells. Cancer and genetic defects can be induced by exposure to X-rays. Because of their effect on rapidly dividing cells, X-rays can also be used to treat and even cure cancer.

The widest use of X-rays is for imaging objects that are opaque to visible light, such as the human body or aircraft parts. In humans, the risk of cell damage is weighed carefully against the benefit of the diagnostic information obtained. However, questions have risen in recent years as to accidental overexposure of some people during CT scans—a mistake at least in part due to poor monitoring of radiation dose.

The ability of X-rays to penetrate matter depends on density, and so an X-ray image can reveal very detailed density information. Figure 24.20 shows an example of the simplest type of X-ray image, an X-ray shadow on film. The amount of information in a simple X-ray image is impressive, but more sophisticated techniques, such as CT scans, can reveal three-dimensional information with details smaller than a millimeter.

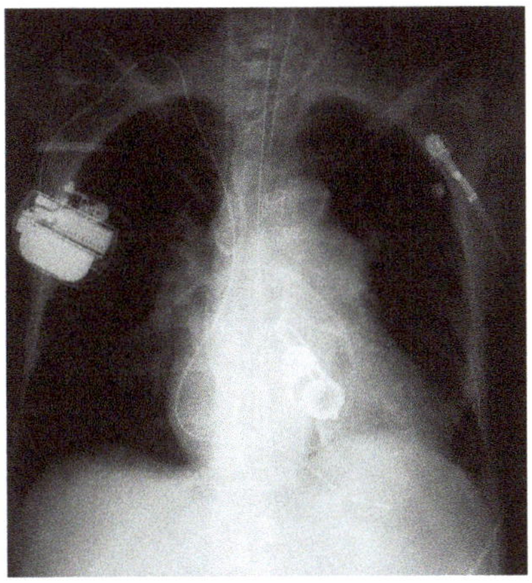

FIGURE 24.20 This shadow X-ray image shows many interesting features, such as artificial heart valves, a pacemaker, and the wires used to close the sternum. (credit: P. P. Urone)

The use of X-ray technology in medicine is called radiology—an established and relatively cheap tool in comparison to more sophisticated technologies. Consequently, X-rays are widely available and used extensively in medical diagnostics. During World War I, mobile X-ray units, advocated by Marie Curie, were used to diagnose soldiers.

Because they can have wavelengths less than 0.01 nm, X-rays can be scattered (a process called X-ray diffraction) to detect the shape of molecules and the structure of crystals. X-ray diffraction was crucial to Crick, Watson, and Wilkins in the determination of the shape of the double-helix DNA molecule.

X-rays are also used as a precise tool for trace-metal analysis in X-ray induced fluorescence, in which the energy of the X-ray emissions are related to the specific types of elements and amounts of materials present.

Gamma Rays

Soon after nuclear radioactivity was first detected in 1896, it was found that at least three distinct types of radiation were being emitted. The most penetrating nuclear radiation was called a **gamma ray (γ ray)** (again a name given because its identity and character were unknown), and it was later found to be an extremely high frequency electromagnetic wave.

In fact, γ rays are any electromagnetic radiation emitted by a nucleus. This can be from natural nuclear decay or induced nuclear processes in nuclear reactors and weapons. The lower end of the γ-ray frequency range overlaps the upper end of the X-ray range, but γ rays can have the highest frequency of any electromagnetic radiation.

Gamma rays have characteristics identical to X-rays of the same frequency—they differ only in source. At higher frequencies, γ rays are more penetrating and more damaging to living tissue. They have many of the same uses as X-rays, including cancer therapy. Gamma radiation from radioactive materials is used in nuclear medicine.

Figure 24.21 shows a medical image based on γ rays. Food spoilage can be greatly inhibited by exposing it to large doses of γ radiation, thereby obliterating responsible microorganisms. Damage to food cells through irradiation occurs as well, and the long-term hazards of consuming radiation-preserved food are unknown and controversial for some groups. Both X-ray and γ-ray technologies are also used in scanning luggage at airports.

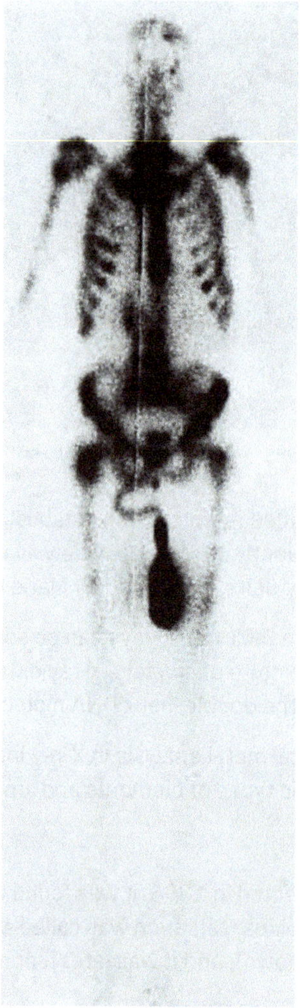

FIGURE 24.21 This is an image of the γ rays emitted by nuclei in a compound that is concentrated in the bones and eliminated through the kidneys. Bone cancer is evidenced by nonuniform concentration in similar structures. For example, some ribs are darker than others. (credit: P. P. Urone)

Detecting Electromagnetic Waves from Space

The entire electromagnetic spectrum is used by researchers for investigating stars, space, and time. Arthur B. C. Walker was a pioneer in X-ray and ultraviolet observations, and designed specialized telescopes and instruments to observe the Sun's atmosphere and corona. His developments significantly advanced our understanding of stars, and some of his developments are currently in use in space telescopes as well as in microchip manufacturing. As noted earlier, Penzias and Wilson detected microwaves to identify the background radiation originating from the Big Bang. Radio telescopes such as the Arecibo Radio Telescope in Puerto Rico and Parkes Observatory in Australia were designed to detect radio waves.

Infrared telescopes need to have their detectors cooled by liquid nitrogen to be able to gather useful signals. Since infrared radiation is predominantly from thermal agitation, if the detectors were not cooled, the vibrations of the molecules in the antenna would be stronger than the signal being collected.

The most famous of these infrared sensitive telescopes is the James Clerk Maxwell Telescope in Hawaii. The earliest telescopes, developed in the seventeenth century, were optical telescopes, collecting visible light. Telescopes in the ultraviolet, X-ray, and γ-ray regions are placed outside the atmosphere on satellites orbiting the Earth.

The Hubble Space Telescope (launched in 1990) gathers ultraviolet radiation as well as visible light. In the X-ray region, there is the Chandra X-ray Observatory (launched in 1999), and in the γ-ray region, there is the new Fermi Gamma-ray Space Telescope (launched in 2008—taking the place of the Compton Gamma Ray Observatory, 1991–2000). The James Webb Space Telescope, launched in late 2021, observes in a lower-frequency portion of the spectrum compared to Hubble. The JWST observes in long-wavelength visible light (red) through infrared, enabling it to detect objects that are further away, older, and fainter than previous telescopes could detect.

PHET EXPLORATIONS

Color Vision

Make a whole rainbow by mixing red, green, and blue light. Change the wavelength of a monochromatic beam or filter white light. View the light as a solid beam, or see the individual photons.

Click to view content (https://openstax.org/books/college-physics-ap-courses-2e/pages/24-3-the-electromagnetic-spectrum)

24.4 Energy in Electromagnetic Waves

LEARNING OBJECTIVES

By the end of this section, you will be able to:

- Explain how the energy and amplitude of an electromagnetic wave are related.
- Given its power output and the heating area, calculate the intensity of a microwave oven's electromagnetic field, as well as its peak electric and magnetic field strengths

Anyone who has used a microwave oven knows there is energy in **electromagnetic waves**. Sometimes this energy is obvious, such as in the warmth of the summer sun. Other times it is subtle, such as the unfelt energy of gamma rays, which can destroy living cells.

Electromagnetic waves can bring energy into a system by virtue of their **electric and magnetic fields**. These fields can exert forces and move charges in the system and, thus, do work on them. If the frequency of the electromagnetic wave is the same as the natural frequencies of the system (such as microwaves at the resonant frequency of water molecules), the transfer of energy is much more efficient.

CONNECTIONS: WAVES AND PARTICLES

The behavior of electromagnetic radiation clearly exhibits wave characteristics. But we shall find in later modules that at high frequencies, electromagnetic radiation also exhibits particle characteristics. These particle characteristics will be used to explain more of the properties of the electromagnetic spectrum and to introduce the formal study of modern physics.

Another startling discovery of modern physics is that particles, such as electrons and protons, exhibit wave characteristics. This simultaneous sharing of wave and particle properties for all submicroscopic entities is one of the great symmetries in nature.

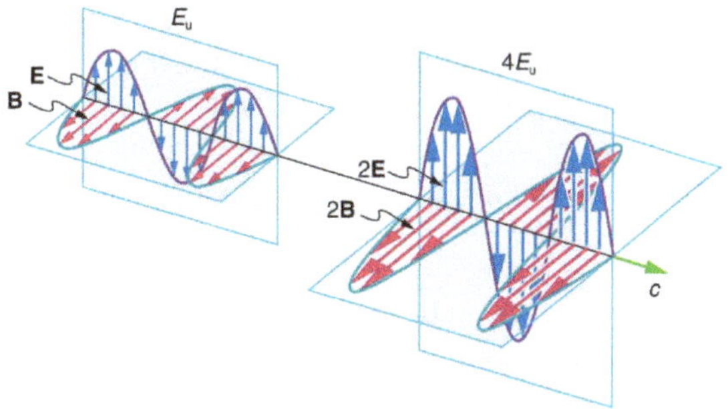

FIGURE 24.22 Energy carried by a wave is proportional to its amplitude squared. With electromagnetic waves, larger E-fields and B-fields exert larger forces and can do more work.

But there is energy in an electromagnetic wave, whether it is absorbed or not. Once created, the fields carry energy away from a source. If absorbed, the field strengths are diminished and anything left travels on. Clearly, the larger the strength of the electric and magnetic fields, the more work they can do and the greater the energy the electromagnetic wave carries.

A wave's energy is proportional to its **amplitude** squared (E^2 or B^2). This is true for waves on guitar strings, for water waves, and for sound waves, where amplitude is proportional to pressure. In electromagnetic waves, the amplitude is the **maximum field strength** of the electric and magnetic fields. (See Figure 24.22.)

Thus the energy carried and the **intensity** I of an electromagnetic wave is proportional to E^2 and B^2. In fact, for a continuous sinusoidal electromagnetic wave, the average intensity I_{ave} is given by

$$I_{\text{ave}} = \frac{c\varepsilon_0 E_0^2}{2}, \tag{24.18}$$

where c is the speed of light, ε_0 is the permittivity of free space, and E_0 is the maximum electric field strength; intensity, as always, is power per unit area (here in W/m^2).

The average intensity of an electromagnetic wave I_{ave} can also be expressed in terms of the magnetic field strength by using the relationship $B = E/c$, and the fact that $\varepsilon_0 = 1/\mu_0 c^2$, where μ_0 is the permeability of free space. Algebraic manipulation produces the relationship

$$I_{\text{ave}} = \frac{cB_0^2}{2\mu_0}, \tag{24.19}$$

where B_0 is the maximum magnetic field strength.

One more expression for I_{ave} in terms of both electric and magnetic field strengths is useful. Substituting the fact that $c \cdot B_0 = E_0$, the previous expression becomes

$$I_{\text{ave}} = \frac{E_0 B_0}{2\mu_0}. \tag{24.20}$$

Whichever of the three preceding equations is most convenient can be used, since they are really just different versions of the same principle: Energy in a wave is related to amplitude squared. Furthermore, since these equations are based on the assumption that the electromagnetic waves are sinusoidal, peak intensity is twice the average; that is, $I_0 = 2I_{\text{ave}}$.

EXAMPLE 24.4

Calculate Microwave Intensities and Fields

On its highest power setting, a certain microwave oven projects 1.00 kW of microwaves onto a 30.0 by 40.0 cm area. (a) What is the intensity in W/m^2? (b) Calculate the peak electric field strength E_0 in these waves. (c) What is the peak magnetic field strength B_0?

Strategy

In part (a), we can find intensity from its definition as power per unit area. Once the intensity is known, we can use the equations below to find the field strengths asked for in parts (b) and (c).

Solution for (a)

Entering the given power into the definition of intensity, and noting the area is 0.300 by 0.400 m, yields

$$I = \frac{P}{A} = \frac{1.00\ \text{kW}}{0.300\ \text{m} \times 0.400\ \text{m}}. \tag{24.21}$$

Here $I = I_{\text{ave}}$, so that

$$I_{\text{ave}} = \frac{1000\ \text{W}}{0.120\ \text{m}^2} = 8.33 \times 10^3\ \text{W/m}^2. \tag{24.22}$$

Note that the peak intensity is twice the average:

$$I_0 = 2I_{\text{ave}} = 1.67 \times 10^4 \text{ W/m}^2. \tag{24.23}$$

Solution for (b)

To find E_0, we can rearrange the first equation given above for I_{ave} to give

$$E_0 = \left(\frac{2I_{\text{ave}}}{c\varepsilon_0}\right)^{1/2}. \tag{24.24}$$

Entering known values gives

$$\begin{aligned} E_0 &= \sqrt{\frac{2(8.33\times10^3 \text{ W/m}^2)}{(3.00\times10^8 \text{ m/s})(8.85\times10^{-12} \text{ C}^2/\text{N}\cdot\text{m}^2)}} \\ &= 2.51 \times 10^3 \text{ V/m}. \end{aligned} \tag{24.25}$$

Solution for (c)

Perhaps the easiest way to find magnetic field strength, now that the electric field strength is known, is to use the relationship given by

$$B_0 = \frac{E_0}{c}. \tag{24.26}$$

Entering known values gives

$$\begin{aligned} B_0 &= \frac{2.51\times10^3 \text{ V/m}}{3.0\times10^8 \text{ m/s}} \\ &= 8.35 \times 10^{-6} \text{ T}. \end{aligned} \tag{24.27}$$

Discussion

As before, a relatively strong electric field is accompanied by a relatively weak magnetic field in an electromagnetic wave, since $B = E/c$, and c is a large number.

PHET EXPLORATIONS

Explore the effect of different types of radiation on various molecules. Choose the type of radiation and the molecules to see how they interact.

Click to view content (https://openstax.org/l/28Moleculeslight)

Glossary

amplitude the height, or magnitude, of an electromagnetic wave

amplitude modulation (AM) a method for placing information on electromagnetic waves by modulating the amplitude of a carrier wave with an audio signal, resulting in a wave with constant frequency but varying amplitude

carrier wave an electromagnetic wave that carries a signal by modulation of its amplitude or frequency

electric field a vector quantity (**E**); the lines of electric force per unit charge, moving radially outward from a positive charge and in toward a negative charge

electric field lines a pattern of imaginary lines that extend between an electric source and charged objects in the surrounding area, with arrows pointed away from positively charged objects and toward negatively charged objects. The more lines in the pattern, the stronger the electric field in that region

electric field strength the magnitude of the electric field, denoted *E*-field

electromagnetic spectrum the full range of wavelengths or frequencies of electromagnetic radiation

electromagnetic waves radiation in the form of waves of electric and magnetic energy

electromotive force (emf) energy produced per unit charge, drawn from a source that produces an electrical current

extremely low frequency (ELF) electromagnetic radiation with wavelengths usually in the range of 0 to 300 Hz, but also about 1kHz

frequency the number of complete wave cycles (up-down-up) passing a given point within one second (cycles/second)

frequency modulation (FM) a method of placing information on electromagnetic waves by modulating the frequency of a carrier wave with an audio signal, producing a wave of constant amplitude but varying frequency

gamma ray (γ ray); extremely high frequency electromagnetic radiation emitted by the nucleus of an atom, either from natural nuclear decay or induced nuclear processes in nuclear reactors and weapons. The lower end of the γ-ray frequency range overlaps the upper end of the X-ray range, but γ rays can have the highest frequency of any electromagnetic radiation

hertz an SI unit denoting the frequency of an electromagnetic wave, in cycles per second

infrared radiation (IR) a region of the electromagnetic spectrum with a frequency range that extends from just below the red region of the visible light spectrum up to the microwave region, or from $0.74\ \mu m$ to $300\ \mu m$

intensity the power of an electric or magnetic field per unit area, for example, Watts per square meter

magnetic field a vector quantity (**B**); can be used to determine the magnetic force on a moving charged particle

magnetic field lines a pattern of continuous, imaginary lines that emerge from and enter into opposite magnetic poles. The density of the lines indicates the magnitude of the magnetic field

magnetic field strength the magnitude of the magnetic field, denoted *B*-field

maximum field strength the maximum amplitude an electromagnetic wave can reach, representing the maximum amount of electric force and/or magnetic flux that the wave can exert

Maxwell's equations a set of four equations that comprise a complete, overarching theory of electromagnetism

microwaves electromagnetic waves with wavelengths in the range from 1 mm to 1 m; they can be produced by currents in macroscopic circuits and devices

oscillate to fluctuate back and forth in a steady beat

radar a common application of microwaves. Radar can determine the distance to objects as diverse as clouds and aircraft, as well as determine the speed of a car or the intensity of a rainstorm

radio waves electromagnetic waves with wavelengths in the range from 1 mm to 100 km; they are produced by currents in wires and circuits and by astronomical phenomena

resonant a system that displays enhanced oscillation when subjected to a periodic disturbance of the same frequency as its natural frequency

***RLC* circuit** an electric circuit that includes a resistor, capacitor and inductor

speed of light in a vacuum, such as space, the speed of light is a constant 3×10^8 m/s

standing wave a wave that oscillates in place, with nodes where no motion happens

thermal agitation the thermal motion of atoms and molecules in any object at a temperature above absolute zero, which causes them to emit and absorb radiation

transverse wave a wave, such as an electromagnetic wave, which oscillates perpendicular to the axis along the line of travel

TV video and audio signals broadcast on electromagnetic waves

ultra-high frequency (UHF) TV channels in an even higher frequency range than VHF, of 470 to 1000 MHz

ultraviolet radiation (UV) electromagnetic radiation in the range extending upward in frequency from violet light and overlapping with the lowest X-ray frequencies, with wavelengths from 400 nm down to about 10 nm

very high frequency (VHF) TV channels utilizing frequencies in the two ranges of 54 to 88 MHz and 174 to 222 MHz

visible light the narrow segment of the electromagnetic spectrum to which the normal human eye responds

wavelength the distance from one peak to the next in a wave

X-ray invisible, penetrating form of very high frequency electromagnetic radiation, overlapping both the ultraviolet range and the γ-ray range

Section Summary

24.1 Maxwell's Equations: Electromagnetic Waves Predicted and Observed

- Electromagnetic waves consist of oscillating electric and magnetic fields and propagate at the speed of light c. They were predicted by Maxwell, who also showed that
  $$c = \frac{1}{\sqrt{\mu_0 \varepsilon_0}},$$
  where μ_0 is the permeability of free space and ε_0 is the permittivity of free space.

- Maxwell's prediction of electromagnetic waves resulted from his formulation of a complete and symmetric theory of electricity and magnetism, known as Maxwell's equations.
- These four equations are paraphrased in this text, rather than presented numerically, and encompass the major laws of electricity and magnetism. First is Gauss's law for electricity, second is Gauss's law for magnetism, third is Faraday's law of induction, including Lenz's law, and fourth is Ampere's law in a symmetric formulation that adds another source of magnetism—changing electric fields.

24.2 Production of Electromagnetic Waves

- Electromagnetic waves are created by oscillating charges (which radiate whenever accelerated) and have the same frequency as the oscillation.
- Since the electric and magnetic fields in most electromagnetic waves are perpendicular to the direction in which the wave moves, it is ordinarily a transverse wave.
- The strengths of the electric and magnetic parts of the wave are related by
  $$\frac{E}{B} = c,$$
  which implies that the magnetic field B is very weak relative to the electric field E.

24.3 The Electromagnetic Spectrum

- The relationship among the speed of propagation, wavelength, and frequency for any wave is given by $v_W = f\lambda$, so that for electromagnetic waves,
  $$c = f\lambda,$$
  where f is the frequency, λ is the wavelength, and c is the speed of light.
- The electromagnetic spectrum is separated into many categories and subcategories, based on the frequency and wavelength, source, and uses of the electromagnetic waves.
- Any electromagnetic wave produced by currents in wires is classified as a radio wave, the lowest frequency electromagnetic waves. Radio waves are divided into many types, depending on their applications, ranging up to microwaves at their highest frequencies.
- Infrared radiation lies below visible light in frequency and is produced by thermal motion and the vibration and rotation of atoms and molecules. Infrared's lower frequencies overlap with the highest-frequency microwaves.
- Visible light is largely produced by electronic transitions in atoms and molecules, and is defined as being detectable by the human eye. Its colors vary with frequency, from red at the lowest to violet at the highest.
- Ultraviolet radiation starts with frequencies just above violet in the visible range and is produced primarily by electronic transitions in atoms and molecules.
- X-rays are created in high-voltage discharges and by electron bombardment of metal targets. Their lowest frequencies overlap the ultraviolet range but extend to much higher values, overlapping at the high end with gamma rays.
- Gamma rays are nuclear in origin and are defined to include the highest-frequency electromagnetic radiation of any type.

24.4 Energy in Electromagnetic Waves

- The energy carried by any wave is proportional to its amplitude squared. For electromagnetic waves, this means intensity can be expressed as

$$I_{\text{ave}} = \frac{c\varepsilon_0 E_0^2}{2},$$

where I_{ave} is the average intensity in W/m^2, and E_0 is the maximum electric field strength of a continuous sinusoidal wave.

- This can also be expressed in terms of the maximum magnetic field strength B_0 as

$$I_{\text{ave}} = \frac{cB_0^2}{2\mu_0}$$

and in terms of both electric and magnetic fields as

$$I_{\text{ave}} = \frac{E_0 B_0}{2\mu_0}.$$

- The three expressions for I_{ave} are all equivalent.

Conceptual Questions

24.2 Production of Electromagnetic Waves

1. The direction of the electric field shown in each part of Figure 24.5 is that produced by the charge distribution in the wire. Justify the direction shown in each part, using the Coulomb force law and the definition of $\mathbf{E} = \mathbf{F}/q$, where q is a positive test charge.

2. Is the direction of the magnetic field shown in Figure 24.6 (a) consistent with the right-hand rule for current (RHR-2) in the direction shown in the figure?

3. Why is the direction of the current shown in each part of Figure 24.6 opposite to the electric field produced by the wire's charge separation?

4. In which situation shown in Figure 24.23 will the electromagnetic wave be more successful in inducing a current in the wire? Explain.

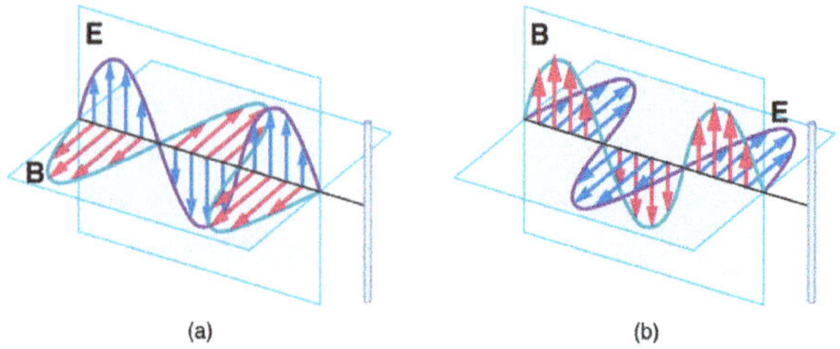

FIGURE 24.23 Electromagnetic waves approaching long straight wires.

5. In which situation shown in Figure 24.24 will the electromagnetic wave be more successful in inducing a current in the loop? Explain.

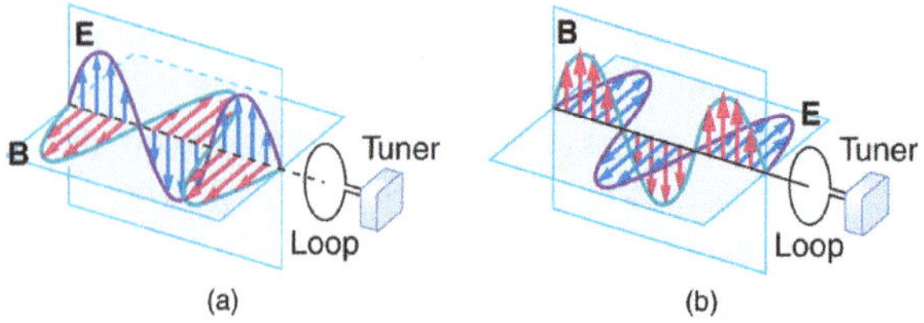

FIGURE 24.24 Electromagnetic waves approaching a wire loop.

6. Should the straight wire antenna of a radio be vertical or horizontal to best receive radio waves broadcast by a vertical transmitter antenna? How should a loop antenna be aligned to best receive the signals? (Note that the direction of the loop that produces the best reception can be used to determine the location of the source. It is used for that purpose in tracking tagged animals in nature studies, for example.)

7. Under what conditions might wires in a DC circuit emit electromagnetic waves?

8. Give an example of interference of electromagnetic waves.

9. Figure 24.25 shows the interference pattern of two radio antennas broadcasting the same signal. Explain how this is analogous to the interference pattern for sound produced by two speakers. Could this be used to make a directional antenna system that broadcasts preferentially in certain directions? Explain.

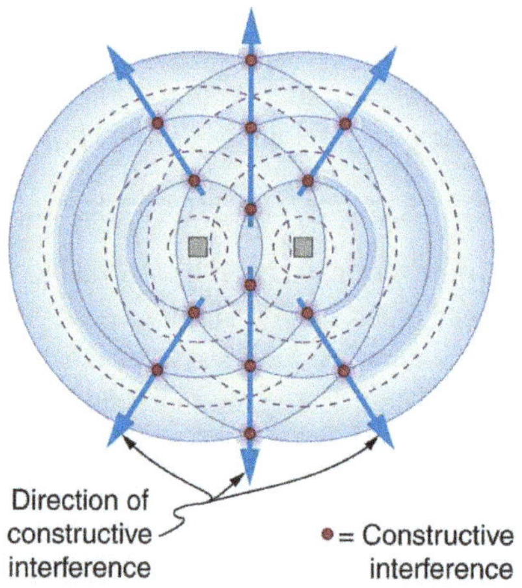

FIGURE 24.25 An overhead view of two radio broadcast antennas sending the same signal, and the interference pattern they produce.

10. Can an antenna be any length? Explain your answer.

24.3 The Electromagnetic Spectrum

11. If you live in a region that has a particular TV

station, you can sometimes pick up some of its audio portion on your FM radio receiver. Explain how this is possible. Does it imply that TV audio is broadcast as FM?

12. Explain why people who have the lens of their eye removed because of cataracts are able to see low-frequency ultraviolet.

13. How do fluorescent soap residues make clothing look "brighter and whiter" in outdoor light? Would this be effective in candlelight?

14. Give an example of resonance in the reception of electromagnetic waves.

15. Illustrate that the size of details of an object that can be detected with electromagnetic waves is related to their wavelength, by comparing details observable with two different types (for example, radar and visible light or infrared and X-rays).

16. Why don't buildings block radio waves as completely as they do visible light?

17. Make a list of some everyday objects and decide whether they are transparent or opaque to each of the types of electromagnetic waves.

18. Your friend says that more patterns and colors can be seen on the wings of birds if viewed in ultraviolet light. Would you agree with your friend? Explain your answer.

19. The rate at which information can be transmitted on an electromagnetic wave is proportional to the frequency of the wave. Is this consistent with the fact that laser telephone transmission at visible frequencies carries far more conversations per optical fiber than conventional electronic transmission in a wire? What is the implication for ELF radio communication with submarines?

20. Give an example of energy carried by an electromagnetic wave.

21. In an MRI scan, a higher magnetic field requires higher frequency radio waves to resonate with the nuclear type whose density and location is being imaged. What effect does going to a larger magnetic field have on the most efficient antenna to broadcast those radio waves? Does it favor a smaller or larger antenna?

22. Laser vision correction often uses an excimer laser that produces 193-nm electromagnetic radiation. This wavelength is extremely strongly absorbed by the cornea and ablates it in a manner that reshapes the cornea to correct vision defects. Explain how the strong absorption helps concentrate the energy in a thin layer and thus give greater accuracy in shaping the cornea. Also explain how this strong absorption limits damage to the lens and retina of the eye.

Problems & Exercises

24.1 Maxwell's Equations: Electromagnetic Waves Predicted and Observed

1. Verify that the correct value for the speed of light c is obtained when numerical values for the permeability and permittivity of free space (μ_0 and ε_0) are entered into the equation $c = \frac{1}{\sqrt{\mu_0 \varepsilon_0}}$.

2. Show that, when SI units for μ_0 and ε_0 are entered, the units given by the right-hand side of the equation in the problem above are m/s.

24.2 Production of Electromagnetic Waves

3. What is the maximum electric field strength in an electromagnetic wave that has a maximum magnetic field strength of $5.00 \times 10^{-4}\ \text{T}$ (about 10 times the Earth's)?

4. The maximum magnetic field strength of an electromagnetic field is $5 \times 10^{-6}\ \text{T}$. Calculate the maximum electric field strength if the wave is traveling in a medium in which the speed of the wave is $0.75c$.

5. Verify the units obtained for magnetic field strength B in Example 24.1 (using the equation $B = \frac{E}{c}$) are in fact teslas (T).

24.3 The Electromagnetic Spectrum

6. (a) Two microwave frequencies are authorized for use in microwave ovens: 900 and 2560 MHz. Calculate the wavelength of each. (b) Which frequency would produce smaller hot spots in foods due to interference effects?

7. (a) Calculate the range of wavelengths for AM radio given its frequency range is 540 to 1600 kHz. (b) Do the same for the FM frequency range of 88.0 to 108 MHz.

8. A radio station utilizes frequencies between commercial AM and FM. What is the frequency of a 11.12-m-wavelength channel?

9. Find the frequency range of visible light, given that

it encompasses wavelengths from 380 to 760 nm.

10. Combing your hair leads to excess electrons on the comb. How fast would you have to move the comb up and down to produce red light?

11. Electromagnetic radiation having a $15.0 - \mu\text{m}$ wavelength is classified as infrared radiation. What is its frequency?

12. Approximately what is the smallest detail observable with a microscope that uses ultraviolet light of frequency 1.20×10^{15} Hz?

13. A radar used to detect the presence of aircraft receives a pulse that has reflected off an object 6×10^{-5} s after it was transmitted. What is the distance from the radar station to the reflecting object?

14. Some radar systems detect the size and shape of objects such as aircraft and geological terrain. Approximately what is the smallest observable detail utilizing 500-MHz radar?

15. Determine the amount of time it takes for X-rays of frequency 3×10^{18} Hz to travel (a) 1 mm and (b) 1 cm.

16. If you wish to detect details of the size of atoms (about 1×10^{-10} m) with electromagnetic radiation, it must have a wavelength of about this size. (a) What is its frequency? (b) What type of electromagnetic radiation might this be?

17. If the Sun suddenly turned off, we would not know it until its light stopped coming. How long would that be, given that the Sun is 1.50×10^{11} m away?

18. Distances in space are often quoted in units of light years, the distance light travels in one year. (a) How many meters is a light year? (b) How many meters is it to Andromeda, the nearest large galaxy, given that it is 2.00×10^{6} light years away? (c) The most distant galaxy yet discovered is 12.0×10^{9} light years away. How far is this in meters?

19. A certain 50.0-Hz AC power line radiates an electromagnetic wave having a maximum electric field strength of 13.0 kV/m. (a) What is the wavelength of this very low frequency electromagnetic wave? (b) What is its maximum magnetic field strength?

20. During normal beating, the heart creates a maximum 4.00-mV potential across 0.300 m of a person's chest, creating a 1.00-Hz electromagnetic wave. (a) What is the maximum electric field strength created? (b) What is the corresponding maximum magnetic field strength in the electromagnetic wave? (c) What is the wavelength of the electromagnetic wave?

21. (a) The ideal size (most efficient) for a broadcast antenna with one end on the ground is one-fourth the wavelength ($\lambda/4$) of the electromagnetic radiation being sent out. If a new radio station has such an antenna that is 50.0 m high, what frequency does it broadcast most efficiently? Is this in the AM or FM band? (b) Discuss the analogy of the fundamental resonant mode of an air column closed at one end to the resonance of currents on an antenna that is one-fourth their wavelength.

22. (a) What is the wavelength of 100-MHz radio waves used in an MRI unit? (b) If the frequencies are swept over a ±1.00 range centered on 100 MHz, what is the range of wavelengths broadcast?

23. (a) What is the frequency of the 193-nm ultraviolet radiation used in laser eye surgery? (b) Assuming the accuracy with which this EM radiation can ablate the cornea is directly proportional to wavelength, how much more accurate can this UV be than the shortest visible wavelength of light?

24. TV-reception antennas for VHF are constructed with cross wires supported at their centers, as shown in Figure 24.26. The ideal length for the cross wires is one-half the wavelength to be received, with the more expensive antennas having one for each channel. Suppose you measure the lengths of the wires for particular channels and find them to be 1.94 and 0.753 m long, respectively. What are the frequencies for these channels?

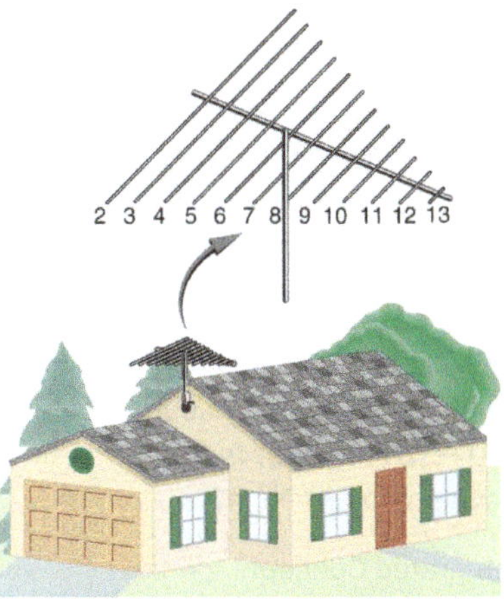

FIGURE 24.26 A television reception antenna has cross wires of various lengths to most efficiently receive different wavelengths.

25. Conversations with astronauts on lunar walks had an echo that was used to estimate the distance to the Moon. The sound spoken by the person on Earth was transformed into a radio signal sent to the Moon, and transformed back into sound on a speaker inside the astronaut's space suit. This sound was picked up by the microphone in the space suit (intended for the astronaut's voice) and sent back to Earth as a radio echo of sorts. If the round-trip time was 2.60 s, what was the approximate distance to the Moon, neglecting any delays in the electronics?

26. Lunar astronauts placed a reflector on the Moon's surface, off which a laser beam is periodically reflected. The distance to the Moon is calculated from the round-trip time. (a) To what accuracy in meters can the distance to the Moon be determined, if this time can be measured to 0.100 ns? (b) What percent accuracy is this, given the average distance to the Moon is 3.84×10^8 m?

27. Radar is used to determine distances to various objects by measuring the round-trip time for an echo from the object. (a) How far away is the planet Venus if the echo time is 1000 s? (b) What is the echo time for a car 75.0 m from a Highway Police radar unit? (c) How accurately (in nanoseconds) must you be able to measure the echo time to an airplane 12.0 km away to determine its distance within 10.0 m?

28. Integrated Concepts
(a) Calculate the ratio of the highest to lowest frequencies of electromagnetic waves the eye can see, given the wavelength range of visible light is from 380 to 760 nm. (b) Compare this with the ratio of highest to lowest frequencies the ear can hear.

29. Integrated Concepts
(a) Calculate the rate in watts at which heat transfer through radiation occurs (almost entirely in the infrared) from $1.0\ \mathrm{m}^2$ of the Earth's surface at night. Assume the emissivity is 0.90, the temperature of the Earth is $15^{\circ}\mathrm{C}$, and that of outer space is 2.7 K. (b) Compare the intensity of this radiation with that coming to the Earth from the Sun during the day, which averages about $800\ \mathrm{W/m}^2$, only half of which is absorbed. (c) What is the maximum magnetic field strength in the outgoing radiation, assuming it is a continuous wave?

24.4 Energy in Electromagnetic Waves

30. What is the intensity of an electromagnetic wave with a peak electric field strength of 125 V/m?

31. Find the intensity of an electromagnetic wave having a peak magnetic field strength of 4.00×10^{-9} T.

32. Assume the helium-neon lasers commonly used in student physics laboratories have power outputs of 0.250 mW. (a) If such a laser beam is projected onto a circular spot 1.00 mm in diameter, what is its intensity? (b) Find the peak magnetic field strength. (c) Find the peak electric field strength.

33. An AM radio transmitter broadcasts 50.0 kW of power uniformly in all directions. (a) Assuming all of the radio waves that strike the ground are completely absorbed, and that there is no absorption by the atmosphere or other objects, what is the intensity 30.0 km away? (Hint: Half the power will be spread over the area of a hemisphere.) (b) What is the maximum electric field strength at this distance?

34. Suppose the maximum safe intensity of microwaves for human exposure is taken to be $1.00\ \mathrm{W/m}^2$. (a) If a radar unit leaks 10.0 W of microwaves (other than those sent by its antenna) uniformly in all directions, how far away must you be to be exposed to an intensity considered to be safe? Assume that the power spreads uniformly over the area of a sphere with no complications from absorption or reflection. (b) What is the maximum electric field strength at the safe intensity? (Note that early radar units leaked more than modern ones do. This caused identifiable health problems, such as cataracts, for people who worked near them.)

35. A 2.50-m-diameter university communications satellite dish receives TV signals that have a maximum electric field strength (for one channel) of $7.50\ \mu\text{V/m}$. (See Figure 24.27.) (a) What is the intensity of this wave? (b) What is the power received by the antenna? (c) If the orbiting satellite broadcasts uniformly over an area of $1.50 \times 10^{13}\ \text{m}^2$ (a large fraction of North America), how much power does it radiate?

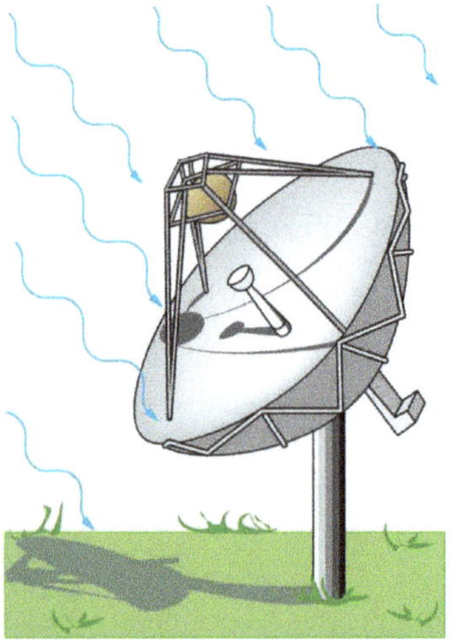

FIGURE 24.27 Satellite dishes receive TV signals sent from orbit. Although the signals are quite weak, the receiver can detect them by being tuned to resonate at their frequency.

36. Lasers can be constructed that produce an extremely high intensity electromagnetic wave for a brief time—called pulsed lasers. They are used to ignite nuclear fusion, for example. Such a laser may produce an electromagnetic wave with a maximum electric field strength of $1.00 \times 10^{11}\ \text{V/m}$ for a time of 1.00 ns. (a) What is the maximum magnetic field strength in the wave? (b) What is the intensity of the beam? (c) What energy does it deliver on a 1.00-mm^2 area?

37. Show that for a continuous sinusoidal electromagnetic wave, the peak intensity is twice the average intensity ($I_0 = 2I_{\text{ave}}$), using either the fact that $E_0 = \sqrt{2}E_{\text{rms}}$, or $B_0 = \sqrt{2}B_{\text{rms}}$, where rms means average (actually root mean square, a type of average).

38. Suppose a source of electromagnetic waves radiates uniformly in all directions in empty space where there are no absorption or interference effects. (a) Show that the intensity is inversely proportional to r^2, the distance from the source squared. (b) Show that the magnitudes of the electric and magnetic fields are inversely proportional to r.

39. Integrated Concepts
An LC circuit with a 5.00-pF capacitor oscillates in such a manner as to radiate at a wavelength of 3.30 m. (a) What is the resonant frequency? (b) What inductance is in series with the capacitor?

40. Integrated Concepts
What capacitance is needed in series with an $800 - \mu\text{H}$ inductor to form a circuit that radiates a wavelength of 196 m?

41. Integrated Concepts
Police radar determines the speed of motor vehicles using the same Doppler-shift technique employed for ultrasound in medical diagnostics. Beats are produced by mixing the double Doppler-shifted echo with the original frequency. If $1.50 \times 10^9\text{-Hz}$ microwaves are used and a beat frequency of 150 Hz is produced, what is the speed of the vehicle? (Assume the same Doppler-shift formulas are valid with the speed of sound replaced by the speed of light.)

42. Integrated Concepts
Assume the mostly infrared radiation from a heat lamp acts like a continuous wave with wavelength $1.50\ \mu\text{m}$. (a) If the lamp's 200-W output is focused on a person's shoulder, over a circular area 25.0 cm in diameter, what is the intensity in W/m^2? (b) What is the peak electric field strength? (c) Find the peak magnetic field strength. (d) How long will it take to increase the temperature of the 4.00-kg shoulder by $2.00^\circ\ \text{C}$, assuming no other heat transfer and given that its specific heat is $3.47 \times 10^3\ \text{J/kg}\cdot{}^\circ\text{C}$?

43. Integrated Concepts
On its highest power setting, a microwave oven increases the temperature of 0.400 kg of spaghetti by 45.0°C in 120 s. (a) What was the rate of power absorption by the spaghetti, given that its specific heat is $3.76 \times 10^3\ \text{J/kg}\cdot{}^\circ\text{C}$? (b) Find the average intensity of the microwaves, given that they are absorbed over a circular area 20.0 cm in diameter. (c) What is the peak electric field strength of the microwave? (d) What is its peak magnetic field strength?

44. Integrated Concepts
Electromagnetic radiation from a 5.00-mW laser is concentrated on a 1.00-mm^2 area. (a) What is the intensity in W/m^2? (b) Suppose a 2.00-nC static

charge is in the beam. What is the maximum electric force it experiences? (c) If the static charge moves at 400 m/s, what maximum magnetic force can it feel?

45. Integrated Concepts
A 200-turn flat coil of wire 30.0 cm in diameter acts as an antenna for FM radio at a frequency of 100 MHz. The magnetic field of the incoming electromagnetic wave is perpendicular to the coil and has a maximum strength of 1.00×10^{-12} T. (a) What power is incident on the coil? (b) What average emf is induced in the coil over one-fourth of a cycle? (c) If the radio receiver has an inductance of $2.50\ \mu\text{H}$, what capacitance must it have to resonate at 100 MHz?

46. Integrated Concepts
If electric and magnetic field strengths vary sinusoidally in time, being zero at $t = 0$, then $E = E_0 \sin 2\pi ft$ and $B = B_0 \sin 2\pi ft$. Let $f = 1.00$ GHz here. (a) When are the field strengths first zero? (b) When do they reach their most negative value? (c) How much time is needed for them to complete one cycle?

47. Unreasonable Results
A researcher measures the wavelength of a 1.20-GHz electromagnetic wave to be 0.500 m. (a) Calculate the speed at which this wave propagates. (b) What is unreasonable about this result? (c) Which assumptions are unreasonable or inconsistent?

48. Unreasonable Results
The peak magnetic field strength in a residential microwave oven is 9.20×10^{-5} T. (a) What is the intensity of the microwave? (b) What is unreasonable about this result? (c) What is wrong about the premise?

49. Unreasonable Results
An LC circuit containing a 2.00-H inductor oscillates at such a frequency that it radiates at a 1.00-m wavelength. (a) What is the capacitance of the circuit? (b) What is unreasonable about this result? (c) Which assumptions are unreasonable or inconsistent?

50. Unreasonable Results
An LC circuit containing a 1.00-pF capacitor oscillates at such a frequency that it radiates at a 300-nm wavelength. (a) What is the inductance of the circuit? (b) What is unreasonable about this result? (c) Which assumptions are unreasonable or inconsistent?

51. Create Your Own ProblemConsider electromagnetic fields produced by high voltage power lines. Construct a problem in which you calculate the intensity of this electromagnetic radiation in W/m^2 based on the measured magnetic field strength of the radiation in a home near the power lines. Assume these magnetic field strengths are known to average less than a μT. The intensity is small enough that it is difficult to imagine mechanisms for biological damage due to it. Discuss how much energy may be radiating from a section of power line several hundred meters long and compare this to the power likely to be carried by the lines. An idea of how much power this is can be obtained by calculating the approximate current responsible for μT fields at distances of tens of meters.

52. Create Your Own ProblemConsider the most recent generation of residential satellite dishes that are a little less than half a meter in diameter. Construct a problem in which you calculate the power received by the dish and the maximum electric field strength of the microwave signals for a single channel received by the dish. Among the things to be considered are the power broadcast by the satellite and the area over which the power is spread, as well as the area of the receiving dish.

53. Critical Thinking (a) Find the magnetic field strength when the electric field strength is 1,250 V/m. (b) If *E* is increased, would *B* be increased, decreased, or remain the same? (c) By what factor would the change in part b be, if any?

Test Prep for AP® Courses

24.2 Production of Electromagnetic Waves

1. If an electromagnetic wave is described as having a frequency of 3 GHz, what are its period and wavelength (in a vacuum)?
a. 3.0×10^9s, 10 cm
b. 3.3×10^{-10}s, 10 cm
c. 3.3×10^{-10}s, 10 m
d. 3.0×10^9s, 10 m

2. Describe the outcome if you attempt to produce a longitudinal electromagnetic wave.

3. A wave is travelling through a medium until it hits

the end of the medium and there is nothing but vacuum beyond. What happens to a mechanical wave? Electromagnetic wave?

a. reflects backward, continues on
b. reflects backward, reflects backward
c. continues on, continues on
d. stops, continues on

4. You're on the moon, skipping around, and your radio breaks. What would be the best way to communicate this problem to your friend, who is also skipping around on the moon: yelling or flashing a light? Why?

5. Given the waveform in Figure 24.5(d), if $T = 3.0 \times 10^{-9}$ s and $E = 5.0 \times 10^{5}$ N/C, which of the following is the correct equation for the wave at the antenna?

a. $\left(5.0 \times 10^{5}\ \text{N/C}\right) \sin\left(2\pi\left(3.0 \times 10^{-9}\ \text{s}\right)t\right)$
b. $\left(5.0 \times 10^{5}\ \text{N/C}\right) \sin\left(\frac{2\pi t}{\left(3.0 \times 10^{-9}\ \text{s}\right)}\right)$
c. $\left(5.0 \times 10^{5}\ \text{N/C}\right) \cos\left(2\pi\left(3.0 \times 10^{-9}\ \text{s}\right)t\right)$
d. $\left(5.0 \times 10^{5}\ \text{N/C}\right) \cos\left(\frac{2\pi t}{\left(3.0 \times 10^{-9}\ \text{s}\right)}\right)$

6. Given the waveform in Figure 24.5(d), if $f = 2.0$ GHz and $E = 6.0 \times 10^{5}$ N/C, what is the correct equation for the magnetic field wave at the antenna?

7. In Heinrich Hertz's spark gap experiment (Figure 24.4), how will the induced sparks in Loop 2 compare to those created in Loop 1?

a. Stronger
b. Weaker
c. Need to know the tuner settings to tell
d. Weaker, but how much depends on the tuner settings.

8. The sun is far away from the Earth, and the intervening space is very close to empty. Yet the tilt of the Earth's axis of rotation relative to the sun results in seasons. Explain why, given what you have learned in this section.

24.3 The Electromagnetic Spectrum

9. The correct ordering from least to greatest wavelength is:

a. ELF, FM radio, microwaves, infrared, red, green, ultraviolet, x-ray, gamma ray
b. ELF, FM radio, microwaves, infrared, green, red, ultraviolet, x-ray, gamma ray
c. gamma ray, x-ray, ultraviolet, red, green, infrared, microwaves, FM radio, ELF
d. gamma ray, x-ray, ultraviolet, green, red, infrared, microwaves, FM radio, ELF

10. Describe how our vision would be different if we could see energy in what we define as the radio spectrum.

24.4 Energy in Electromagnetic Waves

11. An old microwave oven outputs only half the electric field it used to. How much longer does it take to cook things in this microwave oven?

a. Four times as long
b. Twice as long
c. Half the time
d. One fourth the time

12. Describe at least two improvements you could make to a radar set to make it more sensitive (able to detect things at longer ranges). Explain why these would work.

CHAPTER 25

Geometric Optics

FIGURE 25.1 Image seen as a result of reflection of light on a plane smooth surface. (credit: NASA Goddard Photo and Video, via Flickr)

CHAPTER OUTLINE

CONNECTION FOR AP® COURSES Many visual aspects of light result from the transfer of energy in the form of electromagnetic waves (Big Idea 6). Light from this page or screen is formed into an image by the lens of your eye, much like the lens of the camera that make a photograph. Mirrors, like lenses, can also form images that in turn are captured by your eye (Essential Knowledge 6.E.2, Essential Knowledge 6.E.4). In this chapter, you will explore the behavior of light as an electromagnetic wave and learn:

- what makes a diamond sparkle (Essential Knowledge 6.E.3),
- how images are formed by lenses for the purposes of magnification or photography (Essential Knowledge 6.E.5),

- why objects in some mirrors are closer than they appear (Essential Knowledge 6.E.2), and
- why clear mountain streams are always a little bit deeper than they appear to be.

You will examine different ways of thinking about and modeling light and when each method is most appropriate (Enduring Understanding 6.F, Essential Knowledge 6.F.4). You will also learn how to use simple geometry to predict how light will move when crossing from one medium to another, or when passing through a lens, or when reflecting off a curved surface (Enduring Understanding 6.E, Essential Knowledge 6.E.1). With this knowledge, you will be able to predict what kind of image will form when light interacts with matter.

Big Idea 6 Waves can transfer energy and momentum from one location to another without the permanent transfer of mass and serve as a mathematical model for the description of other phenomena.

Enduring Understanding 6.E The direction of propagation of a wave such as light may be changed when the wave encounters an interface between two media.

Essential Knowledge 6.E.1 When light travels from one medium to another, some of the light is transmitted, some is reflected, and some is absorbed. (Qualitative understanding only.)

Essential Knowledge 6.E.2 When light hits a smooth reflecting surface at an angle, it reflects at the same angle on the other side of the line perpendicular to the surface (specular reflection); and this law of reflection accounts for the size and location of images seen in plane mirrors.

Essential Knowledge 6.E.3 When light travels across a boundary from one transparent material to another, the speed of propagation changes. At a non–normal incident angle, the path of the light ray bends closer to the perpendicular in the optically slower substance. This is called refraction.

Essential Knowledge 6.E.4 The reflection of light from surfaces can be used to form images.

Essential Knowledge 6.E.5 The refraction of light as it travels from one transparent medium to another can be used to form images.

Enduring Understanding 6.F Electromagnetic radiation can be modeled as waves or as fundamental particles.

Essential Knowledge 6.F.4 The nature of light requires that different models of light are most appropriate at different scales.

25.1 The Ray Aspect of Light

LEARNING OBJECTIVES

By the end of this section, you will be able to:

- List the ways by which light travels from a source to another location.

There are three ways in which light can travel from a source to another location. (See Figure 25.2.) It can come directly from the source through empty space, such as from the Sun to Earth. Or light can travel through various media, such as air and glass, to the person. Light can also arrive after being reflected, such as by a mirror. In all of these cases, light is modeled as traveling in straight lines called rays. Light may change direction when it encounters objects (such as a mirror) or in passing from one material to another (such as in passing from air to glass), but it then continues in a straight line or as a ray. The word **ray** comes from mathematics and here means a straight line that originates at some point. It is acceptable to visualize light rays as laser rays (or even science fiction depictions of ray guns).

RAY

The word “ray” comes from mathematics and here means a straight line that originates at some point.

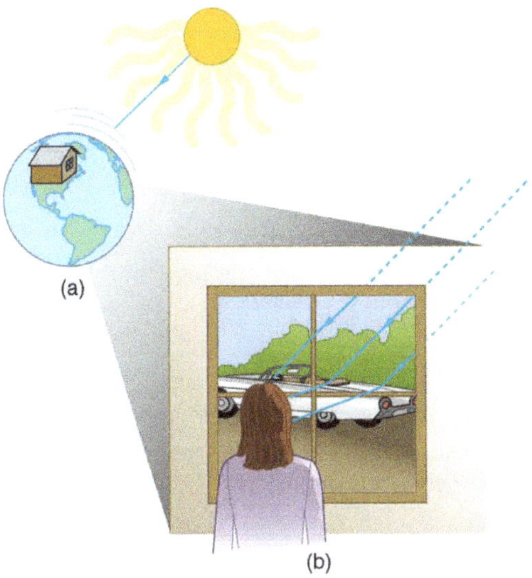

FIGURE 25.2 Three methods for light to travel from a source to another location. (a) Light reaches the upper atmosphere of Earth traveling through empty space directly from the source. (b) Light can reach a person in one of two ways. It can travel through media like air and glass. It can also reflect from an object like a mirror. In the situations shown here, light interacts with objects large enough that it travels in straight lines, like a ray.

Experiments, as well as our own experiences, show that when light interacts with objects several times as large as its wavelength, it travels in straight lines and acts like a ray. Its wave characteristics are not pronounced in such situations. Since the wavelength of light is less than a micron (a thousandth of a millimeter), it acts like a ray in the many common situations in which it encounters objects larger than a micron. For example, when light encounters anything we can observe with unaided eyes, such as a mirror, it acts like a ray, with only subtle wave characteristics. We will concentrate on the ray characteristics in this chapter.

Since light moves in straight lines, changing directions when it interacts with materials, it is described by geometry and simple trigonometry. This part of optics, where the ray aspect of light dominates, is therefore called **geometric optics**. There are two laws that govern how light changes direction when it interacts with matter. These are the law of reflection, for situations in which light bounces off matter, and the law of refraction, for situations in which light passes through matter.

GEOMETRIC OPTICS

The part of optics dealing with the ray aspect of light is called geometric optics.

25.2 The Law of Reflection

LEARNING OBJECTIVES

By the end of this section, you will be able to:

- Explain reflection of light from polished and rough surfaces.

Whenever we look into a mirror, or squint at sunlight glinting from a lake, we are seeing a reflection. When you look at this page, too, you are seeing light reflected from it. Large telescopes use reflection to form an image of stars and other astronomical objects.

The law of reflection is illustrated in Figure 25.3, which also shows how the angles are measured relative to the perpendicular to the surface at the point where the light ray strikes. We expect to see reflections from smooth surfaces, but Figure 25.4 illustrates how a rough surface reflects light. Since the light strikes different parts of the surface at different angles, it is reflected in many different directions, or diffused. Diffused light is what allows us to see a sheet of paper from any angle, as illustrated in Figure 25.5. Many objects, such as people, clothing, leaves, and walls, have rough surfaces and can be seen from all sides. A mirror, on the other hand, has a smooth surface (compared with the wavelength of light) and reflects light at specific angles, as illustrated in Figure 25.6. When the moon reflects from a lake, as shown in Figure 25.7, a combination of these effects takes place.

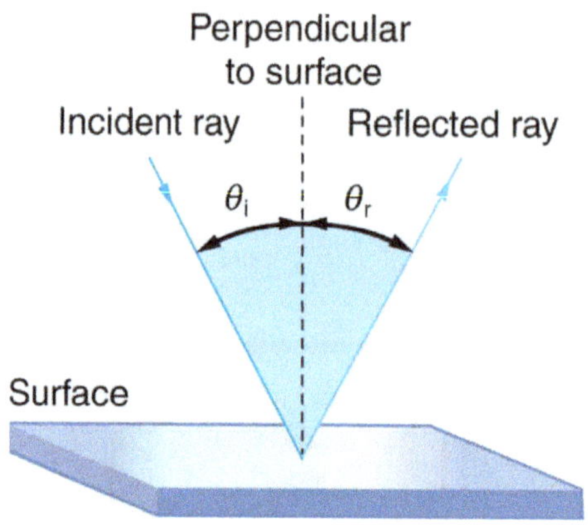

FIGURE 25.3 The law of reflection states that the angle of reflection equals the angle of incidence— $\theta_r = \theta_i$. The angles are measured relative to the perpendicular to the surface at the point where the ray strikes the surface.

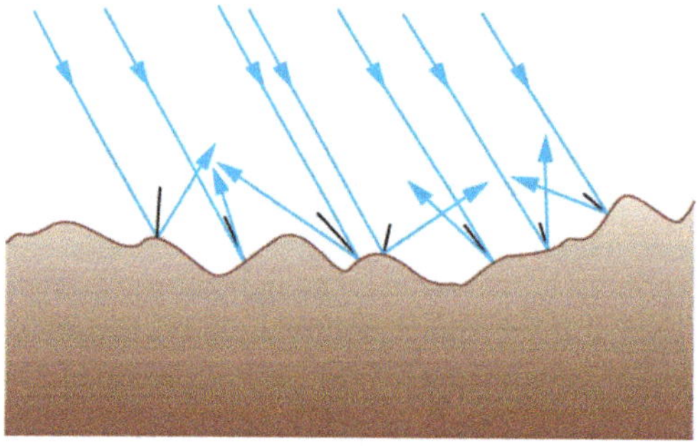

FIGURE 25.4 Light is diffused when it reflects from a rough surface. Here many parallel rays are incident, but they are reflected at many different angles since the surface is rough.

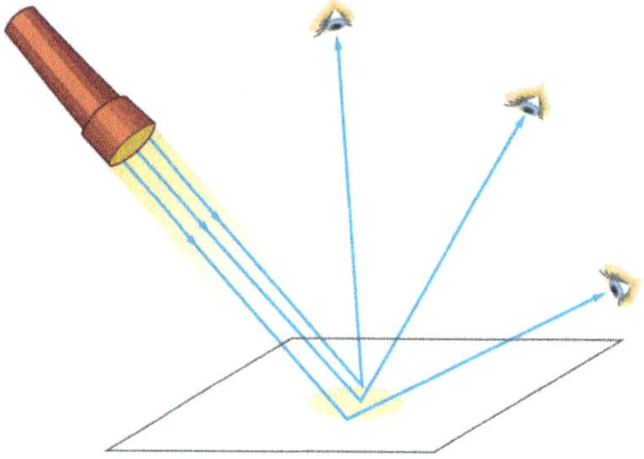

FIGURE 25.5 When a sheet of paper is illuminated with many parallel incident rays, it can be seen at many different angles, because its surface is rough and diffuses the light.

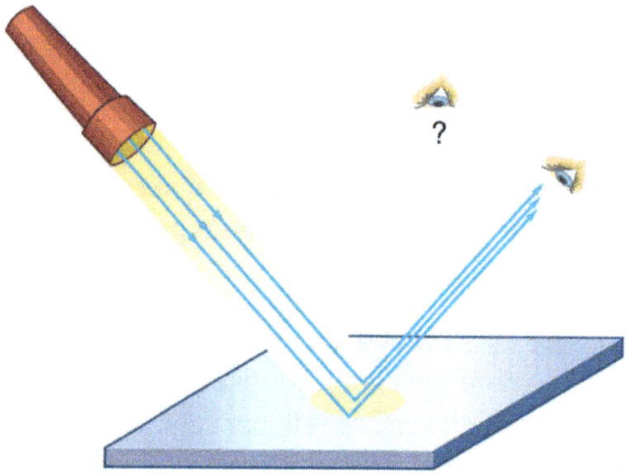

FIGURE 25.6 A mirror illuminated by many parallel rays reflects them in only one direction, since its surface is very smooth. Only the observer at a particular angle will see the reflected light.

FIGURE 25.7 Moonlight is spread out when it is reflected by the lake, since the surface is shiny but uneven. (credit: Diego Torres Silvestre, Flickr)

The law of reflection is very simple: The angle of reflection equals the angle of incidence.

THE LAW OF REFLECTION

The angle of reflection equals the angle of incidence.

When we see ourselves in a mirror, it appears that our image is actually behind the mirror. This is illustrated in Figure 25.8. We see the light coming from a direction determined by the law of reflection. The angles are such that our image is exactly the same distance behind the mirror as we stand away from the mirror. If the mirror is on the wall of a room, the images in it are all behind the mirror, which can make the room seem bigger. Although these mirror images make objects appear to be where they cannot be (like behind a solid wall), the images are not figments of our imagination. Mirror images can be photographed and videotaped by instruments and look just as they do with our eyes (optical instruments themselves). The precise manner in which images are formed by mirrors and lenses will be treated in later sections of this chapter.

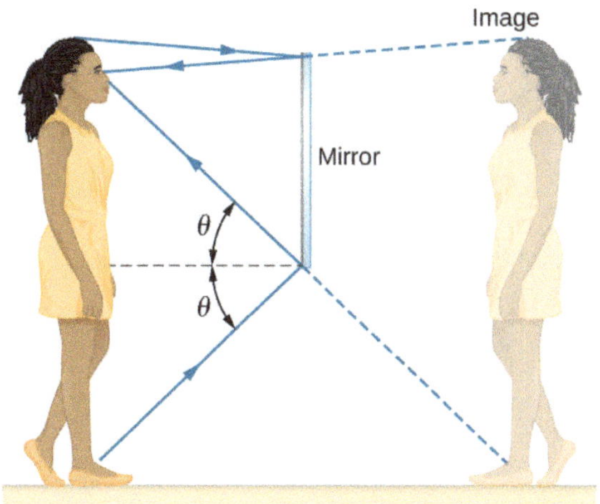

FIGURE 25.8 Our image in a mirror is behind the mirror. The two rays shown are those that strike the mirror at just the correct angles to be reflected into the eyes of the person. The image appears to be in the direction the rays are coming from when they enter the eyes.

TAKE-HOME EXPERIMENT: LAW OF REFLECTION

Take a piece of paper and shine a flashlight at an angle at the paper, as shown in Figure 25.5. Now shine the flashlight at a mirror at an angle. Do your observations confirm the predictions in Figure 25.5 and Figure 25.6? Shine the flashlight on various surfaces and determine whether the reflected light is diffuse or not. You can choose a shiny metallic lid of a pot or your skin. Using the mirror and flashlight, can you confirm the law of reflection? You will need to draw lines on a piece of paper showing the incident and reflected rays. (This part works even better if you use a laser pencil.)

25.3 The Law of Refraction

LEARNING OBJECTIVES

By the end of this section, you will be able to:

- Determine the index of refraction, given the speed of light in a medium.

It is easy to notice some odd things when looking into a fish tank. For example, you may see the same fish appearing to be in two different places. (See Figure 25.9.) This is because light coming from the fish to us changes direction when it leaves the tank, and in this case, it can travel two different paths to get to our eyes. The changing of a light ray's direction (loosely called bending) when it passes through variations in matter is called **refraction**. Refraction is responsible for a tremendous range of optical phenomena, from the action of lenses to voice transmission through optical fibers.

REFRACTION

The changing of a light ray's direction (loosely called bending) when it passes through variations in matter is called refraction.

SPEED OF LIGHT

The speed of light c not only affects refraction, it is one of the central concepts of Einstein's theory of relativity. As the accuracy of the measurements of the speed of light were improved, c was found not to depend on the velocity of the source or the observer. However, the speed of light does vary in a precise manner with the material it traverses. These facts have far-reaching implications, as we will see in Special Relativity. It makes connections between space and time and alters our expectations that all observers measure the same time for the same event, for example. The speed of light is so important that its value in a vacuum is one of the most fundamental constants in nature as well as being one of the four fundamental SI units.

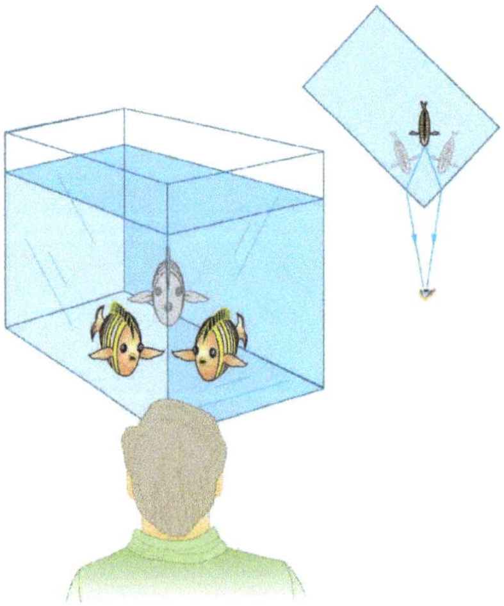

FIGURE 25.9 Looking at the fish tank as shown, we can see the same fish in two different locations, because light changes directions when it passes from water to air. In this case, the light can reach the observer by two different paths, and so the fish seems to be in two different places. This bending of light is called refraction and is responsible for many optical phenomena.

Why does light change direction when passing from one material (medium) to another? It is because light changes speed when going from one material to another. So before we study the law of refraction, it is useful to discuss the speed of light and how it varies in different media.

The Speed of Light

Early attempts to measure the speed of light, such as those made by Galileo, determined that light moved extremely fast, perhaps instantaneously. The first real evidence that light traveled at a finite speed came from the Danish astronomer Ole Roemer in the late 17th century. Roemer had noted that the average orbital period of one of Jupiter's moons, as measured from Earth, varied depending on whether Earth was moving toward or away from Jupiter. He correctly concluded that the apparent change in period was due to the change in distance between Earth and Jupiter and the time it took light to travel this distance. From his 1676 data, a value of the speed of light was calculated to be 2.26×10^8 m/s (only 25% different from today's accepted value). In more recent times, physicists have measured the speed of light in numerous ways and with increasing accuracy. One particularly direct method, used in 1887 by the American physicist Albert Michelson (1852–1931), is illustrated in Figure 25.10. Light reflected from a rotating set of mirrors was reflected from a stationary mirror 35 km away and returned to the rotating mirrors. The time for the light to travel can be determined by how fast the mirrors must rotate for the light to be returned to the observer's eye.

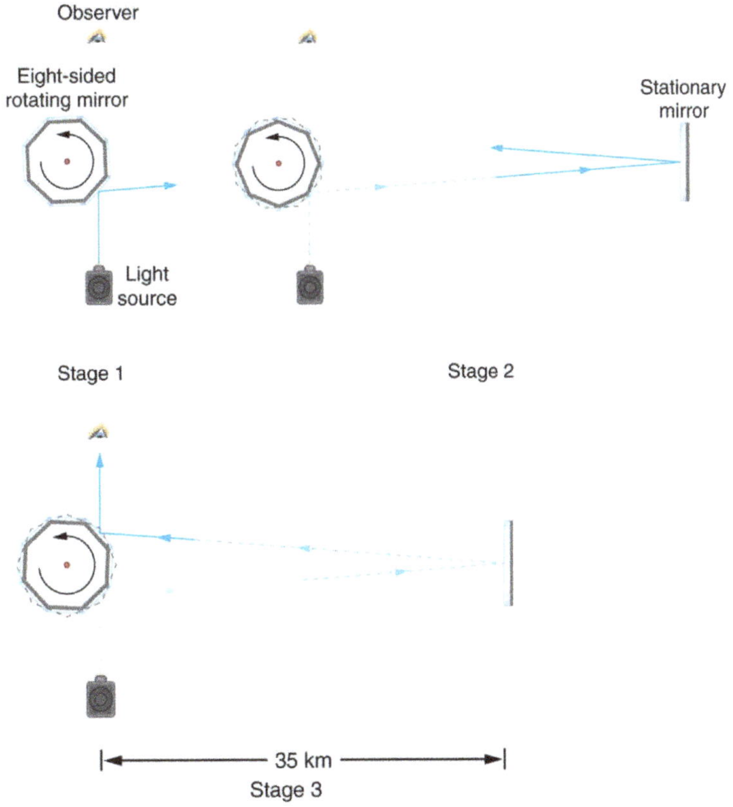

FIGURE 25.10 A schematic of early apparatus used by Michelson and others to determine the speed of light. As the mirrors rotate, the reflected ray is only briefly directed at the stationary mirror. The returning ray will be reflected into the observer's eye only if the next mirror has rotated into the correct position just as the ray returns. By measuring the correct rotation rate, the time for the round trip can be measured and the speed of light calculated. Michelson's calculated value of the speed of light was only 0.04% different from the value used today.

The speed of light is now known to great precision. In fact, the speed of light in a vacuum c is so important that it is accepted as one of the basic physical quantities and has the fixed value

$$c = 2.99792458 \times 10^8 \text{ m/s} \approx 3.00 \times 10^8 \text{ m/s}, \tag{25.1}$$

where the approximate value of 3.00×10^8 m/s is used whenever three-digit accuracy is sufficient. The speed of light through matter is less than it is in a vacuum, because light interacts with atoms in a material. The speed of light depends strongly on the type of material, since its interaction with different atoms, crystal lattices, and other substructures varies. We define the **index of refraction** n of a material to be

$$n = \frac{c}{v}, \tag{25.2}$$

where v is the observed speed of light in the material. Since the speed of light is always less than c in matter and equals c only in a vacuum, the index of refraction is always greater than or equal to one.

VALUE OF THE SPEED OF LIGHT

$$c = 2.99792458 \times 10^8 \text{ m/s} \approx 3.00 \times 10^8 \text{ m/s} \qquad 25.3$$

INDEX OF REFRACTION

$$n = \frac{c}{v} \qquad 25.4$$

That is, $n \geq 1$. Table 25.1 gives the indices of refraction for some representative substances. The values are listed for a particular wavelength of light, because they vary slightly with wavelength. (This can have important effects, such as colors produced by a prism.) Note that for gases, n is close to 1.0. This seems reasonable, since atoms in gases are widely separated and light travels at c in the vacuum between atoms. It is common to take $n = 1$ for gases unless great precision is needed. Although the speed of light v in a medium varies considerably from its value c in a vacuum, it is still a large speed.

Medium	n
Gases at $0°\text{C}$***, 1 atm***	
Air	1.000293
Carbon dioxide	1.00045
Hydrogen	1.000139
Oxygen	1.000271
Liquids at $20°\text{C}$	
Benzene	1.501
Carbon disulfide	1.628
Carbon tetrachloride	1.461
Ethanol	1.361
Glycerine	1.473
Water, fresh	1.333
Solids at $20°\text{C}$	
Diamond	2.419

TABLE 25.1 Index of Refraction in Various Media

Medium	n
Fluorite	1.434
Glass, crown	1.52
Glass, flint	1.66
Ice at 20°C	1.309
Polystyrene	1.49
Plexiglas	1.51
Quartz, crystalline	1.544
Quartz, fused	1.458
Sodium chloride	1.544
Zircon	1.923

TABLE 25.1 Index of Refraction in Various Media

EXAMPLE 25.1

Speed of Light in Matter

Calculate the speed of light in zircon, a material used in jewelry to imitate diamond.

Strategy

The speed of light in a material, v, can be calculated from the index of refraction n of the material using the equation $n = c/v$.

Solution

The equation for index of refraction states that $n = c/v$. Rearranging this to determine v gives

$$v = \frac{c}{n}. \tag{25.5}$$

The index of refraction for zircon is given as 1.923 in Table 25.1, and c is given in the equation for speed of light. Entering these values in the last expression gives

$$\begin{aligned} v &= \frac{3.00\times10^8 \text{ m/s}}{1.923} \\ &= 1.56\times10^8 \text{ m/s}. \end{aligned} \tag{25.6}$$

Discussion

This speed is slightly larger than half the speed of light in a vacuum and is still high compared with speeds we normally experience. The only substance listed in Table 25.1 that has a greater index of refraction than zircon is diamond. We shall see later that the large index of refraction for zircon makes it sparkle more than glass, but less than diamond.

Law of Refraction

Figure 25.11 shows how a ray of light changes direction when it passes from one medium to another. As before, the angles are measured relative to a perpendicular to the surface at the point where the light ray crosses it. (Some of the incident light will be reflected from the surface, but for now we will concentrate on the light that is transmitted.) The change in direction of the light ray depends on how the speed of light changes. The change in the speed of light is related to the indices of refraction of the media involved. In the situations shown in Figure 25.11, medium 2 has a greater index of refraction than medium 1. This means that the speed of light is less in medium 2 than in medium 1. Note that as shown in Figure 25.11(a), the direction of the ray moves closer to the perpendicular when it slows down. Conversely, as shown in Figure 25.11(b), the direction of the ray moves away from the perpendicular when it speeds up. The path is exactly reversible. In both cases, you can imagine what happens by thinking about pushing a lawn mower from a footpath onto grass, and vice versa. Going from the footpath to grass, the front wheels are slowed and pulled to the side as shown. This is the same change in direction as for light when it goes from a fast medium to a slow one. When going from the grass to the footpath, the front wheels can move faster and the mower changes direction as shown. This, too, is the same change in direction as for light going from slow to fast.

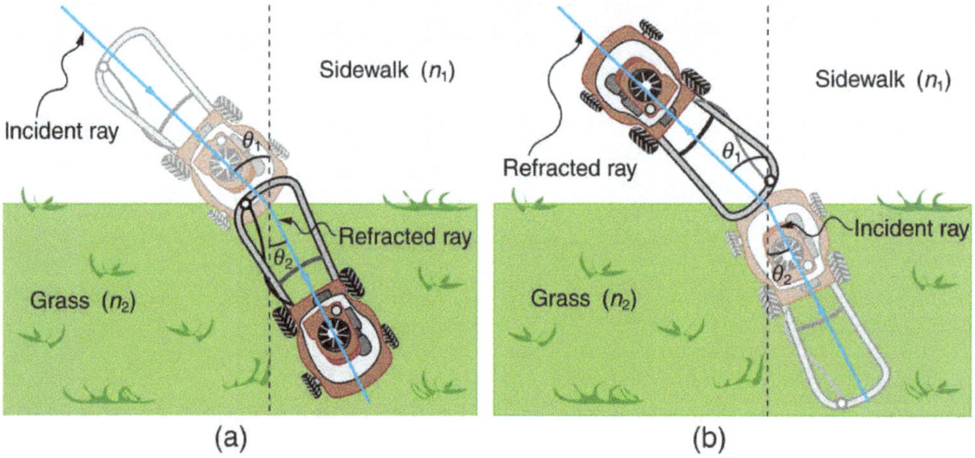

FIGURE 25.11 The change in direction of a light ray depends on how the speed of light changes when it crosses from one medium to another. The speed of light is greater in medium 1 than in medium 2 in the situations shown here. (a) A ray of light moves closer to the perpendicular when it slows down. This is analogous to what happens when a lawn mower goes from a footpath to grass. (b) A ray of light moves away from the perpendicular when it speeds up. This is analogous to what happens when a lawn mower goes from grass to footpath. The paths are exactly reversible.

The amount that a light ray changes its direction depends both on the incident angle and the amount that the speed changes. For a ray at a given incident angle, a large change in speed causes a large change in direction, and thus a large change in angle. The exact mathematical relationship is the **law of refraction**, or "Snell's Law," which is stated in equation form as

$$n_1 \sin \theta_1 = n_2 \sin \theta_2. \quad (25.7)$$

Here n_1 and n_2 are the indices of refraction for medium 1 and 2, and θ_1 and θ_2 are the angles between the rays and the perpendicular in medium 1 and 2, as shown in Figure 25.11. The incoming ray is called the incident ray and the outgoing ray the refracted ray, and the associated angles the incident angle and the refracted angle. The law of refraction is also called Snell's law after the Dutch mathematician Willebrord Snell (1591–1626). While the law has been named after Snell, the Arabian physicist, Ibn Sahl, found the law of refraction in 984 and used it in his work *On Burning Mirrors and Lenses.* Snell's experiments showed that the law of refraction was obeyed and that a characteristic index of refraction n could be assigned to a given medium. Snell was not aware that the speed of light varied in different media, but through experiments he was able to determine indices of refraction from the way light rays changed direction.

THE LAW OF REFRACTION

$$n_1 \sin \theta_1 = n_2 \sin \theta_2 \quad (25.8)$$

TAKE-HOME EXPERIMENT: A BROKEN PENCIL

A classic observation of refraction occurs when a pencil is placed in a glass half filled with water. Do this and observe the shape of the pencil when you look at the pencil sideways, that is, through air, glass, water. Explain your observations. Draw ray diagrams for the situation.

EXAMPLE 25.2

Determine the Index of Refraction from Refraction Data

Find the index of refraction for medium 2 in Figure 25.11(a), assuming medium 1 is air and given the incident angle is 30.0° and the angle of refraction is 22.0°.

Strategy

The index of refraction for air is taken to be 1 in most cases (and up to four significant figures, it is 1.000). Thus $n_1 = 1.00$ here. From the given information, $\theta_1 = 30.0^\circ$ and $\theta_2 = 22.0^\circ$. With this information, the only unknown in Snell's law is n_2, so that it can be used to find this unknown.

Solution

Snell's law is

$$n_1 \sin\theta_1 = n_2 \sin\theta_2. \tag{25.9}$$

Rearranging to isolate n_2 gives

$$n_2 = n_1 \frac{\sin\theta_1}{\sin\theta_2}. \tag{25.10}$$

Entering known values,

$$\begin{aligned} n_2 &= 1.00 \frac{\sin 30.0^\circ}{\sin 22.0^\circ} = \frac{0.500}{0.375} \\ &= 1.33. \end{aligned} \tag{25.11}$$

Discussion

This is the index of refraction for water, and Snell could have determined it by measuring the angles and performing this calculation. He would then have found 1.33 to be the appropriate index of refraction for water in all other situations, such as when a ray passes from water to glass. Today we can verify that the index of refraction is related to the speed of light in a medium by measuring that speed directly.

EXAMPLE 25.3

A Larger Change in Direction

Suppose that in a situation like that in Example 25.2, light goes from air to diamond and that the incident angle is 30.0°. Calculate the angle of refraction θ_2 in the diamond.

Strategy

Again the index of refraction for air is taken to be $n_1 = 1.00$, and we are given $\theta_1 = 30.0^\circ$. We can look up the index of refraction for diamond in Table 25.1, finding $n_2 = 2.419$. The only unknown in Snell's law is θ_2, which we wish to determine.

Solution

Solving Snell's law for $\sin\theta_2$ yields

$$\sin \theta_2 = \frac{n_1}{n_2} \sin \theta_1. \tag{25.12}$$

Entering known values,

$$\sin \theta_2 = \frac{1.00}{2.419} \sin 30.0° = \left(0.413\right)(0.500) = 0.207. \tag{25.13}$$

The angle is thus

$$\theta_2 = \sin^{-1} 0.207 = 11.9°. \tag{25.14}$$

Discussion

For the same $30°$ angle of incidence, the angle of refraction in diamond is significantly smaller than in water ($11.9°$ rather than $22°$—see the preceding example). This means there is a larger change in direction in diamond. The cause of a large change in direction is a large change in the index of refraction (or speed). In general, the larger the change in speed, the greater the effect on the direction of the ray.

25.4 Total Internal Reflection

LEARNING OBJECTIVES

By the end of this section, you will be able to:

- Explain the phenomenon of total internal reflection.
- Describe the workings and uses of fiber optics.
- Analyze the reason for the sparkle of diamonds.

A good-quality mirror may reflect more than 90% of the light that falls on it, absorbing the rest. But it would be useful to have a mirror that reflects all of the light that falls on it. Interestingly, we can produce *total reflection* using an aspect of *refraction*.

Consider what happens when a ray of light strikes the surface between two materials, such as is shown in Figure 25.12(a). Part of the light crosses the boundary and is refracted; the rest is reflected. If, as shown in the figure, the index of refraction for the second medium is less than for the first, the ray bends away from the perpendicular. (Since $n_1 > n_2$, the angle of refraction is greater than the angle of incidence—that is, $\theta_2 > \theta_1$.) Now imagine what happens as the incident angle is increased. This causes θ_2 to increase also. The largest the angle of refraction θ_2 can be is $90°$, as shown in Figure 25.12(b).The **critical angle**θ_c for a combination of materials is defined to be the incident angle θ_1 that produces an angle of refraction of $90°$. That is, θ_c is the incident angle for which $\theta_2 = 90°$. If the incident angle θ_1 is greater than the critical angle, as shown in Figure 25.12(c), then all of the light is reflected back into medium 1, a condition called **total internal reflection**.

CRITICAL ANGLE

The incident angle θ_1 that produces an angle of refraction of $90°$ is called the critical angle, θ_c.

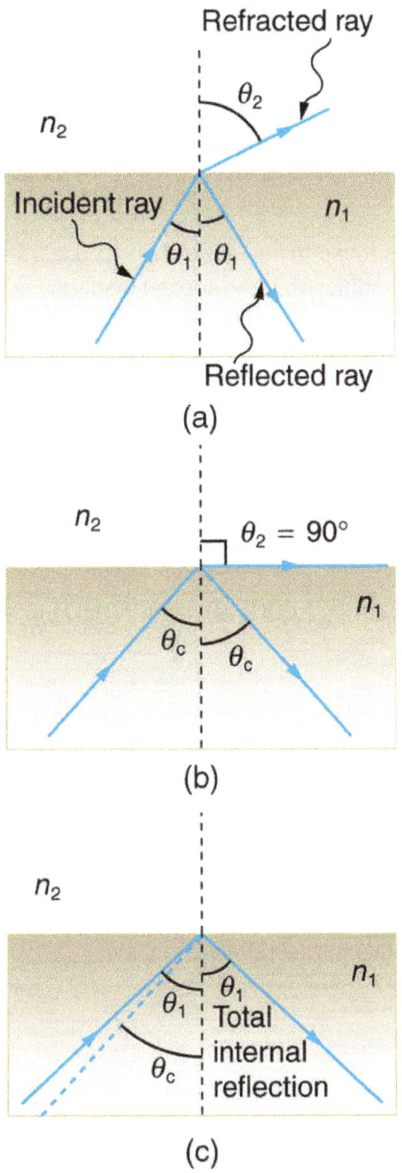

FIGURE 25.12 (a) A ray of light crosses a boundary where the speed of light increases and the index of refraction decreases. That is, $n_2 < n_1$. The ray bends away from the perpendicular. (b) The critical angle θ_c is the one for which the angle of refraction is . (c) Total internal reflection occurs when the incident angle is greater than the critical angle.

Snell's law states the relationship between angles and indices of refraction. It is given by

$$n_1 \sin\theta_1 = n_2 \sin\theta_2. \tag{25.15}$$

When the incident angle equals the critical angle ($\theta_1 = \theta_c$), the angle of refraction is 90° ($\theta_2 = 90^\circ$). Noting that $\sin 90^\circ = 1$, Snell's law in this case becomes

$$n_1 \sin\theta_1 = n_2. \tag{25.16}$$

The critical angle θ_c for a given combination of materials is thus

$$\theta_c = \sin^{-1}(n_2/n_1) \text{ for } n_1 > n_2. \tag{25.17}$$

Total internal reflection occurs for any incident angle greater than the critical angle θ_c, and it can only occur when the second medium has an index of refraction less than the first. Note the above equation is written for a light ray that travels in medium 1 and reflects from medium 2, as shown in the figure.

EXAMPLE 25.4

How Big is the Critical Angle Here?

What is the critical angle for light traveling in a polystyrene (a type of plastic) pipe surrounded by air?

Strategy

The index of refraction for polystyrene is found to be 1.49 in Figure 25.13, and the index of refraction of air can be taken to be 1.00, as before. Thus, the condition that the second medium (air) has an index of refraction less than the first (plastic) is satisfied, and the equation $\theta_c = \sin^{-1}(n_2/n_1)$ can be used to find the critical angle θ_c. Here, then, $n_2 = 1.00$ and $n_1 = 1.49$.

Solution

The critical angle is given by

$$\theta_c = \sin^{-1}(n_2/n_1). \quad 25.18$$

Substituting the identified values gives

$$\theta_c = \sin^{-1}(1.00/1.49) = \sin^{-1}(0.671) = 42.2^\circ. \quad 25.19$$

Discussion

This means that any ray of light inside the plastic that strikes the surface at an angle greater than 42.2° will be totally reflected. This will make the inside surface of the clear plastic a perfect mirror for such rays without any need for the silvering used on common mirrors. Different combinations of materials have different critical angles, but any combination with $n_1 > n_2$ can produce total internal reflection. The same calculation as made here shows that the critical angle for a ray going from water to air is 48.6°, while that from diamond to air is 24.4°, and that from flint glass to crown glass is 66.3°. There is no total reflection for rays going in the other direction—for example, from air to water—since the condition that the second medium must have a smaller index of refraction is not satisfied. A number of interesting applications of total internal reflection follow.

Fiber Optics: Endoscopes to Telephones

Fiber optics is one application of total internal reflection that is in wide use. In communications, it is used to transmit telephone, internet, and cable TV signals. **Fiber optics** employs the transmission of light down fibers of plastic or glass. Because the fibers are thin, light entering one is likely to strike the inside surface at an angle greater than the critical angle and, thus, be totally reflected (See Figure 25.13.) The index of refraction outside the fiber must be smaller than inside, a condition that is easily satisfied by coating the outside of the fiber with a material having an appropriate refractive index. In fact, most fibers have a varying refractive index to allow more light to be guided along the fiber through total internal refraction. Rays are reflected around corners as shown, making the fibers into tiny light pipes.

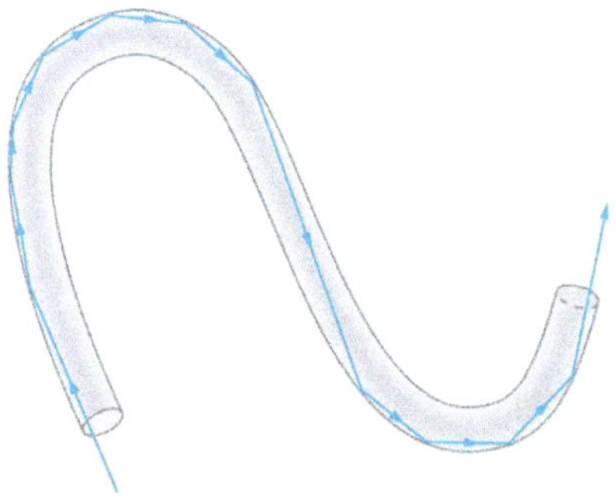

FIGURE 25.13 Light entering a thin fiber may strike the inside surface at large or grazing angles and is completely reflected if these angles exceed the critical angle. Such rays continue down the fiber, even following it around corners, since the angles of reflection and incidence remain large.

Bundles of fibers can be used to transmit an image without a lens, as illustrated in Figure 25.14. The output of a device called an **endoscope** is shown in Figure 25.14(b). Endoscopes are used to explore the body through various orifices or minor incisions. Light is transmitted down one fiber bundle to illuminate internal parts, and the reflected light is transmitted back out through another to be observed. Surgery can be performed, such as arthroscopic surgery on the knee joint, employing cutting tools attached to and observed with the endoscope. Samples can also be obtained, such as by lassoing an intestinal polyp for external examination.

Fiber optics has revolutionized surgical techniques and observations within the body. There are a host of medical diagnostic and therapeutic uses. The flexibility of the fiber optic bundle allows it to navigate around difficult and small regions in the body, such as the intestines, the heart, blood vessels, and joints. Transmission of an intense laser beam to burn away obstructing plaques in major arteries as well as delivering light to activate chemotherapy drugs are becoming commonplace. Optical fibers have in fact enabled microsurgery and remote surgery where the incisions are small and the surgeon's fingers do not need to touch the diseased tissue.

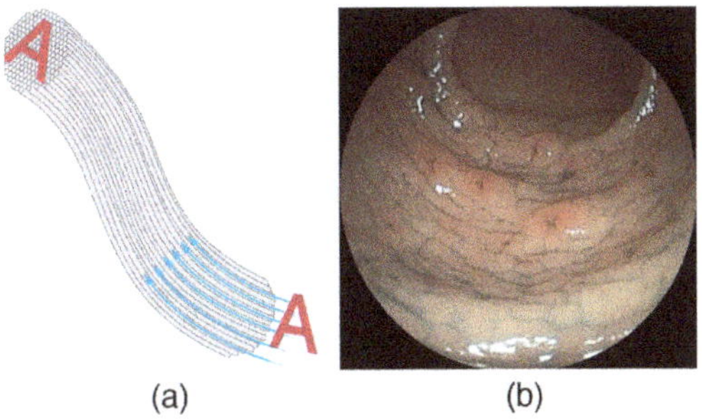

FIGURE 25.14 (a) An image is transmitted by a bundle of fibers that have fixed neighbors. (b) An endoscope is used to probe the body, both transmitting light to the interior and returning an image such as the one shown. (credit: Med_Chaos, Wikimedia Commons)

Fibers in bundles are surrounded by a cladding material that has a lower index of refraction than the core. (See Figure 25.15.) The cladding prevents light from being transmitted between fibers in a bundle. Without cladding, light could pass between fibers in contact, since their indices of refraction are identical. Since no light gets into the cladding (there is total internal reflection back into the core), none can be transmitted between clad fibers that are in contact with one another. The cladding prevents light from escaping out of the fiber; instead most of the light is propagated along the length of the fiber, minimizing the loss of signal and ensuring that a quality image is formed at the other end. The cladding and an additional protective layer make optical fibers flexible and durable.

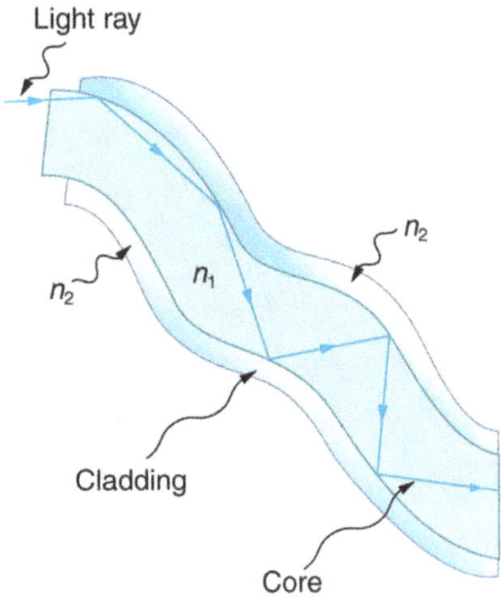

FIGURE 25.15 Fibers in bundles are clad by a material that has a lower index of refraction than the core to ensure total internal reflection, even when fibers are in contact with one another. This shows a single fiber with its cladding.

CLADDING

The cladding prevents light from being transmitted between fibers in a bundle.

Special tiny lenses that can be attached to the ends of bundles of fibers are being designed and fabricated. Light emerging from a fiber bundle can be focused and a tiny spot can be imaged. In some cases the spot can be scanned, allowing quality imaging of a region inside the body. Special minute optical filters inserted at the end of the fiber bundle have the capacity to image tens of microns below the surface without cutting the surface—non-intrusive diagnostics. This is particularly useful for determining the extent of cancers in the stomach and bowel.

Most telephone conversations and Internet communications are now carried by laser signals along optical fibers. Extensive optical fiber cables have been placed on the ocean floor and underground to enable optical communications. Optical fiber communication systems offer several advantages over electrical (copper) based systems, particularly for long distances. The fibers can be made so transparent that light can travel many kilometers before it becomes dim enough to require amplification—much superior to copper conductors. This property of optical fibers is called *low loss*. Lasers emit light with characteristics that allow far more conversations in one fiber than are possible with electric signals on a single conductor. This property of optical fibers is called *high bandwidth*. Optical signals in one fiber do not produce undesirable effects in other adjacent fibers. This property of optical fibers is called *reduced crosstalk*. We shall explore the unique characteristics of laser radiation in a later chapter.

Corner Reflectors and Diamonds

A light ray that strikes an object consisting of two mutually perpendicular reflecting surfaces is reflected back exactly parallel to the direction from which it came. This is true whenever the reflecting surfaces are perpendicular, and it is independent of the angle of incidence. Such an object, shown in Figure 25.16, is called a **corner reflector**, since the light bounces from its inside corner. Many inexpensive reflector buttons on bicycles, cars, and warning signs have corner reflectors designed to return light in the direction from which it originated. It was more expensive for astronauts to place one on the moon. Laser signals can be bounced from that corner reflector to measure the gradually increasing distance to the moon with great precision.

(a)

(b)

FIGURE 25.16 (a) Astronauts placed a corner reflector on the moon to measure its gradually increasing orbital distance. (credit: NASA) (b) The bright spots on these bicycle safety reflectors are reflections of the flash of the camera that took this picture on a dark night. (credit: Julo, Wikimedia Commons)

Corner reflectors are perfectly efficient when the conditions for total internal reflection are satisfied. With common materials, it is easy to obtain a critical angle that is less than 45°. One use of these perfect mirrors is in binoculars, as shown in Figure 25.17. Another use is in periscopes found in submarines.

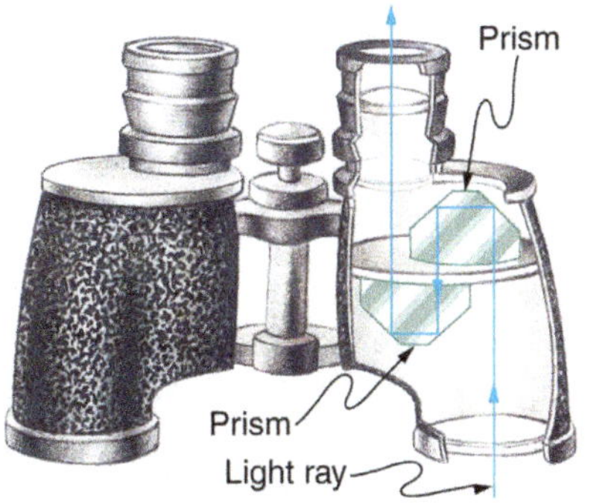

FIGURE 25.17 These binoculars employ corner reflectors with total internal reflection to get light to the observer's eyes.

The Sparkle of Diamonds

Total internal reflection, coupled with a large index of refraction, explains why diamonds sparkle more than other materials. The critical angle for a diamond-to-air surface is only $24.4°$, and so when light enters a diamond, it has trouble getting back out. (See Figure 25.18.) Although light freely enters the diamond, it can exit only if it makes an angle less than $24.4°$. Facets on diamonds are specifically intended to make this unlikely, so that the light can exit only in certain places. Good diamonds are very clear, so that the light makes many internal reflections and is concentrated at the few places it can exit—hence the sparkle. (Zircon is a natural gemstone that has an exceptionally large index of refraction, but not as large as diamond, so it is not as highly prized. Cubic zirconia is manufactured and has an even higher index of refraction (≈ 2.17), but still less than that of diamond.) The colors you see emerging from a sparkling diamond are not due to the diamond's color, which is usually nearly colorless. Those colors result from dispersion, the topic of Dispersion: The Rainbow and Prisms. Colored diamonds get their color from structural defects of the crystal lattice and the inclusion of minute quantities of graphite and other materials. The Argyle Mine in Western Australia produces around 90% of the world's pink, red, champagne, and cognac diamonds, while around 50% of the world's clear diamonds come from central and southern Africa.

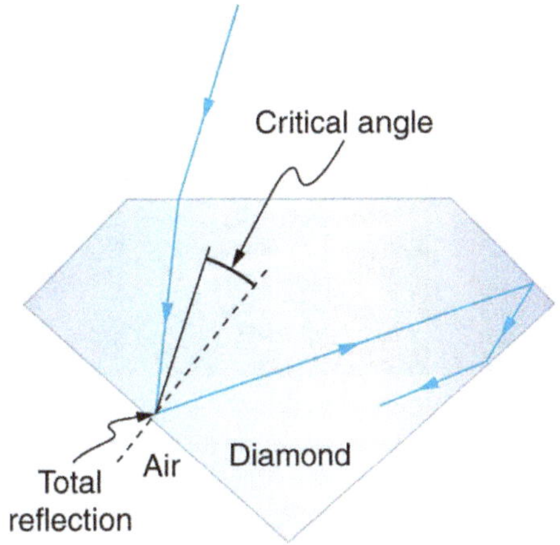

FIGURE 25.18 Light cannot easily escape a diamond, because its critical angle with air is so small. Most reflections are total, and the facets are placed so that light can exit only in particular ways—thus concentrating the light and making the diamond sparkle.

PHET EXPLORATIONS

Bending Light

Explore bending of light between two media with different indices of refraction. See how changing from air to water to glass changes the bending angle. Play with prisms of different shapes and make rainbows.

Click to view content (https://openstax.org/books/college-physics-ap-courses-2e/pages/25-4-total-internal-reflection)

PhET

25.5 Dispersion: The Rainbow and Prisms

LEARNING OBJECTIVES

By the end of this section, you will be able to:

- Explain the phenomenon of dispersion and discuss its advantages and disadvantages.

Everyone enjoys the spectacle and surprise of rainbows. They've been hailed as symbols of hope and spirituality and are the subject of stories and myths across the world's cultures. Just how does sunlight falling on water droplets cause the multicolored image we see, and what else does this phenomenon tell us about light, color, and radiation? Working in his native Persia (now Iran), Kamal al-Din Hasan ibn Ali ibn Hasan al-Farisi (1267–1319) designed a series of innovative experiments to answer this question and clarify the explanations of many earlier scientists. At that time, there were no microscopes to examine tiny drops of water similar to those in the atmosphere, so Farisi created an enormous drop of water. He filled a large glass vessel with water and placed it inside a camera obscura, in which he could carefully control the entry of light. Using a series of careful observations on the resulting multicolored spectra of light, he deduced and confirmed that the droplets split—or decompose—white light into the colors of the rainbow. Farisi's contemporary, Theodoric of Freiberg (in Germany), performed similar experiments using other equipment. Both relied on the prior work of Ibn al-Haytham, often known as the founder of optics and among the first to formalize a scientific method.

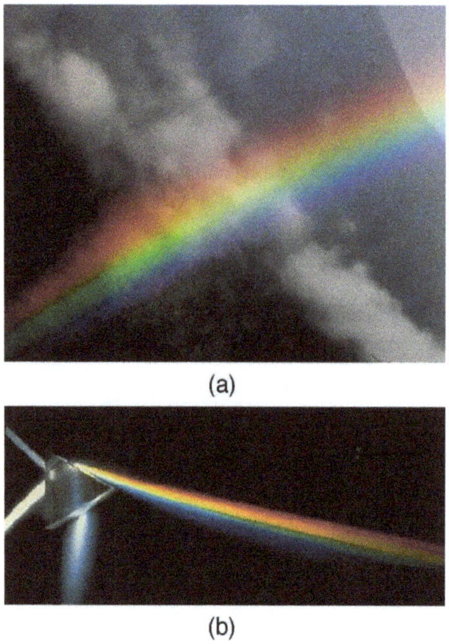

FIGURE 25.19 The colors of the rainbow (a) and those produced by a prism (b) are identical. (credit: Alfredo55, Wikimedia Commons; NASA)

We see about six colors in a rainbow—red, orange, yellow, green, blue, and violet; sometimes indigo is listed, too. Those colors are associated with different wavelengths of light, as shown in Figure 25.20. When our eye receives pure-wavelength light, we tend to see only one of the six colors, depending on wavelength. The thousands of other hues we can sense in other situations are our eye's response to various mixtures of wavelengths. White light, in particular, is a fairly uniform mixture of all visible wavelengths. Sunlight, considered to be white, actually appears to be a bit yellow because of its mixture of wavelengths, but it does contain all visible wavelengths. The sequence of colors in rainbows is the same sequence as the colors plotted versus wavelength in Figure 25.20. What this implies is that white light is spread out according to wavelength in a rainbow. **Dispersion** is defined as the spreading of white light into its full spectrum of wavelengths. More technically, dispersion occurs whenever there is a process that changes the direction of light in a manner that depends on wavelength. Dispersion, as a general phenomenon, can occur for any type of wave and always involves wavelength-dependent processes.

DISPERSION

Dispersion is defined to be the spreading of white light into its full spectrum of wavelengths.

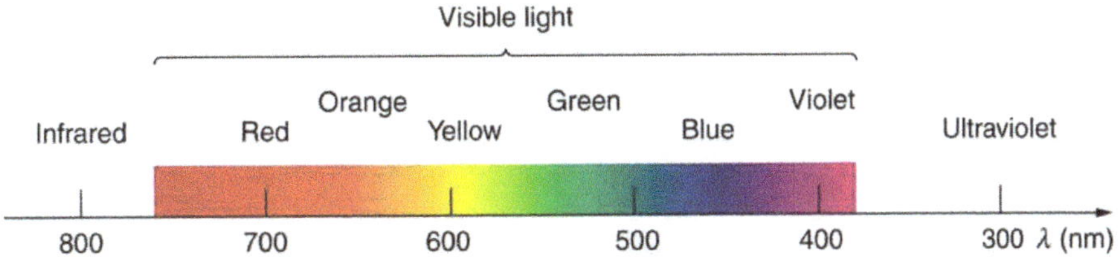

FIGURE 25.20 Even though rainbows are associated with seven colors, the rainbow is a continuous distribution of colors according to wavelengths.

Refraction is responsible for dispersion in rainbows and many other situations. The angle of refraction depends on the index of refraction, as we saw in The Law of Refraction. We know that the index of refraction n depends on the medium. But for a given medium, n also depends on wavelength. (See Table 25.2. Note that, for a given medium, n increases as wavelength decreases and is greatest for violet light. Thus violet light is bent more than red light, as shown for a prism in Figure 25.21(b), and the light is dispersed into the same sequence of wavelengths as seen in Figure 25.19 and Figure 25.20.

MAKING CONNECTIONS: DISPERSION

Any type of wave can exhibit dispersion. Sound waves, all types of electromagnetic waves, and water waves can be dispersed according to wavelength. Dispersion occurs whenever the speed of propagation depends on wavelength, thus separating and spreading out various wavelengths. Dispersion may require special circumstances and can result in spectacular displays such as in the production of a rainbow. This is also true for sound, since all frequencies ordinarily travel at the same speed. If you listen to sound through a long tube, such as a vacuum cleaner hose, you can easily hear it is dispersed by interaction with the tube. Dispersion, in fact, can reveal a great deal about what the wave has encountered that disperses its wavelengths. The dispersion of electromagnetic radiation from outer space, for example, has revealed much about what exists between the stars—the so-called empty space.

Medium	Red (660 nm)	Orange (610 nm)	Yellow (580 nm)	Green (550 nm)	Blue (470 nm)	Violet (410 nm)
Water	1.331	1.332	1.333	1.335	1.338	1.342
Diamond	2.410	2.415	2.417	2.426	2.444	2.458
Glass, crown	1.512	1.514	1.518	1.519	1.524	1.530
Glass, flint	1.662	1.665	1.667	1.674	1.684	1.698
Polystyrene	1.488	1.490	1.492	1.493	1.499	1.506
Quartz, fused	1.455	1.456	1.458	1.459	1.462	1.468

TABLE 25.2 Index of Refraction n in Selected Media at Various Wavelengths

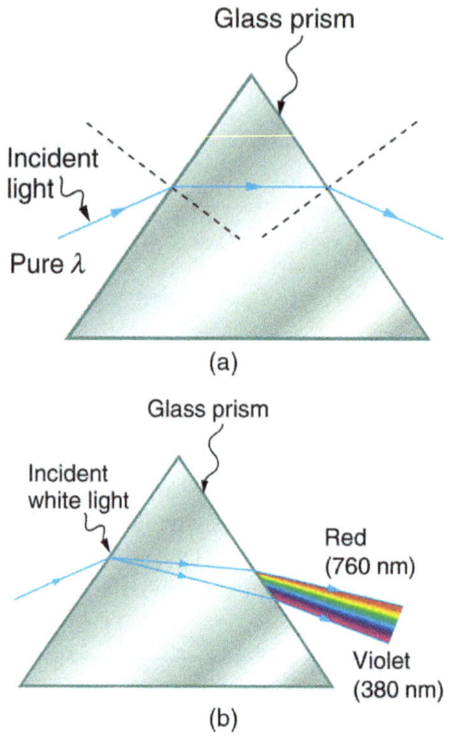

FIGURE 25.21 (a) A pure wavelength of light falls onto a prism and is refracted at both surfaces. (b) White light is dispersed by the prism (shown exaggerated). Since the index of refraction varies with wavelength, the angles of refraction vary with wavelength. A sequence of red to violet is produced, because the index of refraction increases steadily with decreasing wavelength.

Rainbows are produced by a combination of refraction and reflection. You may have noticed that you see a rainbow only when you look away from the sun. Light enters a drop of water and is reflected from the back of the drop, as shown in Figure 25.22. The light is refracted both as it enters and as it leaves the drop. Since the index of refraction of water varies with wavelength, the light is dispersed, and a rainbow is observed, as shown in Figure 25.23 (a). (There is no dispersion caused by reflection at the back surface, since the law of reflection does not depend on wavelength.) The actual rainbow of colors seen by an observer depends on the myriad of rays being refracted and reflected toward the observer's eyes from numerous drops of water. The effect is most spectacular when the background is dark, as in stormy weather, but can also be observed in waterfalls and lawn sprinklers. The arc of a rainbow comes from the need to be looking at a specific angle relative to the direction of the sun, as illustrated in Figure 25.23 (b). (If there are two reflections of light within the water drop, another "secondary" rainbow is produced. This rare event produces an arc that lies above the primary rainbow arc—see Figure 25.23 (c).)

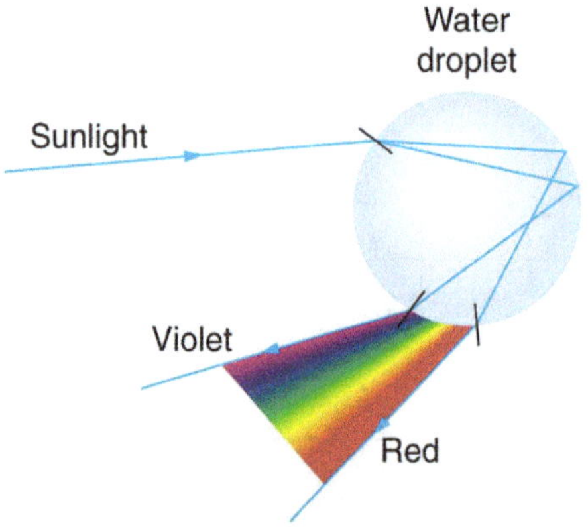

FIGURE 25.22 Part of the light falling on this water drop enters and is reflected from the back of the drop. This light is refracted and dispersed both as it enters and as it leaves the drop.

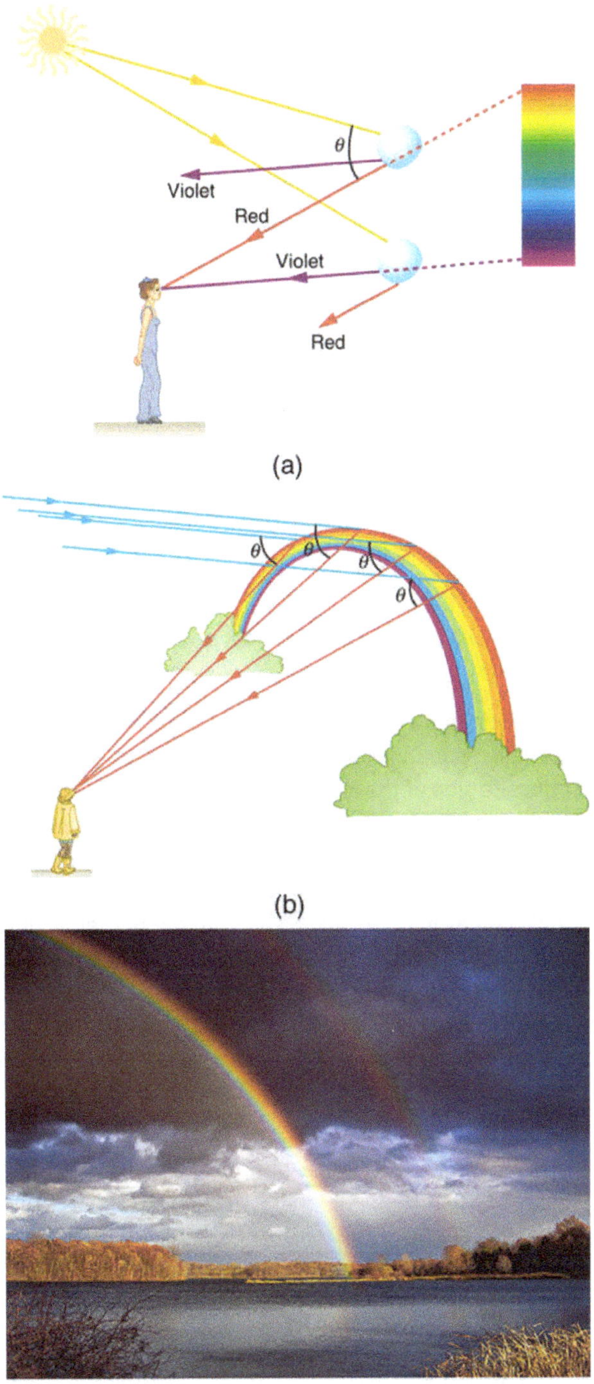

(c)

FIGURE 25.23 (a) Different colors emerge in different directions, and so you must look at different locations to see the various colors of a rainbow. (b) The arc of a rainbow results from the fact that a line between the observer and any point on the arc must make the correct angle with the parallel rays of sunlight to receive the refracted rays. (c) Double rainbow. (credit: Nicholas, Wikimedia Commons)

Dispersion may produce beautiful rainbows, but it can cause problems in optical systems. White light used to transmit messages in a fiber is dispersed, spreading out in time and eventually overlapping with other messages. Since a laser produces a nearly pure wavelength, its light experiences little dispersion, an advantage over white light for transmission of information. In contrast, dispersion of electromagnetic waves coming to us from outer space can be used to determine the amount of matter they pass through. As with many phenomena, dispersion can be useful or a nuisance, depending on the situation and our human goals.

PHET EXPLORATIONS

Geometric Optics

How does a lens form an image? See how light rays are refracted by a lens. Watch how the image changes when you adjust the focal length of the lens, move the object, move the lens, or move the screen.

Click to view content (https://openstax.org/books/college-physics-ap-courses-2e/pages/25-5-dispersion-the-rainbow-and-prisms)

25.6 Image Formation by Lenses

LEARNING OBJECTIVES

By the end of this section, you will be able to:

- List the rules for ray tracking for thin lenses.
- Illustrate the formation of images using the technique of ray tracking.
- Determine power of a lens given the focal length.

Lenses are found in a huge array of optical instruments, ranging from a simple magnifying glass to the eye to a camera's zoom lens. In this section, we will use the law of refraction to explore the properties of lenses and how they form images.

The word *lens* derives from the Latin word for a lentil bean, the shape of which is similar to the convex lens in Figure 25.24. The convex lens shown has been shaped so that all light rays that enter it parallel to its axis cross one another at a single point on the opposite side of the lens. (The axis is defined to be a line normal to the lens at its center, as shown in Figure 25.24.) Such a lens is called a **converging (or convex) lens** for the converging effect it has on light rays. An expanded view of the path of one ray through the lens is shown, to illustrate how the ray changes direction both as it enters and as it leaves the lens. Since the index of refraction of the lens is greater than that of air, the ray moves towards the perpendicular as it enters and away from the perpendicular as it leaves. (This is in accordance with the law of refraction.) Due to the lens's shape, light is thus bent toward the axis at both surfaces. The point at which the rays cross is defined to be the **focal point** F of the lens. The distance from the center of the lens to its focal point is defined to be the **focal length** f of the lens. Figure 25.25 shows how a converging lens, such as that in a magnifying glass, can converge the nearly parallel light rays from the sun to a small spot.

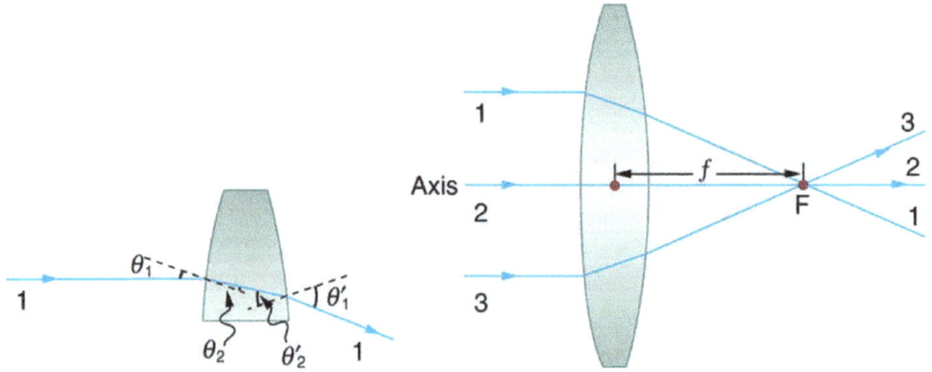

FIGURE 25.24 Rays of light entering a converging lens parallel to its axis converge at its focal point F. (Ray 2 lies on the axis of the lens.) The distance from the center of the lens to the focal point is the lens's focal length f. An expanded view of the path taken by ray 1 shows the perpendiculars and the angles of incidence and refraction at both surfaces.

CONVERGING OR CONVEX LENS

The lens in which light rays that enter it parallel to its axis cross one another at a single point on the opposite side with a converging effect is called converging lens.

FOCAL POINT F

The point at which the light rays cross is called the focal point F of the lens.

FOCAL LENGTH f

The distance from the center of the lens to its focal point is called focal length f.

FIGURE 25.25 Sunlight focused by a converging magnifying glass can burn paper. Light rays from the sun are nearly parallel and cross at the focal point of the lens. The more powerful the lens, the closer to the lens the rays will cross.

The greater effect a lens has on light rays, the more powerful it is said to be. For example, a powerful converging lens will focus parallel light rays closer to itself and will have a smaller focal length than a weak lens. The light will also focus into a smaller and more intense spot for a more powerful lens. The **power** P of a lens is defined to be the inverse of its focal length. In equation form, this is

$$P = \frac{1}{f}. \quad (25.20)$$

POWER P

The **power** P of a lens is defined to be the inverse of its focal length. In equation form, this is

$$P = \frac{1}{f}. \quad (25.21)$$

where f is the focal length of the lens, which must be given in meters (and not cm or mm). The power of a lens P has the unit diopters (D), provided that the focal length is given in meters. That is, $1\ \text{D} = 1/\text{m}$, or $1\ \text{m}^{-1}$. (Note that this power (optical power, actually) is not the same as power in watts defined in Work, Energy, and Energy Resources. It is a concept related to the effect of optical devices on light.) Optometrists prescribe common spectacles and contact lenses in units of diopters.

EXAMPLE 25.5

What is the Power of a Common Magnifying Glass?

Suppose you take a magnifying glass out on a sunny day and you find that it concentrates sunlight to a small spot 8.00 cm away from the lens. What are the focal length and power of the lens?

Strategy

The situation here is the same as those shown in Figure 25.24 and Figure 25.25. The Sun is so far away that the Sun's rays are nearly parallel when they reach Earth. The magnifying glass is a convex (or converging) lens, focusing the nearly parallel rays of sunlight. Thus the focal length of the lens is the distance from the lens to the spot, and its power is the inverse of this distance (in m).

Solution

The focal length of the lens is the distance from the center of the lens to the spot, given to be 8.00 cm. Thus,

$$f = 8.00\text{ cm}. \qquad (25.22)$$

To find the power of the lens, we must first convert the focal length to meters; then, we substitute this value into the equation for power. This gives

$$P = \frac{1}{f} = \frac{1}{0.0800\text{ m}} = 12.5\text{ D}. \qquad (25.23)$$

Discussion

This is a relatively powerful lens. The power of a lens in diopters should not be confused with the familiar concept of power in watts. It is an unfortunate fact that the word "power" is used for two completely different concepts. If you examine a prescription for eyeglasses, you will note lens powers given in diopters. If you examine the label on a motor, you will note energy consumption rate given as a power in watts.

Figure 25.26 shows a concave lens and the effect it has on rays of light that enter it parallel to its axis (the path taken by ray 2 in the figure is the axis of the lens). The concave lens is a **diverging lens**, because it causes the light rays to bend away (diverge) from its axis. In this case, the lens has been shaped so that all light rays entering it parallel to its axis appear to originate from the same point, F, defined to be the focal point of a diverging lens. The distance from the center of the lens to the focal point is again called the focal length f of the lens. Note that the focal length and power of a diverging lens are defined to be negative. For example, if the distance to F in Figure 25.26 is 5.00 cm, then the focal length is $f = -5.00\text{ cm}$ and the power of the lens is $P = -20\text{ D}$. An expanded view of the path of one ray through the lens is shown in the figure to illustrate how the shape of the lens, together with the law of refraction, causes the ray to follow its particular path and be diverged.

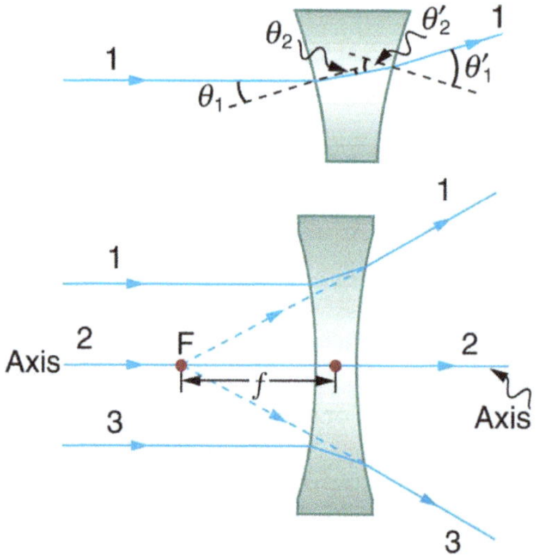

FIGURE 25.26 Rays of light entering a diverging lens parallel to its axis are diverged, and all appear to originate at its focal point F. The dashed lines are not rays—they indicate the directions from which the rays appear to come. The focal length f of a diverging lens is negative. An expanded view of the path taken by ray 1 shows the perpendiculars and the angles of incidence and refraction at both surfaces.

DIVERGING LENS

A lens that causes the light rays to bend away from its axis is called a diverging lens.

As noted in the initial discussion of the law of refraction in The Law of Refraction, the paths of light rays are exactly reversible. This means that the direction of the arrows could be reversed for all of the rays in Figure 25.24 and Figure 25.26. For example, if a point light source is placed at the focal point of a convex lens, as shown in Figure 25.27, parallel light rays emerge from the other side.

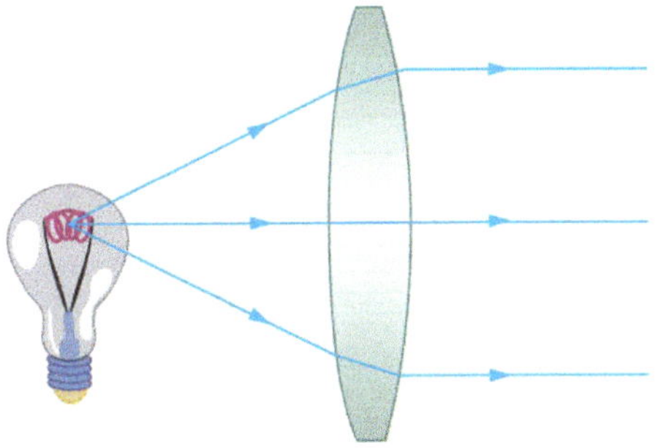

FIGURE 25.27 A small light source, like a light bulb filament, placed at the focal point of a convex lens, results in parallel rays of light emerging from the other side. The paths are exactly the reverse of those shown in Figure 25.24. This technique is used in lighthouses and sometimes in traffic lights to produce a directional beam of light from a source that emits light in all directions.

Ray Tracing and Thin Lenses

Ray tracing is the technique of determining or following (tracing) the paths that light rays take. For rays passing through matter, the law of refraction is used to trace the paths. Here we use ray tracing to help us understand the action of lenses in situations ranging from forming images on film to magnifying small print to correcting nearsightedness. While ray tracing for complicated lenses, such as those found in sophisticated cameras, may require computer techniques, there is a set of simple rules for tracing rays through thin lenses. A **thin lens** is defined to be one whose thickness allows rays to refract, as illustrated in Figure 25.24, but does not allow properties such as dispersion and aberrations. An ideal thin lens has two refracting surfaces but the lens is thin enough to assume that light rays bend only once. A thin symmetrical lens has two focal points, one on either side and both at the same distance from the lens. (See Figure 25.28.) Another important characteristic of a thin lens is that light rays through its center are deflected by a negligible amount, as seen in Figure 25.29.

THIN LENS

A thin lens is defined to be one whose thickness allows rays to refract but does not allow properties such as dispersion and aberrations.

TAKE-HOME EXPERIMENT: A VISIT TO THE OPTICIAN

Look through your eyeglasses (or those of a friend) backward and forward and comment on whether they act like thin lenses.

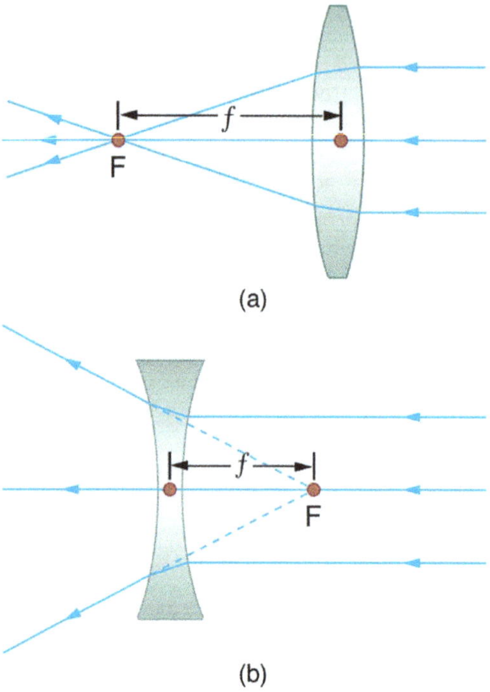

FIGURE 25.28 Thin lenses have the same focal length on either side. (a) Parallel light rays entering a converging lens from the right cross at its focal point on the left. (b) Parallel light rays entering a diverging lens from the right seem to come from the focal point on the right.

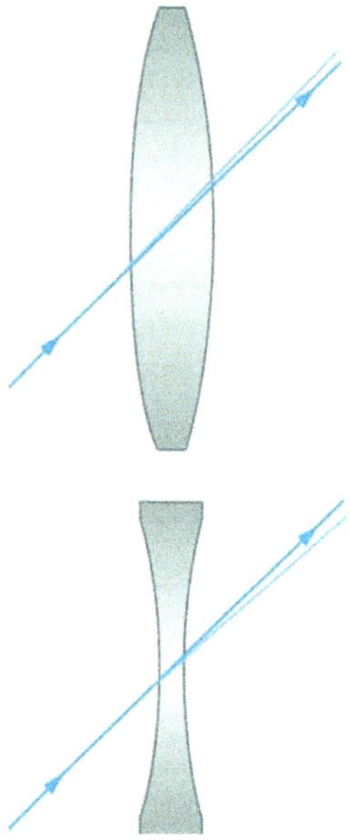

FIGURE 25.29 The light ray through the center of a thin lens is deflected by a negligible amount and is assumed to emerge parallel to its original path (shown as a shaded line).

Using paper, pencil, and a straight edge, ray tracing can accurately describe the operation of a lens. The rules for ray tracing for thin lenses are based on the illustrations already discussed:

1. A ray entering a converging lens parallel to its axis passes through the focal point F of the lens on the other side. (See rays 1 and 3 in Figure 25.24.)
2. A ray entering a diverging lens parallel to its axis seems to come from the focal point F. (See rays 1 and 3 in Figure 25.26.)
3. A ray passing through the center of either a converging or a diverging lens does not change direction. (See Figure 25.29, and see ray 2 in Figure 25.24 and Figure 25.26.)
4. A ray entering a converging lens through its focal point exits parallel to its axis. (The reverse of rays 1 and 3 in Figure 25.24.)
5. A ray that enters a diverging lens by heading toward the focal point on the opposite side exits parallel to the

axis. (The reverse of rays 1 and 3 in Figure 25.26.)

RULES FOR RAY TRACING

1. A ray entering a converging lens parallel to its axis passes through the focal point F of the lens on the other side.
2. A ray entering a diverging lens parallel to its axis seems to come from the focal point F.
3. A ray passing through the center of either a converging or a diverging lens does not change direction.
4. A ray entering a converging lens through its focal point exits parallel to its axis.
5. A ray that enters a diverging lens by heading toward the focal point on the opposite side exits parallel to the axis.

Image Formation by Thin Lenses

In some circumstances, a lens forms an obvious image, such as when a movie projector casts an image onto a screen. In other cases, the image is less obvious. Where, for example, is the image formed by eyeglasses? We will use ray tracing for thin lenses to illustrate how they form images, and we will develop equations to describe the image formation quantitatively.

Consider an object some distance away from a converging lens, as shown in Figure 25.30. To find the location and size of the image formed, we trace the paths of selected light rays originating from one point on the object, in this case the top of the person's head. The figure shows three rays from the top of the object that can be traced using the ray tracing rules given above. (Rays leave this point going in many directions, but we concentrate on only a few with paths that are easy to trace.) The first ray is one that enters the lens parallel to its axis and passes through the focal point on the other side (rule 1). The second ray passes through the center of the lens without changing direction (rule 3). The third ray passes through the nearer focal point on its way into the lens and leaves the lens parallel to its axis (rule 4). The three rays cross at the same point on the other side of the lens. The image of the top of the person's head is located at this point. All rays that come from the same point on the top of the person's head are refracted in such a way as to cross at the point shown. Rays from another point on the object, such as her belt buckle, will also cross at another common point, forming a complete image, as shown. Although three rays are traced in Figure 25.30, only two are necessary to locate the image. It is best to trace rays for which there are simple ray tracing rules. Before applying ray tracing to other situations, let us consider the example shown in Figure 25.30 in more detail.

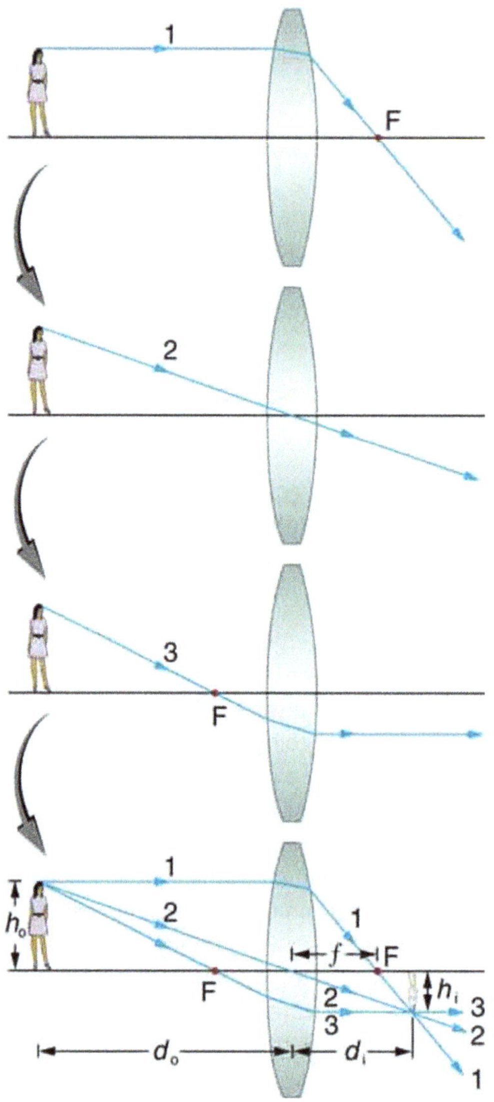

FIGURE 25.30 Ray tracing is used to locate the image formed by a lens. Rays originating from the same point on the object are traced—the three chosen rays each follow one of the rules for ray tracing, so that their paths are easy to determine. The image is located at the point where the rays cross. In this case, a real image—one that can be projected on a screen—is formed.

The image formed in Figure 25.30 is a **real image**, meaning that it can be projected. That is, light rays from one point on the object actually cross at the location of the image and can be projected onto a screen, a piece of film, or the retina of an eye, for example. Figure 25.31 shows how such an image would be projected onto film by a camera lens. This figure also shows how a real image is projected onto the retina by the lens of an eye. Note that the image is there whether it is projected onto a screen or not.

REAL IMAGE

The image in which light rays from one point on the object actually cross at the location of the image and can be projected onto a screen, a piece of film, or the retina of an eye is called a real image.

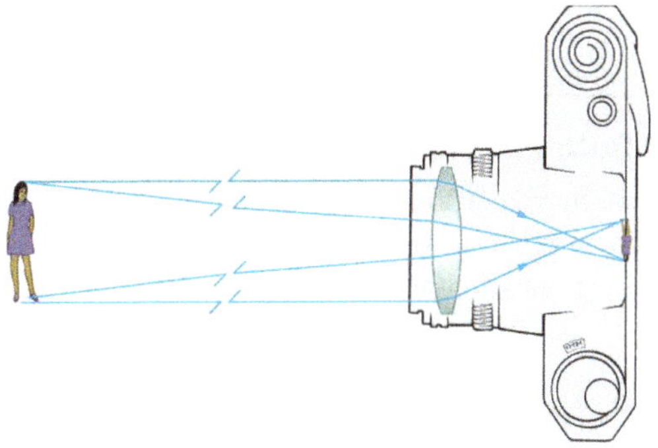
(a)

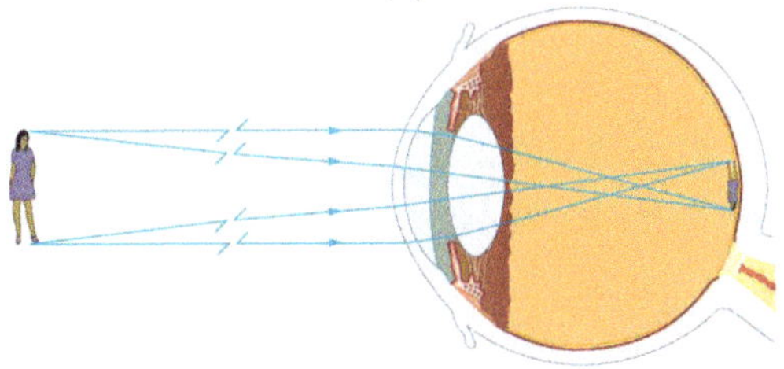
(b)

FIGURE 25.31 Real images can be projected. (a) A real image of the person is projected onto film. (b) The converging nature of the multiple surfaces that make up the eye result in the projection of a real image on the retina.

Several important distances appear in Figure 25.30. We define d_o to be the object distance, the distance of an object from the center of a lens. **Image distance** d_i is defined to be the distance of the image from the center of a lens. The height of the object and height of the image are given the symbols h_o and h_i, respectively. Images that appear upright relative to the object have heights that are positive and those that are inverted have negative heights. Using the rules of ray tracing and making a scale drawing with paper and pencil, like that in Figure 25.30, we can accurately describe the location and size of an image. But the real benefit of ray tracing is in visualizing how images are formed in a variety of situations. To obtain numerical information, we use a pair of equations that can be derived from a geometric analysis of ray tracing for thin lenses. The **thin lens equations** are

$$\frac{1}{d_o} + \frac{1}{d_i} = \frac{1}{f} \tag{25.24}$$

and

$$\frac{h_i}{h_o} = -\frac{d_i}{d_o} = m. \tag{25.25}$$

We define the ratio of image height to object height (h_i/h_o) to be the **magnification** m. (The minus sign in the equation above will be discussed shortly.) The thin lens equations are broadly applicable to all situations involving thin lenses (and "thin" mirrors, as we will see later). We will explore many features of image formation in the following worked examples.

IMAGE DISTANCE

The distance of the image from the center of the lens is called image distance.

THIN LENS EQUATIONS AND MAGNIFICATION

$$\frac{1}{d_o} + \frac{1}{d_i} = \frac{1}{f} \tag{25.26}$$

$$\frac{h_i}{h_o} = -\frac{d_i}{d_o} = m \tag{25.27}$$

EXAMPLE 25.6

Finding the Image of a Light Bulb Filament by Ray Tracing and by the Thin Lens Equations

A clear glass light bulb is placed 0.750 m from a convex lens having a 0.500 m focal length, as shown in Figure 25.32. Use ray tracing to get an approximate location for the image. Then use the thin lens equations to calculate (a) the location of the image and (b) its magnification. Verify that ray tracing and the thin lens equations produce consistent results.

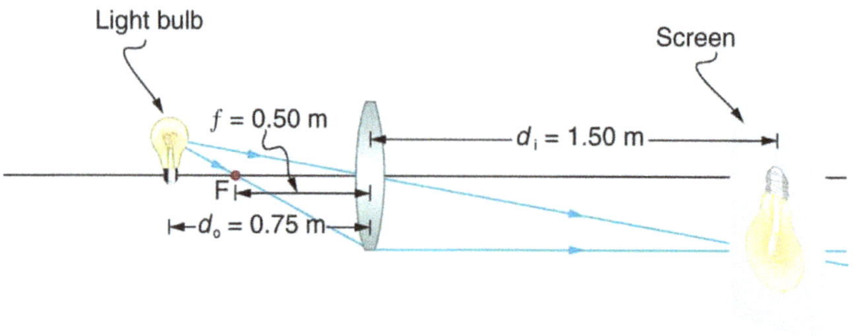

FIGURE 25.32 A light bulb placed 0.750 m from a lens having a 0.500 m focal length produces a real image on a poster board as discussed in the example above. Ray tracing predicts the image location and size.

Strategy and Concept

Since the object is placed farther away from a converging lens than the focal length of the lens, this situation is analogous to those illustrated in Figure 25.30 and Figure 25.31. Ray tracing to scale should produce similar results for d_i. Numerical solutions for d_i and m can be obtained using the thin lens equations, noting that $d_o = 0.750 \text{ m and } f = 0.500 \text{ m.}$

Solutions (Ray tracing)

The ray tracing to scale in Figure 25.32 shows two rays from a point on the bulb's filament crossing about 1.50 m on the far side of the lens. Thus the image distance d_i is about 1.50 m. Similarly, the image height based on ray tracing is greater than the object height by about a factor of 2, and the image is inverted. Thus m is about –2. The minus sign indicates that the image is inverted.

The thin lens equations can be used to find d_i from the given information:

$$\frac{1}{d_o} + \frac{1}{d_i} = \frac{1}{f}. \tag{25.28}$$

Rearranging to isolate d_i gives

$$\frac{1}{d_i} = \frac{1}{f} - \frac{1}{d_o}. \tag{25.29}$$

Entering known quantities gives a value for $1/d_i$:

$$\frac{1}{d_i} = \frac{1}{0.500 \text{ m}} - \frac{1}{0.750 \text{ m}} = \frac{0.667}{\text{m}}. \tag{25.30}$$

This must be inverted to find d_i:

$$d_i = \frac{\text{m}}{0.667} = 1.50 \text{ m}. \tag{25.31}$$

Note that another way to find d_i is to rearrange the equation:

$$\frac{1}{d_i} = \frac{1}{f} - \frac{1}{d_o}. \tag{25.32}$$

This yields the equation for the image distance as:

$$d_i = \frac{fd_o}{d_o - f}. \quad 25.33$$

Note that there is no inverting here.

The thin lens equations can be used to find the magnification m, since both d_i and d_o are known. Entering their values gives

$$m = -\frac{d_i}{d_o} = -\frac{1.50 \text{ m}}{0.750 \text{ m}} = -2.00. \quad 25.34$$

Discussion

Note that the minus sign causes the magnification to be negative when the image is inverted. Ray tracing and the use of the thin lens equations produce consistent results. The thin lens equations give the most precise results, being limited only by the accuracy of the given information. Ray tracing is limited by the accuracy with which you can draw, but it is highly useful both conceptually and visually.

Real images, such as the one considered in the previous example, are formed by converging lenses whenever an object is farther from the lens than its focal length. This is true for movie projectors, cameras, and the eye. We shall refer to these as *case 1* images. A case 1 image is formed when $d_o > f$ and f is positive, as in Figure 25.33(a). (A summary of the three cases or types of image formation appears at the end of this section.)

A different type of image is formed when an object, such as a person's face, is held close to a convex lens. The image is upright and larger than the object, as seen in Figure 25.33(b), and so the lens is called a magnifier. If you slowly pull the magnifier away from the face, you will see that the magnification steadily increases until the image begins to blur. Pulling the magnifier even farther away produces an inverted image as seen in Figure 25.33(a). The distance at which the image blurs, and beyond which it inverts, is the focal length of the lens. To use a convex lens as a magnifier, the object must be closer to the converging lens than its focal length. This is called a *case 2* image. A case 2 image is formed when $d_o < f$ and f is positive.

(a)

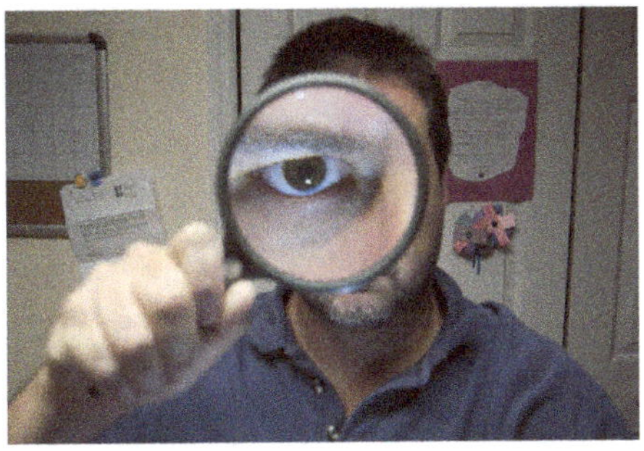

(b)

FIGURE 25.33 (a) When a converging lens is held farther away from the face than the lens's focal length, an inverted image is formed. This is a case 1 image. Note that the image is in focus but the face is not, because the image is much closer to the camera taking this photograph than the face. (credit: DaMongMan, Flickr) (b) A magnified image of a face is produced by placing it closer to the converging lens than its focal length. This is a case 2 image. (credit: Casey Fleser, Flickr)

Figure 25.34 uses ray tracing to show how an image is formed when an object is held closer to a converging lens than its focal length. Rays coming from a common point on the object continue to diverge after passing through the lens, but all appear to originate from a point at the location of the image. The image is on the same side of the lens as the object and is farther away from the lens than the object. This image, like all case 2 images, cannot be projected and, hence, is called a **virtual image**. Light rays only appear to originate at a virtual image; they do not actually pass through that location in space. A screen placed at the location of a virtual image will receive only diffuse light from the object, not focused rays from the lens. Additionally, a screen placed on the opposite side of the lens will receive rays that are still diverging, and so no image will be projected on it. We can see the magnified image with our eyes, because the lens of the eye converges the rays into a real image projected on our retina. Finally, we note that a virtual image is upright and larger than the object, meaning that the magnification is positive and greater than 1.

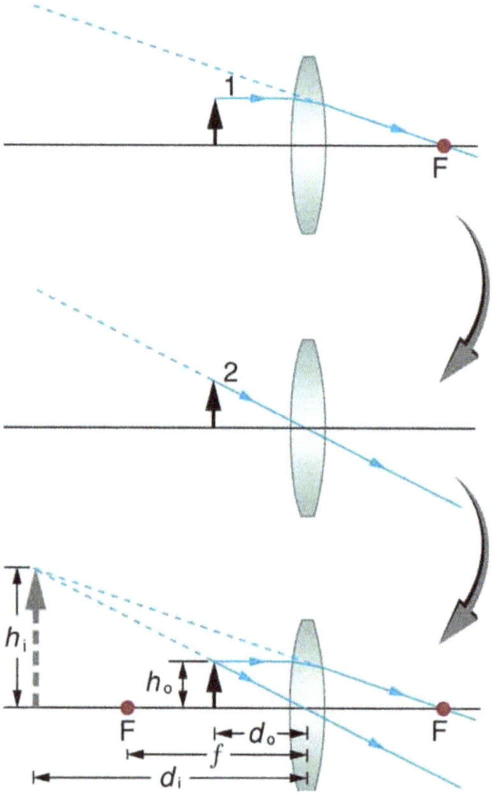

FIGURE 25.34 Ray tracing predicts the image location and size for an object held closer to a converging lens than its focal length. Ray 1 enters parallel to the axis and exits through the focal point on the opposite side, while ray 2 passes through the center of the lens without changing path. The two rays continue to diverge on the other side of the lens, but both appear to come from a common point, locating the upright, magnified, virtual image. This is a case 2 image.

VIRTUAL IMAGE

An image that is on the same side of the lens as the object and cannot be projected on a screen is called a virtual image.

EXAMPLE 25.7

Image Produced by a Magnifying Glass

Suppose the book page in Figure 25.34 (a) is held 7.50 cm from a convex lens of focal length 10.0 cm, such as a typical magnifying glass might have. What magnification is produced?

Strategy and Concept

We are given that $d_o = 7.50 \text{ cm}$ and $f = 10.0 \text{ cm}$, so we have a situation where the object is placed closer to the lens than its focal length. We therefore expect to get a case 2 virtual image with a positive magnification that is greater than 1. Ray tracing produces an image like that shown in Figure 25.34, but we will use the thin lens equations to get numerical solutions in this example.

Solution

To find the magnification m, we try to use magnification equation, $m = -d_i/d_o$. We do not have a value for d_i, so that we must first find the location of the image using lens equation. (The procedure is the same as followed in the preceding example, where d_o and f were known.) Rearranging the magnification equation to isolate d_i gives

$$\frac{1}{d_i} = \frac{1}{f} - \frac{1}{d_o}. \tag{25.35}$$

Entering known values, we obtain a value for $1/d_i$:

$$\frac{1}{d_i} = \frac{1}{10.0 \text{ cm}} - \frac{1}{7.50 \text{ cm}} = \frac{-0.0333}{\text{cm}}. \tag{25.36}$$

This must be inverted to find d_i:

$$d_i = -\frac{\text{cm}}{0.0333} = -30.0 \text{ cm}. \tag{25.37}$$

Now the thin lens equation can be used to find the magnification m, since both d_i and d_o are known. Entering their values gives

$$m = -\frac{d_i}{d_o} = -\frac{-30.0 \text{ cm}}{7.50 \text{ cm}} = 4.00. \tag{25.38}$$

Discussion

A number of results in this example are true of all case 2 images, as well as being consistent with Figure 25.34. Magnification is indeed positive (as predicted), meaning the image is upright. The magnification is also greater than 1, meaning that the image is larger than the object—in this case, by a factor of 4. Note that the image distance is negative. This means the image is on the same side of the lens as the object. Thus the image cannot be projected and is virtual. (Negative values of d_i occur for virtual images.) The image is farther from the lens than the object, since the image distance is greater in magnitude than the object distance. The location of the image is not obvious when you look through a magnifier. In fact, since the image is bigger than the object, you may think the image is closer than the object. But the image is farther away, a fact that is useful in correcting farsightedness, as we shall see in a later section.

A third type of image is formed by a diverging or concave lens. Try looking through eyeglasses meant to correct nearsightedness. (See Figure 25.35.) You will see an image that is upright but smaller than the object. This means that the magnification is positive but less than 1. The ray diagram in Figure 25.36 shows that the image is on the same side of the lens as the object and, hence, cannot be projected—it is a virtual image. Note that the image is closer to the lens than the object. This is a *case 3* image, formed for any object by a negative focal length or diverging lens.

FIGURE 25.35 A car viewed through a concave or diverging lens looks upright. This is a case 3 image. (credit: Daniel Oines, Flickr)

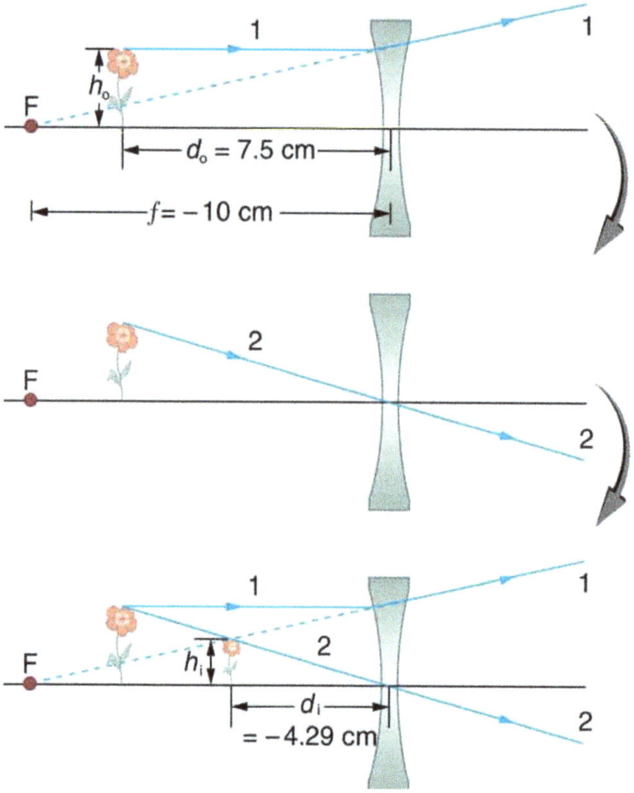

FIGURE 25.36 Ray tracing predicts the image location and size for a concave or diverging lens. Ray 1 enters parallel to the axis and is bent so that it appears to originate from the focal point. Ray 2 passes through the center of the lens without changing path. The two rays appear to come from a common point, locating the upright image. This is a case 3 image, which is closer to the lens than the object and smaller in height.

EXAMPLE 25.8

Image Produced by a Concave Lens

Suppose an object such as a book page is held 7.50 cm from a concave lens of focal length −10.0 cm. Such a lens could be used in eyeglasses to correct pronounced nearsightedness. What magnification is produced?

Strategy and Concept

This example is identical to the preceding one, except that the focal length is negative for a concave or diverging lens. The method of solution is thus the same, but the results are different in important ways.

Solution

To find the magnification m, we must first find the image distance d_i using thin lens equation

$$\frac{1}{d_\text{i}} = \frac{1}{f} - \frac{1}{d_\text{o}}, \qquad 25.39$$

or its alternative rearrangement

$$d_i = \frac{fd_\text{o}}{d_\text{o} - f}. \qquad 25.40$$

We are given that $f = -10.0\text{ cm}$ and $d_\text{o} = 7.50\text{ cm}$. Entering these yields a value for $1/d_\text{i}$:

$$\frac{1}{d_\text{i}} = \frac{1}{-10.0\text{ cm}} - \frac{1}{7.50\text{ cm}} = \frac{-0.2333}{\text{cm}}. \qquad 25.41$$

This must be inverted to find d_i:

$$d_i = -\frac{\text{cm}}{0.2333} = -4.29 \text{ cm.} \quad 25.42$$

Or

$$d_i = \frac{(7.5)(-10)}{(7.5-(-10))} = -75/17.5 = -4.29 \text{ cm.} \quad 25.43$$

Now the magnification equation can be used to find the magnification m, since both d_i and d_o are known. Entering their values gives

$$m = -\frac{d_i}{d_o} = -\frac{-4.29 \text{ cm}}{7.50 \text{ cm}} = 0.571. \quad 25.44$$

Discussion

A number of results in this example are true of all case 3 images, as well as being consistent with Figure 25.36. Magnification is positive (as predicted), meaning the image is upright. The magnification is also less than 1, meaning the image is smaller than the object—in this case, a little over half its size. The image distance is negative, meaning the image is on the same side of the lens as the object. (The image is virtual.) The image is closer to the lens than the object, since the image distance is smaller in magnitude than the object distance. The location of the image is not obvious when you look through a concave lens. In fact, since the image is smaller than the object, you may think it is farther away. But the image is closer than the object, a fact that is useful in correcting nearsightedness, as we shall see in a later section.

Table 25.3 summarizes the three types of images formed by single thin lenses. These are referred to as case 1, 2, and 3 images. Convex (converging) lenses can form either real or virtual images (cases 1 and 2, respectively), whereas concave (diverging) lenses can form only virtual images (always case 3). Real images are always inverted, but they can be either larger or smaller than the object. For example, a slide projector forms an image larger than the slide, whereas a camera makes an image smaller than the object being photographed. Virtual images are always upright and cannot be projected. Virtual images are larger than the object only in case 2, where a convex lens is used. The virtual image produced by a concave lens is always smaller than the object—a case 3 image. We can see and photograph virtual images only by using an additional lens to form a real image.

Type	Formed when	Image type	d_i	m
Case 1	f positive, $d_o > f$	real	positive	negative
Case 2	f positive, $d_o < f$	virtual	negative	positive $m > 1$
Case 3	f negative	virtual	negative	positive $m < 1$

TABLE 25.3 Three Types of Images Formed By Thin Lenses

In Image Formation by Mirrors, we shall see that mirrors can form exactly the same types of images as lenses.

TAKE-HOME EXPERIMENT: CONCENTRATING SUNLIGHT

Find several lenses and determine whether they are converging or diverging. In general those that are thicker near the edges are diverging and those that are thicker near the center are converging. On a bright sunny day take the converging lenses outside and try focusing the sunlight onto a piece of paper. Determine the focal lengths of the lenses. Be careful because the paper may start to burn, depending on the type of lens you have selected.

Problem-Solving Strategies for Lenses

Step 1. Examine the situation to determine that image formation by a lens is involved.

Step 2. Determine whether ray tracing, the thin lens equations, or both are to be employed. A sketch is very useful even if ray tracing is not specifically required by the problem. Write symbols and values on the sketch.

Step 3. Identify exactly what needs to be determined in the problem (identify the unknowns).

Step 4. Make alist of what is given or can be inferred from the problem as stated (identify the knowns). It is helpful to determine whether the situation involves a case 1, 2, or 3 image. While these are just names for types of images, they have certain characteristics (given in Table 25.3) that can be of great use in solving problems.

Step 5. If ray tracing is required, use the ray tracing rules listed near the beginning of this section.

Step 6. Most quantitative problems require the use of the thin lens equations. These are solved in the usual manner by substituting knowns and solving for unknowns. Several worked examples serve as guides.

Step 7. Check to see if the answer is reasonable: Does it make sense? If you have identified the type of image (case 1, 2, or 3), you should assess whether your answer is consistent with the type of image, magnification, and so on.

MISCONCEPTION ALERT

We do not realize that light rays are coming from every part of the object, passing through every part of the lens, and all can be used to form the final image.

We generally feel the entire lens, or mirror, is needed to form an image. Actually, half a lens will form the same, though a fainter, image.

25.7 Image Formation by Mirrors

LEARNING OBJECTIVES

By the end of this section, you will be able to:

- Illustrate image formation in a flat mirror.
- Explain with ray diagrams the formation of an image using spherical mirrors.
- Determine focal length and magnification given radius of curvature, distance of object and image.

We only have to look as far as the nearest bathroom to find an example of an image formed by a mirror. Images in flat mirrors are the same size as the object and are located behind the mirror. Like lenses, mirrors can form a variety of images. For example, dental mirrors may produce a magnified image, just as makeup mirrors do. Security mirrors in shops, on the other hand, form images that are smaller than the object. We will use the law of reflection to understand how mirrors form images, and we will find that mirror images are analogous to those formed by lenses.

Figure 25.37 helps illustrate how a flat mirror forms an image. Two rays are shown emerging from the same point, striking the mirror, and being reflected into the observer's eye. The rays can diverge slightly, and both still get into the eye. If the rays are extrapolated backward, they seem to originate from a common point behind the mirror, locating the image. (The paths of the reflected rays into the eye are the same as if they had come directly from that point behind the mirror.) Using the law of reflection—the angle of reflection equals the angle of incidence—we can see that the image and object are the same distance from the mirror. This is a virtual image, since it cannot be projected—the rays only appear to originate from a common point behind the mirror. Obviously, if you walk behind the mirror, you cannot see the image, since the rays do not go there. But in front of the mirror, the rays behave exactly as if they had come from behind the mirror, so that is where the image is situated.

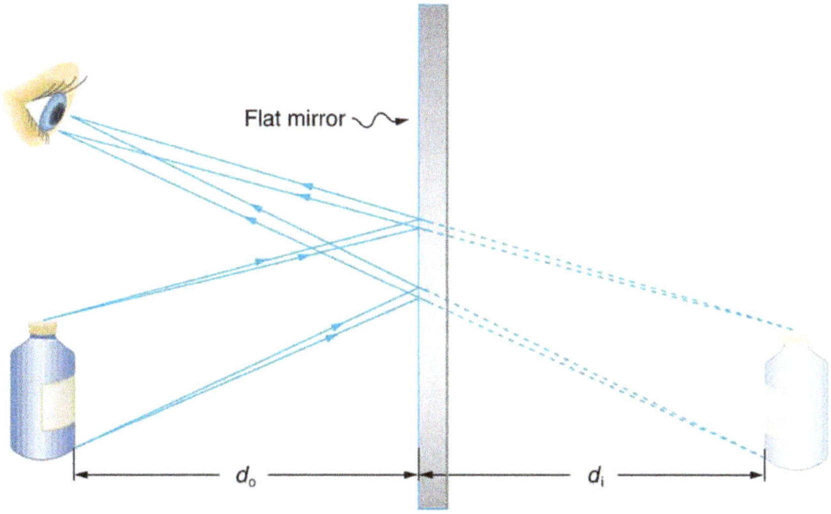

FIGURE 25.37 Two sets of rays from common points on an object are reflected by a flat mirror into the eye of an observer. The reflected rays seem to originate from behind the mirror, locating the virtual image.

Now let us consider the focal length of a mirror—for example, the concave spherical mirrors in Figure 25.38. Rays of light that strike the surface follow the law of reflection. For a mirror that is large compared with its radius of curvature, as in Figure 25.38(a), we see that the reflected rays do not cross at the same point, and the mirror does not have a well-defined focal point. If the mirror had the shape of a parabola, the rays would all cross at a single point, and the mirror would have a well-defined focal point. But parabolic mirrors are much more expensive to make than spherical mirrors. The solution is to use a mirror that is small compared with its radius of curvature, as shown in Figure 25.38(b). (This is the mirror equivalent of the thin lens approximation.) To a very good approximation, this mirror has a well-defined focal point at F that is the focal distance f from the center of the mirror. The focal length f of a concave mirror is positive, since it is a converging mirror.

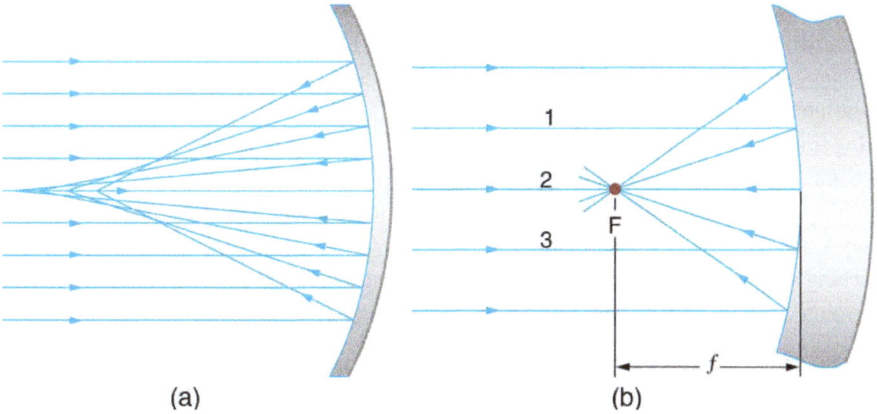

FIGURE 25.38 (a) Parallel rays reflected from a large spherical mirror do not all cross at a common point. (b) If a spherical mirror is small compared with its radius of curvature, parallel rays are focused to a common point. The distance of the focal point from the center of the mirror is its focal length f. Since this mirror is converging, it has a positive focal length.

Just as for lenses, the shorter the focal length, the more powerful the mirror; thus, $P = 1/f$ for a mirror, too. A more strongly curved mirror has a shorter focal length and a greater power. Using the law of reflection and some simple trigonometry, it can be shown that the focal length is half the radius of curvature, or

$$f = \frac{R}{2}, \quad 25.45$$

where R is the radius of curvature of a spherical mirror. The smaller the radius of curvature, the smaller the focal length and, thus, the more powerful the mirror.

The convex mirror shown in Figure 25.39 also has a focal point. Parallel rays of light reflected from the mirror seem to originate from the point F at the focal distance f behind the mirror. The focal length and power of a convex mirror are negative, since it is a diverging mirror.

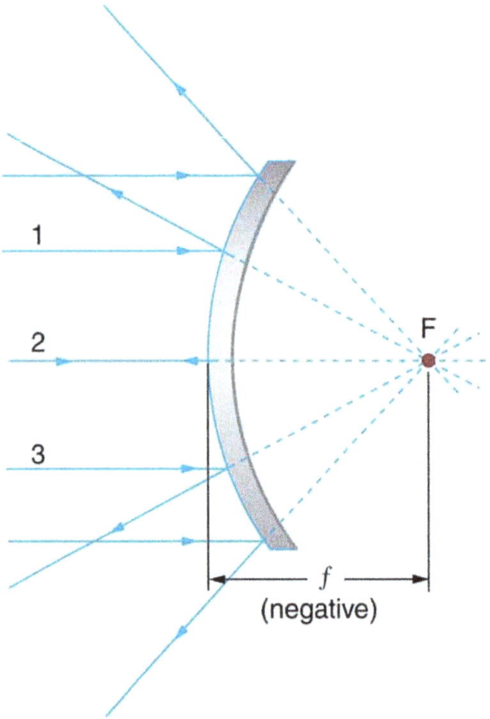

FIGURE 25.39 Parallel rays of light reflected from a convex spherical mirror (small in size compared with its radius of curvature) seem to originate from a well-defined focal point at the focal distance f behind the mirror. Convex mirrors diverge light rays and, thus, have a negative focal length.

Ray tracing is as useful for mirrors as for lenses. The rules for ray tracing for mirrors are based on the illustrations just discussed:

1. A ray approaching a concave converging mirror parallel to its axis is reflected through the focal point F of the mirror on the same side. (See rays 1 and 3 in Figure 25.38(b).)
2. A ray approaching a convex diverging mirror parallel to its axis is reflected so that it seems to come from the focal point F behind the mirror. (See rays 1 and 3 in Figure 25.39.)
3. Any ray striking the center of a mirror is followed by applying the law of reflection; it makes the same angle with the axis when leaving as when approaching. (See ray 2 in Figure 25.40.)
4. A ray approaching a concave converging mirror through its focal point is reflected parallel to its axis. (The reverse of rays 1 and 3 in Figure 25.38.)
5. A ray approaching a convex diverging mirror by heading toward its focal point on the opposite side is reflected parallel to the axis. (The reverse of rays 1 and 3 in Figure 25.39.)

We will use ray tracing to illustrate how images are formed by mirrors, and we can use ray tracing quantitatively to obtain numerical information. But since we assume each mirror is small compared with its radius of curvature, we can use the thin lens equations for mirrors just as we did for lenses.

Consider the situation shown in Figure 25.40, concave spherical mirror reflection, in which an object is placed farther from a concave (converging) mirror than its focal length. That is, f is positive and $d_o > f$, so that we may expect an image similar to the case 1 real image formed by a converging lens. Ray tracing in Figure 25.40 shows that the rays from a common point on the object all cross at a point on the same side of the mirror as the object. Thus a real image can be projected onto a screen placed at this location. The image distance is positive, and the image is inverted, so its magnification is negative. This is a *case 1 image for mirrors.* It differs from the case 1 image for lenses only in that the image is on the same side of the mirror as the object. It is otherwise identical.

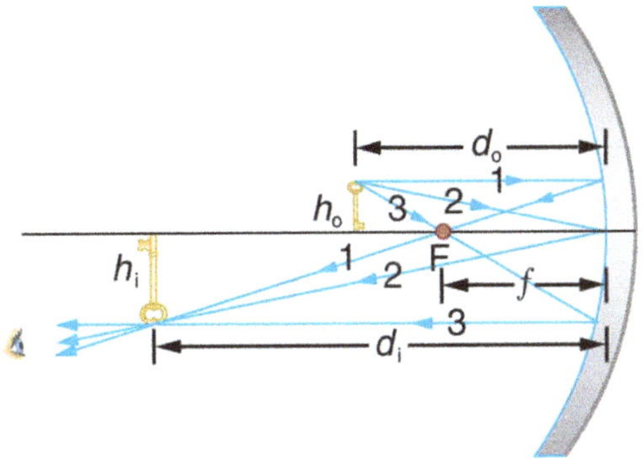

FIGURE 25.40 A case 1 image for a mirror. An object is farther from the converging mirror than its focal length. Rays from a common point on the object are traced using the rules in the text. Ray 1 approaches parallel to the axis, ray 2 strikes the center of the mirror, and ray 3 goes through the focal point on the way toward the mirror. All three rays cross at the same point after being reflected, locating the inverted real image. Although three rays are shown, only two of the three are needed to locate the image and determine its height.

EXAMPLE 25.9

A Concave Reflector

Electric room heaters use a concave mirror to reflect infrared (IR) radiation from hot coils. Note that IR follows the same law of reflection as visible light. Given that the mirror has a radius of curvature of 50.0 cm and produces an image of the coils 3.00 m away from the mirror, where are the coils?

Strategy and Concept

We are given that the concave mirror projects a real image of the coils at an image distance $d_i = 3.00\text{ m}$. The coils are the object, and we are asked to find their location—that is, to find the object distance d_o. We are also given the radius of curvature of the mirror, so that its focal length is $f = R/2 = 25.0\text{ cm}$ (positive since the mirror is concave or converging). Assuming the mirror is small compared with its radius of curvature, we can use the thin lens equations, to solve this problem.

Solution

Since d_i and f are known, thin lens equation can be used to find d_o:

$$\frac{1}{d_o} + \frac{1}{d_i} = \frac{1}{f}. \quad 25.46$$

Rearranging to isolate d_o gives

$$\frac{1}{d_o} = \frac{1}{f} - \frac{1}{d_i}. \quad 25.47$$

Entering known quantities gives a value for $1/d_o$:

$$\frac{1}{d_o} = \frac{1}{0.250\text{ m}} - \frac{1}{3.00\text{ m}} = \frac{3.667}{\text{m}}. \quad 25.48$$

This must be inverted to find d_o:

$$d_o = \frac{1\text{ m}}{3.667} = 27.3\text{ cm}. \quad 25.49$$

Discussion

Note that the object (the filament) is farther from the mirror than the mirror's focal length. This is a case 1 image ($d_o > f$ and f positive), consistent with the fact that a real image is formed. You will get the most concentrated thermal energy directly in front of the mirror and 3.00 m away from it. Generally, this is not desirable, since it could cause burns. Usually, you want the rays to emerge parallel, and this is accomplished by having the filament at the focal point of the mirror.

Note that the filament here is not much farther from the mirror than its focal length and that the image produced is considerably farther away. This is exactly analogous to a slide projector. Placing a slide only slightly farther away from the projector lens than its focal length produces an image significantly farther away. As the object gets closer to the focal distance, the image gets farther away. In fact, as the object distance approaches the focal length, the image distance approaches infinity and the rays are sent out parallel to one another.

EXAMPLE 25.10

Solar Electric Generating System

One of the solar technologies used today for generating electricity is a device (called a parabolic trough or concentrating collector) that concentrates the sunlight onto a blackened pipe that contains a fluid. This heated fluid is pumped to a heat exchanger, where its heat energy is transferred to another system that is used to generate steam—and so generate electricity through a conventional steam cycle. Figure 25.41 shows such a working system in southern California. Concave mirrors are used to concentrate the sunlight onto the pipe. The mirror has the approximate shape of a section of a cylinder. For the problem, assume that the mirror is exactly one-quarter of a full cylinder.

a. If we wish to place the fluid-carrying pipe 40.0 cm from the concave mirror at the mirror's focal point, what will be the radius of curvature of the mirror?
b. Per meter of pipe, what will be the amount of sunlight concentrated onto the pipe, assuming the insolation (incident solar radiation) is $0.900\ \mathrm{kW/m^2}$?
c. If the fluid-carrying pipe has a 2.00-cm diameter, what will be the temperature increase of the fluid per meter of pipe over a period of one minute? Assume all the solar radiation incident on the reflector is absorbed by the pipe, and that the fluid is mineral oil.

Strategy

To solve an *Integrated Concept Problem* we must first identify the physical principles involved. Part (a) is related to the current topic. Part (b) involves a little math, primarily geometry. Part (c) requires an understanding of heat and density.

Solution to (a)

To a good approximation for a concave or semi-spherical surface, the point where the parallel rays from the sun converge will be at the focal point, so $R = 2f = 80.0\ \mathrm{cm}$.

Solution to (b)

The insolation is $900\ \mathrm{W/m^2}$. We must find the cross-sectional area A of the concave mirror, since the power delivered is $900\ \mathrm{W/m^2} \times \mathrm{A}$. The mirror in this case is a quarter-section of a cylinder, so the area for a length L of the mirror is $\mathrm{A} = \frac{1}{4}(2\pi R)\mathrm{L}$. The area for a length of 1.00 m is then

$$\mathrm{A} = \frac{\pi}{2}R(1.00\ \mathrm{m}) = \frac{(3.14)}{2}(0.800\ \mathrm{m})(1.00\ \mathrm{m}) = 1.26\ \mathrm{m}^2. \quad 25.50$$

The insolation on the 1.00-m length of pipe is then

$$\left(9.00 \times 10^2\ \frac{\mathrm{W}}{\mathrm{m}^2}\right)\left(1.26\ \mathrm{m}^2\right) = 1130\ \mathrm{W}. \quad 25.51$$

Solution to (c)

The increase in temperature is given by $Q = mc\Delta T$. The mass m of the mineral oil in the one-meter section of pipe is

$$
\begin{aligned}
m &= \rho V = \rho\pi\left(\frac{d}{2}\right)^2(1.00\text{ m}) \\
&= \left(8.00 \times 10^2 \text{ kg/m}^3\right)(3.14)(0.0100\text{ m})^2(1.00\text{ m}) \\
&= 0.251\text{ kg.}
\end{aligned} \tag{25.52}
$$

Therefore, the increase in temperature in one minute is

$$
\begin{aligned}
\Delta T &= Q/mc \\
&= \frac{(1130\text{ W})(60.0\text{ s})}{(0.251\text{ kg})(1670\text{ J}\cdot\text{kg/°C})} \\
&= 162\text{°C.}
\end{aligned} \tag{25.53}
$$

Discussion for (c)

An array of such pipes in the California desert can provide a thermal output of 250 MW on a sunny day, with fluids reaching temperatures as high as $400°\text{C}$. We are considering only one meter of pipe here, and ignoring heat losses along the pipe.

FIGURE 25.41 Parabolic trough collectors are used to generate electricity in southern California. (credit: kjkolb, Wikimedia Commons)

What happens if an object is closer to a concave mirror than its focal length? This is analogous to a case 2 image for lenses ($d_o < f$ and f positive), which is a magnifier. In fact, this is how makeup mirrors act as magnifiers. Figure 25.42(a) uses ray tracing to locate the image of an object placed close to a concave mirror. Rays from a common point on the object are reflected in such a manner that they appear to be coming from behind the mirror, meaning that the image is virtual and cannot be projected. As with a magnifying glass, the image is upright and larger than the object. This is a *case 2 image for mirrors* and is exactly analogous to that for lenses.

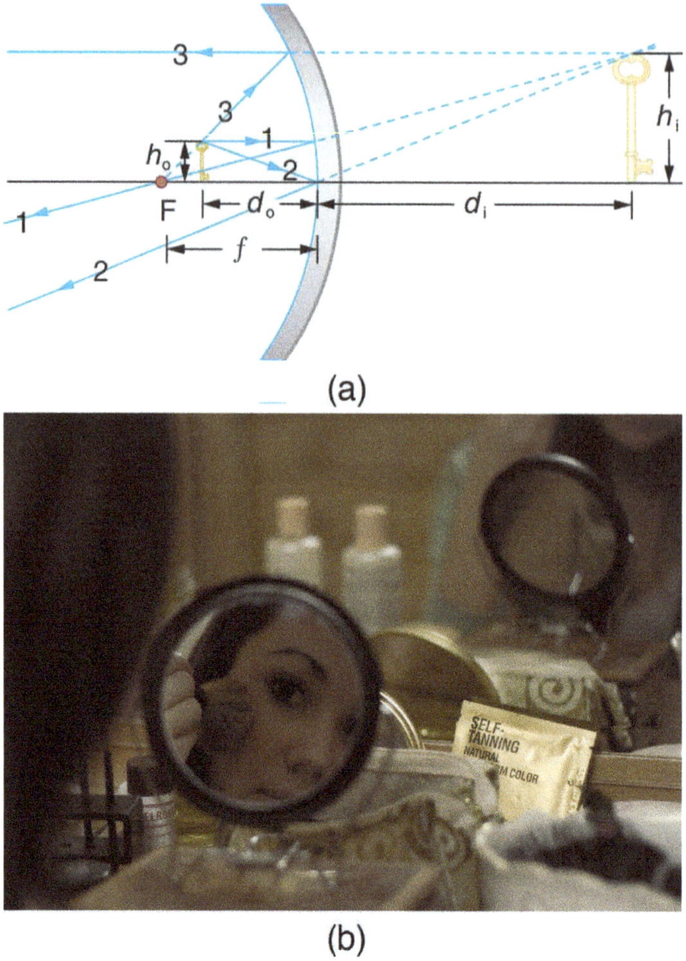

FIGURE 25.42 (a) Case 2 images for mirrors are formed when a converging mirror has an object closer to it than its focal length. Ray 1 approaches parallel to the axis, ray 2 strikes the center of the mirror, and ray 3 approaches the mirror as if it came from the focal point. (b) A magnifying mirror showing the reflection. (credit: Mike Melrose, Flickr)

All three rays appear to originate from the same point after being reflected, locating the upright virtual image behind the mirror and showing it to be larger than the object. (b) Makeup mirrors are perhaps the most common use of a concave mirror to produce a larger, upright image.

A convex mirror is a diverging mirror (f is negative) and forms only one type of image. It is a *case 3* image—one that is upright and smaller than the object, just as for diverging lenses. Figure 25.43(a) uses ray tracing to illustrate the location and size of the case 3 image for mirrors. Since the image is behind the mirror, it cannot be projected and is thus a virtual image. It is also seen to be smaller than the object.

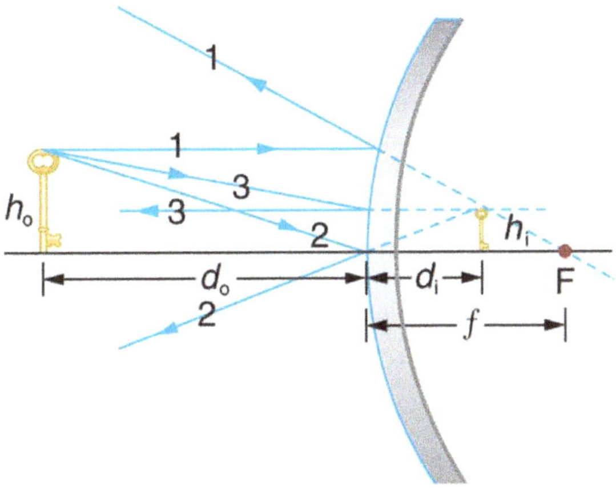

(a)

(b)

FIGURE 25.43 Case 3 images for mirrors are formed by any convex mirror. Ray 1 approaches parallel to the axis, ray 2 strikes the center of the mirror, and ray 3 approaches toward the focal point. All three rays appear to originate from the same point after being reflected, locating the upright virtual image behind the mirror and showing it to be smaller than the object. (b) Security mirrors are convex, producing a smaller, upright image. Because the image is smaller, a larger area is imaged compared to what would be observed for a flat mirror (and hence security is improved). (credit: Laura D'Alessandro, Flickr)

EXAMPLE 25.11

Image in a Convex Mirror

A keratometer is a device used to measure the curvature of the cornea, particularly for fitting contact lenses. Light is reflected from the cornea, which acts like a convex mirror, and the keratometer measures the magnification of the image. The smaller the magnification, the smaller the radius of curvature of the cornea. If the light source is 12.0 cm from the cornea and the image's magnification is 0.0320, what is the cornea's radius of curvature?

Strategy

If we can find the focal length of the convex mirror formed by the cornea, we can find its radius of curvature (the radius of curvature is twice the focal length of a spherical mirror). We are given that the object distance is $d_o = 12.0\text{ cm}$ and that $m = 0.0320$. We first solve for the image distance d_i, and then for f.

Solution

$m = –d_i/d_o$. Solving this expression for d_i gives

$$d_i = -md_o. \qquad 25.54$$

Entering known values yields

$$d_i = –(0.0320)(12.0\text{ cm}) = –0.384\text{ cm}. \qquad 25.55$$

$$\frac{1}{f} = \frac{1}{d_o} + \frac{1}{d_i} \tag{25.56}$$

Substituting known values,

$$\frac{1}{f} = \frac{1}{12.0 \text{ cm}} + \frac{1}{-0.384 \text{ cm}} = \frac{-2.52}{\text{cm}}. \tag{25.57}$$

This must be inverted to find f:

$$f = \frac{\text{cm}}{-2.52} = -0.400 \text{ cm}. \tag{25.58}$$

The radius of curvature is twice the focal length, so that

$$R = 2\,|f| = -0.800 \text{ cm}. \tag{25.59}$$

Discussion

The radius of curvature found here is reasonable for a cornea. The distance from cornea to retina in an adult eye is about 2.0 cm. In practice, many corneas are not spherical, complicating the job of fitting contact lenses. Note that the image distance here is negative, consistent with the fact that the image is behind the mirror, where it cannot be projected. In this section's Problems and Exercises, you will show that for a fixed object distance, the smaller the radius of curvature, the smaller the magnification.

The three types of images formed by mirrors (cases 1, 2, and 3) are exactly analogous to those formed by lenses, as summarized in the table at the end of Image Formation by Lenses. It is easiest to concentrate on only three types of images—then remember that concave mirrors act like convex lenses, whereas convex mirrors act like concave lenses.

TAKE-HOME EXPERIMENT: CONCAVE MIRRORS CLOSE TO HOME

Find a flashlight and identify the curved mirror used in it. Find another flashlight and shine the first flashlight onto the second one, which is turned off. Estimate the focal length of the mirror. You might try shining a flashlight on the curved mirror behind the headlight of a car, keeping the headlight switched off, and determine its focal length.

Problem-Solving Strategy for Mirrors

Step 1. Examine the situation to determine that image formation by a mirror is involved.

Step 2. Refer to the Problem-Solving Strategies for Lenses. The same strategies are valid for mirrors as for lenses with one qualification—use the ray tracing rules for mirrors listed earlier in this section.

Glossary

converging lens a convex lens in which light rays that enter it parallel to its axis converge at a single point on the opposite side

converging mirror a concave mirror in which light rays that strike it parallel to its axis converge at one or more points along the axis

corner reflector an object consisting of two mutually perpendicular reflecting surfaces, so that the light that enters is reflected back exactly parallel to the direction from which it came

critical angle incident angle that produces an angle of refraction of $90°$

dispersion spreading of white light into its full spectrum of wavelengths

diverging lens a concave lens in which light rays that enter it parallel to its axis bend away (diverge) from its axis

diverging mirror a convex mirror in which light rays that strike it parallel to its axis bend away (diverge) from its axis

fiber optics transmission of light down fibers of plastic or glass, applying the principle of total internal reflection

focal length distance from the center of a lens or curved mirror to its focal point

focal point for a converging lens or mirror, the point at which converging light rays cross; for a diverging lens or mirror, the point from which diverging light rays appear to originate

geometric optics part of optics dealing with the ray aspect of light

index of refraction for a material, the ratio of the speed of light in vacuum to that in the material

law of reflection angle of reflection equals the angle of incidence

law of reflection angle of reflection equals the angle of incidence

magnification ratio of image height to object height

mirror smooth surface that reflects light at specific angles, forming an image of the person or object in front of it

power inverse of focal length

rainbow dispersion of sunlight into a continuous distribution of colors according to wavelength, produced by the refraction and reflection of sunlight by water droplets in the sky

ray straight line that originates at some point

real image image that can be projected

refraction changing of a light ray's direction when it passes through variations in matter

virtual image image that cannot be projected

zircon natural gemstone with a large index of refraction

Section Summary

25.1 The Ray Aspect of Light

- A straight line that originates at some point is called a ray.
- The part of optics dealing with the ray aspect of light is called geometric optics.
- Light can travel in three ways from a source to another location: (1) directly from the source through empty space; (2) through various media; (3) after being reflected from a mirror.

25.2 The Law of Reflection

- The angle of reflection equals the angle of incidence.
- A mirror has a smooth surface and reflects light at specific angles.
- Light is diffused when it reflects from a rough surface.
- Mirror images can be photographed and videotaped by instruments.

25.3 The Law of Refraction

- The changing of a light ray's direction when it passes through variations in matter is called refraction.
- The speed of light in vacuum $c = 2.99792458 \times 10^8 \text{ m/s} \approx 3.00 \times 10^8 \text{ m/s}.$
- Index of refraction $n = \frac{c}{v}$, where v is the speed of light in the material, c is the speed of light in vacuum, and n is the index of refraction.
- Snell's law, the law of refraction, is stated in equation form as $n_1 \sin \theta_1 = n_2 \sin \theta_2$.

25.4 Total Internal Reflection

- The incident angle that produces an angle of refraction of $90°$ is called critical angle.
- Total internal reflection is a phenomenon that occurs at the boundary between two mediums, such that if the incident angle in the first medium is greater than the critical angle, then all the light is reflected back into that medium.
- Fiber optics involves the transmission of light down fibers of plastic or glass, applying the principle of total internal reflection.
- Endoscopes are used to explore the body through

various orifices or minor incisions, based on the transmission of light through optical fibers.
- Cladding prevents light from being transmitted between fibers in a bundle.
- Diamonds sparkle due to total internal reflection coupled with a large index of refraction.

25.5 Dispersion: The Rainbow and Prisms

- The spreading of white light into its full spectrum of wavelengths is called dispersion.
- Rainbows are produced by a combination of refraction and reflection and involve the dispersion of sunlight into a continuous distribution of colors.
- Dispersion produces beautiful rainbows but also causes problems in certain optical systems.

25.6 Image Formation by Lenses

- Light rays entering a converging lens parallel to its axis cross one another at a single point on the opposite side.
- For a converging lens, the focal point is the point at which converging light rays cross; for a diverging lens, the focal point is the point from which diverging light rays appear to originate.
- The distance from the center of the lens to its focal point is called the focal length f.
- Power P of a lens is defined to be the inverse of its focal length, $P = \frac{1}{f}$.
- A lens that causes the light rays to bend away from its axis is called a diverging lens.
- Ray tracing is the technique of graphically determining the paths that light rays take.
- The image in which light rays from one point on the object actually cross at the location of the image and can be projected onto a screen, a piece of film, or the retina of an eye is called a real image.
- Thin lens equations are $\frac{1}{d_o} + \frac{1}{d_i} = \frac{1}{f}$ and $\frac{h_i}{h_o} = -\frac{d_i}{d_o} = m$ (magnification).
- The distance of the image from the center of the lens is called image distance.
- An image that is on the same side of the lens as the object and cannot be projected on a screen is called a virtual image.

25.7 Image Formation by Mirrors

- The characteristics of an image formed by a flat mirror are: (a) The image and object are the same distance from the mirror, (b) The image is a virtual image, and (c) The image is situated behind the mirror.
- Image length is half the radius of curvature.
  $$f = \frac{R}{2}$$
- A convex mirror is a diverging mirror and forms only one type of image, namely a virtual image.

Conceptual Questions

25.2 The Law of Reflection

1. Using the law of reflection, explain how powder takes the shine off of a person's nose. What is the name of the optical effect?

25.3 The Law of Refraction

2. Diffusion by reflection from a rough surface is described in this chapter. Light can also be diffused by refraction. Describe how this occurs in a specific situation, such as light interacting with crushed ice.

3. Why is the index of refraction always greater than or equal to 1?

4. Does the fact that the light flash from lightning reaches you before its sound prove that the speed of light is extremely large or simply that it is greater than the speed of sound? Discuss how you could use this effect to get an estimate of the speed of light.

5. Will light change direction toward or away from the perpendicular when it goes from air to water? Water to glass? Glass to air?

6. Explain why an object in water always appears to be at a depth shallower than it actually is? Why do people sometimes sustain neck and spinal injuries when diving into unfamiliar ponds or waters?

7. Explain why a person's legs appear very short when wading in a pool. Justify your explanation with a ray diagram showing the path of rays from the feet to the eye of an observer who is out of the water.

8. Why is the front surface of a thermometer curved as shown?

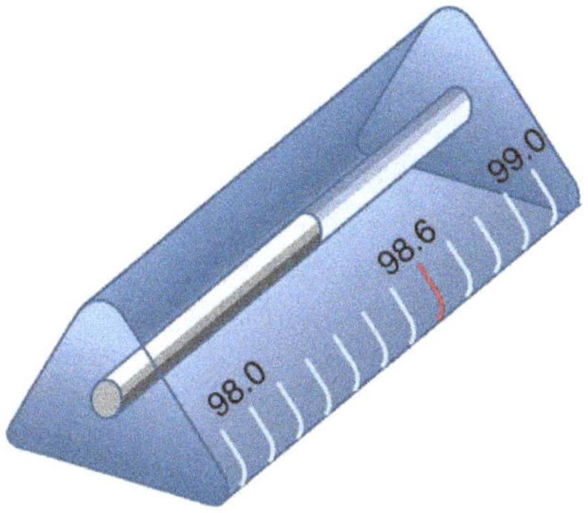

FIGURE 25.44 The curved surface of the thermometer serves a purpose.

9. Suppose light were incident from air onto a material that had a negative index of refraction, say −1.3; where does the refracted light ray go?

25.4 Total Internal Reflection

10. A ring with a colorless gemstone is dropped into water. The gemstone becomes invisible when submerged. Can it be a diamond? Explain.

11. A high-quality diamond may be quite clear and colorless, transmitting all visible wavelengths with little absorption. Explain how it can sparkle with flashes of brilliant color when illuminated by white light.

12. Is it possible that total internal reflection plays a role in rainbows? Explain in terms of indices of refraction and angles, perhaps referring to Figure 25.45. Some of us have seen the formation of a double rainbow. Is it physically possible to observe a triple rainbow?

FIGURE 25.45 Double rainbows are not a very common observance. (credit: InvictusOU812, Flickr)

13. The most common type of mirage is an illusion that light from faraway objects is reflected by a pool of water that is not really there. Mirages are generally observed in deserts, when there is a hot layer of air near the ground. Given that the refractive index of air is lower for air at higher temperatures, explain how mirages can be formed.

25.6 Image Formation by Lenses

14. It can be argued that a flat piece of glass, such as in a window, is like a lens with an infinite focal length. If so, where does it form an image? That is, how are d_{i} and d_{o} related?

15. You can often see a reflection when looking at a sheet of glass, particularly if it is darker on the other side. Explain why you can often see a double image in such circumstances.

16. When you focus a camera, you adjust the distance of the lens from the film. If the camera lens acts like a thin lens, why can it not be a fixed distance from the film for both near and distant objects?

17. A thin lens has two focal points, one on either side, at equal distances from its center, and should behave the same for light entering from either side. Look through your eyeglasses (or those of a friend) backward and forward and comment on whether they are thin lenses.

18. Will the focal length of a lens change when it is submerged in water? Explain.

25.7 Image Formation by Mirrors

19. What are the differences between real and virtual images? How can you tell (by looking) whether an image formed by a single lens or mirror is real or virtual?

20. Can you see a virtual image? Can you photograph one? Can one be projected onto a screen with additional lenses or mirrors? Explain your responses.

21. Is it necessary to project a real image onto a screen for it to exist?

22. At what distance is an image *always* located—at d_{o}, d_{i}, or f?

23. Under what circumstances will an image be located at the focal point of a lens or mirror?

24. What is meant by a negative magnification? What is meant by a magnification that is less than 1 in magnitude?

25. Can a case 1 image be larger than the object even though its magnification is always negative? Explain.

26. Figure 25.46 shows a light bulb between two

mirrors. One mirror produces a beam of light with parallel rays; the other keeps light from escaping without being put into the beam. Where is the filament of the light in relation to the focal point or radius of curvature of each mirror?

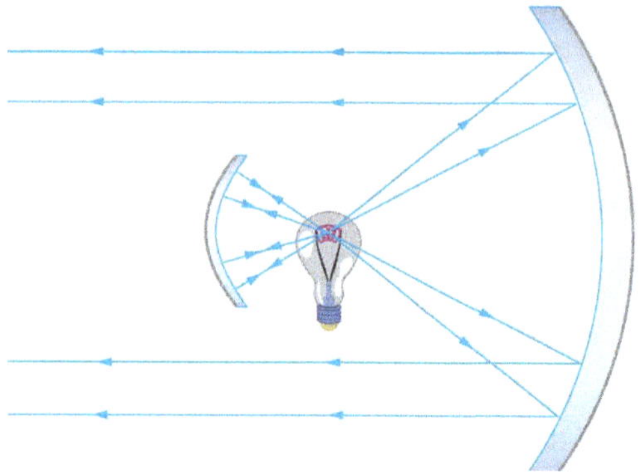

FIGURE 25.46 The two mirrors trap most of the bulb's light and form a directional beam as in a headlight.

27. Devise an arrangement of mirrors allowing you to see the back of your head. What is the minimum number of mirrors needed for this task?

28. If you wish to see your entire body in a flat mirror (from head to toe), how tall should the mirror be? Does its size depend upon your distance away from the mirror? Provide a sketch.

29. It can be argued that a flat mirror has an infinite focal length. If so, where does it form an image? That is, how are d_i and d_o related?

30. Why are diverging mirrors often used for rear-view mirrors in vehicles? What is the main disadvantage of using such a mirror compared with a flat one?

Problems & Exercises

25.1 The Ray Aspect of Light

1. Suppose a man stands in front of a mirror as shown in Figure 25.47. His eyes are 1.65 m above the floor, and the top of his head is 0.13 m higher. Find the height above the floor of the top and bottom of the smallest mirror in which he can see both the top of his head and his feet. How is this distance related to the man's height?

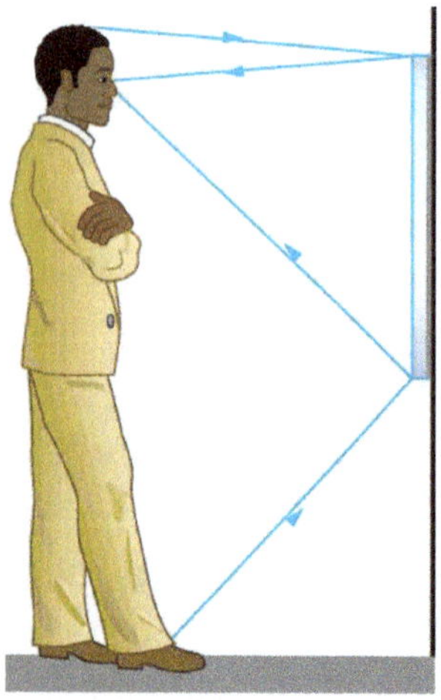

FIGURE 25.47 A full-length mirror is one in which you can see all of yourself. It need not be as big as you, and its size is independent of your distance from it.

25.2 The Law of Reflection

2. Show that when light reflects from two mirrors that meet each other at a right angle, the outgoing ray is parallel to the incoming ray, as illustrated in the following figure.

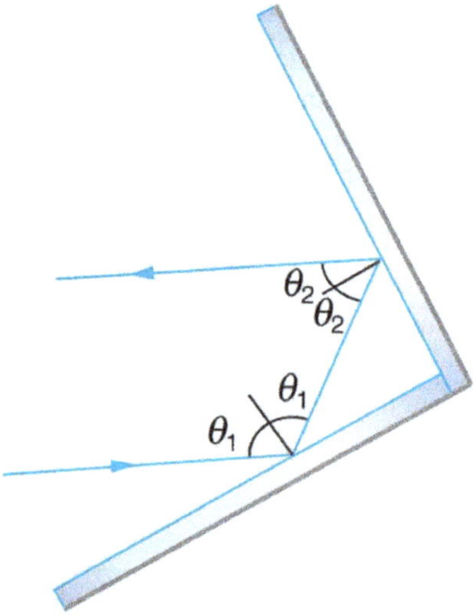

FIGURE 25.48 A corner reflector sends the reflected ray back in a direction parallel to the incident ray, independent of incoming direction.

3. Light shows staged with lasers use moving mirrors to swing beams and create colorful effects. Show that a light ray reflected from a mirror changes direction by 2θ when the mirror is rotated by an angle θ.

4. A flat mirror is neither converging nor diverging. To prove this, consider two rays originating from the same point and diverging at an angle θ. Show that after striking a plane mirror, the angle between their directions remains θ.

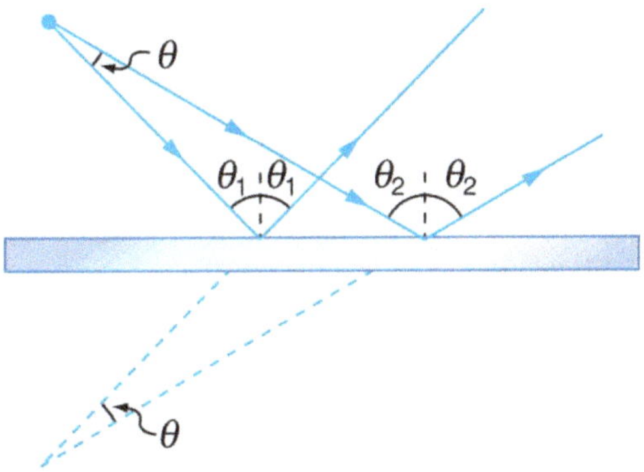

FIGURE 25.49 A flat mirror neither converges nor diverges light rays. Two rays continue to diverge at the same angle after reflection.

25.3 The Law of Refraction

5. What is the speed of light in water? In glycerine?

6. What is the speed of light in air? In crown glass?

7. Calculate the index of refraction for a medium in which the speed of light is 2.012×10^8 m/s, and identify the most likely substance based on Table 25.1.

8. In what substance in Table 25.1 is the speed of light 2.290×10^8 m/s?

9. There was a major collision of an asteroid with the Moon in medieval times. It was described by monks at Canterbury Cathedral in England as a red glow on and around the Moon. How long after the asteroid hit the Moon, which is 3.84×10^5 km away, would the light first arrive on Earth?

10. A scuba diver training in a pool looks at his instructor as shown in Figure 25.50. What angle does the ray from the instructor's face make with the perpendicular to the water at the point where the ray enters? The angle between the ray in the water and the perpendicular to the water is $25.0°$.

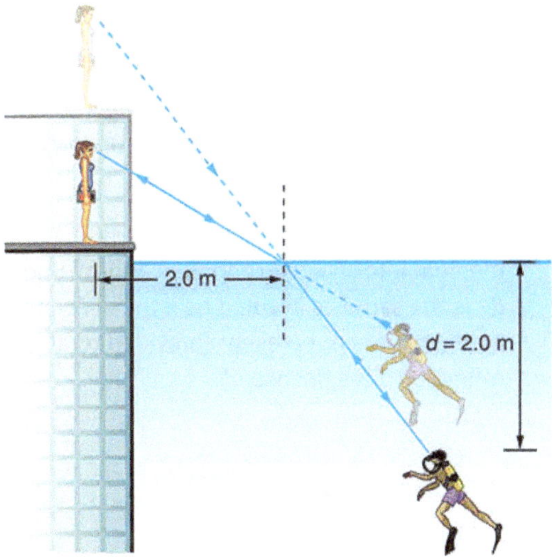

FIGURE 25.50 A scuba diver in a pool and his trainer look at each other.

11. Components of some computers communicate with each other through optical fibers having an index of refraction $n = 1.55$. What time in nanoseconds is required for a signal to travel 0.200 m through such a fiber?

12. (a) Given that the angle between the ray in the water and the perpendicular to the water is $25.0°$, and using information in Figure 25.50, find the height of the instructor's head above the water, noting that you will first have to calculate the angle of refraction. (b) Find the apparent depth of the diver's head below water as seen by the instructor. Assume the diver and the diver's image are the same horizontal distance from the normal.

13. Suppose you have an unknown clear substance immersed in water, and you wish to identify it by finding its index of refraction. You arrange to have a beam of light enter it at an angle of $45.0°$, and you observe the angle of refraction to be $40.3°$. What is the index of refraction of the substance and its likely identity?

14. On the Moon's surface, lunar astronauts placed a corner reflector, off which a laser beam is periodically reflected. The distance to the Moon is calculated from the round-trip time. What percent correction is needed to account for the delay in time due to the slowing of light in Earth's atmosphere? Assume the distance to the Moon is precisely 3.84×10^8 m, and Earth's atmosphere (which varies in density with altitude) is equivalent to a layer 30.0 km thick with a constant index of refraction $n = 1.000293$.

15. Suppose Figure 25.51 represents a ray of light going from air through crown glass into water, such as going into a fish tank. Calculate the amount the ray is displaced by the glass (Δx), given that the incident angle is 40.0° and the glass is 1.00 cm thick.

16. Figure 25.51 shows a ray of light passing from one medium into a second and then a third. Show that θ_3 is the same as it would be if the second medium were not present (provided total internal reflection does not occur).

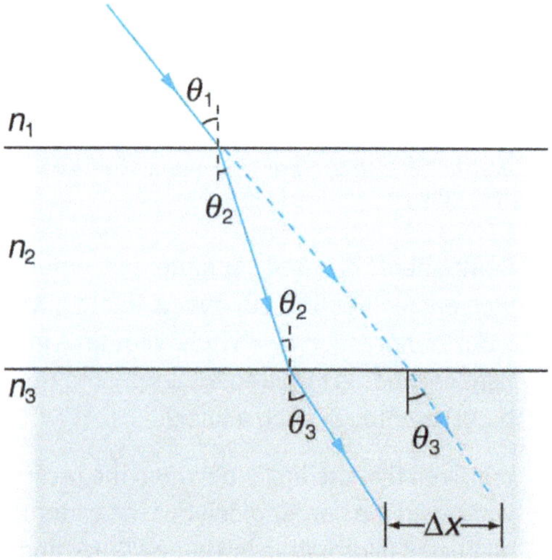

FIGURE 25.51 A ray of light passes from one medium to a third by traveling through a second. The final direction is the same as if the second medium were not present, but the ray is displaced by Δx (shown exaggerated).

17. Unreasonable Results
Suppose light travels from water to another substance, with an angle of incidence of 10.0° and an angle of refraction of 14.9°. (a) What is the index of refraction of the other substance? (b) What is unreasonable about this result? (c) Which assumptions are unreasonable or inconsistent?

18. Construct Your Own Problem
Consider sunlight entering the Earth's atmosphere at sunrise and sunset—that is, at a 90° incident angle. Taking the boundary between nearly empty space and the atmosphere to be sudden, calculate the angle of refraction for sunlight. This lengthens the time the Sun appears to be above the horizon, both at sunrise and sunset. Now construct a problem in which you determine the angle of refraction for different models of the atmosphere, such as various layers of varying density. Your instructor may wish to guide you on the level of complexity to consider and on how the index of refraction varies with air density.

19. Unreasonable Results
Light traveling from water to a gemstone strikes the surface at an angle of 80.0° and has an angle of refraction of 15.2°. (a) What is the speed of light in the gemstone? (b) What is unreasonable about this result? (c) Which assumptions are unreasonable or inconsistent?

25.4 Total Internal Reflection

20. Verify that the critical angle for light going from water to air is 48.6°, as discussed at the end of Example 25.4, regarding the critical angle for light traveling in a polystyrene (a type of plastic) pipe surrounded by air.

21. (a) At the end of Example 25.4, it was stated that the critical angle for light going from diamond to air is 24.4°. Verify this. (b) What is the critical angle for light going from zircon to air?

22. An optical fiber uses flint glass clad with crown glass. What is the critical angle?

23. At what minimum angle will you get total internal reflection of light traveling in water and reflected from ice?

24. Suppose you are using total internal reflection to make an efficient corner reflector. If there is air outside and the incident angle is 45.0°, what must be the minimum index of refraction of the material from which the reflector is made?

25. You can determine the index of refraction of a substance by determining its critical angle. (a) What is the index of refraction of a substance that has a critical angle of 68.4° when submerged in water? What is the substance, based on Table 25.1? (b) What would the critical angle be for this substance in air?

26. A ray of light, emitted beneath the surface of an unknown liquid with air above it, undergoes total internal reflection as shown in Figure 25.52. What is the index of refraction for the liquid and its likely identification?

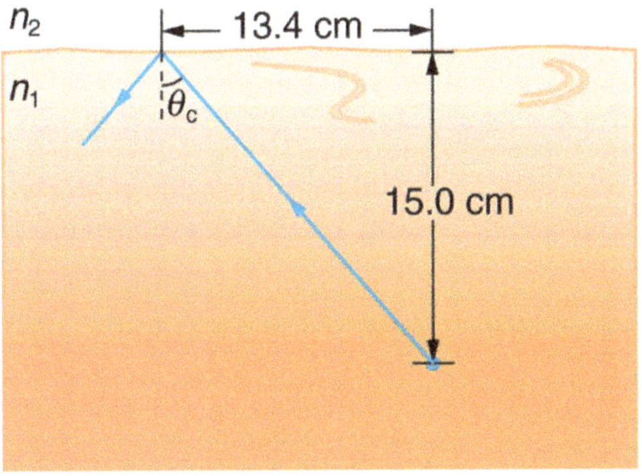

FIGURE 25.52 A light ray inside a liquid strikes the surface at the critical angle and undergoes total internal reflection.

27. A light ray entering an optical fiber surrounded by air is first refracted and then reflected as shown in Figure 25.53. Show that if the fiber is made from crown glass, any incident ray will be totally internally reflected.

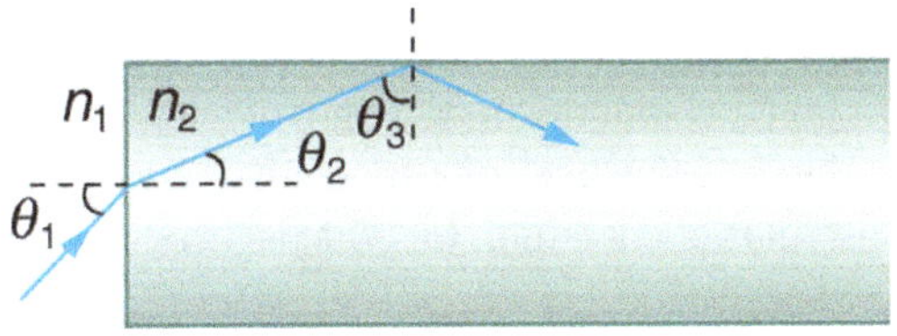

FIGURE 25.53 A light ray enters the end of a fiber, the surface of which is perpendicular to its sides. Examine the conditions under which it may be totally internally reflected.

25.5 Dispersion: The Rainbow and Prisms

28. (a) What is the ratio of the speed of red light to violet light in diamond, based on Table 25.2? (b) What is this ratio in polystyrene? (c) Which is more dispersive?

29. A beam of white light goes from air into water at an incident angle of 75.0°. At what angles are the red (660 nm) and violet (410 nm) parts of the light refracted?

30. By how much do the critical angles for red (660 nm) and violet (410 nm) light differ in a diamond surrounded by air?

31. (a) A narrow beam of light containing yellow (580 nm) and green (550 nm) wavelengths goes from polystyrene to air, striking the surface at a 30.0° incident angle. What is the angle between the colors when they emerge? (b) How far would they have to travel to be separated by 1.00 mm?

32. A parallel beam of light containing orange (610 nm) and violet (410 nm) wavelengths goes from fused quartz to water, striking the surface between them at a 60.0° incident angle. What is the angle between the two colors in water?

33. A ray of 610 nm light goes from air into fused quartz at an incident angle of 55.0°. At what incident angle must 470 nm light enter flint glass to have the same angle of refraction?

34. A narrow beam of light containing red (660 nm) and blue (470 nm) wavelengths travels from air through a 1.00 cm thick flat piece of crown glass and back to air again. The beam strikes at a 30.0° incident angle. (a) At what angles do the two colors emerge? (b) By what distance are the red and blue separated when they emerge?

35. A narrow beam of white light enters a prism made of crown glass at a 45.0° incident angle, as shown in Figure 25.54. At what angles, θ_R and θ_V, do the red (660 nm) and violet (410 nm) components of the light emerge from the prism?

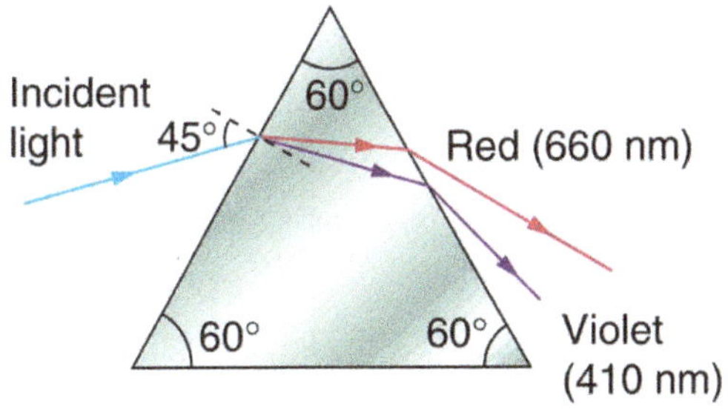

FIGURE 25.54 This prism will disperse the white light into a rainbow of colors. The incident angle is 45.0°, and the angles at which the red and violet light emerge are θ_R and θ_V.

25.6 Image Formation by Lenses

36. What is the power in diopters of a camera lens that has a 50.0 mm focal length?

37. Your camera's zoom lens has an adjustable focal length ranging from 80.0 to 200 mm. What is its range of powers?

38. What is the focal length of 1.75 D reading glasses found on the rack in a pharmacy?

39. You note that your prescription for new eyeglasses is –4.50 D. What will their focal length be?

40. How far from the lens must the film in a camera be, if the lens has a 35.0 mm focal length and is being used to photograph a flower 75.0 cm away? Explicitly show how you follow the steps in the Problem-Solving Strategy for lenses.

41. A certain slide projector has a 100 mm focal length lens. (a) How far away is the screen, if a slide is placed 103 mm from the lens and produces a sharp image? (b) If the slide is 24.0 by 36.0 mm, what are the dimensions of the image?

Explicitly show how you follow the steps in the Problem-Solving Strategy for lenses.

42. A doctor examines a mole with a 15.0 cm focal length magnifying glass held 13.5 cm from the mole (a) Where is the image? (b) What is its magnification? (c) How big is the image of a 5.00 mm diameter mole?

43. How far from a piece of paper must you hold your father's 2.25 D reading glasses to try to burn a hole in the paper with sunlight?

44. A camera with a 50.0 mm focal length lens is being used to photograph a person standing 3.00 m away. (a) How far from the lens must the film be? (b) If the film is 36.0 mm high, what fraction of a 1.75 m tall person will fit on it? (c) Discuss how reasonable this seems, based on your experience in taking or posing for photographs.

45. A camera lens used for taking close-up photographs has a focal length of 22.0 mm. The farthest it can be placed from the film is 33.0 mm. (a) What is the closest object that can be photographed? (b) What is the magnification of this closest object?

46. Suppose your 50.0 mm focal length camera lens is 51.0 mm away from the film in the camera. (a) How far away is an object that is in focus? (b) What is the height of the object if its image is 2.00 cm high?

47. (a) What is the focal length of a magnifying glass that produces a magnification of 3.00 when held 5.00 cm from an object, such as a rare coin? (b) Calculate the power of the magnifier in diopters. (c) Discuss how this power compares to those for store-bought reading glasses (typically 1.0 to 4.0 D). Is the magnifier's power greater, and should it be?

48. What magnification will be produced by a lens of power –4.00 D (such as might be used to correct myopia) if an object is held 25.0 cm away?

49. In Example 25.7, the magnification of a book held 7.50 cm from a 10.0 cm focal length lens was found to be 4.00. (a) Find the magnification for the book when it is held 8.50 cm from the magnifier. (b) Do the same for when it is held 9.50 cm from the magnifier. (c) Comment on the trend in m as the object distance increases as in these two calculations.

50. Suppose a 200 mm focal length telephoto lens is being used to photograph mountains 10.0 km away. (a) Where is the image? (b) What is the height of the image of a 1000 m high cliff on one of the mountains?

51. A camera with a 100 mm focal length lens is used to photograph the sun and moon. What is the height of the image of the sun on the film, given the sun is 1.40×10^6 km in diameter and is 1.50×10^8 km away?

52. Combine thin lens equations to show that the magnification for a thin lens is determined by its focal length and the object distance and is given by $m = f/(f - d_o)$.

25.7 Image Formation by Mirrors

53. What is the focal length of a makeup mirror that has a power of 1.50 D?

54. Some telephoto cameras use a mirror rather than a lens. What radius of curvature mirror is needed to replace a 800 mm focal length telephoto lens?

55. (a) Calculate the focal length of the mirror formed by the shiny back of a spoon that has a 3.00 cm radius of curvature. (b) What is its power in diopters?

56. Find the magnification of the heater element in Example 25.9. Note that its large magnitude helps spread out the reflected energy.

57. What is the focal length of a makeup mirror that produces a magnification of 1.50 when a person's face is 12.0 cm away? Explicitly show how you follow the steps in the Problem-Solving Strategy for Mirrors.

58. A shopper standing 3.00 m from a convex security mirror sees his image with a magnification of 0.250. (a) Where is his image? (b) What is the focal length of the mirror? (c) What is its radius of curvature? Explicitly show how you follow the steps in the Problem-Solving Strategy for Mirrors.

59. An object 1.50 cm high is held 3.00 cm from a person's cornea, and its reflected image is measured to be 0.167 cm high. (a) What is the magnification? (b) Where is the image? (c) Find the radius of curvature of the convex mirror formed by the cornea. (Note that this technique is used by optometrists to measure the curvature of the cornea for contact lens fitting. The instrument used is called a keratometer, or curve measurer.)

60. Ray tracing for a flat mirror shows that the image is located a distance behind the mirror equal to the distance of the object from the mirror. This is stated $d_i = -d_o$, since this is a negative image distance (it is a virtual image). (a) What is the focal length of a flat mirror? (b) What is its power?

61. Show that for a flat mirror $h_i = h_o$, knowing that the image is a distance behind the mirror equal in magnitude to the distance of the object from the mirror.

62. Use the law of reflection to prove that the focal length of a mirror is half its radius of curvature. That is, prove that $f = R/2$. Note this is true for a spherical mirror only if its diameter is small compared with its radius of curvature.

63. Referring to the electric room heater considered in the first example in this section, calculate the intensity of IR radiation in W/m^2 projected by the concave mirror on a person 3.00 m away. Assume that the heating element radiates 1500 W and has an area of 100 cm^2, and that half of the radiated power is reflected and focused by the mirror.

64. Consider a 250-W heat lamp fixed to the ceiling in a bathroom. If the filament in one light burns out then the remaining three still work. Construct a problem in which you determine the resistance of each filament in order to obtain a certain intensity projected on the bathroom floor. The ceiling is 3.0 m high. The problem will need to involve concave mirrors behind the filaments. Your instructor may wish to guide you on the level of complexity to consider in the electrical components.

65. Critical Thinking Light composed of multiple frequencies passes through crown glass. (a) How much faster does the violet component of the light with a wavelength of 410 nm travel in the crown glass than the component of orange light with a wavelength of 610 nm? (b) In a mechanical situation with friction, the longer one surface moves relative to the other, the more the friction acts, slowing the relative motion during the process. Is this the same for light in a medium? (c) In a mechanical situation, it is possible for friction to stop the motion if it occurs over a long enough path. Is this the same for light in a medium? (d) In a mechanical friction situation, once the object slows it will not increase in speed once the friction no longer acts unless another force is present. If a light ray exits a medium into a vacuum, will it go back to a speed of *c* even though that would be an increase in speed not caused by an additional force?

Test Prep for AP® Courses

25.1 The Ray Aspect of Light

1. When light from a distant object reflects off of a concave mirror and comes to a focus some distance in front of the mirror, we model light as a _____ to explain and predict the behavior of light and the formation of an image.

a. wave
b. particle
c. ray
d. all of the above

2. Light of wavelength 500 nm is incident on a narrow slit of width 150 nm. Which model of light most accurately predicts the behavior of the light after it passes through the slit? Explain your answer.

25.2 The Law of Reflection

3. An object is 2 meters in front of a flat mirror. Ray 1 from the object travels in a direction toward the mirror and normal to the mirror's surface. Ray 2 from the object travels at an angle of 5° from the direction of ray 1, and it also reflects off the mirror's surface. At what distance behind the mirror do these two reflected rays appear to converge to form an image?

a. 0.2 m
b. 0.5 m
c. 2 m
d. 4 m

4. Two light rays originate from object A, at a distance of 50 cm in front of a flat mirror, diverging at an angle of 10°. Both of the rays strike a flat mirror and reflect. Two light rays originate from object B, at a distance of 50 cm in front of a convex mirror, diverging at an angle of 10°. Both of the rays strike the convex mirror and reflect. For which object do the reflected rays appear to converge behind the mirror closer to the surface of the mirror, thus forming a closer (larger) image? Explain with the help of a sketch or diagram.

25.3 The Law of Refraction

5. When light travels from air into water, which of the following statements is accurate?

a. The wavelength decreases, and the speed decreases.
b. The wavelength decreases, and the speed

increases.
c. The wavelength increases, and the speed decreases.
d. The wavelength increases, and the speed increases.

6. When a light ray travels from air into glass, which of the following statements is accurate after the light enters the glass?
a. The ray bends away from the normal, and the speed decreases.
b. The ray bends away from the normal, and the speed increases.
c. The ray bends toward the normal, and the speed increases.
d. The ray bends toward the normal, and the speed decreases.

7.

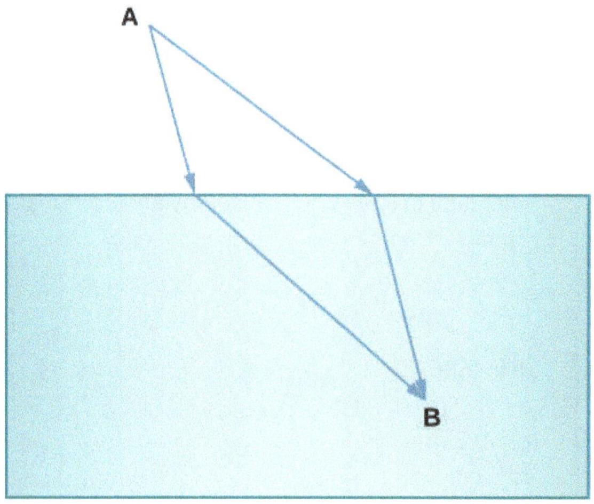

FIGURE 25.55

Two different potential paths from point A to point B are shown. Point A is in the air, and point B is in water. For which of these paths (upper or lower) would light travel from point A to point B faster? Which of the paths more accurately represents how a light ray would travel from point A to point B? Explain.

8. Students in a lab group are given a plastic cube with a hollow cube-shaped space in the middle that fills about half the volume of the cube. The index of refraction of the plastic is known. The hollow space is filled with a gas, and the students are asked to collect the data needed to find the index of refraction of the gas. The students take the following set of measurements:
Angle of incidence of the light in the air above the plastic block: 30°
Angle of refraction of the beam as it enters the plastic from the air: 45°
Angle of refraction of the beam as it enters the plastic from the gas: 45°
The three measurements are shared with a second lab group. Can the second group determine a value for the index of refraction of the gas from only this data?
a. Yes, because they have information about the beam in air and in the plastic above the gas.
b. Yes, because they have information about the beam on both sides of the gas.
c. No, because they need additional information to determine the angle of the beam in the gas.
d. No, because they do not have multiple data points to analyze.

9. Students in a lab group are given a plastic cube with a hollow cube-shaped space in the middle that fills about half the volume of the cube. The index of refraction of the plastic is known. The hollow space is filled with a gas, and the students are asked to collect the data needed to find the index of refraction of the gas. What information would you need to collect, and how would you use this information in order to deduce the index of refraction of the gas in the cube?

10. Light travels through water and crosses a boundary at a non-normal angle into a different fluid with an unknown index of refraction. Which of the following is true about the path of the light after crossing the boundary?
a. If the index of refraction of the fluid is higher than that of water, the light will speed up and turn toward the normal.
b. If the index of refraction of the fluid is higher than that of water, the light will slow down and turn away from the normal.
c. If the index of refraction of the fluid is lower than that of water, the light will speed up and turn away from the normal.
d. If the index of refraction of the fluid is lower than that of water, the light will slow down and turn toward the normal.

11. A laser is fired from a submarine beneath the surface of a lake ($n = 1.33$). The laser emerges from the lake into air with an angle of refraction of 67°. How fast is the light moving through the water? What is the angle of incidence of the laser light when it crosses the boundary between the lake and the air?

25.4 Total Internal Reflection

12. As light travels from air into water, what happens

to the frequency of the light? Consider how the wavelength and speed of light change; then use the relationship between speed, wavelength, and frequency for a wave. What about light that is reflected off the surface of water? What happens to its wavelength, speed, and frequency?

25.6 Image Formation by Lenses

13. An object is 25 cm in front of a converging lens with a focal length of 25 cm. Where will the resulting image be located?

a. 25 cm in front of the lens
b. 25 cm behind the lens
c. 50 cm behind the lens
d. at infinity (either in front of or behind the lens)

14. A detective holds a magnifying glass 5.0 cm above an object he is studying, creating an upright image twice as large as the object. What is the focal length of the lens used for the magnifying glass?

15. A student wishes to predict the magnification of an image given the distance from the object to a converging lens with an unknown index of refraction. What data must the student collect in order to make such a prediction for any object distance?

a. A specific object distance and the image distance associated with that object distance.
b. A specific image distance and a determination of whether the image formed is upright or inverted.
c. The diameter and index of refraction of the lens.
d. The radius of curvature of each side of the lens.

16. Given a converging lens of unknown focal length and unknown index of refraction, explain what materials you would need and what procedure you would follow in order to experimentally determine the focal length of the lens.

25.7 Image Formation by Mirrors

17. A student is testing the properties of a mirror with an unknown radius of curvature. The student notices that no matter how far an object is placed from the mirror, the image seen in the mirror is always upright and smaller than the object. What can the student deduce about this mirror?

a. The mirror is convex.
b. The mirror is flat.
c. The mirror is concave.
d. More information is required to deduce the shape of the mirror.

18. A student notices a small printed sentence at the bottom of the driver's side mirror on her car. It reads, "Objects in the mirror are closer than they appear." Which type of mirror is this (convex, concave, or flat)? How could you confirm the shape of the mirror experimentally?

19. A mirror shows an upright image twice as large as the object when the object is 10 cm away from the mirror. What is the focal length of the mirror?

a. -10 cm
b. 10 cm
c. 20 cm
d. 40 cm

20. A mirror shows an inverted image that is equal in size to the object when the object is 20 cm away from the mirror. Describe the image that will be formed if this object is moved to a distance of 5 cm away from the mirror.

CHAPTER 26

Vision and Optical Instruments

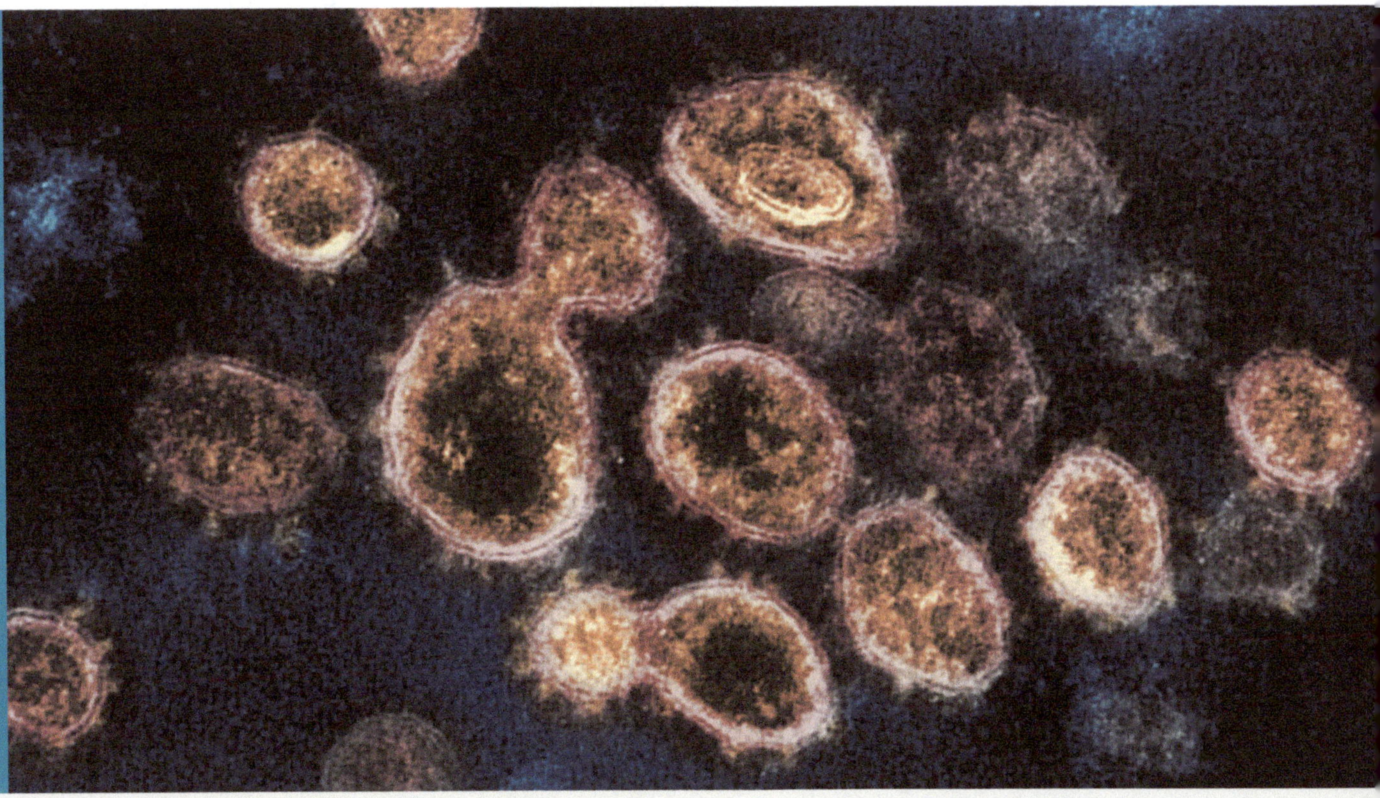

FIGURE 26.1 This transmission electron microscope image shows SARS-CoV-2, the coronavirus that causes COVID-19, isolated from a patient in the U.S. Virus particles are shown emerging from the surface of cells cultured in the lab. The spikes on the outer edge of the virus particles give coronaviruses their name: crown-like. (credit: NIAID-RML, NIH Image Gallery/Flickr)

CHAPTER OUTLINE

CONNECTION FOR AP® COURSES Seeing faces and objects we love and cherish—one's favorite teddy bear, a picture on the wall, or the sun rising over the mountains—is a delight. Intricate images help us understand nature and are invaluable for developing techniques and technologies in order to improve the quality of life. The image of a red blood cell that almost fills the cross-sectional area of a tiny capillary makes us wonder how blood makes it through and does not get stuck. We are able to see bacteria and viruses and understand their structure. It is the knowledge of physics that provides the fundamental understanding and the models required to develop new techniques and instruments. Therefore, physics is called an *enabling science*—it enables development and advancement in other areas. It is through optics and imaging that physics enables advancement in major areas of biosciences.

This chapter builds an understanding of vision and optical instruments on the idea that waves can transfer energy and momentum without the transfer of matter. In support of Big Idea 6, the way light waves travel is addressed using both conceptual and mathematical models. Throughout this unit, the direction of this travel is manipulated through the use of instruments like microscopes and telescopes, in support of Enduring Understanding 6.E.

When light enters a new transparent medium, like the crystalline lens of your eye or the glass lens of a microscope, it is bent either away or toward the line perpendicular to the boundary surface. This process is called “refraction,” as outlined in Essential Knowledge 6.E.3. In both the eye and the microscope, lenses use refraction in order to redirect light and form images. These images, alluded to by Essential Knowledge 6.E.4, can be magnified, shrunk, or inverted, depending upon the lens arrangement.

When a new medium is not fully transparent, the incident light may be reflected or absorbed, and some light may be transmitted. This idea, referenced in Essential Knowledge 6.E.1, is utilized in the construction of telescopes. By relying on the law of reflection and the idea that reflective surfaces can be used to form images, telescopes can be constructed using mirrors to distort the path of light. This distortion allows the person using the telescope to see objects at great distance. While household telescopes utilize wavelengths in the visible light range, telescopes like the Chandra X-ray Observatory and Square Kilometre Array are capable of collecting wavelengths of considerably different size. Essential Knowledge 6.E.2, 6.E.4, and 6.F.1 are all addressed within this telescope discussion.

While ray tracing may easily predict the images formed by lenses and mirrors, only the wave model can be used to describe observations of color. This concept, covered in Section 26.3, underlines Essential Knowledge 6.F.4, the idea that different models of light are appropriate at different scales. The understanding and utilization of both the particle and wave models of light, as described in Enduring Understanding 6.F, is critical to success throughout this chapter.

Big Idea 6 Waves can transfer energy and momentum from one location to another without the permanent transfer of mass and serve as a mathematical model for the description of other phenomena.

Enduring Understanding 6.E The direction of propagation of a wave such as light may be changed when the wave encounters an interface between two media.

Essential Knowledge 6.E.1 When light travels from one medium to another, some of the light is transmitted, some is reflected, and some is absorbed.

Essential Knowledge 6.E.2 When light hits a smooth reflecting surface at an angle, it reflects at the same angle on the other side of the line perpendicular to the surface (specular reflection); and this law of reflection accounts for the size and location of images seen in plane mirrors.

Essential Knowledge 6.E.3 When light travels across a boundary from one transparent material to another, the speed of propagation changes. At a non-normal incident angle, the path of the light ray bends closer to the perpendicular in the optically slower substance. This is called refraction.

Essential Knowledge 6.E.4 The reflection of light from surfaces can be used to form images.

Essential Knowledge 6.E.5 The refraction of light as it travels from one transparent medium to another can be used to form images.

Enduring Understanding 6.F Electromagnetic radiation can be modeled as waves or as fundamental particles.

Essential Knowledge 6.F.1 Types of electromagnetic radiation are characterized by their wavelengths, and certain ranges of wavelength have been given specific names. These include (in order of increasing wavelength spanning a range from picometers to kilometers) gamma rays, x-rays, ultraviolet, visible light, infrared, microwaves, and radio waves.

Essential Knowledge 6.F.4 The nature of light requires that different models of light are most appropriate at different scales.

26.1 Physics of the Eye

LEARNING OBJECTIVES

By the end of this section, you will be able to:

- Explain the image formation by the eye.
- Explain why peripheral images lack detail and color.
- Define refractive indices.
- Analyze the accommodation of the eye for distant and near vision.

Early thinkers had a wide array of theories regarding vision. Euclid and Ptolemy believed that the eyes emitted rays of light; others promoted the idea that objects gave off some particle or substance that was discerned by the eye. Ibn al-Haytham (sometimes called Alhazen), who was mentioned earlier as an originator of the scientific method, conducted a number of experiments to illustrate how the anatomical construction of the eye led to its ability to form images. He recognized that light reflected from objects entered the eye through the lens and was passed to the optic nerve. Al-Haytham did not fully understand the mechanisms involved, but many subsequent discoveries in vision, reflection, and magnification built on his discoveries and methods.

The eye is perhaps the most interesting of all optical instruments. The eye is remarkable in how it forms images and in the richness of detail and color it can detect. However, our eyes commonly need some correction, to reach what is called "normal" vision, but should be called ideal rather than normal. Image formation by our eyes and common vision correction are easy to analyze with the optics discussed in Geometric Optics.

Figure 26.2 shows the basic anatomy of the eye. The cornea and lens form a system that, to a good approximation, acts as a single thin lens. For clear vision, a real image must be projected onto the light-sensitive retina, which lies at a fixed distance from the lens. The lens of the eye adjusts its power to produce an image on the retina for objects at different distances. The center of the image falls on the fovea, which has the greatest density of light receptors and the greatest acuity (sharpness) in the visual field. The variable opening (or pupil) of the eye along with chemical adaptation allows the eye to detect light intensities from the lowest observable to 10^{10} times greater (without damage). This is an incredible range of detection. Our eyes perform a vast number of functions, such as sense direction, movement, sophisticated colors, and distance. Processing of visual nerve impulses begins with interconnections in the retina and continues in the brain. The optic nerve conveys signals received by the eye to the brain.

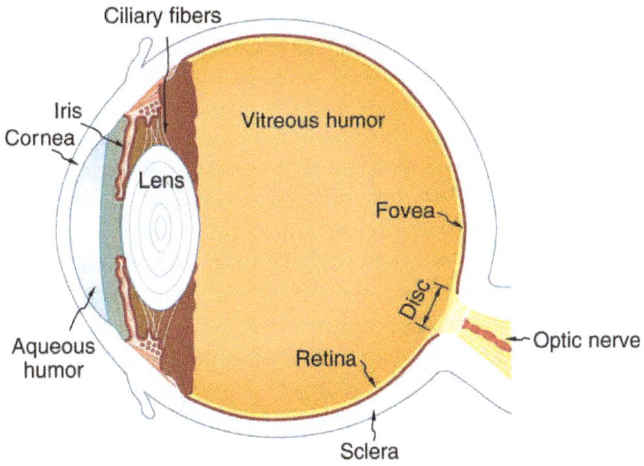

FIGURE 26.2 The cornea and lens of an eye act together to form a real image on the light-sensing retina, which has its densest concentration of receptors in the fovea and a blind spot over the optic nerve. The power of the lens of an eye is adjustable to provide an image on the retina for varying object distances. Layers of tissues with varying indices of refraction in the lens are shown here. However, they have been omitted from other pictures for clarity.

Refractive indices are crucial to image formation using lenses. Table 26.1 shows refractive indices relevant to the eye. The biggest change in the refractive index, and bending of rays, occurs at the cornea rather than the lens. The ray diagram in Figure 26.3 shows image formation by the cornea and lens of the eye. The rays bend according to the refractive indices provided in Table 26.1. The cornea provides about two-thirds of the power of the eye, owing to the fact that speed of light changes considerably while traveling from air into cornea. The lens provides the remaining power needed to produce an image on the retina. The cornea and lens can be treated as a single thin lens, even though the light rays pass through several layers of material (such as cornea, aqueous humor, several layers in the lens, and vitreous humor), changing direction at each interface. The image formed is much like the one produced by a single convex lens. This is a case 1 image. Images formed in the eye are inverted but the brain inverts them once more to make them seem upright.

Material	Index of Refraction
Water	1.33
Air	1.0
Cornea	1.38
Aqueous humor	1.34
Lens	1.41 average (varies throughout the lens, greatest in center)
Vitreous humor	1.34

TABLE 26.1 Refractive Indices Relevant to the Eye

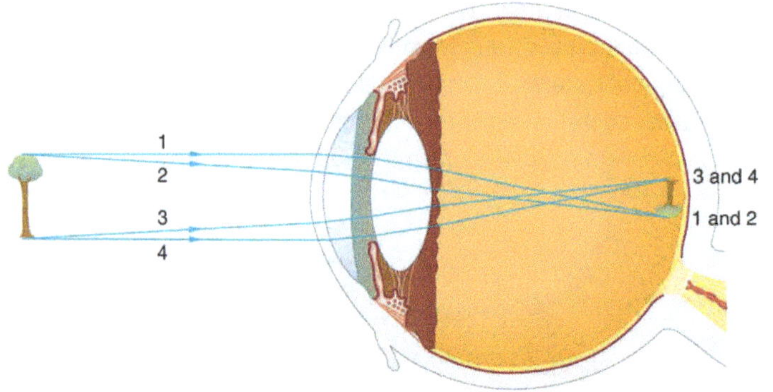

FIGURE 26.3 An image is formed on the retina with light rays converging most at the cornea and upon entering and exiting the lens. Rays from the top and bottom of the object are traced and produce an inverted real image on the retina. The distance to the object is drawn smaller than scale.

As noted, the image must fall precisely on the retina to produce clear vision — that is, the image distance d_i must equal the lens-to-retina distance. Because the lens-to-retina distance does not change, the image distance d_i must be the same for objects at all distances. The eye manages this by varying the power (and focal length) of the lens to accommodate for objects at various distances. The process of adjusting the eye's focal length is called **accommodation**. A person with normal (ideal) vision can see objects clearly at distances ranging from 25 cm to essentially infinity. However, although the near point (the shortest distance at which a sharp focus can be obtained) increases with age (becoming meters for some older people), we will consider it to be 25 cm in our treatment here.

Figure 26.4 shows the accommodation of the eye for distant and near vision. Since light rays from a nearby object can diverge and still enter the eye, the lens must be more converging (more powerful) for close vision than for distant vision. To be more converging, the lens is made thicker by the action of the ciliary muscle surrounding it. The eye is most relaxed when viewing distant objects, one reason that microscopes and telescopes are designed to produce distant images. Vision of very distant objects is called *totally relaxed,* while close vision is termed *accommodated,* with the closest vision being *fully accommodated.*

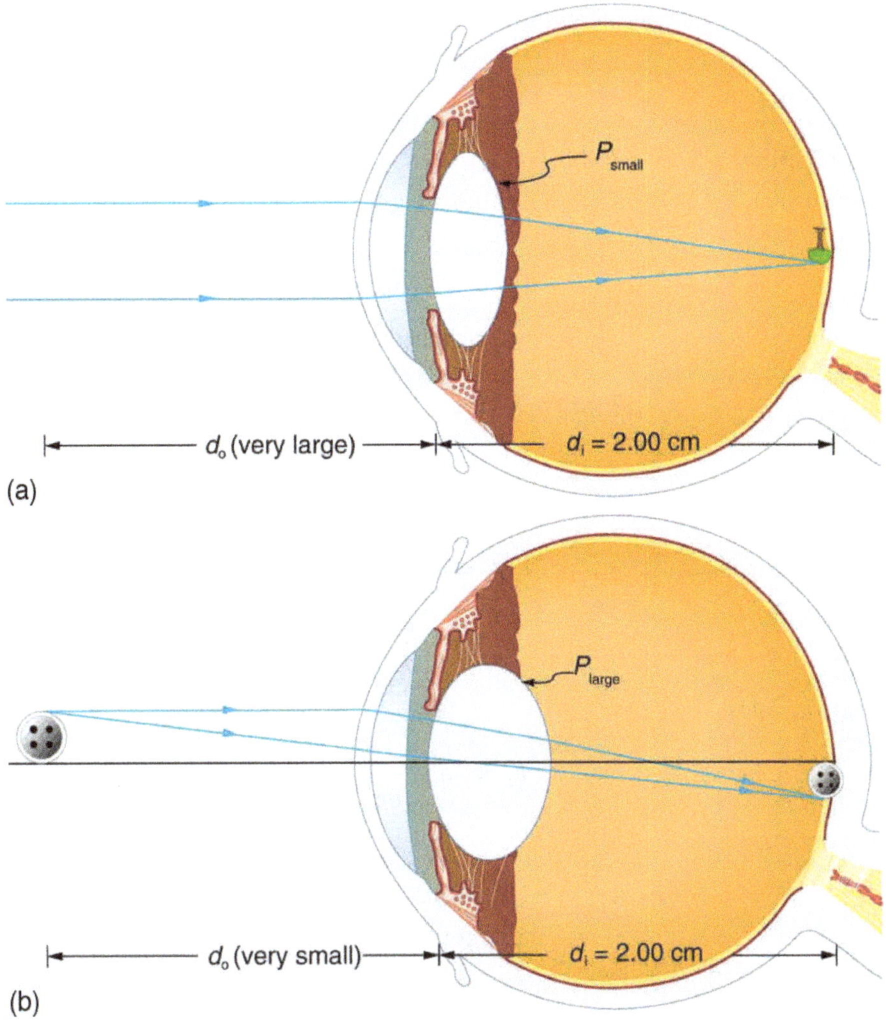

FIGURE 26.4 Relaxed and accommodated vision for distant and close objects. (a) Light rays from the same point on a distant object must be nearly parallel while entering the eye and more easily converge to produce an image on the retina. (b) Light rays from a nearby object can diverge more and still enter the eye. A more powerful lens is needed to converge them on the retina than if they were parallel.

We will use the thin lens equations to examine image formation by the eye quantitatively. First, note the power of a lens is given as $p = 1/f$, so we rewrite the thin lens equations as

$$P = \frac{1}{d_o} + \frac{1}{d_i} \tag{26.1}$$

and

$$\frac{h_i}{h_o} = -\frac{d_i}{d_o} = m. \tag{26.2}$$

We understand that d_i must equal the lens-to-retina distance to obtain clear vision, and that normal vision is possible for objects at distances $d_o = 25 \text{ cm}$ to infinity.

TAKE-HOME EXPERIMENT: THE PUPIL

Look at the central transparent area of someone's eye, the pupil, in normal room light. Estimate the diameter of the pupil. Now turn off the lights and darken the room. After a few minutes turn on the lights and promptly estimate the diameter of the pupil. What happens to the pupil as the eye adjusts to the room light? Explain your observations.

The eye can detect an impressive amount of detail, considering how small the image is on the retina. To get some idea of how small the image can be, consider the following example.

EXAMPLE 26.1

Size of Image on Retina

What is the size of the image on the retina of a 1.20×10^{-2} cm diameter human hair, held at arm's length (60.0 cm) away? Take the lens-to-retina distance to be 2.00 cm.

Strategy

We want to find the height of the image h_i, given the height of the object is $h_\text{o} = 1.20 \times 10^{-2}$ cm. We also know that the object is 60.0 cm away, so that $d_\text{o} = 60.0\text{ cm}$. For clear vision, the image distance must equal the lens-to-retina distance, and so $d_\text{i} = 2.00\text{ cm}$. The equation $\frac{h_\text{i}}{h_\text{o}} = -\frac{d_\text{i}}{d_\text{o}} = m$ can be used to find h_i with the known information.

Solution

The only unknown variable in the equation $\frac{h_\text{i}}{h_\text{o}} = -\frac{d_\text{i}}{d_\text{o}} = m$ is h_i:

$$\frac{h_\text{i}}{h_\text{o}} = -\frac{d_\text{i}}{d_\text{o}}. \tag{26.3}$$

Rearranging to isolate h_i yields

$$h_\text{i} = -h_\text{o} \cdot \frac{d_\text{i}}{d_\text{o}}. \tag{26.4}$$

Substituting the known values gives

$$\begin{aligned} h_\text{i} &= -(1.20 \times 10^{-2}\text{ cm})\frac{2.00\text{ cm}}{60.0\text{ cm}} \\ &= -4.00 \times 10^{-4}\text{ cm}. \end{aligned} \tag{26.5}$$

Discussion

This truly small image is not the smallest discernible—that is, the limit to visual acuity is even smaller than this. Limitations on visual acuity have to do with the wave properties of light and will be discussed in the next chapter. Some limitation is also due to the inherent anatomy of the eye and processing that occurs in our brain.

EXAMPLE 26.2

Power Range of the Eye

Calculate the power of the eye when viewing objects at the greatest and smallest distances possible with normal vision, assuming a lens-to-retina distance of 2.00 cm (a typical value).

Strategy

For clear vision, the image must be on the retina, and so $d_\text{i} = 2.00\text{ cm}$ here. For distant vision, $d_\text{o} \approx \infty$, and for close vision, $d_\text{o} = 25.0\text{ cm}$, as discussed earlier. The equation $P = \frac{1}{d_\text{o}} + \frac{1}{d_\text{i}}$ as written just above, can be used directly to solve for P in both cases, since we know d_i and d_o. Power has units of diopters, where $1\text{ D} = 1/\text{m}$, and so we should express all distances in meters.

Solution

For distant vision,

$$P = \frac{1}{d_\text{o}} + \frac{1}{d_\text{i}} = \frac{1}{\infty} + \frac{1}{0.0200\text{ m}}. \tag{26.6}$$

Since $1/\infty = 0$, this gives

$$P = 0 + 50.0/\text{m} = 50.0\ \text{D (distant vision)}. \tag{26.7}$$

Now, for close vision,

$$\begin{aligned} P &= \frac{1}{d_\text{o}} + \frac{1}{d_\text{i}} = \frac{1}{0.250\ \text{m}} + \frac{1}{0.0200\ \text{m}} \\ &= \frac{4.00}{\text{m}} + \frac{50.0}{\text{m}} = 4.00\ \text{D} + 50.0\ \text{D} \\ &= 54.0\ \text{D (close vision)}. \end{aligned} \tag{26.8}$$

Discussion

For an eye with this typical 2.00 cm lens-to-retina distance, the power of the eye ranges from 50.0 D (for distant totally relaxed vision) to 54.0 D (for close fully accommodated vision), which is an 8% increase. This increase in power for close vision is consistent with the preceding discussion and the ray tracing in Figure 26.4. An 8% ability to accommodate is considered normal but is typical for people who are about 40 years old. Younger people have greater accommodation ability, whereas older people gradually lose the ability to accommodate. When an optometrist identifies accommodation as a problem in elder people, it is most likely due to stiffening of the lens. The lens of the eye changes with age in ways that tend to preserve the ability to see distant objects clearly but do not allow the eye to accommodate for close vision, a condition called **presbyopia** (literally, elder eye). To correct this vision defect, we place a converging, positive power lens in front of the eye, such as found in reading glasses. Commonly available reading glasses are rated by their power in diopters, typically ranging from 1.0 to 3.5 D.

26.2 Vision Correction

LEARNING OBJECTIVES

By the end of this section, you will be able to:

- Identify and discuss common vision defects.
- Explain nearsightedness and farsightedness corrections.
- Explain laser vision correction.

The need for some type of vision correction is very common. Common vision defects are easy to understand, and some are simple to correct. Figure 26.5 illustrates two common vision defects. **Nearsightedness**, or **myopia**, is the inability to see distant objects clearly while close objects are clear. The eye overconverges the nearly parallel rays from a distant object, and the rays cross in front of the retina. More divergent rays from a close object are converged on the retina for a clear image. The distance to the farthest object that can be seen clearly is called the **far point** of the eye (normally infinity). **Farsightedness**, or **hyperopia**, is the inability to see close objects clearly while distant objects may be clear. A farsighted eye does not converge sufficient rays from a close object to make the rays meet on the retina. Less diverging rays from a distant object can be converged for a clear image. The distance to the closest object that can be seen clearly is called the **near point** of the eye (normally 25 cm).

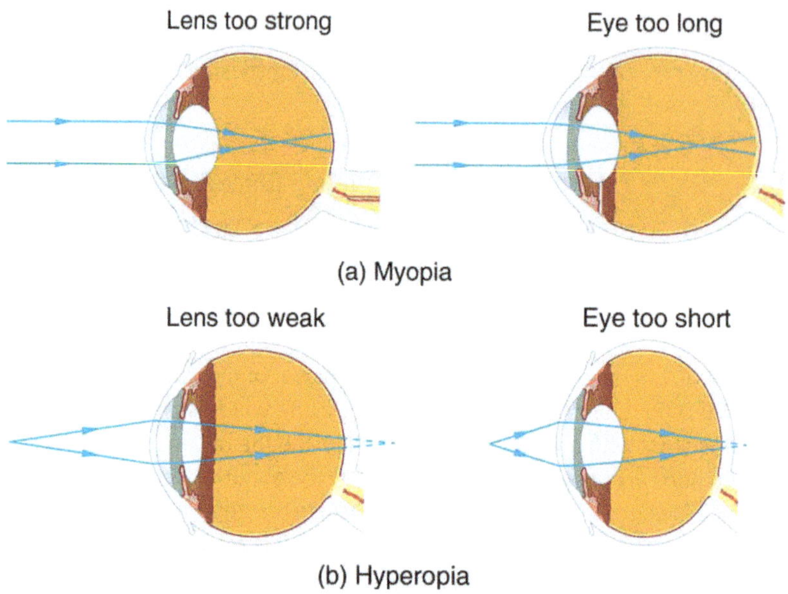

FIGURE 26.5 (a) The nearsighted (myopic) eye converges rays from a distant object in front of the retina; thus, they are diverging when they strike the retina, producing a blurry image. This can be caused by the lens of the eye being too powerful or the length of the eye being too great. (b) The farsighted (hyperopic) eye is unable to converge the rays from a close object by the time they strike the retina, producing blurry close vision. This can be caused by insufficient power in the lens or by the eye being too short.

Since the nearsighted eye over converges light rays, the correction for nearsightedness is to place a diverging spectacle lens in front of the eye. This reduces the power of an eye that is too powerful. Another way of thinking about this is that a diverging spectacle lens produces a case 3 image, which is closer to the eye than the object (see Figure 26.6). To determine the spectacle power needed for correction, you must know the person's far point—that is, you must know the greatest distance at which the person can see clearly. Then the image produced by a spectacle lens must be at this distance or closer for the nearsighted person to be able to see it clearly. It is worth noting that wearing glasses does not change the eye in any way. The eyeglass lens is simply used to create an image of the object at a distance where the nearsighted person can see it clearly. Whereas someone not wearing glasses can see clearly *objects* that fall between their near point and their far point, someone wearing glasses can see *images* that fall between their near point and their far point.

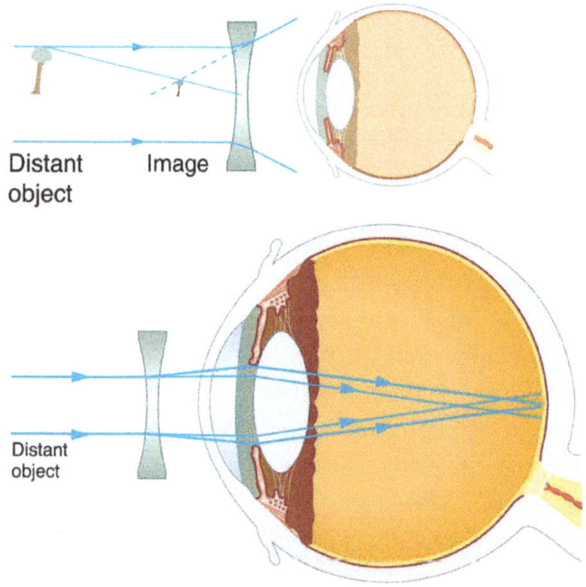

FIGURE 26.6 Correction of nearsightedness requires a diverging lens that compensates for the overconvergence by the eye. The diverging lens produces an image closer to the eye than the object, so that the nearsighted person can see it clearly.

EXAMPLE 26.3

Correcting Nearsightedness

What power of spectacle lens is needed to correct the vision of a nearsighted person whose far point is 30.0 cm? Assume the spectacle (corrective) lens is held 1.50 cm away from the eye by eyeglass frames.

Strategy

You want this nearsighted person to be able to see very distant objects clearly. That means the spectacle lens must produce an image 30.0 cm from the eye for an object very far away. An image 30.0 cm from the eye will be 28.5 cm to the left of the spectacle lens (see Figure 26.6). Therefore, we must get $d_i = -28.5 \text{ cm}$ when $d_o \approx \infty$. The image distance is negative, because it is on the same side of the spectacle as the object.

Solution

Since d_i and d_o are known, the power of the spectacle lens can be found using $P = \frac{1}{d_o} + \frac{1}{d_i}$ as written earlier:

$$P = \frac{1}{d_o} + \frac{1}{d_i} = \frac{1}{\infty} + \frac{1}{-0.285 \text{ m}}. \tag{26.9}$$

Since $1/\infty = 0$, we obtain:

$$P = 0 - 3.51/\text{m} = -3.51 \text{ D}. \tag{26.10}$$

Discussion

The negative power indicates a diverging (or concave) lens, as expected. The spectacle produces a case 3 image closer to the eye, where the person can see it. If you examine eyeglasses for nearsighted people, you will find the lenses are thinnest in the center. Additionally, if you examine a prescription for eyeglasses for nearsighted people, you will find that the prescribed power is negative and given in units of diopters.

Since the farsighted eye under converges light rays, the correction for farsightedness is to place a converging spectacle lens in front of the eye. This increases the power of an eye that is too weak. Another way of thinking about this is that a converging spectacle lens produces a case 2 image, which is farther from the eye than the object (see Figure 26.7). To determine the spectacle power needed for correction, you must know the person's near point—that is, you must know the smallest distance at which the person can see clearly. Then the image produced by a spectacle lens must be at this distance or farther for the farsighted person to be able to see it clearly.

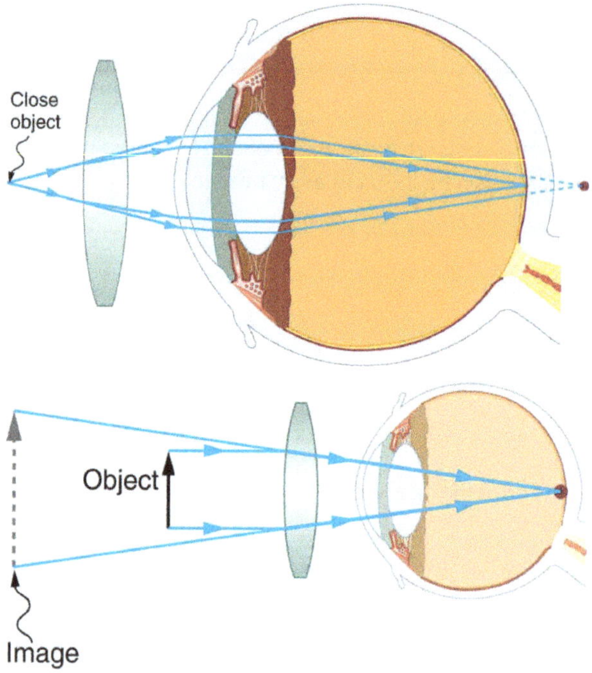

FIGURE 26.7 Correction of farsightedness uses a converging lens that compensates for the under convergence by the eye. The converging lens produces an image farther from the eye than the object, so that the farsighted person can see it clearly.

EXAMPLE 26.4

Correcting Farsightedness

What power of spectacle lens is needed to allow a farsighted person, whose near point is 1.00 m, to see an object clearly that is 25.0 cm away? Assume the spectacle (corrective) lens is held 1.50 cm away from the eye by eyeglass frames.

Strategy

When an object is held 25.0 cm from the person's eyes, the spectacle lens must produce an image 1.00 m away (the near point). An image 1.00 m from the eye will be 98.5 cm to the left of the spectacle lens because the spectacle lens is 1.50 cm from the eye (see Figure 26.7). Therefore, $d_i = -98.5\text{ cm}$. The image distance is negative, because it is on the same side of the spectacle as the object. The object is 23.5 cm to the left of the spectacle, so that $d_o = 23.5\text{ cm}$.

Solution

Since d_i and d_o are known, the power of the spectacle lens can be found using $P = \frac{1}{d_o} + \frac{1}{d_i}$:

$$\begin{aligned} P &= \frac{1}{d_o} + \frac{1}{d_i} = \frac{1}{0.235\text{ m}} + \frac{1}{-0.985\text{ m}} \\ &= 4.26\text{ D} - 1.02\text{ D} = 3.24\text{ D}. \end{aligned} \quad 26.11$$

Discussion

The positive power indicates a converging (convex) lens, as expected. The convex spectacle produces a case 2 image farther from the eye, where the person can see it. If you examine eyeglasses of farsighted people, you will find the lenses to be thickest in the center. In addition, a prescription of eyeglasses for farsighted people has a prescribed power that is positive.

Another common vision defect is **astigmatism**, an unevenness or asymmetry in the focus of the eye. For example, rays passing through a vertical region of the eye may focus closer than rays passing through a horizontal region, resulting in the image appearing elongated. This is mostly due to irregularities in the shape of the cornea but can also be due to lens irregularities or unevenness in the retina. Because of these irregularities, different parts of the lens system produce images at different locations. The eye-brain system can compensate for some of these irregularities, but they generally manifest themselves as less distinct vision or sharper images along certain axes. Figure 26.8 shows a chart used to detect astigmatism. Astigmatism can be at least partially corrected with a spectacle having the opposite irregularity of the eye. If an eyeglass prescription has a cylindrical correction, it is there to correct astigmatism. The normal corrections for short- or farsightedness are spherical corrections, uniform along all axes.

FIGURE 26.8 This chart can detect astigmatism, unevenness in the focus of the eye. Check each of your eyes separately by looking at the center cross (without spectacles if you wear them). If lines along some axes appear darker or clearer than others, you have an astigmatism.

Contact lenses have advantages over glasses beyond their cosmetic aspects. One problem with glasses is that as the eye moves, it is not at a fixed distance from the spectacle lens. Contacts rest on and move with the eye, eliminating this problem. Because contacts cover a significant portion of the cornea, they provide superior peripheral vision compared with eyeglasses. Contacts also correct some corneal astigmatism caused by surface irregularities. The tear layer between the smooth contact and the cornea fills in the irregularities. Since the index of refraction of the tear layer and the cornea are very similar, you now have a regular optical surface in place of an irregular one. If the curvature of a contact lens is not the same as the cornea (as may be necessary with some individuals to obtain a comfortable fit), the tear layer between the contact and cornea acts as a lens. If the tear layer is thinner in the center than at the edges, it has a negative power, for example. Skilled optometrists will adjust the power of the contact to compensate.

Other advances in vision correction demonstrate the interconnectedness and value of scientific research. In the 1980s, Donna Strickland and Gérard Mourou worked on ways to make small but powerful lasers. Up until that time, powerful lasers had to be quite large in order to function properly. Essentially, the intensity of the beam itself would modify the instrument's ability to function and create too much heat to be practical. Strickland and Mourou used ultrashort laser pulses passed over a grating that modified the beam but retained its power. Chirped pulse amplification, as it became known, has been used to develop most of the highest-powered lasers in the world, but also some of the smallest and most common. Decades after their initial discovery, Strickland and Mourou were awarded the Nobel Prize for Physics (with Strickland becoming the third woman to receive the award) partly due to CPA's pivotal role in the increasingly common practice of laser vision correction—an application neither planned during their initial research.

Laser vision correction has progressed rapidly in the last few years. It is the latest and by far the most successful in a series of procedures that correct vision by reshaping the cornea. As noted at the beginning of this section, the cornea accounts for about two-thirds of the power of the eye. Thus, small adjustments of its curvature have the same effect as putting a lens in front of the eye. To a reasonable approximation, the power of multiple lenses placed close together equals the sum of their powers. For example, a concave spectacle lens (for nearsightedness) having $P = -3.00\text{ D}$ has the same effect on vision as reducing the power of the eye itself by 3.00 D. So to correct the eye for nearsightedness, the cornea is flattened to reduce its power. Similarly, to correct for farsightedness, the curvature of the cornea is enhanced to increase the power of the eye—the same effect as the positive power spectacle lens used for farsightedness. Laser vision correction uses high intensity electromagnetic radiation to ablate (to remove material from the surface) and reshape the corneal surfaces.

Today, the most commonly used laser vision correction procedure is *Laser in situ Keratomileusis (LASIK)*. The top layer of the cornea is surgically peeled back and the underlying tissue ablated by multiple bursts of finely controlled ultraviolet radiation produced by an excimer laser. Lasers are used because they not only produce well-focused intense light, but they also emit very pure wavelength electromagnetic radiation that can be controlled more accurately than mixed wavelength light. The 193 nm wavelength UV commonly used is extremely and strongly absorbed by corneal tissue, allowing precise evaporation of very thin layers. A computer controlled program applies more bursts, usually at a rate of 10 per second, to the areas that require deeper removal. Typically a spot less than 1 mm in diameter and about $0.3\ \mu m$ in thickness is removed by each burst. Nearsightedness, farsightedness, and astigmatism can be corrected with an accuracy that produces normal distant vision in more than 90% of the patients, in many cases right away. The corneal flap is replaced; healing takes place rapidly and is nearly painless. More than 1 million Americans per year undergo LASIK (see Figure 26.9).

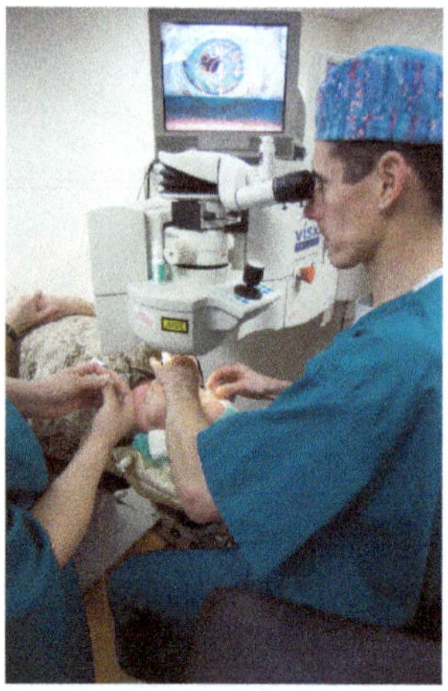

FIGURE 26.9 Laser vision correction is being performed using the LASIK procedure. Reshaping of the cornea by laser ablation is based on a careful assessment of the patient's vision and is computer controlled. The upper corneal layer is temporarily peeled back and minimally disturbed in LASIK, providing for more rapid and less painful healing of the less sensitive tissues below. (credit: U.S. Navy photo by Mass Communication Specialist 1st Class Brien Aho)

26.3 Color and Color Vision

LEARNING OBJECTIVES

By the end of this section, you will be able to:

- Explain the simple theory of color vision.
- Outline the coloring properties of light sources.
- Describe the retinex theory of color vision.

The gift of vision is made richer by the existence of color. Objects and lights abound with thousands of hues that stimulate our eyes, brains, and emotions. Two basic questions are addressed in this brief treatment—what does color mean in scientific terms, and how do we, as humans, perceive it?

Simple Theory of Color Vision

We have already noted that color is associated with the wavelength of visible electromagnetic radiation. When our eyes receive pure-wavelength light, we tend to see only a few colors. Six of these (most often listed) are red, orange, yellow, green, blue, and violet. These are the rainbow of colors produced when white light is dispersed according to different wavelengths. There are thousands of other **hues** that we can perceive. These include brown, teal, gold, pink, and white. One simple theory of color vision implies that all these hues are our eye's response to different combinations of wavelengths. This is true to an extent, but we find that color perception is even subtler than our eye's response for various wavelengths of light.

The two major types of light-sensing cells (photoreceptors) in the retina are **rods and cones**. Rods are more sensitive than cones by a factor of about 1000 and are solely responsible for peripheral vision as well as vision in very dark environments. They are also important for motion detection. There are about 120 million rods in the human retina. Rods do not yield color information. You may notice that you lose color vision when it is very dark, but you retain the ability to discern grey scales.

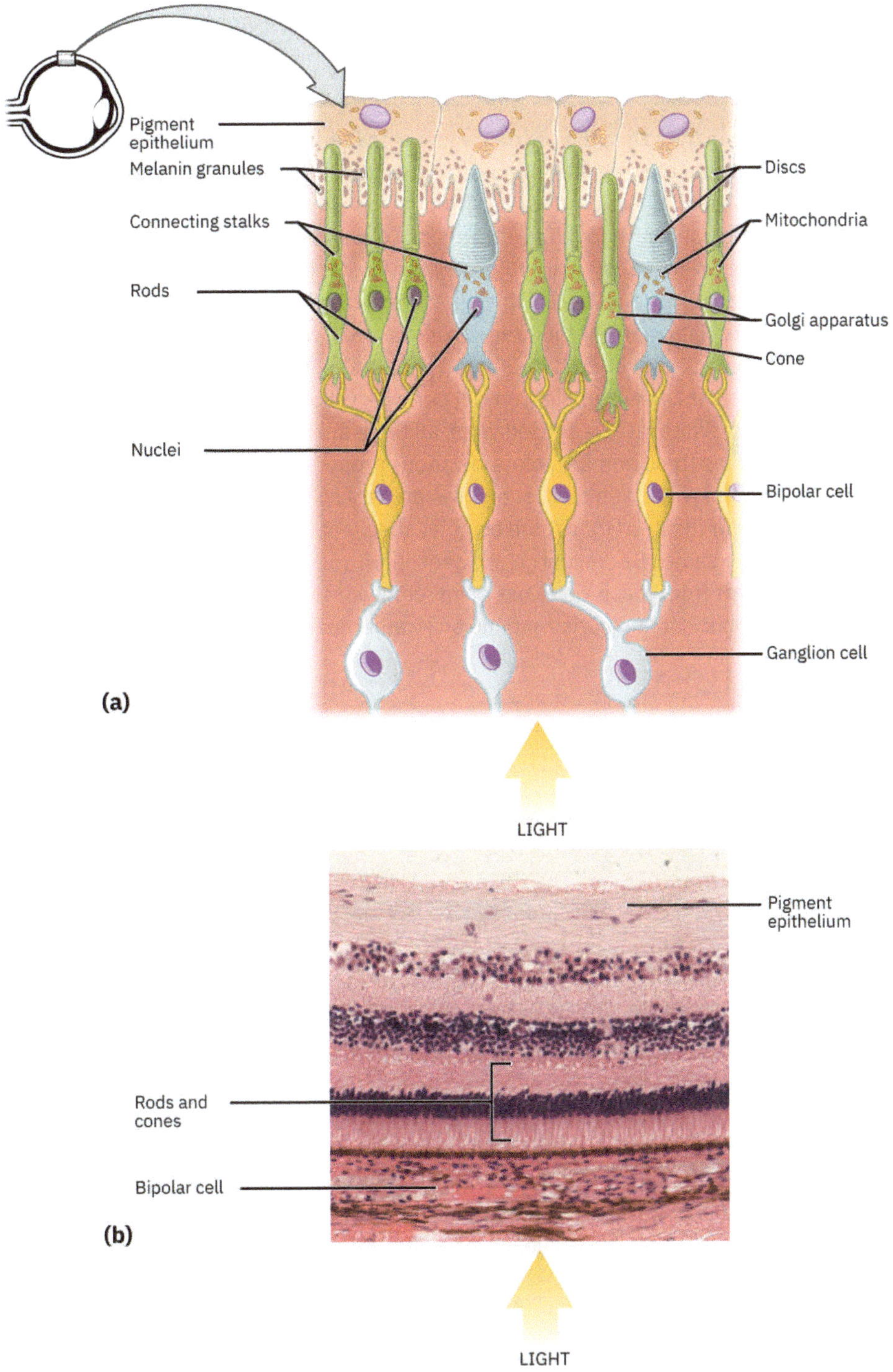

FIGURE 26.10 (a) All photoreceptors have inner segments containing the nucleus and other important organelles and outer segments with membrane arrays containing the photosensitive opsin molecules. Rod outer segments are long columnar shapes with stacks of membrane-bound discs that contain the rhodopsin pigment. Cone outer segments are short, tapered shapes with folds of membrane in place of the discs in the rods. (b) Tissue of the retina shows a dense layer of nuclei of the rods and cones. LM × 800. (Micrograph provided by the Regents of University of Michigan Medical School © 2012)

TAKE-HOME EXPERIMENT: RODS AND CONES

1. Go into a darkened room from a brightly lit room, or from outside in the Sun. How long did it take to start seeing shapes more clearly? What about color? Return to the bright room. Did it take a few minutes before

you could see things clearly?

2. Demonstrate the sensitivity of foveal vision. Look at the letter G in the word ROGERS. What about the clarity of the letters on either side of G?

Cones are most concentrated in the fovea, the central region of the retina. There are no rods here. The fovea is at the center of the macula, a 5 mm diameter region responsible for our central vision. The cones work best in bright light and are responsible for high resolution vision. There are about 6 million cones in the human retina. There are three types of cones, and each type is sensitive to different ranges of wavelengths, as illustrated in Figure 26.11. A **simplified theory of color vision** is that there are three *primary colors* corresponding to the three types of cones. The thousands of other hues that we can distinguish among are created by various combinations of stimulations of the three types of cones. Color television uses a three-color system in which the screen is covered with equal numbers of red, green, and blue phosphor dots. The broad range of hues a viewer sees is produced by various combinations of these three colors. For example, you will perceive yellow when red and green are illuminated with the correct ratio of intensities. White may be sensed when all three are illuminated. Then, it would seem that all hues can be produced by adding three primary colors in various proportions. But there is an indication that color vision is more sophisticated. There is no unique set of three primary colors. Another set that works is yellow, green, and blue. A further indication of the need for a more complex theory of color vision is that various different combinations can produce the same hue. Yellow can be sensed with yellow light, or with a combination of red and green, and also with white light from which violet has been removed. The three-primary-colors aspect of color vision is well established; more sophisticated theories expand on it rather than deny it.

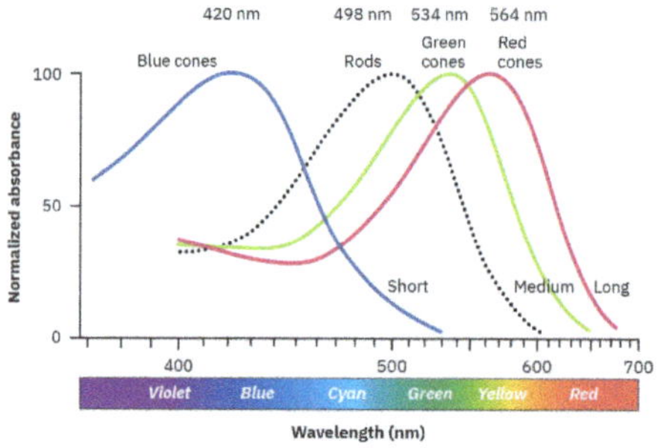

FIGURE 26.11 The image shows the relative sensitivity of the three types of cones, which are named according to wavelengths of greatest sensitivity. Rods are about 1000 times more sensitive, and their curve peaks at about 500 nm. Evidence for the three types of cones comes from direct measurements in animal and human eyes and testing of people with color blindness.

Consider why various objects display color—that is, why are feathers blue and red in a crimson rosella? The *true color of an object* is defined by its absorptive or reflective characteristics. Figure 26.12 shows white light falling on three different objects, one pure blue, one pure red, and one black, as well as pure red light falling on a white object. Other hues are created by more complex absorption characteristics. Pink, for example on a galah cockatoo, can be due to weak absorption of all colors except red. An object can appear a different color under non-white illumination. For example, a pure blue object illuminated with pure red light will *appear* black, because it absorbs all the red light falling on it. But, the true color of the object is blue, which is independent of illumination.

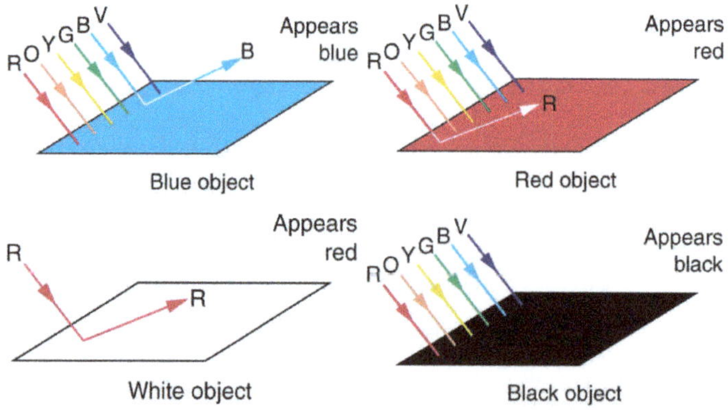

FIGURE 26.12 Absorption characteristics determine the true color of an object. Here, three objects are illuminated by white light, and one by pure red light. White is the equal mixture of all visible wavelengths; black is the absence of light.

Similarly, *light sources have colors* that are defined by the wavelengths they produce. A helium-neon laser emits pure red light. In fact, the phrase "pure red light" is defined by having a sharp constrained spectrum, a characteristic of laser light. The Sun produces a broad yellowish spectrum, fluorescent lights emit bluish-white light, and incandescent lights emit reddish-white hues as seen in Figure 26.13. As you would expect, you sense these colors when viewing the light source directly or when illuminating a white object with them. All of this fits neatly into the simplified theory that a combination of wavelengths produces various hues.

TAKE-HOME EXPERIMENT: EXPLORING COLOR ADDITION

This activity is best done with plastic sheets of different colors as they allow more light to pass through to our eyes. However, thin sheets of paper and fabric can also be used. Overlay different colors of the material and hold them up to a white light. Using the theory described above, explain the colors you observe. You could also try mixing different crayon colors.

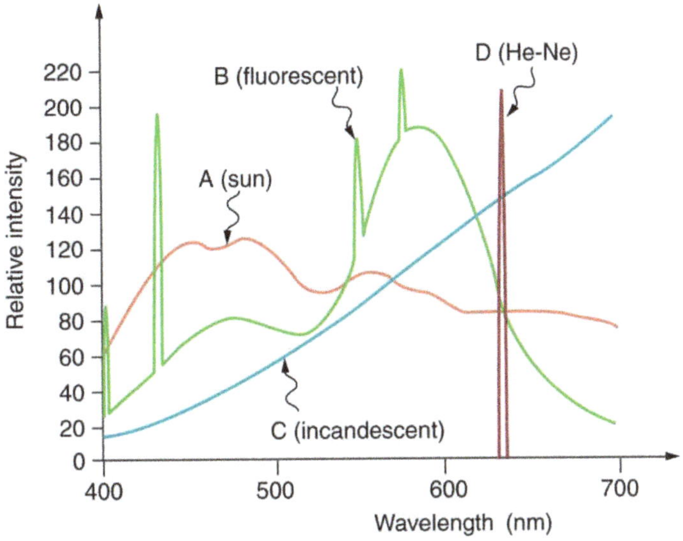

FIGURE 26.13 Emission spectra for various light sources are shown. Curve A is average sunlight at Earth's surface, curve B is light from a fluorescent lamp, and curve C is the output of an incandescent light. The spike for a helium-neon laser (curve D) is due to its pure wavelength emission. The spikes in the fluorescent output are due to atomic spectra—a topic that will be explored later.

Color Constancy and a Modified Theory of Color Vision

The eye-brain color-sensing system can, by comparing various objects in its view, perceive the true color of an object under varying lighting conditions—an ability that is called **color constancy**. We can sense that a white tablecloth, for example, is white whether it is illuminated by sunlight, fluorescent light, or candlelight. The wavelengths entering the eye are quite different in each case, as the graphs in Figure 26.13 imply, but our color vision can detect the true color by comparing the tablecloth with its surroundings.

Theories that take color constancy into account are based on a large body of anatomical evidence as well as perceptual studies. There are nerve connections among the light receptors on the retina, and there are far fewer nerve connections to the brain than there are rods and cones. This means that there is signal processing in the eye before information is sent to the brain. For example, the eye makes comparisons between adjacent light receptors and is very sensitive to edges as seen in Figure 26.14. Rather than responding simply to the light entering the eye, which is uniform in the various rectangles in this figure, the eye responds to the edges and senses false darkness variations.

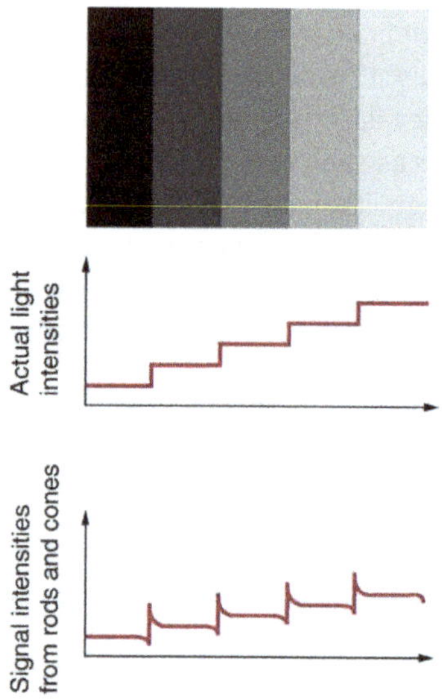

FIGURE 26.14 The importance of edges is shown. Although the grey strips are uniformly shaded, as indicated by the graph immediately below them, they do not appear uniform at all. Instead, they are perceived darker on the dark side and lighter on the light side of the edge, as shown in the bottom graph. This is due to nerve impulse processing in the eye.

One theory that takes various factors into account was advanced by Edwin Land (1909 – 1991), the creative founder of the Polaroid Corporation. Land proposed, based partly on his many elegant experiments, that the three types of cones are organized into systems called **retinexes**. Each retinex forms an image that is compared with the others, and the eye-brain system thus can compare a candle-illuminated white table cloth with its generally reddish surroundings and determine that it is actually white. This **retinex theory of color vision** is an example of modified theories of color vision that attempt to account for its subtleties. One striking experiment performed by Land demonstrates that some type of image comparison may produce color vision. Two pictures are taken of a scene on black-and-white film, one using a red filter, the other a blue filter. Resulting black-and-white slides are then projected and superimposed on a screen, producing a black-and-white image, as expected. Then a red filter is placed in front of the slide taken with a red filter, and the images are again superimposed on a screen. You would expect an image in various shades of pink, but instead, the image appears to humans in full color with all the hues of the original scene. This implies that color vision can be induced by comparison of the black-and-white and red images. Color vision is not completely understood or explained, and the retinex theory is not totally accepted. It is apparent that color vision is much subtler than what a first look might imply.

PHET EXPLORATIONS

Color Vision

Make a whole rainbow by mixing red, green, and blue light. Change the wavelength of a monochromatic beam or filter white light. View the light as a solid beam, or see the individual photons.

Click to view content (https://openstax.org/books/college-physics-ap-courses-2e/pages/26-3-color-and-color-vision)

26.4 Microscopes

LEARNING OBJECTIVES

By the end of this section, you will be able to:

- Investigate different types of microscopes.
- Learn how image is formed in a compound microscope.

Although the eye is marvelous in its ability to see objects large and small, it obviously has limitations to the smallest details it can detect. Human desire to see beyond what is possible with the naked eye led to the use of optical instruments. In this section we will examine microscopes, instruments for enlarging the detail that we cannot see with the unaided eye. The microscope is a multiple-element system having more than a single lens or mirror. (See Figure 26.15) A microscope can be made from two convex lenses. The image formed by the first element becomes the object for the second element. The second element forms its own image, which is the object for the third element, and so on. Ray tracing helps to visualize the image formed. If the device is composed of thin lenses and mirrors that obey the thin lens equations, then it is not difficult to describe their behavior numerically.

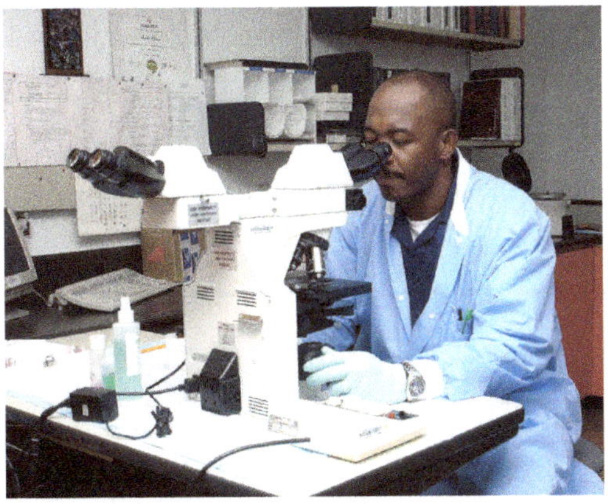

FIGURE 26.15 Multiple lenses and mirrors are used in this microscope. (credit: U.S. Navy photo by Tom Watanabe)

Microscopes were first developed in the early 1600s by eyeglass makers in The Netherlands and Denmark. The simplest **compound microscope** is constructed from two convex lenses as shown schematically in Figure 26.16. The first lens is called the **objective lens**, and has typical magnification values from $5\times$ to $100\times$. In standard microscopes, the objectives are mounted such that when you switch between objectives, the sample remains in focus. Objectives arranged in this way are described as parfocal. The second, the **eyepiece**, also referred to as the ocular, has several lenses which slide inside a cylindrical barrel. The focusing ability is provided by the movement of both the objective lens and the eyepiece. The purpose of a microscope is to magnify small objects, and both lenses contribute to the final magnification. Additionally, the final enlarged image is produced in a location far enough from the observer to be easily viewed, since the eye cannot focus on objects or images that are too close.

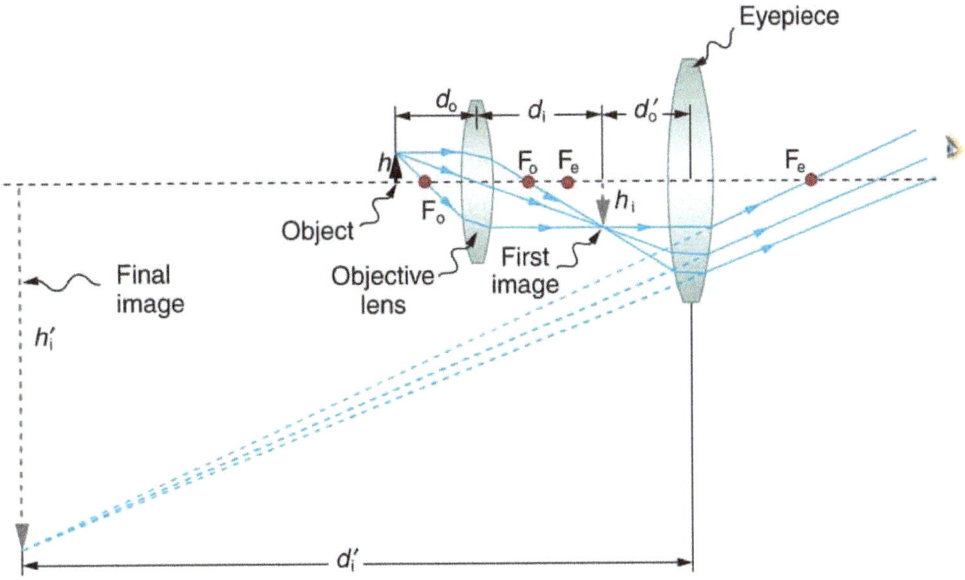

FIGURE 26.16 A compound microscope composed of two lenses, an objective and an eyepiece. The objective forms a case 1 image that is larger than the object. This first image is the object for the eyepiece. The eyepiece forms a case 2 final image that is further magnified.

To see how the microscope in Figure 26.16 forms an image, we consider its two lenses in succession. The object is slightly farther away from the objective lens than its focal length f_o, producing a case 1 image that is larger than the object. This first image is the object for the second lens, or eyepiece. The eyepiece is intentionally located so it can further magnify the image. The eyepiece is placed so that the first image is closer to it than its focal length f_e. Thus the eyepiece acts as a magnifying glass, and the final image is made even larger. The final image remains inverted, but it is farther from the observer, making it easy to view (the eye is most relaxed when viewing distant objects and normally cannot focus closer than 25 cm). Since each lens produces a magnification that multiplies the height of the image, it is apparent that the overall magnification m is the product of the individual magnifications:

$$m = m_o m_e, \tag{26.12}$$

where m_o is the magnification of the objective and m_e is the magnification of the eyepiece. This equation can be generalized for any combination of thin lenses and mirrors that obey the thin lens equations.

OVERALL MAGNIFICATION

The overall magnification of a multiple-element system is the product of the individual magnifications of its elements.

EXAMPLE 26.5

Microscope Magnification

Calculate the magnification of an object placed 6.20 mm from a compound microscope that has a 6.00 mm focal length objective and a 50.0 mm focal length eyepiece. The objective and eyepiece are separated by 23.0 cm.

Strategy and Concept

This situation is similar to that shown in Figure 26.16. To find the overall magnification, we must find the magnification of the objective, then the magnification of the eyepiece. This involves using the thin lens equation.

Solution

The magnification of the objective lens is given as

$$m_o = -\frac{d_i}{d_o}, \tag{26.13}$$

where d_o and d_i are the object and image distances, respectively, for the objective lens as labeled in Figure 26.16. The object distance is given to be $d_o = 6.20\text{ mm}$, but the image distance d_i is not known. Isolating d_i, we have

$$\frac{1}{d_i} = \frac{1}{f_o} - \frac{1}{d_o}, \tag{26.14}$$

where f_o is the focal length of the objective lens. Substituting known values gives

$$\frac{1}{d_i} = \frac{1}{6.00\text{ mm}} - \frac{1}{6.20\text{ mm}} = \frac{0.00538}{\text{mm}}. \tag{26.15}$$

We invert this to find d_i:

$$d_i = 186\text{ mm}. \tag{26.16}$$

Substituting this into the expression for m_o gives

$$m_o = -\frac{d_i}{d_o} = -\frac{186\text{ mm}}{6.20\text{ mm}} = -30.0. \tag{26.17}$$

Now we must find the magnification of the eyepiece, which is given by

$$m_e = -\frac{d_i{}'}{d_o{}'}, \tag{26.18}$$

where $d_i{}'$ and $d_o{}'$ are the image and object distances for the eyepiece (see Figure 26.16). The object distance is the distance of the first image from the eyepiece. Since the first image is 186 mm to the right of the objective and the eyepiece is 230 mm to the right of the objective, the object distance is $d_o{}' = 230\text{ mm} - 186\text{ mm} = 44.0\text{ mm}$. This places the first image closer to the eyepiece than its focal length, so that the eyepiece will form a case 2 image as shown in the figure. We still need to find the location of the final image $d_i{}'$ in order to find the magnification. This is done as before to obtain a value for $1/d_i{}'$:

$$\frac{1}{d_i{}'} = \frac{1}{f_e} - \frac{1}{d_o{}'} = \frac{1}{50.0\text{ mm}} - \frac{1}{44.0\text{ mm}} = -\frac{0.00273}{\text{mm}}. \quad 26.19$$

Inverting gives

$$d_i{}' = -\frac{\text{mm}}{0.00273} = -367\text{ mm}. \quad 26.20$$

The eyepiece's magnification is thus

$$m_e = -\frac{d_i{}'}{d_o{}'} = -\frac{-367\text{ mm}}{44.0\text{ mm}} = 8.33. \quad 26.21$$

So the overall magnification is

$$m = m_o m_e = (-30.0)(8.33) = -250. \quad 26.22$$

Discussion

Both the objective and the eyepiece contribute to the overall magnification, which is large and negative, consistent with Figure 26.16, where the image is seen to be large and inverted. In this case, the image is virtual and inverted, which cannot happen for a single element (case 2 and case 3 images for single elements are virtual and upright). The final image is 367 mm (0.367 m) to the left of the eyepiece. Had the eyepiece been placed farther from the objective, it could have formed a case 1 image to the right. Such an image could be projected on a screen, but it would be behind the head of the person in the figure and not appropriate for direct viewing. The procedure used to solve this example is applicable in any multiple-element system. Each element is treated in turn, with each forming an image that becomes the object for the next element. The process is not more difficult than for single lenses or mirrors, only lengthier.

Normal optical microscopes can magnify up to $1500\times$ with a theoretical resolution of $-0.2\ \mu\text{m}$. The lenses can be quite complicated and are composed of multiple elements to reduce aberrations. Microscope objective lenses are particularly important as they primarily gather light from the specimen. Three parameters describe microscope objectives: the **numerical aperture** (NA), the magnification (m), and the working distance. The NA is related to the light gathering ability of a lens and is obtained using the angle of acceptance θ formed by the maximum cone of rays focusing on the specimen (see Figure 26.17(a)) and is given by

$$NA = n \sin \alpha, \quad 26.23$$

where n is the refractive index of the medium between the lens and the specimen and $\alpha = \theta/2$. As the angle of acceptance given by θ increases, NA becomes larger and more light is gathered from a smaller focal region giving higher resolution. A $0.75NA$ objective gives more detail than a $0.10NA$ objective.

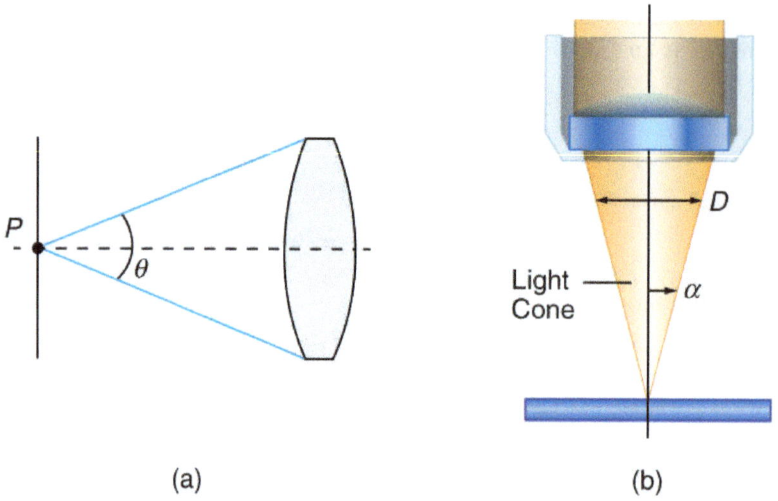

FIGURE 26.17 (a) The numerical aperture (NA) of a microscope objective lens refers to the light-gathering ability of the lens and is calculated using half the angle of acceptance θ. (b) Here, α is half the acceptance angle for light rays from a specimen entering a camera lens, and D is the diameter of the aperture that controls the light entering the lens.

While the numerical aperture can be used to compare resolutions of various objectives, it does not indicate how far the lens could be from the specimen. This is specified by the "working distance," which is the distance (in mm usually) from the front lens element of the objective to the specimen, or cover glass. The higher the NA the closer the lens will be to the specimen and the more chances there are of breaking the cover slip and damaging both the specimen and the lens. The focal length of an objective lens is different than the working distance. This is because objective lenses are made of a combination of lenses and the focal length is measured from inside the barrel. The working distance is a parameter that microscopists can use more readily as it is measured from the outermost lens. The working distance decreases as the NA and magnification both increase.

The term $f/\#$ in general is called the f-number and is used to denote the light per unit area reaching the image plane. In photography, an image of an object at infinity is formed at the focal point and the f-number is given by the ratio of the focal length f of the lens and the diameter D of the aperture controlling the light into the lens (see Figure 26.17(b)). If the acceptance angle is small the NA of the lens can also be used as given below.

$$f/\# = \frac{f}{D} \approx \frac{1}{2NA}. \quad (26.24)$$

As the f-number decreases, the camera is able to gather light from a larger angle, giving wide-angle photography. As usual there is a trade-off. A greater $f/\#$ means less light reaches the image plane. A setting of $f/16$ usually allows one to take pictures in bright sunlight as the aperture diameter is small. In optical fibers, light needs to be focused into the fiber. Figure 26.18 shows the angle used in calculating the NA of an optical fiber.

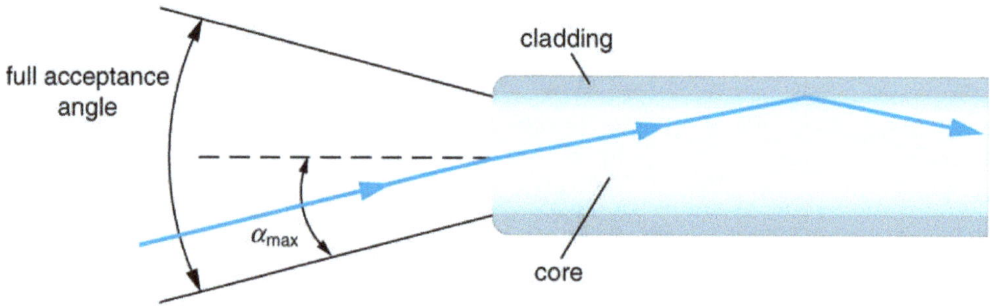

FIGURE 26.18 Light rays enter an optical fiber. The numerical aperture of the optical fiber can be determined by using the angle α_{max}.

Can the NA be larger than 1.00? The answer is 'yes' if we use immersion lenses in which a medium such as oil, glycerine or water is placed between the objective and the microscope cover slip. This minimizes the mismatch in refractive indices as light rays go through different media, generally providing a greater light-gathering ability and an increase in resolution. Figure 26.19 shows light rays when using air and immersion lenses.

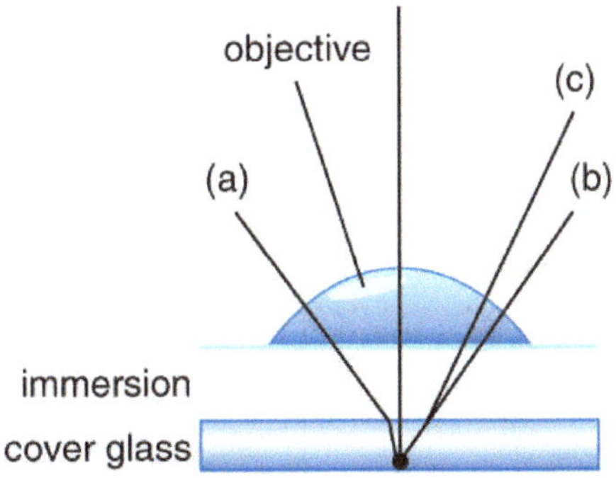

FIGURE 26.19 Light rays from a specimen entering the objective. Paths for immersion medium of air (a), water (b) $(n = 1.33)$, and oil (c) $(n = 1.51)$ are shown. The water and oil immersions allow more rays to enter the objective, increasing the resolution.

When using a microscope we do not see the entire extent of the sample. Depending on the eyepiece and objective lens we see a restricted region which we say is the field of view. The objective is then manipulated in two-dimensions above the sample to view other regions of the sample. Electronic scanning of either the objective or the sample is used in scanning microscopy. The image formed at each point during the scanning is combined using a computer to generate an image of a larger region of the sample at a selected magnification.

When using a microscope, we rely on gathering light to form an image. Hence most specimens need to be illuminated, particularly at higher magnifications, when observing details that are so small that they reflect only small amounts of light. To make such objects easily visible, the intensity of light falling on them needs to be increased. Special illuminating systems called condensers are used for this purpose. The type of condenser that is suitable for an application depends on how the specimen is examined, whether by transmission, scattering or reflecting. See Figure 26.20 for an example of each. White light sources are common and lasers are often used. Laser light illumination tends to be quite intense and it is important to ensure that the light does not result in the degradation of the specimen.

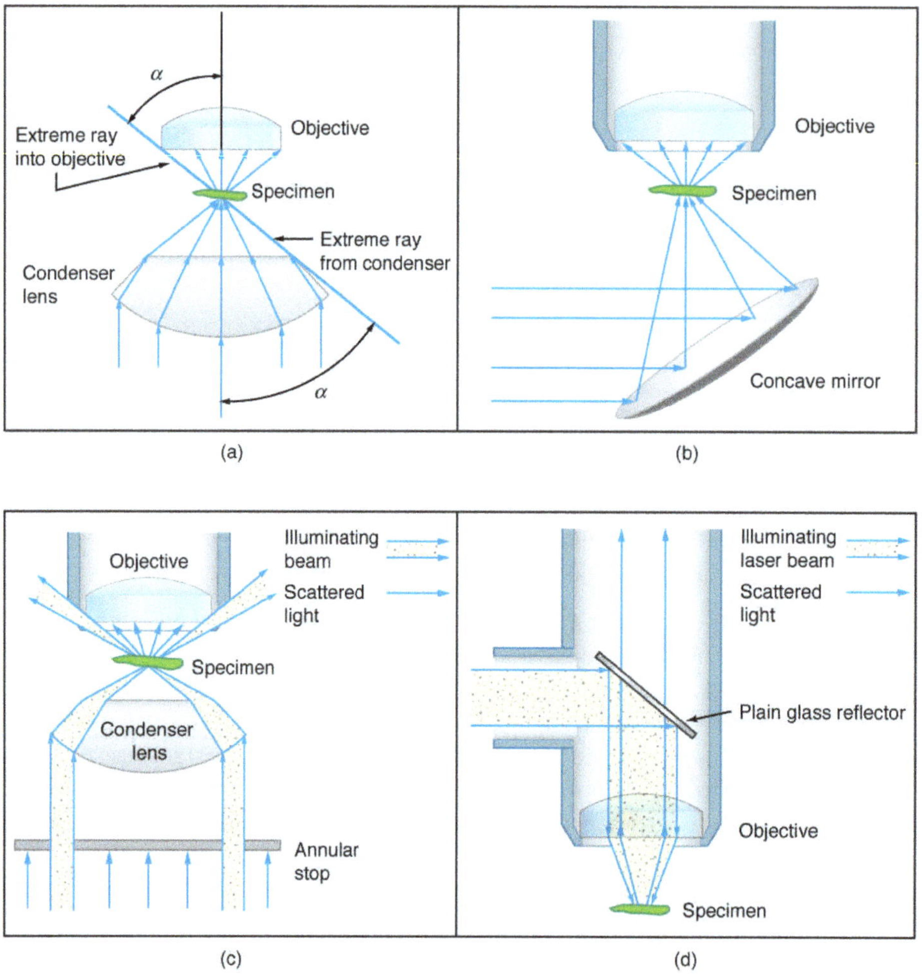

FIGURE 26.20 Illumination of a specimen in a microscope. (a) Transmitted light from a condenser lens. (b) Transmitted light from a mirror condenser. (c) Dark field illumination by scattering (the illuminating beam misses the objective lens). (d) High magnification illumination with reflected light – normally laser light.

We normally associate microscopes with visible light, but x ray and electron microscopes provide greater resolution. The focusing and basic physics is the same as that just described, even though the lenses require different technology. The electron microscope requires vacuum chambers so that the electrons can proceed unheeded. Magnifications of 50 million times provide the ability to determine positions of individual atoms within materials. An electron microscope is shown in Figure 26.21. We do not use our eyes to form images; rather images are recorded electronically and displayed on computers. In fact observing and saving images formed by optical microscopes on computers is now done routinely. Video recordings of what occurs in a microscope can be made for viewing by many people at later dates. Advances in this powerful technology continue. In the 1990s, Pratibha L. Gai invented the environmental transmission electron microscope (ETEM), which was the first device capable of observing individual atoms in chemical reactions.

FIGURE 26.21 An electron microscope has the capability to image individual atoms on a material. The microscope uses vacuum technology, sophisticated detectors and state of the art image processing software. Researchers use the devices in their work on biological and, in the case of Miaofang Chi (pictured), lithium ion battery materials and fuel cell catalysts. (credit: Oak Ridge National Laboratory)

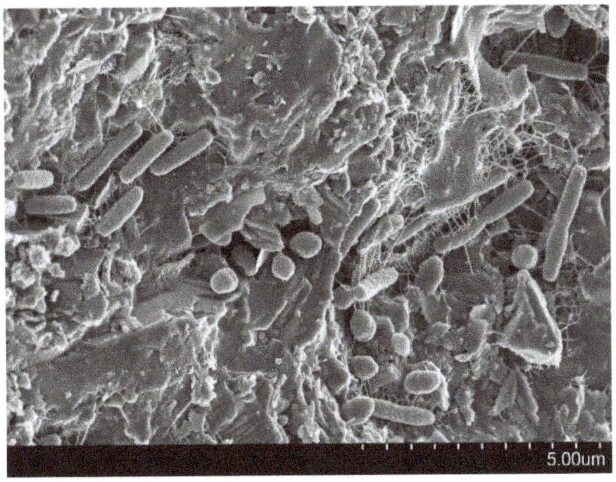

FIGURE 26.22 A natural community of bacteria growing on a single grain of sand, which was imaged using a Scanning Electron Microscope. (credit: The Lewis Lab at Northeastern University. Image created by Anthony D'Onofrio, William H. Fowle, Eric J. Stewart, and Kim Lewis.)

TAKE-HOME EXPERIMENT: MAKE A LENS

Look through a clear glass or plastic bottle and describe what you see. Now fill the bottle with water and describe what you see. Use the water bottle as a lens to produce the image of a bright object and estimate the focal length of the water bottle lens. How is the focal length a function of the depth of water in the bottle?

26.5 Telescopes

LEARNING OBJECTIVES

By the end of this section, you will be able to:

- Outline the invention of a telescope.
- Describe the working of a telescope.

Telescopes are meant for viewing distant objects, producing an image that is larger than the image that can be seen with the unaided eye. Telescopes gather far more light than the eye, allowing dim objects to be observed with greater magnification and better resolution. Although Galileo is often credited with inventing the telescope, he actually did not. What he did was more important. He constructed several early telescopes, was the first to study the heavens with them, and made monumental discoveries using them. Among these are the moons of Jupiter, the craters and mountains on the Moon, the details of sunspots, and the fact that the Milky Way is composed of vast numbers of individual stars.

Figure 26.23(a) shows a telescope made of two lenses, the convex objective and the concave eyepiece, the same construction used by Galileo. Such an arrangement produces an upright image and is used in spyglasses and opera glasses.

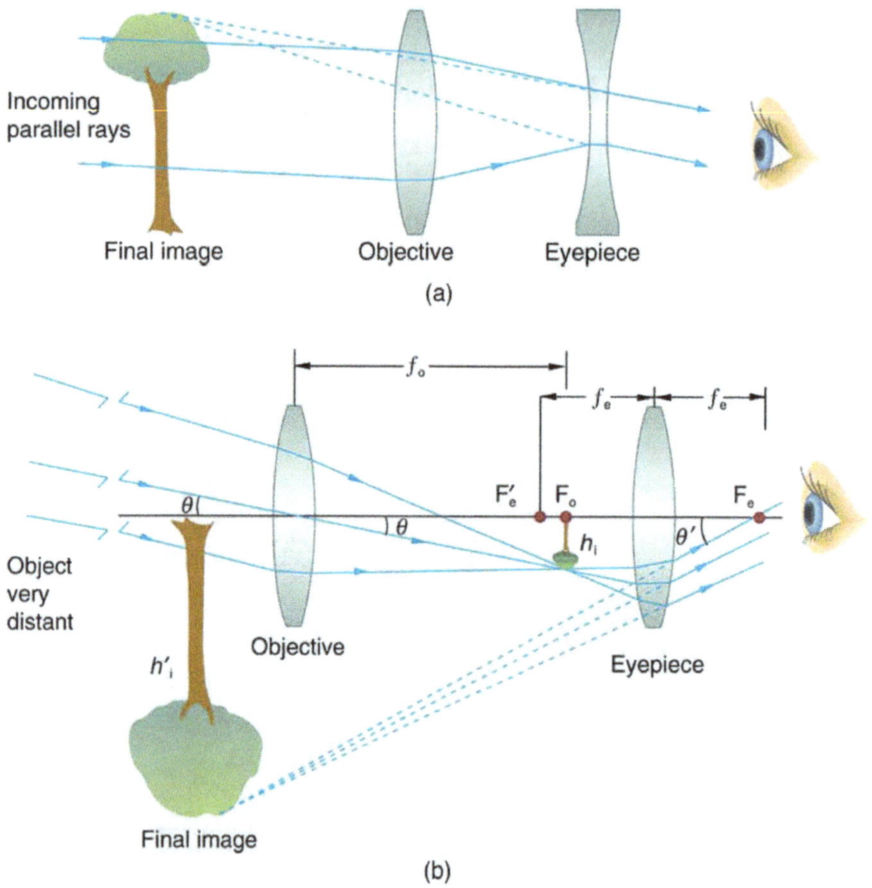

FIGURE 26.23 (a) Galileo made telescopes with a convex objective and a concave eyepiece. These produce an upright image and are used in spyglasses. (b) Most simple telescopes have two convex lenses. The objective forms a case 1 image that is the object for the eyepiece. The eyepiece forms a case 2 final image that is magnified.

The most common two-lens telescope, like the simple microscope, uses two convex lenses and is shown in Figure 26.23(b). The object is so far away from the telescope that it is essentially at infinity compared with the focal lengths of the lenses ($d_o \approx \infty$). The first image is thus produced at $d_i = f_o$, as shown in the figure. To prove this, note that

$$\frac{1}{d_i} = \frac{1}{f_o} - \frac{1}{d_o} = \frac{1}{f_o} - \frac{1}{\infty}. \quad 26.25$$

Because $1/\infty = 0$, this simplifies to

$$\frac{1}{d_i} = \frac{1}{f_o}, \quad 26.26$$

which implies that $d_i = f_o$, as claimed. It is true that for any distant object and any lens or mirror, the image is at the focal length.

The first image formed by a telescope objective as seen in Figure 26.23(b) will not be large compared with what you might see by looking at the object directly. For example, the spot formed by sunlight focused on a piece of paper by a magnifying glass is the image of the Sun, and it is small. The telescope eyepiece (like the microscope eyepiece) magnifies this first image. The distance between the eyepiece and the objective lens is made slightly less than the sum of their focal lengths so that the first image is closer to the eyepiece than its focal length. That is, d_o' is less than f_e, and so the eyepiece forms a case 2 image that is large and to the left for easy viewing. If the angle subtended by an object as viewed by the unaided eye is θ, and the angle subtended by the telescope image is θ', then the **angular magnification** M is defined to be their ratio. That is, $M = \theta'/\theta$. It can be shown that the angular magnification of a telescope is related to the focal lengths of the objective and eyepiece; and is given by

$$M = \frac{\theta'}{\theta} = -\frac{f_o}{f_e}. \tag{26.27}$$

The minus sign indicates the image is inverted. To obtain the greatest angular magnification, it is best to have a long focal length objective and a short focal length eyepiece. The greater the angular magnification M, the larger an object will appear when viewed through a telescope, making more details visible. Limits to observable details are imposed by many factors, including lens quality and atmospheric disturbance.

The image in most telescopes is inverted, which is unimportant for observing the stars but a real problem for other applications, such as telescopes on ships or telescopic gun sights. If an upright image is needed, Galileo's arrangement in Figure 26.23(a) can be used. But a more common arrangement is to use a third convex lens as an eyepiece, increasing the distance between the first two and inverting the image once again as seen in Figure 26.24.

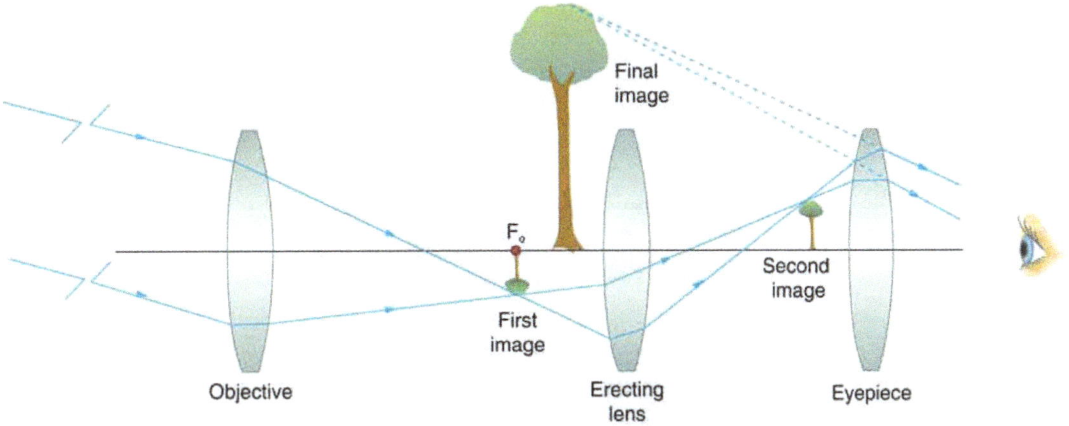

FIGURE 26.24 This arrangement of three lenses in a telescope produces an upright final image. The first two lenses are far enough apart that the second lens inverts the image of the first one more time. The third lens acts as a magnifier and keeps the image upright and in a location that is easy to view.

A telescope can also be made with a concave mirror as its first element or objective, since a concave mirror acts like a convex lens as seen in Figure 26.25. Flat mirrors are often employed in optical instruments to make them more compact or to send light to cameras and other sensing devices. There are many advantages to using mirrors rather than lenses for telescope objectives. Mirrors can be constructed much larger than lenses and can, thus, gather large amounts of light, as needed to view distant galaxies, for example. Large and relatively flat mirrors have very long focal lengths, so that great angular magnification is possible.

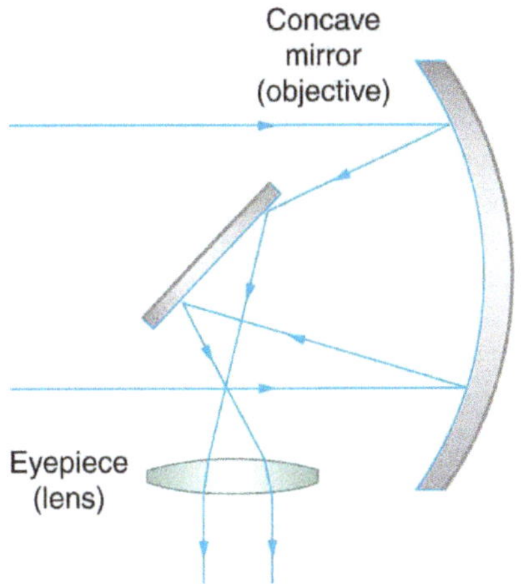

FIGURE 26.25 A two-element telescope composed of a mirror as the objective and a lens for the eyepiece is shown. This telescope forms an image in the same manner as the two-convex-lens telescope already discussed, but it does not suffer from chromatic aberrations. Such telescopes can gather more light, since larger mirrors than lenses can be constructed.

Telescopes, like microscopes, can utilize a range of frequencies from the electromagnetic spectrum. Figure 26.26(a) shows the Australia Telescope Compact Array, which uses six 22-m antennas for mapping the southern skies using radio waves. Figure 26.26(b) shows the focusing of x rays on the Chandra X-ray Observatory—a satellite orbiting earth since 1999 and looking at high temperature events as exploding stars, quasars, and black holes. X rays, with much more energy and shorter wavelengths than RF and light, are mainly absorbed and not reflected when incident perpendicular to the medium. But they can be reflected when incident at small glancing angles, much like a rock will skip on a lake if thrown at a small angle. The mirrors for the Chandra consist of a long barrelled pathway and 4 pairs of mirrors to focus the rays at a point 10 meters away from the entrance. The mirrors are extremely smooth and consist of a glass ceramic base with a thin coating of metal (iridium). Four pairs of precision manufactured mirrors are exquisitely shaped and aligned so that x rays ricochet off the mirrors like bullets off a wall, focusing on a spot.

(a)

(b)

FIGURE 26.26 (a) The Australia Telescope Compact Array at Narrabri (500 km NW of Sydney). (credit: Ian Bailey) (b) The focusing of x rays on the Chandra Observatory, a satellite orbiting earth. X rays ricochet off 4 pairs of mirrors forming a barrelled pathway leading to the focus point. (credit: NASA)

A current exciting development is a collaborative effort involving 17 countries to construct a Square Kilometre Array (SKA) of telescopes capable of covering from 80 MHz to 2 GHz. The initial stage of the project is the construction of the Australian Square Kilometre Array Pathfinder in Western Australia (see Figure 26.27). The project will use cutting-edge technologies such as **adaptive optics** in which the lens or mirror is constructed from lots of carefully aligned tiny lenses and mirrors that can be manipulated using computers. A range of rapidly changing distortions can be minimized by deforming or tilting the tiny lenses and mirrors. The use of adaptive optics in vision correction is a current area of research.

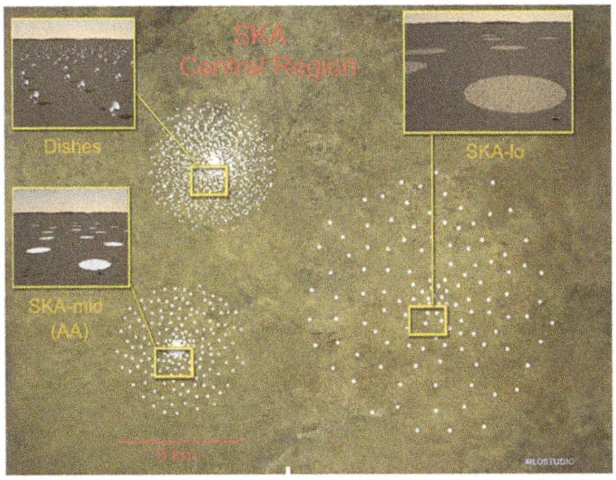

FIGURE 26.27 An artist's impression of the Australian Square Kilometre Array Pathfinder in Western Australia is displayed. (credit: SPDO, XILOSTUDIOS)

26.6 Aberrations

LEARNING OBJECTIVES

By the end of this section, you will be able to:

- Describe optical aberration.

Real lenses behave somewhat differently from how they are modeled using the thin lens equations, producing **aberrations**. An aberration is a distortion in an image. There are a variety of aberrations due to a lens size, material, thickness, and position of the object. One common type of aberration is chromatic aberration, which is related to color. Since the index of refraction of lenses depends on color or wavelength, images are produced at different places and with different magnifications for different colors. (The law of reflection is independent of wavelength, and so mirrors do not have this problem. This is another advantage for mirrors in optical systems such as telescopes.) Figure 26.28(a) shows chromatic aberration for a single convex lens and its partial correction with a two-lens system. Violet rays are bent more than red, since they have a higher index of refraction and are thus focused closer to the lens. The diverging lens partially corrects this, although it is usually not possible to do so completely. Lenses of different materials and having different dispersions may be used. For example an achromatic doublet consisting of a converging lens made of crown glass and a diverging lens made of flint glass in contact can dramatically reduce chromatic aberration (see Figure 26.28(b)).

Quite often in an imaging system the object is off-center. Consequently, different parts of a lens or mirror do not refract or reflect the image to the same point. This type of aberration is called a coma and is shown in Figure 26.29. The image in this case often appears pear-shaped. Another common aberration is spherical aberration where rays converging from the outer edges of a lens converge to a focus closer to the lens and rays closer to the axis focus further (see Figure 26.30). Aberrations due to astigmatism in the lenses of the eyes are discussed in Vision Correction, and a chart used to detect astigmatism is shown in Figure 26.8. Such aberrations and can also be an issue with manufactured lenses.

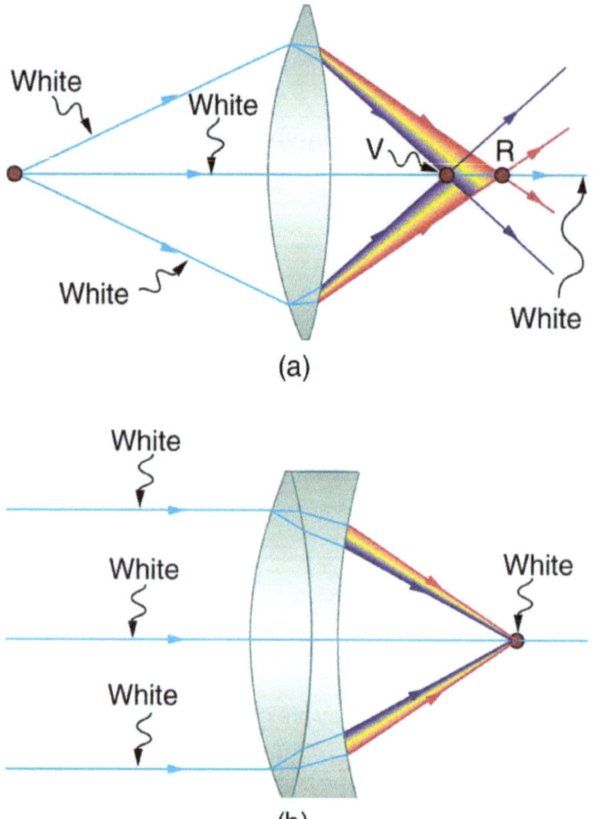

FIGURE 26.28 (a) Chromatic aberration is caused by the dependence of a lens's index of refraction on color (wavelength). The lens is more powerful for violet (V) than for red (R), producing images with different locations and magnifications. (b) Multiple-lens systems can partially correct chromatic aberrations, but they may require lenses of different materials and add to the expense of optical systems such as cameras.

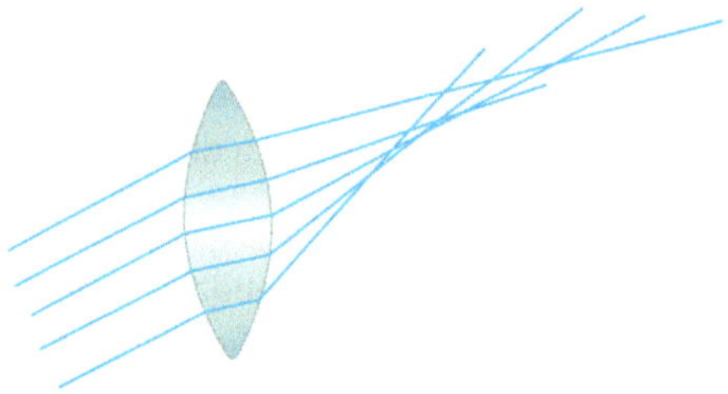

FIGURE 26.29 A coma is an aberration caused by an object that is off-center, often resulting in a pear-shaped image. The rays originate from points that are not on the optical axis and they do not converge at one common focal point.

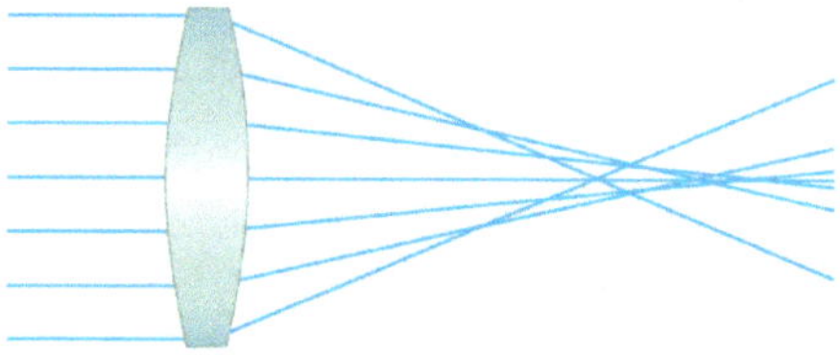

FIGURE 26.30 Spherical aberration is caused by rays focusing at different distances from the lens.

The image produced by an optical system needs to be bright enough to be discerned. It is often a challenge to obtain a sufficiently bright image. The brightness is determined by the amount of light passing through the optical system. The optical components determining the brightness are the diameter of the lens and the diameter of pupils, diaphragms or aperture stops placed in front of lenses. Optical systems often have entrance and exit pupils to specifically reduce aberrations but they inevitably reduce brightness as well. Consequently, optical systems need to strike a balance between the various components used. The iris in the eye dilates and constricts, acting as an entrance pupil. You can see objects more clearly by looking through a small hole made with your hand in the shape of a fist. Squinting, or using a small hole in a piece of paper, also will make the object sharper.

So how are aberrations corrected? The lenses may also have specially shaped surfaces, as opposed to the simple spherical shape that is relatively easy to produce. Expensive camera lenses are large in diameter, so that they can gather more light, and need several elements to correct for various aberrations. Further, advances in materials science have resulted in lenses with a range of refractive indices—technically referred to as graded index (GRIN) lenses. Spectacles often have the ability to provide a range of focusing ability using similar techniques. GRIN lenses are particularly important at the end of optical fibers in endoscopes. Advanced computing techniques allow for a range of corrections on images after the image has been collected and certain characteristics of the optical system are known. Some of these techniques are sophisticated versions of what are available on commercial packages like Adobe Photoshop.

Glossary

aberration failure of rays to converge at one focus because of limitations or defects in a lens or mirror

accommodation the ability of the eye to adjust its focal length is known as accommodation

adaptive optics optical technology in which computers adjust the lenses and mirrors in a device to correct for image distortions

angular magnification a ratio related to the focal lengths of the objective and eyepiece and given as $M = -\frac{f_o}{f_e}$

astigmatism the result of an inability of the cornea to properly focus an image onto the retina

color constancy a part of the visual perception system that allows people to perceive color in a variety of conditions and to see some consistency in the color

compound microscope a microscope constructed from two convex lenses, the first serving as the ocular lens(close to the eye) and the second serving as the objective lens

eyepiece the lens or combination of lenses in an optical instrument nearest to the eye of the observer

far point the object point imaged by the eye onto the retina in an unaccommodated eye

farsightedness another term for hyperopia, the condition of an eye where incoming rays of light reach the retina before they converge into a focused image

hues identity of a color as it relates specifically to the spectrum

hyperopia the condition of an eye where incoming rays of light reach the retina before they converge into a focused image

laser vision correction a medical procedure used to correct astigmatism and eyesight deficiencies such as myopia and hyperopia

myopia a visual defect in which distant objects appear blurred because their images are focused in front of the retina rather than being focused on the retina

near point the point nearest the eye at which an object is accurately focused on the retina at full accommodation

nearsightedness another term for myopia, a visual defect in which distant objects appear blurred because their images are focused in front of the retina rather than being focused on the retina

numerical aperture a number or measure that expresses the ability of a lens to resolve fine detail in an object being observed. Derived by mathematical formula $NA = n \sin \alpha$,
where n is the refractive index of the medium between the lens and the specimen and $\alpha = \theta/2$

objective lens the lens nearest to the object being examined

presbyopia a condition in which the lens of the eye becomes progressively unable to focus on objects close to the viewer

retinex a theory proposed to explain color and brightness perception and constancies; is a combination of the words retina and cortex, which are the two areas responsible for the processing of visual information

retinex theory of color vision the ability to perceive color in an ambient-colored environment

rods and cones two types of photoreceptors in the human retina; rods are responsible for vision at low light levels, while cones are active at higher light levels

simplified theory of color vision a theory that states that there are three primary colors, which correspond to the three types of cones

Section Summary

26.1 Physics of the Eye

- Image formation by the eye is adequately described by the thin lens equations: $P = \frac{1}{d_o} + \frac{1}{d_i}$ and $\frac{h_i}{h_o} = -\frac{d_i}{d_o} = m$.
- The eye produces a real image on the retina by adjusting its focal length and power in a process called accommodation.
- For close vision, the eye is fully accommodated and has its greatest power, whereas for distant vision, it is totally relaxed and has its smallest power.
- The loss of the ability to accommodate with age is called presbyopia, which is corrected by the use of a converging lens to add power for close vision.

26.2 Vision Correction

- Nearsightedness, or myopia, is the inability to see distant objects and is corrected with a diverging lens to reduce power.
- Farsightedness, or hyperopia, is the inability to see close objects and is corrected with a converging lens to increase power.
- In myopia and hyperopia, the corrective lenses

produce images at a distance that the person can see clearly—the far point and near point, respectively.

26.3 Color and Color Vision

- The eye has four types of light receptors—rods and three types of color-sensitive cones.
- The rods are good for night vision, peripheral vision, and motion changes, while the cones are responsible for central vision and color.
- We perceive many hues, from light having mixtures of wavelengths.
- A simplified theory of color vision states that there are three primary colors, which correspond to the three types of cones, and that various combinations of the primary colors produce all the hues.
- The true color of an object is related to its relative absorption of various wavelengths of light. The color of a light source is related to the wavelengths it produces.
- Color constancy is the ability of the eye-brain system to discern the true color of an object illuminated by various light sources.
- The retinex theory of color vision explains color constancy by postulating the existence of three retinexes or image systems, associated with the three types of cones that are compared to obtain sophisticated information.

26.4 Microscopes

- The microscope is a multiple-element system having more than a single lens or mirror.
- Many optical devices contain more than a single lens or mirror. These are analysed by considering each element sequentially. The image formed by the first is the object for the second, and so on. The same ray tracing and thin lens techniques apply to each lens element.
- The overall magnification of a multiple-element system is the product of the magnifications of its individual elements. For a two-element system with an objective and an eyepiece, this is
  $m = m_o m_e$,
  where m_o is the magnification of the objective and m_e is the magnification of the eyepiece, such as for a microscope.
- Microscopes are instruments for allowing us to see detail we would not be able to see with the unaided eye and consist of a range of components.
- The eyepiece and objective contribute to the magnification. The numerical aperture (NA) of an objective is given by
  $NA = n \sin \alpha$
  where n is the refractive index and α the angle of acceptance.
- Immersion techniques are often used to improve the light gathering ability of microscopes. The specimen is illuminated by transmitted, scattered or reflected light though a condenser.
- The f /# describes the light gathering ability of a lens. It is given by
  $f\,/\# = \frac{f}{D} \approx \frac{1}{2NA}$.

26.5 Telescopes

- Simple telescopes can be made with two lenses. They are used for viewing objects at large distances and utilize the entire range of the electromagnetic spectrum.
- The angular magnification M for a telescope is given by
  $M = \frac{\theta'}{\theta} = -\frac{f_o}{f_e}$,
  where θ is the angle subtended by an object viewed by the unaided eye, θ' is the angle subtended by a magnified image, and f_o and f_e are the focal lengths of the objective and the eyepiece.

26.6 Aberrations

- Aberrations or image distortions can arise due to the finite thickness of optical instruments, imperfections in the optical components, and limitations on the ways in which the components are used.
- The means for correcting aberrations range from better components to computational techniques.

Conceptual Questions

26.1 Physics of the Eye

1. If the lens of a person's eye is removed because of cataracts (as has been done since ancient times), why would you expect a spectacle lens of about 16 D to be prescribed?

2. A cataract is cloudiness in the lens of the eye. Is light dispersed or diffused by it?

3. When laser light is shone into a relaxed normal-vision eye to repair a tear by spot-welding the retina to the back of the eye, the rays entering the eye must be parallel. Why?

4. How does the power of a dry contact lens compare

with its power when resting on the tear layer of the eye? Explain.

5. Why is your vision so blurry when you open your eyes while swimming under water? How does a face mask enable clear vision?

26.2 Vision Correction

6. It has become common to replace the cataract-clouded lens of the eye with an internal lens. This intraocular lens can be chosen so that the person has perfect distant vision. Will the person be able to read without glasses? If the person was nearsighted, is the power of the intraocular lens greater or less than the removed lens?

7. If the cornea is to be reshaped (this can be done surgically or with contact lenses) to correct myopia, should its curvature be made greater or smaller? Explain. Also explain how hyperopia can be corrected.

8. If there is a fixed percent uncertainty in LASIK reshaping of the cornea, why would you expect those people with the greatest correction to have a poorer chance of normal distant vision after the procedure?

9. A person with presbyopia has lost some or all of the ability to accommodate the power of the eye. If such a person's distant vision is corrected with LASIK, will she still need reading glasses? Explain.

26.3 Color and Color Vision

10. A pure red object on a black background seems to disappear when illuminated with pure green light. Explain why.

11. What is color constancy, and what are its limitations?

12. There are different types of color blindness related to the malfunction of different types of cones. Why would it be particularly useful to study those rare individuals who are color blind only in one eye or who have a different type of color blindness in each eye?

13. Propose a way to study the function of the rods alone, given they can sense light about 1000 times dimmer than the cones.

26.4 Microscopes

14. Geometric optics describes the interaction of light with macroscopic objects. Why, then, is it correct to use geometric optics to analyse a microscope's image?

15. The image produced by the microscope in Figure 26.16 cannot be projected. Could extra lenses or mirrors project it? Explain.

16. Why not have the objective of a microscope form a case 2 image with a large magnification? (Hint: Consider the location of that image and the difficulty that would pose for using the eyepiece as a magnifier.)

17. What advantages do oil immersion objectives offer?

18. How does the NA of a microscope compare with the NA of an optical fiber?

26.5 Telescopes

19. If you want your microscope or telescope to project a real image onto a screen, how would you change the placement of the eyepiece relative to the objective?

26.6 Aberrations

20. List the various types of aberrations. What causes them and how can each be reduced?

Problems & Exercises

26.1 Physics of the Eye

Unless otherwise stated, the lens-to-retina distance is 2.00 cm.

1. What is the power of the eye when viewing an object 50.0 cm away?

2. Calculate the power of the eye when viewing an object 3.00 m away.

3. (a) The print in many books averages 3.50 mm in height. How high is the image of the print on the retina when the book is held 30.0 cm from the eye?

(b) Compare the size of the print to the sizes of rods and cones in the fovea and discuss the possible details observable in the letters. (The eye-brain system can perform better because of interconnections and higher order image processing.)

4. Suppose a certain person's visual acuity is such that he can see objects clearly that form an image $4.00\ \mu m$ high on his retina. What is the maximum distance at which he can read the 75.0 cm high letters on the side of an airplane?

5. People who do very detailed work close up, such as jewellers, often can see objects clearly at much closer distance than the normal 25 cm.
(a) What is the power of the eyes of a woman who can see an object clearly at a distance of only 8.00 cm?
(b) What is the size of an image of a 1.00 mm object, such as lettering inside a ring, held at this distance?
(c) What would the size of the image be if the object were held at the normal 25.0 cm distance?

26.2 Vision Correction

6. What is the far point of a person whose eyes have a relaxed power of 50.5 D?

7. What is the near point of a person whose eyes have an accommodated power of 53.5 D?

8. (a) A laser vision correction reshaping the cornea of a myopic patient reduces the power of his eye by 9.00 D, with a $\pm 5.0\%$ uncertainty in the final correction. What is the range of diopters for spectacle lenses that this person might need after LASIK procedure? (b) Was the person nearsighted or farsighted before the procedure? How do you know?

9. In a LASIK vision correction, the power of a patient's eye is increased by 3.00 D. Assuming this produces normal close vision, what was the patient's near point before the procedure?

10. What was the previous far point of a patient who had laser vision correction that reduced the power of her eye by 7.00 D, producing normal distant vision for her?

11. A severely myopic patient has a far point of 5.00 cm. By how many diopters should the power of his eye be reduced in laser vision correction to obtain normal distant vision for him?

12. A student's eyes, while reading the blackboard, have a power of 51.0 D. How far is the board from his eyes?

13. The power of a physician's eyes is 53.0 D while examining a patient. How far from her eyes is the feature being examined?

14. A young woman with normal distant vision has a 10.0% ability to accommodate (that is, increase) the power of her eyes. What is the closest object she can see clearly?

15. The far point of a myopic administrator is 50.0 cm. (a) What is the relaxed power of their eyes? (b) If they have the normal 8.00% ability to accommodate, what is the closest object they can see clearly?

16. A very myopic man has a far point of 20.0 cm. What power contact lens (when on the eye) will correct his distant vision?

17. Repeat the previous problem for eyeglasses held 1.50 cm from the eyes.

18. A myopic person sees that their contact lens prescription is -4.00 D. What is their far point?

19. Repeat the previous problem for glasses that are 1.75 cm from the eyes.

20. The contact lens prescription for a mildly farsighted person is 0.750 D, and the person has a near point of 29.0 cm. What is the power of the tear layer between the cornea and the lens if the correction is ideal, taking the tear layer into account?

21. A nearsighted man cannot see objects clearly beyond 20 cm from his eyes. How close must he stand to a mirror in order to see what he is doing when he shaves?

22. A teacher sees that a child's contact lens prescription is 0.750 D. What is the child's near point?

23. Repeat the previous problem for glasses that are 2.20 cm from the eyes.

24. The contact lens prescription for a nearsighted person is -4.00 D and the person has a far point of 22.5 cm. What is the power of the tear layer between the cornea and the lens if the correction is ideal, taking the tear layer into account?

25. Unreasonable Results
A boy has a near point of 50 cm and a far point of 500 cm. Will a -4.00 D lens correct his far point to infinity?

26.4 Microscopes

26. A microscope with an overall magnification of 800 has an objective that magnifies by 200. (a) What is the magnification of the eyepiece? (b) If there are two other objectives that can be used, having magnifications of 100 and 400, what other total magnifications are possible?

27. (a) What magnification is produced by a 0.150 cm focal length microscope objective that is 0.155 cm from the object being viewed? (b) What is the overall magnification if an $8\times$ eyepiece (one that

produces a magnification of 8.00) is used?

28. (a) Where does an object need to be placed relative to a microscope for its 0.500 cm focal length objective to produce a magnification of -400? (b) Where should the 5.00 cm focal length eyepiece be placed to produce a further fourfold (4.00) magnification?

29. You switch from a $1.40NA\ 60\times$ oil immersion objective to a $1.40NA\ 60\times$ oil immersion objective. What are the acceptance angles for each? Compare and comment on the values. Which would you use first to locate the target area on your specimen?

30. An amoeba is 0.305 cm away from the 0.300 cm focal length objective lens of a microscope. (a) Where is the image formed by the objective lens? (b) What is this image's magnification? (c) An eyepiece with a 2.00 cm focal length is placed 20.0 cm from the objective. Where is the final image? (d) What magnification is produced by the eyepiece? (e) What is the overall magnification? (See Figure 26.16.)

31. You are using a standard microscope with a $0.10NA\ 4\times$ objective and switch to a $0.65NA\ 40\times$ objective. What are the acceptance angles for each? Compare and comment on the values. Which would you use first to locate the target area on of your specimen? (See Figure 26.17.)

32. Unreasonable Results
Your friends show you an image through a microscope. They tell you that the microscope has an objective with a 0.500 cm focal length and an eyepiece with a 5.00 cm focal length. The resulting overall magnification is 250,000. Are these viable values for a microscope?

26.5 Telescopes

Unless otherwise stated, the lens-to-retina distance is 2.00 cm.

33. What is the angular magnification of a telescope that has a 100 cm focal length objective and a 2.50 cm focal length eyepiece?

34. Find the distance between the objective and eyepiece lenses in the telescope in the above problem needed to produce a final image very far from the observer, where vision is most relaxed. Note that a telescope is normally used to view very distant objects.

35. A large reflecting telescope has an objective mirror with a $10.0\ \text{m}$ radius of curvature. What angular magnification does it produce when a 3.00 cm focal length eyepiece is used?

36. A small telescope has a concave mirror with a 2.00 m radius of curvature for its objective. Its eyepiece is a 4.00 cm focal length lens. (a) What is the telescope's angular magnification? (b) What angle is subtended by a 25,000 km diameter sunspot? (c) What is the angle of its telescopic image?

37. A $7.5\times$ binocular produces an angular magnification of -7.50, acting like a telescope. (Mirrors are used to make the image upright.) If the binoculars have objective lenses with a 75.0 cm focal length, what is the focal length of the eyepiece lenses?

38. Construct Your Own Problem
Consider a telescope of the type used by Galileo, having a convex objective and a concave eyepiece as illustrated in Figure 26.23(a). Construct a problem in which you calculate the location and size of the image produced. Among the things to be considered are the focal lengths of the lenses and their relative placements as well as the size and location of the object. Verify that the angular magnification is greater than one. That is, the angle subtended at the eye by the image is greater than the angle subtended by the object.

26.6 Aberrations

39. Integrated Concepts
(a) During laser vision correction, a brief burst of 193 nm ultraviolet light is projected onto the cornea of the patient. It makes a spot 1.00 mm in diameter and deposits 0.500 mJ of energy. Calculate the depth of the layer ablated, assuming the corneal tissue has the same properties as water and is initially at 34.0°C. The tissue's temperature is increased to 100°C and evaporated without further temperature increase. (b) Does your answer imply that the shape of the cornea can be finely controlled?

40. Critical Thinking A microscope has the objective lens 6.00 mm from an object. The focal length of the objective lens is 4.00 mm. The eyepiece has a focal length of 50.0 mm and is initially 25.0 mm from the objective lens. (a) The objective lens is moved to 5.00 mm from the objective, effectively lengthening the microscope. How does this affect the magnification of the microscope? (b) Does moving the objective increase closer to the object increase or decrease the magnification, or does it remain the same? (c) Do you think moving the objective from 6 mm to 7 mm from the object will increase or decrease the magnification of the microscope, or will it likely remain the same? (d) What indicates whether the image is upright or inverted?

Test Prep for AP® Courses

26.1 Physics of the Eye

1. A tree that is 3 m tall is viewed from a distance of 25 m. If the cornea-to-retina distance of an ideal eye is 2 cm, how tall is the image of the tree on the observer's retina?

a. 0.24 cm
b. 0.5 cm
c. 0.5 m
d. 0.08 cm

2. Often people with lens-to-retina distances smaller than 2 cm purchase glasses to place in front of their eyes.

a. Explain why people with lens-to-retina distances smaller than 2 cm need glasses.
b. Explain whether the glasses should be composed of converging or diverging lenses.
c. Draw a ray diagram demonstrating the ability to see with and without the glasses.

26.2 Vision Correction

3. Which of the following types of light have a wavelength greater than that of visible light?

I. gamma rays
II. infrared
III. radio
IV. ultraviolet

a. I, II, and III
b. I and IV only
c. II and III only
d. III only

4. In LASIK surgery, a coherent UV light of 193 nm is focused on the corneal tissue.

a. Explain the importance of using light that is all the same wavelength.
b. Explain why UV light is more effective than infrared light at evaporating the corneal tissue.

26.3 Color and Color Vision

5. A student sees a piece of paper sitting on a table. Which of the following would not result in the student observing the paper as yellow?

a. Yellow light shines on a black paper.
b. White light shines on a yellow paper.
c. Yellow light shines on a white paper.
d. Red and green lights shine on a white paper.

6. A white light is projected onto a tablecloth. Using the light reflecting off the tablecloth, an observer determines that the color of the tablecloth is blue.

a. Using the wave model of light, explain how the observer is capable of making this judgment.
b. Describe how using the particle model of light limits our explanation of the observer's judgment.

26.4 Microscopes

7. Which of the following correctly describes the image created by a microscope?

a. The image is real, inverted, and magnified.
b. The image is virtual, inverted, and magnified.
c. The image is real, upright, and magnified.
d. The image is virtual, upright, and magnified.

8. Use the diagram shown below to answer the following questions.

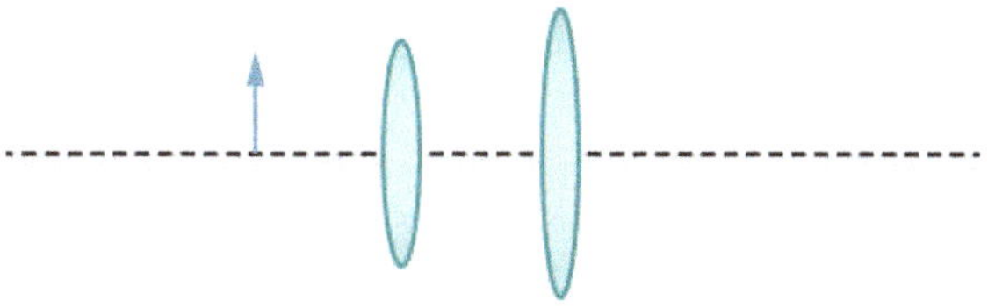

FIGURE 26.31

Draw two rays leaving the arrow shown to the left of both lenses. Use ray tracing to draw the images created by the objective and eyepiece lenses. Label the images as i_o and i_e.

26.5 Telescopes

9. Which of the following is an advantage to using a concave mirror in the construction of a telescope?

I. The telescope can gather more light than a telescope using lenses.
II. The telescope does not suffer from chromatic aberration.
III. The telescope can provide greater magnification than a telescope using lenses.

a. I and III only

b. II only
c. I and II only
d. I, II, and III

10. A spherical mirror is used to construct a telescope.

a. Using the picture below, draw two rays incident on the object mirror and continue their path through the eye lens.

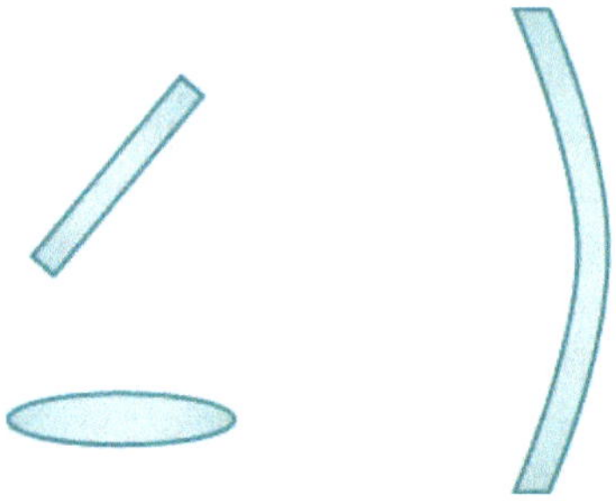

FIGURE 26.32

b. The plane mirror is replaced with a concave lens. Using the picture below, draw the path of two incident rays.

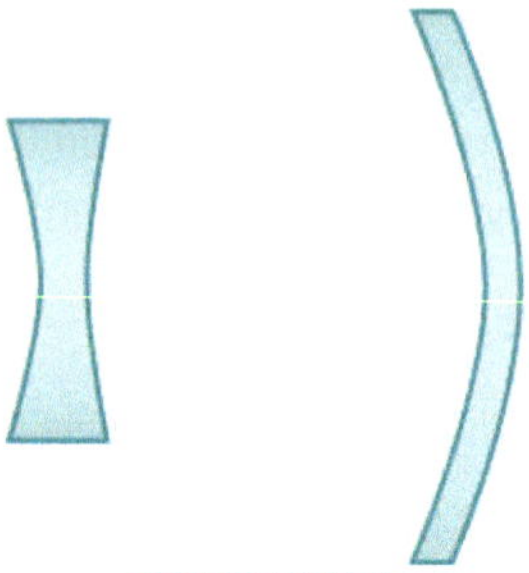

FIGURE 26.33

c. Using the concave lens setup, describe the final image created by the concave lens.

11. Two concave lenses, of focal lengths 500 mm and 20 mm, are used in the construction of a telescope. Given any potential arrangement, what is the largest possible magnification the telescope may have?

a. 100×
b. 10,000×
c. 25×
d. 4×

CHAPTER 27
Wave Optics

FIGURE 27.1 Katharine Burr Blodgett (1898–1979) was a physicist and chemist who made significant advancements in the study of surfaces and thin films. The trough she developed is still used in thousands of labs around the world, and her invention of non-reflective glass has had massive impact in cinema, medical, and scientific research arenas. (credit: Smithsonian Institution)

CHAPTER OUTLINE

CONNECTION FOR AP® COURSES If you have ever looked at the reds, blues, and greens in a sunlit soap bubble and wondered how straw-colored soapy water could produce them, you have hit upon one of the many phenomena that can only be explained by the wave character of light. The same is true for the colors seen in an oil slick or in the light reflected from an optical data disk. These and other interesting phenomena, such as the dispersion of white light into a rainbow of colors when passed through a narrow slit, cannot be explained fully by geometric optics. In these cases, light interacts with objects and exhibits a number of wave characteristics. The branch of optics that considers the behavior of light when it exhibits wave characteristics is called “wave optics” (or sometimes “physical optics”).

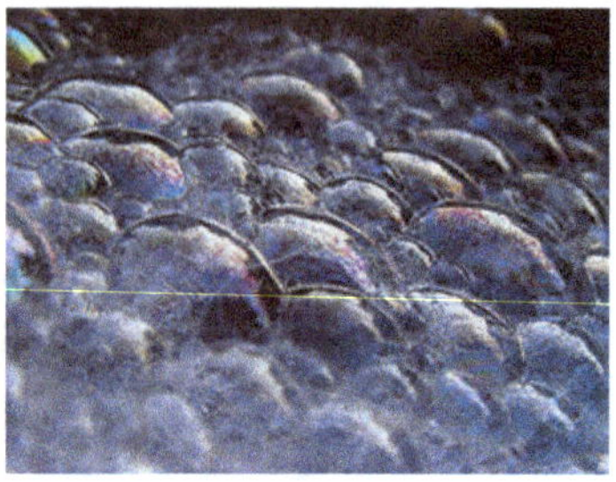

FIGURE 27.2 Multicolored soap bubbles (credit: Scott Robinson, Flickr).

These soap bubbles exhibit brilliant colors when exposed to sunlight. How are the colors produced if they are not pigments in the soap?

This chapter supports Big Idea 6 in its coverage of wave optics by presenting explanations and examples of many phenomena that can only be explained by the wave aspect of light. You will learn how only waves can exhibit diffraction and interference patterns that we observe in light (Enduring Understanding 6.C). As explained by Huygens's principle, diffraction is the bending of waves around the edges of a nontransparent object or after passing through an opening (Essential Knowledge 6.C.4). Interference results from the superposition of two or more traveling waves (Enduring Understanding 6.D, Enduring Understanding 6.D.1). Superposition causes variations in the resultant wave amplitude (Essential Knowledge 6.D.2). The interference can be described as constructive interference, which increases amplitude, and destructive interference, which decreases amplitude. Based on an understanding of diffraction and interference of light, this chapter also explains experimental observations that occur when light passes through an opening or set of openings with dimensions comparable to the wavelength of the light – specifically the effects of double-slit, multiple-slit (Essential Knowledge 6.C.3), and single-slit (Essential Knowledge 6.C.2) openings. Another aspect of light waves that you will learn about in this chapter is polarization, a phenomenon in which light waves all vibrate in a single plane. The explanation for this phenomenon is based on the fact that light is a traveling electromagnetic wave (Enduring Understanding 6.A) that propagates via transverse oscillations of both electric and magnetic field vectors (Enduring Understanding 6.A.1). Light waves can be polarized by passing through filters. Many sunglasses contain polarizing filters to reduce glare, and certain types of 3-D glasses use polarization to create an effect of depth on the movie screen.

Big Idea 6 Waves can transfer energy and momentum from one location to another without the permanent transfer of mass and serve as a mathematical model for the description of other phenomena.

Enduring Understanding 6.A A wave is a traveling disturbance that transfers energy and momentum.

Essential Knowledge 6.A.1 Waves can propagate via different oscillation modes such as transverse and longitudinal.

Enduring Understanding 6.C Only waves exhibit interference and diffraction.

Essential Knowledge 6.C.2 When waves pass through an opening whose dimensions are comparable to the wavelength, a diffraction pattern can be observed.

Essential Knowledge 6.C.3 When waves pass through a set of openings whose spacing is comparable to the wavelength, an interference pattern can be observed. Examples should include monochromatic double-slit interference.

Essential Knowledge 6.C.4 When waves pass by an edge, they can diffract into the "shadow region" behind the edge. Examples should include hearing around corners, but not seeing around them, and water waves bending around obstacles.

Enduring Understanding 6.D Interference and superposition lead to standing waves and beats.

Essential Knowledge 6.D.1 Two or more wave pulses can interact in such a way as to produce amplitude variations in the resultant wave. When two pulses cross, they travel through each other; they do not bounce off each other. Where the pulses overlap, the resulting displacement can be determined by adding the displacements of the two pulses. This is called superposition.

Essential Knowledge 6.D.2 Two or more traveling waves can interact in such a way as to produce amplitude variations in the resultant wave.

27.1 The Wave Aspect of Light: Interference

LEARNING OBJECTIVES

By the end of this section, you will be able to:

- Discuss the wave character of light.
- Identify the changes when light enters a medium.

We know that visible light is the type of electromagnetic wave to which our eyes respond. Like all other electromagnetic waves, it obeys the equation

$$c = f\lambda, \tag{27.1}$$

where $c = 3 \times 10^8$ m/s is the speed of light in vacuum, f is the frequency of the electromagnetic waves, and λ is its wavelength. The range of visible wavelengths is approximately 380 to 760 nm. As is true for all waves, light travels in straight lines and acts like a ray when it interacts with objects several times as large as its wavelength. However, when it interacts with smaller objects, it displays its wave characteristics prominently. Interference is the hallmark of a wave, and in Figure 27.3 both the ray and wave characteristics of light can be seen. The laser beam emitted by the observatory epitomizes a ray, traveling in a straight line. However, passing a pure-wavelength beam through vertical slits with a size close to the wavelength of the beam reveals the wave character of light, as the beam spreads out horizontally into a pattern of bright and dark regions caused by systematic constructive and destructive interference. Rather than spreading out, a ray would continue traveling straight ahead after passing through slits.

MAKING CONNECTIONS: WAVES

The most certain indication of a wave is interference. This wave characteristic is most prominent when the wave interacts with an object that is not large compared with the wavelength. Interference is observed for water waves, sound waves, light waves, and (as we will see in Special Relativity) for matter waves, such as electrons scattered from a crystal.

(a)

(b)

FIGURE 27.3 (a) The laser beam emitted by an observatory acts like a ray, traveling in a straight line. This laser beam is from the Paranal Observatory of the European Southern Observatory. (credit: Yuri Beletsky, European Southern Observatory) (b) A laser beam passing through a grid of vertical slits produces an interference pattern—characteristic of a wave. (credit: Shim'on and Slava Rybka, Wikimedia Commons)

Light has wave characteristics in various media as well as in a vacuum. When light goes from a vacuum to some medium, like water, its speed and wavelength change, but its frequency f remains the same. (We can think of light as a forced oscillation that must have the frequency of the original source.) The speed of light in a medium is $v = c/n$, where n is its index of refraction. If we divide both sides of equation $c = f\lambda$ by n, we get $c/n = v = f\lambda/n$. This implies that $v = f\lambda_{\text{n}}$, where λ_{n} is the **wavelength in a medium** and that

$$\lambda_{\text{n}} = \frac{\lambda}{n}, \qquad 27.2$$

where λ is the wavelength in vacuum and n is the medium's index of refraction. Therefore, the wavelength of light is smaller in any medium than it is in vacuum. In water, for example, which has $n = 1.333$, the range of visible wavelengths is $(380\text{ nm})/1.333$ to $(760\text{ nm})/1.333$, or $\lambda_{\text{n}} = 285\text{ to }570\text{ nm}$. Although wavelengths change while traveling from one medium to another, colors do not, since colors are associated with frequency.

27.2 Huygens's Principle: Diffraction

LEARNING OBJECTIVES

By the end of this section, you will be able to:

- Discuss the propagation of transverse waves.
- Discuss Huygens's principle.
- Explain the bending of light.

Figure 27.4 shows how a transverse wave looks as viewed from above and from the side. A light wave can be imagined to propagate like this, although we do not actually see it wiggling through space. From above, we view the wavefronts (or wave crests) as we would by looking down on the ocean waves. The side view would be a graph of the electric or magnetic field. The view from above is perhaps the most useful in developing concepts about wave optics.

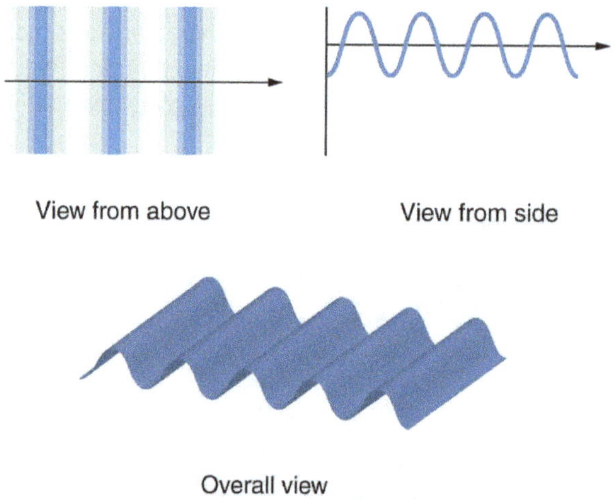

FIGURE 27.4 A transverse wave, such as an electromagnetic wave like light, as viewed from above and from the side. The direction of propagation is perpendicular to the wavefronts (or wave crests) and is represented by an arrow like a ray.

The Dutch scientist Christiaan Huygens (1629–1695) developed a useful technique for determining in detail how and where waves propagate. Starting from some known position, **Huygens's principle** states that:

Every point on a wavefront is a source of wavelets that spread out in the forward direction at the same speed as the wave itself. The new wavefront is a line tangent to all of the wavelets.

Figure 27.5 shows how Huygens's principle is applied. A wavefront is the long edge that moves, for example, the crest or the trough. Each point on the wavefront emits a semicircular wave that moves at the propagation speed v. These are drawn at a time t later, so that they have moved a distance $s = vt$. The new wavefront is a line tangent to the wavelets and is where we would expect the wave to be a time t later. Huygens's principle works for all types of waves, including water waves, sound waves, and light waves. We will find it useful not only in describing how light waves propagate, but also in explaining the laws of reflection and refraction. In addition, we will see that Huygens's principle tells us how and where light rays interfere.

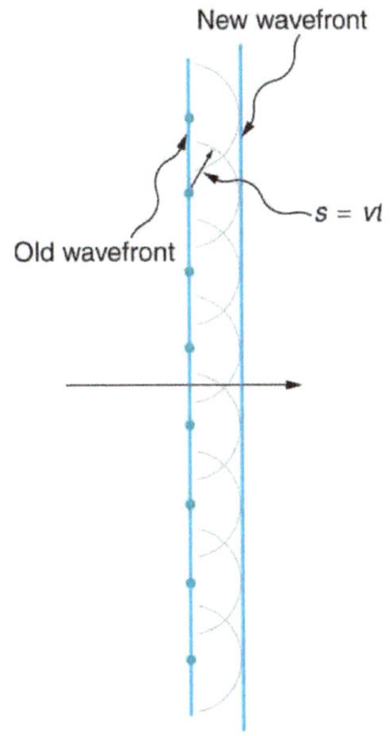

FIGURE 27.5 Huygens's principle applied to a straight wavefront. Each point on the wavefront emits a semicircular wavelet that moves a distance $s = vt$. The new wavefront is a line tangent to the wavelets.

Figure 27.6 shows how a mirror reflects an incoming wave at an angle equal to the incident angle, verifying the law of reflection. As the wavefront strikes the mirror, wavelets are first emitted from the left part of the mirror and then the right. The wavelets closer to the left have had time to travel farther, producing a wavefront traveling in the direction shown.

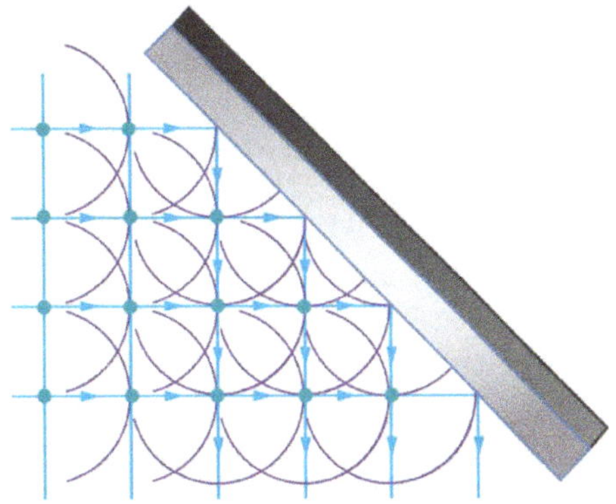

FIGURE 27.6 Huygens's principle applied to a straight wavefront striking a mirror. The wavelets shown were emitted as each point on the wavefront struck the mirror. The tangent to these wavelets shows that the new wavefront has been reflected at an angle equal to the incident angle. The direction of propagation is perpendicular to the wavefront, as shown by the downward-pointing arrows.

The law of refraction can be explained by applying Huygens's principle to a wavefront passing from one medium to another (see Figure 27.7). Each wavelet in the figure was emitted when the wavefront crossed the interface between the media. Since the speed of light is smaller in the second medium, the waves do not travel as far in a given time, and the new wavefront changes direction as shown. This explains why a ray changes direction to become closer to the perpendicular when light slows down. Snell's law can be derived from the geometry in Figure 27.7, but this is left as an exercise for ambitious readers.

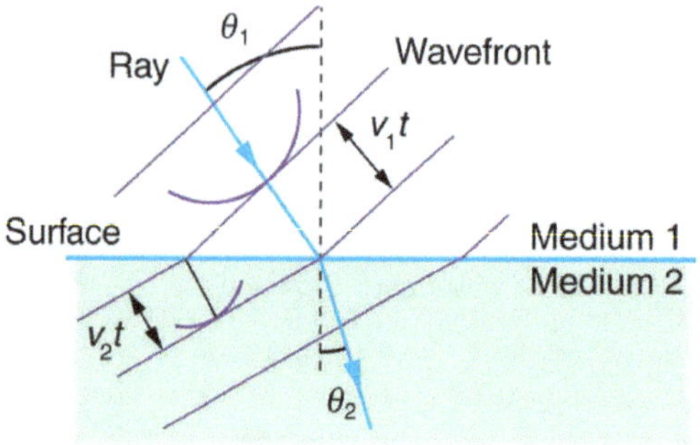

FIGURE 27.7 Huygens's principle applied to a straight wavefront traveling from one medium to another where its speed is less. The ray bends toward the perpendicular, since the wavelets have a lower speed in the second medium.

What happens when a wave passes through an opening, such as light shining through an open door into a dark room? For light, we expect to see a sharp shadow of the doorway on the floor of the room, and we expect no light to bend around corners into other parts of the room. When sound passes through a door, we expect to hear it everywhere in the room and, thus, expect that sound spreads out when passing through such an opening (see Figure 27.8). What is the difference between the behavior of sound waves and light waves in this case? The answer is that light has very short wavelengths and acts like a ray. Sound has wavelengths on the order of the size of the door and bends around corners (for frequency of 1000 Hz, $\lambda = c/f = (330 \text{ m/s})/(1000 \text{ s}^{-1}) = 0.33 \text{ m}$, about three times smaller than the width of the doorway).

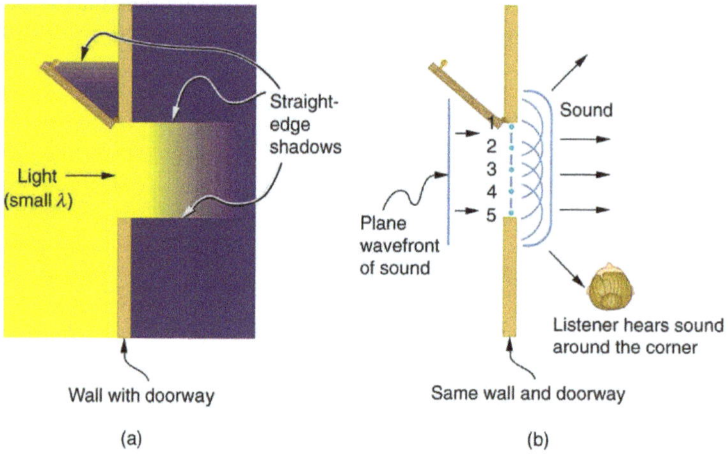

FIGURE 27.8 (a) Light passing through a doorway makes a sharp outline on the floor. Since light's wavelength is very small compared with the size of the door, it acts like a ray. (b) Sound waves bend into all parts of the room, a wave effect, because their wavelength is similar to the size of the door.

If we pass light through smaller openings, often called slits, we can use Huygens's principle to see that light bends as sound does (see Figure 27.9). The bending of a wave around the edges of an opening or an obstacle is called **diffraction**. Diffraction is a wave characteristic and occurs for all types of waves. If diffraction is observed for some phenomenon, it is evidence that the phenomenon is a wave. Thus the horizontal diffraction of the laser beam after it passes through slits in Figure 27.3 is evidence that light is a wave.

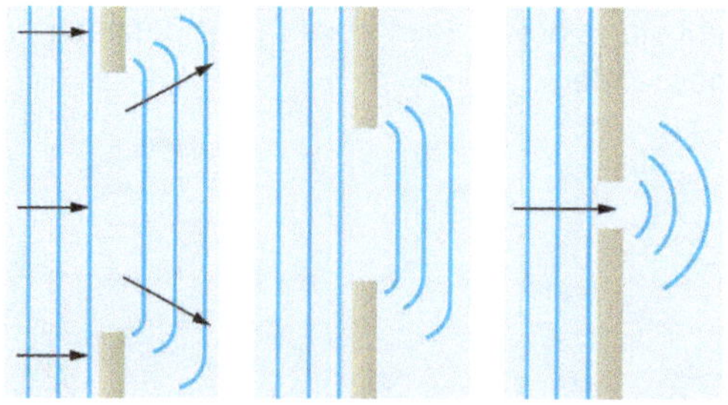

FIGURE 27.9 Huygens's principle applied to a straight wavefront striking an opening. The edges of the wavefront bend after passing through the opening, a process called diffraction. The amount of bending is more extreme for a small opening, consistent with the fact that wave characteristics are most noticeable for interactions with objects about the same size as the wavelength.

27.3 Young's Double Slit Experiment

LEARNING OBJECTIVES

By the end of this section, you will be able to:

- Explain the phenomena of interference.
- Define constructive interference for a double slit and destructive interference for a double slit.

Although Christiaan Huygens thought that light was a wave, Isaac Newton did not. Newton felt that there were other explanations for color, and for the interference and diffraction effects that were observable at the time. Owing to Newton's tremendous stature, his view generally prevailed. The fact that Huygens's principle worked was not considered evidence that was direct enough to prove that light is a wave. The acceptance of the wave character of light came many years later when, in 1801, the English physicist and physician Thomas Young (1773–1829) did his now-classic double slit experiment (see Figure 27.10).

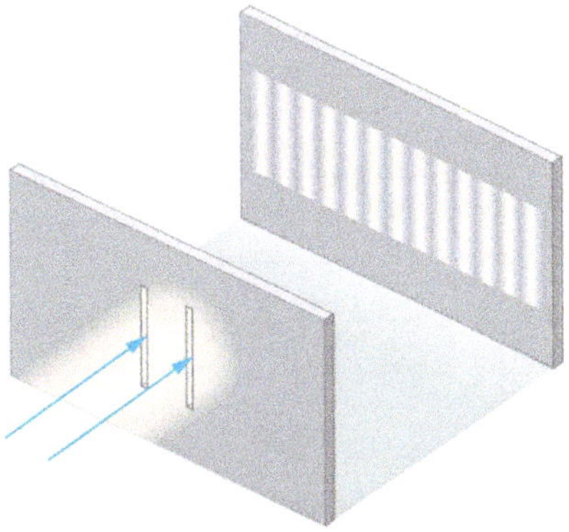

FIGURE 27.10 Young's double slit experiment. Here pure-wavelength light sent through a pair of vertical slits is diffracted into a pattern on the screen of numerous vertical lines spread out horizontally. Without diffraction and interference, the light would simply make two lines on the screen.

Why do we not ordinarily observe wave behavior for light, such as observed in Young's double slit experiment? First, light must interact with something small, such as the closely spaced slits used by Young, to show pronounced wave effects. Furthermore, Young first passed light from a single source (the Sun) through a single slit to make the light somewhat coherent. By **coherent**, we mean waves are in phase or have a definite phase relationship. **Incoherent** means the waves have random phase relationships. Why did Young then pass the light through a double slit? The answer to this question is that two slits provide two coherent light sources that then interfere constructively or destructively. Young used sunlight, where each wavelength forms its own pattern, making the effect more difficult to see. We illustrate the double slit experiment with monochromatic (single λ) light to clarify the effect. Figure 27.11 shows the pure constructive and destructive interference of two waves having the same wavelength and amplitude.

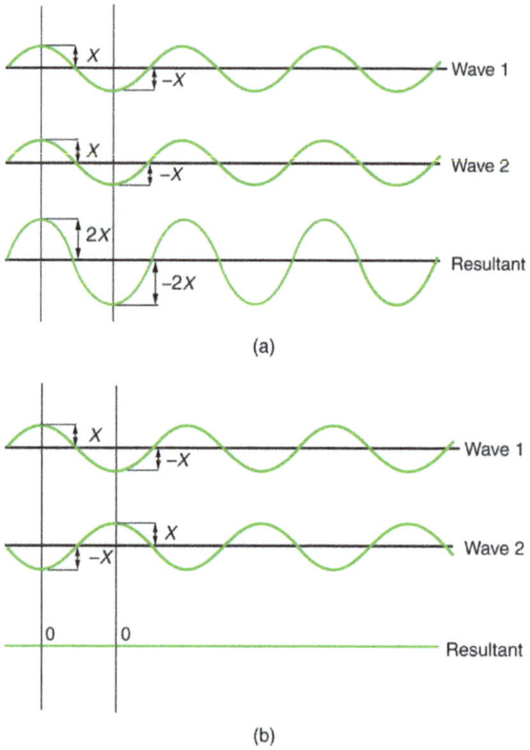

FIGURE 27.11 The amplitudes of waves add. (a) Pure constructive interference is obtained when identical waves are in phase. (b) Pure destructive interference occurs when identical waves are exactly out of phase, or shifted by half a wavelength.

When light passes through narrow slits, it is diffracted into semicircular waves, as shown in Figure 27.12(a). Pure constructive interference occurs where the waves are crest to crest or trough to trough. Pure destructive interference occurs where they are crest to trough. The light must fall on a screen and be scattered into our eyes for us to see the pattern. An analogous pattern for water waves is shown in Figure 27.12(b). Note that regions of constructive and destructive interference move out from the slits at well-defined angles to the original beam. These angles depend on wavelength and the distance between the slits, as we shall see below.

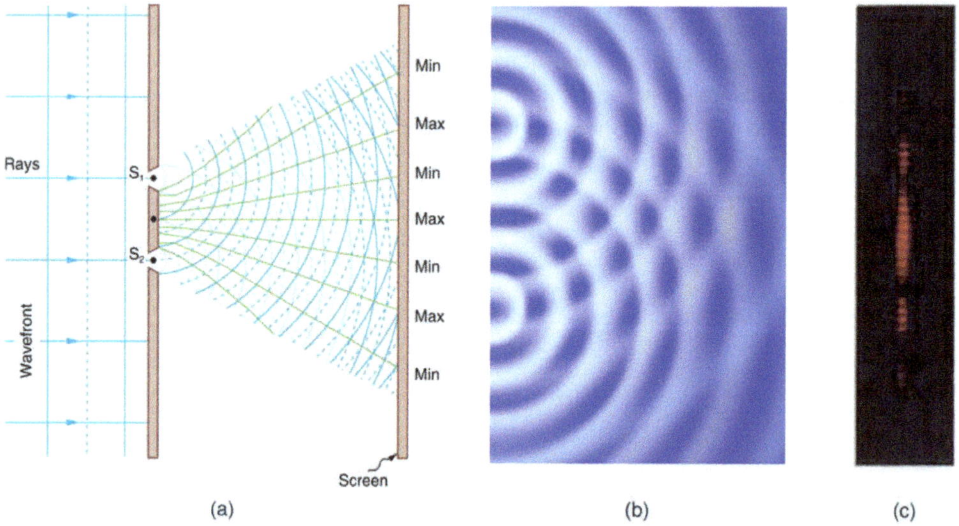

FIGURE 27.12 Double slits produce two coherent sources of waves that interfere. (a) Light spreads out (diffracts) from each slit, because the slits are narrow. These waves overlap and interfere constructively (bright lines) and destructively (dark regions). We can only see this if the light falls onto a screen and is scattered into our eyes. (b) Double slit interference pattern for water waves are nearly identical to that for light. Wave action is greatest in regions of constructive interference and least in regions of destructive interference. (c) When light that has passed through double slits falls on a screen, we see a pattern such as this. (credit: PASCO)

To understand the double slit interference pattern, we consider how two waves travel from the slits to the screen, as illustrated in Figure 27.13. Each slit is a different distance from a given point on the screen. Thus different numbers of wavelengths fit into each path. Waves start out from the slits in phase (crest to crest), but they may end up out of phase (crest to trough) at the screen if the paths differ in length by half a wavelength, interfering destructively as shown in Figure 27.13(a). If the paths differ by a whole wavelength, then the waves arrive in phase (crest to crest) at the screen, interfering constructively as shown in Figure 27.13(b). More generally, if the paths taken by the two waves differ by any half-integral number of wavelengths [$(1/2)\lambda$, $(3/2)\lambda$, $(5/2)\lambda$, etc.], then destructive interference occurs. Similarly, if the paths taken by the two waves differ by any integral number of wavelengths (λ, 2λ, 3λ, etc.), then constructive interference occurs.

TAKE-HOME EXPERIMENT: USING FINGERS AS SLITS

Look at a light, such as a street lamp or incandescent bulb, through the narrow gap between two fingers held close together. What type of pattern do you see? How does it change when you allow the fingers to move a little farther apart? Is it more distinct for a monochromatic source, such as the yellow light from a sodium vapor lamp, than for an incandescent bulb?

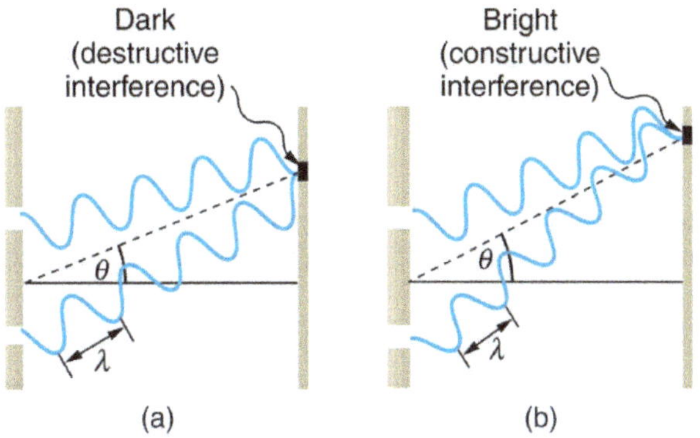

FIGURE 27.13 Waves follow different paths from the slits to a common point on a screen. (a) Destructive interference occurs here, because one path is a half wavelength longer than the other. The waves start in phase but arrive out of phase. (b) Constructive interference occurs here because one path is a whole wavelength longer than the other. The waves start out and arrive in phase.

Figure 27.14 shows how to determine the path length difference for waves traveling from two slits to a common point on a screen. If the screen is a large distance away compared with the distance between the slits, then the angle θ between the path and a line from the slits to the screen (see the figure) is nearly the same for each path. The difference between the paths is shown in the figure; simple trigonometry shows it to be $d \sin \theta$, where d is the distance between the slits. To obtain **constructive interference for a double slit**, the path length difference must be an integral multiple of the wavelength, or

$$d \sin \theta = m\lambda, \text{ for } m = 0, 1, -1, 2, -2, \ldots \text{ (constructive).} \tag{27.3}$$

Similarly, to obtain **destructive interference for a double slit**, the path length difference must be a half-integral multiple of the wavelength, or

$$d \sin \theta = \left(m + \frac{1}{2}\right)\lambda, \text{ for } m = 0, 1, -1, 2, -2, \ldots \text{ (destructive),} \tag{27.4}$$

where λ is the wavelength of the light, d is the distance between slits, and θ is the angle from the original direction of the beam as discussed above. We call m the **order** of the interference. For example, $m = 4$ is fourth-order interference.

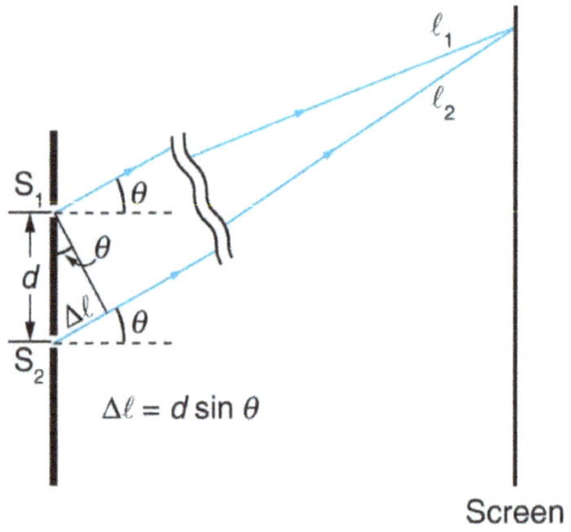

FIGURE 27.14 The paths from each slit to a common point on the screen differ by an amount $d\sin\theta$, assuming the distance to the screen is much greater than the distance between slits (not to scale here).

The equations for double slit interference imply that a series of bright and dark lines are formed. For vertical slits, the light spreads out horizontally on either side of the incident beam into a pattern called interference fringes, illustrated in Figure 27.15. The intensity of the bright fringes falls off on either side, being brightest at the center. The closer the slits are, the more is the spreading of the bright fringes. We can see this by examining the equation

$$d\ \sin\theta = m\lambda, \text{ for } m = 0, 1, \ -1, 2, \ -2, \ \dots . \qquad 27.5$$

For fixed λ and m, the smaller d is, the larger θ must be, since $\sin\theta = m\lambda/d$. This is consistent with our contention that wave effects are most noticeable when the object the wave encounters (here, slits a distance d apart) is small. Small d gives large θ, hence a large effect.

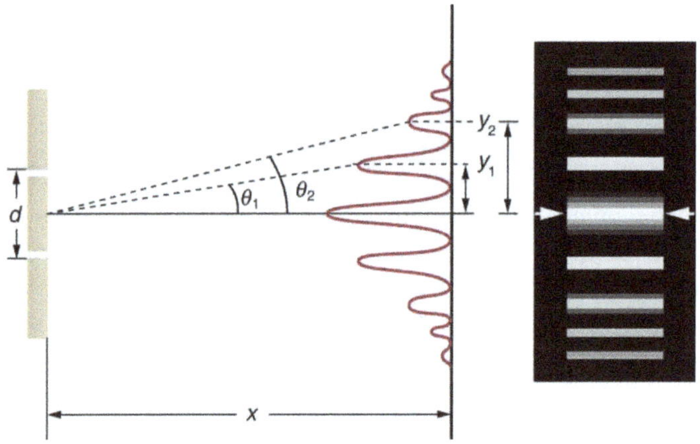

FIGURE 27.15 The interference pattern for a double slit has an intensity that falls off with angle. The photograph shows multiple bright and dark lines, or fringes, formed by light passing through a double slit.

EXAMPLE 27.1

Finding a Wavelength from an Interference Pattern

Suppose you pass light from a He-Ne laser through two slits separated by 0.0100 mm and find that the third bright line on a screen is formed at an angle of 10.95° relative to the incident beam. What is the wavelength of the light?

Strategy

The third bright line is due to third-order constructive interference, which means that $m = 3$. We are given $d = 0.0100\ \text{mm}$ and $\theta = 10.95^\circ$. The wavelength can thus be found using the equation $d\ \sin\theta = m\lambda$ for constructive interference.

Solution

The equation is $d\ \sin\theta = m\lambda$. Solving for the wavelength λ gives

$$\lambda = \frac{d \sin\theta}{m}. \tag{27.6}$$

Substituting known values yields

$$\begin{aligned} \lambda &= \frac{(0.0100 \text{ mm})(\sin 10.95^\circ)}{3} \\ &= 6.33 \times 10^{-4} \text{ mm} = 633 \text{ nm}. \end{aligned} \tag{27.7}$$

Discussion

To three digits, this is the wavelength of light emitted by the common He-Ne laser. Not by coincidence, this red color is similar to that emitted by neon lights. More important, however, is the fact that interference patterns can be used to measure wavelength. Young did this for visible wavelengths. This analytical technique is still widely used to measure electromagnetic spectra. For a given order, the angle for constructive interference increases with λ, so that spectra (measurements of intensity versus wavelength) can be obtained.

EXAMPLE 27.2

Calculating Highest Order Possible

Interference patterns do not have an infinite number of lines, since there is a limit to how big m can be. What is the highest-order constructive interference possible with the system described in the preceding example?

Strategy and Concept

The equation $d \sin\theta = m\lambda$ (for $m = 0, 1, -1, 2, -2, \ldots$) describes constructive interference. For fixed values of d and λ, the larger m is, the larger $\sin\theta$ is. However, the maximum value that $\sin\theta$ can have is 1, for an angle of 90°. (Larger angles imply that light goes backward and does not reach the screen at all.) Let us find which m corresponds to this maximum diffraction angle.

Solution

Solving the equation $d \sin\theta = m\lambda$ for m gives

$$m = \frac{d \sin\theta}{\lambda}. \tag{27.8}$$

Taking $\sin\theta = 1$ and substituting the values of d and λ from the preceding example gives

$$m = \frac{(0.0100 \text{ mm})(1)}{633 \text{ nm}} \approx 15.8. \tag{27.9}$$

Therefore, the largest integer m can be is 15, or

$$m = 15. \tag{27.10}$$

Discussion

The number of fringes depends on the wavelength and slit separation. The number of fringes will be very large for large slit separations. However, if the slit separation becomes much greater than the wavelength, the intensity of the interference pattern changes so that the screen has two bright lines cast by the slits, as expected when light behaves like a ray. We also note that the fringes get fainter further away from the center. Consequently, not all 15 fringes may be observable.

27.4 Multiple Slit Diffraction

LEARNING OBJECTIVES

By the end of this section, you will be able to:

- Discuss the pattern obtained from diffraction grating.
- Explain diffraction grating effects.

An interesting thing happens if you pass light through a large number of evenly spaced parallel slits, called a **diffraction grating**. An interference pattern is created that is very similar to the one formed by a double slit (see Figure 27.16). A diffraction grating can be manufactured by scratching glass with a sharp tool in a number of precisely positioned parallel lines, with the untouched regions acting like slits. These can be photographically mass produced rather cheaply. Diffraction gratings work both for transmission of light, as in Figure 27.16, and for reflection of light, as on butterfly wings and the Australian opal in Figure 27.17 or the CD pictured in the opening photograph of this chapter. In addition to their use as novelty items, diffraction gratings are commonly used for spectroscopic dispersion and analysis of light. What makes them particularly useful is the fact that they form a sharper pattern than double slits do. That is, their bright regions are narrower and brighter, while their dark regions are darker. Figure 27.18 shows idealized graphs demonstrating the sharper pattern. Natural diffraction gratings occur in the feathers of certain birds. Tiny, finger-like structures in regular patterns act as reflection gratings, producing constructive interference that gives the feathers colors not solely due to their pigmentation. This is called iridescence.

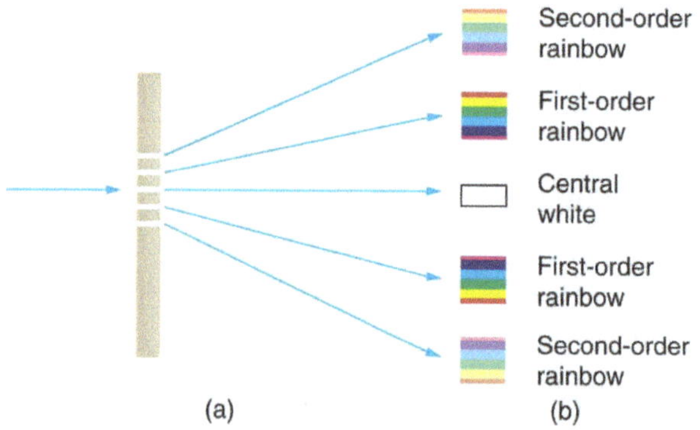

FIGURE 27.16 A diffraction grating is a large number of evenly spaced parallel slits. (a) Light passing through is diffracted in a pattern similar to a double slit, with bright regions at various angles. (b) The pattern obtained for white light incident on a grating. The central maximum is white, and the higher-order maxima disperse white light into a rainbow of colors.

FIGURE 27.17 (a) This Australian opal and (b) the butterfly wings have rows of reflectors that act like reflection gratings, reflecting different colors at different angles. (credits: (a) Opals-On-Black.com, via Flickr (b) whologwhy, Flickr)

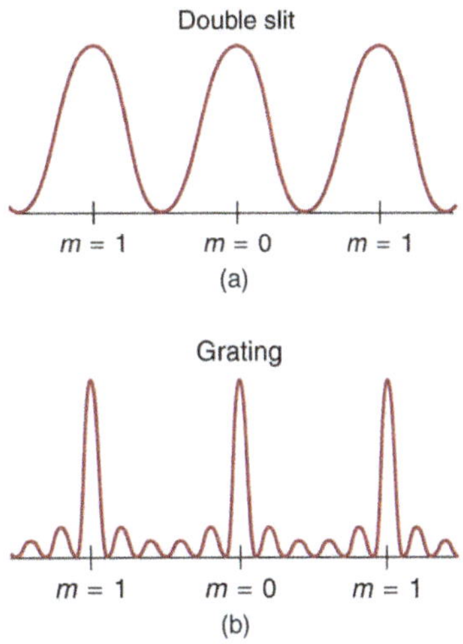

FIGURE 27.18 Idealized graphs of the intensity of light passing through a double slit (a) and a diffraction grating (b) for monochromatic light. Maxima can be produced at the same angles, but those for the diffraction grating are narrower and hence sharper. The maxima become narrower and the regions between darker as the number of slits is increased.

The analysis of a diffraction grating is very similar to that for a double slit (see Figure 27.19). As we know from our discussion of double slits in Young's Double Slit Experiment, light is diffracted by each slit and spreads out after passing through. Rays traveling in the same direction (at an angle θ relative to the incident direction) are shown in the figure. Each of these rays travels a different distance to a common point on a screen far away. The rays start in phase, and they can be in or out of phase when they reach a screen, depending on the difference in the path lengths traveled. As seen in the figure, each ray travels a distance $d \sin \theta$ different from that of its neighbor, where d is the distance between slits. If this distance equals an integral number of wavelengths, the rays all arrive in phase, and constructive interference (a maximum) is obtained. Thus, the condition necessary to obtain **constructive interference for a diffraction grating** is

$$d \sin \theta = m\lambda, \text{ for } m = 0, 1, -1, 2, -2, \ldots \text{ (constructive)}, \quad 27.11$$

where d is the distance between slits in the grating, λ is the wavelength of light, and m is the order of the maximum. Note that this is exactly the same equation as for double slits separated by d. However, the slits are usually closer in diffraction gratings than in double slits, producing fewer maxima at larger angles.

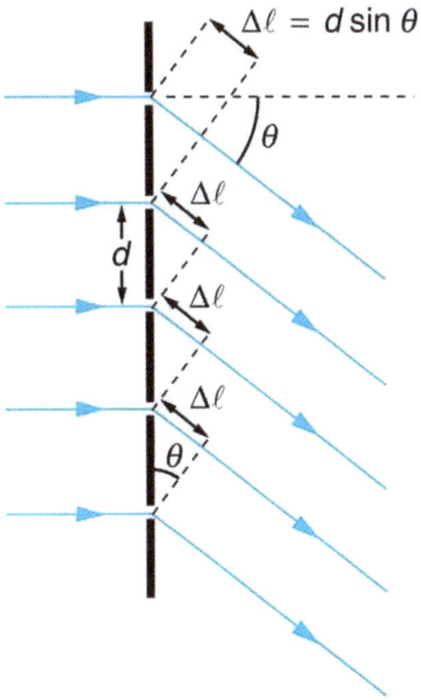

FIGURE 27.19 Diffraction grating showing light rays from each slit traveling in the same direction. Each ray travels a different distance to reach a common point on a screen (not shown). Each ray travels a distance $d \sin \theta$ different from that of its neighbor.

Where are diffraction gratings used? Diffraction gratings are key components of monochromators used, for example, in optical imaging of particular wavelengths from biological or medical samples. A diffraction grating can be chosen to specifically analyze a wavelength emitted by molecules in diseased cells in a biopsy sample or to help excite strategic molecules in the sample with a selected frequency of light. Another vital use is in optical fiber technologies where fibers are designed to provide optimum performance at specific wavelengths. A range of diffraction gratings are available for selecting specific wavelengths for such use.

TAKE-HOME EXPERIMENT: RAINBOWS ON A CD

The spacing d of the grooves in a CD or DVD can be well determined by using a laser and the equation $d\ \sin\theta = m\lambda,$ for $m = 0, 1, -1, 2, -2, \ldots$. However, we can still make a good estimate of this spacing by using white light and the rainbow of colors that comes from the interference. Reflect sunlight from a CD onto a wall and use your best judgment of the location of a strongly diffracted color to find the separation d.

EXAMPLE 27.3

Calculating Typical Diffraction Grating Effects

Diffraction gratings with 10,000 lines per centimeter are readily available. Suppose you have one, and you send a beam of white light through it to a screen 2.00 m away. (a) Find the angles for the first-order diffraction of the shortest and longest wavelengths of visible light (380 and 760 nm). (b) What is the distance between the ends of the rainbow of visible light produced on the screen for first-order interference? (See Figure 27.20.)

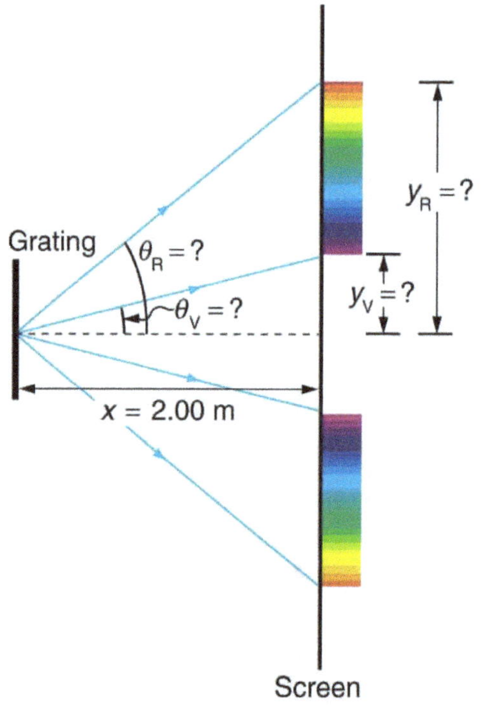

FIGURE 27.20 The diffraction grating considered in this example produces a rainbow of colors on a screen a distance $x = 2.00\,\text{m}$ from the grating. The distances along the screen are measured perpendicular to the x-direction. In other words, the rainbow pattern extends out of the page.

Strategy

The angles can be found using the equation

$$d\ \sin\theta = m\lambda\ (\text{for } m = 0, 1, -1, 2, -2, \ldots) \tag{27.12}$$

once a value for the slit spacing d has been determined. Since there are 10,000 lines per centimeter, each line is separated by $1/10{,}000$ of a centimeter. Once the angles are found, the distances along the screen can be found using simple trigonometry.

Solution for (a)

The distance between slits is $d = (1\text{ cm})/10{,}000 = 1.00 \times 10^{-4}\text{ cm}$ or $1.00 \times 10^{-6}\text{ m}$. Let us call the two angles θ_V for violet (380 nm) and θ_R for red (760 nm). Solving the equation $d \sin \theta_V = m\lambda$ for $\sin \theta_V$,

$$\sin \theta_V = \frac{m\lambda_V}{d}, \qquad 27.13$$

where $m = 1$ for first order and $\lambda_V = 380\text{ nm} = 3.80 \times 10^{-7}\text{ m}$. Substituting these values gives

$$\sin \theta_V = \frac{3.80 \times 10^{-7}\text{ m}}{1.00 \times 10^{-6}\text{ m}} = 0.380. \qquad 27.14$$

Thus the angle θ_V is

$$\theta_V = \sin^{-1} 0.380 = 22.33^\circ. \qquad 27.15$$

Similarly,

$$\sin \theta_R = \frac{7.60 \times 10^{-7}\text{ m}}{1.00 \times 10^{-6}\text{ m}}. \qquad 27.16$$

Thus the angle θ_R is

$$\theta_R = \sin^{-1} 0.760 = 49.46^\circ. \qquad 27.17$$

Notice that in both equations, we reported the results of these intermediate calculations to four significant figures to use with the calculation in part (b).

Solution for (b)

The distances on the screen are labeled y_V and y_R in Figure 27.20. Noting that $\tan \theta = y/x$, we can solve for y_V and y_R. That is,

$$y_V = x \tan \theta_V = (2.00\text{ m})(\tan 22.33^\circ) = 0.815\text{ m} \qquad 27.18$$

and

$$y_R = x \tan \theta_R = (2.00\text{ m})(\tan 49.46^\circ) = 2.338\text{ m}. \qquad 27.19$$

The distance between them is therefore

$$y_R - y_V = 1.52\text{ m}. \qquad 27.20$$

Discussion

The large distance between the red and violet ends of the rainbow produced from the white light indicates the potential this diffraction grating has as a spectroscopic tool. The more it can spread out the wavelengths (greater dispersion), the more detail can be seen in a spectrum. This depends on the quality of the diffraction grating—it must be very precisely made in addition to having closely spaced lines.

27.5 Single Slit Diffraction

LEARNING OBJECTIVES

By the end of this section, you will be able to:

- Discuss the single slit diffraction pattern.

Light passing through a single slit forms a diffraction pattern somewhat different from those formed by double slits or diffraction gratings. Figure 27.21 shows a single slit diffraction pattern. Note that the central maximum is larger than those on either side, and that the intensity decreases rapidly on either side. In contrast, a diffraction grating produces evenly spaced lines that dim slowly on either side of center.

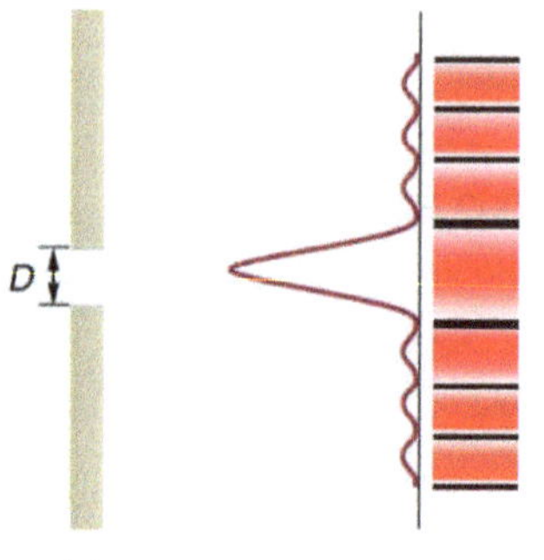

FIGURE 27.21 (a) Single slit diffraction pattern. Monochromatic light passing through a single slit has a central maximum and many smaller and dimmer maxima on either side. The central maximum is six times higher than shown. (b) The drawing shows the bright central maximum and dimmer and thinner maxima on either side.

The analysis of single slit diffraction is illustrated in Figure 27.22. Here we consider light coming from different parts of the *same* slit. According to Huygens's principle, every part of the wavefront in the slit emits wavelets. These are like rays that start out in phase and head in all directions. (Each ray is perpendicular to the wavefront of a wavelet.) Assuming the screen is very far away compared with the size of the slit, rays heading toward a common destination are nearly parallel. When they travel straight ahead, as in Figure 27.22(a), they remain in phase, and a central maximum is obtained. However, when rays travel at an angle θ relative to the original direction of the beam, each travels a different distance to a common location, and they can arrive in or out of phase. In Figure 27.22(b), the ray from the bottom travels a distance of one wavelength λ farther than the ray from the top. Thus a ray from the center travels a distance $\lambda/2$ farther than the one on the left, arrives out of phase, and interferes destructively. A ray from slightly above the center and one from slightly above the bottom will also cancel one another. In fact, each ray from the slit will have another to interfere destructively, and a minimum in intensity will occur at this angle. There will be another minimum at the same angle to the right of the incident direction of the light.

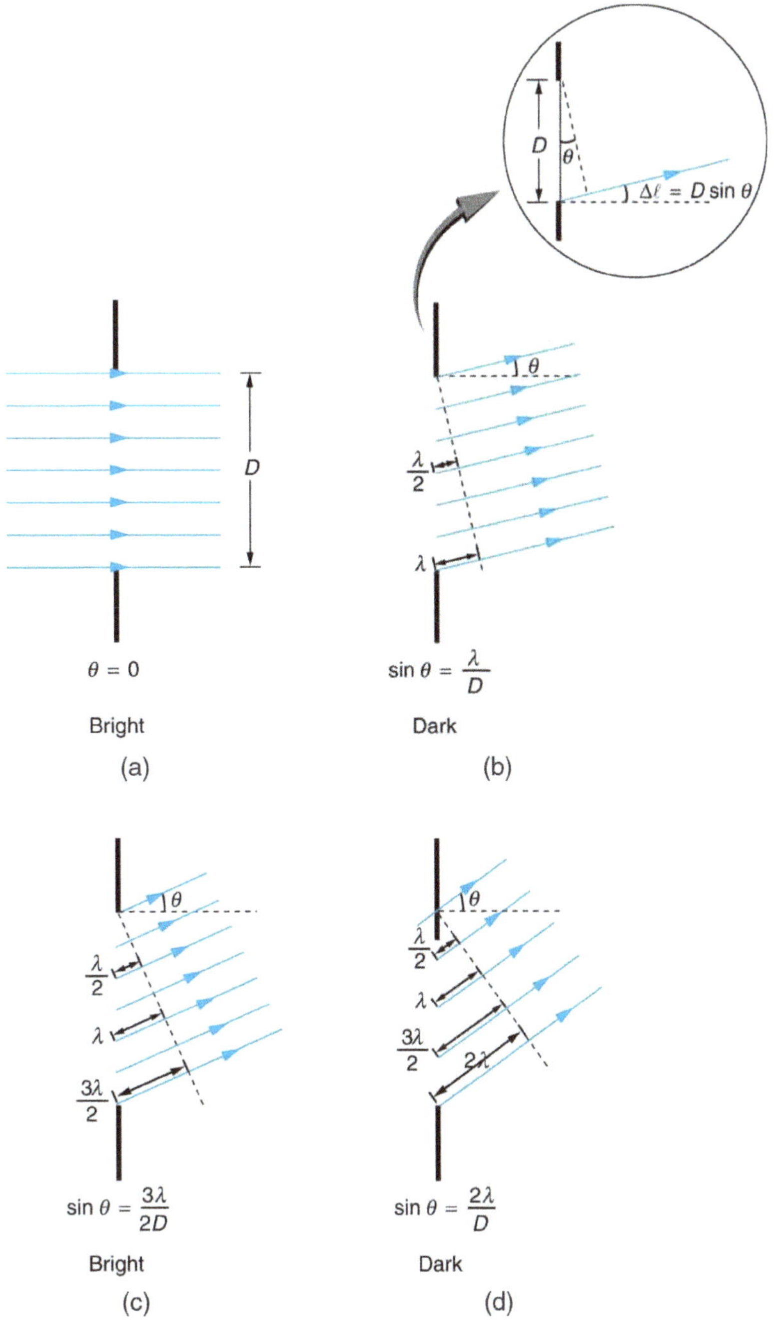

FIGURE 27.22 Light passing through a single slit is diffracted in all directions and may interfere constructively or destructively, depending on the angle. The difference in path length for rays from either side of the slit is seen to be $D \sin \theta$.

At the larger angle shown in Figure 27.22(c), the path lengths differ by $3\lambda/2$ for rays from the top and bottom of the slit. One ray travels a distance λ different from the ray from the bottom and arrives in phase, interfering constructively. Two rays, each from slightly above those two, will also add constructively. Most rays from the slit will have another to interfere with constructively, and a maximum in intensity will occur at this angle. However, all rays do not interfere constructively for this situation, and so the maximum is not as intense as the central maximum. Finally, in Figure 27.22(d), the angle shown is large enough to produce a second minimum. As seen in the figure, the difference in path length for rays from either side of the slit is $D \sin \theta$, and we see that a destructive minimum is obtained when this distance is an integral multiple of the wavelength.

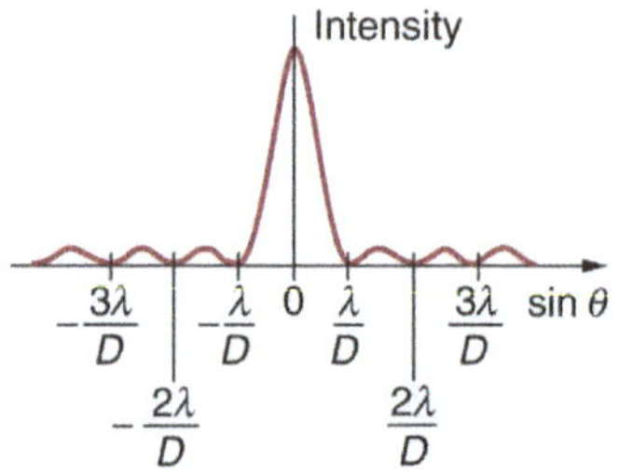

FIGURE 27.23 A graph of single slit diffraction intensity showing the central maximum to be wider and much more intense than those to the sides. In fact the central maximum is six times higher than shown here.

Thus, to obtain **destructive interference for a single slit**,

$$D \sin \theta = m\lambda, \text{ for } m = 1, -1, 2, -2, 3, \dots \text{ (destructive)}, \quad 27.21$$

where D is the slit width, λ is the light's wavelength, θ is the angle relative to the original direction of the light, and m is the order of the minimum. Figure 27.23 shows a graph of intensity for single slit interference, and it is apparent that the maxima on either side of the central maximum are much less intense and not as wide. This is consistent with the illustration in Figure 27.21(b).

EXAMPLE 27.4

Calculating Single Slit Diffraction

Visible light of wavelength 550 nm falls on a single slit and produces its second diffraction minimum at an angle of 45.0° relative to the incident direction of the light. (a) What is the width of the slit? (b) At what angle is the first minimum produced?

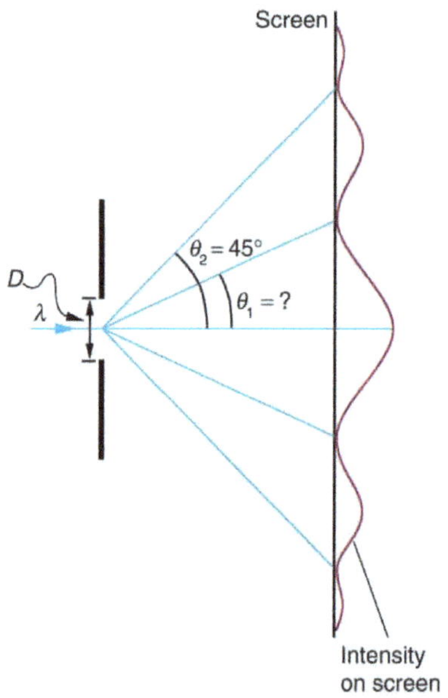

FIGURE 27.24 A graph of the single slit diffraction pattern is analyzed in this example.

Strategy

From the given information, and assuming the screen is far away from the slit, we can use the equation $D \sin \theta = m\lambda$ first to find D, and again to find the angle for the first minimum θ_1.

Solution for (a)

We are given that $\lambda = 550\text{ nm}$, $m = 2$, and $\theta_2 = 45.0^\circ$. Solving the equation $D \sin \theta = m\lambda$ for D and substituting known values gives

$$\begin{aligned} D &= \frac{m\lambda}{\sin\theta_2} = \frac{2(550 \text{ nm})}{\sin 45.0^\circ} \\ &= \frac{1100\times10^{-9}}{0.707} \\ &= 1.56\times10^{-6}. \end{aligned} \quad (27.22)$$

Solution for (b)

Solving the equation $D \sin\theta = m\lambda$ for $\sin\theta_1$ and substituting the known values gives

$$\sin\theta_1 = \frac{m\lambda}{D} = \frac{1\left(550\times10^{-9}\text{ m}\right)}{1.56\times10^{-6}\text{ m}}. \quad (27.23)$$

Thus the angle θ_1 is

$$\theta_1 = \sin^{-1} 0.354 = 20.7^\circ. \quad (27.24)$$

Discussion

We see that the slit is narrow (it is only a few times greater than the wavelength of light). This is consistent with the fact that light must interact with an object comparable in size to its wavelength in order to exhibit significant wave effects such as this single slit diffraction pattern. We also see that the central maximum extends 20.7° on either side of the original beam, for a width of about 41°. The angle between the first and second minima is only about 24° $(45.0^\circ - 20.7^\circ)$. Thus the second maximum is only about half as wide as the central maximum.

27.6 Limits of Resolution: The Rayleigh Criterion

LEARNING OBJECTIVES

By the end of this section, you will be able to:

- Discuss the Rayleigh criterion.

Light diffracts as it moves through space, bending around obstacles, interfering constructively and destructively. While this can be used as a spectroscopic tool—a diffraction grating disperses light according to wavelength, for example, and is used to produce spectra—diffraction also limits the detail we can obtain in images. Figure 27.25(a) shows the effect of passing light through a small circular aperture. Instead of a bright spot with sharp edges, a spot with a fuzzy edge surrounded by circles of light is obtained. This pattern is caused by diffraction similar to that produced by a single slit. Light from different parts of the circular aperture interferes constructively and destructively. The effect is most noticeable when the aperture is small, but the effect is there for large apertures, too.

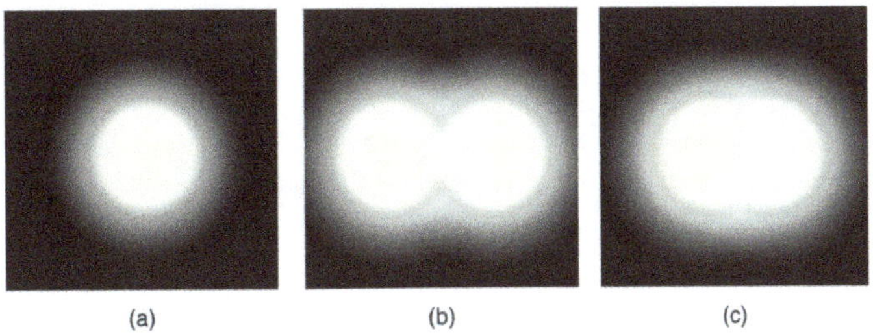

FIGURE 27.25 (a) Monochromatic light passed through a small circular aperture produces this diffraction pattern. (b) Two point light sources that are close to one another produce overlapping images because of diffraction. (c) If they are closer together, they cannot be resolved or distinguished.

How does diffraction affect the detail that can be observed when light passes through an aperture? Figure 27.25(b) shows the diffraction pattern produced by two point light sources that are close to one another. The pattern is similar to that for a single point source, and it is just barely possible to tell that there are two light sources rather than one. If they were closer together, as in Figure 27.25(c), we could not distinguish them, thus limiting the detail or resolution we can obtain. This limit is an inescapable consequence of the wave nature of light.

There are many situations in which diffraction limits the resolution. The acuity of our vision is limited because light passes through the pupil, the circular aperture of our eye. Be aware that the diffraction-like spreading of light is due to the limited diameter of a light beam, not the interaction with an aperture. Thus light passing through a lens with a diameter D shows this effect and spreads, blurring the image, just as light passing through an aperture of diameter D does. So diffraction limits the resolution of any system having a lens or mirror. Telescopes are also limited by diffraction, because of the finite diameter D of their primary mirror.

TAKE-HOME EXPERIMENT: RESOLUTION OF THE EYE

Draw two lines on a white sheet of paper (several mm apart). How far away can you be and still distinguish the two lines? What does this tell you about the size of the eye's pupil? Can you be quantitative? (The size of an adult's pupil is discussed in Physics of the Eye.)

Just what is the limit? To answer that question, consider the diffraction pattern for a circular aperture, which has a central maximum that is wider and brighter than the maxima surrounding it (similar to a slit) [see Figure 27.26(a)]. It can be shown that, for a circular aperture of diameter D, the first minimum in the diffraction pattern occurs at $\theta = 1.22\ \lambda/D$ (providing the aperture is large compared with the wavelength of light, which is the case for most optical instruments). The accepted criterion for determining the diffraction limit to resolution based on this angle was developed by Lord Rayleigh in the 19th century. The **Rayleigh criterion** for the diffraction limit to resolution states that *two images are just resolvable when the center of the diffraction pattern of one is directly over the first minimum of the diffraction pattern of the other.* See Figure 27.26(b). The first minimum is at an angle of $\theta = 1.22\ \lambda/D$, so that two point objects are just resolvable if they are separated by the angle

$$\theta = 1.22\frac{\lambda}{D}, \tag{27.25}$$

where λ is the wavelength of light (or other electromagnetic radiation) and D is the diameter of the aperture, lens, mirror, etc., with which the two objects are observed. In this expression, θ has units of radians.

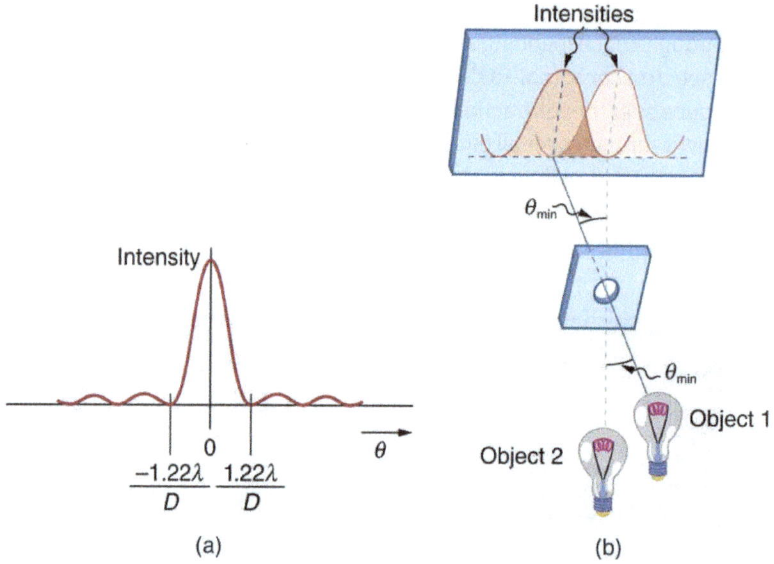

FIGURE 27.26 (a) Graph of intensity of the diffraction pattern for a circular aperture. Note that, similar to a single slit, the central maximum is wider and brighter than those to the sides. (b) Two point objects produce overlapping diffraction patterns. Shown here is the Rayleigh criterion for being just resolvable. The central maximum of one pattern lies on the first minimum of the other.

CONNECTIONS: LIMITS TO KNOWLEDGE

All attempts to observe the size and shape of objects are limited by the wavelength of the probe. Even the small wavelength of light prohibits exact precision. When extremely small wavelength probes as with an electron microscope are used, the system is disturbed, still limiting our knowledge, much as making an electrical measurement alters a circuit. Heisenberg's uncertainty principle asserts that this limit is fundamental and inescapable, as we shall see in quantum mechanics.

EXAMPLE 27.5

Calculating Diffraction Limits of the Hubble Space Telescope

The primary mirror of the orbiting Hubble Space Telescope has a diameter of 2.40 m. Being in orbit, this telescope avoids the degrading effects of atmospheric distortion on its resolution. (a) What is the angle between two just-resolvable point light sources (perhaps two stars)? Assume an average light wavelength of 550 nm. (b) If these two stars are at the 2 million light year distance of the Andromeda galaxy, how close together can they be and still be resolved? (A light year, or ly, is the distance light travels in 1 year.)

Strategy

The Rayleigh criterion stated in the equation $\theta = 1.22\frac{\lambda}{D}$ gives the smallest possible angle θ between point sources, or the best obtainable resolution. Once this angle is found, the distance between stars can be calculated, since we are given how far away they are.

Solution for (a)

The Rayleigh criterion for the minimum resolvable angle is

$$\theta = 1.22\frac{\lambda}{D}. \qquad \text{27.26}$$

Entering known values gives

$$\begin{aligned} \theta &= 1.22\frac{550\times10^{-9}\text{ m}}{2.40\text{ m}} \\ &= 2.80\times10^{-7}\text{ rad.} \end{aligned} \qquad \text{27.27}$$

Solution for (b)

The distance s between two objects a distance r away and separated by an angle θ is $s = r\theta$.

Substituting known values gives

$$\begin{aligned} s &= (2.0\times10^{6}\text{ ly})(2.80\times10^{-7}\text{ rad}) \\ &= 0.56\text{ ly.} \end{aligned} \qquad \text{27.28}$$

Discussion

The angle found in part (a) is extraordinarily small (less than 1/50,000 of a degree), because the primary mirror is so large compared with the wavelength of light. As noticed, diffraction effects are most noticeable when light interacts with objects having sizes on the order of the wavelength of light. However, the effect is still there, and there is a diffraction limit to what is observable. The actual resolution of the Hubble Telescope is not quite as good as that found here. As with all instruments, there are other effects, such as non-uniformities in mirrors or aberrations in lenses that further limit resolution. However, Figure 27.27 gives an indication of the extent of the detail observable with the Hubble because of its size and quality and especially because it is above the Earth's atmosphere.

(a) (b)

FIGURE 27.27 These two photographs of the M82 galaxy give an idea of the observable detail using the Hubble Space Telescope compared with that using a ground-based telescope. (a) On the left is a ground-based image. (credit: Ricnun, Wikimedia Commons) (b) The photo on the right was captured by Hubble. (credit: NASA, ESA, and the Hubble Heritage Team (STScI/AURA))

The answer in part (b) indicates that two stars separated by about half a light year can be resolved. The average distance between stars in a galaxy is on the order of 5 light years in the outer parts and about 1 light year near the galactic center. Therefore, the Hubble can resolve most of the individual stars in Andromeda galaxy, even though it lies at such a huge distance that its light takes 2 million years for its light to reach us. Figure 27.28 shows another mirror used to observe radio waves from outer space.

FIGURE 27.28 A 305-m-diameter natural bowl at Arecibo in Puerto Rico is lined with reflective material, making it into a radio telescope. It is the largest curved focusing dish in the world. Although D for Arecibo is much larger than for the Hubble Telescope, it detects much longer wavelength radiation and its diffraction limit is significantly poorer than Hubble's. Arecibo is still very useful, because important information is carried by radio waves that is not carried by visible light. (credit: Tatyana Temirbulatova, Flickr)

Diffraction is not only a problem for optical instruments but also for the electromagnetic radiation itself. Any beam of light having a finite diameter D and a wavelength λ exhibits diffraction spreading. The beam spreads out with an angle θ given by the equation $\theta = 1.22\frac{\lambda}{D}$. Take, for example, a laser beam made of rays as parallel as possible (angles between rays as close to $\theta = 0^\circ$ as possible) instead spreads out at an angle $\theta = 1.22\ \lambda/D$, where D is the diameter of the beam and λ is its wavelength. This spreading is impossible to observe for a flashlight, because its beam is not very parallel to start with. However, for long-distance transmission of laser beams or microwave signals, diffraction spreading can be significant (see Figure 27.29). To avoid this, we can increase D. This is done for laser light sent to the Moon to measure its distance from the Earth. The laser beam is expanded through a telescope to make D much larger and θ smaller.

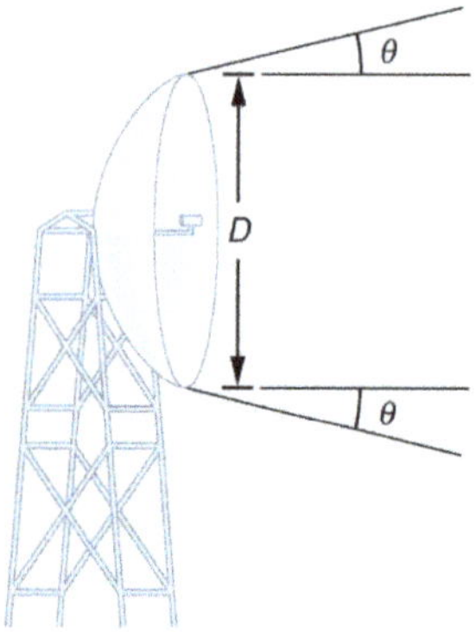

FIGURE 27.29 The beam produced by this microwave transmission antenna will spread out at a minimum angle $\theta = 1.22\ \lambda/D$ due to diffraction. It is impossible to produce a near-parallel beam, because the beam has a limited diameter.

In most biology laboratories, resolution is presented when the use of the microscope is introduced. The ability of a lens to produce sharp images of two closely spaced point objects is called resolution. The smaller the distance x by which two objects can be separated and still be seen as distinct, the greater the resolution. The resolving power of a lens is defined as that distance x. An expression for resolving power is obtained from the Rayleigh criterion. In Figure 27.30(a) we have two point objects separated by a distance x. According to the Rayleigh criterion, resolution is possible when the minimum angular separation is

$$\theta = 1.22\frac{\lambda}{D} = \frac{x}{d}, \tag{27.29}$$

where d is the distance between the specimen and the objective lens, and we have used the small angle approximation (i.e., we have assumed that x is much smaller than d), so that $\tan\theta \approx \sin\theta \approx \theta$.

Therefore, the resolving power is

$$x = 1.22\frac{\lambda d}{D}. \quad 27.30$$

Another way to look at this is by re-examining the concept of Numerical Aperture (NA) discussed in Microscopes. There, NA is a measure of the maximum acceptance angle at which the fiber will take light and still contain it within the fiber. Figure 27.30(b) shows a lens and an object at point P. The NA here is a measure of the ability of the lens to gather light and resolve fine detail. The angle subtended by the lens at its focus is defined to be $\theta = 2\alpha$. From the figure and again using the small angle approximation, we can write

$$\sin\alpha = \frac{D/2}{d} = \frac{D}{2d}. \quad 27.31$$

The NA for a lens is $NA = n\sin\alpha$, where n is the index of refraction of the medium between the objective lens and the object at point P.

From this definition for NA, we can see that

$$x = 1.22\frac{\lambda d}{D} = 1.22\frac{\lambda}{2\sin\alpha} = 0.61\frac{\lambda n}{NA}. \quad 27.32$$

In a microscope, NA is important because it relates to the resolving power of a lens. A lens with a large NA will be able to resolve finer details. Lenses with larger NA will also be able to collect more light and so give a brighter image. Another way to describe this situation is that the larger the NA, the larger the cone of light that can be brought into the lens, and so more of the diffraction modes will be collected. Thus the microscope has more information to form a clear image, and so its resolving power will be higher.

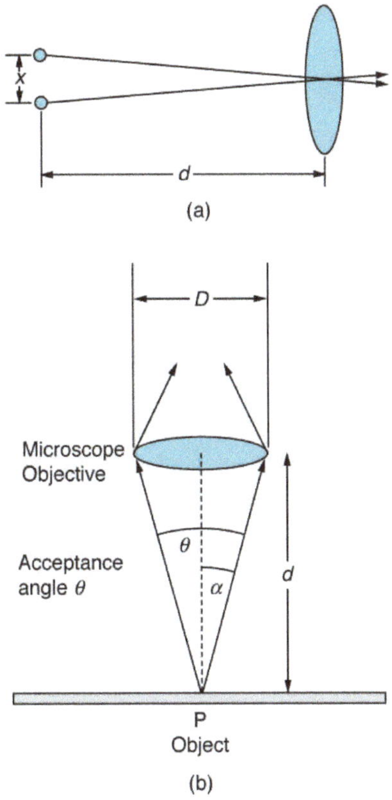

FIGURE 27.30 (a) Two points separated by at distance x and a positioned a distance d away from the objective. (credit: Infopro, Wikimedia Commons) (b) Terms and symbols used in discussion of resolving power for a lens and an object at point P. (credit: Infopro, Wikimedia Commons)

One of the consequences of diffraction is that the focal point of a beam has a finite width and intensity distribution. Consider focusing when only considering geometric optics, shown in Figure 27.31(a). The focal point is infinitely small with a huge intensity and the capacity to incinerate most samples irrespective of the NA of the objective lens. For wave optics, due to diffraction, the focal point spreads to become a focal spot (see Figure 27.31(b)) with the size of the spot decreasing with increasing NA. Consequently, the intensity in the focal spot increases with increasing NA. The higher the NA, the greater the chances of photodegrading the specimen. However, the spot never becomes a true point.

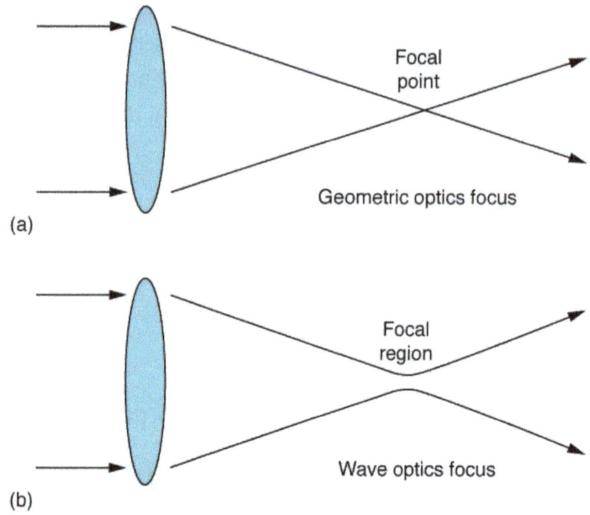

FIGURE 27.31 (a) In geometric optics, the focus is a point, but it is not physically possible to produce such a point because it implies infinite intensity. (b) In wave optics, the focus is an extended region.

27.7 Thin Film Interference

LEARNING OBJECTIVES

By the end of this section, you will be able to:

- Discuss the rainbow formation by thin films.

The bright colors seen in an oil slick floating on water or in a sunlit soap bubble are caused by interference. The brightest colors are those that interfere constructively. This interference is between light reflected from different surfaces of a thin film; thus, the effect is known as **thin film interference**. As noticed before, interference effects are most prominent when light interacts with something having a size similar to its wavelength. A thin film is one having a thickness t smaller than a few times the wavelength of light, λ. Since color is associated indirectly with λ and since all interference depends in some way on the ratio of λ to the size of the object involved, we should expect to see different colors for different thicknesses of a film, as in Figure 27.32. Some of the earliest measurements of such films and their effects were conducted by Agnes Pockels, a self-taught German chemist who investigated the characteristics of soapy and greasy films in water. Using homemade materials, Pockels developed a trough for measuring surface films and began conducting experiments. While scientific and societal barriers for women prevented her from publishing on her own, renowned scientist Lord Rayleigh supported her efforts and pushed for her work to be shared in the journal *Nature*. The trough Pockels invented became the basis for the contemporary version, as described below.

FIGURE 27.32 These soap bubbles exhibit brilliant colors when exposed to sunlight. (credit: Scott Robinson, Flickr)

What causes thin film interference? Figure 27.33 shows how light reflected from the top and bottom surfaces of a film can interfere. Incident light is only partially reflected from the top surface of the film (ray 1). The remainder enters the film and is itself partially reflected from the bottom surface. Part of the light reflected from the bottom surface can emerge from the top of the film (ray 2) and interfere with light reflected from the top (ray 1). Since the ray that enters the film travels a greater distance, it may be in or out of phase with the ray reflected from the top. However, consider for a moment, again, the bubbles in Figure 27.32. The bubbles are darkest where they are thinnest. Furthermore, if you observe a soap bubble carefully, you will note it gets dark at the point where it breaks. For very thin films, the difference in path lengths of ray 1 and ray 2 in Figure 27.33 is negligible; so why should they interfere destructively and not constructively? The answer is that a phase change can occur upon reflection. The rule is as follows:

When light reflects from a medium having an index of refraction greater than that of the medium in which it is traveling, a 180° phase change (or a $\lambda/2$ shift) occurs.

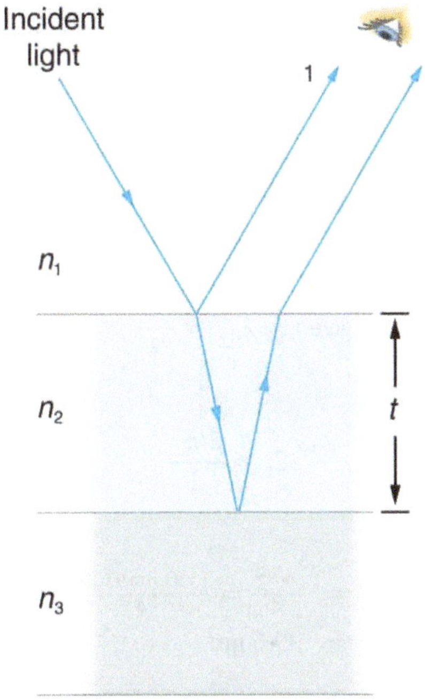

FIGURE 27.33 Light striking a thin film is partially reflected (ray 1) and partially refracted at the top surface. The refracted ray is partially reflected at the bottom surface and emerges as ray 2. These rays will interfere in a way that depends on the thickness of the film and the indices of refraction of the various media.

If the film in Figure 27.33 is a soap bubble (essentially water with air on both sides), then there is a $\lambda/2$ shift for ray 1 and none for ray 2. Thus, when the film is very thin, the path length difference between the two rays is negligible, they are exactly out of phase, and destructive interference will occur at all wavelengths and so the soap bubble will be dark here.

The thickness of the film relative to the wavelength of light is the other crucial factor in thin film interference. Ray 2 in Figure 27.33 travels a greater distance than ray 1. For light incident perpendicular to the surface, ray 2 travels a distance approximately $2t$ farther than ray 1. When this distance is an integral or half-integral multiple of the wavelength in the medium ($\lambda_n = \lambda/n$, where λ is the wavelength in vacuum and n is the index of refraction), constructive or destructive interference occurs, depending also on whether there is a phase change in either ray.

Thin-film interference has created an entire field of research and industrial applications. Its foundations were laid by Irving Langmuir and Katharine Burr Blodgett, working at General Electric in the 1920s and 1930s. Langmuir had pioneered a method for producing ultra-thin layers on materials. Blodgett built on these practices by creating a method to precisely stack and compress these layers in order to produce a film of a desired thickness and quality. The device they developed became known as the Langmuir-Blodgett trough, built from principles developed by Agnes Pockels and still used in laboratories today. The earliest widely applied use of these principles was non-reflective glass, which Blodgett patented in 1938 and which was used almost immediately in the making of the film *Gone With the Wind*. The film is viewed as a tremendous leap in cinematography; cameras, microscopes, telescopes, and many other instruments rely on Blodgett's invention as well.

EXAMPLE 27.6

Calculating Non-reflective Lens Coating Using Thin Film Interference

Sophisticated cameras use a series of several lenses. Light can reflect from the surfaces of these various lenses and degrade image clarity. To limit these reflections, lenses are coated with a thin layer of magnesium fluoride that causes destructive thin film interference. What is the thinnest this film can be, if its index of refraction is 1.38 and it is designed to limit the reflection of 550-nm light, normally the most intense visible wavelength? The index of refraction of glass is 1.52.

Strategy

Refer to Figure 27.33 and use $n_1 = 1.00$ for air, $n_2 = 1.38$, and $n_3 = 1.52$. Both ray 1 and ray 2 will have a $\lambda/2$ shift upon reflection. Thus, to obtain destructive interference, ray 2 will need to travel a half wavelength farther than ray 1. For rays incident perpendicularly, the path length difference is $2t$.

Solution

To obtain destructive interference here,

$$2t = \frac{\lambda_{n_2}}{2}, \qquad 27.33$$

where λ_{n_2} is the wavelength in the film and is given by $\lambda_{n_2} = \frac{\lambda}{n_2}$.

Thus,

$$2t = \frac{\lambda/n_2}{2}. \qquad 27.34$$

Solving for t and entering known values yields

$$\begin{aligned} t &= \frac{\lambda/n_2}{4} = \frac{(550\text{ nm})/1.38}{4} \\ &= 99.6\text{ nm}. \end{aligned} \qquad 27.35$$

Discussion

Films such as the one in this example are most effective in producing destructive interference when the thinnest layer is used, since light over a broader range of incident angles will be reduced in intensity. These films are called non-reflective coatings; this is only an approximately correct description, though, since other wavelengths will only be partially cancelled. Non-reflective coatings are used in car windows and sunglasses.

Thin film interference is most constructive or most destructive when the path length difference for the two rays is an integral or half-integral wavelength, respectively. That is, for rays incident perpendicularly, $2t = \lambda_n, 2\lambda_n, 3\lambda_n, \ldots$ or $2t = \lambda_n/2, 3\lambda_n/2, 5\lambda_n/2, \ldots$. To know whether interference is constructive or destructive, you must also determine if there is a phase change upon reflection. Thin film interference thus depends on film thickness, the wavelength of light, and the refractive indices. For white light incident on a film that varies in thickness, you will observe rainbow colors of constructive interference for various wavelengths as the thickness varies.

EXAMPLE 27.7

Soap Bubbles: More Than One Thickness can be Constructive

(a) What are the three smallest thicknesses of a soap bubble that produce constructive interference for red light with a wavelength of 650 nm? The index of refraction of soap is taken to be the same as that of water. (b) What three smallest thicknesses will give destructive interference?

Strategy and Concept

Use Figure 27.33 to visualize the bubble. Note that $n_1 = n_3 = 1.00$ for air, and $n_2 = 1.333$ for soap (equivalent to water). There is a $\lambda/2$ shift for ray 1 reflected from the top surface of the bubble, and no shift for ray 2 reflected from the bottom surface. To get constructive interference, then, the path length difference ($2t$) must be a half-integral multiple of the wavelength—the first three being $\lambda_n/2$, $3\lambda_n/2$, and $5\lambda_n/2$. To get destructive interference, the path length difference must be an integral multiple of the wavelength—the first three being 0, λ_n, and $2\lambda_n$.

Solution for (a)

Constructive interference occurs here when

$$2t_c = \frac{\lambda_n}{2}, \frac{3\lambda_n}{2}, \frac{5\lambda_n}{2}, \ldots. \quad 27.36$$

The smallest constructive thickness t_c thus is

$$\begin{aligned} t_c &= \frac{\lambda_n}{4} = \frac{\lambda/n}{4} = \frac{(650 \text{ nm})/1.333}{4} \\ &= 122 \text{ nm}. \end{aligned} \quad 27.37$$

The next thickness that gives constructive interference is $t'_c = 3\lambda_n/4$, so that

$$t'_c = 366 \text{ nm}. \quad 27.38$$

Finally, the third thickness producing constructive interference is $t''_c \leq 5\lambda_n/4$, so that

$$t''_c = 610 \text{ nm}. \quad 27.39$$

Solution for (b)

For *destructive interference*, the path length difference here is an integral multiple of the wavelength. The first occurs for zero thickness, since there is a phase change at the top surface. That is,

$$t_d = 0. \quad 27.40$$

The first non-zero thickness producing destructive interference is

$$2t'_d = \lambda_n. \quad 27.41$$

Substituting known values gives

$$\begin{aligned} t'_d &= \frac{\lambda_n}{2} = \frac{\lambda/n}{2} = \frac{(650 \text{ nm})/1.333}{2} \\ &= 244 \text{ nm}. \end{aligned} \quad 27.42$$

Finally, the third destructive thickness is $2t''_d = 2\lambda_n$, so that

$$\begin{aligned} t''_d &= \lambda_n = \frac{\lambda}{n} = \frac{650 \text{ nm}}{1.333} \\ &= 488 \text{ nm}. \end{aligned} \quad 27.43$$

Discussion

If the bubble was illuminated with pure red light, we would see bright and dark bands at very uniform increases in thickness. First would be a dark band at 0 thickness, then bright at 122 nm thickness, then dark at 244 nm, bright at 366 nm, dark at 488 nm, and bright at 610 nm. If the bubble varied smoothly in thickness, like a smooth wedge, then the bands would be evenly spaced.

Another example of thin film interference can be seen when microscope slides are separated (see Figure 27.34). The slides are very flat, so that the wedge of air between them increases in thickness very uniformly. A phase change occurs at the second surface but not the first, and so there is a dark band where the slides touch. The rainbow colors of constructive interference repeat, going from violet to red again and again as the distance between the slides increases. As the layer of air increases, the bands become more difficult to see, because slight changes in incident angle have greater effects on path length differences. If pure-wavelength light instead of white light is used, then bright and dark bands are obtained rather than repeating rainbow colors.

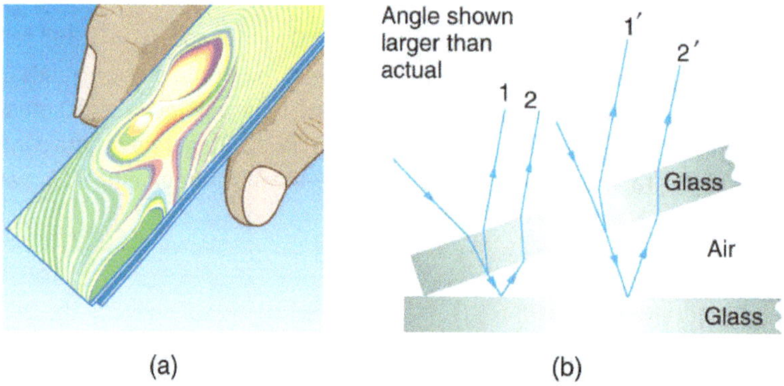

FIGURE 27.34 (a) The rainbow color bands are produced by thin film interference in the air between the two glass slides. (b) Schematic of the paths taken by rays in the wedge of air between the slides.

An important application of thin film interference is found in the manufacturing of optical instruments. A lens or mirror can be compared with a master as it is being ground, allowing it to be shaped to an accuracy of less than a wavelength over its entire surface. Figure 27.35 illustrates the phenomenon called Newton's rings, which occurs when the plane surfaces of two lenses are placed together. (The circular bands are called Newton's rings because Isaac Newton described them and their use in detail. Newton did not discover them; Robert Hooke did, and Newton did not believe they were due to the wave character of light.) Each successive ring of a given color indicates an increase of only one wavelength in the distance between the lens and the blank, so that great precision can be obtained. Once the lens is perfect, there will be no rings.

FIGURE 27.35 "Newton's rings" interference fringes are produced when two plano-convex lenses are placed together with their plane surfaces in contact. The rings are created by interference between the light reflected off the two surfaces as a result of a slight gap between them, indicating that these surfaces are not precisely plane but are slightly convex. (credit: Ulf Seifert, Wikimedia Commons)

The wings of certain moths and butterflies have nearly iridescent colors due to thin film interference. In addition to pigmentation, the wing's color is affected greatly by constructive interference of certain wavelengths reflected from its film-coated surface. Car manufacturers are offering special paint jobs that use thin film interference to produce colors that change with angle. This expensive option is based on variation of thin film path length differences with angle. Security features on credit cards, banknotes, driving licenses and similar items prone to forgery use thin film interference, diffraction gratings, or holograms. Australia led the way with dollar bills printed on polymer with a diffraction grating security feature making the currency difficult to forge. Other countries such as New Zealand and Taiwan are using similar technologies, while the United States currency includes a thin film interference effect.

MAKING CONNECTIONS: TAKE-HOME EXPERIMENT—THIN FILM INTERFERENCE

One feature of thin film interference and diffraction gratings is that the pattern shifts as you change the angle at which you look or move your head. Find examples of thin film interference and gratings around you. Explain how the patterns change for each specific example. Find examples where the thickness changes giving rise to changing colors. If you can find two microscope slides, then try observing the effect shown in Figure 27.34. Try separating one end of the two slides with a hair or maybe a thin piece of paper and observe the effect.

Problem-Solving Strategies for Wave Optics

Step 1. *Examine the situation to determine that interference is involved.* Identify whether slits or thin film interference are considered in the problem.

Step 2. *If slits are involved,* note that diffraction gratings and double slits produce very similar interference patterns, but that gratings have narrower (sharper) maxima. Single slit patterns are characterized by a large central maximum and smaller maxima to the sides.

Step 3. *If thin film interference is involved, take note of the path length difference between the two rays that interfere.* Be certain to use the wavelength in the medium involved, since it differs from the wavelength in vacuum. Note also that there is an additional $\lambda/2$ phase shift when light reflects from a medium with a greater index of refraction.

Step 4. *Identify exactly what needs to be determined in the problem (identify the unknowns).* A written list is useful. Draw a diagram of the situation. Labeling the diagram is useful.

Step 5. *Make a list of what is given or can be inferred from the problem as stated (identify the knowns).*

Step 6. *Solve the appropriate equation for the quantity to be determined (the unknown), and enter the knowns.* Slits, gratings, and the Rayleigh limit involve equations.

Step 7. *For thin film interference, you will have constructive interference for a total shift that is an integral number of wavelengths. You will have destructive interference for a total shift of a half-integral number of wavelengths.* Always keep in mind that crest to crest is constructive whereas crest to trough is destructive.

Step 8. *Check to see if the answer is reasonable: Does it make sense?* Angles in interference patterns cannot be greater than 90°, for example.

27.8 Polarization

LEARNING OBJECTIVES

By the end of this section, you will be able to:

- Discuss the meaning of polarization.
- Discuss the property of optical activity of certain materials.

Polaroid sunglasses are familiar to most of us. They have a special ability to cut the glare of light reflected from water or glass (see Figure 27.36). Polaroids have this ability because of a wave characteristic of light called polarization. What is polarization? How is it produced? What are some of its uses? The answers to these questions are related to the wave character of light.

FIGURE 27.36 These two photographs of a river show the effect of a polarizing filter in reducing glare in light reflected from the surface of water. Part (b) of this figure was taken with a polarizing filter and part (a) was not. As a result, the reflection of clouds and sky observed in part (a) is not observed in part (b). Polarizing sunglasses are particularly useful on snow and water. (credit: Amithshs, Wikimedia Commons)

Light is one type of electromagnetic (EM) wave. As noted earlier, EM waves are *transverse waves* consisting of varying electric and magnetic fields that oscillate perpendicular to the direction of propagation (see Figure 27.37). There are specific directions for the oscillations of the electric and magnetic fields. **Polarization** is the attribute that a wave's oscillations have a definite direction relative to the direction of propagation of the wave. (This is not the same type of polarization as that discussed for the separation of charges.) Waves having such a direction are said to be **polarized**. For an EM wave, we define the **direction of polarization** to be the direction parallel to the electric field. Thus we can think of the electric field arrows as showing the direction of polarization, as in Figure 27.37.

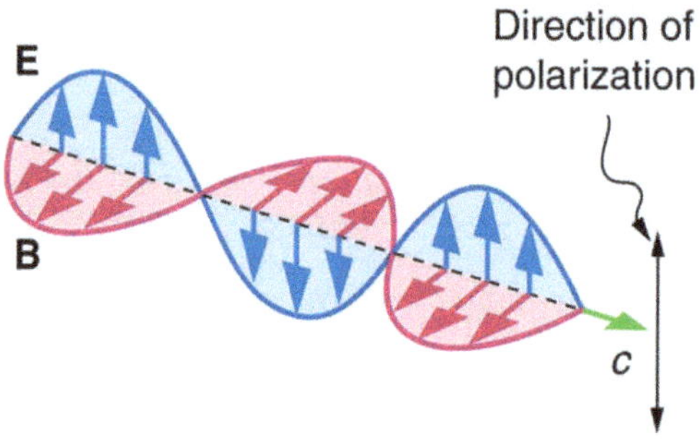

FIGURE 27.37 An EM wave, such as light, is a transverse wave. The electric and magnetic fields are perpendicular to the direction of propagation.

To examine this further, consider the transverse waves in the ropes shown in Figure 27.38. The oscillations in one rope are in a vertical plane and are said to be **vertically polarized**. Those in the other rope are in a horizontal plane and are **horizontally polarized**. If a vertical slit is placed on the first rope, the waves pass through. However, a vertical slit blocks the horizontally polarized waves. For EM waves, the direction of the electric field is analogous to the disturbances on the ropes.

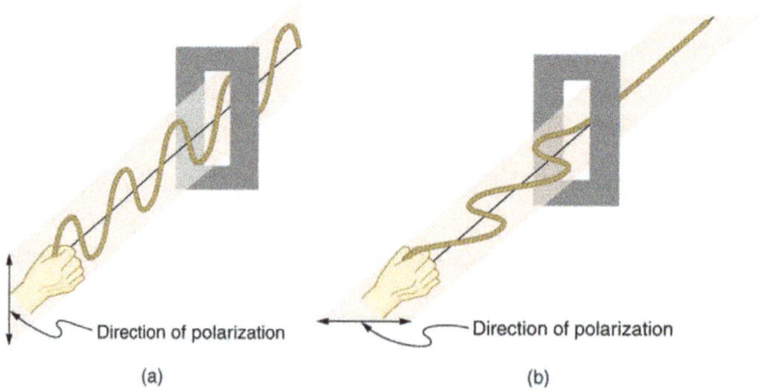

FIGURE 27.38 The transverse oscillations in one rope are in a vertical plane, and those in the other rope are in a horizontal plane. The first is said to be vertically polarized, and the other is said to be horizontally polarized. Vertical slits pass vertically polarized waves and block horizontally polarized waves.

The Sun and many other light sources produce waves that are randomly polarized (see Figure 27.39). Such light is said to be **unpolarized** because it is composed of many waves with all possible directions of polarization. Polaroid materials, invented by the founder of Polaroid Corporation, Edwin Land, act as a *polarizing* slit for light, allowing only polarization in one direction to pass through. Polarizing filters are composed of long molecules aligned in one direction. Thinking of the molecules as many slits, analogous to those for the oscillating ropes, we can understand why only light with a specific polarization can get through. The **axis of a polarizing filter** is the direction along which the filter passes the electric field of an EM wave (see Figure 27.40).

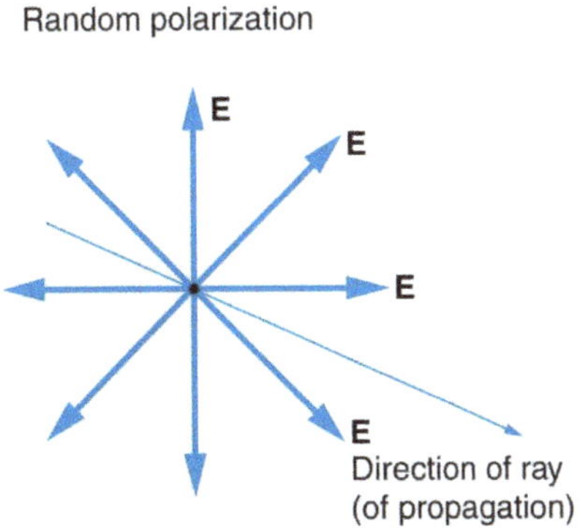

FIGURE 27.39 The slender arrow represents a ray of unpolarized light. The bold arrows represent the direction of polarization of the individual waves composing the ray. Since the light is unpolarized, the arrows point in all directions.

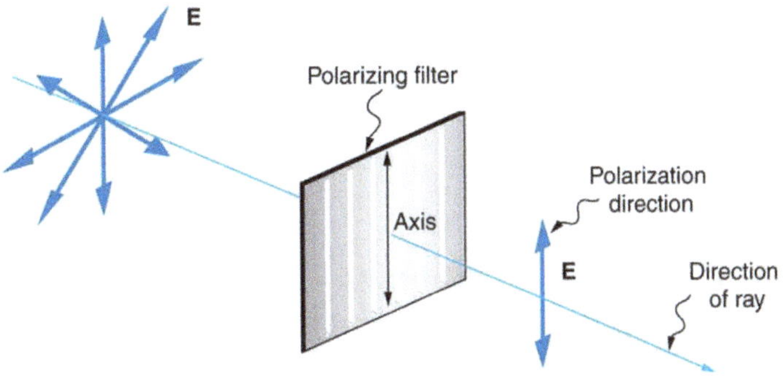

FIGURE 27.40 A polarizing filter has a polarization axis that acts as a slit passing through electric fields parallel to its direction. The direction of polarization of an EM wave is defined to be the direction of its electric field.

Figure 27.41 shows the effect of two polarizing filters on originally unpolarized light. The first filter polarizes the light along its axis. When the axes of the first and second filters are aligned (parallel), then all of the polarized light passed by the first filter is also passed by the second. If the second polarizing filter is rotated, only the component of the light parallel to the second filter's axis is passed. When the axes are perpendicular, no light is passed by the second.

Only the component of the EM wave parallel to the axis of a filter is passed. Let us call the angle between the direction of polarization and the axis of a filter θ. If the electric field has an amplitude E, then the transmitted part of the wave has an amplitude $E \cos \theta$ (see Figure 27.42). Since the intensity of a wave is proportional to its amplitude squared, the intensity I of the transmitted wave is related to the incident wave by

$$I = I_0 \cos^2 \theta, \tag{27.44}$$

where I_0 is the intensity of the polarized wave before passing through the filter. (The above equation is known as Malus's law.)

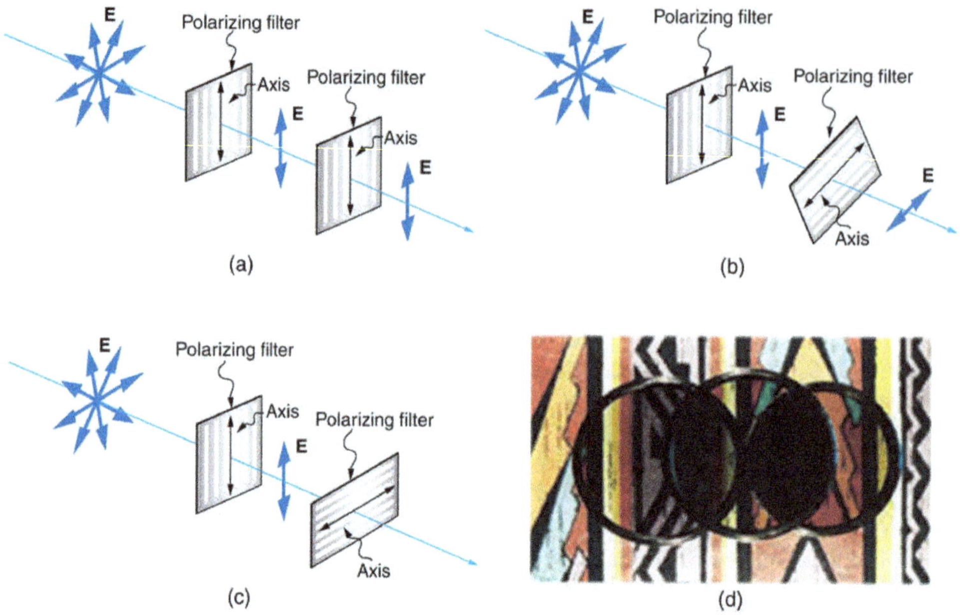

FIGURE 27.41 The effect of rotating two polarizing filters, where the first polarizes the light. (a) All of the polarized light is passed by the second polarizing filter, because its axis is parallel to the first. (b) As the second is rotated, only part of the light is passed. (c) When the second is perpendicular to the first, no light is passed. (d) In this photograph, a polarizing filter is placed above two others. Its axis is perpendicular to the filter on the right (dark area) and parallel to the filter on the left (lighter area). (credit: P.P. Urone)

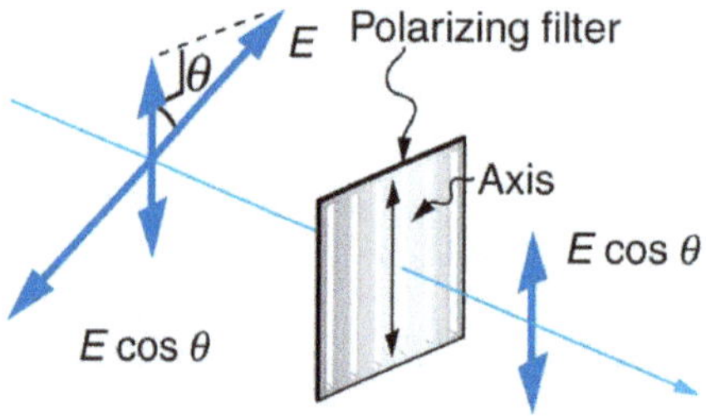

FIGURE 27.42 A polarizing filter transmits only the component of the wave parallel to its axis, $E \cos \theta$, reducing the intensity of any light not polarized parallel to its axis.

EXAMPLE 27.8

Calculating Intensity Reduction by a Polarizing Filter

What angle is needed between the direction of polarized light and the axis of a polarizing filter to reduce its intensity by 90.0%?

Strategy

When the intensity is reduced by 90.0%, it is 10.0% or 0.100 times its original value. That is, $I = 0.100 I_0$. Using this information, the equation $I = I_0 \cos^2 \theta$ can be used to solve for the needed angle.

Solution

Solving the equation $I = I_0 \cos^2 \theta$ for $\cos \theta$ and substituting with the relationship between I and I_0 gives

$$\cos \theta = \sqrt{\frac{I}{I_0}} = \sqrt{\frac{0.100 I_0}{I_0}} = 0.3162. \tag{27.45}$$

Solving for θ yields

$$\theta = \cos^{-1} 0.3162 = 71.6^{\circ}. \tag{27.46}$$

Discussion

A fairly large angle between the direction of polarization and the filter axis is needed to reduce the intensity to 10.0% of its original value. This seems reasonable based on experimenting with polarizing films. It is interesting that, at an angle of $45°$, the intensity is reduced to 50% of its original value (as you will show in this section's Problems & Exercises). Note that $71.6°$ is $18.4°$ from reducing the intensity to zero, and that at an angle of $18.4°$ the intensity is reduced to 90.0% of its original value (as you will also show in Problems & Exercises), giving evidence of symmetry.

Polarization by Reflection

By now you can probably guess that Polaroid sunglasses cut the glare in reflected light because that light is polarized. You can check this for yourself by holding Polaroid sunglasses in front of you and rotating them while looking at light reflected from water or glass. As you rotate the sunglasses, you will notice the light gets bright and dim, but not completely black. This implies the reflected light is partially polarized and cannot be completely blocked by a polarizing filter.

Figure 27.43 illustrates what happens when unpolarized light is reflected from a surface. Vertically polarized light is preferentially refracted at the surface, so that *the reflected light is left more horizontally polarized.* The reasons for this phenomenon are beyond the scope of this text, but a convenient mnemonic for remembering this is to imagine the polarization direction to be like an arrow. Vertical polarization would be like an arrow perpendicular to the surface and would be more likely to stick and not be reflected. Horizontal polarization is like an arrow bouncing on its side and would be more likely to be reflected. Sunglasses with vertical axes would then block more reflected light than unpolarized light from other sources.

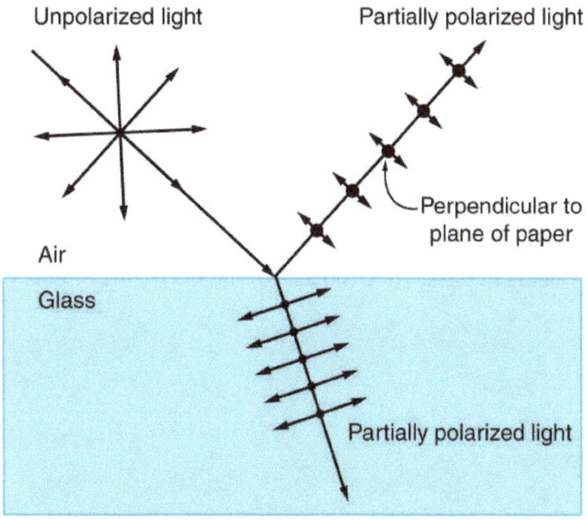

FIGURE 27.43 Polarization by reflection. Unpolarized light has equal amounts of vertical and horizontal polarization. After interaction with a surface, the vertical components are preferentially absorbed or refracted, leaving the reflected light more horizontally polarized. This is akin to arrows striking on their sides bouncing off, whereas arrows striking on their tips go into the surface.

Since the part of the light that is not reflected is refracted, the amount of polarization depends on the indices of refraction of the media involved. It can be shown that **reflected light is completely polarized** at a angle of reflection θ_b, given by

$$\tan \theta_b = \frac{n_2}{n_1}, \quad 27.47$$

where n_1 is the medium in which the incident and reflected light travel and n_2 is the index of refraction of the medium that forms the interface that reflects the light. This equation is known as **Brewster's law**, and θ_b is known as **Brewster's angle**, named after the 19th-century Scottish physicist who discovered them.

THINGS GREAT AND SMALL: ATOMIC EXPLANATION OF POLARIZING FILTERS

Polarizing filters have a polarization axis that acts as a slit. This slit passes electromagnetic waves (often visible light) that have an electric field parallel to the axis. This is accomplished with long molecules aligned perpendicular to the axis as shown in Figure 27.44.

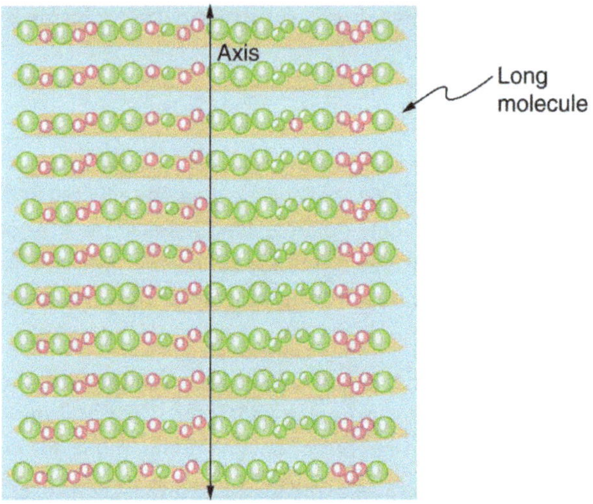

FIGURE 27.44 Long molecules are aligned perpendicular to the axis of a polarizing filter. The component of the electric field in an EM wave perpendicular to these molecules passes through the filter, while the component parallel to the molecules is absorbed.

Figure 27.45 illustrates how the component of the electric field parallel to the long molecules is absorbed. An electromagnetic wave is composed of oscillating electric and magnetic fields. The electric field is strong compared with the magnetic field and is more effective in exerting force on charges in the molecules. The most affected charged particles are the electrons in the molecules, since electron masses are small. If the electron is forced to oscillate, it can absorb energy from the EM wave. This reduces the fields in the wave and, hence, reduces its intensity. In long molecules, electrons can more easily oscillate parallel to the molecule than in the perpendicular direction. The electrons are bound to the molecule and are more restricted in their movement perpendicular to the molecule. Thus, the electrons can absorb EM waves that have a component of their electric field parallel to the molecule. The electrons are much less responsive to electric fields perpendicular to the molecule and will allow those fields to pass. Thus the axis of the polarizing filter is perpendicular to the length of the molecule.

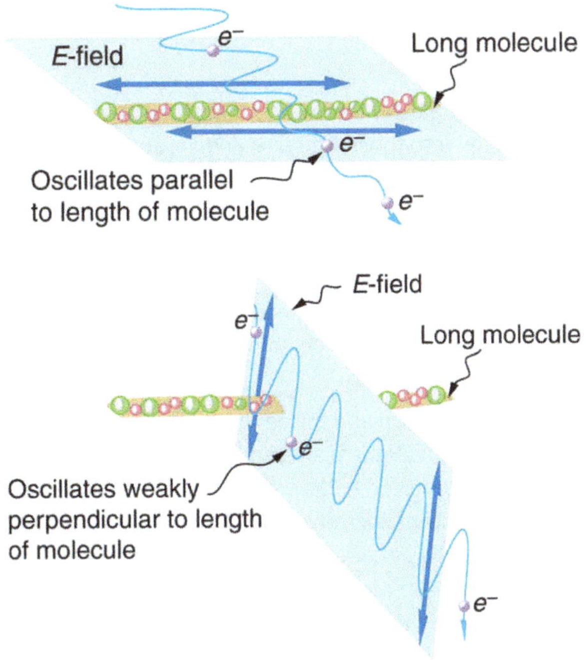

FIGURE 27.45 Artist's conception of an electron in a long molecule oscillating parallel to the molecule. The oscillation of the electron absorbs energy and reduces the intensity of the component of the EM wave that is parallel to the molecule.

EXAMPLE 27.9

Calculating Polarization by Reflection

(a) At what angle will light traveling in air be completely polarized horizontally when reflected from water? (b) From glass?

Strategy

All we need to solve these problems are the indices of refraction. Air has $n_1 = 1.00$, water has $n_2 = 1.333$, and crown glass has $n'_2 = 1.520$. The equation $\tan\theta_b = \frac{n_2}{n_1}$ can be directly applied to find θ_b in each case.

Solution for (a)

Putting the known quantities into the equation

$$\tan\theta_b = \frac{n_2}{n_1} \qquad 27.48$$

gives

$$\tan\theta_b = \frac{n_2}{n_1} = \frac{1.333}{1.00} = 1.333. \qquad 27.49$$

Solving for the angle θ_b yields

$$\theta_b = \tan^{-1} 1.333 = 53.1^\circ. \qquad 27.50$$

Solution for (b)

Similarly, for crown glass and air,

$$\tan\theta'_b = \frac{n'_2}{n_1} = \frac{1.520}{1.00} = 1.52. \qquad 27.51$$

Thus,

$$\theta'_b = \tan^{-1} 1.52 = 56.7°. \qquad (27.52)$$

Discussion

Light reflected at these angles could be completely blocked by a good polarizing filter held with its *axis vertical*. Brewster's angle for water and air are similar to those for glass and air, so that sunglasses are equally effective for light reflected from either water or glass under similar circumstances. Light not reflected is refracted into these media. So at an incident angle equal to Brewster's angle, the refracted light will be slightly polarized vertically. It will not be completely polarized vertically, because only a small fraction of the incident light is reflected, and so a significant amount of horizontally polarized light is refracted.

Polarization by Scattering

If you hold your Polaroid sunglasses in front of you and rotate them while looking at blue sky, you will see the sky get bright and dim. This is a clear indication that light scattered by air is partially polarized. Figure 27.46 helps illustrate how this happens. Since light is a transverse EM wave, it vibrates the electrons of air molecules perpendicular to the direction it is traveling. The electrons then radiate like small antennae. Since they are oscillating perpendicular to the direction of the light ray, they produce EM radiation that is polarized perpendicular to the direction of the ray. When viewing the light along a line perpendicular to the original ray, as in Figure 27.46, there can be no polarization in the scattered light parallel to the original ray, because that would require the original ray to be a longitudinal wave. Along other directions, a component of the other polarization can be projected along the line of sight, and the scattered light will only be partially polarized. Furthermore, multiple scattering can bring light to your eyes from other directions and can contain different polarizations.

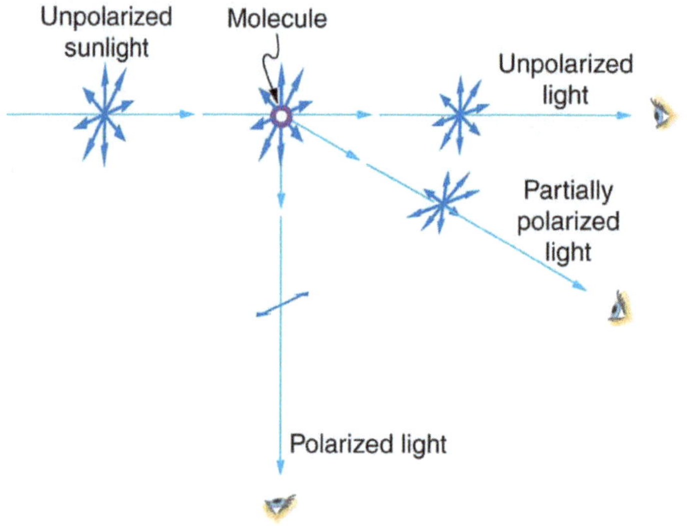

FIGURE 27.46 Polarization by scattering. Unpolarized light scattering from air molecules shakes their electrons perpendicular to the direction of the original ray. The scattered light therefore has a polarization perpendicular to the original direction and none parallel to the original direction.

Photographs of the sky can be darkened by polarizing filters, a trick used by many photographers to make clouds brighter by contrast. Scattering from other particles, such as smoke or dust, can also polarize light. Detecting polarization in scattered EM waves can be a useful analytical tool in determining the scattering source.

There is a range of optical effects used in sunglasses. Besides being Polaroid, other sunglasses have colored pigments embedded in them, while others use non-reflective or even reflective coatings. A recent development is photochromic lenses, which darken in the sunlight and become clear indoors. Photochromic lenses are embedded with organic microcrystalline molecules that change their properties when exposed to UV in sunlight, but become clear in artificial lighting with no UV.

TAKE-HOME EXPERIMENT: POLARIZATION

Find Polaroid sunglasses and rotate one while holding the other still and look at different surfaces and objects. Explain your observations. What is the difference in angle from when you see a maximum intensity to when you see a minimum intensity? Find a reflective glass surface and do the same. At what angle does the glass need to be oriented to give minimum glare?

Liquid Crystals and Other Polarization Effects in Materials

While you are undoubtedly aware of liquid crystal displays (LCDs) found in watches, calculators, computer screens, cellphones, flat screen televisions, and other myriad places, you may not be aware that they are based on polarization. Liquid crystals are so named because their molecules can be aligned even though they are in a liquid. Liquid crystals have the property that they can rotate the polarization of light passing through them by 90°. Furthermore, this property can be turned off by the application of a voltage, as illustrated in Figure 27.47. It is possible to manipulate this characteristic quickly and in small well-defined regions to create the contrast patterns we see in so many LCD devices.

In flat screen LCD televisions, there is a large light at the back of the TV. The light travels to the front screen through millions of tiny units called pixels (picture elements). One of these is shown in Figure 27.47 (a) and (b). Each unit has three cells, with red, blue, or green filters, each controlled independently. When the voltage across a liquid crystal is switched off, the liquid crystal passes the light through the particular filter. One can vary the picture contrast by varying the strength of the voltage applied to the liquid crystal.

FIGURE 27.47 (a) Polarized light is rotated 90° by a liquid crystal and then passed by a polarizing filter that has its axis perpendicular to the original polarization direction. (b) When a voltage is applied to the liquid crystal, the polarized light is not rotated and is blocked by the filter, making the region dark in comparison with its surroundings. (c) LCDs can be made color specific, small, and fast enough to use in computer monitor screens. (credit: Idaho National Laboratory)

Many crystals and solutions rotate the plane of polarization of light passing through them. Such substances are said to be **optically active**. Examples include sugar water, insulin, and collagen (see Figure 27.48). In addition to depending on the type of substance, the amount and direction of rotation depends on a number of factors. Among these is the concentration of the substance, the distance the light travels through it, and the wavelength of light. Optical activity is due to the asymmetric shape of molecules in the substance, such as being helical. Measurements of the rotation of polarized light passing through substances can thus be used to measure concentrations, a standard technique for sugars. It can also give information on the shapes of molecules, such as proteins, and factors that affect their shapes, such as temperature and pH.

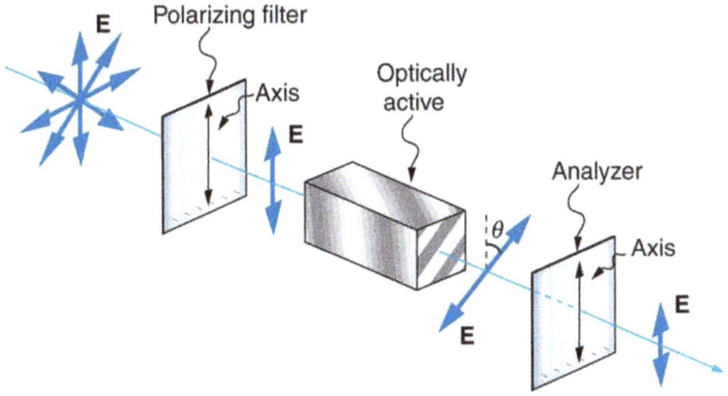

FIGURE 27.48 Optical activity is the ability of some substances to rotate the plane of polarization of light passing through them. The rotation is detected with a polarizing filter or analyzer.

Glass and plastic become optically active when stressed; the greater the stress, the greater the effect. Optical stress analysis on complicated shapes can be performed by making plastic models of them and observing them through crossed filters, as seen in Figure 27.49. It is apparent that the effect depends on wavelength as well as stress. The wavelength dependence is sometimes also used for artistic purposes.

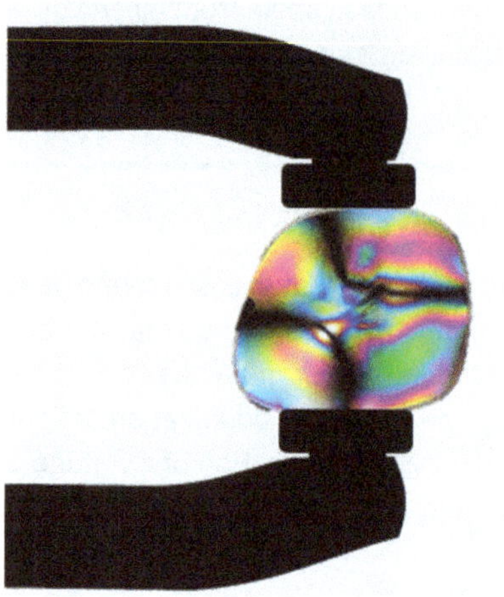

FIGURE 27.49 Optical stress analysis of a plastic lens placed between crossed polarizers. (credit: Infopro, Wikimedia Commons)

Another interesting phenomenon associated with polarized light is the ability of some crystals to split an unpolarized beam of light into two. Such crystals are said to be **birefringent** (see Figure 27.50). Each of the separated rays has a specific polarization. One behaves normally and is called the ordinary ray, whereas the other does not obey Snell's law and is called the extraordinary ray. Birefringent crystals can be used to produce polarized beams from unpolarized light. Some birefringent materials preferentially absorb one of the polarizations. These materials are called dichroic and can produce polarization by this preferential absorption. This is fundamentally how polarizing filters and other polarizers work. The interested reader is invited to further pursue the numerous properties of materials related to polarization.

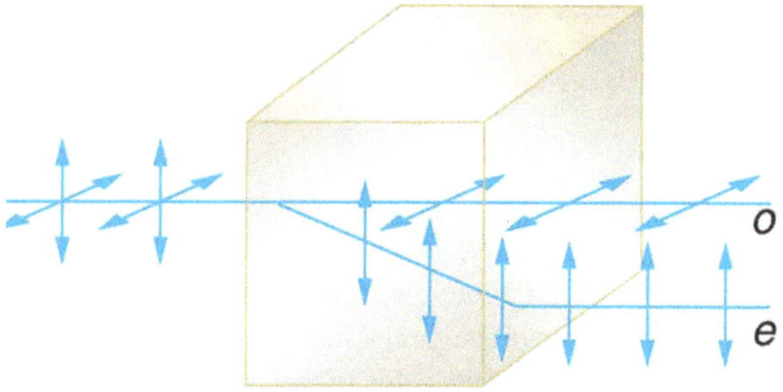

FIGURE 27.50 Birefringent materials, such as the common mineral calcite, split unpolarized beams of light into two. The ordinary ray behaves as expected, but the extraordinary ray does not obey Snell's law.

27.9 *Extended Topic* Microscopy Enhanced by the Wave Characteristics of Light

LEARNING OBJECTIVES

By the end of this section, you will be able to:

- Discuss the different types of microscopes.

Physics research underpins the advancement of developments in microscopy. As we gain knowledge of the wave nature of electromagnetic waves and methods to analyze and interpret signals, new microscopes that enable us to "see" more are being developed. It is the evolution and newer generation of microscopes that are described in this section.

The use of microscopes (microscopy) to observe small details is limited by the wave nature of light. Owing to the fact that light diffracts significantly around small objects, it becomes impossible to observe details significantly smaller than the wavelength of light. One rule of thumb has it that all details smaller than about λ are difficult to observe. Radar, for example, can detect the size of an aircraft, but not its individual rivets, since the wavelength of most radar is several centimeters or greater. Similarly, visible light cannot detect individual atoms, since atoms are about 0.1 nm in size and visible wavelengths range from 380 to 760 nm. Ironically, special techniques used to obtain the best possible resolution with microscopes take advantage of the same wave characteristics of light that ultimately limit the detail.

MAKING CONNECTIONS: WAVES

All attempts to observe the size and shape of objects are limited by the wavelength of the probe. Sonar and medical ultrasound are limited by the wavelength of sound they employ. We shall see that this is also true in electron microscopy, since electrons have a wavelength. Heisenberg's uncertainty principle asserts that this limit is fundamental and inescapable, as we shall see in quantum mechanics.

The most obvious method of obtaining better detail is to utilize shorter wavelengths. **Ultraviolet (UV) microscopes** have been constructed with special lenses that transmit UV rays and utilize photographic or electronic techniques to record images. The shorter UV wavelengths allow somewhat greater detail to be observed, but drawbacks, such as the hazard of UV to living tissue and the need for special detection devices and lenses (which tend to be dispersive in the UV), severely limit the use of UV microscopes. Elsewhere, we will explore practical uses of very short wavelength EM waves, such as x rays, and other short-wavelength probes, such as electrons in electron microscopes, to detect small details.

Another difficulty in microscopy is the fact that many microscopic objects do not absorb much of the light passing through them. The lack of contrast makes image interpretation very difficult. **Contrast** is the difference in intensity between objects and the background on which they are observed. Stains (such as dyes, fluorophores, etc.) are commonly employed to enhance contrast, but these tend to be application specific. More general wave interference techniques can be used to produce contrast. Figure 27.51 shows the passage of light through a sample. Since the indices of refraction differ, the number of wavelengths in the paths differs. Light emerging from the object is thus out of phase with light from the background and will interfere differently, producing enhanced contrast, especially if the light is coherent and monochromatic—as in laser light.

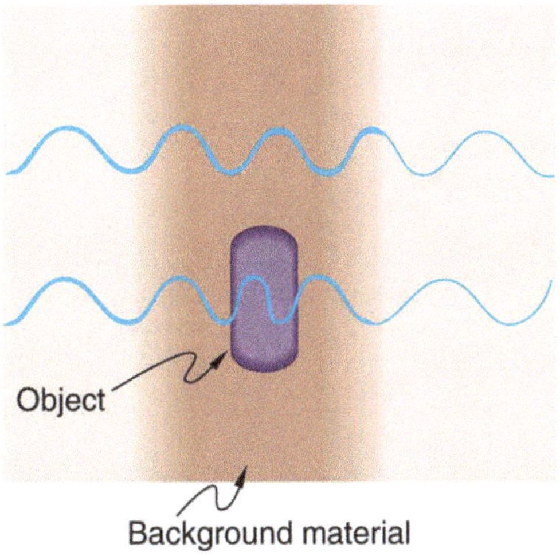

FIGURE 27.51 Light rays passing through a sample under a microscope will emerge with different phases depending on their paths. The object shown has a greater index of refraction than the background, and so the wavelength decreases as the ray passes through it. Superimposing these rays produces interference that varies with path, enhancing contrast between the object and background.

Interference microscopes enhance contrast between objects and background by superimposing a reference beam of light upon the light emerging from the sample. Since light from the background and objects differ in phase, there will be different amounts of constructive and destructive interference, producing the desired contrast in final intensity. Figure 27.52 shows schematically how this is done. Parallel rays of light from a source are split into two beams by a half-silvered mirror. These beams are called the object and reference beams. Each beam passes through identical optical elements, except that the object beam passes through the object we wish to observe microscopically. The light beams are recombined by another half-silvered mirror and interfere. Since the light rays passing through different parts of the object have different phases, interference will be significantly different and, hence, have greater contrast between them.

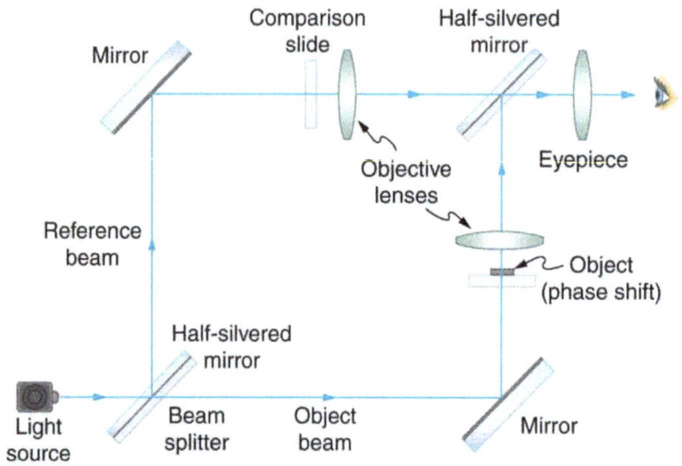

FIGURE 27.52 An interference microscope utilizes interference between the reference and object beam to enhance contrast. The two beams are split by a half-silvered mirror; the object beam is sent through the object, and the reference beam is sent through otherwise identical optical elements. The beams are recombined by another half-silvered mirror, and the interference depends on the various phases emerging from different parts of the object, enhancing contrast.

Another type of microscope utilizing wave interference and differences in phases to enhance contrast is called the **phase-contrast microscope**. While its principle is the same as the interference microscope, the phase-contrast microscope is simpler to use and construct. Its impact (and the principle upon which it is based) was so important that its developer, the Dutch physicist Frits Zernike (1888–1966), was awarded the Nobel Prize in 1953. Figure 27.53 shows the basic construction of a phase-contrast microscope. Phase differences between light passing through the object and background are produced by passing the rays through different parts of a phase plate (so called because it shifts the phase of the light passing through it). These two light rays are superimposed in the image plane, producing contrast due to their interference.

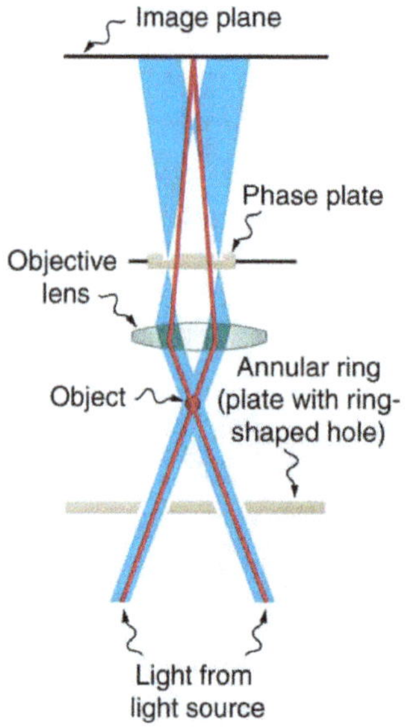

FIGURE 27.53 Simplified construction of a phase-contrast microscope. Phase differences between light passing through the object and background are produced by passing the rays through different parts of a phase plate. The light rays are superimposed in the image plane, producing contrast due to their interference.

A **polarization microscope** also enhances contrast by utilizing a wave characteristic of light. Polarization microscopes are useful for objects that are optically active or birefringent, particularly if those characteristics vary from place to place in the object. Polarized light is sent through the object and then observed through a polarizing filter that is perpendicular to the original polarization direction. Nearly transparent objects can then appear with strong color and in high contrast. Many polarization effects are wavelength dependent, producing color in the processed image. Contrast results from the action of the polarizing filter in passing only components parallel to its axis.

Apart from the UV microscope, the variations of microscopy discussed so far in this section are available as attachments to fairly standard microscopes or as slight variations. The next level of sophistication is provided by commercial **confocal microscopes**, which use the extended focal region shown in Figure 27.31(b) to obtain three-dimensional images rather than two-dimensional images. Here, only a single plane or region of focus is identified; out-of-focus regions above and below this plane are subtracted out by a computer so the image quality is much better. This type of microscope makes use of fluorescence, where a laser provides the excitation light. Laser light passing through a tiny aperture called a pinhole forms an extended focal region within the specimen. The reflected light passes through the objective lens to a second pinhole and the photomultiplier detector, see Figure 27.54. The second pinhole is the key here and serves to block much of the light from points that are not at the focal point of the objective lens. The pinhole is conjugate (coupled) to the focal point of the lens. The second pinhole and detector are scanned, allowing reflected light from a small region or section of the extended focal region to be imaged at any one time. The out-of-focus light is excluded. Each image is stored in a computer, and a full scanned image is generated in a short time. Live cell processes can also be imaged at adequate scanning speeds allowing the imaging of three-dimensional microscopic movement. Confocal microscopy enhances images over conventional optical microscopy, especially for thicker specimens, and so has become quite popular.

The next level of sophistication is provided by microscopes attached to instruments that isolate and detect only a small wavelength band of light—monochromators and spectral analyzers. Here, the monochromatic light from a laser is scattered from the specimen. This scattered light shifts up or down as it excites particular energy levels in the sample. The uniqueness of the observed scattered light can give detailed information about the chemical composition of a given spot on the sample with high contrast—like molecular fingerprints. Applications are in materials science, nanotechnology, and the biomedical field. Fine details in biochemical processes over time can even be detected. The ultimate in microscopy is the electron microscope—to be discussed later. Research is being conducted into the development of new prototype microscopes that can become commercially available, providing better diagnostic and research capacities.

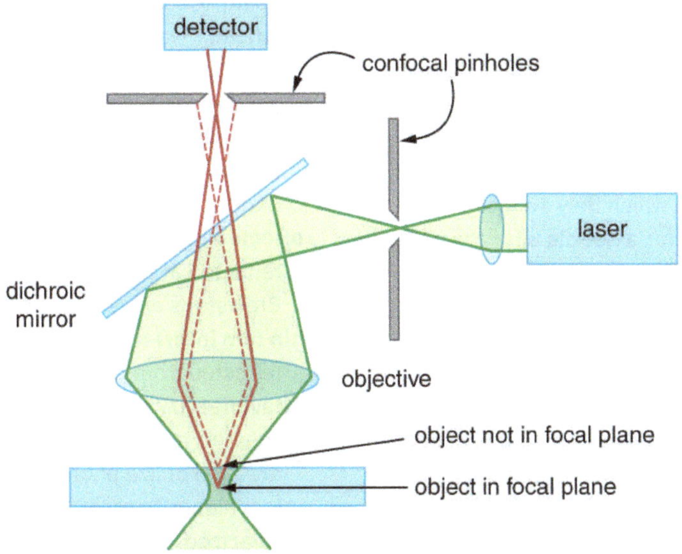

FIGURE 27.54 A confocal microscope provides three-dimensional images using pinholes and the extended depth of focus as described by wave optics. The right pinhole illuminates a tiny region of the sample in the focal plane. In-focus light rays from this tiny region pass through the dichroic mirror and the second pinhole to a detector and a computer. Out-of-focus light rays are blocked. The pinhole is scanned sideways to form an image of the entire focal plane. The pinhole can then be scanned up and down to gather images from different focal planes. The result is a three-dimensional image of the specimen.

Glossary

axis of a polarizing filter the direction along which the filter passes the electric field of an EM wave

birefringent crystals that split an unpolarized beam of light into two beams

Brewster's angle $\theta_b = \tan^{-1}\left(\frac{n_2}{n_1}\right)$, where n_2 is the index of refraction of the medium from which the light is reflected and n_1 is the index of refraction of the medium in which the reflected light travels

Brewster's law $\tan\theta_b = \frac{n_2}{n_1}$, where n_1 is the medium in which the incident and reflected light travel and n_2 is the index of refraction of the medium that forms the interface that reflects the light

coherent waves are in phase or have a definite phase relationship

confocal microscopes microscopes that use the extended focal region to obtain three-dimensional images rather than two-dimensional images

constructive interference for a diffraction grating occurs when the condition $d\ \sin\theta = m\lambda$ (for $m = 0, 1, -1, 2, -2, \ldots$) is satisfied, where d is the distance between slits in the grating, λ is the wavelength of light, and m is the order of the maximum

constructive interference for a double slit the path length difference must be an integral multiple of the wavelength

contrast the difference in intensity between objects and the background on which they are observed

destructive interference for a double slit the path length difference must be a half-integral multiple of the wavelength

destructive interference for a single slit occurs when $D\ \sin\theta = m\lambda$, (for $m = 1, -1, 2, -2, 3, \ldots$), where D is the slit width, λ is the light's wavelength, θ is the angle relative to the original direction of the light, and m is the order of the minimum

diffraction the bending of a wave around the edges of an opening or an obstacle

diffraction grating a large number of evenly spaced parallel slits

direction of polarization the direction parallel to the electric field for EM waves

horizontally polarized the oscillations are in a horizontal plane

Huygens's principle every point on a wavefront is a source of wavelets that spread out in the forward direction at the same speed as the wave itself. The new wavefront is a line tangent to all of the wavelets

incoherent waves have random phase relationships

interference microscopes microscopes that enhance contrast between objects and background by superimposing a reference beam of light upon the light emerging from the sample

optically active substances that rotate the plane of polarization of light passing through them

order the integer m used in the equations for constructive and destructive interference for a double slit

phase-contrast microscope microscope utilizing wave interference and differences in phases to enhance contrast

polarization the attribute that wave oscillations have a definite direction relative to the direction of propagation of the wave

polarization microscope microscope that enhances contrast by utilizing a wave characteristic of light, useful for objects that are optically active

polarized waves having the electric and magnetic field oscillations in a definite direction

Rayleigh criterion two images are just resolvable when the center of the diffraction pattern of one is directly over the first minimum of the diffraction pattern of the other

reflected light that is completely polarized light reflected at the angle of reflection θ_b, known as Brewster's angle

thin film interference interference between light reflected from different surfaces of a thin film

ultraviolet (UV) microscopes microscopes constructed with special lenses that transmit UV rays and utilize photographic or electronic techniques to record images

unpolarized waves that are randomly polarized

vertically polarized the oscillations are in a vertical plane

wavelength in a medium $\lambda_n = \lambda/n$, where λ is the wavelength in vacuum, and n is the index of refraction of the medium

Section Summary

27.1 The Wave Aspect of Light: Interference

- Wave optics is the branch of optics that must be used when light interacts with small objects or whenever the wave characteristics of light are considered.
- Wave characteristics are those associated with interference and diffraction.
- Visible light is the type of electromagnetic wave to which our eyes respond and has a wavelength in

the range of 380 to 760 nm.

- Like all EM waves, the following relationship is valid in vacuum: $c = f\lambda$, where $c = 3 \times 10^8$ m/s is the speed of light, f is the frequency of the electromagnetic wave, and λ is its wavelength in vacuum.
- The wavelength λ_n of light in a medium with index of refraction n is $\lambda_n = \lambda/n$. Its frequency is the same as in vacuum.

27.2 Huygens's Principle: Diffraction

- An accurate technique for determining how and where waves propagate is given by Huygens's principle: Every point on a wavefront is a source of wavelets that spread out in the forward direction at the same speed as the wave itself. The new wavefront is a line tangent to all of the wavelets.
- Diffraction is the bending of a wave around the edges of an opening or other obstacle.

27.3 Young's Double Slit Experiment

- Young's double slit experiment gave definitive proof of the wave character of light.
- An interference pattern is obtained by the superposition of light from two slits.
- There is constructive interference when $d \sin \theta = m\lambda \text{ (for } m = 0, 1, -1, 2, -2, \ldots)$, where d is the distance between the slits, θ is the angle relative to the incident direction, and m is the order of the interference.
- There is destructive interference when $d \sin \theta = \left(m + \frac{1}{2}\right)\lambda \text{ (for } m = 0, 1, -1, 2, -2, \ldots)$.

27.4 Multiple Slit Diffraction

- A diffraction grating is a large collection of evenly spaced parallel slits that produces an interference pattern similar to but sharper than that of a double slit.
- There is constructive interference for a diffraction grating when $d \sin \theta = m\lambda \text{ (for } m = 0, 1, –1, 2, –2, \ldots)$, where d is the distance between slits in the grating, λ is the wavelength of light, and m is the order of the maximum.

27.5 Single Slit Diffraction

- A single slit produces an interference pattern characterized by a broad central maximum with narrower and dimmer maxima to the sides.
- There is destructive interference for a single slit when $D \sin \theta = m\lambda, \text{ (for } m = 1, –1, 2, –2, 3, \ldots)$, where D is the slit width, λ is the light's wavelength, θ is the angle relative to the original direction of the light, and m is the order of the minimum. Note that there is no $m = 0$ minimum.

27.6 Limits of Resolution: The Rayleigh Criterion

- Diffraction limits resolution.
- For a circular aperture, lens, or mirror, the Rayleigh criterion states that two images are just resolvable when the center of the diffraction pattern of one is directly over the first minimum of the diffraction pattern of the other.
- This occurs for two point objects separated by the angle $\theta = 1.22\frac{\lambda}{D}$, where λ is the wavelength of light (or other electromagnetic radiation) and D is the diameter of the aperture, lens, mirror, etc. This equation also gives the angular spreading of a source of light having a diameter D.

27.7 Thin Film Interference

- Thin film interference occurs between the light reflected from the top and bottom surfaces of a film. In addition to the path length difference, there can be a phase change.
- When light reflects from a medium having an index of refraction greater than that of the medium in which it is traveling, a $180°$ phase change (or a $\lambda/2$ shift) occurs.

27.8 Polarization

- Polarization is the attribute that wave oscillations have a definite direction relative to the direction of propagation of the wave.
- EM waves are transverse waves that may be polarized.
- The direction of polarization is defined to be the direction parallel to the electric field of the EM wave.
- Unpolarized light is composed of many rays having random polarization directions.
- Light can be polarized by passing it through a polarizing filter or other polarizing material. The intensity I of polarized light after passing through a polarizing filter is $I = I_0 \cos^2 \theta$, where I_0 is the original intensity and θ is the angle between the direction of polarization and the axis of the filter.
- Polarization is also produced by reflection.
- Brewster's law states that reflected light will be completely polarized at the angle of reflection θ_b, known as Brewster's angle, given by a statement known as Brewster's law: $\tan \theta_b = \frac{n_2}{n_1}$, where n_1 is the medium in which the incident and reflected

light travel and n_2 is the index of refraction of the medium that forms the interface that reflects the light.

- Polarization can also be produced by scattering.
- There are a number of types of optically active substances that rotate the direction of polarization of light passing through them.

27.9 *Extended Topic* Microscopy Enhanced by the Wave Characteristics of Light

- To improve microscope images, various techniques utilizing the wave characteristics of light have been developed. Many of these enhance contrast with interference effects.

Conceptual Questions

27.1 The Wave Aspect of Light: Interference

1. What type of experimental evidence indicates that light is a wave?

2. Give an example of a wave characteristic of light that is easily observed outside the laboratory.

27.2 Huygens's Principle: Diffraction

3. How do wave effects depend on the size of the object with which the wave interacts? For example, why does sound bend around the corner of a building while light does not?

4. Under what conditions can light be modeled like a ray? Like a wave?

5. Go outside in the sunlight and observe your shadow. It has fuzzy edges even if you do not. Is this a diffraction effect? Explain.

6. Why does the wavelength of light decrease when it passes from vacuum into a medium? State which attributes change and which stay the same and, thus, require the wavelength to decrease.

7. Does Huygens's principle apply to all types of waves?

27.3 Young's Double Slit Experiment

8. Young's double slit experiment breaks a single light beam into two sources. Would the same pattern be obtained for two independent sources of light, such as the headlights of a distant car? Explain.

9. Suppose you use the same double slit to perform Young's double slit experiment in air and then repeat the experiment in water. Do the angles to the same parts of the interference pattern get larger or smaller? Does the color of the light change? Explain.

10. Is it possible to create a situation in which there is only destructive interference? Explain.

11. Figure 27.55 shows the central part of the interference pattern for a pure wavelength of red light projected onto a double slit. The pattern is actually a combination of single slit and double slit interference. Note that the bright spots are evenly spaced. Is this a double slit or single slit characteristic? Note that some of the bright spots are dim on either side of the center. Is this a single slit or double slit characteristic? Which is smaller, the slit width or the separation between slits? Explain your responses.

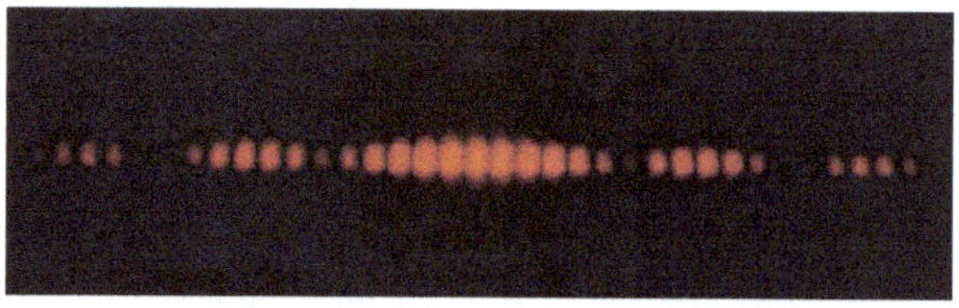

FIGURE 27.55 This double slit interference pattern also shows signs of single slit interference. (credit: PASCO)

27.4 Multiple Slit Diffraction

12. What is the advantage of a diffraction grating over a double slit in dispersing light into a spectrum?

13. What are the advantages of a diffraction grating over a prism in dispersing light for spectral analysis?

14. Can the lines in a diffraction grating be too close together to be useful as a spectroscopic tool for visible light? If so, what type of EM radiation would the grating be suitable for? Explain.

15. If a beam of white light passes through a diffraction grating with vertical lines, the light is dispersed into rainbow colors on the right and left. If a glass prism disperses white light to the right into a rainbow, how does the sequence of colors compare with that produced on the right by a diffraction grating?

16. Suppose pure-wavelength light falls on a diffraction grating. What happens to the interference pattern if the same light falls on a grating that has more lines per centimeter? What happens to the interference pattern if a longer-wavelength light falls on the same grating? Explain how these two effects are consistent in terms of the relationship of wavelength to the distance between slits.

17. Suppose a feather appears green but has no green pigment. Explain in terms of diffraction.

18. It is possible that there is no minimum in the interference pattern of a single slit. Explain why. Is the same true of double slits and diffraction gratings?

27.5 Single Slit Diffraction

19. As the width of the slit producing a single-slit diffraction pattern is reduced, how will the diffraction pattern produced change?

27.6 Limits of Resolution: The Rayleigh Criterion

20. A beam of light always spreads out. Why can a beam not be created with parallel rays to prevent spreading? Why can lenses, mirrors, or apertures not be used to correct the spreading?

27.7 Thin Film Interference

21. What effect does increasing the wedge angle have on the spacing of interference fringes? If the wedge angle is too large, fringes are not observed. Why?

22. How is the difference in paths taken by two originally in-phase light waves related to whether they interfere constructively or destructively? How can this be affected by reflection? By refraction?

23. Is there a phase change in the light reflected from either surface of a contact lens floating on a person's tear layer? The index of refraction of the lens is about 1.5, and its top surface is dry.

24. In placing a sample on a microscope slide, a glass cover is placed over a water drop on the glass slide. Light incident from above can reflect from the top and bottom of the glass cover and from the glass slide below the water drop. At which surfaces will there be a phase change in the reflected light?

25. Answer the above question if the fluid between the two pieces of crown glass is carbon disulfide.

26. While contemplating the food value of a slice of ham, you notice a rainbow of color reflected from its moist surface. Explain its origin.

27. An inventor notices that a soap bubble is dark at its thinnest and realizes that destructive interference is taking place for all wavelengths. How could she use this knowledge to make a non-reflective coating for lenses that is effective at all wavelengths? That is, what limits would there be on the index of refraction and thickness of the coating? How might this be impractical?

28. A non-reflective coating like the one described in Example 27.6 works ideally for a single wavelength and for perpendicular incidence. What happens for other wavelengths and other incident directions? Be specific.

29. Why is it much more difficult to see interference fringes for light reflected from a thick piece of glass than from a thin film? Would it be easier if monochromatic light were used?

27.8 Polarization

30. Under what circumstances is the phase of light changed by reflection? Is the phase related to polarization?

31. Can a sound wave in air be polarized? Explain.

32. No light passes through two perfect polarizing filters with perpendicular axes. However, if a third polarizing filter is placed between the original two, some light can pass. Why is this? Under what circumstances does most of the light pass?

33. Explain what happens to the energy carried by light that it is dimmed by passing it through two crossed polarizing filters.

34. When particles scattering light are much smaller than its wavelength, the amount of scattering is proportional to $1/\lambda^4$. Does this mean there is more scattering for small λ than large λ? How does this relate to the fact that the sky is blue?

35. Using the information given in the preceding question, explain why sunsets are red.

36. When light is reflected at Brewster's angle from a smooth surface, it is 100% polarized parallel to the surface. Part of the light will be refracted into the surface. Describe how you would do an experiment to determine the polarization of the refracted light. What direction would you expect the polarization to have and would you expect it to be 100%?

27.9 *Extended Topic* Microscopy Enhanced by the Wave Characteristics of Light

37. Explain how microscopes can use wave optics to improve contrast and why this is important.

38. A bright white light under water is collimated and directed upon a prism. What range of colors does one see emerging?

Problems & Exercises

27.1 The Wave Aspect of Light: Interference

1. Show that when light passes from air to water, its wavelength decreases to 0.750 times its original value.

2. Find the range of visible wavelengths of light in crown glass.

3. What is the index of refraction of a material for which the wavelength of light is 0.671 times its value in a vacuum? Identify the likely substance.

4. Analysis of an interference effect in a clear solid shows that the wavelength of light in the solid is 329 nm. Knowing this light comes from a He-Ne laser and has a wavelength of 633 nm in air, is the substance zircon or diamond?

5. What is the ratio of thicknesses of crown glass and water that would contain the same number of wavelengths of light?

27.3 Young's Double Slit Experiment

6. At what angle is the first-order maximum for 450-nm wavelength blue light falling on double slits separated by 0.0500 mm?

7. Calculate the angle for the third-order maximum of 580-nm wavelength yellow light falling on double slits separated by 0.100 mm.

8. What is the separation between two slits for which 610-nm orange light has its first maximum at an angle of 30.0°?

9. Find the distance between two slits that produces the first minimum for 410-nm violet light at an angle of 45.0°.

10. Calculate the wavelength of light that has its third minimum at an angle of 30.0° when falling on double slits separated by $3.00\ \mu m$. Explicitly, show how you follow the steps in Problem-Solving Strategies for Wave Optics.

11. What is the wavelength of light falling on double slits separated by $2.00\ \mu m$ if the third-order maximum is at an angle of 60.0°?

12. At what angle is the fourth-order maximum for the situation in Exercise 27.6?

13. What is the highest-order maximum for 400-nm light falling on double slits separated by $25.0\ \mu m$?

14. Find the largest wavelength of light falling on double slits separated by $1.20\ \mu m$ for which there is a first-order maximum. Is this in the visible part of the spectrum?

15. What is the smallest separation between two slits that will produce a second-order maximum for 720-nm red light?

16. (a) What is the smallest separation between two slits that will produce a second-order maximum for any visible light? (b) For all visible light?

17. (a) If the first-order maximum for pure-wavelength light falling on a double slit is at an angle of 10.0°, at what angle is the second-order maximum? (b) What is the angle of the first minimum? (c) What is the highest-order maximum possible here?

18. Figure 27.56 shows a double slit located a distance x from a screen, with the distance from the center of the screen given by y. When the distance d between the slits is relatively large, there will be numerous bright spots, called fringes. Show that, for small angles (where $\sin\theta \approx \theta$, with θ in radians), the distance between fringes is given by $\Delta y = x\lambda/d$.

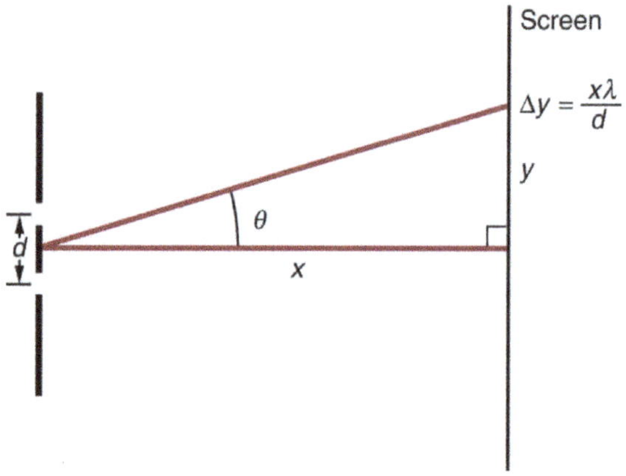

FIGURE 27.56 The distance between adjacent fringes is $\Delta y = x\lambda/d$, assuming the slit separation d is large compared with λ.

19. Using the result of the problem above, calculate the distance between fringes for 633-nm light falling on double slits separated by 0.0800 mm, located 3.00 m from a screen as in Figure 27.56.

20. Using the result of the problem two problems prior, find the wavelength of light that produces

fringes 7.50 mm apart on a screen 2.00 m from double slits separated by 0.120 mm (see Figure 27.56).

27.4 Multiple Slit Diffraction

21. A diffraction grating has 2000 lines per centimeter. At what angle will the first-order maximum be for 520-nm-wavelength green light?

22. Find the angle for the third-order maximum for 580-nm-wavelength yellow light falling on a diffraction grating having 1500 lines per centimeter.

23. How many lines per centimeter are there on a diffraction grating that gives a first-order maximum for 470-nm blue light at an angle of 25.0°?

24. What is the distance between lines on a diffraction grating that produces a second-order maximum for 760-nm red light at an angle of 60.0°?

25. Calculate the wavelength of light that has its second-order maximum at 45.0° when falling on a diffraction grating that has 5000 lines per centimeter.

26. An electric current through hydrogen gas produces several distinct wavelengths of visible light. What are the wavelengths of the hydrogen spectrum, if they form first-order maxima at angles of 24.2°, 25.7°, 29.1°, and 41.0° when projected on a diffraction grating having 10,000 lines per centimeter? Explicitly show how you follow the steps in Problem-Solving Strategies for Wave Optics

27. (a) What do the four angles in the above problem become if a 5000-line-per-centimeter diffraction grating is used? (b) Using this grating, what would the angles be for the second-order maxima? (c) Discuss the relationship between integral reductions in lines per centimeter and the new angles of various order maxima.

28. What is the maximum number of lines per centimeter a diffraction grating can have and produce a complete first-order spectrum for visible light?

29. The yellow light from a sodium vapor lamp *seems* to be of pure wavelength, but it produces two first-order maxima at 36.093° and 36.129° when projected on a 10,000 line per centimeter diffraction grating. What are the two wavelengths to an accuracy of 0.1 nm?

30. What is the spacing between structures in a feather that acts as a reflection grating, given that they produce a first-order maximum for 525-nm light at a 30.0° angle?

31. Structures on a bird feather act like a reflection grating having 8000 lines per centimeter. What is the angle of the first-order maximum for 600-nm light?

32. An opal such as that shown in Figure 27.17 acts like a reflection grating with rows separated by about $8\ \mu m$. If the opal is illuminated normally, (a) at what angle will red light be seen and (b) at what angle will blue light be seen?

33. At what angle does a diffraction grating produces a second-order maximum for light having a first-order maximum at 20.0°?

34. Show that a diffraction grating cannot produce a second-order maximum for a given wavelength of light unless the first-order maximum is at an angle less than 30.0°.

35. If a diffraction grating produces a first-order maximum for the shortest wavelength of visible light at 30.0°, at what angle will the first-order maximum be for the longest wavelength of visible light?

36. (a) Find the maximum number of lines per centimeter a diffraction grating can have and produce a maximum for the smallest wavelength of visible light. (b) Would such a grating be useful for ultraviolet spectra? (c) For infrared spectra?

37. (a) Show that a 30,000-line-per-centimeter grating will not produce a maximum for visible light. (b) What is the longest wavelength for which it does produce a first-order maximum? (c) What is the greatest number of lines per centimeter a diffraction grating can have and produce a complete second-order spectrum for visible light?

38. A He–Ne laser beam is reflected from the surface of a CD onto a wall. The brightest spot is the reflected beam at an angle equal to the angle of incidence. However, fringes are also observed. If the wall is 1.50 m from the CD, and the first fringe is 0.600 m from the central maximum, what is the spacing of grooves on the CD?

39. The analysis shown in the figure below also applies to diffraction gratings with lines separated by a distance d. What is the distance between fringes produced by a diffraction grating having 125 lines per centimeter for 600-nm light, if the screen is 1.50 m away?

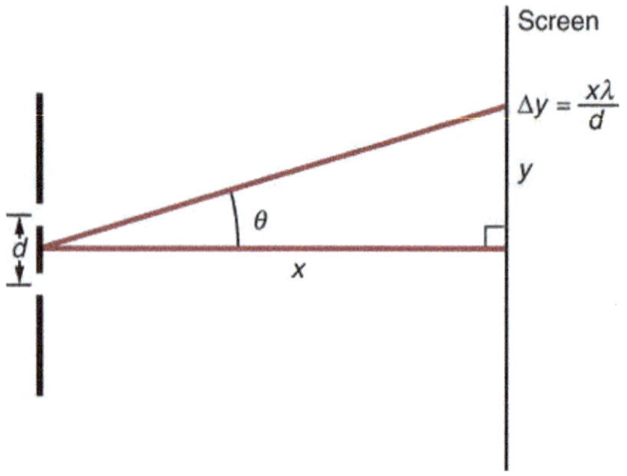

FIGURE 27.57 The distance between adjacent fringes is $\Delta y = x\lambda/d$, assuming the slit separation d is large compared with λ.

40. Unreasonable Results
Red light of wavelength of 700 nm falls on a double slit separated by 400 nm. (a) At what angle is the first-order maximum in the diffraction pattern? (b) What is unreasonable about this result? (c) Which assumptions are unreasonable or inconsistent?

41. Unreasonable Results
(a) What visible wavelength has its fourth-order maximum at an angle of 25.0° when projected on a 25,000-line-per-centimeter diffraction grating? (b) What is unreasonable about this result? (c) Which assumptions are unreasonable or inconsistent?

42. Construct Your Own Problem
Consider a spectrometer based on a diffraction grating. Construct a problem in which you calculate the distance between two wavelengths of electromagnetic radiation in your spectrometer. Among the things to be considered are the wavelengths you wish to be able to distinguish, the number of lines per meter on the diffraction grating, and the distance from the grating to the screen or detector. Discuss the practicality of the device in terms of being able to discern between wavelengths of interest.

27.5 Single Slit Diffraction

43. (a) At what angle is the first minimum for 550-nm light falling on a single slit of width $1.00\ \mu m$? (b) Will there be a second minimum?

44. (a) Calculate the angle at which a $2.00\text{-}\mu m$-wide slit produces its first minimum for 410-nm violet light. (b) Where is the first minimum for 700-nm red light?

45. (a) How wide is a single slit that produces its first minimum for 633-nm light at an angle of 28.0°? (b) At what angle will the second minimum be?

46. (a) What is the width of a single slit that produces its first minimum at 60.0° for 600-nm light? (b) Find the wavelength of light that has its first minimum at 62.0°.

47. Find the wavelength of light that has its third minimum at an angle of 48.6° when it falls on a single slit of width $3.00\ \mu m$.

48. Calculate the wavelength of light that produces its first minimum at an angle of 36.9° when falling on a single slit of width $1.00\ \mu m$.

49. (a) Sodium vapor light averaging 589 nm in wavelength falls on a single slit of width $7.50\ \mu m$. At what angle does it produces its second minimum? (b) What is the highest-order minimum produced?

50. (a) Find the angle of the third diffraction minimum for 633-nm light falling on a slit of width $20.0\ \mu m$. (b) What slit width would place this minimum at 85.0°? Explicitly show how you follow the steps in Problem-Solving Strategies for Wave Optics

51. (a) Find the angle between the first minima for the two sodium vapor lines, which have wavelengths of 589.1 and 589.6 nm, when they fall upon a single slit of width $2.00\ \mu m$. (b) What is the distance between these minima if the diffraction pattern falls on a screen 1.00 m from the slit? (c) Discuss the ease or difficulty of measuring such a distance.

52. (a) What is the minimum width of a single slit (in multiples of λ) that will produce a first minimum for a wavelength λ? (b) What is its minimum width if it produces 50 minima? (c) 1000 minima?

53. (a) If a single slit produces a first minimum at 14.5°, at what angle is the second-order minimum? (b) What is the angle of the third-order minimum? (c) Is there a fourth-order minimum? (d) Use your answers to illustrate how the angular width of the central maximum is about twice the angular width of the next maximum (which is the angle between the first and second minima).

54. A double slit produces a diffraction pattern that is a combination of single and double slit interference. Find the ratio of the width of the slits to the separation between them, if the first minimum of the single slit pattern falls on the fifth maximum of the double slit pattern. (This will greatly reduce the intensity of the fifth maximum.)

55. Integrated Concepts
A water break at the entrance to a harbor consists of a rock barrier with a 50.0-m-wide opening. Ocean waves of 20.0-m wavelength approach the opening straight on. At what angle to the incident direction are the boats inside the harbor most protected against wave action?

56. Integrated Concepts
An aircraft maintenance technician walks past a tall hangar door that acts like a single slit for sound entering the hangar. Outside the door, on a line perpendicular to the opening in the door, a jet engine makes a 600-Hz sound. At what angle with the door will the technician observe the first minimum in sound intensity if the vertical opening is 0.800 m wide and the speed of sound is 340 m/s?

27.6 Limits of Resolution: The Rayleigh Criterion

57. The 300-m-diameter Arecibo radio telescope pictured in Figure 27.28 detects radio waves with a 4.00 cm average wavelength.
(a) What is the angle between two just-resolvable point sources for this telescope?
(b) How close together could these point sources be at the 2 million light year distance of the Andromeda galaxy?

58. Assuming the angular resolution found for the Hubble Telescope in Example 27.5, what is the smallest detail that could be observed on the Moon?

59. Diffraction spreading for a flashlight is insignificant compared with other limitations in its optics, such as spherical aberrations in its mirror. To show this, calculate the minimum angular spreading of a flashlight beam that is originally 5.00 cm in diameter with an average wavelength of 600 nm.

60. (a) What is the minimum angular spread of a 633-nm wavelength He-Ne laser beam that is originally 1.00 mm in diameter?
(b) If this laser is aimed at a mountain cliff 15.0 km away, how big will the illuminated spot be?
(c) How big a spot would be illuminated on the Moon, neglecting atmospheric effects? (This might be done to hit a corner reflector to measure the round-trip time and, hence, distance.) Explicitly show how you follow the steps in Problem-Solving Strategies for Wave Optics.

61. A telescope can be used to enlarge the diameter of a laser beam and limit diffraction spreading. The laser beam is sent through the telescope in opposite the normal direction and can then be projected onto a satellite or the Moon.
(a) If this is done with the Mount Wilson telescope, producing a 2.54-m-diameter beam of 633-nm light, what is the minimum angular spread of the beam (the angle between the beam's maximum and its first zero)?
(b) Neglecting atmospheric effects, what is the size of the spot this beam would make on the Moon, assuming a lunar distance of 3.84×10^8 m?

62. The limit to the eye's acuity is actually related to diffraction by the pupil.
(a) What is the angle between two just-resolvable points of light for a 3.00-mm-diameter pupil, assuming an average wavelength of 550 nm?
(b) Take your result to be the practical limit for the eye. What is the greatest possible distance a car can be from you if you can resolve its two headlights, given they are 1.30 m apart?
(c) What is the distance between two just-resolvable points held at an arm's length (0.800 m) from your eye?
(d) How does your answer to (c) compare to details you normally observe in everyday circumstances?

63. What is the minimum diameter mirror on a telescope that would allow you to see details as small as 5.00 km on the Moon some 384,000 km away? Assume an average wavelength of 550 nm for the light received.

64. You are told not to shoot until you see the whites of their eyes. If the eyes are separated by 6.5 cm and the diameter of your pupil is 5.0 mm, at what distance can you resolve the two eyes using light of wavelength 555 nm?

65. (a) The planet Pluto and its Moon Charon are separated by 19,600 km. Neglecting atmospheric effects, should the 5.08-m-diameter Mount Palomar telescope be able to resolve these bodies when they are 4.50×10^9 km from Earth? Assume an average wavelength of 550 nm.
(b) In actuality, it is just barely possible to discern that Pluto and Charon are separate bodies using an Earth-based telescope. What are the reasons for this?

66. The headlights of a car are 1.3 m apart. What is the maximum distance at which the eye can resolve these two headlights? Take the pupil diameter to be 0.40 cm.

67. When dots are placed on a page from a laser printer, they must be close enough so that you do not see the individual dots of ink. To do this, the separation of the dots must be less than Raleigh's criterion. Take the pupil of the eye to be 3.0 mm and the distance from the paper to the eye of 35 cm; find the minimum separation of two dots such that they cannot be resolved. How many dots per inch (dpi) does this correspond to?

68. Unreasonable Results
An amateur astronomer wants to build a telescope with a diffraction limit that will allow him to see if there are people on the moons of Jupiter.
(a) What diameter mirror is needed to be able to see 1.00 m detail on a Jovian Moon at a distance of 7.50×10^8 km from Earth? The wavelength of light averages 600 nm.
(b) What is unreasonable about this result?
(c) Which assumptions are unreasonable or inconsistent?

69. Construct Your Own Problem
Consider diffraction limits for an electromagnetic wave interacting with a circular object. Construct a problem in which you calculate the limit of angular resolution with a device, using this circular object (such as a lens, mirror, or antenna) to make observations. Also calculate the limit to spatial resolution (such as the size of features observable on the Moon) for observations at a specific distance from the device. Among the things to be considered are the wavelength of electromagnetic radiation used, the size of the circular object, and the distance to the system or phenomenon being observed.

27.7 Thin Film Interference

70. A soap bubble is 100 nm thick and illuminated by white light incident perpendicular to its surface. What wavelength and color of visible light is most constructively reflected, assuming the same index of refraction as water?

71. An oil slick on water is 120 nm thick and illuminated by white light incident perpendicular to its surface. What color does the oil appear (what is the most constructively reflected wavelength), given its index of refraction is 1.40?

72. Calculate the minimum thickness of an oil slick on water that appears blue when illuminated by white light perpendicular to its surface. Take the blue wavelength to be 470 nm and the index of refraction of oil to be 1.40.

73. Find the minimum thickness of a soap bubble that appears red when illuminated by white light perpendicular to its surface. Take the wavelength to be 680 nm, and assume the same index of refraction as water.

74. A film of soapy water ($n = 1.33$) on top of a plastic cutting board has a thickness of 233 nm. What color is most strongly reflected if it is illuminated perpendicular to its surface?

75. What are the three smallest non-zero thicknesses of soapy water ($n = 1.33$) on Plexiglas if it appears green (constructively reflecting 520-nm light) when illuminated perpendicularly by white light? Explicitly show how you follow the steps in Problem Solving Strategies for Wave Optics.

76. Suppose you have a lens system that is to be used primarily for 700-nm red light. What is the second thinnest coating of fluorite (magnesium fluoride) that would be non-reflective for this wavelength?

77. (a) As a soap bubble thins it becomes dark, because the path length difference becomes small compared with the wavelength of light and there is a phase shift at the top surface. If it becomes dark when the path length difference is less than one-fourth the wavelength, what is the thickest the bubble can be and appear dark at all visible wavelengths? Assume the same index of refraction as water. (b) Discuss the fragility of the film considering the thickness found.

78. A film of oil on water will appear dark when it is very thin, because the path length difference becomes small compared with the wavelength of light and there is a phase shift at the top surface. If it becomes dark when the path length difference is less than one-fourth the wavelength, what is the thickest the oil can be and appear dark at all visible wavelengths? Oil has an index of refraction of 1.40.

79. Figure 27.34 shows two glass slides illuminated by pure-wavelength light incident perpendicularly. The top slide touches the bottom slide at one end and rests on a 0.100-mm-diameter hair at the other end, forming a wedge of air. (a) How far apart are the dark bands, if the slides are 7.50 cm long and 589-nm light is used? (b) Is there any difference if the slides are made from crown or flint glass? Explain.

80. Figure 27.34 shows two 7.50-cm-long glass slides illuminated by pure 589-nm wavelength light incident perpendicularly. The top slide touches the bottom slide at one end and rests on some debris at the other end, forming a wedge of air. How thick is the debris, if the dark bands are 1.00 mm apart?

81. Repeat Exercise 27.70, but take the light to be incident at a $45°$ angle.

82. Repeat Exercise 27.71, but take the light to be incident at a $45°$ angle.

83. Unreasonable Results
To save money on making military aircraft invisible to radar, an inventor decides to coat them with a non-reflective material having an index of refraction of 1.20, which is between that of air and the surface of the plane. This, he reasons, should be much cheaper than designing Stealth bombers. (a) What thickness should the coating be to inhibit the reflection of 4.00-cm wavelength radar? (b) What is unreasonable about this result? (c) Which assumptions are unreasonable or inconsistent?

27.8 Polarization

84. What angle is needed between the direction of polarized light and the axis of a polarizing filter to cut its intensity in half?

85. The angle between the axes of two polarizing filters is $45.0°$. By how much does the second filter reduce the intensity of the light coming through the first?

86. If you have completely polarized light of intensity 150 W/m^2, what will its intensity be after passing through a polarizing filter with its axis at an $89.0°$ angle to the light's polarization direction?

87. What angle would the axis of a polarizing filter need to make with the direction of polarized light of intensity 1.00 kW/m^2 to reduce the intensity to 10.0 W/m^2?

88. At the end of Example 27.8, it was stated that the intensity of polarized light is reduced to 90.0% of its original value by passing through a polarizing filter with its axis at an angle of $18.4°$ to the direction of polarization. Verify this statement.

89. Show that if you have three polarizing filters, with the second at an angle of $45°$ to the first and the third at an angle of $90.0°$ to the first, the intensity of light passed by the first will be reduced to 25.0% of its value. (This is in contrast to having only the first and third, which reduces the intensity to zero, so that placing the second between them increases the intensity of the transmitted light.)

90. Prove that, if I is the intensity of light transmitted by two polarizing filters with axes at an angle θ and I' is the intensity when the axes are at an angle $90.0° - \theta$, then $I + I' = I_0,$ the original intensity. (Hint: Use the trigonometric identities $\cos(90.0° - \theta) = \sin\theta$ and $\cos^2\theta + \sin^2\theta = 1$.)

91. At what angle will light reflected from diamond be completely polarized?

92. What is Brewster's angle for light traveling in water that is reflected from crown glass?

93. A scuba diver sees light reflected from the water's surface. At what angle will this light be completely polarized?

94. At what angle is light inside crown glass completely polarized when reflected from water, as in a fish tank?

95. Light reflected at $55.6°$ from a window is completely polarized. What is the window's index of refraction and the likely substance of which it is made?

96. (a) Light reflected at $62.5°$ from a gemstone in a ring is completely polarized. Can the gem be a diamond? (b) At what angle would the light be completely polarized if the gem was in water?

97. If θ_b is Brewster's angle for light reflected from the top of an interface between two substances, and θ'_b is Brewster's angle for light reflected from below, prove that $\theta_b + \theta'_b = 90.0°$.

98. Integrated Concepts
If a polarizing filter reduces the intensity of polarized light to 50.0% of its original value, by how much are the electric and magnetic fields reduced?

99. Integrated Concepts
Suppose you put on two pairs of Polaroid sunglasses with their axes at an angle of $15.0°$. How much longer will it take the light to deposit a given amount of energy in your eye compared with a single pair of sunglasses? Assume the lenses are clear except for their polarizing characteristics.

100. Integrated Concepts
(a) On a day when the intensity of sunlight is 1.00 kW/m^2, a circular lens 0.200 m in diameter focuses light onto water in a black aluminum beaker. Two polarizing sheets of plastic are placed in front of the lens with their axes at an

angle of $20.0°$. Assuming the sunlight is unpolarized and the polarizers are 100% efficient, what is the initial rate of heating of the water in $°C/s$, assuming it is 80.0% absorbed? The aluminum beaker has a mass of 30.0 grams and contains 250 grams of water. (b) Do the polarizing filters get hot? Explain.

101. Critical Thinking A semiconductor laser emits light at 400.0 nm. The light is passed through a grating where 1,000 lines are etched covering a space of 10.00 mm. The light is directed directly at the grating. (a) What is the angle the light beam diffracts for first order diffraction? (b) What is the angle the light beam diffracts for second order diffraction? (c) The laser is changed out. The first order angle of diffraction is now $23.9°$. What wavelength of light does it produce? (d) If a new grating with the spacing between the lines doubled were to replace the one above, what would the new angle be for part a? (e) Would the magnitude of the angle of diffraction be different going left from going right?

Test Prep for AP® Courses

27.2 Huygens's Principle: Diffraction

1. Which of the following statements is true about Huygens's principle of secondary wavelets?
   a. It can be used to explain the particle behavior of waves.
   b. It states that each point on a wavefront can be considered a new wave source.
   c. It can be used to find the velocity of a wave.
   d. All of the above.

2. Explain why the amount of bending that occurs during diffraction depends on the width of the opening through which light passes.

27.3 Young's Double Slit Experiment

3. Superposition of which of the following light waves may produce interference fringes? Select *two* answers.

$\text{Wave}_1 = A_1\sin(2\omega t)$
$\text{Wave}_2 = A_2\sin(4\omega t)$
$\text{Wave}_3 = A_3\sin(2\omega t + \theta)$
$\text{Wave}_4 = A_4\sin(4\omega t + \theta)$.

   a. Wave_1 and Wave_2
   b. Wave_2 and Wave_4
   c. Wave_3 and Wave_1
   d. Wave_4 and Wave_3

4. In a double slit experiment with monochromatic light, the separation between the slits is 2 mm. If the screen is moved by 100 mm toward the slits, the distance between the central bright line and the second bright line changes by 32 µm. Calculate the wavelength of the light used for the experiment.

5. In a double slit experiment, a student measures the maximum and minimum intensities when two waves with equal amplitudes are used. The student then doubles the amplitudes of the two waves and performs the measurements again. Which of the following will remain unchanged?
   a. The intensity of the bright fringe
   b. The intensity of the dark fringe
   c. The difference in the intensities of consecutive bright and dark fringes
   d. None of the above

6. Draw a figure to show the resultant wave produced when two coherent waves (with equal amplitudes x) interact in phase. What is the amplitude of the resultant wave? If the phase difference between the coherent waves is changed to 60°, what will be new amplitude?

7. What will be the amplitude of the central fringe if the amplitudes of the two waves in a double slit experiment are a and $3a$?
   a. $2a$
   b. $4a$
   c. $8a^2$
   d. $16a^2$

8. If the ratio of amplitudes of the two waves in a double slit experiment is 3:4, calculate the ratio of minimum intensity (dark fringe) to maximum intensity (bright fringe).

27.4 Multiple Slit Diffraction

9. Which of the following cannot be a possible outcome of passing white light through several evenly spaced parallel slits?
   a. The central maximum will be white but the higher-order maxima will disperse into a rainbow of colors.
   b. The central maximum and higher-order maxima will be of equal widths.
   c. The lower wavelength components of light will have less diffraction compared to higher wavelength components for all maxima except the central one.
   d. None of the above.

10. White light is passed through a diffraction grating to a screen some distance away. The *n*th-order diffraction angle for the longest wavelength (760 nm) is 53.13°. Find the *n*th-order diffraction angle for the shortest wavelength (380 nm). What will be the change in the two angles if the distance between the screen and the grating is doubled?

27.5 Single Slit Diffraction

11. A diffraction pattern is formed on a screen when light of wavelength 410 nm is passed through a single slit of width 1 µm. If the source light is replaced by another light of wavelength 700 nm, what should be the width of the slit so that the new light produces a pattern with the same spacing?

a. 0.6 µm
b. 1 µm
c. 1.4 µm
d. 1.7 µm

12. Monochromatic light passing through a single slit forms a diffraction pattern on a screen. If the second minimum occurs at an angle of 15°, find the angle for the fourth minimum.

27.6 Limits of Resolution: The Rayleigh Criterion

13. What is the relationship between the width (*W*) of the central diffraction maximum formed through a circular aperture and the size (*S*) of the aperture?

a. *W* increases as *S* increases.
b. *W* decreases as *S* increases.
c. *W* can increase or decrease as *S* decreases.
d. *W* can neither increase nor decrease as *S* decreases.

14. Light from two sources passes through a circular aperture to form images on a screen. State the Rayleigh criterion for the images to be just resolvable and draw a figure to visually explain it.

27.7 Thin Film Interference

15. Which of the following best describes the cause of thin film interference?

a. Light reflecting from a medium having an index of refraction less than that of the medium in which it is traveling.
b. Light reflecting from a medium having an index of refraction greater than that of the medium in which it is traveling.
c. Light changing its wavelength and speed after reflection.
d. Light reflecting from the top and bottom surfaces of a film.

16. A film of magnesium fluoride ($n = 1.38$) is used to coat a glass camera lens ($n = 1.52$). If the thickness of the film is 105 nm, calculate the wavelength of visible light that will have the most limited reflection.

27.8 Polarization

17. Which of the following statements is true for the direction of polarization for a polarized light wave?

a. It is parallel to the direction of propagation and perpendicular to the direction of the electric field.
b. It is perpendicular to the direction of propagation and parallel to the direction of the electric field.
c. It is parallel to the directions of propagation and the electric field.
d. It is perpendicular to the directions of propagation and the electric field.

18. In an experiment, light is passed through two polarizing filters. The image below shows the first filter and axis of polarization.

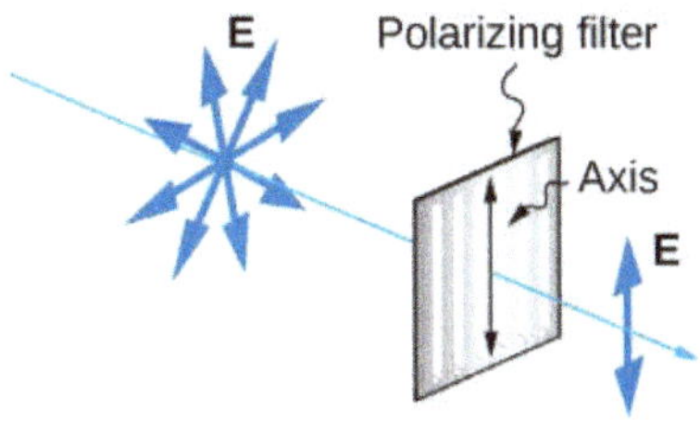

FIGURE 27.58

The intensity of the resulting light (after the first filter) is recorded as I. Three configurations (at different angles) are set up for the second filter, and the intensity of light is recorded for each configuration. The results are shown in the table below:

Set up	Angle of second filter compared to first filter	Intensity of light after second filter
Configuration A	θ_1	I
Configuration B	θ_2	$0.5I$
Configuration C	θ_3	0

TABLE 27.1

Complete the table by calculating θ_1, θ_2, and θ_3.

CHAPTER 28
Special Relativity

FIGURE 28.1 Special relativity has implications and applications ranging from space travel and our understanding of time to everyday technologies such as Global Positioning Systems. In order to be effective, GPS, whether it is a part of a mobile phone or a shark tracking system, must account for relativistic principles such as time dilation. (credit: UW News/Flickr)

CHAPTER OUTLINE

CONNECTION FOR AP® COURSES In this chapter you will be introduced to the theory of special relativity, which was first described by Albert Einstein in the year 1905. The chapter opens with a discussion of Einstein's postulates that form the basis of special relativity. You will learn about an essential physics framework that is used to describe the observations and measurements made by an observer in what is called the "inertial frame of reference" (Enduring Understanding 3.A). Special relativity is a universally accepted theory that defines a relationship between space and time (Essential Knowledge 1.D.3). When the speed of an object approaches the speed of light, Newton's laws no longer hold, which means that classical (Newtonian) mechanics (Enduring Understanding 1.D) is not sufficient to define the physical properties of such a system. This is where special relativity comes into play. Many interesting and counterintuitive physical results follow from the theory of special relativity. In this chapter we will explore the concepts of simultaneity, time dilation, and length contraction.

Further into the chapter you will find information that supports the concepts of relativistic velocity addition, relativistic momentum, and energy (Enduring Understanding 4.C). Learning these concepts will help you understand how the mass (Enduring Understanding 1.C and Essential Knowledge 4.C.4) of an object can appear to be different for different observers and how matter can be converted into energy and then back to matter so that the energy of the system remains conserved. (Essential Knowledge 1.C.4 and Enduring Understanding 5.B). The information and examples presented in the chapter support Big Ideas 1, 3, 4, and 5 of the AP® Physics Curriculum Framework.

The content of this chapter supports:

Big Idea 1 Objects and systems have properties such as mass and charge. Systems may have internal structure.

Enduring Understanding 1.C Objects and systems have properties of inertial mass and gravitational mass that are experimentally verified to be the same and that satisfy conservation principles.

Essential Knowledge 1.C.4 In certain processes, mass can be converted to energy and energy can be converted to mass according to $E = mc^2$, the equation derived from the theory of special relativity.

Enduring Understanding 1.D Classical mechanics cannot describe all properties of objects.

Essential Knowledge 1.D.3 Properties of space and time cannot always be treated as absolute.

Big Idea 3 The interactions of an object with other objects can be described by forces.

Enduring Understanding 3.A All forces share certain common characteristics when considered by observers in inertial reference frames.

Essential Knowledge 3.A.1 An observer in a particular reference frame can describe the motion of an object using such quantities as position, displacement, distance, velocity, speed, and acceleration.

Big Idea 4 Interactions between systems can result in changes in those systems.

Enduring Understanding 4.C Interactions with other objects or systems can change the total energy of a system.

Essential Knowledge 4.C.4 Mass can be converted into energy and energy can be converted into mass.

Big Idea 5 Changes that occur as a result of interactions are constrained by conservation laws.

Enduring Understanding 5.B The energy of a system is conserved.

Essential Knowledge 5.B.11 Beyond the classical approximation, mass is actually part of the internal energy of an object or system with $E = mc^2$.

FIGURE 28.2 Many people think that Albert Einstein (1879–1955) was the greatest physicist of the 20th century. Not only did he develop modern relativity, thus revolutionizing our concept of the universe, he also made fundamental contributions to the foundations of quantum mechanics. (credit: The Library of Congress)

It is important to note that although classical mechanic, in general, and classical relativity, in particular, are limited, they are extremely good approximations for large, slow-moving objects. Otherwise, we could not use classical physics to launch satellites or build bridges. In the classical limit (objects larger than submicroscopic and moving slower than about 1% of the speed of light), relativistic mechanics becomes the same as classical mechanics. This fact will be noted at appropriate places throughout this chapter.

28.1 Einstein's Postulates

LEARNING OBJECTIVES

By the end of this section, you will be able to:

- State and explain both of Einstein's postulates.
- Explain what an inertial frame of reference is.
- Describe one way the speed of light can be changed.

FIGURE 28.3 Special relativity resembles trigonometry in that both are reliable because they are based on postulates that flow one from another in a logical way. (credit: Jon Oakley, Flickr)

Have you ever used the Pythagorean Theorem and gotten a wrong answer? Probably not, unless you made a mistake in either your algebra or your arithmetic. Each time you perform the same calculation, you know that the answer will be the same. Trigonometry is reliable because of the certainty that one part always flows from another in a logical way. Each part is based on a set of postulates, and you can always connect the parts by applying those postulates. Physics is the same way with the exception that *all* parts must describe nature. If we are careful to choose the correct postulates, then our theory will follow and will be verified by experiment.

Einstein essentially did the theoretical aspect of this method for **relativity**. With two deceptively simple postulates and a careful consideration of how measurements are made, he produced the theory of **special relativity.**

Einstein's First Postulate

The first postulate upon which Einstein based the theory of special relativity relates to reference frames. All velocities are measured relative to some frame of reference. For example, a car's motion is measured relative to its starting point or the road it is moving over, a projectile's motion is measured relative to the surface it was launched from, and a planet's orbit is measured relative to the star it is orbiting around. The simplest frames of reference are those that are not accelerated and are not rotating. Newton's first law, the law of inertia, holds exactly in such a frame.

INERTIAL REFERENCE FRAME

An **inertial frame of reference** is a reference frame in which a body at rest remains at rest and a body in motion moves at a constant speed in a straight line unless acted on by an outside force.

The laws of physics seem to be simplest in inertial frames. For example, when you are in a plane flying at a constant altitude and speed, physics seems to work exactly the same as if you were standing on the surface of the Earth. However, in a plane that is taking off, matters are somewhat more complicated. In these cases, the net force on an object, F, is not equal to the product of mass and acceleration, ma. Instead, F is equal to ma plus a fictitious force. This situation is not as simple as in an inertial frame. Not only are laws of physics simplest in inertial frames, but they should be the same in all inertial frames, since there is no preferred frame and no absolute motion. Einstein incorporated these ideas into his **first postulate of special relativity**.

FIRST POSTULATE OF SPECIAL RELATIVITY

The laws of physics are the same and can be stated in their simplest form in all inertial frames of reference.

As with many fundamental statements, there is more to this postulate than meets the eye. The laws of physics include only those that satisfy this postulate. We shall find that the definitions of relativistic momentum and energy must be altered to fit. Another outcome of this postulate is the famous equation $E = mc^2$.

Einstein's Second Postulate

The second postulate upon which Einstein based his theory of special relativity deals with the speed of light. Late in the 19th century, the major tenets of classical physics were well established. Two of the most important were the laws of electricity and magnetism and Newton's laws. In particular, the laws of electricity and magnetism predict that light travels at $c = 3.00 \times 10^8\ \text{m/s}$ in a vacuum, but they do not specify the frame of reference in which light has this speed.

There was a contradiction between this prediction and Newton's laws, in which velocities add like simple vectors. If the latter were true, then two observers moving at different speeds would see light traveling at different speeds. Imagine what a light wave would look like to a person traveling along with it at a speed c. If such a motion were possible then the wave would be stationary relative to the observer. It would have electric and magnetic fields that varied in strength at various distances from the observer but were constant in time. This is not allowed by Maxwell's equations. So either Maxwell's equations are wrong, or an object with mass cannot travel at speed c. Einstein concluded that the latter is true. An object with mass cannot travel at speed c. This conclusion implies that light in a vacuum must always travel at speed c relative to any observer. Maxwell's equations are correct, and Newton's addition of velocities is not correct for light.

Investigations such as Young's double slit experiment in the early-1800s had convincingly demonstrated that light is a wave. Many types of waves were known, and all travelled in some medium. Scientists therefore assumed that a medium carried light, even in a vacuum, and light travelled at a speed c relative to that medium. Starting in the mid-1880s, the American physicist A. A. Michelson, later aided by E. W. Morley, made a series of direct measurements of the speed of light. The results of their measurements were startling.

MICHELSON-MORLEY EXPERIMENT

The **Michelson-Morley experiment** demonstrated that the speed of light in a vacuum is independent of the motion of the Earth about the Sun.

The eventual conclusion derived from this result is that light, unlike mechanical waves such as sound, does not need a medium to carry it. Furthermore, the Michelson-Morley results implied that the speed of light c is independent of the motion of the source relative to the observer. That is, everyone observes light to move at speed c regardless of how they move relative to the source or one another. For a number of years, many scientists tried unsuccessfully to explain these results and still retain the general applicability of Newton's laws.

It was not until 1905, when Einstein published his first paper on special relativity, that the currently accepted conclusion was reached. Based mostly on his analysis that the laws of electricity and magnetism would not allow another speed for light, and only slightly aware of the Michelson-Morley experiment, Einstein detailed his **second postulate of special relativity**.

SECOND POSTULATE OF SPECIAL RELATIVITY

The speed of light c is a constant, independent of the relative motion of the source.

Deceptively simple and counterintuitive, this and the first postulate leave all else open for change. Some fundamental concepts do change. Among the changes are the loss of agreement on the elapsed time for an event, the variation of distance with speed, and the realization that matter and energy can be converted into one another. You will read about these concepts in the following sections.

MISCONCEPTION ALERT: CONSTANCY OF THE SPEED OF LIGHT

The speed of light is a constant $c = 3.00 \times 10^8$ m/s *in a vacuum*. If you remember the effect of the index of refraction from The Law of Refraction, the speed of light is lower in matter.

CHECK YOUR UNDERSTANDING

Explain how special relativity differs from general relativity.

Solution

Special relativity applies only to unaccelerated motion, but general relativity applies to accelerated motion.

28.2 Simultaneity And Time Dilation

LEARNING OBJECTIVES

By the end of this section, you will be able to:

- Describe simultaneity.
- Describe time dilation.
- Calculate γ.
- Compare proper time and the observer's measured time.
- Explain why the twin paradox is a false paradox.

FIGURE 28.4 Elapsed time for a foot race is the same for all observers, but at relativistic speeds, elapsed time depends on the relative motion of the observer and the event that is observed. (credit: Jason Edward Scott Bain, Flickr)

Do time intervals depend on who observes them? Intuitively, we expect the time for a process, such as the elapsed time for a foot race, to be the same for all observers. Our experience has been that disagreements over elapsed time have to do with the accuracy of measuring time. When we carefully consider just how time is measured, however, we will find that elapsed time depends on the relative motion of an observer with respect to the process being measured.

Simultaneity

Consider how we measure elapsed time. If we use a stopwatch, for example, how do we know when to start and stop the watch? One method is to use the arrival of light from the event, such as observing a light turning green to start a drag race. The timing will be more accurate if some sort of electronic detection is used, avoiding human reaction times and other complications.

Now suppose we use this method to measure the time interval between two flashes of light produced by flash lamps. (See Figure 28.5.) Two flash lamps with observer A midway between them are on a rail car that moves to the right relative to observer B. Observer B arranges for the light flashes to be emitted just as A passes B, so that both A and B are equidistant from the lamps when the light is emitted. Observer B measures the time interval between the arrival of the light flashes. According to postulate 2, the speed of light is not affected by the motion of the lamps relative to B. Therefore, light travels equal distances to him at equal speeds. Thus observer B measures the flashes to be simultaneous.

FIGURE 28.5 Observer B measures the elapsed time between the arrival of light flashes as described in the text. Observer A moves with the lamps on a rail car. Observer B views the light flashes occurring simultaneously. Observer B views the light on the right reaching observer A before the light on the left does.

Now consider what observer A sees happening. Since both lamps are the same distance from her in her reference frame and the train is moving to the right, she perceives the flash from the right-hand bulb occurring before the left-hand bulb. Here a relative velocity between observers affects whether two events are observed to be simultaneous. *Simultaneity is not absolute..*

This illustrates the power of clear thinking. We might have guessed incorrectly that if light is emitted simultaneously, then two observers halfway between the sources would see the flashes simultaneously. But careful analysis shows this not to be the case. Einstein was brilliant at this type of *thought experiment* (in German, "Gedankenexperiment"). He very carefully considered how an observation is made and disregarded what might seem obvious. The validity of thought experiments, of course, is determined by actual observation. The genius of Einstein is evidenced by the fact that experiments have repeatedly confirmed his theory of relativity.

In summary: Two events are defined to be simultaneous if an observer measures them as occurring at the same time (such as by receiving light from the events). Two events are not necessarily simultaneous to all observers.

Time Dilation

The consideration of the measurement of elapsed time and simultaneity leads to an important relativistic effect.

TIME DILATION

Time dilation is the phenomenon of time passing slower for an observer who is moving relative to another observer.

Suppose, for example, an astronaut measures the time it takes for light to cross her ship, bounce off a mirror, and return. (See Figure 28.6.) How does the elapsed time the astronaut measures compare with the elapsed time measured for the same event by a person on the Earth? Asking this question (another thought experiment) produces a profound result. We find that the elapsed time for a process depends on who is measuring it. In this case, the time measured by the astronaut is smaller than the time measured by the Earth-bound observer. The passage of time is different for the observers because the distance the light travels in the astronaut's frame is smaller than in the

Earth-bound frame. Light travels at the same speed in each frame, and so it will take longer to travel the greater distance in the Earth-bound frame.

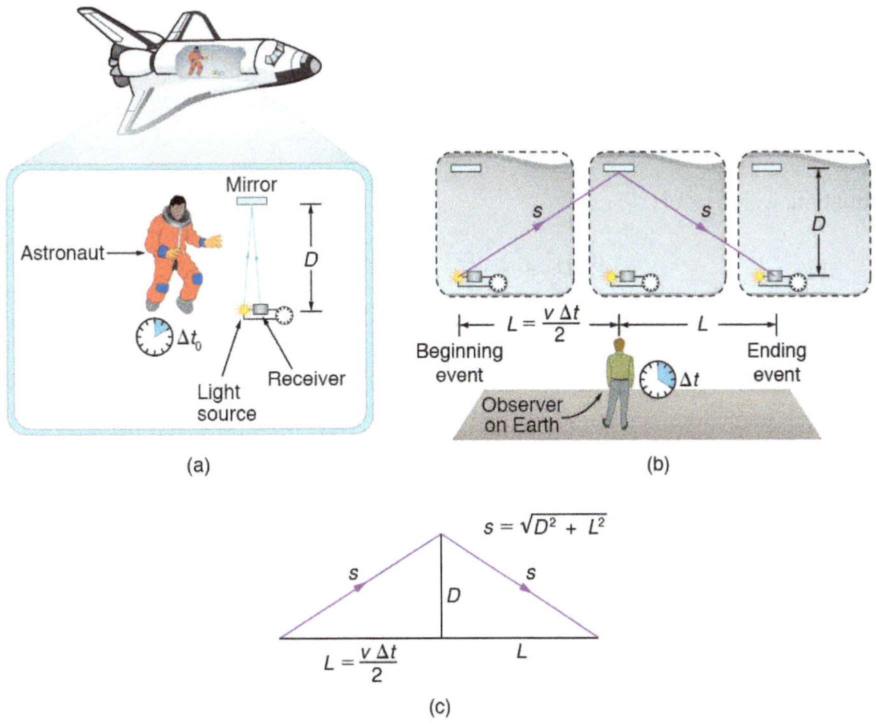

FIGURE 28.6 (a) An astronaut measures the time Δt_0 for light to cross her ship using an electronic timer. Light travels a distance $2D$ in the astronaut's frame. (b) A person on the Earth sees the light follow the longer path $2s$ and take a longer time Δt. (c) These triangles are used to find the relationship between the two distances $2D$ and $2s$.

To quantitatively verify that time depends on the observer, consider the paths followed by light as seen by each observer. (See Figure 28.6(c).) The astronaut sees the light travel straight across and back for a total distance of $2D$, twice the width of her ship. The Earth-bound observer sees the light travel a total distance $2s$. Since the ship is moving at speed v to the right relative to the Earth, light moving to the right hits the mirror in this frame. Light travels at a speed c in both frames, and because time is the distance divided by speed, the time measured by the astronaut is

$$\Delta t_0 = \frac{2D}{c}. \tag{28.1}$$

This time has a separate name to distinguish it from the time measured by the Earth-bound observer.

PROPER TIME

Proper time Δt_0 is the time measured by an observer at rest relative to the event being observed.

In the case of the astronaut observe the reflecting light, the astronaut measures proper time. The time measured by the Earth-bound observer is

$$\Delta t = \frac{2s}{c}. \tag{28.2}$$

To find the relationship between Δt_0 and Δt, consider the triangles formed by D and s. (See Figure 28.6(c).) The third side of these similar triangles is L, the distance the astronaut moves as the light goes across her ship. In the frame of the Earth-bound observer,

$$L = \frac{v\Delta t}{2}. \tag{28.3}$$

Using the Pythagorean Theorem, the distance s is found to be

$$s=\sqrt{D^2+\left(\frac{v\Delta t}{2}\right)^2}. \tag{28.4}$$

Substituting s into the expression for the time interval Δt gives

$$\Delta t=\frac{2s}{c}=\frac{2\sqrt{D^2+\left(\frac{v\Delta t}{2}\right)^2}}{c}. \tag{28.5}$$

We square this equation, which yields

$$(\Delta t)^2=\frac{4\left(D^2+\frac{v^2(\Delta t)^2}{4}\right)}{c^2}=\frac{4D^2}{c^2}+\frac{v^2}{c^2}(\Delta t)^2. \tag{28.6}$$

Note that if we square the first expression we had for Δt_0, we get $(\Delta t_0)^2=\frac{4D^2}{c^2}$. This term appears in the preceding equation, giving us a means to relate the two time intervals. Thus,

$$(\Delta t)^2=(\Delta t_0)^2+\frac{v^2}{c^2}(\Delta t)^2. \tag{28.7}$$

Gathering terms, we solve for Δt:

$$(\Delta t)^2\left(1-\frac{v^2}{c^2}\right)=(\Delta t_0)^2. \tag{28.8}$$

Thus,

$$(\Delta t)^2=\frac{(\Delta t_0)^2}{1-\frac{v^2}{c^2}}. \tag{28.9}$$

Taking the square root yields an important relationship between elapsed times:

$$\Delta t=\frac{\Delta t_0}{\sqrt{1-\frac{v^2}{c^2}}}=\gamma\Delta t_0, \tag{28.10}$$

where

$$\gamma=\frac{1}{\sqrt{1-\frac{v^2}{c^2}}}. \tag{28.11}$$

This equation for Δt is truly remarkable. First, as contended, elapsed time is not the same for different observers moving relative to one another, even though both are in inertial frames. Proper time Δt_0 measured by an observer, like the astronaut moving with the apparatus, is smaller than time measured by other observers. Since those other observers measure a longer time Δt, the effect is called time dilation. The Earth-bound observer sees time dilate (get longer) for a system moving relative to the Earth. Alternatively, according to the Earth-bound observer, time slows in the moving frame, since less time passes there. All clocks moving relative to an observer, including biological clocks such as aging, are observed to run slow compared with a clock stationary relative to the observer.

Note that if the relative velocity is much less than the speed of light ($v<<c$), then $\frac{v^2}{c^2}$ is extremely small, and the elapsed times Δt and Δt_0 are nearly equal. At low velocities, modern relativity approaches classical physics—our everyday experiences have very small relativistic effects.

The equation $\Delta t=\gamma\Delta t_0$ also implies that relative velocity cannot exceed the speed of light. As v approaches c, Δt approaches infinity. This would imply that time in the astronaut's frame stops at the speed of light. If v exceeded c, then we would be taking the square root of a negative number, producing an imaginary value for Δt.

There is considerable experimental evidence that the equation $\Delta t = \gamma \Delta t_0$ is correct. One example is found in cosmic ray particles that continuously rain down on the Earth from deep space. Some collisions of these particles with nuclei in the upper atmosphere result in short-lived particles called muons. The half-life (amount of time for half of a material to decay) of a muon is $1.52\ \mu s$ when it is at rest relative to the observer who measures the half-life. This is the proper time Δt_0. Muons produced by cosmic ray particles have a range of velocities, with some moving near the speed of light. It has been found that the muon's half-life as measured by an Earth-bound observer (Δt) varies with velocity exactly as predicted by the equation $\Delta t = \gamma \Delta t_0$. The faster the muon moves, the longer it lives. We on the Earth see the muon's half-life time dilated—as viewed from our frame, the muon decays more slowly than it does when at rest relative to us.

EXAMPLE 28.1

Calculating Δt for a Relativistic Event: How Long Does a Speedy Muon Live?

Suppose a cosmic ray colliding with a nucleus in the Earth's upper atmosphere produces a muon that has a velocity $v = 0.950c$. The muon then travels at constant velocity and lives $1.52\ \mu s$ as measured in the muon's frame of reference. (You can imagine this as the muon's internal clock.) How long does the muon live as measured by an Earth-bound observer? (See Figure 28.7.)

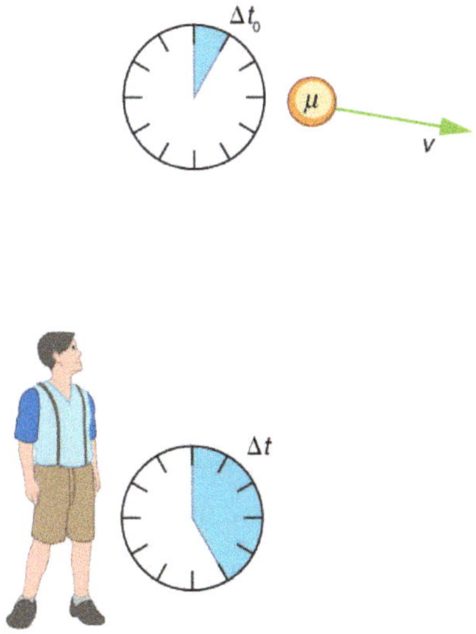

FIGURE 28.7 A muon in the Earth's atmosphere lives longer as measured by an Earth-bound observer than measured by the muon's internal clock.

Strategy

A clock moving with the system being measured observes the proper time, so the time we are given is $\Delta t_0 = 1.52\ \mu s$. The Earth-bound observer measures Δt as given by the equation $\Delta t = \gamma \Delta t_0$. Since we know the velocity, the calculation is straightforward.

Solution

1) Identify the knowns. $v = 0.950c$, $\Delta t_0 = 1.52\ \mu s$

2) Identify the unknown. Δt

3) Choose the appropriate equation.

Use,

$$\Delta t = \gamma \Delta t_0, \tag{28.12}$$

where

$$\gamma = \frac{1}{\sqrt{1 - \frac{v^2}{c^2}}}. \quad 28.13$$

4) Plug the knowns into the equation.

First find γ.

$$\begin{aligned} \gamma &= \frac{1}{\sqrt{1-\frac{v^2}{c^2}}} \\ &= \frac{1}{\sqrt{1-\frac{(0.950c)^2}{c^2}}} \\ &= \frac{1}{\sqrt{1-(0.950)^2}} \\ &= 3.20. \end{aligned} \quad 28.14$$

Use the calculated value of γ to determine Δt.

$$\begin{aligned} \Delta t &= \gamma \Delta t_0 \\ &= (3.20)(1.52\ \mu\text{s}) \\ &= 4.87\ \mu\text{s} \end{aligned} \quad 28.15$$

Discussion

One implication of this example is that since $\gamma = 3.20$ at 95.0% of the speed of light ($v = 0.950c$), the relativistic effects are significant. The two time intervals differ by this factor of 3.20, where classically they would be the same. Something moving at $0.950c$ is said to be highly relativistic.

Another implication of the preceding example is that everything an astronaut does when moving at 95.0% of the speed of light relative to the Earth takes 3.20 times longer when observed from the Earth. Does the astronaut sense this? Only if she looks outside her spaceship. All methods of measuring time in her frame will be affected by the same factor of 3.20. This includes her wristwatch, heart rate, cell metabolism rate, nerve impulse rate, and so on. She will have no way of telling, since all of her clocks will agree with one another because their relative velocities are zero. Motion is relative, not absolute. But what if she does look out the window?

REAL-WORLD CONNECTIONS

It may seem that special relativity has little effect on your life, but it is probably more important than you realize. One of the most common effects is through the Global Positioning System (GPS). Emergency vehicles, package delivery services, electronic maps, and communications devices are just a few of the common uses of GPS, and the GPS system could not work without taking into account relativistic effects. GPS satellites rely on precise time measurements to communicate. The signals travel at relativistic speeds. Without corrections for time dilation, the satellites could not communicate, and the GPS system would fail within minutes.

The Twin Paradox

An intriguing consequence of time dilation is that a space traveler moving at a high velocity relative to the Earth would age less than her Earth-bound twin. Imagine the astronaut moving at such a velocity that $\gamma = 30.0$, as in Figure 28.8. A trip that takes 2.00 years in her frame would take 60.0 years in her Earth-bound twin's frame. Suppose the astronaut traveled 1.00 year to another star system. She briefly explored the area, and then traveled 1.00 year back. If the astronaut was 40 years old when she left, she would be 42 upon her return. Everything on the Earth, however, would have aged 60.0 years. Her twin, if still alive, would be 100 years old.

The situation would seem different to the astronaut. Because motion is relative, the spaceship would seem to be stationary and the Earth would appear to move. (This is the sensation you have when flying in a jet.) If the astronaut looks out the window of the spaceship, she will see time slow down on the Earth by a factor of $\gamma = 30.0$. To her, the Earth-bound sister will have aged only 2/30 (1/15) of a year, while she aged 2.00 years. The two sisters cannot both be correct.

FIGURE 28.8 The twin paradox asks why the traveling twin ages less than the Earth-bound twin. That is the prediction we obtain if we consider the Earth-bound twin's frame. In the astronaut's frame, however, the Earth is moving and time runs slower there. Who is correct?

As with all paradoxes, the premise is faulty and leads to contradictory conclusions. In fact, the astronaut's motion is significantly different from that of the Earth-bound twin. The astronaut accelerates to a high velocity and then decelerates to view the star system. To return to the Earth, she again accelerates and decelerates. The Earth-bound twin does not experience these accelerations. So the situation is not symmetric, and it is not correct to claim that the astronaut will observe the same effects as her Earth-bound twin. If you use special relativity to examine the twin paradox, you must keep in mind that the theory is expressly based on inertial frames, which by definition are not accelerated or rotating. Einstein developed general relativity to deal with accelerated frames and with gravity, a prime source of acceleration. You can also use general relativity to address the twin paradox and, according to general relativity, the astronaut will age less. Some important conceptual aspects of general relativity are discussed in General Relativity and Quantum Gravity of this course.

In 1971, American physicists Joseph Hafele and Richard Keating verified time dilation at low relative velocities by flying extremely accurate atomic clocks around the Earth on commercial aircraft. They measured elapsed time to an accuracy of a few nanoseconds and compared it with the time measured by clocks left behind. Hafele and Keating's results were within experimental uncertainties of the predictions of relativity. Both special and general relativity had to be taken into account, since gravity and accelerations were involved as well as relative motion.

CHECK YOUR UNDERSTANDING

1. What is γ if $v = 0.650c$?

2. A particle travels at 1.90×10^8 m/s and lives 2.10×10^{-8} s when at rest relative to an observer. How long does the particle live as viewed in the laboratory?

Solution

1. $\gamma = \dfrac{1}{\sqrt{1-\frac{v^2}{c^2}}} = \dfrac{1}{\sqrt{1-\frac{(0.650c)^2}{c^2}}} = 1.32$

2. $\Delta t = \dfrac{\Delta t_0}{\sqrt{1-\frac{v^2}{c^2}}} = \dfrac{2.10\times10^{-8}\text{ s}}{\sqrt{1-\frac{(1.90\times10^8\text{ m/s})^2}{(3.00\times10^8\text{ m/s})^2}}} = 2.71 \times 10^{-8}$ s

28.3 Length Contraction

LEARNING OBJECTIVES

By the end of this section, you will be able to:

- Describe proper length.
- Calculate length contraction.
- Explain why we don't notice these effects at everyday scales.

FIGURE 28.9 People might describe distances differently, but at relativistic speeds, the distances really are different. (credit: Corey Leopold, Flickr)

Have you ever driven on a road that seems like it goes on forever? If you look ahead, you might say you have about 10 km left to go. Another traveler might say the road ahead looks like it's about 15 km long. If you both measured the road, however, you would agree. Traveling at everyday speeds, the distance you both measure would be the same. You will read in this section, however, that this is not true at relativistic speeds. Close to the speed of light, distances measured are not the same when measured by different observers.

Proper Length

One thing all observers agree upon is relative speed. Even though clocks measure different elapsed times for the same process, they still agree that relative speed, which is distance divided by elapsed time, is the same. This implies that distance, too, depends on the observer's relative motion. If two observers see different times, then they must also see different distances for relative speed to be the same to each of them.

The muon discussed in Example 28.1 illustrates this concept. To an observer on the Earth, the muon travels at $0.950c$ for $7.05\ \mu s$ from the time it is produced until it decays. Thus it travels a distance

$$L_0 = v\Delta t = (0.950)(3.00 \times 10^8 \text{ m/s})(7.05 \times 10^{-6} \text{ s}) = 2.01 \text{ km} \tag{28.16}$$

relative to the Earth. In the muon's frame of reference, its lifetime is only $2.20\ \mu s$. It has enough time to travel only

$$L = v\Delta t_0 = (0.950)(3.00 \times 10^8 \text{ m/s})(2.20 \times 10^{-6} \text{ s}) = 0.627 \text{ km}. \tag{28.17}$$

The distance between the same two events (production and decay of a muon) depends on who measures it and how they are moving relative to it.

> **PROPER LENGTH**
>
> **Proper length** L_0 is the distance between two points measured by an observer who is at rest relative to both of the points.

The Earth-bound observer measures the proper length L_0, because the points at which the muon is produced and decays are stationary relative to the Earth. To the muon, the Earth, air, and clouds are moving, and so the distance L it sees is not the proper length.

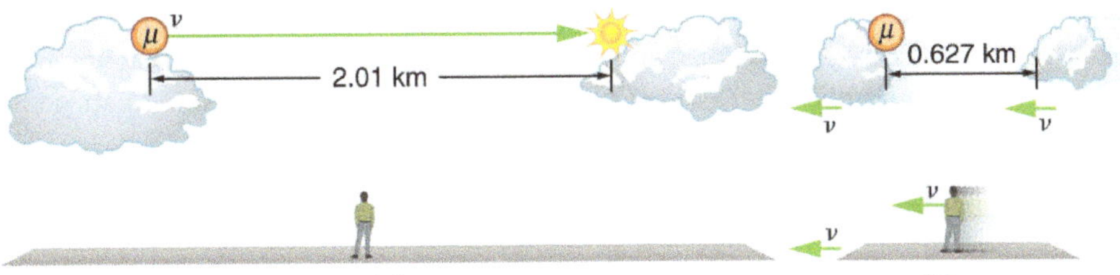

FIGURE 28.10 (a) The Earth-bound observer sees the muon travel 2.01 km between clouds. (b) The muon sees itself travel the same path, but only a distance of 0.627 km. The Earth, air, and clouds are moving relative to the muon in its frame, and all appear to have smaller lengths along the direction of travel.

Length Contraction

To develop an equation relating distances measured by different observers, we note that the velocity relative to the Earth-bound observer in our muon example is given by

$$v = \frac{L_0}{\Delta t}. \tag{28.18}$$

The time relative to the Earth-bound observer is Δt, since the object being timed is moving relative to this observer. The velocity relative to the moving observer is given by

$$v = \frac{L}{\Delta t_0}. \tag{28.19}$$

The moving observer travels with the muon and therefore observes the proper time Δt_0. The two velocities are identical; thus,

$$\frac{L_0}{\Delta t} = \frac{L}{\Delta t_0}. \tag{28.20}$$

We know that $\Delta t = \gamma \Delta t_0$. Substituting this equation into the relationship above gives

$$L = \frac{L_0}{\gamma}. \tag{28.21}$$

Substituting for γ gives an equation relating the distances measured by different observers.

LENGTH CONTRACTION

Length contraction L is the shortening of the measured length of an object moving relative to the observer's frame.

$$L = L_0 \sqrt{1 - \frac{v^2}{c^2}}. \tag{28.22}$$

If we measure the length of anything moving relative to our frame, we find its length L to be smaller than the proper length L_0 that would be measured if the object were stationary. For example, in the muon's reference frame, the distance between the points where it was produced and where it decayed is shorter. Those points are fixed relative to the Earth but moving relative to the muon. Clouds and other objects are also contracted along the direction of motion in the muon's reference frame.

EXAMPLE 28.2

Calculating Length Contraction: The Distance between Stars Contracts when You Travel at High Velocity

Suppose an astronaut, such as the twin discussed in Simultaneity and Time Dilation, travels so fast that $\gamma = 30.00$.

(a) She travels from the Earth to the nearest star system, Alpha Centauri, 4.300 light years (ly) away as measured by an Earth-bound observer. How far apart are the Earth and Alpha Centauri as measured by the astronaut? (b) In terms of c, what is her velocity relative to the Earth? You may neglect the motion of the Earth relative to the Sun. (See Figure 28.11.)

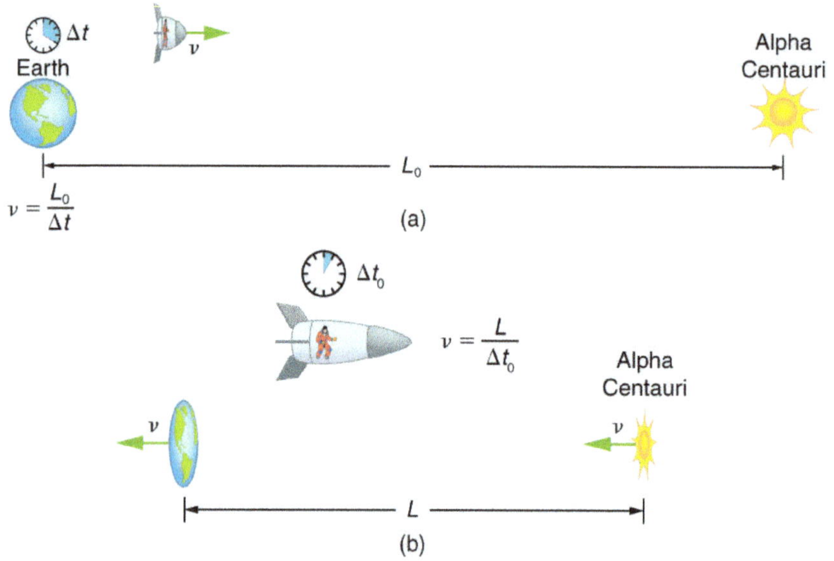

FIGURE 28.11 (a) The Earth-bound observer measures the proper distance between the Earth and the Alpha Centauri. (b) The astronaut observes a length contraction, since the Earth and the Alpha Centauri move relative to her ship. She can travel this shorter distance in a smaller time (her proper time) without exceeding the speed of light.

Strategy

First note that a light year (ly) is a convenient unit of distance on an astronomical scale—it is the distance light travels in a year. For part (a), note that the 4.300 ly distance between the Alpha Centauri and the Earth is the proper distance L_0, because it is measured by an Earth-bound observer to whom both bodies are (approximately) stationary. To the astronaut, the Earth and the Alpha Centauri are moving by at the same velocity, and so the distance between them is the contracted length L. In part (b), we are given γ, and so we can find v by rearranging the definition of γ to express v in terms of c.

Solution for (a)

1. Identify the knowns. $L_0 - 4.300 \text{ ly}; \gamma = 30.00$
2. Identify the unknown. L
3. Choose the appropriate equation. $L = \frac{L_0}{\gamma}$
4. Rearrange the equation to solve for the unknown.

$$\begin{aligned} L &= \frac{L_0}{\gamma} \\ &= \frac{4.300 \text{ ly}}{30.00} \\ &= 0.1433 \text{ ly} \end{aligned} \tag{28.23}$$

Solution for (b)

1. Identify the known. $\gamma = 30.00$
2. Identify the unknown. v in terms of c
3. Choose the appropriate equation. $\gamma = \frac{1}{\sqrt{1-\frac{v^2}{c^2}}}$
4. Rearrange the equation to solve for the unknown.

$$\gamma = \frac{1}{\sqrt{1-\frac{v^2}{c^2}}}$$

$$30.00 = \frac{1}{\sqrt{1-\frac{v^2}{c^2}}} \quad 28.24$$

Squaring both sides of the equation and rearranging terms gives

$$900.0 = \frac{1}{1-\frac{v^2}{c^2}} \quad 28.25$$

so that

$$1 - \frac{v^2}{c^2} = \frac{1}{900.0} \quad 28.26$$

and

$$\frac{v^2}{c^2} = 1 - \frac{1}{900.0} = 0.99888.... \quad 28.27$$

Taking the square root, we find

$$\frac{v}{c} = 0.99944, \quad 28.28$$

which is rearranged to produce a value for the velocity

$$v = 0.9994c. \quad 28.29$$

Discussion

First, remember that you should not round off calculations until the final result is obtained, or you could get erroneous results. This is especially true for special relativity calculations, where the differences might only be revealed after several decimal places. The relativistic effect is large here (γ=30.00), and we see that v is approaching (not equaling) the speed of light. Since the distance as measured by the astronaut is so much smaller, the astronaut can travel it in much less time in her frame.

People could be sent very large distances (thousands or even millions of light years) and age only a few years on the way if they traveled at extremely high velocities. But, like emigrants of centuries past, they would leave the Earth they know forever. Even if they returned, thousands to millions of years would have passed on the Earth, obliterating most of what now exists. There is also a more serious practical obstacle to traveling at such velocities; immensely greater energies than classical physics predicts would be needed to achieve such high velocities. This will be discussed in Relatavistic Energy.

Why don't we notice length contraction in everyday life? The distance to the grocery shop does not seem to depend on whether we are moving or not. Examining the equation $L = L_0\sqrt{1-\frac{v^2}{c^2}}$, we see that at low velocities (v<<c) the lengths are nearly equal, the classical expectation. But length contraction is real, if not commonly experienced. For example, a charged particle, like an electron, traveling at relativistic velocity has electric field lines that are compressed along the direction of motion as seen by a stationary observer. (See Figure 28.12.) As the electron passes a detector, such as a coil of wire, its field interacts much more briefly, an effect observed at particle accelerators such as the 3 km long Stanford Linear Accelerator (SLAC). In fact, to an electron traveling down the beam pipe at SLAC, the accelerator and the Earth are all moving by and are length contracted. The relativistic effect is so great than the accelerator is only 0.5 m long to the electron. It is actually easier to get the electron beam down the pipe, since the beam does not have to be as precisely aimed to get down a short pipe as it would down one 3 km long. This, again, is an experimental verification of the Special Theory of Relativity.

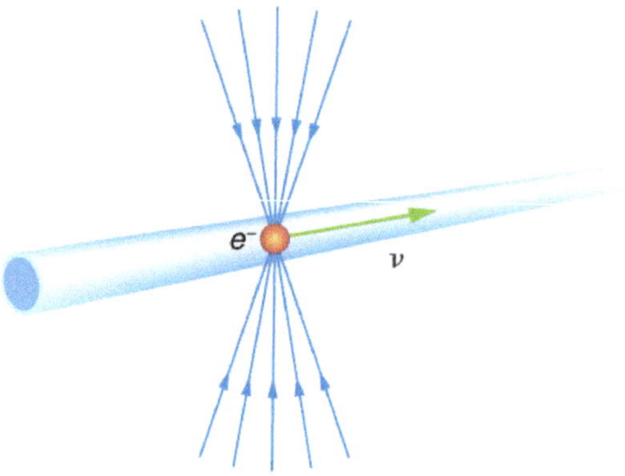

FIGURE 28.12 The electric field lines of a high-velocity charged particle are compressed along the direction of motion by length contraction. This produces a different signal when the particle goes through a coil, an experimentally verified effect of length contraction.

CHECK YOUR UNDERSTANDING

A particle is traveling through the Earth's atmosphere at a speed of $0.750c$. To an Earth-bound observer, the distance it travels is 2.50 km. How far does the particle travel in the particle's frame of reference?

Solution

$$L = L_0\sqrt{1-\frac{v^2}{c^2}} = (2.50\text{ km})\sqrt{1-\frac{(0.750c)^2}{c^2}} = 1.65\text{ km} \tag{28.30}$$

28.4 Relativistic Addition of Velocities

LEARNING OBJECTIVES

By the end of this section, you will be able to:

- Calculate relativistic velocity addition.
- Explain when relativistic velocity addition should be used instead of classical addition of velocities.
- Calculate relativistic Doppler shift.

FIGURE 28.13 The total velocity of a kayak, like this one on the Deerfield River in Massachusetts, is its velocity relative to the water as well as the water's velocity relative to the riverbank. (credit: abkfenris, Flickr)

If you've ever seen a kayak move down a fast-moving river, you know that remaining in the same place would be hard. The river current pulls the kayak along. Pushing the oars back against the water can move the kayak forward in the water, but that only accounts for part of the velocity. The kayak's motion is an example of classical addition of velocities. In classical physics, velocities add as vectors. The kayak's velocity is the vector sum of its velocity relative to the water and the water's velocity relative to the riverbank.

Classical Velocity Addition

For simplicity, we restrict our consideration of velocity addition to one-dimensional motion. Classically, velocities add like regular numbers in one-dimensional motion. (See Figure 28.14.) Suppose, for example, a girl is riding in a sled at a speed 1.0 m/s relative to an observer. She throws a snowball first forward, then backward at a speed of 1.5 m/s relative to the sled. We denote direction with plus and minus signs in one dimension; in this example, forward is positive. Let v be the velocity of the sled relative to the Earth, u the velocity of the snowball relative to the Earth-bound observer, and u' the velocity of the snowball relative to the sled.

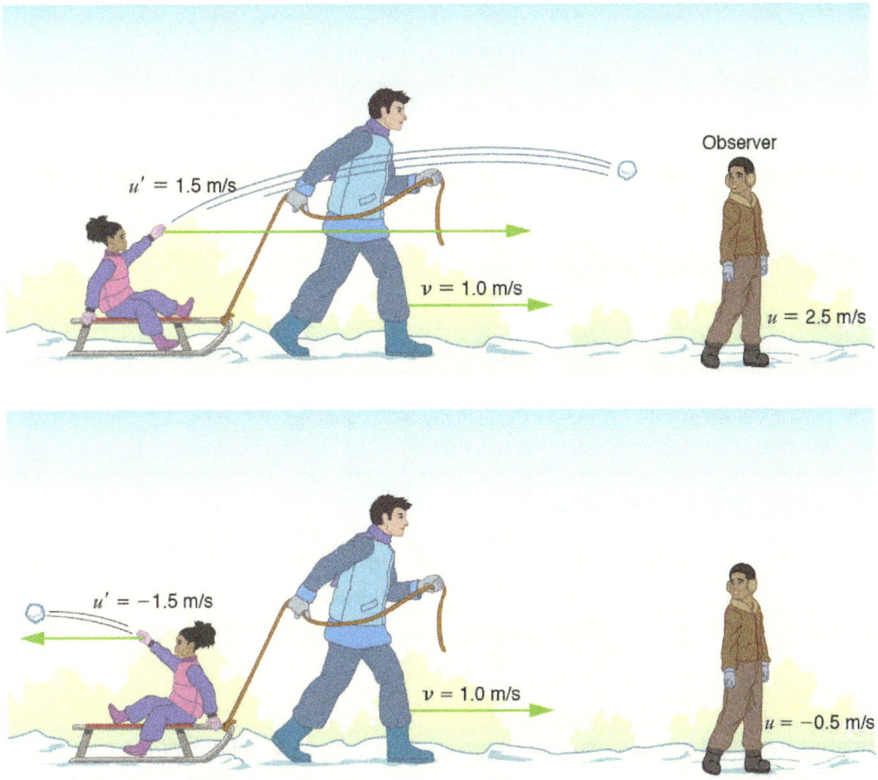

FIGURE 28.14 Classically, velocities add like ordinary numbers in one-dimensional motion. Here the girl throws a snowball forward and then backward from a sled. The velocity of the sled relative to the Earth is v=1.0 m/s. The velocity of the snowball relative to the sled is u', while its velocity relative to the Earth is u. Classically, $u = v + u'$.

CLASSICAL VELOCITY ADDITION

$$u = v + u' \quad (28.31)$$

Thus, when the girl throws the snowball forward, $u = 1.0\text{ m/s} + 1.5\text{ m/s} = 2.5\text{ m/s}$. It makes good intuitive sense that the snowball will head towards the Earth-bound observer faster, because it is thrown forward from a moving vehicle. When the girl throws the snowball backward, $u = 1.0\text{ m/s}+(-1.5\text{ m/s})= -0.5\text{ m/s}$. The minus sign means the snowball moves away from the Earth-bound observer.

Relativistic Velocity Addition

The second postulate of relativity (verified by extensive experimental observation) says that classical velocity addition does not apply to light. Imagine a car traveling at night along a straight road, as in Figure 28.15. If classical velocity addition applied to light, then the light from the car's headlights would approach the observer on the sidewalk at a speed $u = v + c$. But we know that light will move away from the car at speed c relative to the driver of the car, and light will move towards the observer on the sidewalk at speed c, too.

FIGURE 28.15 According to experiment and the second postulate of relativity, light from the car's headlights moves away from the car at speed c and towards the observer on the sidewalk at speed c. Classical velocity addition is not valid.

RELATIVISTIC VELOCITY ADDITION

Either light is an exception, or the classical velocity addition formula only works at low velocities. The latter is the case. The correct formula for one-dimensional **relativistic velocity addition** is

$$u = \frac{v + u'}{1 + \frac{vu'}{c^2}}, \qquad (28.32)$$

where v is the relative velocity between two observers, u is the velocity of an object relative to one observer, and u' is the velocity relative to the other observer. (For ease of visualization, we often choose to measure u in our reference frame, while someone moving at v relative to us measures u'.) Note that the term $\frac{vu'}{c^2}$ becomes very small at low velocities, and $u = \frac{v+u'}{1+\frac{vu'}{c^2}}$ gives a result very close to classical velocity addition. As before, we see that classical velocity addition is an excellent approximation to the correct relativistic formula for small velocities. No wonder that it seems correct in our experience.

EXAMPLE 28.3

Showing that the Speed of Light towards an Observer is Constant (in a Vacuum): The Speed of Light is the Speed of Light

Suppose a spaceship heading directly towards the Earth at half the speed of light sends a signal to us on a laser-produced beam of light. Given that the light leaves the ship at speed c as observed from the ship, calculate the speed at which it approaches the Earth.

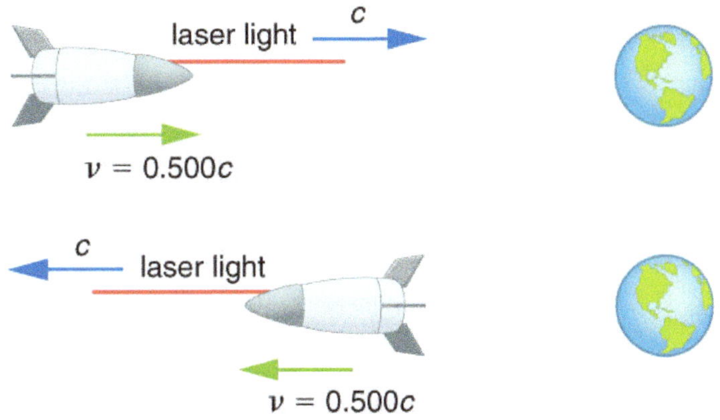

FIGURE 28.16

Strategy

Because the light and the spaceship are moving at relativistic speeds, we cannot use simple velocity addition. Instead, we can determine the speed at which the light approaches the Earth using relativistic velocity addition.

Solution

1. Identify the knowns. $v = 0.500c$; $u' = c$
2. Identify the unknown. u
3. Choose the appropriate equation. $u = \frac{v+u'}{1+\frac{vu'}{c^2}}$
4. Plug the knowns into the equation.

$$\begin{aligned} u &= \frac{v+u'}{1+\frac{vu'}{c^2}} \\ &= \frac{0.500c+c}{1+\frac{(0.500c)(c)}{c^2}} \\ &= \frac{(0.500+1)c}{1+\frac{0.500c^2}{c^2}} \\ &= \frac{1.500c}{1+0.500} \\ &= \frac{1.500c}{1.500} \\ &= c \end{aligned} \tag{28.33}$$

Discussion

Relativistic velocity addition gives the correct result. Light leaves the ship at speed c and approaches the Earth at speed c. The speed of light is independent of the relative motion of source and observer, whether the observer is on the ship or Earth-bound.

Velocities cannot add to greater than the speed of light, provided that v is less than c and u' does not exceed c. The following example illustrates that relativistic velocity addition is not as symmetric as classical velocity addition.

EXAMPLE 28.4

Comparing the Speed of Light towards and away from an Observer: Relativistic Package Delivery

Suppose the spaceship in the previous example is approaching the Earth at half the speed of light and shoots a canister at a speed of $0.750c$. (a) At what velocity will an Earth-bound observer see the canister if it is shot directly towards the Earth? (b) If it is shot directly away from the Earth? (See Figure 28.17.)

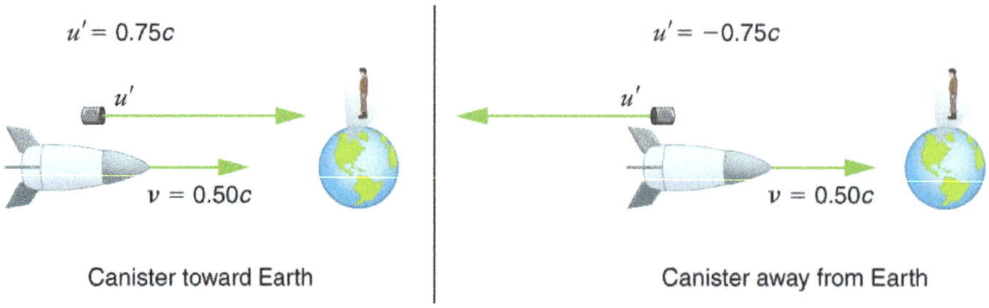

FIGURE 28.17

Strategy

Because the canister and the spaceship are moving at relativistic speeds, we must determine the speed of the canister by an Earth-bound observer using relativistic velocity addition instead of simple velocity addition.

Solution for (a)

1. Identify the knowns. $v=0.500c$; $u' = 0.750c$
2. Identify the unknown. u
3. Choose the appropriate equation. $u=\frac{v+u'}{1+\frac{vu'}{c^2}}$
4. Plug the knowns into the equation.

$$\begin{aligned} u &= \frac{v+u'}{1+\frac{vu'}{c^2}} \\ &= \frac{0.500c+0.750c}{1+\frac{(0.500c)(0.750c)}{c^2}} \\ &= \frac{1.250c}{1+0.375} \\ &= 0.909c \end{aligned} \quad (28.34)$$

Solution for (b)

1. Identify the knowns. $v = 0.500c$; $u' = -0.750c$
2. Identify the unknown. u
3. Choose the appropriate equation. $u = \frac{v+u'}{1+\frac{vu'}{c^2}}$
4. Plug the knowns into the equation.

$$\begin{aligned} u &= \frac{v+u'}{1+\frac{vu'}{c^2}} \\ &= \frac{0.500c+(-0.750c)}{1+\frac{(0.500c)(-0.750c)}{c^2}} \\ &= \frac{-0.250c}{1-0.375} \\ &= -0.400c \end{aligned} \quad (28.35)$$

Discussion

The minus sign indicates velocity away from the Earth (in the opposite direction from v), which means the canister is heading towards the Earth in part (a) and away in part (b), as expected. But relativistic velocities do not add as simply as they do classically. In part (a), the canister does approach the Earth faster, but not at the simple sum of $1.250c$. The total velocity is less than you would get classically. And in part (b), the canister moves away from the Earth at a velocity of $-0.400c$, which is *faster* than the $-0.250c$ you would expect classically. The velocities are not even symmetric. In part (a) the canister moves $0.409c$ faster than the ship relative to the Earth, whereas in part (b) it moves $0.900c$ slower than the ship.

Doppler Shift

Although the speed of light does not change with relative velocity, the frequencies and wavelengths of light do. First discussed for sound waves, a Doppler shift occurs in any wave when there is relative motion between source and observer.

RELATIVISTIC DOPPLER EFFECTS

The observed wavelength of electromagnetic radiation is longer (called a red shift) than that emitted by the source when the source moves away from the observer and shorter (called a blue shift) when the source moves towards the observer.

$$=\lambda_{\text{obs}}=\lambda_s\sqrt{\frac{1+\frac{u}{c}}{1-\frac{u}{c}}}. \tag{28.36}$$

In the Doppler equation, λ_{obs} is the observed wavelength, λ_s is the source wavelength, and u is the relative velocity of the source to the observer. The velocity u is positive for motion away from an observer and negative for motion toward an observer. In terms of source frequency and observed frequency, this equation can be written

$$f_{\text{obs}}=f_s\sqrt{\frac{1-\frac{u}{c}}{1+\frac{u}{c}}}. \tag{28.37}$$

Notice that the – and + signs are different than in the wavelength equation.

CAREER CONNECTION: ASTRONOMER

If you are interested in a career that requires a knowledge of special relativity, there's probably no better connection than astronomy. Astronomers must take into account relativistic effects when they calculate distances, times, and speeds of black holes, galaxies, quasars, and all other astronomical objects. To have a career in astronomy, you need at least an undergraduate degree in either physics or astronomy, but a Master's or doctoral degree is often required. You also need a good background in high-level mathematics.

EXAMPLE 28.5

Calculating a Doppler Shift: Radio Waves from a Receding Galaxy

Suppose a galaxy is moving away from the Earth at a speed $0.825c$. It emits radio waves with a wavelength of 0.525 m. What wavelength would we detect on the Earth?

Strategy

Because the galaxy is moving at a relativistic speed, we must determine the Doppler shift of the radio waves using the relativistic Doppler shift instead of the classical Doppler shift.

Solution

1. Identify the knowns. $u=0.825c$; $\lambda_s = 0.525\ m$
2. Identify the unknown. λ_{obs}
3. Choose the appropriate equation. $\lambda_{\text{obs}}=\lambda_s\sqrt{\frac{1+\frac{u}{c}}{1-\frac{u}{c}}}$
4. Plug the knowns into the equation.

$$\begin{aligned} \lambda_{\text{obs}} &= \lambda_s \sqrt{\frac{1+\frac{u}{c}}{1-\frac{u}{c}}} \\ &= (0.525 \text{ m}) \sqrt{\frac{1+\frac{0.825c}{c}}{1-\frac{0.825c}{c}}} \\ &= 1.70 \text{ m.} \end{aligned} \quad 28.38$$

Discussion

Because the galaxy is moving away from the Earth, we expect the wavelengths of radiation it emits to be redshifted. The wavelength we calculated is 1.70 m, which is redshifted from the original wavelength of 0.525 m.

The relativistic Doppler shift is easy to observe. This equation has everyday applications ranging from Doppler-shifted radar velocity measurements of transportation to Doppler-radar storm monitoring. In astronomical observations, the relativistic Doppler shift provides velocity information such as the motion and distance of stars.

CHECK YOUR UNDERSTANDING

Suppose a space probe moves away from the Earth at a speed $0.350c$. It sends a radio wave message back to the Earth at a frequency of 1.50 GHz. At what frequency is the message received on the Earth?

Solution

$$f_{\text{obs}} = f_s \sqrt{\frac{1-\frac{u}{c}}{1+\frac{u}{c}}} = (1.50 \text{ GHz}) \sqrt{\frac{1-\frac{0.350c}{c}}{1+\frac{0.350c}{c}}} = 1.04 \text{ GHz} \quad 28.39$$

28.5 Relativistic Momentum

LEARNING OBJECTIVES

By the end of this section, you will be able to:

- Calculate relativistic momentum.
- Explain why the only mass it makes sense to talk about is rest mass.

FIGURE 28.18 Momentum is an important concept for these football players from the University of California at Berkeley and the University of California at Davis. Players with more mass often have a larger impact because their momentum is larger. For objects moving at relativistic speeds, the effect is even greater. (credit: John Martinez Pavliga)

In classical physics, momentum is a simple product of mass and velocity. However, we saw in the last section that when special relativity is taken into account, massive objects have a speed limit. What effect do you think mass and velocity have on the momentum of objects moving at relativistic speeds?

Momentum is one of the most important concepts in physics. The broadest form of Newton's second law is stated in terms of momentum. Momentum is conserved whenever the net external force on a system is zero. This makes momentum conservation a fundamental tool for analyzing collisions. All of Work, Energy, and Energy Resources is devoted to momentum, and momentum has been important for many other topics as well, particularly where collisions were involved. We will see that momentum has the same importance in modern physics. Relativistic momentum is conserved, and much of what we know about subatomic structure comes from the analysis of collisions of accelerator-produced relativistic particles.

The first postulate of relativity states that the laws of physics are the same in all inertial frames. Does the law of conservation of momentum survive this requirement at high velocities? The answer is yes, provided that the momentum is defined as follows.

RELATIVISTIC MOMENTUM

Relativistic momentum p is classical momentum multiplied by the relativistic factor γ.

$$p = \gamma m u, \tag{28.40}$$

where m is the **rest mass** of the object, u is its velocity relative to an observer, and the relativistic factor

$$\gamma = \frac{1}{\sqrt{1 - \frac{u^2}{c^2}}}. \tag{28.41}$$

Note that we use u for velocity here to distinguish it from relative velocity v between observers. Only one observer is being considered here. With p defined in this way, total momentum p_{tot} is conserved whenever the net external force is zero, just as in classical physics. Again we see that the relativistic quantity becomes virtually the same as the classical at low velocities. That is, relativistic momentum γmu becomes the classical mu at low velocities, because γ is very nearly equal to 1 at low velocities.

Relativistic momentum has the same intuitive feel as classical momentum. It is greatest for large masses moving at high velocities, but, because of the factor γ, relativistic momentum approaches infinity as u approaches c. (See Figure 28.19.) This is another indication that an object with mass cannot reach the speed of light. If it did, its momentum would become infinite, an unreasonable value.

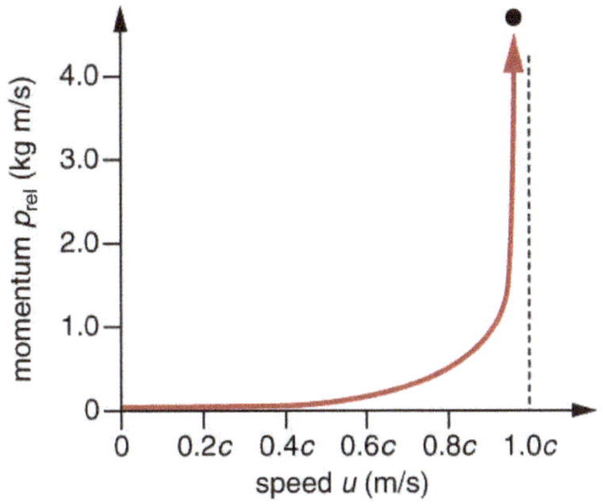

FIGURE 28.19 Relativistic momentum approaches infinity as the velocity of an object approaches the speed of light.

MISCONCEPTION ALERT: RELATIVISTIC MASS AND MOMENTUM

The relativistically correct definition of momentum as $p = \gamma mu$ is sometimes taken to imply that mass varies with velocity: $m_{var} = \gamma m$, particularly in older textbooks. However, note that m is the mass of the object as measured by a person at rest relative to the object. Thus, m is defined to be the rest mass, which could be measured at rest, perhaps using gravity. When a mass is moving relative to an observer, the only way that its mass can be determined is through collisions or other means in which momentum is involved. Since the mass of a moving object cannot be determined independently of momentum, the only meaningful mass is rest mass. Thus, when we use the term mass, assume it to be identical to rest mass.

Relativistic momentum is defined in such a way that the conservation of momentum will hold in all inertial frames. Whenever the net external force on a system is zero, relativistic momentum is conserved, just as is the case for classical momentum. This has been verified in numerous experiments.

In Relativistic Energy, the relationship of relativistic momentum to energy is explored. That subject will produce our first inkling that objects without mass may also have momentum.

CHECK YOUR UNDERSTANDING

What is the momentum of an electron traveling at a speed $0.985c$? The rest mass of the electron is 9.11×10^{-31} kg.

Solution

$$p = \gamma mu = \frac{mu}{\sqrt{1 - \frac{u^2}{c^2}}} = \frac{(9.11 \times 10^{-31}\ \text{kg})(0.985)(3.00 \times 10^8\ \text{m/s})}{\sqrt{1 - \frac{(0.985c)^2}{c^2}}} = 1.56 \times 10^{-21}\ \text{kg} \cdot \text{m/s} \tag{28.42}$$

28.6 Relativistic Energy

LEARNING OBJECTIVES

By the end of this section, you will be able to:

- Compute total energy of a relativistic object.
- Compute the kinetic energy of a relativistic object.
- Describe rest energy, and explain how it can be converted to other forms.
- Explain why massive particles cannot reach C.

FIGURE 28.20 The National Spherical Torus Experiment (NSTX) has a fusion reactor in which hydrogen isotopes undergo fusion to produce helium. In this process, a relatively small mass of fuel is converted into a large amount of energy. (credit: Princeton Plasma Physics Laboratory)

A tokamak is a form of experimental fusion reactor, which can change mass to energy. Accomplishing this requires an understanding of relativistic energy. Nuclear reactors are proof of the conservation of relativistic energy.

Conservation of energy is one of the most important laws in physics. Not only does energy have many important forms, but each form can be converted to any other. We know that classically the total amount of energy in a system remains constant. Relativistically, energy is still conserved, provided its definition is altered to include the possibility of mass changing to energy, as in the reactions that occur within a nuclear reactor. Relativistic energy is intentionally defined so that it will be conserved in all inertial frames, just as is the case for relativistic momentum. As a consequence, we learn that several fundamental quantities are related in ways not known in classical physics. All of these relationships are verified by experiment and have fundamental consequences. The altered definition of energy contains some of the most fundamental and spectacular new insights into nature found in recent history.

Total Energy and Rest Energy

The first postulate of relativity states that the laws of physics are the same in all inertial frames. Einstein showed that the law of conservation of energy is valid relativistically, if we define energy to include a relativistic factor.

TOTAL ENERGY

Total energy E is defined to be

$$E = \gamma mc^2, \qquad 28.43$$

where m is mass, c is the speed of light, $\gamma = \frac{1}{\sqrt{1-\frac{v^2}{c^2}}}$, and v is the velocity of the mass relative to an observer.

There are many aspects of the total energy E that we will discuss—among them are how kinetic and potential energies are included in E, and how E is related to relativistic momentum. But first, note that at rest, total energy is not zero. Rather, when $v = 0$, we have $\gamma = 1$, and an object has rest energy.

REST ENERGY

Rest energy is

$$E_0 = mc^2. \qquad 28.44$$

This is the correct form of Einstein's most famous equation, which for the first time showed that energy is related to the mass of an object at rest. For example, if energy is stored in the object, its rest mass increases. This also implies that mass can be destroyed to release energy. The implications of these first two equations regarding relativistic energy are so broad that they were not completely recognized for some years after Einstein published them in 1907, nor was the experimental proof that they are correct widely recognized at first. Einstein, it should be noted, did understand and describe the meanings and implications of his theory.

EXAMPLE 28.6

Calculating Rest Energy: Rest Energy is Very Large

Calculate the rest energy of a 1.00-g mass.

Strategy

One gram is a small mass—less than half the mass of a penny. We can multiply this mass, in SI units, by the speed of light squared to find the equivalent rest energy.

Solution

1. Identify the knowns. $m = 1.00 \times 10^{-3}$ kg; $c = 3.00 \times 10^8$ m/s
2. Identify the unknown. E_0
3. Choose the appropriate equation. $E_0 = mc^2$
4. Plug the knowns into the equation.

$$\begin{aligned} E_0 &= mc^2 = (1.00 \times 10^{-3}\ \text{kg})(3.00 \times 10^8\ \text{m/s})^2 \\ &= 9.00 \times 10^{13}\ \text{kg} \cdot \text{m}^2/\text{s}^2 \end{aligned} \qquad 28.45$$

5. Convert units.
   Noting that $1\ \text{kg} \cdot \text{m}^2/\text{s}^2 = 1\ \text{J}$, we see the rest mass energy is

$$E_0 = 9.00 \times 10^{13}\ \text{J}. \qquad 28.46$$

Discussion

This is an enormous amount of energy for a 1.00-g mass. We do not notice this energy, because it is generally not available. Rest energy is large because the speed of light c is a large number and c^2 is a very large number, so that mc^2 is huge for any macroscopic mass. The 9.00×10^{13} J rest mass energy for 1.00 g is about twice the energy released by the Hiroshima atomic bomb and about 10,000 times the kinetic energy of a large aircraft carrier. If a way can be found to convert rest mass energy into some other form (and all forms of energy can be converted into one another), then huge amounts of energy can be obtained from the destruction of mass.

Today, the practical applications of *the conversion of mass into another form of energy*, such as in nuclear weapons and nuclear power plants, are well known. But examples also existed when Einstein first proposed the correct form of relativistic energy, and he did describe some of them. Nuclear radiation had been discovered in the previous decade, and it had been a mystery as to where its energy originated. The explanation was that, in certain nuclear processes, a small amount of mass is destroyed and energy is released and carried by nuclear radiation. But the amount of mass destroyed is so small that it is difficult to detect that any is missing. Although Einstein proposed this as the source of energy in the radioactive salts then being studied, it was many years before there was broad recognition that mass could be and, in fact, commonly is converted to energy. (See Figure 28.21.)

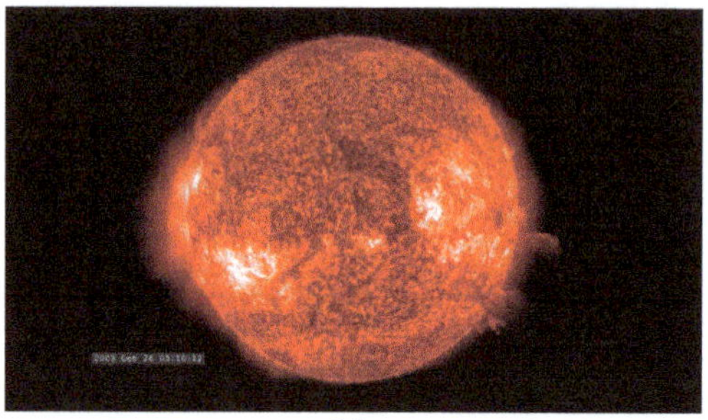

(a)

(b)

FIGURE 28.21 The Sun (a) and the Susquehanna Steam Electric Station (b) both convert mass into energy—the Sun via nuclear fusion, the electric station via nuclear fission. (credits: (a) NASA/Goddard Space Flight Center, Scientific Visualization Studio; (b) U.S. government)

Because of the relationship of rest energy to mass, we now consider mass to be a form of energy rather than something separate. There had not even been a hint of this prior to Einstein's work. Such conversion is now known to be the source of the Sun's energy, the energy of nuclear decay, and even the source of energy keeping Earth's interior hot.

Stored Energy and Potential Energy

What happens to energy stored in an object at rest, such as the energy put into a battery by charging it, or the energy stored in a toy gun's compressed spring? The energy input becomes part of the total energy of the object and, thus, increases its rest mass. All stored and potential energy becomes mass in a system. Why is it we don't ordinarily notice this? In fact, conservation of mass (meaning total mass is constant) was one of the great laws verified by 19th-century science. Why was it not noticed to be incorrect? The following example helps answer these questions.

EXAMPLE 28.7

Calculating Rest Mass: A Small Mass Increase due to Energy Input

A car battery is rated to be able to move 600 ampere-hours ($\text{A}{\cdot}\text{h}$) of charge at 12.0 V. (a) Calculate the increase in rest mass of such a battery when it is taken from being fully depleted to being fully charged. (b) What percent increase is this, given the battery's mass is 20.0 kg?

Strategy

In part (a), we first must find the energy stored in the battery, which equals what the battery can supply in the form of electrical potential energy. Since $\text{PE}_{\text{elec}} = qV$, we have to calculate the charge q in $600\ \text{A}{\cdot}\text{h}$, which is the product of the current I and the time t. We then multiply the result by 12.0 V. We can then calculate the battery's increase in mass using $\Delta E = \text{PE}_{\text{elec}} = (\Delta m)c^2$. Part (b) is a simple ratio converted to a percentage.

Solution for (a)

1. Identify the knowns. $I \cdot t = 600\ \text{A} \cdot \text{h};\ V = 12.0\ \text{V};\ c = 3.00 \times 10^8\ \text{m/s}$
2. Identify the unknown. Δm
3. Choose the appropriate equation. $\text{PE}_{\text{elec}} = (\Delta m)c^2$
4. Rearrange the equation to solve for the unknown. $\Delta m = \dfrac{\text{PE}_{\text{elec}}}{c^2}$
5. Plug the knowns into the equation.

$$\begin{aligned}\Delta m &= \frac{\text{PE}_{\text{elec}}}{c^2}\\ &= \frac{qV}{c^2}\\ &= \frac{(It)V}{c^2}\\ &= \frac{(600\ \text{A}{\cdot}\text{h})(12.0\ \text{V})}{(3.00{\times}10^8)^2}.\end{aligned} \tag{28.47}$$

Write amperes A as coulombs per second (C/s), and convert hours to seconds.

$$\begin{aligned}\Delta m &= \frac{(600\ \text{C/s}{\cdot}\text{h}\left(\frac{3600\ \text{s}}{1\ \text{h}}\right)(12.0\ \text{J/C})}{(3.00{\times}10^8\ \text{m/s})^2}\\ &= \frac{(2.16{\times}10^6\ \text{C})(12.0\ \text{J/C})}{(3.00{\times}10^8\ \text{m/s})^2}\end{aligned} \tag{28.48}$$

Using the conversion $1\ \text{kg} \cdot \text{m}^2/\text{s}^2 = 1\ \text{J}$, we can write the mass as

$\Delta m = 2.88 \times 10^{-10}\ \text{kg}.$

Solution for (b)

1. Identify the knowns. $\Delta m = 2.88 \times 10^{-10}\ \text{kg};\ m = 20.0\ \text{kg}$
2. Identify the unknown. % change
3. Choose the appropriate equation. $\%\ \text{increase} = \frac{\Delta m}{m} \times 100\%$
4. Plug the knowns into the equation.

$$\begin{aligned}\%\ \text{increase} &= \frac{\Delta m}{m} \times 100\%\\ &= \frac{2.88{\times}10^{-10}\ \text{kg}}{20.0\ \text{kg}} \times 100\%\\ &= 1.44 \times 10^{-9}\%.\end{aligned} \tag{28.49}$$

Discussion

Both the actual increase in mass and the percent increase are very small, since energy is divided by c^2, a very large number. We would have to be able to measure the mass of the battery to a precision of a billionth of a percent, or 1 part in 10^{11}, to notice this increase. It is no wonder that the mass variation is not readily observed. In fact, this change in mass is so small that we may question how you could verify it is real. The answer is found in nuclear processes in which the percentage of mass destroyed is large enough to be measured. The mass of the fuel of a nuclear reactor, for example, is measurably smaller when its energy has been used. In that case, stored energy has been released (converted mostly to heat and electricity) and the rest mass has decreased. This is also the case when you use the energy stored in a battery, except that the stored energy is much greater in nuclear processes, making the change in mass measurable in practice as well as in theory.

Kinetic Energy and the Ultimate Speed Limit

Kinetic energy is energy of motion. Classically, kinetic energy has the familiar expression $\frac{1}{2}mv^2$. The relativistic expression for kinetic energy is obtained from the work-energy theorem. This theorem states that the net work on a system goes into kinetic energy. If our system starts from rest, then the work-energy theorem is

$$W_{\text{net}} = \text{KE}. \tag{28.50}$$

Relativistically, at rest we have rest energy $E_0 = mc^2$. The work increases this to the total energy $E = \gamma mc^2$. Thus,

$$W_{\text{net}} = E - E_0 = \gamma mc^2 - mc^2 = (\gamma - 1)mc^2. \tag{28.51}$$

Relativistically, we have $W_{\text{net}} = \text{KE}_{\text{rel}}$.

RELATIVISTIC KINETIC ENERGY

Relativistic kinetic energy is

$$\text{KE}_{\text{rel}} = (\gamma - 1)mc^2. \tag{28.52}$$

When motionless, we have $v = 0$ and

$$\gamma = \frac{1}{\sqrt{1 - \frac{v^2}{c^2}}} = 1, \tag{28.53}$$

so that $\text{KE}_{\text{rel}} = 0$ at rest, as expected. But the expression for relativistic kinetic energy (such as total energy and rest energy) does not look much like the classical $\frac{1}{2}mv^2$. To show that the classical expression for kinetic energy is obtained at low velocities, we note that the binomial expansion for γ at low velocities gives

$$\gamma = 1 + \frac{1}{2}\frac{v^2}{c^2}. \tag{28.54}$$

A binomial expansion is a way of expressing an algebraic quantity as a sum of an infinite series of terms. In some cases, as in the limit of small velocity here, most terms are very small. Thus the expression derived for γ here is not exact, but it is a very accurate approximation. Thus, at low velocities,

$$\gamma - 1 = \frac{1}{2}\frac{v^2}{c^2}. \tag{28.55}$$

Entering this into the expression for relativistic kinetic energy gives

$$\text{KE}_{\text{rel}} = \left[\frac{1}{2}\frac{v^2}{c^2}\right]mc^2 = \frac{1}{2}mv^2 = \text{KE}_{\text{class}}. \tag{28.56}$$

So, in fact, relativistic kinetic energy does become the same as classical kinetic energy when $v << c$.

It is even more interesting to investigate what happens to kinetic energy when the velocity of an object approaches the speed of light. We know that γ becomes infinite as v approaches c, so that KE_{rel} also becomes infinite as the velocity approaches the speed of light. (See Figure 28.22.) An infinite amount of work (and, hence, an infinite amount of energy input) is required to accelerate a mass to the speed of light.

THE SPEED OF LIGHT

No object with mass can attain the speed of light.

So the speed of light is the ultimate speed limit for any particle having mass. All of this is consistent with the fact that velocities less than c always add to less than c. Both the relativistic form for kinetic energy and the ultimate speed limit being c have been confirmed in detail in numerous experiments. No matter how much energy is put into accelerating a mass, its velocity can only approach—not reach—the speed of light.

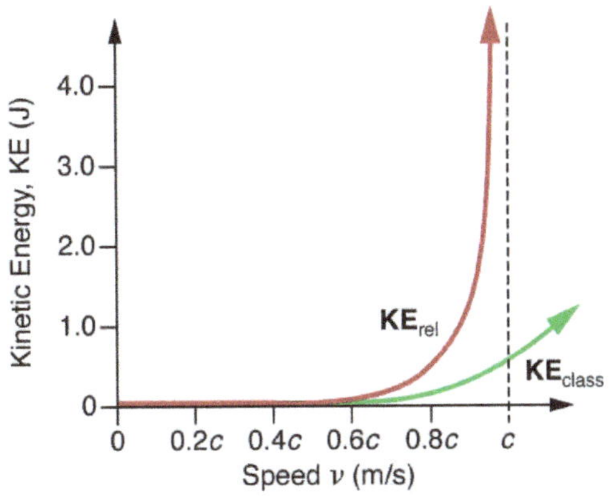

FIGURE 28.22 This graph of $\mathrm{KE}_{\mathrm{rel}}$ versus velocity shows how kinetic energy approaches infinity as velocity approaches the speed of light. It is thus not possible for an object having mass to reach the speed of light. Also shown is $\mathrm{KE}_{\mathrm{class}}$, the classical kinetic energy, which is similar to relativistic kinetic energy at low velocities. Note that much more energy is required to reach high velocities than predicted classically.

EXAMPLE 28.8

Comparing Kinetic Energy: Relativistic Energy Versus Classical Kinetic Energy

An electron has a velocity $v = 0.990c$. (a) Calculate the kinetic energy in MeV of the electron. (b) Compare this with the classical value for kinetic energy at this velocity. (The mass of an electron is 9.11×10^{-31} kg.)

Strategy

The expression for relativistic kinetic energy is always correct, but for (a) it must be used since the velocity is highly relativistic (close to c). First, we will calculate the relativistic factor γ, and then use it to determine the relativistic kinetic energy. For (b), we will calculate the classical kinetic energy (which would be close to the relativistic value if v were less than a few percent of c) and see that it is not the same.

Solution for (a)

1. Identify the knowns. $v = 0.990c$; $m = 9.11 \times 10^{-31}$ kg
2. Identify the unknown. $\mathrm{KE}_{\mathrm{rel}}$
3. Choose the appropriate equation. $\mathrm{KE}_{\mathrm{rel}} = (\gamma - 1)mc^2$
4. Plug the knowns into the equation.
   First calculate γ. We will carry extra digits because this is an intermediate calculation.

$$\begin{aligned}\gamma &= \frac{1}{\sqrt{1-\frac{v^2}{c^2}}} \\ &= \frac{1}{\sqrt{1-\frac{(0.990c)^2}{c^2}}} \\ &= \frac{1}{\sqrt{1-(0.990)^2}} \\ &= 7.0888\end{aligned} \quad 28.57$$

Next, we use this value to calculate the kinetic energy.

$$\begin{aligned}\text{KE}_{\text{rel}} &= (\gamma - 1)\,mc^2 \\ &= (7.0888 - 1)(9.11 \times 10^{-31}\text{ kg})(3.00 \times 10^8\text{ m/s})^2 \\ &= 4.99 \times 10^{-13}\text{ J}\end{aligned} \quad 28.58$$

5. Convert units.

$$\begin{aligned}\text{KE}_{\text{rel}} &= (4.99 \times 10^{-13}\text{ J})\left(\frac{1\text{ MeV}}{1.60\times10^{-13}\text{ J}}\right) \\ &= 3.12\text{ MeV}\end{aligned} \quad 28.59$$

Solution for (b)

1. List the knowns. $v = 0.990c;\ m = 9.11 \times 10^{-31}$ kg
2. List the unknown. KE_{class}
3. Choose the appropriate equation. $\text{KE}_{\text{class}} = \frac{1}{2}mv^2$
4. Plug the knowns into the equation.

$$\begin{aligned}\text{KE}_{\text{class}} &= \frac{1}{2}mv^2 \\ &= \frac{1}{2}(9.00 \times 10^{-31}\text{ kg})(0.990)^2(3.00 \times 10^8\text{ m/s})^2 \\ &= 4.02 \times 10^{-14}\text{ J}\end{aligned} \quad 28.60$$

5. Convert units.

$$\begin{aligned}\text{KE}_{\text{class}} &= 4.02 \times 10^{-14}\text{ J}\left(\frac{1\text{ MeV}}{1.60\times10^{-13}\text{ J}}\right) \\ &= 0.251\text{ MeV}\end{aligned} \quad 28.61$$

Discussion

As might be expected, since the velocity is 99.0% of the speed of light, the classical kinetic energy is significantly off from the correct relativistic value. Note also that the classical value is much smaller than the relativistic value. In fact, $\text{KE}_{\text{rel}}/\text{KE}_{\text{class}} = 12.4$ here. This is some indication of how difficult it is to get a mass moving close to the speed of light. Much more energy is required than predicted classically. Some people interpret this extra energy as going into increasing the mass of the system, but, as discussed in Relativistic Momentum, this cannot be verified unambiguously. What is certain is that ever-increasing amounts of energy are needed to get the velocity of a mass a little closer to that of light. An energy of 3 MeV is a very small amount for an electron, and it can be achieved with present-day particle accelerators. SLAC, for example, can accelerate electrons to over $50 \times 10^9\text{ eV} = 50{,}000\text{ MeV}$.

Is there any point in getting v a little closer to c than 99.0% or 99.9%? The answer is yes. We learn a great deal by doing this. The energy that goes into a high-velocity mass can be converted to any other form, including into entirely new masses. (See Figure 28.23.) Most of what we know about the substructure of matter and the collection of exotic short-lived particles in nature has been learned this way. Particles are accelerated to extremely relativistic energies and made to collide with other particles, producing totally new species of particles. Patterns in the characteristics of these previously unknown particles hint at a basic substructure for all matter. These particles and some of their characteristics will be covered in Particle Physics.

FIGURE 28.23 The Fermi National Accelerator Laboratory, near Batavia, Illinois, was a subatomic particle collider that accelerated protons and antiprotons to attain energies up to 1 Tev (a trillion electronvolts). The circular ponds near the rings were built to dissipate waste heat. This accelerator was shut down in September 2011. (credit: Fermilab, Reidar Hahn)

Relativistic Energy and Momentum

We know classically that kinetic energy and momentum are related to each other, since

$$\text{KE}_{\text{class}} = \frac{p^2}{2m} = \frac{(mv)^2}{2m} = \frac{1}{2}mv^2. \quad 28.62$$

Relativistically, we can obtain a relationship between energy and momentum by algebraically manipulating their definitions. This produces

$$E^2 = (pc)^2 + (mc^2)^2, \quad 28.63$$

where E is the relativistic total energy and p is the relativistic momentum. This relationship between relativistic energy and relativistic momentum is more complicated than the classical, but we can gain some interesting new insights by examining it. First, total energy is related to momentum and rest mass. At rest, momentum is zero, and the equation gives the total energy to be the rest energy mc^2 (so this equation is consistent with the discussion of rest energy above). However, as the mass is accelerated, its momentum p increases, thus increasing the total energy. At sufficiently high velocities, the rest energy term $(mc^2)^2$ becomes negligible compared with the momentum term $(pc)^2$; thus, $E = pc$ at extremely relativistic velocities.

If we consider momentum p to be distinct from mass, we can determine the implications of the equation $E^2 = (pc)^2 + (mc^2)^2$, for a particle that has no mass. If we take m to be zero in this equation, then $E = pc$, or $p = E/c$. Massless particles have this momentum. There are several massless particles found in nature, including photons (these are quanta of electromagnetic radiation). Another implication is that a massless particle must travel at speed c and only at speed c. While it is beyond the scope of this text to examine the relationship in the equation $E^2 = (pc)^2 + (mc^2)^2$, in detail, we can see that the relationship has important implications in special relativity.

PROBLEM-SOLVING STRATEGIES FOR RELATIVITY

1. *Examine the situation to determine that it is necessary to use relativity.* Relativistic effects are related to $\gamma = \frac{1}{\sqrt{1-\frac{v^2}{c^2}}}$, the quantitative relativistic factor. If γ is very close to 1, then relativistic effects are small and differ very little from the usually easier classical calculations.
2. *Identify exactly what needs to be determined in the problem (identify the unknowns).*
3. *Make a list of what is given or can be inferred from the problem as stated (identify the knowns).* Look in particular for information on relative velocity v.
4. *Make certain you understand the conceptual aspects of the problem before making any calculations.* Decide, for example, which observer sees time dilated or length contracted before plugging into equations. If you have thought about who sees what, who is moving with the event being observed, who sees proper time, and so on, you will find it much easier to determine if your calculation is reasonable.
5. *Determine the primary type of calculation to be done to find the unknowns identified above.* You will find the

section summary helpful in determining whether a length contraction, relativistic kinetic energy, or some other concept is involved.

6. *Do not round off during the calculation.* As noted in the text, you must often perform your calculations to many digits to see the desired effect. You may round off at the very end of the problem, but do not use a rounded number in a subsequent calculation.
7. *Check the answer to see if it is reasonable: Does it make sense?* This may be more difficult for relativity, since we do not encounter it directly. But you can look for velocities greater than c or relativistic effects that are in the wrong direction (such as a time contraction where a dilation was expected).

CHECK YOUR UNDERSTANDING

A photon decays into an electron-positron pair. What is the kinetic energy of the electron if its speed is $0.992c$?

Solution

$$\begin{aligned} \text{KE}_{\text{rel}} &= (\gamma - 1)\,mc^2 = \left(\frac{1}{\sqrt{1-\frac{v^2}{c^2}}} - 1\right)mc^2 \\ &= \left(\frac{1}{\sqrt{1-\frac{(0.992c)^2}{c^2}}} - 1\right)(9.11 \times 10^{-31}\text{ kg})(3.00 \times 10^{8}\text{ m/s})^2 = 5.67 \times 10^{-13}\text{ J} \end{aligned} \tag{28.64}$$

Glossary

classical velocity addition the method of adding velocities when $v<<c$; velocities add like regular numbers in one-dimensional motion: $u = v + u'$, where v is the velocity between two observers, u is the velocity of an object relative to one observer, and u' is the velocity relative to the other observer

first postulate of special relativity the idea that the laws of physics are the same and can be stated in their simplest form in all inertial frames of reference

inertial frame of reference a reference frame in which a body at rest remains at rest and a body in motion moves at a constant speed in a straight line unless acted on by an outside force

length contraction L, the shortening of the measured length of an object moving relative to the observer's frame: $L=L_0\sqrt{1-\frac{v^2}{c^2}}=\frac{L_0}{\gamma}$

Michelson-Morley experiment an investigation performed in 1887 that proved that the speed of light in a vacuum is the same in all frames of reference from which it is viewed

proper length L_0; the distance between two points measured by an observer who is at rest relative to both of the points; Earth-bound observers measure proper length when measuring the distance between two points that are stationary relative to the Earth

proper time Δt_0. the time measured by an observer at rest relative to the event being observed: $\Delta t=\frac{\Delta t_0}{\sqrt{1-\frac{v^2}{c^2}}}=\gamma\Delta t_0$, where $\gamma=\frac{1}{\sqrt{1-\frac{v^2}{c^2}}}$

relativistic Doppler effects a change in wavelength of radiation that is moving relative to the observer; the wavelength of the radiation is longer (called a red shift) than that emitted by the source when the source moves away from the observer and shorter (called a blue shift) when the source moves toward the observer; the shifted wavelength is described by the equation $\lambda_{obs}=\lambda_s\sqrt{\frac{1+\frac{u}{c}}{1-\frac{u}{c}}}$ where λ_{obs} is the observed wavelength, λ_s is the source wavelength, and u is the velocity of the source to the observer

relativistic kinetic energy the kinetic energy of an object moving at relativistic speeds: $\text{KE}_{\text{rel}}=(\gamma-1)mc^2$, where $\gamma=\frac{1}{\sqrt{1-\frac{v^2}{c^2}}}$

relativistic momentum p, the momentum of an object moving at relativistic velocity; $p=\gamma mu$, where m is the rest mass of the object, u is its velocity relative to an observer, and the relativistic factor $\gamma=\frac{1}{\sqrt{1-\frac{u^2}{c^2}}}$

relativistic velocity addition the method of adding velocities of an object moving at a relativistic speed: $u=\frac{v+u'}{1+\frac{vu'}{c^2}}$, where v is the relative velocity between two observers, u is the velocity of an object relative to one observer, and u' is the velocity relative to the other observer

relativity the study of how different observers measure the same event

rest energy the energy stored in an object at rest: $E_0=mc^2$

rest mass the mass of an object as measured by a person at rest relative to the object

second postulate of special relativity the idea that the speed of light c is a constant, independent of the source

special relativity the theory that, in an inertial frame of reference, the motion of an object is relative to the frame from which it is viewed or measured

time dilation the phenomenon of time passing slower to an observer who is moving relative to another observer

total energy defined as $E=\gamma mc^2$, where $\gamma=\frac{1}{\sqrt{1-\frac{v^2}{c^2}}}$

twin paradox this asks why a twin traveling at a relativistic speed away and then back towards the Earth ages less than the Earth-bound twin. The premise to the paradox is faulty because the traveling twin is accelerating, and special relativity does not apply to accelerating frames of reference

Section Summary

28.1 Einstein's Postulates

- Relativity is the study of how different observers measure the same event.
- Modern relativity is divided into two parts. Special relativity deals with observers who are in uniform (unaccelerated) motion, whereas general relativity includes accelerated relative motion and gravity. Modern relativity is correct in all circumstances and, in the limit of low velocity and weak gravitation, gives the same predictions as classical relativity.
- An inertial frame of reference is a reference frame in which a body at rest remains at rest and a body

in motion moves at a constant speed in a straight line unless acted on by an outside force.

- Modern relativity is based on Einstein's two postulates. The first postulate of special relativity is the idea that the laws of physics are the same and can be stated in their simplest form in all inertial frames of reference. The second postulate of special relativity is the idea that the speed of light c is a constant, independent of the relative motion of the source.
- The Michelson-Morley experiment demonstrated that the speed of light in a vacuum is independent of the motion of the Earth about the Sun.

28.2 Simultaneity And Time Dilation

- Two events are defined to be simultaneous if an observer measures them as occurring at the same time. They are not necessarily simultaneous to all observers—simultaneity is not absolute.
- Time dilation is the phenomenon of time passing slower for an observer who is moving relative to another observer.
- Observers moving at a relative velocity v do not measure the same elapsed time for an event. Proper time Δt_0 is the time measured by an observer at rest relative to the event being observed. Proper time is related to the time Δt measured by an Earth-bound observer by the equation
$$\Delta t = \frac{\Delta t_0}{\sqrt{1 - \frac{v^2}{c^2}}} = \gamma \Delta t_0,$$
where
$$\gamma = \frac{1}{\sqrt{1 - \frac{v^2}{c^2}}}.$$
- The equation relating proper time and time measured by an Earth-bound observer implies that relative velocity cannot exceed the speed of light.
- The twin paradox asks why a twin traveling at a relativistic speed away and then back towards the Earth ages less than the Earth-bound twin. The premise to the paradox is faulty because the traveling twin is accelerating. Special relativity does not apply to accelerating frames of reference.
- Time dilation is usually negligible at low relative velocities, but it does occur, and it has been verified by experiment.

28.3 Length Contraction

- All observers agree upon relative speed.
- Distance depends on an observer's motion. Proper length L_0 is the distance between two points measured by an observer who is at rest relative to both of the points. Earth-bound observers measure proper length when measuring the distance between two points that are stationary relative to the Earth.
- Length contraction L is the shortening of the measured length of an object moving relative to the observer's frame:
$$L = L_0 \sqrt{1 - \frac{v^2}{c^2}} = \frac{L_0}{\gamma}.$$

28.4 Relativistic Addition of Velocities

- With classical velocity addition, velocities add like regular numbers in one-dimensional motion: $u = v + u'$, where v is the velocity between two observers, u is the velocity of an object relative to one observer, and u' is the velocity relative to the other observer.
- Velocities cannot add to be greater than the speed of light. Relativistic velocity addition describes the velocities of an object moving at a relativistic speed:
$$u = \frac{v + u'}{1 + \frac{vu'}{c^2}}$$
- An observer of electromagnetic radiation sees **relativistic Doppler effects** if the source of the radiation is moving relative to the observer. The wavelength of the radiation is longer (called a red shift) than that emitted by the source when the source moves away from the observer and shorter (called a blue shift) when the source moves toward the observer. The shifted wavelength is described by the equation
$$\lambda_{obs} = \lambda_s \sqrt{\frac{1 + \frac{u}{c}}{1 - \frac{u}{c}}}$$
λ_{obs} is the observed wavelength, λ_s is the source wavelength, and u is the relative velocity of the source to the observer.

28.5 Relativistic Momentum

- The law of conservation of momentum is valid whenever the net external force is zero and for relativistic momentum. Relativistic momentum p is classical momentum multiplied by the relativistic factor γ.
- $p = \gamma m u$, where m is the rest mass of the object, u is its velocity relative to an observer, and the relativistic factor $\gamma = \frac{1}{\sqrt{1 - \frac{u^2}{c^2}}}$.
- At low velocities, relativistic momentum is

equivalent to classical momentum.

- Relativistic momentum approaches infinity as u approaches c. This implies that an object with mass cannot reach the speed of light.
- Relativistic momentum is conserved, just as classical momentum is conserved.

28.6 Relativistic Energy

- Relativistic energy is conserved as long as we define it to include the possibility of mass changing to energy.
- Total Energy is defined as: $E = \gamma mc^2$, where $\gamma = \frac{1}{\sqrt{1-\frac{v^2}{c^2}}}$.
- Rest energy is $E_0 = mc^2$, meaning that mass is a form of energy. If energy is stored in an object, its mass increases. Mass can be destroyed to release energy.
- We do not ordinarily notice the increase or decrease in mass of an object because the change in mass is so small for a large increase in energy.
- The relativistic work-energy theorem is $W_{\text{net}} = E - E_0 = \gamma mc^2 - mc^2 = (\gamma - 1)mc^2$.
- Relativistically, $W_{\text{net}} = \text{KE}_{\text{rel}}$, where KE_{rel} is the relativistic kinetic energy.
- Relativistic kinetic energy is $\text{KE}_{\text{rel}} = (\gamma - 1)mc^2$, where $\gamma = \frac{1}{\sqrt{1-\frac{v^2}{c^2}}}$. At low velocities, relativistic kinetic energy reduces to classical kinetic energy.
- **No object with mass can attain the speed of light** because an infinite amount of work and an infinite amount of energy input is required to accelerate a mass to the speed of light.
- The equation $E^2 = (pc)^2 + (mc^2)^2$ relates the relativistic total energy E and the relativistic momentum p. At extremely high velocities, the rest energy mc^2 becomes negligible, and $E = pc$.

Conceptual Questions

28.1 Einstein's Postulates

1. Which of Einstein's postulates of special relativity includes a concept that does not fit with the ideas of classical physics? Explain.

2. Is Earth an inertial frame of reference? Is the Sun? Justify your response.

3. When you are flying in a commercial jet, it may appear to you that the airplane is stationary and the Earth is moving beneath you. Is this point of view valid? Discuss briefly.

28.2 Simultaneity And Time Dilation

4. Does motion affect the rate of a clock as measured by an observer moving with it? Does motion affect how an observer moving relative to a clock measures its rate?

5. To whom does the elapsed time for a process seem to be longer, an observer moving relative to the process or an observer moving with the process? Which observer measures proper time?

6. How could you travel far into the future without aging significantly? Could this method also allow you to travel into the past?

28.3 Length Contraction

7. To whom does an object seem greater in length, an observer moving with the object or an observer moving relative to the object? Which observer measures the object's proper length?

8. Relativistic effects such as time dilation and length contraction are present for cars and airplanes. Why do these effects seem strange to us?

9. Suppose an astronaut is moving relative to the Earth at a significant fraction of the speed of light. (a) Does he observe the rate of his clocks to have slowed? (b) What change in the rate of Earth-bound clocks does he see? (c) Does his ship seem to him to shorten? (d) What about the distance between stars that lie on lines parallel to his motion? (e) Do he and an Earth-bound observer agree on his velocity relative to the Earth?

28.4 Relativistic Addition of Velocities

10. Explain the meaning of the terms "red shift" and "blue shift" as they relate to the relativistic Doppler effect.

11. What happens to the relativistic Doppler effect when relative velocity is zero? Is this the expected result?

12. Is the relativistic Doppler effect consistent with the classical Doppler effect in the respect that λ_{obs} is larger for motion away?

13. All galaxies farther away than about 50×10^6 ly exhibit a red shift in their emitted light that is proportional to distance, with those farther and farther away having progressively greater red shifts. What does this imply, assuming that the only source of red shift is relative motion? (Hint: At these large distances, it is space itself that is expanding, but the effect on light is the same.)

28.5 Relativistic Momentum

14. How does modern relativity modify the law of conservation of momentum?

15. Is it possible for an external force to be acting on a system and relativistic momentum to be conserved? Explain.

28.6 Relativistic Energy

16. How are the classical laws of conservation of energy and conservation of mass modified by modern relativity?

17. What happens to the mass of water in a pot when it cools, assuming no molecules escape or are added? Is this observable in practice? Explain.

18. Consider a thought experiment. You place an expanded balloon of air on weighing scales outside in the early morning. The balloon stays on the scales and you are able to measure changes in its mass. Does the mass of the balloon change as the day progresses? Discuss the difficulties in carrying out this experiment.

19. The mass of the fuel in a nuclear reactor decreases by an observable amount as it puts out energy. Is the same true for the coal and oxygen combined in a conventional power plant? If so, is this observable in practice for the coal and oxygen? Explain.

20. We know that the velocity of an object with mass has an upper limit of c. Is there an upper limit on its momentum? Its energy? Explain.

21. Given the fact that light travels at c, can it have mass? Explain.

22. If you use an Earth-based telescope to project a laser beam onto the Moon, you can move the spot across the Moon's surface at a velocity greater than the speed of light. Does this violate modern relativity? (Note that light is being sent from the Earth to the Moon, not across the surface of the Moon.)

Problems & Exercises

28.2 Simultaneity And Time Dilation

1. (a) What is γ if $v = 0.250c$? (b) If $v = 0.500c$?

2. (a) What is γ if $v = 0.100c$? (b) If $v = 0.900c$?

3. Particles called π-mesons are produced by accelerator beams. If these particles travel at 2.70×10^8 m/s and live 2.60×10^{-8} s when at rest relative to an observer, how long do they live as viewed in the laboratory?

4. Suppose a particle called a kaon is created by cosmic radiation striking the atmosphere. It moves by you at $0.980c$, and it lives 1.24×10^{-8} s when at rest relative to an observer. How long does it live as you observe it?

5. A neutral π-meson is a particle that can be created by accelerator beams. If one such particle lives 1.40×10^{-16} s as measured in the laboratory, and 0.840×10^{-16} s when at rest relative to an observer, what is its velocity relative to the laboratory?

6. A neutron lives 900 s when at rest relative to an observer. How fast is the neutron moving relative to an observer who measures its life span to be 2065 s?

7. If relativistic effects are to be less than 1%, then γ must be less than 1.01. At what relative velocity is $\gamma = 1.01$?

8. If relativistic effects are to be less than 3%, then γ must be less than 1.03. At what relative velocity is $\gamma = 1.03$?

9. (a) At what relative velocity is $\gamma = 1.50$? (b) At what relative velocity is $\gamma = 100$?

10. (a) At what relative velocity is $\gamma = 2.00$? (b) At what relative velocity is $\gamma = 10.0$?

11. Unreasonable Results
(a) Find the value of γ for the following situation. An Earth-bound observer measures 23.9 h to have passed while signals from a high-velocity space probe indicate that 24.0 h have passed on board. (b) What is unreasonable about this result? (c) Which assumptions are unreasonable or inconsistent?

28.3 Length Contraction

12. A spaceship, 200 m long as seen on board, moves by the Earth at $0.970c$. What is its length as measured by an Earth-bound observer?

13. How fast would a 6.0 m-long sports car have to be going past you in order for it to appear only 5.5 m long?

14. (a) How far does the muon in Example 28.1 travel according to the Earth-bound observer? (b) How far does it travel as viewed by an observer moving with it? Base your calculation on its velocity relative to the Earth and the time it lives (proper time). (c) Verify that these two distances are related through length contraction $\gamma = 3.20$.

15. (a) How long would the muon in Example 28.1 have lived as observed on the Earth if its velocity was $0.0500c$? (b) How far would it have traveled as observed on the Earth? (c) What distance is this in the muon's frame?

16. (a) How long does it take the astronaut in Example 28.2 to travel 4.30 ly at $0.99944c$ (as measured by the Earth-bound observer)? (b) How long does it take according to the astronaut? (c) Verify that these two times are related through time dilation with $\gamma = 30.00$ as given.

17. (a) How fast would an athlete need to be running for a 100-m race to look 100 yd long? (b) Is the answer consistent with the fact that relativistic effects are difficult to observe in ordinary circumstances? Explain.

18. Unreasonable Results
(a) Find the value of γ for the following situation. An astronaut measures the length of her spaceship to be 25.0 m, while an Earth-bound observer measures it to be 100 m. (b) What is unreasonable about this result? (c) Which assumptions are unreasonable or inconsistent?

19. Unreasonable Results
A spaceship is heading directly toward the Earth at a velocity of $0.800c$. The astronaut on board claims that he can send a canister toward the Earth at $1.20c$ relative to the Earth. (a) Calculate the velocity the canister must have relative to the spaceship. (b) What is unreasonable about this result? (c) Which assumptions are unreasonable or inconsistent?

28.4 Relativistic Addition of Velocities

20. Suppose a spaceship heading straight towards the Earth at $0.750c$ can shoot a canister at $0.500c$ relative to the ship. (a) What is the velocity of the canister relative to the Earth, if it is shot directly at the Earth? (b) If it is shot directly away from the Earth?

21. Repeat the previous problem with the ship heading directly away from the Earth.

22. If a spaceship is approaching the Earth at $0.100c$ and a message capsule is sent toward it at $0.100c$ relative to the Earth, what is the speed of the capsule relative to the ship?

23. (a) Suppose the speed of light were only 3000 m/s. A jet fighter moving toward a target on the ground at 800 m/s shoots bullets, each having a muzzle velocity of 1000 m/s. What are the bullets' velocity relative to the target? (b) If the speed of light was this small, would you observe relativistic effects in everyday life? Discuss.

24. If a galaxy moving away from the Earth has a speed of 1000 km/s and emits 656 nm light characteristic of hydrogen (the most common element in the universe). (a) What wavelength would we observe on the Earth? (b) What type of electromagnetic radiation is this? (c) Why is the speed of the Earth in its orbit negligible here?

25. A space probe speeding towards the nearest star moves at $0.250c$ and sends radio information at a broadcast frequency of 1.00 GHz. What frequency is received on the Earth?

26. If two spaceships are heading directly towards each other at $0.800c$, at what speed must a canister be shot from the first ship to approach the other at $0.999c$ as seen by the second ship?

27. Two planets are on a collision course, heading directly towards each other at $0.250c$. A spaceship sent from one planet approaches the second at $0.750c$ as seen by the second planet. What is the velocity of the ship relative to the first planet?

28. When a missile is shot from one spaceship towards another, it leaves the first at $0.950c$ and approaches the other at $0.750c$. What is the relative velocity of the two ships?

29. What is the relative velocity of two spaceships if one fires a missile at the other at $0.750c$ and the other observes it to approach at $0.950c$?

30. Near the center of our galaxy, hydrogen gas is moving directly away from us in its orbit about a black hole. We receive 1900 nm electromagnetic radiation and know that it was 1875 nm when emitted by the hydrogen gas. What is the speed of the gas?

31. A highway patrol officer uses a device that measures the speed of vehicles by bouncing radar off them and measuring the Doppler shift. The outgoing radar has a frequency of 100 GHz and the returning echo has a frequency 15.0 kHz higher. What is the velocity of the vehicle? Note that there are two Doppler shifts in echoes. Be certain not to round off until the end of the problem, because the effect is small.

32. Prove that for any relative velocity v between two observers, a beam of light sent from one to the other will approach at speed c (provided that v is less than c, of course).

33. Show that for any relative velocity v between two observers, a beam of light projected by one directly away from the other will move away at the speed of light (provided that v is less than c, of course).

34. (a) All but the closest galaxies are receding from our own Milky Way Galaxy. If a galaxy 12.0×10^9 ly ly away is receding from us at $0.0.900c$, at what velocity relative to us must we send an exploratory probe to approach the other galaxy at $0.990c$, as measured from that galaxy? (b) How long will it take the probe to reach the other galaxy as measured from the Earth? You may assume that the velocity of the other galaxy remains constant. (c) How long will it then take for a radio signal to be beamed back? (All of this is possible in principle, but not practical.)

28.5 Relativistic Momentum

35. Find the momentum of a helium nucleus having a mass of 6.68×10^{-27} kg that is moving at $0.200c$.

36. What is the momentum of an electron traveling at $0.980c$?

37. (a) Find the momentum of a 1.00×10^9 kg asteroid heading towards the Earth at 30.0 km/s. (b) Find the ratio of this momentum to the classical momentum. (Hint: Use the approximation that $\gamma = 1{+}(1/2)v^2/c^2$ at low velocities.)

38. (a) What is the momentum of a 2000 kg satellite orbiting at 4.00 km/s? (b) Find the ratio of this momentum to the classical momentum. (Hint: Use the approximation that $\gamma = 1{+}(1/2)v^2/c^2$ at low velocities.)

39. What is the velocity of an electron that has a momentum of 3.04×10^{-21} kg·m/s? Note that you must calculate the velocity to at least four digits to see the difference from c.

40. Find the velocity of a proton that has a momentum of 4.48×-10^{-19} kg·m/s.

41. (a) Calculate the speed of a 1.00-μg particle of dust that has the same momentum as a proton moving at $0.999c$. (b) What does the small speed tell us about the mass of a proton compared to even a tiny amount of macroscopic matter?

42. (a) Calculate γ for a proton that has a momentum of 1.00 kg·m/s. (b) What is its speed? Such protons form a rare component of cosmic radiation with uncertain origins.

28.6 Relativistic Energy

43. What is the rest energy of an electron, given its mass is 9.11×10^{-31} kg? Give your answer in joules and MeV.

44. Find the rest energy in joules and MeV of a proton, given its mass is 1.67×10^{-27} kg.

45. If the rest energies of a proton and a neutron (the two constituents of nuclei) are 938.3 and 939.6 MeV respectively, what is the difference in their masses in kilograms?

46. The Big Bang that began the universe is estimated to have released 10^{68} J of energy. How many stars could half this energy create, assuming the average star's mass is 4.00×10^{30} kg?

47. A supernova explosion of a 2.00×10^{31} kg star produces 1.00×10^{44} J of energy. (a) How many kilograms of mass are converted to energy in the explosion? (b) What is the ratio $\Delta m/m$ of mass destroyed to the original mass of the star?

48. (a) Using data from Table 7.1, calculate the mass converted to energy by the fission of 1.00 kg of uranium. (b) What is the ratio of mass destroyed to the original mass, $\Delta m/m$?

49. (a) Using data from Table 7.1, calculate the amount of mass converted to energy by the fusion of 1.00 kg of hydrogen. (b) What is the ratio of mass destroyed to the original mass, $\Delta m/m$? (c) How does this compare with $\Delta m/m$ for the fission of 1.00 kg of uranium?

50. There is approximately 10^{34} J of energy available from fusion of hydrogen in the world's oceans. (a) If 10^{33} J of this energy were utilized, what would be the decrease in mass of the oceans? Assume that 0.08% of the mass of a water molecule is converted to energy during the fusion of hydrogen. (b) How great a volume of water does this correspond to? (c) Comment on whether this is a significant fraction of the total mass of the oceans.

51. A muon has a rest mass energy of 105.7 MeV, and

it decays into an electron and a massless particle. (a) If all the lost mass is converted into the electron's kinetic energy, find γ for the electron. (b) What is the electron's velocity?

52. A π-meson is a particle that decays into a muon and a massless particle. The π-meson has a rest mass energy of 139.6 MeV, and the muon has a rest mass energy of 105.7 MeV. Suppose the π-meson is at rest and all of the missing mass goes into the muon's kinetic energy. How fast will the muon move?

53. (a) Calculate the relativistic kinetic energy of a 1000-kg car moving at 30.0 m/s if the speed of light were only 45.0 m/s. (b) Find the ratio of the relativistic kinetic energy to classical.

54. Alpha decay is nuclear decay in which a helium nucleus is emitted. If the helium nucleus has a mass of 6.80×10^{-27} kg and is given 5.00 MeV of kinetic energy, what is its velocity?

55. (a) Beta decay is nuclear decay in which an electron is emitted. If the electron is given 0.750 MeV of kinetic energy, what is its velocity? (b) Comment on how the high velocity is consistent with the kinetic energy as it compares to the rest mass energy of the electron.

56. A positron is an antimatter version of the electron, having exactly the same mass. When a positron and an electron meet, they annihilate, converting all of their mass into energy. (a) Find the energy released, assuming negligible kinetic energy before the annihilation. (b) If this energy is given to a proton in the form of kinetic energy, what is its velocity? (c) If this energy is given to another electron in the form of kinetic energy, what is its velocity?

57. What is the kinetic energy in MeV of a π-meson that lives 1.40×10^{-16} s as measured in the laboratory, and 0.840×10^{-16} s when at rest relative to an observer, given that its rest energy is 135 MeV?

58. Find the kinetic energy in MeV of a neutron with a measured life span of 2065 s, given its rest energy is 939.6 MeV, and rest life span is 900s.

59. (a) Show that $(pc)^2/(mc^2)^2 = \gamma^2 - 1$. This means that at large velocities $pc >> mc^2$. (b) Is $E \approx pc$ when $\gamma = 30.0$, as for the astronaut discussed in the twin paradox?

60. One cosmic ray neutron has a velocity of $0.250c$ relative to the Earth. (a) What is the neutron's total energy in MeV? (b) Find its momentum. (c) Is $E \approx pc$ in this situation? Discuss in terms of the equation given in part (a) of the previous problem.

61. What is γ for a proton having a mass energy of 938.3 MeV accelerated through an effective potential of 1.0 TV (teravolt) at Fermilab outside Chicago?

62. (a) What is the effective accelerating potential for electrons at the Stanford Linear Accelerator, if $\gamma = 1.00 \times 10^5$ for them? (b) What is their total energy (nearly the same as kinetic in this case) in GeV?

63. (a) Using data from Table 7.1, find the mass destroyed when the energy in a barrel of crude oil is released. (b) Given these barrels contain 200 liters and assuming the density of crude oil is 750 kg/m^3, what is the ratio of mass destroyed to original mass, $\Delta m/m$?

64. (a) Calculate the energy released by the destruction of 1.00 kg of mass. (b) How many kilograms could be lifted to a 10.0 km height by this amount of energy?

65. A Van de Graaff accelerator utilizes a 50.0 MV potential difference to accelerate charged particles such as protons. (a) What is the velocity of a proton accelerated by such a potential? (b) An electron?

66. Suppose you use an average of 500 kW·h of electric energy per month in your home. (a) How long would 1.00 g of mass converted to electric energy with an efficiency of 38.0% last you? (b) How many homes could be supplied at the 500 kW·h per month rate for one year by the energy from the described mass conversion?

67. (a) A nuclear power plant converts energy from nuclear fission into electricity with an efficiency of 35.0%. How much mass is destroyed in one year to produce a continuous 1000 MW of electric power? (b) Do you think it would be possible to observe this mass loss if the total mass of the fuel is 10^4 kg?

68. Nuclear-powered rockets were researched for some years before safety concerns became paramount. (a) What fraction of a rocket's mass would have to be destroyed to get it into a low Earth orbit, neglecting the decrease in gravity? (Assume an orbital altitude of 250 km, and calculate both the kinetic energy (classical) and the gravitational potential energy needed.) (b) If the ship has a mass of 1.00×10^5 kg (100 tons), what total yield nuclear explosion in tons of TNT is needed?

69. The Sun produces energy at a rate of 4.00×10^{26} W by the fusion of hydrogen. (a) How many kilograms of hydrogen undergo fusion each second? (b) If the Sun is 90.0% hydrogen and half of this can undergo fusion before the Sun changes character, how long could it produce energy at its current rate? (c) How many kilograms of mass is the Sun losing per second? (d) What fraction of its mass will it have lost in the time found in part (b)?

70. Unreasonable Results
A proton has a mass of 1.67×10^{-27} kg. A physicist measures the proton's total energy to be 50.0 MeV. (a) What is the proton's kinetic energy? (b) What is unreasonable about this result? (c) Which assumptions are unreasonable or inconsistent?

71. Construct Your Own Problem
Consider a highly relativistic particle. Discuss what is meant by the term "highly relativistic." (Note that, in part, it means that the particle cannot be massless.) Construct a problem in which you calculate the wavelength of such a particle and show that it is very nearly the same as the wavelength of a massless particle, such as a photon, with the same energy. Among the things to be considered are the rest energy of the particle (it should be a known particle) and its total energy, which should be large compared to its rest energy.

72. Construct Your Own Problem
Consider an astronaut traveling to another star at a relativistic velocity. Construct a problem in which you calculate the time for the trip as observed on the Earth and as observed by the astronaut. Also calculate the amount of mass that must be converted to energy to get the astronaut and ship to the velocity travelled. Among the things to be considered are the distance to the star, the velocity, and the mass of the astronaut and ship. Unless your instructor directs you otherwise, do not include any energy given to other masses, such as rocket propellants.

73. Critical Thinking A space rock with a length of 1,000.0 m is moving through space at exactly 0.6 c. (a) If the space rock is moving toward an observer, what is the contracted length observed? (b) If the space rock is moving away from the observer, what is the contracted length observed? (c) Can the object reach the speed of light? (d) If the object were to stop in the observer's reference frame, would it be observed to have proper length?

Test Prep for AP® Courses

28.1 Einstein's Postulates

1. Which of the following statements describes the Michelson-Morley experiment?
   a. The speed of light is independent of the motion of the source relative to the observer.
   b. The speed of light is different in different frames of reference.
   c. The speed of light changes with changes in the observer.
   d. The speed of light is dependent on the motion of the source.

28.4 Relativistic Addition of Velocities

2. What happens when velocities comparable to the speed of light are involved in an observation?
   a. Newton's second law of motion, $F = ma$, governs the motion of the object.
   b. Newton's second law of motion, $F = ma$, no longer governs the dynamics of the object.
   c. Such velocities cannot be determined mathematically.
   d. None of the above

3. How is the relativistic Doppler effect different from the classical Doppler effect?

28.6 Relativistic Energy

4. A mass of 50 g is completely converted into energy. What is the energy that will be obtained when such a conversion takes place?

5. Show that relativistic kinetic energy becomes the same as classical kinetic energy when $v = c$.

6. The relativistic energy of a particle in terms of momentum is given by:
   a. $E = \sqrt{p^2c^2 + m_0^2c^4}$
   b. $E = \sqrt{p^2c^2 + m_0^4c^4}$
   c. $E = \sqrt{p^2c^2 + m_0^2c^2}$
   d. $E = \sqrt{p^2c^4 + m_0^2c^2}$

CHAPTER 29
Quantum Physics

FIGURE 29.1 A black fly imaged by an electron microscope is as monstrous as any science-fiction creature. (credit: U.S. Department of Agriculture via Wikimedia Commons)

CHAPTER OUTLINE

CONNECTION FOR AP® COURSES In this chapter, the basic principles of **quantum mechanics** are introduced. Quantum mechanics is the branch of physics needed to deal with submicroscopic objects. Because these objects are smaller than those, such as computers, books, or cars, that we can observe directly with our senses, and so generally must be observed with the aid of instruments, parts of quantum mechanics seem as foreign and bizarre as the effects of relative motion near the speed of light. Yet through experimental results, quantum mechanics has been shown to be valid. Truth is often stranger than fiction.

Quantum theory was developed initially to explain the behavior of electromagnetic energy in certain situations, such as **blackbody radiation** or the **photoelectric effect**, which could not be understood in terms of classical electrodynamics (Essential Knowledge 1.D.2). In the quantum model, light is treated as a packet of energy called a **photon**, which has both the properties of a wave and a particle (Essential Knowledge 6.F.3). The energy of a photon is directly proportional to its frequency.

This new model for light provided the foundation for one of the most important ideas in quantum theory: wave-particle duality. Just as light has properties of both waves and particles, matter also has the properties of waves and particles (Essential Knowledge 1.D.1). This interpretation of matter and energy explained observations at the atomic level that could not be explained by classical mechanics or electromagnetic theory (Enduring Understanding 1.D). The quantum interpretation of energy and matter at the atomic level, most notably the internal structure of atoms, supports Big Idea 1 of the AP Physics Curriculum Framework.

Big Idea 1 is also supported by the **correspondence principle**. Classical mechanics cannot accurately describe systems at the atomic level, whereas quantum mechanics is able to describe systems at both levels. However, the properties of matter that are described by waves become insignificant at the macroscopic level, so that for large systems of matter, the quantum description closely approaches, or *corresponds to*, the classical description (Essential Knowledge 6.G.1, Essential Knowledge 6.G.2, Essential Knowledge 6.F.3).

Big Ideas 5 and 6 are supported by the descriptions of energy and momentum transfer at the quantum level. Although quantum mechanics overturned a number of fundamental ideas of classical physics, the most important principles, such as energy conservation and momentum conservation, remained intact (Enduring Understanding 5.B, Enduring Understanding 5.D). Quantum mechanics expands on these principles, so that the particle-like behavior of electromagnetic energy describes momentum transfer, while the wave-like behavior of matter accounts for why electrons produce diffraction patterns when they pass through the atomic lattices of crystals.

At the quantum level, the effects of measurement are very different from those at the macroscopic level. Because the wave properties of matter are more prominent for small particles, such as electrons, and a wave does not have a specific location, the position and momentum of matter cannot be measured with absolute precision (Essential Knowledge 1.D.3). Rather, the particle has a certain probability of being in a location interval for a specific momentum, or being located within a particular interval of time for a specific energy (Enduring Understanding 7.C, Essential Knowledge 7.C.1). These probabilistic limits on measurement are described by **Heisenberg's uncertainty principle**, which connects wave-particle duality to the non-absolute properties of space and time. At the quantum level, measurements affect the system being measured, and so restrict the degree to which properties can be known. The discussion of this probabilistic interpretation supports Big Idea 7 of the AP Physics Curriculum Framework.

The concepts in this chapter support:

Big Idea 1 Objects and systems have properties such as mass and charge. Systems may have internal structure.

Enduring Understanding 1.D Classical mechanics cannot describe all properties of objects.

Essential Knowledge 1.D.1 Objects classically thought of as particles can exhibit properties of waves.

Essential Knowledge 1.D.2 Certain phenomena classically thought of as waves can exhibit properties of particles.

Essential Knowledge 1.D.3 Properties of space and time cannot always be treated as absolute.

Big Idea 5 Changes that occur as a result of interactions are constrained by conservation laws.

Enduring Understanding 5.B The energy of a system is conserved.

Essential Knowledge 5.B.8 Energy transfer occurs when photons are absorbed or emitted, for example, by atoms or nuclei.

Enduring Understanding 5.D The linear momentum of a system is conserved.

Essential Knowledge 5.D.1 In a collision between objects, linear momentum is conserved. In an elastic collision, kinetic energy is the same before and after.

Big Idea 6 Waves can transfer energy and momentum from one location to another without the permanent transfer of mass and serve as a mathematical model for the description of other phenomena.

Enduring Understanding 6.F Electromagnetic radiation can be modeled as waves or as fundamental particles.

Essential Knowledge 6.F.3 Photons are individual energy packets of electromagnetic waves, with $E_{\text{photon}} = hf$, where h is Planck's constant and f is the frequency of the associated light wave.

Essential Knowledge 6.F.4 The nature of light requires that different models of light are most appropriate at different scales.

Enduring Understanding 6.G All matter can be modeled as waves or as particles.

Essential Knowledge 6.G.1 Under certain regimes of energy or distance, matter can be modeled as a classical particle.

Essential Knowledge 6.G.2 Under certain regimes of energy or distance, matter can be modeled as a wave. The behavior in these regimes is described by quantum mechanics.

Big Idea 7. The mathematics of probability can be used to describe the behavior of complex systems and to interpret the behavior of quantum mechanical systems.

Enduring Understanding 7.C At the quantum scale, matter is described by a wave function, which leads to a probabilistic description of the microscopic world.

Essential Knowledge 7.C.1 The probabilistic description of matter is modeled by a wave function, which can be assigned to an object and used to describe its motion and interactions. The absolute value of the wave function is related to the probability of finding a particle in some spatial region. (Qualitative treatment only, using graphical analysis.)

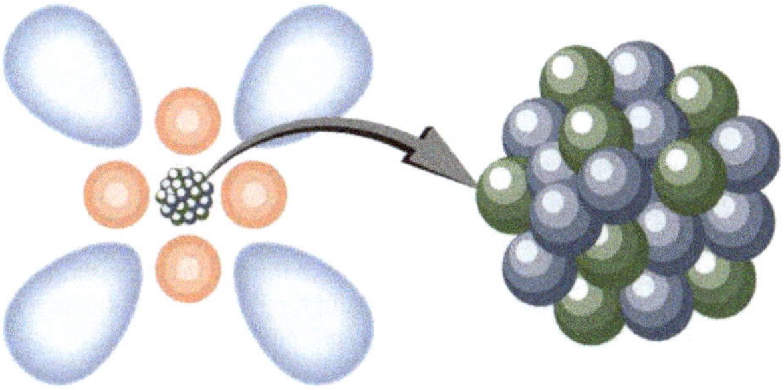

FIGURE 29.2 Atoms and their substructure are familiar examples of objects that require quantum mechanics to be fully explained. Certain of their characteristics, such as the discrete electron shells, are classical physics explanations. In quantum mechanics we conceptualize discrete "electron clouds" around the nucleus.

MAKING CONNECTIONS: REALMS OF PHYSICS

Classical physics is a good approximation of modern physics under conditions first discussed in The Nature of Science and Physics. Quantum mechanics is valid in general, and it must be used rather than classical physics to describe small objects, such as atoms.

Atoms, molecules, and fundamental electron and proton charges are all examples of physical entities that are **quantized**—that is, they appear only in certain discrete values and do not have every conceivable value. Quantized is the opposite of continuous. We cannot have a fraction of an atom, or part of an electron's charge, or 14-1/3 cents, for example. Rather, everything is built of integral multiples of these substructures. Quantum physics is the branch of physics that deals with small objects and the quantization of various entities, including energy and angular momentum. Just as with classical physics, quantum physics has several subfields, such as mechanics and the study of electromagnetic forces. The **correspondence principle** states that in the classical limit (large, slow-moving objects), **quantum mechanics** becomes the same as classical physics. In this chapter, we begin the development of quantum mechanics and its description of the strange submicroscopic world. In later chapters, we will examine many areas, such as atomic and nuclear physics, in which quantum mechanics is crucial.

29.1 Quantization of Energy

LEARNING OBJECTIVES

By the end of this section, you will be able to:

- Explain Max Planck's contribution to the development of quantum mechanics.
- Explain why atomic spectra indicate quantization.

Planck's Contribution

Energy is quantized in some systems, meaning that the system can have only certain energies and not a continuum of energies, unlike the classical case. This would be like having only certain speeds at which a car can travel because its kinetic energy can have only certain values. We also find that some forms of energy transfer take place with discrete lumps of energy. While most of us are familiar with the quantization of matter into lumps called atoms, molecules, and the like, we are less aware that energy, too, can be quantized. Some of the earliest clues about the necessity of quantum mechanics over classical physics came from the quantization of energy.

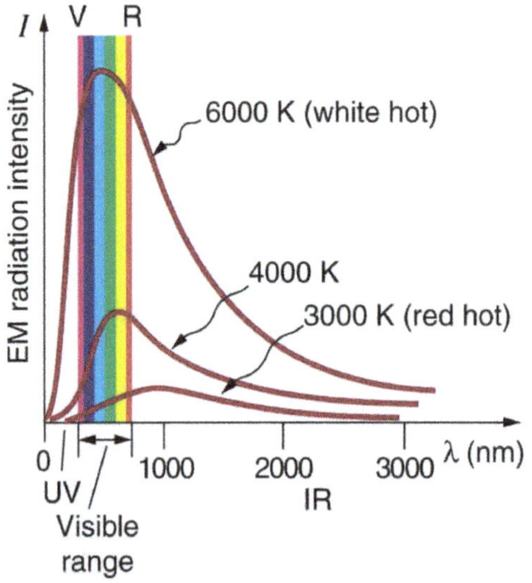

FIGURE 29.3 Graphs of blackbody radiation (from an ideal radiator) at three different radiator temperatures. The intensity or rate of radiation emission increases dramatically with temperature, and the peak of the spectrum shifts toward the visible and ultraviolet parts of the spectrum. The shape of the spectrum cannot be described with classical physics.

Where is the quantization of energy observed? Let us begin by considering the emission and absorption of electromagnetic (EM) radiation. The EM spectrum radiated by a hot solid is linked directly to the solid's temperature. (See Figure 29.3.) An ideal radiator is one that has an emissivity of 1 at all wavelengths and, thus, is jet black. Ideal radiators are therefore called **blackbodies**, and their EM radiation is called **blackbody radiation**. It was discussed that the total intensity of the radiation varies as T^4, the fourth power of the absolute temperature of the body, and that the peak of the spectrum shifts to shorter wavelengths at higher temperatures. All of this seems quite continuous, but it was the curve of the spectrum of intensity versus wavelength that gave a clue that the energies of the atoms in the solid are quantized. In fact, providing a theoretical explanation for the experimentally measured shape of the spectrum was a mystery at the turn of the century. When this "ultraviolet catastrophe" was eventually solved, the answers led to new technologies such as computers and the sophisticated imaging techniques described in earlier chapters. Once again, physics as an enabling science changed the way we live.

The German physicist Max Planck (1858–1947) used the idea that atoms and molecules in a body act like oscillators to absorb and emit radiation. The energies of the oscillating atoms and molecules had to be quantized to correctly describe the shape of the blackbody spectrum. Planck deduced that the energy of an oscillator having a frequency f is given by

$$E = \left(n + \frac{1}{2}\right)hf. \tag{29.1}$$

Here n is any nonnegative integer (0, 1, 2, 3, ….). The symbol h stands for **Planck's constant**, given by

$$h = 6.626 \times 10^{-34}\ \text{J} \cdot \text{s}. \tag{29.2}$$

The equation $E = \left(n + \frac{1}{2}\right)hf$ means that an oscillator having a frequency f (emitting and absorbing EM radiation of frequency f) can have its energy increase or decrease only in *discrete* steps of size

$$\Delta E = hf. \tag{29.3}$$

It might be helpful to mention some macroscopic analogies of this quantization of energy phenomena. This is like a pendulum that has a characteristic oscillation frequency but can swing with only certain amplitudes. Quantization of energy also resembles a standing wave on a string that allows only particular harmonics described by integers. It is also similar to going up and down a hill using discrete stair steps rather than being able to move up and down a continuous slope. Your potential energy takes on discrete values as you move from step to step.

Using the quantization of oscillators, Planck was able to correctly describe the experimentally known shape of the blackbody spectrum. This was the first indication that energy is sometimes quantized on a small scale and earned him the Nobel Prize in Physics in 1918. Although Planck's theory comes from observations of a macroscopic object, its analysis is based on atoms and molecules. It was such a revolutionary departure from classical physics that Planck himself was reluctant to accept his own idea that energy states are not continuous. The general acceptance of Planck's energy quantization was greatly enhanced by Einstein's explanation of the photoelectric effect (discussed in the next section), which took energy quantization a step further. Planck was fully involved in the development of both early quantum mechanics and relativity. He quickly embraced Einstein's special relativity, published in 1905, and in 1906 Planck was the first to suggest the correct formula for relativistic momentum, $p = \gamma mu$.

FIGURE 29.4 The German physicist Max Planck had a major influence on the early development of quantum mechanics, being the first to recognize that energy is sometimes quantized. Planck also made important contributions to special relativity and classical physics. (credit: Library of Congress, Prints and Photographs Division via Wikimedia Commons)

Note that Planck's constant h is a very small number. So for an infrared frequency of 10^{14} Hz being emitted by a blackbody, for example, the difference between energy levels is only $\Delta E = hf$=$(6.63 \times 10^{-34}$ J·s)(10^{14} Hz)= 6.63×10^{-20} J, or about 0.4 eV. This 0.4 eV of energy is significant compared with typical atomic energies, which are on the order of an electron volt, or thermal energies, which are typically fractions of an electron volt. But on a macroscopic or classical scale, energies are typically on the order of joules. Even if macroscopic energies are quantized, the quantum steps are too small to be noticed. This is an example of the correspondence principle. For a large object, quantum mechanics produces results indistinguishable from those of classical physics.

Atomic Spectra

Now let us turn our attention to the *emission and absorption of EM radiation by gases*. The Sun is the most common example of a body containing gases emitting an EM spectrum that includes visible light. We also see examples in neon signs and candle flames. Studies of emissions of hot gases began more than two centuries ago, and it was soon recognized that these emission spectra contained huge amounts of information. The type of gas and its temperature, for example, could be determined. We now know that these EM emissions come from electrons transitioning between energy levels in individual atoms and molecules; thus, they are called **atomic spectra**. Atomic spectra remain an important analytical tool today. Figure 29.5 shows an example of an emission spectrum obtained by passing an electric discharge through a material. One of the most important characteristics of these spectra is that they are discrete. By this we mean that only certain wavelengths, and hence frequencies, are emitted. This is called a line spectrum. If frequency and energy are associated as $\Delta E = hf$, the energies of the electrons in the emitting atoms and molecules are quantized. This is discussed in more detail later in this chapter.

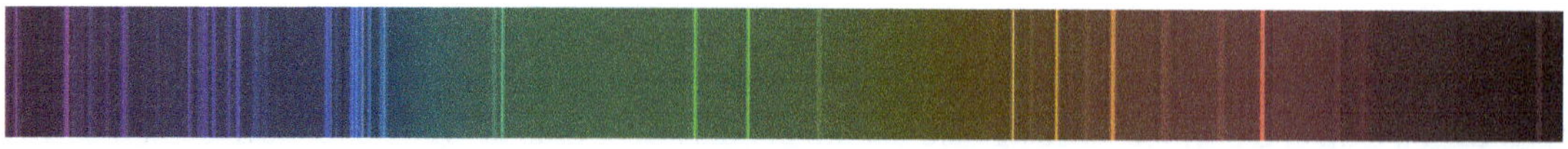

FIGURE 29.5 Emission spectrum of oxygen. When an electrical discharge is passed through a substance, its atoms and molecules absorb energy, which is reemitted as EM radiation. The discrete nature of these emissions implies that the energy states of the atoms and molecules are quantized. Such atomic spectra were used as analytical tools for many decades before it was understood why they are quantized. (credit: Teravolt, Wikimedia Commons)

It was a major puzzle that atomic spectra are quantized. Some of the best minds of 19th-century science failed to explain why this might be. Not until the second decade of the 20th century did an answer based on quantum mechanics begin to emerge. Again a macroscopic or classical body of gas was involved in the studies, but the effect, as we shall see, is due to individual atoms and molecules.

PHET EXPLORATIONS

Models of the Hydrogen Atom

How did scientists figure out the structure of atoms without looking at them? Try out different models by shooting light at the atom. Check how the prediction of the model matches the experimental results.

Click to view content (https://openstax.org/l/28atom_model).

PhET

29.2 The Photoelectric Effect

LEARNING OBJECTIVES

By the end of this section, you will be able to:

- Describe a typical photoelectric-effect experiment.
- Determine the maximum kinetic energy of photoelectrons ejected by photons of one energy or wavelength, when given the maximum kinetic energy of photoelectrons for a different photon energy or wavelength.

When light strikes materials, it can eject electrons from them. This is called the **photoelectric effect**, meaning that light (*photo*) produces electricity. One common use of the photoelectric effect is in light meters, such as those that adjust the automatic iris on various types of cameras. In a similar way, another use is in solar cells, as you probably have in your calculator or have seen on a roof top or a roadside sign. These make use of the photoelectric effect to convert light into electricity for running different devices.

FIGURE 29.6 The photoelectric effect can be observed by allowing light to fall on the metal plate in this evacuated tube. Electrons ejected by the light are collected on the collector wire and measured as a current. A retarding voltage between the collector wire and plate can then be adjusted so as to determine the energy of the ejected electrons. For example, if it is sufficiently negative, no electrons will reach the wire. (credit: P.P. Urone)

This effect has been known for more than a century and can be studied using a device such as that shown in Figure 29.6. This figure shows an evacuated tube with a metal plate and a collector wire that are connected by a variable voltage source, with the collector more negative than the plate. When light (or other EM radiation) strikes the plate in the evacuated tube, it may eject electrons. If the electrons have energy in electron volts (eV) greater than the potential difference between the plate and the wire in volts, some electrons will be collected on the wire. Since the electron energy in eV is qV, where q is the electron charge and V is the potential difference, the electron energy can be measured by adjusting the retarding voltage between the wire and the plate. The voltage that stops the electrons from reaching the wire equals the energy in eV. For example, if -3.00 V barely stops the electrons, their energy is

3.00 eV. The number of electrons ejected can be determined by measuring the current between the wire and plate. The more light, the more electrons; a little circuitry allows this device to be used as a light meter.

What is really important about the photoelectric effect is what Albert Einstein deduced from it. Einstein realized that there were several characteristics of the photoelectric effect that could be explained only if *EM radiation is itself quantized*: the apparently continuous stream of energy in an EM wave is actually composed of energy quanta called photons. In his explanation of the photoelectric effect, Einstein defined a quantized unit or quantum of EM energy, which we now call a **photon**, with an energy proportional to the frequency of EM radiation. In equation form, the **photon energy** is

$$E = hf, \quad (29.4)$$

where E is the energy of a photon of frequency f and h is Planck's constant. This revolutionary idea looks similar to Planck's quantization of energy states in blackbody oscillators, but it is quite different. It is the quantization of EM radiation itself. EM waves are composed of photons and are not continuous smooth waves as described in previous chapters on optics. Their energy is absorbed and emitted in lumps, not continuously. This is exactly consistent with Planck's quantization of energy levels in blackbody oscillators, since these oscillators increase and decrease their energy in steps of hf by absorbing and emitting photons having $E = hf$. We do not observe this with our eyes, because there are so many photons in common light sources that individual photons go unnoticed. (See Figure 29.7.) The next section of the text (Photon Energies and the Electromagnetic Spectrum) is devoted to a discussion of photons and some of their characteristics and implications. For now, we will use the photon concept to explain the photoelectric effect, much as Einstein did.

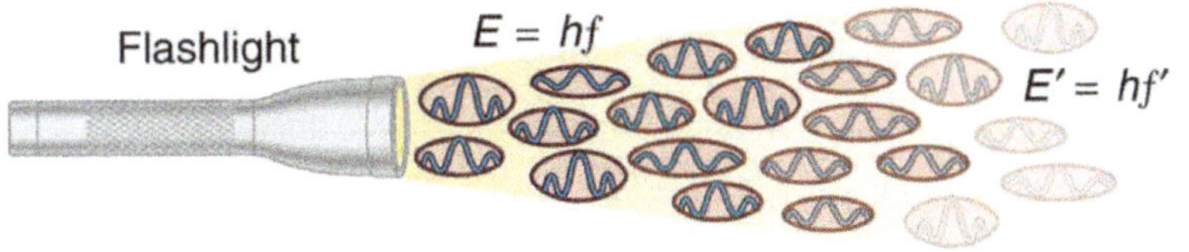

FIGURE 29.7 An EM wave of frequency f is composed of photons, or individual quanta of EM radiation. The energy of each photon is $E = hf$, where h is Planck's constant and f is the frequency of the EM radiation. Higher intensity means more photons per unit area. The flashlight emits large numbers of photons of many different frequencies, hence others have energy $E' = hf'$, and so on.

The photoelectric effect has the properties discussed below. All these properties are consistent with the idea that individual photons of EM radiation are absorbed by individual electrons in a material, with the electron gaining the photon's energy. Some of these properties are inconsistent with the idea that EM radiation is a simple wave. For simplicity, let us consider what happens with monochromatic EM radiation in which all photons have the same energy hf.

1. If we vary the frequency of the EM radiation falling on a material, we find the following: For a given material, there is a threshold frequency f_0 for the EM radiation below which no electrons are ejected, regardless of intensity. Individual photons interact with individual electrons. Thus if the photon energy is too small to break an electron away, no electrons will be ejected. If EM radiation was a simple wave, sufficient energy could be obtained by increasing the intensity.
2. *Once EM radiation falls on a material, electrons are ejected without delay.* As soon as an individual photon of a sufficiently high frequency is absorbed by an individual electron, the electron is ejected. If the EM radiation were a simple wave, several minutes would be required for sufficient energy to be deposited to the metal surface to eject an electron.
3. The number of electrons ejected per unit time is proportional to the intensity of the EM radiation and to no other characteristic. High-intensity EM radiation consists of large numbers of photons per unit area, with all photons having the same characteristic energy hf.
4. If we vary the intensity of the EM radiation and measure the energy of ejected electrons, we find the following: *The maximum kinetic energy of ejected electrons is independent of the intensity of the EM radiation.* Since there are so many electrons in a material, it is extremely unlikely that two photons will interact with the same electron at the same time, thereby increasing the energy given it. Instead (as noted in 3 above), increased intensity results in more electrons of the same energy being ejected. If EM radiation were a simple wave, a higher intensity could give more energy, and higher-energy electrons would be ejected.

5. The kinetic energy of an ejected electron equals the photon energy minus the binding energy of the electron in the specific material. An individual photon can give all of its energy to an electron. The photon's energy is partly used to break the electron away from the material. The remainder goes into the ejected electron's kinetic energy. In equation form, this is given by

$$\mathrm{KE}_e = hf - \mathrm{BE}, \tag{29.5}$$

where KE_e is the maximum kinetic energy of the ejected electron, hf is the photon's energy, and BE is the **binding energy** of the electron to the particular material. (BE is sometimes called the *work function* of the material.) This equation, due to Einstein in 1905, explains the properties of the photoelectric effect quantitatively. An individual photon of EM radiation (it does not come any other way) interacts with an individual electron, supplying enough energy, BE, to break it away, with the remainder going to kinetic energy. The binding energy is $\mathrm{BE} = hf_0$, where f_0 is the threshold frequency for the particular material. Figure 29.8 shows a graph of maximum KE_e versus the frequency of incident EM radiation falling on a particular material.

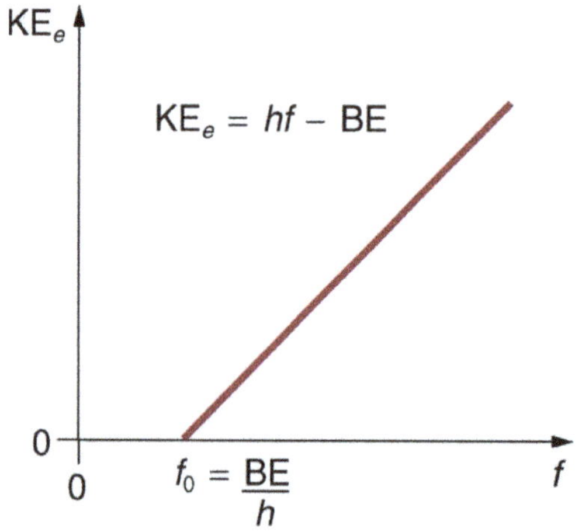

FIGURE 29.8 Photoelectric effect. A graph of the kinetic energy of an ejected electron, KE_e, versus the frequency of EM radiation impinging on a certain material. There is a threshold frequency below which no electrons are ejected, because the individual photon interacting with an individual electron has insufficient energy to break it away. Above the threshold energy, KE_e increases linearly with f, consistent with $\mathrm{KE}_e = hf - \mathrm{BE}$. The slope of this line is h—the data can be used to determine Planck's constant experimentally. Einstein gave the first successful explanation of such data by proposing the idea of photons—quanta of EM radiation.

Einstein's idea that EM radiation is quantized was crucial to the beginnings of quantum mechanics. It is a far more general concept than its explanation of the photoelectric effect might imply. All EM radiation can also be modeled in the form of photons, and the characteristics of EM radiation are entirely consistent with this fact. (As we will see in the next section, many aspects of EM radiation, such as the hazards of ultraviolet (UV) radiation, can be explained *only* by photon properties.) More famous for modern relativity, Einstein planted an important seed for quantum mechanics in 1905, the same year he published his first paper on special relativity. His explanation of the photoelectric effect was the basis for the Nobel Prize awarded to him in 1921. Although his other contributions to theoretical physics were also noted in that award, special and general relativity were not fully recognized in spite of having been partially verified by experiment by 1921. Although hero-worshipped, this great man never received Nobel recognition for his most famous work—relativity.

EXAMPLE 29.1

Calculating Photon Energy and the Photoelectric Effect: A Violet Light

(a) What is the energy in joules and electron volts of a photon of 420-nm violet light? (b) What is the maximum kinetic energy of electrons ejected from calcium by 420-nm violet light, given that the binding energy (or work function) of electrons for calcium metal is 2.71 eV?

Strategy

To solve part (a), note that the energy of a photon is given by $E = hf$. For part (b), once the energy of the photon is calculated, it is a straightforward application of $\mathrm{KE}_e = hf\text{–}\mathrm{BE}$ to find the ejected electron's maximum kinetic energy, since BE is given.

Solution for (a)

Photon energy is given by

$$E = hf \tag{29.6}$$

Since we are given the wavelength rather than the frequency, we solve the familiar relationship $c = f\lambda$ for the frequency, yielding

$$f = \frac{c}{\lambda}. \tag{29.7}$$

Combining these two equations gives the useful relationship

$$E = \frac{hc}{\lambda}. \tag{29.8}$$

Now substituting known values yields

$$E = \frac{\left(6.63 \times 10^{-34}\ \text{J} \cdot \text{s}\right)\left(3.00 \times 10^{8}\ \text{m/s}\right)}{420 \times 10^{-9}\ \text{m}} = 4.74 \times 10^{-19}\ \text{J}. \tag{29.9}$$

Converting to eV, the energy of the photon is

$$E = \left(4.74 \times 10^{-19}\ \text{J}\right)\frac{1\ \text{eV}}{1.6 \times 10^{-19}\ \text{J}} = 2.96\ \text{eV}. \tag{29.10}$$

Solution for (b)

Finding the kinetic energy of the ejected electron is now a simple application of the equation $\text{KE}_e = hf\text{–BE}$. Substituting the photon energy and binding energy yields

$$\text{KE}_e = hf\text{– BE} = 2.96\ \text{eV} - 2.71\ \text{eV} = 0.246\ \text{eV}. \tag{29.11}$$

Discussion

The energy of this 420-nm photon of violet light is a tiny fraction of a joule, and so it is no wonder that a single photon would be difficult for us to sense directly—humans are more attuned to energies on the order of joules. But looking at the energy in electron volts, we can see that this photon has enough energy to affect atoms and molecules. A DNA molecule can be broken with about 1 eV of energy, for example, and typical atomic and molecular energies are on the order of eV, so that the UV photon in this example could have biological effects. The ejected electron (called a *photoelectron*) has a rather low energy, and it would not travel far, except in a vacuum. The electron would be stopped by a retarding potential of but 0.26 eV. In fact, if the photon wavelength were longer and its energy less than 2.71 eV, then the formula would give a negative kinetic energy, an impossibility. This simply means that the 420-nm photons with their 2.96-eV energy are not much above the frequency threshold. You can show for yourself that the threshold wavelength is 459 nm (blue light). This means that if calcium metal is used in a light meter, the meter will be insensitive to wavelengths longer than those of blue light. Such a light meter would be completely insensitive to red light, for example.

PHET EXPLORATIONS

Photoelectric Effect

See how light knocks electrons off a metal target, and recreate the experiment that spawned the field of quantum mechanics.

Click to view content (https://openstax.org/l/28photoelectric).

PhET

29.3 Photon Energies and the Electromagnetic Spectrum

LEARNING OBJECTIVES

By the end of this section, you will be able to:

- Explain the relationship between the energy of a photon in joules or electron volts and its wavelength or frequency.
- Calculate the number of photons per second emitted by a monochromatic source of specific wavelength and power.

Ionizing Radiation

A photon is a quantum of EM radiation. Its energy is given by $E = hf$ and is related to the frequency f and wavelength λ of the radiation by

$$E = hf = \frac{hc}{\lambda}\text{(energy of a photon)}, \quad 29.12$$

where E is the energy of a single photon and c is the speed of light. When working with small systems, energy in eV is often useful. Note that Planck's constant in these units is

$$h = 4.14 \times 10^{-15}\ \text{eV} \cdot \text{s}. \quad 29.13$$

Since many wavelengths are stated in nanometers (nm), it is also useful to know that

$$hc = 1240\ \text{eV} \cdot \text{nm}. \quad 29.14$$

These will make many calculations a little easier.

All EM radiation is composed of photons. Figure 29.9 shows various divisions of the EM spectrum plotted against wavelength, frequency, and photon energy. Previously in this book, photon characteristics were alluded to in the discussion of some of the characteristics of UV, x rays, and γ rays, the first of which start with frequencies just above violet in the visible spectrum. It was noted that these types of EM radiation have characteristics much different than visible light. We can now see that such properties arise because photon energy is larger at high frequencies.

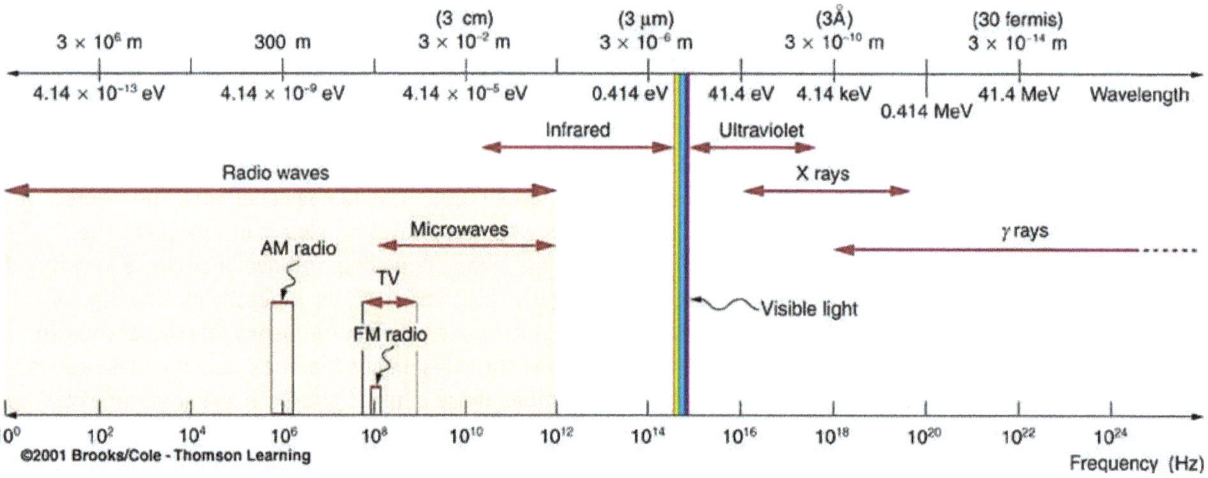

FIGURE 29.9 The EM spectrum, showing major categories as a function of photon energy in eV, as well as wavelength and frequency. Certain characteristics of EM radiation are directly attributable to photon energy alone.

Rotational energies of molecules	10^{-5} eV
Vibrational energies of molecules	0.1 eV
Energy between outer electron shells in atoms	1 eV

TABLE 29.1 Representative Energies for Submicroscopic Effects (Order of Magnitude Only)

Binding energy of a weakly bound molecule	1 eV
Energy of red light	2 eV
Binding energy of a tightly bound molecule	10 eV
Energy to ionize atom or molecule	10 to 1000 eV

TABLE 29.1 Representative Energies for Submicroscopic Effects (Order of Magnitude Only)

Photons act as individual quanta and interact with individual electrons, atoms, molecules, and so on. The energy a photon carries is, thus, crucial to the effects it has. Table 29.1 lists representative submicroscopic energies in eV. When we compare photon energies from the EM spectrum in Figure 29.9 with energies in the table, we can see how effects vary with the type of EM radiation.

Gamma rays, a form of nuclear and cosmic EM radiation, can have the highest frequencies and, hence, the highest photon energies in the EM spectrum. For example, a γ-ray photon with $f = 10^{21}$ Hz has an energy $E = hf = 6.63 \times 10^{-13}\text{ J} = 4.14\text{ MeV}$. This is sufficient energy to ionize thousands of atoms and molecules, since only 10 to 1000 eV are needed per ionization. In fact, γ rays are one type of **ionizing radiation**, as are x rays and UV, because they produce ionization in materials that absorb them. Because so much ionization can be produced, a single γ-ray photon can cause significant damage to biological tissue, killing cells or damaging their ability to properly reproduce. When cell reproduction is disrupted, the result can be cancer, one of the known effects of exposure to ionizing radiation. Since cancer cells are rapidly reproducing, they are exceptionally sensitive to the disruption produced by ionizing radiation. This means that ionizing radiation has positive uses in cancer treatment as well as risks in producing cancer.

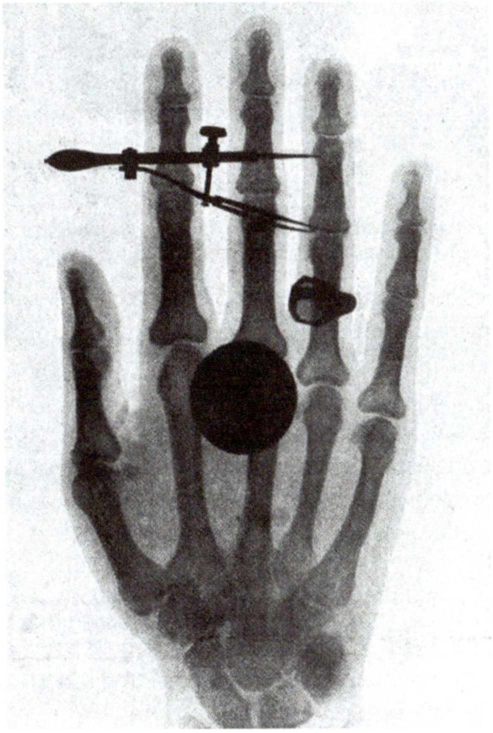

FIGURE 29.10 One of the first x-ray images, taken by Röentgen himself. The hand belongs to Bertha Röentgen, his wife. (credit: Wilhelm Conrad Röntgen, via Wikimedia Commons)

High photon energy also enables γ rays to penetrate materials, since a collision with a single atom or molecule is unlikely to absorb all the γ ray's energy. This can make γ rays useful as a probe, and they are sometimes used in medical imaging. **x rays**, as you can see in Figure 29.9, overlap with the low-frequency end of the γ ray range. Since x rays have energies of keV and up, individual x-ray photons also can produce large amounts of ionization. At lower photon energies, x rays are not as penetrating as γ rays and are slightly less hazardous. X rays are ideal for medical imaging, their most common use, and a fact that was recognized immediately upon their discovery in 1895 by the German physicist W. C. Roentgen (1845–1923). (See Figure 29.10.) Within one year of their discovery, x rays (for a time called Roentgen rays) were used for medical diagnostics. Roentgen received the 1901 Nobel Prize for the discovery of x rays.

CONNECTIONS: CONSERVATION OF ENERGY

Once again, we find that conservation of energy allows us to consider the initial and final forms that energy takes, without having to make detailed calculations of the intermediate steps. Example 29.2 is solved by considering only the initial and final forms of energy.

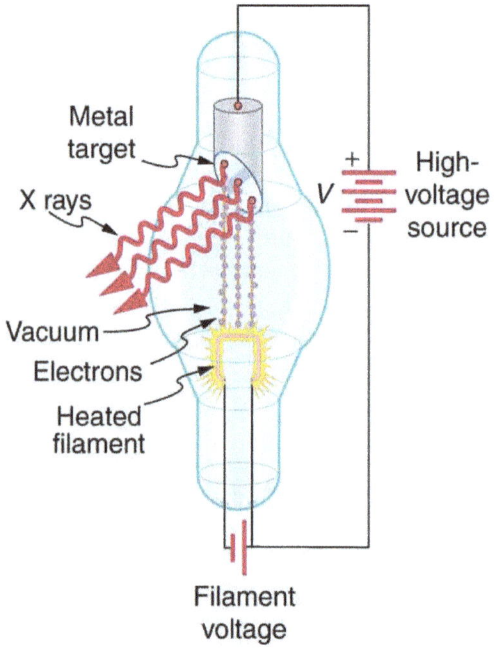

FIGURE 29.11 X rays are produced when energetic electrons strike the copper anode of this cathode ray tube (CRT). Electrons (shown here as separate particles) interact individually with the material they strike, sometimes producing photons of EM radiation.

While γ rays originate in nuclear decay, x rays are produced by the process shown in Figure 29.11. Electrons ejected by thermal agitation from a hot filament in a vacuum tube are accelerated through a high voltage, gaining kinetic energy from the electrical potential energy. When they strike the anode, the electrons convert their kinetic energy to a variety of forms, including thermal energy. But since an accelerated charge radiates EM waves, and since the electrons act individually, photons are also produced. Some of these x-ray photons obtain the kinetic energy of the electron. The accelerated electrons originate at the cathode, so such a tube is called a cathode ray tube (CRT), and various versions of them are found in older TV and computer screens as well as in x-ray machines.

EXAMPLE 29.2

X-ray Photon Energy and X-ray Tube Voltage

Find the maximum energy in eV of an x-ray photon produced by electrons accelerated through a potential difference of 50.0 kV in a CRT like the one in Figure 29.11.

Strategy

Electrons can give all of their kinetic energy to a single photon when they strike the anode of a CRT. (This is something like the photoelectric effect in reverse.) The kinetic energy of the electron comes from electrical potential energy. Thus we can simply equate the maximum photon energy to the electrical potential energy—that is, $hf = qV$.

(We do not have to calculate each step from beginning to end if we know that all of the starting energy qV is converted to the final form hf.)

Solution

The maximum photon energy is $hf = qV$, where q is the charge of the electron and V is the accelerating voltage. Thus,

$$hf = (1.60 \times 10^{-19}\ \text{C})(50.0 \times 10^{3}\ \text{V}). \tag{29.15}$$

From the definition of the electron volt, we know $1\ \text{eV} = 1.60 \times 10^{-19}\ \text{J}$, where $1\ \text{J} = 1\ \text{C} \cdot \text{V}$. Gathering factors and converting energy to eV yields

$$hf = (50.0 \times 10^{3})(1.60 \times 10^{-19}\ \text{C} \cdot \text{V})\left(\frac{1\ \text{eV}}{1.60 \times 10^{-19}\ \text{C} \cdot \text{V}}\right) = (50.0 \times 10^{3})(1\ \text{eV}) = 50.0\ \text{keV}. \tag{29.16}$$

Discussion

This example produces a result that can be applied to many similar situations. If you accelerate a single elementary charge, like that of an electron, through a potential given in volts, then its energy in eV has the same numerical value. Thus a 50.0-kV potential generates 50.0 keV electrons, which in turn can produce photons with a maximum energy of 50 keV. Similarly, a 100-kV potential in an x-ray tube can generate up to 100-keV x-ray photons. Many x-ray tubes have adjustable voltages so that various energy x rays with differing energies, and therefore differing abilities to penetrate, can be generated.

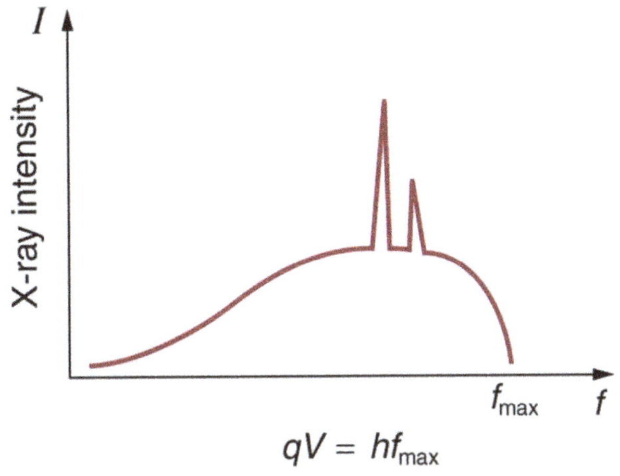

FIGURE 29.12 X-ray spectrum obtained when energetic electrons strike a material. The smooth part of the spectrum is bremsstrahlung, while the peaks are characteristic of the anode material. Both are atomic processes that produce energetic photons known as x-ray photons.

Figure 29.12 shows the spectrum of x rays obtained from an x-ray tube. There are two distinct features to the spectrum. First, the smooth distribution results from electrons being decelerated in the anode material. A curve like this is obtained by detecting many photons, and it is apparent that the maximum energy is unlikely. This decelerating process produces radiation that is called **bremsstrahlung** (German for *braking radiation*). The second feature is the existence of sharp peaks in the spectrum; these are called **characteristic x rays**, since they are characteristic of the anode material. Characteristic x rays come from atomic excitations unique to a given type of anode material. They are akin to lines in atomic spectra, implying the energy levels of atoms are quantized. Phenomena such as discrete atomic spectra and characteristic x rays are explored further in Atomic Physics.

Ultraviolet radiation (approximately 4 eV to 300 eV) overlaps with the low end of the energy range of x rays, but UV is typically lower in energy. UV comes from the de-excitation of atoms that may be part of a hot solid or gas. These atoms can be given energy that they later release as UV by numerous processes, including electric discharge, nuclear explosion, thermal agitation, and exposure to x rays. A UV photon has sufficient energy to ionize atoms and molecules, which makes its effects different from those of visible light. UV thus has some of the same biological effects as γ rays and x rays. For example, it can cause skin cancer and is used as a sterilizer. The major difference is that several UV photons are required to disrupt cell reproduction or kill a bacterium, whereas single γ-ray and X-ray photons can do the same damage. But since UV does have the energy to alter molecules, it can do what visible light cannot. One of the beneficial aspects of UV is that it triggers the production of vitamin D in the skin, whereas visible light has insufficient energy per photon to alter the molecules that trigger this production. Infantile jaundice is treated by exposing the baby to UV (with eye protection), called phototherapy, the beneficial effects of which are thought to be related to its ability to help prevent the buildup of potentially toxic bilirubin in the blood.

EXAMPLE 29.3

Photon Energy and Effects for UV

Short-wavelength UV is sometimes called vacuum UV, because it is strongly absorbed by air and must be studied in a vacuum. Calculate the photon energy in eV for 100-nm vacuum UV, and estimate the number of molecules it could ionize or break apart.

Strategy

Using the equation $E = hf$ and appropriate constants, we can find the photon energy and compare it with energy information in Table 29.1.

Solution

The energy of a photon is given by

$$E = hf = \frac{hc}{\lambda}. \tag{29.17}$$

Using $hc = 1240\ \text{eV} \cdot \text{nm}$, we find that

$$E = \frac{hc}{\lambda} = \frac{1240\ \text{eV} \cdot \text{nm}}{100\ \text{nm}} = 12.4\ \text{eV}. \tag{29.18}$$

Discussion

According to Table 29.1, this photon energy might be able to ionize an atom or molecule, and it is about what is needed to break up a tightly bound molecule, since they are bound by approximately 10 eV. This photon energy could destroy about a dozen weakly bound molecules. Because of its high photon energy, UV disrupts atoms and molecules it interacts with. One good consequence is that all but the longest-wavelength UV is strongly absorbed and is easily blocked by sunglasses. In fact, most of the Sun's UV is absorbed by a thin layer of ozone in the upper atmosphere, protecting sensitive organisms on Earth. Damage to our ozone layer by the addition of such chemicals as CFC's has reduced this protection for us.

Visible Light

The range of photon energies for **visible light** from red to violet is 1.63 to 3.26 eV, respectively (left for this chapter's Problems and Exercises to verify). These energies are on the order of those between outer electron shells in atoms and molecules. This means that these photons can be absorbed by atoms and molecules. A *single* photon can actually stimulate the retina, for example, by altering a receptor molecule that then triggers a nerve impulse. Photons can be absorbed or emitted only by atoms and molecules that have precisely the correct quantized energy step to do so. For example, if a red photon of frequency f encounters a molecule that has an energy step, ΔE, equal to hf, then the photon can be absorbed. Violet flowers absorb red and reflect violet; this implies there is no energy step between levels in the receptor molecule equal to the violet photon's energy, but there is an energy step for the red.

There are some noticeable differences in the characteristics of light between the two ends of the visible spectrum that are due to photon energies. Red light has insufficient photon energy to expose most black-and-white film, and it is thus used to illuminate darkrooms where such film is developed. Since violet light has a higher photon energy, dyes that absorb violet tend to fade more quickly than those that do not. (See Figure 29.13.) Take a look at some faded color posters in a storefront some time, and you will notice that the blues and violets are the last to fade. This is because other dyes, such as red and green dyes, absorb blue and violet photons, the higher energies of which break up their weakly bound molecules. (Complex molecules such as those in dyes and DNA tend to be weakly bound.) Blue and violet dyes reflect those colors and, therefore, do not absorb these more energetic photons, thus suffering less molecular damage.

FIGURE 29.13 Why do the reds, yellows, and greens fade before the blues and violets when exposed to the Sun, as with this poster? The answer is related to photon energy. (credit: Deb Collins, Flickr)

Transparent materials, such as some glasses, do not absorb any visible light, because there is no energy step in the atoms or molecules that could absorb the light. Since individual photons interact with individual atoms, it is nearly impossible to have two photons absorbed simultaneously to reach a large energy step. Because of its lower photon energy, visible light can sometimes pass through many kilometers of a substance, while higher frequencies like UV, x ray, and γ rays are absorbed, because they have sufficient photon energy to ionize the material.

EXAMPLE 29.4

How Many Photons per Second Does a Typical Light Bulb Produce?

Assuming that 10.0% of a 100-W light bulb's energy output is in the visible range (typical for incandescent bulbs) with an average wavelength of 580 nm, calculate the number of visible photons emitted per second.

Strategy

Power is energy per unit time, and so if we can find the energy per photon, we can determine the number of photons per second. This will best be done in joules, since power is given in watts, which are joules per second.

Solution

The power in visible light production is 10.0% of 100 W, or 10.0 J/s. The energy of the average visible photon is found by substituting the given average wavelength into the formula

$$E = \frac{hc}{\lambda}. \tag{29.19}$$

This produces

$$E = \frac{(6.63 \times 10^{-34}\ \text{J} \cdot \text{s})(3.00 \times 10^{8}\ \text{m/s})}{580 \times 10^{-9}\ \text{m}} = 3.43 \times 10^{-19}\ \text{J}. \tag{29.20}$$

The number of visible photons per second is thus

$$\text{photon/s} = \frac{10.0\ \text{J/s}}{3.43 \times 10^{-19}\ \text{J/photon}} = 2.92 \times 10^{19}\ \text{photon/s}. \tag{29.21}$$

Discussion

This incredible number of photons per second is verification that individual photons are insignificant in ordinary human experience. It is also a verification of the correspondence principle—on the macroscopic scale, quantization becomes essentially continuous or classical. Finally, there are so many photons emitted by a 100-W lightbulb that it can be seen by the unaided eye many kilometers away.

Lower-Energy Photons

Infrared radiation (IR) has even lower photon energies than visible light and cannot significantly alter atoms and molecules. IR can be absorbed and emitted by atoms and molecules, particularly between closely spaced states. IR is extremely strongly absorbed by water, for example, because water molecules have many states separated by energies on the order of 10^{-5} eV to 10^{-2} eV, well within the IR and microwave energy ranges. This is why in the IR range, skin is almost jet black, with an emissivity near 1—there are many states in water molecules in the skin that can absorb a large range of IR photon energies. Not all molecules have this property. Air, for example, is nearly transparent to many IR frequencies.

Microwaves are the highest frequencies that can be produced by electronic circuits, although they are also produced naturally. Thus microwaves are similar to IR but do not extend to as high frequencies. There are states in water and other molecules that have the same frequency and energy as microwaves, typically about 10^{-5} eV. This is one reason why food absorbs microwaves more strongly than many other materials, making microwave ovens an efficient way of putting energy directly into food.

Photon energies for both IR and microwaves are so low that huge numbers of photons are involved in any significant energy transfer by IR or microwaves (such as warming yourself with a heat lamp or cooking pizza in the microwave). Visible light, IR, microwaves, and all lower frequencies cannot produce ionization with single photons and do not ordinarily have the hazards of higher frequencies. When visible, IR, or microwave radiation *is* hazardous, such as the inducement of cataracts by microwaves, the hazard is due to huge numbers of photons acting together (not to an accumulation of photons, such as sterilization by weak UV). The negative effects of visible, IR, or microwave radiation can be thermal effects, which could be produced by any heat source. But one difference is that at very high intensity, strong electric and magnetic fields can be produced by photons acting together. Such electromagnetic fields (EMF) can actually ionize materials.

MISCONCEPTION ALERT: HIGH-VOLTAGE POWER LINES

Although some people think that living near high-voltage power lines is hazardous to one's health, ongoing studies of the transient field effects produced by these lines show their strengths to be insufficient to cause damage. Demographic studies also fail to show significant correlation of ill effects with high-voltage power lines. The American Physical Society issued a report over 20 years ago on power-line fields, and additional studies since that time show no consistent, significant link between cancer and power-line fields.

It is virtually impossible to detect individual photons having frequencies below microwave frequencies, because of their low photon energy. But the photons are there. A continuous EM wave can be modeled as photons. At low frequencies, EM waves are generally treated as time- and position-varying electric and magnetic fields with no discernible quantization. This is another example of the correspondence principle in situations involving huge numbers of photons.

PHET EXPLORATIONS

Color Vision

Make a whole rainbow by mixing red, green, and blue light. Change the wavelength of a monochromatic beam or filter white light. View the light as a solid beam, or see the individual photons.

Click to view content (https://openstax.org/books/college-physics-ap-courses-2e/pages/29-3-photon-energies-and-the-electromagnetic-spectrum)

29.4 Photon Momentum

LEARNING OBJECTIVES

By the end of this section, you will be able to:

- Relate the linear momentum of a photon to its energy or wavelength, and apply linear momentum conservation to simple processes involving the emission, absorption, or reflection of photons.
- Account qualitatively for the increase of photon wavelength that is observed, and explain the significance of the Compton wavelength.

Measuring Photon Momentum

The quantum of EM radiation we call a **photon** has properties analogous to those of particles we can see, such as grains of sand. A photon interacts as a unit in collisions or when absorbed, rather than as an extensive wave. Massive quanta, like electrons, also act like macroscopic particles—something we expect, because they are the smallest units of matter. Particles carry momentum as well as energy. Despite photons having no mass, there has long been evidence that EM radiation carries momentum. (Maxwell and others who studied EM waves predicted that they would carry momentum.) It is now a well-established fact that photons *do* have momentum. In fact, photon momentum is suggested by the photoelectric effect, where photons knock electrons out of a substance. Figure 29.14 shows macroscopic evidence of photon momentum.

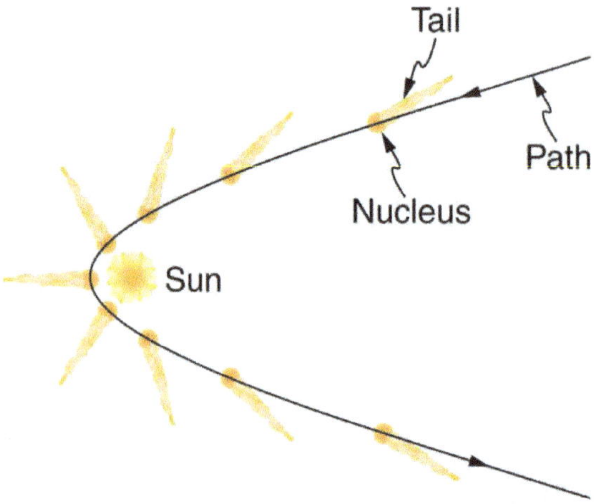

FIGURE 29.14 The tails of the Hale-Bopp comet point away from the Sun, evidence that light has momentum. Dust emanating from the body of the comet forms this tail. Particles of dust are pushed away from the Sun by light reflecting from them. The blue ionized gas tail is also produced by photons interacting with atoms in the comet material. (credit: Geoff Chester, U.S. Navy, via Wikimedia Commons)

Figure 29.14 shows a comet with two prominent tails. What most people do not know about the tails is that they always point *away* from the Sun rather than trailing behind the comet (like the tail of Bo Peep's sheep). Comet tails are composed of gases and dust evaporated from the body of the comet and ionized gas. The dust particles recoil away from the Sun when photons scatter from them. Evidently, photons carry momentum in the direction of their motion (away from the Sun), and some of this momentum is transferred to dust particles in collisions. Gas atoms and molecules in the blue tail are most affected by other particles of radiation, such as protons and electrons emanating from the Sun, rather than by the momentum of photons.

CONNECTIONS: CONSERVATION OF MOMENTUM

Not only is momentum conserved in all realms of physics, but all types of particles are found to have momentum. We expect particles with mass to have momentum, but now we see that massless particles including photons also carry momentum.

Momentum is conserved in quantum mechanics just as it is in relativity and classical physics. Some of the earliest direct experimental evidence of this came from scattering of x-ray photons by electrons in substances, named Compton scattering after the American physicist Arthur H. Compton (1892–1962). Around 1923, Compton observed that x rays scattered from materials had a decreased energy and correctly analyzed this as being due to the scattering of photons from electrons. This phenomenon could be handled as a collision between two particles—a photon and an electron at rest in the material. Energy and momentum are conserved in the collision. (See Figure 29.15) He won a Nobel Prize in 1929 for the discovery of this scattering, now called the **Compton effect**, because it helped prove that **photon momentum** is given by

$$p = \frac{h}{\lambda}, \tag{29.22}$$

where h is Planck's constant and λ is the photon wavelength. (Note that relativistic momentum given as $p = \gamma mu$ is valid only for particles having mass.)

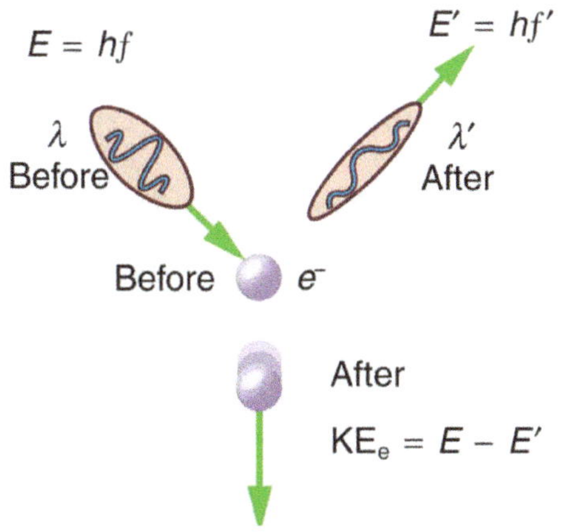

FIGURE 29.15 The Compton effect is the name given to the scattering of a photon by an electron. Energy and momentum are conserved, resulting in a reduction of both for the scattered photon. Studying this effect, Compton verified that photons have momentum.

We can see that photon momentum is small, since $p = h/\lambda$ and h is very small. It is for this reason that we do not ordinarily observe photon momentum. Our mirrors do not recoil when light reflects from them (except perhaps in cartoons). Compton saw the effects of photon momentum because he was observing x rays, which have a small wavelength and a relatively large momentum, interacting with the lightest of particles, the electron.

EXAMPLE 29.5

Electron and Photon Momentum Compared

(a) Calculate the momentum of a visible photon that has a wavelength of 500 nm. (b) Find the velocity of an electron having the same momentum. (c) What is the energy of the electron, and how does it compare with the energy of the photon?

Strategy

Finding the photon momentum is a straightforward application of its definition: $p = \frac{h}{\lambda}$. If we find the photon momentum is small, then we can assume that an electron with the same momentum will be nonrelativistic, making it easy to find its velocity and kinetic energy from the classical formulas.

Solution for (a)

Photon momentum is given by the equation:

$$p = \frac{h}{\lambda}. \tag{29.23}$$

Entering the given photon wavelength yields

$$p = \frac{6.63 \times 10^{-34}\ \text{J} \cdot \text{s}}{500 \times 10^{-9}\ \text{m}} = 1.33 \times 10^{-27}\ \text{kg} \cdot \text{m/s}. \tag{29.24}$$

Solution for (b)

Since this momentum is indeed small, we will use the classical expression $p = mv$ to find the velocity of an electron with this momentum. Solving for v and using the known value for the mass of an electron gives

$$v = \frac{p}{m} = \frac{1.33 \times 10^{-27}\ \text{kg} \cdot \text{m/s}}{9.11 \times 10^{-31}\ \text{kg}} = 1460\ \text{m/s} \approx 1460\ \text{m/s}. \tag{29.25}$$

Solution for (c)

The electron has kinetic energy, which is classically given by

$$\text{KE}_e = \frac{1}{2}mv^2. \tag{29.26}$$

Thus,

$$\text{KE}_e = \frac{1}{2}(9.11 \times 10^{-3}\ \text{kg})(1455\ \text{m/s})^2 = 9.64 \times 10^{-25}\ \text{J}. \tag{29.27}$$

Converting this to eV by multiplying by $(1\ \text{eV})/(1.602 \times 10^{-19}\ \text{J})$ yields

$$\text{KE}_e = 6.02 \times 10^{-6}\ \text{eV}. \tag{29.28}$$

The photon energy E is

$$E = \frac{hc}{\lambda} = \frac{1240\ \text{eV} \cdot \text{nm}}{500\ \text{nm}} = 2.48\ \text{eV}, \tag{29.29}$$

which is about five orders of magnitude greater.

Discussion

Photon momentum is indeed small. Even if we have huge numbers of them, the total momentum they carry is small. An electron with the same momentum has a 1460 m/s velocity, which is clearly nonrelativistic. A more massive particle with the same momentum would have an even smaller velocity. This is borne out by the fact that it takes far less energy to give an electron the same momentum as a photon. But on a quantum-mechanical scale, especially for high-energy photons interacting with small masses, photon momentum is significant. Even on a large scale, photon momentum can have an effect if there are enough of them and if there is nothing to prevent the slow recoil of matter. Comet tails are one example, but there are also proposals to build space sails that use huge low-mass mirrors (made of aluminized Mylar) to reflect sunlight. In the vacuum of space, the mirrors would gradually recoil and could actually take spacecraft from place to place in the solar system. (See Figure 29.16.)

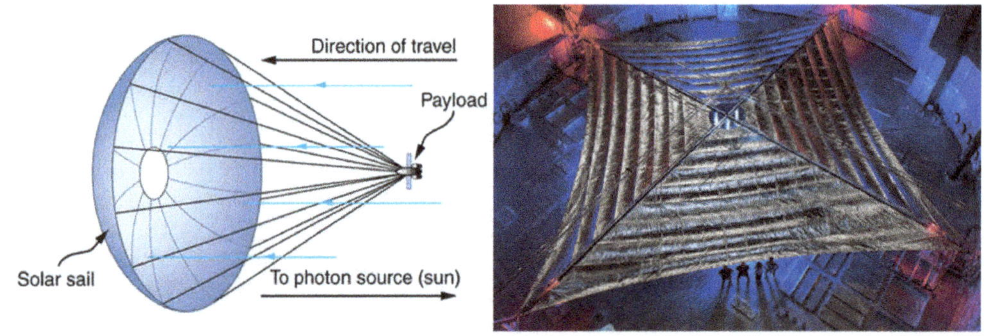

(a) (b)

FIGURE 29.16 (a) Space sails have been proposed that use the momentum of sunlight reflecting from gigantic low-mass sails to propel spacecraft about the solar system. A Russian test model of this (the Cosmos 1) was launched in 2005, but did not make it into orbit due to a rocket failure. (b) A U.S. version of this, labeled LightSail-1, is scheduled for trial launches in the first part of this decade. It will have a 40-m^2 sail. (credit: Kim Newton/NASA)

Relativistic Photon Momentum

There is a relationship between photon momentum p and photon energy E that is consistent with the relation given previously for the relativistic total energy of a particle as $E^2 = (pc)^2 + (mc)^2$. We know m is zero for a photon, but p is not, so that $E^2 = (pc)^2 + (mc^2)^2$ becomes

$$E = pc, \tag{29.30}$$

or

$$p = \frac{E}{c} \text{ (photons).} \tag{29.31}$$

To check the validity of this relation, note that $E = hc/\lambda$ for a photon. Substituting this into $p = E/c$ yields

$$p = (hc/\lambda)/c = \frac{h}{\lambda}, \tag{29.32}$$

as determined experimentally and discussed above. Thus, $p = E/c$ is equivalent to Compton's result $p = h/\lambda$. For a further verification of the relationship between photon energy and momentum, see Example 29.6.

PHOTON DETECTORS

Almost all detection systems talked about thus far—eyes, photographic plates, photomultiplier tubes in microscopes, and CCD cameras—rely on particle-like properties of photons interacting with a sensitive area. A change is caused and either the change is cascaded or zillions of points are recorded to form an image we detect. These detectors are used in biomedical imaging systems, and there is ongoing research into improving the efficiency of receiving photons, particularly by cooling detection systems and reducing thermal effects.

EXAMPLE 29.6

Photon Energy and Momentum

Show that $p = E/c$ for the photon considered in the Example 29.5.

Strategy

We will take the energy E found in Example 29.5, divide it by the speed of light, and see if the same momentum is obtained as before.

Solution

Given that the energy of the photon is 2.48 eV and converting this to joules, we get

$$p = \frac{E}{c} = \frac{(2.48 \text{ eV})(1.60 \times 10^{-19} \text{ J/eV})}{3.00 \times 10^{8} \text{ m/s}} = 1.33 \times 10^{-27} \text{ kg} \cdot \text{m/s}. \tag{29.33}$$

Discussion

This value for momentum is the same as found before (note that unrounded values are used in all calculations to avoid even small rounding errors), an expected verification of the relationship $p = E/c$. This also means the relationship between energy, momentum, and mass given by $E^2 = (pc)^2 + (mc)^2$ applies to both matter and photons. Once again, note that p is not zero, even when m is.

PROBLEM-SOLVING SUGGESTION

Note that the forms of the constants $h = 4.14 \times 10^{-15} \text{ eV} \cdot \text{s}$ and $hc = 1240 \text{ eV} \cdot \text{nm}$ may be particularly useful for this section's Problems and Exercises.

29.5 The Particle-Wave Duality

LEARNING OBJECTIVES

By the end of this section, you will be able to:

- Explain what the term particle-wave duality means, and why it is applied to EM radiation.

We have long known that EM radiation is a wave, capable of interference and diffraction. We now see that light can be modeled as photons, which are massless particles. This may seem contradictory, since we ordinarily deal with large objects that never act like both wave and particle. An ocean wave, for example, looks nothing like a rock. To understand small-scale phenomena, we make analogies with the large-scale phenomena we observe directly. When we say something behaves like a wave, we mean it shows interference effects analogous to those seen in overlapping water waves. (See Figure 29.17.) Two examples of waves are sound and EM radiation. When we say something behaves like a particle, we mean that it interacts as a discrete unit with no interference effects. Examples of particles include electrons, atoms, and photons of EM radiation. How do we talk about a phenomenon that acts like both a particle and a wave?

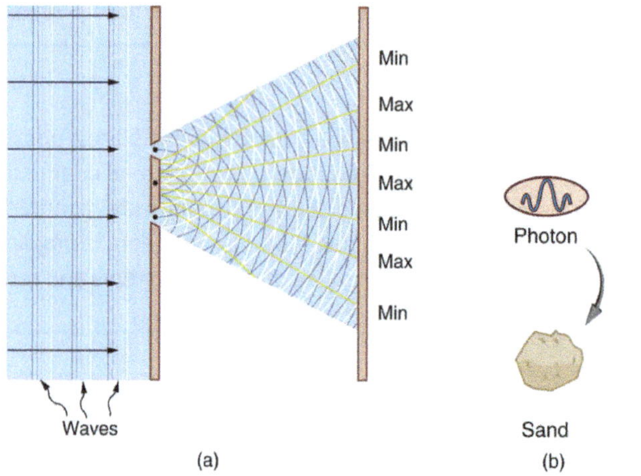

FIGURE 29.17 (a) The interference pattern for light through a double slit is a wave property understood by analogy to water waves. (b) The properties of photons having quantized energy and momentum and acting as a concentrated unit are understood by analogy to macroscopic particles.

There is no doubt that EM radiation interferes and has the properties of wavelength and frequency. There is also no doubt that it behaves as particlesâ€"photons with discrete energy. We call this twofold nature the **particle-wave duality**, meaning that EM radiation has both particle and wave properties. This so-called duality is simply a term for properties of the photon analogous to phenomena we can observe directly, on a macroscopic scale. If this term seems strange, it is because we do not ordinarily observe details on the quantum level directly, and our observations yield either particle *or* wavelike properties, but never both simultaneously.

Since we have a particle-wave duality for photons, and since we have seen connections between photons and matter in that both have momentum, it is reasonable to ask whether there is a particle-wave duality for matter as well. If the EM radiation we once thought to be a pure wave has particle properties, is it possible that matter has wave properties? The answer is yes. The consequences are tremendous, as we will begin to see in the next section.

PHET EXPLORATIONS

Quantum Wave Interference

When do photons, electrons, and atoms behave like particles and when do they behave like waves? Watch waves spread out and interfere as they pass through a double slit, then get detected on a screen as tiny dots. Use quantum detectors to explore how measurements change the waves and the patterns they produce on the screen.

Click to view content (https://openstax.org/l/21intquawavint).

PhET

29.6 The Wave Nature of Matter

LEARNING OBJECTIVES

By the end of this section, you will be able to:

- Describe the Davisson-Germer experiment, and explain how it provides evidence for the wave nature of electrons.

De Broglie Wavelength

In 1923 a French physics graduate student named Prince Louis-Victor de Broglie (1892–1987) made a radical proposal based on the hope that nature is symmetric. If EM radiation has both particle and wave properties, then nature would be symmetric if matter also had both particle and wave properties. If what we once thought of as an unequivocal wave (EM radiation) is also a particle, then what we think of as an unequivocal particle (matter) may also be a wave. De Broglie's suggestion, made as part of his doctoral thesis, was so radical that it was greeted with some skepticism. A copy of his thesis was sent to Einstein, who said it was not only probably correct, but that it might be of fundamental importance. With the support of Einstein and a few other prominent physicists, de Broglie was awarded his doctorate.

De Broglie took both relativity and quantum mechanics into account to develop the proposal that *all particles have a wavelength*, given by

$$\lambda = \frac{h}{p} \text{ (matter and photons)}, \tag{29.34}$$

where h is Planck's constant and p is momentum. This is defined to be the **de Broglie wavelength**. (Note that we already have this for photons, from the equation $p = h/\lambda$.) The hallmark of a wave is interference. If matter is a wave, then it must exhibit constructive and destructive interference. Why isn't this ordinarily observed? The answer is that in order to see significant interference effects, a wave must interact with an object about the same size as its wavelength. Since h is very small, λ is also small, especially for macroscopic objects. A 3-kg bowling ball moving at 10 m/s, for example, has

$$\lambda = h/p = (6.63 \times 10^{-34} \text{ J·s})/[(3 \text{ kg})(10 \text{ m/s})] = 2 \times 10^{-35} \text{ m}. \tag{29.35}$$

This means that to see its wave characteristics, the bowling ball would have to interact with something about 10^{-35} m in size—far smaller than anything known. When waves interact with objects much larger than their wavelength, they show negligible interference effects and move in straight lines (such as light rays in geometric optics). To get easily observed interference effects from particles of matter, the longest wavelength and hence smallest mass possible would be useful. Therefore, this effect was first observed with electrons.

American physicists Clinton J. Davisson and Lester H. Germer in 1925 and, independently, British physicist G. P. Thomson (son of J. J. Thomson, discoverer of the electron) in 1926 scattered electrons from crystals and found diffraction patterns. These patterns are exactly consistent with interference of electrons having the de Broglie wavelength and are somewhat analogous to light interacting with a diffraction grating. (See Figure 29.18.)

CONNECTIONS: WAVES

All microscopic particles, whether massless, like photons, or having mass, like electrons, have wave properties. The relationship between momentum and wavelength is fundamental for all particles.

De Broglie's proposal of a wave nature for all particles initiated a remarkably productive era in which the foundations for quantum mechanics were laid. In 1926, the Austrian physicist Erwin Schrödinger (1887–1961) published four papers in which the wave nature of particles was treated explicitly with wave equations. At the same time, many others began important work. Among them was German physicist Werner Heisenberg (1901–1976) who, among many other contributions to quantum mechanics, formulated a mathematical treatment of the wave nature of matter that used matrices rather than wave equations. We will deal with some specifics in later sections, but it is worth noting that de Broglie's work was a watershed for the development of quantum mechanics. De Broglie was awarded the Nobel Prize in 1929 for his vision, as were Davisson and G. P. Thomson in 1937 for their experimental verification of de Broglie's hypothesis.

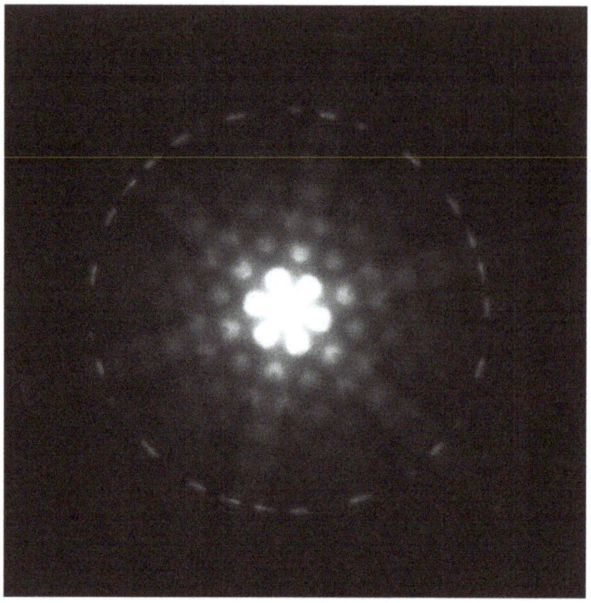

FIGURE 29.18 This diffraction pattern was obtained for electrons diffracted by crystalline silicon. Bright regions are those of constructive interference, while dark regions are those of destructive interference. (credit: Ndthe, Wikimedia Commons)

EXAMPLE 29.7

Electron Wavelength versus Velocity and Energy

For an electron having a de Broglie wavelength of 0.167 nm (appropriate for interacting with crystal lattice structures that are about this size): (a) Calculate the electron's velocity, assuming it is nonrelativistic. (b) Calculate the electron's kinetic energy in eV.

Strategy

For part (a), since the de Broglie wavelength is given, the electron's velocity can be obtained from $\lambda = h/p$ by using the nonrelativistic formula for momentum, $p = mv$. For part (b), once v is obtained (and it has been verified that v is nonrelativistic), the classical kinetic energy is simply $(1/2)mv^2$.

Solution for (a)

Substituting the nonrelativistic formula for momentum ($p = mv$) into the de Broglie wavelength gives

$$\lambda = \frac{h}{p} = \frac{h}{mv}. \qquad 29.36$$

Solving for v gives

$$v = \frac{h}{m\lambda}. \qquad 29.37$$

Substituting known values yields

$$v = \frac{6.63 \times 10^{-34}\ \text{J} \cdot \text{s}}{(9.11 \times 10^{-31}\ \text{kg})(0.167 \times 10^{-9}\ \text{m})} = 4.36 \times 10^{6}\ \text{m/s}. \qquad 29.38$$

Solution for (b)

While fast compared with a car, this electron's speed is not highly relativistic, and so we can comfortably use the classical formula to find the electron's kinetic energy and convert it to eV as requested.

$$\begin{aligned} \text{KE} &= \tfrac{1}{2}mv^2 \\ &= \tfrac{1}{2}(9.11 \times 10^{-31}\ \text{kg})(4.36 \times 10^6\ \text{m/s})^2 \\ &= (86.4 \times 10^{-18}\ \text{J})\left(\frac{1\ \text{eV}}{1.602{\times}10^{-19}\ \text{J}}\right) \\ &= 54.0\ \text{eV} \end{aligned} \tag{29.39}$$

Discussion

This low energy means that these 0.167-nm electrons could be obtained by accelerating them through a 54.0-V electrostatic potential, an easy task. The results also confirm the assumption that the electrons are nonrelativistic, since their velocity is just over 1% of the speed of light and the kinetic energy is about 0.01% of the rest energy of an electron (0.511 MeV). If the electrons had turned out to be relativistic, we would have had to use more involved calculations employing relativistic formulas.

Electron Microscopes

One consequence or use of the wave nature of matter is found in the electron microscope. As we have discussed, there is a limit to the detail observed with any probe having a wavelength. Resolution, or observable detail, is limited to about one wavelength. Since a potential of only 54 V can produce electrons with sub-nanometer wavelengths, it is easy to get electrons with much smaller wavelengths than those of visible light (hundreds of nanometers). Electron microscopes can, thus, be constructed to detect much smaller details than optical microscopes. (See Figure 29.19.)

There are basically two types of electron microscopes. The transmission electron microscope (TEM) accelerates electrons that are emitted from a hot filament (the cathode). The beam is broadened and then passes through the sample. A magnetic lens focuses the beam image onto a fluorescent screen, a photographic plate, or (most probably) a CCD (light sensitive camera), from which it is transferred to a computer. The TEM is similar to the optical microscope, but it requires a thin sample examined in a vacuum. However it can resolve details as small as 0.1 nm (10^{-10} m), providing magnifications of 100 million times the size of the original object. The TEM has allowed us to see individual atoms and structure of cell nuclei.

The scanning electron microscope (SEM) provides images by using secondary electrons produced by the primary beam interacting with the surface of the sample (see Figure 29.19). The SEM also uses magnetic lenses to focus the beam onto the sample. However, it moves the beam around electrically to “scan” the sample in the *x* and *y* directions. A CCD detector is used to process the data for each electron position, producing images like the one at the beginning of this chapter. The SEM has the advantage of not requiring a thin sample and of providing a 3-D view. However, its resolution is about ten times less than a TEM.

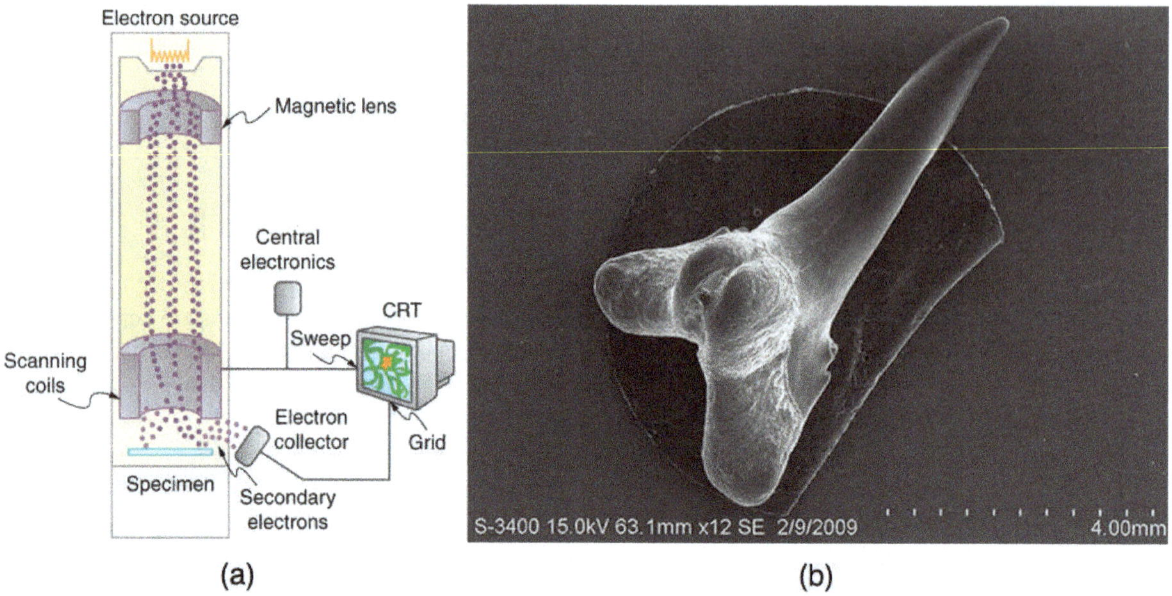

FIGURE 29.19 Schematic of a scanning electron microscope (SEM) (a) used to observe small details, such as those seen in this image of a tooth of a *Himipristis*, a type of shark (b). (credit: Dallas Krentzel, Flickr)

Electrons were the first particles with mass to be directly confirmed to have the wavelength proposed by de Broglie. Subsequently, protons, helium nuclei, neutrons, and many others have been observed to exhibit interference when they interact with objects having sizes similar to their de Broglie wavelength. The de Broglie wavelength for massless particles was well established in the 1920s for photons, and it has since been observed that all massless particles have a de Broglie wavelength $\lambda = h/p$. The wave nature of all particles is a universal characteristic of nature. We shall see in following sections that implications of the de Broglie wavelength include the quantization of energy in atoms and molecules, and an alteration of our basic view of nature on the microscopic scale. The next section, for example, shows that there are limits to the precision with which we may make predictions, regardless of how hard we try. There are even limits to the precision with which we may measure an object's location or energy.

MAKING CONNECTIONS: A SUBMICROSCOPIC DIFFRACTION GRATING

The wave nature of matter allows it to exhibit all the characteristics of other, more familiar, waves. Diffraction gratings, for example, produce diffraction patterns for light that depend on grating spacing and the wavelength of the light. This effect, as with most wave phenomena, is most pronounced when the wave interacts with objects having a size similar to its wavelength. For gratings, this is the spacing between multiple slits.) When electrons interact with a system having a spacing similar to the electron wavelength, they show the same types of interference patterns as light does for diffraction gratings, as shown at top left in Figure 29.20.

Atoms are spaced at regular intervals in a crystal as parallel planes, as shown in the bottom part of Figure 29.20. The spacings between these planes act like the openings in a diffraction grating. At certain incident angles, the paths of electrons scattering from successive planes differ by one wavelength and, thus, interfere constructively. At other angles, the path length differences are not an integral wavelength, and there is partial to total destructive interference. This type of scattering from a large crystal with well-defined lattice planes can produce dramatic interference patterns. It is called *Bragg reflection*, for the father-and-son team who first explored and analyzed it in some detail. The expanded view also shows the path-length differences and indicates how these depend on incident angle θ in a manner similar to the diffraction patterns for x rays reflecting from a crystal.

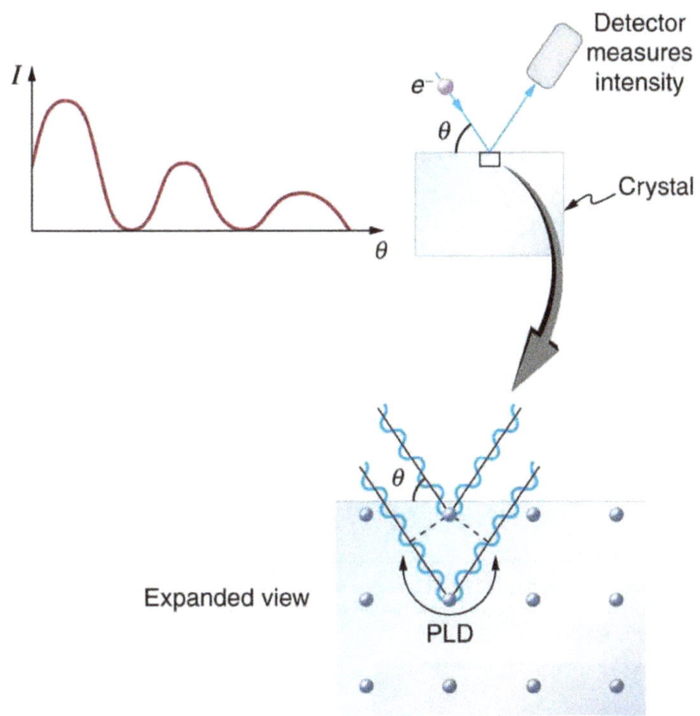

FIGURE 29.20 The diffraction pattern at top left is produced by scattering electrons from a crystal and is graphed as a function of incident angle relative to the regular array of atoms in a crystal, as shown at bottom. Electrons scattering from the second layer of atoms travel farther than those scattered from the top layer. If the path length difference (PLD) is an integral wavelength, there is constructive interference.

Let us take the spacing between parallel planes of atoms in the crystal to be d. As mentioned, if the path length difference (PLD) for the electrons is a whole number of wavelengths, there will be constructive interference—that is, $\text{PLD} = n\lambda (n = 1, 2, 3, \ldots)$. Because $\text{AB} = \text{BC} = d \sin \theta$, we have constructive interference when $n\lambda = 2d \sin \theta$. This relationship is called the *Bragg equation* and applies not only to electrons but also to x rays.

The wavelength of matter is a submicroscopic characteristic that explains a macroscopic phenomenon such as Bragg reflection. Similarly, the wavelength of light is a submicroscopic characteristic that explains the macroscopic phenomenon of diffraction patterns.

29.7 Probability: The Heisenberg Uncertainty Principle

LEARNING OBJECTIVES

By the end of this section, you will be able to:

- Use both versions of Heisenberg's uncertainty principle in calculations.
- Explain the implications of Heisenberg's uncertainty principle for measurements.

Probability Distribution

Matter and photons are waves, implying they are spread out over some distance. What is the position of a particle, such as an electron? Is it at the center of the wave? The answer lies in how you measure the position of an electron. Experiments show that you will find the electron at some definite location, unlike a wave. But if you set up exactly the same situation and measure it again, you will find the electron in a different location, often far outside any experimental uncertainty in your measurement. Repeated measurements will display a statistical distribution of locations that appears wavelike. (See Figure 29.21.)

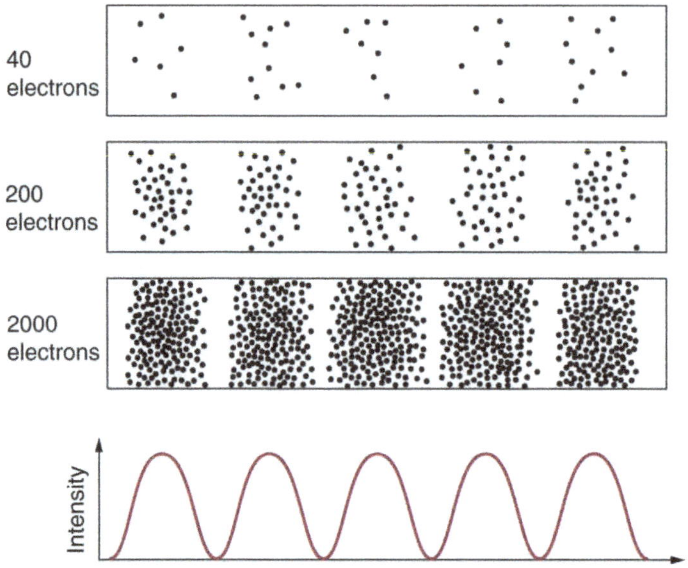

FIGURE 29.21 The building up of the diffraction pattern of electrons scattered from a crystal surface. Each electron arrives at a definite location, which cannot be precisely predicted. The overall distribution shown at the bottom can be predicted as the diffraction of waves having the de Broglie wavelength of the electrons.

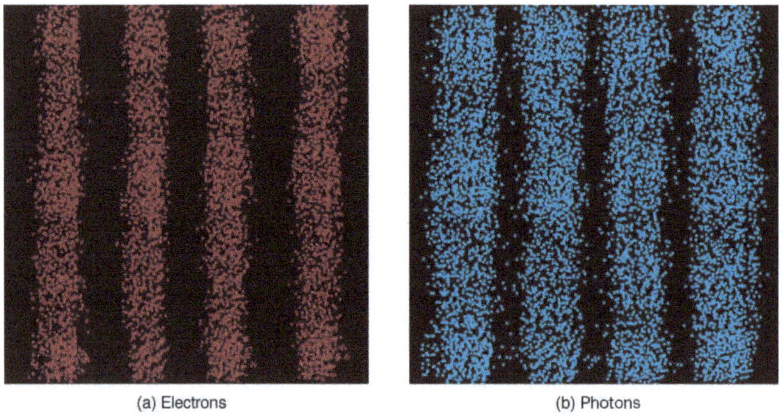

FIGURE 29.22 Double-slit interference for electrons (a) and photons (b) is identical for equal wavelengths and equal slit separations. Both patterns are probability distributions in the sense that they are built up by individual particles traversing the apparatus, the paths of which are not individually predictable.

After de Broglie proposed the wave nature of matter, many physicists, including Schrödinger and Heisenberg, explored the consequences. The idea quickly emerged that, *because of its wave character, a particle's trajectory and destination cannot be precisely predicted for each particle individually.* However, each particle goes to a definite place (as illustrated in Figure 29.21). After compiling enough data, you get a distribution related to the particle's wavelength and diffraction pattern. There is a certain *probability* of finding the particle at a given location, and the overall pattern is called a **probability distribution**. Those who developed quantum mechanics devised equations that predicted the probability distribution in various circumstances.

It is somewhat disquieting to think that you cannot predict exactly where an individual particle will go, or even follow it to its destination. Let us explore what happens if we try to follow a particle. Consider the double-slit patterns obtained for electrons and photons in Figure 29.22. First, we note that these patterns are identical, following $d \sin \theta = m\lambda$, the equation for double-slit constructive interference developed in Photon Energies and the Electromagnetic Spectrum, where d is the slit separation and λ is the electron or photon wavelength.

Both patterns build up statistically as individual particles fall on the detector. This can be observed for photons or electrons—for now, let us concentrate on electrons. You might imagine that the electrons are interfering with one another as any waves do. To test this, you can lower the intensity until there is never more than one electron between the slits and the screen. The same interference pattern builds up! This implies that a particle's probability distribution spans both slits, and the particles actually interfere with themselves. Does this also mean that the electron goes through both slits? An electron is a basic unit of matter that is not divisible. But it is a fair question, and so we should look to see if the electron traverses one slit or the other, or both. One possibility is to have coils around the slits that detect charges moving through them. What is observed is that an electron always goes through one slit or the other; it does not split to go through both. But there is a catch. If you determine that the electron went through one of the slits, you no longer get a double slit pattern—instead, you get single slit interference. There is no escape by using another method of determining which slit the electron went through. Knowing the particle went through one slit forces a single-slit pattern. If you do not observe which slit the electron goes through, you obtain a double-slit pattern.

Heisenberg Uncertainty

How does knowing which slit the electron passed through change the pattern? The answer is fundamentally important—*measurement affects the system being observed.* Information can be lost, and in some cases it is impossible to measure two physical quantities simultaneously to exact precision. For example, you can measure the position of a moving electron by scattering light or other electrons from it. Those probes have momentum themselves, and by scattering from the electron, they change its momentum *in a manner that loses information.* There is a limit to absolute knowledge, even in principle.

FIGURE 29.23 Werner Heisenberg was one of the best of those physicists who developed early quantum mechanics. Not only did his work enable a description of nature on the very small scale, it also changed our view of the availability of knowledge. Although he is universally recognized for his brilliance and the importance of his work (he received the Nobel Prize in 1932, for example), Heisenberg remained in Germany during World War II and headed the German effort to build a nuclear bomb, permanently alienating himself from most of the scientific community. (credit: Author Unknown, via Wikimedia Commons)

It was Werner Heisenberg who first stated this limit to knowledge in 1929 as a result of his work on quantum mechanics and the wave characteristics of all particles. (See Figure 29.23). Specifically, consider simultaneously measuring the position and momentum of an electron (it could be any particle). There is an **uncertainty in position** Δx that is approximately equal to the wavelength of the particle. That is,

$$\Delta x \approx \lambda. \tag{29.40}$$

As discussed above, a wave is not located at one point in space. If the electron's position is measured repeatedly, a spread in locations will be observed, implying an uncertainty in position Δx. To detect the position of the particle, we must interact with it, such as having it collide with a detector. In the collision, the particle will lose momentum. This change in momentum could be anywhere from close to zero to the total momentum of the particle, $p = h/\lambda$. It is not possible to tell how much momentum will be transferred to a detector, and so there is an **uncertainty in momentum** Δp, too. In fact, the uncertainty in momentum may be as large as the momentum itself, which in equation form means that

$$\Delta p \approx \frac{h}{\lambda}. \tag{29.41}$$

The uncertainty in position can be reduced by using a shorter-wavelength electron, since $\Delta x \approx \lambda$. But shortening the wavelength increases the uncertainty in momentum, since $\Delta p \approx h/\lambda$. Conversely, the uncertainty in momentum can be reduced by using a longer-wavelength electron, but this increases the uncertainty in position. Mathematically, you can express this trade-off by multiplying the uncertainties. The wavelength cancels, leaving

$$\Delta x \Delta p \approx h. \tag{29.42}$$

So if one uncertainty is reduced, the other must increase so that their product is $\approx h$.

With the use of advanced mathematics, Heisenberg showed that the best that can be done in a *simultaneous measurement of position and momentum* is

$$\Delta x \Delta p \geq \frac{h}{4\pi}. \tag{29.43}$$

This is known as the **Heisenberg uncertainty principle**. It is impossible to measure position x and momentum p simultaneously with uncertainties Δx and Δp that multiply to be less than $h/4\pi$. Neither uncertainty can be zero. Neither uncertainty can become small without the other becoming large. A small wavelength allows accurate position measurement, but it increases the momentum of the probe to the point that it further disturbs the momentum of a system being measured. For example, if an electron is scattered from an atom and has a wavelength small enough to detect the position of electrons in the atom, its momentum can knock the electrons from their orbits in a manner that loses information about their original motion. It is therefore impossible to follow an electron in its orbit around an atom. If you measure the electron's position, you will find it in a definite location, but the atom will be disrupted. Repeated measurements on identical atoms will produce interesting probability distributions for electrons around the atom, but they will not produce motion information. The probability distributions are referred to as electron clouds or orbitals. The shapes of these orbitals are often shown in general chemistry texts and are discussed in The Wave Nature of Matter Causes Quantization.

EXAMPLE 29.8

Heisenberg Uncertainty Principle in Position and Momentum for an Atom

(a) If the position of an electron in an atom is measured to an accuracy of 0.0100 nm, what is the electron's uncertainty in velocity? (b) If the electron has this velocity, what is its kinetic energy in eV?

Strategy

The uncertainty in position is the accuracy of the measurement, or $\Delta x = 0.0100 \text{ nm}$. Thus the smallest uncertainty in momentum Δp can be calculated using $\Delta x \Delta p \geq h/4\pi$. Once the uncertainty in momentum Δp is found, the uncertainty in velocity can be found from $\Delta p = m\Delta v$.

Solution for (a)

Using the equals sign in the uncertainty principle to express the minimum uncertainty, we have

$$\Delta x \Delta p = \frac{h}{4\pi}. \tag{29.44}$$

Solving for Δp and substituting known values gives

$$\Delta p = \frac{h}{4\pi \Delta x} = \frac{6.63 \times 10^{-34} \text{ J} \cdot \text{s}}{4\pi(1.00 \times 10^{-11} \text{ m})} = 5.28 \times 10^{-24} \text{ kg} \cdot \text{m/s}. \tag{29.45}$$

Thus,

$$\Delta p = 5.28 \times 10^{-24} \text{ kg} \cdot \text{m/s} = m\Delta v. \tag{29.46}$$

Solving for Δv and substituting the mass of an electron gives

$$\Delta v = \frac{\Delta p}{m} = \frac{5.28 \times 10^{-24} \text{ kg} \cdot \text{m/s}}{9.11 \times 10^{-31} \text{ kg}} = 5.79 \times 10^{6} \text{ m/s}. \tag{29.47}$$

Solution for (b)

Although large, this velocity is not highly relativistic, and so the electron's kinetic energy is

$$\begin{aligned} \text{KE}_e &= \frac{1}{2}mv^2 \\ &= \frac{1}{2}(9.11 \times 10^{-31}\ \text{kg})(5.79 \times 10^6\ \text{m/s})^2 \\ &= (1.53 \times 10^{-17}\ \text{J})\left(\frac{1\ \text{eV}}{1.60{\times}10^{-19}\ \text{J}}\right) = 95.5\ \text{eV}. \end{aligned} \quad 29.48$$

Discussion

Since atoms are roughly 0.1 nm in size, knowing the position of an electron to 0.0100 nm localizes it reasonably well inside the atom. This would be like being able to see details one-tenth the size of the atom. But the consequent uncertainty in velocity is large. You certainly could not follow it very well if its velocity is so uncertain. To get a further idea of how large the uncertainty in velocity is, we assumed the velocity of the electron was equal to its uncertainty and found this gave a kinetic energy of 95.5 eV. This is significantly greater than the typical energy difference between levels in atoms (see Table 29.1), so that it is impossible to get a meaningful energy for the electron if we know its position even moderately well.

Why don't we notice Heisenberg's uncertainty principle in everyday life? The answer is that Planck's constant is very small. Thus the lower limit in the uncertainty of measuring the position and momentum of large objects is negligible. We can detect sunlight reflected from Jupiter and follow the planet in its orbit around the Sun. The reflected sunlight alters the momentum of Jupiter and creates an uncertainty in its momentum, but this is totally negligible compared with Jupiter's huge momentum. The correspondence principle tells us that the predictions of quantum mechanics become indistinguishable from classical physics for large objects, which is the case here.

Heisenberg Uncertainty for Energy and Time

There is another form of **Heisenberg's uncertainty principle** for *simultaneous measurements of energy and time*. In equation form,

$$\Delta E \Delta t \geq \frac{h}{4\pi}, \quad 29.49$$

where ΔE is the **uncertainty in energy** and Δt is the **uncertainty in time**. This means that within a time interval Δt, it is not possible to measure energy precisely—there will be an uncertainty ΔE in the measurement. In order to measure energy more precisely (to make ΔE smaller), we must increase Δt. This time interval may be the amount of time we take to make the measurement, or it could be the amount of time a particular state exists, as in the next Example 29.9.

EXAMPLE 29.9

Heisenberg Uncertainty Principle for Energy and Time for an Atom

An atom in an excited state temporarily stores energy. If the lifetime of this excited state is measured to be $1.0{\times}10^{-10}$ s, what is the minimum uncertainty in the energy of the state in eV?

Strategy

The minimum uncertainty in energy ΔE is found by using the equals sign in $\Delta E \Delta t \geq h/4\pi$ and corresponds to a reasonable choice for the uncertainty in time. The largest the uncertainty in time can be is the full lifetime of the excited state, or $\Delta t = 1.0{\times}10^{-10}$ s.

Solution

Solving the uncertainty principle for ΔE and substituting known values gives

$$\Delta E = \frac{h}{4\pi\Delta t} = \frac{6.63 \times 10^{-34}\ \text{J} \cdot \text{s}}{4\pi(1.0\times10^{-10}\ \text{s})} = 5.3 \times 10^{-25}\ \text{J}. \quad 29.50$$

Now converting to eV yields

$$\Delta E = (5.3 \times 10^{-25}\ \text{J})\left(\frac{1\ \text{eV}}{1.6 \times 10^{-19}\ \text{J}}\right) = 3.3 \times 10^{-6}\ \text{eV}. \quad 29.51$$

Discussion

The lifetime of 10^{-10} s is typical of excited states in atoms—on human time scales, they quickly emit their stored energy. An uncertainty in energy of only a few millionths of an eV results. This uncertainty is small compared with typical excitation energies in atoms, which are on the order of 1 eV. So here the uncertainty principle limits the accuracy with which we can measure the lifetime and energy of such states, but not very significantly.

The uncertainty principle for energy and time can be of great significance if the lifetime of a system is very short. Then Δt is very small, and ΔE is consequently very large. Some nuclei and exotic particles have extremely short lifetimes (as small as 10^{-25} s), causing uncertainties in energy as great as many GeV (10^9 eV). Stored energy appears as increased rest mass, and so this means that there is significant uncertainty in the rest mass of short-lived particles. When measured repeatedly, a spread of masses or decay energies are obtained. The spread is ΔE. You might ask whether this uncertainty in energy could be avoided by not measuring the lifetime. The answer is no. Nature knows the lifetime, and so its brevity affects the energy of the particle. This is so well established experimentally that the uncertainty in decay energy is used to calculate the lifetime of short-lived states. Some nuclei and particles are so short-lived that it is difficult to measure their lifetime. But if their decay energy can be measured, its spread is ΔE, and this is used in the uncertainty principle ($\Delta E \Delta t \geq h/4\pi$) to calculate the lifetime Δt.

There is another consequence of the uncertainty principle for energy and time. If energy is uncertain by ΔE, then conservation of energy can be violated by ΔE for a time Δt. Neither the physicist nor nature can tell that conservation of energy has been violated, if the violation is temporary and smaller than the uncertainty in energy. While this sounds innocuous enough, we shall see in later chapters that it allows the temporary creation of matter from nothing and has implications for how nature transmits forces over very small distances.

Finally, note that in the discussion of particles and waves, we have stated that individual measurements produce precise or particle-like results. A definite position is determined each time we observe an electron, for example. But repeated measurements produce a spread in values consistent with wave characteristics. The great theoretical physicist Richard Feynman (1918–1988) commented, "What there are, are particles." When you observe enough of them, they distribute themselves as you would expect for a wave phenomenon. However, what there are as they travel we cannot tell because, when we do try to measure, we affect the traveling.

29.8 The Particle-Wave Duality Reviewed

LEARNING OBJECTIVES

By the end of this section, you will be able to:

- Explain the concept of particle-wave duality, and its scope.

Particle-wave duality—the fact that all particles have wave properties—is one of the cornerstones of quantum mechanics. We first came across it in the treatment of photons, those particles of EM radiation that exhibit both particle and wave properties, but not at the same time. Later it was noted that particles of matter have wave properties as well. The dual properties of particles and waves are found for all particles, whether massless like photons, or having a mass like electrons. (See Figure 29.24.)

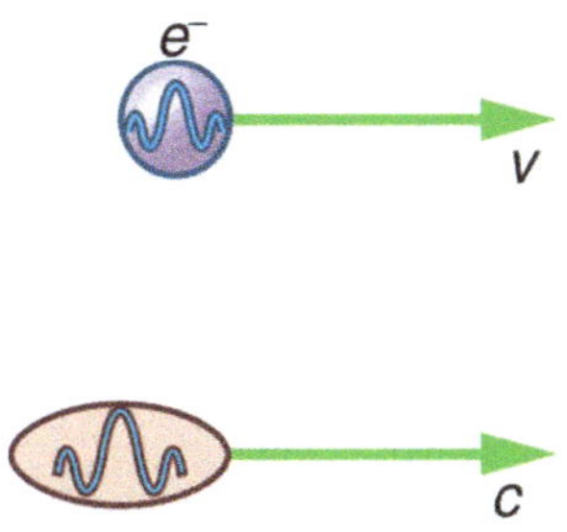

FIGURE 29.24 On a quantum-mechanical scale (i.e., very small), particles with and without mass have wave properties. For example, both electrons and photons have wavelengths but also behave as particles.

There are many submicroscopic particles in nature. Most have mass and are expected to act as particles, or the smallest units of matter. All these masses have wave properties, with wavelengths given by the de Broglie relationship $\lambda = h/p$. So, too, do combinations of these particles, such as nuclei, atoms, and molecules. As a combination of masses becomes large, particularly if it is large enough to be called macroscopic, its wave nature becomes difficult to observe. This is consistent with our common experience with matter.

Some particles in nature are massless. We have only treated the photon so far, but all massless entities travel at the speed of light, have a wavelength, and exhibit particle and wave behaviors. They have momentum given by a rearrangement of the de Broglie relationship, $p = h/\lambda$. In large combinations of these massless particles (such large combinations are common only for photons or EM waves), there is mostly wave behavior upon detection, and the particle nature becomes difficult to observe. This is also consistent with experience. (See Figure 29.25.)

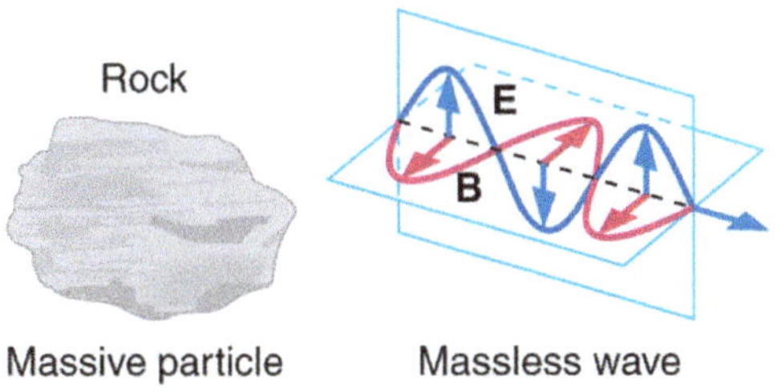

FIGURE 29.25 On a classical scale (macroscopic), particles with mass behave as particles and not as waves. Particles without mass act as waves and not as particles.

The particle-wave duality is a universal attribute. It is another connection between matter and energy. Not only has modern physics been able to describe nature for high speeds and small sizes, it has also discovered new connections and symmetries. There is greater unity and symmetry in nature than was known in the classical era—but they were dreamt of. A beautiful poem written by the English poet William Blake some two centuries ago contains the following four lines:

To see the World in a Grain of Sand

And a Heaven in a Wild Flower

Hold Infinity in the palm of your hand

And Eternity in an hour

Integrated Concepts

The problem set for this section involves concepts from this chapter and several others. Physics is most interesting when applied to general situations involving more than a narrow set of physical principles. For example, photons have momentum, hence the relevance of Linear Momentum and Collisions. The following topics are involved in some or all of the problems in this section:

- Dynamics: Newton's Laws of Motion
- Work, Energy, and Energy Resources
- Linear Momentum and Collisions
- Heat and Heat Transfer Methods

- Electric Potential and Electric Field
- Electric Current, Resistance, and Ohm's Law
- Wave Optics
- Special Relativity

PROBLEM-SOLVING STRATEGY

1. Identify which physical principles are involved.
2. Solve the problem using strategies outlined in the text.

Example 29.10 illustrates how these strategies are applied to an integrated-concept problem.

EXAMPLE 29.10

Recoil of a Dust Particle after Absorbing a Photon

The following topics are involved in this integrated concepts worked example:

Photons (quantum mechanics)
Linear Momentum

TABLE 29.2 Topics

A 550-nm photon (visible light) is absorbed by a $1.00\text{-}\mu\text{g}$ particle of dust in outer space. (a) Find the momentum of such a photon. (b) What is the recoil velocity of the particle of dust, assuming it is initially at rest?

Strategy Step 1

To solve an *integrated-concept problem*, such as those following this example, we must first identify the physical principles involved and identify the chapters in which they are found. Part (a) of this example asks for the *momentum of a photon*, a topic of the present chapter. Part (b) considers *recoil following a collision*, a topic of Linear Momentum and Collisions.

Strategy Step 2

The following solutions to each part of the example illustrate how specific problem-solving strategies are applied. These involve identifying knowns and unknowns, checking to see if the answer is reasonable, and so on.

Solution for (a)

The momentum of a photon is related to its wavelength by the equation:

$$p = \frac{h}{\lambda}. \tag{29.52}$$

Entering the known value for Planck's constant h and given the wavelength λ, we obtain

$$\begin{aligned} p &= \frac{6.63 \times 10^{-34}\ \text{J}\cdot\text{s}}{550 \times 10^{-9}\ \text{m}} \\ &= 1.21 \times 10^{-27}\ \text{kg}\cdot\text{m/s}. \end{aligned} \tag{29.53}$$

Discussion for (a)

This momentum is small, as expected from discussions in the text and the fact that photons of visible light carry small amounts of energy and momentum compared with those carried by macroscopic objects.

Solution for (b)

Conservation of momentum in the absorption of this photon by a grain of dust can be analyzed using the equation:

$$p_1 + p_2 = p'_1 + p'_2 (F_{\text{net}} = 0). \tag{29.54}$$

The net external force is zero, since the dust is in outer space. Let 1 represent the photon and 2 the dust particle. Before the collision, the dust is at rest (relative to some observer); after the collision, there is no photon (it is absorbed). So conservation of momentum can be written

$$p_1 = p'_2 = mv, \tag{29.55}$$

where p_1 is the photon momentum before the collision and p'_2 is the dust momentum after the collision. The mass and recoil velocity of the dust are m and v, respectively. Solving this for v, the requested quantity, yields

$$v = \frac{p}{m}, \tag{29.56}$$

where p is the photon momentum found in part (a). Entering known values (noting that a microgram is 10^{-9} kg) gives

$$\begin{aligned} v &= \frac{1.21 \times 10^{-27}\ \text{kg}\cdot\text{m/s}}{1.00 \times 10^{-9}\ \text{kg}} \\ &= 1.21 \times 10^{-18}\ \text{m/s}. \end{aligned} \tag{29.57}$$

Discussion

The recoil velocity of the particle of dust is extremely small. As we have noted, however, there are immense numbers of photons in sunlight and other macroscopic sources. In time, collisions and absorption of many photons could cause a significant recoil of the dust, as observed in comet tails.

Glossary

atomic spectra the electromagnetic emission from atoms and molecules

binding energy also called the *work function*; the amount of energy necessary to eject an electron from a material

blackbody an ideal radiator, which can radiate equally well at all wavelengths

blackbody radiation the electromagnetic radiation from a blackbody

bremsstrahlung German for *braking radiation*; produced when electrons are decelerated

characteristic x rays x rays whose energy depends on the material they were produced in

Compton effect the phenomenon whereby x rays scattered from materials have decreased energy

correspondence principle in the classical limit (large, slow-moving objects), quantum mechanics becomes the same as classical physics

de Broglie wavelength the wavelength possessed by a particle of matter, calculated by $\lambda = h/p$

gamma ray also γ-ray; highest-energy photon in the EM spectrum

Heisenberg's uncertainty principle a fundamental limit to the precision with which pairs of quantities (momentum and position, and energy and time) can be measured

infrared radiation photons with energies slightly less than red light

ionizing radiation radiation that ionizes materials that absorb it

microwaves photons with wavelengths on the order of a micron (μm)

particle-wave duality the property of behaving like either a particle or a wave; the term for the phenomenon that all particles have wave characteristics

photoelectric effect the phenomenon whereby some materials eject electrons when light is shined on them

photon a quantum, or particle, of electromagnetic radiation

photon energy the amount of energy a photon has; $E = hf$

photon momentum the amount of momentum a photon has, calculated by $p = \frac{h}{\lambda} = \frac{E}{c}$

Planck's constant $h = 6.626 \times 10^{-34}\ \text{J} \cdot \text{s}$

probability distribution the overall spatial distribution of probabilities to find a particle at a given location

quantized the fact that certain physical entities exist only with particular discrete values and not every conceivable value

quantum mechanics the branch of physics that deals with small objects and with the quantization of various entities, especially energy

ultraviolet radiation UV; ionizing photons slightly more energetic than violet light

uncertainty in energy lack of precision or lack of knowledge of precise results in measurements of energy

uncertainty in momentum lack of precision or lack of knowledge of precise results in measurements of momentum

uncertainty in position lack of precision or lack of knowledge of precise results in measurements of position

uncertainty in time lack of precision or lack of knowledge of precise results in measurements of time

visible light the range of photon energies the human eye can detect

x ray EM photon between γ-ray and UV in energy

Section Summary

29.1 Quantization of Energy

- The first indication that energy is sometimes quantized came from blackbody radiation, which is the emission of EM radiation by an object with an emissivity of 1.
- Planck recognized that the energy levels of the emitting atoms and molecules were quantized, with only the allowed values of $E = \left(n + \frac{1}{2}\right)hf$, where n is any non-negative integer (0, 1, 2, 3, ...).
- h is Planck's constant, whose value is $h = 6.626 \times 10^{-34}\ \text{J} \cdot \text{s}.$
- Thus, the oscillatory absorption and emission energies of atoms and molecules in a blackbody could increase or decrease only in steps of size $\Delta E = hf$ where f is the frequency of the oscillatory nature of the absorption and emission of EM radiation.
- Another indication of energy levels being quantized in atoms and molecules comes from the lines in atomic spectra, which are the EM emissions of individual atoms and molecules.

29.2 The Photoelectric Effect

- The photoelectric effect is the process in which EM

radiation ejects electrons from a material.

- Einstein proposed photons to be quanta of EM radiation having energy $E = hf$, where f is the frequency of the radiation.
- All EM radiation is composed of photons. As Einstein explained, all characteristics of the photoelectric effect are due to the interaction of individual photons with individual electrons.
- The maximum kinetic energy KE_e of ejected electrons (photoelectrons) is given by $\text{KE}_e = hf - \text{BE}$, where hf is the photon energy and BE is the binding energy (or work function) of the electron to the particular material.

29.3 Photon Energies and the Electromagnetic Spectrum

- Photon energy is responsible for many characteristics of EM radiation, being particularly noticeable at high frequencies.
- Photons have both wave and particle characteristics.

29.4 Photon Momentum

- Photons have momentum, given by $p = \frac{h}{\lambda}$, where λ is the photon wavelength.
- Photon energy and momentum are related by $p = \frac{E}{c}$, where $E = hf = hc/\lambda$ for a photon.

29.5 The Particle-Wave Duality

- EM radiation can behave like either a particle or a wave.
- This is termed particle-wave duality.

29.6 The Wave Nature of Matter

- Particles of matter also have a wavelength, called the de Broglie wavelength, given by $\lambda = \frac{h}{p}$, where p is momentum.
- Matter is found to have the same *interference characteristics* as any other wave.

29.7 Probability: The Heisenberg Uncertainty Principle

- Matter is found to have the same interference characteristics as any other wave.
- There is now a probability distribution for the location of a particle rather than a definite position.
- Another consequence of the wave character of all particles is the Heisenberg uncertainty principle, which limits the precision with which certain physical quantities can be known simultaneously. For position and momentum, the uncertainty principle is $\Delta x \Delta p \geq \frac{h}{4\pi}$, where Δx is the uncertainty in position and Δp is the uncertainty in momentum.
- For energy and time, the uncertainty principle is $\Delta E \Delta t \geq \frac{h}{4\pi}$ where ΔE is the uncertainty in energy and Δt is the uncertainty in time.
- These small limits are fundamentally important on the quantum-mechanical scale.

29.8 The Particle-Wave Duality Reviewed

- The particle-wave duality refers to the fact that all particles—those with mass and those without mass—have wave characteristics.
- This is a further connection between mass and energy.

Conceptual Questions

29.1 Quantization of Energy

1. Give an example of a physical entity that is quantized. State specifically what the entity is and what the limits are on its values.

2. Give an example of a physical entity that is not quantized, in that it is continuous and may have a continuous range of values.

3. What aspect of the blackbody spectrum forced Planck to propose quantization of energy levels in its atoms and molecules?

4. If Planck's constant were large, say 10^{34} times greater than it is, we would observe macroscopic entities to be quantized. Describe the motions of a child's swing under such circumstances.

5. Why don't we notice quantization in everyday events?

29.2 The Photoelectric Effect

6. Is visible light the only type of EM radiation that can cause the photoelectric effect?

7. Which aspects of the photoelectric effect cannot be explained without photons? Which can be explained without photons? Are the latter inconsistent with the existence of photons?

8. Is the photoelectric effect a direct consequence of the wave character of EM radiation or of the particle character of EM radiation? Explain briefly.

9. Insulators (nonmetals) have a higher BE than metals, and it is more difficult for photons to eject electrons from insulators. Discuss how this relates to the free charges in metals that make them good conductors.

10. If you pick up and shake a piece of metal that has electrons in it free to move as a current, no electrons fall out. Yet if you heat the metal, electrons can be boiled off. Explain both of these facts as they relate to the amount and distribution of energy involved with shaking the object as compared with heating it.

29.3 Photon Energies and the Electromagnetic Spectrum

11. Why are UV, x rays, and γ rays called ionizing radiation?

12. How can treating food with ionizing radiation help keep it from spoiling? UV is not very penetrating. What else could be used?

13. Some television tubes are CRTs. They use an approximately 30-kV accelerating potential to send electrons to the screen, where the electrons stimulate phosphors to emit the light that forms the pictures we watch. Would you expect x rays also to be created?

14. Tanning salons use "safe" UV with a longer wavelength than some of the UV in sunlight. This "safe" UV has enough photon energy to trigger the tanning mechanism. Is it likely to be able to cause cell damage and induce cancer with prolonged exposure?

15. Your pupils dilate when visible light intensity is reduced. Does wearing sunglasses that lack UV blockers increase or decrease the UV hazard to your eyes? Explain.

16. One could feel heat transfer in the form of infrared radiation from a large nuclear bomb detonated in the atmosphere 75 km from you. However, none of the profusely emitted x rays or γ rays reaches you. Explain.

17. Can a single microwave photon cause cell damage? Explain.

18. In an x-ray tube, the maximum photon energy is given by $hf = qV$. Would it be technically more correct to say $hf = qV + \text{BE}$, where BE is the binding energy of electrons in the target anode? Why isn't the energy stated the latter way?

29.4 Photon Momentum

19. Which formula may be used for the momentum of all particles, with or without mass?

20. Is there any measurable difference between the momentum of a photon and the momentum of matter?

21. Why don't we feel the momentum of sunlight when we are on the beach?

29.6 The Wave Nature of Matter

22. How does the interference of water waves differ from the interference of electrons? How are they analogous?

23. Describe one type of evidence for the wave nature of matter.

24. Describe one type of evidence for the particle nature of EM radiation.

29.7 Probability: The Heisenberg Uncertainty Principle

25. What is the Heisenberg uncertainty principle? Does it place limits on what can be known?

29.8 The Particle-Wave Duality Reviewed

26. In what ways are matter and energy related that were not known before the development of relativity and quantum mechanics?

Problems & Exercises

29.1 Quantization of Energy

1. A LiBr molecule oscillates with a frequency of 1.7×10^{13} Hz. (a) What is the difference in energy in eV between allowed oscillator states? (b) What is the approximate value of n for a state having an energy of 1.0 eV?

2. The difference in energy between allowed oscillator states in HBr molecules is 0.330 eV. What is the oscillation frequency of this molecule?

3. A physicist is watching a 15-kg orangutan at a zoo swing lazily in a tire at the end of a rope. He (the physicist) notices that each oscillation takes 3.00 s and hypothesizes that the energy is quantized. (a) What is the difference in energy in joules between allowed oscillator states? (b) What is the value of n for a state where the energy is 5.00 J? (c) Can the quantization be observed?

29.2 The Photoelectric Effect

4. What is the longest-wavelength EM radiation that can eject a photoelectron from silver, given that the binding energy is 4.73 eV? Is this in the visible range?

5. Find the longest-wavelength photon that can eject an electron from potassium, given that the binding energy is 2.24 eV. Is this visible EM radiation?

6. What is the binding energy in eV of electrons in magnesium, if the longest-wavelength photon that can eject electrons is 337 nm?

7. Calculate the binding energy in eV of electrons in aluminum, if the longest-wavelength photon that can eject them is 304 nm.

8. What is the maximum kinetic energy in eV of electrons ejected from sodium metal by 450-nm EM radiation, given that the binding energy is 2.28 eV?

9. UV radiation having a wavelength of 120 nm falls on gold metal, to which electrons are bound by 4.82 eV. What is the maximum kinetic energy of the ejected photoelectrons?

10. Violet light of wavelength 400 nm ejects electrons with a maximum kinetic energy of 0.860 eV from sodium metal. What is the binding energy of electrons to sodium metal?

11. UV radiation having a 300-nm wavelength falls on uranium metal, ejecting 0.500-eV electrons. What is the binding energy of electrons to uranium metal?

12. What is the wavelength of EM radiation that ejects 2.00-eV electrons from calcium metal, given that the binding energy is 2.71 eV? What type of EM radiation is this?

13. Find the wavelength of photons that eject 0.100-eV electrons from potassium, given that the binding energy is 2.24 eV. Are these photons visible?

14. What is the maximum velocity of electrons ejected from a material by 80-nm photons, if they are bound to the material by 4.73 eV?

15. Photoelectrons from a material with a binding energy of 2.71 eV are ejected by 420-nm photons. Once ejected, how long does it take these electrons to travel 2.50 cm to a detection device?

16. A laser with a power output of 2.00 mW at a wavelength of 400 nm is projected onto calcium metal. (a) How many electrons per second are ejected? (b) What power is carried away by the electrons, given that the binding energy is 2.71 eV?

17. (a) Calculate the number of photoelectrons per second ejected from a 1.00-mm ^{2} area of sodium metal by 500-nm EM radiation having an intensity of 1.30 kW/m^2 (the intensity of sunlight above the Earth's atmosphere). (b) Given that the binding energy is 2.28 eV, what power is carried away by the electrons? (c) The electrons carry away less power than brought in by the photons. Where does the other power go? How can it be recovered?

18. Unreasonable Results
Red light having a wavelength of 700 nm is projected onto magnesium metal to which electrons are bound by 3.68 eV. (a) Use $\text{KE}_e = hf - \text{BE}$ to calculate the kinetic energy of the ejected electrons. (b) What is unreasonable about this result? (c) Which assumptions are unreasonable or inconsistent?

19. Unreasonable Results
(a) What is the binding energy of electrons to a material from which 4.00-eV electrons are ejected by 400-nm EM radiation? (b) What is unreasonable about this result? (c) Which assumptions are unreasonable or inconsistent?

29.3 Photon Energies and the Electromagnetic Spectrum

20. What is the energy in joules and eV of a photon in a radio wave from an AM station that has a 1530-kHz broadcast frequency?

21. (a) Find the energy in joules and eV of photons in radio waves from an FM station that has a 90.0-MHz broadcast frequency. (b) What does this imply about the number of photons per second that the radio station must broadcast?

22. Calculate the frequency in hertz of a 1.00-MeV γ-ray photon.

23. (a) What is the wavelength of a 1.00-eV photon? (b) Find its frequency in hertz. (c) Identify the type of EM radiation.

24. Do the unit conversions necessary to show that $hc = 1240 \text{ eV} \cdot \text{nm}$, as stated in the text.

25. Confirm the statement in the text that the range of photon energies for visible light is 1.63 to 3.26 eV, given that the range of visible wavelengths is 380 to 760 nm.

26. (a) Calculate the energy in eV of an IR photon of frequency 2.00×10^{13} Hz. (b) How many of these photons would need to be absorbed simultaneously by a tightly bound molecule to break it apart? (c) What is the energy in eV of a γ ray of frequency 3.00×10^{20} Hz? (d) How many tightly bound molecules could a single such γ ray break apart?

27. Prove that, to three-digit accuracy, $h = 4.14 \times 10^{-15}\ \text{eV} \cdot \text{s}$, as stated in the text.

28. (a) What is the maximum energy in eV of photons produced in a CRT using a 25.0-kV accelerating potential, such as a color TV? (b) What is their frequency?

29. What is the accelerating voltage of an x-ray tube that produces x rays with a shortest wavelength of 0.0103 nm?

30. (a) What is the ratio of power outputs by two microwave ovens having frequencies of 950 and 2560 MHz, if they emit the same number of photons per second? (b) What is the ratio of photons per second if they have the same power output?

31. How many photons per second are emitted by the antenna of a microwave oven, if its power output is 1.00 kW at a frequency of 2560 MHz?

32. Some satellites use nuclear power. (a) If such a satellite emits a 1.00-W flux of γ rays having an average energy of 0.500 MeV, how many are emitted per second? (b) These γ rays affect other satellites. How far away must another satellite be to only receive one γ ray per second per square meter?

33. (a) If the power output of a 650-kHz radio station is 50.0 kW, how many photons per second are produced? (b) If the radio waves are broadcast uniformly in all directions, find the number of photons per second per square meter at a distance of 100 km. Assume no reflection from the ground or absorption by the air.

34. How many x-ray photons per second are created by an x-ray tube that produces a flux of x rays having a power of 1.00 W? Assume the average energy per photon is 75.0 keV.

35. (a) How far away must you be from a 650-kHz radio station with power 50.0 kW for there to be only one photon per second per square meter? Assume no reflections or absorption, as if you were in deep outer space. (b) Discuss the implications for detecting intelligent life in other solar systems by detecting their radio broadcasts.

36. Assuming that 10.0% of a 100-W light bulb's energy output is in the visible range (typical for incandescent bulbs) with an average wavelength of 580 nm, and that the photons spread out uniformly and are not absorbed by the atmosphere, how far away would you be if 500 photons per second enter the 3.00-mm diameter pupil of your eye? (This number easily stimulates the retina.)

37. Construct Your Own Problem
Consider a laser pen. Construct a problem in which you calculate the number of photons per second emitted by the pen. Among the things to be considered are the laser pen's wavelength and power output. Your instructor may also wish for you to determine the minimum diffraction spreading in the beam and the number of photons per square centimeter the pen can project at some large distance. In this latter case, you will also need to consider the output size of the laser beam, the distance to the object being illuminated, and any absorption or scattering along the way.

29.4 Photon Momentum

38. (a) Find the momentum of a 4.00-cm-wavelength microwave photon. (b) Discuss why you expect the answer to (a) to be very small.

39. (a) What is the momentum of a 0.0100-nm-wavelength photon that could detect details of an atom? (b) What is its energy in MeV?

40. (a) What is the wavelength of a photon that has a momentum of $5.00 \times 10^{-29}\ \text{kg} \cdot \text{m/s}$? (b) Find its energy in eV.

41. (a) A γ-ray photon has a momentum of $8.00 \times 10^{-21}\ \text{kg} \cdot \text{m/s}$. What is its wavelength? (b) Calculate its energy in MeV.

42. (a) Calculate the momentum of a photon having a wavelength of $2.50\ \mu\text{m}$. (b) Find the velocity of an electron having the same momentum. (c) What is the kinetic energy of the electron, and how does it compare with that of the photon?

43. Repeat the previous problem for a 10.0-nm-wavelength photon.

44. (a) Calculate the wavelength of a photon that has the same momentum as a proton moving at 1.00% of the speed of light. (b) What is the energy of the photon in MeV? (c) What is the kinetic energy of the proton in MeV?

45. (a) Find the momentum of a 100-keV x-ray photon. (b) Find the equivalent velocity of a neutron with the same momentum. (c) What is the neutron's kinetic energy in keV?

46. Take the ratio of relativistic rest energy, $E = \gamma mc^2 mc^2$, to relativistic momentum, $p = \gamma mu$, and show that in the limit that mass approaches zero, you find $E/p = c$.

47. Construct Your Own Problem
Consider a space sail such as mentioned in Example 29.5. Construct a problem in which you calculate the light pressure on the sail in $\mathrm{N/m^2}$ produced by reflecting sunlight. Also calculate the force that could be produced and how much effect that would have on a spacecraft. Among the things to be considered are the intensity of sunlight, its average wavelength, the number of photons per square meter this implies, the area of the space sail, and the mass of the system being accelerated.

48. Unreasonable Results
A car feels a small force due to the light it sends out from its headlights, equal to the momentum of the light divided by the time in which it is emitted. (a) Calculate the power of each headlight, if they exert a total force of 2.00×10^{-2} N backward on the car. (b) What is unreasonable about this result? (c) Which assumptions are unreasonable or inconsistent?

29.6 The Wave Nature of Matter

49. At what velocity will an electron have a wavelength of 1.00 m?

50. What is the wavelength of an electron moving at 3.00% of the speed of light?

51. At what velocity does a proton have a 6.00-fm wavelength (about the size of a nucleus)? Assume the proton is nonrelativistic. (1 femtometer = 10^{-15} m.)

52. What is the velocity of a 0.400-kg billiard ball if its wavelength is 7.50 cm (large enough for it to interfere with other billiard balls)?

53. Find the wavelength of a proton moving at 1.00% of the speed of light.

54. Experiments are performed with ultracold neutrons having velocities as small as 1.00 m/s. (a) What is the wavelength of such a neutron? (b) What is its kinetic energy in eV?

55. (a) Find the velocity of a neutron that has a 6.00-fm wavelength (about the size of a nucleus). Assume the neutron is nonrelativistic. (b) What is the neutron's kinetic energy in MeV?

56. What is the wavelength of an electron accelerated through a 30.0-kV potential, as in a TV tube?

57. What is the kinetic energy of an electron in a TEM having a 0.0100-nm wavelength?

58. (a) Calculate the velocity of an electron that has a wavelength of $1.00\ \mu\mathrm{m}$. (b) Through what voltage must the electron be accelerated to have this velocity?

59. The velocity of a proton emerging from a Van de Graaff accelerator is 25.0% of the speed of light. (a) What is the proton's wavelength? (b) What is its kinetic energy, assuming it is nonrelativistic? (c) What was the equivalent voltage through which it was accelerated?

60. The kinetic energy of an electron accelerated in an x-ray tube is 100 keV. Assuming it is nonrelativistic, what is its wavelength?

61. Unreasonable Results
(a) Assuming it is nonrelativistic, calculate the velocity of an electron with a 0.100-fm wavelength (small enough to detect details of a nucleus). (b) What is unreasonable about this result? (c) Which assumptions are unreasonable or inconsistent?

29.7 Probability: The Heisenberg Uncertainty Principle

62. (a) If the position of an electron in a membrane is measured to an accuracy of $1.00\ \mu\mathrm{m}$, what is the electron's minimum uncertainty in velocity? (b) If the electron has this velocity, what is its kinetic energy in eV? (c) What are the implications of this energy, comparing it to typical molecular binding energies?

63. (a) If the position of a chlorine ion in a membrane is measured to an accuracy of $1.00\ \mu\mathrm{m}$, what is its minimum uncertainty in velocity, given its mass is 5.86×10^{-26} kg? (b) If the ion has this velocity, what is its kinetic energy in eV, and how does this compare with typical molecular binding energies?

64. Suppose the velocity of an electron in an atom is known to an accuracy of 2.0×10^3 m/s (reasonably accurate compared with orbital velocities). What is the electron's minimum uncertainty in position, and how does this compare with the approximate 0.1-nm size of the atom?

65. The velocity of a proton in an accelerator is known to an accuracy of 0.250% of the speed of light. (This could be small compared with its velocity.) What is the smallest possible uncertainty in its position?

66. A relatively long-lived excited state of an atom has a lifetime of 3.00 ms. What is the minimum uncertainty in its energy?

67. (a) The lifetime of a highly unstable nucleus is 10^{-20} s. What is the smallest uncertainty in its decay energy? (b) Compare this with the rest energy of an electron.

68. The decay energy of a short-lived particle has an uncertainty of 1.0 MeV due to its short lifetime. What is the smallest lifetime it can have?

69. The decay energy of a short-lived nuclear excited state has an uncertainty of 2.0 eV due to its short lifetime. What is the smallest lifetime it can have?

70. What is the approximate uncertainty in the mass of a muon, as determined from its decay lifetime?

71. Derive the approximate form of Heisenberg's uncertainty principle for energy and time, $\Delta E \Delta t \approx h$, using the following arguments: Since the position of a particle is uncertain by $\Delta x \approx \lambda$, where λ is the wavelength of the photon used to examine it, there is an uncertainty in the time the photon takes to traverse Δx. Furthermore, the photon has an energy related to its wavelength, and it can transfer some or all of this energy to the object being examined. Thus the uncertainty in the energy of the object is also related to λ. Find Δt and ΔE; then multiply them to give the approximate uncertainty principle.

29.8 The Particle-Wave Duality Reviewed

72. Integrated Concepts
The 54.0-eV electron in Example 29.7 has a 0.167-nm wavelength. If such electrons are passed through a double slit and have their first maximum at an angle of 25.0°, what is the slit separation d?

73. Integrated Concepts
An electron microscope produces electrons with a 2.00-pm wavelength. If these are passed through a 1.00-nm single slit, at what angle will the first diffraction minimum be found?

74. Integrated Concepts
A certain heat lamp emits 200 W of mostly IR radiation averaging 1500 nm in wavelength. (a) What is the average photon energy in joules? (b) How many of these photons are required to increase the temperature of a person's shoulder by 2.0°C, assuming the affected mass is 4.0 kg with a specific heat of $0.83\ \text{kcal/kg}\cdot{}^\circ\text{C}$. Also assume no other significant heat transfer. (c) How long does this take?

75. Integrated Concepts
On its high power setting, a microwave oven produces 900 W of 2560 MHz microwaves. (a) How many photons per second is this? (b) How many photons are required to increase the temperature of a 0.500-kg mass of pasta by 45.0°C, assuming a specific heat of $0.900\ \text{kcal/kg}\cdot{}^\circ\text{C}$? Neglect all other heat transfer. (c) How long must the microwave operator wait for their pasta to be ready?

76. Integrated Concepts
(a) Calculate the amount of microwave energy in joules needed to raise the temperature of 1.00 kg of soup from 20.0°C to 100°C. (b) What is the total momentum of all the microwave photons it takes to do this? (c) Calculate the velocity of a 1.00-kg mass with the same momentum. (d) What is the kinetic energy of this mass?

77. Integrated Concepts
(a) What is γ for an electron emerging from the Stanford Linear Accelerator with a total energy of 50.0 GeV? (b) Find its momentum. (c) What is the electron's wavelength?

78. Integrated Concepts
(a) What is γ for a proton having an energy of 1.00 TeV, produced by the Fermilab accelerator? (b) Find its momentum. (c) What is the proton's wavelength?

79. Integrated Concepts
An electron microscope passes 1.00-pm-wavelength electrons through a circular aperture $2.00\ \mu\text{m}$ in diameter. What is the angle between two just-resolvable point sources for this microscope?

80. Integrated Concepts
(a) Calculate the velocity of electrons that form the same pattern as 450-nm light when passed through a double slit. (b) Calculate the kinetic

energy of each and compare them. (c) Would either be easier to generate than the other? Explain.

81. Integrated Concepts
(a) What is the separation between double slits that produces a second-order minimum at 45.0° for 650-nm light? (b) What slit separation is needed to produce the same pattern for 1.00-keV protons.

82. Integrated Concepts
A laser with a power output of 2.00 mW at a wavelength of 400 nm is projected onto calcium metal. (a) How many electrons per second are ejected? (b) What power is carried away by the electrons, given that the binding energy is 2.71 eV? (c) Calculate the current of ejected electrons. (d) If the photoelectric material is electrically insulated and acts like a 2.00-pF capacitor, how long will current flow before the capacitor voltage stops it?

83. Integrated Concepts
One problem with x rays is that they are not sensed. Calculate the temperature increase of a researcher exposed in a few seconds to a nearly fatal accidental dose of x rays under the following conditions. The energy of the x-ray photons is 200 keV, and 4.00×10^{13} of them are absorbed per kilogram of tissue, the specific heat of which is $0.830\ \text{kcal/kg} \cdot {}^{\circ}\text{C}$. (Note that medical diagnostic x-ray machines *cannot* produce an intensity this great.)

84. Integrated Concepts
A 1.00-fm photon has a wavelength short enough to detect some information about nuclei. (a) What is the photon momentum? (b) What is its energy in joules and MeV? (c) What is the (relativistic) velocity of an electron with the same momentum? (d) Calculate the electron's kinetic energy.

85. Integrated Concepts
The momentum of light is exactly reversed when reflected straight back from a mirror, assuming negligible recoil of the mirror. Thus the change in momentum is twice the photon momentum. Suppose light of intensity $1.00\ \text{kW/m}^2$ reflects from a mirror of area $2.00\ \text{m}^2$. (a) Calculate the energy reflected in 1.00 s. (b) What is the momentum imparted to the mirror? (c) Using the most general form of Newton's second law, what is the force on the mirror? (d) Does the assumption of no mirror recoil seem reasonable?

86. Integrated Concepts
Sunlight above the Earth's atmosphere has an intensity of $1.30\ \text{kW/m}^2$. If this is reflected straight back from a mirror that has only a small recoil, the light's momentum is exactly reversed, giving the mirror twice the incident momentum. (a) Calculate the force per square meter of mirror. (b) Very low mass mirrors can be constructed in the near weightlessness of space, and attached to a spaceship to sail it. Once done, the average mass per square meter of the spaceship is 0.100 kg. Find the acceleration of the spaceship if all other forces are balanced. (c) How fast is it moving 24 hours later?

87. Critical Thinking A photon of light with a wavelength of 550.0 nm is involved in a collision with an electron. Use $6.63 \times 10^{-34} \text{m}^2\ \text{kg/s}$ for Planck's constant. (a) How much momentum does the photon have before the collision? (b) If the wavelength of the photon leaving the collision is 650.0 nm, how much momentum does the photon have? (c) Does the momentum have to be conserved in every direction? (d) Does a longer wavelength imply more or less momentum than a shorter wavelength?

Test Prep for AP® Courses

29.1 Quantization of Energy

1. The visible spectrum of sunlight shows a range of colors from red to violet. This spectrum has numerous dark lines spread throughout it. Noting that the surface of the Sun is much cooler than the interior, so that the surface is comparable to a cool gas through which light passes, which of the following statements correctly explains the dark lines?

a. The cooler, denser surface material scatters certain wavelengths of light, forming dark lines.
b. The atoms at the surface absorb certain wavelengths of light, causing the dark lines at those wavelengths.
c. The atoms in the Sun's interior emit light of specific wavelength, so that parts of the spectrum are dark.
d. The atoms at the surface are excited by the high interior temperatures, so that the dark lines are merely wavelengths at which those atoms don't emit energy.

2. A log in a fireplace burns for nearly an hour, at which point it consists mostly of small, hot embers. These embers glow a bright orange and whitish-yellow color. Describe the characteristics of the energy of this system, both in terms of energy transfer and the quantum behavior of blackbodies.

29.2 The Photoelectric Effect

3. A metal exposed to a beam of light with a wavelength equal to or shorter than a specific wavelength emits electrons. What property of light, as described in the quantum explanation of blackbody radiation, accounts for this photoelectric process?
   a. The energy of light increases as its speed increases.
   b. The energy of light increases as its intensity increases.
   c. The energy of light increases as its frequency increases.
   d. The energy of light increases as its wavelength increases.

4. During his experiments that confirmed the existence of electromagnetic waves, Heinrich Hertz used a spark across a gap between two electrodes to provide the rapidly changing electric current that produced electromagnetic waves. He noticed, however, that production of the spark required a lower voltage in a well-lighted laboratory than when the room was dark. Describe how this curious event can be explained in terms of the quantum interpretation of the photoelectric effect.

29.3 Photon Energies and the Electromagnetic Spectrum

5. A microwave oven produces electromagnetic radiation in the radio portion of the spectrum. These microwave photons are absorbed by water molecules, resulting in an increase in the molecules' rotational energies. This added energy is transferred by heat to the surrounding food, which as a result becomes hot very quickly. If the energy absorbed by a water molecule is 1.0×10^{-5} eV, what is the corresponding wavelength of the microwave photons?
   a. 1.22 GHz
   b. 2.45 GHz
   c. 4.90 GHz
   d. 9.80 Hz

6. In the intensity versus frequency curve for x rays (Figure 29.12), the intensity is mostly a smooth curve associated with *bremsstrahlung* ("breaking radiation"). However, there are two spikes (characteristic x rays) that exhibit high-intensity output. Explain how the smooth curve can be described by classical electrodynamics, whereas the peaks require a quantum mechanical interpretation. (Recall that the acceleration or deceleration of electric charges causes the emission of electromagnetic radiation.)

29.4 Photon Momentum

7. The mass of a proton is 1.67×10^{-27} kg. If a proton has the same momentum as a photon with a wavelength of 325 nm, what is its speed?
   a. 2.73×10^{-3} m/s
   b. 0.819 m/s
   c. 1.22 m/s
   d. 2.71×10^{4} m/s

8. A strip of metal foil with a mass of 5.00×10^{-7} kg is suspended in a vacuum and exposed to a pulse of light. The velocity of the foil changes from zero to 1.00×10^{-3} m/s in the same direction as the initial light pulse, and the light pulse is entirely reflected from the surface of the foil. Given that the wavelength of the light is 450 nm, and assuming that this wavelength is the same before and after the collision, how many photons in the pulse collide with the foil?

9. In an experiment in which the Compton effect is observed, a "gamma ray" photon with a wavelength of 5.00×10^{-13} m scatters from an electron. If the change in the electron energy is 1.60×10^{-15} J, what is the wavelength of the photon after the collision with the electron?
   a. 4.95×10^{-13} m
   b. 4.98×10^{-13} m
   c. 5.02×10^{-13} m
   d. 5.05×10^{-13} m

10. Consider two experiments involving a metal sphere with a radius of 2.00 μm that is suspended in a vacuum. In one experiment, a pulse of *N* photons reflects from the surface of the sphere, causing the sphere to acquire momentum. In a second experiment, an identical pulse of photons is completely absorbed by the sphere, so that the sphere acquires momentum. Identify each type of collision as either elastic or inelastic, and, assuming that the change in the photon wavelength can be ignored, use linear momentum conservation to derive the expression for the momentum of the sphere in each experiment.

29.5 The Particle-Wave Duality

11. The ground state of a certain type of atom has energy of $-E_0$. What is the wavelength of a photon with enough energy to ionize the atom when it is in the ground state, so that the ejected electron has kinetic energy equal to $2E_0$?

a. $\lambda = \frac{hc}{3E_0}$
b. $\lambda = \frac{hc}{2E_0}$
c. $\lambda = \frac{hc}{E_0}$
d. $\lambda = \frac{2hc}{E_0}$

12. While the quantum model explains many physical processes that the classical model cannot, it must be consistent with those processes that the classical model does explain. Energy and momentum conservation are fundamental principles of classical physics. Use the Compton and photoelectric effects to explain how these conservation principles carry over to the quantum model of light.

29.6 The Wave Nature of Matter

13. The least massive particle known to exist is the electron neutrino. Though scientists once believed that it had no mass, like the photon, they have now determined that this particle has an extremely low mass, equivalent to a few electron volts. Assuming a mass of 2.2 eV/c^2 (or 3.9×10^{-36} kg) and a speed of 4.4×10^6 m/s, which of the following values equals the neutrino's de Broglie wavelength?

a. 3.8×10^{-5} m
b. 4.7×10^{-7} m
c. 1.7×10^{-10} m
d. 8.9×10^{-14} m

14. Using the definition of the de Broglie wavelength, explain how wavelike properties of matter increase with a decrease in mass or decrease in speed. Use as examples an electron (mass = 9.11×10^{-31} kg) with a speed of 5.0×10^6 m/s and a proton (mass = 1.67×10^{-27} kg) with a speed of 8.0×10^6 m/s.

15. In a Davisson-Germer type of experiment, a crystal with a parallel-plane separation (d) of 9.1×10^{-2} nm produces constructive interference with an electron beam at an angle of $\theta = 50°$. Which of the following is the maximum de Broglie wavelength for these electrons?

a. 0.07nm
b. 0.09 nm
c. 0.14 nm
d. 0.21 nm

16. In a Davisson-Germer experiment, electrons with a speed of 6.5×10^6 m/s exhibit third-order ($n = 3$) constructive interference for a crystal with unknown plane separation, d. Given an angle of incidence of $\theta = 45°$, compute the value for d. Compare the de Broglie wavelength to electromagnetic radiation with the same wavelength. (Recall that the mass of the electron is 9.11×10^{-31} kg.)

29.8 The Particle-Wave Duality Reviewed

17. Which of the following describes one of the main features of wave-particle duality?

a. As speed increases, the wave nature of matter becomes more evident.
b. As momentum decreases, the particle nature of matter becomes more evident.
c. As energy increases, the wave nature of matter becomes easier to observe.
d. As mass increases, the wave nature of matter is less easy to observe.

18. Explain why Heisenberg's uncertainty principle limits the precision with which either momentum or position of a subatomic particle can be known, but becomes less applicable for matter at the macroscopic level.

CHAPTER 30
Atomic Physics

FIGURE 30.1 Individual carbon atoms are visible in this image of a carbon nanotube made by a scanning tunneling electron microscope. (credit: Taner Yildirim, National Institute of Standards and Technology, via Wikimedia Commons)

CHAPTER OUTLINE

CONNECTION FOR AP® COURSES Have you ever wondered how we know the composition of the Sun? After all, we cannot travel there to physically collect a sample due to the extreme conditions. Fortunately, our understanding of the internal structure of atoms gives us the tools to identify the elements in the Sun's outer layers due to an atomic "fingerprint" in the Sun's spectrum. You will learn about atoms and their substructures, as well as how these substructures determine the behavior of the atom, such as the absorption and emission of energy by electrons within an atom.

You will learn the stories of how we discovered the various properties of an atom (Essential Knowledge 1.A.4) through clever and imaginative experimentation (such as the Millikan oil drop experiment) and interpretation (such as Brownian motion). You will also learn about the probabilistic description we use to describe the nature of electrons (Essential Knowledge 7.C.1). At this scale, electrons can be thought of as discrete particles, but they also behave in a way that is consistent with a wave model of matter (Enduring Understanding 7.C). You will learn how we use the wave model to understand the energy levels in an atom (Essential Knowledge 7.C.2) and the properties of electrons.

The content in this chapter supports:

Big Idea 1 Objects and systems have properties such as mass and charge. Systems may have internal structure.

Enduring Understanding 1.A The internal structure of a system determines many properties of the system.

Essential Knowledge 1.A.4 Atoms have internal structures that determine their properties.

Essential Knowledge 1.A.5 Systems have properties determined by the properties and interactions of their constituent atomic and molecular substructures.

Enduring Understanding 1.B Electric charge is a property of an object or system that affects its interactions with other objects or systems containing charge.

Essential Knowledge 1.B.3 The smallest observed unit of charge that can be isolated is the electron charge, also known as the elementary charge.

Big Idea 5 Changes that occur as a result of interactions are constrained by conservation laws.

Enduring Understanding 5.B The energy of a system is conserved.

Essential Knowledge 5.B.8 Energy transfer occurs when photons are absorbed or emitted, for example, by atoms or nuclei.

Big Idea 7 The mathematics of probability can be used to describe the behavior of complex systems and to interpret the behavior of quantum mechanical systems.

Enduring Understanding 7.C At the quantum scale, matter is described by a wave function, which leads to a probabilistic description of the microscopic world.

Essential Knowledge 7.C.1 The probabilistic description of matter is modeled by a wave function, which can be assigned to an object and used to describe its motion and interactions. The absolute value of the wave function is related to the probability of finding a particle in some spatial region.

Essential Knowledge 7.C.2 The allowed states for an electron in an atom can be calculated from the wave model of an electron.

Essential Knowledge 7.C.4 Photon emission and absorption processes are described by probability.

30.1 Discovery of the Atom

LEARNING OBJECTIVES

By the end of this section, you will be able to:

- Describe the basic structure of the atom, the substructure of all matter.

How do we know that atoms are really there if we cannot see them with our eyes? A brief account of the progression from the proposal of atoms by the Greeks to the first direct evidence of their existence follows.

People have long speculated about the structure of matter and the existence of atoms. The earliest significant ideas to survive are due to the ancient Greeks in the fifth century BCE, especially those of the philosophers Leucippus and Democritus. (There is some evidence that philosophers in both India and China made similar speculations, at about the same time.) They considered the question of whether a substance can be divided without limit into ever smaller pieces. There are only a few possible answers to this question. One is that infinitesimally small subdivision is possible. Another is what Democritus in particular believed—that there is a smallest unit that cannot be further subdivided. Democritus called this the **atom**. We now know that atoms themselves can be subdivided, but their identity is destroyed in the process, so the Greeks were correct in a respect. The Greeks also felt that atoms were in constant motion, another correct notion.

The Greeks and others speculated about the properties of atoms, proposing that only a few types existed and that all matter was formed as various combinations of these types. The famous proposal that the basic elements were earth, air, fire, and water was brilliant, but incorrect. The Greeks had identified the most common examples of the four states of matter (solid, gas, plasma, and liquid), rather than the basic elements. More than 2000 years passed before observations could be made with equipment capable of revealing the true nature of atoms.

Over the centuries, discoveries were made regarding the properties of substances and their chemical reactions. Certain systematic features were recognized, but similarities between common and rare elements resulted in efforts to transmute them (lead into gold, in particular) for financial gain. Secrecy was endemic. Alchemists discovered and rediscovered many facts but did not make them broadly available. As the Middle Ages ended, alchemy gradually faded, and the science of chemistry arose. It was no longer possible, nor considered desirable, to keep discoveries secret. Collective knowledge grew, and by the beginning of the 19th century, an important fact was well established—the masses of reactants in specific chemical reactions always have a particular mass ratio. This is very strong indirect evidence that there are basic units (atoms and molecules) that have these same mass ratios. The English chemist John Dalton (1766–1844) did much of this work, with significant contributions by the Italian physicist Amedeo Avogadro (1776–1856). It was Avogadro who developed the idea of a fixed number of atoms and molecules in a mole, and this special number is called Avogadro's number in his honor. The Austrian physicist Johann Josef Loschmidt was the first to measure the value of the constant in 1865 using the kinetic theory of gases.

PATTERNS AND SYSTEMATICS

The recognition and appreciation of patterns has enabled us to make many discoveries. The periodic table of elements was proposed as an organized summary of the known elements long before all elements had been discovered, and it led to many other discoveries. We shall see in later chapters that patterns in the properties of subatomic particles led to the proposal of quarks as their underlying structure, an idea that is still bearing fruit.

Knowledge of the properties of elements and compounds grew, culminating in the mid-19th-century development of the periodic table of the elements by Dmitri Mendeleev (1834–1907), the great Russian chemist. Mendeleev proposed an ingenious array that highlighted the periodic nature of the properties of elements. Believing in the systematics of the periodic table, he also predicted the existence of then-unknown elements to complete it. Once these elements were discovered and determined to have properties predicted by Mendeleev, his periodic table became universally accepted.

Also during the 19th century, the kinetic theory of gases was developed. Kinetic theory is based on the existence of atoms and molecules in random thermal motion and provides a microscopic explanation of the gas laws, heat transfer, and thermodynamics (see Introduction to Temperature, Kinetic Theory, and the Gas Laws and Introduction to Laws of Thermodynamics). Kinetic theory works so well that it is another strong indication of the existence of atoms. But it is still indirect evidence—individual atoms and molecules had not been observed. There were heated debates about the validity of kinetic theory until direct evidence of atoms was obtained.

The first truly direct evidence of atoms is credited to Robert Brown, a Scottish botanist. In 1827, he noticed that tiny pollen grains suspended in still water moved about in complex paths. This can be observed with a microscope for any small particles in a fluid. The motion is caused by the random thermal motions of fluid molecules colliding with particles in the fluid, and it is now called **Brownian motion**. (See Figure 30.2.) Statistical fluctuations in the numbers of molecules striking the sides of a visible particle cause it to move first this way, then that. Although the molecules cannot be directly observed, their effects on the particle can be. By examining Brownian motion, the size of molecules can be calculated. The smaller and more numerous they are, the smaller the fluctuations in the numbers striking different sides.

FIGURE 30.2 The position of a pollen grain in water, measured every few seconds under a microscope, exhibits Brownian motion. Brownian motion is due to fluctuations in the number of atoms and molecules colliding with a small mass, causing it to move about in complex paths. This is nearly direct evidence for the existence of atoms, providing a satisfactory alternative explanation cannot be found.

It was Albert Einstein who, starting in his epochal year of 1905, published several papers that explained precisely how Brownian motion could be used to measure the size of atoms and molecules. (In 1905 Einstein created special relativity, proposed photons as quanta of EM radiation, and produced a theory of Brownian motion that allowed the size of atoms to be determined. All of this was done in his spare time, since he worked days as a patent examiner. Any one of these very basic works could have been the crowning achievement of an entire career—yet Einstein did even more in later years.) Their sizes were only approximately known to be 10^{-10} m, based on a comparison of latent heat of vaporization and surface tension made in about 1805 by Thomas Young of double-slit fame and the famous astronomer and mathematician Simon Laplace.

Using Einstein's ideas, the French physicist Jean-Baptiste Perrin (1870–1942) carefully observed Brownian motion; not only did he confirm Einstein's theory, he also produced accurate sizes for atoms and molecules. Since molecular weights and densities of materials were well established, knowing atomic and molecular sizes allowed a precise value for Avogadro's number to be obtained. (If we know how big an atom is, we know how many fit into a certain volume.) Perrin also used these ideas to explain atomic and molecular agitation effects in sedimentation, and he received the 1926 Nobel Prize for his achievements. Most scientists were already convinced of the existence of atoms, but the accurate observation and analysis of Brownian motion was conclusive—it was the first truly direct evidence.

A huge array of direct and indirect evidence for the existence of atoms now exists. For example, it has become possible to accelerate ions (much as electrons are accelerated in cathode-ray tubes) and to detect them individually as well as measure their masses (see More Applications of Magnetism for a discussion of mass spectrometers). Other devices that observe individual atoms, such as the scanning tunneling electron microscope, will be discussed elsewhere. (See Figure 30.3.) All of our understanding of the properties of matter is based on and consistent with the atom. The atom's substructures, such as electron shells and the nucleus, are both interesting and important. The nucleus in turn has a substructure, as do the particles of which it is composed. These topics, and the question of whether there is a smallest basic structure to matter, will be explored in later parts of the text.

FIGURE 30.3 Individual atoms can be detected with devices such as the scanning tunneling electron microscope that produced this image of individual gold atoms on a graphite substrate. (credit: Erwin Rossen, Eindhoven University of Technology, via Wikimedia Commons)

30.2 Discovery of the Parts of the Atom: Electrons and Nuclei

LEARNING OBJECTIVES

By the end of this section, you will be able to:

- Describe how electrons were discovered.
- Explain the Millikan oil drop experiment.
- Describe Rutherford's gold foil experiment.
- Describe Rutherford's planetary model of the atom.

Just as atoms are a substructure of matter, electrons and nuclei are substructures of the atom. The experiments that were used to discover electrons and nuclei reveal some of the basic properties of atoms and can be readily understood using ideas such as electrostatic and magnetic force, already covered in previous chapters.

CHARGES AND ELECTROMAGNETIC FORCES

In previous discussions, we have noted that positive charge is associated with nuclei and negative charge with electrons. We have also covered many aspects of the electric and magnetic forces that affect charges. We will now explore the discovery of the electron and nucleus as substructures of the atom and examine their contributions to the properties of atoms.

The Electron

Gas discharge tubes, such as that shown in Figure 30.4, consist of an evacuated glass tube containing two metal electrodes and a rarefied gas. When a high voltage is applied to the electrodes, the gas glows. These tubes were the precursors to today's neon lights. They were first studied seriously by Heinrich Geissler, a German inventor and glassblower, starting in the 1860s. The English scientist William Crookes, among others, continued to study what for some time were called Crookes tubes, wherein electrons are freed from atoms and molecules in the rarefied gas inside the tube and are accelerated from the cathode (negative) to the anode (positive) by the high potential. These "*cathode rays*" collide with the gas atoms and molecules and excite them, resulting in the emission of electromagnetic (EM) radiation that makes the electrons' path visible as a ray that spreads and fades as it moves away from the cathode.

Gas discharge tubes today are most commonly called **cathode-ray tubes**, because the rays originate at the cathode. Crookes showed that the electrons carry momentum (they can make a small paddle wheel rotate). He also found that their normally straight path is bent by a magnet in the direction expected for a negative charge moving away from the cathode. These were the first direct indications of electrons and their charge.

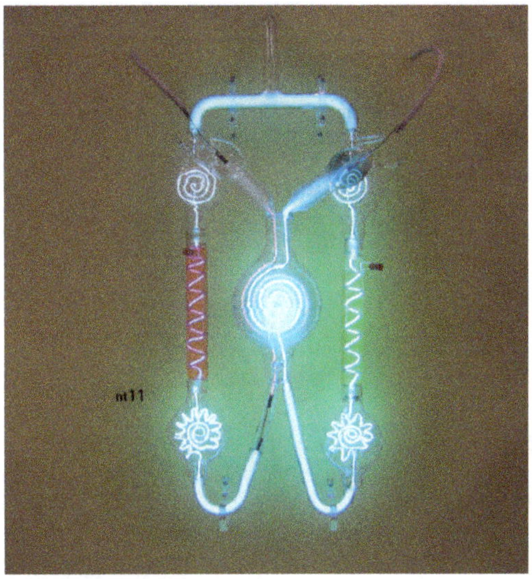

FIGURE 30.4 A gas discharge tube glows when a high voltage is applied to it. Electrons emitted from the cathode are accelerated toward the anode; they excite atoms and molecules in the gas, which glow in response. Once called Geissler tubes and later Crookes tubes, they are now known as cathode-ray tubes (CRTs) and are found in older TVs, computer screens, and x-ray machines. When a magnetic field is applied, the beam bends in the direction expected for negative charge. (credit: Paul Downey, Flickr)

The English physicist J. J. Thomson (1856–1940) improved and expanded the scope of experiments with gas discharge tubes. (See Figure 30.5 and Figure 30.6.) He verified the negative charge of the cathode rays with both magnetic and electric fields. Additionally, he collected the rays in a metal cup and found an excess of negative charge. Thomson was also able to measure the ratio of the charge of the electron to its mass, q_e/m_e—an important step to finding the actual values of both q_e and m_e. Figure 30.7 shows a cathode-ray tube, which produces a narrow beam of electrons that passes through charging plates connected to a high-voltage power supply. An electric field $\mathbf{E}$ is produced between the charging plates, and the cathode-ray tube is placed between the poles of a magnet so that the electric field $\mathbf{E}$ is perpendicular to the magnetic field $\mathbf{B}$ of the magnet. These fields, being perpendicular to each other, produce opposing forces on the electrons. As discussed for mass spectrometers in More Applications of Magnetism, if the net force due to the fields vanishes, then the velocity of the charged particle is $v = E/B$. In this manner, Thomson determined the velocity of the electrons and then moved the beam up and down by adjusting the electric field.

FIGURE 30.5 J. J. Thomson (credit: www.firstworldwar.com, via Wikimedia Commons)

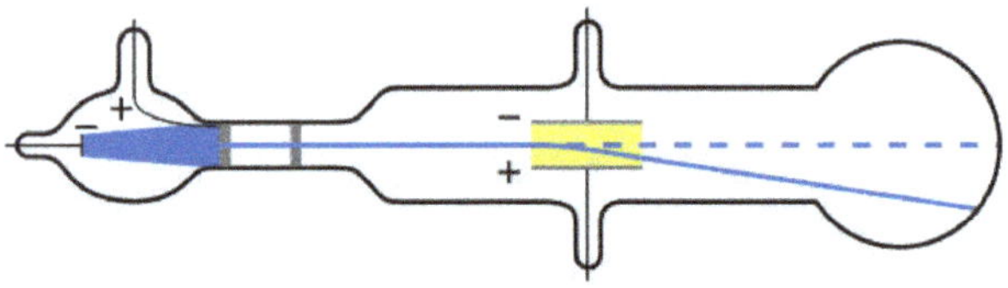

FIGURE 30.6 Diagram of Thomson's CRT. (credit: Kurzon, Wikimedia Commons)

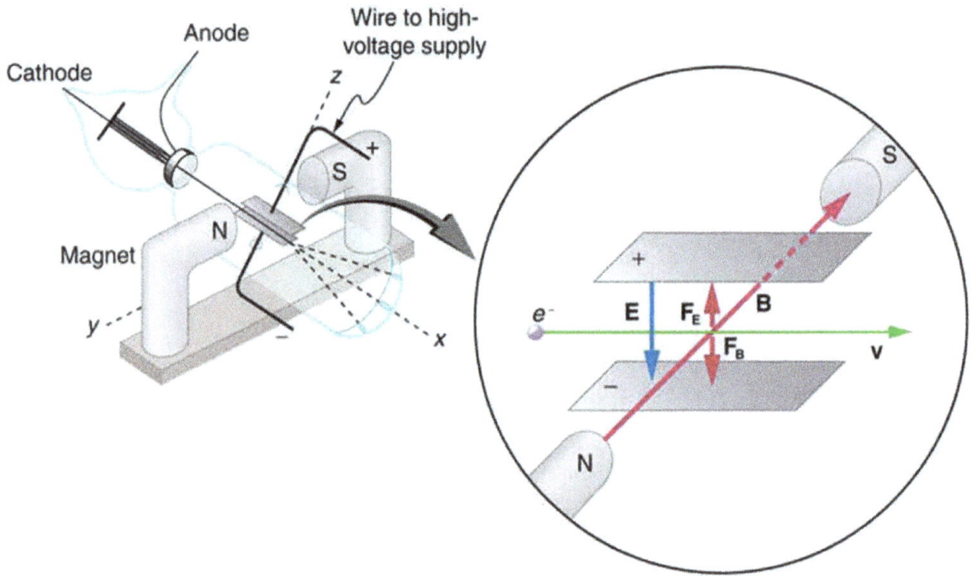

FIGURE 30.7 This schematic shows the electron beam in a CRT passing through crossed electric and magnetic fields and causing phosphor to glow when striking the end of the tube.

To see how the amount of deflection is used to calculate q_e/m_e, note that the deflection is proportional to the electric force on the electron:

$$F = q_e E. \tag{30.1}$$

But the vertical deflection is also related to the electron's mass, since the electron's acceleration is

$$a = \frac{F}{m_e}. \tag{30.2}$$

The value of F is not known, since q_e was not yet known. Substituting the expression for electric force into the expression for acceleration yields

$$a = \frac{F}{m_e} = \frac{q_e E}{m_e}. \quad (30.3)$$

Gathering terms, we have

$$\frac{q_e}{m_e} = \frac{a}{E}. \quad (30.4)$$

The deflection is analyzed to get a, and E is determined from the applied voltage and distance between the plates; thus, $\frac{q_e}{m_e}$ can be determined. With the velocity known, another measurement of $\frac{q_e}{m_e}$ can be obtained by bending the beam of electrons with the magnetic field. Since $F_{\text{mag}} = q_e vB = m_e a$, we have $q_e / m_e = a / vB$. Consistent results are obtained using magnetic deflection.

What is so important about q_e / m_e, the ratio of the electron's charge to its mass? The value obtained is

$$\frac{q_e}{m_e} = -1.76 \times 10^{11} \text{ C/kg (electron)}. \quad (30.5)$$

This is a huge number, as Thomson realized, and it implies that the electron has a very small mass. It was known from electroplating that about 10^8 C/kg is needed to plate a material, a factor of about 1000 less than the charge per kilogram of electrons. Thomson went on to do the same experiment for positively charged hydrogen ions (now known to be bare protons) and found a charge per kilogram about 1000 times smaller than that for the electron, implying that the proton is about 1000 times more massive than the electron. Today, we know more precisely that

$$\frac{q_p}{m_p} = 9.58 \times 10^7 \text{ C/kg (proton)}, \quad (30.6)$$

where q_p is the charge of the proton and m_p is its mass. This ratio (to four significant figures) is 1836 times less charge per kilogram than for the electron. Since the charges of electrons and protons are equal in magnitude, this implies $m_p = 1836 m_e$.

Thomson performed a variety of experiments using differing gases in discharge tubes and employing other methods, such as the photoelectric effect, for freeing electrons from atoms. He always found the same properties for the electron, proving it to be an independent particle. For his work, the important pieces of which he began to publish in 1897, Thomson was awarded the 1906 Nobel Prize in Physics. In retrospect, it is difficult to appreciate how astonishing it was to find that the atom has a substructure. Thomson himself said, "It was only when I was convinced that the experiment left no escape from it that I published my belief in the existence of bodies smaller than atoms."

Thomson attempted to measure the charge of individual electrons, but his method could determine its charge only to the order of magnitude expected.

Since Faraday's experiments with electroplating in the 1830s, it had been known that about 100,000 C per mole was needed to plate singly ionized ions. Dividing this by the number of ions per mole (that is, by Avogadro's number), which was approximately known, the charge per ion was calculated to be about 1.6×10^{-19} C, close to the actual value.

An American physicist, Robert Millikan (1868–1953) (see Figure 30.8), decided to improve upon Thomson's experiment for measuring q_e and was eventually forced to try another approach, which is now a classic experiment performed by students. The Millikan oil drop experiment is shown in Figure 30.9.

FIGURE 30.8 Robert Millikan (credit: Unknown Author, via Wikimedia Commons)

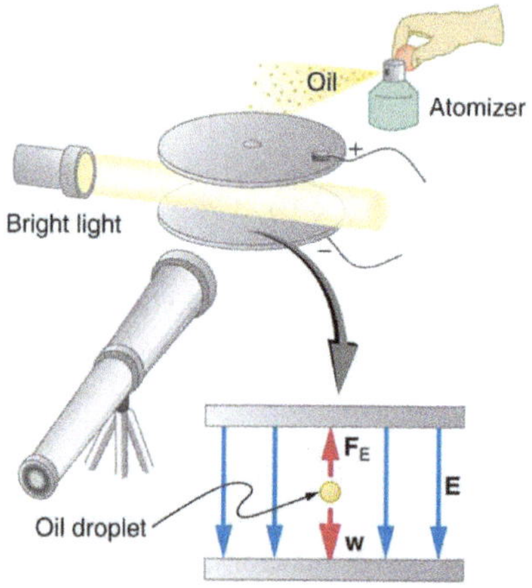

FIGURE 30.9 The Millikan oil drop experiment produced the first accurate direct measurement of the charge on electrons, one of the most fundamental constants in nature. Fine drops of oil become charged when sprayed. Their movement is observed between metal plates with a potential applied to oppose the gravitational force. The balance of gravitational and electric forces allows the calculation of the charge on a drop. The charge is found to be quantized in units of -1.6×10^{-19} C, thus determining directly the charge of the excess and missing electrons on the oil drops.

In the Millikan oil drop experiment, fine drops of oil are sprayed from an atomizer. Some of these are charged by the process and can then be suspended between metal plates by a voltage between the plates. In this situation, the weight of the drop is balanced by the electric force:

$$m_{\text{drop}} g = q_e E \tag{30.7}$$

The electric field is produced by the applied voltage, hence, $E = V/d$, and V is adjusted to just balance the drop's weight. The drops can be seen as points of reflected light using a microscope, but they are too small to directly measure their size and mass. The mass of the drop is determined by observing how fast it falls when the voltage is turned off. Since air resistance is very significant for these submicroscopic drops, the more massive drops fall faster than the less massive, and sophisticated sedimentation calculations can reveal their mass. Oil is used rather than water, because it does not readily evaporate, and so mass is nearly constant. Once the mass of the drop is known, the charge of the electron is given by rearranging the previous equation:

$$q = \frac{m_{\text{drop}} g}{E} = \frac{m_{\text{drop}} g d}{V}, \tag{30.8}$$

where d is the separation of the plates and V is the voltage that holds the drop motionless. (The same drop can be observed for several hours to see that it really is motionless.) By 1913 Millikan had measured the charge of the electron q_e to an accuracy of 1%, and he improved this by a factor of 10 within a few years to a value of -1.60×10^{-19} C. He also observed that all charges were multiples of the basic electron charge and that sudden changes could occur in which electrons were added or removed from the drops. For this very fundamental direct measurement of q_e and for his studies of the photoelectric effect, Millikan was awarded the 1923 Nobel Prize in Physics.

With the charge of the electron known and the charge-to-mass ratio known, the electron's mass can be calculated. It is

$$m = \frac{q_e}{\left(\frac{q_e}{m_e}\right)}. \quad 30.9$$

Substituting known values yields

$$m_e = \frac{-1.60 \times 10^{-19}\ \text{C}}{-1.76 \times 10^{11}\ \text{C/kg}} \quad 30.10$$

or

$$m_e = 9.11 \times 10^{-31}\ \text{kg}\ \ \text{(electron's mass)}, \quad 30.11$$

where the round-off errors have been corrected. The mass of the electron has been verified in many subsequent experiments and is now known to an accuracy of better than one part in one million. It is an incredibly small mass and remains the smallest known mass of any particle that has mass. (Some particles, such as photons, are massless and cannot be brought to rest, but travel at the speed of light.) A similar calculation gives the masses of other particles, including the proton. To three digits, the mass of the proton is now known to be

$$m_p = 1.67 \times 10^{-27}\ \text{kg}\ \ \text{(proton's mass)}, \quad 30.12$$

which is nearly identical to the mass of a hydrogen atom. What Thomson and Millikan had done was to prove the existence of one substructure of atoms, the electron, and further to show that it had only a tiny fraction of the mass of an atom. The nucleus of an atom contains most of its mass, and the nature of the nucleus was completely unanticipated.

Another important characteristic of quantum mechanics was also beginning to emerge. All electrons are identical to one another. The charge and mass of electrons are not average values; rather, they are unique values that all electrons have. This is true of other fundamental entities at the submicroscopic level. All protons are identical to one another, and so on.

The Nucleus

Here, we examine the first direct evidence of the size and mass of the nucleus. In later chapters, we will examine many other aspects of nuclear physics, but the basic information on nuclear size and mass is so important to understanding the atom that we consider it here.

Nuclear radioactivity was discovered in 1896, and it was soon the subject of intense study by a number of the best scientists in the world. Among them was New Zealander Lord Ernest Rutherford, who made numerous fundamental discoveries and earned the title of "father of nuclear physics." Born in Nelson, Rutherford did his postgraduate studies at the Cavendish Laboratories in England before taking up a position at McGill University in Canada where he did the work that earned him a Nobel Prize in Chemistry in 1908. In the area of atomic and nuclear physics, there is much overlap between chemistry and physics, with physics providing the fundamental enabling theories. He returned to England in later years and had six future Nobel Prize winners as students. Rutherford used nuclear radiation to directly examine the size and mass of the atomic nucleus. The experiment he devised is shown in Figure 30.10. A radioactive source that emits alpha radiation was placed in a lead container with a hole in one side to produce a beam of alpha particles, which are a type of ionizing radiation ejected by the nuclei of a radioactive source. A thin gold foil was placed in the beam, and the scattering of the alpha particles was observed by the glow they caused when they struck a phosphor screen.

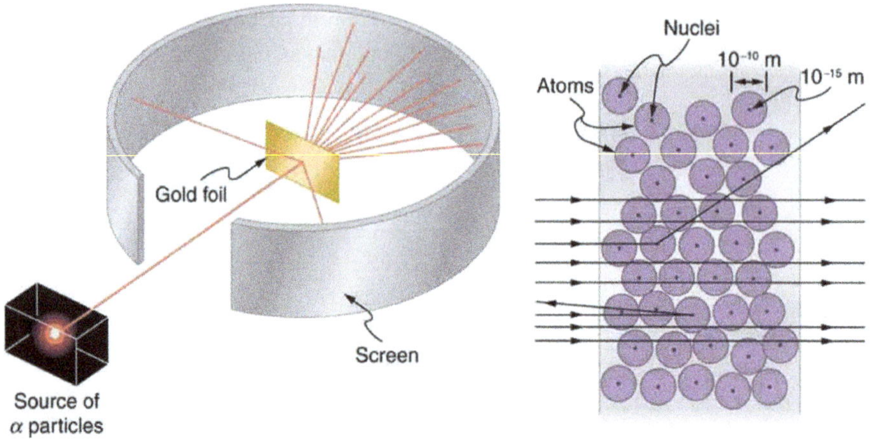

FIGURE 30.10 Rutherford's experiment gave direct evidence for the size and mass of the nucleus by scattering alpha particles from a thin gold foil. Alpha particles with energies of about 5 MeV are emitted from a radioactive source (which is a small metal container in which a specific amount of a radioactive material is sealed), are collimated into a beam, and fall upon the foil. The number of particles that penetrate the foil or scatter to various angles indicates that gold nuclei are very small and contain nearly all of the gold atom's mass. This is particularly indicated by the alpha particles that scatter to very large angles, much like a soccer ball bouncing off a goalie's head.

Alpha particles were known to be the doubly charged positive nuclei of helium atoms that had kinetic energies on the order of 5 MeV when emitted in nuclear decay, which is the disintegration of the nucleus of an unstable nuclide by the spontaneous emission of charged particles. These particles interact with matter mostly via the Coulomb force, and the manner in which they scatter from nuclei can reveal nuclear size and mass. This is analogous to observing how a bowling ball is scattered by an object you cannot see directly. Because the alpha particle's energy is so large compared with the typical energies associated with atoms (MeV versus eV), you would expect the alpha particles to simply crash through a thin foil much like a supersonic bowling ball would crash through a few dozen rows of bowling pins. Thomson had envisioned the atom to be a small sphere in which equal amounts of positive and negative charge were distributed evenly. The incident massive alpha particles would suffer only small deflections in such a model. Instead, Rutherford and his collaborators found that alpha particles occasionally were scattered to large angles, some even back in the direction from which they came! Detailed analysis using conservation of momentum and energy—particularly of the small number that came straight back—implied that gold nuclei are very small compared with the size of a gold atom, contain almost all of the atom's mass, and are tightly bound. Since the gold nucleus is several times more massive than the alpha particle, a head-on collision would scatter the alpha particle straight back toward the source. In addition, the smaller the nucleus, the fewer alpha particles that would hit one head on.

Although the results of the experiment were published by his colleagues in 1909, it took Rutherford two years to convince himself of their meaning. Like Thomson before him, Rutherford was reluctant to accept such radical results. Nature on a small scale is so unlike our classical world that even those at the forefront of discovery are sometimes surprised. Rutherford later wrote: "It was almost as incredible as if you fired a 15-inch shell at a piece of tissue paper and it came back and hit you. On consideration, I realized that this scattering backwards ... [meant] ... the greatest part of the mass of the atom was concentrated in a tiny nucleus." In 1911, Rutherford published his analysis together with a proposed model of the atom. The size of the nucleus was determined to be about 10^{-15} m, or 100,000 times smaller than the atom. This implies a huge density, on the order of 10^{15} g/cm^3, vastly unlike any macroscopic matter. Also implied is the existence of previously unknown nuclear forces to counteract the huge repulsive Coulomb forces among the positive charges in the nucleus. Huge forces would also be consistent with the large energies emitted in nuclear radiation.

The small size of the nucleus also implies that the atom is mostly empty inside. In fact, in Rutherford's experiment, most alphas went straight through the gold foil with very little scattering, since electrons have such small masses and since the atom was mostly empty with nothing for the alpha to hit. There were already hints of this at the time Rutherford performed his experiments, since energetic electrons had been observed to penetrate thin foils more easily than expected. Figure 30.11 shows a schematic of the atoms in a thin foil with circles representing the size of the atoms (about 10^{-10} m) and dots representing the nuclei. (The dots are not to scale—if they were, you would need a microscope to see them.) Most alpha particles miss the small nuclei and are only slightly scattered by electrons. Occasionally, (about once in 8000 times in Rutherford's experiment), an alpha hits a nucleus head-on and is scattered straight backward.

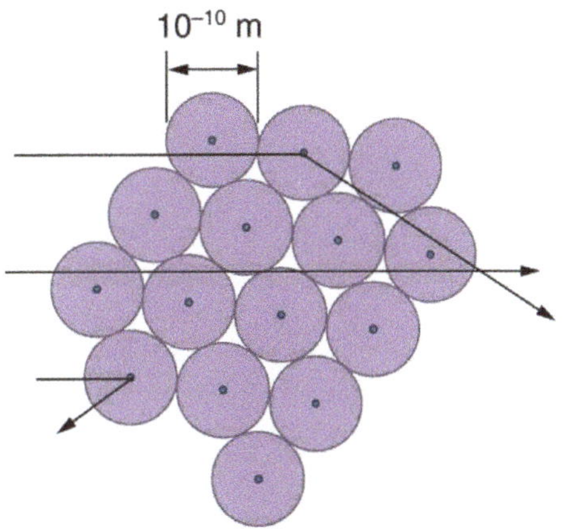

FIGURE 30.11 An expanded view of the atoms in the gold foil in Rutherford's experiment. Circles represent the atoms (about 10^{-10} m in diameter), while the dots represent the nuclei (about 10^{-15} m in diameter). To be visible, the dots are much larger than scale. Most alpha particles crash through but are relatively unaffected because of their high energy and the electron's small mass. Some, however, head straight toward a nucleus and are scattered straight back. A detailed analysis gives the size and mass of the nucleus.

Based on the size and mass of the nucleus revealed by his experiment, as well as the mass of electrons, Rutherford proposed the **planetary model of the atom**. The planetary model of the atom pictures low-mass electrons orbiting a large-mass nucleus. The sizes of the electron orbits are large compared with the size of the nucleus, with mostly vacuum inside the atom. This picture is analogous to how low-mass planets in our solar system orbit the large-mass Sun at distances large compared with the size of the sun. In the atom, the attractive Coulomb force is analogous to gravitation in the planetary system. (See Figure 30.12.) Note that a model or mental picture is needed to explain experimental results, since the atom is too small to be directly observed with visible light.

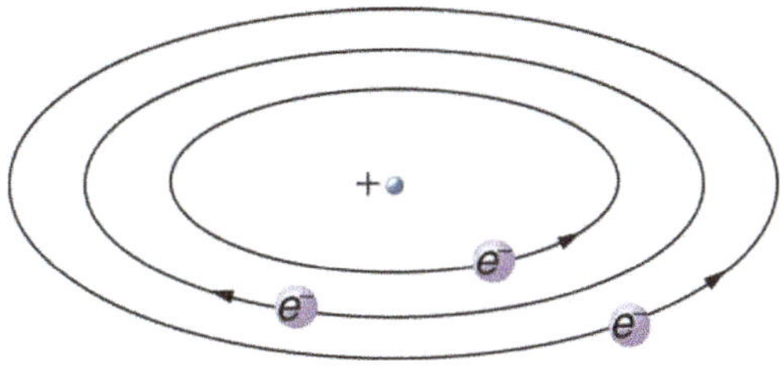

FIGURE 30.12 Rutherford's planetary model of the atom incorporates the characteristics of the nucleus, electrons, and the size of the atom. This model was the first to recognize the structure of atoms, in which low-mass electrons orbit a very small, massive nucleus in orbits much larger than the nucleus. The atom is mostly empty and is analogous to our planetary system.

Rutherford's planetary model of the atom was crucial to understanding the characteristics of atoms, and their interactions and energies, as we shall see in the next few sections. Also, it was an indication of how different nature is from the familiar classical world on the small, quantum mechanical scale. The discovery of a substructure to all matter in the form of atoms and molecules was now being taken a step further to reveal a substructure of atoms that was simpler than the 92 elements then known. We have continued to search for deeper substructures, such as those inside the nucleus, with some success. In later chapters, we will follow this quest in the discussion of quarks and other elementary particles, and we will look at the direction the search seems now to be heading.

PHET EXPLORATIONS

Rutherford Scattering

How did Rutherford figure out the structure of the atom without being able to see it? Simulate the famous experiment in which he disproved the Plum Pudding model of the atom by observing alpha particles bouncing off atoms and determining that they must have a small core.

Click to view content (https://openstax.org/books/college-physics-ap-courses-2e/pages/30-2-discovery-of-the-parts-of-the-atom-electrons-and-nuclei)

30.3 Bohr's Theory of the Hydrogen Atom

LEARNING OBJECTIVES

By the end of this section, you will be able to:

- Describe the mysteries of atomic spectra.
- Explain Bohr's theory of the hydrogen atom.
- Explain Bohr's planetary model of the atom.
- Illustrate energy state using the energy-level diagram.
- Describe the triumphs and limits of Bohr's theory.

The great Danish physicist Niels Bohr (1885–1962) made immediate use of Rutherford's planetary model of the atom. (Figure 30.13). Bohr became convinced of its validity and spent part of 1912 at Rutherford's laboratory. In 1913, after returning to Copenhagen, he began publishing his theory of the simplest atom, hydrogen, based on the planetary model of the atom. For decades, many questions had been asked about atomic characteristics. From their sizes to their spectra, much was known about atoms, but little had been explained in terms of the laws of physics. Bohr's theory explained the atomic spectrum of hydrogen and established new and broadly applicable principles in quantum mechanics.

FIGURE 30.13 Niels Bohr, Danish physicist, used the planetary model of the atom to explain the atomic spectrum and size of the hydrogen atom. His many contributions to the development of atomic physics and quantum mechanics, his personal influence on many students and colleagues, and his personal integrity, especially in the face of Nazi oppression, earned him a prominent place in history. (credit: Unknown Author, via Wikimedia Commons)

Mysteries of Atomic Spectra

As noted in Quantization of Energy , the energies of some small systems are quantized. Atomic and molecular emission and absorption spectra have been known for over a century to be discrete (or quantized). (See Figure 30.14.) Maxwell and others had realized that there must be a connection between the spectrum of an atom and its structure, something like the resonant frequencies of musical instruments. But, in spite of years of efforts by many great minds, no one had a workable theory. (It was a running joke that any theory of atomic and molecular spectra could be destroyed by throwing a book of data at it, so complex were the spectra.) Following Einstein's proposal of photons with quantized energies directly proportional to their wavelengths, it became even more evident that electrons in atoms can exist only in discrete orbits.

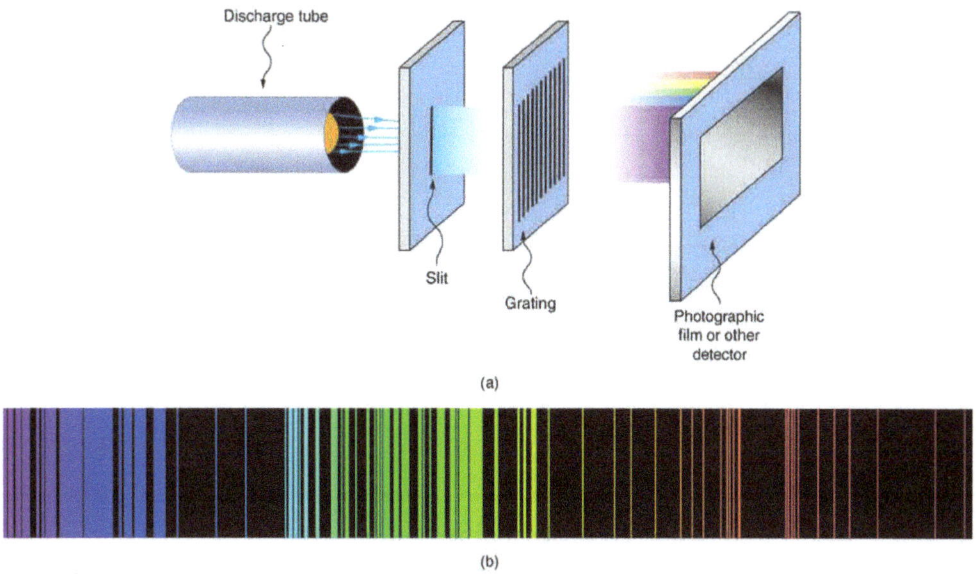

FIGURE 30.14 Part (a) shows, from left to right, a discharge tube, slit, and diffraction grating producing a line spectrum. Part (b) shows the emission line spectrum for iron. The discrete lines imply quantized energy states for the atoms that produce them. The line spectrum for each element is unique, providing a powerful and much used analytical tool, and many line spectra were well known for many years before they could be explained with physics. (credit for (b): Yttrium91, Wikimedia Commons)

In some cases, it had been possible to devise formulas that described the emission spectra. As you might expect, the simplest atom—hydrogen, with its single electron—has a relatively simple spectrum. The hydrogen spectrum had been observed in the infrared (IR), visible, and ultraviolet (UV), and several series of spectral lines had been observed. (See Figure 30.15.) These series are named after early researchers who studied them in particular depth.

The observed **hydrogen-spectrum wavelengths** can be calculated using the following formula:

$$\frac{1}{\lambda} = R\left(\frac{1}{n_\text{f}^2} - \frac{1}{n_\text{i}^2}\right), \quad 30.13$$

where λ is the wavelength of the emitted EM radiation and R is the **Rydberg constant**, determined by the experiment to be

$$R = 1.097 \times 10^7/\text{m (or m}^{-1}). \quad 30.14$$

The constant n_f is a positive integer associated with a specific series. For the Lyman series, $n_\text{f} = 1$; for the Balmer series, $n_\text{f} = 2$; for the Paschen series, $n_\text{f} = 3$; and so on. The Lyman series is entirely in the UV, while part of the Balmer series is visible with the remainder UV. The Paschen series and all the rest are entirely IR. There are apparently an unlimited number of series, although they lie progressively farther into the infrared and become difficult to observe as n_f increases. The constant n_i is a positive integer, but it must be greater than n_f. Thus, for the Balmer series, $n_\text{f} = 2$ and $n_\text{i} = 3, 4, 5, 6, ...$ Note that n_i can approach infinity. While the formula in the wavelengths equation was just a recipe designed to fit data and was not based on physical principles, it did imply a deeper meaning. Balmer first devised the formula for his series alone, and it was later found to describe all the other series by using different values of n_f. Bohr was the first to comprehend the deeper meaning. Again, we see the interplay between experiment and theory in physics. Experimentally, the spectra were well established, an equation was found to fit the experimental data, but the theoretical foundation was missing.

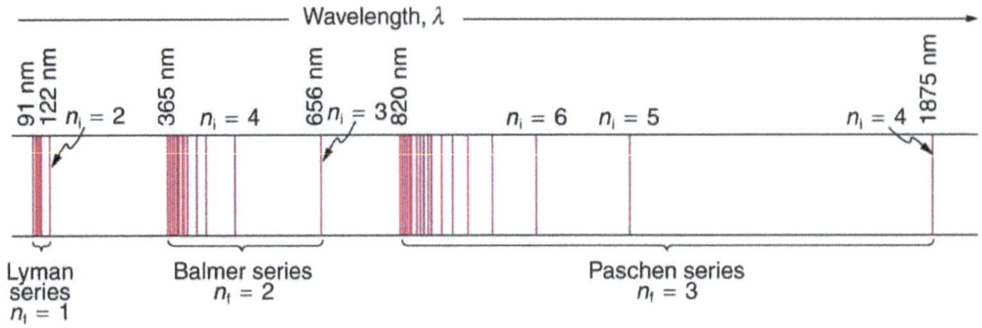

FIGURE 30.15 A schematic of the hydrogen spectrum shows several series named for those who contributed most to their determination. Part of the Balmer series is in the visible spectrum, while the Lyman series is entirely in the UV, and the Paschen series and others are in the IR. Values of n_f and n_i are shown for some of the lines.

EXAMPLE 30.1

Calculating Wave Interference of a Hydrogen Line

What is the distance between the slits of a grating that produces a first-order maximum for the second Balmer line at an angle of 15°?

Strategy and Concept

For an Integrated Concept problem, we must first identify the physical principles involved. In this example, we need to know (a) the wavelength of light as well as (b) conditions for an interference maximum for the pattern from a double slit. Part (a) deals with a topic of the present chapter, while part (b) considers the wave interference material of Wave Optics.

Solution for (a)

Hydrogen spectrum wavelength. The Balmer series requires that $n_f = 2$. The first line in the series is taken to be for $n_i = 3$, and so the second would have $n_i = 4$.

The calculation is a straightforward application of the wavelength equation. Entering the determined values for n_f and n_i yields

$$\begin{aligned}\frac{1}{\lambda} &= R\left(\frac{1}{n_f^2} - \frac{1}{n_i^2}\right) \\ &= \left(1.097 \times 10^7\ \text{m}^{-1}\right)\left(\frac{1}{2^2} - \frac{1}{4^2}\right) \\ &= 2.057 \times 10^6\ \text{m}^{-1}.\end{aligned} \tag{30.15}$$

Inverting to find λ gives

$$\begin{aligned}\lambda &= \frac{1}{2.057\times10^6\ \text{m}^{-1}} = 486 \times 10^{-9}\ \text{m} \\ &= 486\ \text{nm}.\end{aligned} \tag{30.16}$$

Discussion for (a)

This is indeed the experimentally observed wavelength, corresponding to the second (blue-green) line in the Balmer series. More impressive is the fact that the same simple recipe predicts *all* of the hydrogen spectrum lines, including new ones observed in subsequent experiments. What is nature telling us?

Solution for (b)

Double-slit interference (Wave Optics). To obtain constructive interference for a double slit, the path length difference from two slits must be an integral multiple of the wavelength. This condition was expressed by the equation

$$d \sin \theta = m\lambda, \tag{30.17}$$

where d is the distance between slits and θ is the angle from the original direction of the beam. The number m is the order of the interference; $m = 1$ in this example. Solving for d and entering known values yields

$$d = \frac{(1)(486 \text{ nm})}{\sin 15^\circ} = 1.88 \times 10^{-6} \text{ m}. \quad 30.18$$

Discussion for (b)

This number is similar to those used in the interference examples of Introduction to Quantum Physics (and is close to the spacing between slits in commonly used diffraction glasses).

Bohr's Solution for Hydrogen

Bohr was able to derive the formula for the hydrogen spectrum using basic physics, the planetary model of the atom, and some very important new proposals. His first proposal is that only certain orbits are allowed: we say that *the orbits of electrons in atoms are quantized.* Each orbit has a different energy, and electrons can move to a higher orbit by absorbing energy and drop to a lower orbit by emitting energy. If the orbits are quantized, the amount of energy absorbed or emitted is also quantized, producing discrete spectra. Photon absorption and emission are among the primary methods of transferring energy into and out of atoms. The energies of the photons are quantized, and their energy is explained as being equal to the change in energy of the electron when it moves from one orbit to another. In equation form, this is

$$\Delta E = hf = E_{\text{i}} - E_{\text{f}}. \quad 30.19$$

Here, ΔE is the change in energy between the initial and final orbits, and hf is the energy of the absorbed or emitted photon. It is quite logical (that is, expected from our everyday experience) that energy is involved in changing orbits. A blast of energy is required for the space shuttle, for example, to climb to a higher orbit. What is not expected is that atomic orbits should be quantized. This is not observed for satellites or planets, which can have any orbit given the proper energy. (See Figure 30.16.)

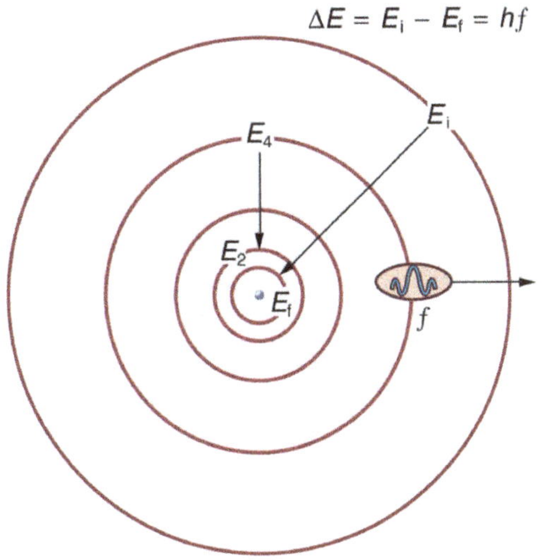

FIGURE 30.16 The planetary model of the atom, as modified by Bohr, has the orbits of the electrons quantized. Only certain orbits are allowed, explaining why atomic spectra are discrete (quantized). The energy carried away from an atom by a photon comes from the electron dropping from one allowed orbit to another and is thus quantized. This is likewise true for atomic absorption of photons.

Figure 30.17 shows an **energy-level diagram**, a convenient way to display energy states. In the present discussion, we take these to be the allowed energy levels of the electron. Energy is plotted vertically with the lowest or ground state at the bottom and with excited states above. Given the energies of the lines in an atomic spectrum, it is possible (although sometimes very difficult) to determine the energy levels of an atom. Energy-level diagrams are used for many systems, including molecules and nuclei. A theory of the atom or any other system must predict its energies based on the physics of the system.

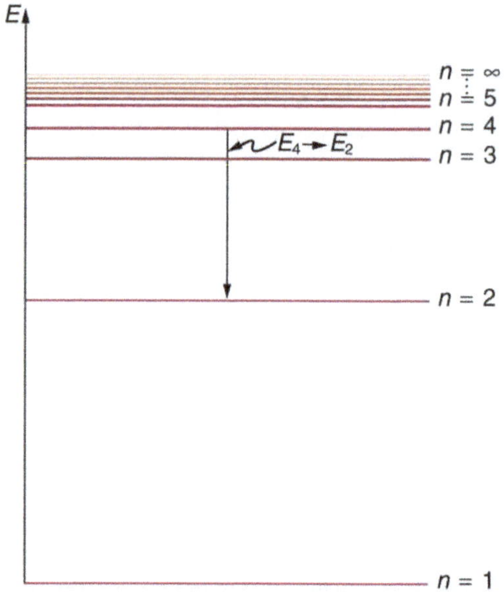

FIGURE 30.17 An energy-level diagram plots energy vertically and is useful in visualizing the energy states of a system and the transitions between them. This diagram is for the hydrogen-atom electrons, showing a transition between two orbits having energies E_4 and E_2.

Bohr was clever enough to find a way to calculate the electron orbital energies in hydrogen. This was an important first step that has been improved upon, but it is well worth repeating here, because it does correctly describe many characteristics of hydrogen. Assuming circular orbits, Bohr proposed that the **angular momentum L of an electron in its orbit is quantized**, that is, it has only specific, discrete values. The value for L is given by the formula

$$L = m_e v r_n = n\frac{h}{2\pi}(n = 1, 2, 3, \ldots), \qquad 30.20$$

where L is the angular momentum, m_e is the electron's mass, r_n is the radius of the n th orbit, and h is Planck's constant. Note that angular momentum is $L = I\omega$. For a small object at a radius r, $I = mr^2$ and $\omega = v/r$, so that $L = \left(mr^2\right)(v/r) = mvr$. Quantization says that this value of mvr can only be equal to $h/2$, $2h/2$, $3h/2$, etc. At the time, Bohr himself did not know why angular momentum should be quantized, but using this assumption he was able to calculate the energies in the hydrogen spectrum, something no one else had done at the time.

From Bohr's assumptions, we will now derive a number of important properties of the hydrogen atom from the classical physics we have covered in the text. We start by noting the centripetal force causing the electron to follow a circular path is supplied by the Coulomb force. To be more general, we note that this analysis is valid for any single-electron atom. So, if a nucleus has Z protons ($Z = 1$ for hydrogen, 2 for helium, etc.) and only one electron, that atom is called a **hydrogen-like atom**. The spectra of hydrogen-like ions are similar to hydrogen, but shifted to higher energy by the greater attractive force between the electron and nucleus. The magnitude of the centripetal force is $m_e v^2/r_n$, while the Coulomb force is $k\left(Zq_e\right)(q_e)/r_n^2$. The tacit assumption here is that the nucleus is more massive than the stationary electron, and the electron orbits about it. This is consistent with the planetary model of the atom. Equating these,

$$k\frac{Zq_e^2}{r_n^2} = \frac{m_e v^2}{r_n} \text{ (Coulomb = centripetal).} \qquad 30.21$$

Angular momentum quantization is stated in an earlier equation. We solve that equation for v, substitute it into the above, and rearrange the expression to obtain the radius of the orbit. This yields:

$$r_n = \frac{n^2}{Z}a_B, \text{ for allowed orbits}(n = 1,2,3, \ldots), \qquad 30.22$$

where a_B is defined to be the **Bohr radius**, since for the lowest orbit ($n = 1$) and for hydrogen ($Z = 1$), $r_1 = a_B$. It is left for this chapter's Problems and Exercises to show that the Bohr radius is

$$a_{\mathrm{B}} = \frac{h^2}{4\pi^2 m_e k q_e^2} = 0.529 \times 10^{-10}\ \mathrm{m}. \tag{30.23}$$

These last two equations can be used to calculate the **radii of the allowed (quantized) electron orbits in any hydrogen-like atom**. It is impressive that the formula gives the correct size of hydrogen, which is measured experimentally to be very close to the Bohr radius. The earlier equation also tells us that the orbital radius is proportional to n^2, as illustrated in Figure 30.18.

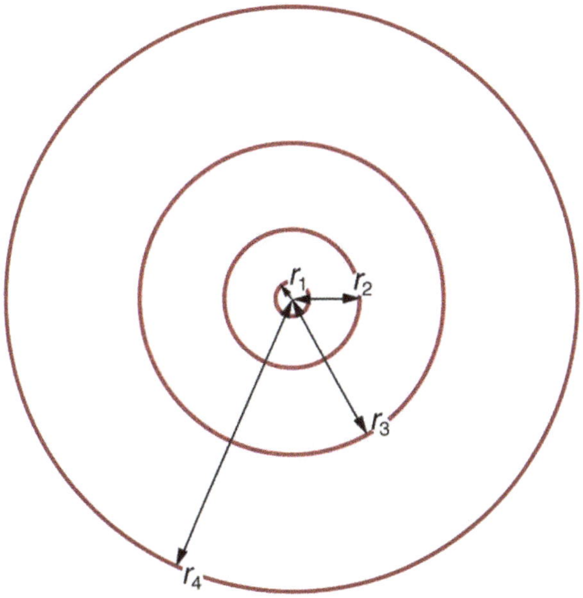

FIGURE 30.18 The allowed electron orbits in hydrogen have the radii shown. These radii were first calculated by Bohr and are given by the equation $r_n = \frac{n^2}{Z} a_{\mathrm{B}}$. The lowest orbit has the experimentally verified diameter of a hydrogen atom.

To get the electron orbital energies, we start by noting that the electron energy is the sum of its kinetic and potential energy:

$$E_n = \mathrm{KE} + \mathrm{PE}. \tag{30.24}$$

Kinetic energy is the familiar $KE = (1/2)m_e v^2$, assuming the electron is not moving at relativistic speeds. Potential energy for the electron is electrical, or $PE = q_e V$, where V is the potential due to the nucleus, which looks like a point charge. The nucleus has a positive charge Zq_e ; thus, $V = kZq_e/r_n$, recalling an earlier equation for the potential due to a point charge. Since the electron's charge is negative, we see that $PE = -kZq_e/r_n$. Entering the expressions for KE and PE, we find

$$E_n = \frac{1}{2} m_e v^2 - k\frac{Zq_e^2}{r_n}. \tag{30.25}$$

Now we substitute r_n and v from earlier equations into the above expression for energy. Algebraic manipulation yields

$$E_n = -\frac{Z^2}{n^2} E_0 (n = 1, 2, 3, ...) \tag{30.26}$$

for the orbital **energies of hydrogen-like atoms**. Here, E_0 is the **ground-state energy** $(n = 1)$ for hydrogen $(Z = 1)$ and is given by

$$E_0 = \frac{2\pi^2 q_e^4 m_e k^2}{h^2} = 13.6\ \mathrm{eV}. \tag{30.27}$$

Thus, for hydrogen,

$$E_n = -\frac{13.6\ \mathrm{eV}}{n^2} (n = 1, 2, 3, ...). \tag{30.28}$$

Figure 30.19 shows an energy-level diagram for hydrogen that also illustrates how the various spectral series for hydrogen are related to transitions between energy levels.

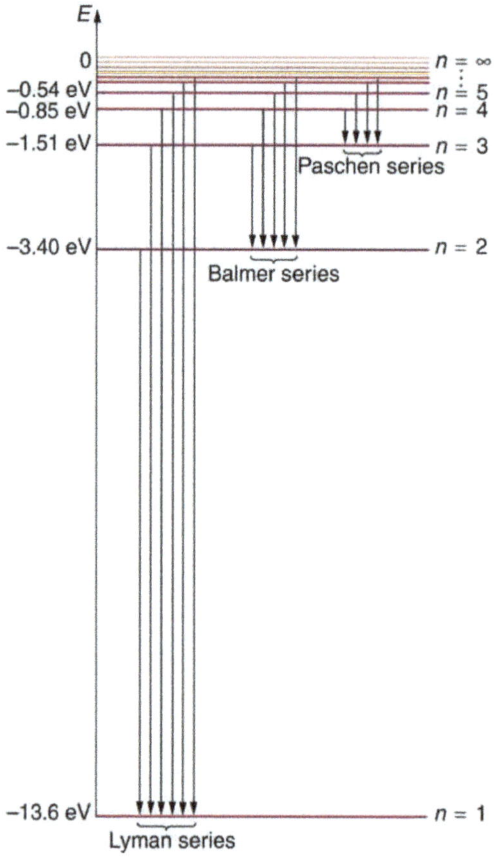

FIGURE 30.19 Energy-level diagram for hydrogen showing the Lyman, Balmer, and Paschen series of transitions. The orbital energies are calculated using the above equation, first derived by Bohr.

Electron total energies are negative, since the electron is bound to the nucleus, analogous to being in a hole without enough kinetic energy to escape. As n approaches infinity, the total energy becomes zero. This corresponds to a free electron with no kinetic energy, since r_n gets very large for large n, and the electric potential energy thus becomes zero. Thus, 13.6 eV is needed to ionize hydrogen (to go from −13.6 eV to 0, or unbound), an experimentally verified number. Given more energy, the electron becomes unbound with some kinetic energy. For example, giving 15.0 eV to an electron in the ground state of hydrogen strips it from the atom and leaves it with 1.4 eV of kinetic energy.

Finally, let us consider the energy of a photon emitted in a downward transition, given by the equation to be

$$\Delta E = hf = E_{\text{i}} - E_{\text{f}}. \tag{30.29}$$

Substituting $E_n = (-13.6\ \text{eV}/n^2)$, we see that

$$hf = (13.6\ \text{eV})\left(\frac{1}{n_{\text{f}}^2} - \frac{1}{n_{\text{i}}^2}\right). \tag{30.30}$$

Dividing both sides of this equation by hc gives an expression for $1/\lambda$:

$$\frac{hf}{hc} = \frac{f}{c} = \frac{1}{\lambda} = \frac{(13.6\ \text{eV})}{hc}\left(\frac{1}{n_{\text{f}}^2} - \frac{1}{n_{\text{i}}^2}\right). \tag{30.31}$$

It can be shown that

$$\left(\frac{13.6\ \text{eV}}{hc}\right) = \frac{(13.6\ \text{eV})\left(1.602 \times 10^{-19}\ \text{J/eV}\right)}{\left(6.626 \times 10^{-34}\ \text{J·s}\right)\left(2.998 \times 10^{8}\ \text{m/s}\right)} = 1.097 \times 10^{7}\ \text{m}^{-1} = R \tag{30.32}$$

is the **Rydberg constant**. Thus, we have used Bohr's assumptions to derive the formula first proposed by Balmer years earlier as a recipe to fit experimental data.

$$\frac{1}{\lambda} = R\left(\frac{1}{n_\mathrm{f}^2} - \frac{1}{n_\mathrm{i}^2}\right) \tag{30.33}$$

We see that Bohr's theory of the hydrogen atom answers the question as to why this previously known formula describes the hydrogen spectrum. It is because the energy levels are proportional to $1/n^2$, where n is a non-negative integer. A downward transition releases energy, and so n_i must be greater than n_f. The various series are those where the transitions end on a certain level. For the Lyman series, $n_\mathrm{f} = 1$ – that is, all the transitions end in the ground state (see also Figure 30.19). For the Balmer series, $n_\mathrm{f} = 2$, or all the transitions end in the first excited state; and so on. What was once a recipe is now based in physics, and something new is emerging—angular momentum is quantized.

Triumphs and Limits of the Bohr Theory

Bohr did what no one had been able to do before. Not only did he explain the spectrum of hydrogen, he correctly calculated the size of the atom from basic physics. Some of his ideas are broadly applicable. Electron orbital energies are quantized in all atoms and molecules. Angular momentum is quantized. The electrons do not spiral into the nucleus, as expected classically (accelerated charges radiate, so that the electron orbits classically would decay quickly, and the electrons would sit on the nucleus—matter would collapse). These are major triumphs.

But there are limits to Bohr's theory. It cannot be applied to multielectron atoms, even one as simple as a two-electron helium atom. Bohr's model is what we call *semiclassical*. The orbits are quantized (nonclassical) but are assumed to be simple circular paths (classical). As quantum mechanics was developed, it became clear that there are no well-defined orbits; rather, there are clouds of probability. Bohr's theory also did not explain that some spectral lines are doublets (split into two) when examined closely. We shall examine many of these aspects of quantum mechanics in more detail, but it should be kept in mind that Bohr did not fail. Rather, he made very important steps along the path to greater knowledge and laid the foundation for all of atomic physics that has since evolved.

PHET EXPLORATIONS

Models of the Hydrogen Atom

How did scientists figure out the structure of atoms without looking at them? Try out different models by shooting light at the atom. Check how the prediction of the model matches the experimental results.

Click to view content (https://openstax.org/l/28atom_model).

30.4 X Rays: Atomic Origins and Applications

LEARNING OBJECTIVES

By the end of this section, you will be able to:

- Define x-ray tube and its spectrum.
- Show the x-ray characteristic energy.
- Specify the use of x rays in medical observations.
- Explain the use of x rays in CT scanners in diagnostics.

Each type of atom (or element) has its own characteristic electromagnetic spectrum. **X rays** lie at the high-frequency end of an atom's spectrum and are characteristic of the atom as well. In this section, we explore characteristic x rays and some of their important applications.

We have previously discussed x rays as a part of the electromagnetic spectrum in Photon Energies and the Electromagnetic Spectrum. That module illustrated how an x-ray tube (a specialized CRT) produces x rays. Electrons emitted from a hot filament are accelerated with a high voltage, gaining significant kinetic energy and striking the anode.

There are two processes by which x rays are produced in the anode of an x-ray tube. In one process, the deceleration of electrons produces x rays, and these x rays are called *bremsstrahlung*, or braking radiation. The second process is atomic in nature and produces *characteristic x rays*, so called because they are characteristic of the anode material. The x-ray spectrum in Figure 30.20 is typical of what is produced by an x-ray tube, showing a broad curve of bremsstrahlung radiation with characteristic x-ray peaks on it.

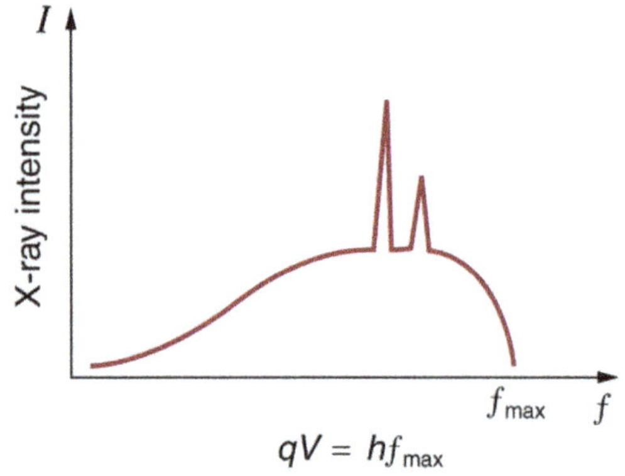

FIGURE 30.20 X-ray spectrum obtained when energetic electrons strike a material, such as in the anode of a CRT. The smooth part of the spectrum is bremsstrahlung radiation, while the peaks are characteristic of the anode material. A different anode material would have characteristic x-ray peaks at different frequencies.

The spectrum in Figure 30.20 is collected over a period of time in which many electrons strike the anode, with a variety of possible outcomes for each hit. The broad range of x-ray energies in the bremsstrahlung radiation indicates that an incident electron's energy is not usually converted entirely into photon energy. The highest-energy x ray produced is one for which all of the electron's energy was converted to photon energy. Thus the accelerating voltage and the maximum x-ray energy are related by conservation of energy. Electric potential energy is converted to kinetic energy and then to photon energy, so that $E_{\text{max}} = hf_{\text{max}} = q_e V$. Units of electron volts are convenient. For example, a 100-kV accelerating voltage produces x-ray photons with a maximum energy of 100 keV.

Some electrons excite atoms in the anode. Part of the energy that they deposit by collision with an atom results in one or more of the atom's inner electrons being knocked into a higher orbit or the atom being ionized. When the anode's atoms de-excite, they emit characteristic electromagnetic radiation. The most energetic of these are produced when an inner-shell vacancy is filled—that is, when an $n = 1$ or $n = 2$ shell electron has been excited to a higher level, and another electron falls into the vacant spot. A *characteristic x ray* (see Photon Energies and the Electromagnetic Spectrum) is electromagnetic (EM) radiation emitted by an atom when an inner-shell vacancy is filled. Figure 30.21 shows a representative energy-level diagram that illustrates the labeling of characteristic x rays. X rays created when an electron falls into an $n = 1$ shell vacancy are called K_α when they come from the next higher level; that is, an $n = 2$ to $n = 1$ transition. The labels $K, L, M, \ldots$ come from the older alphabetical labeling of shells starting with K rather than using the principal quantum numbers 1, 2, 3, ... A more energetic K_β x ray is produced when an electron falls into an $n = 1$ shell vacancy from the $n = 3$ shell; that is, an $n = 3$ to $n = 1$ transition. Similarly, when an electron falls into the $n = 2$ shell from the $n = 3$ shell, an L_α x ray is created. The energies of these x rays depend on the energies of electron states in the particular atom and, thus, are characteristic of that element: every element has it own set of x-ray energies. This property can be used to identify elements, for example, to find trace (small) amounts of an element in an environmental or biological sample.

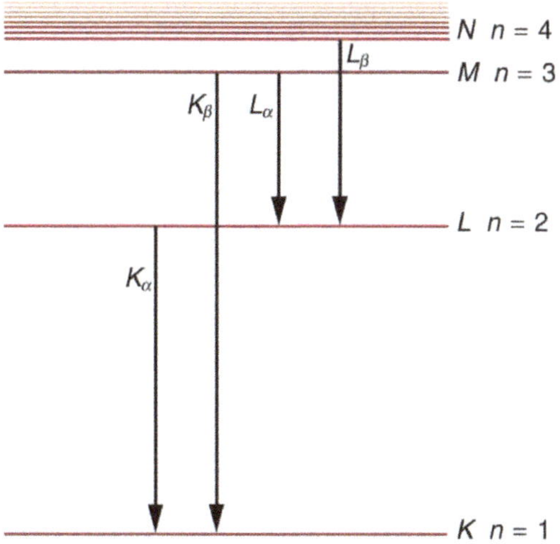

FIGURE 30.21 A characteristic x ray is emitted when an electron fills an inner-shell vacancy, as shown for several transitions in this approximate energy level diagram for a multiple-electron atom. Characteristic x rays are labeled according to the shell that had the vacancy and the shell from which the electron came. A K_α x ray, for example, is produced when an electron coming from the $n = 2$ shell fills the $n = 1$ shell vacancy.

EXAMPLE 30.2

Characteristic X-Ray Energy

Calculate the approximate energy of a K_α x ray from a tungsten anode in an x-ray tube.

Strategy

How do we calculate energies in a multiple-electron atom? In the case of characteristic x rays, the following approximate calculation is reasonable. Characteristic x rays are produced when an inner-shell vacancy is filled. Inner-shell electrons are nearer the nucleus than others in an atom and thus feel little net effect from the others. This is similar to what happens inside a charged conductor, where its excess charge is distributed over the surface so that it produces no electric field inside. It is reasonable to assume the inner-shell electrons have hydrogen-like energies, as given by $E_n = -\frac{Z^2}{n^2}E_0(n = 1, 2, 3, ...)$. As noted, a K_α x ray is produced by an $n = 2$ to $n = 1$ transition. Since there are two electrons in a filled K shell, a vacancy would leave one electron, so that the effective charge would be $Z - 1$ rather than Z. For tungsten, $Z = 74$, so that the effective charge is 73.

Solution

$E_n = -\frac{Z^2}{n^2}E_0(n = 1, 2, 3, ...)$ gives the orbital energies for hydrogen-like atoms to be $E_n = -(Z^2/n^2)E_0$, where $E_0 = 13.6 \text{ eV}$. As noted, the effective Z is 73. Now the K_α x-ray energy is given by

$$E_{K_\alpha} = \Delta E = E_\text{i} - E_\text{f} = E_2 - E_1, \tag{30.34}$$

where

$$E_1 = -\frac{Z^2}{1^2}E_0 = -\frac{73^2}{1}\left(13.6 \text{ eV}\right) = -72.5 \text{ keV} \tag{30.35}$$

and

$$E_2 = -\frac{Z^2}{2^2}E_0 = -\frac{73^2}{4}\left(13.6 \text{ eV}\right) = -18.1 \text{ keV}. \tag{30.36}$$

Thus,

$$E_{K_\alpha} = -18.1 \text{ keV} - \left(-72.5 \text{ keV}\right) = 54.4 \text{ keV}. \tag{30.37}$$

Discussion

This large photon energy is typical of characteristic x rays from heavy elements. It is large compared with other atomic emissions because it is produced when an inner-shell vacancy is filled, and inner-shell electrons are tightly bound. Characteristic x ray energies become progressively larger for heavier elements because their energy increases approximately as Z^2. Significant accelerating voltage is needed to create these inner-shell vacancies. In the case of tungsten, at least 72.5 kV is needed, because other shells are filled and you cannot simply bump one electron to a higher filled shell. Tungsten is a common anode material in x-ray tubes; so much of the energy of the impinging electrons is absorbed, raising its temperature, that a high-melting-point material like tungsten is required.

Medical and Other Diagnostic Uses of X-rays

All of us can identify diagnostic uses of x-ray photons. Among these are the universal dental and medical x rays that have become an essential part of medical diagnostics. (See Figure 30.23 and Figure 30.24.) X rays are also used to inspect our luggage at airports, as shown in Figure 30.22, and for early detection of cracks in crucial aircraft components. An x ray is not only a noun meaning high-energy photon, it also is an image produced by x rays, and it has been made into a familiar verb—to be x-rayed.

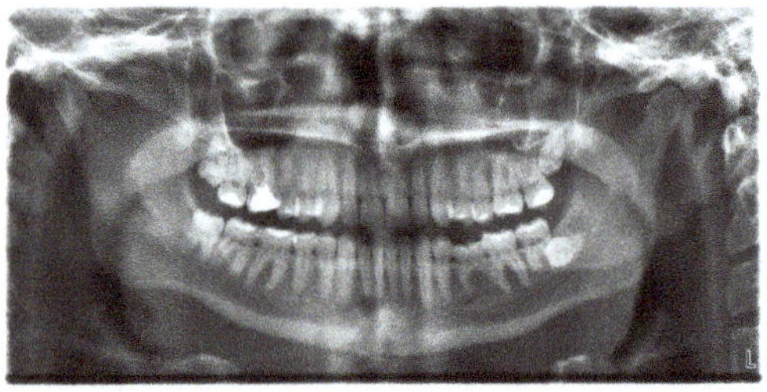

FIGURE 30.22 An x-ray image reveals fillings in a person's teeth. (credit: Dmitry G, Wikimedia Commons)

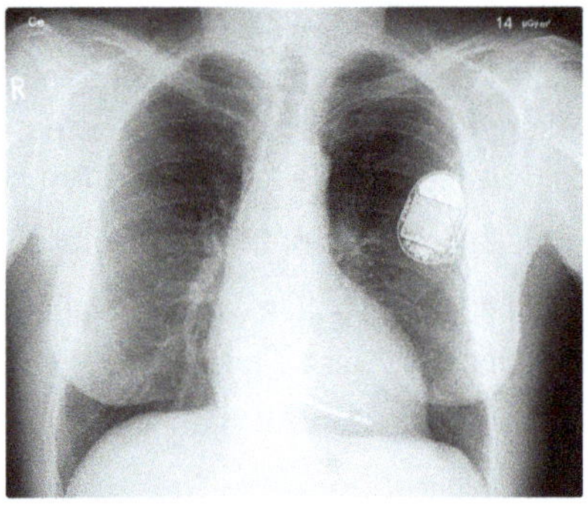

FIGURE 30.23 This x-ray image of a person's chest shows many details, including an artificial pacemaker. (credit: Sunzi99, Wikimedia Commons)

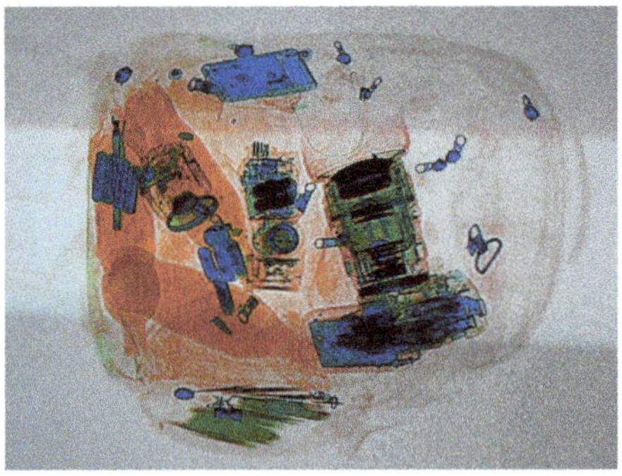

FIGURE 30.24 This x-ray image shows the contents of a piece of luggage. The denser the material, the darker the shadow. (credit: IDuke, Wikimedia Commons)

The most common x-ray images are simple shadows. Since x-ray photons have high energies, they penetrate materials that are opaque to visible light. The more energy an x-ray photon has, the more material it will penetrate. So an x-ray tube may be operated at 50.0 kV for a chest x ray, whereas it may need to be operated at 100 kV to examine a broken leg in a cast. The depth of penetration is related to the density of the material as well as to the energy of the photon. The denser the material, the fewer x-ray photons get through and the darker the shadow. Thus x rays excel at detecting breaks in bones and in imaging other physiological structures, such as some tumors, that differ in density from surrounding material. Because of their high photon energy, x rays produce significant ionization in materials and damage cells in biological organisms. Modern uses minimize exposure to the patient and eliminate exposure to others. Biological effects of x rays will be explored in the next chapter along with other types of ionizing radiation such as those produced by nuclei.

As the x-ray energy increases, the Compton effect (see Photon Momentum) becomes more important in the attenuation of the x rays. Here, the x ray scatters from an outer electron shell of the atom, giving the ejected electron some kinetic energy while losing energy itself. The probability for attenuation of the x rays depends upon the number of electrons present (the material's density) as well as the thickness of the material. Chemical composition of the medium, as characterized by its atomic number Z, is not important here. Low-energy x rays provide better contrast (sharper images). However, due to greater attenuation and less scattering, they are more absorbed by thicker materials. Greater contrast can be achieved by injecting a substance with a large atomic number, such as barium or iodine. The structure of the part of the body that contains the substance (e.g., the gastro-intestinal tract or the abdomen) can easily be seen this way.

Breast cancer is the second-leading cause of death among women worldwide. Early detection can be very effective, hence the importance of x-ray diagnostics. A mammogram cannot diagnose a malignant tumor, only give evidence of a lump or region of increased density within the breast. X-ray absorption by different types of soft tissue is very similar, so contrast is difficult; this is especially true for younger women, who typically have denser breasts. For older women who are at greater risk of developing breast cancer, the presence of more fat in the breast gives the lump or tumor more contrast. MRI (Magnetic resonance imaging) has recently been used as a supplement to conventional x rays to improve detection and eliminate false positives. The subject's radiation dose from x rays will be treated in a later chapter.

A standard x ray gives only a two-dimensional view of the object. Dense bones might hide images of soft tissue or organs. If you took another x ray from the side of the person (the first one being from the front), you would gain additional information. While shadow images are sufficient in many applications, far more sophisticated images can be produced with modern technology. Figure 30.25 shows the use of a computed tomography (CT) scanner, also called computed axial tomography (CAT) scanner. X rays are passed through a narrow section (called a slice) of the patient's body (or body part) over a range of directions. An array of many detectors on the other side of the patient registers the x rays. The system is then rotated around the patient and another image is taken, and so on. The x-ray tube and detector array are mechanically attached and so rotate together. Complex computer image processing of the relative absorption of the x rays along different directions produces a highly-detailed image. Different slices are taken as the patient moves through the scanner on a table. Multiple images of different slices can also be computer analyzed to produce three-dimensional information, sometimes enhancing specific types of tissue, as shown in Figure 30.26. G. Hounsfield (UK) and A. Cormack (US) won the Nobel Prize in Medicine in 1979 for their development of computed tomography.

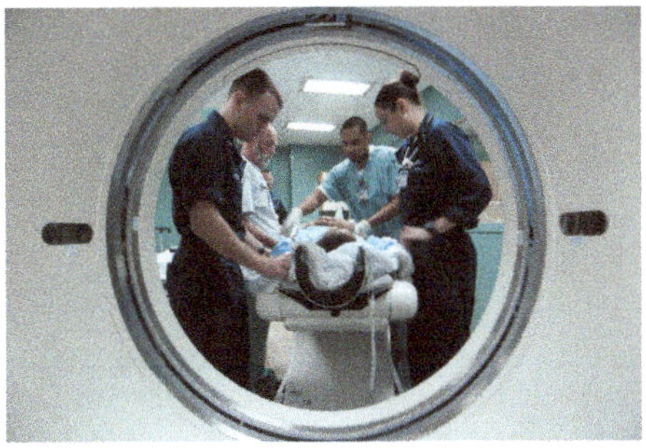

FIGURE 30.25 A patient being positioned in a CT scanner aboard the hospital ship USNS Mercy. The CT scanner passes x rays through slices of the patient's body (or body part) over a range of directions. The relative absorption of the x rays along different directions is computer analyzed to produce highly detailed images. Three-dimensional information can be obtained from multiple slices. (credit: Rebecca Moat, U.S. Navy)

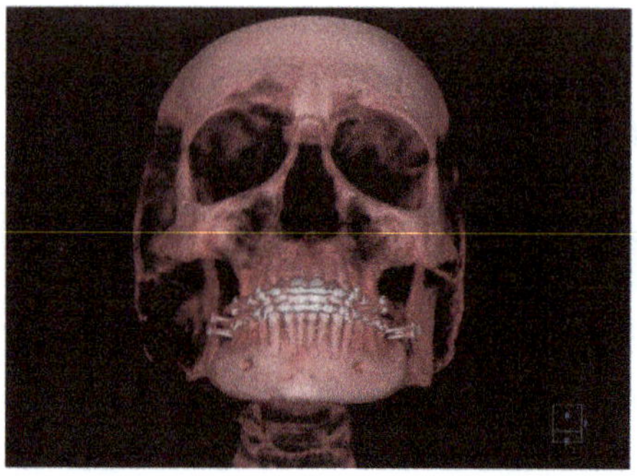

FIGURE 30.26 This three-dimensional image of a skull was produced by computed tomography, involving analysis of several x-ray slices of the head. (credit: Emailshankar, Wikimedia Commons)

X-Ray Diffraction and Crystallography

Since x-ray photons are very energetic, they have relatively short wavelengths. For example, the 54.4-keV K_α x ray of Example 30.2 has a wavelength $\lambda = hc/E = 0.0228 \text{ nm}$. Thus, typical x-ray photons act like rays when they encounter macroscopic objects, like teeth, and produce sharp shadows; however, since atoms are on the order of 0.1 nm in size, x rays can be used to detect the location, shape, and size of atoms and molecules. The process is called **x-ray diffraction**, because it involves the diffraction and interference of x rays to produce patterns that can be analyzed for information about the structures that scattered the x rays. Perhaps the most famous example of x-ray diffraction is the discovery of the double-helix structure of DNA in 1953 by an international team of scientists working at the Cavendish Laboratory—American James Watson, Englishman Francis Crick, and New Zealand–born Maurice Wilkins. Using x-ray diffraction data produced by Rosalind Franklin, they were the first to discern the structure of DNA that is so crucial to life. For this, Watson, Crick, and Wilkins were awarded the 1962 Nobel Prize in Physiology or Medicine. There is much debate and controversy over the issue that Rosalind Franklin was not included in the prize.

Figure 30.27 shows a diffraction pattern produced by the scattering of x rays from a crystal. This process is known as x-ray crystallography because of the information it can yield about crystal structure, and it was the type of data Rosalind Franklin supplied to Watson and Crick for DNA. Not only do x rays confirm the size and shape of atoms, they give information on the atomic arrangements in materials. For example, current research in high-temperature superconductors involves complex materials whose lattice arrangements are crucial to obtaining a superconducting material. These can be studied using x-ray crystallography.

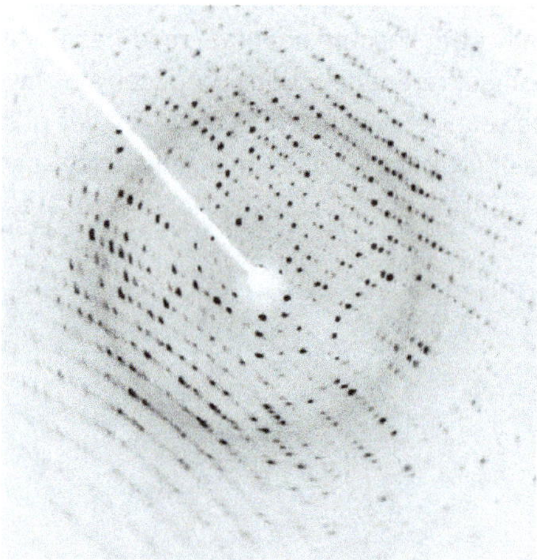

FIGURE 30.27 X-ray diffraction from the crystal of a protein, hen egg lysozyme, produced this interference pattern. Analysis of the pattern yields information about the structure of the protein. (credit: Del45, Wikimedia Commons)

Historically, the scattering of x rays from crystals was used to prove that x rays are energetic EM waves. This was suspected from the time of the discovery of x rays in 1895, but it was not until 1912 that the German Max von Laue (1879–1960) convinced two of his colleagues to scatter x rays from crystals. If a diffraction pattern is obtained, he reasoned, then the x rays must be waves, and their wavelength could be determined. (The spacing of atoms in various crystals was reasonably well known at the time, based on good values for Avogadro's number.) The experiments were convincing, and the 1914 Nobel Prize in Physics was given to von Laue for his suggestion leading to the proof that x rays are EM waves. In 1915, the unique father-and-son team of Sir William Henry Bragg and his son Sir William Lawrence Bragg were awarded a joint Nobel Prize for inventing the x-ray spectrometer and the then-new science of x-ray analysis. The elder Bragg had migrated to Australia from England just after graduating in mathematics. He learned physics and chemistry during his career at the University of Adelaide. The younger Bragg was born in Adelaide but went back to the Cavendish Laboratories in England to a career in x-ray and neutron crystallography; he provided support for Watson, Crick, and Wilkins for their work on unraveling the mysteries of DNA and to Max Perutz for his 1962 Nobel Prize-winning work on the structure of hemoglobin. Here again, we witness the enabling nature of physics—establishing instruments and designing experiments as well as solving mysteries in the biomedical sciences.

Certain other uses for x rays will be studied in later chapters. X rays are useful in the treatment of cancer because of the inhibiting effect they have on cell reproduction. X rays observed coming from outer space are useful in determining the nature of their sources, such as neutron stars and possibly black holes. Created in nuclear bomb explosions, x rays can also be used to detect clandestine atmospheric tests of these weapons. X rays can cause excitations of atoms, which then fluoresce (emitting characteristic EM radiation), making x-ray-induced fluorescence a valuable analytical tool in a range of fields from art to archaeology.

30.5 Applications of Atomic Excitations and De-Excitations

LEARNING OBJECTIVES

By the end of this section, you will be able to:

- Define and discuss fluorescence.
- Define metastable.
- Describe how laser emission is produced.
- Explain population inversion.
- Define and discuss holography.

Many properties of matter and phenomena in nature are directly related to atomic energy levels and their associated excitations and de-excitations. The color of a rose, the output of a laser, and the transparency of air are but a few examples. (See Figure 30.28.) While it may not appear that glow-in-the-dark pajamas and lasers have much in common, they are in fact different applications of similar atomic de-excitations.

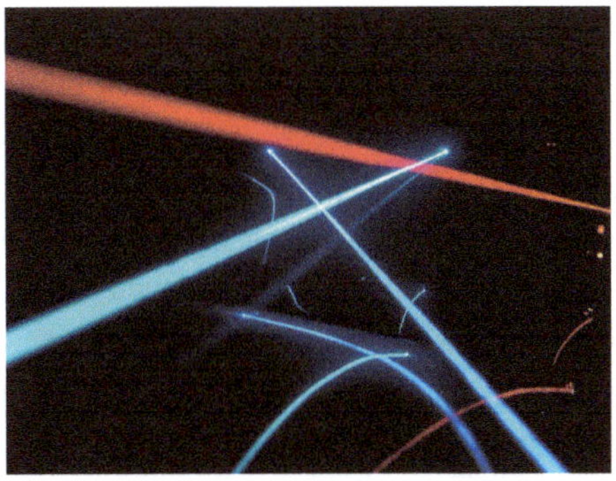

FIGURE 30.28 Light from a laser is based on a particular type of atomic de-excitation. (credit: Jeff Keyzer)

The color of a material is due to the ability of its atoms to absorb certain wavelengths while reflecting or reemitting others. A simple red material, for example a tomato, absorbs all visible wavelengths except red. This is because the atoms of its hydrocarbon pigment (lycopene) have levels separated by a variety of energies corresponding to all visible photon energies except red. Air is another interesting example. It is transparent to visible light, because there are few energy levels that visible photons can excite in air molecules and atoms. Visible light, thus, cannot be absorbed. Furthermore, visible light is only weakly scattered by air, because visible wavelengths are so much greater than the sizes of the air molecules and atoms. Light must pass through kilometers of air to scatter enough to cause red sunsets and blue skies.

Fluorescence and Phosphorescence

The ability of a material to emit various wavelengths of light is similarly related to its atomic energy levels. Figure

30.29 shows a scorpion illuminated by a UV lamp, sometimes called a black light. Some rocks also glow in black light, the particular colors being a function of the rock's mineral composition. Black lights are also used to make certain posters glow.

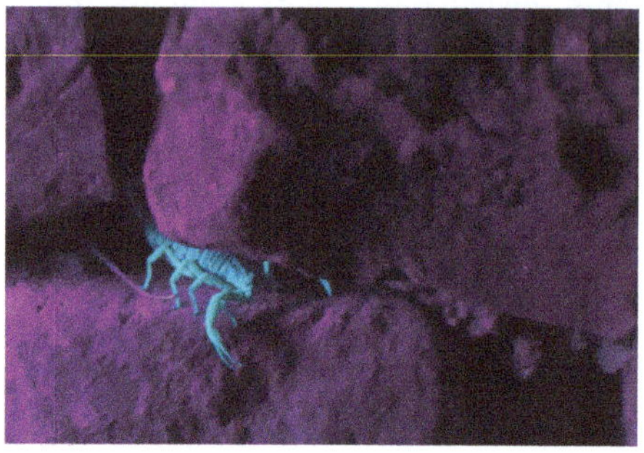

FIGURE 30.29 Objects glow in the visible spectrum when illuminated by an ultraviolet (black) light. Emissions are characteristic of the mineral involved, since they are related to its energy levels. In the case of scorpions, proteins near the surface of their skin give off the characteristic blue glow. This is a colorful example of fluorescence in which excitation is induced by UV radiation while de-excitation occurs in the form of visible light. (credit: Ken Bosma, Flickr)

In the fluorescence process, an atom is excited to a level several steps above its ground state by the absorption of a relatively high-energy UV photon. This is called **atomic excitation**. Once it is excited, the atom can de-excite in several ways, one of which is to re-emit a photon of the same energy as excited it, a single step back to the ground state. This is called **atomic de-excitation**. All other paths of de-excitation involve smaller steps, in which lower-energy (longer wavelength) photons are emitted. Some of these may be in the visible range, such as for the scorpion in Figure 30.29. **Fluorescence** is defined to be any process in which an atom or molecule, excited by a photon of a given energy, and de-excites by emission of a lower-energy photon.

Fluorescence can be induced by many types of energy input. Fluorescent paint, dyes, and even soap residues in clothes make colors seem brighter in sunlight by converting some UV into visible light. X rays can induce fluorescence, as is done in x-ray fluoroscopy to make brighter visible images. Electric discharges can induce fluorescence, as in so-called neon lights and in gas-discharge tubes that produce atomic and molecular spectra. Common fluorescent lights use an electric discharge in mercury vapor to cause atomic emissions from mercury atoms. The inside of a fluorescent light is coated with a fluorescent material that emits visible light over a broad spectrum of wavelengths. By choosing an appropriate coating, fluorescent lights can be made more like sunlight or like the reddish glow of candlelight, depending on needs. Fluorescent lights are more efficient in converting electrical energy into visible light than incandescent filaments (about four times as efficient), the blackbody radiation of which is primarily in the infrared due to temperature limitations.

This atom is excited to one of its higher levels by absorbing a UV photon. It can de-excite in a single step, re-emitting a photon of the same energy, or in several steps. The process is called fluorescence if the atom de-excites in smaller steps, emitting energy different from that which excited it. Fluorescence can be induced by a variety of energy inputs, such as UV, x-rays, and electrical discharge.

The spectacular Waitomo caves on North Island in New Zealand provide a natural habitat for glow-worms. The glow-worms hang up to 70 silk threads of about 30 or 40 cm each to trap prey that fly towards them in the dark. The fluorescence process is very efficient, with nearly 100% of the energy input turning into light. (In comparison, fluorescent lights are about 20% efficient.)

Fluorescence has many uses in biology and medicine. It is commonly used to label and follow a molecule within a cell. Such tagging allows one to study the structure of DNA and proteins. Fluorescent dyes and antibodies are usually used to tag the molecules, which are then illuminated with UV light and their emission of visible light is observed. Since the fluorescence of each element is characteristic, identification of elements within a sample can be done this way.

Figure 30.30 shows a commonly used fluorescent dye called fluorescein. Below that, Figure 30.31 reveals the diffusion of a fluorescent dye in water by observing it under UV light.

FIGURE 30.30 Fluorescein, shown here in powder form, is used to dye laboratory samples. (credit: Benjah-bmm27, Wikimedia Commons)

FIGURE 30.31 Here, fluorescent powder is added to a beaker of water. The mixture gives off a bright glow under ultraviolet light. (credit: Bricksnite, Wikimedia Commons)

NANO-CRYSTALS

Recently, a new class of fluorescent materials has appeared—"nano-crystals." These are single-crystal molecules less than 100 nm in size. The smallest of these are called "quantum dots." These semiconductor indicators are very small (2–6 nm) and provide improved brightness. They also have the advantage that all colors can be excited with the same incident wavelength. They are brighter and more stable than organic dyes and have a longer lifetime than conventional phosphors. They have become an excellent tool for long-term studies of cells, including migration and morphology. (Figure 30.32.)

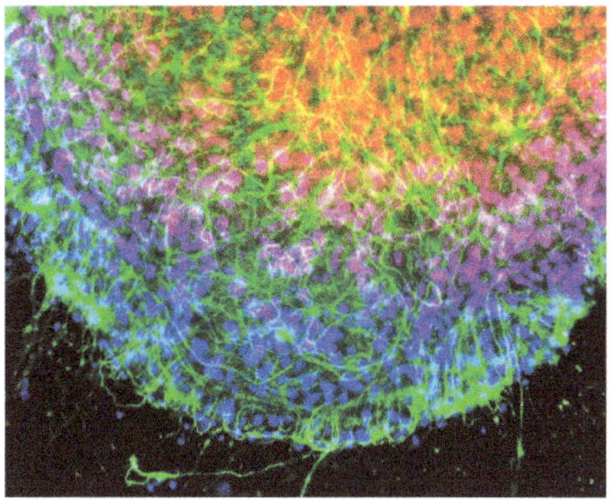

FIGURE 30.32 Microscopic image of chicken cells using nano-crystals of a fluorescent dye. Cell nuclei exhibit blue fluorescence while neurofilaments exhibit green. (credit: Weerapong Prasongchean, Wikimedia Commons)

Once excited, an atom or molecule will usually spontaneously de-excite quickly. (The electrons raised to higher levels are attracted to lower ones by the positive charge of the nucleus.) Spontaneous de-excitation has a very short mean lifetime of typically about 10^{-8} s. However, some levels have significantly longer lifetimes, ranging up to milliseconds to minutes or even hours. These energy levels are inhibited and are slow in de-exciting because their quantum numbers differ greatly from those of available lower levels. Although these level lifetimes are short in human terms, they are many orders of magnitude longer than is typical and, thus, are said to be **metastable**, meaning relatively stable. **Phosphorescence** is the de-excitation of a metastable state. Glow-in-the-dark materials, such as luminous dials on some watches and clocks and on children's toys and pajamas, are made of phosphorescent substances. Visible light excites the atoms or molecules to metastable states that decay slowly, releasing the stored excitation energy partially as visible light. In some ceramics, atomic excitation energy can be frozen in after the ceramic has cooled from its firing. It is very slowly released, but the ceramic can be induced to phosphoresce by heating—a process called “thermoluminescence.” Since the release is slow, thermoluminescence can be used to date antiquities. The less light emitted, the older the ceramic. (See Figure 30.33.)

FIGURE 30.33 Atoms frozen in an excited state when this Chinese ceramic figure was fired can be stimulated to de-excite and emit EM radiation by heating a sample of the ceramic—a process called thermoluminescence. Since the states slowly de-excite over centuries, the amount of thermoluminescence decreases with age, making it possible to use this effect to date and authenticate antiquities. This figure dates from the 11th century. (credit: Vassil, Wikimedia Commons)

Lasers

Lasers today are commonplace. Lasers are used to read bar codes at stores and in libraries, laser shows are staged for entertainment, laser printers produce high-quality images at relatively low cost, and lasers send prodigious numbers of telephone messages through optical fibers. Among other things, lasers are also employed in surveying, weapons guidance, tumor eradication, retinal welding, and for reading DVDs, Blu-rays, and computer or game console CD-ROMs.

Why do lasers have so many varied applications? The answer is that lasers produce single-wavelength EM radiation that is also very coherent—that is, the emitted photons are in phase. Laser output can, thus, be more precisely manipulated than incoherent mixed-wavelength EM radiation from other sources. The reason laser output is so pure and coherent is based on how it is produced, which in turn depends on a metastable state in the lasing material. Suppose a material had the energy levels shown in Figure 30.34. When energy is put into a large collection of these atoms, electrons are raised to all possible levels. Most return to the ground state in less than about 10^{-8} s, but those in the metastable state linger. This includes those electrons originally excited to the metastable state and those that fell into it from above. It is possible to get a majority of the atoms into the metastable state, a condition called a **population inversion**.

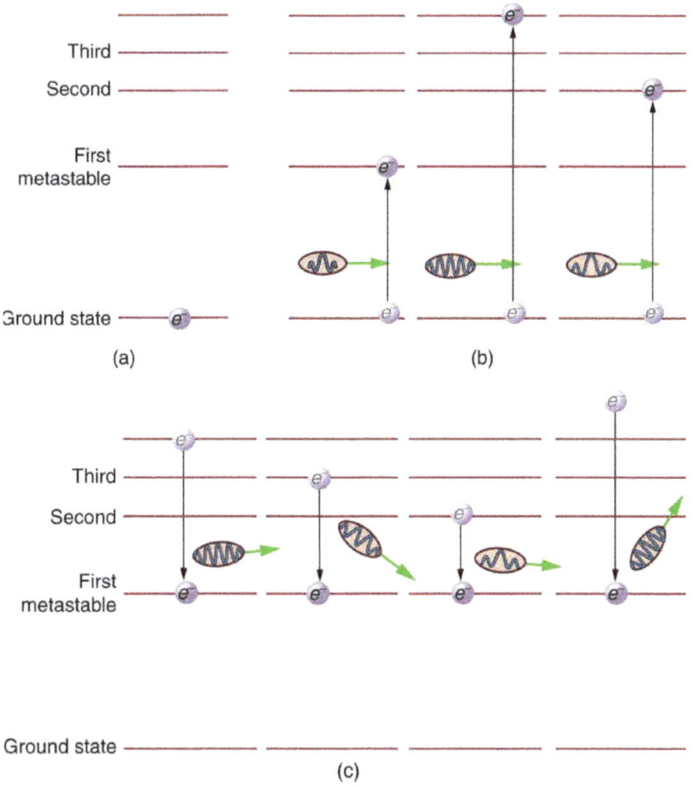

FIGURE 30.34 (a) Energy-level diagram for an atom showing the first few states, one of which is metastable. (b) Massive energy input excites atoms to a variety of states. (c) Most states decay quickly, leaving electrons only in the metastable and ground state. If a majority of electrons are in the metastable state, a population inversion has been achieved.

Once a population inversion is achieved, a very interesting thing can happen, as shown in Figure 30.35. An electron spontaneously falls from the metastable state, emitting a photon. This photon finds another atom in the metastable state and stimulates it to decay, emitting a second photon of *the same wavelength and in phase* with the first, and so on. **Stimulated emission** is the emission of electromagnetic radiation in the form of photons of a given frequency, triggered by photons of the same frequency. For example, an excited atom, with an electron in an energy orbit higher than normal, releases a photon of a specific frequency when the electron drops back to a lower energy orbit. If this photon then strikes another electron in the same high-energy orbit in another atom, another photon of the same frequency is released. The emitted photons and the triggering photons are always in phase, have the same polarization, and travel in the same direction. The probability of absorption of a photon is the same as the probability of stimulated emission, and so a majority of atoms must be in the metastable state to produce energy. Einstein (again Einstein, and back in 1917!) was one of the important contributors to the understanding of stimulated emission of radiation. Decades before the technology was invented to even experiment with laser generation, Einstein was the first to realize that stimulated emission and absorption are equally probable. The laser acts as a temporary energy storage device that subsequently produces a massive energy output of single-wavelength, in-phase photons.

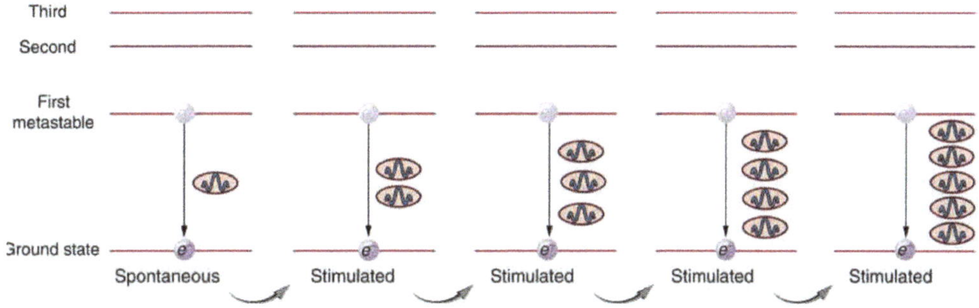

FIGURE 30.35 One atom in the metastable state spontaneously decays to a lower level, producing a photon that goes on to stimulate another atom to de-excite. The second photon has exactly the same energy and wavelength as the first and is in phase with it. Both go on to stimulate the emission of other photons. A population inversion is necessary for there to be a net production rather than a net absorption of

the photons.

The name **laser** is an acronym for light amplification by stimulated emission of radiation, the process just described. The process was proposed and developed following the advances in quantum physics. A joint Nobel Prize was awarded in 1964 to American Charles Townes (1915–), and Nikolay Basov (1922–2001) and Aleksandr Prokhorov (1916–2002), from the Soviet Union, for the development of lasers. The Nobel Prize in 1981 went to Arthur Schawlow (1921-1999) for pioneering laser applications. The original devices were called masers, because they produced microwaves. The first working laser was created in 1960 at Hughes Research labs (CA) by T. Maiman. It used a pulsed high-powered flash lamp and a ruby rod to produce red light. Today the name laser is used for all such devices developed to produce a variety of wavelengths, including microwave, infrared, visible, and ultraviolet radiation. Figure 30.36 shows how a laser can be constructed to enhance the stimulated emission of radiation. Energy input can be from a flash tube, electrical discharge, or other sources, in a process sometimes called optical pumping. A large percentage of the original pumping energy is dissipated in other forms, but a population inversion must be achieved. Mirrors can be used to enhance stimulated emission by multiple passes of the radiation back and forth through the lasing material. One of the mirrors is semitransparent to allow some of the light to pass through. The laser output from a laser is a mere 1% of the light passing back and forth in a laser.

As described earlier in the section on laser vision correction, Donna Strickland and Gérard Mourou, working at University of Rochester, developed a method to greatly increase the power of lasers, while also enabling them to be miniaturized. By passing the light over a specific type of grating, their method segments (or chirps) the delivery of the beam components in a matter that generates little heat at the source. Chirped pulse amplification is now used in some of the world's most powerful lasers as well as those commonly used to make precise microcuts or burns in medical applications. Strickland and Mourou were awarded the Nobel Prize in 1918.

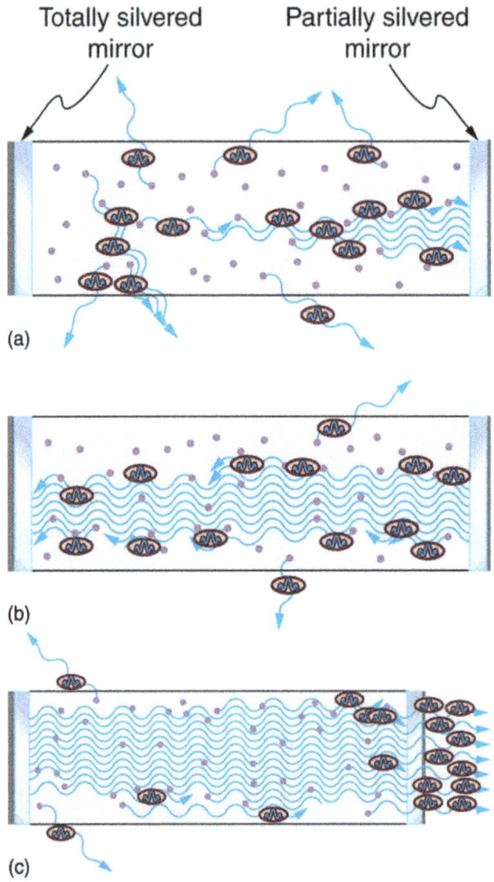

FIGURE 30.36 Typical laser construction has a method of pumping energy into the lasing material to produce a population inversion. (a) Spontaneous emission begins with some photons escaping and others stimulating further emissions. (b) and (c) Mirrors are used to enhance the probability of stimulated emission by passing photons through the material several times.

Lasers are constructed from many types of lasing materials, including gases, liquids, solids, and semiconductors. But all lasers are based on the existence of a metastable state or a phosphorescent material. Some lasers produce continuous output; others are pulsed in bursts as brief as 10^{-14} s. Some laser outputs are fantastically powerful—some greater than 10^{12} W—but the more common, everyday lasers produce something on the order of 10^{-3} W. The helium-neon laser that produces a familiar red light is very common. Figure 30.37 shows the energy levels of helium and neon, a pair of noble gases that work well together. An electrical discharge is passed through a helium-neon gas mixture in which the number of atoms of helium is ten times that of neon. The first excited state of helium is metastable and, thus, stores energy. This energy is easily transferred by collision to neon atoms, because they have an excited state at nearly the same energy as that in helium. That state in neon is also metastable, and this is the one that produces the laser output. (The most likely transition is to the nearby state, producing 1.96 eV photons, which have a wavelength of 633 nm and appear red.) A population inversion can be produced in neon, because there are so many more helium atoms and these put energy into the neon. Helium-neon lasers often have continuous output, because the population inversion can be maintained even while lasing occurs. Probably the most common lasers in use today, including the common laser pointer, are semiconductor or diode lasers, made of silicon. Here, energy is pumped into the material by passing a current in the device to excite the electrons. Special coatings on the ends and fine cleavings of the semiconductor material allow light to bounce back and forth and a tiny fraction to emerge as laser light. Diode lasers can usually run continually and produce outputs in the milliwatt range.

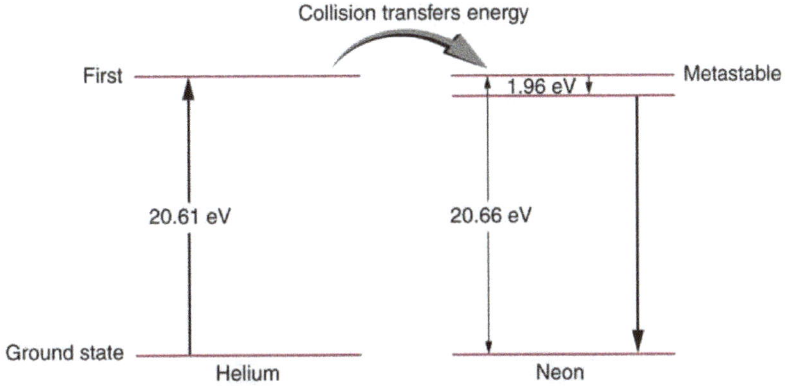

FIGURE 30.37 Energy levels in helium and neon. In the common helium-neon laser, an electrical discharge pumps energy into the metastable states of both atoms. The gas mixture has about ten times more helium atoms than neon atoms. Excited helium atoms easily de-excite by transferring energy to neon in a collision. A population inversion in neon is achieved, allowing lasing by the neon to occur.

There are many medical applications of lasers. Lasers have the advantage that they can be focused to a small spot. They also have a well-defined wavelength. Many types of lasers are available today that provide wavelengths from the ultraviolet to the infrared. This is important, as one needs to be able to select a wavelength that will be preferentially absorbed by the material of interest. Objects appear a certain color because they absorb all other visible colors incident upon them. What wavelengths are absorbed depends upon the energy spacing between electron orbitals in that molecule. Unlike the hydrogen atom, biological molecules are complex and have a variety of absorption wavelengths or lines. But these can be determined and used in the selection of a laser with the appropriate wavelength. Water is transparent to the visible spectrum but will absorb light in the UV and IR regions. Blood (hemoglobin) strongly reflects red but absorbs most strongly in the UV.

Laser surgery uses a wavelength that is strongly absorbed by the tissue it is focused upon. One example of a medical application of lasers is shown in Figure 30.38. A detached retina can result in total loss of vision. Burns made by a laser focused to a small spot on the retina form scar tissue that can hold the retina in place, salvaging the patient's vision. Other light sources cannot be focused as precisely as a laser due to refractive dispersion of different wavelengths. Similarly, laser surgery in the form of cutting or burning away tissue is made more accurate because laser output can be very precisely focused and is preferentially absorbed because of its single wavelength. Depending upon what part or layer of the retina needs repairing, the appropriate type of laser can be selected. For the repair of tears in the retina, a green argon laser is generally used. This light is absorbed well by tissues containing blood, so coagulation or "welding" of the tear can be done.

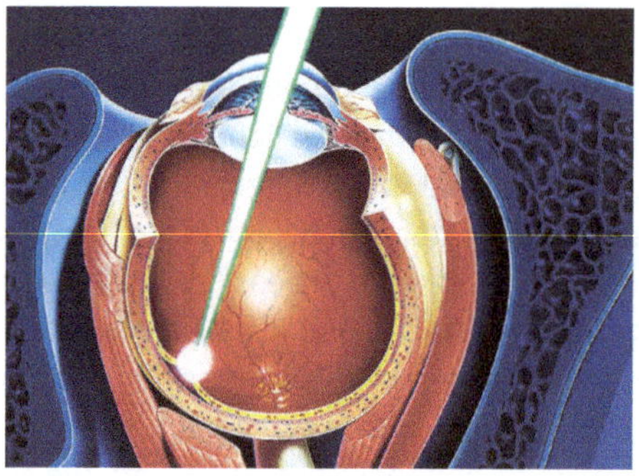

FIGURE 30.38 A detached retina is burned by a laser designed to focus on a small spot on the retina, the resulting scar tissue holding it in place. The lens of the eye is used to focus the light, as is the device bringing the laser output to the eye.

In dentistry, the use of lasers is rising. Lasers are most commonly used for surgery on the soft tissue of the mouth. They can be used to remove ulcers, stop bleeding, and reshape gum tissue. Their use in cutting into bones and teeth is not quite so common; here the erbium YAG (yttrium aluminum garnet) laser is used.

The massive combination of lasers shown in Figure 30.39 can be used to induce nuclear fusion, the energy source of the sun and hydrogen bombs. Since lasers can produce very high power in very brief pulses, they can be used to focus an enormous amount of energy on a small glass sphere containing fusion fuel. Not only does the incident energy increase the fuel temperature significantly so that fusion can occur, it also compresses the fuel to great density, enhancing the probability of fusion. The compression or implosion is caused by the momentum of the impinging laser photons.

FIGURE 30.39 This system of lasers at Lawrence Livermore Laboratory is used to ignite nuclear fusion. A tremendous burst of energy is focused on a small fuel pellet, which is imploded to the high density and temperature needed to make the fusion reaction proceed. (credit: Lawrence Livermore National Laboratory, Lawrence Livermore National Security, LLC, and the Department of Energy)

Before being largely replaced by streaming services and other storage methods, music CDs and DVDs were extremely common. They store information digitally and have a much larger information-storage capacity than their predecessors, audio and video cassette tapes. An entire encyclopedia can be stored on a single CD. Figure 30.40 illustrates how the information is stored and read from the CD. Pits made in the CD by a laser can be tiny and very accurately spaced to record digital information. These are read by having an inexpensive solid-state infrared laser beam scatter from pits as the CD spins, revealing their digital pattern and the information encoded upon them.

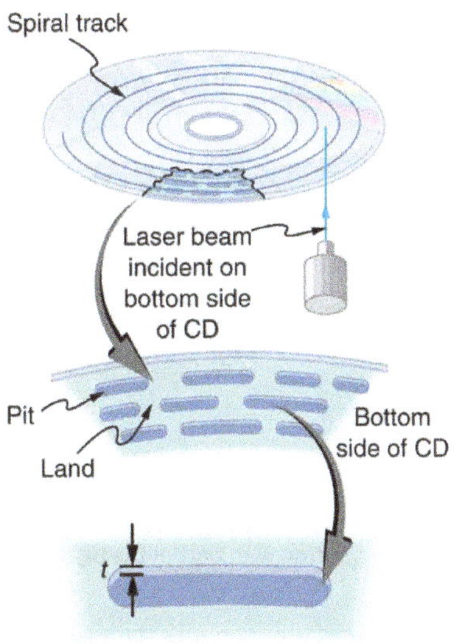

FIGURE 30.40 A CD has digital information stored in the form of laser-created pits on its surface. These in turn can be read by detecting the laser light scattered from the pit. Large information capacity is possible because of the precision of the laser. Shorter-wavelength lasers enable greater storage capacity.

Holograms, such as those in Figure 30.41, are true three-dimensional images recorded on film by lasers. Holograms are used for amusement, decoration on novelty items and magazine covers, security on credit cards and driver's licenses (a laser and other equipment is needed to reproduce them), and for serious three-dimensional information storage. You can see that a hologram is a true three-dimensional image, because objects change relative position in the image when viewed from different angles.

FIGURE 30.41 Credit cards commonly have holograms for logos, making them difficult to reproduce (credit: Dominic Alves, Flickr)

The name **hologram** means "entire picture" (from the Greek *holo*, as in holistic), because the image is three-dimensional. **Holography** is the process of producing holograms and, although they are recorded on photographic film, the process is quite different from normal photography. Holography uses light interference or wave optics, whereas normal photography uses geometric optics. Figure 30.42 shows one method of producing a hologram. Coherent light from a laser is split by a mirror, with part of the light illuminating the object. The remainder, called the reference beam, shines directly on a piece of film. Light scattered from the object interferes with the reference beam, producing constructive and destructive interference. As a result, the exposed film looks foggy, but close examination reveals a complicated interference pattern stored on it. Where the interference was constructive, the film (a negative actually) is darkened. Holography is sometimes called lensless photography, because it uses the wave characteristics of light as contrasted to normal photography, which uses geometric optics and so requires lenses.

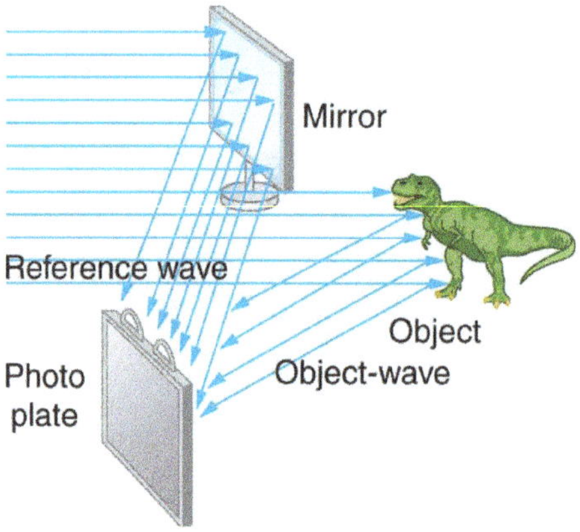

FIGURE 30.42 Production of a hologram. Single-wavelength coherent light from a laser produces a well-defined interference pattern on a piece of film. The laser beam is split by a partially silvered mirror, with part of the light illuminating the object and the remainder shining directly on the film.

Light falling on a hologram can form a three-dimensional image. The process is complicated in detail, but the basics can be understood as shown in Figure 30.43, in which a laser of the same type that exposed the film is now used to illuminate it. The myriad tiny exposed regions of the film are dark and block the light, while less exposed regions allow light to pass. The film thus acts much like a collection of diffraction gratings with various spacings. Light passing through the hologram is diffracted in various directions, producing both real and virtual images of the object used to expose the film. The interference pattern is the same as that produced by the object. Moving your eye to various places in the interference pattern gives you different perspectives, just as looking directly at the object would. The image thus looks like the object and is three-dimensional like the object.

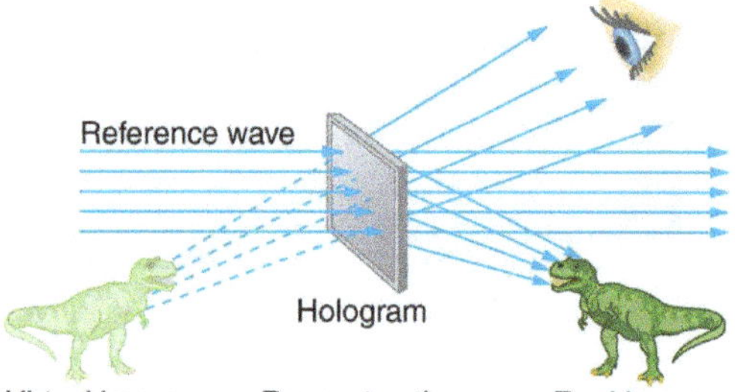

FIGURE 30.43 A transmission hologram is one that produces real and virtual images when a laser of the same type as that which exposed the hologram is passed through it. Diffraction from various parts of the film produces the same interference pattern as the object that was used to expose it.

The hologram illustrated in Figure 30.43 is a transmission hologram. Holograms that are viewed with reflected light, such as the white light holograms on credit cards, are reflection holograms and are more common. White light holograms often appear a little blurry with rainbow edges, because the diffraction patterns of various colors of light are at slightly different locations due to their different wavelengths. Further uses of holography include all types of 3-D information storage, such as of statues in museums and engineering studies of structures and 3-D images of human organs. Invented in the late 1940s by Dennis Gabor (1900–1979), who won the 1971 Nobel Prize in Physics for his work, holography became far more practical with the development of the laser. Since lasers produce coherent single-wavelength light, their interference patterns are more pronounced. The precision is so great that it is even possible to record numerous holograms on a single piece of film by just changing the angle of the film for each successive image. This is how the holograms that move as you walk by them are produced—a kind of lensless movie.

In a similar way, in the medical field, holograms have allowed complete 3-D holographic displays of objects from a stack of images. Storing these images for future use is relatively easy. With the use of an endoscope, high-resolution 3-D holographic images of internal organs and tissues can be made.

30.6 The Wave Nature of Matter Causes Quantization

LEARNING OBJECTIVES

By the end of this section, you will be able to:

- Explain Bohr's model of atom.
- Define and describe quantization of angular momentum.
- Calculate the angular momentum for an orbit of atom.
- Define and describe the wave-like properties of matter.

After visiting some of the applications of different aspects of atomic physics, we now return to the basic theory that was built upon Bohr's atom. Einstein once said it was important to keep asking the questions we eventually teach children not to ask. Why is angular momentum quantized? You already know the answer. Electrons have wave-like properties, as de Broglie later proposed. They can exist only where they interfere constructively, and only certain orbits meet proper conditions, as we shall see in the next module.

Following Bohr's initial work on the hydrogen atom, a decade was to pass before de Broglie proposed that matter has wave properties. The wave-like properties of matter were subsequently confirmed by observations of electron interference when scattered from crystals. Electrons can exist only in locations where they interfere constructively. How does this affect electrons in atomic orbits? When an electron is bound to an atom, its wavelength must fit into a small space, something like a standing wave on a string. (See Figure 30.44.) Allowed orbits are those orbits in which an electron constructively interferes with itself. Not all orbits produce constructive interference. Thus only certain orbits are allowed—the orbits are quantized.

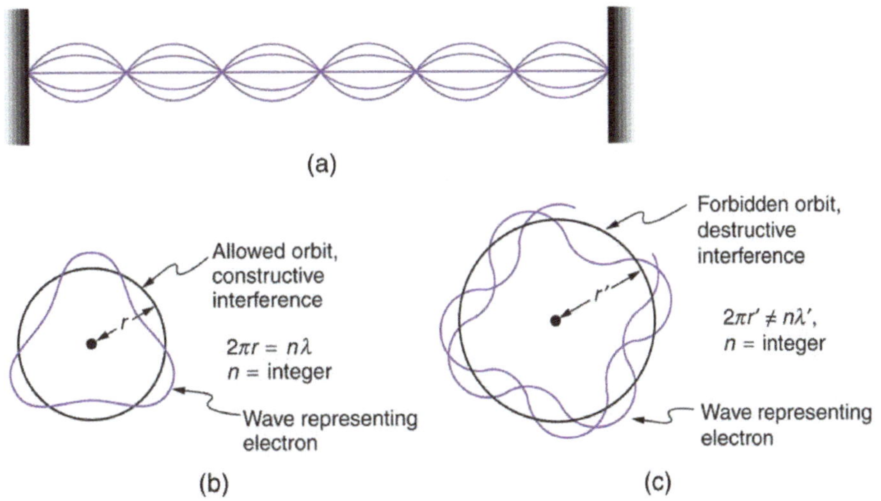

FIGURE 30.44 (a) Waves on a string have a wavelength related to the length of the string, allowing them to interfere constructively. (b) If we imagine the string bent into a closed circle, we get a rough idea of how electrons in circular orbits can interfere constructively. (c) If the wavelength does not fit into the circumference, the electron interferes destructively; it cannot exist in such an orbit.

For a circular orbit, constructive interference occurs when the electron's wavelength fits neatly into the circumference, so that wave crests always align with crests and wave troughs align with troughs, as shown in Figure 30.44 (b). More precisely, when an integral multiple of the electron's wavelength equals the circumference of the orbit, constructive interference is obtained. In equation form, the *condition for constructive interference and an allowed electron orbit* is

$$n\lambda_n = 2\pi r_n (n = 1, 2, 3 \ldots), \quad (30.38)$$

where λ_n is the electron's wavelength and r_n is the radius of that circular orbit. The de Broglie wavelength is $\lambda = h/p = h/mv$, and so here $\lambda = h/m_e v$. Substituting this into the previous condition for constructive interference produces an interesting result:

$$\frac{nh}{m_e v} = 2\pi r_n. \quad (30.39)$$

Rearranging terms, and noting that $L = mvr$ for a circular orbit, we obtain the quantization of angular momentum as the condition for allowed orbits:

$$L = m_e v r_n = n\frac{h}{2\pi}(n = 1, 2, 3 ...). \tag{30.40}$$

This is what Bohr was forced to hypothesize as the rule for allowed orbits, as stated earlier. We now realize that it is the condition for constructive interference of an electron in a circular orbit. Figure 30.45 illustrates this for $n = 3$ and $n = 4$.

WAVES AND QUANTIZATION

The wave nature of matter is responsible for the quantization of energy levels in bound systems. Only those states where matter interferes constructively exist, or are "allowed." Since there is a lowest orbit where this is possible in an atom, the electron cannot spiral into the nucleus. It cannot exist closer to or inside the nucleus. The wave nature of matter is what prevents matter from collapsing and gives atoms their sizes.

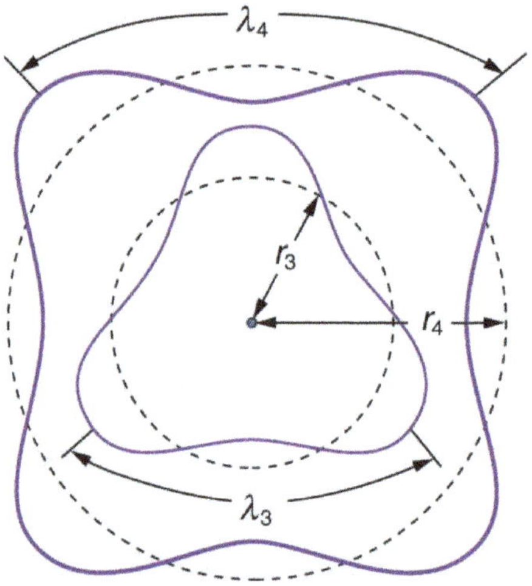

FIGURE 30.45 The third and fourth allowed circular orbits have three and four wavelengths, respectively, in their circumferences.

Because of the wave character of matter, the idea of well-defined orbits gives way to a model in which there is a cloud of probability, consistent with Heisenberg's uncertainty principle. Figure 30.46 shows how this applies to the ground state of hydrogen. If you try to follow the electron in some well-defined orbit using a probe that has a small enough wavelength to get some details, you will instead knock the electron out of its orbit. Each measurement of the electron's position will find it to be in a definite location somewhere near the nucleus. Repeated measurements reveal a cloud of probability like that in the figure, with each speck the location determined by a single measurement. There is not a well-defined, circular-orbit type of distribution. Nature again proves to be different on a small scale than on a macroscopic scale.

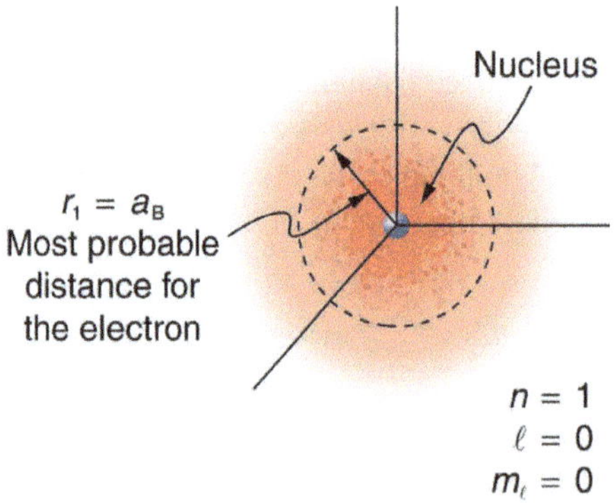

FIGURE 30.46 The ground state of a hydrogen atom has a probability cloud describing the position of its electron. The probability of finding the electron is proportional to the darkness of the cloud. The electron can be closer or farther than the Bohr radius, but it is very unlikely to be a great distance from the nucleus.

There are many examples in which the wave nature of matter causes quantization in bound systems such as the atom. Whenever a particle is confined or bound to a small space, its allowed wavelengths are those which fit into that space. For example, the particle in a box model describes a particle free to move in a small space surrounded by impenetrable barriers. This is true in blackbody radiators (atoms and molecules) as well as in atomic and molecular spectra. Various atoms and molecules will have different sets of electron orbits, depending on the size and complexity of the system. When a system is large, such as a grain of sand, the tiny particle waves in it can fit in so many ways that it becomes impossible to see that the allowed states are discrete. Thus the correspondence principle is satisfied. As systems become large, they gradually look less grainy, and quantization becomes less evident. Unbound systems (small or not), such as an electron freed from an atom, do not have quantized energies, since their wavelengths are not constrained to fit in a certain volume.

PHET EXPLORATIONS

Quantum Wave Interference

When do photons, electrons, and atoms behave like particles and when do they behave like waves? Watch waves spread out and interfere as they pass through a double slit, then get detected on a screen as tiny dots. Use quantum detectors to explore how measurements change the waves and the patterns they produce on the screen.

Click to view content (https://openstax.org/l/21intquawavint).

30.7 Patterns in Spectra Reveal More Quantization

LEARNING OBJECTIVES

By the end of this section, you will be able to:

- State and discuss the Zeeman effect.
- Define orbital magnetic field.
- Define orbital angular momentum.
- Define space quantization.

High-resolution measurements of atomic and molecular spectra show that the spectral lines are even more complex than they first appear. In this section, we will see that this complexity has yielded important new information about electrons and their orbits in atoms.

In order to explore the substructure of atoms (and knowing that magnetic fields affect moving charges), the Dutch physicist Hendrik Lorentz (1853–1930) suggested that his student Pieter Zeeman (1865–1943) study how spectra might be affected by magnetic fields. What they found became known as the **Zeeman effect**, which involved spectral lines being split into two or more separate emission lines by an external magnetic field, as shown in Figure 30.47. For their discoveries, Zeeman and Lorentz shared the 1902 Nobel Prize in Physics.

Zeeman splitting is complex. Some lines split into three lines, some into five, and so on. But one general feature is that the amount the split lines are separated is proportional to the applied field strength, indicating an interaction with a moving charge. The splitting means that the quantized energy of an orbit is affected by an external magnetic field, causing the orbit to have several discrete energies instead of one. Even without an external magnetic field, very precise measurements showed that spectral lines are doublets (split into two), apparently by magnetic fields within the atom itself.

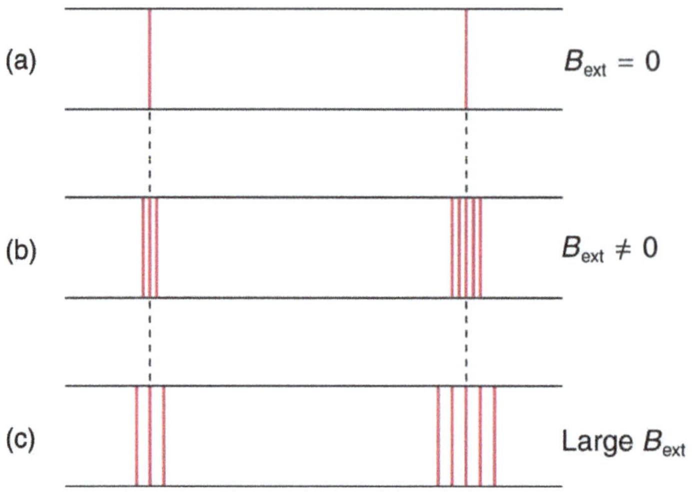

FIGURE 30.47 The Zeeman effect is the splitting of spectral lines when a magnetic field is applied. The number of lines formed varies, but the spread is proportional to the strength of the applied field. (a) Two spectral lines with no external magnetic field. (b) The lines split when the field is applied. (c) The splitting is greater when a stronger field is applied.

Bohr's theory of circular orbits is useful for visualizing how an electron's orbit is affected by a magnetic field. The circular orbit forms a current loop, which creates a magnetic field of its own, $\mathbf{B}_{\text{orb}}$ as seen in Figure 30.48. Note that the **orbital magnetic field** $\mathbf{B}_{\text{orb}}$ and the **orbital angular momentum** $\mathbf{L}_{\text{orb}}$ are along the same line. The external magnetic field and the orbital magnetic field interact; a torque is exerted to align them. A torque rotating a system through some angle does work so that there is energy associated with this interaction. Thus, orbits at different angles to the external magnetic field have different energies. What is remarkable is that the energies are quantized—the magnetic field splits the spectral lines into several discrete lines that have different energies. This means that only certain angles are allowed between the orbital angular momentum and the external field, as seen in Figure 30.49.

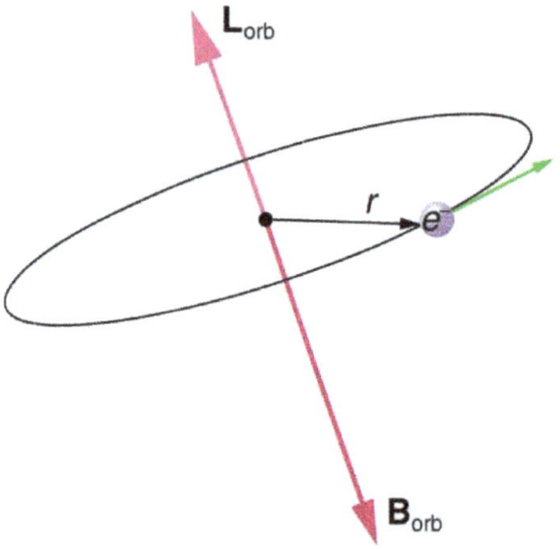

FIGURE 30.48 The approximate picture of an electron in a circular orbit illustrates how the current loop produces its own magnetic field, called $\mathbf{B}_{\text{orb}}$. It also shows how $\mathbf{B}_{\text{orb}}$ is along the same line as the orbital angular momentum $\mathbf{L}_{\text{orb}}$.

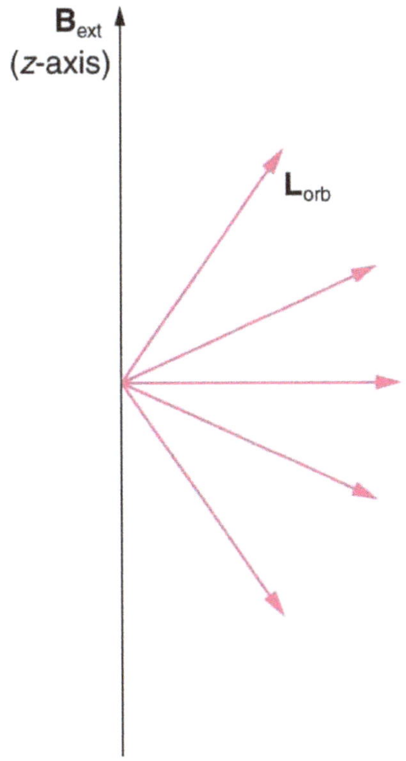

FIGURE 30.49 Only certain angles are allowed between the orbital angular momentum and an external magnetic field. This is implied by the fact that the Zeeman effect splits spectral lines into several discrete lines. Each line is associated with an angle between the external magnetic field and magnetic fields due to electrons and their orbits.

We already know that the magnitude of angular momentum is quantized for electron orbits in atoms. The new insight is that the *direction of the orbital angular momentum is also quantized*. The fact that the orbital angular momentum can have only certain directions is called **space quantization**. Like many aspects of quantum mechanics, this quantization of direction is totally unexpected. On the macroscopic scale, orbital angular momentum, such as that of the moon around the earth, can have any magnitude and be in any direction.

Detailed treatment of space quantization began to explain some complexities of atomic spectra, but certain patterns seemed to be caused by something else. As mentioned, spectral lines are actually closely spaced doublets, a characteristic called **fine structure**, as shown in Figure 30.50. The doublet changes when a magnetic field is applied, implying that whatever causes the doublet interacts with a magnetic field. In 1925, Sem Goudsmit and George Uhlenbeck, two Dutch physicists, successfully argued that electrons have properties analogous to a macroscopic charge spinning on its axis. Electrons, in fact, have an internal or intrinsic angular momentum called **intrinsic spin $\mathbf{S}$**. Since electrons are charged, their intrinsic spin creates an **intrinsic magnetic field $\mathbf{B}_{\text{int}}$**, which interacts with their orbital magnetic field $\mathbf{B}_{\text{orb}}$. Furthermore, *electron intrinsic spin is quantized in magnitude and direction*, analogous to the situation for orbital angular momentum. The spin of the electron can have only one magnitude, and its direction can be at only one of two angles relative to a magnetic field, as seen in Figure 30.51. We refer to this as spin up or spin down for the electron. Each spin direction has a different energy; hence, spectroscopic lines are split into two. Spectral doublets are now understood as being due to electron spin.

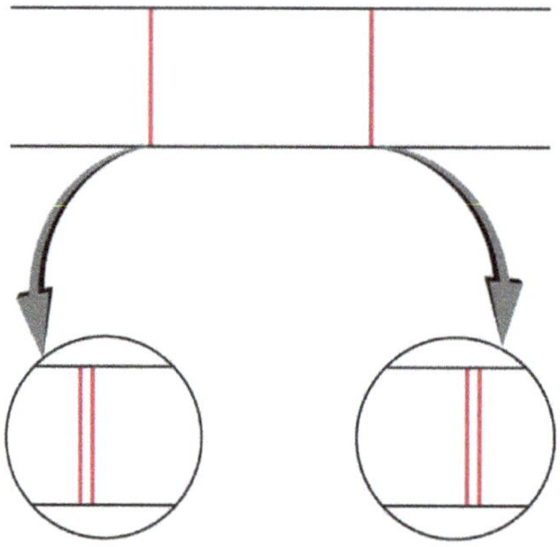

FIGURE 30.50 Fine structure. Upon close examination, spectral lines are doublets, even in the absence of an external magnetic field. The electron has an intrinsic magnetic field that interacts with its orbital magnetic field.

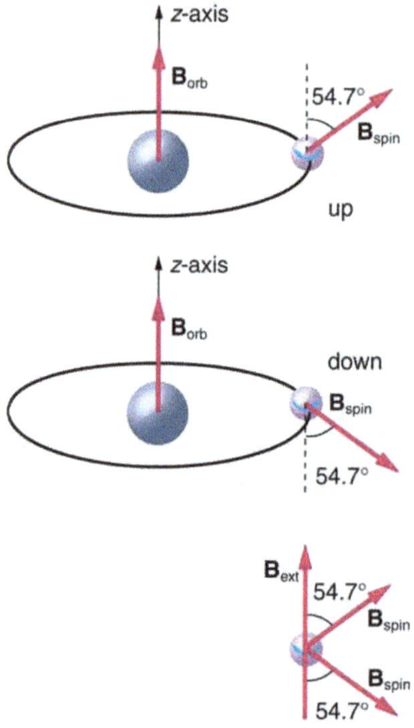

FIGURE 30.51 The intrinsic magnetic field $\mathbf{B}_{\text{int}}$ of an electron is attributed to its spin, $\mathbf{S}$, roughly pictured to be due to its charge spinning on its axis. This is only a crude model, since electrons seem to have no size. The spin and intrinsic magnetic field of the electron can make only one of two angles with another magnetic field, such as that created by the electron's orbital motion. Space is quantized for spin as well as for orbital angular momentum.

These two new insights—that the direction of angular momentum, whether orbital or spin, is quantized, and that electrons have intrinsic spin—help to explain many of the complexities of atomic and molecular spectra. In magnetic resonance imaging, it is the way that the intrinsic magnetic field of hydrogen and biological atoms interact with an external field that underlies the diagnostic fundamentals.

30.8 Quantum Numbers and Rules

LEARNING OBJECTIVES

By the end of this section, you will be able to:

- Define quantum number.
- Calculate angle of angular momentum vector with an axis.
- Define spin quantum number.

Physical characteristics that are quantized—such as energy, charge, and angular momentum—are of such importance that names and symbols are given to them. The values of quantized entities are expressed in terms of **quantum numbers**, and the rules governing them are of the utmost importance in determining what nature is and does. This section covers some of the more important quantum numbers and rules—all of which apply in chemistry, material science, and far beyond the realm of atomic physics, where they were first discovered. Once again, we see how physics makes discoveries which enable other fields to grow.

The *energy states of bound systems are quantized*, because the particle wavelength can fit into the bounds of the system in only certain ways. This was elaborated for the hydrogen atom, for which the allowed energies are expressed as $E_n \propto 1/n^2$, where $n = 1, 2, 3, ...$ We define n to be the principal quantum number that labels the basic states of a system. The lowest-energy state has $n = 1$, the first excited state has $n = 2$, and so on. Thus the allowed values for the principal quantum number are

$$n = 1, 2, 3, ... \tag{30.41}$$

This is more than just a numbering scheme, since the energy of the system, such as the hydrogen atom, can be expressed as some function of n, as can other characteristics (such as the orbital radii of the hydrogen atom).

The fact that the *magnitude of angular momentum is quantized* was first recognized by Bohr in relation to the hydrogen atom; it is now known to be true in general. With the development of quantum mechanics, it was found that the magnitude of angular momentum L can have only the values

$$L = \sqrt{l(l+1)}\frac{h}{2\pi} \quad (l = 0, 1, 2, ..., n-1), \tag{30.42}$$

where l is defined to be the **angular momentum quantum number**. The rule for l in atoms is given in the parentheses. Given n, the value of l can be any integer from zero up to $n - 1$. For example, if $n = 4$, then l can be 0, 1, 2, or 3.

Note that for $n = 1$, l can only be zero. This means that the ground-state angular momentum for hydrogen is actually zero, not $h/2\pi$ as Bohr proposed. The picture of circular orbits is not valid, because there would be angular momentum for any circular orbit. A more valid picture is the cloud of probability shown for the ground state of hydrogen in Figure 30.46. The electron actually spends time in and near the nucleus. The reason the electron does not remain in the nucleus is related to Heisenberg's uncertainty principle—the electron's energy would have to be much too large to be confined to the small space of the nucleus. Now the first excited state of hydrogen has $n = 2$, so that l can be either 0 or 1, according to the rule in $L = \sqrt{l(l+1)}\frac{h}{2\pi}$. Similarly, for $n = 3$, l can be 0, 1, or 2. It is often most convenient to state the value of l, a simple integer, rather than calculating the value of L from $L = \sqrt{l(l+1)}\frac{h}{2\pi}$. For example, for $l = 2$, we see that

$$L = \sqrt{2(2+1)}\frac{h}{2\pi} = \sqrt{6}\frac{h}{2\pi} = 0.390h = 2.58 \times 10^{-34}\ \text{J} \cdot \text{s}. \tag{30.43}$$

It is much simpler to state $l = 2$.

As recognized in the Zeeman effect, the *direction of angular momentum is quantized*. We now know this is true in all circumstances. It is found that the component of angular momentum along one direction in space, usually called the z-axis, can have only certain values of L_z. The direction in space must be related to something physical, such as the direction of the magnetic field at that location. This is an aspect of relativity. Direction has no meaning if there is nothing that varies with direction, as does magnetic force. The allowed values of L_z are

$$L_z = m_l \frac{h}{2\pi} \quad (m_l = -l, -l+1, ..., -1, 0, 1, ... l-1, l), \tag{30.44}$$

where L_z is the **z-component of the angular momentum** and m_l is the angular momentum projection quantum number. The rule in parentheses for the values of m_l is that it can range from $-l$ to l in steps of one. For example, if $l = 2$, then m_l can have the five values −2, −1, 0, 1, and 2. Each m_l corresponds to a different energy in the presence of a magnetic field, so that they are related to the splitting of spectral lines into discrete parts, as discussed in the preceding section. If the z-component of angular momentum can have only certain values, then the angular momentum can have only certain directions, as illustrated in Figure 30.52.

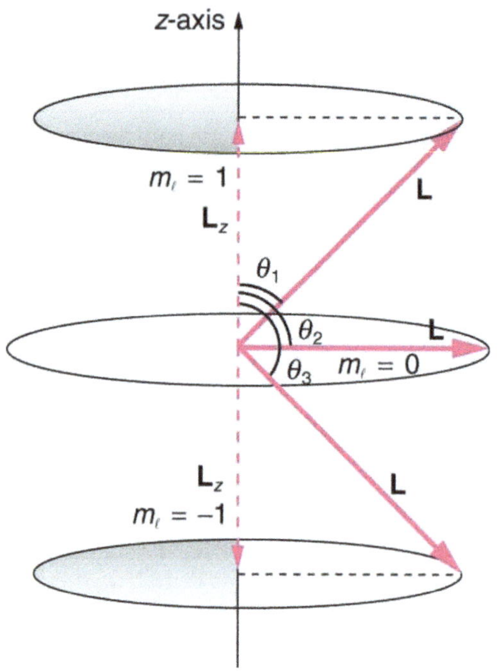

FIGURE 30.52 The component of a given angular momentum along the z-axis (defined by the direction of a magnetic field) can have only certain values; these are shown here for $l = 1$, for which $m_l = -1, 0, \text{and} +1$. The direction of L is quantized in the sense that it can have only certain angles relative to the z-axis.

EXAMPLE 30.3

What Are the Allowed Directions?

Calculate the angles that the angular momentum vector $\mathbf{L}$ can make with the z-axis for $l = 1$, as illustrated in Figure 30.52.

Strategy

Figure 30.52 represents the vectors $\mathbf{L}$ and $\mathbf{L}_z$ as usual, with arrows proportional to their magnitudes and pointing in the correct directions. $\mathbf{L}$ and $\mathbf{L}_z$ form a right triangle, with $\mathbf{L}$ being the hypotenuse and $\mathbf{L}_z$ the adjacent side. This means that the ratio of $\mathbf{L}_z$ to $\mathbf{L}$ is the cosine of the angle of interest. We can find $\mathbf{L}$ and $\mathbf{L}_z$ using $L = \sqrt{l(l+1)}\frac{h}{2\pi}$ and $L_z = m\frac{h}{2\pi}$.

Solution

We are given $l = 1$, so that m_l can be +1, 0, or −1. Thus L has the value given by $L = \sqrt{l(l+1)}\frac{h}{2\pi}$.

$$L = \frac{\sqrt{l(l+1)}h}{2\pi} = \frac{\sqrt{2}h}{2\pi} \tag{30.45}$$

L_z can have three values, given by $L_z = m_l\frac{h}{2\pi}$.

$$L_z = m_l\frac{h}{2\pi} = \begin{cases} \frac{h}{2\pi}, & m_l = +1 \\ 0, & m_l = 0 \\ -\frac{h}{2\pi}, & m_l = -1 \end{cases} \tag{30.46}$$

As can be seen in Figure 30.52, $\cos\theta = \mathrm{L_z/L}$, and so for $m_l = +1$, we have

$$\cos\theta_1 = \frac{L_Z}{L} = \frac{\frac{h}{2\pi}}{\frac{\sqrt{2}h}{2\pi}} = \frac{1}{\sqrt{2}} = 0.707. \tag{30.47}$$

Thus,

$$\theta_1 = \cos^{-1} 0.707 = 45.0^\circ. \tag{30.48}$$

Similarly, for $m_l = 0$, we find $\cos\theta_2 = 0$; thus,

$$\theta_2 = \cos^{-1} 0 = 90.0^\circ. \tag{30.49}$$

And for $m_l = -1$,

$$\cos\theta_3 = \frac{L_Z}{L} = \frac{-\frac{h}{2\pi}}{\frac{\sqrt{2}h}{2\pi}} = -\frac{1}{\sqrt{2}} = -0.707, \tag{30.50}$$

so that

$$\theta_3 = \cos^{-1}(-0.707) = 135.0^\circ. \tag{30.51}$$

Discussion

The angles are consistent with the figure. Only the angle relative to the z-axis is quantized. L can point in any direction as long as it makes the proper angle with the z-axis. Thus the angular momentum vectors lie on cones as illustrated. This behavior is not observed on the large scale. To see how the correspondence principle holds here, consider that the smallest angle (θ_1 in the example) is for the maximum value of $m_l = 0$, namely $m_l = l$. For that smallest angle,

$$\cos\theta = \frac{L_z}{L} = \frac{l}{\sqrt{l(l+1)}}, \tag{30.52}$$

which approaches 1 as l becomes very large. If $\cos\theta = 1$, then $\theta = 0^\circ$. Furthermore, for large l, there are many values of m_l, so that all angles become possible as l gets very large.

Intrinsic Spin Angular Momentum Is Quantized in Magnitude and Direction

There are two more quantum numbers of immediate concern. Both were first discovered for electrons in conjunction with fine structure in atomic spectra. It is now well established that electrons and other fundamental particles have *intrinsic spin*, roughly analogous to a planet spinning on its axis. This spin is a fundamental characteristic of particles, and only one magnitude of intrinsic spin is allowed for a given type of particle. Intrinsic angular momentum is quantized independently of orbital angular momentum. Additionally, the direction of the spin is also quantized. It has been found that the **magnitude of the intrinsic (internal) spin angular momentum**, s, of an electron is given by

$$S = \sqrt{s(s+1)}\frac{h}{2\pi} \quad (s = 1/2 \text{ for electrons}), \tag{30.53}$$

where s is defined to be the **spin quantum number**. This is very similar to the quantization of L given in $L = \sqrt{l(l+1)}\frac{h}{2\pi}$, except that the only value allowed for s for electrons is 1/2.

The *direction of intrinsic spin is quantized*, just as is the direction of orbital angular momentum. The direction of spin angular momentum along one direction in space, again called the z-axis, can have only the values

$$S_z = m_s\frac{h}{2\pi} \quad \left(m_s = -\frac{1}{2}, +\frac{1}{2}\right) \tag{30.54}$$

for electrons. S_z is the **z-component of spin angular momentum** and m_s is the **spin projection quantum number**. For electrons, s can only be 1/2, and m_s can be either +1/2 or −1/2. Spin projection m_s=+1/2 is referred to as *spin up*, whereas $m_s = -1/2$ is called *spin down*. These are illustrated in Figure 30.51.

INTRINSIC SPIN

In later chapters, we will see that intrinsic spin is a characteristic of all subatomic particles. For some particles s is half-integral, whereas for others s is integral—there are crucial differences between half-integral spin particles and integral spin particles. Protons and neutrons, like electrons, have $s = 1/2$, whereas photons have $s = 1$, and other particles called pions have $s = 0$, and so on.

To summarize, the state of a system, such as the precise nature of an electron in an atom, is determined by its particular quantum numbers. These are expressed in the form (n, l, m_l, m_s)—see Table 30.1 *For electrons in atoms,* the principal quantum number can have the values $n = 1, 2, 3, ...$ Once n is known, the values of the angular momentum quantum number are limited to $l = 1, 2, 3, ..., n - 1$. For a given value of l, the angular momentum projection quantum number can have only the values $m_l = -l, \ -l + 1, ..., -1, 0, 1, ..., l - 1, l$. Electron spin is independent of $n, l,$ and m_l, always having $s = 1/2$. The spin projection quantum number can have two values, $m_s = 1/2 \text{ or } -1/2$.

Name	Symbol	Allowed values
Principal quantum number	n	$1, 2, 3, ...$
Angular momentum	l	$0, 1, 2, ...n - 1$
Angular momentum projection	m_l	$-l, \ -l + 1, ..., -1, 0, 1, ..., l - 1, l \text{ (or } 0, \pm 1, \pm 2, ..., \ \pm l)$
Spin[1]	s	$1/2 \text{(electrons)}$
Spin projection	m_s	$-1/2, \ +1/2$

TABLE 30.1 Atomic Quantum Numbers

Figure 30.53 shows several hydrogen states corresponding to different sets of quantum numbers. Note that these clouds of probability are the locations of electrons as determined by making repeated measurements—each measurement finds the electron in a definite location, with a greater chance of finding the electron in some places rather than others. With repeated measurements, the pattern of probability shown in the figure emerges. The clouds of probability do not look like nor do they correspond to classical orbits. The uncertainty principle actually prevents us and nature from knowing how the electron gets from one place to another, and so an orbit really does not exist as such. Nature on a small scale is again much different from that on the large scale.

1 The spin quantum number s is usually not stated, since it is always 1/2 for electrons

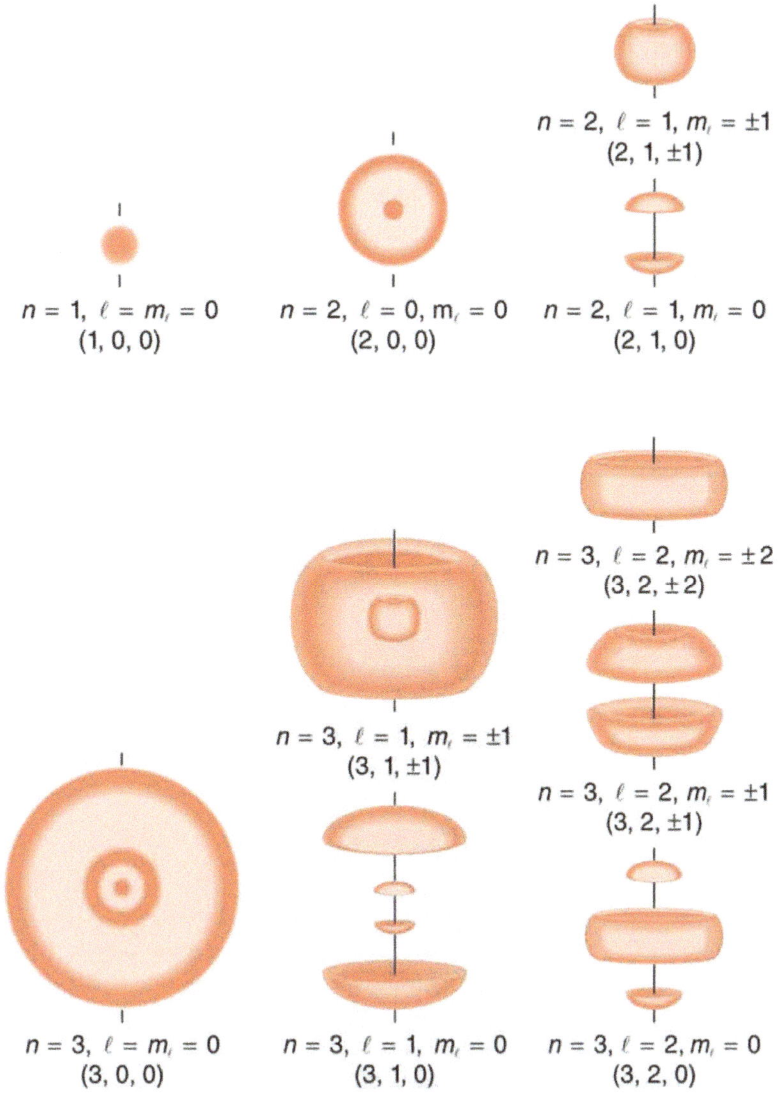

FIGURE 30.53 Probability clouds for the electron in the ground state and several excited states of hydrogen. The nature of these states is determined by their sets of quantum numbers, here given as (n, l, m_l). The ground state is (0, 0, 0); one of the possibilities for the second excited state is (3, 2, 1). The probability of finding the electron is indicated by the shade of color; the darker the coloring the greater the chance of finding the electron.

We will see that the quantum numbers discussed in this section are valid for a broad range of particles and other systems, such as nuclei. Some quantum numbers, such as intrinsic spin, are related to fundamental classifications of subatomic particles, and they obey laws that will give us further insight into the substructure of matter and its interactions.

30.9 The Pauli Exclusion Principle

LEARNING OBJECTIVES

By the end of this section, you will be able to:

- Define the composition of an atom along with its electrons, neutrons, and protons.
- Explain the Pauli exclusion principle and its application to the atom.
- Specify the shell and subshell symbols and their positions.
- Define the position of electrons in different shells of an atom.
- State the position of each element in the periodic table according to shell filling.

Multiple-Electron Atoms

All atoms except hydrogen are multiple-electron atoms. The physical and chemical properties of elements are directly related to the number of electrons a neutral atom has. The periodic table of the elements groups elements with similar properties into columns. This systematic organization is related to the number of electrons in a neutral atom, called the **atomic number**, Z. We shall see in this section that the exclusion principle is key to the underlying explanations, and that it applies far beyond the realm of atomic physics.

In 1925, the Austrian physicist Wolfgang Pauli (see Figure 30.54) proposed the following rule: No two electrons can have the same set of quantum numbers. That is, no two electrons can be in the same state. This statement is known as the **Pauli exclusion principle**, because it excludes electrons from being in the same state. The Pauli exclusion principle is extremely powerful and very broadly applicable. It applies to any identical particles with half-integral intrinsic spin—that is, having $s = 1/2, 3/2, \ldots$ Thus no two electrons can have the same set of quantum numbers.

PAULI EXCLUSION PRINCIPLE

No two electrons can have the same set of quantum numbers. That is, no two electrons can be in the same state.

FIGURE 30.54 The Austrian physicist Wolfgang Pauli (1900–1958) played a major role in the development of quantum mechanics. He proposed the exclusion principle; hypothesized the existence of an important particle, called the neutrino, before it was directly observed; made fundamental contributions to several areas of theoretical physics; and influenced many students who went on to do important work of their own. (credit: Nobel Foundation, via Wikimedia Commons)

Let us examine how the exclusion principle applies to electrons in atoms. The quantum numbers involved were defined in Quantum Numbers and Rules as n, l, m_l, s, and m_s. Since s is always $1/2$ for electrons, it is redundant to list s, and so we omit it and specify the state of an electron by a set of four numbers (n, l, m_l, m_s). For example, the quantum numbers $(2, 1, 0, -1/2)$ completely specify the state of an electron in an atom.

Since no two electrons can have the same set of quantum numbers, there are limits to how many of them can be in the same energy state. Note that n determines the energy state in the absence of a magnetic field. So we first choose n, and then we see how many electrons can be in this energy state or energy level. Consider the $n = 1$ level, for example. The only value l can have is 0 (see Table 30.1 for a list of possible values once n is known), and thus m_l can only be 0. The spin projection m_s can be either $+1/2$ or $-1/2$, and so there can be two electrons in the $n = 1$ state. One has quantum numbers $(1, 0, 0, +1/2)$, and the other has $(1, 0, 0, -1/2)$. Figure 30.55 illustrates that there can be one or two electrons having $n = 1$, but not three.

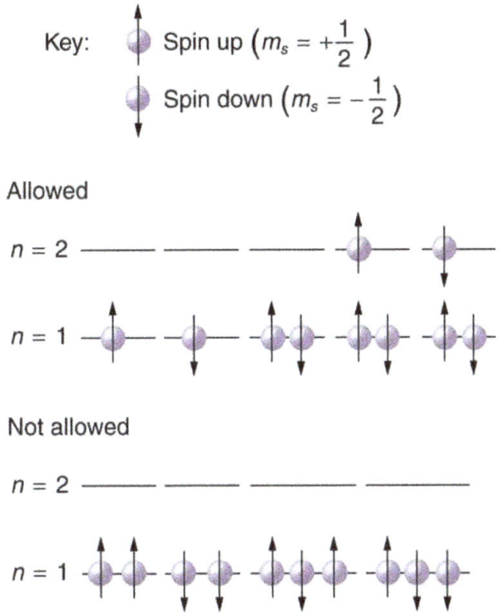

FIGURE 30.55 The Pauli exclusion principle explains why some configurations of electrons are allowed while others are not. Since electrons cannot have the same set of quantum numbers, a maximum of two can be in the $n = 1$ level, and a third electron must reside in the higher-energy $n = 2$ level. If there are two electrons in the $n = 1$ level, their spins must be in opposite directions. (More precisely, their spin projections must differ.)

Shells and Subshells

Because of the Pauli exclusion principle, only hydrogen and helium can have all of their electrons in the $n = 1$ state. Lithium (see the periodic table) has three electrons, and so one must be in the $n = 2$ level. This leads to the concept of shells and shell filling. As we progress up in the number of electrons, we go from hydrogen to helium, lithium, beryllium, boron, and so on, and we see that there are limits to the number of electrons for each value of n. Higher values of the shell n correspond to higher energies, and they can allow more electrons because of the various combinations of l, m_l, and m_s that are possible. Each value of the principal quantum number n thus corresponds to an atomic **shell** into which a limited number of electrons can go. Shells and the number of electrons in them determine the physical and chemical properties of atoms, since it is the outermost electrons that interact most with anything outside the atom.

The probability clouds of electrons with the lowest value of l are closest to the nucleus and, thus, more tightly bound. Thus when shells fill, they start with $l = 0$, progress to $l = 1$, and so on. Each value of l thus corresponds to a **subshell**.

The table given below lists symbols traditionally used to denote shells and subshells.

Shell	Subshell	
n	l	***Symbol***
1	0	s
2	1	p
3	2	d
4	3	f

TABLE 30.2 Shell and Subshell Symbols

Shell	Subshell	
5	4	g
	5	h
	6[2]	i

TABLE 30.2 Shell and Subshell Symbols

To denote shells and subshells, we write nl with a number for n and a letter for l. For example, an electron in the $n = 1$ state must have $l = 0$, and it is denoted as a $1s$ electron. Two electrons in the $n = 1$ state is denoted as $1s^2$. Another example is an electron in the $n = 2$ state with $l = 1$, written as $2p$. The case of three electrons with these quantum numbers is written $2p^3$. This notation, called spectroscopic notation, is generalized as shown in Figure 30.56.

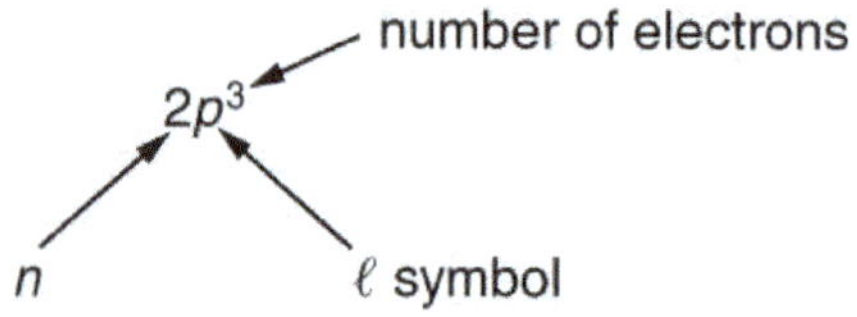

FIGURE 30.56

Counting the number of possible combinations of quantum numbers allowed by the exclusion principle, we can determine how many electrons it takes to fill each subshell and shell.

EXAMPLE 30.4

How Many Electrons Can Be in This Shell?

List all the possible sets of quantum numbers for the $n = 2$ shell, and determine the number of electrons that can be in the shell and each of its subshells.

Strategy

Given $n = 2$ for the shell, the rules for quantum numbers limit l to be 0 or 1. The shell therefore has two subshells, labeled $2s$ and $2p$. Since the lowest l subshell fills first, we start with the $2s$ subshell possibilities and then proceed with the $2p$ subshell.

Solution

It is convenient to list the possible quantum numbers in a table, as shown below.

2 It is unusual to deal with subshells having l greater than 6, but when encountered, they continue to be labeled in alphabetical order.

n	*ℓ*	m_l	m_s	Subshell	Total in subshell	Total in shell
2	0	0	+1/2	2*s*	2	8
2	0	0	−1/2			
2	1	1	+1/2	2*p*	6	
2	1	1	−1/2			
2	1	0	+1/2			
2	1	0	−1/2			
2	1	−1	+1/2			
2	1	−1	−1/2			

FIGURE 30.57

Discussion

It is laborious to make a table like this every time we want to know how many electrons can be in a shell or subshell. There exist general rules that are easy to apply, as we shall now see.

The number of electrons that can be in a subshell depends entirely on the value of l. Once l is known, there are a fixed number of values of m_l, each of which can have two values for m_s First, since m_l goes from $-l$ to l in steps of 1, there are $2l+1$ possibilities. This number is multiplied by 2, since each electron can be spin up or spin down. Thus the *maximum number of electrons that can be in a subshell* is $2(2l+1)$.

For example, the $2s$ subshell in Example 30.4 has a maximum of 2 electrons in it, since $2(2l+1)=2(0+1)=2$ for this subshell. Similarly, the $2p$ subshell has a maximum of 6 electrons, since $2(2l+1)=2(2+1)=6$. For a shell, the maximum number is the sum of what can fit in the subshells. Some algebra shows that the *maximum number of electrons that can be in a shell* is $2n^2$.

For example, for the first shell $n=1$, and so $2n^2=2$. We have already seen that only two electrons can be in the $n=1$ shell. Similarly, for the second shell, $n=2$, and so $2n^2=8$. As found in Example 30.4, the total number of electrons in the $n=2$ shell is 8.

EXAMPLE 30.5

Subshells and Totals for $n=3$

How many subshells are in the $n=3$ shell? Identify each subshell, calculate the maximum number of electrons that will fit into each, and verify that the total is $2n^2$.

Strategy

Subshells are determined by the value of l; thus, we first determine which values of l are allowed, and then we apply the equation "maximum number of electrons that can be in a subshell $=2(2l+1)$" to find the number of electrons in each subshell.

Solution

Since $n=3$, we know that l can be 0, 1, or 2; thus, there are three possible subshells. In standard notation, they are labeled the $3s$, $3p$, and $3d$ subshells. We have already seen that 2 electrons can be in an s state, and 6 in a p state, but let us use the equation "maximum number of electrons that can be in a subshell = $2(2l+1)$" to calculate the maximum number in each:

$$\begin{aligned}
&3s \text{ has } l = 0; \text{ thus, } 2(2l+1)= 2(0+1)= 2 \\
&3p \text{ has } l = 1; \text{ thus, } 2(2l+1)= 2(2+1)= 6 \\
&3d \text{ has } l = 2; \text{ thus, } 2(2l+1)= 2(4+1)= 10 \\
&\text{Total} = 18 \\
&(\text{in the } n = 3 \text{ shell})
\end{aligned} \tag{30.55}$$

The equation "maximum number of electrons that can be in a shell = $2n^2$" gives the maximum number in the $n = 3$ shell to be

$$\text{Maximum number of electrons} = 2n^2 = 2(3)^2 = 2(9)= 18. \tag{30.56}$$

Discussion

The total number of electrons in the three possible subshells is thus the same as the formula $2n^2$. In standard (spectroscopic) notation, a filled $n = 3$ shell is denoted as $3s^2 3p^6 3d^{10}$. Shells do not fill in a simple manner. Before the $n = 3$ shell is completely filled, for example, we begin to find electrons in the $n = 4$ shell.

Shell Filling and the Periodic Table

Table 30.3 shows electron configurations for the first 20 elements in the periodic table, starting with hydrogen and its single electron and ending with calcium. The Pauli exclusion principle determines the maximum number of electrons allowed in each shell and subshell. But the order in which the shells and subshells are filled is complicated because of the large numbers of interactions between electrons.

Element	Number of electrons (Z)	Ground state configuration					
H	1	$1s^1$					
He	2	$1s^2$					
Li	3	$1s^2$	$2s^1$				
Be	4	"	$2s^2$				
B	5	"	$2s^2$	$2p^1$			
C	6	"	$2s^2$	$2p^2$			
N	7	"	$2s^2$	$2p^3$			
O	8	"	$2s^2$	$2p^4$			
F	9	"	$2s^2$	$2p^5$			
Ne	10	"	$2s^2$	$2p^6$			
Na	11	"	$2s^2$	$2p^6$	$3s^1$		
Mg	12	"	"	"	$3s^2$		
Al	13	"	"	"	$3s^2$	$3p^1$	

TABLE 30.3 Electron Configurations of Elements Hydrogen Through Calcium

Element	Number of electrons (Z)	Ground state configuration					
Si	14	"	"	"	$3s^2$	$3p^2$	
P	15	"	"	"	$3s^2$	$3p^3$	
S	16	"	"	"	$3s^2$	$3p^4$	
Cl	17	"	"	"	$3s^2$	$3p^5$	
Ar	18	"	"	"	$3s^2$	$3p^6$	
K	19	"	"	"	$3s^2$	$3p^6$	$4s^1$
Ca	20	"	"	"	"	"	$4s^2$

TABLE 30.3 Electron Configurations of Elements Hydrogen Through Calcium

Examining the above table, you can see that as the number of electrons in an atom increases from 1 in hydrogen to 2 in helium and so on, the lowest-energy shell gets filled first—that is, the $n = 1$ shell fills first, and then the $n = 2$ shell begins to fill. Within a shell, the subshells fill starting with the lowest l, or with the s subshell, then the p, and so on, usually until all subshells are filled. The first exception to this occurs for potassium, where the $4s$ subshell begins to fill before any electrons go into the $3d$ subshell. The next exception is not shown in Table 30.3; it occurs for rubidium, where the $5s$ subshell starts to fill before the $4d$ subshell. The reason for these exceptions is that $l = 0$ electrons have probability clouds that penetrate closer to the nucleus and, thus, are more tightly bound (lower in energy).

Figure 30.58 shows the periodic table of the elements, through element 118. Of special interest are elements in the main groups, namely, those in the columns numbered 1, 2, 13, 14, 15, 16, 17, and 18.

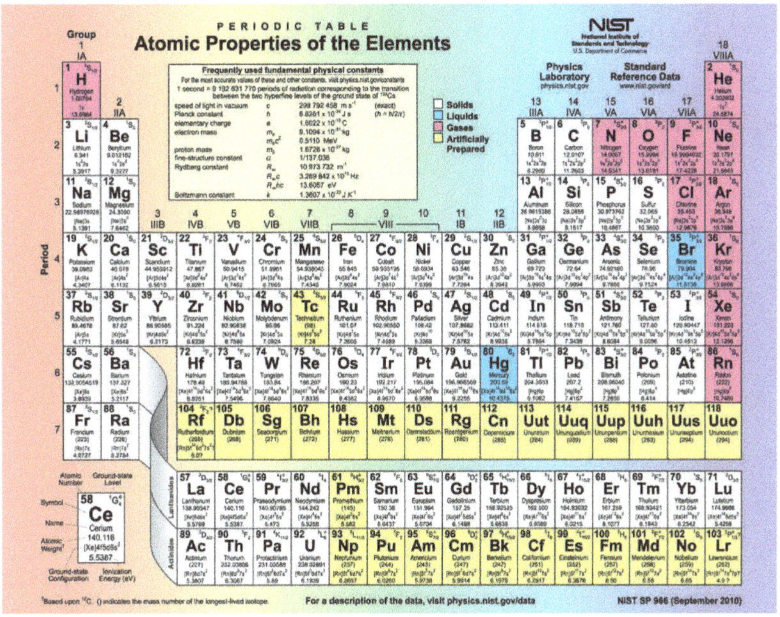

FIGURE 30.58 Periodic table of the elements (credit: National Institute of Standards and Technology, U.S. Department of Commerce)

The number of electrons in the outermost subshell determines the atom's chemical properties, since it is these electrons that are farthest from the nucleus and thus interact most with other atoms. If the outermost subshell can accept or give up an electron easily, then the atom will be highly reactive chemically. Each group in the periodic table is characterized by its outermost electron configuration. Perhaps the most familiar is Group 18 (Group VIII), the noble gases (helium, neon, argon, etc.). These gases are all characterized by a filled outer subshell that is particularly stable. This means that they have large ionization energies and do not readily give up an electron. Furthermore, if they were to accept an extra electron, it would be in a significantly higher level and thus loosely bound. Chemical reactions often involve sharing electrons. Noble gases can be forced into unstable chemical compounds only under high pressure and temperature.

Group 17 (Group VII) contains the halogens, such as fluorine, chlorine, iodine and bromine, each of which has one less electron than a neighboring noble gas. Each halogen has 5 p electrons (a p^5 configuration), while the p subshell can hold 6 electrons. This means the halogens have one vacancy in their outermost subshell. They thus readily accept an extra electron (it becomes tightly bound, closing the shell as in noble gases) and are highly reactive chemically. The halogens are also likely to form singly negative ions, such as Cl^-, fitting an extra electron into the vacancy in the outer subshell. In contrast, alkali metals, such as sodium and potassium, all have a single s electron in their outermost subshell (an s^1 configuration) and are members of Group 1 (Group I). These elements easily give up their extra electron and are thus highly reactive chemically. As you might expect, they also tend to form singly positive ions, such as Na^+, by losing their loosely bound outermost electron. They are metals (conductors), because the loosely bound outer electron can move freely.

Of course, other groups are also of interest. Carbon, silicon, and germanium, for example, have similar chemistries and are in Group 4 (Group IV). Carbon, in particular, is extraordinary in its ability to form many types of bonds and to be part of long chains, such as inorganic molecules. The large group of what are called transitional elements is characterized by the filling of the d subshells and crossing of energy levels. Heavier groups, such as the lanthanide series, are more complex—their shells do not fill in simple order. But the groups recognized by chemists such as Mendeleev have an explanation in the substructure of atoms.

Glossary

angular momentum quantum number a quantum number associated with the angular momentum of electrons

atom basic unit of matter, which consists of a central, positively charged nucleus surrounded by negatively charged electrons

atomic de-excitation process by which an atom transfers from an excited electronic state back to the ground state electronic configuration; often occurs by emission of a photon

atomic excitation a state in which an atom or ion acquires the necessary energy to promote one or more of its electrons to electronic states higher in energy than their ground state

atomic number the number of protons in the nucleus of an atom

Bohr radius the mean radius of the orbit of an electron around the nucleus of a hydrogen atom in its ground state

Brownian motion the continuous random movement of particles of matter suspended in a liquid or gas

cathode-ray tube a vacuum tube containing a source of electrons and a screen to view images

double-slit interference an experiment in which waves or particles from a single source impinge upon two slits so that the resulting interference pattern may be observed

energies of hydrogen-like atoms Bohr formula for energies of electron states in hydrogen-like atoms: $E_n = -\frac{Z^2}{n^2}E_0 (n = 1, 2, 3, \ldots)$

energy-level diagram a diagram used to analyze the energy level of electrons in the orbits of an atom

fine structure the splitting of spectral lines of the hydrogen spectrum when the spectral lines are examined at very high resolution

fluorescence any process in which an atom or molecule, excited by a photon of a given energy, de-excites by emission of a lower-energy photon

hologram means *entire picture* (from the Greek word *holo*, as in holistic), because the image produced is three dimensional

holography the process of producing holograms

hydrogen spectrum wavelengths the wavelengths of visible light from hydrogen; can be calculated by $\frac{1}{\lambda} = R\left(\frac{1}{n_f^2} - \frac{1}{n_i^2}\right)$

hydrogen-like atom any atom with only a single electron

intrinsic magnetic field the magnetic field generated due to the intrinsic spin of electrons

intrinsic spin the internal or intrinsic angular momentum of electrons

laser acronym for light amplification by stimulated emission of radiation

magnitude of the intrinsic (internal) spin angular momentum given by $S = \sqrt{s(s+1)}\frac{h}{2\pi}$

metastable a state whose lifetime is an order of magnitude longer than the most short-lived states

orbital angular momentum an angular momentum that corresponds to the quantum analog of classical angular momentum

orbital magnetic field the magnetic field generated due to the orbital motion of electrons

Pauli exclusion principle a principle that states that no two electrons can have the same set of quantum numbers; that is, no two electrons can be in the same state

phosphorescence the de-excitation of a metastable state

planetary model of the atom the most familiar model or illustration of the structure of the atom

population inversion the condition in which the majority of atoms in a sample are in a metastable state

quantum numbers the values of quantized entities, such as energy and angular momentum

Rydberg constant a physical constant related to the atomic spectra with an established value of $1.097 \times 10^7 \text{ m}^{-1}$

shell a probability cloud for electrons that has a single principal quantum number

space quantization the fact that the orbital angular momentum can have only certain directions

spin projection quantum number quantum number that can be used to calculate the intrinsic electron angular momentum along the z-axis

spin quantum number the quantum number that parameterizes the intrinsic angular momentum (or spin angular momentum, or simply spin) of a given particle

stimulated emission emission by atom or molecule in which an excited state is stimulated to decay, most readily caused by a photon of the same energy that is necessary to excite the state

subshell the probability cloud for electrons that has a single angular momentum quantum number l

x rays a form of electromagnetic radiation

x-ray diffraction a technique that provides the detailed information about crystallographic structure of natural and manufactured materials

z-component of spin angular momentum component of intrinsic electron spin along the z

-axis

z-component of the angular momentum component of orbital angular momentum of electron along the z -axis

Zeeman effect the effect of external magnetic fields on spectral lines

Section Summary

30.1 Discovery of the Atom

- Atoms are the smallest unit of elements; atoms combine to form molecules, the smallest unit of compounds.
- The first direct observation of atoms was in Brownian motion.
- Analysis of Brownian motion gave accurate sizes for atoms (10^{-10} m on average) and a precise value for Avogadro's number.

30.2 Discovery of the Parts of the Atom: Electrons and Nuclei

- Atoms are composed of negatively charged electrons, first proved to exist in cathode-ray-tube experiments, and a positively charged nucleus.
- All electrons are identical and have a charge-to-mass ratio of
  $$\frac{q_e}{m_e} = -1.76 \times 10^{11} \text{ C/kg}.$$
- The positive charge in the nuclei is carried by particles called protons, which have a charge-to-mass ratio of
  $$\frac{q_p}{m_p} = 9.57 \times 10^{7} \text{ C/kg}.$$
- Mass of electron,
  $$m_e = 9.11 \times 10^{-31} \text{ kg}.$$
- Mass of proton,
  $$m_p = 1.67 \times 10^{-27} \text{ kg}.$$
- The planetary model of the atom pictures electrons orbiting the nucleus in the same way that planets orbit the sun.

30.3 Bohr's Theory of the Hydrogen Atom

- The planetary model of the atom pictures electrons orbiting the nucleus in the way that planets orbit the sun. Bohr used the planetary model to develop the first reasonable theory of hydrogen, the simplest atom. Atomic and molecular spectra are quantized, with hydrogen spectrum wavelengths given by the formula
  $$\frac{1}{\lambda} = R\left(\frac{1}{n_\text{f}^2} - \frac{1}{n_\text{i}^2}\right),$$
  where λ is the wavelength of the emitted EM radiation and R is the Rydberg constant, which has the value
  $$R = 1.097 \times 10^{7} \text{ m}^{-1}.$$
- The constants n_i and n_f are positive integers, and n_i must be greater than n_f.
- Bohr correctly proposed that the energy and radii of the orbits of electrons in atoms are quantized, with energy for transitions between orbits given by
  $$\Delta E = hf = E_\text{i} - E_\text{f},$$
  where ΔE is the change in energy between the initial and final orbits and hf is the energy of an absorbed or emitted photon. It is useful to plot orbital energies on a vertical graph called an energy-level diagram.
- Bohr proposed that the allowed orbits are circular and must have quantized orbital angular momentum given by
  $$L = m_e v r_n = n\frac{h}{2\pi}(n = 1, 2, 3 \ldots),$$
  where L is the angular momentum, r_n is the radius of the nth orbit, and h is Planck's constant. For all one-electron (hydrogen-like) atoms, the radius of an orbit is given by
  $$r_n = \frac{n^2}{Z}a_\text{B}(\text{allowed orbits } n = 1, 2, 3, ...),$$
  Z is the atomic number of an element (the number of electrons is has when neutral) and a_B is defined to be the Bohr radius, which is
  $$a_\text{B} = \frac{h^2}{4\pi^2 m_e k q_e^2} = 0.529 \times 10^{-10} \text{ m}.$$
- Furthermore, the energies of hydrogen-like atoms are given by
  $$E_n = -\frac{Z^2}{n^2}E_0(n = 1, 2, 3 ...),$$
  where E_0 is the ground-state energy and is given by
  $$E_0 = \frac{2\pi^2 q_e^4 m_e k^2}{h^2} = 13.6 \text{ eV}.$$
  Thus, for hydrogen,
  $$E_n = -\frac{13.6 \text{ eV}}{n^2}(n, =, 1, 2, 3 ...).$$
- The Bohr Theory gives accurate values for the energy levels in hydrogen-like atoms, but it has been improved upon in several respects.

30.4 X Rays: Atomic Origins and Applications

- X rays are relatively high-frequency EM radiation. They are produced by transitions between inner-shell electron levels, which produce x rays characteristic of the atomic element, or by decelerating electrons.

- X rays have many uses, including medical diagnostics and x-ray diffraction.

30.5 Applications of Atomic Excitations and De-Excitations

- An important atomic process is fluorescence, defined to be any process in which an atom or molecule is excited by absorbing a photon of a given energy and de-excited by emitting a photon of a lower energy.
- Some states live much longer than others and are termed metastable.
- Phosphorescence is the de-excitation of a metastable state.
- Lasers produce coherent single-wavelength EM radiation by stimulated emission, in which a metastable state is stimulated to decay.
- Lasing requires a population inversion, in which a majority of the atoms or molecules are in their metastable state.

30.6 The Wave Nature of Matter Causes Quantization

- Quantization of orbital energy is caused by the wave nature of matter. Allowed orbits in atoms occur for constructive interference of electrons in the orbit, requiring an integral number of wavelengths to fit in an orbit's circumference; that is,
$n\lambda_n = 2\pi r_n (n = 1, 2, 3 \ldots),$
where λ_n is the electron's de Broglie wavelength.
- Owing to the wave nature of electrons and the Heisenberg uncertainty principle, there are no well-defined orbits; rather, there are clouds of probability.
- Bohr correctly proposed that the energy and radii of the orbits of electrons in atoms are quantized, with energy for transitions between orbits given by
$\Delta E = hf = E_{\mathrm{i}} - E_{\mathrm{f}},$
where ΔE is the change in energy between the initial and final orbits and hf is the energy of an absorbed or emitted photon.
- It is useful to plot orbit energies on a vertical graph called an energy-level diagram.
- The allowed orbits are circular, Bohr proposed, and must have quantized orbital angular momentum given by
$L = m_e v r_n = n\dfrac{h}{2\pi} (n = 1, 2, 3 \ldots),$
where L is the angular momentum, r_n is the radius of orbit n, and h is Planck's constant.

30.7 Patterns in Spectra Reveal More Quantization

- The Zeeman effect—the splitting of lines when a magnetic field is applied—is caused by other quantized entities in atoms.
- Both the magnitude and direction of orbital angular momentum are quantized.
- The same is true for the magnitude and direction of the intrinsic spin of electrons.

30.8 Quantum Numbers and Rules

- Quantum numbers are used to express the allowed values of quantized entities. The principal quantum number n labels the basic states of a system and is given by
$n = 1, 2, 3, \ldots.$
- The magnitude of angular momentum is given by
$L = \sqrt{l(l+1)}\dfrac{h}{2\pi} \quad (l = 0, 1, 2, \ldots, n-1),$
where l is the angular momentum quantum number. The direction of angular momentum is quantized, in that its component along an axis defined by a magnetic field, called the z-axis is given by
$$L_z = m_l \frac{h}{2\pi}$$
$(m_l, =, -, l, ,, -, l, +, 1, \ldots, ,, ,-, 1, 0, 1, \ldots, ,l, -, 1,, ,l),$
L_z is the z-component of the angular momentum and m_l is the angular momentum projection quantum number. Similarly, the electron's intrinsic spin angular momentum s is given by
$S = \sqrt{s(s+1)}\dfrac{h}{2\pi} \quad (s = 1/2 \text{ for electrons}),$
s is defined to be the spin quantum number. Finally, the direction of the electron's spin along the z-axis is given by
$S_z = m_s \dfrac{h}{2\pi} \quad \left(m_s = -\dfrac{1}{2}, +\dfrac{1}{2}\right),$
where S_z is the z-component of spin angular momentum and m_s is the spin projection quantum number. Spin projection $m_s = +1/2$ is referred to as spin up, whereas $m_s = -1/2$ is called spin down. Table 30.1 summarizes the atomic quantum numbers and their allowed values.

30.9 The Pauli Exclusion Principle

- The state of a system is completely described by a complete set of quantum numbers. This set is written as (n, l, m_l, m_s).
- The Pauli exclusion principle says that no two electrons can have the same set of quantum numbers; that is, no two electrons can be in the same state.

- This exclusion limits the number of electrons in atomic shells and subshells. Each value of n corresponds to a shell, and each value of l corresponds to a subshell.
- The maximum number of electrons that can be in a subshell is $2(2l + 1)$.
- The maximum number of electrons that can be in a shell is $2n^2$.

Conceptual Questions

30.1 Discovery of the Atom

1. Name three different types of evidence for the existence of atoms.

2. Explain why patterns observed in the periodic table of the elements are evidence for the existence of atoms, and why Brownian motion is a more direct type of evidence for their existence.

3. If atoms exist, why can't we see them with visible light?

30.2 Discovery of the Parts of the Atom: Electrons and Nuclei

4. What two pieces of evidence allowed the first calculation of m_e, the mass of the electron?
(a) The ratios q_e/m_e and q_p/m_p.
(b) The values of q_e and E_B.
(c) The ratio q_e/m_e and q_e.
Justify your response.

5. How do the allowed orbits for electrons in atoms differ from the allowed orbits for planets around the sun? Explain how the correspondence principle applies here.

30.3 Bohr's Theory of the Hydrogen Atom

6. How do the allowed orbits for electrons in atoms differ from the allowed orbits for planets around the sun? Explain how the correspondence principle applies here.

7. Explain how Bohr's rule for the quantization of electron orbital angular momentum differs from the actual rule.

8. What is a hydrogen-like atom, and how are the energies and radii of its electron orbits related to those in hydrogen?

30.4 X Rays: Atomic Origins and Applications

9. Explain why characteristic x rays are the most energetic in the EM emission spectrum of a given element.

10. Why does the energy of characteristic x rays become increasingly greater for heavier atoms?

11. Observers at a safe distance from an atmospheric test of a nuclear bomb feel its heat but receive none of its copious x rays. Why is air opaque to x rays but transparent to infrared?

12. Lasers are used to burn and read CDs. Explain why a laser that emits blue light would be capable of burning and reading more information than one that emits infrared.

13. Crystal lattices can be examined with x rays but not UV. Why?

14. CT scanners do not detect details smaller than about 0.5 mm. Is this limitation due to the wavelength of x rays? Explain.

30.5 Applications of Atomic Excitations and De-Excitations

15. How do the allowed orbits for electrons in atoms differ from the allowed orbits for planets around the sun? Explain how the correspondence principle applies here.

16. Atomic and molecular spectra are discrete. What does discrete mean, and how are discrete spectra related to the quantization of energy and electron orbits in atoms and molecules?

17. Hydrogen gas can only absorb EM radiation that has an energy corresponding to a transition in the atom, just as it can only emit these discrete energies. When a spectrum is taken of the solar corona, in which a broad range of EM wavelengths are passed through very hot hydrogen gas, the absorption spectrum shows all the features of the emission spectrum. But when such EM radiation passes through room-temperature hydrogen gas, only the Lyman series is absorbed. Explain the difference.

18. Lasers are used to burn and read CDs. Explain why a laser that emits blue light would be capable of burning and reading more information than one that emits infrared.

19. The coating on the inside of fluorescent light tubes absorbs ultraviolet light and subsequently emits visible light. An inventor claims that he is able to do the reverse process. Is the inventor's claim possible?

20. What is the difference between fluorescence and phosphorescence?

21. How can you tell that a hologram is a true three-dimensional image and that those in 3-D movies are not?

30.6 The Wave Nature of Matter Causes Quantization

22. How is the de Broglie wavelength of electrons related to the quantization of their orbits in atoms and molecules?

30.7 Patterns in Spectra Reveal More Quantization

23. What is the Zeeman effect, and what type of quantization was discovered because of this effect?

30.8 Quantum Numbers and Rules

24. Define the quantum numbers n, l, m_l, s, and m_s.

25. For a given value of n, what are the allowed values of l?

26. For a given value of l, what are the allowed values of m_l? What are the allowed values of m_l for a given value of n? Give an example in each case.

27. List all the possible values of s and m_s for an electron. Are there particles for which these values are different? The same?

30.9 The Pauli Exclusion Principle

28. Identify the shell, subshell, and number of electrons for the following: (a) $2p^3$. (b) $4d^9$. (c) $3s^1$. (d) $5g^{16}$.

29. Which of the following are not allowed? State which rule is violated for any that are not allowed. (a) $1p^3$ (b) $2p^8$ (c) $3g^{11}$ (d) $4f^2$

Problems & Exercises

30.1 Discovery of the Atom

1. Using the given charge-to-mass ratios for electrons and protons, and knowing the magnitudes of their charges are equal, what is the ratio of the proton's mass to the electron's? (Note that since the charge-to-mass ratios are given to only three-digit accuracy, your answer may differ from the accepted ratio in the fourth digit.)

2. (a) Calculate the mass of a proton using the charge-to-mass ratio given for it in this chapter and its known charge. (b) How does your result compare with the proton mass given in this chapter?

3. If someone wanted to build a scale model of the atom with a nucleus 1.00 m in diameter, how far away would the nearest electron need to be?

30.2 Discovery of the Parts of the Atom: Electrons and Nuclei

4. Rutherford found the size of the nucleus to be about 10^{-15} m. This implied a huge density. What would this density be for gold?

5. In Millikan's oil-drop experiment, one looks at a small oil drop held motionless between two plates. Take the voltage between the plates to be 2033 V, and the plate separation to be 2.00 cm. The oil drop (of density $0.81\ \text{g/cm}^3$) has a diameter of 4.0×10^{-6} m. Find the charge on the drop, in terms of electron units.

6. (a) An aspiring physicist wants to build a scale model of a hydrogen atom for her science fair project. If the atom is 1.00 m in diameter, how big should she try to make the nucleus?
(b) How easy will this be to do?

30.3 Bohr's Theory of the Hydrogen Atom

7. By calculating its wavelength, show that the first line in the Lyman series is UV radiation.

8. Find the wavelength of the third line in the Lyman series, and identify the type of EM radiation.

9. Look up the values of the quantities in $a_B = \dfrac{h^2}{4\pi^2 m_e k q_e^2}$, and verify that the Bohr radius a_B is 0.529×10^{-10} m.

10. Verify that the ground state energy E_0 is 13.6 eV by using $E_0 = \dfrac{2\pi^2 q_e^4 m_e k^2}{h^2}$.

11. If a hydrogen atom has its electron in the $n = 4$ state, how much energy in eV is needed to ionize it?

12. A hydrogen atom in an excited state can be ionized with less energy than when it is in its ground state. What is n for a hydrogen atom if 0.850 eV of energy can ionize it?

13. Find the radius of a hydrogen atom in the $n = 2$ state according to Bohr's theory.

14. Show that $(13.6\ \text{eV})/hc = 1.097 \times 10^7\ \text{m} = R$ (Rydberg's constant), as discussed in the text.

15. What is the smallest-wavelength line in the Balmer series? Is it in the visible part of the spectrum?

16. Show that the entire Paschen series is in the infrared part of the spectrum. To do this, you only need to calculate the shortest wavelength in the series.

17. Do the Balmer and Lyman series overlap? To answer this, calculate the shortest-wavelength Balmer line and the longest-wavelength Lyman line.

18. (a) Which line in the Balmer series is the first one in the UV part of the spectrum?
(b) How many Balmer series lines are in the visible part of the spectrum?
(c) How many are in the UV?

19. A wavelength of $4.653\ \mu\text{m}$ is observed in a hydrogen spectrum for a transition that ends in the $n_\text{f} = 5$ level. What was n_i for the initial level of the electron?

20. A singly ionized helium ion has only one electron and is denoted He^+. What is the ion's radius in the ground state compared to the Bohr radius of hydrogen atom?

21. A beryllium ion with a single electron (denoted Be^{3+}) is in an excited state with radius the same as that of the ground state of hydrogen.
(a) What is n for the Be^{3+} ion?
(b) How much energy in eV is needed to ionize the ion from this excited state?

22. Atoms can be ionized by thermal collisions, such as at the high temperatures found in the solar corona. One such ion is C^{+5}, a carbon atom with only a single electron.
(a) By what factor are the energies of its hydrogen-like levels greater than those of hydrogen?
(b) What is the wavelength of the first line in this ion's Paschen series?
(c) What type of EM radiation is this?

23. Verify Equations $r_n = \frac{n^2}{Z} a_\text{B}$ and $a_\text{B} = \frac{h^2}{4\pi^2 m_e k q_e^2} = 0.529 \times 10^{-10}\ \text{m}$ using the approach stated in the text. That is, equate the Coulomb and centripetal forces and then insert an expression for velocity from the condition for angular momentum quantization.

24. The wavelength of the four Balmer series lines for hydrogen are found to be 410.3, 434.2, 486.3, and 656.5 nm. What average percentage difference is found between these wavelength numbers and those predicted by $\frac{1}{\lambda} = R\left(\frac{1}{n_\text{f}^2} - \frac{1}{n_\text{i}^2}\right)$? It is amazing how well a simple formula (disconnected originally from theory) could duplicate this phenomenon.

30.4 X Rays: Atomic Origins and Applications

25. (a) What is the shortest-wavelength x-ray radiation that can be generated in an x-ray tube with an applied voltage of 50.0 kV? (b) Calculate the photon energy in eV. (c) Explain the relationship of the photon energy to the applied voltage.

26. A color television tube also generates some x rays when its electron beam strikes the screen. What is the shortest wavelength of these x rays, if a 30.0-kV potential is used to accelerate the electrons? (Note that TVs have shielding to prevent these x rays from exposing viewers.)

27. An x ray tube has an applied voltage of 100 kV. (a) What is the most energetic x-ray photon it can produce? Express your answer in electron volts and joules. (b) Find the wavelength of such an X–ray.

28. The maximum characteristic x-ray photon energy comes from the capture of a free electron into a K shell vacancy. What is this photon energy in keV for tungsten, assuming the free electron has no initial kinetic energy?

29. What are the approximate energies of the K_α and K_β x rays for copper?

30.5 Applications of Atomic Excitations and De-Excitations

30. Figure 30.37 shows the energy-level diagram for neon. (a) Verify that the energy of the photon emitted when neon goes from its metastable state to the one immediately below is equal to 1.96 eV. (b) Show that the wavelength of this radiation is 633 nm. (c) What wavelength is emitted when the neon makes a direct transition to its ground state?

31. A helium-neon laser is pumped by electric discharge. What wavelength electromagnetic radiation would be needed to pump it? See Figure 30.37 for energy-level information.

32. Ruby lasers have chromium atoms doped in an aluminum oxide crystal. The energy level diagram for chromium in a ruby is shown in Figure 30.59. What wavelength is emitted by a ruby laser?

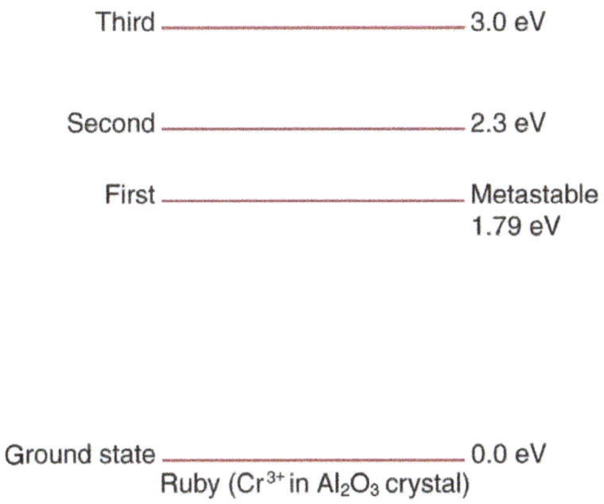

FIGURE 30.59 Chromium atoms in an aluminum oxide crystal have these energy levels, one of which is metastable. This is the basis of a ruby laser. Visible light can pump the atom into an excited state above the metastable state to achieve a population inversion.

33. (a) What energy photons can pump chromium atoms in a ruby laser from the ground state to its second and third excited states? (b) What are the wavelengths of these photons? Verify that they are in the visible part of the spectrum.

34. Some of the most powerful lasers are based on the energy levels of neodymium in solids, such as glass, as shown in Figure 30.60. (a) What average wavelength light can pump the neodymium into the levels above its metastable state? (b) Verify that the 1.17 eV transition produces $1.06\ \mu m$ radiation.

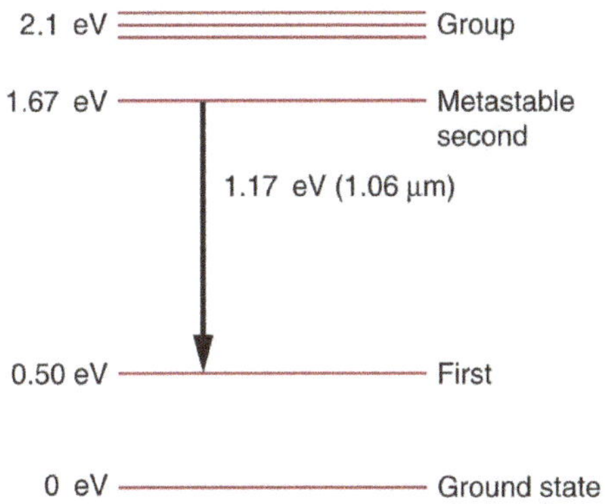

FIGURE 30.60 Neodymium atoms in glass have these energy levels, one of which is metastable. The group of levels above the metastable state is convenient for achieving a population inversion, since photons of many different energies can be absorbed by atoms in the ground state.

30.8 Quantum Numbers and Rules

35. If an atom has an electron in the $n = 5$ state with $m_l = 3$, what are the possible values of l?

36. An atom has an electron with $m_l = 2$. What is the smallest value of n for this electron?

37. What are the possible values of m_l for an electron in the $n = 4$ state?

38. What, if any, constraints does a value of $m_l = 1$ place on the other quantum numbers for an electron in an atom?

39. (a) Calculate the magnitude of the angular momentum for an $l = 1$ electron. (b) Compare your answer to the value Bohr proposed for the $n = 1$ state.

40. (a) What is the magnitude of the angular momentum for an $l = 1$ electron? (b) Calculate the magnitude of the electron's spin angular momentum. (c) What is the ratio of these angular momenta?

41. Repeat Exercise 30.40 for $l = 3$.

42. (a) How many angles can L make with the z-axis for an $l = 2$ electron? (b) Calculate the value of the smallest angle.

43. What angles can the spin s of an electron make with the z-axis?

30.9 The Pauli Exclusion Principle

44. (a) How many electrons can be in the $n = 4$ shell? (b) What are its subshells, and how many electrons can be in each?

45. (a) What is the minimum value of 1 for a subshell that has 11 electrons in it?
(b) If this subshell is in the $n = 5$ shell, what is the spectroscopic notation for this atom?

46. (a) If one subshell of an atom has 9 electrons in it, what is the minimum value of l? (b) What is the spectroscopic notation for this atom, if this subshell is part of the $n = 3$ shell?

47. (a) List all possible sets of quantum numbers (n, l, m_l, m_s) for the $n = 3$ shell, and determine the number of electrons that can be in the shell and each of its subshells.
(b) Show that the number of electrons in the shell equals $2n^2$ and that the number in each subshell is $2(2l + 1)$.

48. Which of the following spectroscopic notations are not allowed? (a) $5s^1$ (b) $1d^1$ (c) $4s^3$ (d) $3p^7$ (e) $5g^{15}$. State which rule is violated for each that is not allowed.

49. Which of the following spectroscopic notations are allowed (that is, which violate none of the rules regarding values of quantum numbers)? (a) $1s^1$ (b) $1d^3$ (c) $4s^2$ (d) $3p^7$ (e) $6h^{20}$

50. (a) Using the Pauli exclusion principle and the rules relating the allowed values of the quantum numbers (n, l, m_l, m_s), prove that the maximum number of electrons in a subshell is $2n^2$.
(b) In a similar manner, prove that the maximum number of electrons in a shell is $2n^2$.

51. Integrated Concepts
Estimate the density of a nucleus by calculating the density of a proton, taking it to be a sphere 1.2 fm in diameter. Compare your result with the value estimated in this chapter.

52. Integrated Concepts
The electric and magnetic forces on an electron in the CRT in Figure 30.7 are supposed to be in opposite directions. Verify this by determining the direction of each force for the situation shown. Explain how you obtain the directions (that is, identify the rules used).

53. (a) What is the distance between the slits of a diffraction grating that produces a first-order maximum for the first Balmer line at an angle of 20.0°?
(b) At what angle will the fourth line of the Balmer series appear in first order?
(c) At what angle will the second-order maximum be for the first line?

54. Integrated Concepts
A galaxy moving away from the earth has a speed of $0.0100c$. What wavelength do we observe for an $n_\text{i} = 7$ to $n_\text{f} = 2$ transition for hydrogen in that galaxy?

55. Integrated Concepts
Calculate the velocity of a star moving relative to the earth if you observe a wavelength of 91.0 nm for ionized hydrogen capturing an electron directly into the lowest orbital (that is, a $n_\text{i} = \infty$ to $n_\text{f} = 1$, or a Lyman series transition).

56. Integrated Concepts
In a Millikan oil-drop experiment using a setup like that in Figure 30.9, a 500-V potential difference is applied to plates separated by 2.50 cm. (a) What is the mass of an oil drop having two extra electrons that is suspended motionless by the field between the plates? (b) What is the diameter of the drop, assuming it is a sphere with the density of olive oil?

57. Integrated Concepts
What double-slit separation would produce a first-order maximum at 3.00° for 25.0-keV x rays? The small answer indicates that the wave character of x rays is best determined by having them interact with very small objects such as atoms and molecules.

58. Integrated Concepts
In a laboratory experiment designed to duplicate Thomson's determination of q_e/m_e, a beam of electrons having a velocity of 6.00×10^7 m/s enters a 5.00×10^{-3} T magnetic field. The beam moves perpendicular to the field in a path having a 6.80-cm radius of curvature. Determine q_e/m_e from these observations, and compare the result with the known value.

59. Integrated Concepts
Find the value of l, the orbital angular momentum quantum number, for the moon around the earth. The extremely large value obtained implies that it is impossible to tell the difference between adjacent quantized orbits for macroscopic objects.

60. Integrated Concepts
Particles called muons exist in cosmic rays and can be created in particle accelerators. Muons are very similar to electrons, having the same charge and spin, but they have a mass 207 times greater. When muons are captured by an atom, they orbit just like an electron but with a smaller radius, since the mass in $a_\text{B} = \frac{h^2}{4\pi^2 m_e k q_e^2} = 0.529 \times 10^{-10}$ m is 207 m_e.
(a) Calculate the radius of the $n = 1$ orbit for a muon in a uranium ion ($Z = 92$).
(b) Compare this with the 7.5-fm radius of a uranium nucleus. Note that since the muon orbits inside the electron, it falls into a hydrogen-like orbit. Since your answer is less than the radius of the nucleus, you can see that the photons emitted as the muon falls into its lowest orbit can give information about the nucleus.

61. Integrated Concepts
Calculate the minimum amount of energy in joules needed to create a population inversion in a helium-neon laser containing 1.00×10^{-4} moles of neon.

62. Integrated Concepts
A carbon dioxide laser used in surgery emits infrared radiation with a wavelength of 10.6 μm. In 1.00 ms, this laser raised the temperature of $1.00\ \text{cm}^3$ of flesh to 100°C and evaporated it.

(a) How many photons were required? You may assume flesh has the same heat of vaporization as water. (b) What was the minimum power output during the flash?

63. Integrated Concepts
Suppose an MRI scanner uses 100-MHz radio waves.
(a) Calculate the photon energy.
(b) How does this compare to typical molecular binding energies?

64. Integrated Concepts
(a) An excimer laser used for vision correction emits 193-nm UV. Calculate the photon energy in eV.
(b) These photons are used to evaporate corneal tissue, which is very similar to water in its properties. Calculate the amount of energy needed per molecule of water to make the phase change from liquid to gas. That is, divide the heat of vaporization in kJ/kg by the number of water molecules in a kilogram.
(c) Convert this to eV and compare to the photon energy. Discuss the implications.

65. Integrated Concepts
A neighboring galaxy rotates on its axis so that stars on one side move toward us as fast as 200 km/s, while those on the other side move away as fast as 200 km/s. This causes the EM radiation we receive to be Doppler shifted by velocities over the entire range of ±200 km/s. What range of wavelengths will we observe for the 656.0-nm line in the Balmer series of hydrogen emitted by stars in this galaxy. (This is called line broadening.)

66. Integrated Concepts
A pulsar is a rapidly spinning remnant of a supernova. It rotates on its axis, sweeping hydrogen along with it so that hydrogen on one side moves toward us as fast as 50.0 km/s, while that on the other side moves away as fast as 50.0 km/s. This means that the EM radiation we receive will be Doppler shifted over a range of $\pm 50.0 \text{ km/s}$. What range of wavelengths will we observe for the 91.20-nm line in the Lyman series of hydrogen? (Such line broadening is observed and actually provides part of the evidence for rapid rotation.)

67. Integrated Concepts
Prove that the velocity of charged particles moving along a straight path through perpendicular electric and magnetic fields is $v = E/B$. Thus crossed electric and magnetic fields can be used as a velocity selector independent of the charge and mass of the particle involved.

68. Unreasonable Results
(a) What voltage must be applied to an X-ray tube to obtain 0.0100-fm-wavelength X-rays for use in exploring the details of nuclei? (b) What is unreasonable about this result? (c) Which assumptions are unreasonable or inconsistent?

69. Unreasonable Results
A student in a physics laboratory observes a hydrogen spectrum with a diffraction grating for the purpose of measuring the wavelengths of the emitted radiation. In the spectrum, she observes a yellow line and finds its wavelength to be 589 nm. (a) Assuming this is part of the Balmer series, determine n_i, the principal quantum number of the initial state. (b) What is unreasonable about this result? (c) Which assumptions are unreasonable or inconsistent?

70. Construct Your Own Problem
The solar corona is so hot that most atoms in it are ionized. Consider a hydrogen-like atom in the corona that has only a single electron. Construct a problem in which you calculate selected spectral energies and wavelengths of the Lyman, Balmer, or other series of this atom that could be used to identify its presence in a very hot gas. You will need to choose the atomic number of the atom, identify the element, and choose which spectral lines to consider.

71. Construct Your Own Problem
Consider the Doppler-shifted hydrogen spectrum received from a rapidly receding galaxy. Construct a problem in which you calculate the energies of selected spectral lines in the Balmer series and examine whether they can be described with a formula like that in the equation $\frac{1}{\lambda} = R\left(\frac{1}{n_f^2} - \frac{1}{n_i^2}\right)$, but with a different constant R.

72. Critical Thinking (a) For carbon, calculate the energy when an electron falls from $n = 3$ to $n = 2$, then from $n = 2$ to $n = 1$. Then add these for the total energy released in the process. (b) Calculate the energy released when the electron falls directly from $n = 3$ to $n = 1$. (c) Are the energies in part a and in part b the same?

Test Prep for AP® Courses

30.2 Discovery of the Parts of the Atom: Electrons and Nuclei

1. In an experiment, three microscopic latex spheres are sprayed into a chamber and become charged with $+3e$, $+5e$, and $-3e$, respectively. Later, all three spheres collide simultaneously and then separate. Which of the following are possible values for the final charges on the spheres? Select two answers.
   a. $+4e, -4e, +5e$
   b. $-4e, +4.5e, +4.5e$
   c. $+5e, -8e, +7e$
   d. $+6e, +6e, -7e$

2. In Millikan's oil drop experiment, he experimented with various voltage differences between two plates to determine what voltage was necessary to hold a drop motionless. He deduced that the charge on the oil drop could be found by setting the gravitational force on the drop (pointing downward) equal to the electric force (pointing upward):
   $m_{\text{drop}}g = qE,$
   where m_{drop} is the mass of the oil drop, g is the gravitational acceleration (9.8 m/s^2), q is the net charge of the oil drop, and E is the electric field between the plates. Millikan deduced that the charge on an electron, e, is 1.6×10^{-19} C.
   For a system of oil drops of equal mass (1.0×10^{-15} kilograms), describe what value or values of the electric field would hold the drops motionless.

30.3 Bohr's Theory of the Hydrogen Atom

3. A hypothetical one-electron atom in its highest excited state can only emit photons of energy $2E$, $3E$, and $5E$ before reaching the ground state. Which of the following represents the complete set of energy levels for this atom?
   a. $0, 3E, 5E$
   b. $0, 2E, 3E$
   c. $0, 2E, 3E, 5E$
   d. $0, 5E, 8E, 10E$

4. The Lyman series of photons each have an energy capable of exciting the electron of a hydrogen atom from the ground state (energy level 1) to energy levels 2, 3, 4, etc. The wavelengths of the first five photons in this series are 121.6 nm, 102.6 nm, 97.3 nm, 95.0 nm, and 93.8 nm. The ground state energy of hydrogen is −13.6 eV. Based on the wavelengths of the Lyman series, calculate the energies of the first five excited states above ground level for a hydrogen atom to the nearest 0.1 eV.

5. The ground state of a certain type of atom has energy $-E_0$. What is the wavelength of a photon with enough energy to ionize an atom in the ground state and give the ejected electron a kinetic energy of $2E_0$?
   a. $\frac{hc}{3E_0}$
   b. $\frac{hc}{2E_0}$
   c. $\frac{hc}{E_0}$
   d. $\frac{2hc}{E_0}$

6. An electron in a hydrogen atom is initially in energy level 2 (E_2 = -3.4 eV). (a) What frequency of photon must be absorbed by the atom in order for the electron to transition to energy level 3 (E_3 = -1.5 eV)? (b) What frequency of photon must be emitted by the atom in order for the electron to transition to energy level 1 (E_1 = -13.6 eV)?

30.5 Applications of Atomic Excitations and De-Excitations

7. A sample of hydrogen gas confined to a tube is initially at room temperature. As the gas is heated, the observer notices that the gas begins to glow with a pale pink color. Careful study of the spectrum shows that the light spectrum is not continuous. Instead, the hydrogen gas is only emitting visible wavelength photons of four specific colors, which combine to form the overall color to the human eye. What is the best way to explain this behavior?
   a. As the gas heats up, atoms have more and more collisions and close approaches, so frictional heating causes the gas to glow.
   b. As the gas heats up, the electrons within the hydrogen atoms are excited to high energy levels. As the electrons transition to lower energies, they emit light of specific colors.
   c. As the gas heats up, more and more collisions occur, and the energy lost in these inelastic collisions is converted into light.
   d. As the gas heats up, the turbulence of the gas within the tube causes friction between the gas and the walls of the container, causing the gas to glow.

8. A rock is illuminated with high energy ultraviolet light. This causes the rock to emit visible light. Explain what is happening in the atomic substructure of the rock that causes this effect, which we call fluorescence.

9. Which of the following is the best way of explaining why the leaves on a given tree are green?
   a. The molecules in the leaves absorb all visible light but strongly reflect green light.
   b. The molecules in the leaves absorb green light and reflect other visible light.
   c. The molecules are excited by external light sources, and their electrons emit green light when they are de-excited to a lower energy level within the molecules.
   d. The molecules glow with a characteristic green energy in order to balance the absorption of energy due to light and heat from their surroundings.

10. Explain what phosphorescence is and how it differs from fluorescence. Which process typically takes longer and why?

11. An electron is excited from the ground state of an atom (energy level 1) into a highly excited state (energy level 8). Which of the following electron behaviors represents the fluorescence effect by the atom?
    a. The electron remains at level 8 for a very long time, then transitions up to level 9.
    b. The electron transitions directly down from level 8 to level 1.
    c. The electron transitions from level 8 to level 1 and then returns quickly to level 8.
    d. The electron transitions from level 8 to level 6, then to level 5, then to level 3, then to level 1.

12. Describe the process of fluorescence in terms of the emission of photons as electron transitions between energy states. Specifically, explain how this process differs from ordinary atomic emission.

30.6 The Wave Nature of Matter Causes Quantization

13.

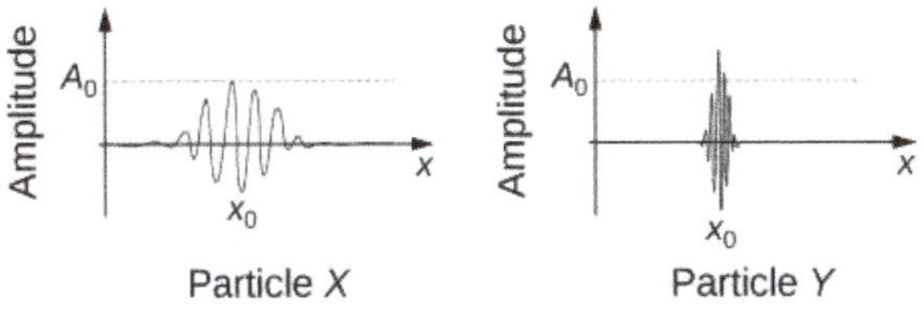

FIGURE 30.61 This figure shows graphical representations of the wave functions of two particles, X and Y, that are moving in the positive x-direction. The maximum amplitude of particle X's wave function is A_0. Which particle has a greater probability of being located at position x_0 at this instant, and why?

   a. Particle X, because the wave function of particle X spends more time passing through x_0 than the wave function of particle Y.
   b. Particle X, because the wave function of particle X has a longer wavelength than the wave function of particle Y.
   c. Particle Y, because the wave function of particle Y is narrower than the wave function of particle X.
   d. Particle Y, because the wave function of particle Y has a greater amplitude near x_0 than the wave function of particle X.

14. In Figure 30.61, explain qualitatively the difference in the wave functions of particle X and particle Y. Which particle is more likely to be found at a larger distance from the coordinate x_0 and why? Which particle is more likely be found exactly at x_0 and why?

15. For an electron with a de Broglie wavelength λ, which of the following orbital circumferences within the atom would be disallowed? Select two answers.
    a. $0.5\,\lambda$
    b. λ
    c. $1.5\,\lambda$
    d. $2\,\lambda$

16. We have discovered that an electron's orbit must contain an integer number of de Broglie wavelengths. Explain why, under ordinary conditions, this makes it impossible for electrons to spiral in to merge with the positively charged nucleus.

CHAPTER 31
Radioactivity and Nuclear Physics

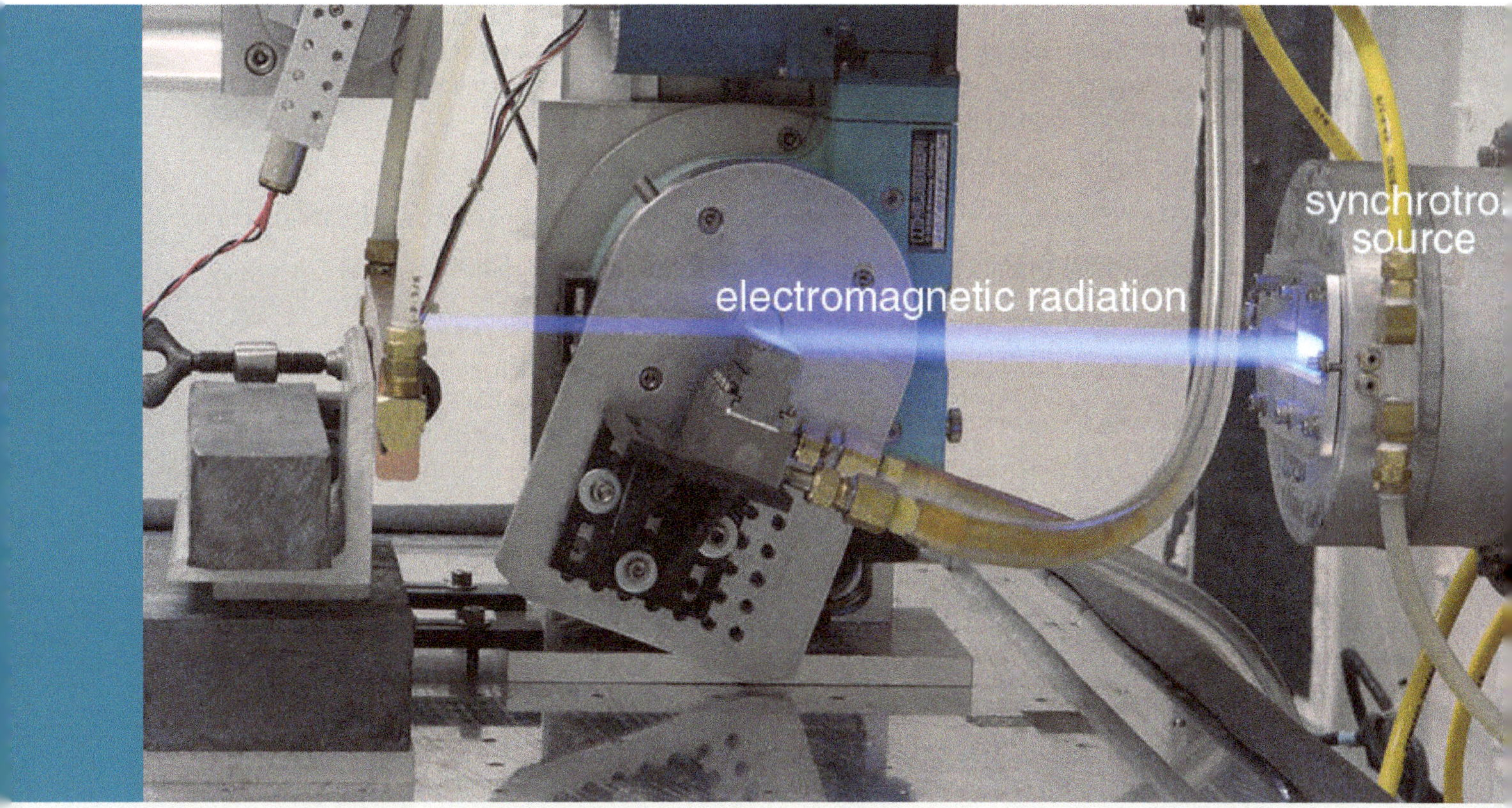

FIGURE 31.1 The synchrotron source produces electromagnetic radiation, as evident from the visible glow. (credit: United States Department of Energy, via Wikimedia Commons)

CHAPTER OUTLINE

CONNECTION FOR AP® COURSES In this chapter, students will explore radioactivity and nuclear physics. Students will learn about the structure and properties of a nucleus (Enduring Understanding 1.A, Essential Knowledge 1.A.3), supporting Big Idea 1. Students will also study the forces that govern the behavior of the nucleus, including the weak force and the strong force (Enduring Understanding 3.G). This supports Big Idea 3 by explaining that interactions can be described by forces, such as the strong force between nucleons holding the nucleus together.

Students will also learn the conservation laws associated with nuclear physics, such as conservation of energy (Enduring Understanding 5.B), conservation of charge (Enduring Understanding 5.C) and conservation of nucleon number (Enduring Understanding 5.G). Students will study the processes that can be described using conservation laws (Big Idea 5), such as radioactive decay, nuclear absorption and emission of nuclear energy, usually regulated by photons (Essential Knowledge 5.B.8). As part of the study of conservation laws, students will explore the consequences of charge conservation (Essential Knowledge 5.C.1) during radioactive decay and during interactions between nuclei (Essential Knowledge 5.C.2). Students will also learn how conservation of nucleon number determines which nuclear reactions can occur (Essential Knowledge 5.G.1). Students will also study types of nuclear radiation, radioactivity, and the binding energy of a nucleus.

This chapter also supports Big Idea 7 by exploring how probability can describe the behavior of quantum mechanical systems. Students will study the process of radioactive decay, which can be described by probability theory. Students will also explore examples demonstrating spontaneous radioactive decay as a probabilistic statistical process (Essential Knowledge 7.C.3), thus making a connection between modeling matter with a wave function and probabilistic description of the microscopic world (Enduring Understanding 7.C).

The content in this chapter supports:

Big Idea 1 Objects and systems have properties such as mass and charge. Systems may have internal structure.

Enduring Understanding 1.A The internal structure of a system determines many properties of the system.

Essential Knowledge 1.A.3 Nuclei have internal structures that determine their properties.

Big Idea 3 The interactions of an object with other objects can be described by forces.

Enduring Understanding 3.G Certain types of forces are considered fundamental.

Essential Knowledge 3.G.3 The strong force is exerted at nuclear scales and dominates the interactions of nucleons.

Big Idea 5 Changes that occur as a result of interactions are constrained by conservation laws.

Enduring Understanding 5.B The energy of a system is conserved.

Essential Knowledge 5.B.8 Energy transfer occurs when photons are absorbed or emitted, for example, by atoms or nuclei.

Enduring Understanding 5.C The electric charge of a system is conserved.

Essential Knowledge 5.C.1 Electric charge is conserved in nuclear and elementary particle reactions, even when elementary particles are produced or destroyed. Examples should include equations representing nuclear decay.

Essential Knowledge 5.C.2 The exchange of electric charges among a set of objects in a system conserves electric charge.

Enduring Understanding 5.G Nucleon number is conserved.

Essential Knowledge 5.G.1 The possible nuclear reactions are constrained by the law of conservation of nucleon number.

Big Idea 7 The mathematics of probability can be used to describe the behavior of complex systems and to interpret the behavior of quantum mechanical systems.

Enduring Understanding 7.C At the quantum scale, matter is described by a wave function, which leads to a probabilistic description of the microscopic world.

Essential Knowledge 7.C.3 The spontaneous radioactive decay of an individual nucleus is described by probability.

31.1 Nuclear Radioactivity

LEARNING OBJECTIVES

By the end of this section, you will be able to:

- Explain nuclear radiation.
- Explain the types of radiation—alpha emission, beta emission, and gamma emission.
- Explain the ionization of radiation in an atom.
- Define the range of radiation.

The discovery and study of nuclear radioactivity quickly revealed evidence of revolutionary new physics. In addition, uses for nuclear radiation also emerged quickly—for example, people such as Ernest Rutherford used it to determine the size of the nucleus and devices were painted with radon-doped paint to make them glow in the dark (see Figure 31.2). We therefore begin our study of nuclear physics with the discovery and basic features of nuclear radioactivity.

FIGURE 31.2 The dials of this World War II aircraft glow in the dark, because they are painted with radium-doped phosphorescent paint. It is a poignant reminder of the dual nature of radiation. Although radium paint dials are conveniently visible day and night, they emit radon, a radioactive gas that is hazardous and is not directly sensed. (credit: U.S. Air Force Photo)

Discovery of Nuclear Radioactivity

In 1896, the French physicist Antoine Henri Becquerel (1852–1908) accidentally found that a uranium-rich mineral called pitchblende emits invisible, penetrating rays that can darken a photographic plate enclosed in an opaque envelope. The rays therefore carry energy; but amazingly, the pitchblende emits them continuously without any energy input. This is an apparent violation of the law of conservation of energy, one that we now understand is due to the conversion of a small amount of mass into energy, as related in Einstein's famous equation $E = mc^2$. It was soon evident that Becquerel's rays originate in the nuclei of the atoms and have other unique characteristics. The emission of these rays is called **nuclear radioactivity** or simply **radioactivity**. The rays themselves are called **nuclear radiation**. A nucleus that spontaneously destroys part of its mass to emit radiation is said to **decay** (a term also used to describe the emission of radiation by atoms in excited states). A substance or object that emits nuclear radiation is said to be **radioactive**.

Two types of experimental evidence imply that Becquerel's rays originate deep in the heart (or nucleus) of an atom. First, the radiation is found to be associated with certain elements, such as uranium. Radiation does not vary with chemical state—that is, uranium is radioactive whether it is in the form of an element or compound. In addition, radiation does not vary with temperature, pressure, or ionization state of the uranium atom. Since all of these factors affect electrons in an atom, the radiation cannot come from electron transitions, as atomic spectra do. The huge energy emitted during each event is the second piece of evidence that the radiation cannot be atomic. Nuclear radiation has energies of the order of 10^6 eV per event, which is much greater than the typical atomic energies (a few eV), such as that observed in spectra and chemical reactions, and more than ten times as high as the most energetic characteristic x rays. Becquerel did not vigorously pursue his discovery for very long. In 1898, Marie Curie (1867–1934), then a graduate student married to the already well-known French physicist Pierre Curie (1859–1906), began her doctoral study of Becquerel's rays. She and her husband soon discovered two new radioactive elements, which she named *polonium* (after her native land) and *radium* (because it radiates). These two new elements filled holes in the periodic table and, further, displayed much higher levels of radioactivity per gram of material than uranium. Over a period of four years, working under poor conditions and spending their own funds, the Curies processed more than a ton of uranium ore to isolate a gram of radium salt. Radium became highly sought after, because it was about two million times as radioactive as uranium. Curie's radium salt glowed visibly from the radiation that took its toll on them and other unaware researchers. Shortly after completing her Ph.D., both Curies and Becquerel shared the 1903 Nobel Prize in physics for their work on radioactivity. Pierre was killed in a horse cart accident in 1906, but Marie continued her study of radioactivity for nearly 30 more years. Awarded the 1911 Nobel Prize in chemistry for her discovery of two new elements, she remains the only person to win Nobel Prizes in physics and chemistry. Marie's radioactive fingerprints on some pages of her notebooks can still expose film, and she suffered from radiation-induced lesions. She died of leukemia likely caused by radiation, but she was active in research almost until her death in 1934. The following year, her daughter and son-in-law, Irene and Frederic Joliot-Curie, were awarded the Nobel Prize in chemistry for their discovery of artificially induced radiation, adding to a remarkable family legacy.

Alpha, Beta, and Gamma

Research begun by people such as New Zealander Ernest Rutherford soon after the discovery of nuclear radiation indicated that different types of rays are emitted. Eventually, three types were distinguished and named **alpha(α)**, **beta(β)**, and **gamma(γ)**, because, like x-rays, their identities were initially unknown. Figure 31.3 shows what happens if the rays are passed through a magnetic field. The γs are unaffected, while the α s and β s are deflected in opposite directions, indicating the α s are positive, the β s negative, and the γ s uncharged. Rutherford used both magnetic and electric fields to show that α s have a positive charge twice the magnitude of an electron, or $+2\,|q_e|$. In the process, he found the α s charge to mass ratio to be several thousand times smaller than the electron's. Later on, Rutherford collected α s from a radioactive source and passed an electric discharge through them, obtaining the spectrum of recently discovered helium gas. Among many important discoveries made by Rutherford and his collaborators was the proof that α *radiation is the emission of a helium nucleus.* Rutherford won the Nobel Prize in chemistry in 1908 for his early work. He continued to make important contributions until his death in 1934.

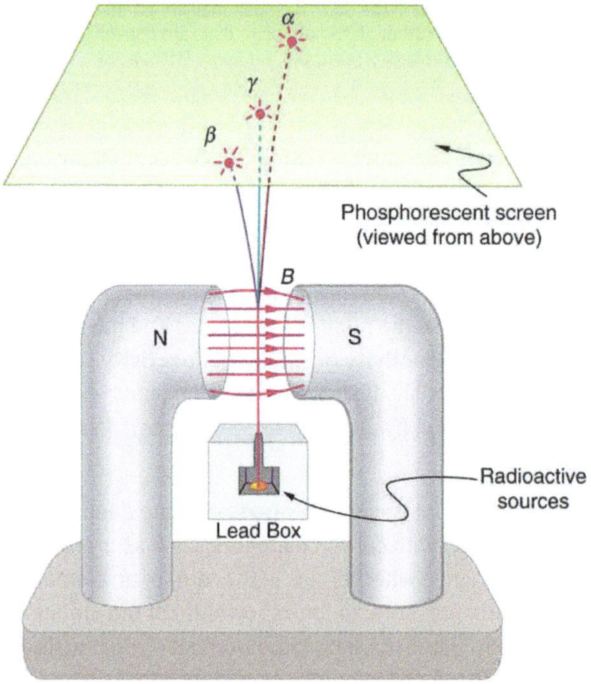

FIGURE 31.3 Alpha, beta, and gamma rays are passed through a magnetic field on the way to a phosphorescent screen. The α s and β s bend in opposite directions, while the γ s are unaffected, indicating a positive charge for α s, negative for β s, and neutral for γ s. Consistent results are obtained with electric fields. Collection of the radiation offers further confirmation from the direct measurement of excess charge.

Other researchers had already proved that β s are negative and have the same mass and same charge-to-mass ratio as the recently discovered electron. By 1902, it was recognized that β *radiation is the emission of an electron.* Although β s are electrons, they do not exist in the nucleus before it decays and are not ejected atomic electrons—the electron is created in the nucleus at the instant of decay.

Since γ s remain unaffected by electric and magnetic fields, it is natural to think they might be photons. Evidence for this grew, but it was not until 1914 that this was proved by Rutherford and collaborators. By scattering γ radiation from a crystal and observing interference, they demonstrated that γ *radiation is the emission of a high-energy photon by a nucleus.* In fact, γ radiation comes from the de-excitation of a nucleus, just as an x ray comes from the de-excitation of an atom. The names "γ ray" and "x ray" identify the source of the radiation. At the same energy, γ rays and x rays are otherwise identical.

Type of Radiation	Range
α-Particles	A sheet of paper, a few cm of air, fractions of a mm of tissue
β-Particles	A thin aluminum plate, or tens of cm of tissue
γ Rays	Several cm of lead or meters of concrete

TABLE 31.1 Properties of Nuclear Radiation

Ionization and Range

Two of the most important characteristics of α, β, and γ rays were recognized very early. All three types of nuclear radiation produce *ionization* in materials, but they penetrate different distances in materials—that is, they have different *ranges*. Let us examine why they have these characteristics and what are some of the consequences.

Like x rays, nuclear radiation in the form of α s, β s, and γ s has enough energy per event to ionize atoms and molecules in any material. The energy emitted in various nuclear decays ranges from a few keV to more than $10\ \mathrm{MeV}$, while only a few eV are needed to produce ionization. The effects of x rays and nuclear radiation on biological tissues and other materials, such as solid state electronics, are directly related to the ionization they produce. All of them, for example, can damage electronics or kill cancer cells. In addition, methods for detecting x rays and nuclear radiation are based on ionization, directly or indirectly. All of them can ionize the air between the plates of a capacitor, for example, causing it to discharge. This is the basis of inexpensive personal radiation monitors, such as pictured in Figure 31.4. Apart from α, β, and γ, there are other forms of nuclear radiation as well, and these also produce ionization with similar effects. We define **ionizing radiation** as any form of radiation that produces ionization whether nuclear in origin or not, since the effects and detection of the radiation are related to ionization.

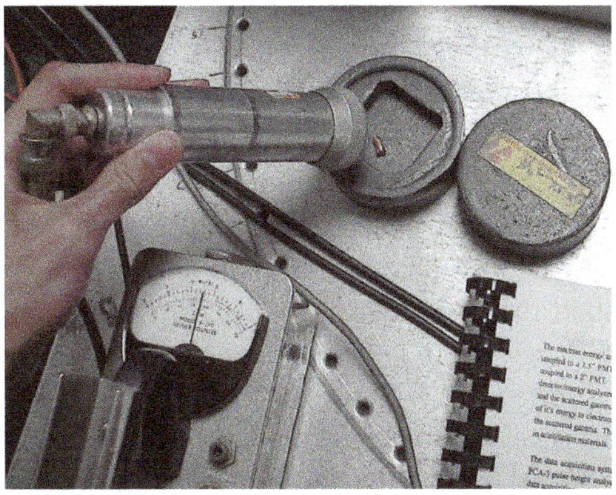

FIGURE 31.4 These dosimeters (literally, dose meters) are personal radiation monitors that detect the amount of radiation by the discharge of a rechargeable internal capacitor. The amount of discharge is related to the amount of ionizing radiation encountered, a measurement of dose. One dosimeter is shown in the charger. Its scale is read through an eyepiece on the top. (credit: L. Chang, Wikimedia Commons)

The **range of radiation** is defined to be the distance it can travel through a material. Range is related to several factors, including the energy of the radiation, the material encountered, and the type of radiation (see Figure 31.5). The higher the *energy*, the greater the range, all other factors being the same. This makes good sense, since radiation loses its energy in materials primarily by producing ionization in them, and each ionization of an atom or a molecule requires energy that is removed from the radiation. The amount of ionization is, thus, directly proportional to the energy of the particle of radiation, as is its range.

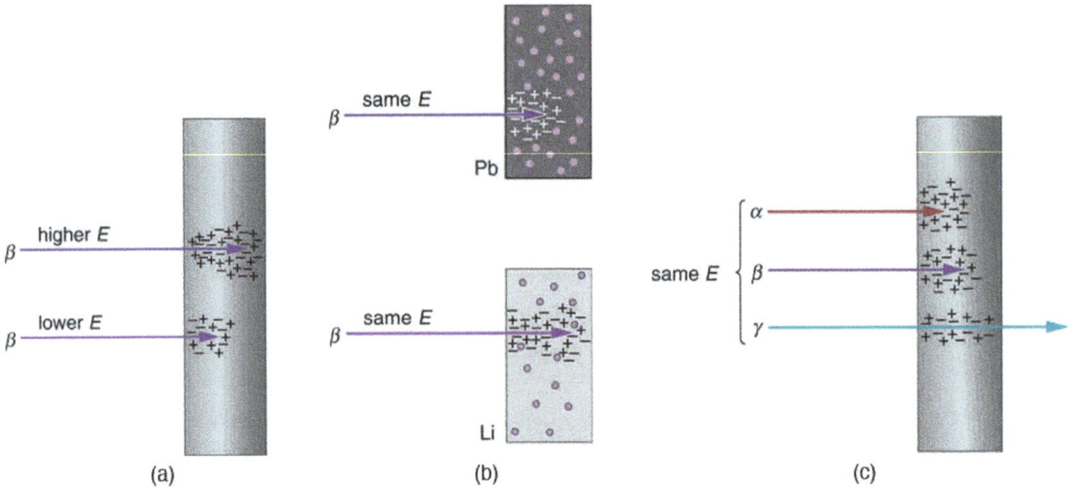

FIGURE 31.5 The penetration or range of radiation depends on its energy, the material it encounters, and the type of radiation. (a) Greater energy means greater range. (b) Radiation has a smaller range in materials with high electron density. (c) Alphas have the smallest range, betas have a greater range, and gammas penetrate the farthest.

Radiation can be absorbed or shielded by materials, such as the lead aprons dentists drape on us when taking x rays. Lead is a particularly effective shield compared with other materials, such as plastic or air. How does the range of radiation depend on *material*? Ionizing radiation interacts best with charged particles in a material. Since electrons have small masses, they most readily absorb the energy of the radiation in collisions. The greater the density of a material and, in particular, the greater the density of electrons within a material, the smaller the range of radiation.

COLLISIONS

Conservation of energy and momentum often results in energy transfer to a less massive object in a collision. This was discussed in detail in Work, Energy, and Energy Resources, for example.

Different *types* of radiation have different ranges when compared at the same energy and in the same material. Alphas have the shortest range, betas penetrate farther, and gammas have the greatest range. This is directly related to charge and speed of the particle or type of radiation. At a given energy, each α, β, or γ will produce the same number of ionizations in a material (each ionization requires a certain amount of energy on average). The more readily the particle produces ionization, the more quickly it will lose its energy. The effect of *charge* is as follows: The α has a charge of $+2q_e$, the β has a charge of $-q_e$, and the γ is uncharged. The electromagnetic force exerted by the α is thus twice as strong as that exerted by the β and it is more likely to produce ionization. Although chargeless, the γ does interact weakly because it is an electromagnetic wave, but it is less likely to produce ionization in any encounter. More quantitatively, the change in momentum Δp given to a particle in the material is $\Delta p = F\Delta t$, where F is the force the α, β, or γ exerts over a time Δt. The smaller the charge, the smaller is F and the smaller is the momentum (and energy) lost. Since the speed of alphas is about 5% to 10% of the speed of light, classical (non-relativistic) formulas apply.

The *speed* at which they travel is the other major factor affecting the range of α s, β s, and γ s. The faster they move, the less time they spend in the vicinity of an atom or a molecule, and the less likely they are to interact. Since α s and β s are particles with mass (helium nuclei and electrons, respectively), their energy is kinetic, given classically by $\frac{1}{2}mv^2$. The mass of the β particle is thousands of times less than that of the α s, so that β s must travel much faster than α s to have the same energy. Since β s move faster (most at relativistic speeds), they have less time to interact than α s. Gamma rays are photons, which must travel at the speed of light. They are even less likely to interact than a β, since they spend even less time near a given atom (and they have no charge). The range of γ s is thus greater than the range of β s.

Alpha radiation from radioactive sources has a range much less than a millimeter of biological tissues, usually not enough to even penetrate the dead layers of our skin. On the other hand, the same α radiation can penetrate a few centimeters of air, so mere distance from a source prevents α radiation from reaching us. This makes α radiation relatively safe for our body compared to β and γ radiation. Typical β radiation can penetrate a few millimeters of tissue or about a meter of air. Beta radiation is thus hazardous even when not ingested. The range of β s in lead is about a millimeter, and so it is easy to store β sources in lead radiation-proof containers. Gamma rays have a much greater range than either αs or βs. In fact, if a given thickness of material, like a lead brick, absorbs 90% of the γs, then a second lead brick will only absorb 90% of what got through the first. Thus, γs do not have a well-defined range; we can only cut down the amount that gets through. Typically, γs can penetrate many meters of air, go right through our bodies, and are effectively shielded (that is, reduced in intensity to acceptable levels) by many centimeters of lead. One benefit of γs is that they can be used as radioactive tracers (see Figure 31.6).

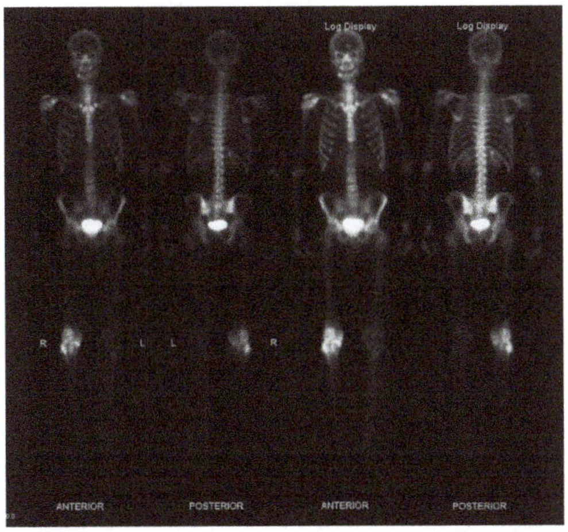

FIGURE 31.6 This image of the concentration of a radioactive tracer in a patient's body reveals where the most active bone cells are, an indication of bone cancer. A short-lived radioactive substance that locates itself selectively is given to the patient, and the radiation is measured with an external detector. The emitted γ radiation has a sufficient range to leave the body—the range of α s and β s is too small for them to be observed outside the patient. (credit: Kieran Maher, Wikimedia Commons)

PHET EXPLORATIONS

Beta Decay

Build an atom out of protons, neutrons, and electrons, and see how the element, charge, and mass change. Then play a game to test your ideas!

Click to view content (https://openstax.org/l/21betadecayvid).

31.2 Radiation Detection and Detectors

LEARNING OBJECTIVES

By the end of this section, you will be able to:

- Explain the working principle of a Geiger tube.
- Define and discuss radiation detectors.

It is well known that ionizing radiation affects us but does not trigger nerve impulses. Newspapers carry stories about unsuspecting victims of radiation poisoning who fall ill with radiation sickness, such as burns and blood count changes, but who never felt the radiation directly. This makes the detection of radiation by instruments more than an important research tool. This section is a brief overview of radiation detection and some of its applications.

Human Application

The first direct detection of radiation was Becquerel's fogged photographic plate. Photographic film is still the most common detector of ionizing radiation, being used routinely in medical and dental x rays. Nuclear radiation is also captured on film, such as seen in Figure 31.7. The mechanism for film exposure by ionizing radiation is similar to that by photons. A quantum of energy interacts with the emulsion and alters it chemically, thus exposing the film. The quantum come from an α-particle, β-particle, or photon, provided it has more than the few eV of energy needed to induce the chemical change (as does all ionizing radiation). The process is not 100% efficient, since not all incident radiation interacts and not all interactions produce the chemical change. The amount of film darkening is related to exposure, but the darkening also depends on the type of radiation, so that absorbers and other devices must be used to obtain energy, charge, and particle-identification information.

FIGURE 31.7 Film badges contain film similar to that used in this dental x-ray film and is sandwiched between various absorbers to determine the penetrating ability of the radiation as well as the amount. (credit: Werneuchen, Wikimedia Commons)

Another very common **radiation detector** is the **Geiger tube**. The clicking and buzzing sound we hear in dramatizations and documentaries, as well as in our own physics labs, is usually an audio output of events detected by a Geiger counter. These relatively inexpensive radiation detectors are based on the simple and sturdy Geiger tube, shown schematically in Figure 31.8(b). A conducting cylinder with a wire along its axis is filled with an insulating gas so that a voltage applied between the cylinder and wire produces almost no current. Ionizing radiation passing through the tube produces free ion pairs (each pair consisting of one positively charged particle and one negatively charged particle) that are attracted to the wire and cylinder, forming a current that is detected as a count. The word count implies that there is no information on energy, charge, or type of radiation with a simple Geiger counter. They do not detect every particle, since some radiation can pass through without producing enough ionization to be detected. However, Geiger counters are very useful in producing a prompt output that reveals the existence and relative intensity of ionizing radiation.

(a)
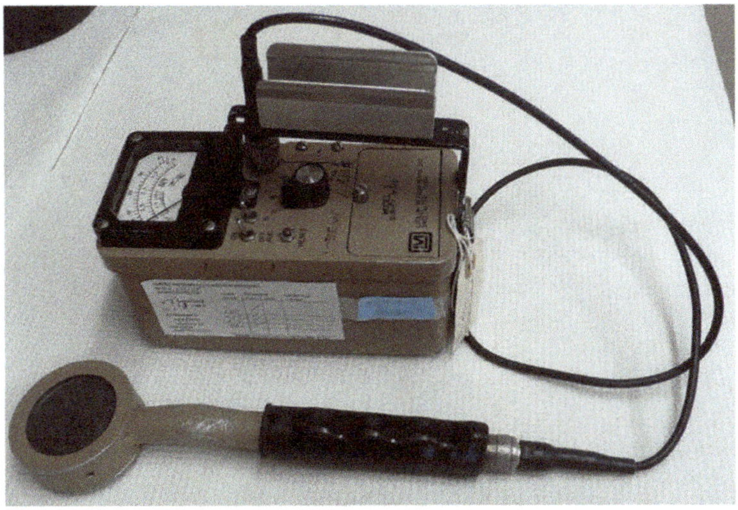

(b)
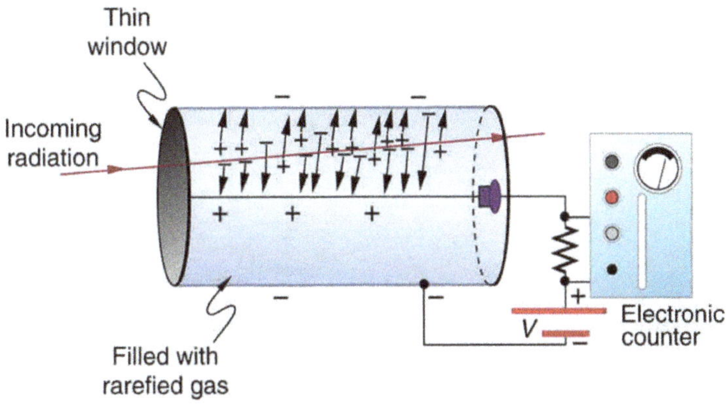

FIGURE 31.8 (a) Geiger counters such as this one are used for prompt monitoring of radiation levels, generally giving only relative intensity and not identifying the type or energy of the radiation. (credit: TimVickers, Wikimedia Commons) (b) Voltage applied between the cylinder and wire in a Geiger tube causes ions and electrons produced by radiation passing through the gas-filled cylinder to move towards them. The resulting current is detected and registered as a count.

Another radiation detection method records light produced when radiation interacts with materials. The energy of the radiation is sufficient to excite atoms in a material that may fluoresce, such as the phosphor used by Rutherford's group. Materials called **scintillators** use a more complex collaborative process to convert radiation energy into light. Scintillators may be liquid or solid, and they can be very efficient. Their light output can provide information about the energy, charge, and type of radiation. Scintillator light flashes are very brief in duration, enabling the detection of a huge number of particles in short periods of time. Scintillator detectors are used in a variety of research and diagnostic applications. Among these are the detection by satellite-mounted equipment of the radiation from distant galaxies, the analysis of radiation from a person indicating body burdens, and the detection of exotic particles in accelerator laboratories.

Light from a scintillator is converted into electrical signals by devices such as the **photomultiplier** tube shown schematically in Figure 31.9. These tubes are based on the photoelectric effect, which is multiplied in stages into a cascade of electrons, hence the name photomultiplier. Light entering the photomultiplier strikes a metal plate, ejecting an electron that is attracted by a positive potential difference to the next plate, giving it enough energy to eject two or more electrons, and so on. The final output current can be made proportional to the energy of the light entering the tube, which is in turn proportional to the energy deposited in the scintillator. Very sophisticated information can be obtained with scintillators, including energy, charge, particle identification, direction of motion, and so on.

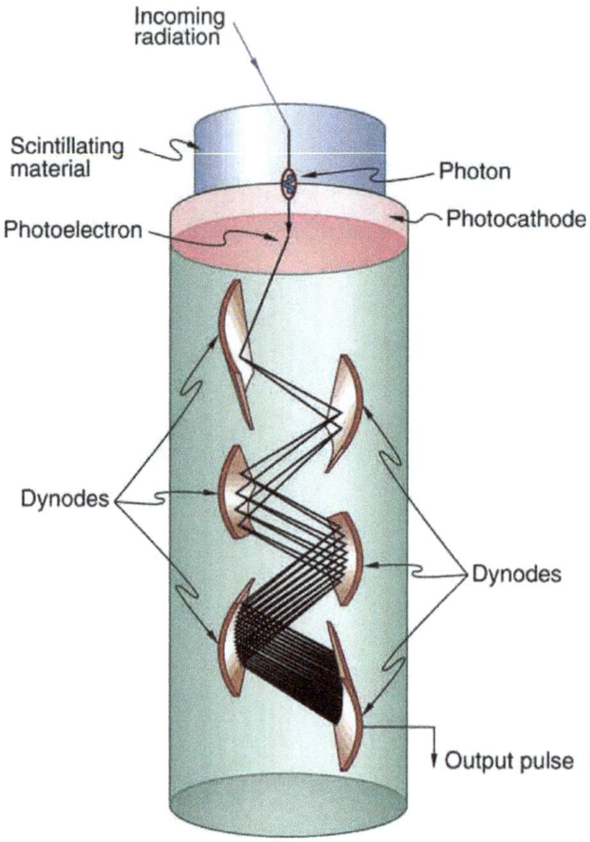

FIGURE 31.9 Photomultipliers use the photoelectric effect on the photocathode to convert the light output of a scintillator into an electrical signal. Each successive dynode has a more-positive potential than the last and attracts the ejected electrons, giving them more energy. The number of electrons is thus multiplied at each dynode, resulting in an easily detected output current.

Solid-state radiation detectors convert ionization produced in a semiconductor (like those found in computer chips) directly into an electrical signal. Semiconductors can be constructed that do not conduct current in one particular direction. When a voltage is applied in that direction, current flows only when ionization is produced by radiation, similar to what happens in a Geiger tube. Further, the amount of current in a solid-state detector is closely related to the energy deposited and, since the detector is solid, it can have a high efficiency (since ionizing radiation is stopped in a shorter distance in solids fewer particles escape detection). As with scintillators, very sophisticated information can be obtained from solid-state detectors.

PHET EXPLORATIONS

Radioactive Dating Game

Learn about different types of radiometric dating, such as carbon dating. Understand how decay and half life work to enable radiometric dating to work. Play a game that tests your ability to match the percentage of the dating element that remains to the age of the object.

Click to view content (https://openstax.org/l/02radioactive_dating_game).

31.3 Substructure of the Nucleus

LEARNING OBJECTIVES

By the end of this section, you will be able to:

- Define and discuss the nucleus in an atom.
- Define atomic number.
- Define and discuss isotopes.
- Calculate the density of the nucleus.
- Explain nuclear force.

What is inside the nucleus? Why are some nuclei stable while others decay? (See Figure 31.10.) Why are there different types of decay (α, β and γ)? Why are nuclear decay energies so large? Pursuing natural questions like these has led to far more fundamental discoveries than you might imagine.

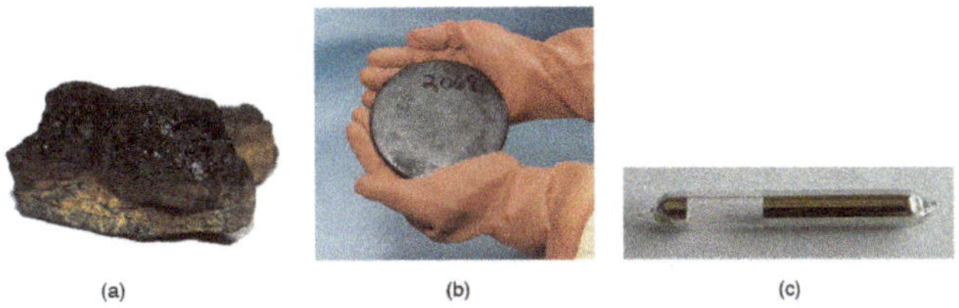

FIGURE 31.10 Why is most of the carbon in this coal stable (a), while the uranium in the disk (b) slowly decays over billions of years? Why is cesium in this ampule (c) even less stable than the uranium, decaying in far less than 1/1,000,000 the time? What is the reason uranium and cesium undergo different types of decay (α and β, respectively)? (credits: (a) Bresson Thomas, Wikimedia Commons; (b) U.S. Department of Energy; (c) Tomihahndorf, Wikimedia Commons)

We have already identified **protons** as the particles that carry positive charge in the nuclei. However, there are actually *two* types of particles in the nuclei—the *proton* and the *neutron*, referred to collectively as **nucleons**, the constituents of nuclei. As its name implies, the **neutron** is a neutral particle ($q = 0$) that has nearly the same mass and intrinsic spin as the proton. Table 31.2 compares the masses of protons, neutrons, and electrons. Note how close the proton and neutron masses are, but the neutron is slightly more massive once you look past the third digit. Both nucleons are much more massive than an electron. In fact, $m_p = 1836 m_e$ (as noted in Medical Applications of Nuclear Physics and $m_n = 1839 m_e$.

Table 31.2 also gives masses in terms of mass units that are more convenient than kilograms on the atomic and nuclear scale. The first of these is the *unified **atomic mass** unit* (u), defined as

$$1 \text{ u} = 1.6605 \times 10^{-27} \text{ kg}. \quad \text{31.1}$$

This unit is defined so that a neutral carbon ^{12}C atom has a mass of exactly 12 u. Masses are also expressed in units of MeV/c^2. These units are very convenient when considering the conversion of mass into energy (and vice versa), as is so prominent in nuclear processes. Using $E = mc^2$ and units of m in MeV/c^2, we find that c^2 cancels and E comes out conveniently in MeV. For example, if the rest mass of a proton is converted entirely into energy, then

$$E = mc^2 = (938.27 \text{ MeV}/c^2)c^2 = 938.27 \text{ MeV}. \quad \text{31.2}$$

It is useful to note that 1 u of mass converted to energy produces 931.5 MeV, or

$$1 \text{ u} = 931.5 \text{ MeV}/c^2. \quad \text{31.3}$$

All properties of a nucleus are determined by the number of protons and neutrons it has. A specific combination of protons and neutrons is called a **nuclide** and is a unique nucleus. The following notation is used to represent a particular nuclide:

$$^{A}_{Z}\text{X}_N, \quad \text{31.4}$$

where the symbols A, X, Z, and N are defined as follows: The *number of protons in a nucleus* is the **atomic number** Z, as defined in Medical Applications of Nuclear Physics. X is the *symbol for the element*, such as Ca for calcium. However, once Z is known, the element is known; hence, Z and X are redundant. For example, $Z = 20$ is always calcium, and calcium always has $Z = 20$. N is the *number of neutrons* in a nucleus. In the notation for a nuclide, the subscript N is usually omitted. The symbol A is defined as the number of nucleons or the *total number* *of protons and neutrons,*

$$A = N + Z, \quad 31.5$$

where A is also called the **mass number**. This name for A is logical; the mass of an atom is nearly equal to the mass of its nucleus, since electrons have so little mass. The mass of the nucleus turns out to be nearly equal to the sum of the masses of the protons and neutrons in it, which is proportional to A. In this context, it is particularly convenient to express masses in units of u. Both protons and neutrons have masses close to 1 u, and so the mass of an atom is close to A u. For example, in an oxygen nucleus with eight protons and eight neutrons, $A = 16$, and its mass is 16 u. As noticed, the unified atomic mass unit is defined so that a neutral carbon atom (actually a ^{12}C atom) has a mass of *exactly* 12 $\textbf{u}$. Carbon was chosen as the standard, partly because of its importance in organic chemistry (see Appendix A).

Particle	Symbol	kg	u	MeV/c^2
Proton	p	1.67262×10^{-27}	1.007276	938.27
Neutron	n	1.67493×10^{-27}	1.008665	939.57
Electron	e	9.1094×10^{-31}	0.00054858	0.511

TABLE 31.2 Masses of the Proton, Neutron, and Electron

Let us look at a few examples of nuclides expressed in the $^{A}_{Z}\text{X}_N$ notation. The nucleus of the simplest atom, hydrogen, is a single proton, or $^{1}_{1}\text{H}$ (the zero for no neutrons is often omitted). To check this symbol, refer to the periodic table—you see that the atomic number Z of hydrogen is 1. Since you are given that there are no neutrons, the mass number A is also 1. Suppose you are told that the helium nucleus or α particle has two protons and two neutrons. You can then see that it is written $^{4}_{2}\text{He}_2$. There is a scarce form of hydrogen found in nature called deuterium; its nucleus has one proton and one neutron and, hence, twice the mass of common hydrogen. The symbol for deuterium is, thus, $^{2}_{1}\text{H}_1$ (sometimes D is used, as for deuterated water D_2O). An even rarer—and radioactive—form of hydrogen is called tritium, since it has a single proton and two neutrons, and it is written $^{3}_{1}\text{H}_2$. These three varieties of hydrogen have nearly identical chemistries, but the nuclei differ greatly in mass, stability, and other characteristics. Nuclei (such as those of hydrogen) having the same Z and different N s are defined to be **isotopes** of the same element.

There is some redundancy in the symbols A, X, Z, and N. If the element X is known, then Z can be found in a periodic table and is always the same for a given element. If both A and X are known, then N can also be determined (first find Z; then, $N = A - Z$). Thus the simpler notation for nuclides is

$$^{A}\text{X}, \quad 31.6$$

which is sufficient and is most commonly used. For example, in this simpler notation, the three isotopes of hydrogen are ^{1}H, ^{2}H, and ^{3}H, while the α particle is ^{4}He. We read this backward, saying helium-4 for ^{4}He, or uranium-238 for ^{238}U. So for ^{238}U, should we need to know, we can determine that $Z = 92$ for uranium from the periodic table, and, thus, $N = 238 - 92 = 146$.

A variety of experiments indicate that a nucleus behaves something like a tightly packed ball of nucleons, as illustrated in Figure 31.11. These nucleons have large kinetic energies and, thus, move rapidly in very close contact. Nucleons can be separated by a large force, such as in a collision with another nucleus, but resist strongly being pushed closer together. The most compelling evidence that nucleons are closely packed in a nucleus is that the **radius of a nucleus**, *r*, is found to be given approximately by

$$r = r_0 A^{1/3}, \quad 31.7$$

where $r_0 = 1.2\ \text{fm}$ and A is the mass number of the nucleus. Note that $r^3 \propto A$. Since many nuclei are spherical, and the volume of a sphere is $V = (4/3)\pi r^3$, we see that $V \propto A$—that is, the volume of a nucleus is proportional to the number of nucleons in it. This is what would happen if you pack nucleons so closely that there is no empty space between them.

FIGURE 31.11 A model of the nucleus.

Nucleons are held together by nuclear forces and resist both being pulled apart and pushed inside one another. The volume of the nucleus is the sum of the volumes of the nucleons in it, here shown in different colors to represent protons and neutrons.

EXAMPLE 31.1

How Small and Dense Is a Nucleus?

(a) Find the radius of an iron-56 nucleus. (b) Find its approximate density in kg/m^3, approximating the mass of ^{56}Fe to be 56 u.

Strategy and Concept

(a) Finding the radius of ^{56}Fe is a straightforward application of $r = r_0 A^{1/3}$, given $A = 56$. (b) To find the approximate density, we assume the nucleus is spherical (this one actually is), calculate its volume using the radius found in part (a), and then find its density from $\rho = m/V$. Finally, we will need to convert density from units of u/fm^3 to kg/m^3.

Solution

(a) The radius of a nucleus is given by

$$r = r_0 A^{1/3}. \tag{31.8}$$

Substituting the values for r_0 and A yields

$$\begin{aligned} r &= (1.2\text{ fm})(56)^{1/3} = (1.2\text{ fm})(3.83) \\ &= 4.6\text{ fm}. \end{aligned} \tag{31.9}$$

(b) Density is defined to be $\rho = m/V$, which for a sphere of radius r is

$$\rho = \frac{m}{V} = \frac{m}{(4/3)\pi r^3}. \tag{31.10}$$

Substituting known values gives

$$\begin{aligned} \rho &= \frac{56\text{ u}}{(1.33)(3.14)(4.6\text{ fm})^3} \\ &= 0.138\text{ u/fm}^3. \end{aligned} \tag{31.11}$$

Converting to units of kg/m^3, we find

$$\begin{aligned} \rho &= (0.138\text{ u/fm}^3)(1.66 \times 10^{-27}\text{ kg/u})\left(\frac{1\text{ fm}}{10^{-15}\text{ m}}\right) \\ &= 2.3 \times 10^{17}\text{ kg/m}^3. \end{aligned} \tag{31.12}$$

Discussion

(a) The radius of this medium-sized nucleus is found to be approximately 4.6 fm, and so its diameter is about 10 fm, or 10^{-14} m. In our discussion of Rutherford's discovery of the nucleus, we noticed that it is about 10^{-15} m in diameter (which is for lighter nuclei), consistent with this result to an order of magnitude. The nucleus is much smaller in diameter than the typical atom, which has a diameter of the order of 10^{-10} m.

(b) The density found here is so large as to cause disbelief. It is consistent with earlier discussions we have had about the nucleus being very small and containing nearly all of the mass of the atom. Nuclear densities, such as found here, are about 2×10^{14} times greater than that of water, which has a density of "only" $10^3\ \text{kg/m}^3$. One cubic meter of nuclear matter, such as found in a neutron star, has the same mass as a cube of water 61 km on a side.

Nuclear Forces and Stability

What forces hold a nucleus together? The nucleus is very small and its protons, being positive, exert tremendous repulsive forces on one another. (The Coulomb force increases as charges get closer, since it is proportional to $1/r^2$, even at the tiny distances found in nuclei.) The answer is that two previously unknown forces hold the nucleus together and make it into a tightly packed ball of nucleons. These forces are called the *weak and strong nuclear forces.* Nuclear forces are so short ranged that they fall to zero strength when nucleons are separated by only a few fm. However, like glue, they are strongly attracted when the nucleons get close to one another. The strong nuclear force is about 100 times more attractive than the repulsive EM force, easily holding the nucleons together. Nuclear forces become extremely repulsive if the nucleons get too close, making nucleons strongly resist being pushed inside one another, something like ball bearings.

The fact that nuclear forces are very strong is responsible for the very large energies emitted in nuclear decay. During decay, the forces do work, and since work is force times the distance ($W = Fd \cos \theta$), a large force can result in a large emitted energy. In fact, we know that there are *two* distinct nuclear forces because of the different types of nuclear decay—the strong nuclear force is responsible for α decay, while the weak nuclear force is responsible for β decay.

The many stable and unstable nuclei we have explored, and the hundreds we have not discussed, can be arranged in a table called the **chart of the nuclides**, a simplified version of which is shown in Figure 31.12. Nuclides are located on a plot of N versus Z. Examination of a detailed chart of the nuclides reveals patterns in the characteristics of nuclei, such as stability, abundance, and types of decay, analogous to but more complex than the systematics in the periodic table of the elements.

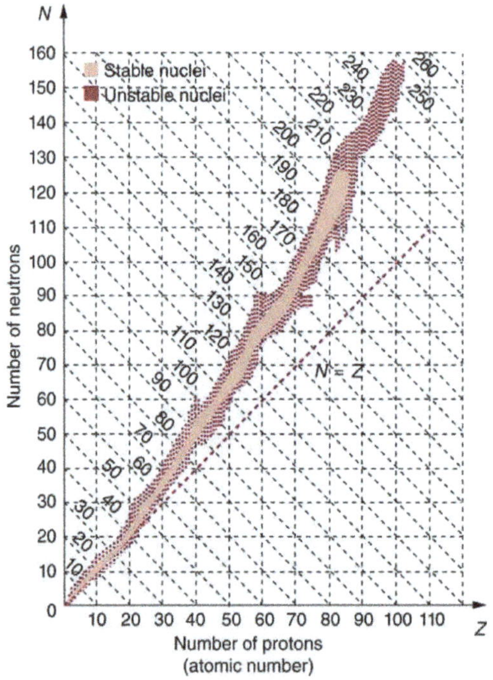

FIGURE 31.12 Simplified chart of the nuclides, a graph of N versus Z for known nuclides. The patterns of stable and unstable nuclides reveal characteristics of the nuclear forces. The dashed line is for $N = Z$. Numbers along diagonals are mass numbers A.

In principle, a nucleus can have any combination of protons and neutrons, but Figure 31.12 shows a definite pattern for those that are stable. For low-mass nuclei, there is a strong tendency for N and Z to be nearly equal. This means that the nuclear force is more attractive when $N = Z$. More detailed examination reveals greater stability when N and Z are even numbers—nuclear forces are more attractive when neutrons and protons are in pairs. For increasingly higher masses, there are progressively more neutrons than protons in stable nuclei. This is due to the ever-growing repulsion between protons. Since nuclear forces are short ranged, and the Coulomb force is long ranged, an excess of neutrons keeps the protons a little farther apart, reducing Coulomb repulsion. Decay modes of nuclides out of the region of stability consistently produce nuclides closer to the region of stability. There are more stable nuclei having certain numbers of protons and neutrons, called **magic numbers**. Magic numbers indicate a shell structure for the nucleus in which closed shells are more stable. Nuclear shell theory has been very successful in explaining nuclear energy levels, nuclear decay, and the greater stability of nuclei with closed shells. We have been producing ever-heavier transuranic elements since the early 1940s, and we have now produced the element with $Z = 118$. There are theoretical predictions of an island of relative stability for nuclei with such high Z s.

FIGURE 31.13 The German-born American physicist Maria Goeppert Mayer (1906–1972) shared the 1963 Nobel Prize in physics with J. Jensen for the creation of the nuclear shell model. This successful nuclear model has nucleons filling shells analogous to electron shells in atoms. It was inspired by patterns observed in nuclear properties. (credit: Nobel Foundation via Wikimedia Commons)

31.4 Nuclear Decay and Conservation Laws

LEARNING OBJECTIVES

By the end of this section, you will be able to:

- Define and discuss nuclear decay.
- State the conservation laws.
- Explain parent and daughter nucleus.
- Calculate the energy emitted during nuclear decay.

Nuclear **decay** has provided an amazing window into the realm of the very small. Nuclear decay gave the first indication of the connection between mass and energy, and it revealed the existence of two of the four basic forces in nature. In this section, we explore the major modes of nuclear decay; and, like those who first explored them, we will discover evidence of previously unknown particles and conservation laws.

Some nuclides are stable, apparently living forever. Unstable nuclides decay (that is, they are radioactive), eventually producing a stable nuclide after many decays. We call the original nuclide the **parent** and its decay products the **daughters**. Some radioactive nuclides decay in a single step to a stable nucleus. For example, $^{60}\mathrm{Co}$ is unstable and decays directly to $^{60}\mathrm{Ni}$, which is stable. Others, such as $^{238}\mathrm{U}$, decay to another unstable nuclide, resulting in a **decay series** in which each subsequent nuclide decays until a stable nuclide is finally produced. The decay series that starts from $^{238}\mathrm{U}$ is of particular interest, since it produces the radioactive isotopes $^{226}\mathrm{Ra}$ and $^{210}\mathrm{Po}$, which the Curies first discovered (see Figure 31.14). Radon gas is also produced ($^{222}\mathrm{Rn}$ in the series), an increasingly recognized naturally occurring hazard. Since radon is a noble gas, it emanates from materials, such as soil, containing even trace amounts of $^{238}\mathrm{U}$ and can be inhaled. The decay of radon and its daughters produces internal damage. The $^{238}\mathrm{U}$ decay series ends with $^{206}\mathrm{Pb}$, a stable isotope of lead.

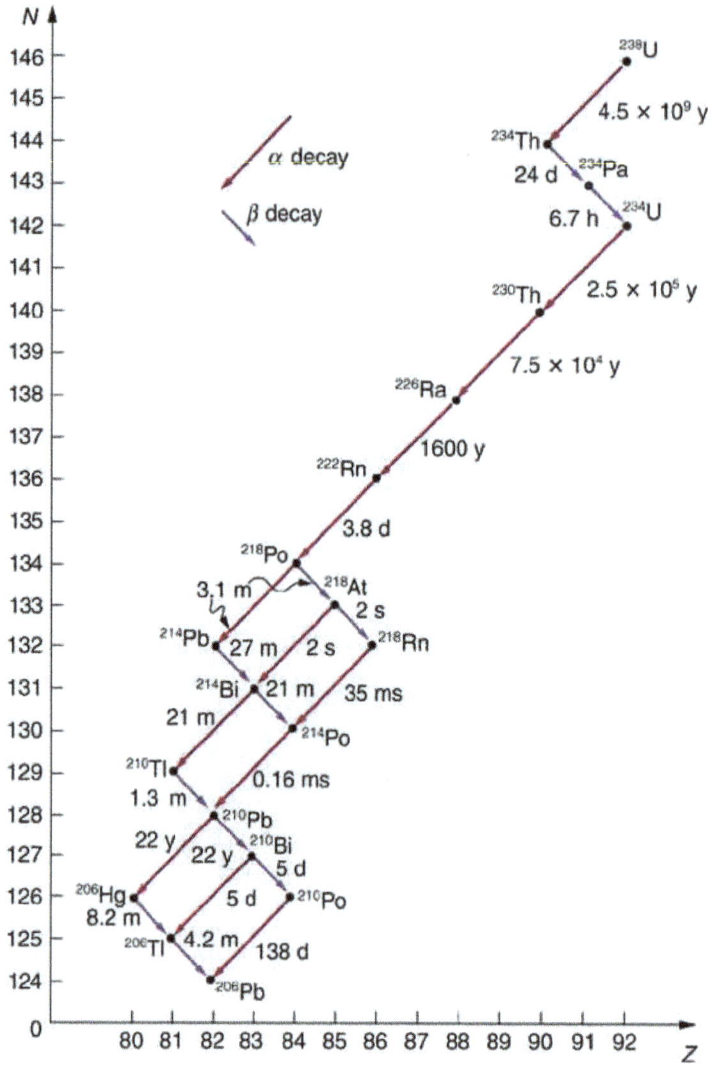

FIGURE 31.14 The decay series produced by $^{238}\mathrm{U}$, the most common uranium isotope. Nuclides are graphed in the same manner as in the chart of nuclides. The type of decay for each member of the series is shown, as well as the half-lives. Note that some nuclides decay by more than one mode. You can see why radium and polonium are found in uranium ore. A stable isotope of lead is the end product of the series.

Note that the daughters of α decay shown in Figure 31.14 always have two fewer protons and two fewer neutrons than the parent. This seems reasonable, since we know that α decay is the emission of a $^{4}\mathrm{He}$ nucleus, which has two protons and two neutrons. The daughters of β decay have one less neutron and one more proton than their parent. Beta decay is a little more subtle, as we shall see. No γ decays are shown in the figure, because they do not produce a daughter that differs from the parent.

Alpha Decay

In **alpha decay**, a $^{4}\mathrm{He}$ nucleus simply breaks away from the parent nucleus, leaving a daughter with two fewer protons and two fewer neutrons than the parent (see Figure 31.15). One example of α decay is shown in Figure 31.14 for $^{238}\mathrm{U}$. Another nuclide that undergoes α decay is $^{239}\mathrm{Pu}$. The decay equations for these two nuclides are

$$^{238}\mathrm{U} \rightarrow {}^{234}\mathrm{Th}^{234}_{92} + {}^{4}\mathrm{He} \tag{31.13}$$

and

$$^{239}\mathrm{Pu} \rightarrow {}^{235}\mathrm{U} + {}^{4}\mathrm{He}. \tag{31.14}$$

FIGURE 31.15 Alpha decay is the separation of a ^4He nucleus from the parent. The daughter nucleus has two fewer protons and two fewer neutrons than the parent. Alpha decay occurs spontaneously only if the daughter and ^4He nucleus have less total mass than the parent.

If you examine the periodic table of the elements, you will find that Th has $Z = 90$, two fewer than U, which has $Z = 92$. Similarly, in the second **decay equation**, we see that U has two fewer protons than Pu, which has $Z = 94$. The general rule for α decay is best written in the format $^A_Z\text{X}_N$. If a certain nuclide is known to α decay (generally this information must be looked up in a table of isotopes, such as in Appendix B), its α **decay equation** is

$$^A_Z\text{X}_N \rightarrow {}^{A-4}_{Z-2}\text{Y}_{N-2} + {}^4_2\text{He}_2 \quad (\alpha \text{ decay}) \tag{31.15}$$

where Y is the nuclide that has two fewer protons than X, such as Th having two fewer than U. So if you were told that ^{239}Pu α decays and were asked to write the complete decay equation, you would first look up which element has two fewer protons (an atomic number two lower) and find that this is uranium. Then since four nucleons have broken away from the original 239, its atomic mass would be 235.

It is instructive to examine conservation laws related to α decay. You can see from the equation $^A_Z\text{X}_N \rightarrow {}^{A-4}_{Z-2}\text{Y}_{N-2} + {}^4_2\text{He}_2$ that total charge is conserved. Linear and angular momentum are conserved, too. Although conserved angular momentum is not of great consequence in this type of decay, conservation of linear momentum has interesting consequences. If the nucleus is at rest when it decays, its momentum is zero. In that case, the fragments must fly in opposite directions with equal-magnitude momenta so that total momentum remains zero. This results in the α particle carrying away most of the energy, as a bullet from a heavy rifle carries away most of the energy of the powder burned to shoot it. Total mass–energy is also conserved: the energy produced in the decay comes from conversion of a fraction of the original mass. As discussed in Atomic Physics, the general relationship is

$$E = (\Delta m)c^2. \tag{31.16}$$

Here, E is the **nuclear reaction energy** (the reaction can be nuclear decay or any other reaction), and Δm is the difference in mass between initial and final products. When the final products have less total mass, Δm is positive, and the reaction releases energy (is exothermic). When the products have greater total mass, the reaction is endothermic (Δm is negative) and must be induced with an energy input. For α decay to be spontaneous, the decay products must have smaller mass than the parent.

EXAMPLE 31.2

Alpha Decay Energy Found from Nuclear Masses

Find the energy emitted in the α decay of ^{239}Pu.

Strategy

Nuclear reaction energy, such as released in α decay, can be found using the equation $E = (\Delta m)c^2$. We must first find Δm, the difference in mass between the parent nucleus and the products of the decay. This is easily done using masses given in Appendix A.

Solution

The decay equation was given earlier for ^{239}Pu; it is

$$^{239}\text{Pu} \rightarrow {}^{235}\text{U} + {}^4\text{He}. \tag{31.17}$$

Thus the pertinent masses are those of ^{239}Pu, ^{235}U, and the α particle or ^4He, all of which are listed in Appendix A. The initial mass was $m(^{239}\text{Pu}) = 239.052157\text{ u}$. The final mass is the sum $m(^{235}\text{U}) + m(^4\text{He}) = 235.043924\text{ u} + 4.002602\text{ u} = 239.046526\text{ u}$. Thus,

$$\begin{aligned} \Delta m &= m(^{239}\text{Pu}) - [m(^{235}\text{U}) + m(^{4}\text{He})] \\ &= 239.052157\ \text{u} - 239.046526\ \text{u} \\ &= 0.0005631\ \text{u}. \end{aligned} \quad (31.18)$$

Now we can find E by entering Δm into the equation:

$$E = (\Delta m)c^2 = (0.005631\ \text{u})c^2. \quad (31.19)$$

We know $1\ \text{u} = 931.5\ \text{MeV}/c^2$, and so

$$E = (0.005631)(931.5\ \text{MeV}/c^2)(c^2) = 5.25\ \text{MeV}. \quad (31.20)$$

Discussion

The energy released in this α decay is in the MeV range, about 10^6 times as great as typical chemical reaction energies, consistent with many previous discussions. Most of this energy becomes kinetic energy of the α particle (or ^4He nucleus), which moves away at high speed. The energy carried away by the recoil of the ^{235}U nucleus is much smaller in order to conserve momentum. The ^{235}U nucleus can be left in an excited state to later emit photons (γ rays). This decay is spontaneous and releases energy, because the products have less mass than the parent nucleus. The question of why the products have less mass will be discussed in Binding Energy. Note that the masses given in Appendix A are atomic masses of neutral atoms, including their electrons. The mass of the electrons is the same before and after α decay, and so their masses subtract out when finding Δm. In this case, there are 94 electrons before and after the decay.

Beta Decay

There are actually *three* types of **beta decay**. The first discovered was "ordinary" beta decay and is called β^- decay or electron emission. The symbol β^- represents *an electron emitted in nuclear beta decay.* Cobalt-60 is a nuclide that β^- decays in the following manner:

$$^{60}\text{Co} \rightarrow {}^{60}\text{Ni} + \beta^- + \text{neutrino}. \quad (31.21)$$

The **neutrino** is a particle emitted in beta decay that was unanticipated and is of fundamental importance. The neutrino was not even proposed in theory until more than 20 years after beta decay was known to involve electron emissions. Neutrinos are so difficult to detect that the first direct evidence of them was not obtained until 1953. Neutrinos are nearly massless, have no charge, and do not interact with nucleons via the strong nuclear force. Traveling approximately at the speed of light, they have little time to affect any nucleus they encounter. This is, owing to the fact that they have no charge (and they are not EM waves), they do not interact through the EM force. They do interact via the relatively weak and very short range weak nuclear force. Consequently, neutrinos escape almost any detector and penetrate almost any shielding. However, neutrinos do carry energy, angular momentum (they are fermions with half-integral spin), and linear momentum away from a beta decay. When accurate measurements of beta decay were made, it became apparent that energy, angular momentum, and linear momentum were not accounted for by the daughter nucleus and electron alone. Either a previously unsuspected particle was carrying them away, or three conservation laws were being violated. Wolfgang Pauli made a formal proposal for the existence of neutrinos in 1930. The Italian-born American physicist Enrico Fermi (1901–1954) gave neutrinos their name, meaning little neutral ones, when he developed a sophisticated theory of beta decay (see Figure 31.16). Part of Fermi's theory was the identification of the weak nuclear force as being distinct from the strong nuclear force and in fact responsible for beta decay. Chinese-born physicist Chien-Shiung Wu, who had developed a number of processes critical to the Manhattan Project and related research, set out to investigate Fermi's theory and some experiments whose failures had cast the theory in doubt. She first identified a number of flaws in her contemporaries' methods and materials, and then designed an experimental method that would avoid the same errors. Wu verified Fermi's theory and went on to establish the core principles of beta decay, which would become critical to further work in nuclear physics.

FIGURE 31.16 (a) Enrico Fermi made significant contributions both as an experimentalist and a theorist. His many contributions to theoretical physics included the identification of the weak nuclear force. The fermi (fm) is named after him, as are an entire class of subatomic particles (fermions), an element (Fermium), and a major research laboratory (Fermilab). (credit: United States Department of Energy, Office of Public Affairs). (b) Chien-Shiung Wu undertook the experimentation to verify Fermi's theory of beta decay. She became the world's expert on the subject, and contributed to work that led to a Nobel Prize, even though she was denied the award. (credit: Smithsonian Institute)

The neutrino also reveals a new conservation law. There are various families of particles, one of which is the electron family. We propose that the number of members of the electron family is constant in any process or any closed system. In our example of beta decay, there are no members of the electron family present before the decay, but after, there is an electron and a neutrino. So electrons are given an electron family number of $+1$. The neutrino in β^- decay is an **electron's antineutrino**, given the symbol $\bar{\nu}_e$, where ν is the Greek letter nu, and the subscript e means this neutrino is related to the electron. The bar indicates this is a particle of **antimatter**. (All particles have antimatter counterparts that are nearly identical except that they have the opposite charge. Antimatter is almost entirely absent on Earth, but it is found in nuclear decay and other nuclear and particle reactions as well as in outer space.) The electron's antineutrino $\bar{\nu}_e$, being antimatter, has an electron family number of -1. The total is zero, before and after the decay. The new conservation law, obeyed in all circumstances, states that the *total electron family number is constant*. An electron cannot be created without also creating an antimatter family member. This law is analogous to the conservation of charge in a situation where total charge is originally zero, and equal amounts of positive and negative charge must be created in a reaction to keep the total zero.

If a nuclide ${}^{A}_{Z}\text{X}_N$ is known to β^- decay, then its β^- decay equation is

$$ {}^{A}_{Z}\text{X}_N \rightarrow {}_{Z+1}^{\ \ \ A}\text{Y}_{N-1} + \beta^- + \bar{\nu}_e \ (\beta^- \text{ decay}), \quad 31.22 $$

where Y is the nuclide having one more proton than X (see Figure 31.17). So if you know that a certain nuclide β^- decays, you can find the daughter nucleus by first looking up Z for the parent and then determining which element has atomic number $Z+1$. In the example of the β^- decay of ${}^{60}\text{Co}$ given earlier, we see that $Z = 27$ for Co and $Z = 28$ is Ni. It is as if one of the neutrons in the parent nucleus decays into a proton, electron, and neutrino. In fact, neutrons outside of nuclei do just that—they live only an average of a few minutes and β^- decay in the following manner:

$$ \text{n} \rightarrow \text{p} + \beta^- + \bar{\nu}_e. \quad 31.23 $$

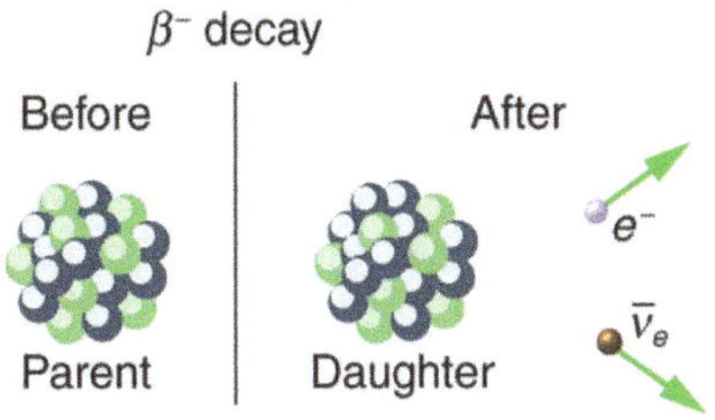

FIGURE 31.17 In β^- decay, the parent nucleus emits an electron and an antineutrino. The daughter nucleus has one more proton and one less neutron than its parent. Neutrinos interact so weakly that they are almost never directly observed, but they play a fundamental role in particle physics.

We see that charge is conserved in β^- decay, since the total charge is Z before and after the decay. For example, in ${}^{60}\text{Co}$ decay, total charge is 27 before decay, since cobalt has $Z = 27$. After decay, the daughter nucleus is Ni, which has $Z = 28$, and there is an electron, so that the total charge is also $28 + (-1)$ or 27. Angular momentum is conserved, but not obviously (you have to examine the spins and angular momenta of the final products in detail to verify this). Linear momentum is also conserved, again imparting most of the decay energy to the electron and the antineutrino, since they are of low and zero mass, respectively. Another new conservation law is obeyed here and elsewhere in nature. *The total number of nucleons A is conserved.* In ^{60}Co decay, for example, there are 60 nucleons before and after the decay. Note that total A is also conserved in α decay. Also note that the total number of protons changes, as does the total number of neutrons, so that total Z and total N are *not* conserved in β^- decay, as they are in α decay. Energy released in β^- decay can be calculated given the masses of the parent and products.

EXAMPLE 31.3

β^- Decay Energy from Masses

Find the energy emitted in the β^- decay of ^{60}Co.

Strategy and Concept

As in the preceding example, we must first find Δm, the difference in mass between the parent nucleus and the products of the decay, using masses given in Appendix A. Then the emitted energy is calculated as before, using $E = (\Delta m)c^2$. The initial mass is just that of the parent nucleus, and the final mass is that of the daughter nucleus and the electron created in the decay. The neutrino is massless, or nearly so. However, since the masses given in Appendix A are for neutral atoms, the daughter nucleus has one more electron than the parent, and so the extra electron mass that corresponds to the β^- is included in the atomic mass of Ni. Thus,

$$\Delta m = m(^{60}\text{Co}) - m(^{60}\text{Ni}). \tag{31.24}$$

Solution

The β^- decay equation for ^{60}Co is

$$^{60}_{27}\text{Co}_{33} \rightarrow {}^{60}_{28}\text{Ni}_{32} + \beta^- + \bar{\nu}_e. \tag{31.25}$$

As noticed,

$$\Delta m = m(^{60}\text{Co}) - m(^{60}\text{Ni}). \tag{31.26}$$

Entering the masses found in Appendix A gives

$$\Delta m = 59.933820 \text{ u} - 59.930789 \text{ u} = 0.003031 \text{ u}. \tag{31.27}$$

Thus,

$$E = (\Delta m)c^2 = (0.003031 \text{ u})c^2. \tag{31.28}$$

Using $1 \text{ u} = 931.5 \text{ MeV}/c^2$, we obtain

$$E = (0.003031)(931.5 \text{ MeV}/c^2)(c^2) = 2.82 \text{ MeV}. \tag{31.29}$$

Discussion and Implications

Perhaps the most difficult thing about this example is convincing yourself that the β^- mass is included in the atomic mass of ^{60}Ni. Beyond that are other implications. Again the decay energy is in the MeV range. This energy is shared by all of the products of the decay. In many ^{60}Co decays, the daughter nucleus ^{60}Ni is left in an excited state and emits photons (γ rays). Most of the remaining energy goes to the electron and neutrino, since the recoil kinetic energy of the daughter nucleus is small. One final note: the electron emitted in β^- decay is created in the nucleus at the time of decay.

The second type of beta decay is less common than the first. It is β^+ decay. Certain nuclides decay by the emission of a *positive* electron. This is **antielectron** or **positron decay** (see Figure 31.18).

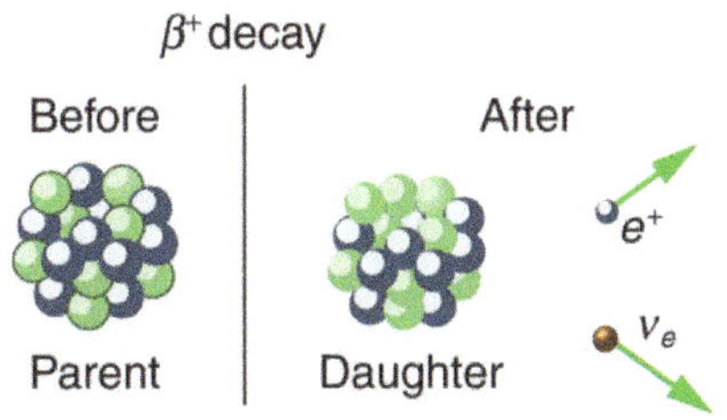

FIGURE 31.18 β^+ decay is the emission of a positron that eventually finds an electron to annihilate, characteristically producing gammas in opposite directions.

The antielectron is often represented by the symbol e^+, but in beta decay it is written as β^+ to indicate the antielectron was emitted in a nuclear decay. Antielectrons are the antimatter counterpart to electrons, being nearly identical, having the same mass, spin, and so on, but having a positive charge and an electron family number of -1. When a **positron** encounters an electron, there is a mutual annihilation in which all the mass of the antielectron-electron pair is converted into pure photon energy. (The reaction, $e^+ + e^- \rightarrow \gamma + \gamma$, conserves electron family number as well as all other conserved quantities.) If a nuclide ${}^{A}_{Z}\mathrm{X}_N$ is known to β^+ decay, then its **β^+ decay equation** is

$$ {}^{A}_{Z}\mathrm{X}_N \rightarrow {}_{Z-1}^{\ \ A}\mathrm{Y}_{N+1} + \beta^+ + \nu_e \text{ } (\beta^+ \text{ decay}), \quad 31.30 $$

where Y is the nuclide having one less proton than X (to conserve charge) and ν_e is the symbol for the **electron's neutrino**, which has an electron family number of $+1$. Since an antimatter member of the electron family (the β^+) is created in the decay, a matter member of the family (here the ν_e) must also be created. Given, for example, that ${}^{22}\mathrm{Na}$ β^+ decays, you can write its full decay equation by first finding that $Z = 11$ for ${}^{22}\mathrm{Na}$, so that the daughter nuclide will have $Z = 10$, the atomic number for neon. Thus the β^+ decay equation for ${}^{22}\mathrm{Na}$ is

$$ {}^{22}_{11}\mathrm{Na}_{11} \rightarrow {}^{22}_{10}\mathrm{Ne}_{12} + \beta^+ + \nu_e. \quad 31.31 $$

In β^+ decay, it is as if one of the protons in the parent nucleus decays into a neutron, a positron, and a neutrino. Protons do not do this outside of the nucleus, and so the decay is due to the complexities of the nuclear force. Note again that the total number of nucleons is constant in this and any other reaction. To find the energy emitted in β^+ decay, you must again count the number of electrons in the neutral atoms, since atomic masses are used. The daughter has one less electron than the parent, and one electron mass is created in the decay. Thus, in β^+ decay,

$$ \Delta m = m(\text{parent}) - [\, m(\text{daughter}) + 2m_e], \quad 31.32 $$

since we use the masses of neutral atoms.

Electron capture is the third type of beta decay. Here, a nucleus captures an inner-shell electron and undergoes a nuclear reaction that has the same effect as β^+ decay. Electron capture is sometimes denoted by the letters EC. We know that electrons cannot reside in the nucleus, but this is a nuclear reaction that consumes the electron and occurs spontaneously only when the products have less mass than the parent plus the electron. If a nuclide ${}^{A}_{Z}\mathrm{X}_N$ is known to undergo electron capture, then its **electron capture equation** is

$$ {}^{A}_{Z}\mathrm{X}_N + e^- \rightarrow {}_{Z-1}^{\ \ A}\mathrm{Y}_{N+1} + \nu_e (\text{electron capture, or EC}). \quad 31.33 $$

Any nuclide that can β^+ decay can also undergo electron capture (and often does both). The same conservation laws are obeyed for EC as for β^+ decay. It is good practice to confirm these for yourself.

All forms of beta decay occur because the parent nuclide is unstable and lies outside the region of stability in the chart of nuclides. Those nuclides that have relatively more neutrons than those in the region of stability will β^- decay to produce a daughter with fewer neutrons, producing a daughter nearer the region of stability. Similarly, those nuclides having relatively more protons than those in the region of stability will β^- decay or undergo electron capture to produce a daughter with fewer protons, nearer the region of stability.

Gamma Decay

Gamma decay is the simplest form of nuclear decay—it is the emission of energetic photons by nuclei left in an excited state by some earlier process. Protons and neutrons in an excited nucleus are in higher orbitals, and they fall to lower levels by photon emission (analogous to electrons in excited atoms). Nuclear excited states have lifetimes typically of only about 10^{-14} s, an indication of the great strength of the forces pulling the nucleons to lower states. The γ decay equation is simply

$$^{A}_{Z}\text{X}^{*}_{N} \rightarrow {}^{A}_{Z}\text{X}_{N} + \gamma_1 + \gamma_2 + \cdots \ (\gamma \text{ decay}) \quad 31.34$$

where the asterisk indicates the nucleus is in an excited state. There may be one or more γ s emitted, depending on how the nuclide de-excites. In radioactive decay, γ emission is common and is preceded by γ or β decay. For example, when ^{60}Co β^- decays, it most often leaves the daughter nucleus in an excited state, written $^{60}\text{Ni}^*$. Then the nickel nucleus quickly γ decays by the emission of two penetrating γ s:

$$^{60}\text{Ni}^* \rightarrow {}^{60}\text{Ni} + \gamma_1 + \gamma_2. \quad 31.35$$

These are called cobalt γ rays, although they come from nickel—they are used for cancer therapy, for example. It is again constructive to verify the conservation laws for gamma decay. Finally, since γ decay does not change the nuclide to another species, it is not prominently featured in charts of decay series, such as that in Figure 31.14.

There are other types of nuclear decay, but they occur less commonly than α, β, and γ decay. Spontaneous fission is the most important of the other forms of nuclear decay because of its applications in nuclear power and weapons. It is covered in the next chapter.

31.5 Half-Life and Activity

LEARNING OBJECTIVES

By the end of this section, you will be able to:

- Define half-life.
- Define dating.
- Calculate age of old objects by radioactive dating.

Unstable nuclei decay. However, some nuclides decay faster than others. For example, radium and polonium, discovered by the Curies, decay faster than uranium. This means they have shorter lifetimes, producing a greater rate of decay. In this section we explore half-life and activity, the quantitative terms for lifetime and rate of decay.

Half-Life

Why use a term like half-life rather than lifetime? The answer can be found by examining Figure 31.19, which shows how the number of radioactive nuclei in a sample decreases with time. The *time in which half of the original number of nuclei decay* is defined as the **half-life**, $t_{1/2}$. Half of the remaining nuclei decay in the next half-life. Further, half of that amount decays in the following half-life. Therefore, the number of radioactive nuclei decreases from N to $N/2$ in one half-life, then to $N/4$ in the next, and to $N/8$ in the next, and so on. If N is a large number, then *many* half-lives (not just two) pass before all of the nuclei decay. Nuclear decay is an example of a purely statistical process. A more precise definition of half-life is that *each nucleus has a 50% chance of living for a time equal to one half-life* $t_{1/2}$. Thus, if N is reasonably large, half of the original nuclei decay in a time of one half-life. If an individual nucleus makes it through that time, it still has a 50% chance of surviving through another half-life. Even if it happens to make it through hundreds of half-lives, it still has a 50% chance of surviving through one more. The probability of decay is the same no matter when you start counting. This is like random coin flipping. The chance of heads is 50%, no matter what has happened before.

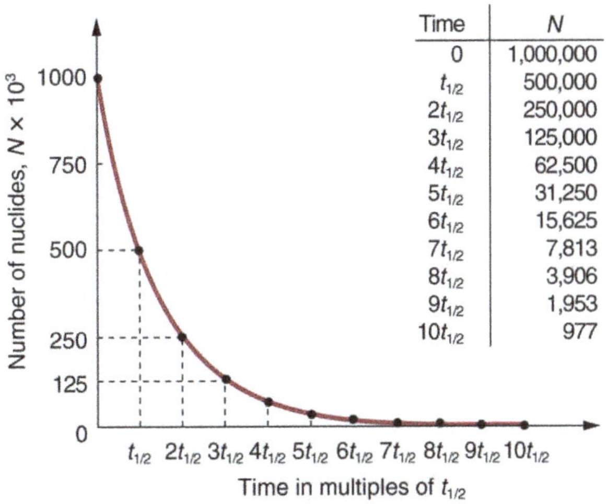

Time	N
0	1,000,000
$t_{1/2}$	500,000
$2t_{1/2}$	250,000
$3t_{1/2}$	125,000
$4t_{1/2}$	62,500
$5t_{1/2}$	31,250
$6t_{1/2}$	15,625
$7t_{1/2}$	7,813
$8t_{1/2}$	3,906
$9t_{1/2}$	1,953
$10t_{1/2}$	977

FIGURE 31.19 Radioactive decay reduces the number of radioactive nuclei over time. In one half-life $t_{1/2}$, the number decreases to half of its original value. Half of what remains decay in the next half-life, and half of those in the next, and so on. This is an exponential decay, as seen in the graph of the number of nuclei present as a function of time.

There is a tremendous range in the half-lives of various nuclides, from as short as 10^{-23} s for the most unstable, to more than 10^{16} y for the least unstable, or about 46 orders of magnitude. Nuclides with the shortest half-lives are those for which the nuclear forces are least attractive, an indication of the extent to which the nuclear force can depend on the particular combination of neutrons and protons. The concept of half-life is applicable to other subatomic particles, as will be discussed in Particle Physics. It is also applicable to the decay of excited states in atoms and nuclei. The following equation gives the quantitative relationship between the original number of nuclei present at time zero (N_0) and the number (N) at a later time t:

$$N = N_0 e^{-\lambda t}, \tag{31.36}$$

where $e = 2.71828...$ is the base of the natural logarithm, and λ is the **decay constant** for the nuclide. The shorter the half-life, the larger is the value of λ, and the faster the exponential $e^{-\lambda t}$ decreases with time. The relationship between the decay constant λ and the half-life $t_{1/2}$ is

$$\lambda = \frac{\ln(2)}{t_{1/2}} \approx \frac{0.693}{t_{1/2}}. \tag{31.37}$$

To see how the number of nuclei declines to half its original value in one half-life, let $t = t_{1/2}$ in the exponential in the equation $N = N_0 e^{-\lambda t}$. This gives $N = N_0 e^{-\lambda t} = N_0 e^{-0.693} = 0.500 N_0$. For integral numbers of half-lives, you can just divide the original number by 2 over and over again, rather than using the exponential relationship. For example, if ten half-lives have passed, we divide N by 2 ten times. This reduces it to $N/1024$. For an arbitrary time, not just a multiple of the half-life, the exponential relationship must be used.

Radioactive dating is a clever use of naturally occurring radioactivity. Its most famous application is **carbon-14 dating**. Carbon-14 has a half-life of 5730 years and is produced in a nuclear reaction induced when solar neutrinos strike ^{14}N in the atmosphere. Radioactive carbon has the same chemistry as stable carbon, and so it mixes into the ecosphere, where it is consumed and becomes part of every living organism. Carbon-14 has an abundance of 1.3 parts per trillion of normal carbon. Thus, if you know the number of carbon nuclei in an object (perhaps determined by mass and Avogadro's number), you multiply that number by 1.3×10^{-12} to find the number of ^{14}C nuclei in the object. When an organism dies, carbon exchange with the environment ceases, and ^{14}C is not replenished as it decays. By comparing the abundance of ^{14}C in an artifact, such as mummy wrappings, with the normal abundance in living tissue, it is possible to determine the artifact's age (or time since death). Carbon-14 dating can be used for biological tissues as old as 50 or 60 thousand years, but is most accurate for younger samples, since the abundance of ^{14}C nuclei in them is greater. Very old biological materials contain no ^{14}C at all. There are instances in which the date of an artifact can be determined by other means, such as historical knowledge or tree-ring counting. These cross-references have confirmed the validity of carbon-14 dating and permitted us to calibrate the technique as well. Carbon-14 dating revolutionized parts of archaeology and is of such importance that it earned the 1960 Nobel Prize in chemistry for its developer, the American chemist Willard Libby (1908–1980).

One of the most famous cases of carbon-14 dating involves the Shroud of Turin, a long piece of fabric purported to be the burial shroud of Jesus (see Figure 31.20). This relic was first displayed in Turin in 1354 and was denounced as a fraud at that time by a French bishop. Its remarkable negative imprint of an apparently crucified body resembles the then-accepted image of Jesus, and so the shroud was never disregarded completely and remained controversial over the centuries. Carbon-14 dating was not performed on the shroud until 1988, when the process had been refined to the point where only a small amount of material needed to be destroyed. Samples were tested at three independent laboratories, each being given four pieces of cloth, with only one unidentified piece from the shroud, to avoid prejudice. All three laboratories found samples of the shroud contain 92% of the ^{14}C found in living tissues, allowing the shroud to be dated (see Example 31.4).

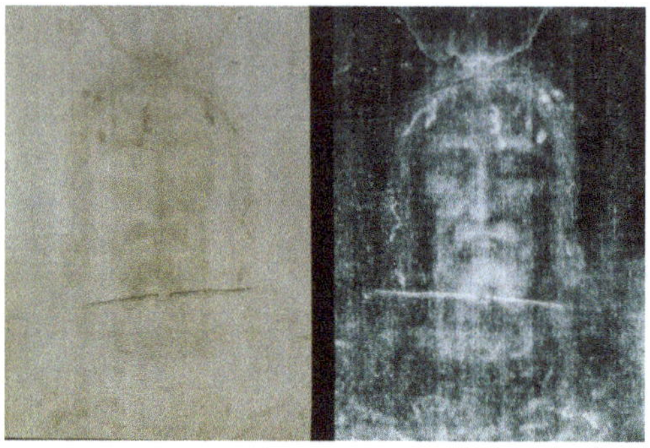

FIGURE 31.20 Part of the Shroud of Turin, which shows a remarkable negative imprint likeness of Jesus complete with evidence of crucifixion wounds. The shroud first surfaced in the 14th century and was only recently carbon-14 dated. It has not been determined how the image was placed on the material. (credit: Butko, Wikimedia Commons)

EXAMPLE 31.4

How Old Is the Shroud of Turin?

Calculate the age of the Shroud of Turin given that the amount of ^{14}C found in it is 92% of that in living tissue.

Strategy

Knowing that 92% of the ^{14}C remains means that $N/N_0 = 0.92$. Therefore, the equation $N = N_0 e^{-\lambda t}$ can be used to find λt. We also know that the half-life of ^{14}C is 5730 y, and so once λt is known, we can use the equation $\lambda = \frac{0.693}{t_{1/2}}$ to find λ and then find t as requested. Here, we postulate that the decrease in ^{14}C is solely due to nuclear decay.

Solution

Solving the equation $N = N_0 e^{-\lambda t}$ for N/N_0 gives

$$\frac{N}{N_0} = e^{-\lambda t}. \tag{31.38}$$

Thus,

$$0.92 = e^{-\lambda t}. \tag{31.39}$$

Taking the natural logarithm of both sides of the equation yields

$$\ln 0.92 = -\lambda t \tag{31.40}$$

so that

$$-0.0834 = -\lambda t. \tag{31.41}$$

Rearranging to isolate t gives

$$t = \frac{0.0834}{\lambda}. \tag{31.42}$$

Now, the equation $\lambda = \frac{0.693}{t_{1/2}}$ can be used to find λ for ^{14}C. Solving for λ and substituting the known half-life gives

$$\lambda = \frac{0.693}{t_{1/2}} = \frac{0.693}{5730\text{ y}}. \quad (31.43)$$

We enter this value into the previous equation to find t:

$$t = \frac{0.0834}{\frac{0.693}{5730\text{ y}}} = 690\text{ y}. \quad (31.44)$$

Discussion

This dates the material in the shroud to 1988–690 = a.d. 1300. Our calculation is only accurate to two digits, so that the year is rounded to 1300. The values obtained at the three independent laboratories gave a weighted average date of a.d. 1320 ± 60. The uncertainty is typical of carbon-14 dating and is due to the small amount of ^{14}C in living tissues, the amount of material available, and experimental uncertainties (reduced by having three independent measurements). It is meaningful that the date of the shroud is consistent with the first record of its existence and inconsistent with the period in which Jesus lived.

There are other forms of radioactive dating. Rocks, for example, can sometimes be dated based on the decay of ^{238}U. The decay series for ^{238}U ends with ^{206}Pb, so that the ratio of these nuclides in a rock is an indication of how long it has been since the rock solidified. The original composition of the rock, such as the absence of lead, must be known with some confidence. However, as with carbon-14 dating, the technique can be verified by a consistent body of knowledge. Since ^{238}U has a half-life of 4.5×10^9 y, it is useful for dating only very old materials, showing, for example, that the oldest rocks on Earth solidified about 3.5×10^9 years ago.

Activity, the Rate of Decay

What do we mean when we say a source is highly radioactive? Generally, this means the number of decays per unit time is very high. We define **activity** R to be the **rate of decay** expressed in decays per unit time. In equation form, this is

$$R = \frac{\Delta N}{\Delta t} \quad (31.45)$$

where ΔN is the number of decays that occur in time Δt. The SI unit for activity is one decay per second and is given the name **becquerel** (Bq) in honor of the discoverer of radioactivity. That is,

$$1\text{ Bq} = 1\text{ decay/s}. \quad (31.46)$$

Activity R is often expressed in other units, such as decays per minute or decays per year. One of the most common units for activity is the **curie** (Ci), defined to be the activity of 1 g of ^{226}Ra, in honor of Marie Curie's work with radium. The definition of curie is

$$1\text{ Ci} = 3.70 \times 10^{10}\text{ Bq}, \quad (31.47)$$

or 3.70×10^{10} decays per second. A curie is a large unit of activity, while a becquerel is a relatively small unit. $1\text{ MBq} = 100\text{ microcuries }(\mu\text{Ci})$. In countries like Australia and New Zealand that adhere more to SI units, most radioactive sources, such as those used in medical diagnostics or in physics laboratories, are labeled in Bq or megabecquerel (MBq).

Intuitively, you would expect the activity of a source to depend on two things: the amount of the radioactive substance present, and its half-life. The greater the number of radioactive nuclei present in the sample, the more will decay per unit of time. The shorter the half-life, the more decays per unit time, for a given number of nuclei. So activity R should be proportional to the number of radioactive nuclei, N, and inversely proportional to their half-life, $t_{1/2}$. In fact, your intuition is correct. It can be shown that the activity of a source is

$$R = \frac{0.693N}{t_{1/2}} \quad (31.48)$$

where N is the number of radioactive nuclei present, having half-life $t_{1/2}$. This relationship is useful in a variety of calculations, as the next two examples illustrate.

EXAMPLE 31.5

How Great Is the ^{14}C Activity in Living Tissue?

Calculate the activity due to ^{14}C in 1.00 kg of carbon found in a living organism. Express the activity in units of Bq and Ci.

Strategy

To find the activity R using the equation $R = \frac{0.693N}{t_{1/2}}$, we must know N and $t_{1/2}$. The half-life of ^{14}C can be found in Appendix B, and was stated above as 5730 y. To find N, we first find the number of ^{12}C nuclei in 1.00 kg of carbon using the concept of a mole. As indicated, we then multiply by 1.3×10^{-12} (the abundance of ^{14}C in a carbon sample from a living organism) to get the number of ^{14}C nuclei in a living organism.

Solution

One mole of carbon has a mass of 12.0 g, since it is nearly pure ^{12}C. (A mole has a mass in grams equal in magnitude to A found in the periodic table.) Thus the number of carbon nuclei in a kilogram is

$$N(^{12}\text{C}) = \frac{6.02\times10^{23}\text{ mol}^{-1}}{12.0\text{ g/mol}}\times(1000\text{ g}) = 5.02\times10^{25}. \quad 31.49$$

So the number of ^{14}C nuclei in 1 kg of carbon is

$$N(^{14}\text{C}) = (5.02\times10^{25})(1.3\times10^{-12}) = 6.52\times10^{13}. \quad 31.50$$

Now the activity R is found using the equation $R = \frac{0.693N}{t_{1/2}}$.

Entering known values gives

$$R = \frac{0.693(6.52\times10^{13})}{5730\text{ y}} = 7.89\times10^{9}\text{ y}^{-1}, \quad 31.51$$

or 7.89×10^{9} decays per year. To convert this to the unit Bq, we simply convert years to seconds. Thus,

$$R = (7.89\times10^{9}\text{ y}^{-1})\frac{1.00\text{ y}}{3.16\times10^{7}\text{ s}} = 250\text{ Bq}, \quad 31.52$$

or 250 decays per second. To express R in curies, we use the definition of a curie,

$$R = \frac{250\text{ Bq}}{3.7\times10^{10}\text{ Bq/Ci}} = 6.76\times10^{-9}\text{ Ci}. \quad 31.53$$

Thus,

$$R = 6.76\text{ nCi}. \quad 31.54$$

Discussion

Our own bodies contain kilograms of carbon, and it is intriguing to think there are hundreds of ^{14}C decays per second taking place in us. Carbon-14 and other naturally occurring radioactive substances in our bodies contribute to the background radiation we receive. The small number of decays per second found for a kilogram of carbon in this example gives you some idea of how difficult it is to detect ^{14}C in a small sample of material. If there are 250 decays per second in a kilogram, then there are 0.25 decays per second in a gram of carbon in living tissue. To observe this, you must be able to distinguish decays from other forms of radiation, in order to reduce background noise. This becomes more difficult with an old tissue sample, since it contains less ^{14}C, and for samples more than

50 thousand years old, it is impossible.

Human-made (or artificial) radioactivity has been produced for decades and has many uses. Some of these include medical therapy for cancer, medical imaging and diagnostics, and food preservation by irradiation. Many applications as well as the biological effects of radiation are explored in Medical Applications of Nuclear Physics, but it is clear that radiation is hazardous. A number of tragic examples of this exist, one of the most disastrous being the meltdown and fire at the Chernobyl reactor complex in the Ukraine (see Figure 31.21). Several radioactive isotopes were released in huge quantities, contaminating many thousands of square kilometers and directly affecting hundreds of thousands of people. The most significant releases were of ^{131}I, ^{90}Sr, ^{137}Cs, ^{239}Pu, ^{238}U, and ^{235}U. Estimates are that the total amount of radiation released was about 100 million curies.

Human and Medical Applications

FIGURE 31.21 The Chernobyl reactor. More than 100 people died soon after its meltdown, and there will be thousands of deaths from radiation-induced cancer in the future. While the accident was due to a series of human errors, the cleanup efforts were heroic. Most of the immediate fatalities were firefighters and reactor personnel. (credit: Elena Filatova)

EXAMPLE 31.6

What Mass of ^{137}Cs Escaped Chernobyl?

It is estimated that the Chernobyl disaster released 6.0 MCi of ^{137}Cs into the environment. Calculate the mass of ^{137}Cs released.

Strategy

We can calculate the mass released using Avogadro's number and the concept of a mole if we can first find the number of nuclei N released. Since the activity R is given, and the half-life of ^{137}Cs is found in Appendix B to be 30.2 y, we can use the equation $R = \frac{0.693N}{t_{1/2}}$ to find N.

Solution

Solving the equation $R = \frac{0.693N}{t_{1/2}}$ for N gives

$$N = \frac{Rt_{1/2}}{0.693}. \quad 31.55$$

Entering the given values yields

$$N = \frac{(6.0\text{ MCi})(30.2\text{ y})}{0.693}. \quad 31.56$$

Converting curies to becquerels and years to seconds, we get

$$\begin{aligned} N &= \frac{(6.0\times10^{6}\text{ Ci})(3.7\times10^{10}\text{ Bq/Ci})(30.2\text{ y})(3.16\times10^{7}\text{ s/y})}{0.693} \\ &= 3.1\times10^{26}. \end{aligned} \quad 31.57$$

One mole of a nuclide ${}^{A}X$ has a mass of A grams, so that one mole of ${}^{137}\text{Cs}$ has a mass of 137 g. A mole has 6.02×10^{23} nuclei. Thus the mass of ${}^{137}\text{Cs}$ released was

$$\begin{aligned} m &= \left(\frac{137\text{ g}}{6.02 \times 10^{23}}\right)(3.1 \times 10^{26}) = 70 \times 10^{3}\text{ g} \\ &= 70\text{ kg}. \end{aligned} \quad (31.58)$$

Discussion

While 70 kg of material may not be a very large mass compared to the amount of fuel in a power plant, it is extremely radioactive, since it only has a 30-year half-life. Six megacuries (6.0 MCi) is an extraordinary amount of activity but is only a fraction of what is produced in nuclear reactors. Similar amounts of the other isotopes were also released at Chernobyl. Although the chances of such a disaster may have seemed small, the consequences were extremely severe, requiring greater caution than was used. More will be said about safe reactor design in the next chapter, but it should be noted that more recent reactors have a fundamentally safer design.

Activity R decreases in time, going to half its original value in one half-life, then to one-fourth its original value in the next half-life, and so on. Since $R = \frac{0.693N}{t_{1/2}}$, the activity decreases as the number of radioactive nuclei decreases. The equation for R as a function of time is found by combining the equations $N = N_0 e^{-\lambda t}$ and $R = \frac{0.693N}{t_{1/2}}$, yielding

$$R = R_0 e^{-\lambda t}, \quad (31.59)$$

where R_0 is the activity at $t = 0$. This equation shows exponential decay of radioactive nuclei. For example, if a source originally has a 1.00-mCi activity, it declines to 0.500 mCi in one half-life, to 0.250 mCi in two half-lives, to 0.125 mCi in three half-lives, and so on. For times other than whole half-lives, the equation $R = R_0 e^{-\lambda t}$ must be used to find R.

PHET EXPLORATIONS

Alpha Decay

Watch alpha particles escape from a polonium nucleus, causing radioactive alpha decay. See how random decay times relate to the half life.

Click to view content (https://openstax.org/l/02alphadecay).

31.6 Binding Energy

LEARNING OBJECTIVES

By the end of this section, you will be able to:

- Define and discuss binding energy.
- Calculate the binding energy per nucleon of a particle.

The more tightly bound a system is, the stronger the forces that hold it together and the greater the energy required to pull it apart. We can therefore learn about nuclear forces by examining how tightly bound the nuclei are. We define the **binding energy** (BE) of a nucleus to be *the energy required to completely disassemble it into separate protons and neutrons.* We can determine the BE of a nucleus from its rest mass. The two are connected through Einstein's famous relationship $E = (\Delta m)c^2$. A bound system has a *smaller* mass than its separate constituents; the more tightly the nucleons are bound together, the smaller the mass of the nucleus.

Imagine pulling a nuclide apart as illustrated in Figure 31.22. Work done to overcome the nuclear forces holding the nucleus together puts energy into the system. By definition, the energy input equals the binding energy BE. The pieces are at rest when separated, and so the energy put into them increases their total rest mass compared with what it was when they were glued together as a nucleus. That mass increase is thus $\Delta m = \text{BE}/c^2$. This difference in mass is known as *mass defect*. It implies that the mass of the nucleus is less than the sum of the masses of its constituent protons and neutrons. A nuclide ${}^{A}\mathrm{X}$ has Z protons and N neutrons, so that the difference in mass is

$$\Delta m = (Zm_p + Nm_n) - m_{\text{tot}}. \tag{31.60}$$

Thus,

$$\text{BE} = (\Delta m)c^2 = [(Zm_p + Nm_n) - m_{\text{tot}}]c^2, \tag{31.61}$$

where m_{tot} is the mass of the nuclide ${}^{A}\mathrm{X}$, m_p is the mass of a proton, and m_n is the mass of a neutron. Traditionally, we deal with the masses of neutral atoms. To get atomic masses into the last equation, we first add Z electrons to m_{tot}, which gives $m({}^{A}\mathrm{X})$, the atomic mass of the nuclide. We then add Z electrons to the Z protons, which gives $Zm({}^{1}\mathrm{H})$, or Z times the mass of a hydrogen atom. Thus the binding energy of a nuclide ${}^{A}\mathrm{X}$ is

$$\text{BE} = \left\{[Zm({}^{1}\mathrm{H}) + Nm_n] - m({}^{A}X)\right\}c^2. \tag{31.62}$$

The atomic masses can be found in Appendix A, most conveniently expressed in unified atomic mass units u ($1\ \text{u} = 931.5\ \text{MeV}/c^2$). BE is thus calculated from known atomic masses.

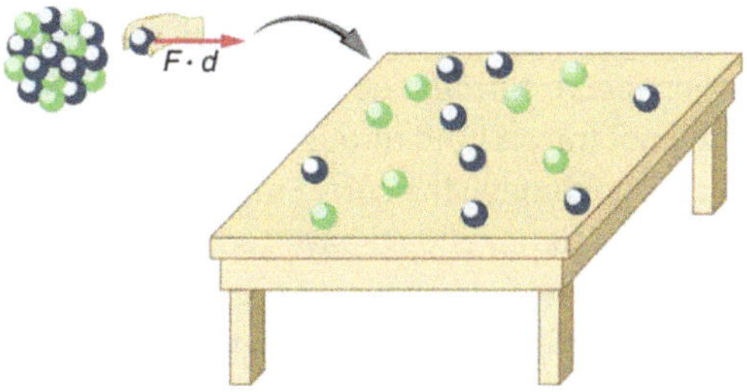

FIGURE 31.22 Work done to pull a nucleus apart into its constituent protons and neutrons increases the mass of the system. The work to disassemble the nucleus equals its binding energy BE. A bound system has less mass than the sum of its parts, especially noticeable in the nuclei, where forces and energies are very large.

THINGS GREAT AND SMALL

Nuclear Decay Helps Explain Earth's Hot Interior

A puzzle created by radioactive dating of rocks is resolved by radioactive heating of Earth's interior. This intriguing story is another example of how small-scale physics can explain large-scale phenomena.

Radioactive dating plays a role in determining the approximate age of the Earth. The oldest rocks on Earth solidified about 3.5×10^9 years ago—a number determined by uranium-238 dating. These rocks could only have solidified once the surface of the Earth had cooled sufficiently. The temperature of the Earth at formation can be estimated based on gravitational potential energy of the assemblage of pieces being converted to thermal energy. Using heat transfer concepts discussed in Thermodynamics it is then possible to calculate how long it would take for the surface to cool to rock-formation temperatures. The result is about 10^9 years. The first rocks formed have been solid for 3.5×10^9 years, so that the age of the Earth is approximately 4.5×10^9 years. There is a large body of other types of evidence (both Earth-bound and solar system characteristics are used) that supports this age. The puzzle is that, given its age and initial temperature, the center of the Earth should be much cooler than it is today (see Figure 31.23).

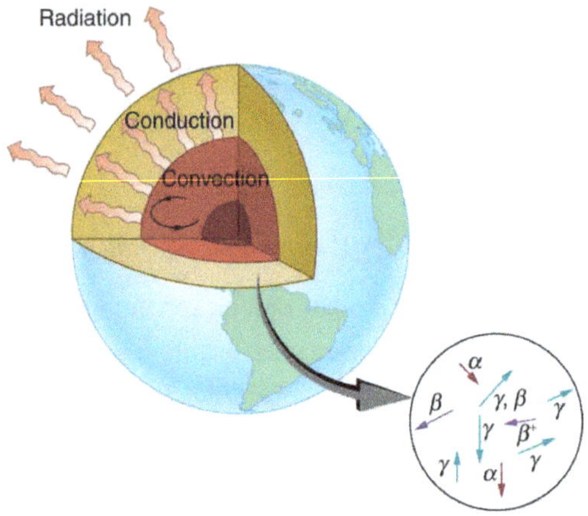

FIGURE 31.23 The center of the Earth cools by well-known heat transfer methods. Convection in the liquid regions and conduction move thermal energy to the surface, where it radiates into cold, dark space. Given the age of the Earth and its initial temperature, it should have cooled to a lower temperature by now. The blowup shows that nuclear decay releases energy in the Earth's interior. This energy has slowed the cooling process and is responsible for the interior still being molten.

Danish geophysicist Inge Lehmann was the first to properly interpret seismological data from earthquakes as evidence that the Earth had a solid inner core surrounded by a liquid outer core. Shear or transverse waves cannot travel through a liquid and are not transmitted through the Earth's core. Yet compression or longitudinal waves can pass through a liquid and do go through the core. From this information, the temperature of the interior can be estimated. As noticed, the interior should have cooled more from its initial temperature in the 4.5×10^9 years since its formation. In fact, it should have taken no more than about 10^9 years to cool to its present temperature. What is keeping it hot? The answer seems to be radioactive decay of primordial elements that were part of the material that formed the Earth (see the blowup in Figure 31.23).

Nuclides such as ^{238}U and ^{40}K have half-lives similar to or longer than the age of the Earth, and their decay still contributes energy to the interior. Some of the primordial radioactive nuclides have unstable decay products that also release energy— ^{238}U has a long decay chain of these. Further, there were more of these primordial radioactive nuclides early in the life of the Earth, and thus the activity and energy contributed were greater then (perhaps by an order of magnitude). The amount of power created by these decays per cubic meter is very small. However, since a huge volume of material lies deep below the surface, this relatively small amount of energy cannot escape quickly. The power produced near the surface has much less distance to go to escape and has a negligible effect on surface temperatures.

A final effect of this trapped radiation merits mention. Alpha decay produces helium nuclei, which form helium atoms when they are stopped and capture electrons. Most of the helium on Earth is obtained from wells and is produced in this manner. Any helium in the atmosphere will escape in geologically short times because of its high thermal velocity.

What patterns and insights are gained from an examination of the binding energy of various nuclides? First, we find that BE is approximately proportional to the number of nucleons A in any nucleus. About twice as much energy is needed to pull apart a nucleus like ^{24}Mg compared with pulling apart ^{12}C, for example. To help us look at other effects, we divide BE by A and consider the **binding energy per nucleon**, BE/A. The graph of BE/A in Figure 31.24 reveals some very interesting aspects of nuclei. We see that the binding energy per nucleon averages about 8 MeV, but is lower for both the lightest and heaviest nuclei. This overall trend, in which nuclei with A equal to about 60 have the greatest BE/A and are thus the most tightly bound, is due to the combined characteristics of the attractive nuclear forces and the repulsive Coulomb force. It is especially important to note two things—the strong nuclear force is about 100 times stronger than the Coulomb force, *and* the nuclear forces are shorter in range compared to the Coulomb force. So, for low-mass nuclei, the nuclear attraction dominates and each added nucleon forms bonds with all others, causing progressively heavier nuclei to have progressively greater values of BE/A. This continues up to $A \approx 60$, roughly corresponding to the mass number of iron. Beyond that, new nucleons added to a nucleus will be too far from some others to feel their nuclear attraction. Added protons, however, feel the repulsion of all other protons, since the Coulomb force is longer in range. Coulomb repulsion grows for progressively heavier nuclei, but nuclear attraction remains about the same, and so BE/A becomes smaller. This is why stable nuclei heavier than $A \approx 40$ have more neutrons than protons. Coulomb repulsion is reduced by having more neutrons to keep the protons farther apart (see Figure 31.25).

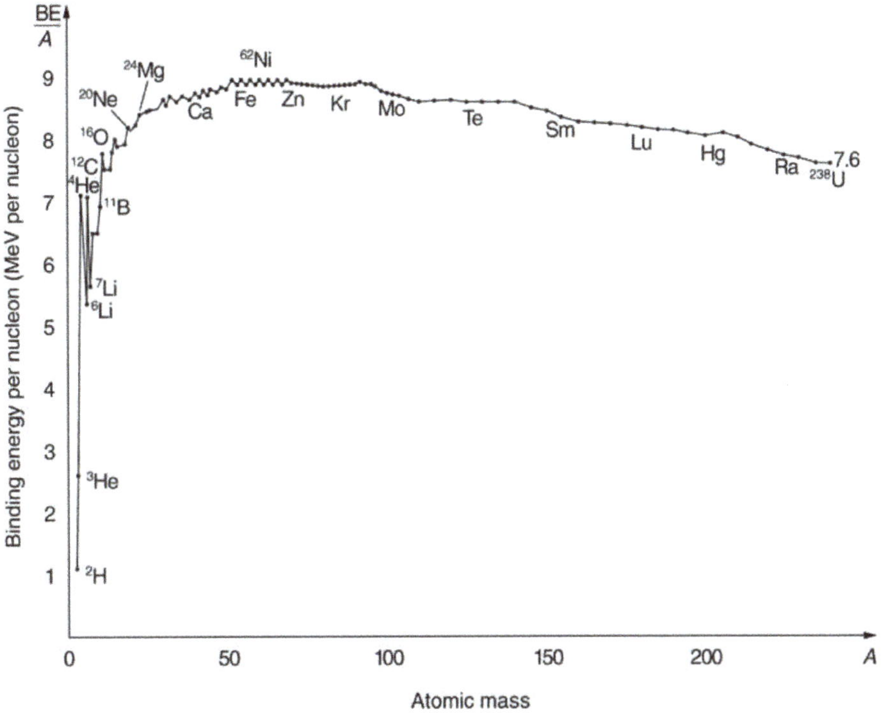

FIGURE 31.24 A graph of average binding energy per nucleon, BE/A, for stable nuclei. The most tightly bound nuclei are those with A near 60, where the attractive nuclear force has its greatest effect. At higher A s, the Coulomb repulsion progressively reduces the binding energy per nucleon, because the nuclear force is short ranged. The spikes on the curve are very tightly bound nuclides and indicate shell closures.

FIGURE 31.25 The nuclear force is attractive and stronger than the Coulomb force, but it is short ranged. In low-mass nuclei, each nucleon feels the nuclear attraction of all others. In larger nuclei, the range of the nuclear force, shown for a single nucleon, is smaller than the size of the nucleus, but the Coulomb repulsion from all protons reaches all others. If the nucleus is large enough, the Coulomb repulsion can add to overcome the nuclear attraction.

There are some noticeable spikes on the BE/A graph, which represent particularly tightly bound nuclei. These spikes reveal further details of nuclear forces, such as confirming that closed-shell nuclei (those with magic numbers of protons or neutrons or both) are more tightly bound. The spikes also indicate that some nuclei with even numbers for Z and N, and with $Z = N$, are exceptionally tightly bound. This finding can be correlated with some of the cosmic abundances of the elements. The most common elements in the universe, as determined by observations of atomic spectra from outer space, are hydrogen, followed by $^4\mathrm{He}$, with much smaller amounts of $^{12}\mathrm{C}$ and other elements. It should be noted that the heavier elements are created in supernova explosions, while the lighter ones are produced by nuclear fusion during the normal life cycles of stars, as will be discussed in subsequent chapters. The most common elements have the most tightly bound nuclei. It is also no accident that one of the most tightly bound light nuclei is $^4\mathrm{He}$, emitted in α decay.

EXAMPLE 31.7

What Is BE/A for an Alpha Particle?

Calculate the binding energy per nucleon of $^4\mathrm{He}$, the α particle.

Strategy

To find BE/A, we first find BE using the Equation $\mathrm{BE} = \{[Zm(^1\mathrm{H}) + Nm_n] - m(^A\mathrm{X})\}\, c^2$ and then divide by A. This is straightforward once we have looked up the appropriate atomic masses in Appendix A.

Solution

The binding energy for a nucleus is given by the equation

$$\mathrm{BE} = \{[Zm(^1\mathrm{H}) + Nm_n] - m(^A\mathrm{X})\}\, c^2. \quad 31.63$$

For $^4\mathrm{He}$, we have $Z = N = 2$; thus,

$$\mathrm{BE} = \{[2m(^1\mathrm{H}) + 2m_n] - m(^4\mathrm{He})\}\, c^2. \quad 31.64$$

Appendix A gives these masses as $m(^4\mathrm{He}) = 4.002602\ \mathrm{u}$, $m(^1\mathrm{H}) = 1.007825\ \mathrm{u}$, and $m_n = 1.008665\ \mathrm{u}$. Thus,

$$\mathrm{BE} = (0.030378\ \mathrm{u})c^2. \quad 31.65$$

Noting that $1\ \mathrm{u} = 931.5\ \mathrm{MeV}/c^2$, we find

$$\mathrm{BE} = (0.030378)(931.5\ \mathrm{MeV}/c^2)c^2 = 28.3\ \mathrm{MeV}. \quad 31.66$$

Since $A = 4$, we see that BE/A is this number divided by 4, or

$$\mathrm{BE}/A = 7.07\ \mathrm{MeV/nucleon}. \quad 31.67$$

Discussion

This is a large binding energy per nucleon compared with those for other low-mass nuclei, which have $\mathrm{BE}/A \approx 3\ \mathrm{MeV/nucleon}$. This indicates that $^4\mathrm{He}$ is tightly bound compared with its neighbors on the chart of the nuclides. You can see the spike representing this value of BE/A for $^4\mathrm{He}$ on the graph in Figure 31.24. This is why $^4\mathrm{He}$ is stable. Since $^4\mathrm{He}$ is tightly bound, it has less mass than other $A = 4$ nuclei and, therefore, cannot spontaneously decay into them. The large binding energy also helps to explain why some nuclei undergo α decay. Smaller mass in the decay products can mean energy release, and such decays can be spontaneous. Further, it can happen that two protons and two neutrons in a nucleus can randomly find themselves together, experience the exceptionally large nuclear force that binds this combination, and act as a $^4\mathrm{He}$ unit within the nucleus, at least for a while. In some cases, the $^4\mathrm{He}$ escapes, and α decay has then taken place.

There is more to be learned from nuclear binding energies. The general trend in BE/A is fundamental to energy production in stars, and to fusion and fission energy sources on Earth, for example. This is one of the applications of nuclear physics covered in Medical Applications of Nuclear Physics. The abundance of elements on Earth, in stars, and in the universe as a whole is related to the binding energy of nuclei and has implications for the continued expansion of the universe.

Problem-Solving Strategies

For Reaction And Binding Energies and Activity Calculations in Nuclear Physics

1. *Identify exactly what needs to be determined in the problem (identify the unknowns).* This will allow you to decide whether the energy of a decay or nuclear reaction is involved, for example, or whether the problem is primarily concerned with activity (rate of decay).
2. *Make a list of what is given or can be inferred from the problem as stated (identify the knowns).*
3. *For reaction and binding-energy problems, we use atomic rather than nuclear masses.* Since the masses of neutral atoms are used, you must count the number of electrons involved. If these do not balance (such as in β^+ decay), then an energy adjustment of 0.511 MeV per electron must be made. Also note that atomic masses

may not be given in a problem; they can be found in tables.

4. *For problems involving activity, the relationship of activity to half-life, and the number of nuclei given in the equation* $R = \frac{0.693N}{t_{1/2}}$ *can be very useful.* Owing to the fact that number of nuclei is involved, you will also need to be familiar with moles and Avogadro's number.
5. *Perform the desired calculation; keep careful track of plus and minus signs as well as powers of 10.*
6. *Check the answer to see if it is reasonable: Does it make sense?* Compare your results with worked examples and other information in the text. (Heeding the advice in Step 5 will also help you to be certain of your result.) You must understand the problem conceptually to be able to determine whether the numerical result is reasonable.

PHET EXPLORATIONS

Nuclear Fission

Start a chain reaction, or introduce non-radioactive isotopes to prevent one. Control energy production in a nuclear reactor!

Click to view content (https://openstax.org/l/16fission).

31.7 Tunneling

LEARNING OBJECTIVES

By the end of this section, you will be able to:

- Define and discuss tunneling.
- Define potential barrier.
- Explain quantum tunneling.

Protons and neutrons are *bound* inside nuclei, that means energy must be supplied to break them away. The situation is analogous to a marble in a bowl that can roll around but lacks the energy to get over the rim. It is bound inside the bowl (see Figure 31.26). If the marble could get over the rim, it would gain kinetic energy by rolling down outside. However classically, if the marble does not have enough kinetic energy to get over the rim, it remains forever trapped in its well.

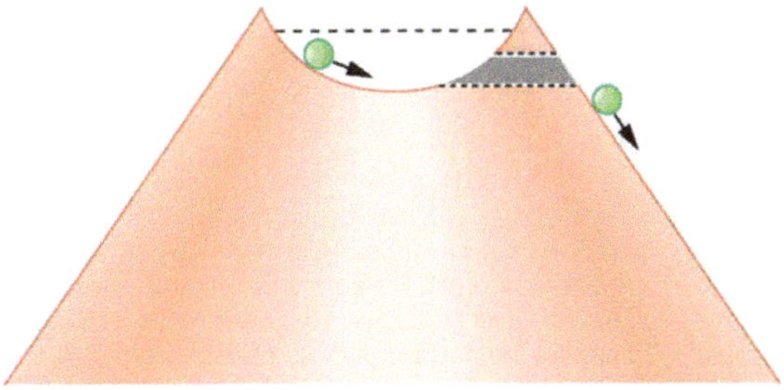

FIGURE 31.26 The marble in this semicircular bowl at the top of a volcano has enough kinetic energy to get to the altitude of the dashed line, but not enough to get over the rim, so that it is trapped forever. If it could find a tunnel through the barrier, it would escape, roll downhill, and gain kinetic energy.

In a nucleus, the attractive nuclear potential is analogous to the bowl at the top of a volcano (where the "volcano" refers only to the shape). Protons and neutrons have kinetic energy, but it is about 8 MeV less than that needed to get out (see Figure 31.27). That is, they are bound by an average of 8 MeV per nucleon. The slope of the hill outside the bowl is analogous to the repulsive Coulomb potential for a nucleus, such as for an α particle outside a positive nucleus. In α decay, two protons and two neutrons spontaneously break away as a ^4He unit. Yet the protons and neutrons do not have enough kinetic energy to get over the rim. So how does the α particle get out?

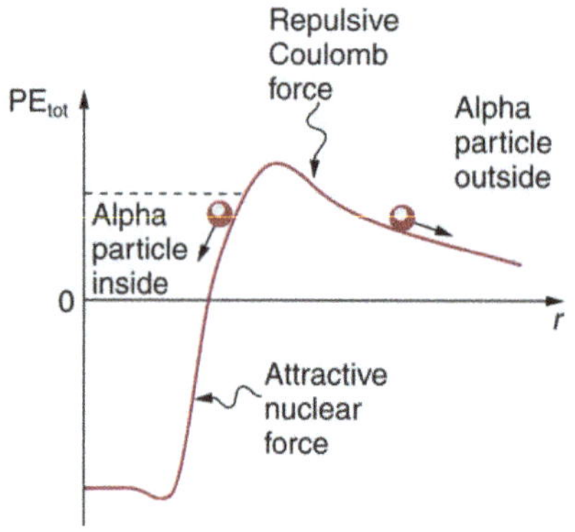

FIGURE 31.27 Nucleons within an atomic nucleus are bound or trapped by the attractive nuclear force, as shown in this simplified potential energy curve. An α particle outside the range of the nuclear force feels the repulsive Coulomb force. The α particle inside the nucleus does not have enough kinetic energy to get over the rim, yet it does manage to get out by quantum mechanical tunneling.

The answer was supplied in 1928 by the Russian physicist George Gamow (1904–1968). The α particle tunnels through a region of space it is forbidden to be in, and it comes out of the side of the nucleus. Like an electron making a transition between orbits around an atom, it travels from one point to another without ever having been in between. Figure 31.28 indicates how this works. The wave function of a quantum mechanical particle varies smoothly, going from within an atomic nucleus (on one side of a potential energy barrier) to outside the nucleus (on the other side of the potential energy barrier). Inside the barrier, the wave function does not become zero but decreases exponentially, and we do not observe the particle inside the barrier. The probability of finding a particle is related to the square of its wave function, and so there is a small probability of finding the particle outside the barrier, which implies that the particle can tunnel through the barrier. This process is called **barrier penetration** or **quantum mechanical tunneling**. This concept was developed in theory by J. Robert Oppenheimer (who led the development of the first nuclear bombs during World War II) and was used by Gamow and others to describe α decay.

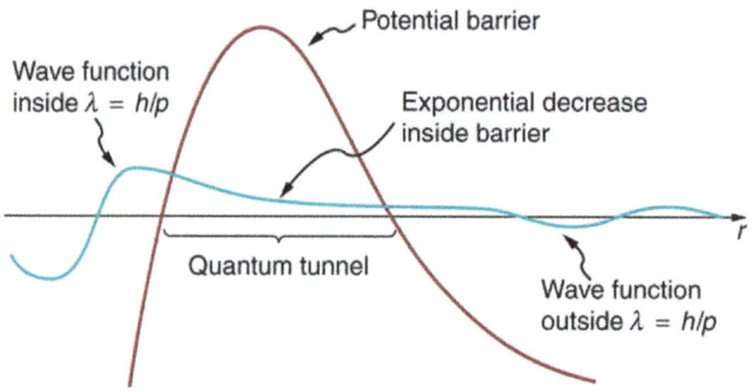

FIGURE 31.28 The wave function representing a quantum mechanical particle must vary smoothly, going from within the nucleus (to the left of the barrier) to outside the nucleus (to the right of the barrier). Inside the barrier, the wave function does not abruptly become zero; rather, it decreases exponentially. Outside the barrier, the wave function is small but finite, and there it smoothly becomes sinusoidal. Owing to the fact that there is a small probability of finding the particle outside the barrier, the particle can tunnel through the barrier.

Good ideas explain more than one thing. In addition to qualitatively explaining how the four nucleons in an α particle can get out of the nucleus, the detailed theory also explains quantitatively the half-life of various nuclei that undergo α decay. This description is what Gamow and others devised, and it works for α decay half-lives that vary by 17 orders of magnitude. Experiments have shown that the more energetic the α decay of a particular nuclide is, the shorter is its half-life. **Tunneling** explains this in the following manner: For the decay to be more energetic, the nucleons must have more energy in the nucleus and should be able to ascend a little closer to the rim. The barrier is therefore not as thick for more energetic decay, and the exponential decrease of the wave function inside the barrier is not as great. Thus the probability of finding the particle outside the barrier is greater, and the half-life is shorter.

Tunneling as an effect also occurs in quantum mechanical systems other than nuclei. Electrons trapped in solids can tunnel from one object to another if the barrier between the objects is thin enough. The process is the same in principle as described for α decay. It is far more likely for a thin barrier than a thick one. Scanning tunneling electron microscopes function on this principle. The current of electrons that travels between a probe and a sample tunnels through a barrier and is very sensitive to its thickness, allowing detection of individual atoms as shown in Figure

31.29.

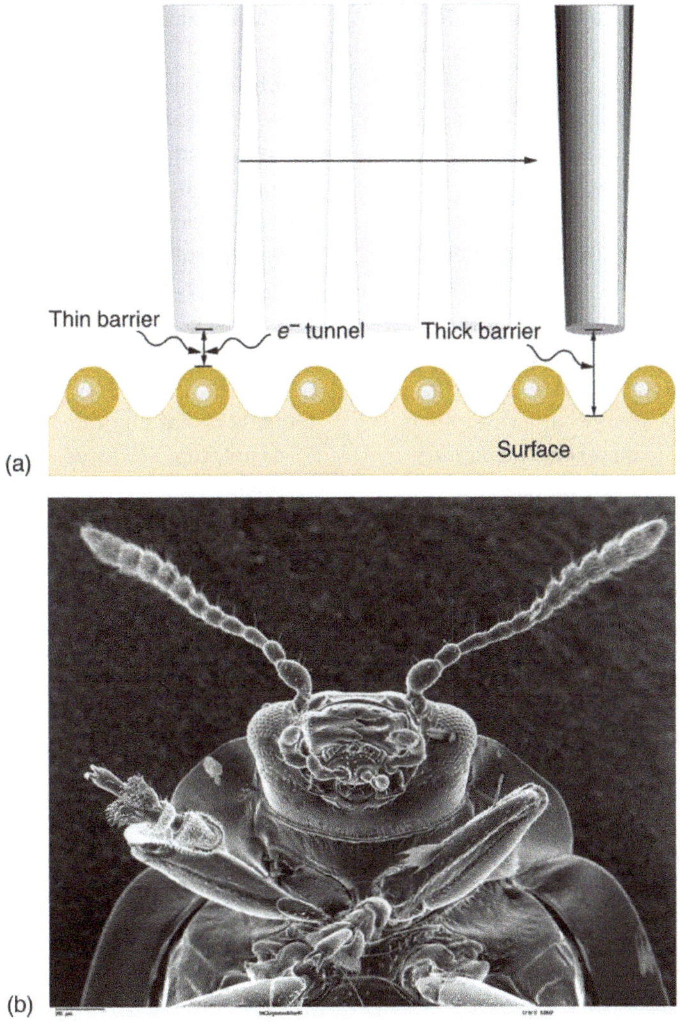

FIGURE 31.29 (a) A scanning tunneling electron microscope can detect extremely small variations in dimensions, such as individual atoms. Electrons tunnel quantum mechanically between the probe and the sample. The probability of tunneling is extremely sensitive to barrier thickness, so that the electron current is a sensitive indicator of surface features. (b) Head and mouthparts of *Coleoptera Chrysomelidea* as seen through an electron microscope (credit: Louisa Howard, Dartmouth College)

PHET EXPLORATIONS

Quantum Tunneling and Wave Packets

Watch quantum "particles" tunnel through barriers. Explore the properties of the wave functions that describe these particles.

Click to view content (https://openstax.org/l/21intquatanvid).

Glossary

activity the rate of decay for radioactive nuclides

alpha decay type of radioactive decay in which an atomic nucleus emits an alpha particle

alpha rays one of the types of rays emitted from the nucleus of an atom

antielectron another term for positron

antimatter composed of antiparticles

atomic mass the total mass of the protons, neutrons, and electrons in a single atom

atomic number number of protons in a nucleus

barrier penetration quantum mechanical effect whereby a particle has a nonzero probability to cross through a potential energy barrier despite not having sufficient energy to pass over the barrier; also called quantum mechanical tunneling

becquerel SI unit for rate of decay of a radioactive material

beta decay type of radioactive decay in which an atomic nucleus emits a beta particle

beta rays one of the types of rays emitted from the nucleus of an atom

binding energy the energy needed to separate nucleus into individual protons and neutrons

binding energy per nucleon the binding energy calculated per nucleon; it reveals the details of the nuclear force—larger the BE/A, the more stable the nucleus

carbon-14 dating a radioactive dating technique based on the radioactivity of carbon-14

chart of the nuclides a table comprising stable and unstable nuclei

curie the activity of 1g of ^{226}Ra, equal to $3.70 \times 10^{10}\ \text{Bq}$

daughter the nucleus obtained when parent nucleus decays and produces another nucleus following the rules and the conservation laws

decay the process by which an atomic nucleus of an unstable atom loses mass and energy by emitting ionizing particles

decay constant quantity that is inversely proportional to the half-life and that is used in equation for number of nuclei as a function of time

decay equation the equation to find out how much of a radioactive material is left after a given period of time

decay series process whereby subsequent nuclides decay until a stable nuclide is produced

electron capture the process in which a proton-rich nuclide absorbs an inner atomic electron and simultaneously emits a neutrino

electron capture equation equation representing the electron capture

electron's antineutrino antiparticle of electron's neutrino

electron's neutrino a subatomic elementary particle which has no net electric charge

gamma decay type of radioactive decay in which an atomic nucleus emits a gamma particle

gamma rays one of the types of rays emitted from the nucleus of an atom

Geiger tube a very common radiation detector that usually gives an audio output

half-life the time in which there is a 50% chance that a nucleus will decay

ionizing radiation radiation (whether nuclear in origin or not) that produces ionization whether nuclear in origin or not

isotopes nuclei having the same Z and different Ns

magic numbers a number that indicates a shell structure for the nucleus in which closed shells are more stable

mass number number of nucleons in a nucleus

neutrino an electrically neutral, weakly interacting elementary subatomic particle

neutron a neutral particle that is found in a nucleus

nuclear radiation rays that originate in the nuclei of atoms, the first examples of which were discovered by Becquerel

nuclear reaction energy the energy created in a nuclear reaction

nucleons the particles found inside nuclei

nucleus a region consisting of protons and neutrons at the center of an atom

nuclide a type of atom whose nucleus has specific numbers of protons and neutrons

parent the original state of nucleus before decay

photomultiplier a device that converts light into electrical signals

positron the particle that results from positive beta decay; also known as an antielectron

positron decay type of beta decay in which a proton is converted to a neutron, releasing a positron and a neutrino

protons the positively charged nucleons found in a nucleus

quantum mechanical tunneling quantum mechanical effect whereby a particle has a nonzero probability to cross through a potential energy barrier despite not having sufficient energy to pass over the barrier; also called barrier penetration

radiation detector a device that is used to detect and track the radiation from a radioactive reaction

radioactive a substance or object that emits nuclear radiation

radioactive dating an application of radioactive decay in which the age of a material is determined by the amount of radioactivity of a particular type that occurs

radioactivity the emission of rays from the nuclei of atoms

radius of a nucleus the radius of a nucleus is $r = r_0 A^{1/3}$

range of radiation the distance that the radiation can travel through a material

rate of decay the number of radioactive events per unit time

scintillators a radiation detection method that records light produced when radiation interacts with materials

solid-state radiation detectors semiconductors fabricated to directly convert incident radiation into electrical current

tunneling a quantum mechanical process of potential energy barrier penetration

Section Summary

31.1 Nuclear Radioactivity

- Some nuclei are radioactive—they spontaneously decay destroying some part of their mass and emitting energetic rays, a process called nuclear radioactivity.
- Nuclear radiation, like x rays, is ionizing radiation, because energy sufficient to ionize matter is emitted in each decay.
- The range (or distance traveled in a material) of ionizing radiation is directly related to the charge of the emitted particle and its energy, with greater-charge and lower-energy particles having the shortest ranges.
- Radiation detectors are based directly or indirectly upon the ionization created by radiation, as are the effects of radiation on living and inert materials.

31.2 Radiation Detection and Detectors

- Radiation detectors are based directly or indirectly upon the ionization created by radiation, as are the effects of radiation on living and inert materials.

31.3 Substructure of the Nucleus

- Two particles, both called nucleons, are found inside nuclei. The two types of nucleons are protons and neutrons; they are very similar, except that the proton is positively charged while the neutron is neutral. Some of their characteristics are given in Table 31.2 and compared with those of the electron. A mass unit convenient to atomic and nuclear processes is the unified atomic mass unit (u), defined to be
  $1\text{ u} = 1.6605 \times 10^{-27}\text{ kg} = 931.46\text{ MeV}/c^2.$
- A nuclide is a specific combination of protons and neutrons, denoted by
  ${}^{A}_{Z}\text{X}_N \text{ or simply} {}^{A}\text{X},$
  Z is the number of protons or atomic number, X is the symbol for the element, N is the number of neutrons, and A is the mass number or the total number of protons and neutrons,
  $A = N + Z.$
- Nuclides having the same Z but different N are isotopes of the same element.
- The radius of a nucleus, r, is approximately
  $r = r_0 A^{1/3},$
  where $r_0 = 1.2\text{ fm}$. Nuclear volumes are proportional to A. There are two nuclear forces, the weak and the strong. Systematics in nuclear stability seen on the chart of the nuclides indicate that there are shell closures in nuclei for values of Z and N equal to the magic numbers, which correspond to highly stable nuclei.

31.4 Nuclear Decay and Conservation Laws

- When a parent nucleus decays, it produces a daughter nucleus following rules and conservation laws. There are three major types of nuclear decay, called alpha (α), beta (β), and gamma (γ). The α decay equation is
  ${}^{A}_{Z}\text{X}_N \rightarrow {}^{A-4}_{Z-2}\text{Y}_{N-2} + {}^{4}_{2}\text{He}_2.$
- Nuclear decay releases an amount of energy E related to the mass destroyed Δm by
  $E = (\Delta m)c^2.$
- There are three forms of beta decay. The β^- decay equation is
  ${}^{A}_{Z}\text{X}_N \rightarrow {}^{A}_{Z+1}\text{Y}_{N-1} + \beta^- + \bar{\nu}_e.$
- The β^+ decay equation is
  ${}^{A}_{Z}\text{X}_N \rightarrow {}^{A}_{Z-1}\text{Y}_{N+1} + \beta^+ + \nu_e.$
- The electron capture equation is
  ${}^{A}_{Z}\text{X}_N + e^- \rightarrow {}^{A}_{Z-1}\text{Y}_{N+1} + \nu_e.$
- β^- is an electron, β^+ is an antielectron or positron, ν_e represents an electron's neutrino, and $\bar{\nu}_e$ is an electron's antineutrino. In addition to all previously known conservation laws, two new ones arise— conservation of electron family number and conservation of the total number of nucleons. The γ decay equation is
  ${}^{A}_{Z}\text{X}^*_N \rightarrow {}^{A}_{Z}\text{X}_N + \gamma_1 + \gamma_2 + \cdots$
  γ is a high-energy photon originating in a nucleus.

31.5 Half-Life and Activity

- Half-life $t_{1/2}$ is the time in which there is a 50% chance that a nucleus will decay. The number of nuclei N as a function of time is
$N = N_0 e^{-\lambda t}$,
where N_0 is the number present at $t = 0$, and λ is the decay constant, related to the half-life by
$\lambda = \frac{0.693}{t_{1/2}}$.
- One of the applications of radioactive decay is radioactive dating, in which the age of a material is determined by the amount of radioactive decay that occurs. The rate of decay is called the activity R:
$R = \frac{\Delta N}{\Delta t}$.
- The SI unit for R is the becquerel (Bq), defined by $1 \text{ Bq} = 1 \text{ decay/s}$.
- R is also expressed in terms of curies (Ci), where $1 \text{ Ci} = 3.70 \times 10^{10} \text{ Bq}$.
- The activity R of a source is related to N and $t_{1/2}$ by
$R = \frac{0.693N}{t_{1/2}}$.
- Since N has an exponential behavior as in the equation $N = N_0 e^{-\lambda t}$, the activity also has an exponential behavior, given by
$R = R_0 e^{-\lambda t}$,
where R_0 is the activity at $t = 0$.

31.6 Binding Energy

- The binding energy (BE) of a nucleus is the energy needed to separate it into individual protons and neutrons. In terms of atomic masses,
$\text{BE} = \{[Zm(^1\text{H}) + Nm_n] - m(^A\text{X})\} c^2$,
where $m(^1\text{H})$ is the mass of a hydrogen atom, $m(^A\text{X})$ is the atomic mass of the nuclide, and m_n is the mass of a neutron. Patterns in the binding energy per nucleon, BE/A, reveal details of the nuclear force. The larger the BE/A, the more stable the nucleus.

31.7 Tunneling

- Tunneling is a quantum mechanical process of potential energy barrier penetration. The concept was first applied to explain α decay, but tunneling is found to occur in other quantum mechanical systems.

Conceptual Questions

31.1 Nuclear Radioactivity

1. Suppose the range for $5.0 \text{ MeV}\alpha$ ray is known to be 2.0 mm in a certain material. Does this mean that every $5.0 \text{ MeV}\alpha$ a ray that strikes this material travels 2.0 mm, or does the range have an average value with some statistical fluctuations in the distances traveled? Explain.

2. What is the difference between γ rays and characteristic x rays? Is either necessarily more energetic than the other? Which can be the most energetic?

3. Ionizing radiation interacts with matter by scattering from electrons and nuclei in the substance. Based on the law of conservation of momentum and energy, explain why electrons tend to absorb more energy than nuclei in these interactions.

4. What characteristics of radioactivity show it to be nuclear in origin and not atomic?

5. What is the source of the energy emitted in radioactive decay? Identify an earlier conservation law, and describe how it was modified to take such processes into account.

6. Consider Figure 31.3. If an electric field is substituted for the magnetic field with positive charge instead of the north pole and negative charge instead of the south pole, in which directions will the α, β, and γ rays bend?

7. Explain how an α particle can have a larger range in air than a β particle with the same energy in lead.

8. Arrange the following according to their ability to act as radiation shields, with the best first and worst last. Explain your ordering in terms of how radiation loses its energy in matter.
(a) A solid material with low density composed of low-mass atoms.
(b) A gas composed of high-mass atoms.
(c) A gas composed of low-mass atoms.
(d) A solid with high density composed of high-mass atoms.

9. Often, when people have to work around radioactive materials spills, we see them wearing white coveralls (usually a plastic material). What types of radiation (if any) do you think these suits protect the worker from, and how?

31.2 Radiation Detection and Detectors

10. Is it possible for light emitted by a scintillator to be too low in frequency to be used in a photomultiplier tube? Explain.

31.3 Substructure of the Nucleus

11. The weak and strong nuclear forces are basic to the structure of matter. Why we do not experience them directly?

12. Define and make clear distinctions between the terms neutron, nucleon, nucleus, nuclide, and neutrino.

13. What are isotopes? Why do different isotopes of the same element have similar chemistries?

31.4 Nuclear Decay and Conservation Laws

14. Star Trek fans have often heard the term "antimatter drive." Describe how you could use a magnetic field to trap antimatter, such as produced by nuclear decay, and later combine it with matter to produce energy. Be specific about the type of antimatter, the need for vacuum storage, and the fraction of matter converted into energy.

15. What conservation law requires an electron's neutrino to be produced in electron capture? Note that the electron no longer exists after it is captured by the nucleus.

16. Neutrinos are experimentally determined to have an extremely small mass. Huge numbers of neutrinos are created in a supernova at the same time as massive amounts of light are first produced. When the 1987A supernova occurred in the Large Magellanic Cloud, visible primarily in the Southern Hemisphere and some 100,000 light-years away from Earth, neutrinos from the explosion were observed at about the same time as the light from the blast. How could the relative arrival times of neutrinos and light be used to place limits on the mass of neutrinos?

17. What do the three types of beta decay have in common that is distinctly different from alpha decay?

31.5 Half-Life and Activity

18. In a 3×10^9-year-old rock that originally contained some ^{238}U, which has a half-life of 4.5×10^9 years, we expect to find some ^{238}U remaining in it. Why are ^{226}Ra, ^{222}Rn, and ^{210}Po also found in such a rock, even though they have much shorter half-lives (1600 years, 3.8 days, and 138 days, respectively)?

19. Does the number of radioactive nuclei in a sample decrease to *exactly* half its original value in one half-life? Explain in terms of the statistical nature of radioactive decay.

20. Radioactivity depends on the nucleus and not the atom or its chemical state. Why, then, is one kilogram of uranium more radioactive than one kilogram of uranium hexafluoride?

21. Explain how a bound system can have less mass than its components. Why is this not observed classically, say for a building made of bricks?

22. Spontaneous radioactive decay occurs only when the decay products have less mass than the parent, and it tends to produce a daughter that is more stable than the parent. Explain how this is related to the fact that more tightly bound nuclei are more stable. (Consider the binding energy per nucleon.)

23. To obtain the most precise value of BE from the equation $\text{BE}=[ZM(^1\text{H})+Nm_n]c^2 - m(^A\text{X})c^2$, we should take into account the binding energy of the electrons in the neutral atoms. Will doing this produce a larger or smaller value for BE? Why is this effect usually negligible?

24. How does the finite range of the nuclear force relate to the fact that BE/A is greatest for A near 60?

31.6 Binding Energy

25. Why is the number of neutrons greater than the number of protons in stable nuclei having A greater than about 40, and why is this effect more pronounced for the heaviest nuclei?

31.7 Tunneling

26. A physics student caught breaking conservation laws is imprisoned. She leans against the cell wall hoping to tunnel out quantum mechanically. Explain why her chances are negligible. (This is so in any classical situation.)

27. When a nucleus α decays, does the α particle move continuously from inside the nucleus to outside? That is, does it travel each point along an imaginary line from inside to out? Explain.

Problems & Exercises

31.2 Radiation Detection and Detectors

1. The energy of 30.0 eV is required to ionize a molecule of the gas inside a Geiger tube, thereby producing an ion pair. Suppose a particle of ionizing radiation deposits 0.500 MeV of energy in this Geiger tube. What maximum number of ion pairs can it create?

2. A particle of ionizing radiation creates 4000 ion pairs in the gas inside a Geiger tube as it passes through. What minimum energy was deposited, if 30.0 eV is required to create each ion pair?

3. (a) Repeat Exercise 31.2, and convert the energy to joules or calories. (b) If all of this energy is converted to thermal energy in the gas, what is its temperature increase, assuming $50.0\ \text{cm}^3$ of ideal gas at 0.250-atm pressure? (The small answer is consistent with the fact that the energy is large on a quantum mechanical scale but small on a macroscopic scale.)

4. Suppose a particle of ionizing radiation deposits 1.0 MeV in the gas of a Geiger tube, all of which goes to creating ion pairs. Each ion pair requires 30.0 eV of energy. (a) The applied voltage sweeps the ions out of the gas in $1.00\ \mu\text{s}$. What is the current? (b) This current is smaller than the actual current since the applied voltage in the Geiger tube accelerates the separated ions, which then create other ion pairs in subsequent collisions. What is the current if this last effect multiplies the number of ion pairs by 900?

31.3 Substructure of the Nucleus

5. Verify that a 2.3×10^{17} kg mass of water at normal density would make a cube 60 km on a side, as claimed in Example 31.1. (This mass at nuclear density would make a cube 1.0 m on a side.)

6. Find the length of a side of a cube having a mass of 1.0 kg and the density of nuclear matter, taking this to be $2.3 \times 10^{17}\ \text{kg/m}^3$.

7. What is the radius of an α particle?

8. Find the radius of a ^{238}Pu nucleus. ^{238}Pu is a manufactured nuclide that is used as a power source on some space probes.

9. (a) Calculate the radius of ^{58}Ni, one of the most tightly bound stable nuclei.
(b) What is the ratio of the radius of ^{58}Ni to that of ^{258}Ha, one of the largest nuclei ever made? Note that the radius of the largest nucleus is still much smaller than the size of an atom.

10. The unified atomic mass unit is defined to be $1\ \text{u} = 1.6605 \times 10^{-27}\ \text{kg}$. Verify that this amount of mass converted to energy yields 931.5 MeV. Note that you must use four-digit or better values for c and $|q_e|$.

11. What is the ratio of the velocity of a β particle to that of an α particle, if they have the same nonrelativistic kinetic energy?

12. If a 1.50-cm-thick piece of lead can absorb 90.0% of the γ rays from a radioactive source, how many centimeters of lead are needed to absorb all but 0.100% of the γ rays?

13. The detail observable using a probe is limited by its wavelength. Calculate the energy of a γ-ray photon that has a wavelength of 1×10^{-16} m, small enough to detect details about one-tenth the size of a nucleon. Note that a photon having this energy is difficult to produce and interacts poorly with the nucleus, limiting the practicability of this probe.

14. (a) Show that if you assume the average nucleus is spherical with a radius $r = r_0 A^{1/3}$, and with a mass of A u, then its density is independent of A.
(b) Calculate that density in u/fm^3 and kg/m^3, and compare your results with those found in Example 31.1 for ^{56}Fe.

15. What is the ratio of the velocity of a 5.00-MeV β ray to that of an α particle with the same kinetic energy? This should confirm that βs travel much faster than αs even when relativity is taken into consideration. (See also Exercise 31.11.)

16. (a) What is the kinetic energy in MeV of a β ray that is traveling at $0.998c$? This gives some idea of how energetic a β ray must be to travel at nearly the same speed as a γ ray. (b) What is the velocity of the γ ray relative to the β ray?

31.4 Nuclear Decay and Conservation Laws

In the following eight problems, write the complete decay equation for the given nuclide in the complete $^A_Z\text{X}_N$ notation. Refer to the periodic table for values of Z.

17. β^- decay of ^3H (tritium), a manufactured isotope of hydrogen used in some digital watch displays, and manufactured primarily for use in hydrogen

bombs.

18. β^- decay of ^{40}K, a naturally occurring rare isotope of potassium responsible for some of our exposure to background radiation.

19. β^+ decay of ^{50}Mn.

20. β^+ decay of ^{52}Fe.

21. Electron capture by ^{7}Be.

22. Electron capture by ^{106}In.

23. α decay of ^{210}Po, the isotope of polonium in the decay series of ^{238}U that was discovered by the Curies. A favorite isotope in physics labs, since it has a short half-life and decays to a stable nuclide.

24. α decay of ^{226}Ra, another isotope in the decay series of ^{238}U, first recognized as a new element by the Curies. Poses special problems because its daughter is a radioactive noble gas.

In the following four problems, identify the parent nuclide and write the complete decay equation in the $^{A}_{Z}\text{X}_N$ notation. Refer to the periodic table for values of Z.

25. β^- decay producing ^{137}Ba. The parent nuclide is a major waste product of reactors and has chemistry similar to potassium and sodium, resulting in its concentration in your cells if ingested.

26. β^- decay producing ^{90}Y. The parent nuclide is a major waste product of reactors and has chemistry similar to calcium, so that it is concentrated in bones if ingested (^{90}Y is also radioactive.)

27. α decay producing ^{228}Ra. The parent nuclide is nearly 100% of the natural element and is found in gas lantern mantles and in metal alloys used in jets (^{228}Ra is also radioactive).

28. α decay producing ^{208}Pb. The parent nuclide is in the decay series produced by ^{232}Th, the only naturally occurring isotope of thorium.

29. When an electron and positron annihilate, both their masses are destroyed, creating two equal energy photons to preserve momentum. (a) Confirm that the annihilation equation $e^+ + e^- \rightarrow \gamma + \gamma$ conserves charge, electron family number, and total number of nucleons. To do this, identify the values of each before and after the annihilation. (b) Find the energy of each γ ray, assuming the electron and positron are initially nearly at rest. (c) Explain why the two γ rays travel in exactly opposite directions if the center of mass of the electron-positron system is initially at rest.

30. Confirm that charge, electron family number, and the total number of nucleons are all conserved by the rule for α decay given in the equation $^{A}_{Z}\text{X}_N \rightarrow {}^{A-4}_{Z-2}\text{Y}_{N-2} + {}^{4}_{2}\text{He}_2$. To do this, identify the values of each before and after the decay.

31. Confirm that charge, electron family number, and the total number of nucleons are all conserved by the rule for β^- decay given in the equation $^{A}_{Z}\text{X}_N \rightarrow {}^{A}_{Z+1}\text{Y}_{N-1} + \beta^- + \bar{\nu}_e$. To do this, identify the values of each before and after the decay.

32. Confirm that charge, electron family number, and the total number of nucleons are all conserved by the rule for β^- decay given in the equation $^{A}_{Z}\text{X}_N \rightarrow {}^{A}_{Z-1}\text{Y}_{N-1} + \beta^- + \nu_e$. To do this, identify the values of each before and after the decay.

33. Confirm that charge, electron family number, and the total number of nucleons are all conserved by the rule for electron capture given in the equation $^{A}_{Z}\text{X}_N + e^- \rightarrow {}^{A}_{Z-1}\text{Y}_{N+1} + \nu_e$. To do this, identify the values of each before and after the capture.

34. A rare decay mode has been observed in which ^{222}Ra emits a ^{14}C nucleus. (a) The decay equation is $^{222}\text{Ra} \rightarrow^{A} \text{X} + ^{14}\text{C}$. Identify the nuclide ^{A}X. (b) Find the energy emitted in the decay. The mass of ^{222}Ra is 222.015353 u.

35. (a) Write the complete α decay equation for ^{226}Ra.
(b) Find the energy released in the decay.

36. (a) Write the complete α decay equation for ^{249}Cf.
(b) Find the energy released in the decay.

37. (a) Write the complete β^- decay equation for the neutron. (b) Find the energy released in the decay.

38. (a) Write the complete β^- decay equation for ^{90}Sr, a major waste product of nuclear reactors.
(b) Find the energy released in the decay.

39. Calculate the energy released in the β^+ decay of ^{22}Na, the equation for which is given in the text. The masses of ^{22}Na and ^{22}Ne are 21.994434 and 21.991383 u, respectively.

40. (a) Write the complete β^+ decay equation for ^{11}C.

(b) Calculate the energy released in the decay. The masses of ^{11}C and ^{11}B are 11.011433 and 11.009305 u, respectively.

41. (a) Calculate the energy released in the α decay of ^{238}U.
(b) What fraction of the mass of a single ^{238}U is destroyed in the decay? The mass of ^{234}Th is 234.043593 u.
(c) Although the fractional mass loss is large for a single nucleus, it is difficult to observe for an entire macroscopic sample of uranium. Why is this?

42. (a) Write the complete reaction equation for electron capture by ^{7}Be.
(b) Calculate the energy released.

43. (a) Write the complete reaction equation for electron capture by ^{15}O.
(b) Calculate the energy released.

31.5 Half-Life and Activity

Data from the appendices and the periodic table may be needed for these problems.

44. An old campfire is uncovered during an archaeological dig. Its charcoal is found to contain less than 1/1000 the normal amount of ^{14}C. Estimate the minimum age of the charcoal, noting that $2^{10} = 1024$.

45. A ^{60}Co source is labeled 4.00 mCi, but its present activity is found to be 1.85×10^7 Bq. (a) What is the present activity in mCi? (b) How long ago did it actually have a 4.00-mCi activity?

46. (a) Calculate the activity R in curies of 1.00 g of ^{226}Ra. (b) Discuss why your answer is not exactly 1.00 Ci, given that the curie was originally supposed to be exactly the activity of a gram of radium.

47. Show that the activity of the ^{14}C in 1.00 g of ^{12}C found in living tissue is 0.250 Bq.

48. Mantles for gas lanterns contain thorium, because it forms an oxide that can survive being heated to incandescence for long periods of time. Natural thorium is almost 100% ^{232}Th, with a half-life of 1.405×10^{10} y. If an average lantern mantle contains 300 mg of thorium, what is its activity?

49. Cow's milk produced near nuclear reactors can be tested for as little as 1.00 pCi of ^{131}I per liter, to check for possible reactor leakage. What mass of ^{131}I has this activity?

50. (a) Natural potassium contains ^{40}K, which has a half-life of 1.277×10^9 y. What mass of ^{40}K in a person would have a decay rate of 4140 Bq? (b) What is the fraction of ^{40}K in natural potassium, given that the person has 140 g in his body? (These numbers are typical for a 70-kg adult.)

51. There is more than one isotope of natural uranium. If a researcher isolates 1.00 mg of the relatively scarce ^{235}U and finds this mass to have an activity of 80.0 Bq, what is its half-life in years?

52. ^{50}V has one of the longest known radioactive half-lives. In a difficult experiment, a researcher found that the activity of 1.00 kg of ^{50}V is 1.75 Bq. What is the half-life in years?

53. You can sometimes find deep red crystal vases in antique stores, called uranium glass because their color was produced by doping the glass with uranium. Look up the natural isotopes of uranium and their half-lives, and calculate the activity of such a vase assuming it has 2.00 g of uranium in it. Neglect the activity of any daughter nuclides.

54. A tree falls in a forest. How many years must pass before the ^{14}C activity in 1.00 g of the tree's carbon drops to 1.00 decay per hour?

55. What fraction of the ^{40}K that was on Earth when it formed 4.5×10^9 years ago is left today?

56. A 5000-Ci ^{60}Co source used for cancer therapy is considered too weak to be useful when its activity falls to 3500 Ci. How long after its manufacture does this happen?

57. Natural uranium is 0.7200% ^{235}U and 99.27% ^{238}U. What were the percentages of ^{235}U and ^{238}U in natural uranium when Earth formed 4.5×10^9 years ago?

58. The β^- particles emitted in the decay of ^{3}H (tritium) interact with matter to create light in a glow-in-the-dark exit sign. At the time of manufacture, such a sign contains 15.0 Ci of ^{3}H. (a) What is the mass of the tritium? (b) What is its activity 5.00 y after manufacture?

59. World War II aircraft had instruments with glowing radium-painted dials (see Figure 31.2). The activity of one such instrument was 1.0×10^5 Bq when new. (a) What mass of ^{226}Ra was present? (b) After some years, the phosphors on the dials deteriorated chemically, but the radium did not escape. What is the activity of this instrument 57.0 years after it was made?

60. (a) The ^{210}Po source used in a physics laboratory is labeled as having an activity of $1.0\ \mu\text{Ci}$ on the date it was prepared. A student measures the radioactivity of this source with a Geiger counter and observes 1500 counts per minute. She notices that the source was prepared 120 days before her lab. What fraction of the decays is she observing with her apparatus? (b) Identify some of the reasons that only a fraction of the α s emitted are observed by the detector.

61. Armor-piercing shells with depleted uranium cores are fired by aircraft at tanks. (The high density of the uranium makes them effective.) The uranium is called depleted because it has had its ^{235}U removed for reactor use and is nearly pure ^{238}U. Depleted uranium has been erroneously called non-radioactive. To demonstrate that this is wrong: (a) Calculate the activity of 60.0 g of pure ^{238}U. (b) Calculate the activity of 60.0 g of natural uranium, neglecting the ^{234}U and all daughter nuclides.

62. The ceramic glaze on a red-orange Fiestaware plate is U_2O_3 and contains 50.0 grams of ^{238}U, but very little ^{235}U. (a) What is the activity of the plate? (b) Calculate the total energy that will be released by the ^{238}U decay. (c) If energy is worth 12.0 cents per $\text{kW} \cdot \text{h}$, what is the monetary value of the energy emitted? (These plates went out of production some 30 years ago, but are still available as collectibles.)

63. Large amounts of depleted uranium (^{238}U) are available as a by-product of uranium processing for reactor fuel and weapons. Uranium is very dense and makes good counter weights for aircraft. Suppose you have a 4000-kg block of ^{238}U. (a) Find its activity. (b) How many calories per day are generated by thermalization of the decay energy? (c) Do you think you could detect this as heat? Explain.

64. The *Galileo* space probe was launched on its long journey past several planets in 1989, with an ultimate goal of Jupiter. Its power source is 11.0 kg of ^{238}Pu, a by-product of nuclear weapons plutonium production. Electrical energy is generated thermoelectrically from the heat produced when the 5.59-MeV α particles emitted in each decay crash to a halt inside the plutonium and its shielding. The half-life of ^{238}Pu is 87.7 years. (a) What was the original activity of the ^{238}Pu in becquerel? (b) What power was emitted in kilowatts? (c) What power was emitted 12.0 y after launch? You may neglect any extra energy from daughter nuclides and any losses from escaping γ rays.

65. Construct Your Own Problem
Consider the generation of electricity by a radioactive isotope in a space probe, such as described in Exercise 31.64. Construct a problem in which you calculate the mass of a radioactive isotope you need in order to supply power for a long space flight. Among the things to consider are the isotope chosen, its half-life and decay energy, the power needs of the probe and the length of the flight.

66. Unreasonable Results
A nuclear physicist finds $1.0\ \mu\text{g}$ of ^{236}U in a piece of uranium ore and assumes it is primordial since its half-life is 2.3×10^7 y. (a) Calculate the amount of ^{236}Uthat would had to have been on Earth when it formed 4.5×10^9 y ago for $1.0\ \mu\text{g}$ to be left today. (b) What is unreasonable about this result? (c) What assumption is responsible?

67. Unreasonable Results
(a) Repeat Exercise 31.57 but include the 0.0055% natural abundance of ^{234}U with its 2.45×10^5 y half-life. (b) What is unreasonable about this result? (c) What assumption is responsible? (d) Where does the ^{234}U come from if it is not primordial?

68. Unreasonable Results
The manufacturer of a smoke alarm decides that the smallest current of α radiation he can detect is $1.00\ \mu\text{A}$. (a) Find the activity in curies of an α emitter that produces a $1.00\ \mu\text{A}$ current of α particles. (b) What is unreasonable about this result? (c) What assumption is responsible?

31.6 Binding Energy

69. ^2H is a loosely bound isotope of hydrogen. Called deuterium or heavy hydrogen, it is stable but relatively rare—it is 0.015% of natural hydrogen. Note that deuterium has $Z = N$, which should tend to make it more tightly bound, but both are odd numbers. Calculate BE/A, the binding energy per nucleon, for ^2H and compare it with the approximate value obtained from the graph in Figure 31.24.

70. ^{56}Fe is among the most tightly bound of all nuclides. It is more than 90% of natural iron. Note that ^{56}Fe has even numbers of both protons and neutrons. Calculate BE/A, the binding energy per

nucleon, for ^{56}Fe and compare it with the approximate value obtained from the graph in Figure 31.24.

71. ^{209}Bi is the heaviest stable nuclide, and its BE/A is low compared with medium-mass nuclides. Calculate BE/A, the binding energy per nucleon, for ^{209}Bi and compare it with the approximate value obtained from the graph in Figure 31.24.

72. (a) Calculate BE/A for ^{235}U, the rarer of the two most common uranium isotopes. (b) Calculate BE/A for ^{238}U. (Most of uranium is ^{238}U.) Note that ^{238}U has even numbers of both protons and neutrons. Is the BE/A of ^{238}U significantly different from that of ^{235}U?

73. (a) Calculate BE/A for ^{12}C. Stable and relatively tightly bound, this nuclide is most of natural carbon. (b) Calculate BE/A for ^{14}C. Is the difference in BE/A between ^{12}C and ^{14}C significant? One is stable and common, and the other is unstable and rare.

74. The fact that BE/A is greatest for A near 60 implies that the range of the nuclear force is about the diameter of such nuclides. (a) Calculate the diameter of an $A = 60$ nucleus. (b) Compare BE/A for ^{58}Ni and ^{90}Sr. The first is one of the most tightly bound nuclides, while the second is larger and less tightly bound.

75. The purpose of this problem is to show in three ways that the binding energy of the electron in a hydrogen atom is negligible compared with the masses of the proton and electron. (a) Calculate the mass equivalent in u of the 13.6-eV binding energy of an electron in a hydrogen atom, and compare this with the mass of the hydrogen atom obtained from Appendix A. (b) Subtract the mass of the proton given in Table 31.2 from the mass of the hydrogen atom given in Appendix A. You will find the difference is equal to the electron's mass to three digits, implying the binding energy is small in comparison. (c) Take the ratio of the binding energy of the electron (13.6 eV) to the energy equivalent of the electron's mass (0.511 MeV). (d) Discuss how your answers confirm the stated purpose of this problem.

76. Unreasonable Results
A particle physicist discovers a neutral particle with a mass of 2.02733 u that he assumes is two neutrons bound together. (a) Find the binding energy. (b) What is unreasonable about this result? (c) What assumptions are unreasonable or inconsistent?

31.7 Tunneling

77. Derive an approximate relationship between the energy of α decay and half-life using the following data. It may be useful to graph the log of $t_{1/2}$ against E_α to find some straight-line relationship.

Nuclide	E_α (MeV)	$t_{1/2}$
^{216}Ra	9.5	0.18 μs
^{194}Po	7.0	0.7 s
^{240}Cm	6.4	27 d
^{226}Ra	4.91	1600 y
^{232}Th	4.1	1.4×10^{10} y

TABLE 31.3 Energy and Half-Life for α Decay

78. Integrated Concepts
A 2.00-T magnetic field is applied perpendicular to the path of charged particles in a bubble chamber. What is the radius of curvature of the path of a 10 MeV proton in this field? Neglect any slowing along its path.

79. (a) Write the decay equation for the α decay of ^{235}U. (b) What energy is released in this decay? The mass of the daughter nuclide is 231.036298 u. (c) Assuming the residual nucleus is formed in its ground state, how much energy goes to the α particle?

80. Unreasonable Results
The relatively scarce naturally occurring calcium isotope ^{48}Ca has a half-life of about 2×10^{16} y. (a) A small sample of this isotope is labeled as having an activity of 1.0 Ci. What is the mass of the ^{48}Ca in the sample? (b) What is unreasonable about this result? (c) What assumption is responsible?

81. Unreasonable Results
A physicist scatters γ rays from a substance and sees evidence of a nucleus 7.5×10^{-13} m in radius. (a) Find the atomic mass of such a nucleus. (b) What is unreasonable about this result? (c) What is unreasonable about the assumption?

82. Unreasonable Results
A frazzled theoretical physicist reckons that all

conservation laws are obeyed in the decay of a proton into a neutron, positron, and neutrino (as in β^+ decay of a nucleus) and sends a paper to a journal to announce the reaction as a possible end of the universe due to the spontaneous decay of protons. (a) What energy is released in this decay? (b) What is unreasonable about this result? (c) What assumption is responsible?

83. Construct Your Own Problem
Consider the decay of radioactive substances in the Earth's interior. The energy emitted is converted to thermal energy that reaches the earth's surface and is radiated away into cold dark space. Construct a problem in which you estimate the activity in a cubic meter of earth rock? And then calculate the power generated. Calculate how much power must cross each square meter of the Earth's surface if the power is dissipated at the same rate as it is generated. Among the things to consider are the activity per cubic meter, the energy per decay, and the size of the Earth.

84. Critical Thinking (a) What is the density of ^{235}U in u/fm^3? (b) If ^{235}U splits into ^{141}Ba and $^{92}\text{Kr} + 3$ neutrons, how does the density of ^{235}U compare with the density of each element it splits into?

Test Prep for AP® Courses

31.1 Nuclear Radioactivity

1. A nucleus is observed to emit a γ ray with a frequency of 6.3×10^{19} Hz. What must happen to the nucleus as a consequence?
   a. The nucleus must gain 0.26 MeV.
   b. The nucleus must also emit an α particle of energy 0.26 MeV in the opposite direction.
   c. The nucleus must lose 0.26 MeV.
   d. The nucleus must also emit a β particle of energy 0.26 MeV in the opposite direction.

2. A uranium nucleus emits an α particle. Assuming charge is conserved, the resulting nucleus must be
   a. thorium
   b. plutonium
   c. radium
   d. curium

31.3 Substructure of the Nucleus

3. A typical carbon nucleus contains 6 neutrons and 6 protons. The 6 protons are all positively charged and in very close proximity, with separations on the order of 10^{-15} meters, which should result in an enormous repulsive force. What prevents the nucleus from dismantling itself due to the repulsion of the electric force?
   a. The attractive nature of the strong nuclear force overpowers the electric force.
   b. The weak nuclear force barely offsets the electric force.
   c. Magnetic forces generated by the orbiting electrons create a stable minimum in which the nuclear charged particles reside.
   d. The attractive electric force of the surrounding electrons is equal in all directions and cancels out, leaving no net electric force.

31.4 Nuclear Decay and Conservation Laws

4. A nucleus in an excited state undergoes γ decay, losing 1.33 MeV when emitting a γ ray. In order to conserve energy in the reaction, what frequency must the γ ray have?

5. $^{241}_{95}\text{Am}$ is commonly used in smoke detectors because its α decay process provides a useful tool for detecting the presence of smoke particles. When $^{241}_{95}\text{Am}$ undergoes α decay, what is the resulting nucleus? If $^{241}_{95}\text{Am}$ were to undergo β decay, what would be the resulting nucleus? Explain each answer.

6. For β decay, the nucleus releases a negative charge. In order for charge to be conserved overall, the nucleus must gain a positive charge, increasing its atomic number by 1, resulting in $^{241}_{96}\text{Cm}$.
A $^{14}_{6}\text{C}$ nucleus undergoes a decay process, and the resulting nucleus is $^{14}_{7}\text{N}$. What is the value of the charge released by the original nucleus?
   a. +1
   b. 0
   c. -1
   d. -2

7. Explain why the overall charge of the nucleus is increased by +1 during the β decay process.

8. Identify the missing particle based upon conservation principles:
$^{14}_{7}\text{N} + ^{4}_{2}\text{He} \rightarrow X + ^{17}_{8}\text{O}$
   a. $^{2}_{1}\text{H}$
   b. $^{1}_{1}\text{H}$
   c. $^{12}_{6}\text{C}$
   d. $^{12}_{6}\text{C}$

e. $^{8}_{4}\text{Be}$

9. Are the following reactions possible? For each, explain why or why not.

a. $^{238}_{92}\text{U} \rightarrow {}^{234}_{88}\text{Ra} + {}^{4}_{2}\text{He}$
b. $^{223}_{88}\text{Ra} \rightarrow {}^{209}_{82}\text{Pb} + {}^{14}_{6}\text{C}$
c. $^{14}_{6}\text{C} \rightarrow {}^{14}_{7}\text{N} + e^{-} + \bar{\upsilon}_{e}$
d. $^{24}_{12}\text{Mg} \rightarrow {}^{23}_{11}\text{Na} + e^{+} + \upsilon_{e}$

31.5 Half-Life and Activity

10. A radioactive sample has N atoms initially. After 3 half-lives have elapsed, how many atoms remain?

a. N/3
b. N/6
c. N/8
d. N/27

11. When $^{215}_{84}\text{Po}$ decays, the product is $^{211}_{82}\text{Pb}$. The half-life of this decay process is 1.78 ms. If the initial sample contains 3.4 x 10^{17} parent nuclei, how many are remaining after 35 ms have elapsed? What kind of decay process is this (alpha, beta, or gamma)?

31.6 Binding Energy

12. Binding energy is a measure of how much work must be done against nuclear forces in order to disassemble a nucleus into its constituent parts. For example, the amount of energy in order to disassemble $^{4}_{2}\text{He}$ into 2 protons and 2 neutrons requires 28.3 MeV of work to be done on the nuclear particles. Describe the force that makes it so difficult to pull a nucleus apart. Would it be accurate to say that the electric force plays a role in the forces within a nucleus? Explain why or why not.

CHAPTER 32
Medical Applications of Nuclear Physics

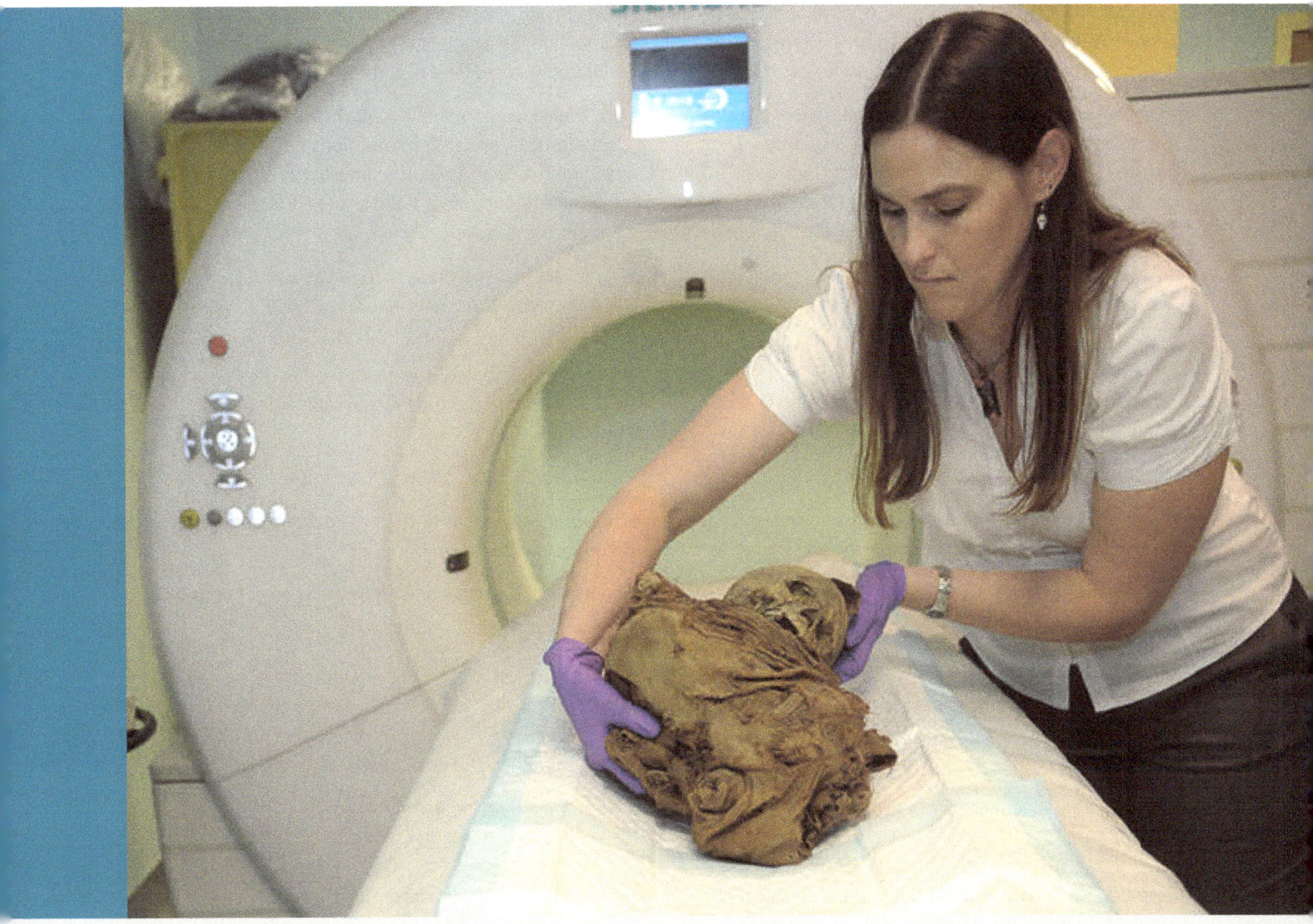

FIGURE 32.1 Tori Randall, Ph.D., curator for the Department of Physical Anthropology at the San Diego Museum of Man, prepares a 550-year-old Peruvian mummy for a CT scan at Naval Medical Center San Diego. (credit: U.S. Navy photo by Mass Communication Specialist 3rd Class Samantha A. Lewis)

CHAPTER OUTLINE

CONNECTION FOR AP® COURSES Applications of nuclear physics have become an integral part of modern life. From a bone scan that detects a cancer to a radioiodine treatment that cures another, nuclear radiation has many diagnostic and therapeutic applications in medicine. In addition nuclear radiation is used in other useful scanning applications. The fission power reactor and the hope of controlled fusion have made nuclear energy a part of our plans for the future. That said, the destructive potential of nuclear weapons haunts us, as does the possibility of nuclear reactor accidents.

Nuclear physics revealed many secrets of nature, but full exploitation of the technology remains controversial as it is intertwined with human values. Because of its great potential for alleviation of suffering and its power as a giant-scale destroyer of life, nuclear physics is typically viewed with ambivalence. Nuclear physics is a classic example of the truism that applications of technology can be good or evil, but knowledge itself is neither.

This chapter focuses on medical applications of nuclear physics. The sections on fusion and fission address the ideas that objects and systems have properties, such as mass (Big Idea 1), and that interactions between systems can result in changes in those systems (Big Idea 4). The changes that occur as a result of interactions always satisfy conservation laws (Big Idea 5). The mass conservation (Enduring Understanding 1.C) and energy conservation (Enduring Understanding 5.B) are replaced by the law of conservation of mass-energy.

In nuclear fusion and fission reactions, so much potential energy is lost that the mass of the products of a reaction are measurably less than the mass of the reactants (Essential Knowledge 1.C.4, Essential Knowledge 4.C.4) in accordance with the equation $E = mc^2$. This equation explains that mass is part of the internal energy of an object or system (Essential Knowledge 5.B.11). In addition, the number of nucleons is conserved in these nuclear reactions (Enduring Understanding 5.G), and that determines which nuclear reactions are possible (Essential Knowledge 5.G.1).

Big Idea 1 Objects and systems have properties such as mass and charge. Systems may have internal structure.

Enduring Understanding 1.C Objects and systems have properties of inertial mass and gravitational mass that are experimentally verified to be the same and that satisfy conservation principles.

Essential Knowledge 1.C.4 In certain processes, mass can be converted to energy and energy can be converted to mass according to $E = mc^2$, the equation derived from the theory of special relativity.

Big Idea 4 Interactions between systems can result in changes in those systems.

Enduring Understanding 4.C Interactions with other objects or systems can change the total energy of a system.

Essential Knowledge 4.C.4 Mass can be converted into energy and energy can be converted into mass.

Big Idea 5 Changes that occur as a result of interactions are constrained by conservation laws.

Enduring Understanding 5.B The energy of a system is conserved.

Essential Knowledge 5.B.11 Beyond the classical approximation, mass is actually part of the internal energy of an object or system with $E = mc^2$.

Enduring Understanding 5.G Nucleon number is conserved.

Essential Knowledge 5.G.1 The possible nuclear reactions are constrained by the law of conservation of nucleon number.

32.1 Diagnostics and Medical Imaging

LEARNING OBJECTIVES

By the end of this section, you will be able to:

- Explain the working principle behind an anger camera.
- Describe the SPECT and PET imaging techniques.

Most medical and related applications of nuclear physics are driven, at their core, by the difference between a radioactive substance and a non-radioactive substance. One of the first such methods is the precision measurement and detection method known as radioimmunoassay (RIA). Developed by Rosalyn Sussman Yalow and Solomon Berson in the late 1950s, RIA relies on the principle of competitive binding. For the particular substance being measured, a sample containing a radioactive isotope is prepared. A known quantity of antibodies is then introduced. By measuring the amount of "unbound" antibodies after the reaction, technicians can detect and measure the precise amount of the target substance. Radioimmunoassay is essential in cancer screening, hepatitis diagnosis, narcotics investigation, and other analyses.

A host of medical imaging techniques employ nuclear radiation. What makes nuclear radiation so useful? First, γ radiation can easily penetrate tissue; hence, it is a useful probe to monitor conditions inside the body. Second, nuclear radiation depends on the nuclide and not on the chemical compound it is in, so that a radioactive nuclide can be put into a compound designed for specific purposes. The compound is said to be **tagged**. A tagged compound used for medical purposes is called a **radiopharmaceutical**. Radiation detectors external to the body can determine the location and concentration of a radiopharmaceutical to yield medically useful information. For example, certain drugs are concentrated in inflamed regions of the body, and this information can aid diagnosis and treatment as seen in Figure 32.2. Another application utilizes a radiopharmaceutical which the body sends to bone cells, particularly those that are most active, to detect cancerous tumors or healing points. Images can then be produced of such bone scans. Radioisotopes are also used to determine the functioning of body organs, such as blood flow, heart muscle activity, and iodine uptake in the thyroid gland.

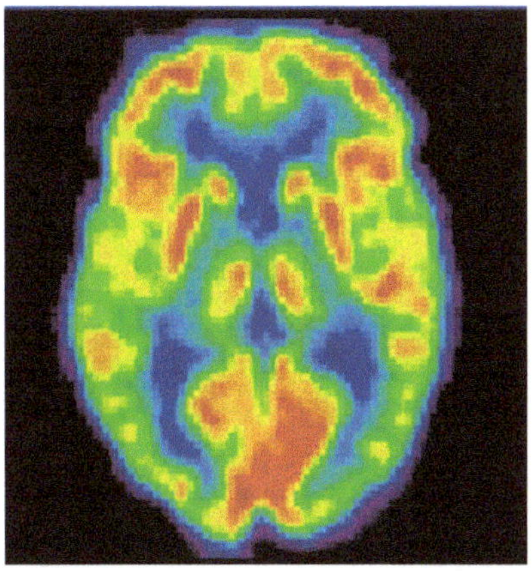

FIGURE 32.2 A radiopharmaceutical is used to produce this brain image of a patient with Alzheimer's disease. Certain features are computer enhanced. (credit: National Institutes of Health)

Medical Application

Table 32.1 lists certain medical diagnostic uses of radiopharmaceuticals, including isotopes and activities that are typically administered. Many organs can be imaged with a variety of nuclear isotopes replacing a stable element by a radioactive isotope. One common diagnostic employs iodine to image the thyroid, since iodine is concentrated in that organ. The most active thyroid cells, including cancerous cells, concentrate the most iodine and, therefore, emit the most radiation. Conversely, hypothyroidism is indicated by lack of iodine uptake. Note that there is more than one isotope that can be used for several types of scans. Another common nuclear diagnostic is the thallium scan for the cardiovascular system, particularly used to evaluate blockages in the coronary arteries and examine heart activity. The salt TlCl can be used, because it acts like NaCl and follows the blood. Gallium-67 accumulates where there is rapid cell growth, such as in tumors and sites of infection. Hence, it is useful in cancer imaging. Usually, the patient receives the injection one day and has a whole body scan 3 or 4 days later because it can take several days for the gallium to build up.

Procedure, isotope	Typical activity (mCi), where $1 \text{ mCi} = 3.7 \times 10^7 \text{ Bq}$
Brain scan	
$^{99\text{m}}\text{Tc}$	7.5
$^{113\text{m}}\text{In}$	7.5

TABLE 32.1 Diagnostic Uses of Radiopharmaceuticals

Procedure, isotope	Typical activity (mCi), where $1 \text{ mCi} = 3.7 \times 10^7 \text{ Bq}$
^{11}C (PET)	20
^{13}N (PET)	20
^{15}O (PET)	50
^{18}F (PET)	10
Lung scan	
$^{99\text{m}}\text{Tc}$	2
^{133}Xe	7.5
Cardiovascular blood pool	
^{131}I	0.2
$^{99\text{m}}\text{Tc}$	2
Cardiovascular arterial flow	
^{201}Tl	3
^{24}Na	7.5
Thyroid scan	
^{131}I	0.05
^{123}I	0.07
Liver scan	
^{198}Au (colloid)	0.1
$^{99\text{m}}\text{Tc}$ (colloid)	2
Bone scan	
^{85}Sr	0.1
$^{99\text{m}}\text{Tc}$	10
Kidney scan	

TABLE 32.1 Diagnostic Uses of Radiopharmaceuticals

Procedure, isotope	Typical activity (mCi), where $1\ \text{mCi} = 3.7 \times 10^7\ \text{Bq}$
^{197}Hg	0.1
$^{99\text{m}}\text{Tc}$	1.5

TABLE 32.1 Diagnostic Uses of Radiopharmaceuticals

Note that Table 32.1 lists many diagnostic uses for $^{99\text{m}}\text{Tc}$, where "m" stands for a metastable state of the technetium nucleus. Perhaps 80 percent of all radiopharmaceutical procedures employ $^{99\text{m}}\text{Tc}$ because of its many advantages. One is that the decay of its metastable state produces a single, easily identified 0.142-MeV γ ray. Additionally, the radiation dose to the patient is limited by the short 6.0-h half-life of $^{99\text{m}}\text{Tc}$. And, although its half-life is short, it is easily and continuously produced on site. The basic process for production is neutron activation of molybdenum, which quickly β decays into $^{99\text{m}}\text{Tc}$. Technetium-99m can be attached to many compounds to allow the imaging of the skeleton, heart, lungs, kidneys, etc.

Figure 32.3 shows one of the simpler methods of imaging the concentration of nuclear activity, employing a device called an **Anger camera** or **gamma camera**. A piece of lead with holes bored through it collimates γ rays emerging from the patient, allowing detectors to receive γ rays from specific directions only. The computer analysis of detector signals produces an image. One of the disadvantages of this detection method is that there is no depth information (i.e., it provides a two-dimensional view of the tumor as opposed to a three-dimensional view), because radiation from any location under that detector produces a signal.

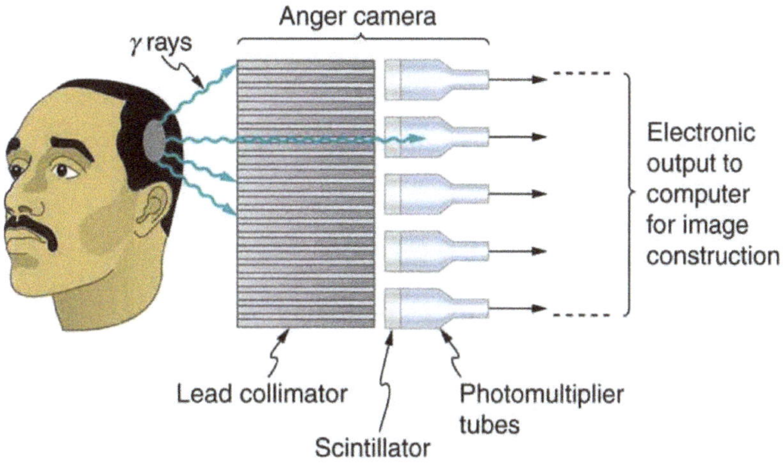

FIGURE 32.3 An Anger or gamma camera consists of a lead collimator and an array of detectors. Gamma rays produce light flashes in the scintillators. The light output is converted to an electrical signal by the photomultipliers. A computer constructs an image from the detector output.

Imaging techniques much like those in x-ray computed tomography (CT) scans use nuclear activity in patients to form three-dimensional images. Figure 32.4 shows a patient in a circular array of detectors that may be stationary or rotated, with detector output used by a computer to construct a detailed image. This technique is called **single-photon-emission computed tomography(SPECT)** or sometimes simply SPET. The spatial resolution of this technique is poor, about 1 cm, but the contrast (i.e. the difference in visual properties that makes an object distinguishable from other objects and the background) is good.

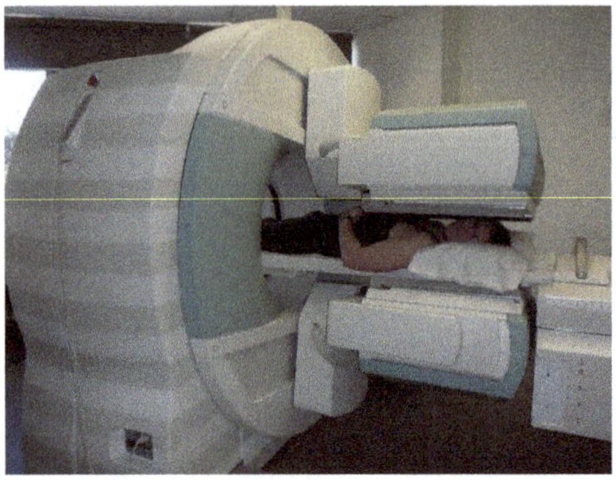

FIGURE 32.4 SPECT uses a geometry similar to a CT scanner to form an image of the concentration of a radiopharmaceutical compound. (credit: Woldo, Wikimedia Commons)

Images produced by β^+ emitters have become important in recent years. When the emitted positron (β^+) encounters an electron, mutual annihilation occurs, producing two γ rays. These γ rays have identical 0.511-MeV energies (the energy comes from the destruction of an electron or positron mass) and they move directly away from one another, allowing detectors to determine their point of origin accurately, as shown in Figure 32.5. The system is called **positron emission tomography (PET)**. It requires detectors on opposite sides to simultaneously (i.e., at the same time) detect photons of 0.511-MeV energy and utilizes computer imaging techniques similar to those in SPECT and CT scans. Examples of β^+ -emitting isotopes used in PET are ^{11}C, ^{13}N, ^{15}O, and ^{18}F, as seen in Table 32.1. This list includes C, N, and O, and so they have the advantage of being able to function as tags for natural body compounds. Its resolution of 0.5 cm is better than that of SPECT; the accuracy and sensitivity of PET scans make them useful for examining the brain's anatomy and function. The brain's use of oxygen and water can be monitored with ^{15}O. PET is used extensively for diagnosing brain disorders. It can note decreased metabolism in certain regions prior to a confirmation of Alzheimer's disease. PET can locate regions in the brain that become active when a person carries out specific activities, such as speaking, closing their eyes, and so on.

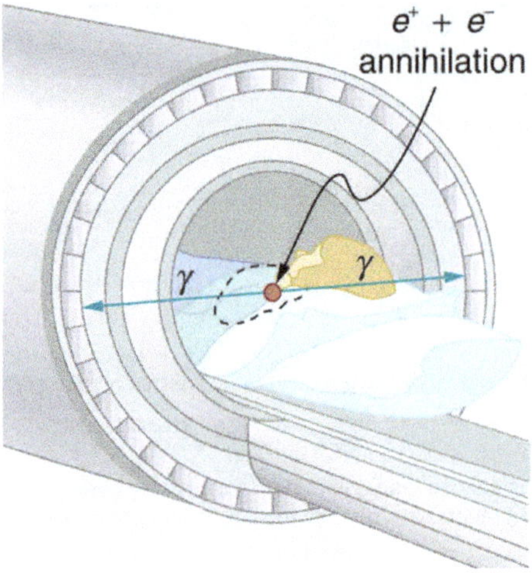

FIGURE 32.5 A PET system takes advantage of the two identical γ-ray photons produced by positron-electron annihilation. These γ rays are emitted in opposite directions, so that the line along which each pair is emitted is determined. Various events detected by several pairs of detectors are then analyzed by the computer to form an accurate image.

PHET EXPLORATIONS

Simplified MRI

Is it a tumor? Magnetic Resonance Imaging (MRI) can tell. Your head is full of tiny radio transmitters (the nuclear spins of the hydrogen nuclei of your water molecules). In an MRI unit, these little radios can be made to broadcast their positions, giving a detailed picture of the inside of your head.

Click to view content (https://openstax.org/l/02simplemri).

32.2 Biological Effects of Ionizing Radiation

LEARNING OBJECTIVES

By the end of this section, you will be able to:

- Define various units of radiation.
- Describe RBE.

We hear many seemingly contradictory things about the biological effects of ionizing radiation. It can cause cancer, burns, and hair loss, yet it is used to treat and even cure cancer. How do we understand these effects? Once again, there is an underlying simplicity in nature, even in complicated biological organisms. All the effects of ionizing radiation on biological tissue can be understood by knowing that **ionizing radiation affects molecules within cells, particularly DNA molecules.**

Let us take a brief look at molecules within cells and how cells operate. Cells have long, double-helical DNA molecules containing chemical codes called genetic codes that govern the function and processes undertaken by the cell. It is for unraveling the double-helical structure of DNA that James Watson, Francis Crick, and Maurice Wilkins received the Nobel Prize. Damage to DNA consists of breaks in chemical bonds or other changes in the structural features of the DNA chain, leading to changes in the genetic code. In human cells, we can have as many as a million individual instances of damage to DNA per cell per day. It is remarkable that DNA contains codes that check whether the DNA is damaged or can repair itself. It is like an auto check and repair mechanism. This repair ability of DNA is vital for maintaining the integrity of the genetic code and for the normal functioning of the entire organism. It should be constantly active and needs to respond rapidly. The rate of DNA repair depends on various factors such as the cell type and age of the cell. A cell with a damaged ability to repair DNA, which could have been induced by ionizing radiation, can do one of the following:

- The cell can go into an irreversible state of dormancy, known as senescence.
- The cell can initiate programmed cell death.
- The cell can go into unregulated cell division leading to tumors and cancers.

Since ionizing radiation damages the DNA, which is critical in cell reproduction, it has its greatest effect on cells that rapidly reproduce, including most types of cancer. Thus, cancer cells are more sensitive to radiation than normal cells and can be killed by it easily. Cancer is characterized by a malfunction of cell reproduction, and can also be caused by ionizing radiation. Without contradiction, ionizing radiation can be both a cure and a cause.

To discuss quantitatively the biological effects of ionizing radiation, we need a radiation dose unit that is directly related to those effects. All effects of radiation are assumed to be directly proportional to the amount of ionization produced in the biological organism. The amount of ionization is in turn proportional to the amount of deposited energy. Therefore, we define a **radiation dose unit** called the **rad**, as $1/100$ of a joule of ionizing energy deposited per kilogram of tissue, which is

$$1 \text{ rad} = 0.01 \text{ J/kg}. \tag{32.1}$$

For example, if a 50.0-kg person is exposed to ionizing radiation over her entire body and she absorbs 1.00 J, then her whole-body radiation dose is

$$(1.00 \text{ J})/(50.0 \text{ kg}) = 0.0200 \text{ J/kg} = 2.00 \text{ rad}. \tag{32.2}$$

If the same 1.00 J of ionizing energy were absorbed in her 2.00-kg forearm alone, then the dose to the forearm would be

$$(1.00 \text{ J})/(2.00 \text{ kg}) = 0.500 \text{ J/kg} = 50.0 \text{ rad}, \tag{32.3}$$

and the unaffected tissue would have a zero rad dose. While calculating radiation doses, you divide the energy absorbed by the mass of affected tissue. You must specify the affected region, such as the whole body or forearm in addition to giving the numerical dose in rads. The SI unit for radiation dose is the **gray (Gy)**, which is defined to be

$$1 \text{ Gy} = 1 \text{ J/kg} = 100 \text{ rad}. \tag{32.4}$$

However, the rad is still commonly used. Although the energy per kilogram in 1 rad is small, it has significant effects since the energy causes ionization. The energy needed for a single ionization is a few eV, or less than 10^{-18} J. Thus, 0.01 J of ionizing energy can create a huge number of ion pairs and have an effect at the cellular level.

The effects of ionizing radiation may be directly proportional to the dose in rads, but they also depend on the type of radiation and the type of tissue. That is, for a given dose in rads, the effects depend on whether the radiation is α, β, γ, x-ray, or some other type of ionizing radiation. In the earlier discussion of the range of ionizing radiation, it was noted that energy is deposited in a series of ionizations and not in a single interaction. Each ion pair or ionization requires a certain amount of energy, so that the number of ion pairs is directly proportional to the amount of the deposited ionizing energy. But, if the range of the radiation is small, as it is for α s, then the ionization and the damage created is more concentrated and harder for the organism to repair, as seen in Figure 32.6. Concentrated damage is more difficult for biological organisms to repair than damage that is spread out, so short-range particles have greater biological effects. The **relative biological effectiveness** (RBE) or **quality factor** (QF) is given in Table 32.2 for several types of ionizing radiation—the effect of the radiation is directly proportional to the RBE. A dose unit more closely related to effects in biological tissue is called the **roentgen equivalent man** or rem and is defined to be the dose in rads multiplied by the relative biological effectiveness.

$$\text{rem} = \text{rad} \times \text{RBE} \tag{32.5}$$

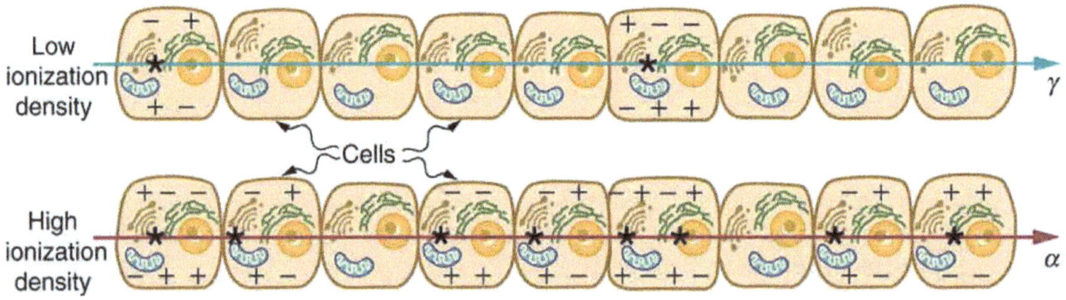

FIGURE 32.6 The image shows ionization created in cells by α and γ radiation. Because of its shorter range, the ionization and damage created by α is more concentrated and harder for the organism to repair. Thus, the RBE for α s is greater than the RBE for γ s, even though they create the same amount of ionization at the same energy.

So, if a person had a whole-body dose of 2.00 rad of γ radiation, the dose in rem would be $(2.00 \text{ rad})(1) = 2.00 \text{ rem whole body}$. If the person had a whole-body dose of 2.00 rad of α radiation, then the dose in rem would be $(2.00 \text{ rad})(20) = 40.0 \text{ rem whole body}$. The α s would have 20 times the effect on the person than the γ s for the same deposited energy. The SI equivalent of the rem is the **sievert** (Sv), defined to be $\text{Sv} = \text{Gy} \times \text{RBE}$, so that

$$1 \text{ Sv} = 1 \text{ Gy} \times \text{RBE} = 100 \text{ rem}. \tag{32.6}$$

The RBEs given in Table 32.2 are approximate, but they yield certain insights. For example, the eyes are more sensitive to radiation, because the cells of the lens do not repair themselves. Neutrons cause more damage than γ rays, although both are neutral and have large ranges, because neutrons often cause secondary radiation when they are captured. Note that the RBEs are 1 for higher-energy β s, γ s, and x-rays, three of the most common types of radiation. For those types of radiation, the numerical values of the dose in rem and rad are identical. For example, 1 rad of γ radiation is also 1 rem. For that reason, rads are still widely quoted rather than rem. Table 32.3 summarizes the units that are used for radiation.

MISCONCEPTION ALERT: ACTIVITY VS. DOSE

"Activity" refers to the radioactive source while "dose" refers to the amount of energy from the radiation that is deposited in a person or object.

A high level of activity doesn't mean much if a person is far away from the source. The activity R of a source depends upon the quantity of material (kg) as well as the half-life. A short half-life will produce many more disintegrations per second. Recall that $R = \frac{0.693N}{t_{1/2}}$. Also, the activity decreases exponentially, which is seen in the equation $R = R_0 e^{-\lambda t}$.

Type and energy of radiation	RBE[1]
X-rays	1
γ rays	1
β rays greater than 32 keV	1
βrays less than 32 keV	1.7
Neutrons, thermal to slow (<20 keV)	2–5
Neutrons, fast (1–10 MeV)	10 (body), 32 (eyes)
Protons (1–10 MeV)	10 (body), 32 (eyes)
α rays from radioactive decay	10–20
Heavy ions from accelerators	10–20

TABLE 32.2 Relative Biological Effectiveness

Quantity	SI unit name	Definition	Former unit	Conversion
Activity	Becquerel (bq)	decay/s	Curie (Ci)	$1 \text{ Bq} = 2.7 \times 10^{-11} \text{ Ci}$
Absorbed dose	Gray (Gy)	1 J/kg	rad	$\text{Gy} = 100 \text{ rad}$
Dose Equivalent	Sievert (Sv)	1 J/kg × RBE	rem	$\text{Sv} = 100 \text{ rem}$

TABLE 32.3 Units for Radiation

The large-scale effects of radiation on humans can be divided into two categories: immediate effects and long-term effects. Table 32.4 gives the immediate effects of whole-body exposures received in less than one day. If the radiation exposure is spread out over more time, greater doses are needed to cause the effects listed. This is due to the body's ability to partially repair the damage. Any dose less than 100 mSv (10 rem) is called a **low dose**, 0.1 Sv to 1 Sv (10 to 100 rem) is called a **moderate dose**, and anything greater than 1 Sv (100 rem) is called a **high dose**. There is no known way to determine after the fact if a person has been exposed to less than 10 mSv.

Dose in Sv [2]	Effect
0–0.10	No observable effect.
0.1 – 1	Slight to moderate decrease in white blood cell counts.
0.5	Temporary sterility; 0.35 for women, 0.50 for men.
1 – 2	Significant reduction in blood cell counts, brief nausea and vomiting. Rarely fatal.

TABLE 32.4 Immediate Effects of Radiation (Adults, Whole Body, Single Exposure)

1 Values approximate, difficult to determine.
2 Multiply by 100 to obtain dose in rem.

Dose in Sv [2]	Effect
2 – 5	Nausea, vomiting, hair loss, severe blood damage, hemorrhage, fatalities.
4.5	LD50/32. Lethal to 50% of the population within 32 days after exposure if not treated.
5 – 20	Worst effects due to malfunction of small intestine and blood systems. Limited survival.
>20	Fatal within hours due to collapse of central nervous system.

TABLE 32.4 Immediate Effects of Radiation (Adults, Whole Body, Single Exposure)

Immediate effects are explained by the effects of radiation on cells and the sensitivity of rapidly reproducing cells to radiation. The first clue that a person has been exposed to radiation is a change in blood count, which is not surprising since blood cells are the most rapidly reproducing cells in the body. At higher doses, nausea and hair loss are observed, which may be due to interference with cell reproduction. Cells in the lining of the digestive system also rapidly reproduce, and their destruction causes nausea. When the growth of hair cells slows, the hair follicles become thin and break off. High doses cause significant cell death in all systems, but the lowest doses that cause fatalities do so by weakening the immune system through the loss of white blood cells.

The two known long-term effects of radiation are cancer and genetic defects. Both are directly attributable to the interference of radiation with cell reproduction. For high doses of radiation, the risk of cancer is reasonably well known from studies of exposed groups. Hiroshima and Nagasaki survivors and a smaller number of people exposed by their occupation, such as radium dial painters, have been fully documented. Chernobyl victims will be studied for many decades, with some data already available. For example, a significant increase in childhood thyroid cancer has been observed. The risk of a radiation-induced cancer for low and moderate doses is generally *assumed* to be proportional to the risk known for high doses. Under this assumption, any dose of radiation, no matter how small, involves a risk to human health. This is called the **linear hypothesis** and it may be prudent, but it *is* controversial. There is some evidence that, unlike the immediate effects of radiation, the long-term effects are cumulative and there is little self-repair. This is analogous to the risk of skin cancer from UV exposure, which is known to be cumulative.

There is a latency period for the onset of radiation-induced cancer of about 2 years for leukemia and 15 years for most other forms. The person is at risk for at least 30 years after the latency period. Omitting many details, the overall risk of a radiation-induced cancer death per year per rem of exposure is about 10 in a million, which can be written as $10/10^6 \text{ rem} \cdot \text{y}$.

If a person receives a dose of 1 rem, his risk each year of dying from radiation-induced cancer is 10 in a million and that risk continues for about 30 years. The lifetime risk is thus 300 in a million, or 0.03 percent. Since about 20 percent of all worldwide deaths are from cancer, the increase due to a 1 rem exposure is impossible to detect demographically. But 100 rem (1 Sv), which was the dose received by the average Hiroshima and Nagasaki survivor, causes a 3 percent risk, which can be observed in the presence of a 20 percent normal or natural incidence rate.

The incidence of genetic defects induced by radiation is about one-third that of cancer deaths, but is much more poorly known. The lifetime risk of a genetic defect due to a 1 rem exposure is about 100 in a million or $3.3/10^6 \text{ rem} \cdot \text{y}$, but the normal incidence is 60,000 in a million. Evidence of such a small increase, tragic as it is, is nearly impossible to obtain. For example, there is no evidence of increased genetic defects among the offspring of Hiroshima and Nagasaki survivors. Animal studies do not seem to correlate well with effects on humans and are not very helpful. For both cancer and genetic defects, the approach to safety has been to use the linear hypothesis, which is likely to be an overestimate of the risks of low doses. Certain researchers even claim that low doses are *beneficial*. **Hormesis** is a term used to describe generally favorable biological responses to low exposures of toxins or radiation. Such low levels may help certain repair mechanisms to develop or enable cells to adapt to the effects of the low exposures. Positive effects may occur at low doses that could be a problem at high doses.

Even the linear hypothesis estimates of the risks are relatively small, and the average person is not exposed to large amounts of radiation. Table 32.5 lists average annual background radiation doses from natural and artificial sources for Australia, the United States, Germany, and world-wide averages. Cosmic rays are partially shielded by the atmosphere, and the dose depends upon altitude and latitude, but the average is about 0.40 mSv/y. A good example of the variation of cosmic radiation dose with altitude comes from the airline industry. Monitored personnel show an average of 2 mSv/y. A 12-hour flight might give you an exposure of 0.02 to 0.03 mSv.

Doses from the Earth itself are mainly due to the isotopes of uranium, thorium, and potassium, and vary greatly by location. Some places have great natural concentrations of uranium and thorium, yielding doses ten times as high as the average value. Internal doses come from foods and liquids that we ingest. Fertilizers containing phosphates have potassium and uranium. So we are all a little radioactive. Carbon-14 has about 66 Bq/kg radioactivity whereas fertilizers may have more than 3000 Bq/kg radioactivity. Medical and dental diagnostic exposures are mostly from x-rays. It should be noted that x-ray doses tend to be localized and are becoming much smaller with improved techniques. Table 32.6 shows typical doses received during various diagnostic x-ray examinations. Note the large dose from a CT scan. While CT scans only account for less than 20 percent of the x-ray procedures done today, they account for about 50 percent of the annual dose received.

Radon is usually more pronounced underground and in buildings with low air exchange with the outside world. Almost all soil contains some ^{226}Ra and ^{222}Rn, but radon is lower in mainly sedimentary soils and higher in granite soils. Thus, the exposure to the public can vary greatly, even within short distances. Radon can diffuse from the soil into homes, especially basements. The estimated exposure for ^{222}Rn is controversial. Recent studies indicate there is more radon in homes than had been realized, and it is speculated that radon may be responsible for 20 percent of lung cancers, being particularly hazardous to those who also smoke. Many countries have introduced limits on allowable radon concentrations in indoor air, often requiring the measurement of radon concentrations in a house prior to its sale. Ironically, it could be argued that the higher levels of radon exposure and their geographic variability, taken with the lack of demographic evidence of any effects, means that low-level radiation is *less* dangerous than previously thought.

Radiation Protection

Laws regulate radiation doses to which people can be exposed. The greatest occupational whole-body dose that is allowed depends upon the country and is about 20 to 50 mSv/y and is rarely reached by medical and nuclear power workers. Higher doses are allowed for the hands. Much lower doses are permitted for the reproductive organs and the fetuses of pregnant women. Inadvertent doses to the public are limited to $1/10$ of occupational doses, except for those caused by nuclear power, which cannot legally expose the public to more than $1/1000$ of the occupational limit or 0.05 mSv/y (5 mrem/y). This has been exceeded in the United States only at the time of the Three Mile Island (TMI) accident in 1979. Chernobyl is another story. Extensive monitoring with a variety of radiation detectors is performed to assure radiation safety. Increased ventilation in uranium mines has lowered the dose there to about 1 mSv/y.

Source	**Dose (mSv/y)**[3]			
Source	Australia	Germany	United States	World
Natural Radiation - external				
Cosmic Rays	0.30	0.28	0.30	0.39
Soil, building materials	0.40	0.40	0.30	0.48
Radon gas	0.90	1.1	2.0	1.2
Natural Radiation - internal				

3 Multiply by 100 to obtain dose in mrem/y.

Source	Dose (mSv/y)[3]			
^{40}K, ^{14}C, ^{226}Ra	0.24	0.28	0.40	0.29
Medical & Dental	0.80	0.90	0.53	0.40
TOTAL	2.6	3.0	3.5	2.8

TABLE 32.5 Background Radiation Sources and Average Doses

To physically limit radiation doses, we use **shielding**, increase the **distance** from a source, and limit the **time of exposure**.

Figure 32.7 illustrates how these are used to protect both the patient and the dental technician when an x-ray is taken. Shielding absorbs radiation and can be provided by any material, including sufficient air. The greater the distance from the source, the more the radiation spreads out. The less time a person is exposed to a given source, the smaller is the dose received by the person. Doses from most medical diagnostics have decreased in recent years due to faster films that require less exposure time.

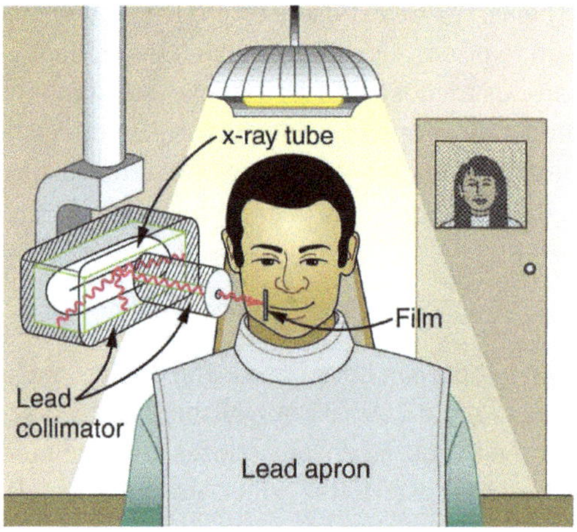

FIGURE 32.7 A lead apron is placed over the dental patient and shielding surrounds the x-ray tube to limit exposure to tissue other than the tissue that is being imaged. Fast films limit the time needed to obtain images, reducing exposure to the imaged tissue. The technician stands a few meters away behind a lead-lined door with a lead glass window, reducing her occupational exposure.

Procedure	Effective dose (mSv)
Chest	0.02
Dental	0.01
Skull	0.07
Leg	0.02
Mammogram	0.40
Barium enema	7.0
Upper GI	3.0

TABLE 32.6 Typical Doses Received During Diagnostic X-ray Exams

Procedure	Effective dose (mSv)
CT head	2.0
CT abdomen	10.0

TABLE 32.6 Typical Doses Received During Diagnostic X-ray Exams

Problem-Solving Strategy

You need to follow certain steps for dose calculations, which are

Step 1. *Examine the situation to determine that a person is exposed to ionizing radiation.*

Step 2. *Identify exactly what needs to be determined in the problem (identify the unknowns).* The most straightforward problems ask for a dose calculation.

Step 3. *Make a list of what is given or can be inferred from the problem as stated (identify the knowns).* Look for information on the type of radiation, the energy per event, the activity, and the mass of tissue affected.

Step 4. *For dose calculations, you need to determine the energy deposited.* This may take one or more steps, depending on the given information.

Step 5. *Divide the deposited energy by the mass of the affected tissue.* Use units of joules for energy and kilograms for mass. To calculate the dose in Gy, use the definition that 1 Gy = 1 J/kg.

Step 6. *To calculate the dose in mSv, determine the RBE (QF) of the radiation.* Recall that $1\text{ mSv} = 1\text{ mGy} \times \text{RBE (or } 1\text{ rem} = 1\text{ rad} \times \text{RBE)}.$

Step 7. *Check the answer to see if it is reasonable: Does it make sense?* The dose should be consistent with the numbers given in the text for diagnostic, occupational, and therapeutic exposures.

EXAMPLE 32.1

Dose from Inhaled Plutonium

Calculate the dose in rem/y for the lungs of a weapons plant employee who inhales and retains an activity of $1.00\ \mu\text{Ci of }^{239}\text{Pu}$ in an accident. The mass of affected lung tissue is 2.00 kg, the plutonium decays by emission of a 5.23-MeV α particle, and you may assume the higher value of the RBE for α s from Table 32.2.

Strategy

Dose in rem is defined by $1\text{ rad} = 0.01\text{ J/kg}$ and $\text{rem} = \text{rad} \times \text{RBE}$. The energy deposited is divided by the mass of tissue affected and then multiplied by the RBE. The latter two quantities are given, and so the main task in this example will be to find the energy deposited in one year. Since the activity of the source is given, we can calculate the number of decays, multiply by the energy per decay, and convert MeV to joules to get the total energy.

Solution

The activity $R = 1.00\ \mu\text{Ci} = 3.70 \times 10^4\text{ Bq} = 3.70 \times 10^4$ decays/s. So, the number of decays per year is obtained by multiplying by the number of seconds in a year:

$$\left(3.70 \times 10^4\text{ decays/s}\right)\left(3.16 \times 10^7\text{ s}\right) = 1.17 \times 10^{12}\text{ decays.} \quad 32.7$$

Thus, the ionizing energy deposited per year is

$$E = \left(1.17 \times 10^{12}\text{ decays}\right)(5.23\text{ MeV/decay}) \times \left(\frac{1.60 \times 10^{-13}\text{ J}}{\text{MeV}}\right) = 0.978\text{ J.} \quad 32.8$$

Dividing by the mass of the affected tissue gives

$$\frac{E}{\text{mass}} = \frac{0.978\ \text{J}}{2.00\ \text{kg}} = 0.489\ \text{J/kg}. \tag{32.9}$$

One Gray is 1.00 J/kg, and so the dose in Gy is

$$\text{dose in Gy} = \frac{0.489\ \text{J/kg}}{1.00\ (\text{J/kg})/\text{Gy}} = 0.489\ \text{Gy}. \tag{32.10}$$

Now, the dose in Sv is

$$\text{dose in Sv} = \text{Gy} \times \text{RBE} \tag{32.11}$$

$$= (0.489\ \text{Gy})(20) = 9.8\ \text{Sv}. \tag{32.12}$$

Discussion

First note that the dose is given to two digits, because the RBE is (at best) known only to two digits. By any standard, this yearly radiation dose is high and will have a devastating effect on the health of the worker. Worse yet, plutonium has a long radioactive half-life and is not readily eliminated by the body, and so it will remain in the lungs. Being an α emitter makes the effects 10 to 20 times worse than the same ionization produced by β s, γ rays, or x-rays. An activity of $1.00\ \mu\text{Ci}$ is created by only $16\ \mu\text{g}$ of ^{239}Pu (left as an end-of-chapter problem to verify), partly justifying claims that plutonium is the most toxic substance known. Its actual hazard depends on how likely it is to be spread out among a large population and then ingested. The Chernobyl disaster's deadly legacy, for example, has nothing to do with the plutonium it put into the environment.

Risk versus Benefit

Medical doses of radiation are also limited. Diagnostic doses are generally low and have further lowered with improved techniques and faster films. With the possible exception of routine dental x-rays, radiation is used diagnostically only when needed so that the low risk is justified by the benefit of the diagnosis. Chest x-rays give the lowest doses—about 0.1 mSv to the tissue affected, with less than 5 percent scattering into tissues that are not directly imaged. Other x-ray procedures range upward to about 10 mSv in a CT scan, and about 5 mSv (0.5 rem) per dental x-ray, again both only affecting the tissue imaged. Medical images with radiopharmaceuticals give doses ranging from 1 to 5 mSv, usually localized. One exception is the thyroid scan using ^{131}I. Because of its relatively long half-life, it exposes the thyroid to about 0.75 Sv. The isotope ^{123}I is more difficult to produce, but its short half-life limits thyroid exposure to about 15 mSv.

PHET EXPLORATIONS

Alpha Decay

Watch alpha particles escape from a polonium nucleus, causing radioactive alpha decay. See how random decay times relate to the half life.

Click to view content (https://openstax.org/l/02alphadecay).

32.3 Therapeutic Uses of Ionizing Radiation

LEARNING OBJECTIVES

By the end of this section, you will be able to:

- Explain the concept of radiotherapy and list typical doses for cancer therapy.

Therapeutic applications of ionizing radiation, called radiation therapy or **radiotherapy**, have existed since the discovery of x-rays and nuclear radioactivity. Today, radiotherapy is used almost exclusively for cancer therapy, where it saves thousands of lives and improves the quality of life and longevity of many it cannot save. Radiotherapy may be used alone or in combination with surgery and chemotherapy (drug treatment) depending on the type of cancer and the response of the patient. A careful examination of all available data has established that radiotherapy's beneficial effects far outweigh its long-term risks.

Medical Application

The earliest uses of ionizing radiation on humans were mostly harmful, with many at the level of snake oil as seen in Figure 32.8. Radium-doped cosmetics that glowed in the dark were used around the time of World War I. As recently as the 1950s, radon mine tours were promoted as healthful and rejuvenating—those who toured were exposed but gained no benefits. Radium salts were sold as health elixirs for many years. The gruesome death of a wealthy industrialist, who became psychologically addicted to the brew, alerted the unsuspecting to the dangers of radium salt elixirs. Most abuses finally ended after the legislation in the 1950s.

FIGURE 32.8 The properties of radiation were once touted for far more than its modern use in cancer therapy. Until 1932, radium was advertised for a variety of uses, often with tragic results. (credit: Struthious Bandersnatch.)

Radiotherapy is effective against cancer because cancer cells reproduce rapidly and, consequently, are more sensitive to radiation. The central problem in radiotherapy is to make the dose for cancer cells as high as possible while limiting the dose for normal cells. The ratio of abnormal cells killed to normal cells killed is called the **therapeutic ratio**, and all radiotherapy techniques are designed to enhance this ratio. Radiation can be concentrated in cancerous tissue by a number of techniques. One of the most prevalent techniques for well-defined tumors is a geometric technique shown in Figure 32.9. A narrow beam of radiation is passed through the patient from a variety of directions with a common crossing point in the tumor. This concentrates the dose in the tumor while spreading it out over a large volume of normal tissue. The external radiation can be x-rays, $^{60}\mathrm{Co}$ γ rays, or ionizing-particle beams produced by accelerators. Accelerator-produced beams of neutrons, π-mesons, and heavy ions such as nitrogen nuclei have been employed, and these can be quite effective. These particles have larger QFs or RBEs and sometimes can be better localized, producing a greater therapeutic ratio. But accelerator radiotherapy is much more expensive and less frequently employed than other forms.

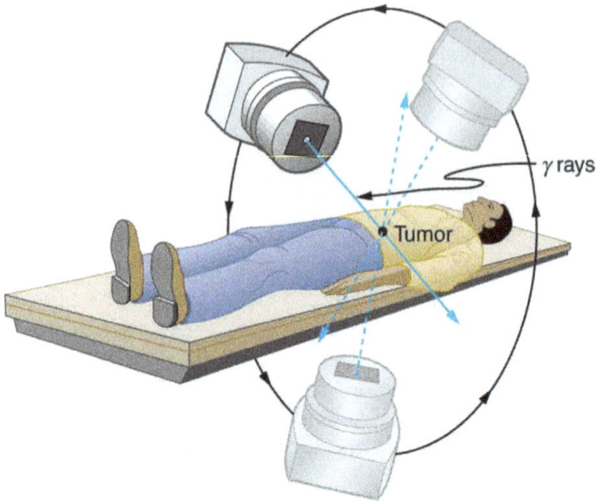

FIGURE 32.9 The ^{60}Co source of γ-radiation is rotated around the patient so that the common crossing point is in the tumor, concentrating the dose there. This geometric technique works for well-defined tumors.

Another form of radiotherapy uses chemically inert radioactive implants. One use is for prostate cancer. Radioactive seeds (about 40 to 100 and the size of a grain of rice) are placed in the prostate region. The isotopes used are usually ^{135}I (6-month half life) or ^{103}Pd (3-month half life). Alpha emitters have the dual advantages of a large QF and a small range for better localization.

Radiopharmaceuticals are used for cancer therapy when they can be localized well enough to produce a favorable therapeutic ratio. Thyroid cancer is commonly treated utilizing radioactive iodine. Thyroid cells concentrate iodine, and cancerous thyroid cells are more aggressive in doing this. An ingenious use of radiopharmaceuticals in cancer therapy tags antibodies with radioisotopes. Antibodies produced by a patient to combat his cancer are extracted, cultured, loaded with a radioisotope, and then returned to the patient. The antibodies are concentrated almost entirely in the tissue they developed to fight, thus localizing the radiation in abnormal tissue. The therapeutic ratio can be quite high for short-range radiation. There is, however, a significant dose for organs that eliminate radiopharmaceuticals from the body, such as the liver, kidneys, and bladder. As with most radiotherapy, the technique is limited by the tolerable amount of damage to the normal tissue.

Table 32.7 lists typical therapeutic doses of radiation used against certain cancers. The doses are large, but not fatal because they are localized and spread out in time. Protocols for treatment vary with the type of cancer and the condition and response of the patient. Three to five 200-rem treatments per week for a period of several weeks is typical. Time between treatments allows the body to repair normal tissue. This effect occurs because damage is concentrated in the abnormal tissue, and the abnormal tissue is more sensitive to radiation. Damage to normal tissue limits the doses. You will note that the greatest doses are given to any tissue that is not rapidly reproducing, such as in the adult brain. Lung cancer, on the other end of the scale, cannot ordinarily be cured with radiation because of the sensitivity of lung tissue and blood to radiation. But radiotherapy for lung cancer does alleviate symptoms and prolong life and is therefore justified in some cases.

Type of Cancer	Typical dose (Sv)
Lung	10–20
Hodgkin's disease	40–45
Skin	40–50
Ovarian	50–75

TABLE 32.7 Cancer Radiotherapy

Type of Cancer	Typical dose (Sv)
Breast	50–80+
Brain	80+
Neck	80+
Bone	80+
Soft tissue	80+
Thyroid	80+

TABLE 32.7 Cancer Radiotherapy

Finally, it is interesting to note that chemotherapy employs drugs that interfere with cell division and is, thus, also effective against cancer. It also has almost the same side effects, such as nausea and hair loss, and risks, such as the inducement of another cancer.

32.4 Food Irradiation

LEARNING OBJECTIVES

By the end of this section, you will be able to:

- Define food irradiation low dose, and free radicals.

Ionizing radiation is widely used to sterilize medical supplies, such as bandages, and consumer products, such as tampons. Worldwide, it is also used to irradiate food, an application that promises to grow in the future. **Food irradiation** is the treatment of food with ionizing radiation. It is used to reduce pest infestation and to delay spoilage and prevent illness caused by microorganisms. Food irradiation is controversial. Proponents see it as superior to pasteurization, preservatives, and insecticides, supplanting dangerous chemicals with a more effective process. Opponents see its safety as unproven, perhaps leaving worse toxic residues as well as presenting an environmental hazard at treatment sites. In developing countries, food irradiation might increase crop production by 25.0% or more, and reduce food spoilage by a similar amount. It is used chiefly to treat spices and some fruits, and in some countries, red meat, poultry, and vegetables. Over 40 countries have approved food irradiation at some level.

Food irradiation exposes food to large doses of γ rays, x-rays, or electrons. These photons and electrons induce no nuclear reactions and thus create *no residual radioactivity*. (Some forms of ionizing radiation, such as neutron irradiation, cause residual radioactivity. These are not used for food irradiation.) The γ source is usually ^{60}Co or ^{137}Cs, the latter isotope being a major by-product of nuclear power. Cobalt-60 γ rays average 1.25 MeV, while those of ^{137}Cs are 0.67 MeV and are less penetrating. X-rays used for food irradiation are created with voltages of up to 5 million volts and, thus, have photon energies up to 5 MeV. Electrons used for food irradiation are accelerated to energies up to 10 MeV. The higher the energy per particle, the more penetrating the radiation is and the more ionization it can create. Figure 32.10 shows a typical γ-irradiation plant.

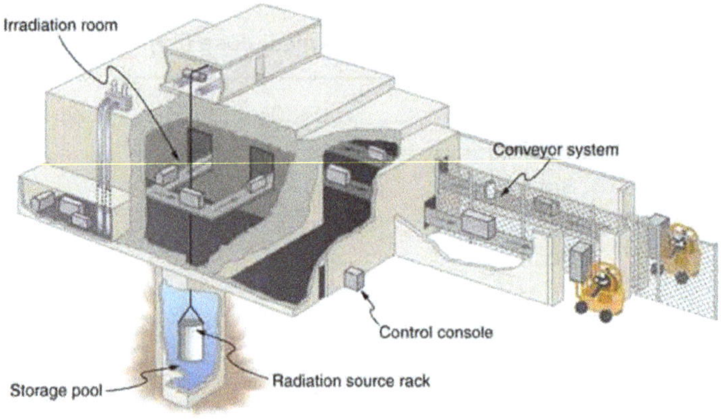

FIGURE 32.10 A food irradiation plant has a conveyor system to pass items through an intense radiation field behind thick shielding walls. The γ source is lowered into a deep pool of water for safe storage when not in use. Exposure times of up to an hour expose food to doses up to 10^4 Gy.

Owing to the fact that food irradiation seeks to destroy organisms such as insects and bacteria, much larger doses than those fatal to humans must be applied. Generally, the simpler the organism, the more radiation it can tolerate. (Cancer cells are a partial exception, because they are rapidly reproducing and, thus, more sensitive.) Current licensing allows up to 1000 Gy to be applied to fresh fruits and vegetables, called a *low dose* in food irradiation. Such a dose is enough to prevent or reduce the growth of many microorganisms, but about 10,000 Gy is needed to kill salmonella, and even more is needed to kill fungi. Doses greater than 10,000 Gy are considered to be high doses in food irradiation and product sterilization.

The effectiveness of food irradiation varies with the type of food. Spices and many fruits and vegetables have dramatically longer shelf lives. These also show no degradation in taste and no loss of food value or vitamins. If not for the mandatory labeling, such foods subjected to low-level irradiation (up to 1000 Gy) could not be distinguished from untreated foods in quality. However, some foods actually spoil faster after irradiation, particularly those with high water content like lettuce and peaches. Others, such as milk, are given a noticeably unpleasant taste. High-level irradiation produces significant and chemically measurable changes in foods. It produces about a 15% loss of nutrients and a 25% loss of vitamins, as well as some change in taste. Such losses are similar to those that occur in ordinary freezing and cooking.

How does food irradiation work? Ionization produces a random assortment of broken molecules and ions, some with unstable oxygen- or hydrogen-containing molecules known as **free radicals**. These undergo rapid chemical reactions, producing perhaps four or five thousand different compounds called **radiolytic products**, some of which make cell function impossible by breaking cell membranes, fracturing DNA, and so on. How safe is the food afterward? Critics argue that the radiolytic products present a lasting hazard, perhaps being carcinogenic. However, the safety of irradiated food is not known precisely. We do know that low-level food irradiation produces no compounds in amounts that can be measured chemically. This is not surprising, since trace amounts of several thousand compounds may be created. We also know that there have been no observable negative short-term effects on consumers. Long-term effects may show up if large number of people consume large quantities of irradiated food, but no effects have appeared due to the small amounts of irradiated food that are consumed regularly. The case for safety is supported by testing of animal diets that were irradiated; no transmitted genetic effects have been observed. Food irradiation (at least up to a million rad) has been endorsed by the World Health Organization and the UN Food and Agricultural Organization. Finally, the hazard to consumers, if it exists, must be weighed against the benefits in food production and preservation. It must also be weighed against the very real hazards of existing insecticides and food preservatives.

32.5 Fusion

LEARNING OBJECTIVES

By the end of this section, you will be able to:

- Define nuclear fusion.
- Discuss processes to achieve practical fusion energy generation.

While basking in the warmth of the summer sun, a student reads of the latest breakthrough in achieving sustained thermonuclear power and vaguely recalls hearing about the cold fusion controversy. The three are connected. The Sun's energy is produced by nuclear fusion (see Figure 32.11). Thermonuclear power is the name given to the use of controlled nuclear fusion as an energy source. While research in the area of thermonuclear power is progressing, high temperatures and containment difficulties remain. The cold fusion controversy centered around unsubstantiated claims of practical fusion power at room temperatures.

FIGURE 32.11 The Sun's energy is produced by nuclear fusion. (credit: Spiralz)

Nuclear fusion is a reaction in which two nuclei are combined, or *fused*, to form a larger nucleus. We know that all nuclei have less mass than the sum of the masses of the protons and neutrons that form them. The missing mass times c^2 equals the binding energy of the nucleus—the greater the binding energy, the greater the missing mass. We also know that BE/A, the binding energy per nucleon, is greater for medium-mass nuclei and has a maximum at Fe (iron). This means that if two low-mass nuclei can be fused together to form a larger nucleus, energy can be released. The larger nucleus has a greater binding energy and less mass per nucleon than the two that combined. Thus mass is destroyed in the fusion reaction, and energy is released (see Figure 32.12). On average, fusion of low-mass nuclei releases energy, but the details depend on the actual nuclides involved.

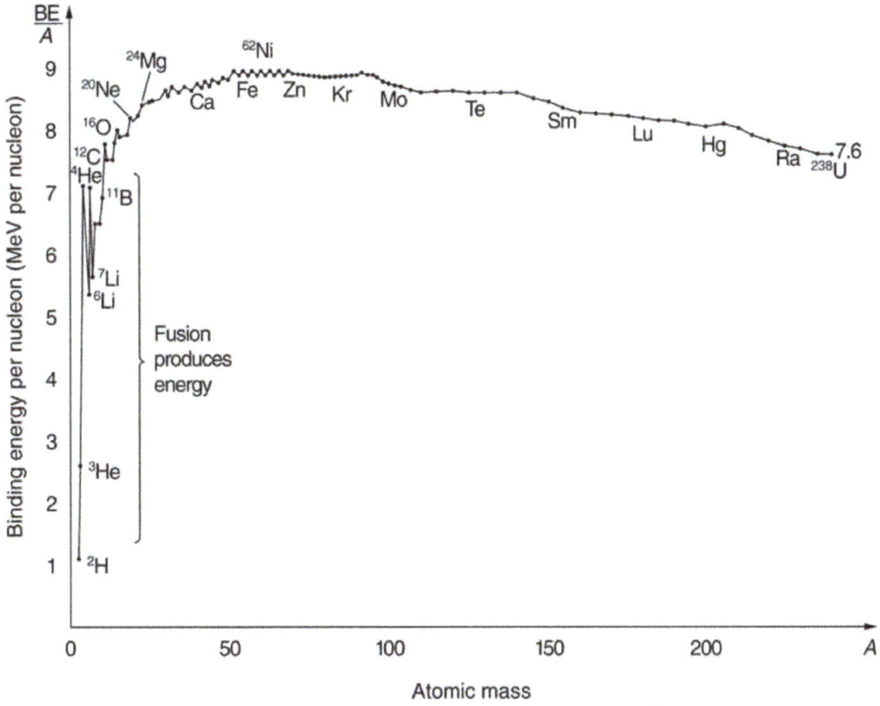

FIGURE 32.12 Fusion of light nuclei to form medium-mass nuclei destroys mass, because BE/A is greater for the product nuclei. The larger BE/A is, the less mass per nucleon, and so mass is converted to energy and released in these fusion reactions.

The major obstruction to fusion is the Coulomb repulsion between nuclei. Since the attractive nuclear force that can fuse nuclei together is short ranged, the repulsion of like positive charges must be overcome to get nuclei close enough to induce fusion. Figure 32.13 shows an approximate graph of the potential energy between two nuclei as a function of the distance between their centers. The graph is analogous to a hill with a well in its center. A ball rolled from the right must have enough kinetic energy to get over the hump before it falls into the deeper well with a net gain in energy. So it is with fusion. If the nuclei are given enough kinetic energy to overcome the electric potential energy due to repulsion, then they can combine, release energy, and fall into a deep well. One way to accomplish this is to heat fusion fuel to high temperatures so that the kinetic energy of thermal motion is sufficient to get the nuclei together.

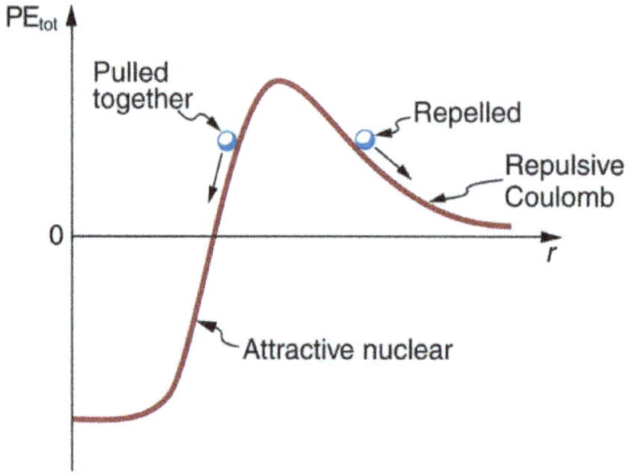

FIGURE 32.13 Potential energy between two light nuclei graphed as a function of distance between them. If the nuclei have enough kinetic energy to get over the Coulomb repulsion hump, they combine, release energy, and drop into a deep attractive well. Tunneling through the barrier is important in practice. The greater the kinetic energy and the higher the particles get up the barrier (or the lower the barrier), the more likely the tunneling.

You might think that, in the core of our Sun, nuclei are coming into contact and fusing. However, in fact, temperatures on the order of $10^8\,\text{K}$ are needed to actually get the nuclei in contact, exceeding the core temperature of the Sun. Quantum mechanical tunneling is what makes fusion in the Sun possible, and tunneling is an important process in most other practical applications of fusion, too. Since the probability of tunneling is extremely sensitive to barrier height and width, increasing the temperature greatly increases the rate of fusion. The closer reactants get to one another, the more likely they are to fuse (see Figure 32.14). Thus most fusion in the Sun and other stars takes place at their centers, where temperatures are highest. Moreover, high temperature is needed for thermonuclear power to be a practical source of energy.

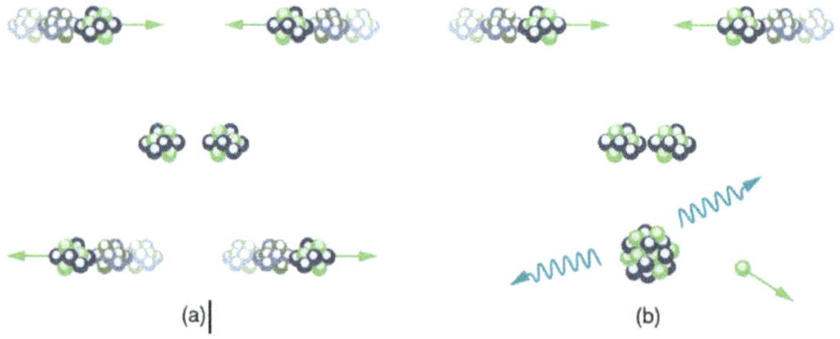

FIGURE 32.14 (a) Two nuclei heading toward each other slow down, then stop, and then fly away without touching or fusing. (b) At higher energies, the two nuclei approach close enough for fusion via tunneling. The probability of tunneling increases as they approach, but they do not have to touch for the reaction to occur.

The Sun produces energy by fusing protons or hydrogen nuclei ^1H (by far the Sun's most abundant nuclide) into helium nuclei ^4He. The principal sequence of fusion reactions forms what is called the **proton-proton cycle**:

$$^1\text{H} + {}^1\text{H} \rightarrow {}^2\text{H} + e^+ + v_e \qquad (0.42\text{ MeV}) \tag{32.13}$$

$$^1\text{H} + {}^2\text{H} \rightarrow {}^3\text{He} + \gamma \qquad (5.49\text{ MeV}) \tag{32.14}$$

$$^3\text{He} + {}^3\text{He} \rightarrow {}^4\text{He} + {}^1\text{H} + {}^1\text{H} \qquad (12.86\text{ MeV}) \tag{32.15}$$

where e^+ stands for a positron and v_e is an electron neutrino. (The energy in parentheses is *released* by the reaction.) Note that the first two reactions must occur twice for the third to be possible, so that the cycle consumes six protons (^1H) but gives back two. Furthermore, the two positrons produced will find two electrons and annihilate to form four more γ rays, for a total of six. The overall effect of the cycle is thus

$$2e^- + 4^1\text{H} \rightarrow {}^4\text{He} + 2\nu_e + 6\gamma \qquad (26.7\ \text{MeV}) \qquad 32.16$$

where the 26.7 MeV includes the annihilation energy of the positrons and electrons and is distributed among all the reaction products. The solar interior is dense, and the reactions occur deep in the Sun where temperatures are highest. It takes about 32,000 years for the energy to diffuse to the surface and radiate away. However, the neutrinos escape the Sun in less than two seconds, carrying their energy with them, because they interact so weakly that the Sun is transparent to them. Negative feedback in the Sun acts as a thermostat to regulate the overall energy output. For instance, if the interior of the Sun becomes hotter than normal, the reaction rate increases, producing energy that expands the interior. This cools it and lowers the reaction rate. Conversely, if the interior becomes too cool, it contracts, increasing the temperature and reaction rate (see Figure 32.15). Stars like the Sun are stable for billions of years, until a significant fraction of their hydrogen has been depleted. What happens then is discussed in Frontiers of Physics.

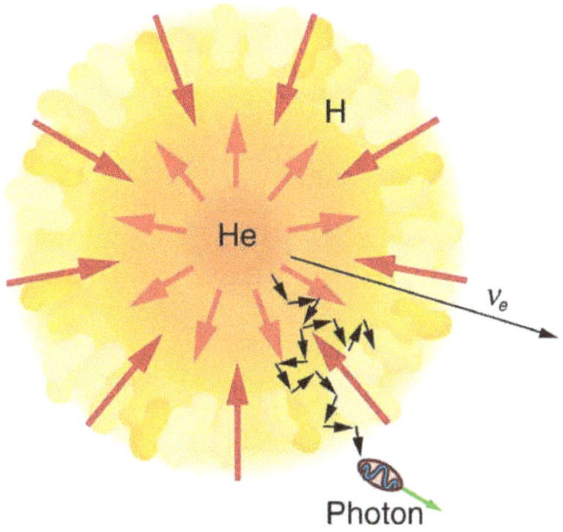

FIGURE 32.15 Nuclear fusion in the Sun converts hydrogen nuclei into helium; fusion occurs primarily at the boundary of the helium core, where temperature is highest and sufficient hydrogen remains. Energy released diffuses slowly to the surface, with the exception of neutrinos, which escape immediately. Energy production remains stable because of negative feedback effects.

Theories of the proton-proton cycle (and other energy-producing cycles in stars) were pioneered by the German-born, American physicist Hans Bethe (1906–2005), starting in 1938. He was awarded the 1967 Nobel Prize in physics for this work, and he has made many other contributions to physics and society. Neutrinos produced in these cycles escape so readily that they provide us an excellent means to test these theories and study stellar interiors. Detectors have been constructed and operated for more than four decades now to measure solar neutrinos (see Figure 32.16). Although solar neutrinos are detected and neutrinos were observed from Supernova 1987A (Figure 32.17), too few solar neutrinos were observed to be consistent with predictions of solar energy production. After many years, this solar neutrino problem was resolved with a blend of theory and experiment that showed that the neutrino does indeed have mass. It was also found that there are three types of neutrinos, each associated with a different type of nuclear decay.

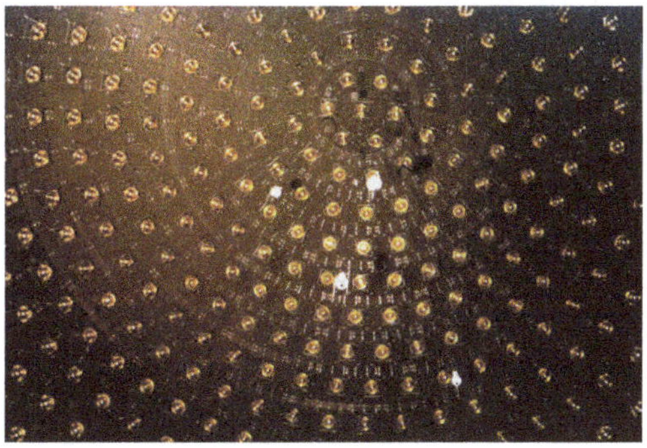

FIGURE 32.16 This array of photomultiplier tubes is part of the large solar neutrino detector at the Fermi National Accelerator Laboratory in Illinois. In these experiments, the neutrinos interact with heavy water and produce flashes of light, which are detected by the photomultiplier tubes. In spite of its size and the huge flux of neutrinos that strike it, very few are detected each day since they interact so weakly. This, of course, is the same reason they escape the Sun so readily. (credit: Fred Ullrich)

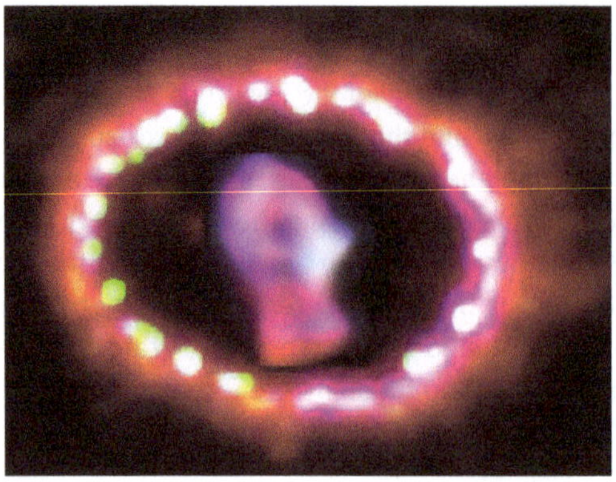

FIGURE 32.17 Supernovas are the source of elements heavier than iron. Energy released powers nucleosynthesis. Spectroscopic analysis of the ring of material ejected by Supernova 1987A observable in the southern hemisphere, shows evidence of heavy elements. The study of this supernova also provided indications that neutrinos might have mass. (credit: NASA, ESA, and P. Challis)

The proton-proton cycle is not a practical source of energy on Earth, in spite of the great abundance of hydrogen ($^{1}\mathrm{H}$). The reaction $^{1}\mathrm{H} + {}^{1}\mathrm{H} \rightarrow {}^{2}\mathrm{H} + e^{+} + v_{\mathrm{e}}$ has a very low probability of occurring. (This is why our Sun will last for about ten billion years.) However, a number of other fusion reactions are easier to induce. Among them are:

$$^{2}\mathrm{H} + {}^{2}\mathrm{H} \rightarrow {}^{3}\mathrm{H} + {}^{1}\mathrm{H} \qquad (4.03\ \mathrm{MeV}) \tag{32.17}$$

$$^{2}\mathrm{H} + {}^{2}\mathrm{H} \rightarrow {}^{3}\mathrm{He} + n \qquad (3.27\ \mathrm{MeV}) \tag{32.18}$$

$$^{2}\mathrm{H} + {}^{3}\mathrm{H} \rightarrow {}^{4}\mathrm{He} + n \qquad (17.59\ \mathrm{MeV}) \tag{32.19}$$

$$^{2}\mathrm{H} + {}^{2}\mathrm{H} \rightarrow {}^{4}\mathrm{He} + \gamma \qquad (23.85\ \mathrm{MeV}). \tag{32.20}$$

Deuterium ($^{2}\mathrm{H}$) is about 0.015% of natural hydrogen, so there is an immense amount of it in sea water alone. In addition to an abundance of deuterium fuel, these fusion reactions produce large energies per reaction (in parentheses), but they do not produce much radioactive waste. Tritium ($^{3}\mathrm{H}$) is radioactive, but it is consumed as a fuel (the reaction $^{2}\mathrm{H} + {}^{3}\mathrm{H} \rightarrow {}^{4}\mathrm{He} + n$), and the neutrons and γs can be shielded. The neutrons produced can also be used to create more energy and fuel in reactions like

$$n + {}^{1}\mathrm{H} \rightarrow {}^{2}\mathrm{H} + \gamma \qquad (20.68\ \mathrm{MeV}) \tag{32.21}$$

and

$$n + {}^{1}\mathrm{H} \rightarrow {}^{2}\mathrm{H} + \gamma \qquad (2.22\ \mathrm{MeV}). \tag{32.22}$$

Note that these last two reactions, and $^{2}\mathrm{H} + {}^{2}\mathrm{H} \rightarrow {}^{4}\mathrm{He} + \gamma$, put most of their energy output into the γ ray, and such energy is difficult to utilize.

The three keys to practical fusion energy generation are to achieve the temperatures necessary to make the reactions likely, to raise the density of the fuel, and to confine it long enough to produce large amounts of energy. These three factors—temperature, density, and time—complement one another, and so a deficiency in one can be compensated for by the others. **Ignition** is defined to occur when the reactions produce enough energy to be self-sustaining after external energy input is cut off. This goal, which must be reached before commercial plants can be a reality, has not been achieved. Another milestone, called **break-even**, occurs when the fusion power produced equals the heating power input. Break-even has nearly been reached and gives hope that ignition and commercial plants may become a reality in a few decades.

Two techniques have shown considerable promise. The first of these is called **magnetic confinement** and uses the property that charged particles have difficulty crossing magnetic field lines. The tokamak, shown in Figure 32.18, has shown particular promise. The tokamak's toroidal coil confines charged particles into a circular path with a helical twist due to the circulating ions themselves. In 1995, the Tokamak Fusion Test Reactor at Princeton in the US achieved world-record plasma temperatures as high as 500 million degrees Celsius. This facility operated between 1982 and 1997. A joint international effort is underway in France to build a tokamak-type reactor that will be the stepping stone to commercial power. ITER, as it is called, will be a full-scale device that aims to demonstrate the feasibility of fusion energy. It will generate 500 MW of power for extended periods of time and will achieve break-even conditions. It will study plasmas in conditions similar to those expected in a fusion power plant. Completion is scheduled for 2018.

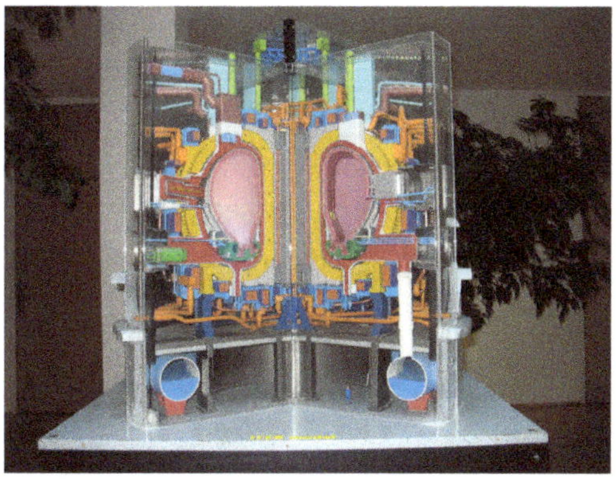

FIGURE 32.18 (a) Artist's rendition of ITER, a tokamak-type fusion reactor being built in southern France. It is hoped that this gigantic machine will reach the break-even point. Completion is scheduled for 2018. (credit: Stephan Mosel, Flickr)

The second promising technique aims multiple lasers at tiny fuel pellets filled with a mixture of deuterium and tritium. Huge power input heats the fuel, evaporating the confining pellet and crushing the fuel to high density with the expanding hot plasma produced. This technique is called **inertial confinement**, because the fuel's inertia prevents it from escaping before significant fusion can take place. Higher densities have been reached than with tokamaks, but with smaller confinement times. In 2009, the Lawrence Livermore Laboratory (CA) completed a laser fusion device with 192 ultraviolet laser beams that are focused upon a D-T pellet (see Figure 32.19).

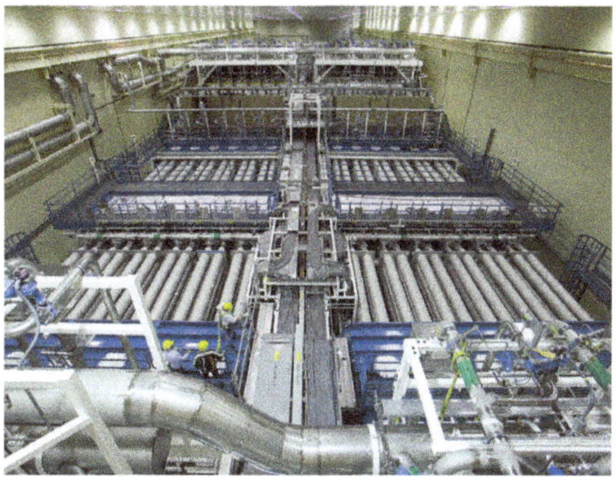

FIGURE 32.19 National Ignition Facility (CA). This image shows a laser bay where 192 laser beams will focus onto a small D-T target, producing fusion. (credit: Lawrence Livermore National Laboratory, Lawrence Livermore National Security, LLC, and the Department of Energy)

EXAMPLE 32.2

Calculating Energy and Power from Fusion

(a) Calculate the energy released by the fusion of a 1.00-kg mixture of deuterium and tritium, which produces helium. There are equal numbers of deuterium and tritium nuclei in the mixture.

(b) If this takes place continuously over a period of a year, what is the average power output?

Strategy

According to $^2\text{H} + {}^3\text{H} \rightarrow {}^4\text{He} + n$, the energy per reaction is 17.59 MeV. To find the total energy released, we must find the number of deuterium and tritium atoms in a kilogram. Deuterium has an atomic mass of about 2 and tritium has an atomic mass of about 3, for a total of about 5 g per mole of reactants or about 200 mol in 1.00 kg. To get a more precise figure, we will use the atomic masses from Appendix A. The power output is best expressed in watts, and so the energy output needs to be calculated in joules and then divided by the number of seconds in a year.

Solution for (a)

The atomic mass of deuterium (^{2}H) is 2.014102 u, while that of tritium (^{3}H) is 3.016049 u, for a total of 5.032151 u per reaction. So a mole of reactants has a mass of 5.03 g, and in 1.00 kg there are $(1000 \text{ g})/(5.03 \text{ g/mol}) = 198.8 \text{ mol of reactants}$. The number of reactions that take place is therefore

$$(198.8 \text{ mol})\left(6.02 \times 10^{23} \text{ mol}^{-1}\right) = 1.20 \times 10^{26} \text{ reactions.} \tag{32.23}$$

The total energy output is the number of reactions times the energy per reaction:

$$\begin{aligned} E &= \left(1.20 \times 10^{26} \text{ reactions}\right)(17.59 \text{ MeV/reaction})\left(1.602 \times 10^{-13} \text{ J/MeV}\right) \\ &= 3.37 \times 10^{14} \text{ J.} \end{aligned} \tag{32.24}$$

Solution for (b)

Power is energy per unit time. One year has 3.16×10^7 s, so

$$\begin{aligned} P &= \frac{E}{t} = \frac{3.37 \times 10^{14} \text{ J}}{3.16 \times 10^7 \text{ s}} \\ &= 1.07 \times 10^7 \text{ W} = 10.7 \text{ MW.} \end{aligned} \tag{32.25}$$

Discussion

By now we expect nuclear processes to yield large amounts of energy, and we are not disappointed here. The energy output of 3.37×10^{14} J from fusing 1.00 kg of deuterium and tritium is equivalent to 2.6 million gallons of gasoline and about eight times the energy output of the bomb that destroyed Hiroshima. Yet the average backyard swimming pool has about 6 kg of deuterium in it, so that fuel is plentiful if it can be utilized in a controlled manner. The average power output over a year is more than 10 MW, impressive but a bit small for a commercial power plant. About 32 times this power output would allow generation of 100 MW of electricity, assuming an efficiency of one-third in converting the fusion energy to electrical energy.

32.6 Fission

LEARNING OBJECTIVES

By the end of this section, you will be able to:

- Define nuclear fission.
- Discuss how fission fuel reacts and describe what it produces.
- Describe controlled and uncontrolled chain reactions.

Nuclear fission is a reaction in which a nucleus is split (or *fissured*). Controlled fission is a reality, whereas controlled fusion is a hope for the future. Hundreds of nuclear fission power plants around the world attest to the fact that controlled fission is practical and, at least in the short term, economical, as seen in Figure 32.20. Whereas nuclear power was of little interest for decades following TMI and Chernobyl (and now Fukushima Daiichi), growing concerns over global warming has brought nuclear power back on the table as a viable energy alternative. By the end of 2009, there were 442 reactors operating in 30 countries, providing 15% of the world's electricity. France provides over 75% of its electricity with nuclear power, while the US has 104 operating reactors providing 20% of its electricity. Australia and New Zealand have none. China is building nuclear power plants at the rate of one start every month.

FIGURE 32.20 The people living near this nuclear power plant have no measurable exposure to radiation that is traceable to the plant. About 16% of the world's electrical power is generated by controlled nuclear fission in such plants. The cooling towers are the most prominent features but are not unique to nuclear power. The reactor is in the small domed building to the left of the towers. (credit: Kalmthouts)

Fission is the opposite of fusion and releases energy only when heavy nuclei are split. As noted in Fusion, energy is released if the products of a nuclear reaction have a greater binding energy per nucleon (BE/A) than the parent nuclei. Figure 32.21 shows that BE/A is greater for medium-mass nuclei than heavy nuclei, implying that when a heavy nucleus is split, the products have less mass per nucleon, so that mass is destroyed and energy is released in the reaction. The amount of energy per fission reaction can be large, even by nuclear standards. The graph in Figure 32.21 shows BE/A to be about 7.6 MeV/nucleon for the heaviest nuclei (A about 240), while BE/A is about 8.6 MeV/nucleon for nuclei having A about 120. Thus, if a heavy nucleus splits in half, then about 1 MeV per nucleon, or approximately 240 MeV per fission, is released. This is about 10 times the energy per fusion reaction, and about 100 times the energy of the average α, β, or γ decay.

EXAMPLE 32.3

Calculating Energy Released by Fission

Calculate the energy released in the following spontaneous fission reaction:

$$^{238}\text{U} \rightarrow {}^{95}\text{Sr} + {}^{140}\text{Xe} + 3n \tag{32.26}$$

given the atomic masses to be $m(^{238}\text{U}) = 238.050784\ \text{u}$, $m(^{95}\text{Sr}) = 94.919388\ \text{u}$, $m(^{140}\text{Xe}) = 139.921610\ \text{u}$, and $m(n) = 1.008665\ \text{u}$.

Strategy

As always, the energy released is equal to the mass destroyed times c^2 , so we must find the difference in mass between the parent ^{238}U and the fission products.

Solution

The products have a total mass of

$$\begin{aligned} m_{\text{products}} &= 94.919388\ \text{u} + 139.921610\ \text{u} + 3(1.008665\ \text{u}) \\ &= 237.866993\ \text{u}. \end{aligned} \tag{32.27}$$

The mass lost is the mass of ^{238}U minus m_{products}, or

$$\Delta m = 238.050784\ \text{u} - 237.8669933\ \text{u} = 0.183791\ \text{u}, \tag{32.28}$$

so the energy released is

$$\begin{aligned} E &= (\Delta m)c^2 \\ &= (0.183791\ \text{u})\frac{931.5\ \text{MeV}/c^2}{\text{u}}c^2 = 171.2\ \text{MeV}. \end{aligned} \tag{32.29}$$

Discussion

A number of important things arise in this example. The 171-MeV energy released is large, but a little less than the earlier estimated 240 MeV. This is because this fission reaction produces neutrons and does not split the nucleus into two equal parts. Fission of a given nuclide, such as ^{238}U, does not always produce the same products. Fission is a statistical process in which an entire range of products are produced with various probabilities. Most fission produces neutrons, although the number varies with each fission. This is an extremely important aspect of fission, because *neutrons can induce more fission*, enabling self-sustaining chain reactions.

Spontaneous fission can occur, but this is usually not the most common decay mode for a given nuclide. For example, ^{238}U can spontaneously fission, but it decays mostly by α emission. Neutron-induced fission is crucial as seen in Figure 32.21. Being chargeless, even low-energy neutrons can strike a nucleus and be absorbed once they feel the attractive nuclear force. Large nuclei are described by a **liquid drop model** with surface tension and oscillation modes, because the large number of nucleons act like atoms in a drop. The neutron is attracted and thus, deposits energy, causing the nucleus to deform as a liquid drop. If stretched enough, the nucleus narrows in the middle. The number of nucleons in contact and the strength of the nuclear force binding the nucleus together are reduced. Coulomb repulsion between the two ends then succeeds in fissioning the nucleus, which pops like a water drop into two large pieces and a few neutrons. **Neutron-induced fission** can be written as

$$n + {}^{A}\text{X} \rightarrow \text{FF}_1 + \text{FF}_2 + xn, \tag{32.30}$$

where FF_1 and FF_2 are the two daughter nuclei, called **fission fragments**, and x is the number of neutrons produced. Most often, the masses of the fission fragments are not the same. Most of the released energy goes into the kinetic energy of the fission fragments, with the remainder going into the neutrons and excited states of the fragments. Since neutrons can induce fission, a self-sustaining chain reaction is possible, provided more than one neutron is produced on average — that is, if $x > 1$ in $n + {}^{A}\text{X} \rightarrow \text{FF}_1 + \text{FF}_2 + xn$. This can also be seen in Figure 32.22.

An example of a typical neutron-induced fission reaction is

$$n + {}^{235}_{92}\text{U} \rightarrow {}^{142}_{56}\text{Ba} + {}^{91}_{36}\text{Kr} + 3n. \tag{32.31}$$

Note that in this equation, the total charge remains the same (is conserved): $92 + 0 = 56 + 36$. Also, as far as whole numbers are concerned, the mass is constant: $1 + 235 = 142 + 91 + 3$. This is not true when we consider the masses out to 6 or 7 significant places, as in the previous example.

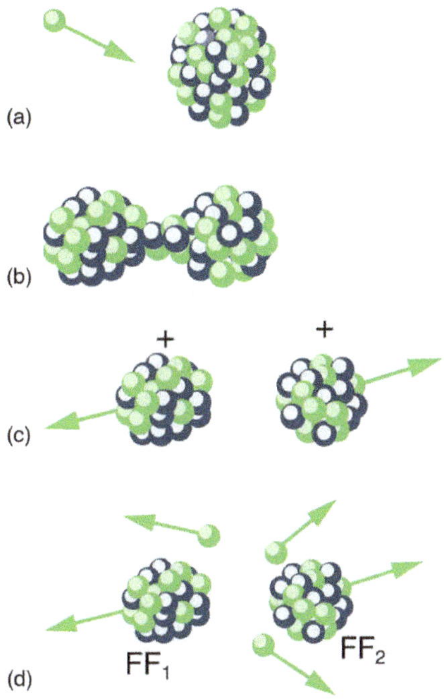

FIGURE 32.21 Neutron-induced fission is shown. First, energy is put into this large nucleus when it absorbs a neutron. Acting like a struck liquid drop, the nucleus deforms and begins to narrow in the middle. Since fewer nucleons are in contact, the repulsive Coulomb force is able to break the nucleus into two parts with some neutrons also flying away.

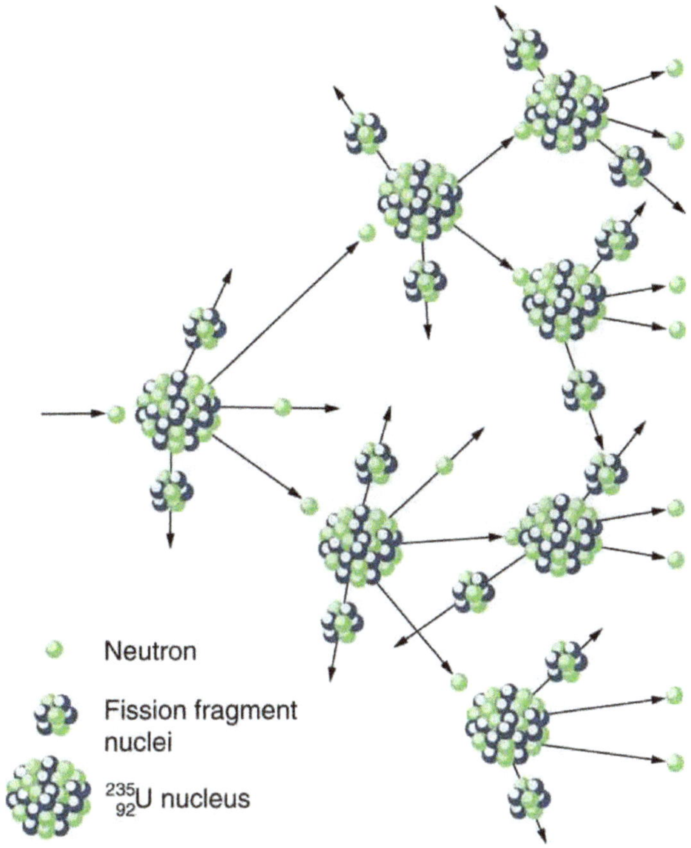

FIGURE 32.22 A chain reaction can produce self-sustained fission if each fission produces enough neutrons to induce at least one more fission. This depends on several factors, including how many neutrons are produced in an average fission and how easy it is to make a particular type of nuclide fission.

Not every neutron produced by fission induces fission. Some neutrons escape the fissionable material, while others interact with a nucleus without making it fission. We can enhance the number of fissions produced by neutrons by having a large amount of fissionable material. The minimum amount necessary for self-sustained fission of a given nuclide is called its **critical mass**. Some nuclides, such as ^{239}Pu, produce more neutrons per fission than others, such as ^{235}U. Additionally, some nuclides are easier to make fission than others. In particular, ^{235}U and ^{239}Pu are easier to fission than the much more abundant ^{238}U. Both factors affect critical mass, which is smallest for ^{239}Pu.

The reason ^{235}U and ^{239}Pu are easier to fission than ^{238}U is that the nuclear force is more attractive for an even number of neutrons in a nucleus than for an odd number. Consider that $^{235}_{92}\text{U}_{143}$ has 143 neutrons, and $^{239}_{94}\text{P}_{145}$ has 145 neutrons, whereas $^{238}_{92}\text{U}_{146}$ has 146. When a neutron encounters a nucleus with an odd number of neutrons, the nuclear force is more attractive, because the additional neutron will make the number even. About 2-MeV more energy is deposited in the resulting nucleus than would be the case if the number of neutrons was already even. This extra energy produces greater deformation, making fission more likely. Thus, ^{235}U and ^{239}Pu are superior fission fuels. The isotope ^{235}U is only 0.72 % of natural uranium, while ^{238}U is 99.27%, and ^{239}Pu does not exist in nature. Australia has the largest deposits of uranium in the world, standing at 28% of the total. This is followed by Kazakhstan and Canada. The US has only 3% of global reserves.

Most fission reactors utilize ^{235}U, which is separated from ^{238}U at some expense. This is called enrichment. The most common separation method is gaseous diffusion of uranium hexafluoride (UF_6) through membranes. Since ^{235}U has less mass than ^{238}U, its UF_6 molecules have higher average velocity at the same temperature and diffuse faster. Another interesting characteristic of ^{235}U is that it preferentially absorbs very slow moving neutrons (with energies a fraction of an eV), whereas fission reactions produce fast neutrons with energies in the order of an MeV. To make a self-sustained fission reactor with ^{235}U, it is thus necessary to slow down ("thermalize") the neutrons. Water is very effective, since neutrons collide with protons in water molecules and lose energy. Figure 32.23 shows a schematic of a reactor design, called the pressurized water reactor.

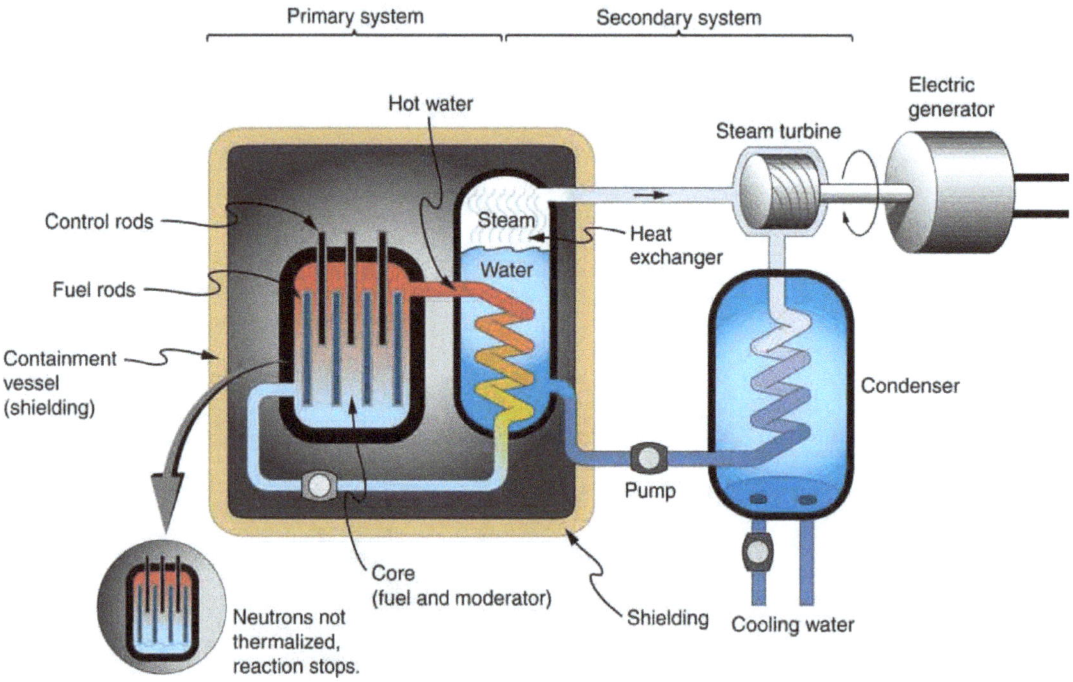

FIGURE 32.23 A pressurized water reactor is cleverly designed to control the fission of large amounts of ^{235}U, while using the heat produced in the fission reaction to create steam for generating electrical energy. Control rods adjust neutron flux so that criticality is obtained, but not exceeded. In case the reactor overheats and boils the water away, the chain reaction terminates, because water is needed to thermalize the neutrons. This inherent safety feature can be overwhelmed in extreme circumstances.

Control rods containing nuclides that very strongly absorb neutrons are used to adjust neutron flux. To produce large power, reactors contain hundreds to thousands of critical masses, and the chain reaction easily becomes self-sustaining, a condition called **criticality**. Neutron flux should be carefully regulated to avoid an exponential increase in fissions, a condition called **supercriticality**. Control rods help prevent overheating, perhaps even a meltdown or explosive disassembly. The water that is used to thermalize neutrons, necessary to get them to induce fission in ^{235}U, and achieve criticality, provides a negative feedback for temperature increases. In case the reactor overheats and boils the water to steam or is breached, the absence of water kills the chain reaction. Considerable heat, however, can still be generated by the reactor's radioactive fission products. Other safety features, thus, need to be incorporated in the event of a *loss of coolant* accident, including auxiliary cooling water and pumps.

EXAMPLE 32.4

Calculating Energy from a Kilogram of Fissionable Fuel

Calculate the amount of energy produced by the fission of 1.00 kg of ^{235}U, given the average fission reaction of ^{235}U produces 200 MeV.

Strategy

The total energy produced is the number of ^{235}U atoms times the given energy per ^{235}U fission. We should therefore find the number of ^{235}U atoms in 1.00 kg.

Solution

The number of ^{235}U atoms in 1.00 kg is Avogadro's number times the number of moles. One mole of ^{235}U has a mass of 235.04 g; thus, there are $(1000\text{ g})/(235.04\text{ g/mol}) = 4.25\text{ mol}$. The number of ^{235}U atoms is therefore,

$$(4.25\text{ mol})\left(6.02\times10^{23}\ ^{235}\text{U/mol}\right) = 2.56\times10^{24}\ ^{235}\text{U}. \quad 32.32$$

So the total energy released is

$$\begin{aligned} E &= \left(2.56\times10^{24}\ ^{235}\text{U}\right)\left(\frac{200\text{ MeV}}{^{235}\text{U}}\right)\left(\frac{1.60\times10^{-13}\text{ J}}{\text{MeV}}\right) \\ &= 8.21\times10^{13}\text{ J}. \end{aligned} \quad 32.33$$

Discussion

This is another impressively large amount of energy, equivalent to about 14,000 barrels of crude oil or 600,000 gallons of gasoline. But, it is only one-fourth the energy produced by the fusion of a kilogram mixture of deuterium and tritium as seen in Example 32.2. Even though each fission reaction yields about ten times the energy of a fusion reaction, the energy per kilogram of fission fuel is less, because there are far fewer moles per kilogram of the heavy nuclides. Fission fuel is also much more scarce than fusion fuel, and less than 1% of uranium (the ^{235}U) is readily usable.

One nuclide already mentioned is ^{239}Pu, which has a 24,120-y half-life and does not exist in nature. Plutonium-239 is manufactured from ^{238}U in reactors, and it provides an opportunity to utilize the other 99% of natural uranium as an energy source. The following reaction sequence, called **breeding**, produces ^{239}Pu. Breeding begins with neutron capture by ^{238}U:

$$^{238}\text{U} + n \rightarrow {}^{239}\text{U} + \gamma. \quad 32.34$$

Uranium-239 then β^- decays:

$$^{239}\text{U} \rightarrow {}^{239}\text{Np} + \beta^- + v_e(\text{t}_{1/2} = 23\text{ min}). \quad 32.35$$

Neptunium-239 also β^- decays:

$$^{239}\text{Np} \rightarrow {}^{239}\text{Pu} + \beta^- + v_e(\text{t}_{1/2} = 2.4\text{ d}). \quad 32.36$$

Plutonium-239 builds up in reactor fuel at a rate that depends on the probability of neutron capture by ^{238}U (all reactor fuel contains more ^{238}U than ^{235}U). Reactors designed specifically to make plutonium are called **breeder reactors**. They seem to be inherently more hazardous than conventional reactors, but it remains unknown whether their hazards can be made economically acceptable. The four reactors at Chernobyl, including the one that was destroyed, were built to breed plutonium and produce electricity. These reactors had a design that was significantly different from the pressurized water reactor illustrated above.

Plutonium-239 has advantages over ^{235}U as a reactor fuel — it produces more neutrons per fission on average, and it is easier for a thermal neutron to cause it to fission. It is also chemically different from uranium, so it is inherently easier to separate from uranium ore. This means ^{239}Pu has a particularly small critical mass, an advantage for nuclear weapons.

PHET EXPLORATIONS

Nuclear Fission

Start a chain reaction, or introduce non-radioactive isotopes to prevent one. Control energy production in a nuclear reactor!

Click to view content (https://openstax.org/l/16fission).

32.7 Nuclear Weapons

LEARNING OBJECTIVES

By the end of this section, you will be able to:

- Discuss different types of fission and thermonuclear bombs.
- Explain the ill effects of nuclear explosion.

The world was in turmoil when fission was discovered in 1938. The discovery of fission, made by two German physicists, Otto Hahn and Fritz Strassman, was quickly verified by two Jewish refugees from Nazi Germany, Lise Meitner and her nephew Otto Frisch. Fermi, among others, soon found that not only did neutrons induce fission; more neutrons were produced during fission. The possibility of a self-sustained chain reaction was immediately recognized by leading scientists the world over. The enormous energy known to be in nuclei, but considered inaccessible, now seemed to be available on a large scale.

Within months after the announcement of the discovery of fission, Adolf Hitler banned the export of uranium from newly occupied Czechoslovakia. It seemed that the military value of uranium had been recognized in Nazi Germany, and that a serious effort to build a nuclear bomb had begun.

Alarmed scientists, many of them who fled Nazi Germany, decided to take action. None was more famous or revered than Einstein. It was felt that his help was needed to get the American government to make a serious effort at nuclear weapons as a matter of survival. Leo Szilard, an escaped Hungarian physicist, took a draft of a letter to Einstein, who, although pacifistic, signed the final version. The letter was for President Franklin Roosevelt, warning of the German potential to build extremely powerful bombs of a new type. It was sent in August of 1939, just before the German invasion of Poland that marked the start of World War II.

It was not until December 6, 1941, the day before the Japanese attack on Pearl Harbor, that the United States made a massive commitment to building a nuclear bomb. The top secret Manhattan Project was a crash program aimed at beating the Germans. It was carried out in remote locations, such as Los Alamos, New Mexico, whenever possible, and eventually came to cost billions of dollars and employ the efforts of more than 100,000 people. J. Robert Oppenheimer (1904–1967), whose talent and ambitions made him ideal, was chosen to head the project. The first major step was made by Enrico Fermi and his group in December 1942, when they achieved the first self-sustained nuclear reactor. This first "atomic pile", built in a squash court at the University of Chicago, used carbon blocks to thermalize neutrons. It not only proved that the chain reaction was possible, it began the era of nuclear reactors. Glenn Seaborg, an American chemist and physicist, received the Nobel Prize in physics in 1951 for discovery of several transuranic elements, including plutonium. Carbon-moderated reactors are relatively inexpensive and simple in design and are still used for breeding plutonium, such as at Chernobyl, where two such reactors remain in operation.

Plutonium was recognized as easier to fission with neutrons and, hence, a superior fission material very early in the Manhattan Project. Plutonium availability was uncertain, and so a uranium bomb was developed simultaneously. Figure 32.24 shows a gun-type bomb, which takes two subcritical uranium masses and blows them together. To get an appreciable yield, the critical mass must be held together by the explosive charges inside the cannon barrel for a few microseconds. Since the buildup of the uranium chain reaction is relatively slow, the device to hold the critical mass together can be relatively simple. Owing to the fact that the rate of spontaneous fission is low, a neutron source is triggered at the same time the critical mass is assembled.

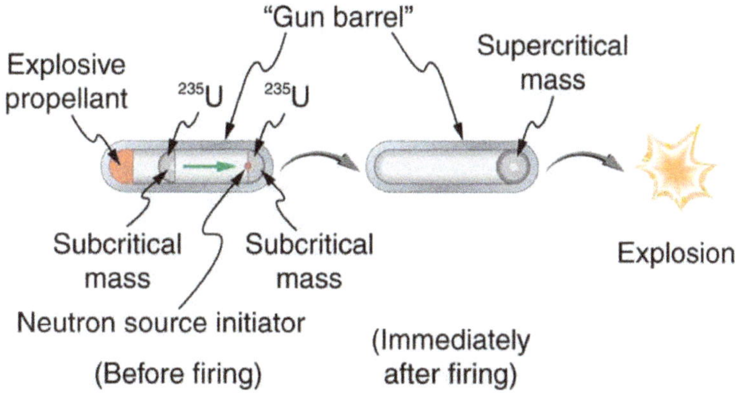

FIGURE 32.24 A gun-type fission bomb for ^{235}U utilizes two subcritical masses forced together by explosive charges inside a cannon barrel. The energy yield depends on the amount of uranium and the time it can be held together before it disassembles itself.

Plutonium's special properties necessitated a more sophisticated critical mass assembly, shown schematically in Figure 32.25. A spherical mass of plutonium is surrounded by shape charges (high explosives that release most of their blast in one direction) that implode the plutonium, crushing it into a smaller volume to form a critical mass. The implosion technique is faster and more effective, because it compresses three-dimensionally rather than one-dimensionally as in the gun-type bomb. Again, a neutron source must be triggered at just the correct time to initiate the chain reaction.

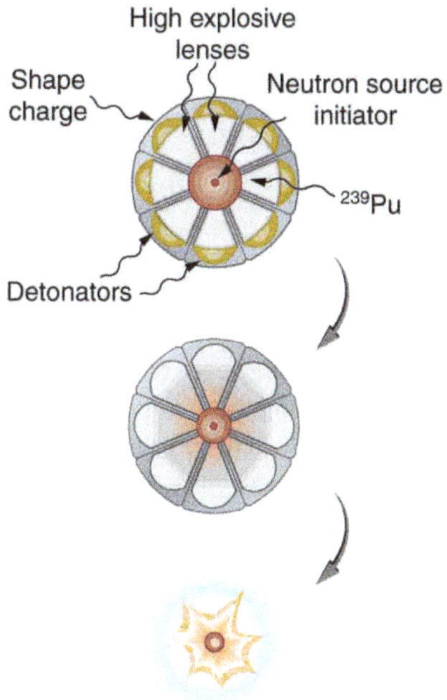

FIGURE 32.25 An implosion created by high explosives compresses a sphere of ^{239}Pu into a critical mass. The superior fissionability of plutonium has made it the universal bomb material.

Owing to its complexity, the plutonium bomb needed to be tested before there could be any attempt to use it. On July 16, 1945, the test named Trinity was conducted in the isolated Alamogordo Desert about 200 miles south of Los Alamos (see Figure 32.26). A new age had begun. The yield of this device was about 10 kilotons (kT), the equivalent of 5000 of the largest conventional bombs.

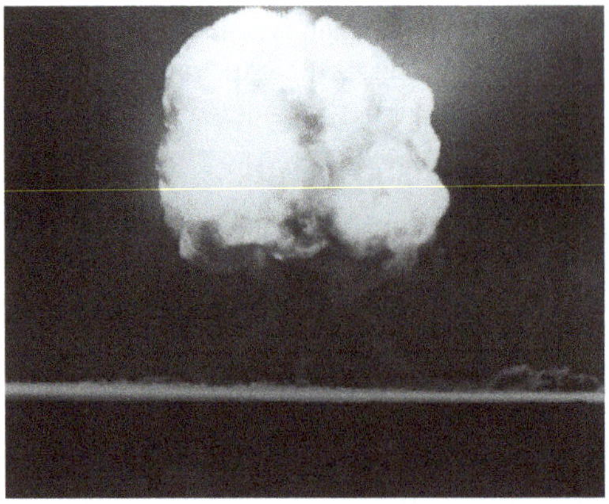

FIGURE 32.26 Trinity test (1945), the first nuclear bomb (credit: United States Department of Energy)

Although Germany surrendered on May 7, 1945, Japan had been steadfastly refusing to surrender for many months, forcing large casualties. Invasion plans by the Allies estimated a million casualties of their own and untold losses of Japanese lives. The bomb was viewed as a way to end the war. The first was a uranium bomb dropped on Hiroshima on August 6. Its yield of about 15 kT destroyed the city and killed an estimated 80,000 people, with 100,000 more being seriously injured (see Figure 32.27). The second was a plutonium bomb dropped on Nagasaki only three days later, on August 9. Its 20 kT yield killed at least 50,000 people, something less than Hiroshima because of the hilly terrain and the fact that it was a few kilometers off target. The Japanese were told that one bomb a week would be dropped until they surrendered unconditionally, which they did on August 14. In actuality, the United States had only enough plutonium for one more and as yet unassembled bomb.

FIGURE 32.27 Destruction in Hiroshima (credit: United States Federal Government)

Knowing that fusion produces several times more energy per kilogram of fuel than fission, some scientists pushed the idea of a fusion bomb starting very early on. Calling this bomb the Super, they realized that it could have another advantage over fission—high-energy neutrons would aid fusion, while they are ineffective in ^{239}Pu fission. Thus the fusion bomb could be virtually unlimited in energy release. The first such bomb was detonated by the United States on October 31, 1952, at Eniwetok Atoll with a yield of 10 megatons (MT), about 670 times that of the fission bomb that destroyed Hiroshima. The USSR followed with a fusion device of their own in August 1953, and a weapons race, beyond the aim of this text to discuss, continued until the end of the Cold War.

Figure 32.28 shows a simple diagram of how a thermonuclear bomb is constructed. A fission bomb is exploded next to fusion fuel in the solid form of lithium deuteride. Before the shock wave blows it apart, γ rays heat and compress the fuel, and neutrons create tritium through the reaction $n + ^6\text{Li} \rightarrow ^3\text{H} + ^4\text{He}$. Additional fusion and fission fuels are enclosed in a dense shell of ^{238}U. The shell reflects some of the neutrons back into the fuel to enhance its fusion, but at high internal temperatures fast neutrons are created that also cause the plentiful and inexpensive ^{238}U to fission, part of what allows thermonuclear bombs to be so large.

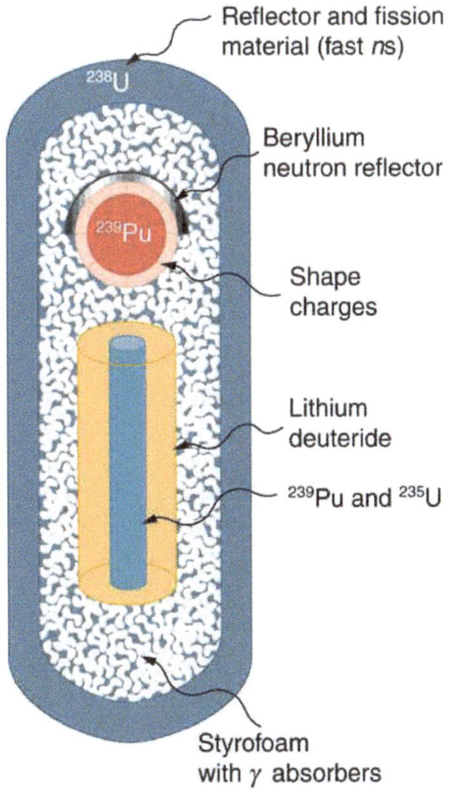

FIGURE 32.28 This schematic of a fusion bomb (H-bomb) gives some idea of how the ^{239}Pu fission trigger is used to ignite fusion fuel. Neutrons and γ rays transmit energy to the fusion fuel, create tritium from deuterium, and heat and compress the fusion fuel. The outer shell of ^{238}U serves to reflect some neutrons back into the fuel, causing more fusion, and it boosts the energy output by fissioning itself when neutron energies become high enough.

The energy yield and the types of energy produced by nuclear bombs can be varied. Energy yields in current arsenals range from about 0.1 kT to 20 MT, although the USSR once detonated a 67 MT device. Nuclear bombs differ from conventional explosives in more than size. Figure 32.29 shows the approximate fraction of energy output in various forms for conventional explosives and for two types of nuclear bombs. Nuclear bombs put a much larger fraction of their output into thermal energy than do conventional bombs, which tend to concentrate the energy in blast. Another difference is the immediate and residual radiation energy from nuclear weapons. This can be adjusted to put more energy into radiation (the so-called neutron bomb) so that the bomb can be used to irradiate advancing troops without killing friendly troops with blast and heat.

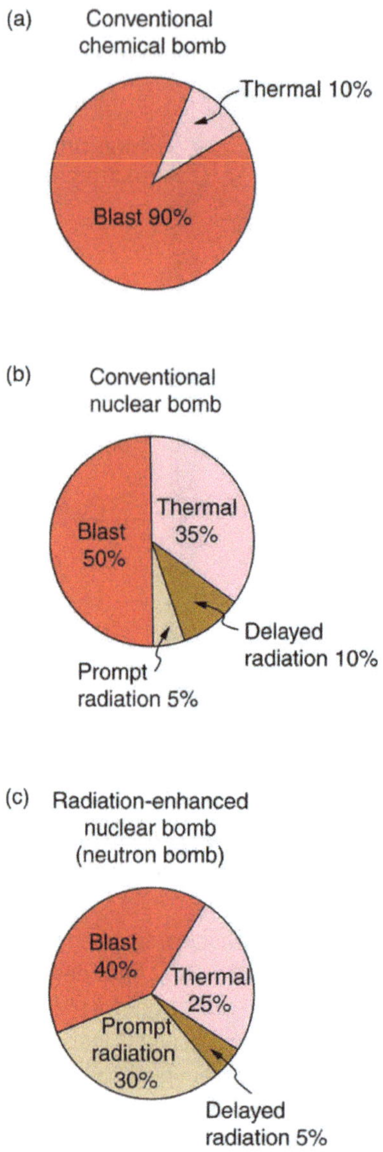

FIGURE 32.29 Approximate fractions of energy output by conventional and two types of nuclear weapons. In addition to yielding more energy than conventional weapons, nuclear bombs put a much larger fraction into thermal energy. This can be adjusted to enhance the radiation output to be more effective against troops. An enhanced radiation bomb is also called a neutron bomb.

At its peak in 1986, the combined arsenals of the United States and the Soviet Union totaled about 60,000 nuclear warheads. In addition, the British, French, and Chinese each have several hundred bombs of various sizes, and a few other countries have a small number. Nuclear weapons are generally divided into two categories. Strategic nuclear weapons are those intended for military targets, such as bases and missile complexes, and moderate to large cities. There were about 20,000 strategic weapons in 1988. Tactical weapons are intended for use in smaller battles. Since the collapse of the Soviet Union and the end of the Cold War in 1989, most of the 32,000 tactical weapons (including Cruise missiles, artillery shells, land mines, torpedoes, depth charges, and backpacks) have been demobilized, and parts of the strategic weapon systems are being dismantled with warheads and missiles being disassembled. According to the Treaty of Moscow of 2002, Russia and the United States have been required to reduce their strategic nuclear arsenal down to about 2000 warheads each.

A few small countries have built or are capable of building nuclear bombs, as are some terrorist groups. Two things are needed—a minimum level of technical expertise and sufficient fissionable material. The first is easy. Fissionable material is controlled but is also available. There are international agreements and organizations that attempt to control nuclear proliferation, but it is increasingly difficult given the availability of fissionable material and the small amount needed for a crude bomb. The production of fissionable fuel itself is technologically difficult. However, the presence of large amounts of such material worldwide, though in the hands of a few, makes control and accountability crucial.

Glossary

Anger camera a common medical imaging device that uses a scintillator connected to a series of photomultipliers

break-even when fusion power produced equals the heating power input

breeder reactors reactors that are designed specifically to make plutonium

breeding reaction process that produces ^{239}Pu

critical mass minimum amount necessary for self-sustained fission of a given nuclide

criticality condition in which a chain reaction easily becomes self-sustaining

fission fragments a daughter nuclei

food irradiation treatment of food with ionizing radiation

free radicals ions with unstable oxygen- or hydrogen-containing molecules

gamma camera another name for an Anger camera

gray (Gy) the SI unit for radiation dose which is defined to be $1\ \text{Gy} = 1\ \text{J/kg} = 100\ \text{rad}$

high dose a dose greater than 1 Sv (100 rem)

hormesis a term used to describe generally favorable biological responses to low exposures of toxins or radiation

ignition when a fusion reaction produces enough energy to be self-sustaining after external energy input is cut off

inertial confinement a technique that aims multiple lasers at tiny fuel pellets evaporating and crushing them to high density

linear hypothesis assumption that risk is directly proportional to risk from high doses

liquid drop model a model of nucleus (only to understand some of its features) in which nucleons in a nucleus act like atoms in a drop

low dose a dose less than 100 mSv (10 rem)

magnetic confinement a technique in which charged particles are trapped in a small region because of difficulty in crossing magnetic field lines

moderate dose a dose from 0.1 Sv to 1 Sv (10 to 100 rem)

neutron-induced fission fission that is initiated after the absorption of neutron

nuclear fission reaction in which a nucleus splits

nuclear fusion a reaction in which two nuclei are combined, or fused, to form a larger nucleus

positron emission tomography (PET) tomography technique that uses β^+ emitters and detects the two annihilation γ rays, aiding in source localization

proton-proton cycle the combined reactions $^1H+^1H \rightarrow ^2H+e^++v_e$, $^1H+^2H \rightarrow ^3He+\gamma$, and $^3He+^3He \rightarrow ^4He+^1H+^1H$

quality factor same as relative biological effectiveness

rad the ionizing energy deposited per kilogram of tissue

radiolytic products compounds produced due to chemical reactions of free radicals

radiopharmaceutical compound used for medical imaging

radiotherapy the use of ionizing radiation to treat ailments

relative biological effectiveness (RBE) a number that expresses the relative amount of damage that a fixed amount of ionizing radiation of a given type can inflict on biological tissues

roentgen equivalent man (rem) a dose unit more closely related to effects in biological tissue

shielding a technique to limit radiation exposure

sievert the SI equivalent of the rem

single-photon-emission computed tomography (SPECT) tomography performed with γ-emitting radiopharmaceuticals

supercriticality an exponential increase in fissions

tagged process of attaching a radioactive substance to a chemical compound

therapeutic ratio the ratio of abnormal cells killed to normal cells killed

Section Summary

32.1 Diagnostics and Medical Imaging

- Radiopharmaceuticals are compounds that are used for medical imaging and therapeutics.
- The process of attaching a radioactive substance is called tagging.
- Table 32.1 lists certain diagnostic uses of radiopharmaceuticals including the isotope and activity typically used in diagnostics.
- One common imaging device is the Anger camera, which consists of a lead collimator, radiation detectors, and an analysis computer.
- Tomography performed with γ-emitting radiopharmaceuticals is called SPECT and has the advantages of x-ray CT scans coupled with organ- and function-specific drugs.
- PET is a similar technique that uses β^+ emitters and detects the two annihilation γ rays, which aid to localize the source.

32.2 Biological Effects of Ionizing Radiation

- The biological effects of ionizing radiation are due to two effects it has on cells: interference with cell reproduction, and destruction of cell function.
- A radiation dose unit called the rad is defined in terms of the ionizing energy deposited per kilogram of tissue:
  $1 \text{ rad} = 0.01 \text{ J/kg}.$
- The SI unit for radiation dose is the gray (Gy), which is defined to be $1 \text{ Gy} = 1 \text{ J/kg} = 100 \text{ rad}.$
- To account for the effect of the type of particle creating the ionization, we use the relative biological effectiveness (RBE) or quality factor (QF) given in Table 32.2 and define a unit called the roentgen equivalent man (rem) as
  $\text{rem} = \text{rad} \times \text{RBE}.$
- Particles that have short ranges or create large ionization densities have RBEs greater than unity. The SI equivalent of the rem is the sievert (Sv), defined to be
  $\text{Sv} = \text{Gy} \times \text{RBE and } 1 \text{ Sv} = 100 \text{ rem}.$
- Whole-body, single-exposure doses of 0.1 Sv or less are low doses while those of 0.1 to 1 Sv are moderate, and those over 1 Sv are high doses. Some immediate radiation effects are given in Table 32.4. Effects due to low doses are not observed, but their risk is assumed to be directly proportional to those of high doses, an assumption known as the linear hypothesis. Long-term effects are cancer deaths at the rate of $10/10^6 \text{ rem} \cdot \text{y}$and genetic defects at roughly one-third this rate. Background radiation doses and sources are given in Table 32.5. World-wide average radiation exposure from natural sources, including radon, is about 3 mSv, or 300 mrem. Radiation protection utilizes shielding, distance, and time to limit exposure.

32.3 Therapeutic Uses of Ionizing Radiation

- Radiotherapy is the use of ionizing radiation to treat ailments, now limited to cancer therapy.
- The sensitivity of cancer cells to radiation enhances the ratio of cancer cells killed to normal cells killed, which is called the therapeutic ratio.
- Doses for various organs are limited by the tolerance of normal tissue for radiation. Treatment is localized in one region of the body and spread out in time.

32.4 Food Irradiation

- Food irradiation is the treatment of food with ionizing radiation.
- Irradiating food can destroy insects and bacteria by creating free radicals and radiolytic products that can break apart cell membranes.
- Food irradiation has produced no observable negative short-term effects for humans, but its long-term effects are unknown.

32.5 Fusion

- Nuclear fusion is a reaction in which two nuclei are combined to form a larger nucleus. It releases energy when light nuclei are fused to form medium-mass nuclei.
- Fusion is the source of energy in stars, with the proton-proton cycle,
  $$^1\text{H} + {}^1\text{H} \rightarrow {}^2\text{H} + e^+ + v_e \quad (0.42 \text{ MeV})$$
  $$^1\text{H} + {}^2\text{H} \rightarrow {}^3\text{He} + \gamma \quad (5.49 \text{ MeV})$$
  $$^3\text{He} + {}^3\text{He} \rightarrow {}^4\text{He} + {}^1\text{H} + {}^1\text{H} \quad (12.86 \text{ MeV})$$
  being the principal sequence of energy-producing reactions in our Sun.
- The overall effect of the proton-proton cycle is
  $$2e^- + 4{}^1\text{H} \rightarrow {}^4\text{He} + 2v_e + 6\gamma \quad (26.7 \text{ MeV}),$$
  where the 26.7 MeV includes the energy of the positrons emitted and annihilated.
- Attempts to utilize controlled fusion as an energy source on Earth are related to deuterium and tritium, and the reactions play important roles.
- Ignition is the condition under which controlled fusion is self-sustaining; it has not yet been achieved. Break-even, in which the fusion energy output is as great as the external energy input, has nearly been achieved.
- Magnetic confinement and inertial confinement are the two methods being developed for heating fuel to sufficiently high temperatures, at sufficient density, and for sufficiently long times to achieve ignition. The first method uses magnetic fields and the second method uses the momentum of impinging laser beams for confinement.

32.6 Fission

- Nuclear fission is a reaction in which a nucleus is split.
- Fission releases energy when heavy nuclei are split into medium-mass nuclei.
- Self-sustained fission is possible, because neutron-induced fission also produces neutrons that can induce other fissions,
  $n + {}^A X \rightarrow \text{FF}_1 + \text{FF}_2 + xn$, where FF_1 and FF_2 are the two daughter nuclei, or fission fragments, and x is the number of neutrons produced.
- A minimum mass, called the critical mass, should be present to achieve criticality.

- More than a critical mass can produce supercriticality.
- The production of new or different isotopes (especially ^{239}Pu) by nuclear transformation is called breeding, and reactors designed for this purpose are called breeder reactors.

32.7 Nuclear Weapons

- There are two types of nuclear weapons—fission bombs use fission alone, whereas thermonuclear bombs use fission to ignite fusion.
- Both types of weapons produce huge numbers of nuclear reactions in a very short time.
- Energy yields are measured in kilotons or megatons of equivalent conventional explosives and range from 0.1 kT to more than 20 MT.
- Nuclear bombs are characterized by far more thermal output and nuclear radiation output than conventional explosives.

Conceptual Questions

32.1 Diagnostics and Medical Imaging

1. In terms of radiation dose, what is the major difference between medical diagnostic uses of radiation and medical therapeutic uses?
2. One of the methods used to limit radiation dose to the patient in medical imaging is to employ isotopes with short half-lives. How would this limit the dose?

32.2 Biological Effects of Ionizing Radiation

3. Isotopes that emit α radiation are relatively safe outside the body and exceptionally hazardous inside. Yet those that emit γ radiation are hazardous outside and inside. Explain why.
4. Why is radon more closely associated with inducing lung cancer than other types of cancer?
5. The RBE for low-energy βs is 1.7, whereas that for higher-energy βs is only 1. Explain why, considering how the range of radiation depends on its energy.
6. Which methods of radiation protection were used in the device shown in the first photo in Figure 32.30? Which were used in the situation shown in the second photo?

(a) (b)

FIGURE 32.30 (a) This x-ray fluorescence machine is one of the thousands used in shoe stores to produce images of feet as a check on the fit of shoes. They are unshielded and remain on as long as the feet are in them, producing doses much greater than medical images. Children were fascinated with them. These machines were used in shoe stores until laws preventing such unwarranted radiation exposure were enacted in the 1950s. (credit: Andrew Kuchling) (b) Now that we know the effects of exposure to radioactive material, safety is a priority. (credit: U.S. Navy)

7. What radioisotope could be a problem in homes built of cinder blocks made from uranium mine tailings? (This is true of homes and schools in certain regions near uranium mines.)
8. Are some types of cancer more sensitive to radiation than others? If so, what makes them more sensitive?
9. Suppose a person swallows some radioactive material by accident. What information is needed to be able to assess possible damage?

32.3 Therapeutic Uses of Ionizing Radiation

10. Radiotherapy is more likely to be used to treat cancer in elderly patients than in young ones. Explain why. Why is radiotherapy used to treat young people at all?

32.4 Food Irradiation

11. Does food irradiation leave the food radioactive? To what extent is the food altered chemically for low and high doses in food irradiation?

12. Compare a low dose of radiation to a human with a low dose of radiation used in food treatment.

13. Suppose one food irradiation plant uses a $^{137}\mathrm{Cs}$ source while another uses an equal activity of $^{60}\mathrm{Co}$. Assuming equal fractions of the γ rays from the sources are absorbed, why is more time needed to get the same dose using the $^{137}\mathrm{Cs}$ source?

32.5 Fusion

14. Why does the fusion of light nuclei into heavier nuclei release energy?

15. Energy input is required to fuse medium-mass nuclei, such as iron or cobalt, into more massive nuclei. Explain why.

16. In considering potential fusion reactions, what is the advantage of the reaction $^2\mathrm{H} + {}^3\mathrm{H} \rightarrow {}^4\mathrm{He} + n$ over the reaction $^2\mathrm{H} + {}^2\mathrm{H} \rightarrow {}^3\mathrm{He} + n$?

17. Give reasons justifying the contention made in the text that energy from the fusion reaction $^2\mathrm{H} + {}^2\mathrm{H} \rightarrow {}^4\mathrm{He} + \gamma$ is relatively difficult to capture and utilize.

32.6 Fission

18. Explain why the fission of heavy nuclei releases energy. Similarly, why is it that energy input is required to fission light nuclei?

19. Explain, in terms of conservation of momentum and energy, why collisions of neutrons with protons will thermalize neutrons better than collisions with oxygen.

20. The ruins of the Chernobyl reactor are enclosed in a huge concrete structure built around it after the accident. Some rain penetrates the building in winter, and radioactivity from the building increases. What does this imply is happening inside?

21. Since the uranium or plutonium nucleus fissions into several fission fragments whose mass distribution covers a wide range of pieces, would you expect more residual radioactivity from fission than fusion? Explain.

22. The core of a nuclear reactor generates a large amount of thermal energy from the decay of fission products, even when the power-producing fission chain reaction is turned off. Would this residual heat be greatest after the reactor has run for a long time or short time? What if the reactor has been shut down for months?

23. How can a nuclear reactor contain many critical masses and not go supercritical? What methods are used to control the fission in the reactor?

24. Why can heavy nuclei with odd numbers of neutrons be induced to fission with thermal neutrons, whereas those with even numbers of neutrons require more energy input to induce fission?

25. Why is a conventional fission nuclear reactor not able to explode as a bomb?

32.7 Nuclear Weapons

26. What are some of the reasons that plutonium rather than uranium is used in all fission bombs and as the trigger in all fusion bombs?

27. Use the laws of conservation of momentum and energy to explain how a shape charge can direct most of the energy released in an explosion in a specific direction. (Note that this is similar to the situation in guns and cannons—most of the energy goes into the bullet.)

28. How does the lithium deuteride in the thermonuclear bomb shown in Figure 32.28 supply tritium ($^3\mathrm{H}$) as well as deuterium ($^2\mathrm{H}$)?

29. Fallout from nuclear weapons tests in the atmosphere is mainly $^{90}\mathrm{Sr}$ and $^{137}\mathrm{Cs}$, which have 28.6- and 32.2-y half-lives, respectively. Atmospheric tests were terminated in most countries in 1963, although China only did so in 1980. It has been found that environmental activities of these two isotopes are decreasing faster than their half-lives. Why might this be?

Problems & Exercises

32.1 Diagnostics and Medical Imaging

1. A neutron generator uses an α source, such as radium, to bombard beryllium, inducing the reaction $^4\text{He} + {}^9\text{Be} \rightarrow {}^{12}\text{C} + n$. Such neutron sources are called RaBe sources, or PuBe sources if they use plutonium to get the α s. Calculate the energy output of the reaction in MeV.

2. Neutrons from a source (perhaps the one discussed in the preceding problem) bombard natural molybdenum, which is 24 percent ^{98}Mo. What is the energy output of the reaction $^{98}\text{Mo} + n \rightarrow {}^{99}\text{Mo} + \gamma$? The mass of ^{98}Mo is given in Appendix A: Atomic Masses, and that of ^{99}Mo is 98.907711 u.

3. The purpose of producing ^{99}Mo (usually by neutron activation of natural molybdenum, as in the preceding problem) is to produce $^{99\text{m}}\text{Tc}$. Using the rules, verify that the β^- decay of ^{99}Mo produces $^{99\text{m}}\text{Tc}$. (Most $^{99\text{m}}\text{Tc}$ nuclei produced in this decay are left in a metastable excited state denoted $^{99\text{m}}\text{Tc}$.)

4. (a) Two annihilation γ rays in a PET scan originate at the same point and travel to detectors on either side of the patient. If the point of origin is 9.00 cm closer to one of the detectors, what is the difference in arrival times of the photons? (This could be used to give position information, but the time difference is small enough to make it difficult.) (b) How accurately would you need to be able to measure arrival time differences to get a position resolution of 1.00 mm?

5. Table 32.1 indicates that 7.50 mCi of $^{99\text{m}}\text{Tc}$ is used in a brain scan. What is the mass of technetium?

6. The activities of ^{131}I and ^{123}I used in thyroid scans are given in Table 32.1 to be 50 and $70\ \mu\text{Ci}$, respectively. Find and compare the masses of ^{131}I and ^{123}I in such scans, given their respective half-lives are 8.04 d and 13.2 h. The masses are so small that the radioiodine is usually mixed with stable iodine as a carrier to ensure normal chemistry and distribution in the body.

7. (a) Neutron activation of sodium, which is $100\%{}^{23}\text{Na}$, produces ^{24}Na, which is used in some heart scans, as seen in Table 32.1. The equation for the reaction is $^{23}\text{Na} + n \rightarrow {}^{24}\text{Na} + \gamma$. Find its energy output, given the mass of ^{24}Na is 23.990962 u.

   (b) What mass of ^{24}Na produces the needed 5.0-mCi activity, given its half-life is 15.0 h?

32.2 Biological Effects of Ionizing Radiation

8. What is the dose in mSv for: (a) a 0.1 Gy x-ray? (b) 2.5 mGy of neutron exposure to the eye? (c) 1.5 mGy of α exposure?

9. Find the radiation dose in Gy for: (a) A 10-mSv fluoroscopic x-ray series. (b) 50 mSv of skin exposure by an α emitter. (c) 160 mSv of β^- and γ rays from the ^{40}K in your body.

10. How many Gy of exposure is needed to give a cancerous tumor a dose of 40 Sv if it is exposed to α activity?

11. What is the dose in Sv in a cancer treatment that exposes the patient to 200 Gy of γ rays?

12. One half the γ rays from $^{99\text{m}}\text{Tc}$ are absorbed by a 0.170-mm-thick lead shielding. Half of the γ rays that pass through the first layer of lead are absorbed in a second layer of equal thickness. What thickness of lead will absorb all but one in 1000 of these γ rays?

13. A plumber at a nuclear power plant receives a whole-body dose of 30 mSv in 15 minutes while repairing a crucial valve. Find the radiation-induced yearly risk of death from cancer and the chance of genetic defect from this maximum allowable exposure.

14. In the 1980s, the term picowave was used to describe food irradiation in order to overcome public resistance by playing on the well-known safety of microwave radiation. Find the energy in MeV of a photon having a wavelength of a picometer.

15. Find the mass of ^{239}Pu that has an activity of $1.00\ \mu\text{Ci}$.

32.3 Therapeutic Uses of Ionizing Radiation

16. A beam of 168-MeV nitrogen nuclei is used for cancer therapy. If this beam is directed onto a 0.200-kg tumor and gives it a 2.00-Sv dose, how many nitrogen nuclei were stopped? (Use an RBE of 20 for heavy ions.)

17. (a) If the average molecular mass of compounds in food is 50.0 g, how many molecules are there in 1.00 kg of food? (b) How many ion pairs are created in 1.00 kg of food, if it is exposed to 1000

Sv and it takes 32.0 eV to create an ion pair? (c) Find the ratio of ion pairs to molecules. (d) If these ion pairs recombine into a distribution of 2000 new compounds, how many parts per billion is each?

18. Calculate the dose in Sv to the chest of a patient given an x-ray under the following conditions. The x-ray beam intensity is $1.50\ \text{W/m}^2$, the area of the chest exposed is $0.0750\ \text{m}^2$, 35.0% of the x-rays are absorbed in 20.0 kg of tissue, and the exposure time is 0.250 s.

19. (a) A cancer patient is exposed to γ rays from a 5000-Ci ^{60}Co transillumination unit for 32.0 s. The γ rays are collimated in such a manner that only 1.00% of them strike the patient. Of those, 20.0% are absorbed in a tumor having a mass of 1.50 kg. What is the dose in rem to the tumor, if the average γ energy per decay is 1.25 MeV? None of the β s from the decay reach the patient. (b) Is the dose consistent with stated therapeutic doses?

20. What is the mass of ^{60}Co in a cancer therapy transillumination unit containing 5.00 kCi of ^{60}Co?

21. Large amounts of ^{65}Zn are produced in copper exposed to accelerator beams. While machining contaminated copper, a physicist ingests $50.0\ \mu\text{Ci}$ of ^{65}Zn. Each ^{65}Zn decay emits an average γ-ray energy of 0.550 MeV, 40.0% of which is absorbed in the scientist's 75.0-kg body. What dose in mSv is caused by this in one day?

22. Naturally occurring ^{40}K is listed as responsible for 16 mrem/y of background radiation. Calculate the mass of ^{40}K that must be inside the 55-kg body of a woman to produce this dose. Each ^{40}K decay emits a 1.32-MeV β, and 50% of the energy is absorbed inside the body.

23. (a) Background radiation due to ^{226}Ra averages only 0.01 mSv/y, but it can range upward depending on where a person lives. Find the mass of ^{226}Ra in the 80.0-kg body of a man who receives a dose of 2.50-mSv/y from it, noting that each ^{226}Ra decay emits a 4.80-MeV α particle. You may neglect dose due to daughters and assume a constant amount, evenly distributed due to balanced ingestion and bodily elimination. (b) Is it surprising that such a small mass could cause a measurable radiation dose? Explain.

24. The annual radiation dose from ^{14}C in our bodies is 0.01 mSv/y. Each ^{14}C decay emits a β^- averaging 0.0750 MeV. Taking the fraction of ^{14}C to be 1.3×10^{-12} N of normal ^{12}C, and assuming the body is 13% carbon, estimate the fraction of the decay energy absorbed. (The rest escapes, exposing those close to you.)

25. If everyone in Australia received an extra 0.05 mSv per year of radiation, what would be the increase in the number of cancer deaths per year? (Assume that time had elapsed for the effects to become apparent.) Assume that there are 200×10^{-4} deaths per Sv of radiation per year. What percent of the actual number of cancer deaths recorded is this?

32.5 Fusion

26. Verify that the total number of nucleons, total charge, and electron family number are conserved for each of the fusion reactions in the proton-proton cycle in
$^1\text{H} + {}^1\text{H} \rightarrow {}^2\text{H} + e^+ + \upsilon_e$,
$^1\text{H} + {}^2\text{H} \rightarrow {}^3\text{He} + \gamma$,
and
$^3\text{He} + {}^3\text{He} \rightarrow {}^4\text{He} + {}^1\text{H} + {}^1\text{H}$.
(List the value of each of the conserved quantities before and after each of the reactions.)

27. Calculate the energy output in each of the fusion reactions in the proton-proton cycle, and verify the values given in the above summary.

28. Show that the total energy released in the proton-proton cycle is 26.7 MeV, considering the overall effect in $^1\text{H} + {}^1\text{H} \rightarrow {}^2\text{H} + e^+ + \upsilon_e$, $^1\text{H} + {}^2\text{H} \rightarrow {}^3\text{He} + \gamma$, and $^3\text{He} + {}^3\text{He} \rightarrow {}^4\text{He} + {}^1\text{H} + {}^1\text{H}$ and being certain to include the annihilation energy.

29. Verify by listing the number of nucleons, total charge, and electron family number before and after the cycle that these quantities are conserved in the overall proton-proton cycle in
$2e^- + 4{}^1\text{H} \rightarrow {}^4\text{He} + 2\upsilon_e + 6\gamma$.

30. The energy produced by the fusion of a 1.00-kg mixture of deuterium and tritium was found in Example Calculating Energy and Power from Fusion. Approximately how many kilograms would be required to supply the annual energy use in the United States?

31. Tritium is naturally rare, but can be produced by the reaction $n + {}^2\text{H} \rightarrow {}^3\text{H} + \gamma$. How much energy in MeV is released in this neutron capture?

32. Two fusion reactions mentioned in the text are

$n + {}^3\text{He} \to {}^4\text{He} + \gamma$
and
$n + {}^1\text{H} \to {}^2\text{H} + \gamma.$
Both reactions release energy, but the second also creates more fuel. Confirm that the energies produced in the reactions are 20.58 and 2.22 MeV, respectively. Comment on which product nuclide is most tightly bound, ${}^4\text{He}$ or ${}^2\text{H}$.

33. (a) Calculate the number of grams of deuterium in an 80,000-L swimming pool, given deuterium is 0.0150% of natural hydrogen.
(b) Find the energy released in joules if this deuterium is fused via the reaction
${}^2\text{H} + {}^2\text{H} \to {}^3\text{He} + n.$
(c) Could the neutrons be used to create more energy?
(d) Discuss the amount of this type of energy in a swimming pool as compared to that in, say, a gallon of gasoline, also taking into consideration that water is far more abundant.

34. How many kilograms of water are needed to obtain the 198.8 mol of deuterium, assuming that deuterium is 0.01500% (by number) of natural hydrogen?

35. The power output of the Sun is 4×10^{26} W.
(a) If 90% of this is supplied by the proton-proton cycle, how many protons are consumed per second?
(b) How many neutrinos per second should there be per square meter at the Earth from this process? This huge number is indicative of how rarely a neutrino interacts, since large detectors observe very few per day.

36. Another set of reactions that result in the fusing of hydrogen into helium in the Sun and especially in hotter stars is called the carbon cycle. It is

$$\begin{aligned}
{}^{12}\text{C} + {}^1\text{H} &\to {}^{13}\text{N} + \gamma, \\
{}^{13}\text{N} &\to {}^{13}\text{C} + e^+ + v_e, \\
{}^{13}\text{C} + {}^1\text{H} &\to {}^{14}\text{N} + \gamma, \\
{}^{14}\text{N} + {}^1\text{H} &\to {}^{15}\text{O} + \gamma, \\
{}^{15}\text{O} &\to {}^{15}\text{N} + e^+ + v_e, \\
{}^{15}\text{N} + {}^1\text{H} &\to {}^{12}\text{C} + {}^4\text{He}.
\end{aligned}$$

Write down the overall effect of the carbon cycle (as was done for the proton-proton cycle in $2e^- + 4{}^1\text{H} \to {}^4\text{He} + 2v_e + 6\gamma$). Note the number of protons (${}^1\text{H}$) required and assume that the positrons (e^+) annihilate electrons to form more γ rays.

37. (a) Find the total energy released in MeV in each carbon cycle (elaborated in the above problem) including the annihilation energy.
(b) How does this compare with the proton-proton cycle output?

38. Verify that the total number of nucleons, total charge, and electron family number are conserved for each of the fusion reactions in the carbon cycle given in the above problem. (List the value of each of the conserved quantities before and after each of the reactions.)

39. Integrated Concepts
The laser system tested for inertial confinement can produce a 100-kJ pulse only 1.00 ns in duration. (a) What is the power output of the laser system during the brief pulse?
(b) How many photons are in the pulse, given their wavelength is $1.06\ \mu\text{m}$?
(c) What is the total momentum of all these photons?
(d) How does the total photon momentum compare with that of a single 1.00 MeV deuterium nucleus?

40. Integrated Concepts
Find the amount of energy given to the ${}^4\text{He}$ nucleus and to the γ ray in the reaction $n + ^3\text{He} \to ^4\text{He} + \gamma$, using the conservation of momentum principle and taking the reactants to be initially at rest. This should confirm the contention that most of the energy goes to the γ ray.

41. Integrated Concepts
(a) What temperature gas would have atoms moving fast enough to bring two ${}^3\text{He}$ nuclei into contact? Note that, because both are moving, the average kinetic energy only needs to be half the electric potential energy of these doubly charged nuclei when just in contact with one another.
(b) Does this high temperature imply practical difficulties for doing this in controlled fusion?

42. Integrated Concepts
(a) Estimate the years that the deuterium fuel in the oceans could supply the energy needs of the world. Assume world energy consumption to be ten times that of the United States which is 8×10^{19} J/y and that the deuterium in the oceans could be converted to energy with an efficiency of 32%. You must estimate or look up the amount of water in the oceans and take the deuterium content to be 0.015% of natural hydrogen to find the mass of deuterium available. Note that approximate energy yield of deuterium is

3.37×10^{14} J/kg.
(b) Comment on how much time this is by any human measure. (It is not an unreasonable result, only an impressive one.)

32.6 Fission

43. (a) Calculate the energy released in the neutron-induced fission (similar to the spontaneous fission in Example 32.3)
$n + {}^{238}\text{U} \rightarrow {}^{96}\text{Sr} + {}^{140}\text{Xe} + 3n$,
given $m({}^{96}\text{Sr}) = 95.921750$ u and $m({}^{140}\text{Xe}) = 139.92164$. (b) This result is about 6 MeV greater than the result for spontaneous fission. Why? (c) Confirm that the total number of nucleons and total charge are conserved in this reaction.

44. (a) Calculate the energy released in the neutron-induced fission reaction
$n + {}^{235}\text{U} \rightarrow {}^{92}\text{Kr} + {}^{142}\text{Ba} + 2n$,
given $m({}^{92}\text{Kr}) = 91.926269$ u and
$m({}^{142}\text{Ba}) = 141.916361$ u.
(b) Confirm that the total number of nucleons and total charge are conserved in this reaction.

45. (a) Calculate the energy released in the neutron-induced fission reaction
$n + {}^{239}\text{Pu} \rightarrow {}^{96}\text{Sr} + {}^{140}\text{Ba} + 4n$,
given $m({}^{96}\text{Sr}) = 95.921750$ u and
$m({}^{140}\text{Ba}) = 139.910581$ u.
(b) Confirm that the total number of nucleons and total charge are conserved in this reaction.

46. Confirm that each of the reactions listed for plutonium breeding just following Example 32.4 conserves the total number of nucleons, the total charge, and electron family number.

47. Breeding plutonium produces energy even before any plutonium is fissioned. (The primary purpose of the four nuclear reactors at Chernobyl was breeding plutonium for weapons. Electrical power was a by-product used by the civilian population.) Calculate the energy produced in each of the reactions listed for plutonium breeding just following Example 32.4. The pertinent masses are
$m({}^{239}\text{U}) = 239.054289$ u,
$m({}^{239}\text{Np}) = 239.052932$ u, and
$m({}^{239}\text{Pu}) = 239.052157$ u.

48. The naturally occurring radioactive isotope ${}^{232}\text{Th}$ does not make good fission fuel, because it has an even number of neutrons; however, it can be bred into a suitable fuel (much as ${}^{238}\text{U}$ is bred into ${}^{239}\text{P}$).
(a) What are Z and N for ${}^{232}\text{Th}$?
(b) Write the reaction equation for neutron captured by ${}^{232}\text{Th}$ and identify the nuclide ${}^{A}X$ produced in $n + {}^{232}\text{Th} \rightarrow {}^{A}X + \gamma$.
(c) The product nucleus β^- decays, as does its daughter. Write the decay equations for each, and identify the final nucleus.
(d) Confirm that the final nucleus has an odd number of neutrons, making it a better fission fuel.
(e) Look up the half-life of the final nucleus to see if it lives long enough to be a useful fuel.

49. The electrical power output of a large nuclear reactor facility is 900 MW. It has a 35.0% efficiency in converting nuclear power to electrical.
(a) What is the thermal nuclear power output in megawatts?
(b) How many ${}^{235}\text{U}$ nuclei fission each second, assuming the average fission produces 200 MeV?
(c) What mass of ${}^{235}\text{U}$ is fissioned in one year of full-power operation?

50. A large power reactor that has been in operation for some months is turned off, but residual activity in the core still produces 150 MW of power. If the average energy per decay of the fission products is 1.00 MeV, what is the core activity in curies?

32.7 Nuclear Weapons

51. Find the mass converted into energy by a 12.0-kT bomb.

52. What mass is converted into energy by a 1.00-MT bomb?

53. Fusion bombs use neutrons from their fission trigger to create tritium fuel in the reaction $n + {}^{6}\text{Li} \rightarrow {}^{3}\text{H} + {}^{4}\text{He}$. What is the energy released by this reaction in MeV?

54. It is estimated that the total explosive yield of all the nuclear bombs in existence currently is about 4,000 MT.
(a) Convert this amount of energy to kilowatt-hours, noting that $1\ \text{kW} \cdot \text{h} = 3.60 \times 10^6$ J.
(b) What would the monetary value of this energy be if it could be converted to electricity costing 10 cents per kW·h?

55. A radiation-enhanced nuclear weapon (or neutron bomb) can have a smaller total yield and still produce more prompt radiation than a conventional nuclear bomb. This allows the use of neutron bombs to kill nearby advancing enemy forces with radiation without blowing up your own forces with the blast. For a 0.500-kT radiation-enhanced weapon and a 1.00-kT conventional nuclear bomb: (a) Compare the blast yields. (b) Compare the prompt radiation yields.

56. (a) How many ^{239}Pu nuclei must fission to produce a 20.0-kT yield, assuming 200 MeV per fission? (b) What is the mass of this much ^{239}Pu?

57. Assume one-fourth of the yield of a typical 320-kT strategic bomb comes from fission reactions averaging 200 MeV and the remainder from fusion reactions averaging 20 MeV.
(a) Calculate the number of fissions and the approximate mass of uranium and plutonium fissioned, taking the average atomic mass to be 238.
(b) Find the number of fusions and calculate the approximate mass of fusion fuel, assuming an average total atomic mass of the two nuclei in each reaction to be 5.
(c) Considering the masses found, does it seem reasonable that some missiles could carry 10 warheads? Discuss, noting that the nuclear fuel is only a part of the mass of a warhead.

58. This problem gives some idea of the magnitude of the energy yield of a small tactical bomb. Assume that half the energy of a 1.00-kT nuclear depth charge set off under an aircraft carrier goes into lifting it out of the water—that is, into gravitational potential energy. How high is the carrier lifted if its mass is 90,000 tons?

59. It is estimated that weapons tests in the atmosphere have deposited approximately 9 MCi of ^{90}Sr on the surface of the earth. Find the mass of this amount of ^{90}Sr.

60. A 1.00-MT bomb exploded a few kilometers above the ground deposits 25.0% of its energy into radiant heat.
(a) Find the calories per cm^2 at a distance of 10.0 km by assuming a uniform distribution over a spherical surface of that radius.
(b) If this heat falls on a person's body, what temperature increase does it cause in the affected tissue, assuming it is absorbed in a layer 1.00-cm deep?

61. Integrated Concepts
One scheme to put nuclear weapons to nonmilitary use is to explode them underground in a geologically stable region and extract the geothermal energy for electricity production. There was a total yield of about 4,000 MT in the combined arsenals in 2006. If 1.00 MT per day could be converted to electricity with an efficiency of 10.0%:
(a) What would the average electrical power output be?
(b) How many years would the arsenal last at this rate?

62. Critical Thinking A spherical target in a body is being targeted with β^{+} radiation. The target is centered at $(0.00, 2.00, 3.00)$ on a grid that is in centimeters. The target has a radius of 0.500 centimeters. (a) What two points on the *x*-axis are at the extremes of where the positrons annihilate the electrons? (b) What two points on the *y*-axis are at the extremes of where the positrons annihilate the electrons? (c) What can be said about the directions of the pair of gamma rays that result from the annihilations? (d) Can the use of β^{+} give information in three dimensions?

Test Prep for AP® Courses

32.2 Biological Effects of Ionizing Radiation

1. A patient receives *A* rad of radiation as part of her treatment and absorbs *E* J of energy. The RBE of the radiation particles is *R*. If the RBE is increased to 1.5*R*, what will be the energy absorbed by the patient?
a. 1.5*E* J
b. *E* J
c. 0.75*E* J
d. 0.67*E* J

2. If a 90-kg person is exposed to 50 mrem of alpha particles (with RBE of 16), calculate the dosage (in rad) received by the person. What is the amount of energy absorbed by the person?

32.5 Fusion

3.

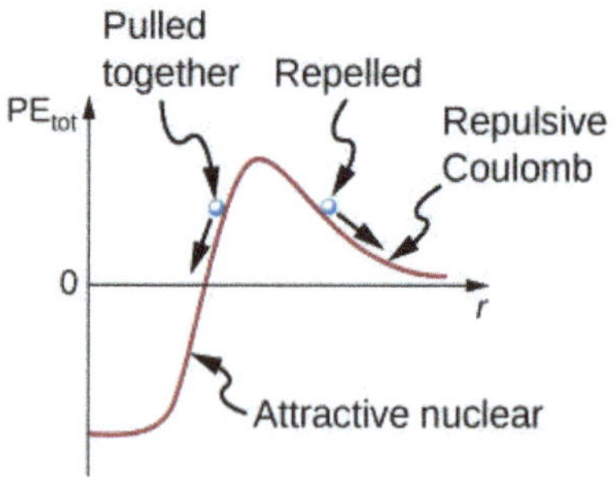

FIGURE 32.31

This figure shows a graph of the potential energy

between two light nuclei as a function of the distance between them. Fusion can occur between the nuclei if the distance is

a. large so that kinetic energy is low.
b. large so that potential energy is low.
c. small so that nuclear attractive force can overcome Coulomb's repulsion.
d. small so that nuclear attractive force cannot overcome Coulomb's repulsion.

4. In a nuclear fusion reaction, 2 g of hydrogen is converted into 1.985 g of helium. What is the energy released?

a. 4.5×10^{3} J
b. 4.5×10^{6} J
c. 1.35×10^{12} J
d. 1.35×10^{15} J

5. When deuterium and tritium nuclei fuse to produce helium, what else is produced?

a. positron
b. proton
c. α-particle
d. neutron

6. Suppose two deuterium nuclei are fused to produce helium.

a. Write the equation for the fusion reaction.
b. Calculate the difference between the masses of reactants and products.
c. Using the result calculated in (b), find the energy produced in the fusion reaction.

Assume that the mass of deuterium is 2.014102 u, the mass of helium is 4.002603 u and 1 u = 1.66×10^{-27} kg.

32.6 Fission

7. Which of the following statements about nuclear fission is true?

a. No new elements can be produced in a fission reaction.
b. Energy released in fission reactions is generally less than that from fusion reactions.
c. In a fission reaction, two light nuclei are combined into a heavier one.
d. Fission reactions can be explained on the basis of the conservation of mass-energy.

8. What is the energy obtained when 10 g of mass is converted to energy with an efficiency of 70%?

a. 3.93×10^{27} MeV
b. 3.93×10^{30} MeV
c. 5.23×10^{27} MeV
d. 5.23×10^{30} MeV

9. In a neutron-induced fission reaction of ^{239}Pu, which of the following is produced along with ^{96}Sr and four neutrons?

a. $^{139}_{56}\text{Ba}$
b. $^{140}_{56}\text{Ba}$
c. $^{139}_{54}\text{Xe}$
d. $^{140}_{54}\text{Xe}$

10. When ^{235}U is bombarded with one neutron, the following fission reaction occurs:

$$^{235}_{92}\text{U} + n \rightarrow {}^{141}_{56}\text{Ba} + {}^{92}_{y}\text{Kr} + xn.$$

a. Find the values for x and y.
b. Assuming that the mass of ^{235}U is 235.04 u, the mass of ^{141}Ba is 140.91 u, the mass of ^{92}Kr is 91.93 u, and the mass of n is 1.01 u, a student calculates the energy released in the fission reaction as 2.689×10^{-8}, but forgets to write the unit. Find the correct unit and convert the answer to MeV.

CHAPTER 33
Particle Physics

FIGURE 33.1 Part of the Large Hadron Collider at CERN, on the border of Switzerland and France. The LHC is a particle accelerator, designed to study fundamental particles. (credit: Image Editor, Flickr)

CHAPTER OUTLINE

CONNECTION FOR AP® COURSES Continuing to use ideas that would be familiar to the ancient Greeks, we look for smaller and smaller structures in nature, hoping ultimately to find and understand the most fundamental building blocks. Atomic physics deals with the smallest units of elements and compounds. Through the study of atomic physics, we have found a relatively small number of atoms with systematic properties that explain a tremendous range of phenomena.

Nuclear physics is concerned with the nuclei of atoms and their substructures, supporting Big Idea 1, that systems have internal structure. Furthermore, the internal structure of a system determines many properties of the system (Enduring Understanding 1.A). Here, a smaller number of components—the proton and neutron—make up all nuclei. Neutrons and protons are composed of quarks. Electrons, neutrinos, photons, and quarks are examples of fundamental particles. The positive electric charge on protons and neutral charge on neutrons result from their quark compositions (Essential Knowledge 1.A.2).

This chapter divides elementary particles into fundamental particles as objects that do not have internal structure and composed particles whose properties are defined by their substructures (Essential Knowledge 1.A.2). The magnetic dipole moment, related to the properties of spin (angular momentum) and charge, is an intrinsic property of some fundamental particles such as the electron (Essential Knowledge 1.E.6). This property is the fundamental source of magnetic behavior in matter (Enduring Understanding 1.E).

Exploring the systematic behavior of interactions among particles has revealed even more about matter, forces, and energy. Mass and electric charge are properties of matter that are conserved (Enduring Understanding 1.C). The total energy of the system is also conserved (Enduring Understanding 5.B). In quantum mechanical systems, mass is actually part of the internal energy of an object or system (Essential Knowledge 5.B.11). It has been discovered experimentally that, due to certain interactions between systems, mass can be converted to energy and energy can be converted to mass (Essential Knowledge 1.C.4, Essential Knowledge 4.C.4), supporting Big Idea 4. These process can also lead to changes in the total energy of the system (Enduring Understanding 4.C).

Particle physics deals with the substructures of atoms and nuclei and is particularly aimed at finding those truly fundamental particles that have no further substructure. In general, any system can be viewed as a collection of objects, where objects do not have internal structure (Essential Knowledge 1.A.1). Just as in atomic and nuclear physics, we have found a complex array of particles and properties with systematic characteristics analogous to the periodic table and the chart of nuclides. We have discovered that changes in the systems are constrained by the conservation laws, supporting Big Idea 5. In the case of elementary particles, these conservation laws include mass-energy conservation and conservation of electric charge (Enduring Understanding 5.C). Electric charge is conserved in elementary particle reactions, even when elementary particles are produced or destroyed (Essential Knowledge 5.C.1).

The chapter revisits the ideas of fundamental forces (Enduring Understanding 3.G) and their fields in connection to elementary particles. This supports Big Ideas 2 and 3, because these particles are carriers of a specific force that provides existence of the field in space (Enduring Understanding 2.A). The field is simply the macroscopic outcome of all these force-carrying particles. The approximate relative strength and range of the gravitational force (Essential Knowledge 3.G.1), electromagnetic force (Essential Knowledge 3.G.2), strong force (Essential Knowledge 3.G.3) and weak force are considered in relation to the properties of their carrier particles. The details of these considerations go beyond AP® expectations.

An underlying structure is apparent, and there is some reason to think that we *are* finding particles that have no substructure. Of course, we have been in similar situations before. For example, atoms were once thought to be the ultimate substructure. Perhaps we will find deeper and deeper structures and never come to an ultimate substructure. We may never really know, as indicated in Figure 33.2.

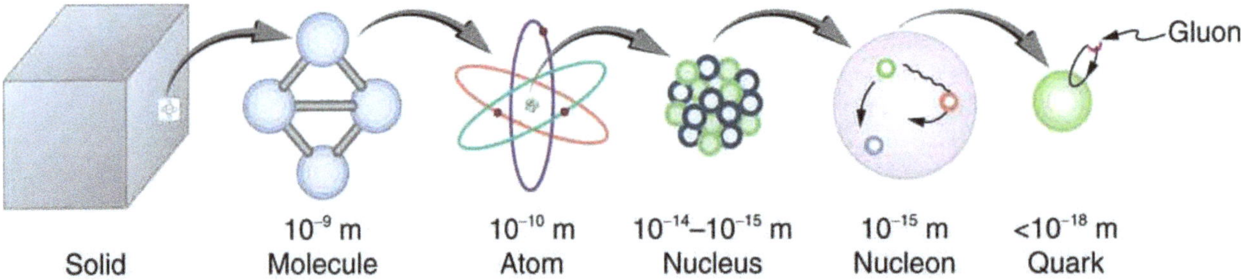

FIGURE 33.2 The properties of matter are based on substructures called molecules and atoms. Molecules are formed from atoms. Atoms have the substructure of a nucleus with orbiting electrons, the interactions of which explain atomic properties. Protons and neutrons, the interactions of which explain the stability and abundance of elements, form the substructure of nuclei. Protons and neutrons are not fundamental—they are composed of quarks. Like electrons and a few other particles, quarks may be fundamental building blocks, lacking any further substructure. But the story is not complete, because quarks and electrons may have substructure smaller than is presently observable.

This chapter covers the basics of particle physics as we know it today. An amazing convergence of topics is evolving in modern particle physics. We find that some particles are intimately related to forces, and that nature on the smallest scale may have a defining influence on the large-scale character of the universe. The study of particle physics is an adventure beyond even the best science fiction, because it is not only fantastic, it is real.

Big Idea 1 Objects and systems have properties such as mass and charge. Systems may have internal structure.

Enduring Understanding 1.A The internal structure of a system determines many properties of the system.

Essential Knowledge 1.A.1 A system is an object or a collection of objects. Objects are treated as having no internal structure.

Essential Knowledge 1.A.2 Fundamental particles have no internal structure.

Enduring Understanding 1.C Objects and systems have properties of inertial mass and gravitational mass that are experimentally verified to be the same and that satisfy conservation principles.

Essential Knowledge 1.C.4 In certain processes, mass can be converted to energy and energy can be converted to mass according to $E = mc^2$, the equation derived from the theory of special relativity.

Enduring Understanding 1.E Materials have many macroscopic properties that result from the arrangement and interactions of the atoms and molecules that make up the material.

Essential Knowledge 1.E.6 Matter has a property called magnetic dipole moment.

a. Magnetic dipole moment is a fundamental source of magnetic behavior of matter and an intrinsic property of some fundamental particles such as the electron.

Big Idea 2 Fields existing in space can be used to explain interactions.

Enduring Understanding 2.A A field associates a value of some physical quantity with every point in space. Field models are useful for describing interactions that occur at a distance (long-range forces) as well as a variety of other physical phenomena.

Big Idea 3 The interactions of an object with other objects can be described by forces.

Enduring Understanding 3.G Certain types of forces are considered fundamental.

Essential Knowledge 3.G.1: Gravitational forces are exerted at all scales and dominate at the largest distance and mass scales.

Essential Knowledge 3.G.2 Electromagnetic forces are exerted at all scales and can dominate at the human scale.

Essential Knowledge 3.G.3 The strong force is exerted at nuclear scales and dominates the interactions of nucleons.

Big Idea 4 Interactions between systems can result in changes in those systems.

Enduring Understanding 4.C Interactions with other objects or systems can change the total energy of a system.

Essential Knowledge 4.C.4 Mass can be converted into energy and energy can be converted into mass.

Big Idea 5. Changes that occur as a result of interactions are constrained by conservation laws.

Enduring Understanding 5.B The energy of a system is conserved.

Essential Knowledge 5.B.11 Beyond the classical approximation, mass is actually part of the internal energy of an object or system with $E = mc^2$.

Enduring Understanding 5.C The electric charge of a system is conserved.

Essential Knowledge 5.C.1 Electric charge is conserved in nuclear and elementary particle reactions, even when elementary particles are produced or destroyed. Examples should include equations representing nuclear decay.

33.1 The Yukawa Particle and the Heisenberg Uncertainty Principle Revisited

LEARNING OBJECTIVES

By the end of this section, you will be able to:

- Define Yukawa particle.
- State the Heisenberg uncertainty principle.
- Describe pion.
- Estimate the mass of a pion.
- Explain meson.

Particle physics as we know it today began with the ideas of Hideki Yukawa in 1935. Physicists had long been concerned with how forces are transmitted, finding the concept of fields, such as electric and magnetic fields to be very useful. A field surrounds an object and carries the force exerted by the object through space. Yukawa was interested in the strong nuclear force in particular and found an ingenious way to explain its short range. His idea is a blend of particles, forces, relativity, and quantum mechanics that is applicable to all forces. Yukawa proposed that force is transmitted by the exchange of particles (called carrier particles). The field consists of these carrier particles.

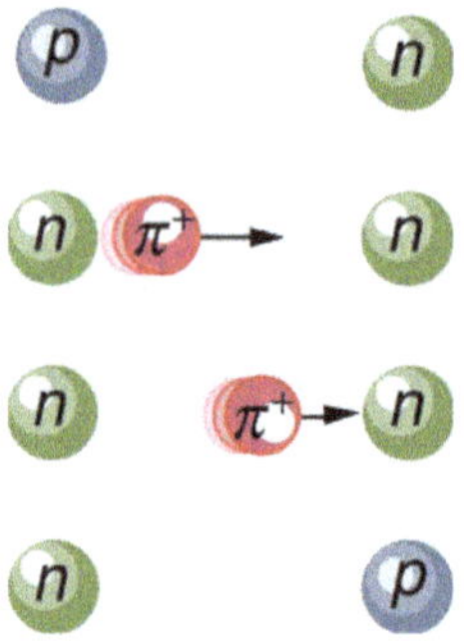

FIGURE 33.3 The strong nuclear force is transmitted between a proton and neutron by the creation and exchange of a pion. The pion is created through a temporary violation of conservation of mass-energy and travels from the proton to the neutron and is recaptured. It is not directly observable and is called a virtual particle. Note that the proton and neutron change identity in the process. The range of the force is limited by the fact that the pion can only exist for the short time allowed by the Heisenberg uncertainty principle. Yukawa used the finite range of the strong nuclear force to estimate the mass of the pion; the shorter the range, the larger the mass of the carrier particle.

Specifically for the strong nuclear force, Yukawa proposed that a previously unknown particle, now called a **pion**, is exchanged between nucleons, transmitting the force between them. Figure 33.3 illustrates how a pion would carry a force between a proton and a neutron. The pion has mass and can only be created by violating the conservation of mass-energy. This is allowed by the Heisenberg uncertainty principle if it occurs for a sufficiently short period of time. As discussed in Probability: The Heisenberg Uncertainty Principle the Heisenberg uncertainty principle relates the uncertainties ΔE in energy and Δt in time by

$$\Delta E \Delta t \geq \frac{h}{4\pi}, \tag{33.1}$$

where h is Planck's constant. Therefore, conservation of mass-energy can be violated by an amount ΔE for a time $\Delta t \approx \frac{h}{4\pi\Delta E}$ in which time no process can detect the violation. This allows the temporary creation of a particle of mass m, where $\Delta E = mc^2$. The larger the mass and the greater the ΔE, the shorter is the time it can exist. This means the range of the force is limited, because the particle can only travel a limited distance in a finite amount of time. In fact, the maximum distance is $d \approx c\Delta t$, where c is the speed of light. The pion must then be captured and, thus, cannot be directly observed because that would amount to a permanent violation of mass-energy conservation. Such particles (like the pion above) are called **virtual particles**, because they cannot be directly observed but their *effects* can be directly observed. Realizing all this, Yukawa used the information on the range of the strong nuclear force to estimate the mass of the pion, the particle that carries it. The steps of his reasoning are approximately retraced in the following worked example:

EXAMPLE 33.1

Calculating the Mass of a Pion

Taking the range of the strong nuclear force to be about 1 fermi (10^{-15} m), calculate the approximate mass of the pion carrying the force, assuming it moves at nearly the speed of light.

Strategy

The calculation is approximate because of the assumptions made about the range of the force and the speed of the pion, but also because a more accurate calculation would require the sophisticated mathematics of quantum mechanics. Here, we use the Heisenberg uncertainty principle in the simple form stated above, as developed in Probability: The Heisenberg Uncertainty Principle. First, we must calculate the time Δt that the pion exists, given that the distance it travels at nearly the speed of light is about 1 fermi. Then, the Heisenberg uncertainty principle can be solved for the energy ΔE, and from that the mass of the pion can be determined. We will use the units of MeV/c^2 for mass, which are convenient since we are often considering converting mass to energy and vice versa.

Solution

The distance the pion travels is $d \approx c\Delta t$, and so the time during which it exists is approximately

$$\begin{aligned}\Delta t &\approx \frac{d}{c} = \frac{10^{-15}\ \text{m}}{3.0\times10^{8}\ \text{m/s}} \\ &\approx 3.3 \times 10^{-24}\ \text{s}.\end{aligned} \quad 33.2$$

Now, solving the Heisenberg uncertainty principle for ΔE gives

$$\Delta E \approx \frac{h}{4\pi\Delta t} \approx \frac{6.63 \times 10^{-34}\ \text{J}\cdot\text{s}}{4\pi\left(3.3 \times 10^{-24}\ \text{s}\right)}. \quad 33.3$$

Solving this and converting the energy to MeV gives

$$\Delta E \approx \left(1.6 \times 10^{-11}\ \text{J}\right)\frac{1\ \text{MeV}}{1.6 \times 10^{-13}\ \text{J}} = 100\ \text{MeV}. \quad 33.4$$

Mass is related to energy by $\Delta E = mc^2$, so that the mass of the pion is $m = \Delta E/c^2$, or

$$m \approx 100\ \text{MeV}/c^2. \quad 33.5$$

Discussion

This is about 200 times the mass of an electron and about one-tenth the mass of a nucleon. No such particles were known at the time Yukawa made his bold proposal.

Yukawa's proposal of particle exchange as the method of force transfer is intriguing. But how can we verify his proposal if we cannot observe the virtual pion directly? If sufficient energy is in a nucleus, it would be possible to free the pion—that is, to create its mass from external energy input. This can be accomplished by collisions of energetic particles with nuclei, but energies greater than 100 MeV are required to conserve both energy and momentum. In 1947, pions were observed in cosmic-ray experiments, which were designed to supply a small flux of high-energy protons that may collide with nuclei. Soon afterward, accelerators of sufficient energy were creating pions in the laboratory under controlled conditions. Three pions were discovered, two with charge and one neutral, and given the symbols π^+, π^-, and π^0, respectively. The masses of π^+ and π^- are identical at $139.6\ \text{MeV}/c^2$, whereas π^0 has a mass of $135.0\ \text{MeV}/c^2$. These masses are close to the predicted value of $100\ \text{MeV}/c^2$ and, since they are intermediate between electron and nucleon masses, the particles are given the name **meson** (now an entire class of particles, as we shall see in Particles, Patterns, and Conservation Laws).

The pions, or π-mesons as they are also called, have masses close to those predicted and feel the strong nuclear force. Another previously unknown particle, now called the muon, was discovered during cosmic-ray experiments in 1936 (one of its discoverers, Seth Neddermeyer, also originated the idea of implosion for plutonium bombs). Since the mass of a muon is around $106\ \text{MeV}/c^2$, at first it was thought to be the particle predicted by Yukawa. But it was soon realized that muons do not feel the strong nuclear force and could not be Yukawa's particle. Their role was unknown, causing the respected physicist I. I. Rabi to comment, "Who ordered that?" This remains a valid question today. We have discovered hundreds of subatomic particles; the roles of some are only partially understood. But there are various patterns and relations to forces that have led to profound insights into nature's secrets.

33.2 The Four Basic Forces

LEARNING OBJECTIVES

By the end of this section, you will be able to:

- State the four basic forces.
- Explain the Feynman diagram for the exchange of a virtual photon between two positive charges.
- Define QED.
- Describe the Feynman diagram for the exchange of a between a proton and a neutron.

As first discussed in Problem-Solving Strategies and mentioned at various points in the text since then, there are only four distinct basic forces in all of nature. This is a remarkably small number considering the myriad phenomena they explain. Particle physics is intimately tied to these four forces. Certain fundamental particles, called carrier particles, carry these forces, and all particles can be classified according to which of the four forces they feel. The table given below summarizes important characteristics of the four basic forces.

Force	Approximate relative strength	Range	+/–[1]	Carrier particle
Gravity	10^{-38}	∞	+ only	Graviton (conjectured)
Electromagnetic	10^{-2}	∞	+/ –	Photon (observed)
Weak force	10^{-13}	$< 10^{-18}$ m	+/ –	W^+, W^-, Z^0 (observed[2])
Strong force	1	$< 10^{-15}$ m	+/ –	Gluons (conjectured[3])

TABLE 33.1 Properties of the Four Basic Forces

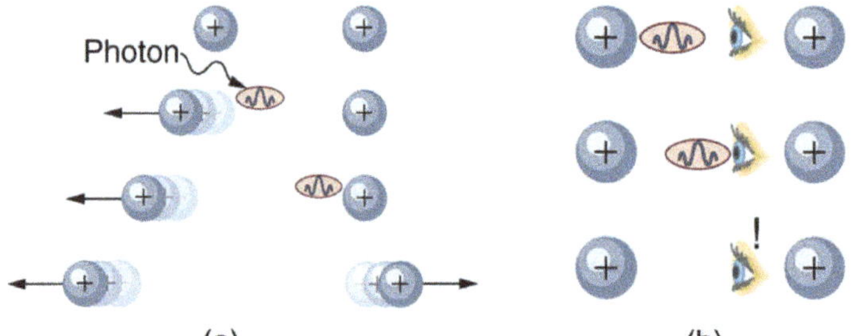

FIGURE 33.4 The first image shows the exchange of a virtual photon transmitting the electromagnetic force between charges, just as virtual pion exchange carries the strong nuclear force between nucleons. The second image shows that the photon cannot be directly observed in its passage, because this would disrupt it and alter the force. In this case it does not get to the other charge.

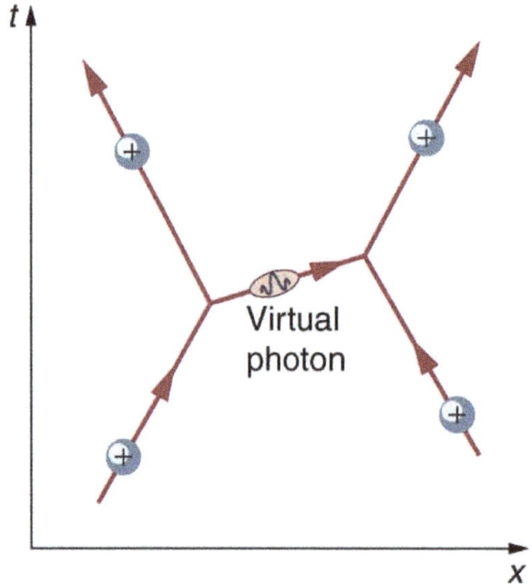

FIGURE 33.5 The Feynman diagram for the exchange of a virtual photon between two positive charges illustrates how the electromagnetic force is transmitted on a quantum mechanical scale. Time is graphed vertically while the distance is graphed horizontally. The two positive charges are seen to be repelled by the photon exchange.

Although these four forces are distinct and differ greatly from one another under all but the most extreme circumstances, we can see similarities among them. (In GUTs: the Unification of Forces, we will discuss how the four

1 + attractive; - repulsive; + /– both.
2 Predicted by theory and first observed in 1983.
3 Eight proposed—indirect evidence of existence. Underlie meson exchange.

forces may be different manifestations of a single unified force.) Perhaps the most important characteristic among the forces is that they are all transmitted by the exchange of a carrier particle, exactly like what Yukawa had in mind for the strong nuclear force. Each carrier particle is a virtual particle—it cannot be directly observed while transmitting the force. Figure 33.4 shows the exchange of a virtual photon between two positive charges. The photon cannot be directly observed in its passage, because this would disrupt it and alter the force.

Figure 33.5 shows a way of graphing the exchange of a virtual photon between two positive charges. This graph of time versus position is called a **Feynman diagram**, after the brilliant American physicist Richard Feynman (1918–1988) who developed it.

Figure 33.6 is a Feynman diagram for the exchange of a virtual pion between a proton and a neutron representing the same interaction as in Figure 33.3. Feynman diagrams are not only a useful tool for visualizing interactions at the quantum mechanical level, they are also used to calculate details of interactions, such as their strengths and probability of occurring. Feynman was one of the theorists who developed the field of **quantum electrodynamics** (QED), which is the quantum mechanics of electromagnetism. QED has been spectacularly successful in describing electromagnetic interactions on the submicroscopic scale. Feynman was an inspiring teacher, had a colorful personality, and made a profound impact on generations of physicists. He shared the 1965 Nobel Prize with Julian Schwinger and S. I. Tomonaga for work in QED with its deep implications for particle physics.

Why is it that particles called gluons are listed as the carrier particles for the strong nuclear force when, in The Yukawa Particle and the Heisenberg Uncertainty Principle Revisited, we saw that pions apparently carry that force? The answer is that pions are exchanged but they have a substructure and, as we explore it, we find that the strong force is actually related to the indirectly observed but more fundamental **gluons**. In fact, all the carrier particles are thought to be fundamental in the sense that they have no substructure. Another similarity among carrier particles is that they are all bosons (first mentioned in Patterns in Spectra Reveal More Quantization), having integral intrinsic spins.

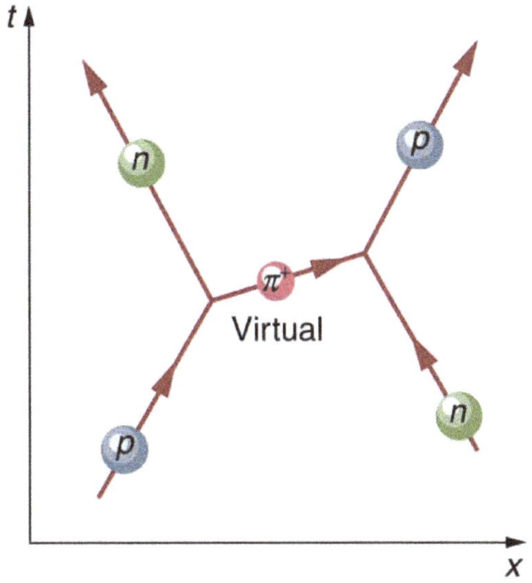

FIGURE 33.6 The image shows a Feynman diagram for the exchange of a π^+ between a proton and a neutron, carrying the strong nuclear force between them. This diagram represents the situation shown more pictorially in Figure 33.4.

There is a relationship between the mass of the carrier particle and the range of the force. The photon is massless and has energy. So, the existence of (virtual) photons is possible only by virtue of the Heisenberg uncertainty principle and can travel an unlimited distance. Thus, the range of the electromagnetic force is infinite. This is also true for gravity. It is infinite in range because its carrier particle, the graviton, has zero rest mass. (Gravity is the most difficult of the four forces to understand on a quantum scale because it affects the space and time in which the others act. But gravity is so weak that its effects are extremely difficult to observe quantum mechanically. We shall explore it further in General Relativity and Quantum Gravity). The W^+, W^-, and Z^0 particles that carry the weak nuclear force have mass, accounting for the very short range of this force. In fact, the W^+, W^-, and Z^0 are about 1000 times more massive than pions, consistent with the fact that the range of the weak nuclear force is about 1/1000 that of the strong nuclear force. Gluons are actually massless, but since they act inside massive carrier particles like pions, the strong nuclear force is also short ranged.

The relative strengths of the forces given in the Table 33.1 are those for the most common situations. When particles are brought very close together, the relative strengths change, and they may become identical at extremely close range. As we shall see in GUTs: the Unification of Forces, carrier particles may be altered by the energy required to bring particles very close together—in such a manner that they become identical.

33.3 Accelerators Create Matter from Energy

LEARNING OBJECTIVES

By the end of this section, you will be able to:

- State the principle of a cyclotron.
- Explain the principle of a synchrotron.
- Describe the voltage needed by an accelerator between accelerating tubes.
- State Fermilab's accelerator principle.

Before looking at all the particles we now know about, let us examine some of the machines that created them. The fundamental process in creating previously unknown particles is to accelerate known particles, such as protons or electrons, and direct a beam of them toward a target. Collisions with target nuclei provide a wealth of information, such as information obtained by Rutherford using energetic helium nuclei from natural α radiation. But if the energy of the incoming particles is large enough, new matter is sometimes created in the collision. The more energy input or ΔE, the more matter m can be created, since $m = \Delta E/c^2$. Limitations are placed on what can occur by known conservation laws, such as conservation of mass-energy, momentum, and charge. Even more interesting are the unknown limitations provided by nature. Some expected reactions do occur, while others do not, and still other unexpected reactions may appear. New laws are revealed, and the vast majority of what we know about particle physics has come from accelerator laboratories. It is the particle physicist's favorite indoor sport, which is partly inspired by theory.

Early Accelerators

An early accelerator is a relatively simple, large-scale version of the electron gun. The **Van de Graaff** (named after the Dutch physicist), which you have likely seen in physics demonstrations, is a small version of the ones used for nuclear research since their invention for that purpose in 1932. For more, see Figure 33.7. These machines are electrostatic, creating potentials as great as 50 MV, and are used to accelerate a variety of nuclei for a range of experiments. Energies produced by Van de Graaffs are insufficient to produce new particles, but they have been instrumental in exploring several aspects of the nucleus. Another, equally famous, early accelerator is the **cyclotron**, invented in 1930 by the American physicist, E. O. Lawrence (1901–1958). For a visual representation with more detail, see Figure 33.8. Cyclotrons use fixed-frequency alternating electric fields to accelerate particles. The particles spiral outward in a magnetic field, making increasingly larger radius orbits during acceleration. This clever arrangement allows the successive addition of electric potential energy and so greater particle energies are possible than in a Van de Graaff. Lawrence was involved in many early discoveries and in the promotion of physics programs in American universities. He was awarded the 1939 Nobel Prize in Physics for the cyclotron and nuclear activations, and he has an element and two major laboratories named for him.

A **synchrotron** is a version of a cyclotron in which the frequency of the alternating voltage and the magnetic field strength are increased as the beam particles are accelerated. Particles are made to travel the same distance in a shorter time with each cycle in fixed-radius orbits. A ring of magnets and accelerating tubes, as shown in Figure 33.9, are the major components of synchrotrons. Accelerating voltages are synchronized (i.e., occur at the same time) with the particles to accelerate them, hence the name. Magnetic field strength is increased to keep the orbital radius constant as energy increases. High-energy particles require strong magnetic fields to steer them, so superconducting magnets are commonly employed. Still limited by achievable magnetic field strengths, synchrotrons need to be very large at very high energies, since the radius of a high-energy particle's orbit is very large. Radiation caused by a magnetic field accelerating a charged particle perpendicular to its velocity is called **synchrotron radiation** in honor of its importance in these machines. Synchrotron radiation has a characteristic spectrum and polarization, and can be recognized in cosmic rays, implying large-scale magnetic fields acting on energetic and charged particles in deep space. Synchrotron radiation produced by accelerators is sometimes used as a source of intense energetic electromagnetic radiation for research purposes.

FIGURE 33.7 An artist's rendition of a Van de Graaff generator.

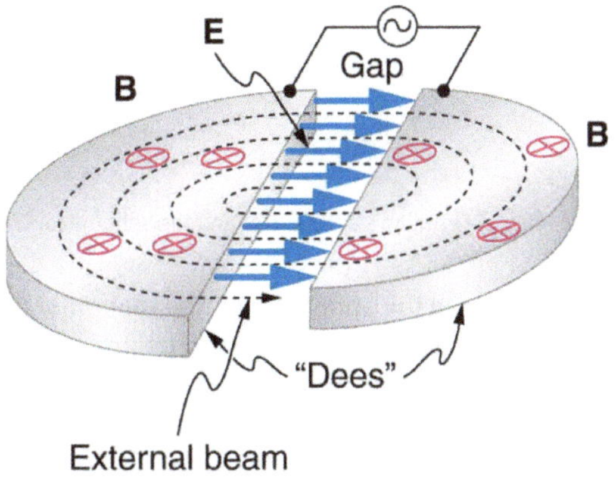

FIGURE 33.8 Cyclotrons use a magnetic field to cause particles to move in circular orbits. As the particles pass between the plates of the Ds, the voltage across the gap is oscillated to accelerate them twice in each orbit.

Modern Behemoths and Colliding Beams

Physicists have built ever-larger machines, first to reduce the wavelength of the probe and obtain greater detail, then to put greater energy into collisions to create new particles. Each major energy increase brought new information, sometimes producing spectacular progress, motivating the next step. One major innovation was driven by the desire to create more massive particles. Since momentum needs to be conserved in a collision, the particles created by a beam hitting a stationary target should recoil. This means that part of the energy input goes into recoil kinetic energy, significantly limiting the fraction of the beam energy that can be converted into new particles. One solution to this problem is to have head-on collisions between particles moving in opposite directions. **Colliding beams** are made to meet head-on at points where massive detectors are located. Since the total incoming momentum is zero, it is possible to create particles with momenta and kinetic energies near zero. Particles with masses equivalent to twice the beam energy can thus be created. Another innovation is to create the antimatter counterpart of the beam particle, which thus has the opposite charge and circulates in the opposite direction in the same beam pipe. For a schematic representation, see Figure 33.10.

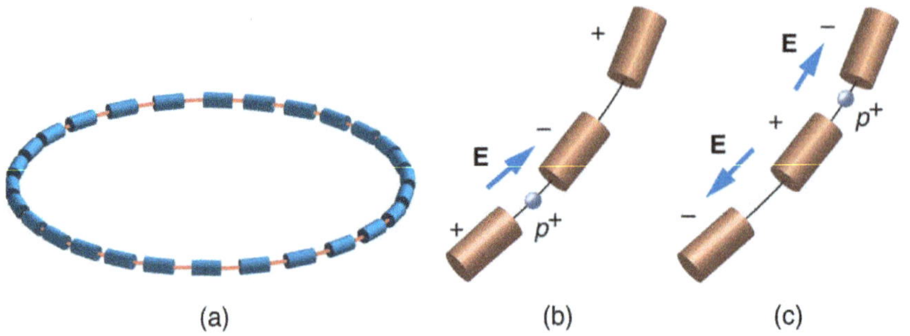

FIGURE 33.9 (a) A synchrotron has a ring of magnets and accelerating tubes. The frequency of the accelerating voltages is increased to cause the beam particles to travel the same distance in shorter time. The magnetic field should also be increased to keep each beam burst traveling in a fixed-radius path. Limits on magnetic field strength require these machines to be very large in order to accelerate particles to very high energies. (b) A positive particle is shown in the gap between accelerating tubes. (c) While the particle passes through the tube, the potentials are reversed so that there is another acceleration at the next gap. The frequency of the reversals needs to be varied as the particle is accelerated to achieve successive accelerations in each gap.

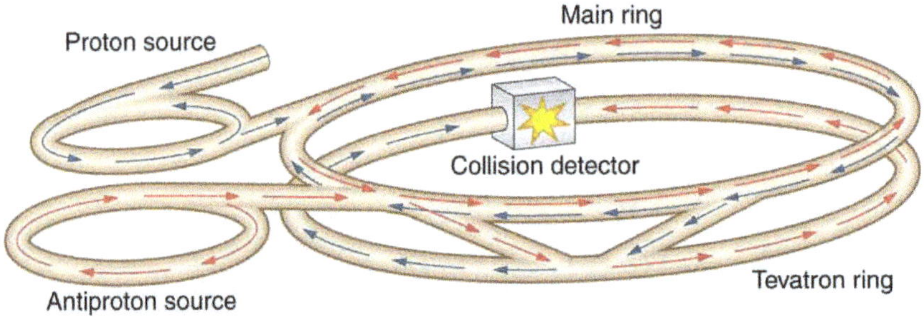

FIGURE 33.10 This schematic shows the two rings of Fermilab's accelerator and the scheme for colliding protons and antiprotons (not to scale).

Detectors capable of finding the new particles in the spray of material that emerges from colliding beams are as impressive as the accelerators. While the Fermilab Tevatron had proton and antiproton beam energies of about 1 TeV, so that it can create particles up to $2\ \text{TeV}/c^2$, the Large Hadron Collider (LHC) at the European Center for Nuclear Research (CERN) has achieved beam energies of 3.5 TeV, so that it has a 7-TeV collision energy; CERN hopes to double the beam energy in 2014. The now-canceled Superconducting Super Collider was being constructed in Texas with a design energy of 20 TeV to give a 40-TeV collision energy. It was to be an oval 30 km in diameter. Its cost as well as the politics of international research funding led to its demise.

In addition to the large synchrotrons that produce colliding beams of protons and antiprotons, there are other large electron-positron accelerators. The oldest of these was a straight-line or **linear accelerator**, called the Stanford Linear Accelerator (SLAC), which accelerated particles up to 50 GeV as seen in Figure 33.11. Positrons created by the accelerator were brought to the same energy and collided with electrons in specially designed detectors. Linear accelerators use accelerating tubes similar to those in synchrotrons, but aligned in a straight line. This helps eliminate synchrotron radiation losses, which are particularly severe for electrons made to follow curved paths. CERN had an electron-positron collider appropriately called the Large Electron-Positron Collider (LEP), which accelerated particles to 100 GeV and created a collision energy of 200 GeV. It was 8.5 km in diameter, while the SLAC machine was 3.2 km long.

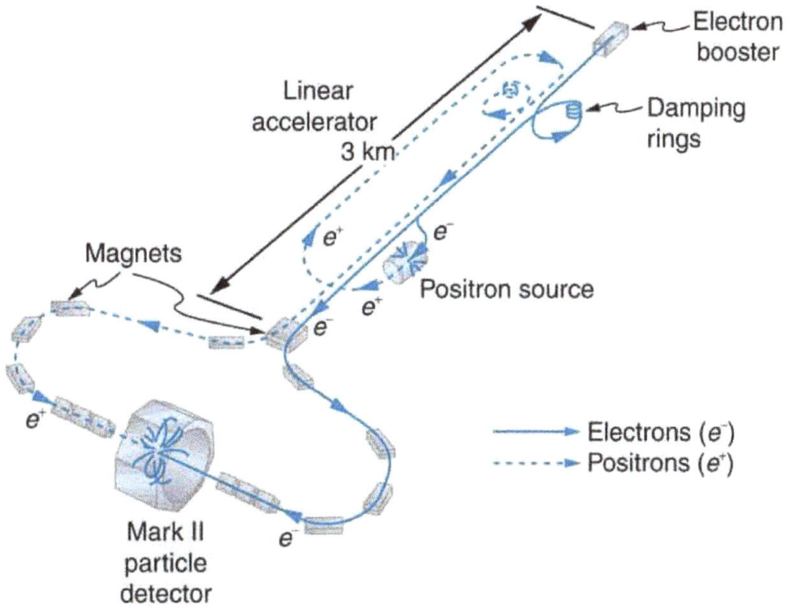

FIGURE 33.11 The Stanford Linear Accelerator was 3.2 km long and had the capability of colliding electron and positron beams. SLAC was also used to probe nucleons by scattering extremely short wavelength electrons from them. This produced the first convincing evidence of a quark structure inside nucleons in an experiment analogous to those performed by Rutherford long ago.

EXAMPLE 33.2

Calculating the Voltage Needed by the Accelerator Between Accelerating Tubes

A linear accelerator designed to produce a beam of 800-MeV protons has 2000 accelerating tubes. What average voltage must be applied between tubes (such as in the gaps in Figure 33.9) to achieve the desired energy?

Strategy

The energy given to the proton in each gap between tubes is $\text{PE}_{\text{elec}} = qV$ where q is the proton's charge and V is the potential difference (voltage) across the gap. Since $q = q_e = 1.6 \times 10^{-19}$ C and $1 \text{ eV} = (1 \text{ V})(1.6 \times 10^{-19} \text{ C})$, the proton gains 1 eV in energy for each volt across the gap that it passes through. The AC voltage applied to the tubes is timed so that it adds to the energy in each gap. The effective voltage is the sum of the gap voltages and equals 800 MV to give each proton an energy of 800 MeV.

Solution

There are 2000 gaps and the sum of the voltages across them is 800 MV; thus,

$$V_{\text{gap}} = \frac{800 \text{ MV}}{2000} = 400 \text{ kV}. \tag{33.6}$$

Discussion

A voltage of this magnitude is not difficult to achieve in a vacuum. Much larger gap voltages would be required for higher energy, such as those at the 50-GeV SLAC facility. Synchrotrons are aided by the circular path of the accelerated particles, which can orbit many times, effectively multiplying the number of accelerations by the number of orbits. This makes it possible to reach energies greater than 1 TeV.

33.4 Particles, Patterns, and Conservation Laws

LEARNING OBJECTIVES

By the end of this section, you will be able to:

- Define matter and antimatter.
- Outline the differences between hadrons and leptons.
- State the differences between mesons and baryons.

In the early 1930s only a small number of subatomic particles were known to exist—the proton, neutron, electron, photon and, indirectly, the neutrino. Nature seemed relatively simple in some ways, but mysterious in others. Why, for example, should the particle that carries positive charge be almost 2000 times as massive as the one carrying negative charge? Why does a neutral particle like the neutron have a magnetic moment? Does this imply an internal structure with a distribution of moving charges? Why is it that the electron seems to have no size other than its wavelength, while the proton and neutron are about 1 fermi in size? So, while the number of known particles was small and they explained a great deal of atomic and nuclear phenomena, there were many unexplained phenomena and hints of further substructures.

Things soon became more complicated, both in theory and in the prediction and discovery of new particles. In 1928, the British physicist P.A.M. Dirac (see Figure 33.12) developed a highly successful relativistic quantum theory that laid the foundations of quantum electrodynamics (QED). His theory, for example, explained electron spin and magnetic moment in a natural way. But Dirac's theory also predicted negative energy states for free electrons. By 1931, Dirac, along with Oppenheimer, realized this was a prediction of positively charged electrons (or positrons). In 1932, American physicist Carl Anderson discovered the positron in cosmic ray studies. The positron, or e^+ , is the same particle as emitted in β^+ decay and was the first antimatter that was discovered. In 1935, Yukawa predicted pions as the carriers of the strong nuclear force, and they were eventually discovered. Muons were discovered in cosmic ray experiments in 1937, and they seemed to be heavy, unstable versions of electrons and positrons. After World War II, accelerators energetic enough to create these particles were built. Not only were predicted and known particles created, but many unexpected particles were observed. Initially called elementary particles, their numbers proliferated to dozens and then hundreds, and the term "particle zoo" became the physicist's lament at the lack of simplicity. But patterns were observed in the particle zoo that led to simplifying ideas such as quarks, as we shall soon see.

FIGURE 33.12 P.A.M. Dirac's theory of relativistic quantum mechanics not only explained a great deal of what was known, it also predicted antimatter. (credit: Cambridge University, Cavendish Laboratory)

Matter and Antimatter

The positron was only the first example of antimatter. Every particle in nature has an antimatter counterpart, although some particles, like the photon, are their own antiparticles. Antimatter has charge opposite to that of matter (for example, the positron is positive while the electron is negative) but is nearly identical otherwise, having the same mass, intrinsic spin, half-life, and so on. When a particle and its antimatter counterpart interact, they annihilate one another, usually totally converting their masses to pure energy in the form of photons as seen in Figure 33.13. Neutral particles, such as neutrons, have neutral antimatter counterparts, which also annihilate when they interact. Certain neutral particles are their own antiparticle and live correspondingly short lives. For example, the neutral pion π^0 is its own antiparticle and has a half-life about 10^{-8} shorter than π^+ and π^-, which are each other's antiparticles. Without exception, nature is symmetric—all particles have antimatter counterparts. For example, antiprotons and antineutrons were first created in accelerator experiments in 1956 and the antiproton is negative. Antihydrogen atoms, consisting of an antiproton and antielectron, were observed in 1995 at CERN, too. It is possible to contain large-scale antimatter particles such as antiprotons by using electromagnetic traps that confine the particles within a magnetic field so that they don't annihilate with other particles. However, particles of the same charge repel each other, so the more particles that are contained in a trap, the more energy is needed to power the magnetic field that contains them. It is not currently possible to store a significant quantity of antiprotons. At any rate, we now see that negative charge is associated with both low-mass (electrons) and high-mass particles (antiprotons) and the apparent asymmetry is not there. But this knowledge does raise another question—why is there such a predominance of matter and so little antimatter? Possible explanations emerge later in this and the next chapter.

Hadrons and Leptons

Particles can also be revealingly grouped according to what forces they feel between them. All particles (even those that are massless) are affected by gravity, since gravity affects the space and time in which particles exist. All charged particles are affected by the electromagnetic force, as are neutral particles that have an internal distribution of charge (such as the neutron with its magnetic moment). Special names are given to particles that feel the strong and weak nuclear forces. **Hadrons** are particles that feel the strong nuclear force, whereas **leptons** are particles that do not. The proton, neutron, and the pions are examples of hadrons. The electron, positron, muons, and neutrinos are examples of leptons, the name meaning low mass. Leptons feel the weak nuclear force. In fact, all particles feel the weak nuclear force. This means that hadrons are distinguished by being able to feel both the strong and weak nuclear forces.

Table 33.2 lists the characteristics of some of the most important subatomic particles, including the directly observed carrier particles for the electromagnetic and weak nuclear forces, all leptons, and some hadrons. Several hints related to an underlying substructure emerge from an examination of these particle characteristics. Note that the carrier particles are called **gauge bosons**. First mentioned in Patterns in Spectra Reveal More Quantization, a **boson** is a particle with zero or an integer value of intrinsic spin (such as $s = 0, 1, 2, ...$), whereas a **fermion** is a particle with a half-integer value of intrinsic spin ($s = 1/2, 3/2, ...$). Fermions obey the Pauli exclusion principle whereas bosons do not. All the known and conjectured carrier particles are bosons.

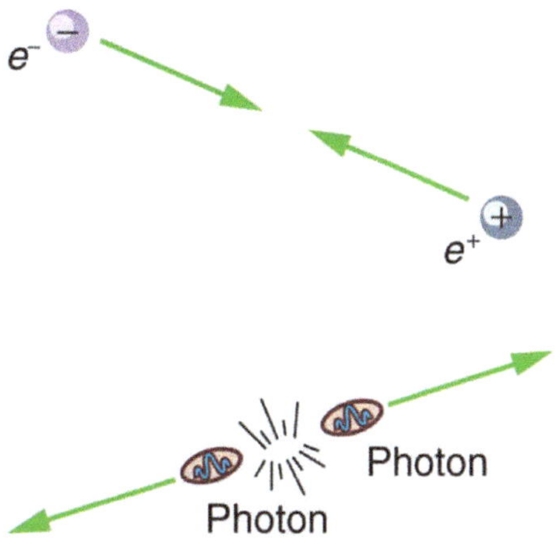

FIGURE 33.13 When a particle encounters its antiparticle, they annihilate, often producing pure energy in the form of photons. In this case, an electron and a positron convert all their mass into two identical energy rays, which move away in opposite directions to keep total momentum zero as it was before. Similar annihilations occur for other combinations of a particle with its antiparticle, sometimes producing more particles while obeying all conservation laws.

Category	Particle name	Symbol	Antiparticle	Rest mass (MeV/c^2)	B	L_e	L_μ	L_τ	S	Lifetime[4] (s)
Gauge	Photon	γ	Self	0	0	0	0	0	0	Stable
Bosons	W	W^+	W^-	80.39×10^3	0	0	0	0	0	1.6×10^{-25}

TABLE 33.2 Selected Particle Characteristics[7]

4 Lifetimes are traditionally given as $t_{1/2}/0.693$ (which is $1/\lambda$, the inverse of the decay constant).
7 The lower of the $\mp$ or $\pm$ symbols are the values for antiparticles.

Category	Particle name	Symbol	Antiparticle	Rest mass (MeV/c^2)	B	L_e	L_μ	L_τ	S	Lifetime[4] (s)
	Z	Z^0	Self	91.19×10^3	0	0	0	0	0	1.32×10^{-25}
Leptons	Electron	e^-	e^+	0.511	0	±1	0	0	0	Stable
	Neutrino (e)	ν_e	$\bar{\nu}_e$	$0(7.0\mathrm{eV})$[5]	0	±1	0	0	0	Stable
	Muon	μ^-	μ^+	105.7	0	0	±1	0	0	2.20×10^{-6}
	Neutrino (μ)	υ_μ	$\bar{\upsilon}_\mu$	$0(< 0.27)$	0	0	±1	0	0	Stable
	Tau	τ^-	τ^+	1777	0	0	0	±1	0	2.91×10^{-13}
	Neutrino (τ)	υ_τ	$\bar{\upsilon}_\tau$	$0(< 31)$	0	0	0	±1	0	Stable
Hadrons (selected)										
Mesons	Pion	π^+	π^-	139.6	0	0	0	0	0	2.60×10^{-8}
		π^0	Self	135.0	0	0	0	0	0	8.4×10^{-17}
	Kaon	K^+	K^-	493.7	0	0	0	0	±1	1.24×10^{-8}
		K^0	$\bar{K}^0$	497.6	0	0	0	0	±1	0.90×10^{-10}
	Eta	η^0	Self	547.9	0	0	0	0	0	2.53×10^{-19}
(many other mesons known)										
Baryons	Proton	p	$\bar{p}$	938.3	± 1	0	0	0	0	Stable[6]
	Neutron	n	$\bar{n}$	939.6	± 1	0	0	0	0	882
	Lambda	Λ^0	$\bar{\Lambda}^0$	1115.7	± 1	0	0	0	∓1	2.63×10^{-10}
	Sigma	Σ^+	$\bar{\Sigma}^-$	1189.4	± 1	0	0	0	∓1	0.80×10^{-10}
		Σ^0	$\bar{\Sigma}^0$	1192.6	± 1	0	0	0	∓1	7.4×10^{-20}

TABLE 33.2 Selected Particle Characteristics[7]

5 Neutrino masses may be zero. Experimental upper limits are given in parentheses.
6 Experimental lower limit is $>5 \times 10^{32}$ for proposed mode of decay.

Category	Particle name	Symbol	Antiparticle	Rest mass (MeV/c^2)	B	L_e	L_μ	L_τ	S	Lifetime[4] (s)
		Σ^-	$\overline{\Sigma}^+$	1197.4	± 1	0	0	0	∓ 1	1.48 × 10 $^{-10}$
	Xi	Ξ^0	$\overline{\Xi}^0$	1314.9	± 1	0	0	0	∓ 2	2.90 × 10 $^{-10}$
		Ξ^-	Ξ^+	1321.7	± 1	0	0	0	∓ 2	1.64 × 10 $^{-10}$
	Omega	Ω^-	Ω^+	1672.5	± 1	0	0	0	∓ 3	0.82 × 10 $^{-10}$
(many other baryons known)										

TABLE 33.2 Selected Particle Characteristics[7]

All known leptons are listed in the table given above. There are only six leptons (and their antiparticles), and they seem to be fundamental in that they have no apparent underlying structure. Leptons have no discernible size other than their wavelength, so that we know they are pointlike down to about 10^{-18} m. The leptons fall into three families, implying three conservation laws for three quantum numbers. One of these was known from β decay, where the existence of the electron's neutrino implied that a new quantum number, called the **electron family number** L_e is conserved. Thus, in β decay, an antielectron's neutrino $\overline{\upsilon}_e$ must be created with $L_e = -1$ when an electron with L_e=+1 is created, so that the total remains 0 as it was before decay.

Once the muon was discovered in cosmic rays, its decay mode was found to be

$$\mu^- \to e^- + \overline{\upsilon}_e + \upsilon_\mu, \tag{33.7}$$

which implied another "family" and associated conservation principle. The particle υ_μ is a muon's neutrino, and it is created to conserve **muon family number** L_μ. So muons are leptons with a family of their own, and **conservation of total** L_μ also seems to be obeyed in many experiments.

More recently, a third lepton family was discovered when τ particles were created and observed to decay in a manner similar to muons. One principal decay mode is

$$\tau^- \to \mu^- + \overline{\upsilon}_\mu + \upsilon_\tau. \tag{33.8}$$

Conservation of total L_τ seems to be another law obeyed in many experiments. In fact, particle experiments have found that lepton family number is not universally conserved, due to neutrino "oscillations," or transformations of neutrinos from one family type to another.

Mesons and Baryons

Now, note that the hadrons in the table given above are divided into two subgroups, called mesons (originally for medium mass) and baryons (the name originally meaning large mass). The division between mesons and baryons is actually based on their observed decay modes and is not strictly associated with their masses. **Mesons** are hadrons that can decay to leptons and leave no hadrons, which implies that mesons are not conserved in number. **Baryons** are hadrons that always decay to another baryon. A new physical quantity called **baryon number** B seems to always be conserved in nature and is listed for the various particles in the table given above. Mesons and leptons have $B = 0$ so that they can decay to other particles with $B = 0$. But baryons have B=+1 if they are matter, and $B = -1$ if they are antimatter. The **conservation of total baryon number** is a more general rule than first noted in nuclear physics, where it was observed that the total number of nucleons was always conserved in nuclear reactions and decays. That rule in nuclear physics is just one consequence of the conservation of the total baryon number.

Forces, Reactions, and Reaction Rates

The forces that act between particles regulate how they interact with other particles. For example, pions feel the strong force and do not penetrate as far in matter as do muons, which do not feel the strong force. (This was the way those who discovered the muon knew it could not be the particle that carries the strong force—its penetration or range was too great for it to be feeling the strong force.) Similarly, reactions that create other particles, like cosmic rays interacting with nuclei in the atmosphere, have greater probability if they are caused by the strong force than if they are caused by the weak force. Such knowledge has been useful to physicists while analyzing the particles produced by various accelerators.

The forces experienced by particles also govern how particles interact with themselves if they are unstable and decay. For example, the stronger the force, the faster they decay and the shorter is their lifetime. An example of a nuclear decay via the strong force is ${}^{8}\text{Be} \rightarrow \alpha + \alpha$ with a lifetime of about 10^{-16} s. The neutron is a good example of decay via the weak force. The process $n \rightarrow p + e^{-} + \overline{v}_e$ has a longer lifetime of 882 s. The weak force causes this decay, as it does all β decay. An important clue that the weak force is responsible for β decay is the creation of leptons, such as e^{-} and $\overline{v}_e$. None would be created if the strong force was responsible, just as no leptons are created in the decay of ${}^{8}\text{Be}$. The systematics of particle lifetimes is a little simpler than nuclear lifetimes when hundreds of particles are examined (not just the ones in the table given above). Particles that decay via the weak force have lifetimes mostly in the range of 10^{-16} to 10^{-12} s, whereas those that decay via the strong force have lifetimes mostly in the range of 10^{-16} to 10^{-23} s. Turning this around, if we measure the lifetime of a particle, we can tell if it decays via the weak or strong force.

Yet another quantum number emerges from decay lifetimes and patterns. Note that the particles Λ, Σ, Ξ, and Ω decay with lifetimes on the order of 10^{-10} s (the exception is Σ^0, whose short lifetime is explained by its particular quark substructure.), implying that their decay is caused by the weak force alone, although they are hadrons and feel the strong force. The decay modes of these particles also show patterns—in particular, certain decays that should be possible within all the known conservation laws do not occur. Whenever something is possible in physics, it will happen. If something does not happen, it is forbidden by a rule. All this seemed strange to those studying these particles when they were first discovered, so they named a new quantum number **strangeness**, given the symbol S in the table given above. The values of strangeness assigned to various particles are based on the decay systematics. It is found that **strangeness is conserved by the strong force**, which governs the production of most of these particles in accelerator experiments. However, **strangeness is *not conserved* by the weak force**. This conclusion is reached from the fact that particles that have long lifetimes decay via the weak force and do not conserve strangeness. All of this also has implications for the carrier particles, since they transmit forces and are thus involved in these decays.

EXAMPLE 33.3

Calculating Quantum Numbers in Two Decays

(a) The most common decay mode of the Ξ^{-} particle is $\Xi^{-} \rightarrow \Lambda^{0} + \pi^{-}$. Using the quantum numbers in the table given above, show that strangeness changes by 1, baryon number and charge are conserved, and lepton family numbers are unaffected.

(b) Is the decay $K^{+} \rightarrow \mu^{+} + v_{\mu}$ allowed, given the quantum numbers in the table given above?

Strategy

In part (a), the conservation laws can be examined by adding the quantum numbers of the decay products and comparing them with the parent particle. In part (b), the same procedure can reveal if a conservation law is broken or not.

Solution for (a)

Before the decay, the Ξ^{-} has strangeness $S = -2$. After the decay, the total strangeness is –1 for the Λ^{0}, plus 0 for the π^{-}. Thus, total strangeness has gone from –2 to –1 or a change of +1. Baryon number for the Ξ^{-} is $B = +1$ before the decay, and after the decay the Λ^{0} has $B = +1$ and the π^{-} has $B = 0$ so that the total baryon number remains +1. Charge is −1 before the decay, and the total charge after is also $0 - 1 = -1$. Lepton numbers for all the particles are zero, and so lepton numbers are conserved.

Discussion for (a)

The Ξ^- decay is caused by the weak interaction, since strangeness changes, and it is consistent with the relatively long 1.64×10^{-10}-s lifetime of the Ξ^-.

Solution for (b)

The decay $K^+ \rightarrow \mu^+ + \nu_\mu$ is allowed if charge, baryon number, mass-energy, and lepton numbers are conserved. Strangeness can change due to the weak interaction. Charge is conserved as $s \rightarrow d$. Baryon number is conserved, since all particles have $B = 0$. Mass-energy is conserved in the sense that the K^+ has a greater mass than the products, so that the decay can be spontaneous. Lepton family numbers are conserved at 0 for the electron and tau family for all particles. The muon family number is $L_\mu = 0$ before and $L_\mu = -1 + 1 = 0$ after. Strangeness changes from +1 before to 0 + 0 after, for an allowed change of 1. The decay is allowed by all these measures.

Discussion for (b)

This decay is not only allowed by our reckoning, it is, in fact, the primary decay mode of the K^+ meson and is caused by the weak force, consistent with the long 1.24×10^{-8}-s lifetime.

There are hundreds of particles, all hadrons, not listed in Table 33.2, most of which have shorter lifetimes. The systematics of those particle lifetimes, their production probabilities, and decay products are completely consistent with the conservation laws noted for lepton families, baryon number, and strangeness, but they also imply other quantum numbers and conservation laws. There are a finite, and in fact relatively small, number of these conserved quantities, however, implying a finite set of substructures. Additionally, some of these short-lived particles resemble the excited states of other particles, implying an internal structure. All of this jigsaw puzzle can be tied together and explained relatively simply by the existence of fundamental substructures. Leptons seem to be fundamental structures. Hadrons seem to have a substructure called quarks. Quarks: Is That All There Is? explores the basics of the underlying quark building blocks.

FIGURE 33.14 Murray Gell-Mann (b. 1929) proposed quarks as a substructure of hadrons in 1963 and was already known for his work on the concept of strangeness. Although quarks have never been directly observed, several predictions of the quark model were quickly confirmed, and their properties explain all known hadron characteristics. Gell-Mann was awarded the Nobel Prize in 1969. (credit: Luboš Motl)

33.5 Quarks: Is That All There Is?

LEARNING OBJECTIVES

By the end of this section, you will be able to:

- Define fundamental particle.
- Describe quark and antiquark.
- List the flavors of quark.
- Outline the quark composition of hadrons.
- Determine quantum numbers from quark composition.

Quarks have been mentioned at various points in this text as fundamental building blocks and members of the exclusive club of truly elementary particles. Note that an elementary or **fundamental particle** has no substructure (it is not made of other particles) and has no finite size other than its wavelength. This does not mean that fundamental particles are stable—some decay, while others do not. Keep in mind that *all* leptons seem to be fundamental, whereas*no* hadrons are fundamental. There is strong evidence that **quarks** are the fundamental building blocks of hadrons as seen in Figure 33.15. Quarks are the second group of fundamental particles (leptons are the first). The third and perhaps final group of fundamental particles is the carrier particles for the four basic forces. Leptons, quarks, and carrier particles may be all there is. In this module we will discuss the quark substructure of hadrons and its relationship to forces as well as indicate some remaining questions and problems.

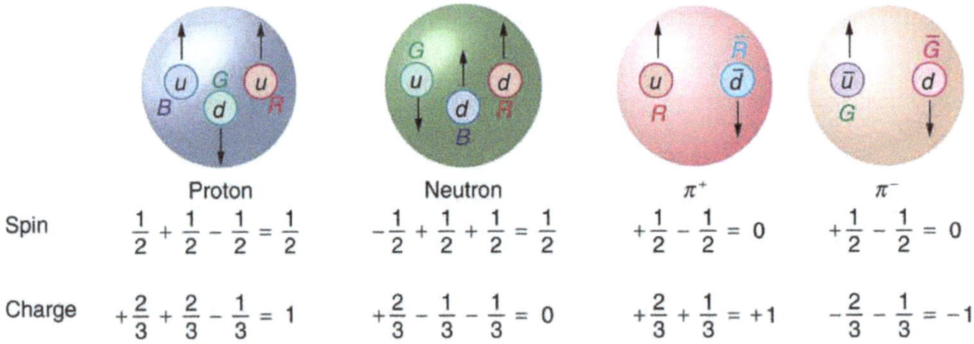

FIGURE 33.15 All baryons, such as the proton and neutron shown here, are composed of three quarks. All mesons, such as the pions shown here, are composed of a quark-antiquark pair. Arrows represent the spins of the quarks, which, as we shall see, are also colored. The colors are such that they need to add to white for any possible combination of quarks.

Conception of Quarks

Quarks were first proposed independently by American physicists Murray Gell-Mann and George Zweig in 1963. Their quaint name was taken by Gell-Mann from a James Joyce novel—Gell-Mann was also largely responsible for the concept and name of strangeness. (Whimsical names are common in particle physics, reflecting the personalities of modern physicists.) Originally, three quark types—or **flavors**—were proposed to account for the then-known mesons and baryons. These quark flavors are named **up** (*u*), **down** (*d*), and **strange** (*s*). All quarks have half-integral spin and are thus fermions. All mesons have integral spin while all baryons have half-integral spin. Therefore, mesons should be made up of an even number of quarks while baryons need to be made up of an odd number of quarks. Figure 33.15 shows the quark substructure of the proton, neutron, and two pions. The most radical proposal by Gell-Mann and Zweig is the fractional charges of quarks, which are $\pm\left(\frac{2}{3}\right)q_e$ and $\left(\frac{1}{3}\right)q_e$, whereas all directly observed particles have charges that are integral multiples of q_e. Note that the fractional value of the quark does not violate the fact that the *e* is the smallest unit of charge that is observed, because a free quark cannot exist. Table 33.3 lists characteristics of the six quark flavors that are now thought to exist. Discoveries made since 1963 have required extra quark flavors, which are divided into three families quite analogous to leptons.

How Does it Work?

To understand how these quark substructures work, let us specifically examine the proton, neutron, and the two pions pictured in Figure 33.15 before moving on to more general considerations. First, the proton *p* is composed of the three quarks *uud*, so that its total charge is $+\left(\frac{2}{3}\right)q_e+\left(\frac{2}{3}\right)q_e-\left(\frac{1}{3}\right)q_e=q_e$, as expected. With the spins aligned as in the figure, the proton's intrinsic spin is $+\left(\frac{1}{2}\right)+\left(\frac{1}{2}\right)-\left(\frac{1}{2}\right)=\left(\frac{1}{2}\right)$, also as expected. Note that the spins of the up quarks are aligned, so that they would be in the same state except that they have different colors (another quantum number to be elaborated upon a little later). Quarks obey the Pauli exclusion principle. Similar comments apply to the neutron *n*, which is composed of the three quarks *udd*. Note also that the neutron is made of charges that add to zero but move internally, producing its well-known magnetic moment. When the neutron β^- decays, it does so by changing the flavor of one of its quarks. Writing neutron β^- decay in terms of quarks,

$$n \rightarrow p + \beta^- + \bar{v}_e \text{ becomes } udd \rightarrow uud + \beta^- + \bar{v}_e. \tag{33.9}$$

We see that this is equivalent to a down quark changing flavor to become an up quark:

$$d \rightarrow u + \beta^- + \bar{v}_e \tag{33.10}$$

Name	Symbol	Antiparticle	Spin	Charge	B[8]	S	c	b	t	Mass (GeV/c^2)[9]
Up	u	$\bar{u}$	1/2	$\pm\frac{2}{3}q_e$	$\pm\frac{1}{3}$	0	0	0	0	0.005
Down	d	$\bar{d}$	1/2	$\mp\frac{1}{3}q_e$	$\pm\frac{1}{3}$	0	0	0	0	0.008
Strange	s	$\bar{s}$	1/2	$\mp\frac{1}{3}q_e$	$\pm\frac{1}{3}$	∓1	0	0	0	0.50
Charmed	c	$\bar{c}$	1/2	$\pm\frac{2}{3}q_e$	$\pm\frac{1}{3}$	0	±1	0	0	1.6
Bottom	b	$\bar{b}$	1/2	$\mp\frac{1}{3}q_e$	$\pm\frac{1}{3}$	0	0	∓1	0	5
Top	t	$\bar{t}$	1/2	$\pm\frac{2}{3}q_e$	$\pm\frac{1}{3}$	0	0	0	±1	173

TABLE 33.3 Quarks and Antiquarks[10]

Particle	Quark Composition
Mesons	
π^+	$u\bar{d}$
π^-	$\bar{u}d$
π^0	$u\bar{u}$, $d\bar{d}$ mixture[11]
η^0	$u\bar{u}$, $d\bar{d}$ mixture[12]
K^0	$d\bar{s}$

TABLE 33.4 Quark Composition of Selected Hadrons[15]

8 ***B*** is baryon number, *S* is strangeness, ***c*** is charm, ***b*** is bottomness, ***t*** is topness.
9 Values are approximate, are not directly observable, and vary with model.
10 The lower of the $\pm$ symbols are the values for antiquarks.
11 These two mesons are different mixtures, but each is its own antiparticle, as indicated by its quark composition.
12 These two mesons are different mixtures, but each is its own antiparticle, as indicated by its quark composition.
15 These two mesons are different mixtures, but each is its own antiparticle, as indicated by its quark composition.

Particle	Quark Composition
$\overline{K}^0$	$\overline{d}s$
K^+	$u\overline{s}$
K^-	$\overline{u}s$
J/ψ	$c\overline{c}$
Υ	$b\overline{b}$
Baryons[13, 14]	
p	uud
n	udd
Δ^0	udd
Δ^+	uud
Δ^-	ddd
Δ^{++}	uuu
Λ^0	uds
Σ^0	uds
Σ^+	uus
Σ^-	dds
Ξ^0	uss
Ξ^-	dss
Ω^-	sss

TABLE 33.4 Quark Composition of Selected Hadrons[15]

This is an example of the general fact that **the weak nuclear force can change the flavor of a quark**. By general, we mean that any quark can be converted to any other (change flavor) by the weak nuclear force. Not only can we get $d \to u$, we can also get $u \to d$. Furthermore, the strange quark can be changed by the weak force, too, making $s \to u$ and $s \to d$ possible. This explains the violation of the conservation of strangeness by the weak force noted in the preceding section. Another general fact is that **the strong nuclear force cannot change the flavor of a quark.**

Again, from Figure 33.15, we see that the π^+ meson (one of the three pions) is composed of an up quark plus an antidown quark, or $u\overline{d}$. Its total charge is thus $+\left(\frac{2}{3}\right)q_e + \left(\frac{1}{3}\right)q_e = q_e$, as expected. Its baryon number is 0, since it

13 Antibaryons have the antiquarks of their counterparts. The antiproton $\overline{p}$ is $\overline{u}\overline{u}\overline{d}$, for example.
14 Baryons composed of the same quarks are different states of the same particle. For example, the Δ^+ is an excited state of the proton.

has a quark and an antiquark with baryon numbers $+\left(\frac{1}{3}\right)-\left(\frac{1}{3}\right)=0$. The π^+ half-life is relatively long since, although it is composed of matter and antimatter, the quarks are different flavors and the weak force should cause the decay by changing the flavor of one into that of the other. The spins of the u and $\bar{d}$ quarks are antiparallel, enabling the pion to have spin zero, as observed experimentally. Finally, the π^- meson shown in Figure 33.15 is the antiparticle of the π^+ meson, and it is composed of the corresponding quark antiparticles. That is, the π^+ meson is $u\bar{d}$, while the π^- meson is $\bar{u}d$. These two pions annihilate each other quickly, because their constituent quarks are each other's antiparticles.

Two general rules for combining quarks to form hadrons are:

1. Baryons are composed of three quarks, and antibaryons are composed of three antiquarks.
2. Mesons are combinations of a quark and an antiquark.

One of the clever things about this scheme is that only integral charges result, even though the quarks have fractional charge.

All Combinations are Possible

All quark combinations are possible. Table 33.4 lists some of these combinations. When Gell-Mann and Zweig proposed the original three quark flavors, particles corresponding to all combinations of those three had not been observed. The pattern was there, but it was incomplete—much as had been the case in the periodic table of the elements and the chart of nuclides. The Ω^- particle, in particular, had not been discovered but was predicted by quark theory. Its combination of three strange quarks, sss, gives it a strangeness of -3 (see Table 33.2) and other predictable characteristics, such as spin, charge, approximate mass, and lifetime. If the quark picture is complete, the Ω^- should exist. It was first observed in 1964 at Brookhaven National Laboratory and had the predicted characteristics as seen in Figure 33.16. The discovery of the Ω^- was convincing indirect evidence for the existence of the three original quark flavors and boosted theoretical and experimental efforts to further explore particle physics in terms of quarks.

PATTERNS AND PUZZLES: ATOMS, NUCLEI, AND QUARKS

Patterns in the properties of atoms allowed the periodic table to be developed. From it, previously unknown elements were predicted and observed. Similarly, patterns were observed in the properties of nuclei, leading to the chart of nuclides and successful predictions of previously unknown nuclides. Now with particle physics, patterns imply a quark substructure that, if taken literally, predicts previously unknown particles. These have now been observed in another triumph of underlying unity.

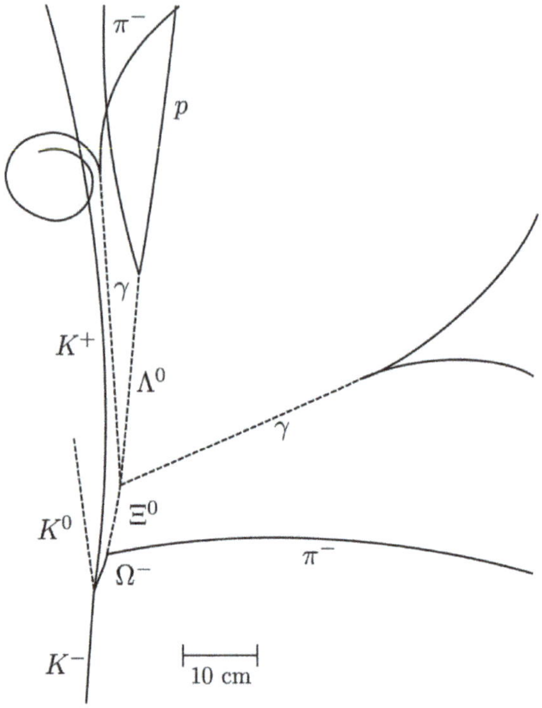

FIGURE 33.16 The image relates to the discovery of the Ω^-. It is a secondary reaction in which an accelerator-produced K^- collides with a proton via the strong force and conserves strangeness to produce the Ω^- with characteristics predicted by the quark model. As with other predictions of previously unobserved particles, this gave a tremendous boost to quark theory. (credit: Brookhaven National Laboratory)

EXAMPLE 33.4

Quantum Numbers From Quark Composition

Verify the quantum numbers given for the Ξ^0 particle in Table 33.2 by adding the quantum numbers for its quark composition as given in Table 33.4.

Strategy

The composition of the Ξ^0 is given as uss in Table 33.4. The quantum numbers for the constituent quarks are given in Table 33.3. We will not consider spin, because that is not given for the Ξ^0. But we can check on charge and the other quantum numbers given for the quarks.

Solution

The total charge of *uss* is $+\left(\frac{2}{3}\right)q_e - \left(\frac{1}{3}\right)q_e - \left(\frac{1}{3}\right)q_e = 0$, which is correct for the Ξ^0. The baryon number is $+\left(\frac{1}{3}\right)+\left(\frac{1}{3}\right)+\left(\frac{1}{3}\right)= 1$, also correct since the Ξ^0 is a matter baryon and has $B = 1$, as listed in Table 33.2. Its strangeness is $S = 0 - 1 - 1 = -2$, also as expected from Table 33.2. Its charm, bottomness, and topness are 0, as are its lepton family numbers (it is not a lepton).

Discussion

This procedure is similar to what the inventors of the quark hypothesis did when checking to see if their solution to the puzzle of particle patterns was correct. They also checked to see if all combinations were known, thereby predicting the previously unobserved Ω^- as the completion of a pattern.

Now, Let Us Talk About Direct Evidence

At first, physicists expected that, with sufficient energy, we should be able to free quarks and observe them directly. This has not proved possible. There is still no direct observation of a fractional charge or any isolated quark. When large energies are put into collisions, other particles are created—but no quarks emerge. There is nearly direct evidence for quarks that is quite compelling. By 1967, experiments at SLAC scattering 20-GeV electrons from protons had produced results like Rutherford had obtained for the nucleus nearly 60 years earlier. The SLAC scattering experiments showed unambiguously that there were three pointlike (meaning they had sizes considerably smaller than the probe's wavelength) charges inside the proton as seen in Figure 33.17. This evidence made all but the most skeptical admit that there was validity to the quark substructure of hadrons.

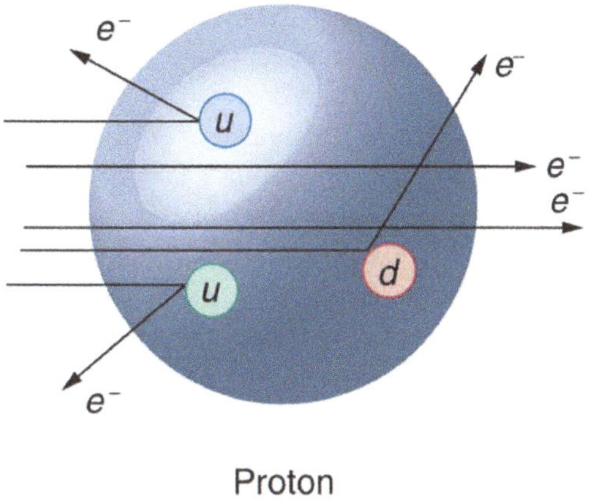

FIGURE 33.17 Scattering of high-energy electrons from protons at facilities like SLAC produces evidence of three point-like charges consistent with proposed quark properties. This experiment is analogous to Rutherford's discovery of the small size of the nucleus by scattering α particles. High-energy electrons are used so that the probe wavelength is small enough to see details smaller than the proton.

More recent and higher-energy experiments have produced jets of particles in collisions, highly suggestive of three quarks in a nucleon. Since the quarks are very tightly bound, energy put into separating them pulls them only so far apart before it starts being converted into other particles. More energy produces more particles, not a separation of quarks. Conservation of momentum requires that the particles come out in jets along the three paths in which the quarks were being pulled. Note that there are only three jets, and that other characteristics of the particles are consistent with the three-quark substructure.

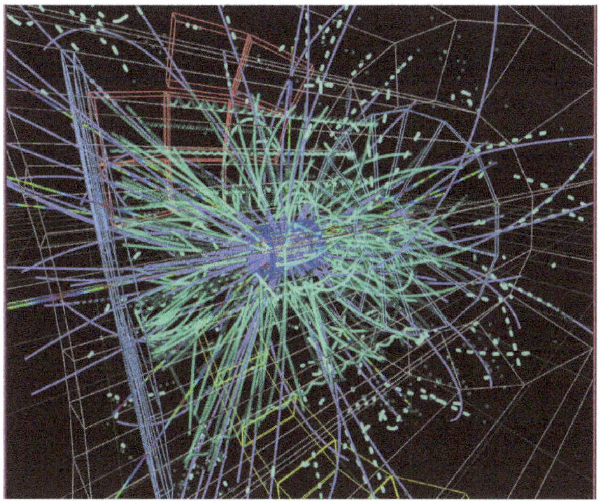

FIGURE 33.18 Simulation of a proton-proton collision at 14-TeV center-of-mass energy in the ALICE detector at CERN LHC. The lines follow particle trajectories and the cyan dots represent the energy depositions in the sensitive detector elements. (credit: Matevž Tadel)

Quarks Have Their Ups and Downs

The quark model actually lost some of its early popularity because the original model with three quarks had to be modified. The up and down quarks seemed to compose normal matter as seen in Table 33.4, while the single strange quark explained strangeness. Why didn't it have a counterpart? A fourth quark flavor called **charm** (*c*) was proposed as the counterpart of the strange quark to make things symmetric—there would be two normal quarks (*u* and *d*) and two exotic quarks (*s* and *c*). Furthermore, at that time only four leptons were known, two normal and two exotic. It was attractive that there would be four quarks and four leptons. The problem was that no known particles contained a charmed quark. Suddenly, in November of 1974, two groups (one headed by C. C. Ting at Brookhaven National Laboratory and the other by Burton Richter at SLAC) independently and nearly simultaneously discovered a new meson with characteristics that made it clear that its substructure is $c\bar{c}$. It was called *J* by one group and psi (ψ) by the other and now is known as the J/ψ meson. Since then, numerous particles have been discovered containing the charmed quark, consistent in every way with the quark model. The discovery of the J/ψ meson had such a rejuvenating effect on quark theory that it is now called the November Revolution. Ting and Richter shared the 1976 Nobel Prize.

History quickly repeated itself. In 1975, the tau (τ) was discovered, and a third family of leptons emerged as seen in Table 33.2). Theorists quickly proposed two more quark flavors called **top** (*t*) or truth and **bottom** (*b*) or beauty to keep the number of quarks the same as the number of leptons. And in 1976, the upsilon (Υ) meson was discovered and shown to be composed of a bottom and an antibottom quark or $b\bar{b}$, quite analogous to the J/ψ being $c\bar{c}$ as seen in Table 33.4. Being a single flavor, these mesons are sometimes called bare charm and bare bottom and reveal the characteristics of their quarks most clearly. Other mesons containing bottom quarks have since been observed. In 1995, two groups at Fermilab confirmed the top quark's existence, completing the picture of six quarks listed in Table 33.3. Each successive quark discovery—first c, then b, and finally t —has required higher energy because each has higher mass. Quark masses in Table 33.3 are only approximately known, because they are not directly observed. They must be inferred from the masses of the particles they combine to form.

What's Color got to do with it?—A Whiter Shade of Pale

As mentioned and shown in Figure 33.15, quarks carry another quantum number, which we call **color**. Of course, it is not the color we sense with visible light, but its properties are analogous to those of three primary and three secondary colors. Specifically, a quark can have one of three color values we call **red** (R), **green** (G), and **blue** (B) in analogy to those primary visible colors. Antiquarks have three values we call **antired or cyan** $(\bar{R})$, **antigreen or magenta** $(\bar{G})$, and **antiblue or yellow** $(\bar{B})$ in analogy to those secondary visible colors. The reason for these names is that when certain visual colors are combined, the eye sees white. The analogy of the colors combining to white is used to explain why baryons are made of three quarks, why mesons are a quark and an antiquark, and why we cannot isolate a single quark. The force between the quarks is such that their combined colors produce white. This is illustrated in Figure 33.19. A baryon must have one of each primary color or RGB, which produces white. A meson must have a primary color and its anticolor, also producing white.

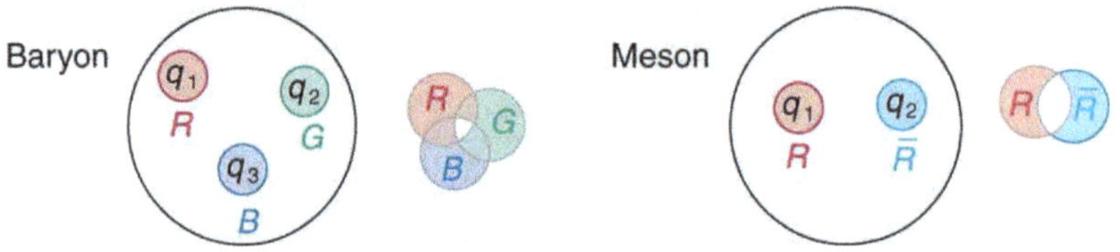

FIGURE 33.19 The three quarks composing a baryon must be RGB, which add to white. The quark and antiquark composing a meson must be a color and anticolor, here $R\bar{R}$ also adding to white. The force between systems that have color is so great that they can neither be separated nor exist as colored.

Why must hadrons be white? The color scheme is intentionally devised to explain why baryons have three quarks and mesons have a quark and an antiquark. Quark color is thought to be similar to charge, but with more values. An ion, by analogy, exerts much stronger forces than a neutral molecule. When the color of a combination of quarks is white, it is like a neutral atom. The forces a white particle exerts are like the polarization forces in molecules, but in hadrons these leftovers are the strong nuclear force. When a combination of quarks has color other than white, it exerts *extremely* large forces—even larger than the strong force—and perhaps cannot be stable or permanently separated. This is part of the **theory of quark confinement**, which explains how quarks can exist and yet never be isolated or directly observed. Finally, an extra quantum number with three values (like those we assign to color) is necessary for quarks to obey the Pauli exclusion principle. Particles such as the Ω^-, which is composed of three strange quarks, sss, and the Δ^{++}, which is three up quarks, *uuu*, can exist because the quarks have different colors and do not have the same quantum numbers. Color is consistent with all observations and is now widely accepted. Quark theory including color is called **quantum chromodynamics** (QCD), also named by Gell-Mann.

The Three Families

Fundamental particles are thought to be one of three types—leptons, quarks, or carrier particles. Each of those three types is further divided into three analogous families as illustrated in Figure 33.20. We have examined leptons and quarks in some detail. Each has six members (and their six antiparticles) divided into three analogous families. The first family is normal matter, of which most things are composed. The second is exotic, and the third more exotic and more massive than the second. The only stable particles are in the first family, which also has unstable members.

Always searching for symmetry and similarity, physicists have also divided the carrier particles into three families, omitting the graviton. Gravity is special among the four forces in that it affects the space and time in which the other forces exist and is proving most difficult to include in a Theory of Everything or TOE (to stub the pretension of such a theory). Gravity is thus often set apart. It is not certain that there is meaning in the groupings shown in Figure 33.20, but the analogies are tempting. In the past, we have been able to make significant advances by looking for analogies and patterns, and this is an example of one under current scrutiny. There are connections between the families of leptons, in that the τ decays into the μ and the μ into the e. Similarly for quarks, the higher families eventually decay into the lowest, leaving only u and d quarks. We have long sought connections between the forces in nature. Since these are carried by particles, we will explore connections between gluons, $W^{\pm}$ and Z^0, and photons as part of the search for unification of forces discussed in GUTs: The Unification of Forces..

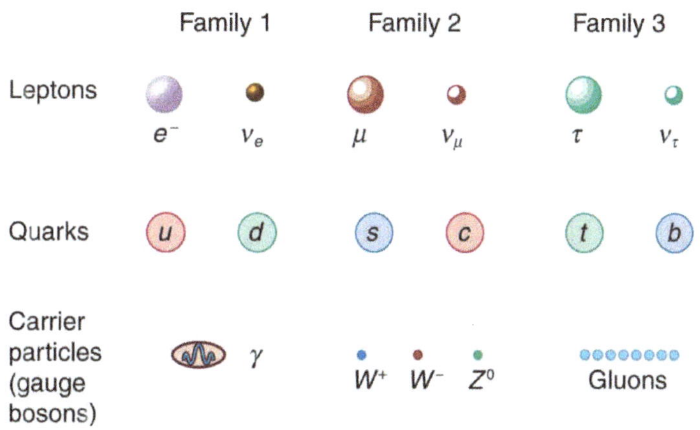

FIGURE 33.20 The three types of particles are leptons, quarks, and carrier particles. Each of those types is divided into three analogous families, with the graviton left out.

33.6 GUTs: The Unification of Forces

LEARNING OBJECTIVES

By the end of this section, you will be able to:

- State the grand unified theory.
- Explain the electroweak theory.
- Define gluons.
- Describe the principle of quantum chromodynamics.
- Define the standard model.

Present quests to show that the four basic forces are different manifestations of a single unified force follow a long tradition. In the 19th century, the distinct electric and magnetic forces were shown to be intimately connected and are now collectively called the electromagnetic force. More recently, the weak nuclear force has been shown to be connected to the electromagnetic force in a manner suggesting that a theory may be constructed in which all four forces are unified. Certainly, there are similarities in how forces are transmitted by the exchange of carrier particles, and the carrier particles themselves (the gauge bosons in Table 33.2) are also similar in important ways. The analogy to the unification of electric and magnetic forces is quite good—the four forces are distinct under normal circumstances, but there are hints of connections even on the atomic scale, and there may be conditions under which the forces are intimately related and even indistinguishable. The search for a correct theory linking the forces, called the **Grand Unified Theory (GUT)**, is explored in this section in the realm of particle physics. Frontiers of Physics expands the story in making a connection with cosmology, on the opposite end of the distance scale.

Figure 33.21 is a Feynman diagram showing how the weak nuclear force is transmitted by the carrier particle Z^0, similar to the diagrams in Figure 33.5 and Figure 33.6 for the electromagnetic and strong nuclear forces. In the 1960s, a gauge theory, called **electroweak theory**, was developed by Steven Weinberg, Sheldon Glashow, and Abdus Salam and proposed that the electromagnetic and weak forces are identical at sufficiently high energies. One of its predictions, in addition to describing both electromagnetic and weak force phenomena, was the existence of the W^+, W^-, and Z^0 carrier particles. Not only were three particles having spin 1 predicted, the mass of the W^+ and W^- was predicted to be $81\ \text{GeV}/c^2$, and that of the Z^0 was predicted to be $90\ \text{GeV}/c^2$. (Their masses had to be about 1000 times that of the pion, or about $100\ \text{GeV}/c^2$, since the range of the weak force is about 1000 times less than the strong force carried by virtual pions.) In 1983, these carrier particles were observed at CERN with the predicted characteristics, including masses having the predicted values as seen in Table 33.2. This was another triumph of particle theory and experimental effort, resulting in the 1984 Nobel Prize to the experiment's group leaders Carlo Rubbia and Simon van der Meer. Theorists Weinberg, Glashow, and Salam had already been honored with the 1979 Nobel Prize for other aspects of electroweak theory.

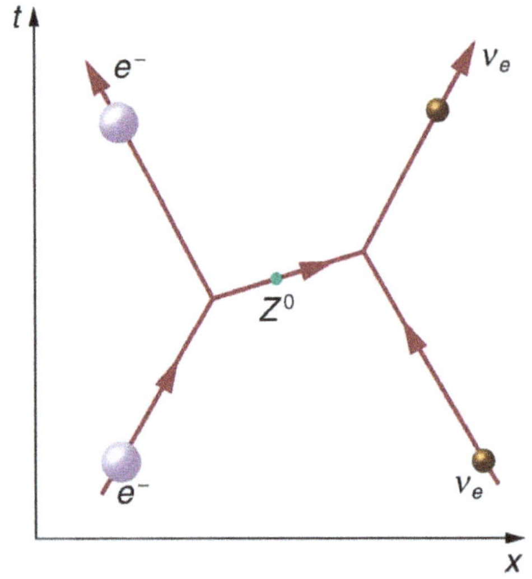

FIGURE 33.21 The exchange of a virtual Z^0 carries the weak nuclear force between an electron and a neutrino in this Feynman diagram. The Z^0 is one of the carrier particles for the weak nuclear force that has now been created in the laboratory with characteristics predicted by electroweak theory.

Although the weak nuclear force is very short ranged ($< 10^{-18}$ m, as indicated in Table 33.1), its effects on atomic levels can be measured given the extreme precision of modern techniques. Since electrons spend some time in the nucleus, their energies are affected, and spectra can even indicate new aspects of the weak force, such as the possibility of other carrier particles. So systems many orders of magnitude larger than the range of the weak force supply evidence of electroweak unification in addition to evidence found at the particle scale.

Gluons (g) are the proposed carrier particles for the strong nuclear force, although they are not directly observed. Like quarks, gluons may be confined to systems having a total color of white. Less is known about gluons than the fact that they are the carriers of the weak and certainly of the electromagnetic force. QCD theory calls for eight gluons, all massless and all spin 1. Six of the gluons carry a color and an anticolor, while two do not carry color, as illustrated in Figure 33.22(a). There is indirect evidence of the existence of gluons in nucleons. When high-energy electrons are scattered from nucleons and evidence of quarks is seen, the momenta of the quarks are smaller than they would be if there were no gluons. That means that the gluons carrying force between quarks also carry some momentum, inferred by the already indirect quark momentum measurements. At any rate, the gluons carry color charge and can change the colors of quarks when exchanged, as seen in Figure 33.22(b). In the figure, a red down quark interacts with a green strange quark by sending it a gluon. That gluon carries red away from the down quark and leaves it green, because it is an $R\overline{G}$ (red-antigreen) gluon. (Taking antigreen away leaves you green.) Its antigreenness kills the green in the strange quark, and its redness turns the quark red.

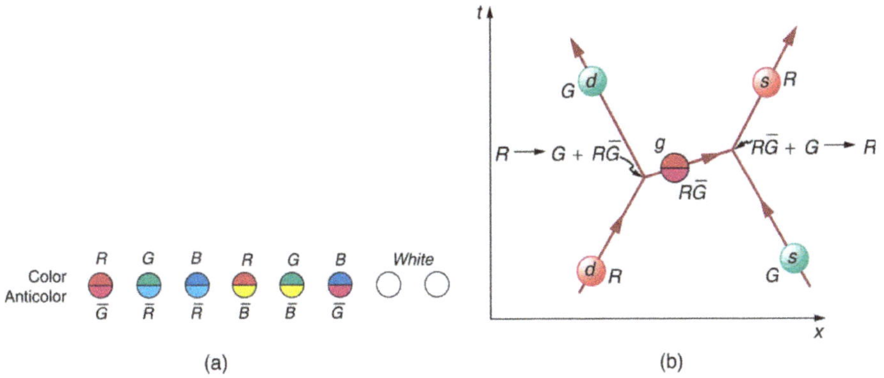

FIGURE 33.22 In figure (a), the eight types of gluons that carry the strong nuclear force are divided into a group of six that carry color and a group of two that do not. Figure (b) shows that the exchange of gluons between quarks carries the strong force and may change the color of a quark.

The strong force is complicated, since observable particles that feel the strong force (hadrons) contain multiple quarks. Figure 33.23 shows the quark and gluon details of pion exchange between a proton and a neutron as illustrated earlier in Figure 33.3 and Figure 33.6. The quarks within the proton and neutron move along together exchanging gluons, until the proton and neutron get close together. As the u quark leaves the proton, a gluon creates a pair of virtual particles, a d quark and a $\bar{d}$ antiquark. The d quark stays behind and the proton turns into a neutron, while the u and $\bar{d}$ move together as a π^+ (Table 33.4 confirms the $u\bar{d}$ composition for the π^+.) The $\bar{d}$ annihilates a d quark in the neutron, the u joins the neutron, and the neutron becomes a proton. A pion is exchanged and a force is transmitted.

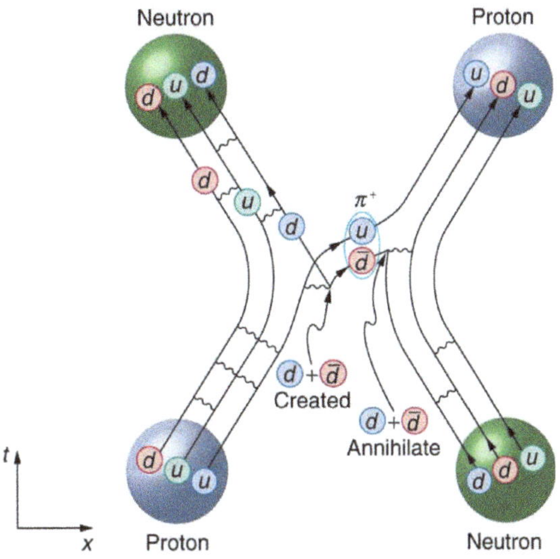

FIGURE 33.23 This Feynman diagram is the same interaction as shown in Figure 33.6, but it shows the quark and gluon details of the strong force interaction.

It is beyond the scope of this text to go into more detail on the types of quark and gluon interactions that underlie the observable particles, but the theory (**quantum chromodynamics** or QCD) is very self-consistent. So successful have QCD and the electroweak theory been that, taken together, they are called the **Standard Model**. Advances in knowledge are expected to modify, but not overthrow, the Standard Model of particle physics and forces.

MAKING CONNECTIONS: UNIFICATION OF FORCES

Grand Unified Theory (GUT) is successful in describing the four forces as distinct under normal circumstances, but connected in fundamental ways. Experiments have verified that the weak and electromagnetic force become identical at very small distances and provide the GUT description of the carrier particles for the forces. GUT predicts that the other forces become identical under conditions so extreme that they cannot be tested in the laboratory, although there may be lingering evidence of them in the evolution of the universe. GUT is also successful in describing a system of carrier particles for all four forces, but there is much to be done, particularly in the realm of gravity.

How can forces be unified? They are definitely distinct under most circumstances, for example, being carried by different particles and having greatly different strengths. But experiments show that at extremely small distances, the strengths of the forces begin to become more similar. In fact, electroweak theory's prediction of the W^+, W^-, and Z^0 carrier particles was based on the strengths of the two forces being identical at extremely small distances as seen in Figure 33.24. As discussed in case of the creation of virtual particles for extremely short times, the small distances or short ranges correspond to the large masses of the carrier particles and the correspondingly large energies needed to create them. Thus, the energy scale on the horizontal axis of Figure 33.24 corresponds to smaller and smaller distances, with 100 GeV corresponding to approximately, $10^{-18}\,\mathrm{m}$ for example. At that distance, the strengths of the EM and weak forces are the same. To test physics at that distance, energies of about 100 GeV must be put into the system, and that is sufficient to create and release the W^+, W^-, and Z^0 carrier particles. At those and higher energies, the masses of the carrier particles becomes less and less relevant, and the Z^0 in particular resembles the massless, chargeless, spin 1 photon. In fact, there is enough energy when things are pushed to even smaller distances to transform the, and Z^0 into massless carrier particles more similar to photons and gluons. These have not been observed experimentally, but there is a prediction of an associated particle called the **Higgs boson**. The mass of this particle is not predicted with nearly the certainty with which the mass of the W^+, W^-, and Z^0 particles were predicted, but it was hoped that the Higgs boson could be observed at the now-canceled Superconducting Super Collider (SSC). Ongoing experiments at the Large Hadron Collider at CERN have presented some evidence for a Higgs boson with a mass of 125 GeV, and there is a possibility of a direct discovery during 2012. The existence of this more massive particle would give validity to the theory that the carrier particles are identical under certain circumstances.

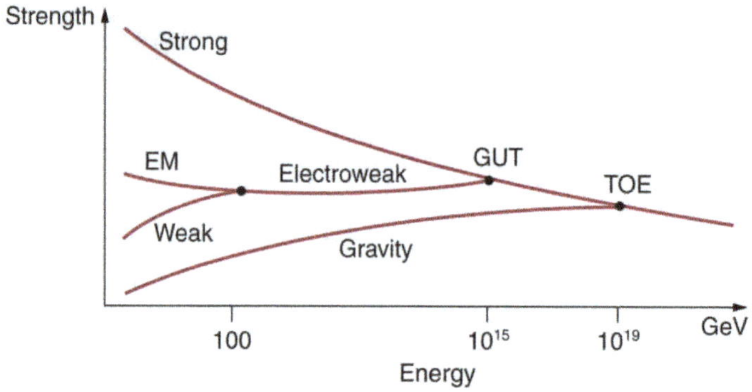

FIGURE 33.24 The relative strengths of the four basic forces vary with distance and, hence, energy is needed to probe small distances. At ordinary energies (a few eV or less), the forces differ greatly as indicated in Table 33.1. However, at energies available at accelerators, the weak and EM forces become identical, or unified. Unfortunately, the energies at which the strong and electroweak forces become the same are unreachable even in principle at any conceivable accelerator. The universe may provide a laboratory, and nature may show effects at ordinary energies that give us clues about the validity of this graph.

The small distances and high energies at which the electroweak force becomes identical with the strong nuclear force are not reachable with any conceivable human-built accelerator. At energies of about 10^{14} GeV (16,000 J per particle), distances of about 10^{-30} m can be probed. Such energies are needed to test theory directly, but these are about 10^{10} higher than the proposed giant SSC would have had, and the distances are about 10^{-12} smaller than any structure we have direct knowledge of. This would be the realm of various GUTs, of which there are many since there is no constraining evidence at these energies and distances. Past experience has shown that any time you probe so many orders of magnitude further (here, about 10^{12}), you find the unexpected. Even more extreme are the energies and distances at which gravity is thought to unify with the other forces in a TOE. Most speculative and least constrained by experiment are TOEs, one of which is called **Superstring theory**. Superstrings are entities that are 10^{-35} m in scale and act like one-dimensional oscillating strings and are also proposed to underlie all particles, forces, and space itself.

At the energy of GUTs, the carrier particles of the weak force would become massless and identical to gluons. If that happens, then both lepton and baryon conservation would be violated. We do not see such violations, because we do not encounter such energies. However, there is a tiny probability that, at ordinary energies, the virtual particles that violate the conservation of baryon number may exist for extremely small amounts of time (corresponding to very small ranges). All GUTs thus predict that the proton should be unstable, but would decay with an extremely long lifetime of about 10^{31} y. The predicted decay mode is

$$p \to \pi^0 + e^+, \text{(proposed proton decay)} \quad 33.11$$

which violates both conservation of baryon number and electron family number. Although 10^{31} y is an extremely long time (about 10^{21} times the age of the universe), there are a lot of protons, and detectors have been constructed to look for the proposed decay mode as seen in Figure 33.25. It is somewhat comforting that proton decay has not been detected, and its experimental lifetime is now greater than 5×10^{32} y. This does not prove GUTs wrong, but it does place greater constraints on the theories, benefiting theorists in many ways.

From looking increasingly inward at smaller details for direct evidence of electroweak theory and GUTs, we turn around and look to the universe for evidence of the unification of forces. In the 1920s, the expansion of the universe was discovered. Thinking backward in time, the universe must once have been very small, dense, and extremely hot. At a tiny fraction of a second after the fabled Big Bang, forces would have been unified and may have left their fingerprint on the existing universe. This, one of the most exciting forefronts of physics, is the subject of Frontiers of Physics.

FIGURE 33.25 In the Tevatron accelerator at Fermilab, protons and antiprotons collide at high energies, and some of those collisions could result in the production of a Higgs boson in association with a *W* boson. When the *W* boson decays to a high-energy lepton and a neutrino, the detector triggers on the lepton, whether it is an electron or a muon. (credit: D. J. Miller)

Glossary

baryon number a conserved physical quantity that is zero for mesons and leptons and ± 1 for baryons and antibaryons, respectively

baryons hadrons that always decay to another baryon

boson particle with zero or an integer value of intrinsic spin

bottom a quark flavor

charm a quark flavor, which is the counterpart of the strange quark

colliding beams head-on collisions between particles moving in opposite directions

color a quark flavor

conservation of total baryon number a general rule based on the observation that the total number of nucleons was always conserved in nuclear reactions and decays

conservation of total electron family number a general rule stating that the total electron family number stays the same through an interaction

conservation of total muon family number a general rule stating that the total muon family number stays the same through an interaction

cyclotron accelerator that uses fixed-frequency alternating electric fields and fixed magnets to accelerate particles in a circular spiral path

down the second-lightest of all quarks

electron family number the number ± 1 that is assigned to all members of the electron family, or the number 0 that is assigned to all particles not in the electron family

electroweak theory theory showing connections between EM and weak forces

fermion particle with a half-integer value of intrinsic spin

Feynman diagram a graph of time versus position that describes the exchange of virtual particles between subatomic particles

flavors quark type

fundamental particle particle with no substructure

gauge boson particle that carries one of the four forces

gluons eight proposed particles which carry the strong force

gluons exchange particles, analogous to the exchange of photons that gives rise to the electromagnetic force between two charged particles

grand unified theory theory that shows unification of the strong and electroweak forces

hadrons particles that feel the strong nuclear force

Higgs boson a massive particle that, if observed, would give validity to the theory that carrier particles are identical under certain circumstances

leptons particles that do not feel the strong nuclear force

linear accelerator accelerator that accelerates particles in a straight line

meson hadrons that can decay to leptons and leave no hadrons

meson particle whose mass is intermediate between the electron and nucleon masses

muon family number the number ± 1 that is assigned to all members of the muon family, or the number 0 that is assigned to all particles not in the muon family

particle physics the study of and the quest for those truly fundamental particles having no substructure

pion particle exchanged between nucleons, transmitting the force between them

quantum chromodynamics quark theory including color

quantum chromodynamics the governing theory of connecting quantum number color to gluons

quantum electrodynamics the theory of electromagnetism on the particle scale

quark an elementary particle and a fundamental constituent of matter

standard model combination of quantum chromodynamics and electroweak theory

strange the third lightest of all quarks

strangeness a physical quantity assigned to various particles based on decay systematics

superstring theory a theory of everything based on vibrating strings some 10^{-35} m in length

synchrotron a version of a cyclotron in which the frequency of the alternating voltage and the magnetic field strength are increased as the beam particles are accelerated

synchrotron radiation radiation caused by a magnetic field accelerating a charged particle perpendicular to its velocity

tau family number the number ± 1 that is assigned to all members of the tau family, or the number 0 that is assigned to all particles not in the tau family

theory of quark confinement explains how quarks can exist and yet never be isolated or directly observed

top a quark flavor

up the lightest of all quarks

Van de Graaff early accelerator: simple, large-scale version of the electron gun

virtual particles particles which cannot be directly observed but their effects can be directly observed

Section Summary

33.1 The Yukawa Particle and the Heisenberg Uncertainty Principle Revisited

- Yukawa's idea of virtual particle exchange as the carrier of forces is crucial, with virtual particles being formed in temporary violation of the conservation of mass-energy as allowed by the Heisenberg uncertainty principle.

33.2 The Four Basic Forces

- The four basic forces and their carrier particles are summarized in the Table 33.1.
- Feynman diagrams are graphs of time versus position and are highly useful pictorial representations of particle processes.
- The theory of electromagnetism on the particle scale is called quantum electrodynamics (QED).

33.3 Accelerators Create Matter from Energy

- A variety of particle accelerators have been used to explore the nature of subatomic particles and to test predictions of particle theories.
- Modern accelerators used in particle physics are either large synchrotrons or linear accelerators.
- The use of colliding beams makes much greater energy available for the creation of particles, and collisions between matter and antimatter allow a greater range of final products.

33.4 Particles, Patterns, and Conservation Laws

- All particles of matter have an antimatter counterpart that has the opposite charge and certain other quantum numbers as seen in Table 33.2. These matter-antimatter pairs are otherwise very similar but will annihilate when brought together. Known particles can be divided into three major groups—leptons, hadrons, and carrier particles (gauge bosons).
- Leptons do not feel the strong nuclear force and are further divided into three groups—electron family designated by electron family number L_e; muon family designated by muon family number L_μ; and tau family designated by tau family number L_τ. The family numbers are not universally conserved due to neutrino oscillations.
- Hadrons are particles that feel the strong nuclear force and are divided into baryons, with the baryon family number B being conserved, and mesons.

33.5 Quarks: Is That All There Is?

- Hadrons are thought to be composed of quarks, with baryons having three quarks and mesons having a quark and an antiquark.
- The characteristics of the six quarks and their antiquark counterparts are given in Table 33.3, and the quark compositions of certain hadrons are given in Table 33.4.
- Indirect evidence for quarks is very strong, explaining all known hadrons and their quantum numbers, such as strangeness, charm, topness, and bottomness.
- Quarks come in six flavors and three colors and occur only in combinations that produce white.
- Fundamental particles have no further substructure, not even a size beyond their de Broglie wavelength.
- There are three types of fundamental particles—leptons, quarks, and carrier particles. Each type is divided into three analogous families as indicated in Figure 33.20.

33.6 GUTs: The Unification of Forces

- Attempts to show unification of the four forces are called Grand Unified Theories (GUTs) and have been partially successful, with connections proven between EM and weak forces in electroweak theory.
- The strong force is carried by eight proposed particles called gluons, which are intimately connected to a quantum number called color—their governing theory is thus called quantum chromodynamics (QCD). Taken together, QCD and the electroweak theory are widely accepted as the Standard Model of particle physics.
- Unification of the strong force is expected at such high energies that it cannot be directly tested, but it may have observable consequences in the as-yet unobserved decay of the proton and topics to be discussed in the next chapter. Although unification of forces is generally anticipated, much remains to be done to prove its validity.

Conceptual Questions

33.3 Accelerators Create Matter from Energy

1. The total energy in the beam of an accelerator is far greater than the energy of the individual beam particles. Why isn't this total energy available to create a single extremely massive particle?
2. Synchrotron radiation takes energy from an accelerator beam and is related to acceleration. Why would you expect the problem to be more severe for electron accelerators than proton accelerators?
3. What two major limitations prevent us from building high-energy accelerators that are physically small?
4. What are the advantages of colliding-beam accelerators? What are the disadvantages?

33.4 Particles, Patterns, and Conservation Laws

5. Large quantities of antimatter isolated from normal matter should behave exactly like normal matter. An antiatom, for example, composed of positrons, antiprotons, and antineutrons should have the same atomic spectrum as its matter counterpart. Would you be able to tell it is antimatter by its emission of antiphotons? Explain briefly.
6. Massless particles are not only neutral, they are chargeless (unlike the neutron). Why is this so?
7. Massless particles must travel at the speed of light, while others cannot reach this speed. Why are all massless particles stable? If evidence is found that neutrinos spontaneously decay into other particles, would this imply they have mass?
8. When a star erupts in a supernova explosion, huge numbers of electron neutrinos are formed in nuclear reactions. Such neutrinos from the 1987A supernova in the relatively nearby Magellanic Cloud were observed within hours of the initial brightening, indicating they traveled to earth at approximately the speed of light. Explain how this data can be used to set an upper limit on the mass of the neutrino, noting that if the mass is small the neutrinos could travel very close to the speed of light and have a reasonable energy (on the order of MeV).
9. Theorists have had spectacular success in predicting previously unknown particles. Considering past theoretical triumphs, why should we bother to perform experiments?
10. What lifetime do you expect for an antineutron isolated from normal matter?
11. Why does the η^0 meson have such a short lifetime compared to most other mesons?
12. (a) Is a hadron always a baryon?
(b) Is a baryon always a hadron?
(c) Can an unstable baryon decay into a meson, leaving no other baryon?
13. Explain how conservation of baryon number is responsible for conservation of total atomic mass (total number of nucleons) in nuclear decay and reactions.

33.5 Quarks: Is That All There Is?

14. The quark flavor change $d \rightarrow u$ takes place in β^- decay. Does this mean that the reverse quark flavor change $u \rightarrow d$ takes place in β^+ decay? Justify your response by writing the decay in terms of the quark constituents, noting that it looks as if a proton is converted into a neutron in β^+ decay.
15. Explain how the weak force can change strangeness by changing quark flavor.
16. Beta decay is caused by the weak force, as are all reactions in which strangeness changes. Does this imply that the weak force can change quark flavor? Explain.
17. Why is it easier to see the properties of the *c*, *b*, and *t* quarks in mesons having composition W^- or $t\bar{t}$ rather than in baryons having a mixture of quarks, such as *udb*?
18. How can quarks, which are fermions, combine to form bosons? Why must an even number combine to form a boson? Give one example by stating the quark substructure of a boson.
19. What evidence is cited to support the contention that the gluon force between quarks is greater than the strong nuclear force between hadrons? How is this related to color? Is it also related to quark confinement?
20. Discuss how we know that π-mesons (π^+, π, π^0) are not fundamental particles and are not the basic carriers of the strong force.
21. An antibaryon has three antiquarks with colors $\overline{R}\overline{G}\overline{B}$. What is its color?

22. Suppose leptons are created in a reaction. Does this imply the weak force is acting? (for example, consider β decay.)

23. How can the lifetime of a particle indicate that its decay is caused by the strong nuclear force? How can a change in strangeness imply which force is responsible for a reaction? What does a change in quark flavor imply about the force that is responsible?

24. (a) Do all particles having strangeness also have at least one strange quark in them?
(b) Do all hadrons with a strange quark also have nonzero strangeness?

25. The sigma-zero particle decays mostly via the reaction $\Sigma^0 \rightarrow \Lambda^0 + \gamma$. Explain how this decay and the respective quark compositions imply that the Σ^0 is an excited state of the Λ^0.

26. What do the quark compositions and other quantum numbers imply about the relationships between the Δ^+ and the proton? The Δ^0 and the neutron?

27. Discuss the similarities and differences between the photon and the Z^0 in terms of particle properties, including forces felt.

28. Identify evidence for electroweak unification.

29. The quarks in a particle are confined, meaning individual quarks cannot be directly observed. Are gluons confined as well? Explain

33.6 GUTs: The Unification of Forces

30. If a GUT is proven, and the four forces are unified, it will still be correct to say that the orbit of the moon is determined by the gravitational force. Explain why.

31. If the Higgs boson is discovered and found to have mass, will it be considered the ultimate carrier of the weak force? Explain your response.

32. Gluons and the photon are massless. Does this imply that the W^+, W^-, and Z^0 are the ultimate carriers of the weak force?

Problems & Exercises

33.1 The Yukawa Particle and the Heisenberg Uncertainty Principle Revisited

1. A virtual particle having an approximate mass of $10^{14}\ \text{GeV}/c^2$ may be associated with the unification of the strong and electroweak forces. For what length of time could this virtual particle exist (in temporary violation of the conservation of mass-energy as allowed by the Heisenberg uncertainty principle)?

2. Calculate the mass in GeV/c^2 of a virtual carrier particle that has a range limited to 10^{-30} m by the Heisenberg uncertainty principle. Such a particle might be involved in the unification of the strong and electroweak forces.

3. Another component of the strong nuclear force is transmitted by the exchange of virtual *K*-mesons. Taking *K*-mesons to have an average mass of $495\ \text{MeV}/c^2$, what is the approximate range of this component of the strong force?

33.2 The Four Basic Forces

4. (a) Find the ratio of the strengths of the weak and electromagnetic forces under ordinary circumstances.
(b) What does that ratio become under circumstances in which the forces are unified?

5. The ratio of the strong to the weak force and the ratio of the strong force to the electromagnetic force become 1 under circumstances where they are unified. What are the ratios of the strong force to those two forces under normal circumstances?

33.3 Accelerators Create Matter from Energy

6. At full energy, protons in the 2.00-km-diameter Fermilab synchrotron travel at nearly the speed of light, since their energy is about 1000 times their rest mass energy.
(a) How long does it take for a proton to complete one trip around?
(b) How many times per second will it pass through the target area?

7. Suppose a W^- created in a bubble chamber lives for 5.00×10^{-25} s. What distance does it move in this time if it is traveling at 0.900 *c*? Since this distance is too short to make a track, the presence of the W^- must be inferred from its decay products. Note that the time is longer than the given W^- lifetime, which can be due to the statistical nature of decay or time dilation.

8. What length track does a π^+ traveling at 0.100 *c* leave in a bubble chamber if it is created there and lives for 2.60×10^{-8} s? (Those moving faster or living longer may escape the detector before decaying.)

9. The 3.20-km-long SLAC produces a beam of 50.0-GeV electrons. If there are 15,000 accelerating tubes, what average voltage must be across the gaps between them to achieve this energy?

10. Because of energy loss due to synchrotron radiation in the LHC at CERN, only 5.00 MeV is added to the energy of each proton during each revolution around the main ring. How many revolutions are needed to produce 7.00-TeV (7000 GeV) protons, if they are injected with an initial energy of 8.00 GeV?

11. A proton and an antiproton collide head-on, with each having a kinetic energy of 7.00 TeV (such as in the LHC at CERN). How much collision energy is available, taking into account the annihilation of the two masses? (Note that this is not significantly greater than the extremely relativistic kinetic energy.)

12. When an electron and positron collide at the SLAC facility, they each have 50.0 GeV kinetic energies. What is the total collision energy available, taking into account the annihilation energy? Note that the annihilation energy is insignificant, because the electrons are highly relativistic.

33.4 Particles, Patterns, and Conservation Laws

13. The π^0 is its own antiparticle and decays in the following manner: $\pi^0 \rightarrow \gamma + \gamma$. What is the energy of each γ ray if the π^0 is at rest when it decays?

14. The primary decay mode for the negative pion is $\pi^- \rightarrow \mu^- + \bar{\nu}_\mu$. What is the energy release in MeV in this decay?

15. The mass of a theoretical particle that may be associated with the unification of the electroweak and strong forces is $10^{14}\ \mathrm{GeV}/c^2$.
(a) How many proton masses is this?
(b) How many electron masses is this? (This indicates how extremely relativistic the accelerator would have to be in order to make the particle, and how large the relativistic quantity γ would have to be.)

16. The decay mode of the negative muon is $\mu^- \rightarrow e^- + \bar{\nu}_e + \nu_\mu$.
(a) Find the energy released in MeV.
(b) Verify that charge and lepton family numbers are conserved.

17. The decay mode of the positive tau is $\tau^+ \rightarrow \mu^+ + \nu_\mu + \bar{\nu}_\tau$.
(a) What energy is released?
(b) Verify that charge and lepton family numbers are conserved.
(c) The τ^+ is the antiparticle of the τ^-.Verify that all the decay products of the τ^+ are the antiparticles of those in the decay of the τ^- given in the text.

18. The principal decay mode of the sigma zero is $\Sigma^0 \rightarrow \Lambda^0 + \gamma$.
(a) What energy is released?
(b) Considering the quark structure of the two baryons, does it appear that the Σ^0 is an excited state of the Λ^0?
(c) Verify that strangeness, charge, and baryon number are conserved in the decay.
(d) Considering the preceding and the short lifetime, can the weak force be responsible? State why or why not.

19. (a) What is the uncertainty in the energy released in the decay of a π^0 due to its short lifetime?
(b) What fraction of the decay energy is this, noting that the decay mode is $\pi^0 \rightarrow \gamma + \gamma$ (so that all the π^0 mass is destroyed)?

20. (a) What is the uncertainty in the energy released in the decay of a τ^- due to its short lifetime?
(b) Is the uncertainty in this energy greater than or less than the uncertainty in the mass of the tau neutrino? Discuss the source of the uncertainty.

33.5 Quarks: Is That All There Is?

21. (a) Verify from its quark composition that the Δ^+ particle could be an excited state of the proton.
(b) There is a spread of about 100 MeV in the decay energy of the Δ^+, interpreted as uncertainty due to its short lifetime. What is its approximate lifetime?
(c) Does its decay proceed via the strong or weak force?

22. Accelerators such as the Triangle Universities Meson Facility (TRIUMF) in British Columbia produce secondary beams of pions by having an intense primary proton beam strike a target. Such "meson factories" have been used for many years to study the interaction of pions with nuclei and, hence, the strong nuclear force. One reaction that occurs is $\pi^+ + p \rightarrow \Delta^{++} \rightarrow \pi^+ + p$, where the Δ^{++} is a very short-lived particle. The graph in Figure 33.26 shows

the probability of this reaction as a function of energy. The width of the bump is the uncertainty in energy due to the short lifetime of the Δ^{++}.
(a) Find this lifetime.
(b) Verify from the quark composition of the particles that this reaction annihilates and then re-creates a d quark and a $\bar{d}$ antiquark by writing the reaction and decay in terms of quarks.
(c) Draw a Feynman diagram of the production and decay of the Δ^{++} showing the individual quarks involved.

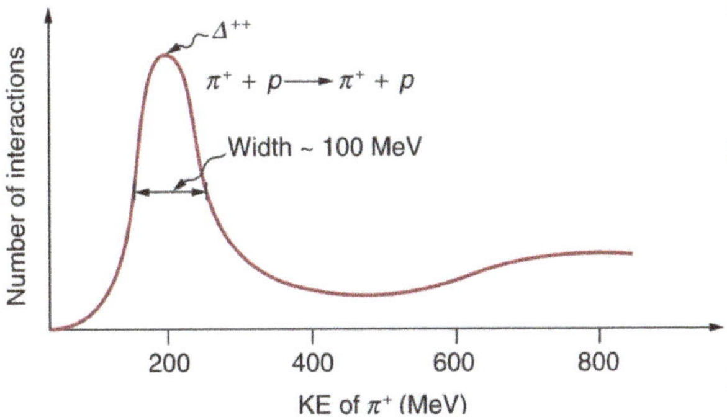

FIGURE 33.26 This graph shows the probability of an interaction between a π^+ and a proton as a function of energy. The bump is interpreted as a very short lived particle called a Δ^{++}. The approximately 100-MeV width of the bump is due to the short lifetime of the Δ^{++}.

23. The reaction $\pi^+ + p \rightarrow \Delta^{++}$ (described in the preceding problem) takes place via the strong force. (a) What is the baryon number of the Δ^{++} particle?
(b) Draw a Feynman diagram of the reaction showing the individual quarks involved.

24. One of the decay modes of the omega minus is $\Omega^- \rightarrow \Xi^0 + \pi^-$.
(a) What is the change in strangeness?
(b) Verify that baryon number and charge are conserved, while lepton numbers are unaffected.
(c) Write the equation in terms of the constituent quarks, indicating that the weak force is responsible.

25. Repeat the previous problem for the decay mode $\Omega^- \rightarrow \Lambda^0 + K^-$.

26. One decay mode for the eta-zero meson is $\eta^0 \rightarrow \gamma + \gamma$.
(a) Find the energy released.
(b) What is the uncertainty in the energy due to the short lifetime?
(c) Write the decay in terms of the constituent quarks.
(d) Verify that baryon number, lepton numbers, and charge are conserved.

27. One decay mode for the eta-zero meson is $\eta^0 \rightarrow \pi^0 + \pi^0$.
(a) Write the decay in terms of the quark constituents.
(b) How much energy is released?
(c) What is the ultimate release of energy, given the decay mode for the pi zero is $\pi^0 \rightarrow \gamma + \gamma$?

28. Is the decay $n \rightarrow e^+ + e^-$ possible considering the appropriate conservation laws? State why or why not.

29. Is the decay $\mu^- \rightarrow e^- + \nu_e + \nu_\mu$ possible considering the appropriate conservation laws? State why or why not.

30. (a) Is the decay $\Lambda^0 \rightarrow n + \pi^0$ possible considering the appropriate conservation laws? State why or why not.
(b) Write the decay in terms of the quark constituents of the particles.

31. (a) Is the decay $\Sigma^- \rightarrow n + \pi^-$ possible considering the appropriate conservation laws? State why or why not. (b) Write the decay in terms of the quark constituents of the particles.

32. The only combination of quark colors that produces a white baryon is *RGB*. Identify all the color combinations that can produce a white meson.

33. (a) Three quarks form a baryon. How many combinations of the six known quarks are there if all combinations are possible?
(b) This number is less than the number of known baryons. Explain why.

34. (a) Show that the conjectured decay of the proton, $p \rightarrow \pi^0 + e^+$, violates conservation of baryon number and conservation of lepton number.
(b) What is the analogous decay process for the antiproton?

35. Verify the quantum numbers given for the Ω^+ in Table 33.2 by adding the quantum numbers for its quark constituents as inferred from Table 33.4.

36. Verify the quantum numbers given for the proton and neutron in Table 33.2 by adding the quantum numbers for their quark constituents as given in Table 33.4.

37. (a) How much energy would be released if the proton did decay via the conjectured reaction $p \rightarrow \pi^0 + e^+$?
(b) Given that the π^0 decays to two γ s and that the e^+ will find an electron to annihilate, what

total energy is ultimately produced in proton decay?
(c) Why is this energy greater than the proton's total mass (converted to energy)?

38. (a) Find the charge, baryon number, strangeness, charm, and bottomness of the J/Ψ particle from its quark composition.
(b) Do the same for the Υ particle.

39. There are particles called *D*-mesons. One of them is the D^+ meson, which has a single positive charge and a baryon number of zero, also the value of its strangeness, topness, and bottomness. It has a charm of $+1$. What is its quark configuration?

40. There are particles called bottom mesons or *B*-mesons. One of them is the B^- meson, which has a single negative charge; its baryon number is zero, as are its strangeness, charm, and topness. It has a bottomness of -1. What is its quark configuration?

41. (a) What particle has the quark composition $\overline{u}\overline{u}\overline{d}$?
(b) What should its decay mode be?

42. (a) Show that all combinations of three quarks produce integral charges. Thus baryons must have integral charge.
(b) Show that all combinations of a quark and an antiquark produce only integral charges. Thus mesons must have integral charge.

33.6 GUTs: The Unification of Forces

43. Integrated Concepts
The intensity of cosmic ray radiation decreases rapidly with increasing energy, but there are occasionally extremely energetic cosmic rays that create a shower of radiation from all the particles they create by striking a nucleus in the atmosphere as seen in the figure given below. Suppose a cosmic ray particle having an energy of 10^{10} GeV converts its energy into particles with masses averaging $200\ \text{MeV}/c^2$. (a) How many particles are created? (b) If the particles rain down on a 1.00-km^2 area, how many particles are there per square meter?

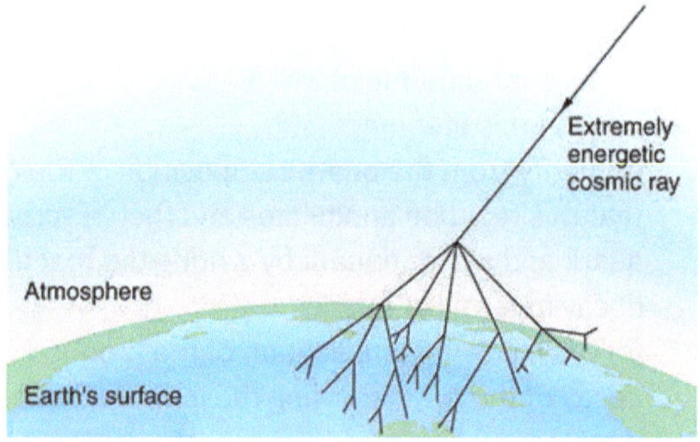

FIGURE 33.27 An extremely energetic cosmic ray creates a shower of particles on earth. The energy of these rare cosmic rays can approach a joule (about 10^{10} GeV) and, after multiple collisions, huge numbers of particles are created from this energy. Cosmic ray showers have been observed to extend over many square kilometers.

44. Integrated Concepts
Assuming conservation of momentum, what is the energy of each γ ray produced in the decay of a neutral at rest pion, in the reaction $\pi^0 \rightarrow \gamma + \gamma$?

45. Integrated Concepts
What is the wavelength of a 50-GeV electron, which is produced at SLAC? This provides an idea of the limit to the detail it can probe.

46. Integrated Concepts
(a) Calculate the relativistic quantity $\gamma = \frac{1}{\sqrt{1-v^2/c^2}}$ for 1.00-TeV protons produced at Fermilab. (b) If such a proton created a π^+ having the same speed, how long would its life be in the laboratory? (c) How far could it travel in this time?

47. Integrated Concepts
The primary decay mode for the negative pion is $\pi^- \rightarrow \mu^- + \overline{\nu}_\mu$. (a) What is the energy release in MeV in this decay? (b) Using conservation of momentum, how much energy does each of the decay products receive, given the π^- is at rest when it decays? You may assume the muon antineutrino is massless and has momentum $p = E/c$, just like a photon.

48. Integrated Concepts
Plans for an accelerator that produces a secondary beam of *K*-mesons to scatter from nuclei, for the purpose of studying the strong force, call for them to have a kinetic energy of 500 MeV. (a) What would the relativistic quantity $\gamma = \frac{1}{\sqrt{1-v^2/c^2}}$ be for these particles? (b) How long would their average lifetime be in the laboratory? (c) How far could they travel in this time?

49. Integrated Concepts
Suppose you are designing a proton decay experiment and you can detect 50 percent of the proton decays in a tank of water. (a) How many kilograms of water would you need to see one decay per month, assuming a lifetime of 10^{31} y? (b) How many cubic meters of water is this? (c) If the actual lifetime is 10^{33} y, how long would you have to wait on an average to see a single proton decay?

50. Integrated Concepts
In supernovas, neutrinos are produced in huge amounts. They were detected from the 1987A supernova in the Magellanic Cloud, which is about 120,000 light years away from the Earth (relatively close to our Milky Way galaxy). If neutrinos have a mass, they cannot travel at the speed of light, but if their mass is small, they can get close. (a) Suppose a neutrino with a $7\text{-eV}/c^2$ mass has a kinetic energy of 700 keV. Find the relativistic quantity $\gamma = \frac{1}{\sqrt{1-v^2/c^2}}$ for it. (b) If the neutrino leaves the 1987A supernova at the same time as a photon and both travel to Earth, how much sooner does the photon arrive? This is not a large time difference, given that it is impossible to know which neutrino left with which photon and the poor efficiency of the neutrino detectors. Thus, the fact that neutrinos were observed within hours of the brightening of the supernova only places an upper limit on the neutrino's mass. (Hint: You may need to use a series expansion to find v for the neutrino, since its γ is so large.)

51. Construct Your Own Problem
Consider an ultrahigh-energy cosmic ray entering the Earth's atmosphere (some have energies approaching a joule). Construct a problem in which you calculate the energy of the particle based on the number of particles in an observed cosmic ray shower. Among the things to consider are the average mass of the shower particles, the average number per square meter, and the extent (number of square meters covered) of the shower. Express the energy in eV and joules.

52. Construct Your Own Problem
Consider a detector needed to observe the proposed, but extremely rare, decay of an electron. Construct a problem in which you calculate the amount of matter needed in the detector to be able to observe the decay, assuming that it has a signature that is clearly identifiable. Among the things to consider are the estimated half life (long for rare events), and the number of decays per unit time that you wish to observe, as well as the number of electrons in the detector substance.

53. Critical Thinking (a) How much mass is converted to energy when a proton and antiproton annihilate each other? (b) How much energy is produced in the conversion above? (c) If energy were to produce a proton-antiproton pair, how much energy would this take? (d) What characteristic other than one being antimatter is different for a proton and an antiproton?

Test Prep for AP® Courses

33.2 The Four Basic Forces

1. Two intact (not ionized) hydrogen atoms are 10 cm apart. Which of the following are true?
   a. Gravity, though very weak, is acting between them.
   b. The neutral charge means the electromagnetic force between them can be ignored.
   c. The range is too long for the strong force to be involved.
   d. All of the above.

2. Explain why we only need to concern ourselves with gravitational force to describe the orbit of the Earth around the Sun.

3. Consider four forces: the gravitational force between the Earth and the Sun; the electrostatic force between the Earth and the Sun; the gravitational force between the proton and electron in a hydrogen atom, and the electrostatic force between the proton and electron in a hydrogen atom. What is the proper ordering of the magnitude of these forces, from greatest to least?
   a. gravity, Earth-Sun; electrostatic, Earth-Sun; gravity, hydrogen; electrostatic, hydrogen
   b. electrostatic, Earth-Sun; gravity, Earth-Sun; electrostatic, hydrogen; gravity, hydrogen
   c. gravity, Earth-Sun; gravity, hydrogen; electrostatic, hydrogen; electrostatic, Earth-Sun
   d. gravity, Earth-Sun; electrostatic, hydrogen; gravity, hydrogen; electrostatic, Earth-Sun

4. Deep within a nucleon, which is the stronger force between two quarks, gravity or the weak force? Why do you think so?

5. Consider the Earth-Moon system. If we were to place equal charges on the Earth and the Moon, how large would they need to be for the electrostatic repulsion to counteract the gravitational attraction?
   a. 5.1×10^{13} C
   b. 5.7×10^{13} C
   c. 6.7×10^{13} C
   d. 3.3×10^{27} C

6. What is the strength of the magnetic field created by the orbiting Moon, at the center of the orbit, in the system in the previous problem? (Treat the charge going around in orbit as a current loop.) How does this compare with the strength of the Earth's intrinsic magnetic field?

7. An atomic nucleus consists of positively charged protons and neutral neutrons, so the electrostatic repulsion should destroy it by making the protons fly apart. This doesn't happen because:
   a. The strong force is ~100 times stronger than electromagnetism.
   b. The weak force generates massive particles that hold it together.
   c. Electromagnetism is sometimes attractive.
   d. Gravity is always attractive.

8. The atomic number of an atom is the number of protons in that atom's nucleus. Make a prediction as to what happens to electromagnetic repulsion as the atomic number gets larger. Then, make a further prediction about what this implies about the number of neutrons in heavy nuclei.

33.3 Accelerators Create Matter from Energy

9. Which of the below was the first hint that conservation of mass and conservation of energy might need to be combined into one concept?
   a. The Van de Graaff generator.
   b. New particles showing up in accelerators.
   c. Yukawa's theory.
   d. They were always related.

10. How fast would two 7.0-kg bowling balls each have to be going in a collision to have enough spare energy to create a 0.10-kg tennis ball? (Ignore relativistic effects.) Can you explain why we don't see this in daily situations?

11. Use the information in Table 33.2 to answer the following questions.
    Taking only energy and mass into consideration, what is the minimum amount of kinetic energy a K^- must have when colliding with a stationary proton to produce an Ω?
   a. 240.5 MeV
   b. 120.0 MeV
   c. 15.5 MeV
   d. 57.6 GeV

12. Using only energy-mass considerations, how many K^0 could a Z boson decay into? How many electrons and positrons could be produced this way?

13. A π^+ and a π^- are moving toward each other extremely slowly. When they collide, two π^0 are produced. How fast are they going? (Ignore relativistic effects.)
   a. Barely moving
   b. 1.0×10^7 m/s
   c. 2.0×10^7 m/s
   d. 7.8×10^7 m/s

14. Assume that when a free neutron decays, it transforms into a proton and an electron. Calculate the kinetic energy of the electron.

33.4 Particles, Patterns, and Conservation Laws

15. When a π^- decays, the products may include:
   a. A positron.
   b. A muon.
   c. A proton.
   d. All of the above.

16. Notice in Table 33.2 that the neutron has a half-life of 882 seconds. This is only for a free neutron, not bound with other neutrons and protons in a nucleus. Given the other particles in the table, and using both their charge and masses, what do you think the most likely decay products for a neutron are? Justify your answer.

33.5 Quarks: Is That All There Is?

17. How many pointlike particles would an experiment scattering high energy electrons from any meson discover within the meson?
   a. 1
   b. 2
   c. 3
   d. 4

18.

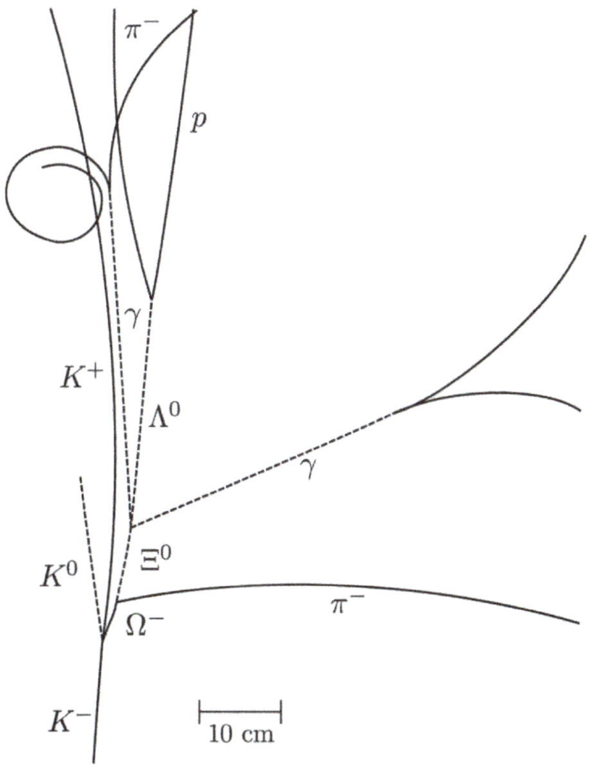

FIGURE 33.28

In this figure, a K⁻ initially hits a proton, and creates three new particles. Identify them, and explain how quark flavors are conserved.

CHAPTER 34

Frontiers of Physics

FIGURE 34.1 This galaxy is ejecting huge jets of matter, powered by an immensely massive black hole at its center. (credit: X-ray: NASA/CXC/CfA/R. Kraft et al.)

CHAPTER OUTLINE

CONNECTION FOR AP® COURSES There is mystery, surprise, adventure, and discovery in exploring new frontiers. The search for answers is that much more intriguing because the answer to any question always leads to new questions. As our understanding of nature becomes more complete, nature still retains its sense of mystery and never loses its ability to awe us.

Looking through the lens of physics allows us to look both backward and forward in time, and we can discern marvelous patterns in nature with its myriad rules and complex connections. Moreover, we continue looking ever deeper and ever further, probing the basic structure of matter, energy, space, and time, and wondering about the scope of the universe, its beginnings, and its future.

The Big Ideas that we have been supporting and justifying throughout the previous chapters will now be used as a framework to investigate and justify new ideas. With the concepts, qualitative and quantitative problem-solving skills, the connections among topics, and all the rest of the coursework you have mastered, you will be more able to deeply appreciate the treatments that follow.

34.1 Cosmology and Particle Physics

LEARNING OBJECTIVES

By the end of this section, you will be able to:

- Discuss the expansion of the universe.
- Explain the Big Bang.

Look at the sky on some clear night when you are away from city lights. There you will see thousands of individual stars and a faint glowing background of millions more. The Milky Way, as it has been called since ancient times, is an arm of our galaxy of stars—the word *galaxy* coming from the Greek word *galaxias*, meaning milky. We know a great deal about our Milky Way galaxy and of the billions of other galaxies beyond its fringes. But they still provoke wonder and awe (see Figure 34.2). And there are still many questions to be answered. Most remarkable when we view the universe on the large scale is that once again explanations of its character and evolution are tied to the very small scale. Particle physics and the questions being asked about the very small scales may also have their answers in the very large scales.

FIGURE 34.2 Take a moment to contemplate these clusters of galaxies, photographed by the Hubble Space Telescope. Trillions of stars linked by gravity in fantastic forms, glowing with light and showing evidence of undiscovered matter. What are they like, these myriad stars? How did they evolve? What can they tell us of matter, energy, space, and time? (credit: NASA, ESA, K. Sharon (Tel Aviv University) and E. Ofek (Caltech))

As has been noted in numerous Things Great and Small vignettes, this is not the first time the large has been explained by the small and vice versa. Newton realized that the nature of gravity on Earth that pulls an apple to the ground could explain the motion of the moon and planets so much farther away. Minute atoms and molecules explain the chemistry of substances on a much larger scale. Decays of tiny nuclei explain the hot interior of the Earth. Fusion of nuclei likewise explains the energy of stars. Today, the patterns in particle physics seem to be explaining the evolution and character of the universe. And the nature of the universe has implications for unexplored regions of particle physics.

Cosmology is the study of the character and evolution of the universe. What are the major characteristics of the universe as we know them today? First, there are approximately 10^{11} galaxies in the observable part of the universe. An average galaxy contains more than 10^{11} stars, with our Milky Way galaxy being larger than average, both in its number of stars and its dimensions. Ours is a spiral-shaped galaxy with a diameter of about 100,000 light years and a thickness of about 2000 light years in the arms with a central bulge about 10,000 light years across. The Sun lies about 30,000 light years from the center near the galactic plane. There are significant clouds of gas, and there is a halo of less-dense regions of stars surrounding the main body. (See Figure 34.3.) Evidence strongly suggests the existence of a large amount of additional matter in galaxies that does not produce light—the mysterious dark matter we shall later discuss.

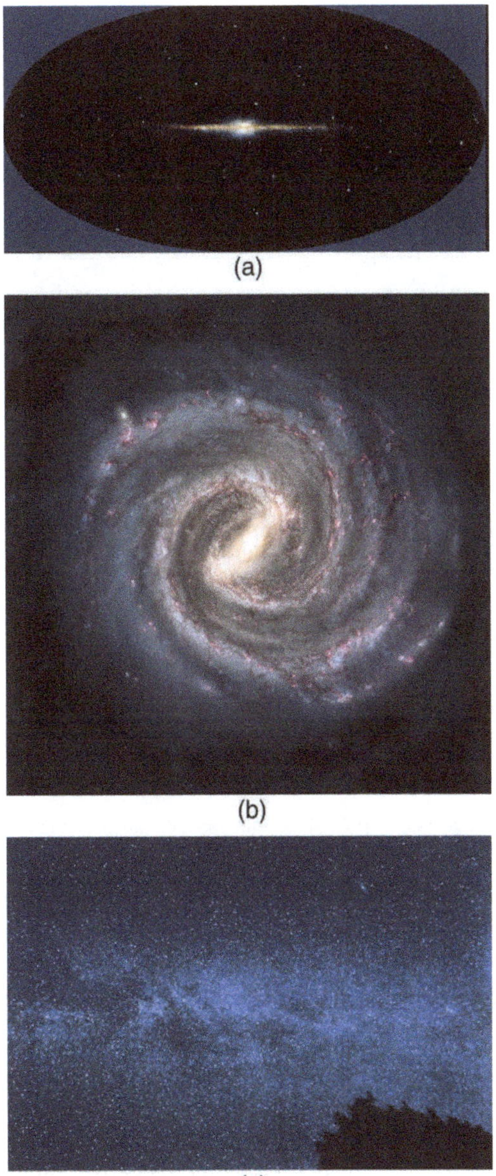

(a) (b) (c)

FIGURE 34.3 The Milky Way galaxy is typical of large spiral galaxies in its size, its shape, and the presence of gas and dust. We are fortunate to be in a location where we can see out of the galaxy and observe the vastly larger and fascinating universe around us. (a) Side view. (b) View from above. (c) The Milky Way as seen from Earth. (credits: (a) NASA, (b) Nick Risinger, (c) Andy)

Distances are great even within our galaxy and are measured in light years (the distance traveled by light in one year). The average distance between galaxies is on the order of a million light years, but it varies greatly with galaxies forming clusters such as shown in Figure 34.2. The Magellanic Clouds, for example, are small galaxies close to our own, some 160,000 light years from Earth. The Andromeda galaxy is a large spiral galaxy like ours and lies 2 million light years away. It is just visible to the naked eye as an extended glow in the Andromeda constellation. Andromeda is the closest large galaxy in our local group, and we can see some individual stars in it with our larger telescopes. The most distant known galaxy is 14 billion light years from Earth—a truly incredible distance. (See Figure 34.4.)

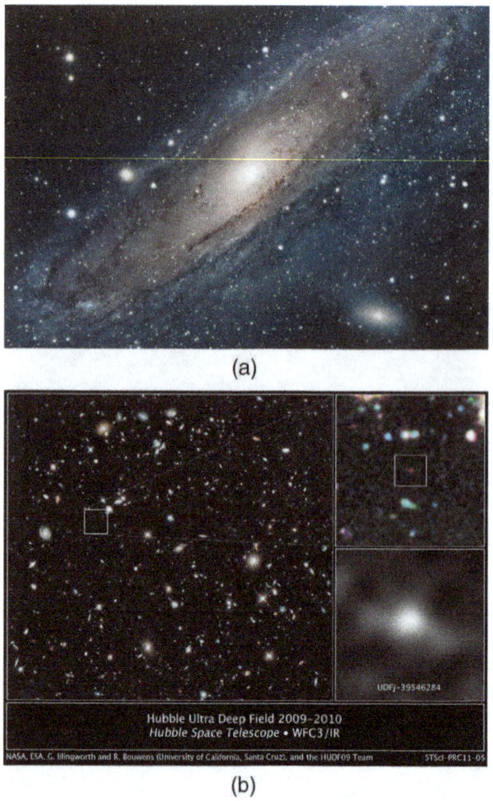

FIGURE 34.4 (a) Andromeda is the closest large galaxy, at 2 million light years distance, and is very similar to our Milky Way. The blue regions harbor young and emerging stars, while dark streaks are vast clouds of gas and dust. A smaller satellite galaxy is clearly visible. (b) The box indicates what may be the most distant known galaxy, estimated to be 13 billion light years from us. It exists in a much older part of the universe. (credit: NASA, ESA, G. Illingworth (University of California, Santa Cruz), R. Bouwens (University of California, Santa Cruz and Leiden University), and the HUDF09 Team)

Consider the fact that the light we receive from these vast distances has been on its way to us for a long time. In fact, the time in years is the same as the distance in light years. For example, the Andromeda galaxy is 2 million light years away, so that the light now reaching us left it 2 million years ago. If we could be there now, Andromeda would be different. Similarly, light from the most distant galaxy left it 14 billion years ago. We have an incredible view of the past when looking great distances. We can try to see if the universe was different then—if distant galaxies are more tightly packed or have younger-looking stars, for example, than closer galaxies, in which case there has been an evolution in time. But the problem is that the uncertainties in our data are great. Cosmology is almost typified by these large uncertainties, so that we must be especially cautious in drawing conclusions. One consequence is that there are more questions than answers, and so there are many competing theories. Another consequence is that any hard data produce a major result. Discoveries of some importance are being made on a regular basis, the hallmark of a field in its golden age.

Perhaps the most important characteristic of the universe is that all galaxies except those in our local cluster seem to be moving away from us at speeds proportional to their distance from our galaxy. It looks as if a gigantic explosion, universally called the **Big Bang**, threw matter out some billions of years ago. This amazing conclusion is based on the pioneering work of Edwin Hubble (1889–1953), the American astronomer. In the 1920s, Hubble first demonstrated conclusively that other galaxies, many previously called nebulae or clouds of stars, were outside our own. He then found that all but the closest galaxies have a red shift in their hydrogen spectra that is proportional to their distance. The explanation is that there is a **cosmological red shift** due to the expansion of space itself. The photon wavelength is stretched in transit from the source to the observer. Double the distance, and the red shift is doubled. While this cosmological red shift is often called a Doppler shift, it is not—space itself is expanding. There is no center of expansion in the universe. All observers see themselves as stationary; the other objects in space appear to be moving away from them. Hubble was directly responsible for discovering that the universe was much larger than had previously been imagined and that it had this amazing characteristic of rapid expansion.

Universal expansion on the scale of galactic clusters (that is, galaxies at smaller distances are not uniformly receding from one another) is an integral part of modern cosmology. For galaxies farther away than about 50 Mly (50 million light years), the expansion is uniform with variations due to local motions of galaxies within clusters. A representative recession velocity v can be obtained from the simple formula

$$v = H_0 d, \quad (34.1)$$

where d is the distance to the galaxy and H_0 is the **Hubble constant**. The Hubble constant is a central concept in cosmology. Its value is determined by taking the slope of a graph of velocity versus distance, obtained from red shift measurements, such as shown in Figure 34.5. We shall use an approximate value of $H_0 = 20 \text{ (km/s)/Mly}$. Thus, $v = H_0 d$ is an average behavior for all but the closest galaxies. For example, a galaxy 100 Mly away (as determined by its size and brightness) typically moves away from us at a speed of $v = (20 \text{ (km/s)/Mly})(100 \text{ Mly}) = 2000 \text{ km/s}$. There can be variations in this speed due to so-called local motions or interactions with neighboring galaxies. Conversely, if a galaxy is found to be moving away from us at speed of 100,000 km/s based on its red shift, it is at a distance

$d = v/H_0 = (10{,}000 \text{ km/s})/(20 \text{ (km/s)/Mly}) = 5000 \text{ Mly} = 5 \text{ Gly}$ or $5 \times 10^9 \text{ ly}$. This last calculation is approximate, because it assumes the expansion rate was the same 5 billion years ago as now. A similar calculation in Hubble's measurement changed the notion that the universe is in a steady state.

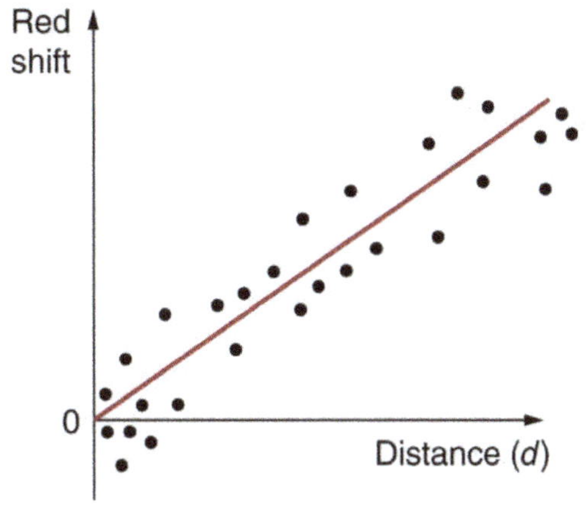

FIGURE 34.5 This graph of red shift versus distance for galaxies shows a linear relationship, with larger red shifts at greater distances, implying an expanding universe. The slope gives an approximate value for the expansion rate. (credit: John Cub).

One of the most intriguing developments recently has been the discovery that the expansion of the universe may be *faster now* than in the past, rather than slowing due to gravity as expected. Various groups have been looking, in particular, at supernovas in moderately distant galaxies (less than 1 Gly) to get improved distance measurements. Those distances are larger than expected for the observed galactic red shifts, implying the expansion was slower when that light was emitted. This has cosmological consequences that are discussed in Dark Matter and Closure. The first results, published in 1999, are only the beginning of emerging data, with astronomy now entering a data-rich era.

Figure 34.6 shows how the recession of galaxies looks like the remnants of a gigantic explosion, the famous Big Bang. Extrapolating backward in time, the Big Bang would have occurred between 13 and 15 billion years ago when all matter would have been at a point. Questions instantly arise. What caused the explosion? What happened before the Big Bang? Was there a before, or did time start then? Will the universe expand forever, or will gravity reverse it into a Big Crunch? And is there other evidence of the Big Bang besides the well-documented red shifts?

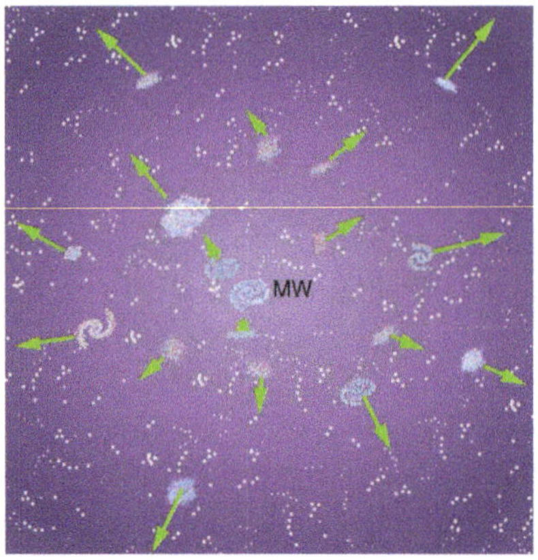

FIGURE 34.6 Galaxies are flying apart from one another, with the more distant moving faster as if a primordial explosion expelled the matter from which they formed. The most distant known galaxies move nearly at the speed of light relative to us.

The Russian-born American physicist George Gamow (1904–1968) was among the first to note that, if there was a Big Bang, the remnants of the primordial fireball should still be evident and should be blackbody radiation. Since the radiation from this fireball has been traveling to us since shortly after the Big Bang, its wavelengths should be greatly stretched. It will look as if the fireball has cooled in the billions of years since the Big Bang. Gamow and collaborators predicted in the late 1940s that there should be blackbody radiation from the explosion filling space with a characteristic temperature of about 7 K. Such blackbody radiation would have its peak intensity in the microwave part of the spectrum. (See Figure 34.7.) In 1964, Arno Penzias and Robert Wilson, two American scientists working with Bell Telephone Laboratories on a low-noise radio antenna, detected the radiation and eventually recognized it for what it is.

Figure 34.7(b) shows the spectrum of this microwave radiation that permeates space and is of cosmic origin. It is the most perfect blackbody spectrum known, and the temperature of the fireball remnant is determined from it to be $2.725 \pm 0.\ 002\ \text{K}$. The detection of what is now called the **cosmic microwave background** (CMBR) was so important (generally considered as important as Hubble's detection that the galactic red shift is proportional to distance) that virtually every scientist has accepted the expansion of the universe as fact. Penzias and Wilson shared the 1978 Nobel Prize in Physics for their discovery.

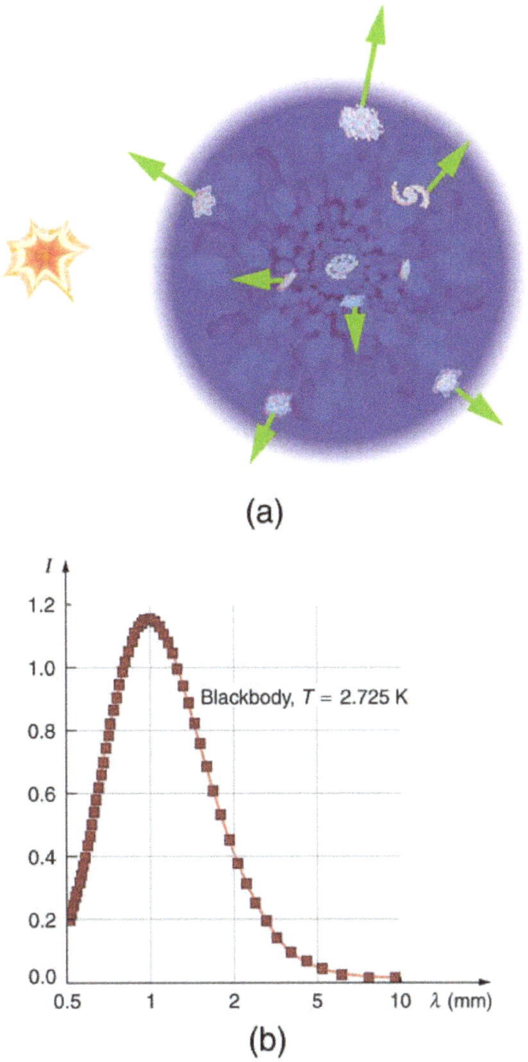

FIGURE 34.7 (a) The Big Bang is used to explain the present observed expansion of the universe. It was an incredibly energetic explosion some 10 to 20 billion years ago. After expanding and cooling, galaxies form inside the now-cold remnants of the primordial fireball. (b) The spectrum of cosmic microwave radiation is the most perfect blackbody spectrum ever detected. It is characteristic of a temperature of 2.725 K, the expansion-cooled temperature of the Big Bang's remnant. This radiation can be measured coming from any direction in space not obscured by some other source. It is compelling evidence of the creation of the universe in a gigantic explosion, already indicated by galactic red shifts.

MAKING CONNECTIONS: COSMOLOGY AND PARTICLE PHYSICS

There are many connections of cosmology—by definition involving physics on the largest scale—with particle physics—by definition physics on the smallest scale. Among these are the dominance of matter over antimatter, the nearly perfect uniformity of the cosmic microwave background, and the mere existence of galaxies.

Matter versus antimatter We know from direct observation that antimatter is rare. The Earth and the solar system are nearly pure matter. Space probes and cosmic rays give direct evidence—the landing of the Viking probes on Mars would have been spectacular explosions of mutual annihilation energy if Mars were antimatter. We also know that most of the universe is dominated by matter. This is proven by the lack of annihilation radiation coming to us from space, particularly the relative absence of 0.511-MeV γ rays created by the mutual annihilation of electrons and positrons. It seemed possible that there could be entire solar systems or galaxies made of antimatter in perfect symmetry with our matter-dominated systems. But the interactions between stars and galaxies would sometimes bring matter and antimatter together in large amounts. The annihilation radiation they would produce is simply not observed. Antimatter in nature is created in particle collisions and in β^+ decays, but only in small amounts that quickly annihilate, leaving almost pure matter surviving.

Particle physics seems symmetric in matter and antimatter. Why isn't the cosmos? The answer is that particle physics is not quite perfectly symmetric in this regard. The decay of one of the neutral K-mesons, for example, preferentially creates more matter than antimatter. This is caused by a fundamental small asymmetry in the basic forces. This small asymmetry produced slightly more matter than antimatter in the early universe. If there was only one part in 10^9 more matter (a small asymmetry), the rest would annihilate pair for pair, leaving nearly pure matter to form the stars and galaxies we see today. So the vast number of stars we observe may be only a tiny remnant of the original matter created in the Big Bang. Here at last we see a very real and important asymmetry in nature. Rather than be disturbed by an asymmetry, most physicists are impressed by how small it is. Furthermore, if the universe were completely symmetric, the mutual annihilation would be more complete, leaving far less matter to form us and the universe we know.

How can something so old have so few wrinkles? A troubling aspect of cosmic microwave background radiation (CMBR) was soon recognized. True, the CMBR verified the Big Bang, had the correct temperature, and had a blackbody spectrum as expected. But the CMBR was *too* smooth—it looked identical in every direction. Galaxies and other similar entities could not be formed without the existence of fluctuations in the primordial stages of the universe and so there should be hot and cool spots in the CMBR, nicknamed wrinkles, corresponding to dense and sparse regions of gas caused by turbulence or early fluctuations. Over time, dense regions would contract under gravity and form stars and galaxies. Why aren't the fluctuations there? (This is a good example of an answer producing more questions.) Furthermore, galaxies are observed very far from us, so that they formed very long ago. The problem was to explain how galaxies could form so early and so quickly after the Big Bang if its remnant fingerprint is perfectly smooth. The answer is that if you look very closely, the CMBR is not perfectly smooth, only extremely smooth.

A satellite called the Cosmic Background Explorer (COBE) carried an instrument that made very sensitive and accurate measurements of the CMBR. In April of 1992, there was extraordinary publicity of COBE's first results—there were small fluctuations in the CMBR. Further measurements were carried out by experiments including NASA's Wilkinson Microwave Anisotropy Probe (WMAP), which launched in 2001. Data from WMAP provided a much more detailed picture of the CMBR fluctuations. (See Figure 34.7.) These amount to temperature fluctuations of only $200\ \mu\text{k}$ out of 2.7 K, better than one part in 1000. The WMAP experiment will be followed up by the European Space Agency's Planck Surveyor, which launched in 2009.

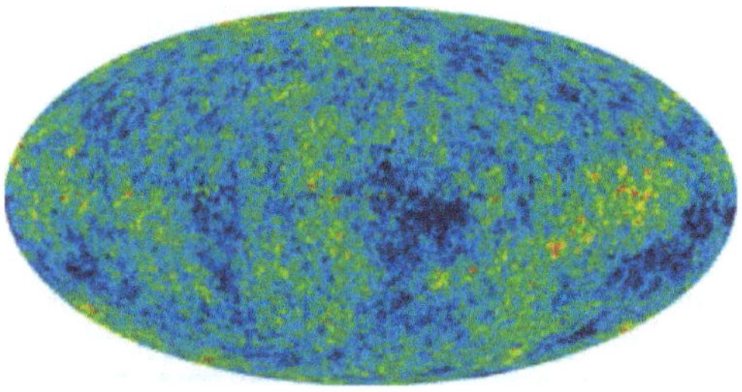

FIGURE 34.8 This map of the sky uses color to show fluctuations, or wrinkles, in the cosmic microwave background observed with the WMAP spacecraft. The Milky Way has been removed for clarity. Red represents higher temperature and higher density, while blue is lower temperature and density. The fluctuations are small, less than one part in 1000, but these are still thought to be the cause of the eventual formation of galaxies. (credit: NASA/WMAP Science Team)

Let us now examine the various stages of the overall evolution of the universe from the Big Bang to the present, illustrated in Figure 34.9. Note that scientific notation is used to encompass the many orders of magnitude in time, energy, temperature, and size of the universe. Going back in time, the two lines approach but do not cross (there is no zero on an exponential scale). Rather, they extend indefinitely in ever-smaller time intervals to some infinitesimal point.

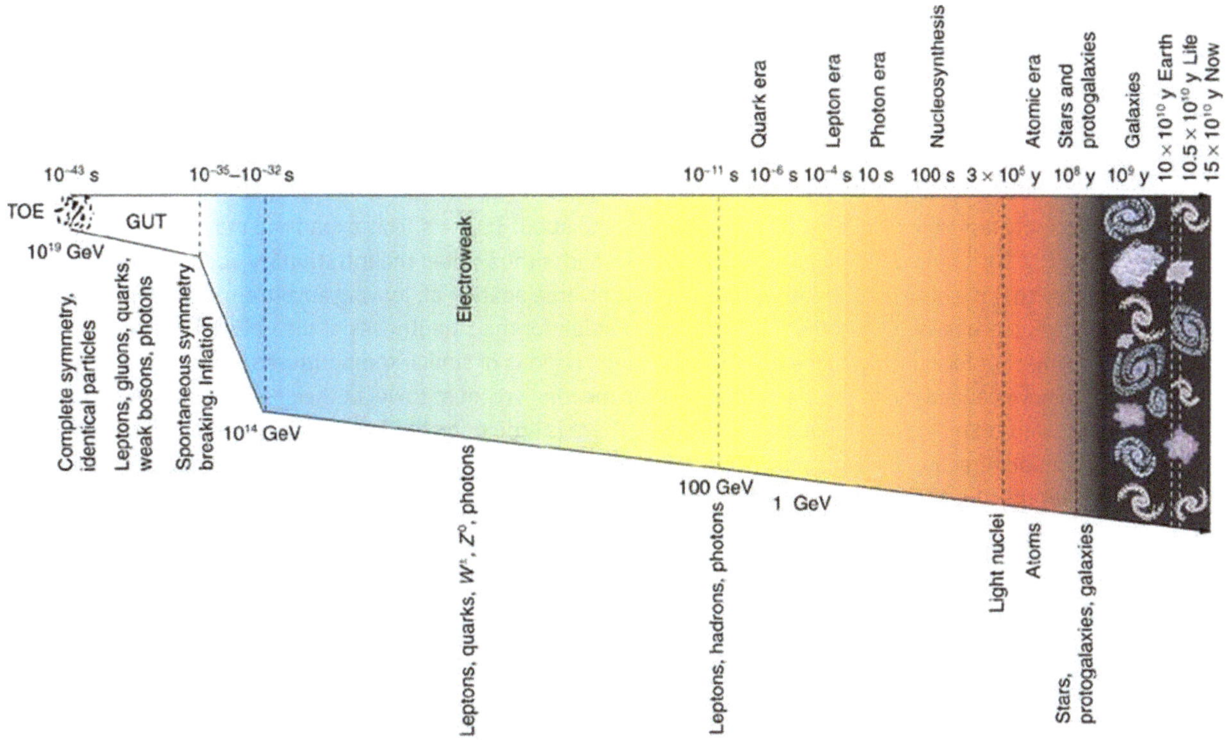

FIGURE 34.9 The evolution of the universe from the Big Bang onward is intimately tied to the laws of physics, especially those of particle physics at the earliest stages. The universe is relativistic throughout its history. Theories of the unification of forces at high energies may be verified by their shaping of the universe and its evolution.

Going back in time is equivalent to what would happen if expansion stopped and gravity pulled all the galaxies together, compressing and heating all matter. At a time long ago, the temperature and density were too high for stars and galaxies to exist. Before then, there was a time when the temperature was too great for atoms to exist. And farther back yet, there was a time when the temperature and density were so great that nuclei could not exist. Even farther back in time, the temperature was so high that average kinetic energy was great enough to create short-lived particles, and the density was high enough to make this likely. When we extrapolate back to the point of $W^{\pm}$ and Z^0 production (thermal energies reaching 1 TeV, or a temperature of about 10^{15} K), we reach the limits of what we know directly about particle physics. This is at a time about 10^{-12} s after the Big Bang. While 10^{-12} s may seem to be negligibly close to the instant of creation, it is not. There are important stages before this time that are tied to the unification of forces. At those stages, the universe was at extremely high energies and average particle separations were smaller than we can achieve with accelerators. What happened in the early stages before 10^{-12} s is crucial to all later stages and is possibly discerned by observing present conditions in the universe. One of these is the smoothness of the CMBR.

Names are given to early stages representing key conditions. The stage before 10^{-11} s back to 10^{-34} s is called the **electroweak epoch**, because the electromagnetic and weak forces become identical for energies above about 100 GeV. As discussed earlier, theorists expect that the strong force becomes identical to and thus unified with the electroweak force at energies of about 10^{14} GeV. The average particle energy would be this great at 10^{-34} s after the Big Bang, if there are no surprises in the unknown physics at energies above about 1 TeV. At the immense energy of 10^{14} GeV (corresponding to a temperature of about 10^{26} K), the $W^{\pm}$ and Z^0 carrier particles would be transformed into massless gauge bosons to accomplish the unification. Before 10^{-34} s back to about 10^{-43} s, we have Grand Unification in the **GUT epoch**, in which all forces except gravity are identical. At 10^{-43} s, the average energy reaches the immense 10^{19} GeV needed to unify gravity with the other forces in TOE, the Theory of Everything. Before that time is the **TOE epoch**, but we have almost no idea as to the nature of the universe then, since we have no workable theory of quantum gravity. We call the hypothetical unified force **superforce**.

Now let us imagine starting at TOE and moving forward in time to see what type of universe is created from various events along the way. As temperatures and average energies decrease with expansion, the universe reaches the stage where average particle separations are large enough to see differences between the strong and electroweak forces (at about 10^{-35} s). After this time, the forces become distinct in almost all interactions—they are no longer unified or symmetric. This transition from GUT to electroweak is an example of **spontaneous symmetry breaking**, in which conditions spontaneously evolved to a point where the forces were no longer unified, breaking that symmetry. This is analogous to a phase transition in the universe, and a clever proposal by American physicist Alan Guth in the early 1980s ties it to the smoothness of the CMBR. Guth proposed that spontaneous symmetry breaking (like a phase transition during cooling of normal matter) released an immense amount of energy that caused the universe to expand extremely rapidly for the brief time from 10^{-35} s to about 10^{-32} s. This expansion may have been by an incredible factor of 10^{50} or more in the size of the universe and is thus called the **inflationary scenario**. One result of this inflation is that it would stretch the wrinkles in the universe nearly flat, leaving an extremely smooth CMBR. While speculative, there is as yet no other plausible explanation for the smoothness of the CMBR. Unless the CMBR is not really cosmic but local in origin, the distances between regions of similar temperatures are too great for any coordination to have caused them, since any coordination mechanism must travel at the speed of light. Again, particle physics and cosmology are intimately entwined. There is little hope that we may be able to test the inflationary scenario directly, since it occurs at energies near 10^{14} GeV, vastly greater than the limits of modern accelerators. But the idea is so attractive that it is incorporated into most cosmological theories.

Characteristics of the present universe may help us determine the validity of this intriguing idea. Additionally, the recent indications that the universe's expansion rate may be *increasing* (see Dark Matter and Closure) could even imply that we are *in* another inflationary epoch.

It is important to note that, if conditions such as those found in the early universe could be created in the laboratory, we would see the unification of forces directly today. The forces have not changed in time, but the average energy and separation of particles in the universe have. As discussed in The Four Basic Forces, the four basic forces in nature are distinct under most circumstances found today. The early universe and its remnants provide evidence from times when they were unified under most circumstances.

34.2 General Relativity and Quantum Gravity

LEARNING OBJECTIVES

By the end of this section, you will be able to:

- Explain the effect of gravity on light.
- Discuss black hole.
- Explain quantum gravity.

When we talk of black holes or the unification of forces, we are actually discussing aspects of general relativity and quantum gravity. We know from Special Relativity that relativity is the study of how different observers measure the same event, particularly if they move relative to one another. Einstein's theory of **general relativity** describes all types of relative motion including accelerated motion and the effects of gravity. General relativity encompasses special relativity and classical relativity in situations where acceleration is zero and relative velocity is small compared with the speed of light. Many aspects of general relativity have been verified experimentally, some of which are better than science fiction in that they are bizarre but true. **Quantum gravity** is the theory that deals with particle exchange of gravitons as the mechanism for the force, and with extreme conditions where quantum mechanics and general relativity must both be used. A good theory of quantum gravity does not yet exist, but one will be needed to understand how all four forces may be unified. If we are successful, the theory of quantum gravity will encompass all others, from classical physics to relativity to quantum mechanics—truly a Theory of Everything (TOE).

General Relativity

Einstein first considered the case of no observer acceleration when he developed the revolutionary special theory of relativity, publishing his first work on it in 1905. By 1916, he had laid the foundation of general relativity, again almost on his own. Much of what Einstein did to develop his ideas was to mentally analyze certain carefully and clearly defined situations—doing this is to perform a **thought experiment**. Figure 34.10 illustrates a thought experiment like the ones that convinced Einstein that light must fall in a gravitational field. Think about what a person feels in an elevator that is accelerated upward. It is identical to being in a stationary elevator in a gravitational field. The feet of a person are pressed against the floor, and objects released from hand fall with identical accelerations. In fact, it is not possible, without looking outside, to know what is happening—acceleration upward or gravity. This led Einstein to correctly postulate that acceleration and gravity will produce identical effects in all situations. So, if acceleration affects light, then gravity will, too. Figure 34.10 shows the effect of acceleration on a beam of light shone horizontally at one wall. Since the accelerated elevator moves up during the time light travels across the elevator, the beam of light strikes low, seeming to the person to bend down. (Normally a tiny effect, since the speed of light is so great.) The same effect must occur due to gravity, Einstein reasoned, since there is no way to tell the effects of gravity acting downward from acceleration of the elevator upward. Thus gravity affects the path of light, even though we think of gravity as acting between masses and photons are massless.

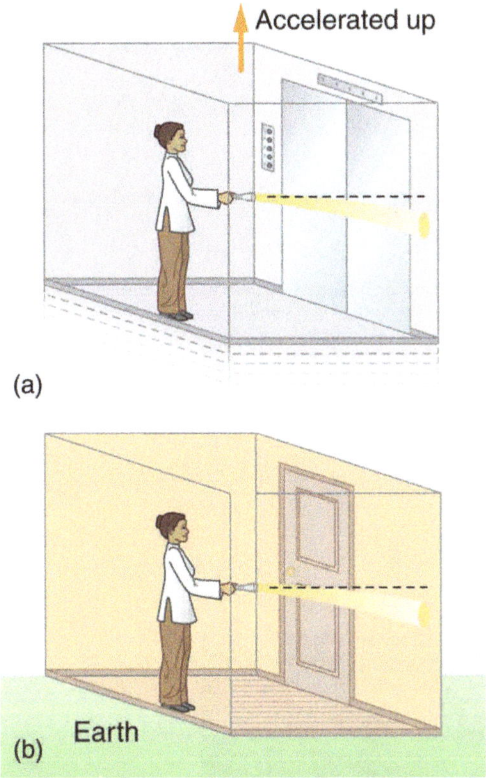

FIGURE 34.10 (a) A beam of light emerges from a flashlight in an upward-accelerating elevator. Since the elevator moves up during the time the light takes to reach the wall, the beam strikes lower than it would if the elevator were not accelerated. (b) Gravity has the same effect on light, since it is not possible to tell whether the elevator is accelerating upward or acted upon by gravity.

Einstein's theory of general relativity got its first verification in 1919 when starlight passing near the Sun was observed during a solar eclipse. (See Figure 34.11.) During an eclipse, the sky is darkened and we can briefly see stars. Those in a line of sight nearest the Sun should have a shift in their apparent positions. Not only was this shift observed, but it agreed with Einstein's predictions well within experimental uncertainties. This discovery created a scientific and public sensation. Einstein was now a folk hero as well as a very great scientist. The bending of light by matter is equivalent to a bending of space itself, with light following the curve. This is another radical change in our concept of space and time. It is also another connection that any particle with mass or energy (massless photons) is affected by gravity.

There are several current forefront efforts related to general relativity. One is the observation and analysis of gravitational lensing of light. Another is analysis of the definitive proof of the existence of black holes. Direct observation of gravitational waves or moving wrinkles in space is being searched for. Theoretical efforts are also being aimed at the possibility of time travel and wormholes into other parts of space due to black holes.

Gravitational lensing As you can see in Figure 34.11, light is bent toward a mass, producing an effect much like a converging lens (large masses are needed to produce observable effects). On a galactic scale, the light from a distant galaxy could be "lensed" into several images when passing close by another galaxy on its way to Earth. Einstein predicted this effect, but he considered it unlikely that we would ever observe it. A number of cases of this effect have now been observed; one is shown in Figure 34.12. This effect is a much larger scale verification of general relativity. But such gravitational lensing is also useful in verifying that the red shift is proportional to distance. The red shift of the intervening galaxy is always less than that of the one being lensed, and each image of the lensed galaxy has the same red shift. This verification supplies more evidence that red shift is proportional to distance. Confidence that the multiple images are not different objects is bolstered by the observations that if one image varies in brightness over time, the others also vary in the same manner.

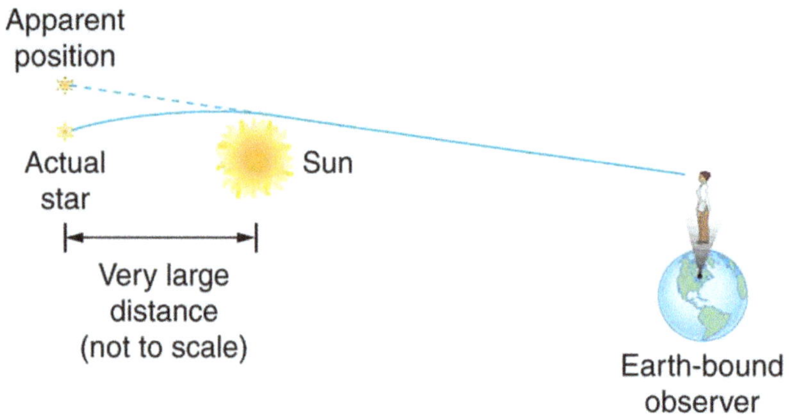

FIGURE 34.11 This schematic shows how light passing near a massive body like the Sun is curved toward it. The light that reaches the Earth then seems to be coming from different locations than the known positions of the originating stars. Not only was this effect observed, the amount of bending was precisely what Einstein predicted in his general theory of relativity.

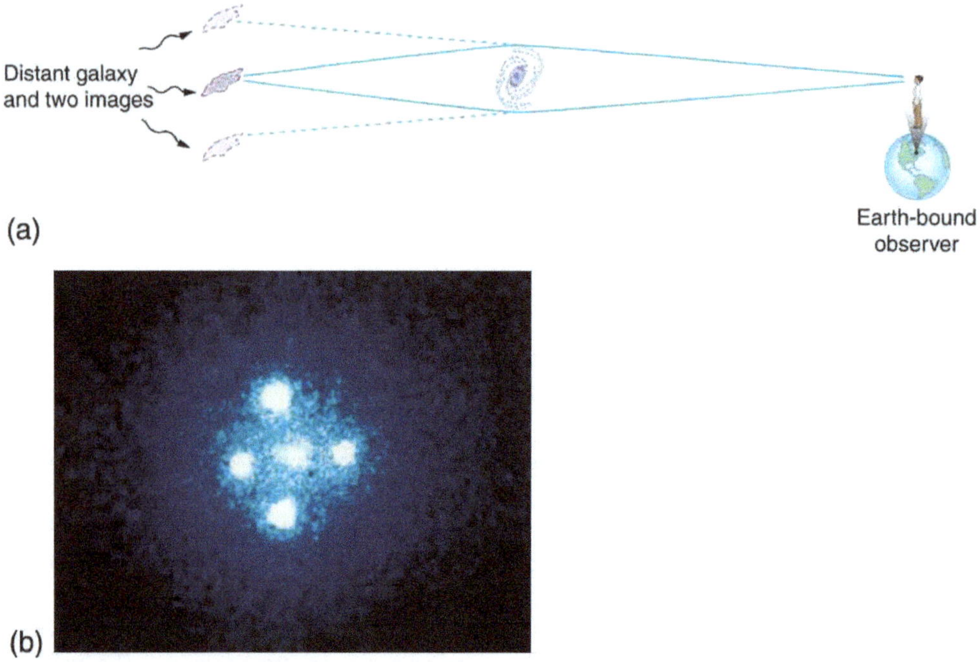

FIGURE 34.12 (a) Light from a distant galaxy can travel different paths to the Earth because it is bent around an intermediary galaxy by gravity. This produces several images of the more distant galaxy. (b) The images around the central galaxy are produced by gravitational lensing. Each image has the same spectrum and a larger red shift than the intermediary. (credit: NASA, ESA, and STScI)

Black holes **Black holes** are objects having such large gravitational fields that things can fall in, but nothing, not even light, can escape. Bodies, like the Earth or the Sun, have what is called an **escape velocity**. If an object moves straight up from the body, starting at the escape velocity, it will just be able to escape the gravity of the body. The greater the acceleration of gravity on the body, the greater is the escape velocity. As long ago as the late 1700s, it was proposed that if the escape velocity is greater than the speed of light, then light cannot escape. Simon Laplace (1749–1827), the French astronomer and mathematician, even incorporated this idea of a dark star into his writings. But the idea was dropped after Young's double slit experiment showed light to be a wave. For some time, light was thought not to have particle characteristics and, thus, could not be acted upon by gravity. The idea of a black hole was very quickly reincarnated in 1916 after Einstein's theory of general relativity was published. It is now thought that black holes can form in the supernova collapse of a massive star, forming an object perhaps 10 km across and having a mass greater than that of our Sun. It is interesting that several prominent physicists who worked on the concept, including Einstein, firmly believed that nature would find a way to prohibit such objects.

Black holes are difficult to observe directly, because they are small and no light comes directly from them. In fact, no light comes from inside the **event horizon**, which is defined to be at a distance from the object at which the escape velocity is exactly the speed of light. The radius of the event horizon is known as the **Schwarzschild radius** R_S and is given by

$$R_S = \frac{2GM}{c^2}, \tag{34.2}$$

where G is the universal gravitational constant, M is the mass of the body, and c is the speed of light. The event horizon is the edge of the black hole and R_S is its radius (that is, the size of a black hole is twice R_S). Since G is small and c^2 is large, you can see that black holes are extremely small, only a few kilometers for masses a little greater than the Sun's. The object itself is inside the event horizon.

Physics near a black hole is fascinating. Gravity increases so rapidly that, as you approach a black hole, the tidal effects tear matter apart, with matter closer to the hole being pulled in with much more force than that only slightly farther away. This can pull a companion star apart and heat inflowing gases to the point of producing X rays. (See Figure 34.13.) We have observed X rays from certain binary star systems that are consistent with such a picture. This is not quite proof of black holes, because the X rays could also be caused by matter falling onto a neutron star. These objects were first discovered in 1967 by the British astrophysicists, Jocelyn Bell and Anthony Hewish. **Neutron stars** are literally a star composed of neutrons. They are formed by the collapse of a star's core in a supernova, during which electrons and protons are forced together to form neutrons (the reverse of neutron β decay). Neutron stars are slightly larger than a black hole of the same mass and will not collapse further because of resistance by the strong force. However, neutron stars cannot have a mass greater than about eight solar masses or they must collapse to a black hole. With recent improvements in our ability to resolve small details, such as with the orbiting Chandra X-ray Observatory, it has become possible to measure the masses of X-ray-emitting objects by observing the motion of companion stars and other matter in their vicinity. What has emerged is a plethora of X-ray-emitting objects too massive to be neutron stars. This evidence is considered conclusive and the existence of black holes is widely accepted. These black holes are concentrated near galactic centers.

We also have evidence that supermassive black holes may exist at the cores of many galaxies, including the Milky Way. Such a black hole might have a mass millions or even billions of times that of the Sun, and it would probably have formed when matter first coalesced into a galaxy billions of years ago. Supporting this is the fact that very distant galaxies are more likely to have abnormally energetic cores. Some of the moderately distant galaxies, and hence among the younger, are known as **quasars** and emit as much or more energy than a normal galaxy but from a region less than a light year across. Quasar energy outputs may vary in times less than a year, so that the energy-emitting region must be less than a light year across. The best explanation of quasars is that they are young galaxies with a supermassive black hole forming at their core, and that they become less energetic over billions of years. In closer superactive galaxies, we observe tremendous amounts of energy being emitted from very small regions of space, consistent with stars falling into a black hole at the rate of one or more a month. The Hubble Space Telescope (1994) observed an accretion disk in the galaxy M87 rotating rapidly around a region of extreme energy emission. (See Figure 34.13.) A jet of material being ejected perpendicular to the plane of rotation gives further evidence of a supermassive black hole as the engine.

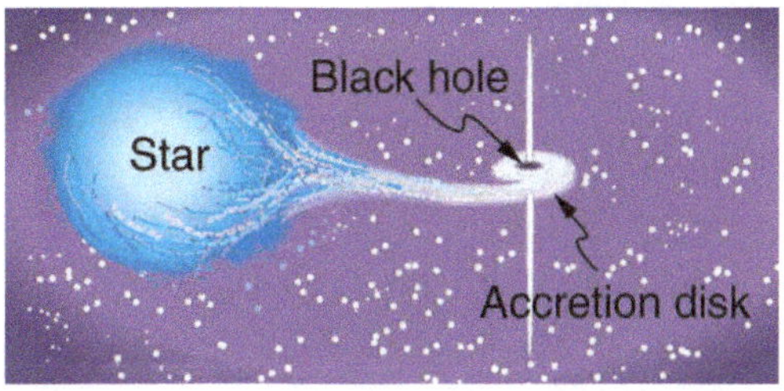

FIGURE 34.13 A black hole is shown pulling matter away from a companion star, forming a superheated accretion disk where X rays are emitted before the matter disappears forever into the hole. The in-fall energy also ejects some material, forming the two vertical spikes. (See also the photograph in the Introduction to Frontiers of Physics.) There are several X-ray-emitting objects in space that are consistent with this picture and are likely to be black holes.

Gravitational waves If a massive object distorts the space around it, like the foot of a water bug on the surface of a pond, then movement of the massive object should create waves in space like those on a pond. **Gravitational waves** are mass-created distortions in space that propagate at the speed of light and are predicted by general relativity. Since gravity is by far the weakest force, extreme conditions are needed to generate significant gravitational waves. Gravity near binary neutron star systems is so great that significant gravitational wave energy is radiated as the two neutron stars orbit one another. American astronomers, Joseph Taylor and Russell Hulse, measured changes in the orbit of such a binary neutron star system. They found its orbit to change precisely as predicted by general relativity, a strong indication of gravitational waves, and were awarded the 1993 Nobel Prize. But direct detection of gravitational waves on Earth would be conclusive. For many years, various attempts have been made to detect gravitational waves by observing vibrations induced in matter distorted by these waves. American physicist Joseph Weber pioneered this field in the 1960s, but no conclusive events have been observed. (No gravity wave detectors were in operation at the time of the 1987A supernova, unfortunately.) There are now several ambitious systems of gravitational wave detectors in use around the world. These include the LIGO (Laser Interferometer Gravitational Wave Observatory) system with two laser interferometer detectors, one in the state of Washington and another in Louisiana (See Figure 34.15) and the VIRGO (Variability of Irradiance and Gravitational Oscillations) facility in Italy with a single detector.

Quantum Gravity

Black holes radiate Quantum gravity is important in those situations where gravity is so extremely strong that it has effects on the quantum scale, where the other forces are ordinarily much stronger. The early universe was such a place, but black holes are another. The first significant connection between gravity and quantum effects was made by the Russian physicist Yakov Zel'dovich in 1971, and other significant advances followed from the British physicist Stephen Hawking. (See Figure 34.16.) These two showed that black holes could radiate away energy by quantum effects just outside the event horizon (nothing can escape from inside the event horizon). Black holes are, thus, expected to radiate energy and shrink to nothing, although extremely slowly for most black holes. The mechanism is the creation of a particle-antiparticle pair from energy in the extremely strong gravitational field near the event horizon. One member of the pair falls into the hole and the other escapes, conserving momentum. (See Figure 34.17.) When a black hole loses energy and, hence, rest mass, its event horizon shrinks, creating an even greater gravitational field. This increases the rate of pair production so that the process grows exponentially until the black hole is nuclear in size. A final burst of particles and γ rays ensues. This is an extremely slow process for black holes about the mass of the Sun (produced by supernovas) or larger ones (like those thought to be at galactic centers), taking on the order of 10^{67} years or longer! Smaller black holes would evaporate faster, but they are only speculated to exist as remnants of the Big Bang. Searches for characteristic γ-ray bursts have produced events attributable to more mundane objects like neutron stars accreting matter.

FIGURE 34.14 This Hubble Space Telescope photograph shows the extremely energetic core of the NGC 4261 galaxy. With the superior resolution of the orbiting telescope, it has been possible to observe the rotation of an accretion disk around the energy-producing object as well as to map jets of material being ejected from the object. A supermassive black hole is consistent with these observations, but other possibilities are not quite eliminated. (credit: NASA and ESA)

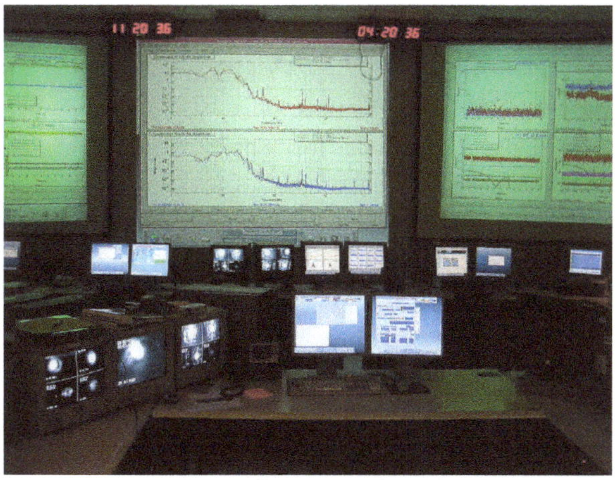

FIGURE 34.15 The control room of the LIGO gravitational wave detector. Gravitational waves will cause extremely small vibrations in a mass in this detector, which will be detected by laser interferometer techniques. Such detection in coincidence with other detectors and with astronomical events, such as supernovas, would provide direct evidence of gravitational waves. (credit: Tobin Fricke)

FIGURE 34.16 Stephen Hawking (b. 1942) has made many contributions to the theory of quantum gravity. Hawking is a long-time survivor of ALS and has produced popular books on general relativity, cosmology, and quantum gravity. (credit: Lwp Kommunikáció)

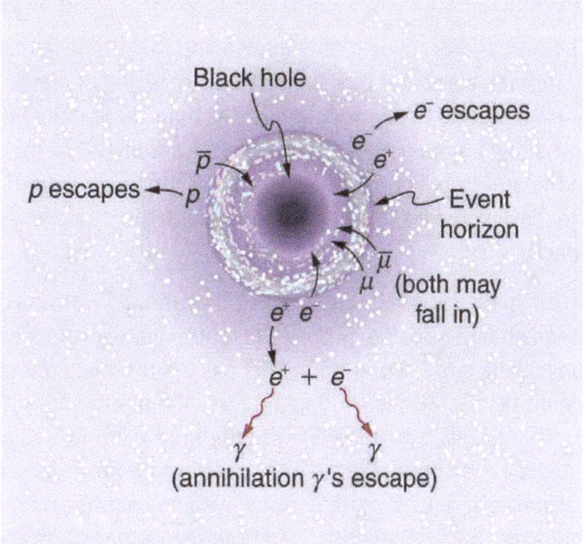

FIGURE 34.17 Gravity and quantum mechanics come into play when a black hole creates a particle-antiparticle pair from the energy in its gravitational field. One member of the pair falls into the hole while the other escapes, removing energy and shrinking the black hole. The search is on for the characteristic energy.

Wormholes and time travel The subject of time travel captures the imagination. Theoretical physicists, such as the American Kip Thorne, have treated the subject seriously, looking into the possibility that falling into a black hole could result in popping up in another time and place—a trip through a so-called wormhole. Time travel and wormholes appear in innumerable science fiction dramatizations, but the consensus is that time travel is not possible in theory. While still debated, it appears that quantum gravity effects inside a black hole prevent time travel due to the creation of particle pairs. Direct evidence is elusive.

The shortest time Theoretical studies indicate that, at extremely high energies and correspondingly early in the universe, quantum fluctuations may make time intervals meaningful only down to some finite time limit. Early work indicated that this might be the case for times as long as 10^{-43} s, the time at which all forces were unified. If so, then it would be meaningless to consider the universe at times earlier than this. Subsequent studies indicate that the crucial time may be as short as 10^{-95} s. But the point remains—quantum gravity seems to imply that there is no such thing as a vanishingly short time. Time may, in fact, be grainy with no meaning to time intervals shorter than some tiny but finite size.

The future of quantum gravity Not only is quantum gravity in its infancy, no one knows how to get started on a theory of gravitons and unification of forces. The energies at which TOE should be valid may be so high (at least 10^{19} GeV) and the necessary particle separation so small (less than 10^{-35} m) that only indirect evidence can provide clues. For some time, the common lament of theoretical physicists was one so familiar to struggling students—how do you even get started? But Hawking and others have made a start, and the approach many theorists have taken is called Superstring theory, the topic of the Superstrings.

34.3 Superstrings

LEARNING OBJECTIVES

By the end of this section, you will be able to:

- Define Superstring theory.
- Explain the relationship between Superstring theory and the Big Bang.

Introduced earlier in GUTS: The Unification of Forces **Superstring theory** is an attempt to unify gravity with the other three forces and, thus, must contain quantum gravity. The main tenet of Superstring theory is that fundamental particles, including the graviton that carries the gravitational force, act like one-dimensional vibrating strings. Since gravity affects the time and space in which all else exists, Superstring theory is an attempt at a Theory of Everything (TOE). Each independent quantum number is thought of as a separate dimension in some super space (analogous to the fact that the familiar dimensions of space are independent of one another) and is represented by a different type of Superstring. As the universe evolved after the Big Bang and forces became distinct (spontaneous symmetry breaking), some of the dimensions of superspace are imagined to have curled up and become unnoticed.

Forces are expected to be unified only at extremely high energies and at particle separations on the order of 10^{-35} m. This could mean that Superstrings must have dimensions or wavelengths of this size or smaller. Just as quantum gravity may imply that there are no time intervals shorter than some finite value, it also implies that there may be no sizes smaller than some tiny but finite value. That may be about 10^{-35} m. If so, and if Superstring theory can explain all it strives to, then the structures of Superstrings are at the lower limit of the smallest possible size and can have no further substructure. This would be the ultimate answer to the question the ancient Greeks considered. There is a finite lower limit to space.

Not only is Superstring theory in its infancy, it deals with dimensions about 17 orders of magnitude smaller than the 10^{-18} m details that we have been able to observe directly. It is thus relatively unconstrained by experiment, and there are a host of theoretical possibilities to choose from. This has led theorists to make choices subjectively (as always) on what is the most elegant theory, with less hope than usual that experiment will guide them. It has also led to speculation of alternate universes, with their Big Bangs creating each new universe with a random set of rules. These speculations may not be tested even in principle, since an alternate universe is by definition unattainable. It is something like exploring a self-consistent field of mathematics, with its axioms and rules of logic that are not consistent with nature. Such endeavors have often given insight to mathematicians and scientists alike and occasionally have been directly related to the description of new discoveries.

34.4 Dark Matter and Closure

LEARNING OBJECTIVES

By the end of this section, you will be able to:

- Discuss the existence of dark matter.
- Explain neutrino oscillations and their consequences.

One of the most exciting problems in physics today is the fact that there is far more matter in the universe than we can see. The motion of stars in galaxies and the motion of galaxies in clusters imply that there is about 10 times as much mass as in the luminous objects we can see. The indirectly observed non-luminous matter is called **dark matter**. Why is dark matter a problem? For one thing, we do not know what it is. It may well be 90% of all matter in the universe, yet there is a possibility that it is of a completely unknown form—a stunning discovery if verified. Dark matter has implications for particle physics. It may be possible that neutrinos actually have small masses or that there are completely unknown types of particles. Dark matter also has implications for cosmology, since there may be enough dark matter to stop the expansion of the universe. That is another problem related to dark matter—we do not know how much there is. We keep finding evidence for more matter in the universe, and we have an idea of how much it would take to eventually stop the expansion of the universe, but whether there is enough is still unknown.

Evidence

The first clues that there is more matter than meets the eye came from the Swiss-born American astronomer Fritz Zwicky in the 1930s; major work was also done by the American astronomer Vera Rubin. Zwicky measured the velocities of stars orbiting the galaxy, using the relativistic Doppler shift of their spectra (see Figure 34.18(a)). He found that velocity varied with distance from the center of the galaxy, as graphed in Figure 34.18(b). If the mass of the galaxy was concentrated in its center, as are its luminous stars, the velocities should decrease as the square root of the distance from the center. Instead, the velocity curve is almost flat, implying that there is a tremendous amount of matter in the galactic halo. Using instruments and methods that offered a greater degree of precision, Rubin investigated the movement of spiral galaxies and observed that their outermost reaches were rotating as quickly as their centers. She also calculated that the rotational velocity of galaxies should have been enough to cause them to fly apart, unless there was a significant discrepancy between their observable matter and their actual matter. This became known as the galaxy rotation problem, which can be "solved" by the presence of unobserved or dark matter. Although not immediately recognized for its significance, such measurements have now been made for many galaxies, with similar results. Further, studies of galactic clusters have also indicated that galaxies have a mass distribution greater than that obtained from their brightness (proportional to the number of stars), which also extends into large halos surrounding the luminous parts of galaxies. Observations of other EM wavelengths, such as radio waves and X rays, have similarly confirmed the existence of dark matter. Take, for example, X rays in the relatively dark space between galaxies, which indicates the presence of previously unobserved hot, ionized gas (see Figure 34.18(c)).

Theoretical Yearnings for Closure

Is the universe open or closed? That is, will the universe expand forever or will it stop, perhaps to contract? This, until recently, was a question of whether there is enough gravitation to stop the expansion of the universe. In the past few years, it has become a question of the combination of gravitation and what is called the **cosmological constant**. The cosmological constant was invented by Einstein to prohibit the expansion or contraction of the universe. At the time he developed general relativity, Einstein considered that an illogical possibility. The cosmological constant was discarded after Hubble discovered the expansion, but has been re-invoked in recent years.

Gravitational attraction between galaxies is slowing the expansion of the universe, but the amount of slowing down is not known directly. In fact, the cosmological constant can counteract gravity's effect. As recent measurements indicate, the universe is expanding *faster* now than in the past—perhaps a "modern inflationary era" in which the dark energy is thought to be causing the expansion of the present-day universe to accelerate. If the expansion rate were affected by gravity alone, we should be able to see that the expansion rate between distant galaxies was once greater than it is now. However, measurements show it was *less* than now. We can, however, calculate the amount of slowing based on the average density of matter we observe directly. Here we have a definite answer—there is far less visible matter than needed to stop expansion. The **critical density** ρ_c is defined to be the density needed to just halt universal expansion in a universe with no cosmological constant. It is estimated to be about

$$\rho_c \approx 10^{-26}\ \text{kg/m}^3. \tag{34.3}$$

However, this estimate of ρ_c is only good to about a factor of two, due to uncertainties in the expansion rate of the universe. The critical density is equivalent to an average of only a few nucleons per cubic meter, remarkably small and indicative of how truly empty intergalactic space is. Luminous matter seems to account for roughly 0.5% to 2% of the critical density, far less than that needed for closure. Taking into account the amount of dark matter we detect indirectly and all other types of indirectly observed normal matter, there is only 10% to 40% of what is needed for closure. If we are able to refine the measurements of expansion rates now and in the past, we will have our answer regarding the curvature of space and we will determine a value for the cosmological constant to justify this observation. Finally, the most recent measurements of the CMBR have implications for the cosmological constant, so it is not simply a device concocted for a single purpose.

After the recent experimental discovery of the cosmological constant, most researchers feel that the universe should be just barely open. Since matter can be thought to curve the space around it, we call an open universe **negatively curved**. This means that you can in principle travel an unlimited distance in any direction. A universe that is closed is called **positively curved**. This means that if you travel far enough in any direction, you will return to your starting point, analogous to circumnavigating the Earth. In between these two is a **flat (zero curvature) universe**. The recent discovery of the cosmological constant has shown the universe is very close to flat, and will expand forever. Why do theorists feel the universe is flat? Flatness is a part of the inflationary scenario that helps explain the flatness of the microwave background. In fact, since general relativity implies that matter creates the space in which it exists, there is a special symmetry to a flat universe.

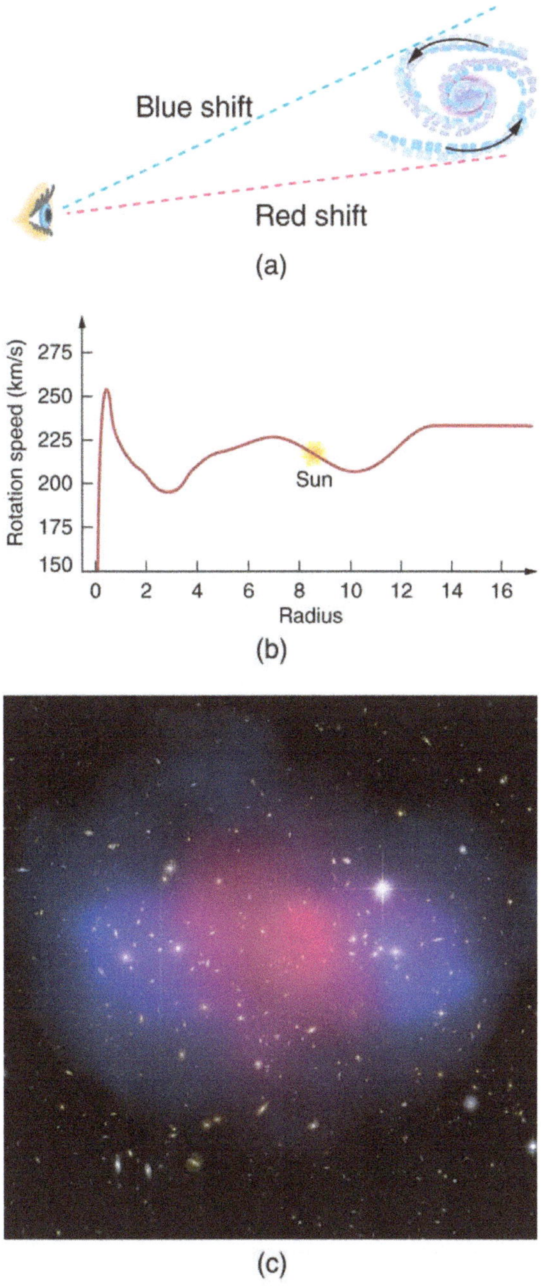

FIGURE 34.18 Evidence for dark matter: (a) We can measure the velocities of stars relative to their galaxies by observing the Doppler shift in emitted light, usually using the hydrogen spectrum. These measurements indicate the rotation of a spiral galaxy. (b) A graph of velocity versus distance from the galactic center shows that the velocity does not decrease as it would if the matter were concentrated in luminous stars. The flatness of the curve implies a massive galactic halo of dark matter extending beyond the visible stars. (c) This is a computer-generated image of X rays from a galactic cluster. The X rays indicate the presence of otherwise unseen hot clouds of ionized gas in the regions of space previously considered more empty. (credit: NASA, ESA, CXC, M. Bradac (University of California, Santa Barbara), and S. Allen (Stanford University))

What Is the Dark Matter We See Indirectly?

There is no doubt that dark matter exists, but its form and the amount in existence are two facts that are still being studied vigorously. As always, we seek to explain new observations in terms of known principles. However, as more discoveries are made, it is becoming more and more difficult to explain dark matter as a known type of matter.

One of the possibilities for normal matter is being explored using the Hubble Space Telescope and employing the lensing effect of gravity on light (see Figure 34.19). Stars glow because of nuclear fusion in them, but planets are visible primarily by reflected light. Jupiter, for example, is too small to ignite fusion in its core and become a star, but we can see sunlight reflected from it, since we are relatively close. If Jupiter orbited another star, we would not be able to see it directly. The question is open as to how many planets or other bodies smaller than about 1/1000 the mass of the Sun are there. If such bodies pass between us and a star, they will not block the star's light, being too small, but they will form a gravitational lens, as discussed in General Relativity and Quantum Gravity.

In a process called **microlensing**, light from the star is focused and the star appears to brighten in a characteristic manner. Searches for dark matter in this form are particularly interested in galactic halos because of the huge amount of mass that seems to be there. Such microlensing objects are thus called **massive compact halo objects**, or **MACHOs**. To date, a few MACHOs have been observed, but not predominantly in galactic halos, nor in the numbers needed to explain dark matter.

MACHOs are among the most conventional of unseen objects proposed to explain dark matter. Others being actively pursued are red dwarfs, which are small dim stars, but too few have been seen so far, even with the Hubble Telescope, to be of significance. Old remnants of stars called white dwarfs are also under consideration, since they contain about a solar mass, but are small as the Earth and may dim to the point that we ordinarily do not observe them. While white dwarfs are known, old dim ones are not. Yet another possibility is the existence of large numbers of smaller than stellar mass black holes left from the Big Bang—here evidence is entirely absent.

There is a very real possibility that dark matter is composed of the known neutrinos, which may have small, but finite, masses. As discussed earlier, neutrinos are thought to be massless, but we only have upper limits on their masses, rather than knowing they are exactly zero. So far, these upper limits come from difficult measurements of total energy emitted in the decays and reactions in which neutrinos are involved. There is an amusing possibility of proving that neutrinos have mass in a completely different way.

We have noted in Particles, Patterns, and Conservation Laws that there are three flavors of neutrinos (v_e, υ_μ, and υ_τ) and that the weak interaction could change quark flavor. It should also change neutrino flavor—that is, any type of neutrino could change spontaneously into any other, a process called **neutrino oscillations**. However, this can occur only if neutrinos have a mass. Why? Crudely, because if neutrinos are massless, they must travel at the speed of light and time will not pass for them, so that they cannot change without an interaction. In 1999, results began to be published containing convincing evidence that neutrino oscillations do occur. Using the Super-Kamiokande detector in Japan, the oscillations have been observed and are being verified and further explored at present at the same facility and others.

Neutrino oscillations may also explain the low number of observed solar neutrinos. Detectors for observing solar neutrinos are specifically designed to detect electron neutrinos v_e produced in huge numbers by fusion in the Sun. A large fraction of electron neutrinos v_e may be changing flavor to muon neutrinos υ_μ on their way out of the Sun, possibly enhanced by specific interactions, reducing the flux of electron neutrinos to observed levels. There is also a discrepancy in observations of neutrinos produced in cosmic ray showers. While these showers of radiation produced by extremely energetic cosmic rays should contain twice as many υ_μ s as v_e s, their numbers are nearly equal. This may be explained by neutrino oscillations from muon flavor to electron flavor. Massive neutrinos are a particularly appealing possibility for explaining dark matter, since their existence is consistent with a large body of known information and explains more than dark matter. The question is not settled at this writing.

The most radical proposal to explain dark matter is that it consists of previously unknown leptons (sometimes obtusely referred to as non-baryonic matter). These are called **weakly interacting massive particles**, or **WIMPs**, and would also be chargeless, thus interacting negligibly with normal matter, except through gravitation. One proposed group of WIMPs would have masses several orders of magnitude greater than nucleons and are sometimes called **neutralinos**. Others are called **axions** and would have masses about 10^{-10} that of an electron mass. Both neutralinos and axions would be gravitationally attached to galaxies, but because they are chargeless and only feel the weak force, they would be in a halo rather than interact and coalesce into spirals, and so on, like normal matter (see Figure 34.20).

FIGURE 34.19 The Hubble Space Telescope is producing exciting data with its corrected optics and with the absence of atmospheric distortion. It has observed some MACHOs, disks of material around stars thought to precede planet formation, black hole candidates, and collisions of comets with Jupiter. (credit: NASA (crew of STS-125))

FIGURE 34.20 Dark matter may shepherd normal matter gravitationally in space, as this stream moves the leaves. Dark matter may be invisible and even move through the normal matter, as neutrinos penetrate us without small-scale effect. (credit: Shinichi Sugiyama)

Some particle theorists have built WIMPs into their unified force theories and into the inflationary scenario of the evolution of the universe so popular today. These particles would have been produced in just the correct numbers to make the universe flat, shortly after the Big Bang. The proposal is radical in the sense that it invokes entirely new forms of matter, in fact *two* entirely new forms, in order to explain dark matter and other phenomena. WIMPs have the extra burden of automatically being very difficult to observe directly. This is somewhat analogous to quark confinement, which guarantees that quarks are there, but they can never be seen directly. One of the primary goals of the LHC at CERN, however, is to produce and detect WIMPs. At any rate, before WIMPs are accepted as the best explanation, all other possibilities utilizing known phenomena will have to be shown inferior. Should that occur, we will be in the unanticipated position of admitting that, to date, all we know is only 10% of what exists. A far cry from the days when people firmly believed themselves to be not only the center of the universe, but also the reason for its existence.

34.5 Complexity and Chaos

LEARNING OBJECTIVES

By the end of this section, you will be able to:

- Explain complex systems.
- Discuss chaotic behavior of different systems.

Much of what impresses us about physics is related to the underlying connections and basic simplicity of the laws we have discovered. The language of physics is precise and well defined because many basic systems we study are simple enough that we can perform controlled experiments and discover unambiguous relationships. Our most spectacular successes, such as the prediction of previously unobserved particles, come from the simple underlying patterns we have been able to recognize. But there are systems of interest to physicists that are inherently complex. The simple laws of physics apply, of course, but complex systems may reveal patterns that simple systems do not. The emerging field of **complexity** is devoted to the study of complex systems, including those outside the traditional bounds of physics. Of particular interest is the ability of complex systems to adapt and evolve.

What are some examples of complex adaptive systems? One is the primordial ocean. When the oceans first formed, they were a random mix of elements and compounds that obeyed the laws of physics and chemistry. In a relatively short geological time (about 500 million years), life had emerged. Laboratory simulations indicate that the emergence of life was far too fast to have come from random combinations of compounds, even if driven by lightning and heat. There must be an underlying ability of the complex system to organize itself, resulting in the self-replication we recognize as life. Living entities, even at the unicellular level, are highly organized and systematic. Systems of living organisms are themselves complex adaptive systems. The grandest of these evolved into the biological system we have today, leaving traces in the geological record of steps taken along the way.

Complexity as a discipline examines complex systems, how they adapt and evolve, looking for similarities with other complex adaptive systems. Can, for example, parallels be drawn between biological evolution and the evolution of *economic systems*? Economic systems do emerge quickly, they show tendencies for self-organization, they are complex (in the number and types of transactions), and they adapt and evolve. Biological systems do all the same types of things. There are other examples of complex adaptive systems being studied for fundamental similarities. *Cultures* show signs of adaptation and evolution. The comparison of different cultural evolutions may bear fruit as well as comparisons to biological evolution. *Science* also is a complex system of human interactions, like culture and economics, that adapts to new information and political pressure, and evolves, usually becoming more organized rather than less. Those who study *creative thinking* also see parallels with complex systems. Humans sometimes organize almost random pieces of information, often subconsciously while doing other things, and come up with brilliant creative insights. The development of *language* is another complex adaptive system that may show similar tendencies. *Artificial intelligence* is an overt attempt to devise an adaptive system that will self-organize and evolve in the same manner as an intelligent living being learns. These are a few of the broad range of topics being studied by those who investigate complexity. There are now institutes, journals, and meetings, as well as popularizations of the emerging topic of complexity.

In traditional physics, the discipline of complexity may yield insights in certain areas. Thermodynamics treats systems on the average, while statistical mechanics deals in some detail with complex systems of atoms and molecules in random thermal motion. Yet there is organization, adaptation, and evolution in those complex systems. Non-equilibrium phenomena, such as heat transfer and phase changes, are characteristically complex in detail, and new approaches to them may evolve from complexity as a discipline. Crystal growth is another example of self-organization spontaneously emerging in a complex system. Alloys are also inherently complex mixtures that show certain simple characteristics implying some self-organization. The organization of iron atoms into magnetic domains as they cool is another. Perhaps insights into these difficult areas will emerge from complexity. But at the minimum, the discipline of complexity is another example of human effort to understand and organize the universe around us, partly rooted in the discipline of physics.

A predecessor to complexity is the topic of chaos, which has been widely publicized and has become a discipline of its own. It is also based partly in physics and treats broad classes of phenomena from many disciplines. **Chaos** is a word used to describe systems whose outcomes are extremely sensitive to initial conditions. The orbit of the planet Pluto, for example, may be chaotic in that it can change tremendously due to small interactions with other planets. This makes its long-term behavior impossible to predict with precision, just as we cannot tell precisely where a decaying Earth satellite will land or how many pieces it will break into. But the discipline of chaos has found ways to deal with such systems and has been applied to apparently unrelated systems. For example, the heartbeat of people with certain types of potentially lethal arrhythmias seems to be chaotic, and this knowledge may allow more sophisticated monitoring and recognition of the need for intervention.

Chaos is related to complexity. Some chaotic systems are also inherently complex; for example, vortices in a fluid as opposed to a double pendulum. Both are chaotic and not predictable in the same sense as other systems. But there can be organization in chaos and it can also be quantified. Examples of chaotic systems are beautiful fractal patterns such as in Figure 34.21. Some chaotic systems exhibit self-organization, a type of stable chaos. The orbits of the planets in our solar system, for example, may be chaotic (we are not certain yet). But they are definitely organized and systematic, with a simple formula describing the orbital radii of the first eight planets *and* the asteroid belt. Large-scale vortices in Jupiter's atmosphere are chaotic, but the Great Red Spot is a stable self-organization of rotational energy. (See Figure 34.22.) The Great Red Spot has been in existence for at least 400 years and is a complex self-adaptive system.

The emerging field of complexity, like the now almost traditional field of chaos, is partly rooted in physics. Both attempt to see similar systematics in a very broad range of phenomena and, hence, generate a better understanding of them. Time will tell what impact these fields have on more traditional areas of physics as well as on the other disciplines they relate to.

FIGURE 34.21 This image is related to the Mandelbrot set, a complex mathematical form that is chaotic. The patterns are infinitely fine as you look closer and closer, and they indicate order in the presence of chaos. (credit: Gilberto Santa Rosa)

FIGURE 34.22 The Great Red Spot on Jupiter is an example of self-organization in a complex and chaotic system. Smaller vortices in Jupiter's atmosphere behave chaotically, but the triple-Earth-size spot is self-organized and stable for at least hundreds of years. (credit: NASA)

34.6 High-temperature Superconductors

LEARNING OBJECTIVES

By the end of this section, you will be able to:

- Identify superconductors and their uses.
- Discuss the need for a high-T_c superconductor.

Superconductors are materials with a resistivity of zero. They are familiar to the general public because of their practical applications and have been mentioned at a number of points in the text. Because the resistance of a piece of superconductor is zero, there are no heat losses for currents through them; they are used in magnets needing high currents, such as in MRI machines, and could cut energy losses in power transmission. But most superconductors must be cooled to temperatures only a few kelvin above absolute zero, a costly procedure limiting their practical applications. In the past decade, tremendous advances have been made in producing materials that become superconductors at relatively high temperatures. There is hope that room temperature superconductors may someday be manufactured.

Superconductivity was discovered accidentally in 1911 by the Dutch physicist H. Kamerlingh Onnes (1853–1926) when he used liquid helium to cool mercury. Onnes had been the first person to liquefy helium a few years earlier and was surprised to observe the resistivity of a mediocre conductor like mercury drop to zero at a temperature of 4.2 K. We define the temperature at which and below which a material becomes a superconductor to be its **critical temperature**, denoted by T_c. (See Figure 34.23.) Progress in understanding how and why a material became a superconductor was relatively slow, with the first workable theory coming in 1957. Certain other elements were also found to become superconductors, but all had T_c s less than 10 K, which are expensive to maintain. Although Onnes received a Nobel prize in 1913, it was primarily for his work with liquid helium.

In 1986, a breakthrough was announced—a ceramic compound was found to have an unprecedented T_c of 35 K. It looked as if much higher critical temperatures could be possible, and by early 1988 another ceramic (this of thallium, calcium, barium, copper, and oxygen) had been found to have $T_c = 125\text{ K}$ (see Figure 34.24.) The economic potential of perfect conductors saving electric energy is immense for T_c s above 77 K, since that is the temperature of liquid nitrogen. Although liquid helium has a boiling point of 4 K and can be used to make materials superconducting, it costs about \$5 per liter. Liquid nitrogen boils at 77 K, but only costs about \$0.30 per liter. There was general euphoria at the discovery of these complex ceramic superconductors, but this soon subsided with the sobering difficulty of forming them into usable wires. The first commercial use of a high temperature superconductor is in an electronic filter for cellular phones. High-temperature superconductors are used in experimental apparatus, and they are actively being researched, particularly in thin film applications.

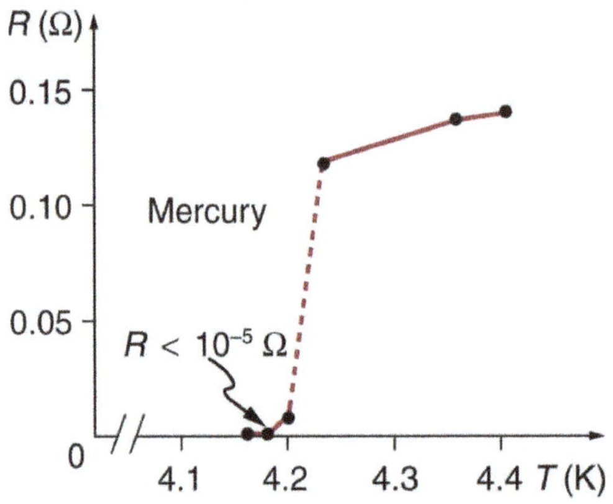

FIGURE 34.23 A graph of resistivity versus temperature for a superconductor shows a sharp transition to zero at the critical temperature T_C. High temperature superconductors have verifiable T_C s greater than 125 K, well above the easily achieved 77-K temperature of liquid nitrogen.

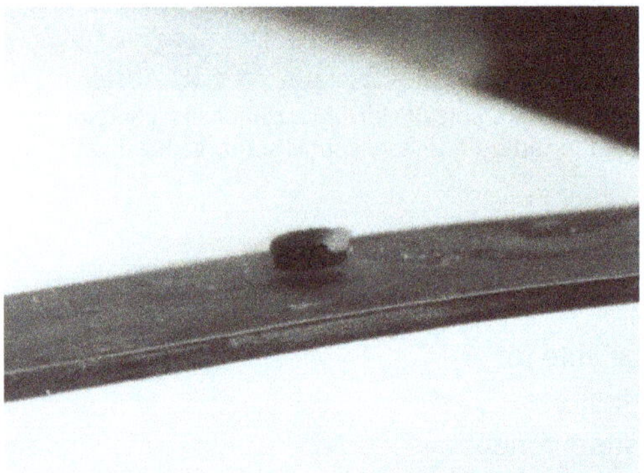

FIGURE 34.24 One characteristic of a superconductor is that it excludes magnetic flux and, thus, repels other magnets. The small magnet levitated above a high-temperature superconductor, which is cooled by liquid nitrogen, gives evidence that the material is superconducting. When the material warms and becomes conducting, magnetic flux can penetrate it, and the magnet will rest upon it. (credit: Saperaud)

The search is on for even higher T_c superconductors, many of complex and exotic copper oxide ceramics, sometimes including strontium, mercury, or yttrium as well as barium, calcium, and other elements. Room temperature (about 293 K) would be ideal, but any temperature close to room temperature is relatively cheap to produce and maintain. There are persistent reports of T_c s over 200 K and some in the vicinity of 270 K. Unfortunately, these observations are not routinely reproducible, with samples losing their superconducting nature once heated and recooled (cycled) a few times (see Figure 34.25.) They are now called USOs or unidentified superconducting objects, out of frustration and the refusal of some samples to show high T_c even though produced in the same manner as others. Reproducibility is crucial to discovery, and researchers are justifiably reluctant to claim the breakthrough they all seek. Time will tell whether USOs are real or an experimental quirk.

The theory of ordinary superconductors is difficult, involving quantum effects for widely separated electrons traveling through a material. Electrons couple in a manner that allows them to get through the material without losing energy to it, making it a superconductor. High- T_c superconductors are more difficult to understand theoretically, but theorists seem to be closing in on a workable theory. The difficulty of understanding how electrons can sneak through materials without losing energy in collisions is even greater at higher temperatures, where vibrating atoms should get in the way. Discoverers of high T_c may feel something analogous to what a politician once said upon an unexpected election victory—"I wonder what we did right?"

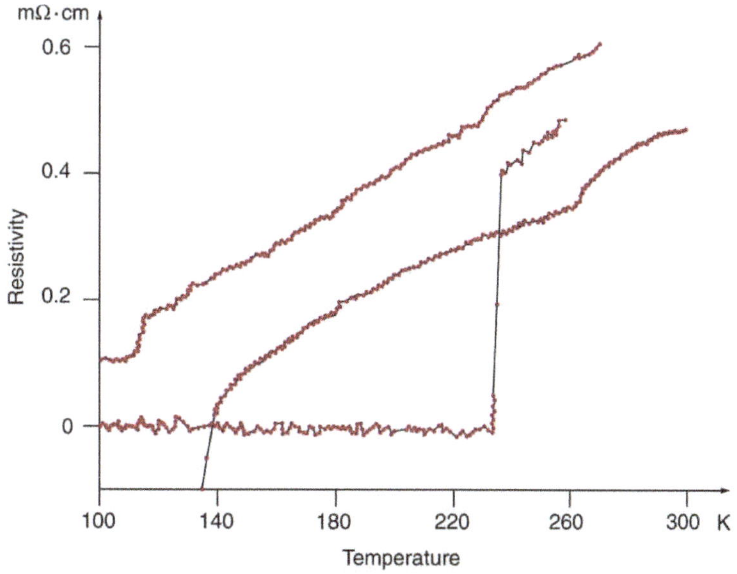

(a)

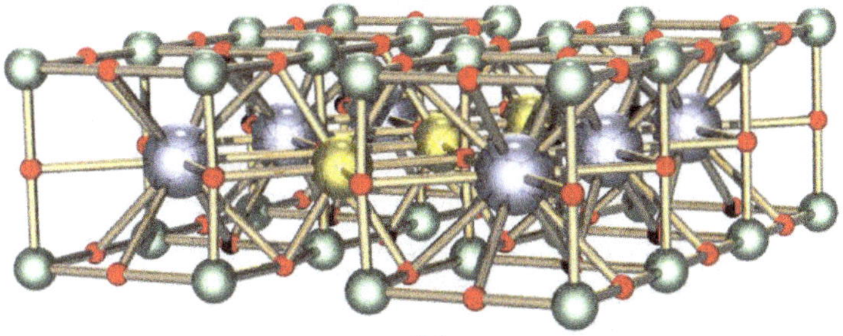
(b)

FIGURE 34.25 (a) This graph, adapted from an article in *Physics Today,* shows the behavior of a single sample of a high-temperature superconductor in three different trials. In one case the sample exhibited a T_c of about 230 K, whereas in the others it did not become superconducting at all. The lack of reproducibility is typical of forefront experiments and prohibits definitive conclusions. (b) This colorful diagram shows the complex but systematic nature of the lattice structure of a high-temperature superconducting ceramic. (credit: en:Cadmium, Wikimedia Commons)

34.7 Some Questions We Know to Ask

LEARNING OBJECTIVES

By the end of this section, you will be able to:

- Identify sample questions to be asked on the largest scales.
- Identify sample questions to be asked on the intermediate scale.
- Identify sample questions to be asked on the smallest scales.

Throughout the text we have noted how essential it is to be curious and to ask questions in order to first understand what is known, and then to go a little farther. Some questions may go unanswered for centuries; others may not have answers, but some bear delicious fruit. Part of discovery is knowing which questions to ask. You have to know something before you can even phrase a decent question. As you may have noticed, the mere act of asking a question can give you the answer. The following questions are a sample of those physicists now know to ask and are representative of the forefronts of physics. Although these questions are important, they will be replaced by others if answers are found to them. The fun continues.

On the Largest Scale

1. *Is the universe open or closed*? Theorists would like it to be just barely closed and evidence is building toward that conclusion. Recent measurements in the expansion rate of the universe and in CMBR support a flat universe. There is a connection to small-scale physics in the type and number of particles that may contribute to closing the universe.
2. *What is dark matter*? It is definitely there, but we really do not know what it is. Conventional possibilities are being ruled out, but one of them still may explain it. The answer could reveal whole new realms of physics and the disturbing possibility that most of what is out there is unknown to us, a completely different form of matter.
3. *How do galaxies form*? They exist since very early in the evolution of the universe and it remains difficult to understand how they evolved so quickly. The recent finer measurements of fluctuations in the CMBR may yet allow us to explain galaxy formation.
4. *What is the nature of various-mass black holes*? Only recently have we become confident that many black hole candidates cannot be explained by other, less exotic possibilities. But we still do not know much about how they form, what their role in the history of galactic evolution has been, and the nature of space in their vicinity. However, so many black holes are now known that correlations between black hole mass and galactic nuclei characteristics are being studied.
5. *What is the mechanism for the energy output of quasars*? These distant and extraordinarily energetic objects now seem to be early stages of galactic evolution with a supermassive black-hole-devouring material. Connections are now being made with galaxies having energetic cores, and there is evidence consistent with less consuming, supermassive black holes at the center of older galaxies. New instruments are allowing us to see deeper into our own galaxy for evidence of our own massive black hole.
6. *Where do the γ bursts come from*? We see bursts of γ rays coming from all directions in space, indicating the sources are very distant objects rather than something associated with our own galaxy. Some γ bursts finally are being correlated with known sources so that the possibility they may originate in binary neutron star interactions or black holes eating a companion neutron star can be explored.

On the Intermediate Scale

1. *How do phase transitions take place on the microscopic scale*? We know a lot about phase transitions, such as water freezing, but the details of how they occur molecule by molecule are not well understood. Similar questions about specific heat a century ago led to early quantum mechanics. It is also an example of a complex adaptive system that may yield insights into other self-organizing systems.
2. *Is there a way to deal with nonlinear phenomena that reveals underlying connections*? Nonlinear phenomena lack a direct or linear proportionality that makes analysis and understanding a little easier. There are implications for nonlinear optics and broader topics such as chaos.
3. *How do high-T_c superconductors become resistanceless at such high temperatures*? Understanding how they work may help make them more practical or may result in surprises as unexpected as the discovery of superconductivity itself.
4. *There are magnetic effects in materials we do not understand—how do they work*? Although beyond the scope of this text, there is a great deal to learn in condensed matter physics (the physics of solids and liquids). We may find surprises analogous to lasing, the quantum Hall effect, and the quantization of magnetic flux. Complexity may play a role here, too.

On the Smallest Scale

1. *Are quarks and leptons fundamental, or do they have a substructure*? The higher energy accelerators that are just completed or being constructed may supply some answers, but there will also be input from cosmology and other systematics.
2. *Why do leptons have integral charge while quarks have fractional charge*? If both are fundamental and analogous as thought, this question deserves an answer. It is obviously related to the previous question.
3. *Why are there three families of quarks and leptons*? First, does this imply some relationship? Second, why three and only three families?
4. *Are all forces truly equal (unified) under certain circumstances*? They don't have to be equal just because we

want them to be. The answer may have to be indirectly obtained because of the extreme energy at which we think they are unified.

5. *Are there other fundamental forces*? There was a flurry of activity with claims of a fifth and even a sixth force a few years ago. Interest has subsided, since those forces have not been detected consistently. Moreover, the proposed forces have strengths similar to gravity, making them extraordinarily difficult to detect in the presence of stronger forces. But the question remains; and if there are no other forces, we need to ask why only four and why these four.
6. *Is the proton stable*? We have discussed this in some detail, but the question is related to fundamental aspects of the unification of forces. We may never know from experiment that the proton is stable, only that it is very long lived.
7. *Are there magnetic monopoles*? Many particle theories call for very massive individual north- and south-pole particles—magnetic monopoles. If they exist, why are they so different in mass and elusiveness from electric charges, and if they do not exist, why not?
8. *Do neutrinos have mass*? Definitive evidence has emerged for neutrinos having mass. The implications are significant, as discussed in this chapter. There are effects on the closure of the universe and on the patterns in particle physics.
9. *What are the systematic characteristics of high- Z nuclei*? All elements with $Z = 118$ or less (with the exception of 115 and 117) have now been discovered. It has long been conjectured that there may be an island of relative stability near $Z = 114$, and the study of the most recently discovered nuclei will contribute to our understanding of nuclear forces.

These lists of questions are not meant to be complete or consistently important—you can no doubt add to it yourself. There are also important questions in topics not broached in this text, such as certain particle symmetries, that are of current interest to physicists. Hopefully, the point is clear that no matter how much we learn, there always seems to be more to know. Although we are fortunate to have the hard-won wisdom of those who preceded us, we can look forward to new enlightenment, undoubtedly sprinkled with surprise.

Glossary

axions a type of WIMPs having masses about 10^{-10} of an electron mass

Big Bang a gigantic explosion that threw out matter a few billion years ago

black holes objects having such large gravitational fields that things can fall in, but nothing, not even light, can escape

chaos word used to describe systems the outcomes of which are extremely sensitive to initial conditions

complexity an emerging field devoted to the study of complex systems

cosmic microwave background the spectrum of microwave radiation of cosmic origin

cosmological constant a theoretical construct intimately related to the expansion and closure of the universe

cosmological red shift the photon wavelength is stretched in transit from the source to the observer because of the expansion of space itself

cosmology the study of the character and evolution of the universe

critical density the density of matter needed to just halt universal expansion

critical temperature the temperature at which and below which a material becomes a superconductor

dark matter indirectly observed non-luminous matter

electroweak epoch the stage before 10^{-11} back to 10^{-34} after the Big Bang

escape velocity takeoff velocity when kinetic energy just cancels gravitational potential energy

event horizon the distance from the object at which the escape velocity is exactly the speed of light

flat (zero curvature) universe a universe that is infinite but not curved

general relativity Einstein's theory thatdescribes all types of relative motion including accelerated motion and the effects of gravity

gravitational waves mass-created distortions in space that propagate at the speed of light and that are predicted by general relativity

GUT epoch the time period from 10^{-43} to 10^{-34} after the Big Bang, when Grand Unification Theory, in which all forces except gravity are identical, governed the universe

Hubble constant a central concept in cosmology whose value is determined by taking the slope of a graph of velocity versus distance, obtained from red shift measurements

inflationary scenario the rapid expansion of the universe by an incredible factor of 10^{-50} for the brief time from 10^{-35} to about 10^{-32}s

MACHOs massive compact halo objects; microlensing objects of huge mass

microlensing a process in which light from a distant star is focused and the star appears to brighten in a characteristic manner, when a small body (smaller than about 1/1000 the mass of the Sun) passes between us and the star

negatively curved an open universe that expands forever

neutralinos a type of WIMPs having masses several orders of magnitude greater than nucleon masses

neutrino oscillations a process in which any type of neutrino could change spontaneously into any other

neutron stars literally a star composed of neutrons

positively curved a universe that is closed and eventually contracts

Quantum gravity the theory that deals with particle exchange of gravitons as the mechanism for the force

quasars the moderately distant galaxies that emit as much or more energy than a normal galaxy

Schwarzschild radius the radius of the event horizon

spontaneous symmetry breaking the transition from GUT to electroweak where the forces were no longer unified

Superconductors materials with resistivity of zero

superforce hypothetical unified force in TOE epoch

Superstring theory a theory to unify gravity with the other three forces in which the fundamental particles are considered to act like one-dimensional vibrating strings

thought experiment mental analysis of certain carefully and clearly defined situations to develop an idea

TOE epoch before 10^{-43} after the Big Bang

WIMPs weakly interacting massive particles; chargeless leptons (non-baryonic matter) interacting negligibly with normal matter

Section Summary

34.1 Cosmology and Particle Physics

- Cosmology is the study of the character and evolution of the universe.
- The two most important features of the universe are the cosmological red shifts of its galaxies being proportional to distance and its cosmic microwave background (CMBR). Both support the notion that there was a gigantic explosion, known as the Big Bang that created the universe.

- Galaxies farther away than our local group have, on an average, a recessional velocity given by
$$v = H_0 d,$$
where d is the distance to the galaxy and H_0 is the Hubble constant, taken to have the average value $H_0 = 20 \text{ km/s} \cdot \text{Mly}$.
- Explanations of the large-scale characteristics of the universe are intimately tied to particle physics.
- The dominance of matter over antimatter and the smoothness of the CMBR are two characteristics that are tied to particle physics.
- The epochs of the universe are known back to very shortly after the Big Bang, based on known laws of physics.
- The earliest epochs are tied to the unification of forces, with the electroweak epoch being partially understood, the GUT epoch being speculative, and the TOE epoch being highly speculative since it involves an unknown single superforce.
- The transition from GUT to electroweak is called spontaneous symmetry breaking. It released energy that caused the inflationary scenario, which in turn explains the smoothness of the CMBR.

34.2 General Relativity and Quantum Gravity

- Einstein's theory of general relativity includes accelerated frames and, thus, encompasses special relativity and gravity. Created by use of careful thought experiments, it has been repeatedly verified by real experiments.
- One direct result of this behavior of nature is the gravitational lensing of light by massive objects, such as galaxies, also seen in the microlensing of light by smaller bodies in our galaxy.
- Another prediction is the existence of black holes, objects for which the escape velocity is greater than the speed of light and from which nothing can escape.
- The event horizon is the distance from the object at which the escape velocity equals the speed of light c. It is called the Schwarzschild radius R_S and is given by
$$R_S = \frac{2GM}{c^2},$$
where G is the universal gravitational constant, and M is the mass of the body.
- Physics is unknown inside the event horizon, and the possibility of wormholes and time travel are being studied.
- Candidates for black holes may power the extremely energetic emissions of quasars, distant objects that seem to be early stages of galactic evolution.
- Neutron stars are stellar remnants, having the density of a nucleus, that hint that black holes could form from supernovas, too.
- Gravitational waves are wrinkles in space, predicted by general relativity but not yet observed, caused by changes in very massive objects.
- Quantum gravity is an incompletely developed theory that strives to include general relativity, quantum mechanics, and unification of forces (thus, a TOE).
- One unconfirmed connection between general relativity and quantum mechanics is the prediction of characteristic radiation from just outside black holes.

34.3 Superstrings

- Superstring theory holds that fundamental particles are one-dimensional vibrations analogous to those on strings and is an attempt at a theory of quantum gravity.

34.4 Dark Matter and Closure

- Dark matter is non-luminous matter detected in and around galaxies and galactic clusters.
- It may be 10 times the mass of the luminous matter in the universe, and its amount may determine whether the universe is open or closed (expands forever or eventually stops).
- The determining factor is the critical density of the universe and the cosmological constant, a theoretical construct intimately related to the expansion and closure of the universe.
- The critical density ρ_c is the density needed to just halt universal expansion. It is estimated to be approximately 10^{-26} kg/m^3.
- An open universe is negatively curved, a closed universe is positively curved, whereas a universe with exactly the critical density is flat.
- Dark matter's composition is a major mystery, but it may be due to the suspected mass of neutrinos or a completely unknown type of leptonic matter.
- If neutrinos have mass, they will change families, a process known as neutrino oscillations, for which there is growing evidence.

34.5 Complexity and Chaos

- Complexity is an emerging field, rooted primarily in physics, that considers complex adaptive systems and their evolution, including self-organization.
- Complexity has applications in physics and many

other disciplines, such as biological evolution.

- Chaos is a field that studies systems whose properties depend extremely sensitively on some variables and whose evolution is impossible to predict.
- Chaotic systems may be simple or complex.
- Studies of chaos have led to methods for understanding and predicting certain chaotic behaviors.

34.6 High-temperature Superconductors

- High-temperature superconductors are materials that become superconducting at temperatures well above a few kelvin.
- The critical temperature T_c is the temperature below which a material is superconducting.
- Some high-temperature superconductors have verified T_c s above 125 K, and there are reports of T_c s as high as 250 K.

34.7 Some Questions We Know to Ask

- On the largest scale, the questions which can be asked may be about dark matter, dark energy, black holes, quasars, and other aspects of the universe.
- On the intermediate scale, we can query about gravity, phase transitions, nonlinear phenomena, high- T_c superconductors, and magnetic effects on materials.
- On the smallest scale, questions may be about quarks and leptons, fundamental forces, stability of protons, and existence of monopoles.

Conceptual Questions

34.1 Cosmology and Particle Physics

1. Explain why it only *appears* that we are at the center of expansion of the universe and why an observer in another galaxy would see the same relative motion of all but the closest galaxies away from her.

2. If there is no observable edge to the universe, can we determine where its center of expansion is? Explain.

3. If the universe is infinite, does it have a center? Discuss.

4. Another known cause of red shift in light is the source being in a high gravitational field. Discuss how this can be eliminated as the source of galactic red shifts, given that the shifts are proportional to distance and not to the size of the galaxy.

5. If some unknown cause of red shift—such as light becoming "tired" from traveling long distances through empty space—is discovered, what effect would there be on cosmology?

6. Olbers's paradox poses an interesting question: If the universe is infinite, then any line of sight should eventually fall on a star's surface. Why then is the sky dark at night? Discuss the commonly accepted evolution of the universe as a solution to this paradox.

7. If the cosmic microwave background radiation (CMBR) is the remnant of the Big Bang's fireball, we expect to see hot and cold regions in it. What are two causes of these wrinkles in the CMBR? Are the observed temperature variations greater or less than originally expected?

8. The decay of one type of K-meson is cited as evidence that nature favors matter over antimatter. Since mesons are composed of a quark and an antiquark, is it surprising that they would preferentially decay to one type over another? Is this an asymmetry in nature? Is the predominance of matter over antimatter an asymmetry?

9. Distances to local galaxies are determined by measuring the brightness of stars, called Cepheid variables, that can be observed individually and that have absolute brightnesses at a standard distance that are well known. Explain how the measured brightness would vary with distance as compared with the absolute brightness.

10. Distances to very remote galaxies are estimated based on their apparent type, which indicate the number of stars in the galaxy, and their measured brightness. Explain how the measured brightness would vary with distance. Would there be any correction necessary to compensate for the red shift of the galaxy (all distant galaxies have significant red shifts)? Discuss possible causes of uncertainties in these measurements.

11. If the smallest meaningful time interval is greater than zero, will the lines in Figure 34.9 ever meet?

34.2 General Relativity and Quantum Gravity

12. Quantum gravity, if developed, would be an improvement on both general relativity and quantum mechanics, but more mathematically difficult. Under what circumstances would it be necessary to use quantum gravity? Similarly, under what circumstances could general relativity be used? When could special relativity, quantum mechanics, or classical physics be used?

13. Does observed gravitational lensing correspond to a converging or diverging lens? Explain briefly.

14. Suppose you measure the red shifts of all the images produced by gravitational lensing, such as in Figure 34.12.You find that the central image has a red shift less than the outer images, and those all have the same red shift. Discuss how this not only shows that the images are of the same object, but also implies that the red shift is not affected by taking different paths through space. Does it imply that cosmological red shifts are not caused by traveling through space (light getting tired, perhaps)?

15. What are gravitational waves, and have they yet been observed either directly or indirectly?

16. Is the event horizon of a black hole the actual physical surface of the object?

17. Suppose black holes radiate their mass away and the lifetime of a black hole created by a supernova is about 10^{67} years. How does this lifetime compare with the accepted age of the universe? Is it surprising that we do not observe the predicted characteristic radiation?

34.4 Dark Matter and Closure

18. Discuss the possibility that star velocities at the edges of galaxies being greater than expected is due to unknown properties of gravity rather than to the existence of dark matter. Would this mean, for example, that gravity is greater or smaller than expected at large distances? Are there other tests that could be made of gravity at large distances, such as observing the motions of neighboring galaxies?

19. How does relativistic time dilation prohibit neutrino oscillations if they are massless?

20. If neutrino oscillations do occur, will they violate conservation of the various lepton family numbers (L_e, L_μ, and L_τ)? Will neutrino oscillations violate conservation of the total number of leptons?

21. Lacking direct evidence of WIMPs as dark matter, why must we eliminate all other possible explanations based on the known forms of matter before we invoke their existence?

34.5 Complexity and Chaos

22. Must a complex system be adaptive to be of interest in the field of complexity? Give an example to support your answer.

23. State a necessary condition for a system to be chaotic.

34.6 High-temperature Superconductors

24. What is critical temperature T_c? Do all materials have a critical temperature? Explain why or why not.

25. Explain how good thermal contact with liquid nitrogen can keep objects at a temperature of 77 K (liquid nitrogen's boiling point at atmospheric pressure).

26. Not only is liquid nitrogen a cheaper coolant than liquid helium, its boiling point is higher (77 K vs. 4.2 K). How does higher temperature help lower the cost of cooling a material? Explain in terms of the rate of heat transfer being related to the temperature difference between the sample and its surroundings.

34.7 Some Questions We Know to Ask

27. For experimental evidence, particularly of previously unobserved phenomena, to be taken seriously it must be reproducible or of sufficiently high quality that a single observation is meaningful. Supernova 1987A is not reproducible. How do we know observations of it were valid? The fifth force is not broadly accepted. Is this due to lack of reproducibility or poor-quality experiments (or both)? Discuss why forefront experiments are more subject to observational problems than those involving established phenomena.

28. Discuss whether you think there are limits to what humans can understand about the laws of physics. Support your arguments.

Problems & Exercises

34.1 Cosmology and Particle Physics

1. Find the approximate mass of the luminous matter in the Milky Way galaxy, given it has approximately 10^{11} stars of average mass 1.5 times that of our Sun.

2. Find the approximate mass of the dark and

luminous matter in the Milky Way galaxy. Assume the luminous matter is due to approximately 10^{11} stars of average mass 1.5 times that of our Sun, and take the dark matter to be 10 times as massive as the luminous matter.

3. (a) Estimate the mass of the luminous matter in the known universe, given there are 10^{11} galaxies, each containing 10^{11} stars of average mass 1.5 times that of our Sun. (b) How many protons (the most abundant nuclide) are there in this mass? (c) Estimate the total number of particles in the observable universe by multiplying the answer to (b) by two, since there is an electron for each proton, and then by 10^{9}, since there are far more particles (such as photons and neutrinos) in space than in luminous matter.

4. If a galaxy is 500 Mly away from us, how fast do we expect it to be moving and in what direction?

5. On average, how far away are galaxies that are moving away from us at 2.0% of the speed of light?

6. Our solar system orbits the center of the Milky Way galaxy. Assuming a circular orbit 30,000 ly in radius and an orbital speed of 250 km/s, how many years does it take for one revolution? Note that this is approximate, assuming constant speed and circular orbit, but it is representative of the time for our system and local stars to make one revolution around the galaxy.

7. (a) What is the approximate speed relative to us of a galaxy near the edge of the known universe, some 10 Gly away? (b) What fraction of the speed of light is this? Note that we have observed galaxies moving away from us at greater than $0.9c$.

8. (a) Calculate the approximate age of the universe from the average value of the Hubble constant, $H_0 = 20\text{ km/s}\cdot\text{Mly}$. To do this, calculate the time it would take to travel 1 Mly at a constant expansion rate of 20 km/s. (b) If deceleration is taken into account, would the actual age of the universe be greater or less than that found here? Explain.

9. Assuming a circular orbit for the Sun about the center of the Milky Way galaxy, calculate its orbital speed using the following information: The mass of the galaxy is equivalent to a single mass 1.5×10^{11} times that of the Sun (or $3 \times 10^{41}\text{ kg}$), located 30,000 ly away.

10. (a) What is the approximate force of gravity on a 70-kg person due to the Andromeda galaxy, assuming its total mass is 10^{13} that of our Sun and acts like a single mass 2 Mly away? (b) What is the ratio of this force to the person's weight? Note that Andromeda is the closest large galaxy.

11. Andromeda galaxy is the closest large galaxy and is visible to the naked eye. Estimate its brightness relative to the Sun, assuming it has luminosity 10^{12} times that of the Sun and lies 2 Mly away.

12. (a) A particle and its antiparticle are at rest relative to an observer and annihilate (completely destroying both masses), creating two γ rays of equal energy. What is the characteristic γ-ray energy you would look for if searching for evidence of proton-antiproton annihilation? (The fact that such radiation is rarely observed is evidence that there is very little antimatter in the universe.) (b) How does this compare with the 0.511-MeV energy associated with electron-positron annihilation?

13. The average particle energy needed to observe unification of forces is estimated to be 10^{19} GeV. (a) What is the rest mass in kilograms of a particle that has a rest mass of $10^{19}\text{ GeV}/c^2$? (b) How many times the mass of a hydrogen atom is this?

14. The peak intensity of the CMBR occurs at a wavelength of 1.1 mm. (a) What is the energy in eV of a 1.1-mm photon? (b) There are approximately 10^{9} photons for each massive particle in deep space. Calculate the energy of 10^{9} such photons. (c) If the average massive particle in space has a mass half that of a proton, what energy would be created by converting its mass to energy? (d) Does this imply that space is "matter dominated"? Explain briefly.

15. (a) What Hubble constant corresponds to an approximate age of the universe of 10^{10} y? To get an approximate value, assume the expansion rate is constant and calculate the speed at which two galaxies must move apart to be separated by 1 Mly (present average galactic separation) in a time of 10^{10} y. (b) Similarly, what Hubble constant corresponds to a universe approximately 2×10^{10}-y old?

16. Show that the velocity of a star orbiting its galaxy in a circular orbit is inversely proportional to the square root of its orbital radius, assuming the mass of the stars inside its orbit acts like a single mass at the center of the galaxy. You may use an equation from a previous chapter to support your conclusion, but you must justify its use and define all terms used.

17. The core of a star collapses during a supernova, forming a neutron star. Angular momentum of the core is conserved, and so the neutron star spins rapidly. If the initial core radius is 5.0×10^5 km and it collapses to 10.0 km, find the neutron star's angular velocity in revolutions per second, given the core's angular velocity was originally 1 revolution per 30.0 days.

18. Using data from the previous problem, find the increase in rotational kinetic energy, given the core's mass is 1.3 times that of our Sun. Where does this increase in kinetic energy come from?

19. Distances to the nearest stars (up to 500 ly away) can be measured by a technique called parallax, as shown in Figure 34.26. What are the angles θ_1 and θ_2 relative to the plane of the Earth's orbit for a star 4.0 ly directly above the Sun?

20. (a) Use the Heisenberg uncertainty principle to calculate the uncertainty in energy for a corresponding time interval of 10^{-43} s. (b) Compare this energy with the 10^{19} GeV unification-of-forces energy and discuss why they are similar.

21. Construct Your Own Problem
Consider a star moving in a circular orbit at the edge of a galaxy. Construct a problem in which you calculate the mass of that galaxy in kg and in multiples of the solar mass based on the velocity of the star and its distance from the center of the galaxy.

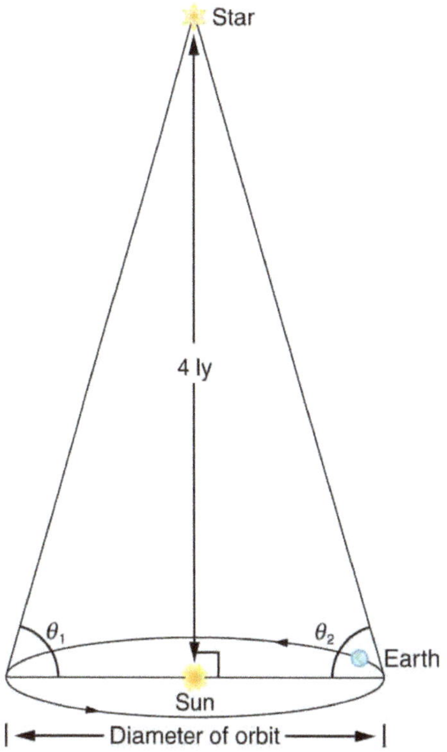

FIGURE 34.26 Distances to nearby stars are measured using triangulation, also called the parallax method. The angle of line of sight to the star is measured at intervals six months apart, and the distance is calculated by using the known diameter of the Earth's orbit. This can be done for stars up to about 500 ly away.

34.2 General Relativity and Quantum Gravity

22. What is the Schwarzschild radius of a black hole that has a mass eight times that of our Sun? Note that stars must be more massive than the Sun to form black holes as a result of a supernova.

23. Black holes with masses smaller than those formed in supernovas may have been created in the Big Bang. Calculate the radius of one that has a mass equal to the Earth's.

24. Supermassive black holes are thought to exist at the center of many galaxies.
(a) What is the radius of such an object if it has a mass of 10^9 Suns?
(b) What is this radius in light years?

25. Construct Your Own Problem
Consider a supermassive black hole near the center of a galaxy. Calculate the radius of such an object based on its mass. You must consider how much mass is reasonable for these large objects, and which is now nearly directly observed. (Information on black holes posted on the Web by NASA and other agencies is reliable, for example.)

34.3 Superstrings

26. The characteristic length of entities in Superstring theory is approximately 10^{-35} m.
(a) Find the energy in GeV of a photon of this wavelength.
(b) Compare this with the average particle energy of 10^{19} GeV needed for unification of forces.

34.4 Dark Matter and Closure

27. If the dark matter in the Milky Way were composed entirely of MACHOs (evidence shows it is not), approximately how many would there have to be? Assume the average mass of a MACHO is 1/1000 that of the Sun, and that dark matter has a mass 10 times that of the luminous Milky Way galaxy with its 10^{11} stars of average mass 1.5 times the Sun's mass.

28. The critical mass density needed to just halt the expansion of the universe is approximately $10^{-26}\ \text{kg/m}^3$.
(a) Convert this to $\text{eV}/c^2 \cdot \text{m}^3$.
(b) Find the number of neutrinos per cubic meter needed to close the universe if their average mass is $7\ \text{eV}/c^2$ and they have negligible kinetic energies.

29. Assume the average density of the universe is 0.1 of the critical density needed for closure. What is the average number of protons per cubic meter, assuming the universe is composed mostly of hydrogen?

30. To get an idea of how empty deep space is on the average, perform the following calculations:
(a) Find the volume our Sun would occupy if it had an average density equal to the critical density of $10^{-26}\ \text{kg/m}^3$ thought necessary to halt the expansion of the universe.
(b) Find the radius of a sphere of this volume in light years.
(c) What would this radius be if the density were that of luminous matter, which is approximately 5% that of the critical density?
(d) Compare the radius found in part (c) with the 4-ly average separation of stars in the arms of the Milky Way.

34.6 High-temperature Superconductors

31. A section of superconducting wire carries a current of 100 A and requires 1.00 L of liquid nitrogen per hour to keep it below its critical temperature. For it to be economically advantageous to use a superconducting wire, the cost of cooling the wire must be less than the cost of energy lost to heat in the wire. Assume that the cost of liquid nitrogen is $0.30 per liter, and that electric energy costs $0.10 per kW·h. What is the resistance of a normal wire that costs as much in wasted electric energy as the cost of liquid nitrogen for the superconductor?

32. Critical Thinking Assume two galaxies are 2.00×10^2 Mly apart. (a) How fast are they separating due to space expansion? (b) Now suppose a third galaxy is located 2.00×10^2 Mly along a line that is a perpendicular bisector of the line segment between the first two galaxies. How fast is this galaxy separating from either of the other two galaxies? (c) Why would the third galaxy appear to be receding from both of the initially mentioned galaxies at the same rate? (d) How would the apparent motion be detected?

APPENDIX A

Atomic Masses

Atomic Number, Z	Name	Atomic Mass Number, A	Symbol	Atomic Mass (u)	Percent Abundance or Decay Mode	Half-life, $t_{1/2}$
0	neutron	1	n	1.008 665	β^-	10.37 min
1	Hydrogen	1	^1H	1.007 825	99.985%	
	Deuterium	2	^2H or D	2.014 102	0.015%	
	Tritium	3	^3H or T	3.016 050	β^-	12.33 y
2	Helium	3	^3He	3.016 030	$1.38 \times 10^{-4}\%$	
		4	^4He	4.002 603	$\approx 100\%$	
3	Lithium	6	^6Li	6.015 121	7.5%	
		7	^7Li	7.016 003	92.5%	
4	Beryllium	7	^7Be	7.016 928	EC	53.29 d
		9	^9Be	9.012 182	100%	
5	Boron	10	^{10}B	10.012 937	19.9%	
		11	^{11}B	11.009 305	80.1%	
6	Carbon	11	^{11}C	11.011 432	EC, β^+	

TABLE A1 Atomic Masses

Atomic Number, Z	Name	Atomic Mass Number, A	Symbol	Atomic Mass (u)	Percent Abundance or Decay Mode	Half-life, $t_{1/2}$
		12	^{12}C	12.000 000	98.90%	
		13	^{13}C	13.003 355	1.10%	
		14	^{14}C	14.003 241	β^-	5730 y
7	Nitrogen	13	^{13}N	13.005 738	β^+	9.96 min
		14	^{14}N	14.003 074	99.63%	
		15	^{15}N	15.000 108	0.37%	
8	Oxygen	15	^{15}O	15.003 065	EC, β^+	122 s
		16	^{16}O	15.994 915	99.76%	
		18	^{18}O	17.999 160	0.200%	
9	Fluorine	18	^{18}F	18.000 937	EC, β^+	1.83 h
		19	^{19}F	18.998 403	100%	
10	Neon	20	^{20}Ne	19.992 435	90.51%	
		22	^{22}Ne	21.991 383	9.22%	
11	Sodium	22	^{22}Na	21.994 434	β^+	2.602 y
		23	^{23}Na	22.989 767	100%	

TABLE A1 Atomic Masses

Atomic Number, Z	Name	Atomic Mass Number, A	Symbol	Atomic Mass (u)	Percent Abundance or Decay Mode	Half-life, $t_{1/2}$
		24	^{24}Na	23.990 961	β^-	14.96 h
12	Magnesium	24	^{24}Mg	23.985 042	78.99%	
13	Aluminum	27	^{27}Al	26.981 539	100%	
14	Silicon	28	^{28}Si	27.976 927	92.23%	2.62h
		31	^{31}Si	30.975 362	β^-	
15	Phosphorus	31	^{31}P	30.973 762	100%	
		32	^{32}P	31.973 907	β^-	14.28 d
16	Sulfur	32	^{32}S	31.972 070	95.02%	
		35	^{35}S	34.969 031	β^-	87.4 d
17	Chlorine	35	^{35}Cl	34.968 852	75.77%	
		37	^{37}Cl	36.965 903	24.23%	
18	Argon	40	^{40}Ar	39.962 384	99.60%	
19	Potassium	39	^{39}K	38.963 707	93.26%	
		40	^{40}K	39.963 999	0.0117%, EC, β^-	1.28×10^9 y
20	Calcium	40	^{40}Ca	39.962 591	96.94%	

TABLE A1 Atomic Masses

Atomic Number, Z	Name	Atomic Mass Number, A	Symbol	Atomic Mass (u)	Percent Abundance or Decay Mode	Half-life, $t_{1/2}$
21	Scandium	45	^{45}Sc	44.955 910	100%	
22	Titanium	48	^{48}Ti	47.947 947	73.8%	
23	Vanadium	51	^{51}V	50.943 962	99.75%	
24	Chromium	52	^{52}Cr	51.940 509	83.79%	
25	Manganese	55	^{55}Mn	54.938 047	100%	
26	Iron	56	^{56}Fe	55.934 939	91.72%	
27	Cobalt	59	^{59}Co	58.933 198	100%	
		60	^{60}Co	59.933 819	β^-	5.271 y
28	Nickel	58	^{58}Ni	57.935 346	68.27%	
		60	^{60}Ni	59.930 788	26.10%	
29	Copper	63	^{63}Cu	62.939 598	69.17%	
		65	^{65}Cu	64.927 793	30.83%	
30	Zinc	64	^{64}Zn	63.929 145	48.6%	
		66	^{66}Zn	65.926 034	27.9%	
31	Gallium	69	^{69}Ga	68.925 580	60.1%	

TABLE A1 Atomic Masses

Atomic Number, Z	Name	Atomic Mass Number, A	Symbol	Atomic Mass (u)	Percent Abundance or Decay Mode	Half-life, $t_{1/2}$
32	Germanium	72	^{72}Ge	71.922 079	27.4%	
		74	^{74}Ge	73.921 177	36.5%	
33	Arsenic	75	^{75}As	74.921 594	100%	
34	Selenium	80	^{80}Se	79.916 520	49.7%	
35	Bromine	79	^{79}Br	78.918 336	50.69%	
36	Krypton	84	^{84}Kr	83.911 507	57.0%	
37	Rubidium	85	^{85}Rb	84.911 794	72.17%	
38	Strontium	86	^{86}Sr	85.909 267	9.86%	
		88	^{88}Sr	87.905 619	82.58%	
		90	^{90}Sr	89.907 738	β^-	28.8 y
39	Yttrium	89	^{89}Y	88.905 849	100%	
		90	^{90}Y	89.907 152	β^-	64.1 h
40	Zirconium	90	^{90}Zr	89.904 703	51.45%	
41	Niobium	93	^{93}Nb	92.906 377	100%	
42	Molybdenum	98	^{98}Mo	97.905 406	24.13%	

TABLE A1 Atomic Masses

Atomic Number, Z	Name	Atomic Mass Number, A	Symbol	Atomic Mass (u)	Percent Abundance or Decay Mode	Half-life, $t_{1/2}$
43	Technetium	98	^{98}Tc	97.907 215	β^-	$4.2 \times 10^6 y$
44	Ruthenium	102	^{102}Ru	101.904 348	31.6%	
45	Rhodium	103	^{103}Rh	102.905 500	100%	
46	Palladium	106	^{106}Pd	105.903 478	27.33%	
47	Silver	107	^{107}Ag	106.905 092	51.84%	
		109	^{109}Ag	108.904 757	48.16%	
48	Cadmium	114	^{114}Cd	113.903 357	28.73%	
49	Indium	115	^{115}In	114.903 880	95.7%, β^-	$4.4 \times 10^{14} y$
50	Tin	120	^{120}Sn	119.902 200	32.59%	
51	Antimony	121	^{121}Sb	120.903 821	57.3%	
52	Tellurium	130	^{130}Te	129.906 229	33.8%, β^-	$2.5 \times 10^{21} y$
53	Iodine	127	^{127}I	126.904 473	100%	
		131	^{131}I	130.906 114	β^-	8.040 d
54	Xenon	132	^{132}Xe	131.904 144	26.9%	
		136	^{136}Xe	135.907 214	8.9%	

TABLE A1 Atomic Masses

Atomic Number, Z	Name	Atomic Mass Number, A	Symbol	Atomic Mass (u)	Percent Abundance or Decay Mode	Half-life, $t_{1/2}$
55	Cesium	133	^{133}Cs	132.905 429	100%	
		134	^{134}Cs	133.906 696	EC, β^-	2.06 y
56	Barium	137	^{137}Ba	136.905 812	11.23%	
		138	^{138}Ba	137.905 232	71.70%	
57	Lanthanum	139	^{139}La	138.906 346	99.91%	
58	Cerium	140	^{140}Ce	139.905 433	88.48%	
59	Praseodymium	141	^{141}Pr	140.907 647	100%	
60	Neodymium	142	^{142}Nd	141.907 719	27.13%	
61	Promethium	145	^{145}Pm	144.912 743	EC, α	17.7 y
62	Samarium	152	^{152}Sm	151.919 729	26.7%	
63	Europium	153	^{153}Eu	152.921 225	52.2%	
64	Gadolinium	158	^{158}Gd	157.924 099	24.84%	
65	Terbium	159	^{159}Tb	158.925 342	100%	
66	Dysprosium	164	^{164}Dy	163.929 171	28.2%	
67	Holmium	165	^{165}Ho	164.930 319	100%	

TABLE A1 Atomic Masses

Atomic Number, Z	Name	Atomic Mass Number, A	Symbol	Atomic Mass (u)	Percent Abundance or Decay Mode	Half-life, $t_{1/2}$
68	Erbium	166	^{166}Er	165.930 290	33.6%	
69	Thulium	169	^{169}Tm	168.934 212	100%	
70	Ytterbium	174	^{174}Yb	173.938 859	31.8%	
71	Lutecium	175	^{175}Lu	174.940 770	97.41%	
72	Hafnium	180	^{180}Hf	179.946 545	35.10%	
73	Tantalum	181	^{181}Ta	180.947 992	99.98%	
74	Tungsten	184	^{184}W	183.950 928	30.67%	
75	Rhenium	187	^{187}Re	186.955 744	62.6%, β^-	4.6×10^{10}y
76	Osmium	191	^{191}Os	190.960 920	β^-	15.4 d
		192	^{192}Os	191.961 467	41.0%	
77	Iridium	191	^{191}Ir	190.960 584	37.3%	
		193	^{193}Ir	192.962 917	62.7%	
78	Platinum	195	^{195}Pt	194.964 766	33.8%	
79	Gold	197	^{197}Au	196.966 543	100%	
		198	^{198}Au	197.968 217	β^-	2.696 d

TABLE A1 Atomic Masses

Atomic Number, Z	Name	Atomic Mass Number, A	Symbol	Atomic Mass (u)	Percent Abundance or Decay Mode	Half-life, $t_{1/2}$
80	Mercury	199	^{199}Hg	198.968 253	16.87%	
		202	^{202}Hg	201.970 617	29.86%	
81	Thallium	205	^{205}Tl	204.974 401	70.48%	
82	Lead	206	^{206}Pb	205.974 440	24.1%	
		207	^{207}Pb	206.975 872	22.1%	
		208	^{208}Pb	207.976 627	52.4%	
		210	^{210}Pb	209.984 163	α, β^-	22.3 y
		211	^{211}Pb	210.988 735	β^-	36.1 min
		212	^{212}Pb	211.991 871	β^-	10.64 h
83	Bismuth	209	^{209}Bi	208.980 374	100%	
		211	^{211}Bi	210.987 255	α, β^-	2.14 min
84	Polonium	210	^{210}Po	209.982 848	α	138.38 d
85	Astatine	218	^{218}At	218.008 684	α, β^-	1.6 s
86	Radon	222	^{222}Rn	222.017 570	α	3.82 d
87	Francium	223	^{223}Fr	223.019 733	α, β^-	21.8 min

TABLE A1 Atomic Masses

Atomic Number, Z	Name	Atomic Mass Number, A	Symbol	Atomic Mass (u)	Percent Abundance or Decay Mode	Half-life, $t_{1/2}$
88	Radium	226	^{226}Ra	226.025 402	α	$1.60 \times 10^3 y$
89	Actinium	227	^{227}Ac	227.027 750	α, β^-	21.8 y
90	Thorium	228	^{228}Th	228.028 715	α	1.91 y
		232	^{232}Th	232.038 054	100%, α	$1.41 \times 10^{10} y$
91	Protactinium	231	^{231}Pa	231.035 880	α	$3.28 \times 10^4 y$
92	Uranium	233	^{233}U	233.039 628	α	$1.59 \times 10^3 y$
		235	^{235}U	235.043 924	0.720%, α	$7.04 \times 10^8 y$
		236	^{236}U	236.045 562	α	$2.34 \times 10^7 y$
		238	^{238}U	238.050 784	99.2745%, α	$4.47 \times 10^9 y$
		239	^{239}U	239.054 289	β^-	23.5 min
93	Neptunium	239	^{239}Np	239.052 933	β^-	2.355 d
94	Plutonium	239	^{239}Pu	239.052 157	α	$2.41 \times 10^4 y$
95	Americium	243	^{243}Am	243.061 375	α, fission	$7.37 \times 10^3 y$
96	Curium	245	^{245}Cm	245.065 483	α	$8.50 \times 10^3 y$
97	Berkelium	247	^{247}Bk	247.070 300	α	$1.38 \times 10^3 y$

TABLE A1 Atomic Masses

Atomic Number, Z	Name	Atomic Mass Number, A	Symbol	Atomic Mass (u)	Percent Abundance or Decay Mode	Half-life, $t_{1/2}$
98	Californium	249	^{249}Cf	249.074 844	α	351 y
99	Einsteinium	254	^{254}Es	254.088 019	α, β^-	276 d
100	Fermium	253	^{253}Fm	253.085 173	EC, α	3.00 d
101	Mendelevium	255	^{255}Md	255.091 081	EC, α	27 min
102	Nobelium	255	^{255}No	255.093 260	EC, α	3.1 min
103	Lawrencium	257	^{257}Lr	257.099 480	EC, α	0.646 s
104	Rutherfordium	261	^{261}Rf	261.108 690	α	1.08 min
105	Dubnium	262	^{262}Db	262.113 760	α, fission	34 s
106	Seaborgium	263	^{263}Sg	263.11 86	α, fission	0.8 s
107	Bohrium	262	^{262}Bh	262.123 1	α	0.102 s
108	Hassium	264	^{264}Hs	264.128 5	α	0.08 ms
109	Meitnerium	266	^{266}Mt	266.137 8	α	3.4 ms

TABLE A1 Atomic Masses

APPENDIX B

Selected Radioactive Isotopes

Decay modes are α, β^-, β^+, electron capture (EC) and isomeric transition (IT). EC results in the same daughter nucleus as would β^+ decay. IT is a transition from a metastable excited state. Energies for $\beta^\pm$ decays are the maxima; average energies are roughly one-half the maxima.

Isotope	$t_{1/2}$	DecayMode(s)	Energy(MeV)	Percent		γ-Ray Energy(MeV)	Percent
^{3}H	12.33 y	β^-	0.0186	100%			
^{14}C	5730 y	β^-	0.156	100%			
^{13}N	9.96 min	β^+	1.20	100%			
^{22}Na	2.602 y	β^+	0.55	90%	γ	1.27	100%
^{32}P	14.28 d	β^-	1.71	100%			
^{35}S	87.4 d	β^-	0.167	100%			
^{36}Cl	3.00×10^5 y	β^-	0.710	100%			
^{40}K	1.28×10^9 y	β^-	1.31	89%			
^{43}K	22.3 h	β^-	0.827	87%	γs	0.373	87%
						0.618	87%
^{45}Ca	165 d	β^-	0.257	100%			
^{51}Cr	27.70 d	EC			γ	0.320	10%
^{52}Mn	5.59d	β^+	3.69	28%	γs	1.33	28%
						1.43	28%
^{52}Fe	8.27 h	β^+	1.80	43%		0.169	43%
						0.378	43%
^{59}Fe	44.6 d	β^-s	0.273	45%	γs	1.10	57%
			0.466	55%		1.29	43%

TABLE B1 Selected Radioactive Isotopes

Isotope	$t_{1/2}$	DecayMode(s)	Energy(MeV)	Percent		γ-Ray Energy(MeV)	Percent
^{60}Co	5.271 y	β^-	0.318	100%	γs	1.17	100%
						1.33	100%
^{65}Zn	244.1 d	EC			γ	1.12	51%
^{67}Ga	78.3 h	EC			γs	0.0933	70%
						0.185	35%
						0.300	19%
						others	
^{75}Se	118.5 d	EC			γs	0.121	20%
						0.136	65%
						0.265	68%
						0.280	20%
						others	
^{86}Rb	18.8 d	β^-s	0.69	9%	γ	1.08	9%
			1.77	91%			
^{85}Sr	64.8 d	EC			γ	0.514	100%
^{90}Sr	28.8 y	β^-	0.546	100%			
^{90}Y	64.1 h	β^-	2.28	100%			
^{99m}Tc	6.02 h	IT			γ	0.142	100%
^{113m}In	99.5 min	IT			γ	0.392	100%
^{123}I	13.0 h	EC			γ	0.159	$\approx$100%
^{131}I	8.040 d	β^-s	0.248	7%	γs	0.364	85%
			0.607	93%		others	
			others				
^{129}Cs	32.3 h	EC			γs	0.0400	35%

TABLE B1 Selected Radioactive Isotopes

Isotope	$t_{1/2}$	DecayMode(s)	Energy(MeV)	Percent		γ-Ray Energy(MeV)	Percent
						0.372	32%
						0.411	25%
						others	
^{137}Cs	30.17 y	$\beta^- s$	0.511	95%	γ	0.662	95%
			1.17	5%			
^{140}Ba	12.79 d	β^-	1.035	$\approx 100\%$	γs	0.030	25%
						0.044	65%
						0.537	24%
						others	
^{198}Au	2.696 d	β^-	1.161	$\approx 100\%$	γ	0.412	$\approx 100\%$
^{197}Hg	64.1 h	EC			γ	0.0733	100%
^{210}Po	138.38 d	α	5.41	100%			
^{226}Ra	1.60×10^3 y	αs	4.68	5%	γ	0.186	100%
			4.87	95%			
^{235}U	7.038×10^8 y	α	4.68	$\approx 100\%$	γs	numerous	<0.400%
^{238}U	4.468×10^9 y	αs	4.22	23%	γ	0.050	23%
			4.27	77%			
^{237}Np	2.14×10^6 y	αs	numerous		γs	numerous	<0.250%
			4.96 (max.)				
^{239}Pu	2.41×10^4 y	αs	5.19	11%	γs	7.5×10^{-5}	73%
			5.23	15%		0.013	15%
			5.24	73%		0.052	10%
						others	
^{243}Am	7.37×10^3 y	αs	Max. 5.44		γs	0.075	

TABLE B1 Selected Radioactive Isotopes

Isotope	$t_{1/2}$	DecayMode(s)	Energy(MeV)	Percent		γ-Ray Energy(MeV)	Percent
			5.37	88%		others	
			5.32	11%			
			others				

TABLE B1 Selected Radioactive Isotopes

APPENDIX C

Useful Information

This appendix is broken into several tables.

- Table C1, Important Constants
- Table C2, Submicroscopic Masses
- Table C3, Solar System Data
- Table C4, Metric Prefixes for Powers of Ten and Their Symbols
- Table C5, The Greek Alphabet
- Table C6, SI units
- Table C7, Selected British Units
- Table C8, Other Units
- Table C9, Useful Formulae

Symbol	Meaning	Best Value	Approximate Value
c	Speed of light in vacuum	2.99792458×10^8 m/s	3.00×10^8 m/s
G	Gravitational constant	$6.67408(31) \times 10^{-11}$ N · m²/kg²	6.67×10^{-11} N · m²/kg²
N_A	Avogadro's number	$6.02214076 \times 10^{23}$	6.02×10^{23}
k	Boltzmann's constant	1.380649×10^{-23} J/K	1.38×10^{-23} J/K
R	Gas constant	8.3144621(75) J/mol · K	8.31 J/mol · K = 1.99 cal/mol · K = 0.0821 atm · L/mol · K
σ	Stefan-Boltzmann constant	$5.670373(21) \times 10^{-8}$ W/m² · K	5.67×10^{-8} W/m² · K
k	Coulomb force constant	$8.987551788... \times 10^9$ N · m²/C²	8.99×10^9 N · m²/C²
q_e	Charge on electron	$-1.602176634 \times 10^{-19}$ C	-1.60×10^{-19} C
ε_0	Permittivity of free space	$8.854187817... \times 10^{-12}$ C²/N · m²	8.85×10^{-12} C²/N · m²
μ_0	Permeability of free space	$4\pi \times 10^{-7}$ T · m/A	1.26×10^{-6} T · m/A
h	Planck's constant	$6.62607015 \times 10^{-34}$ J · s	6.63×10^{-34} J · s

TABLE C1 Important Constants [1]

1 Stated values are according to the National Institute of Standards and Technology Reference on Constants, Units, and Uncertainty, www.physics.nist.gov/cuu (http://www.physics.nist.gov/cuu) (accessed May 18, 2012). Values in parentheses are the uncertainties in the last digits. Numbers without uncertainties are exact as defined.

Symbol	Meaning	Best Value	Approximate Value
m_e	Electron mass	$9.10938291(40) \times 10^{-31}$ kg	9.11×10^{-31} kg
m_p	Proton mass	$1.672621777(74) \times 10^{-27}$ kg	1.6726×10^{-27} kg
m_n	Neutron mass	$1.674927351(74) \times 10^{-27}$ kg	1.6749×10^{-27} kg
u	Atomic mass unit	$1.660538921(73) \times 10^{-27}$ kg	1.6605×10^{-27} kg

TABLE C2 Submicroscopic Masses[2]

Sun	mass	1.99×10^{30} kg
	average radius	6.96×10^{8} m
	Earth-sun distance (average)	1.496×10^{11} m
Earth	mass	5.9736×10^{24} kg
	average radius	6.376×10^{6} m
	orbital period	3.16×10^{7} s
Moon	mass	7.35×10^{22} kg
	average radius	1.74×10^{6} m
	orbital period (average)	2.36×10^{6} s
	Earth-moon distance (average)	3.84×10^{8} m

TABLE C3 Solar System Data

Prefix	Symbol	Value	Prefix	Symbol	Value
tera	T	10^{12}	deci	d	10^{-1}
giga	G	10^{9}	centi	c	10^{-2}
mega	M	10^{6}	milli	m	10^{-3}
kilo	k	10^{3}	micro	μ	10^{-6}
hecto	h	10^{2}	nano	n	10^{-9}

TABLE C4 Metric Prefixes for Powers of Ten and Their Symbols

2 Stated values are according to the National Institute of Standards and Technology Reference on Constants, Units, and Uncertainty, www.physics.nist.gov/cuu (http://www.physics.nist.gov/cuu) (accessed May 18, 2012). Values in parentheses are the uncertainties in the last digits. Numbers without uncertainties are exact as defined.

Prefix	Symbol	Value	Prefix	Symbol	Value
deka	da	10^1	pico	p	10^{-12}
–	–	$10^0 (= 1)$	femto	f	10^{-15}

TABLE C4 Metric Prefixes for Powers of Ten and Their Symbols

Alpha	Α	α	Eta	Η	η	Nu	Ν	ν	Tau	Τ	τ
Beta	Β	β	Theta	Θ	θ	Xi	Ξ	ξ	Upsilon	Υ	υ
Gamma	Γ	γ	Iota	Ι	ι	Omicron	Ο	o	Phi	Φ	ϕ
Delta	Δ	δ	Kappa	Κ	κ	Pi	Π	π	Chi	Χ	χ
Epsilon	Ε	ε	Lambda	Λ	λ	Rho	Ρ	ρ	Psi	Ψ	ψ
Zeta	Ζ	ζ	Mu	Μ	μ	Sigma	Σ	σ	Omega	Ω	ω

TABLE C5 The Greek Alphabet

	Entity	Abbreviation	Name
Fundamental units	Length	m	meter
	Mass	kg	kilogram
	Time	s	second
	Current	A	ampere
Supplementary unit	Angle	rad	radian
Derived units	Force	$N = kg \cdot m/s^2$	newton
	Energy	$J = kg \cdot m^2/s^2$	joule
	Power	$W = J/s$	watt
	Pressure	$Pa = N/m^2$	pascal
	Frequency	$Hz = 1/s$	hertz
	Electronic potential	$V = J/C$	volt
	Capacitance	$F = C/V$	farad
	Charge	$C = s \cdot A$	coulomb

TABLE C6 SI Units

	Entity	Abbreviation	Name
	Resistance	$\Omega = \text{V/A}$	ohm
	Magnetic field	$\text{T} = \text{N/(A} \cdot \text{m)}$	tesla
	Nuclear decay rate	$\text{Bq} = 1/\text{s}$	becquerel

TABLE C6 SI Units

Length	1 inch (in.)= 2.54 cm (exactly)
	1 foot (ft)= 0.3048 m
	1 mile (mi)= 1.609 km
Force	1 pound (lb)= 4.448 N
Energy	1 British thermal unit (Btu)= 1.055×10^3 J
Power	1 horsepower (hp)= 746 W
Pressure	$1\ \text{lb/in}^2 = 6.895 \times 10^3$ Pa

TABLE C7 Selected British Units

Length	1 light year (ly) = 9.46×10^{15} m
	1 astronomical unit (au) = 1.50×10^{11} m
	1 nautical mile = 1.852 km
	1 angstrom(Å) = 10^{-10} m
Area	1 acre (ac) = $4.05 \times 10^3\ \text{m}^2$
	1 square foot (ft^2) = $9.29 \times 10^{-2}\ \text{m}^2$
	1 barn (b) = $10^{-28}\ \text{m}^2$
Volume	1 liter (L) = $10^{-3}\ \text{m}^3$
	1 U.S. gallon (gal) = $3.785 \times 10^{-3}\ \text{m}^3$
Mass	1 solar mass = 1.99×10^{30} kg
	1 metric ton = 10^3 kg
	1 atomic mass unit (u) = 1.6605×10^{-27} kg

TABLE C8 Other Units

Time	1 year (y) = 3.16×10^7 s
	1 day (d) = 86,400 s
Speed	1 mile per hour (mph) = 1.609 km/h
	1 nautical mile per hour (naut) = 1.852 km/h
Angle	1 degree (°) = 1.745×10^{-2} rad
	1 minute of arc (′) = 1/60 degree
	1 second of arc (″) = 1/60 minute of arc
	1 grad = 1.571×10^{-2} rad
Energy	1 kiloton TNT (kT) = 4.2×10^{12} J
	1 kilowatt hour ($\text{kW} \cdot h$) = 3.60×10^6 J
	1 food calorie (kcal) = 4186 J
	1 calorie (cal) = 4.186 J
	1 electron volt (eV) = 1.60×10^{-19} J
Pressure	1 atmosphere (atm) = 1.013×10^5 Pa
	1 millimeter of mercury (mm Hg) = 133.3 Pa
	1 torricelli (torr) = 1 mm Hg = 133.3 Pa
Nuclear decay rate	1 curie (Ci) = 3.70×10^{10} Bq

TABLE C8 Other Units

Circumference of a circle with radius r or diameter d	$C = 2\pi r = \pi d$
Area of a circle with radius r or diameter d	$A = \pi r^2 = \pi d^2/4$
Area of a sphere with radius r	$A = 4\pi r^2$
Volume of a sphere with radius r	$V = (4/3)\left(\pi r^3\right)$

TABLE C9 Useful Formulae

APPENDIX D

Glossary of Key Symbols and Notation

In this glossary, key symbols and notation are briefly defined.

Symbol	Definition
$\overline{\text{any symbol}}$	average (indicated by a bar over a symbol—e.g., $\bar{v}$ is average velocity)
°C	Celsius degree
°F	Fahrenheit degree
//	parallel
$\perp$	perpendicular
$\propto$	proportional to
$\pm$	plus or minus
$_0$	zero as a subscript denotes an initial value
α	alpha rays
α	angular acceleration
α	temperature coefficient(s) of resistivity
β	beta rays
β	sound level
β	volume coefficient of expansion
β^-	electron emitted in nuclear beta decay
β^+	positron decay
γ	gamma rays
γ	surface tension
$\gamma = 1/\sqrt{1 - v^2/c^2}$	a constant used in relativity
Δ	change in whatever quantity follows

TABLE D1

Symbol	Definition
δ	uncertainty in whatever quantity follows
ΔE	change in energy between the initial and final orbits of an electron in an atom
ΔE	uncertainty in energy
Δm	difference in mass between initial and final products
ΔN	number of decays that occur
Δp	change in momentum
Δp	uncertainty in momentum
$\Delta \mathrm{PE}_{\mathrm{g}}$	change in gravitational potential energy
$\Delta \theta$	rotation angle
Δs	distance traveled along a circular path
Δt	uncertainty in time
Δt_0	proper time as measured by an observer at rest relative to the process
ΔV	potential difference
Δx	uncertainty in position
ε_0	permittivity of free space
η	viscosity
θ	angle between the force vector and the displacement vector
θ	angle between two lines
θ	contact angle
θ	direction of the resultant
θ_b	Brewster's angle
θ_c	critical angle
κ	dielectric constant
λ	decay constant of a nuclide

TABLE D1

Symbol	Definition
λ	wavelength
λ_n	wavelength in a medium
μ_0	permeability of free space
μ_k	coefficient of kinetic friction
μ_s	coefficient of static friction
v_e	electron neutrino
π^+	positive pion
π^-	negative pion
π^0	neutral pion
ρ	density
ρ_c	critical density, the density needed to just halt universal expansion
ρ_{fl}	fluid density
$\bar{\rho}_{obj}$	average density of an object
ρ/ρ_w	specific gravity
τ	characteristic time constant for a resistance and inductance (RL) or resistance and capacitance (RC) circuit
τ	characteristic time for a resistor and capacitor (RC) circuit
τ	torque
Υ	upsilon meson
Φ	magnetic flux
ϕ	phase angle
Ω	ohm (unit)
ω	angular velocity
A	ampere (current unit)
A	area

TABLE D1

Symbol	Definition
A	cross-sectional area
A	total number of nucleons
a	acceleration
a_{B}	Bohr radius
a_{c}	centripetal acceleration
a_{t}	tangential acceleration
AC	alternating current
AM	amplitude modulation
atm	atmosphere
B	baryon number
B	blue quark color
$\overline{B}$	antiblue (yellow) antiquark color
b	quark flavor bottom or beauty
B	bulk modulus
B	magnetic field strength
$\mathrm{B}_{\mathrm{int}}$	electron's intrinsic magnetic field
$\mathrm{B}_{\mathrm{orb}}$	orbital magnetic field
BE	binding energy of a nucleus—it is the energy required to completely disassemble it into separate protons and neutrons
BE/A	binding energy per nucleon
Bq	becquerel—one decay per second
C	capacitance (amount of charge stored per volt)
C	coulomb (a fundamental SI unit of charge)
C_{p}	total capacitance in parallel
C_{s}	total capacitance in series

TABLE D1

Symbol	Definition
CG	center of gravity
CM	center of mass
c	quark flavor charm
c	specific heat
c	speed of light
Cal	kilocalorie
cal	calorie
COP_{hp}	heat pump's coefficient of performance
COP_{ref}	coefficient of performance for refrigerators and air conditioners
$\cos\theta$	cosine
$\cot\theta$	cotangent
$\csc\theta$	cosecant
D	diffusion constant
d	displacement
d	quark flavor down
dB	decibel
d_{i}	distance of an image from the center of a lens
d_{o}	distance of an object from the center of a lens
DC	direct current
E	electric field strength
ε	emf (voltage) or Hall electromotive force
emf	electromotive force
E	energy of a single photon
E	nuclear reaction energy

TABLE D1

Symbol	Definition
E	relativistic total energy
E	total energy
E_0	ground state energy for hydrogen
E_0	rest energy
EC	electron capture
E_{cap}	energy stored in a capacitor
Eff	efficiency—the useful work output divided by the energy input
Eff_C	Carnot efficiency
E_{in}	energy consumed (food digested in humans)
E_{ind}	energy stored in an inductor
E_{out}	energy output
e	emissivity of an object
e^+	antielectron or positron
eV	electron volt
F	farad (unit of capacitance, a coulomb per volt)
F	focal point of a lens
$\mathbf{F}$	force
F	magnitude of a force
F	restoring force
F_{B}	buoyant force
F_{c}	centripetal force
F_{i}	force input
$\mathbf{F}_{\text{net}}$	net force
F_{o}	force output

TABLE D1

Symbol	Definition
FM	frequency modulation
f	focal length
f	frequency
f_0	resonant frequency of a resistance, inductance, and capacitance (RLC) series circuit
f_0	threshold frequency for a particular material (photoelectric effect)
f_1	fundamental
f_2	first overtone
f_3	second overtone
f_B	beat frequency
f_k	magnitude of kinetic friction
f_s	magnitude of static friction
G	gravitational constant
G	green quark color
$\overline{G}$	antigreen (magenta) antiquark color
g	acceleration due to gravity
g	gluons (carrier particles for strong nuclear force)
h	change in vertical position
h	height above some reference point
h	maximum height of a projectile
h	Planck's constant
hf	photon energy
h_i	height of the image
h_o	height of the object
I	electric current

TABLE D1

Symbol	Definition
I	intensity
I	intensity of a transmitted wave
I	moment of inertia (also called rotational inertia)
I_0	intensity of a polarized wave before passing through a filter
I_{ave}	average intensity for a continuous sinusoidal electromagnetic wave
I_{rms}	average current
J	joule
J/Ψ	Joules/psi meson
K	kelvin
k	Boltzmann constant
k	force constant of a spring
K_α	x rays created when an electron falls into an $n = 1$ shell vacancy from the $n = 3$ shell
K_β	x rays created when an electron falls into an $n = 2$ shell vacancy from the $n = 3$ shell
kcal	kilocalorie
KE	translational kinetic energy
KE + PE	mechanical energy
KE_e	kinetic energy of an ejected electron
KE_{rel}	relativistic kinetic energy
KE_{rot}	rotational kinetic energy
$\overline{\text{KE}}$	thermal energy
kg	kilogram (a fundamental SI unit of mass)
L	angular momentum
L	liter
L	magnitude of angular momentum

TABLE D1

Symbol	Definition
L	self-inductance
ℓ	angular momentum quantum number
L_α	x rays created when an electron falls into an $n = 2$ shell
L_e	electron total family number
L_μ	muon family total number
L_τ	tau family total number
L_f	heat of fusion
L_f and L_v	latent heat coefficients
L_orb	orbital angular momentum
L_s	heat of sublimation
L_v	heat of vaporization
L_z	z - component of the angular momentum
M	angular magnification
M	mutual inductance
m	indicates metastable state
m	magnification
m	mass
m	mass of an object as measured by a person at rest relative to the object
m	meter (a fundamental SI unit of length)
m	order of interference
m	overall magnification (product of the individual magnifications)
$m\left({}^A\mathrm{X}\right)$	atomic mass of a nuclide
MA	mechanical advantage
m_e	magnification of the eyepiece

TABLE D1

Symbol	Definition
m_e	mass of the electron
m_ℓ	angular momentum projection quantum number
m_n	mass of a neutron
m_{o}	magnification of the objective lens
mol	mole
m_p	mass of a proton
m_{s}	spin projection quantum number
N	magnitude of the normal force
N	newton
N	normal force
N	number of neutrons
n	index of refraction
n	number of free charges per unit volume
N_{A}	Avogadro's number
N_{r}	Reynolds number
$\text{N} \cdot \text{m}$	newton-meter (work-energy unit)
$\text{N} \cdot \text{m}$	newtons times meters (SI unit of torque)
OE	other energy
P	power
P	power of a lens
P	pressure
p	momentum
p	momentum magnitude
p	relativistic momentum

TABLE D1

Symbol	Definition
$\mathbf{p}_{\text{tot}}$	total momentum
$\mathbf{p}'_{\text{tot}}$	total momentum some time later
P_{abs}	absolute pressure
P_{atm}	atmospheric pressure
P_{atm}	standard atmospheric pressure
PE	potential energy
PE_{el}	elastic potential energy
PE_{elec}	electric potential energy
PE_{s}	potential energy of a spring
P_{g}	gauge pressure
P_{in}	power consumption or input
P_{out}	useful power output going into useful work or a desired, form of energy
Q	latent heat
Q	net heat transferred into a system
Q	flow rate—volume per unit time flowing past a point
$+Q$	positive charge
$-Q$	negative charge
q	electron charge
q_p	charge of a proton
q	test charge
QF	quality factor
R	activity, the rate of decay
R	radius of curvature of a spherical mirror
R	red quark color

TABLE D1

Symbol	Definition
$\overline{R}$	antired (cyan) quark color
R	resistance
$\mathbf{R}$	resultant or total displacement
R	Rydberg constant
R	universal gas constant
r	distance from pivot point to the point where a force is applied
r	internal resistance
$r_{\perp}$	perpendicular lever arm
r	radius of a nucleus
r	radius of curvature
r	resistivity
r or rad	radiation dose unit
rem	roentgen equivalent man
rad	radian
RBE	relative biological effectiveness
RC	resistor and capacitor circuit
rms	root mean square
r_n	radius of the *n*th H-atom orbit
R_{p}	total resistance of a parallel connection
R_{s}	total resistance of a series connection
R_{s}	Schwarzschild radius
S	entropy
$\mathbf{S}$	intrinsic spin (intrinsic angular momentum)
S	magnitude of the intrinsic (internal) spin angular momentum

TABLE D1

Symbol	Definition
S	shear modulus
S	strangeness quantum number
s	quark flavor strange
s	second (fundamental SI unit of time)
s	spin quantum number
$\mathbf{s}$	total displacement
$\sec\theta$	secant
$\sin\theta$	sine
s_z	z-component of spin angular momentum
T	period—time to complete one oscillation
T	temperature
T_c	critical temperature—temperature below which a material becomes a superconductor
T	tension
T	tesla (magnetic field strength B)
t	quark flavor top or truth
t	time
$t_{1/2}$	half-life—the time in which half of the original nuclei decay
$\tan\theta$	tangent
U	internal energy
u	quark flavor up
u	unified atomic mass unit
$\mathbf{u}$	velocity of an object relative to an observer
$\mathbf{u}'$	velocity relative to another observer
V	electric potential

TABLE D1

Symbol	Definition
V	terminal voltage
V	volt (unit)
V	volume
$\mathbf{v}$	relative velocity between two observers
v	speed of light in a material
$\mathbf{v}$	velocity
$\bar{\mathbf{v}}$	average fluid velocity
$V_\mathrm{B} - V_\mathrm{A}$	change in potential
$\mathbf{v}_\mathrm{d}$	drift velocity
V_p	transformer input voltage
V_rms	rms voltage
V_s	transformer output voltage
$\mathbf{v}_\mathrm{tot}$	total velocity
v_w	propagation speed of sound or other wave
$\mathbf{v}_\mathrm{w}$	wave velocity
W	work
W	net work done by a system
W	watt
w	weight
w_fl	weight of the fluid displaced by an object
W_c	total work done by all conservative forces
W_nc	total work done by all nonconservative forces
W_out	useful work output
X	amplitude

TABLE D1

Symbol	Definition
X	symbol for an element
${}_{A}^{Z}X_N$	notation for a particular nuclide
x	deformation or displacement from equilibrium
x	displacement of a spring from its undeformed position
x	horizontal axis
X_C	capacitive reactance
X_L	inductive reactance
x_rms	root mean square diffusion distance
y	vertical axis
Y	elastic modulus or Young's modulus
Z	atomic number (number of protons in a nucleus)
Z	impedance

TABLE D1

ANSWER KEY

Chapter 1

Problems & Exercises

1.
(a) 27.8 m/s

(b) 62.1 mph

3.
$$\frac{1.0\text{ m}}{\text{s}} = \frac{1.0\text{ m}}{\text{s}} \times \frac{3600\text{ s}}{1\text{ hr}} \times \frac{1\text{ km}}{1000\text{ m}}$$
$= 3.6\text{ km/h}$.

5.
length: 377 ft; 4.53×10^3 in. width: 280 ft; 3.3×10^3 in.

7.
8.847 km

9.
(a) 1.3×10^{-9} m

(b) 40 km/My

11.
2 kg

13.
(a) 85.5 to 94.5 km/h

(b) 53.1 to 58.7 mi/h

15.
(a) 7.6×10^7 beats

(b) 7.57×10^7 beats

(c) 7.57×10^7 beats

17.
(a) 3

(b) 3

(c) 3

19.
(a) 2.2%

(b) 59 to 61 km/h

21.
80 ± 3 beats/min

23.
2.8 h

25.

$11 \pm 1\ \text{cm}^3$

27.
$12.06 \pm 0.04\ \text{m}^2$

29.
Sample answer: 2×10^9 heartbeats

31.
Sample answer: 2×10^{31} if an average human lifetime is taken to be about 70 years.

33.
Sample answer: 50 atoms

35.
Sample answers:

(a) 10^{12} cells/hummingbird

(b) 10^{16} cells/human

Chapter 2

Problems & Exercises

1.
(a) 7 m

(b) 7 m

(c) $+7\ \text{m}$

3.
a. $8\ \text{m} + 2\ \text{m} + 3\ \text{m} = \underline{13\ \text{m}}$

b. $\underline{9\ \text{m}}$

c. $\Delta x = 11\ \text{m} - 2\ \text{m} = \underline{9\ \text{m}}$

5.
(a) $3.0 \times 10^4\ \text{m/s}$

(b) 0 m/s

7.
2×10^7 years

9.
$34.689\ \text{m/s} = 124.88\ \text{km/h}$

11.
(a) $40.0\ \text{km/h}$

(b) 34.3 km/h, 25° S of E.

(c) average speed $= 3.20\ \text{km/h}$, $\overline{v} = 0$.

13.
384,000 km

15.
(a) 6.61×10^{15} rev/s

(b) 0 m/s

16.

$4.29\ \text{m/s}^2$

18.
(a) $1.43\ \text{s}$

(b) $-2.50\ \text{m/s}^2$

20.
(a) $10.8\ \text{m/s}$

(b)

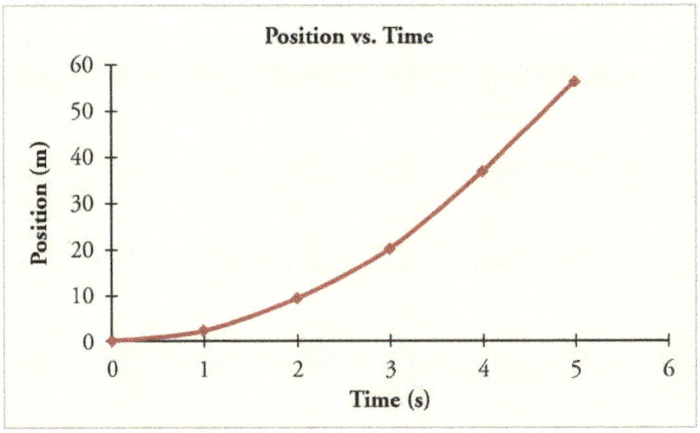

21.
38.9 m/s (about 87 miles per hour)

23.
(a) $16.5\ \text{s}$

(b) $13.5\ \text{s}$

(c) $-2.68\ \text{m/s}^2$

25.
(a) $20.0\ \text{m}$

(b) $-1.00\ \text{m/s}$

(c) This result does not really make sense. If the runner starts at 9.00 m/s and decelerates at $2.00\ \text{m/s}^2$, then she will have stopped after 4.50 s. If she continues to decelerate, she will be running backwards.

27.
$0.799\ \text{m}$

29.
(a) $28.0\ \text{m/s}$

(b) $50.9\ \text{s}$

(c) 7.68 km to accelerate and 713 m to decelerate

31.
(a) $51.4\ \text{m}$

(b) $17.1\ \text{s}$

33.
(a) $-80.4\ \text{m/s}^2$

(b) $9.33 \times 10^{-2}\ \text{s}$

35.
(a) 7.7 m/s

(b) $-15 \times 10^2\text{ m/s}^2$. This is about 3 times the deceleration of the pilots, who were falling from thousands of meters high!

37.
(a) 32.6 m/s^2

(b) 162 m/s

(c) $v > v_{max}$, because the assumption of constant acceleration is not valid for a dragster. A dragster changes gears, and would have a greater acceleration in first gear than second gear than third gear, etc. The acceleration would be greatest at the beginning, so it would not be accelerating at 32.6 m/s^2 during the last few meters, but substantially less, and the final velocity would be less than 162 m/s.

39.
104 s

40.
(a) $v = 12.2\text{ m/s}; a = 4.07\text{ m/s}^2$

(b) $v = 11.2\text{ m/s}$

41.
(a) $y_1 = 6.28\text{ m}; v_1 = 10.1\text{ m/s}$

(b) $y_2 = 10.1\text{ m}; v_2 = 5.20\text{ m/s}$

(c) $y_3 = 11.5\text{ m}; v_3 = 0.300\text{ m/s}$

(d) $y_4 = 10.4\text{ m}; v_4 = -4.60\text{ m/s}$

43.
$v_0 = 4.95\text{ m/s}$

45.
(a) $a = -9.80\text{ m/s}^2; v_0 = 13.0\text{ m/s}; y_0 = 0\text{ m}$

(b) $v = 0\text{m/s}$. Unknown is distance y to top of trajectory, where velocity is zero. Use equation $v^2 = v_0^2 + 2a(y - y_0)$ because it contains all known values except for y, so we can solve for y. Solving for y gives

$$\begin{aligned} v^2 - v_0^2 &= 2a(y - y_0) \\ \frac{v^2 - v_0^2}{2a} &= y - y_0 \\ y &= y_0 + \frac{v^2 - v_0^2}{2a} = 0\text{ m} + \frac{(0\text{ m/s})^2 - (13.0\text{ m/s})^2}{2(-9.80\text{ m/s}^2)} = 8.62\text{ m} \end{aligned}$$

Dolphins measure about 2 meters long and can jump several times their length out of the water, so this is a reasonable result.

(c) 2.65 s

47.

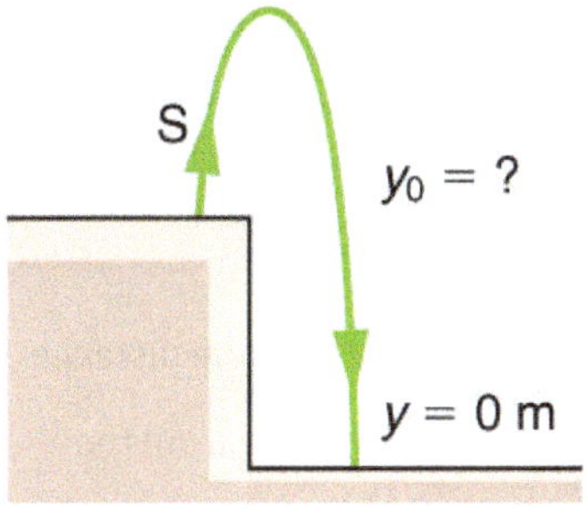

(a) 8.26 m

(b) 0.717 s

49.
1.91 s

51.
(a) 94.0 m

(b) 3.13 s

53.
(a) -70.0 m/s (downward)

(b) 6.10 s

55.
(a) 19.6 m

(b) 18.5 m

57.
(a) 305 m

(b) 262 m, -29.2 m/s

(c) 8.91 s

59.
(a) 115 m/s

(b) 5.0 m/s^2

61.

$$v = \frac{(11.7 - 6.95) \times 10^3 \text{ m}}{(40.0 - 20.0) \text{ s}} = 238 \text{ m/s}$$

63.

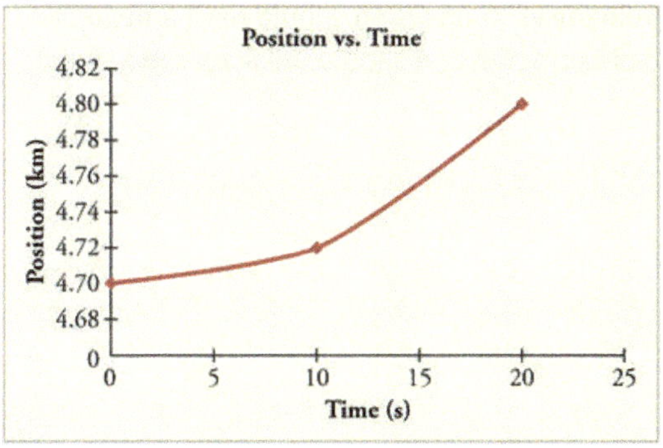

65.
(a) 6 m/s

(b) 12 m/s

(c) $3\ \text{m/s}^2$

(d) 10 s

67.
(a) Car A is traveling faster at the checkpoint because it must go past the speed of car B to reach the same distance.

(b) i. Yes, the equation is consistent with the answer because the speed of car A is only a constant away from the correct answer. ii. Yes, the equation makes sense because $V = 2V_0$.

(c)

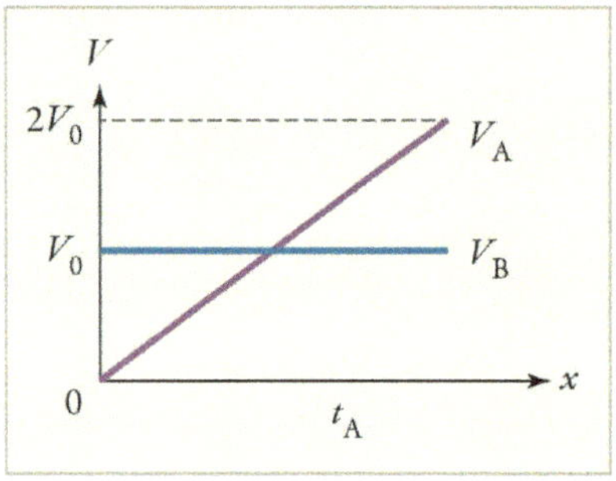

FIGURE 2.67

Test Prep for AP® Courses

1.
(a)

3.
(a) Use tape to mark off two distances on the track — one for cart *A* before the collision and one for the combined carts after the collision. Push cart *A* to give it an initial speed. Use a stopwatch to measure the time it takes for the cart(s) to cross the marked distances. The speeds are the distances divided by the times.

(b) If the measurement errors are of the same magnitude, they will have a greater effect after the collision. The speed of the combined carts will be less than the initial speed of cart *A*. As a result, these errors will be a greater percentage of the actual velocity value after the collision occurs. (Note: Other arguments could properly be made for 'more error before the collision' and error that 'equally affects both sets of measurement.')

5.
The position vs. time graph should be represented with a positively sloped line whose slope steadily decreases to zero. The *y*-intercept of the graph may be any value. The line on the velocity vs. time graph should have a positive *y*-intercept and a negative slope. Because the final velocity of the book is zero, the line should finish on the *x*-axis.

The position vs. time graph should be represented with a negatively sloped line whose slope steadily decreases to zero. The *y*-intercept of the graph may be any value. The line on the velocity vs. time graph should have a negative *y*-intercept and a positive slope. Because the final velocity of the book is zero, the line should finish on the *x*-axis.]

7.
(c)

Chapter 3

Problems & Exercises

1.
(a) $480\ \text{m}$

(b) $379\ \text{m},\ 18.4^\circ$ east of north

3.

north component 3.21 km, east component 3.83 km

5.
$19.5\text{ m}, 4.65°$ south of west

7.
(a) $26.6\text{ m}, 65.1°$ north of east

(b) $26.6\text{ m}, 65.1°$ south of west

9.
$52.9\text{ m}, 90.1°$ with respect to the *x*-axis.

11.
x-component 4.41 m/s

y-component 5.07 m/s

13.
(a) 1.56 km

(b) 120 m east

15.
North-component 87.0 km, east-component 87.0 km

17.
30.8 m, 35.8 west of north

19.
(a) $30.8\text{ m}, 54.2°$ south of west

(b) $30.8\text{ m}, 54.2°$ north of east

21.
18.4 km south, then 26.2 km west(b) 31.5 km at $45.0°$ south of west, then 5.56 km at $45.0°$ west of north

23.
$7.34\text{ km}, 63.5°$ south of east

25.
$$\begin{aligned} x &= 1.30\text{ m} \times 10^2 \\ y &= 30.9\text{ m}. \end{aligned}$$

27.
(a) 3.50 s

(b) 28.6 m/s (c) 34.3 m/s

(d) 44.7 m/s, $50.2°$ below horizontal

29.
(a) $18.4°$

(b) The arrow will go over the branch.

31.
$$R = \frac{v_0^2}{\sin 2\theta_0 g}$$

For $\theta = 45°, \quad R = \frac{v_0^2}{g}$

$R = 91.8\text{ m}$ for $v_0 = 30\text{ m/s}$; $R = 163\text{ m}$ for $v_0 = 40\text{ m/s}$; $R = 255\text{ m}$ for $v_0 = 50\text{ m/s}$.

33.
(a) 560 m/s

(b) 8.00×10^3 m

(c) 80.0 m. This error is not significant because it is only 1% of the answer in part (b).

35.
1.50 m, assuming launch angle of $45°$

37.
$\theta = 6.1°$

yes, the ball lands at 5.3 m from the net

39.
(a) −0.486 m

(b) The larger the muzzle velocity, the smaller the deviation in the vertical direction, because the time of flight would be smaller. Air resistance would have the effect of decreasing the time of flight, therefore increasing the vertical deviation.

41.
4.23 m. No, the owl is not lucky; he misses the nest.

43.
No, the maximum range (neglecting air resistance) is about 92 m.

45.
15.0 m/s

47.
(a) 24.2 m/s

(b) The ball travels a total of 57.4 m with the brief gust of wind.

49.
$y - y_0 = 0 = v_{0y}t - \frac{1}{2}gt^2 = (v_0 \sin\theta)t - \frac{1}{2}gt^2$,

so that $t = \frac{2(v_0 \sin\theta)}{g}$

$x - x_0 = v_{0x}t = (v_0 \cos\theta)t = R$, and substituting for t gives:

$$R = v_0 \cos\theta\left(\frac{2v_0 \sin\theta}{g}\right) = \frac{2v_0^2 \sin\theta \cos\theta}{g}$$

since $2 \sin\theta \cos\theta = \sin 2\theta$, the range is:

$$R = \frac{{v_0}^2 \sin 2\theta}{g}.$$

52.
(a) 35.8 km, $45°$ south of east

(b) 5.53 m/s, $45°$ south of east

(c) 56.1 km, $45°$ south of east

54.
(a) 0.70 m/s faster

(b) Second runner wins

(c) 4.17 m

56.
17.0 m/s, 22.1°

58.
(a) 230 m/s, 8.0° south of west

(b) The wind should make the plane travel slower and more to the south, which is what was calculated.

60.
(a) 63.5 m/s

(b) 29.6 m/s

62.
6.68 m/s, 53.3° south of west

64.
(a) $H_{\text{average}} = 14.9\frac{\text{km/s}}{\text{Mly}}$

(b) 20.2 billion years

66.
1.72 m/s, 42.3° north of east

71.
(a) Since $\sin^2 50 > \sin^2 40$, then B reaches the greatest height.

(b) i. Yes, it is consistent because $\sin 50 > \sin 40$. ii. No, it does not make sense because *y* is proportional to $\sin^2 \theta$.

(c)

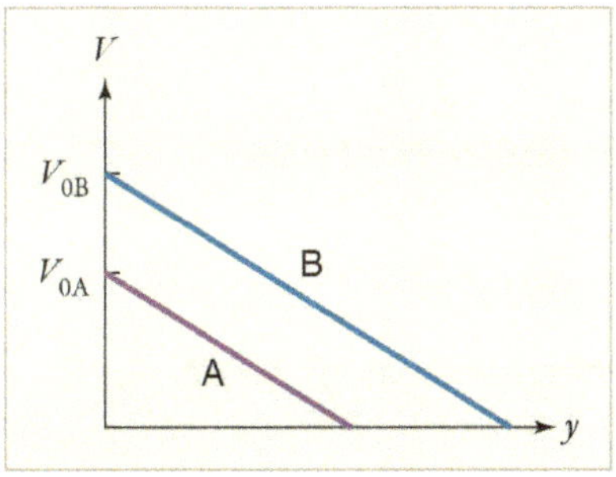

FIGURE 3.61

Test Prep for AP® Courses

1.
(d)

3.
We would need to know the horizontal and vertical positions of each ball at several times. From that data, we could deduce the velocities over several time intervals and also the accelerations (both horizontal and vertical) for each ball over several time intervals.

5.
The graph of the ball's vertical velocity over time should begin at 4.90 m/s during the time interval 0 - 0.1 sec (there should be a data point at t = 0.05 sec, v = 4.90 m/s). It should then have a slope of -9.8 m/s^2, crossing through v = 0 at t = 0.55 sec and ending at v = -0.98 m/s at t = 0.65 sec.

The graph of the ball's horizontal velocity would be a constant positive value, a flat horizontal line at some positive velocity from t = 0 until t = 0.7 sec.

Chapter 4

Problems & Exercises

1.
265 N

3.
$13.3\ \text{m/s}^2$

7.
(a) $12\ \text{m/s}^2$.

(b) The acceleration is not one-fourth of what it was with all rockets burning because the frictional force is still as large as it was with all rockets burning.

9.
(a) The system is the child in the wagon plus the wagon.

(b)

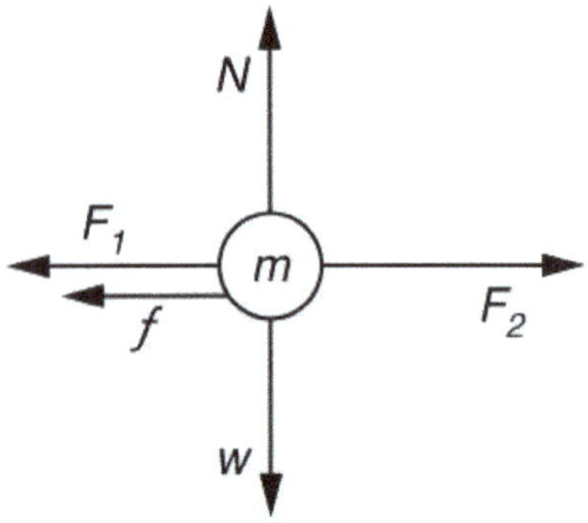

(c) $a = 0.130\ \text{m/s}^2$ in the direction of the second child's push.

(d) $a = 0.00\ \text{m/s}^2$

11.
(a) $3.68 \times 10^3\ \text{N}$. This force is 5.00 times greater than his weight.

(b) 3750 N; 11.3° above horizontal

13.
$1.5 \times 10^3\ \text{N}$, 150 kg, 150 kg

15.
Force on shell: $2.64 \times 10^7\ \text{N}$

Force exerted on ship = $-2.64 \times 10^7\ \text{N}$, by Newton's third law

17.
a. $0.11\ \text{m/s}^2$
b. $1.2 \times 10^4\ \text{N}$

19.
(a) $7.84 \times 10^{-4}\ \text{N}$

(b) $1.89 \times 10^{-3}\ \text{N}$. This is 2.41 times the tension in the vertical strand.

21.
Newton's second law applied in vertical direction gives

$$F_y = F - 2T \sin\theta = 0$$
$$F = 2T \sin\theta$$

$T = \frac{F}{2 \sin \theta}.$

23.

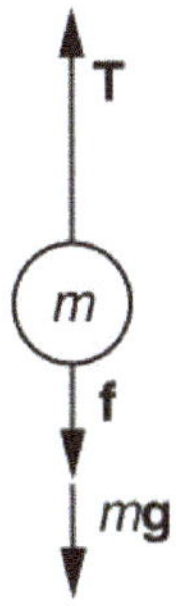

Using the free-body diagram:

$F_{\text{net}} = T - f - mg = ma,$

so that

$a = \frac{T-f-mg}{m} = \frac{1.250\times10^7\ \text{N}-4.50\times10^6\ N-(5.00\times10^5\ \text{kg})(9.80\ \text{m/s}^2)}{5.00\times10^5\ \text{kg}} = 6.20\ \text{m/s}^2.$

25.

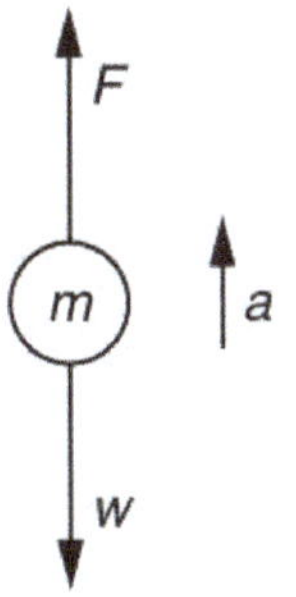

1. Use Newton's laws of motion.
2. Given : $a = 4.00g = (4.00)(9.80\ \text{m/s}^2) = 39.2\ \text{m/s}^2$; $m = 70.0$ kg,
   Find: F.
3. $\sum F = +F - w = ma$, so that $F = ma + w = ma + mg = m(a+g)$.
   $F = (70.0\ \text{kg})[(39.2\ \text{m/s}^2) + (9.80\ \text{m/s}^2)] = 3.43 \times 10^3\ \text{N}$. The force exerted by the high-jumper is actually down on the ground, but F is up from the ground and makes him jump.
4. This result is reasonable, since it is quite possible for a person to exert a force of the magnitude of 10^3 N.

27.
(a) 4.41×10^5 N

(b) 1.50×10^5 N

29.
(a) 910 N

(b) 1.11×10^3 N

31.
$a = 0.139$ m/s, $\theta = 12.4°$ north of east

33.
1. Use Newton's laws since we are looking for forces.

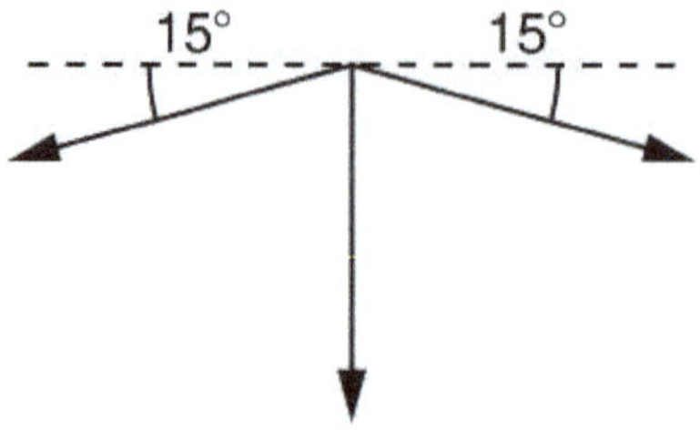

2. Draw a free-body diagram:
3. The tension is given as $T = 25.0\text{ N}$. Find F_{app}. Using Newton's laws gives: $\Sigma F_y = 0$, so that applied force is due to the *y*-components of the two tensions: $F_{app} = 2T\sin\theta = 2(25.0\text{ N})\sin(15°) = 12.9\text{ N}$
The *x*-components of the tension cancel. $\sum F_x = 0$.
4. This seems reasonable, since the applied tensions should be greater than the force applied to the tooth.

40.
10.2 m/s^2, $4.67°$ from vertical

42.

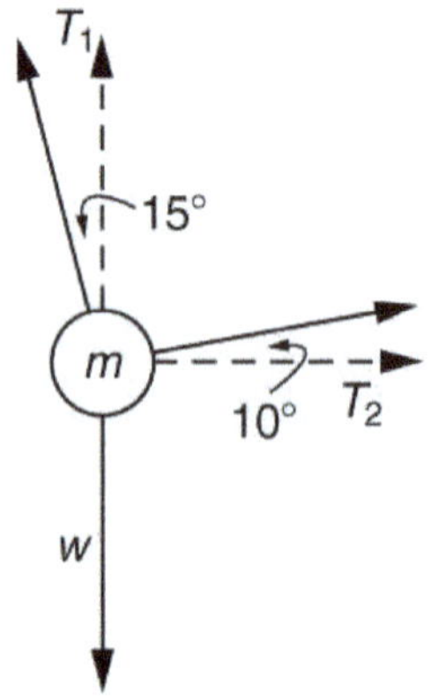

$T_1 = 736\text{ N}$

$T_2 = 194\text{ N}$

44.
(a) 7.43 m/s

(b) 2.97 m

46.
(a) 4.20 m/s

(b) 29.4 m/s^2

(c) $4.31 \times 10^3\text{ N}$

48.
(a) 47.1 m/s

(b) $2.47 \times 10^3\text{ m/s}^2$

(c) $6.18 \times 10^3\text{ N}$. The average force is 252 times the shell's weight.

52.
(a) 1×10^{-13}

(b) 1×10^{-11}

54.
10^2

55.
(a) Box A travels faster at the finishing distance since a greater force with equal mass results in a greater acceleration. Also, a greater acceleration over the same distance results in a greater final speed.

(b) i. Yes, it is consistent because a greater force results in a greater final speed. ii. It does not make sense because $V = \sqrt{2(f/m)x} = \mathrm{K}\sqrt{(F)}$.

(c)

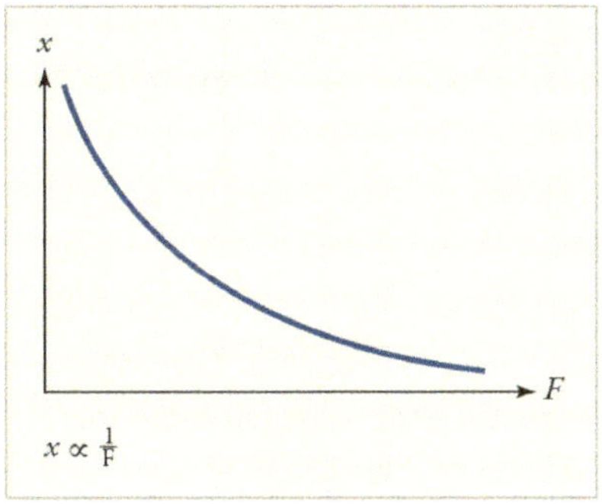

FIGURE 4.41

Test Prep for AP® Courses

1.

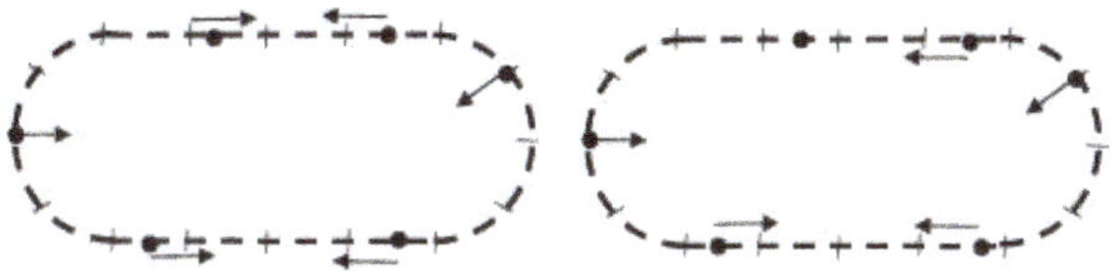
FIGURE 4.44

Car X is shown on the left, and Car Y is shown on the right.

i.

Car X takes longer to accelerate and does not spend any time traveling at top speed. Car Y accelerates over a shorter time and spends time going at top speed. So Car Y must cover the straightaways in a shorter time. Curves take the same time, so Car Y must overall take a shorter time.

ii.

The only difference in the calculations for the time of one segment of linear acceleration is the difference in distances. That shows that Car X takes longer to accelerate. The equation $\frac{d}{4v_c} = t_c$ corresponds to Car Y traveling for a time at top speed.

Substituting $a = \frac{v_c}{t_1}$ into the displacement equation in part (b) ii gives $D = \frac{3}{2}v_c t_1$. This shows that a car takes less time to reach its maximum speed when it accelerates over a shorter distance. Therefore, Car Y reaches its maximum speed more quickly, and spends more time at its maximum speed than Car X does, as argued in part (b) i.

3.
A body cannot exert a force on itself. The hawk may accelerate as a result of several forces. The hawk may accelerate toward Earth as a result of the force due to gravity. The hawk may accelerate as a result of the additional force exerted on it by wind. The hawk may accelerate as a result of orienting its body to create less air resistance, thus increasing the net force forward.

5.
(a) A soccer player, gravity, air, and friction commonly exert forces on a soccer ball being kicked.

(b) Gravity and the surrounding water commonly exert forces on a dolphin jumping. (The dolphin moves its muscles to exert a force on the water. The water exerts an equal force on the dolphin, resulting in the dolphin's motion.)

(c) Gravity and air exert forces on a parachutist drifting to Earth.

7.
(c)

9.

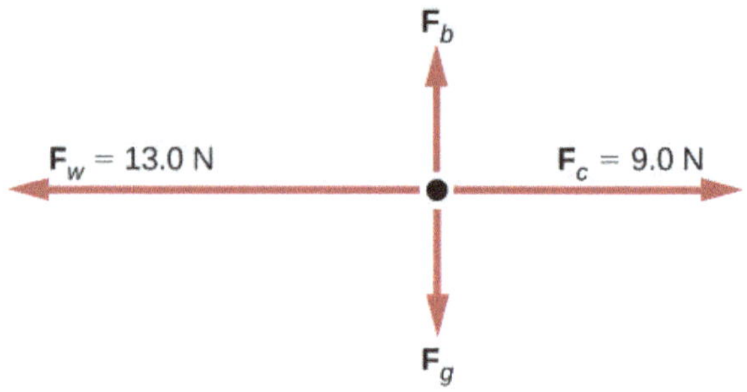

FIGURE 4.45

The diagram consists of a black dot in the center and two small red arrows pointing up (Fb) and down (Fg) and two long red arrows pointing right (Fc = 9.0 N) and left (Fw=13.0 N).

In the diagram, F_g represents the force due to gravity on the balloon, and F_b represents the buoyant force. These two forces are equal in magnitude and opposite in direction. F_c represents the force of the current. F_w represents the force of the wind. The net force on the balloon will be $F_w - F_c = 4.0$ N and the balloon will accelerate in the direction the wind is blowing.

11.
Since $m = F/a$, the parachutist has a mass of $539 \quad \text{N}/9.8 \text{ km/s}^2 = 55 \quad \text{kg}$.

For the first 2 s, the parachutist accelerates at 9.8 m/s^2.

$$\begin{aligned} v &= at \\ &= 9.8\frac{\text{m}}{\text{s}^2} \bullet 2\text{s} \\ &= 19.6 \quad \frac{\text{m}}{\text{s}} \end{aligned}$$

Her speed after 2 s is 19.6 m/s.

From 2 s to 10 s, the net force on the parachutist is 539 N – 615 N, or 76 N upward.

$$\begin{aligned} a &= \frac{F}{m} \\ &= \frac{-76 \quad \text{N}}{55 \quad \text{kg}} \\ &= -1.4 \quad \frac{\text{m}}{\text{s}^2} \end{aligned}$$

Since $v = v_0 + at$, $v = 19.6 \quad \text{m/s}^2 + (-1.4 \quad \text{m/s}^2)(8\text{s}) \quad = 8.4 \quad \text{m/s}^2$.

At 10 s, the parachutist is falling to Earth at 8.4 m/s.

13.
The system includes the gardener and the wheelbarrow with its contents. The following forces are important to include: the weight of the wheelbarrow, the weight of the gardener, the normal force for the wheelbarrow and the gardener, the force of the gardener pushing against the ground and the equal force of the ground pushing back against the gardener, and any friction in the wheelbarrow's wheels.

15.
The system undergoing acceleration is the two figure skaters together.

Net force = $120 \quad \text{N} \quad - \quad 5.0 \quad \text{N} \quad = \quad 115 \quad \text{N}$.

Total mass = $40 \quad \text{kg} + 50 \text{ kg} = 90 \text{ kg}.$

Using Newton’s second law, we have that

$$\begin{aligned} a &= \frac{F}{m} \\ &= \frac{115 \quad \text{N}}{90 \quad \text{kg}} \\ &= 1.28 \quad \frac{\text{m}}{\text{s}^2} \end{aligned}$$

The pair accelerates forward at 1.28 m/s^2.

17.
The force of tension must equal the force of gravity plus the force necessary to accelerate the mass. $F = mg$ can be used to calculate the first, and $F = ma$ can be used to calculate the second.

For gravity:

$$F = mg$$

$$= (120.0 \quad \text{kg})(9.8 \quad \text{m/s}^2)$$

$$= 1205.4 \quad \text{N}$$

For acceleration:

$$F = ma$$

$$= (120.0 \quad \text{kg})(1.3 \quad \text{m/s}^2)$$

$$= 159.9 \quad \text{N}$$

The total force of tension in the cable is 1176 N + 156 N = 1332 N.

19.
(b)

21.

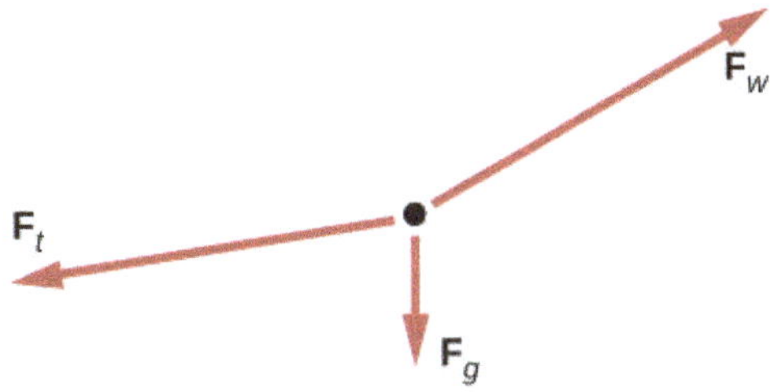

FIGURE 4.47

The diagram has a black dot and three solid red arrows pointing away from the dot. Arrow Ft is long and pointing to the left and slightly down. Arrow Fw is also long and is a bit below a diagonal line halfway between pointing up and pointing to the right. A short arrow Fg is pointing down.

$\mathbf{F}_g$ is the force on the kite due to gravity.

$\mathbf{F}_w$ is the force exerted on the kite by the wind.

$\mathbf{F}_t$ is the force of tension in the string holding the kite. It must balance the vector sum of the other two forces for the kite to float stationary in the air.

23.
(b)

25.

(d)

27.
A free-body diagram would show a northward force of 64 N and a westward force of 38 N. The net force is equal to the sum of the two applied forces. It can be found using the Pythagorean theorem:

$$F_{\text{net}} = \sqrt{F_x{}^2 + F_y{}^w}$$
$$= \sqrt{(38 \text{ N})^2 + (64 \text{ N})^2}$$
$$= 74.4 \text{ N}$$

Since $a = \frac{F}{m}$,

$$a = \frac{74.4 \text{ N}}{825 \text{ kg}}$$
$$= 0.09 \text{ m/s}^2$$

The boulder will accelerate at 0.09 m/s^2.

29.
(b)

31.
(b)

33.
(d)

Chapter 5

Problems & Exercises

1.
5.00 N

4.
(a) 588 N

(b) 1.96 m/s^2

6.
(a) 3.29 m/s^2

(b) 3.52 m/s^2

(c) 980 N; 945 N

10.
1.83 m/s^2

14.
(a) 4.20 m/s^2

(b) 2.74 m/s^2

(c) –0.195 m/s^2

16.
(a) 1.03×10^6 N

(b) 3.48×10^5 N

18.
(a) 51.0 N

(b) 0.720 m/s^2

20.
$115 \text{ m/s}; 414 \text{ km/hr}$

22.
$25.1 \text{ m/s}; 9.90 \text{ m/s}$

24.
2.9

26.
$$[\eta]= \frac{[F_s]}{[r][v]} = \frac{\text{kg} \cdot \text{m/s}^2}{\text{m} \cdot \text{m/s}} = \frac{\text{kg}}{\text{m} \cdot \text{s}}$$

28.
$0.76 \text{ kg/m} \cdot \text{s}$

29.
$1.90 \times 10^{-3} \text{ cm}$

31.
(a)1 mm
(b) This does seem reasonable, since the lead does seem to shrink a little when you push on it.

33.
(a)9 cm
(b)This seems reasonable for nylon climbing rope, since it is not supposed to stretch that much.

35.
8.59 mm

37.
$1.49 \times 10^{-7} \text{ m}$

39.
(a) $3.99 \times 10^{-7} \text{ m}$

(b) $9.67 \times 10^{-8} \text{ m}$

41.
$4 \times 10^6 \text{ N/m}^2$. This is about 36 atm, greater than a typical jar can withstand.

43.
1.4 cm

45.
(a) Bead A has the larger radius because both have the same weight and drag force. Since A takes longer to fall, its speed is less and, therefore, it must have larger area or radius.

(b) i. This equation is not consistent because it shows that the bead that took longer to fall has a smaller radius. ii. It does not make sense because *r* is proportional to *t*.

(c)

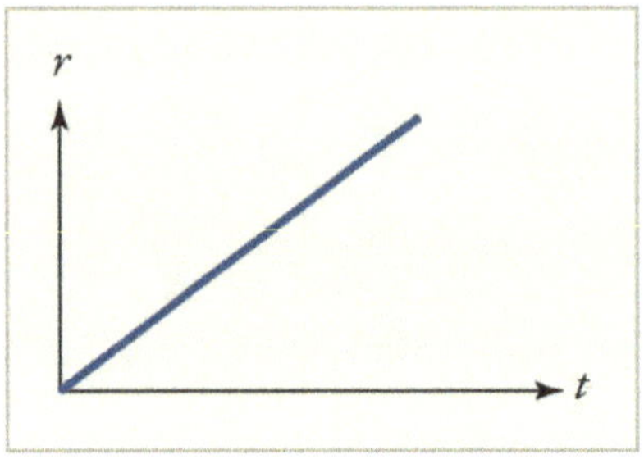

FIGURE 5.23

Test Prep for AP® Courses

1.
(b)

3.
(c)

Chapter 6

Problems & Exercises

1.
723 km

3.
5×10^7 rotations

5.
117 rad/s

7.
76.2 rad/s

728 rpm

8.
(a) 33.3 rad/s

(b) 500 N

(c) 40.8 m

10.
12.9 rev/min

12.
4×10^{21} m

14.
a) 3.47×10^4 m/s^2, 3.55×10^3 g

b) 51.1 m/s

16.
a) 31.4 rad/s

b) 118 m/s

c) 384 m/s

d)The centripetal acceleration felt by Olympic skaters is 12 times larger than the acceleration due to gravity. That's quite a lot of acceleration in itself. The centripetal acceleration felt by Button's nose was 39.2 times larger than the acceleration due to gravity. It is no wonder that he ruptured small blood vessels in his spins.

18.
a) 0.524 km/s

b) 29.7 km/s

20.
(a) 1.35×10^3 rpm

(b) 8.47×10^3 m/s^2

(c) 8.47×10^{-12} N

(d) 865

21.
(a) 16.6 m/s

(b) 19.6 m/s^2

(c)

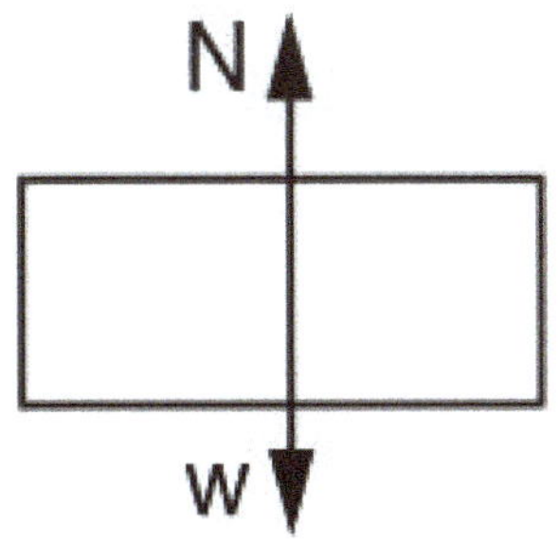

(d) 1.76×10^3 N or $3.00\ w$, that is, the normal force (upward) is three times her weight.

(e) This answer seems reasonable, since she feels like she's being forced into the chair MUCH stronger than just by gravity.

22.
a) 40.5 m/s^2

b) 905 N

c) The force in part (b) is very large. The acceleration in part (a) is too much, about 4 g.

d) The speed of the swing is too large. At the given velocity at the bottom of the swing, there is enough kinetic energy to send the child all the way over the top, ignoring friction.

23.
a) 483 N

b) 17.4 N

c) 2.24 times her weight, 0.0807 times her weight

25.
4.14°

27.
a) 24.6 m

b) 36.6 m/s^2

c) $a_c = 3.73\ g$. This does not seem too large, but it is clear that bobsledders feel a lot of force on them going through sharply banked turns.

29.
a) 2.56 rad/s

b) $5.71°$

30.
a) 16.2 m/s

b) 0.234

32.
a) 1.84

b) A coefficient of friction this much greater than 1 is unreasonable .

c) The assumed speed is too great for the tight curve.

33.
a) $5.979 \times 10^{24}\ \text{kg}$

b) This is identical to the best value to three significant figures.

35.
a) $1.62\ \ \text{m/s}^2$

b) $3.75\ \ \text{m/s}^2$

37.
a) $3.42 \times 10^{-5}\ \ \text{m/s}^2$

b) $3.34 \times 10^{-5}\ \ \text{m/s}^2$

The values are nearly identical. One would expect the gravitational force to be the same as the centripetal force at the core of the system.

39.
a) $7.01 \times 10^{-7}\ \text{N}$

b) $1.35 \times 10^{-6}\ \text{N}, 0.521$

41.
a) $1.66 \times 10^{-10}\ \ \text{m/s}^2$

b) $2.17 \times 10^{5}\ \ \text{m/s}$

42.
a) $2.937 \times 10^{17}\ \text{kg}$

b) 4.91×10^{-8}

of the Earth's mass.

c) The mass of the mountain and its fraction of the Earth's mass are too great.

d) The gravitational force assumed to be exerted by the mountain is too great.

44.
$1.98 \times 10^{30}\ \text{kg}$

46.
$\frac{M_J}{M_E} = 316$

48.
a) $2.11 \times 10^{4}\ \ \text{m/s}$

b) 1.05×10^4 m/s

c) 2.86×10^{-7} s

d) 1.83×10^8 N

e) 2.22×10^5 J

49.
a) 5.08×10^3 km

b) This radius is unreasonable because it is less than the radius of earth.

c) The premise of a one-hour orbit is inconsistent with the known radius of the earth.

51.
(a) The normal force is greatest at point B. At point A, the normal force and the weight are the net force; at point B, only the normal force points in the same direction as the net force.

(b) i. This is not consistent because a larger radius should decease the net force and tension, not increase it. ii. This does not make sense because $F_c = mv^2/r$.

(c)

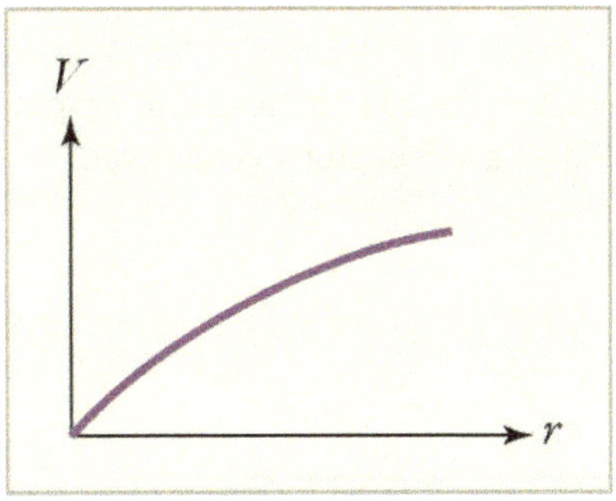

FIGURE 6.36

Test Prep for AP® Courses

1.
(a)

3.
(b)

5.
(b)

Chapter 7

Problems & Exercises

1.
$3.00 \text{ J} = 7.17 \times 10^{-4}$ kcal

3.
(a) 5.92×10^5 J

(b) -5.88×10^5 J

(c) The net force is zero.

5.
3.14×10^3 J

7.

(a) $-700\ \text{J}$

(b) 0

(c) 700 J

(d) 38.6 N

(e) 0

9.
1/250

11.
$1.1 \times 10^{10}\ \text{J}$

13.
$2.8 \times 10^{3}\ \text{N}$

15.
102 N

16.
(a) $1.96 \times 10^{16}\ \text{J}$

(b) The ratio of gravitational potential energy in the lake to the energy stored in the bomb is 0.52. That is, the energy stored in the lake is approximately half that in a 9-megaton fusion bomb.

18.
(a) 1.8 J

(b) 8.6 J

20.
$$v_f = \sqrt{2gh + {v_0}^2} = \sqrt{2(9.80\ \text{m/s}^2)(-0.180\ \text{m}) + (2.00\ \text{m/s})^2} = 0.687\ \text{m/s}$$

22.
$7.81 \times 10^{5}\ \text{N/m}$

24.
9.46 m/s

26.
4×10^{4} molecules

27.
Equating $\Delta \text{PE}_\text{g}$ and ΔKE, we obtain $v = \sqrt{2gh + {v_0}^2} = \sqrt{2(9.80\ \text{m/s}^2)(20.0\ \text{m}) + (15.0\ \text{m/s})^2} = 24.8\ \text{m/s}$

29.
(a) 25×10^{6} years

(b) This is much, much longer than human time scales.

30.
2×10^{-10}

32.
(a) 40

(b) 8 million

34.
$149

36.
(a) 208 W

(b) 141 s

38.
(a) 3.20 s

(b) 4.04 s

40.
(a) $9.46\times10^{7}\text{ J}$

(b) 2.54 y

42.
Identify knowns: $m = 950\text{ kg}$, slope angle $\theta = 2.00°$, $v = 3.00\text{ m/s}$, $f = 600\text{ N}$

Identify unknowns: power P of the car, force F that car applies to road

Solve for unknown:

$$P = \frac{W}{t} = \frac{Fd}{t} = F\left(\frac{d}{t}\right) = Fv,$$

where F is parallel to the incline and must oppose the resistive forces and the force of gravity:

$$F = f + w = 600\text{ N} + mg\sin\theta$$

Insert this into the expression for power and solve:

$$\begin{aligned} P &= (f + mg\sin\theta)v \\ &= \left[600\text{ N} + (950\text{ kg})\left(9.80\text{ m/s}^2\right)\sin 2°\right](30.0\text{ m/s}) \\ &= 2.77\times10^{4}\text{ W} \end{aligned}$$

About 28 kW (or about 37 hp) is reasonable for a car to climb a gentle incline.

44.
(a) 9.5 min

(b) 69 flights of stairs

46.
641 W, 0.860 hp

48.
31 g

50.
14.3%

52.
(a) $3.21\times10^{4}\text{ N}$

(b) $2.35\times10^{3}\text{ N}$

(c) Ratio of net force to weight of person is 41.0 in part (a); 3.00 in part (b)

54.
(a) 108 kJ

(b) 599 W

56.
(a) 144 J

(b) 288 W

58.
(a) 2.50×10^{12} J

(b) 2.52%

(c) 1.4×10^4 kg (14 metric tons)

60.
(a) 294 N

(b) 118 J

(c) 49.0 W

62.
(a) 0.500 m/s^2

(b) 62.5 N

(c) Assuming the acceleration of the swimmer decreases linearly with time over the 5.00 s interval, the frictional force must therefore be increasing linearly with time, since $f = F - ma$. If the acceleration decreases linearly with time, the velocity will contain a term dependent on time squared (t^2). Therefore, the water resistance will not depend linearly on the velocity.

64.
(a) 16.1×10^3 N

(b) 3.22×10^5 J

(c) 5.66 m/s

(d) 4.00 kJ

66.
(a) 4.65×10^3 kcal

(b) 38.8 kcal/min

(c) This power output is higher than the highest value on Table 7.5, which is about 35 kcal/min (corresponding to 2415 watts) for sprinting.

(d) It would be impossible to maintain this power output for 2 hours (imagine sprinting for 2 hours!).

69.
(a) 4.32 m/s

(b) 3.47×10^3 N

(c) 8.93 kW

70.
(a) Box A has the greatest speed since it has the greatest work done; work equals change in kinetic energy and thus fastest speed.

(b) i. Yes, this equation is consistent. An increased force or distance increases the work done, and thus increases the change in kinesthetic energy. ii. No, this equation does not make sense.

(c)

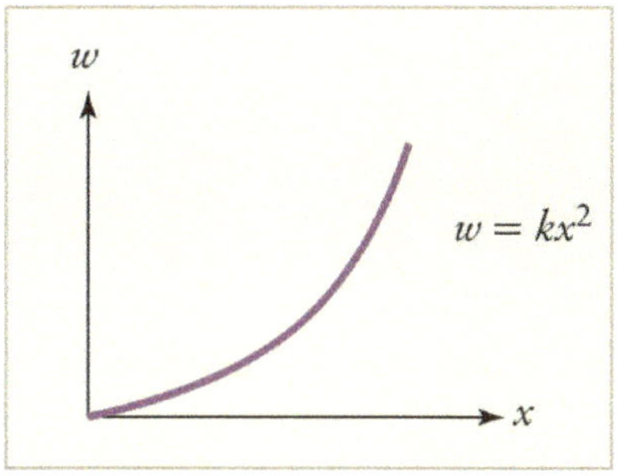

FIGURE 7.44

Test Prep for AP® Courses

1.
(b)

3.
(d)

5.
(a)

7.
The kinetic energy should change in the form of −cos, with an initial value of 0 or slightly above, and ending at the same level.

9.
Any force acting perpendicular will have no effect on kinetic energy. Obvious examples are gravity and the normal force, but others include wind directly from the side and rain or other precipitation falling straight down.

11.
Note that the wind is pushing from behind and one side, so your KE will increase. The net force has components of 1400 N in the direction of travel and 212 N perpendicular to the direction of travel. So the net force is 1420 N at 8.5 degrees from the direction of travel.

13.
Gravity has a component perpendicular to the cannon (and to displacement, so it is irrelevant) and has a component parallel to the cannon. The latter is equal to 9.8 N. Thus the net force in the direction of the displacement is 45 N – 9.8 N, and the kinetic energy is 53 J.

15.
The potato cannon (and many other projectile launchers) above is an option, with a force launching the projectile, friction, potentially gravity depending on the direction it is pointed, etc. A drag (or other) car accelerating is another possibility.

17.
The kinetic energy of the rear wagon increases. The front wagon does not, until the rear wagon collides with it. The total system may be treated by its center of mass, halfway between the wagons, and its energy increases by the same amount as the sum of the two individual wagons.

19.
(d)

21.
0.049 J; 0.041 m, 0.25 m

23.
20 m high, 20 m/s.

25.

(a)

27.
(d)

29.
(c)

31.
(b)

33.
(c)

35.
(c)

37.
(c), (d)

39.
(a)

41.
(b)

Chapter 8

Problems & Exercises

1.
(a) $1.50 \times 10^4 \text{ kg} \cdot \text{m/s}$

(b) 625 to 1

(c) $6.66 \times 10^2 \text{ kg} \cdot \text{m/s}$

3.
(a) $8.00 \times 10^4 \text{ m/s}$

(b) $1.20 \times 10^6 \text{ kg} \cdot \text{m/s}$

(c) Because the momentum of the airplane is 3 orders of magnitude smaller than of the ship, the ship will not recoil very much. The recoil would be -0.0100 m/s, which is probably not noticeable.

5.
54 s

7.
$9.00 \times 10^3 \text{ N}$

9.
a) $2.40 \times 10^3 \text{ N}$ toward the leg

b) The force on each hand would have the same magnitude as that found in part (a) (but in opposite directions by Newton's third law) because the change in momentum and the time interval are the same.

11.
a) $800 \text{ kg} \cdot \text{m/s}$ away from the wall

b) 1.20 m/s away from the wall

13.
(a) $1.50 \times 10^6 \text{ N}$ away from the dashboard

(b) 1.00×10^5 N away from the dashboard

15.
4.69×10^5 N in the boat's original direction of motion

17.
2.10×10^3 N away from the wall

19.

$$\mathbf{p} = m\mathbf{v} \Rightarrow p^2 = m^2 v^2 \Rightarrow \frac{p^2}{m} = mv^2$$

$$\Rightarrow \frac{p^2}{2m} = \frac{1}{2}mv^2 = KE$$

$$KE = \frac{p^2}{2m}$$

21.
60.0 g

23.
0.122 m/s

25.
In a collision with an identical car, momentum is conserved. Afterwards $v_f = 0$ for both cars. The change in momentum will be the same as in the crash with the tree. However, the force on the body is not determined since the time is not known. A padded stop will reduce injurious force on body.

27.
22.4 m/s in the same direction as the original motion

29.
0.250 m/s

31.
(a) 86.4 N perpendicularly away from the bumper

(b) 0.389 J

(c) 64.0%

33.
(a) 8.06 m/s

(b) -56.0 J

(c)(i) 7.88 m/s; (ii) -223 J

35.
(a) 0.163 m/s in the direction of motion of the more massive satellite

(b) 81.6 J

(c) 8.70×10^{-2} m/s in the direction of motion of the less massive satellite, 81.5 J. Because there are no external forces, the velocity of the center of mass of the two-satellite system is unchanged by the collision. The two velocities calculated above are the velocity of the center of mass in each of the two different individual reference frames. The loss in KE is the same in both reference frames because the KE lost to internal forces (heat, friction, etc.) is the same regardless of the coordinate system chosen.

37.
0.704 m/s

−2.25 m/s

38.

(a) 4.58 m/s away from the bullet

(b) 31.5 J

(c) −0.491 m/s

(d) 3.38 J

40.
(a) 1.02×10^{-6} m/s

(b) 5.63×10^{20} J (almost all KE lost)

(c) Recoil speed is 6.79×10^{-17} m/s, energy lost is 6.25×10^{9} J. The plume will not affect the momentum result because the plume is still part of the Moon system. The plume may affect the kinetic energy result because a significant part of the initial kinetic energy may be transferred to the kinetic energy of the plume particles.

42.
24.8 m/s

44.
(a) 4.00 kg

(b) 210 J

(c) The clown does work to throw the barbell, so the kinetic energy comes from the muscles of the clown. The muscles convert the chemical potential energy of ATP into kinetic energy.

45.
(a) 3.00 m/s, $60°$ below x-axis

(b) Find speed of first puck after collision: $0 = mv'_1 \sin 30° - mv'_2 \sin 60° \Rightarrow v'_1 = v_2 \frac{\sin 60°}{\sin 30°} = 5.196$ m/s

Verify that ratio of initial to final KE equals one: $$\left.\begin{array}{l} \text{KE} = \frac{1}{2}mv_1{}^2 = 18m \text{ J} \\ \text{KE} = \frac{1}{2}mv'_1{}^2 + \frac{1}{2}mv'_2{}^2 = 18m \text{ J} \end{array}\right\} \frac{\text{KE}}{\text{KE}'} = 1.00$$

47.
(a) -2.26 m/s

(b) 7.63×10^{3} J

(c) The ground will exert a normal force to oppose recoil of the cannon in the vertical direction. The momentum in the vertical direction is transferred to the earth. The energy is transferred into the ground, making a dent where the cannon is. After long barrages, cannon have erratic aim because the ground is full of divots.

49.
(a) 5.36×10^{5} m/s at $-29.5°$

(b) 7.52×10^{-13} J

51.
We are given that $m_1 = m_2 \equiv m$. The given equations then become:

$$v_1 = v_1 \cos \theta_1 + v_2 \cos \theta_2$$
and

$$0 = v'_1 \sin \theta_1 + v'_2 \sin \theta_2.$$
Square each equation to get

$$\begin{array}{lll} v_1{}^2 & = & v'_1{}^2 \cos^2 \theta_1 + v'_2{}^2 \cos^2 \theta_2 + 2v'_1 v'_2 \cos \theta_1 \cos \theta_2 \\ 0 & = & v'_1{}^2 \sin^2 \theta_1 + v'_2{}^2 \sin^2 \theta_2 + 2v'_1 v'_2 \sin \theta_1 \sin \theta_2. \end{array}$$
Add these two equations and simplify:

$$
\begin{aligned}
v_1^2 &= {v'_1}^2 + {v'_2}^2 + 2v'_1 v'_2(\cos\theta_1 \cos\theta_2 + \sin\theta_1 \sin\theta_2) \\
&= {v'_1}^2 + {v'_2}^2 + 2v'_1 v'_2\left[\tfrac{1}{2}\cos(\theta_1 - \theta_2) + \tfrac{1}{2}\cos(\theta_1 + \theta_2) + \tfrac{1}{2}\cos(\theta_1 - \theta_2) - \tfrac{1}{2}\cos(\theta_1 + \theta_2)\right] \\
&= {v'_1}^2 + {v'_2}^2 + 2v'_1 v'_2 \cos(\theta_1 - \theta_2).
\end{aligned}
$$

Multiply the entire equation by $\frac{1}{2}m$ to recover the kinetic energy:

$$\frac{1}{2}m{v_1}^2 = \frac{1}{2}m{v'_1}^2 + \frac{1}{2}m{v'_2}^2 + mv'_1 v'_2 \cos(\theta_1 - \theta_2)$$

53.
39.2 m/s^2

55.
4.16×10^3 m/s

57.
The force needed to give a small mass Δm an acceleration $a_{\Delta m}$ is $F = \Delta m a_{\Delta m}$. To accelerate this mass in the small time interval Δt requires $v_e = a_{\Delta m}\Delta t$, so $F = v_e \frac{\Delta m}{\Delta t}$. By Newton's third law, this force is equal in magnitude to the thrust force acting on the rocket, so $F_{\text{thrust}} = v_e \frac{\Delta m}{\Delta t}$, where all quantities are positive. Applying Newton's second law to the rocket gives $F_{\text{thrust}} - mg = ma \Rightarrow a = \frac{v_e}{m}\frac{\Delta m}{\Delta t} - g$, where m is the mass of the rocket and unburnt fuel.

60.
2.63×10^3 kg

61.
(a) 0.421 m/s away from the ejected fluid.

(b) 0.237 J.

Test Prep for AP® Courses

1.
(b)

3.
(b)

5.
(a)

7.
(c) (based on calculation of $F = \frac{m\Delta v}{\Delta t}$)

9.
(c)

11.
(d)

13.
(b)

15.
(d)

17.
(b)

19.
(c)

21.

(b)

23.
(c)

25.
(b)

27.
(a)

29.
(c)

31.
(b)

33.
(a)

35.
(b)

37.
(a)

39.
(a)

41.
(d)

43.
(c). Because of conservation of momentum, the final velocity of the combined mass must be 4.286 m/s. The initial kinetic energy is $(0.5)(2.0)(15)^2 = 225\text{ J}$. The final kinetic energy is $(0.5)(7.0)(4.286)^2 = 64\text{ J}$, so the difference is −161 J.

45.
(a)

47.
(d)

49.
(c)

51.
(b)

Chapter 9

Problems & Exercises

1.
a) $46.8\text{ N}\cdot\text{m}$

b) It does not matter at what height you push. The torque depends on only the magnitude of the force applied and the perpendicular distance of the force's application from the hinges. (Children don't have a tougher time opening a door because they push lower than adults, they have a tougher time because they don't push far enough from the hinges.)

3.
23.3 N

5.
Given:

$$\begin{aligned} m_1 &= 26.0\text{ kg}, m_2 = 32.0\text{ kg}, m_s = 12.0\text{ kg}, \\ r_1 &= 1.60\text{ m}, r_s = 0.160\text{ m, find (a) } r_{2,} \text{ (b) } F_p \end{aligned}$$

a) Since children are balancing:

$$\begin{aligned} &\text{net } \tau_{cw} = -\text{net } \tau_{ccw} \\ \Rightarrow &\ w_1 r_1 + m_s\, g r_s = w_2 r_2 \end{aligned}$$

So, solving for r_2 gives:

$$\begin{aligned} r_2 &= \frac{w_1 r_1 + m_s\, g r_s}{w_2} = \frac{m_1\, g r_1 + m_s\, g r_s}{m_2 g} = \frac{m_1 r_1 + m_s r_s}{m_2} \\ &= \frac{(26.0\text{ kg})(1.60\text{ m}) + (12.0\text{ kg})(0.160\text{ m})}{32.0\text{ kg}} \\ &= 1.36\text{ m} \end{aligned}$$

b) Since the children are not moving:

$$\begin{aligned} &\text{net } F = 0 = F_p - w_1 - w_2 - w_s \\ &\quad \Rightarrow F_p = w_1 + w_2 + w_s \end{aligned}$$

So that

$$\begin{aligned} F_p &= (26.0\text{ kg} + 32.0\text{ kg} + 12.0\text{ kg})(9.80\text{ m/s}^2) \\ &= 686\text{ N} \end{aligned}$$

6.
$F_{wall} = 1.43\times10^3\text{ N}$

8.
a) 2.55×10^3 N, 16.3° to the left of vertical (i.e., toward the wall)

b) 0.292

10.
$F_B = 2.12\times10^4\text{ N}$

12.
a) 0.167, or about one-sixth of the weight is supported by the opposite shore.

b) $F = 2.0\times10^4\text{ N}$, straight up.

14.
a) 21.6 N

b) 21.6 N

16.
350 N directly upwards

19.
25

50 N

21.
a) MA = 18.5

b) $F_i = 29.1\text{ N}$

c) 510 N downward

23.

1.3×10^3 N

25.
a) $T = 299$ N

b) 897 N upward

26.
$$\begin{aligned} F_B &= 470 \text{ N}; r_1 = 4.00 \text{ cm}; w_a = 2.50 \text{ kg}; r_2 = 16.0 \text{ cm}; w_b = 4.00 \text{ kg}; r_3 = 38.0 \text{ cm} \\ F_E &= w_a\left(\frac{r_2}{r_1} - 1\right) + w_b\left(\frac{r_3}{r_1} - 1\right) \\ &= (2.50 \text{ kg})(9.80 \text{ m/s}^2)\left(\frac{16.0 \text{ cm}}{4.0 \text{ cm}} - 1\right) \\ &\quad + (4.00 \text{ kg})(9.80 \text{ m/s}^2)\left(\frac{38.0 \text{ cm}}{4.00 \text{ cm}} - 1\right) \\ &= 407 \text{ N} \end{aligned}$$

28.
$$1.1 \times 10^3 \text{ N}$$
$\theta = 190^\circ$ ccw from positive x axis

30.
$F_V = 97 \text{ N}, \theta = 59^\circ$

32.
(a) 25 N downward

(b) 75 N upward

33.
(a) $F_A = 2.21 \times 10^3$ N upward

(b) $F_B = 2.94 \times 10^3$ N downward

35.
(a) $F_{\text{teeth on bullet}} = 1.2 \times 10^2$ N upward

(b) $F_J = 84$ N downward

37.
(a) 147 N downward

(b) 1680 N, 3.4 times her weight

(c) 118 J

(d) 49.0 W

39.
a) $\bar{x}_2 = 2.33$ m

b) The seesaw is 3.0 m long, and hence, there is only 1.50 m of board on the other side of the pivot. The second child is off the board.

c) The position of the first child must be shortened, i.e. brought closer to the pivot.

Test Prep for AP® Courses

1.
(a)

3.
Both objects are in equilibrium. However, they will respond differently if a force is applied to their sides. If the cone placed on its base is displaced to the side, its center of gravity will remain over its base and it will return to its

original position. When the traffic cone placed on its tip is displaced to the side, its center of gravity will drift from its base, causing a torque that will accelerate it to the ground.

5.
(d)

7.
a. $\mathbf{F}_L$ = 7350 N, $\mathbf{F}_R$ = 2450 N
b. As the car moves to the right side of the bridge, $\mathbf{F}_L$ will decrease and $\mathbf{F}_R$ will increase. (At exactly halfway across the bridge, $\mathbf{F}_L$ and $\mathbf{F}_R$ will both be 4900 N.)

9.
The student should mention that the guiding principle behind simple machines is the second condition of equilibrium. Though the torque leaving a machine must be equivalent to torque entering a machine, the same requirement does not exist for forces. As a result, by decreasing the lever arm to the existing force, the size of the existing force will be increased. The mechanical advantage will be equivalent to the ratio of the forces exiting and entering the machine.

11.
a. The force placed on your bicep muscle will be greater than the force placed on the dumbbell. The bicep muscle is closer to your elbow than the downward force placed on your hand from the dumbbell. Because the elbow is the pivot point of the system, this results in a decreased lever arm for the bicep. As a result, the force on the bicep must be greater than that placed on the dumbbell. (How much greater? The ratio between the bicep and dumbbell forces is equal to the inverted ratio of their distances from the elbow. If the dumbbell is ten times further from the elbow than the bicep, the force on the bicep will be 200 pounds!)
b. The force placed on your bicep muscle will decrease. As the forearm lifts the dumbbell, it will get closer to the elbow. As a result, the torque placed on the arm from the weight will decrease and the countering torque created by the bicep muscle will do so as well.

Chapter 10

Problems & Exercises

1.
$\omega = 0.737 \text{ rev/s}$

3.
(a) -0.26 rad/s^2

(b) 27 rev

5.
(a) 80 rad/s^2

(b) 1.0 rev

7.
(a) 45.7 s

(b) 116 rev

9.
a) 600 rad/s^2

b) 450 rad/s

c) 21.0 m/s

10.
(a) 0.338 s

(b) 0.0403 rev

(c) 0.313 s

12.
$0.50\ \text{kg} \cdot \text{m}^2$

14.
(a) $50.4\ \text{N} \cdot \text{m}$

(b) $17.1\ \text{rad/s}^2$

(c) $17.0\ \text{rad/s}^2$

16.
$3.96 \times 10^{18}\ \text{s}$

or $1.26 \times 10^{11}\ \text{y}$

18.
$$I_{end} = I_{center} + m\left(\frac{l}{2}\right)^2$$
Thus, $I_{center} = I_{end} - \frac{1}{4}ml^2 = \frac{1}{3}ml^2 - \frac{1}{4}ml^2 = \frac{1}{12}ml^2$

19.
(a) 2.0 ms

(b) The time interval is too short.

(c) The moment of inertia is much too small, by one to two orders of magnitude. A torque of $500\ \text{N} \cdot \text{m}$ is reasonable.

20.
(a) 17,500 rpm

(b) This angular velocity is very high for a disk of this size and mass. The radial acceleration at the edge of the disk is > 50,000 gs.

(c) Flywheel mass and radius should both be much greater, allowing for a lower spin rate (angular velocity).

21.
(a) 185 J

(b) 0.0785 rev

(c) $W = 9.81\ \text{N}$

23.
(a) $2.57 \times 10^{29}\ \text{J}$

(b) $\text{KE}_{\text{rot}} = 2.65 \times 10^{33}\ \text{J}$

25.
$\text{KE}_{\text{rot}} = 434\ \text{J}$

27.
(a) $128\ \text{rad/s}$

(b) $19.9\ \text{m}$

29.
(a) $10.4\ \text{rad/s}^2$

(b) net $W = 6.11\ \text{J}$

34.
(a) 1.49 kJ

(b) $2.52 \times 10^4\ \text{N}$

36.
(a) $2.66 \times 10^{40}\ \text{kg} \cdot \text{m}^2/\text{s}$

(b) $7.07 \times 10^{33}\ \text{kg} \cdot \text{m}^2/\text{s}$

The angular momentum of the Earth in its orbit around the Sun is 3.77×10^6 times larger than the angular momentum of the Earth around its axis.

38.
$22.5\ \text{kg} \cdot \text{m}^2/\text{s}$

40.
25.3 rpm

43.
(a) $0.156\ \text{rad/s}$

(b) $1.17 \times 10^{-2}\ \text{J}$

(c) $0.188\ \text{kg} \cdot \text{m/s}$

45.
(a) 3.13 rad/s

(b) Initial KE = 438 J, final KE = 438 J

47.
(a) 1.70 rad/s

(b) Initial KE = 22.5 J, final KE = 2.04 J

(c) $1.50\ \text{kg} \cdot \text{m/s}$

48.
(a) $5.64 \times 10^{33}\ \text{kg} \cdot \text{m}^2/\text{s}$

(b) $1.39 \times 10^{22}\ \text{N} \cdot \text{m}$

(c) $2.17 \times 10^{15}\ \text{N}$

Test Prep for AP® Courses

1.
(b)

3.
(d)

5.
(d)

You are given a thin rod of length 1.0 m and mass 2.0 kg, a small lead weight of 0.50 kg, and a not-so-small lead weight of 1.0 kg. The rod has three holes, one in each end and one through the middle, which may either hold a pivot point or one of the small lead weights.

7.
(a)

9.
(c)

11.
(a)

13.
(a)

15.
(b)

17.
(c)

19.
(b)

21.
(b)

23.
(c)

25.
(d)

27.
A door on hinges is a rotational system. When you push or pull on the door handle, the angular momentum of the system changes. If a weight is hung on the door handle, then pushing on the door with the same force will cause a different increase in angular momentum. If you push or pull near the hinges with the same force, the resulting angular momentum of the system will also be different.

29.
Since the globe is stationary to start with,

$$\tau = \frac{\Delta L}{\Delta t}$$

$$\tau \cdot \Delta t = \Delta L$$

By substituting,

120 N•m • 1.2 s = 144 N•m•s.

The angular momentum of the globe after 1.2 s is 144 N•m•s.

Chapter 11

Problems & Exercises

1.
1.610 cm^3

3.
(a) 2.58 g

(b) The volume of your body increases by the volume of air you inhale. The average density of your body decreases when you take a deep breath, because the density of air is substantially smaller than the average density of the body before you took the deep breath.

4.
2.70 g/cm^3

6.
(a) 0.163 m

(b) Equivalent to 19.4 gallons, which is reasonable

8.

$7.9 \times 10^2 \text{ kg/m}^3$

9.
15.8 g/cm^3

10.
(a) 10^{18} kg/m^3

(b) $2 \times 10^4 \text{ m}$

11.
$3.59 \times 10^6 \text{ Pa}$; or 521 lb/in^2

13.
$2.36 \times 10^3 \text{ N}$

14.
0.760 m

16.

$$\begin{aligned}(h\rho g)_{\text{units}} &= (\text{m})(\text{kg/m}^3)(\text{m/s}^2) = (\text{kg} \cdot \text{m}^2)/(\text{m}^3 \cdot \text{s}^2) \\ &= (\text{kg} \cdot \text{m/s}^2)(1/\text{m}^2) \\ &= \text{N/m}^2\end{aligned}$$

18.
(a) 20.5 mm Hg

(b) The range of pressures in the eye is 12–24 mm Hg, so the result in part (a) is within that range

20.
$1.09 \times 10^3 \text{ N/m}^2$

22.
24.0 N

24.
$2.55 \times 10^7 \text{ Pa}$; or 251 atm

26.
$5.76 \times 10^3 \text{ N}$ extra force

28.
(a) $V = d_\text{i} A_\text{i} = d_\text{o} A_\text{o} \Rightarrow d_\text{o} = d_\text{i} \left(\frac{A_\text{i}}{A_\text{o}} \right)$.

Now, using equation:

$$\frac{F_1}{A_1} = \frac{F_2}{A_2} \Rightarrow F_\text{o} = F_\text{i} \left(\frac{A_\text{o}}{A_\text{i}} \right).$$

Finally,

$$W_\text{o} = F_\text{o} d_\text{o} = \left(\frac{F_\text{i} A_\text{o}}{A_\text{i}} \right) \left(\frac{d_\text{i} A_\text{i}}{A_\text{o}} \right) = F_\text{i} d_\text{i} = W_\text{i}.$$

In other words, the work output equals the work input.

(b) If the system is not moving, friction would not play a role. With friction, we know there are losses, so that $W_\text{out} = W_\text{in} - W_\text{f}$; therefore, the work output is less than the work input. In other words, with friction, you need to push harder on the input piston than was calculated for the nonfriction case.

29.
Balloon:

$$P_g = 5.00 \text{ cm } H_2O,$$
$$P_{abs} = 1.035 \times 10^3 \text{ cm } H_2O.$$

Jar:

$$P_g = -50.0 \text{ mm Hg},$$
$$P_{abs} = 710 \text{ mm Hg}.$$

31.
4.08 m

33.
$$\Delta P = 38.7 \text{ mm Hg},$$
$$\text{Leg blood pressure} = \frac{159}{119}.$$

35.
22.4 cm^2

36.
91.7%

38.
815 kg/m^3

40.
(a) 41.4 g

(b) 41.4 cm^3

(c) 1.09 g/cm^3

42.
(a) 39.5 g

(b) 50 cm^3

(c) 0.79 g/cm^3

It is ethyl alcohol.

44.
8.21 N

46.
(a) 960 kg/m^3

(b) 6.34%

She indeed floats more in seawater.

48.
(a) 0.24

(b) 0.68

(c) Yes, the cork will float because $\rho_{obj} < \rho_{\text{ethyl alcohol}} (0.678 \text{ g/cm}^3 < 0.79 \text{ g/cm}^3)$

50.
The difference is 0.006%.

52.
$$F_{net} = F_2 - F_1 = P_2 A - P_1 A = (P_2 - P_1) A$$
$$= (h_2 \rho_{fl} g - h_1 \rho_{fl} g) A$$

$=(h_2 - h_1)\rho_{fl} g A$

where ρ_{fl} = density of fluid. Therefore,

$F_{net} = (h_2 - h_1)A\rho_{fl} g = V_{fl}\rho_{fl} g = m_{fl} g = w_{fl}$

where is w_{fl} the weight of the fluid displaced.

54.
$592\ N/m^2$

56.
2.23×10^{-2} mm Hg

58.
(a) 1.65×10^{-3} m

(b) 3.71×10^{-4} m

60.
6.32×10^{-2} N/m

Based on the values in table, the fluid is probably glycerin.

62.

$$\begin{aligned} P_w &= 14.6\ N/m^2, \\ P_a &= 4.46\ N/m^2, \\ P_{sw} &= 7.40\ N/m^2. \end{aligned}$$

Alcohol forms the most stable bubble, since the absolute pressure inside is closest to atmospheric pressure.

64.
5.1°

This is near the value of $\theta = 0^\circ$ for most organic liquids.

66.
-2.78

The ratio is negative because water is raised whereas mercury is lowered.

68.
479 N

70.
1.96 N

71.
-63.0 cm H_2O

73.
(a) $3.81 \times 10^3\ N/m^2$

(b) 28.7 mm Hg, which is sufficient to trigger micturition reflex

75.
(a) 13.6 m water

(b) 76.5 cm water

77.
(a) 3.98×10^6 Pa

(b) 2.1×10^{-3} cm

79.
(a) 2.97 cm

(b) 3.39×10^{-6} J

(c) Work is done by the surface tension force through an effective distance $h/2$ to raise the column of water.

81.
(a) 2.01×10^{4} N

(b) 1.17×10^{-3} m

(c) 2.56×10^{10} N/m^2

83.
(a) 1.38×10^{4} N

(b) 2.81×10^{7} N/m^2

(c) 283 N

85.
(a) 867 N

(b) This is too much force to exert with a hand pump.

(c) The assumed radius of the pump is too large; it would be nearly two inches in diameter—too large for a pump or even a master cylinder. The pressure is reasonable for bicycle tires.

Test Prep for AP® Courses

1.
(e)

3.
(a) 100 kg/m^3 (b) 60% (c) yes; yes (76% will be submerged) (d) answers vary

Chapter 12

Problems & Exercises

1.
2.78 cm^3/s

3.
27 cm/s

5.
(a) 0.75 m/s

(b) 0.13 m/s

7.
(a) 40.0 cm^2

(b) 5.09×10^{7}

9.
(a) 22 h

(b) 0.016 s

11.
(a) 12.6 m/s

(b) 0.0800 m^3/s

(c) No, independent of density.

13.
(a) 0.402 L/s

(b) 0.584 cm

15.
(a) $127\ \text{cm}^3/\text{s}$

(b) 0.890 cm

17.
$$\begin{aligned} P &= \frac{\text{Force}}{\text{Area}}, \\ (P)_{\text{units}} &= \text{N/m}^2 = \text{N} \cdot \text{m/m}^3 = \text{J/m}^3 \\ &= \text{energy/volume} \end{aligned}$$

19.
184 mm Hg

21.
$2.54 \times 10^5\ \text{N}$

23.
(a) $1.58 \times 10^6\ \text{N/m}^2$

(b) 163 m

25.
(a) $9.56 \times 10^8\ \text{W}$

(b) 1.4

27.
1.26 W

29.
(a) $3.02 \times 10^{-3}\ \text{N}$

(b) 1.03×10^{-3}

31.
$1.60\ \text{cm}^3/\text{min}$

33.
$8.7 \times 10^{-11}\ \text{m}^3/\text{s}$

35.
0.316

37.
(a) 1.52

(b) Turbulence will decrease the flow rate of the blood, which would require an even larger increase in the pressure difference, leading to higher blood pressure.

39.
$225\ \text{mPa} \cdot \text{s}$
41.
$0.138\ \text{Pa} \cdot \text{s},$
or

Olive oil.

43.
(a) $1.62 \times 10^4\ \text{N/m}^2$

(b) $0.111\ \text{cm}^3\text{/s}$

(c)10.6 cm

45.
1.59

47.
$2.95 \times 10^6\ \text{N/m}^2$ (gauge pressure)

51.
$N_\text{R} = 1.99 \times 10^2 < 2000$

53.
(a) nozzle: 1.27×10^5 , not laminar

(b) hose: 3.51×10^4, not laminar.

55.
2.54 << 2000, laminar.

57.
1.02 m/s

$1.28 \times 10^{-2}\ \text{L/s}$

59.
(a)$\geq 13.0\ \text{m}$

(b) $2.68 \times 10^{-6}\ \text{N/m}^2$

61.
(a) 23.7 atm or $344\ \text{lb/in}^2$

(b) The pressure is much too high.

(c) The assumed flow rate is very high for a garden hose.

(d) 5.27×10^6 > > 3000, turbulent, contrary to the assumption of laminar flow when using this equation.

62.
$1.41 \times 10^{-3}\ \text{m}$

64.
$1.3 \times 10^2\ \text{s}$

66.
0.391 s

Test Prep for AP® Courses

1.
(c)

3.
(a)

5.
(a)

7.
(a)

9.
(d)

Chapter 13

Problems & Exercises

1.
102ºF

3.
20.0ºC and 25.6ºC

5.
9890ºF

7.
(a) 22.2ºC

(b)
$$\begin{aligned} \Delta T(\text{ºF}) &= T_2(\text{ºF})-T_1(\text{ºF}) \\ &= \tfrac{9}{5}T_2(\text{ºC})+32.0\text{º} - \left(\tfrac{9}{5}T_1(\text{ºC})+32.0\text{º}\right) \\ &= \tfrac{9}{5}(T_2(\text{ºC})-T_1(\text{ºC})) = \tfrac{9}{5}\Delta T(\text{ºC}) \end{aligned}$$

9.
169.98 m

11.
5.4×10^{-6} m

13.
Because the area gets smaller, the price of the land DECREASES by ~$17,000.

15.
$$\begin{aligned} V &= V_0 + \Delta V = V_0(1 + \beta \Delta T) \\ &= (60.00\text{ L})\left[1 + \left(950 \times 10^{-6}/\text{ºC}\right)(35.0\text{ºC} - 15.0\text{ºC})\right] \\ &= 61.1\text{ L} \end{aligned}$$

17.
(a) 9.35 mL

(b) 7.56 mL

19.
0.832 mm

21.
We know how the length changes with temperature: $\Delta L = \alpha L_0 \Delta T$. Also we know that the volume of a cube is related to its length by $V = L^3$, so the final volume is then $V = V_0 + \Delta V = (L_0 + \Delta L)^3$. Substituting for ΔL gives

$V = (L_0 + \alpha L_0 \Delta T)^3 = L_0^3(1 + \alpha \Delta T)^3$.
Now, because $\alpha \Delta T$ is small, we can use the binomial expansion:

$V \approx L_0^3(1 + 3\alpha \Delta \text{T}) = L_0^3 + 3\alpha L_0^3 \Delta T$.
So writing the length terms in terms of volumes gives $V = V_0 + \Delta V \approx V_0 + 3\alpha V_0 \Delta T$, and so

$\Delta V = \beta V_0 \Delta T \approx 3\alpha V_0 \Delta T$, or $\beta \approx 3\alpha$.
22.
1.62 atm

24.

(a) 0.136 atm

(b) 0.135 atm. The difference between this value and the value from part (a) is negligible.

26.
(a) $nRT = (\text{mol})(\text{J/mol} \cdot \text{K})(\text{K}) = \text{J}$

(b) $nRT = (\text{mol})(\text{cal/mol} \cdot \text{K})(\text{K}) = \text{cal}$

(c)
$$\begin{aligned} nRT &= (\text{mol})(\text{L} \cdot \text{atm/mol} \cdot \text{K})(\text{K}) \\ &= \text{L} \cdot \text{atm} = (\text{m}^3)(\text{N/m}^2) \\ &= \text{N} \cdot \text{m} = \text{J} \end{aligned}$$

28.
7.86×10^{-2} mol

30.
(a) $6.02 \times 10^5\ \text{km}^3$

(b) 6.02×10^8 km

32.
-73.9°C

34.
(a) $9.14 \times 10^6\ \text{N/m}^2$

(b) $8.23 \times 10^6\ \text{N/m}^2$

(c) 2.16 K

(d) No. The final temperature needed is much too low to be easily achieved for a large object.

36.
41 km

38.
(a) 3.7×10^{-17} Pa

(b) $6.0 \times 10^{17}\ \text{m}^3$

(c) 8.4×10^2 km

39.
1.25×10^3 m/s

41.
(a) 1.20×10^{-19} J

(b) 1.24×10^{-17} J

43.
458 K

45.
1.95×10^7 K

47.
6.09×10^5 m/s

49.
7.89×10^4 Pa

51.

(a) 1.99×10^5 Pa

(b) 0.97 atm

53.
3.12×10^4 Pa

55.
78.3%

57.
(a) 2.12×10^4 Pa

(b) 1.06 %

59.
(a) 8.80×10^{-2} g

(b) 6.30×10^3 Pa; the two values are nearly identical.

61.
82.3%

63.
4.77°C

65.
38.3 m

67.
$\frac{\left(F_B / w_{Cu}\right)}{\left(F_B / w_{Cu}\right)'} = 1.02$. The buoyant force supports nearly the exact same amount of force on the copper block in both circumstances.

69.
(a) 4.41×10^{10} mol/m^3

(b) It's unreasonably large.

(c) At high pressures such as these, the ideal gas law can no longer be applied. As a result, unreasonable answers come up when it is used.

71.
(a) 7.03×10^8 m/s

(b) The velocity is too high—it's greater than the speed of light.

(c) The assumption that hydrogen inside a supernova behaves as an idea gas is responsible, because of the great temperature and density in the core of a star. Furthermore, when a velocity greater than the speed of light is obtained, classical physics must be replaced by relativity, a subject not yet covered.

Test Prep for AP® Courses

1.
(a), (c)

3.
(d)

5.
(b)

7.

(a) 7.29×10^{-21} J; (b) 352K or 79°C

Chapter 14

Problems & Exercises

1.
5.02×10^8 J

3.
3.07×10^3 J

5.
$0.171°C$

7.
10.8

9.
617 W

11.
35.9 kcal

13.
(a) 591 kcal

(b) 4.94×10^3 s

15.
13.5 W

17.
(a) 148 kcal

(b) 0.418 s, 3.34 s, 4.19 s, 22.6 s, 0.456 s

19.
33.0 g

20.
(a) 9.67 L

(b) Crude oil is less dense than water, so it floats on top of the water, thereby exposing it to the oxygen in the air, which it uses to burn. Also, if the water is under the oil, it is less efficient in absorbing the heat generated by the oil.

22.
a) 319 kcal

b) $2.00°C$

24.
$20.6°C$

26.
4.38 kg

28.
(a) 1.57×10^4 kcal

(b) $18.3 \text{ kW} \cdot \text{h}$

(c) 1.29×10^4 kcal

30.
(a) 1.01×10^3 W

(b) One

32.
84.0 W

34.
2.59 kg

36.
(a) 39.7 W

(b) 820 kcal

38.
35 to 1, window to wall

40.
1.05×10^3 K

42.
(a) 83 W

(b) 24 times that of a double pane window.

44.
20.0 W, 17.2% of 2400 kcal per day

45.
10 m/s

47.
85.7°C

49.
1.48 kg

51.
2×10^4 MW

53.
(a) 97.2 J

(b) 29.2 W

(c) 9.49 W

(d) The total rate of heat loss would be $29.2 \text{ W} + 9.49 \text{ W} = 38.7 \text{ W}$. While sleeping, our body consumes 83 W of power, while sitting it consumes 120 to 210 W. Therefore, the total rate of heat loss from breathing will not be a major form of heat loss for this person.

55.
−21.7 kW
Note that the negative answer implies heat loss to the surroundings.

57.
−266 kW

59.
−36.0 W

61.
(a) 1.31%

(b) 20.5%

63.
(a) -15.0 kW

(b) 4.2 cm

65.
(a) $48.5°C$

(b) A pure white object reflects more of the radiant energy that hits it, so a white tent would prevent more of the sunlight from heating up the inside of the tent, and the white tunic would prevent that heat which entered the tent from heating the rider. Therefore, with a white tent, the temperature would be lower than $48.5°C$, and the rate of radiant heat transferred to the rider would be less than 20.0 W.

67.
(a) 3×10^{17} J

(b) 1×10^{13} kg

(c) When a large meteor hits the ocean, it causes great tidal waves, dissipating large amount of its energy in the form of kinetic energy of the water.

69.
(a) $3.44 \times 10^5 \text{ m}^3/\text{s}$

(b) This is equivalent to 12 million cubic feet of air per second. That is tremendous. This is too large to be dissipated by heating the air by only $5°C$. Many of these cooling towers use the circulation of cooler air over warmer water to increase the rate of evaporation. This would allow much smaller amounts of air necessary to remove such a large amount of heat because evaporation removes larger quantities of heat than was considered in part (a).

71.
20.9 min

73.
(a) 3.96×10^{-2} g

(b) 96.2 J

(c) 16.0 W

75.
(a) 1.102

(b) 2.79×10^4 J

(c) 12.6 J. This will not cause a significant cooling of the air because it is much less than the energy found in part (b), which is the energy required to warm the air from $20.0°C$ to $50.0°C$.

76.
(a) $36°C$

(b) Any temperature increase greater than about $3°C$ would be unreasonably large. In this case the final temperature of the person would rise to $73°C$ $(163°F)$.

(c) The assumption of 95% heat retention is unreasonable.

78.
(a) 1.46 kW

(b) Very high power loss through a window. An electric heater of this power can keep an entire room warm.

(c) The surface temperatures of the window do not differ by as great an amount as assumed. The inner surface will be warmer, and the outer surface will be cooler.

Test Prep for AP® Courses

1.
(c)

3.
(a)

5.
(b)

7.
(a)

9.
(d)

Chapter 15

Problems & Exercises

1.
1.6×10^9 J

3.
-9.30×10^8 J

5.
(a) -1.0×10^4 J, or -2.39 kcal

(b) 5.00%

7.
(a) 122 W

(b) 2.10×10^6 J

(c) Work done by the motor is 1.61×10^7 J ;thus the motor produces 7.67 times the work done by the man

9.
(a) 492 kJ

(b) This amount of heat is consistent with the fact that you warm quickly when exercising. Since the body is inefficient, the excess heat produced must be dissipated through sweating, breathing, etc.

10.
2.09×10^4 J

12.
(a) $W = P\Delta V = 1.76 \times 10^5$ J

(b) $W = Fd = 1.76 \times 10^5$ J. Yes, the answer is the same.

14.
$W = 4.5 \times 10^3$ J

16.
W is not equal to the difference between the heat input and the heat output.

20.
(a) 18.5 kJ

(b) 54.1%

22.
(a) 1.32×10^9 J

(b) 4.68×10^9 J

24.
(a) 3.80×10^9 J

(b) 0.667 barrels

26.
(a) 8.30×10^{12} J, which is 3.32% of 2.50×10^{14} J .

(b) -8.30×10^{12} J, where the negative sign indicates a reduction in heat transfer to the environment.

28.
403ºC

30.
(a) 244ºC

(b) 477ºC

(c)Yes, since automobiles engines cannot get too hot without overheating, their efficiency is limited.

32.
(a) $Eff_1 = 1 - \frac{T_{c,1}}{T_{h,1}} = 1 - \frac{543\text{ K}}{723\text{ K}} = 0.249 \text{ or } 24.9\%$

(b) $Eff_2 = 1 - \frac{423\text{ K}}{543\text{ K}} = 0.221 \text{ or } 22.1\%$

(c) $Eff_1 = 1 - \frac{T_{c,1}}{T_{h,1}} \Rightarrow T_{c,1} = T_{h,1}(1,-,eff_1)$ similarly, $T_{c,2} = T_{h,2}(1 - Eff_2)$

$$T_{c,2} = T_{h,1}(1 - Eff_1)(1 - Eff_2) \equiv T_{h,1}\left(1 - Eff_{\text{overall}}\right)$$

using $T_{h,2} = T_{c,1}$ in above equation gives $\therefore \left(1 - Eff_{\text{overall}}\right) = (1 - Eff_1)(1 - Eff_2)$

$$Eff_{\text{overall}} = 1 - (1 - 0.249)(1 - 0.221) = 41.5\%$$

(d) $Eff_{\text{overall}} = 1 - \frac{423\text{ K}}{723\text{ K}} = 0.415 \text{ or } 41.5\%$

34.
The heat transfer to the cold reservoir is $Q_c = Q_h - W = 25\text{ kJ} - 12\text{ kJ} = 13\text{ kJ}$, so the efficiency is $Eff = 1 - \frac{Q_c}{Q_h} = 1 - \frac{13\text{ kJ}}{25\text{ kJ}} = 0.48$. The Carnot efficiency is $Eff_C = 1 - \frac{T_c}{T_h} = 1 - \frac{300\text{ K}}{600\text{ K}} = 0.50$. The actual efficiency is 96% of the Carnot efficiency, which is much higher than the best-ever achieved of about 70%, so her scheme is likely to be fraudulent.

36.
(a) –56.3ºC

(b) The temperature is too cold for the output of a steam engine (the local environment). It is below the freezing point of water.

(c) The assumed efficiency is too high.

37.
4.82

39.
0.311

41.
(a) 4.61

(b) 1.66×10^8 J or 3.97×10^4 kcal

(c) To transfer 1.66×10^8 J, heat pump costs $1.00, natural gas costs $1.34.

43.
27.6ºC

45.
(a) 1.44×10^7 J

(b) 40 cents

(c) This cost seems quite realistic; it says that running an air conditioner all day would cost $9.59 (if it ran continuously).

47.
(a) 9.78×10^4 J/K

(b) In order to gain more energy, we must generate it from things within the house, like a heat pump, human bodies, and other appliances. As you know, we use a lot of energy to keep our houses warm in the winter because of the loss of heat to the outside.

49.
8.01×10^5 J

51.
(a) 1.04×10^{31} J/K

(b) 3.28×10^{31} J

53.
199 J/K

55.
(a) 2.47×10^{14} J

(b) 1.60×10^{14} J

(c) 2.85×10^{10} J/K

(d) 8.29×10^{12} J

57.
It should happen twice in every 1.27×10^{30} s or once in every 6.35×10^{29} s

$$\left(6.35 \times 10^{29}\ \text{s}\right)\left(\frac{1\ \text{h}}{3600\ \text{s}}\right)\left(\frac{1\ \text{d}}{24\ \text{h}}\right)\left(\frac{1\ \text{y}}{365.25\ \text{d}}\right) = 2.0 \times 10^{22}\ \text{y}$$

59.
(a) 3.0×10^{29}

(b) 24%

61.
(a) -2.38×10^{-23} J/K

(b) 5.6 times more likely

(c) If you were betting on two heads and 8 tails, the odds of breaking even are 252 to 45, so on average you would break even. So, no, you wouldn't bet on odds of 252 to 45.

63.
(b) 7

(c) 64

(d) 9.38%

(e) 3.33 times more likely (20 to 6)

Test Prep for AP® Courses

1.
(d)

3.
(a)

5.
(b)

7.
(c)

9.
(d)

11.
(a)

13.
(c)

15.
(b)

Chapter 16

Problems & Exercises

1.
(a) $1.23 \times 10^3 \text{ N/m}$

(b) 6.88 kg

(c) 4.00 mm

3.
(a) 889 N/m

(b) 133 N

5.
(a) $6.53 \times 10^3 \text{ N/m}$

(b) Yes

7.
16.7 ms

8.
0.400 s/beats

9.
400 Hz

10.
12,500 Hz

11.
1.50 kHz

12.
(a) 93.8 m/s

(b) 11.3×10^3 rev/min

13.
2.37 N/m

15.
0.389 kg

18.
94.7 kg

21.
1.94 s

22.
6.21 cm

24.
2.01 s

26.
2.23 Hz

28.
(a) 2.99541 s

(b) Since the period is related to the square root of the acceleration of gravity, when the acceleration changes by 1% the period changes by $(0.01)^2 = 0.01\%$ so it is necessary to have at least 4 digits after the decimal to see the changes.

30.
(a) Period increases by a factor of 1.41 ($\sqrt{2}$)

(b) Period decreases to 97.5% of old period

32.
Slow by a factor of 2.45

34.
length must increase by 0.0116%.

35.
(a) 1.99 Hz

(b) 50.2 cm

(c) 1.40 Hz, 71.0 cm

36.
(a) 3.95×10^6 N/m

(b) 7.90×10^6 J

37.
a). 0.266 m/s

b). 3.00 J

39.
$\pm\frac{\sqrt{3}}{2}$

42.
384 J

44.
(a). 0.123 m

(b). −0.600 J

(c). 0.300 J. The rest of the energy may go into heat caused by friction and other damping forces.

46.
(a) 5.00×10^5 J

(b) 1.20×10^3 s

47.
$t = 9.26$ d

49.
$f = 40.0$ Hz

51.
$v_\mathrm{w} = 16.0$ m/s

53.
$\lambda = 700$ m

55.
$d = 34.0$ cm

57.
$f = 4$ Hz

59.
462 Hz,

4 Hz

61.
(a) 3.33 m/s

(b) 1.25 Hz

63.
0.225 W

65.
7.07

67.
16.0 d

68.
2.50 kW

70.
3.38×10^{-5} W/m^2

Test Prep for AP® Courses

1.
(d)

3.

(b)

5.
The frequency is given by

$$f = \frac{1}{T} = \frac{50 \quad cycles}{30s} = 1.66 \quad Hz$$

Time period is:

$$T = \frac{1}{f} = \frac{1}{1.66} = 0.6 \quad \text{s}$$

7.
(c)

9.
The energy of the particle at the center of the oscillation is given by

$$E = \frac{1}{2}mv^2 = \frac{1}{2} \times 0.2 \quad \text{kg} \times (5 \text{ m·s}^{-1})^2 = 2.5 \quad \text{J}$$

11.
(b)

13.
19.7 J

15.
(c)

17.

$$d = \frac{k}{2\mu_K mg}\left(X^2 - \frac{\mu_K mg}{k}\right)^2 \ where \ k = 50 \ \text{N} \cdot \text{m}^{-1} \ \mu_k = 0.06 \ m = 0.5\text{kg}$$

$$d = \frac{50\text{N} \cdot \text{m}^{-1}}{2 \times 0.06 \times 9.8\text{m} \cdot \text{s}^{-2}}\left((0.2)^2 - \left(\frac{(0.06 \times 0.5\text{kg} \times 9.8\text{m} \cdot \text{s}^{-2})^2}{(50\text{N} \cdot \text{m}^{-1})^2}\right)\right) = 1.698 \quad \text{m}$$

19.
The waves coming from a tuning fork are mechanical waves that are longitudinal in nature, whereas electromagnetic waves are transverse in nature.

21.
The sound energy coming out of an instrument depends on its size. The sound waves produced are relative to the size of the musical instrument. A smaller instrument such as a tambourine will produce a high-pitched sound (higher frequency, shorter wavelength), whereas a larger instrument such as a drum will produce a deeper sound (lower frequency, longer wavelength).

23.
$2\pi \quad \text{m}$

25.
The student explains the principle of superposition and then shows two waves adding up to form a bigger wave when a crest adds with a crest and a trough with another trough. Also the student shows a wave getting cancelled out when a crest meets a trough and vice versa.

27.
The student must note that the shape of the wave remains the same and there is first an overlap and then receding of the waves.

29.

(c)

Chapter 17

Problems & Exercises

1.
0.288 m

3.
332 m/s

5.
$$\begin{aligned} v_{\text{w}} &= (331 \text{ m/s})\sqrt{\frac{T}{273 \text{ K}}} = (331 \text{ m/s})\sqrt{\frac{293 \text{ K}}{273 \text{ K}}} \\ &= 343 \text{ m/s} \end{aligned}$$

7.
0.223

9.
(a) 7.70 m

(b) This means that sonar is good for spotting and locating large objects, but it isn't able to resolve smaller objects, or detect the detailed shapes of objects. Objects like ships or large pieces of airplanes can be found by sonar, while smaller pieces must be found by other means.

11.
(a) 18.0 ms, 17.1 ms

(b) 5.00%

(c) This uncertainty could definitely cause difficulties for the bat, if it didn't continue to use sound as it closed in on its prey. A 5% uncertainty could be the difference between catching the prey around the neck or around the chest, which means that it could miss grabbing its prey.

12.
$3.16 \times 10^{-4} \text{ W/m}^2$

14.
$3.04 \times 10^{-4} \text{ W/m}^2$

16.
106 dB

18.
(a) 93 dB

(b) 83 dB

20.
(a) 50.1

(b) 5.01×10^{-3} or $\frac{1}{200}$

22.
70.0 dB

24.
100

26.
$1.45 \times 10^{-3} \text{ J}$

28.
28.2 dB

30.

(a) 878 Hz

(b) 735 Hz

32.

3.79×10^3 Hz

34.

(a) 12.9 m/s

(b) 193 Hz

36.

First eagle hears 4.23×10^3 Hz

Second eagle hears 3.56×10^3 Hz

38.

0.7 Hz

40.

0.3 Hz, 0.2 Hz, 0.5 Hz

42.

(a) 256 Hz

(b) 512 Hz

44.

180 Hz, 270 Hz, 360 Hz

46.

1.56 m

48.

(a) 0.334 m

(b) 259 Hz

50.

3.39 to 4.90 kHz

52.

(a) 367 Hz

(b) 1.07 kHz

54.

(a) $f_n = n(47.6 \text{ Hz}),\ n = 1, 3, 5, \ldots, 419$

(b) $f_n = n(95.3 \text{ Hz}),\ n = 1, 2, 3, \ldots, 210$

55.

1×10^6 km

57.

498.5 or 501.5 Hz

59.

82 dB

61.

approximately 48, 9, 0, −7, and 20 dB, respectively

63.

(a) 23 dB

(b) 70 dB

65.
Five factors of 10

67.
(a) $2 \times 10^{-10}\ \text{W/m}^2$

(b) $2 \times 10^{-13}\ \text{W/m}^2$

69.
2.5

71.
1.26

72.
170 dB

74.
103 dB

76.
(a) 1.00

(b) 0.823

(c) Gel is used to facilitate the transmission of the ultrasound between the transducer and the patient's body.

78.
(a) $77.0\ \mu\text{m}$

(b) Effective penetration depth = 3.85 cm, which is enough to examine the eye.

(c) $16.6\ \mu\text{m}$

80.
(a) $5.78 \times 10^{-4}\ \text{m}$

(b) $2.67 \times 10^{6}\ \text{Hz}$

82.
(a) $v_\text{w} = 1540\ \text{m/s} = f\lambda \Rightarrow \lambda = \frac{1540\ \text{m/s}}{100 \times 10^3\ \text{Hz}} = 0.0154\ \text{m} < 3.50\ \text{m}$. Because the wavelength is much shorter than the distance in question, the wavelength is not the limiting factor.

(b) 4.55 ms

84.
974 Hz

(Note: extra digits were retained in order to show the difference.)

Test Prep for AP® Courses

1.
(b)

3.
(e)

5.
(c)

7.
Answers vary. Students could include a sketch showing an increased amplitude when two waves occupy the same location. Students could also cite conceptual evidence such as sound waves passing through each other.

9.
(d)

11.
(c)

13.
(a)

15.
(c)

17.
(b)

18.
Striking the end of a protruding ruler would create transverse waves, not sound waves. Any measurable, audible sound would come from the repetitive striking of the ruler against the desk. The student is confused about the speed of sound through solids versus the speed of sound in air.

19.
(a), (b)

21.
(c)

Chapter 18

Problems & Exercises

1.
(a) 1.25×10^{10}

(b) 3.13×10^{12}

3.
-600 C

5.
1.03×10^{12}

7.
9.09×10^{-13}

9.
1.48×10^{8} C

15.
(a) 2.12×10^{5} N/C

(b) one charge of $+q$

17.
(a) 0.252 N to the left

(b) $x = 6.07$ cm

19.
(a)The electric field at the center of the square will be straight up, since q_a and q_b are positive and q_c and q_d are

negative and all have the same magnitude.

(b) 2.04×10^7 N/C (upward)

21.
0.102 N, in the $-y$ direction

23.
(a) $\vec{E} = 4.36 \times 10^3$ N/C, 35.0°, below the horizontal.

(b) No

25.
(a) 0.263 N

(b) If the charges are distributed over some area, there will be a concentration of charge along the side closest to the oppositely charged object. This effect will increase the net force.

27.
The separation decreased by a factor of 5.

31.

$$\begin{aligned} F &= k\frac{|q_1 q_2|}{r^2} = ma \Rightarrow a = \frac{kq^2}{mr^2} \\ &= \frac{\left(9.00\times10^9 \text{ N}\cdot\text{m}^2/\text{C}^2\right)\left(1.60\times10^{-19} \text{ m}\right)^2}{\left(1.67\times10^{-27} \text{ kg}\right)\left(2.00\times10^{-9} \text{ m}\right)^2} \\ &= 3.45 \times 10^{16} \text{ m/s}^2 \end{aligned}$$

32.
(a) 3.2

(b) If the distance increases by 3.2, then the force will decrease by a factor of 10 ; if the distance decreases by 3.2, then the force will increase by a factor of 10. Either way, the force changes by a factor of 10.

34.
(a) 1.04×10^{-9} C

(b) This charge is approximately 1 nC, which is consistent with the magnitude of charge typical for static electricity

37.
1.02×10^{-11}

39.
a. 0.859 m beyond negative charge on line connecting two charges
b. 0.109 m from lesser charge on line connecting two charges

42.
8.75×10^{-4} N

44.
(a) 6.94×10^{-8} C

(b) 6.25 N/C

46.
(a) 300 N/C (east)

(b) 4.80×10^{-17} N (east)

52.
(a) 5.58×10^{-11} N/C

(b)the coulomb force is extraordinarily stronger than gravity

54.
(a) $-6.76\times10^5\ \text{C}$

(b) $2.63\times10^{13}\ \text{m/s}^2\ \text{(upward)}$

(c) $2.45\times10^{-18}\ \text{kg}$

56.
The charge q_2 is 9 times greater than q_1.

69.
(a) The forces are balanced in the *x*-direction, so the net force is vertical. It is composed of the sum of the vertical components of the Coulomb force and the gravitational force.

$$\mathbf{F}_y = -2\left(\frac{kq_1q_2}{r^2} + G\frac{m_1m_2}{r^2}\right)\cos 45^\circ =$$

$$-2\left(\frac{8.99\times10^9(1.00\times10^{-9})(2.00\times10^{-9})}{8} + 6.67\times10^{-11}\frac{(10.0)(10.0)}{8}\right)$$

$$\cos 45^\circ = -4.36\times10^{-9}\ \text{N}$$

(b) No, it is in a metastable position. Since it cannot move horizontally, it cannot traverse any part of the track.

$$\mathbf{F}_x = -\left(\frac{kq_1q_2}{4} + G\frac{m_1m_2}{4}\right)\frac{1}{2} + \left(\frac{kq_1q_2}{12} + G\frac{m_1m_2}{12}\right)\frac{\sqrt{3}}{2} =$$

(c) $$-\left(\frac{8.99\times10^9(-1.00\times10^{-9})(2.00\times10^{-9})}{4}\frac{1}{2} - 6.67\times10^{-11}\frac{(10.0)(10.0)}{4}\frac{1}{2}\right)$$

$$+\left(\frac{8.99\times10^9(-1.00\times10^{-9})(2.00\times10^{-9})}{12}\frac{\sqrt{3}}{2} - 6.67\times10^{-11}\frac{(10.0)(10.0)}{12}\frac{\sqrt{3}}{2}\right)\text{N} = 2.60\times10^{-9}\ \text{N}$$

$$\mathbf{F}_y = -\left(\frac{kq_1q_2}{4} + G\frac{m_1m_2}{4}\right)\frac{\sqrt{3}}{2} - \left(\frac{kq_1q_2}{12} + G\frac{m_1m_2}{12}\right)\frac{1}{2} = -2.08\times10^{-9}\ \text{N}$$

$$-\left(\frac{8.99\times10^9(1.00\times10^{-9})(2.00\times10^{-9})}{4}\frac{\sqrt{3}}{2} - 6.67\times10^{-11}\frac{(10.0)(10.0)}{4}\frac{\sqrt{3}}{2}\right)$$

$$-\left(\frac{8.99\times10^9(1.00\times10^{-9})(2.00\times10^{-9})}{12}\frac{1}{2} + 6.67\times10^{-11}\frac{(10.0)(10.0)}{12}\frac{1}{2}\right)\text{N} = -6.36\times10^{-9}\ \text{N}$$

(d) Yes.

(e) It will reach $(1, -\sqrt{3})$ before it will change direction.

(f) The metastable positions where there is no component in one direction are $(0,0)$, $(4,0)$, $(2,2)$, and $(2,-2)$. They number 4.

Test Prep for AP® Courses

1.
(b)

3.
(c)

5.
(a)

7.
(b)

9.
(a) -0.1 C, (b) 1.1 C, (c) Both charges will be equal to 1 C, law of conservation of charge, (d) 0.9 C

11.
W is negative, X is positive, Y is negative, Z is neutral.

13.
(c)

15.
(c)

17.
(b)

19.
a) Ball 1 will have positive charge and Ball 2 will have negative charge. b) The negatively charged rod attracts positive charge of Ball 1. The electrons of Ball 1 are transferred to Ball 2, making it negatively charged. c) If Ball 2 is grounded while the rod is still there, it will lose its negative charge to the ground. d) Yes, Ball 1 will be positively charged and Ball 2 will be negatively charge.

21.
(c)

23.
decrease by 77.78%.

25.
(a)

27.
(d)

29.
(a) 3.60×10^{10} N, (b) It will become 1/4 of the original value; hence it will be equal to 8.99×10^{9} N

31.
(c)

33.
(a)

35.
(b)

37.
(a) 350 N/C, (b) west, (c) 5.6×10−17 N, (d) west.

39.
(b)

41.
(a) i) Field vectors near objects point toward negatively charged objects and away from positively charged objects.

(a) ii) The vectors closest to *R* and *T* are about the same length and start at about the same distance. We have that $q_R/d^2 = q_T/d^2$, so the charge on *R* is about the same as the charge on *T*. The closest vectors around *S* are about the same length as those around *R* and *T*. The vectors near *S* start at about 6 units away, while vectors near *R* and *T* start at about 4 units. We have that $q_R/d^2 = q_S/D^2$, so $q_S/q_R = D^2/d^2 = 36/16 = 2.25$, and so the charge on *S* is about twice that on *R* and *T*.

(b)

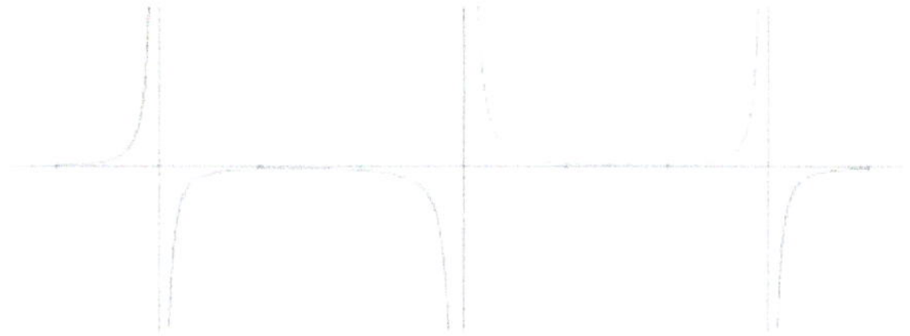

FIGURE 18.65 A vector diagram.

(c)

$$E = k\left[-\frac{q}{(d+x)^2} + \frac{2q}{(x)^2} + \frac{q}{(d-x)^2}\right]$$

(d) The statement is not true. The vector diagram shows field vectors in this region with nonzero length, and the vectors not shown have even greater lengths. The equation in part (c) shows that, when $0 < x < d$, the denominator of the negative term is always greater than the denominator of the third term, but the numerator is the same. So the negative term always has a smaller magnitude than the third term and since the second term is positive the sum of the terms is always positive.

Chapter 19

Problems & Exercises

1.
42.8

4.
1.00×10^5 K

6.
(a) 4×10^4 W

(b) A defibrillator does not cause serious burns because the skin conducts electricity well at high voltages, like those used in defibrillators. The gel used aids in the transfer of energy to the body, and the skin doesn't absorb the energy, but rather lets it pass through to the heart.

8.
(a) 7.40×10^3 C

(b) 1.54×10^{20} electrons per second

9.
3.89×10^6 C

11.
(a) 1.44×10^{12} V

(b) This voltage is very high. A 10.0 cm diameter sphere could never maintain this voltage; it would discharge.

(c) An 8.00 C charge is more charge than can reasonably be accumulated on a sphere of that size.

15.
(a) 3.00 kV

(b) 750 V

17.
(a) No. The electric field strength between the plates is 2.5×10^6 V/m, which is lower than the breakdown strength for air (3.0×10^6 V/m).

(b) 1.7 mm

19.
44.0 mV

21.
15 kV

23.
(a) 800 KeV

(b) 25.0 km

24.
144 V

26.
(a) 1.80 km

(b) A charge of 1 C is a very large amount of charge; a sphere of radius 1.80 km is not practical.

28.
-2.22×10^{-13} C

30.
(a) 3.31×10^{6} V

(b) 152 MeV

32.
(a) 2.78×10^{-7} C

(b) 2.00×10^{-10} C

35.
(a) 2.96×10^{9} m/s

(b) This velocity is far too great. It is faster than the speed of light.

(c) The assumption that the speed of the electron is far less than that of light and that the problem does not require a relativistic treatment produces an answer greater than the speed of light.

46.
21.6 mC

48.
80.0 mC

50.
20.0 kV

52.
667 pF

54.
(a) 4.4 μF

(b) 4.0×10^{-5} C

56.
(a) 14.2 kV

(b) The voltage is unreasonably large, more than 100 times the breakdown voltage of nylon.

(c) The assumed charge is unreasonably large and cannot be stored in a capacitor of these dimensions.

57.
0.293 μF

59.
3.08 μF in series combination, 13.0 μF in parallel combination

60.
2.79 μF

62.
(a) –3.00 μF

(b) You cannot have a negative value of capacitance.

(c) The assumption that the capacitors were hooked up in parallel, rather than in series, was incorrect. A parallel connection always produces a greater capacitance, while here a smaller capacitance was assumed. This could happen only if the capacitors are connected in series.

63.
(a) 405 J

(b) 90.0 mC

64.
(a) 3.16 kV

(b) 25.3 mC

66.
(a) 1.42×10^{-5} C, 6.38×10^{-5} J

(b) 8.46×10^{-5} C, 3.81×10^{-4} J

67.
(a) 4.43×10^{-12} F

(b) 0.452 V

(c) 4.52×10^{-10} J

70.
(a) 133 F

(b) Such a capacitor would be too large to carry with a truck. The size of the capacitor would be enormous.

(c) It is unreasonable to assume that a capacitor can store the amount of energy needed.

Test Prep for AP® Courses

1.
(d)

3.
(b)

5.
(c)

7.
(a)

9.
(b)

11.

(b)

13.
(a)

15.
(c)

17.
(b)

19.
(a)

21.
(d)

23.
(d)

25.
(a)

27.
(b)

29.
(c)

31.
(d)

33.
(a)

35.
(c)

37.
(c)

39.
(b)

41.
(a)

43.
(d)

Chapter 20

Problems & Exercises

1.
0.278 mA

3.
0.250 A

5.
1.50ms

7.

(a) $1.67 k\Omega$

(b) If a 50 times larger resistance existed, keeping the current about the same, the power would be increased by a factor of about 50 (based on the equation $P = I^2 R$), causing much more energy to be transferred to the skin, which could cause serious burns. The gel used reduces the resistance, and therefore reduces the power transferred to the skin.

9.
(a) 0.120 C

(b) 7.50×10^{17} electrons

11.
96.3 s

13.
(a) 7.81×10^{14} He^{++} nuclei/s

(b) 4.00×10^{3} s

(c) 7.71×10^{8} s

15.
-1.13×10^{-4} m/s

17.
9.42×10^{13} electrons

18.
0.833 A

20.
7.33×10^{-2} Ω

22.
(a) 0.300 V

(b) 1.50 V

(c) The voltage supplied to whatever appliance is being used is reduced because the total voltage drop from the wall to the final output of the appliance is fixed. Thus, if the voltage drop across the extension cord is large, the voltage drop across the appliance is significantly decreased, so the power output by the appliance can be significantly decreased, reducing the ability of the appliance to work properly.

24.
0.104 Ω

26.
2.8×10^{-2} m

28.
1.10×10^{-3} A

30.
$-5°C$ to $45°C$

32.
1.03

34.
0.06%

36.
$-17°C$

38.
(a) $4.7\ \Omega$ (total)

(b) 3.0% decrease

40.
$2.00\times10^{12}\ \text{W}$

44.
(a) 1.50 W

(b) 7.50 W

46.
$\frac{V^2}{\Omega} = \frac{V^2}{V/A} = AV = \left(\frac{C}{s}\right)\left(\frac{J}{C}\right) = \frac{J}{s} = 1\ \text{W}$

48.
$1\ \text{kW} \cdot \text{h} = \left(\frac{1\times10^3\ \text{J}}{1\ \text{s}}\right)(1\ \text{h})\left(\frac{3600\ \text{s}}{1\ \text{h}}\right) = 3.60\times10^6\ \text{J}$

50.
$438/y

52.
$6.25

54.
1.58 h

56.
$3.94 billion/year

58.
25.5 W

60.
(a) $2.00\times10^9\ \text{J}$

(b) 769 kg

62.
45.0 s

64.
(a) 343 A

(b) $2.17\times10^3\ \text{A}$

(c) $1.10\times10^3\ \text{A}$

66.
(a) $1.23\times10^3\ \text{kg}$

(b) $2.64\times10^3\ \text{kg}$

69.
(a) $2.08\times10^5\ \text{A}$

(b) $4.33\times10^4\ \text{MW}$

(c) The transmission lines dissipate more power than they are supposed to transmit.

(d) A voltage of 480 V is unreasonably low for a transmission voltage. Long-distance transmission lines are kept at much higher voltages (often hundreds of kilovolts) to reduce power losses.

73.
480 V

75.
2.50 ms

77.
(a) 4.00 kA

(b) 16.0 MW

(c) 16.0%

79.
2.40 kW

81.
(a) 4.0

(b) 0.50

(c) 4.0

83.
(a) 1.39 ms

(b) 4.17 ms

(c) 8.33 ms

85.
(a) 194 kW

(b) 880 A

87.
(a) 0.400 mA, no effect

(b) 26.7 mA, muscular contraction for duration of the shock (can't let go)

89.
$1.20 \times 10^5\ \Omega$

91.
(a) $1.00\ \Omega$

(b) 14.4 kW

93.
Temperature increases $860^\circ\ \text{C}$. It is very likely to be damaging.

95.
80 beats/minute

97.

(a)
$$\frac{3.25 \times 10^{-3}}{1}\text{j/s} = Power = I^2 R = \frac{1}{r^2}\frac{(2.50)^2(1.72 \times 10^{-8})(1.25)}{\pi}\text{jm}^2/\text{s}$$
$$r = \sqrt{\frac{(2.50)^2(1.72 \times 10^{-8})(1.25)}{0.00325\pi}} = 3.63\ \text{mm}$$

(b) $Power = \frac{(2.50)^2(1.74\times10^{-8})(1.25)}{(3.63\times10^{-3})^2\pi}$ j/s, so 3.28 j of energy is expended in 1 s. Since α is specified in the chart to only two significant figures, round to 3.3 j.

(c) Since the energy dissipation is directly proportional to the resistivity, the increase of 0.01% in energy dissipation is when the resistivity increases 1%. Or, $1.01 = 1 + 0.0039\Delta T. T = 23°C$.

Test Prep for AP® Courses

1.
(a)

3.
10 A

5.
(a)

7.
3.2 Ω, 2.19 A

9.
(b), (d)

11.
9.72×10^{-8} Ω•m

13.
18 Ω

15.
10:3 or 3.33

Chapter 21

Problems & Exercises

1.
(a) 2.75 kΩ

(b) 27.5 Ω

3.
(a) 786 Ω

(b) 20.3 Ω

5.
29.6 W

7.
(a) 0.74 A

(b) 0.742 A

9.
(a) 60.8 W

(b) 3.18 kW

11.
(a) $$R_s = R_1 + R_2$$
$$\Rightarrow R_s \approx R_1 (R_1 >> R_2)$$

(b) $\frac{1}{R_p} = \frac{1}{R_1} + \frac{1}{R_2} = \frac{R_1+R_2}{R_1 R_2}$,

so that

$$R_p = \frac{R_1 R_2}{R_1+R_2} \approx \frac{R_1 R_2}{R_1} = R_2 (R_1 >> R_2).$$

13.
(a) $-400\ \text{k}\Omega$

(b) Resistance cannot be negative.

(c) Series resistance is said to be less than one of the resistors, but it must be greater than any of the resistors.

14.
2.00 V

16.
2.9994 V

18.
$0.375\ \Omega$

21.
(a) 0.658 A

(b) 0.997 W

(c) 0.997 W; yes

23.
(a) 200 A

(b) 10.0 V

(c) 2.00 kW

(d) $0.1000\ \Omega$; 80.0 A, 4.0 V, 320 W

25.
(a) $0.400\ \Omega$

(b) No, there is only one independent equation, so only *r* can be found.

29.
(a) −0.120 V

(b) $-1.41 \times 10^{-2}\ \Omega$

(c) Negative terminal voltage; negative load resistance.

(d) The assumption that such a cell could provide 8.50 A is inconsistent with its internal resistance.

31.
$-I_2 R_2 + \text{emf}_1 - I_2 r_1 + I_3 R_3 + I_3 r_2 - \text{emf}_2 = 0$

35.
$I_3 = I_1 + I_2$

37.
$\text{emf}_2 - I_2 r_2 - I_2 R_2 + I_1 R_5 + I_1 r_1 - \text{emf}_1 + I_1 R_1 = 0$

39.
(a) $\text{I}_1 = 4.75\ \text{A}$

(b) $\text{I}_2 = -3.5\ \text{A}$

(c) $\text{I}_3 = 8.25\ \text{A}$

41.
(a) No, you would get inconsistent equations to solve.

(b) $I_1 \neq I_2 + I_3$. The assumed currents violate the junction rule.

42.
$30\ \mu A$

44.
$1.98\ \text{k}\Omega$

46.
$1.25\times10^{-4}\ \Omega$

48.
(a) $3.00\ \text{M}\Omega$

(b) $2.99\ \text{k}\Omega$

50.
(a) 1.58 mA

(b) 1.5848 V (need four digits to see the difference)

(c) 0.99990 (need five digits to see the difference from unity)

52.
$15.0\ \mu\text{A}$

54.
(a)

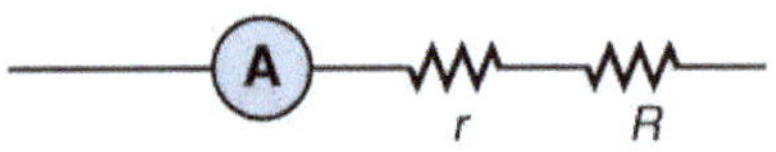

(b) $10.02\ \Omega$

(c) 0.9980, or a 2.0×10^{-1} percent decrease

(d) 1.002, or a 2.0×10^{-1} percent increase

(e) Not significant.

56.
(a) $-66.7\ \Omega$

(b) You can't have negative resistance.

(c) It is unreasonable that I_G is greater than I_{tot} (see Figure 21.30). You cannot achieve a full-scale deflection using a current less than the sensitivity of the galvanometer.

57.
24.0 V

59.
$1.56\ \text{k}\Omega$

61.
(a) 2.00 V

(b) $9.68\ \Omega$

62.
$\text{Range} = 5.00\ \Omega \text{ to } 5.00\ \text{k}\Omega$
63.

range 4.00 to 30.0 MΩ

65.
(a) 2.50 μF

(b) 2.00 s

67.
86.5%

69.
(a) 1.25 kΩ

(b) 30.0 ms

71.
(a) 20.0 s

(b) 120 s

(c) 16.0 ms

73.
1.73×10^{-2} s

74.
3.33×10^{-3} Ω

76.
(a) 4.99 s

(b) 3.87°C

(c) 31.1 kΩ

(d) No

80.

(a) $P = \frac{V^2}{R} = \frac{(1.00\times10^2)^2}{2.50\times10^3}\text{w} = 4.00 \text{ W}$

$$\frac{1}{R_{eq}} = \frac{2}{R_1}$$

(b) $R_{eq} = \frac{R_1}{2} = 1.25 \times 10^3\,\Omega$

$$P = \frac{V^2}{R} = \frac{(1.00\times10^2)^2}{1.25\times10^3}\text{ W} = 8\text{W}$$

$$R_{eq} = R_1 + R_2 = 2R_1$$

(c) $P = \frac{V^2}{R} = \frac{(1.00\times10^2)^2}{5.00\times10^3}\text{W} = 2\text{W}$

(d) In the parallel case current passes through each branch, so more current is passed through the resistor system. In the series, the higher resistance of the circuit allows less current to flow. $P = IV$ is proportional to the current when the voltage does not change.

(e) The parallel combination delivers more energy in a given time period.

Test Prep for AP® Courses

1.
(a), (b)

3.

(b)

5.
(a) 4-Ω resistor; (b) combination of 20-Ω, 20-Ω, and 10-Ω resistors; (c) 20 W in each 20-Ω resistor, 40 W in 10-Ω resistor, 64 W in 4-Ω resistor, total 144W total in resistors, output power is 144 W, yes they are equal (law of conservation of energy); (d) 4 Ω and 3 Ω for part (a) and no change for part (b); (e) no effect, it will remain the same.

7.
0.25 Ω, 0.50 Ω, no change

9.
a. (c)

b. (c)

c. (d)

d. (d)

11.

a. $I_1 + I_3 = I_2$
b. $E_1 - I_1R_1 - I_2R_2 - I_1r_1 = 0$; $- E_2 + I_1R_1 - I_3R_3 - I_3r_2 = 0$
c. $I_1 = 8/15$ A, $I_2 = 7/15$ A and $I_3 = -1/15$ A
d. $I_1 = 2/5$ A, $I_2 = 3/5$ A and $I_3 = 1/5$ A
e. $P_{E1} = 18/5$ W and $P_{R1} = 24/25$ W, $P_{R2} = 54/25$ W, $P_{R3} = 12/25$ W. Yes, $P_{E1} = P_{R1} + P_{R2} + P_{R3}$
f. R_3, losses in the circuit

13.
(a) 20 mA, Figure 21.37, 5.5 s; (b) 24 mA, Figure 21.29, 2 s

Chapter 22

Problems & Exercises

1.
(a) Left (West)

(b) Into the page

(c) Up (North)

(d) No force

(e) Right (East)

(f) Down (South)

3.
(a) East (right)

(b) Into page

(c) South (down)

5.
(a) Into page

(b) West (left)

(c) Out of page

7.
7.50×10^{-7} N perpendicular to both the magnetic field lines and the velocity

9.

(a) 3.01×10^{-5} T

(b) This is slightly less then the magnetic field strength of 5×10^{-5} T at the surface of the Earth, so it is consistent.

11.
(a) 6.67×10^{-10} C (taking the Earth's field to be 5.00×10^{-5} T)

(b) Less than typical static, therefore difficult

12.
4.27 m

14.
(a) 0.261 T

(b) This strength is definitely obtainable with today's technology. Magnetic field strengths of 0.500 T are obtainable with permanent magnets.

16.
4.36×10^{-4} m

18.
(a) 3.00 kV/m

(b) 30.0 V

20.
0.173 m

22.
7.50×10^{-4} V

24.
(a) 1.18×10^{3} m/s

(b) Once established, the Hall emf pushes charges one direction and the magnetic force acts in the opposite direction resulting in no net force on the charges. Therefore, no current flows in the direction of the Hall emf. This is the same as in a current-carrying conductor—current does not flow in the direction of the Hall emf.

26.
11.3 mV

28.
1.16 μV

30.
2.00 T

31.
(a) west (left)

(b) into page

(c) north (up)

(d) no force

(e) east (right)

(f) south (down)

33.
(a) into page

(b) west (left)

(c) out of page

35.
(a) 2.50 N

(b) This is about half a pound of force per 100 m of wire, which is much less than the weight of the wire itself. Therefore, it does not cause any special concerns.

37.
1.80 T

39.
(a) 30°

(b) 4.80 N

41.
(a) τ decreases by 5.00% if B decreases by 5.00%

(b) 5.26% increase

43.
10.0 A

45.
$\mathrm{A} \cdot \mathrm{m}^2 \cdot \mathrm{T} = \mathrm{A} \cdot \mathrm{m}^2 \left(\frac{\mathrm{N}}{\mathrm{A} \cdot \mathrm{m}}\right) = \mathrm{N} \cdot \mathrm{m}.$

47.
$3.48 \times 10^{-26}\ \mathrm{N} \cdot \mathrm{m}$

49.
(a) $0.666\ \mathrm{N} \cdot \mathrm{m}$ west

(b) This is not a very significant torque, so practical use would be limited. Also, the current would need to be alternated to make the loop rotate (otherwise it would oscillate).

50.
(a) 8.53 N, repulsive

(b) This force is repulsive and therefore there is never a risk that the two wires will touch and short circuit.

52.
400 A in the opposite direction

54.
(a) $1.67 \times 10^{-3}\ \mathrm{N/m}$

(b) $3.33 \times 10^{-3}\ \mathrm{N/m}$

(c) Repulsive

(d) No, these are very small forces

56.
(a) Top wire: $2.65 \times 10^{-4}\ \mathrm{N/m}$ s, 10.9° to left of up

(b) Lower left wire: $3.61 \times 10^{-4}\ \mathrm{N/m}$, 13.9° down from right

(c) Lower right wire: $3.46 \times 10^{-4}\ \mathrm{N/m}$, 30.0° down from left

58.
(a) right-into page, left-out of page

(b) right-out of page, left-into page

(c) right-out of page, left-into page

60.
(a) clockwise

(b) clockwise as seen from the left

(c) clockwise as seen from the right

61.
1.01×10^{13} T

63.
(a) 4.80×10^{-4} T

(b) Zero

(c) If the wires are not paired, the field is about 10 times stronger than Earth's magnetic field and so could severely disrupt the use of a compass.

65.
39.8 A

67.
(a) 3.14×10^{-5} T

(b) 0.314 T

69.
7.55×10^{-5} T, 23.4°

71.
10.0 A

73.
(a) 9.09×10^{-7} N upward

(b) 3.03×10^{-5} m/s^2

75.
60.2 cm

77.
(a) 1.02×10^{3} N/m^2

(b) Not a significant fraction of an atmosphere

79.
17.0×10^{-4} %/°C

81.
18.3 MHz

83.
(a) Straight up

(b) 6.00×10^{-4} N/m

(c) 94.1 μm

(d)2.47 Ω/m, 49.4 V/m

85.
(a) 571 C

(b) Impossible to have such a large separated charge on such a small object.

(c) The 1.00-N force is much too great to be realistic in the Earth's field.

87.
(a) 2.40×10^{6} m/s

(b) The speed is too high to be practical $\leq$ 1% speed of light

(c) The assumption that you could reasonably generate such a voltage with a single wire in the Earth's field is unreasonable

89.
(a) 25.0 kA

(b) This current is unreasonably high. It implies a total power delivery in the line of 50.0x10^9 W, which is much too high for standard transmission lines.

(c)100 meters is a long distance to obtain the required field strength. Also coaxial cables are used for transmission lines so that there is virtually no field for DC power lines, because of cancellation from opposing currents. The surveyor's concerns are not a problem for his magnetic field measurements.

92.
(a) $F = qvB \sin \theta$
Since $\sin \theta = 0, \; F = 0$ for the first electron.
For the second and third electrons, $\sin \theta = 1$.
So, $F = (1.60 \times 10^{-19}\text{C})(5.00 \times 10^{7}\,\text{m/s})(2.00 \times 10^{-7}\,\text{T}) = 1.60 \times 10^{-18}\text{N}$.

(b) The first electron moves in a straight line. The other two electrons take a circular path.

(c) The first electron will never return to the origin. The other two will return.

$$r = \frac{(9.11\times10^{-11})(5.00\times10^{7})}{(1.60\times10^{-19})(2.00\times10^{-7})}\text{m}$$

$$v = \frac{r}{t}$$

$$t = \frac{(9.11\times10^{-11})}{(1.60\times10^{-19})(2.00\times10^{-7})}\text{s} = 2.85 \times 10^{15}\,\text{s}$$

Test Prep for AP® Courses

1.
(a)

3.
(b)

5.
(b)

7.
(a)

9.
(b)

11.
(e)

13.
(c)

15.
(c)

Chapter 23

Problems & Exercises

1.
Zero

3.
(a) CCW

(b) CW

(c) No current induced

5.
(a) 1 CCW, 2 CCW, 3 CW

(b) 1, 2, and 3 no current induced

(c) 1 CW, 2 CW, 3 CCW

9.
(a) 3.04 mV
(b) As a lower limit on the ring, estimate R = 1.00 mΩ. The heat transferred will be 2.31 mJ. This is not a significant amount of heat.

11.
0.157 V

13.
proportional to $\frac{1}{r}$

17.
(a) 0.630 V

(b) No, this is a very small emf.

19.
2.22 m/s

25.
(a) 10.0 N

(b) 2.81×10^{8} J

(c) 0.36 m/s

(d) For a week-long mission (168 hours), the change in velocity will be 60 m/s, or approximately 1%. In general, a decrease in velocity would cause the orbit to start spiraling inward because the velocity would no longer be sufficient to keep the circular orbit. The long-term consequences are that the shuttle would require a little more fuel to maintain the desired speed, otherwise the orbit would spiral slightly inward.

28.
474 V

30.
0.247 V

32.
(a) 50

(b) yes

34.

(a) 0.477 T

(b) This field strength is small enough that it can be obtained using either a permanent magnet or an electromagnet.

36.
(a) 5.89 V

(b) At t=0

(c) 0.393 s

(d) 0.785 s

38.
(a) 1.92×10^6 rad/s

(b) This angular velocity is unreasonably high, higher than can be obtained for any mechanical system.

(c) The assumption that a voltage as great as 12.0 kV could be obtained is unreasonable.

39.
(a) $12.00\ \Omega$

(b) 1.67 A

41.
72.0 V

43.
$0.100\ \Omega$

44.
(a) 30.0

(b) 9.75×10^{-2} A

46.
(a) 20.0 mA

(b) 2.40 W

(c) Yes, this amount of power is quite reasonable for a small appliance.

48.
(a) 0.063 A

(b) Greater input current needed.

50.
(a) 2.2

(b) 0.45

(c) 0.20, or 20.0%

52.
(a) 335 MV

(b) way too high, well beyond the breakdown voltage of air over reasonable distances

(c) input voltage is too high

54.
(a) 15.0 V

(b) 75.0 A

(c) yes

55.
1.80 mH

57.
3.60 V

61.
(a) 31.3 kV

(b) 125 kJ

(c) 1.56 MW

(d) No, it is not surprising since this power is very high.

63.
(a) 1.39 mH

(b) 3.33 V

(c) Zero

65.
60.0 mH

67.
(a) 200 H

(b) $5.00°C$

69.
500 H

71.
$50.0\ \Omega$

73.
1.00×10^{-18} s to 0.100 s

75.
95.0%

77.
(a) 24.6 ms

(b) 26.7 ms

(c) 9% difference, which is greater than the inherent uncertainty in the given parameters.

79.
531 Hz

81.
1.33 nF

83.
(a) 2.55 A

(b) 1.53 mA

85.
$63.7\ \mu H$

87.

(a) 21.2 mH

(b) $8.00\ \Omega$

89.
(a) 3.18 mF

(b) $16.7\ \Omega$

92.
(a) $40.02\ \Omega$ at 60.0 Hz, $193\ \Omega$ at 10.0 kHz

(b) At 60 Hz, with a capacitor, $Z=531\ \Omega$, over 13 times as high as without the capacitor. The capacitor makes a large difference at low frequencies. At 10 kHz, with a capacitor $Z=190\ \Omega$, about the same as without the capacitor. The capacitor has a smaller effect at high frequencies.

94.
(a) $529\ \Omega$ at 60.0 Hz, $185\ \Omega$ at 10.0 kHz

(b) These values are close to those obtained in Example 23.12 because at low frequency the capacitor dominates and at high frequency the inductor dominates. So in both cases the resistor makes little contribution to the total impedance.

96.
9.30 nF to 101 nF

98.
3.17 pF

100.
(a) $1.31\ \mu\text{H}$

(b) 1.66 pF

102.
(a) $12.8\ \text{k}\Omega$

(b) $1.31\ \text{k}\Omega$

(c) 31.9 mA at 500 Hz, 312 mA at 7.50 kHz

(d) 82.2 kHz

(e) 0.408 A

104.
(a) 0.159

(b) 80.9°

(c) 26.4 W

(d) 166 W

106.
16.0 W

107.
(a) $|\text{emf}| = 1\frac{\Delta\phi}{\Delta t} = \frac{1.000(0.02000)}{100}\text{V} = 0.0002000\ \text{V}$

(b) $|\text{emf}| = 2\frac{\Delta\phi}{\Delta t} = \frac{2(0.2500)(0.02000)}{100}\text{V} = 0.0001000\ \text{V}$

(c) The average emf is 0 since the loops are made by a wire that crosses, so the voltage from each loop cancels the emf from the other.

(d) No.

Test Prep for AP® Courses

1.
(c)

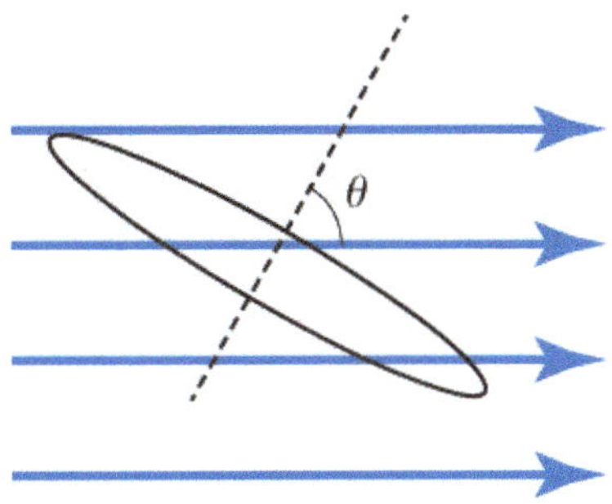

FIGURE 23.58

3.
(c)

5.
(a), (d)

7.
(c)

Chapter 24

Problems & Exercises

3.
150 kV/m

6.
(a) 33.3 cm (900 MHz) 11.7 cm (2560 MHz)

(b) The microwave oven with the smaller wavelength would produce smaller hot spots in foods, corresponding to the one with the frequency 2560 MHz.

8.
26.96 MHz

10.
5.0×10^{14} Hz

12.

$$\lambda = \frac{c}{f} = \frac{3.00 \times 10^8 \text{ m/s}}{1.20 \times 10^{15} \text{ Hz}} = 2.50 \times 10^{-7} \text{ m}$$

14.
0.600 m

16.

(a) $f = \frac{c}{\lambda} = \frac{3.00 \times 10^8 \text{ m/s}}{1 \times 10{-10} \text{ m}} = 3 \times 10^{18} \text{ Hz}$

(b) X-rays

19.
(a) 6.00×10^6 m

(b) 4.33×10^{-5} T

21.
(a) 1.50×10^{6} Hz, AM band
(b) The resonance of currents on an antenna that is 1/4 their wavelength is analogous to the fundamental resonant mode of an air column closed at one end, since the tube also has a length equal to 1/4 the wavelength of the fundamental oscillation.

23.
(a) 1.55×10^{15} Hz

(b) The shortest wavelength of visible light is 380 nm, so that

$$\frac{\lambda_{\text{visible}}}{\lambda_{\text{UV}}} = \frac{380\text{ nm}}{193\text{ nm}} = 1.97.$$

In other words, the UV radiation is 97% more accurate than the shortest wavelength of visible light, or almost twice as accurate!

25.
3.90×10^{8} m

27.
(a) 1.50×10^{11} m

(b) $0.500\ \mu$s

(c) 66.7 ns

29.
(a) $-3.5 \times 10^{2}\ \text{W/m}^2$

(b) 88%

(c) $1.7\ \mu$T

30.

$$\begin{aligned} I &= \frac{c\varepsilon_0 E_0^2}{2} \\ &= \frac{(3.00\times10^8\text{ m/s})(8.85\times10^{-12}\text{C}^2/\text{N}\cdot\text{m}^2)(125\text{ V/m})^2}{2} \\ &= 20.7\text{ W/m}^2 \end{aligned}$$

32.

(a) $I = \frac{P}{A} = \frac{P}{\pi r^2} = \frac{0.250\times10^{-3}\text{ W}}{\pi(0.500\times10^{-3}\text{ m})^2} = 318\text{ W/m}^2$

(b)

$$\begin{aligned} I_{\text{ave}} &= \frac{cB_0^2}{2\mu_0} \Rightarrow B_0 = \left(\frac{2\mu_0 I}{c}\right)^{1/2} \\ &= \left(\frac{2(4\pi\times10^{-7}\text{ T}\cdot\text{m/A})(318.3\text{ W/m}^2)}{3.00\times10^8\text{ m/s}}\right)^{1/2} \\ &= 1.63\times10^{-6}\text{ T} \end{aligned}$$

(c)

$$\begin{aligned} E_0 &= cB_0 = (3.00\times10^8\text{ m/s})(1.633\times10^{-6}\text{ T}) \\ &= 4.90\times10^2\text{ V/m} \end{aligned}$$

34.
(a) 89.2 cm

(b) 27.4 V/m

36.
(a) 333 T

(b) $1.33 \times 10^{19}\ \text{W/m}^2$

(c) 13.3 kJ

38.
(a) $I = \frac{P}{A} = \frac{P}{4\pi r^2} \propto \frac{1}{r^2}$

(b) $I \propto E_0^2,\ B_0^2 \Rightarrow E_0^2,\ B_0^2 \propto \frac{1}{r^2} \Rightarrow E_0,\ B_0 \propto \frac{1}{r}$

40.
13.5 pF

42.
(a) $4.07\ \text{kW/m}^2$

(b) 1.75 kV/m

(c) $5.84\ \mu\text{T}$

(d) 2 min 19 s

44.
(a) $5.00 \times 10^3\ \text{W/m}^2$

(b) $3.88 \times 10^{-6}\ \text{N}$

(c) $5.18 \times 10^{-12}\ \text{N}$

46.
(a) $t = 0$

(b) $7.50 \times 10^{-10}\ \text{s}$

(c) $1.00 \times 10^{-9}\ \text{s}$

48.
(a) $1.01 \times 10^6\ \text{W/m}^2$

(b) Much too great for an oven.

(c) The assumed magnetic field is unreasonably large.

50.
(a) $2.53 \times 10^{-20}\ \text{H}$

(b) L is much too small.

(c) The wavelength is unreasonably small.

53.
(a)
$$B = \frac{E}{c}$$
$$B = \frac{1250}{3.00 \times 10^8}\text{T} = 4.17 \times 10^{-6}\ \text{T}$$

(b) *E* would increase.

(c) It would be by $1/c$.

Test Prep for AP® Courses

1.
(b)

3.
(a)

5.
(d)

7.
(d)

9.
(d)

11.
(a)

Chapter 25

Problems & Exercises

1.
Top 1.715 m from floor, bottom 0.825 m from floor. Height of mirror is 0.890 m, or precisely one-half the height of the person.

5.
$2.25 \times 10^8 \text{ m/s}$ in water

$2.04 \times 10^8 \text{ m/s}$ in glycerine

7.
1.490, polystyrene

9.
1.28 s

11.
1.03 ns

13.
$n = 1.46$, fused quartz

17.
(a) 0.898

(b) Can't have $n < 1.00$ since this would imply a speed greater than c.

(c) Refracted angle is too big relative to the angle of incidence.

19.
(a) $\frac{c}{5.00}$

(b) Speed of light too slow, since index is much greater than that of diamond.

(c) Angle of refraction is unreasonable relative to the angle of incidence.

22.
66.3°

24.

> 1.414

26.
1.50, benzene

29.
46.5°, red; 46.0°, violet

31.
(a) 0.043°

(b) 1.33 m

33.
71.3°

35.
53.5°, red; 55.2°, violet

37.
5.00 to 12.5 D

39.
−0.222 m

41.
(a) 3.43 m

(b) 0.800 by 1.20 m

42.
(a) −1.35 m (on the object side of the lens).

(b) +10.0

(c) 5.00 cm

43.
44.4 cm

45.
(a) 6.60 cm

(b) −0.500

47.
(a) +7.50 cm

(b) 13.3 D

(c) Much greater

49.
(a) +6.67

(b) +20.0

(c) The magnification increases without limit (to infinity) as the object distance increases to the limit of the focal distance.

51.
−0.933 mm

53.
+0.667 m

55.
(a) -1.5×10^{-2} m

(b)-66.7 D

57.
+0.360 m (concave)

59.
(a) +0.111

(b) -0.334 cm (behind “mirror”)

(c) 0.752cm

61.
$$m = \frac{h_\text{i}}{h_\text{o}} = -\frac{d_\text{i}}{d_\text{o}} = -\frac{-d_\text{o}}{d_\text{o}} = \frac{d_\text{o}}{d_\text{o}} = 1 \Rightarrow h_\text{i} = h_\text{o}$$

63.
$6.82\ \text{kW/m}^2$

65.
(a)
$$v_{610} = \frac{3.00\times10^8}{1.530}\text{m/s},\ v_{410} = \frac{3.00\times10^8}{1.514}\text{m/s}$$
$$3.00 \times 10^8 \left(\frac{1}{1.514} - \frac{1}{1.530}\right)\text{m/s} = 2.07 \times 10^6\ \text{m/s}$$

(b) No.

(c) No.

(d) Yes.

Test Prep for AP® Courses

1.
(c)

3.
(c)

5.
(a)

7.
Since light bends toward the normal upon entering a medium with a higher index of refraction, the upper path is a more accurate representation of a light ray moving from A to B.

9.
First, measure the angle of incidence and the angle of refraction for light entering the plastic from air. Since the two angles can be measured and the index of refraction of air is known, the student can solve for the index of refraction of the plastic.

Next, measure the angle of incidence and the angle of refraction for light entering the gas from the plastic. Since the two angles can be measured and the index of refraction of the plastic is known, the student can solve for the index of refraction of the gas.

11.
The speed of light in a medium is simply c/n, so the speed of light in water is 2.25×10^8 m/s. From Snell’s law, the angle of incidence is 44°.

13.
(d)

15.
(a)

17.
(a)

19.
(b)

Chapter 26

Problems & Exercises

1.
52.0 D

3.
(a) –0.233 mm

(b) The size of the rods and the cones is smaller than the image height, so we can distinguish letters on a page.

5.
(a) +62.5 D

(b) –0.250 mm

(c) –0.0800 mm

6.
2.00 m

8.
(a) ±0.45 D

(b) The person was nearsighted because the patient was myopic and the power was reduced.

10.
0.143 m

12.
1.00 m

14.
20.0 cm

16.
–5.00 D

18.
25.0 cm

20.
–0.198 D

22.
30.8 cm

24.
–0.444 D

26.
(a) 4.00

(b) 1600

28.
(a) 0.501 cm

(b) Eyepiece should be 204 cm behind the objective lens.

30.
(a) +18.3 cm (on the eyepiece side of the objective lens)

(b) -60.0

(c) -11.3 cm (on the objective side of the eyepiece)

(d) +6.67

(e) -400

33.
-40.0

35.
-1.67

37.
$+10.0 \text{ cm}$

39.
(a) $0.251\ \mu\text{m}$

(b) Yes, this thickness implies that the shape of the cornea can be very finely controlled, producing normal distant vision in more than 90% of patients.

40.
$$\frac{1}{d_i} + \frac{1}{d_0} = \frac{1}{f}\frac{1}{d_i} = \frac{1}{f} - \frac{1}{d_0} = \frac{1}{4.00 \text{ mm}} - \frac{1}{6.00 \text{ mm}}$$
$$d_i = 12.0 \text{ mm}$$
(a) $m_0 = -\frac{d_i}{d_0} = -\frac{12.0}{6.00} = -2.00$
$$\frac{1}{d'_i} + \frac{1}{d'_0} = \frac{1}{f}\frac{1}{d'_i} = \frac{1}{f} - \frac{1}{d'_0} = \frac{1}{50 \text{ mm}} - \frac{1}{13.0 \text{ mm}}$$
$$d'_i = -17.6 \text{ mm}$$
$$m_e = -\frac{-17.6}{13} = 1.35$$
$$m = -2(1.35) = -2.70$$
$$\frac{1}{d_i} + \frac{1}{d_0} = \frac{1}{f}\frac{1}{d_i} = \frac{1}{f} - \frac{1}{d_0} = \frac{1}{4.00 \text{ mm}} - \frac{1}{5.00 \text{ mm}}$$
$$d_i = 20.0 \text{ mm}$$
$$m_0 = -\frac{d_i}{d_0} = -\frac{20.0}{5.00} = -4.00$$
$$\frac{1}{d'_i} + \frac{1}{d'_0} = \frac{1}{f}\frac{1}{d'_i} = \frac{1}{f} - \frac{1}{d'_0} = \frac{1}{50 \text{ mm}} - \frac{1}{5.00 \text{ mm}}$$
$$d'_i = -5.56 \text{ mm}$$
$$m_e = -\frac{-5.56}{5} = 1.11$$
$$m = -4(1.11) = -4.44$$

(b) It increased.

(c) The magnification should decrease.

(d) In both cases the image is inverted.

Test Prep for AP® Courses

1.

(a)

3.
(c)

5.
(a)

7.
(b)

9.
(d)

11.
(c)

Chapter 27

Problems & Exercises

1.
$1/1.333 = 0.750$

3.
1.49, Polystyrene

5.
0.877 glass to water

6.
0.516°

8.
1.22×10^{-6} m

10.
600 nm

12.
2.06°

14.
1200 nm (not visible)

16.
(a) 760 nm

(b) 1520 nm

18.
For small angles $\sin\theta - \tan\theta \approx \theta$ (in radians).

For two adjacent fringes we have,

$d\ \sin\theta_{\mathrm{m}} = m\lambda$
and

$d\ \sin\theta_{\mathrm{m+1}} = (m+1)\lambda$
Subtracting these equations gives

$$d(\sin\theta_{m+1} - \sin\theta_m) = [(m+1) - m]\lambda$$

$$d(\theta_{m+1} - \theta_m) = \lambda$$

$$\tan\theta_m = \frac{y_m}{x} \approx \theta_m \Rightarrow d\left(\frac{y_{m+1}}{x} - \frac{y_m}{x}\right) = \lambda$$

$$d\frac{\Delta y}{x} = \lambda \Rightarrow \Delta y = \frac{x\lambda}{d}$$

20.
450 nm

21.
5.97°

23.
8.99×10^3

25.
707 nm

27.
(a) 11.8°, 12.5°, 14.1°, 19.2°

(b) 24.2°, 25.7°, 29.1°, 41.0°

(c) Decreasing the number of lines per centimeter by a factor of x means that the angle for the x-order maximum is the same as the original angle for the first-order maximum.

29.
589.1 nm and 589.6 nm

31.
28.7°

33.
43.2°

35.
90.0°

37.
(a) The longest wavelength is 333.3 nm, which is not visible.

(b) 333 nm (UV)

(c) 6.58×10^3 cm

39.
1.13×10^{-2} m

41.
(a) 42.3 nm

(b) Not a visible wavelength

The number of slits in this diffraction grating is too large. Etching in integrated circuits can be done to a resolution of 50 nm, so slit separations of 400 nm are at the limit of what we can do today. This line spacing is too small to produce diffraction of light.

43.
(a) 33.4°

(b) No

45.

(a) 1.35×10^{-6} m

(b) 69.9°

47.
750 nm

49.
(a) 9.04°

(b) 12

51.
(a) 0.0150°

(b) 0.262 mm

(c) This distance is not easily measured by human eye, but under a microscope or magnifying glass it is quite easily measurable.

53.
(a) 30.1°

(b) 48.7°

(c) No

(d) $2\theta_1$ =(2)(14.5°)= 29°, $\theta_2 - \theta_1$ = 30.05° – 14.5°=15.56°. Thus, 29° ≈(2)(15.56°)= 31.1°.

55.
23.6° and 53.1°

57.
(a) 1.63×10^{-4} rad

(b) 326 ly

59.
1.46×10^{-5} rad

61.
(a) 3.04×10^{-7} rad

(b) Diameter of 235 m

63.
5.15 cm

65.
(a) Yes. Should easily be able to discern.

(b) The fact that it is just barely possible to discern that these are separate bodies indicates the severity of atmospheric aberrations.

70.
532 nm (green)

72.
83.9 nm

74.
620 nm (orange)

76.
380 nm

78.
33.9 nm

80.
4.42×10^{-5} m

82.
The oil film will appear black, since the reflected light is not in the visible part of the spectrum.

84.
45.0º

86.
45.7 mW/m^2

88.
90.0%

90.
I_0

92.
48.8º

94.
41.2º

96.
(a) 1.92, not diamond (Zircon)

(b) 55.2º

98.
$B_2 = 0.707\ B_1$

100.
(a) 2.07×10^{-2} °C/s

(b) Yes, the polarizing filters get hot because they absorb some of the lost energy from the sunlight.

101.
(a) $\sin\theta = \frac{4.00\times10^{-7}}{10^{-6}} = 0.400\ \theta = 0.400 = 23.6°$

(b) $\sin\theta = \frac{(2)(4.00\times10^{-7})}{10^{-6}}0.800\ \theta = 0.800 = 53.1°$

(c) $\sin 23.9° = \frac{x}{10^{-6}\ \text{cm}}\ x = \sin 23.9°(10^{-6}) = 4.05 \times 10^{-7} = 405\ \text{nm}$

(d) $\sin\theta = \frac{4.00\times10^{-7}}{2.00\times10^{-6}} = 0.200\ \theta = 0.200 = 11.5°$

(e) No.

Test Prep for AP® Courses

1.
(b)

3.
(b) and (c)

5.
(b)

7.
(b)

9.
(b)

11.
(d)

13.
(b)

15.
(d)

17.
(b)

Chapter 28

Problems & Exercises

1.
(a) 1.0328

(b) 1.15

3.
5.96×10^{-8} s

5.
$0.800c$

7.
$0.140c$

9.
(a) $0.745c$

(b) $0.99995c$ (to five digits to show effect)

11.
(a) 0.996

(b) γ cannot be less than 1.

(c) Assumption that time is longer in moving ship is unreasonable.

12.
48.6 m

14.
(a) 1.387 km = 1.39 km

(b) 0.433 km

(c) $L = \frac{L_0}{\gamma} = \frac{1.387 \times 10^3 \text{ m}}{3.20} = 433.4 \text{ m} = 0.433 \text{ km}$

Thus, the distances in parts (a) and (b) are related when $\gamma = 3.20$.

16.
(a) 4.303 y (to four digits to show any effect)

(b) 0.1434 y

(c) $\Delta t = \gamma \Delta t_0 \Rightarrow \gamma = \frac{\Delta t}{\Delta t_0} = \frac{4.303 \text{ y}}{0.1434 \text{ y}} = 30.0$

Thus, the two times are related when $\gamma = 30.00$.

18.
(a) 0.250

(b) γ must be ≥1

(c) The Earth-bound observer must measure a shorter length, so it is unreasonable to assume a longer length.

20.
(a) $0.909c$

(b) $0.400c$

22.
$0.198c$

24.
a) 658 nm

b) red

c) $v/c = 9.92 \times 10^{-5}$ (negligible)

26.
$0.991c$

28.
$-0.696c$

30.
$0.01324c$

32.
$u' = c$, so

$$\begin{aligned} u &= \frac{v+u'}{1+(vu'/c^2)} = \frac{v+c}{1+(vc/c^2)} = \frac{v+c}{1+(v/c)} \\ &= \frac{c(v+c)}{c+v} = c \end{aligned}$$

34.
a) $0.99947c$

b) 1.2064×10^{11} y

c) 1.2058×10^{11} y (all to sufficient digits to show effects)

35.
$4.09 \times 10^{-19} \text{ kg} \cdot \text{m/s}$

37.
(a) $3.000000015 \times 10^{13} \text{ kg} \cdot \text{m/s}$.

(b) Ratio of relativistic to classical momenta equals 1.000000005 (extra digits to show small effects)

39.
2.9957×10^{8} m/s

41.
(a) 1.121×10^{-8} m/s

(b) The small speed tells us that the mass of a proton is substantially smaller than that of even a tiny amount of macroscopic matter!

43.
8.20×10^{-14} J

0.512 MeV

45.
2.3×10^{-30} kg

47.
(a) 1.11×10^{27} kg

(b) 5.56×10^{-5}

49.
7.1×10^{-3} kg

7.1×10^{-3}

The ratio is greater for hydrogen.

51.
208

$0.999988c$

53.
6.92×10^{5} J

1.54

55.
(a) $0.914c$

(b) The rest mass energy of an electron is 0.511 MeV, so the kinetic energy is approximately 150% of the rest mass energy. The electron should be traveling close to the speed of light.

57.
90.0 MeV

59.
(a)
$$E^2 = p^2c^2 + m^2c^4 = \gamma^2 m^2 c^4, \text{ so that}$$
$$p^2c^2 = (\gamma^2 - 1)m^2c^4 \text{ , and therefore}$$
$$\frac{(pc)^2}{(mc^2)^2} = \gamma^2 - 1$$

(b) yes

61.
1.07×10^{3}

63.
6.56×10^{-8} kg

4.37×10^{-10}

65.
$0.314c$

$0.99995c$

67.
(a) 1.00 kg

(b) This much mass would be measurable, but probably not observable just by looking because it is 0.01% of the total mass.

69.
(a) 6.3×10^{11} kg/s

(b) 4.5×10^{10} y

(c) 4.44×10^{9} kg

(d) 0.32%

73.
(a) $L = 1000.0\sqrt{1 - \frac{(0.6c)^2}{c^2}} = 800.00 \text{ m}$

(b) $L = 1000.0\sqrt{1 - \frac{(0.6c)^2}{c^2}} = 800.00 \text{ m}$

(c) No.

(d) Yes.

Test Prep for AP® Courses

1.
(a)

3.
The relativistic Doppler effect takes into account the special relativity concept of time dilation and also does not require a medium of propagation to be used as a point of reference (light does not require a medium for propagation).

5.
Relativistic kinetic energy is given as $\text{KE}_{\text{rel}} = (\gamma - 1)mc^2$

where $\gamma = \frac{1}{\sqrt{1-\frac{v^2}{c^2}}}$

Classical kinetic energy is given as $\text{KE}_{\text{class}} = \frac{1}{2}mv^2$

At low velocities $v = 0$, a binomial expansion and subsequent approximation of γ gives:

$\gamma = 1 + \frac{1v^2}{2c^2}$ or $\gamma - 1 = \frac{1v^2}{2c^2}$

Substituting $\gamma - 1$ in the expression for KE_{rel} gives

$\text{KE}_{\text{rel}} = \left[\frac{1v^2}{2c^2}\right]mc^2 = \frac{1}{2}mv^2 = \text{KE}_{\text{class}}$

Hence, relativistic kinetic energy becomes classical kinetic energy when $v \ll c$.

Chapter 29

Problems & Exercises

1.
(a) 0.070 eV

(b) 14

3.
(a) 2.21×10^{34} J

(b) 2.26×10^{34}

(c) No

4.
263 nm

6.
3.69 eV

8.
0.483 eV

10.
2.25 eV

12.
(a) 264 nm

(b) Ultraviolet

14.
1.95×10^6 m/s

16.
(a) 4.02×10^{15} /s

(b) 0.256 mW

18.
(a) –1.90 eV

(b) Negative kinetic energy

(c) That the electrons would be knocked free.

20.
6.34×10^{-9} eV, 1.01×10^{-27} J

22.
2.42×10^{20} Hz

24.
$$\begin{aligned} hc &= \left(6.62607 \times 10^{-34}\ \text{J} \cdot \text{s}\right)\left(2.99792 \times 10^{8}\ \text{m/s}\right)\left(\frac{10^9\ \text{nm}}{1\ \text{m}}\right)\left(\frac{1.00000\ \text{eV}}{1.60218 \times 10^{-19}\ \text{J}}\right) \\ &= 1239.84\ \text{eV} \cdot \text{nm} \\ &\approx 1240\ \text{eV} \cdot \text{nm} \end{aligned}$$

26.
(a) 0.0829 eV

(b) 121

(c) 1.24 MeV

(d) 1.24×10^5

28.
(a) 25.0×10^3 eV

(b) 6.04×10^{18} Hz

30.
(a) 2.69

(b) 0.371

32.
(a) 1.25×10^{13} photons/s

(b) 997 km

34.
8.33×10^{13} photons/s

36.
181 km

38.
(a) 1.66×10^{-32} kg · m/s

(b) The wavelength of microwave photons is large, so the momentum they carry is very small.

40.
(a) 13.3 μm

(b) 9.38×10^{-2} eV

42.
(a) 2.65×10^{-28} kg · m/s

(b) 291 m/s

(c) electron 3.86×10^{-26} J, photon 7.96×10^{-20} J, ratio 2.06×10^{6}

44.
(a) 1.32×10^{-13} m

(b) 9.39 MeV

(c) 4.70×10^{-2} MeV

46.
$E = \gamma mc^2 mc^2$ and $P = \gamma mu$, so

$$\frac{E}{P} = \frac{\gamma mc^2}{\gamma mu} = \frac{c^2}{u}.$$

As the mass of particle approaches zero, its velocity u will approach c, so that the ratio of energy to momentum in this limit is

$$\lim_{m \to 0} \frac{E}{P} = \frac{c^2}{c} = c$$

which is consistent with the equation for photon energy.

48.
(a) 3.00×10^{6} W

(b) Headlights are way too bright.

(c) Force is too large.

49.
7.28×10^{-4} m

51.
6.62×10^{7} m/s

53.
1.32×10^{-13} m

55.
(a) 6.62×10^{7} m/s

(b) 22.9 MeV

57.
15.1 keV
59.
(a) 5.29 fm

(b) 4.70×10^{-12} J

(c) 29.4 MV

61.
(a) 7.28×10^{12} m/s

(b) This is thousands of times the speed of light (an impossibility).

(c) The assumption that the electron is non-relativistic is unreasonable at this wavelength.

62.
(a) 57.9 m/s

(b) 9.55×10^{-9} eV

(c) From Table 29.1, we see that typical molecular binding energies range from about 1eV to 10 eV, therefore the result in part (b) is approximately 9 orders of magnitude smaller than typical molecular binding energies.

64.
29 nm,

290 times greater

66.
1.10×10^{-13} eV

68.
3.3×10^{-22} s

70.
2.66×10^{-46} kg

72.
0.395 nm

74.
(a) 1.3×10^{-19} J

(b) 2.1×10^{23}

(c) 1.4×10^{2} s

76.
(a) 3.35×10^{5} J

(b) 1.12×10^{-3} kg · m/s

(c) 1.12×10^{-3} m/s

(d) 6.23×10^{-7} J

78.

(a) 1.06×10^3

(b) 5.33×10^{-16} kg · m/s

(c) 1.24×10^{-18} m

80.

(a) 1.62×10^3 m/s

(b) 4.42×10^{-19} J for photon, 1.19×10^{-24} J for electron, photon energy is 3.71×10^5 times greater

(c) The light is easier to make because 450-nm light is blue light and therefore easy to make. Creating electrons with 7.43 μeV of energy would not be difficult, but would require a vacuum.

81.

(a) 2.30×10^{-6} m

(b) 3.20×10^{-12} m

83.

3.69×10^{-4} °C

85.

(a) 2.00 kJ

(b) 1.33×10^{-5} kg · m/s

(c) 1.33×10^{-5} N

(d) yes

87.

(a) $p = \frac{h}{\lambda} = \frac{6.63\times10^{-34}}{550\times10^{-9}}\text{kg m/s} = 1.21\text{ kg} \times 10^{-27}\text{ m/s}$

(b) $p = \frac{h}{\lambda} = \frac{6.63\times10^{-34}}{650\times10^{-9}}\text{kg m/s} = 1.02 \times 10^{-27}\text{kg m/s}$

(c) Yes, conservation of momentum applies.

(d) The photon with the longer wavelength has less momentum than the one with the shorter wavelength.

Test Prep for AP® Courses

1.

(b)

3.

(c)

5.

(b)

7.

(c)

9.

(c)

11.

(a)

13.

(a)

15.
(c)

17.
(d)

Chapter 30

Problems & Exercises

1.
1.84×10^3

3.
50 km

4.
$6 \times 10^{20}\ \text{kg/m}^3$

6.
(a) $10.0\ \mu\text{m}$

(b) It isn't hard to make one of approximately this size. It would be harder to make it exactly $10.0\ \mu\text{m}$.

7.
$\frac{1}{\lambda} = R\left(\frac{1}{n_\text{f}^2} - \frac{1}{n_\text{i}^2}\right) \Rightarrow \lambda = \frac{1}{R}\left[\frac{(n_\text{i} \cdot n_\text{f})^2}{n_\text{i}^2 - n_\text{f}^2}\right];\ n_\text{i} = 2,\ n_\text{f} = 1,$ so that

$\lambda = \left(\frac{\text{m}}{1.097 \times 10^7}\right)\left[\frac{(2 \times 1)^2}{2^2 - 1^2}\right] = 1.22 \times 10^{-7}\ \text{m} = 122\ \text{nm}$, which is UV radiation.

9.
$$a_\text{B} = \frac{h^2}{4\pi^2 m_e k Z q_e^2} = \frac{(6.626 \times 10^{-34}\ \text{J} \cdot \text{s})^2}{4\pi^2 (9.109 \times 10^{-31}\ \text{kg})(8.988 \times 10^9\ \text{N} \cdot \text{m}^2/\text{C}^2)(1)(1.602 \times 10^{-19}\ \text{C})^2} = 0.529 \times 10^{-10}\ \text{m}$$

11.
0.850 eV

13.
$2.12 \times 10^{-10}\ \text{m}$

15.
365 nm

It is in the ultraviolet.

17.
No overlap

365 nm

122 nm

19.
7

21.
(a) 2

(b) 54.4 eV

23.
$\frac{kZq_e^2}{r_n^2} = \frac{m_e V^2}{r_n}$, so that $r_n = \frac{kZq_e^2}{m_e V^2} = \frac{kZq_e^2}{m_e}\frac{1}{V^2}$. From the equation $m_e v r_n = n\frac{h}{2\pi}$, we can substitute for the

velocity, giving: $r_n = \frac{kZq_e^2}{m_e} \cdot \frac{4\pi^2 m_e^2 r_n^2}{n^2 h^2}$ so that $r_n = \frac{n^2}{Z} \frac{h^2}{4\pi^2 m_e k q_e^2} = \frac{n^2}{Z} a_\mathrm{B}$, where $a_\mathrm{B} = \frac{h^2}{4\pi^2 m_e k q_e^2}$.

25.
(a) 0.248×10^{-10} m

(b) 50.0 keV

(c) The photon energy is simply the applied voltage times the electron charge, so the value of the voltage in volts is the same as the value of the energy in electron volts.

27.
(a) 100×10^3 eV, 1.60×10^{-14} J

(b) 0.124×10^{-10} m

29.
(a) 8.00 keV

(b) 9.48 keV

30.
(a) 1.96 eV

(b) (1240 eV·nm)/(1.96 eV)= 633 nm

(c) 60.0 nm

32.
693 nm

34.
(a) 590 nm

(b) (1240 eV·nm)/(1.17 eV)= 1.06 µm

35.
$l = 4, 3$ are possible since $l < n$ and $|m_l| \leq l$.

37.
$n = 4 \Rightarrow l = 3, 2, 1, 0 \Rightarrow m_l = \pm 3, \ \pm 2, \ \pm 1, 0$ are possible.

39.
(a) 1.49×10^{-34} J · s

(b) 1.06×10^{-34} J · s

41.
(a) 3.66×10^{-34} J · s

(b) $s = 9.13 \times 10^{-35}$ J · s

(c) $\frac{L}{S} = \frac{\sqrt{12}}{\sqrt{3/4}} = 4$

43.
$\theta = 54.7^\circ, 125.3^\circ$

44.
(a) 32. (b) 2 in s, 6 in p, 10 in d, and 14 in f, for a total of 32.

46.
(a) 2

(b) $3d^9$

48.
(b) $n \geq l$ is violated,

(c) cannot have 3 electrons in s subshell since $3 > (2l + 1) = 2$

(d) cannot have 7 electrons in p subshell since $7 > (2l + 1) = 2(2 + 1) = 6$

50.
(a) The number of different values of m_l is $\pm l, \pm(l - 1), ..., 0$ for each $l > 0$ and one for $l = 0 \Rightarrow (2l + 1)$. Also an overall factor of 2 since each m_l can have m_s equal to either $+1/2$ or $-1/2 \Rightarrow 2(2l + 1)$.

(b) for each value of l, you get $2(2l + 1)$

$= 0, 1, 2, ..., (n-1) \Rightarrow 2\{[(2)(0)+1]+[(2)(1)+1]+.... +[(2)(n - 1)+1]\}= 2\underbrace{[1 + 3 + ...+(2n - 3)+(2n - 1)]}_{n \text{ terms}}$ to see that the expression in the box is $= n^2$, imagine taking $(n - 1)$ from the last term and adding it to first term $= 2[1+(n-1)+3 + ...+(2n - 3)+(2n - 1)-(n - 1)]= 2[n + 3 + ...+(2n - 3)+n]$. Now take $(n - 3)$ from penultimate term and add to the second term $2\underbrace{[n + n + ... + n + n]}_{n \text{ terms}} = 2n^2$.

52.
The electric force on the electron is up (toward the positively charged plate). The magnetic force is down (by the RHR).

54.
401 nm

56.
(a) 6.54×10^{-16} kg

(b) 5.54×10^{-7} m

58.
1.76×10^{11} C/kg, which agrees with the known value of 1.759×10^{11} C/kg to within the precision of the measurement

60.
(a) 2.78 fm

(b) 0.37 of the nuclear radius.

62.
(a) 1.34×10^{23}

(b) 2.52 MW

64.
(a) 6.42 eV

(b) 7.27×10^{-20} J/molecule

(c) 0.454 eV, 14.1 times less than a single UV photon. Therefore, each photon will evaporate approximately 14 molecules of tissue. This gives the surgeon a rather precise method of removing corneal tissue from the surface of the eye.

66.
91.18 nm to 91.22 nm

68.
(a) 1.24×10^{11} V

(b) The voltage is extremely large compared with any practical value.

(c) The assumption of such a short wavelength by this method is unreasonable.

72.

$$E = -\frac{z^2}{n^2}$$

(a) $$E_3 - E_2 = -\left(\frac{6^2}{3^2} - \frac{6^2}{2^2}\right)13.6eV = 68.0eV$$

$$E_3 - E_2 = -\left(\frac{6^2}{2^2} - \frac{6^2}{1^2}\right)13.6eV = 367eV$$

$$E = 435eV$$

(b) $E_3 - E_2 = -\left(\frac{6^2}{3^2} - \frac{6^2}{1^2}\right)13.6eV = 435eV$

(c) Yes.

Test Prep for AP® Courses

1.
(a), (d)

3.
(a)

5.
(a)

7.
(b)

9.
(a)

11.
(d)

Chapter 31

Problems & Exercises

1.
1.67×10^4

5.

$$m = \rho V = \rho d^3 \Rightarrow a = \left(\frac{m}{\rho}\right)^{1/3} = \left(\frac{2.3 \times 10^{17}\text{ kg}}{1000\text{ kg/m}^3}\right)^{\frac{1}{3}}$$
$$= 61 \times 10^3\text{ m} = 61\text{ km}$$

7.
1.9 fm

9.
(a) 4.6 fm

(b) 0.61 to 1

11.
85.4 to 1

13.
12.4 GeV

15.

19.3 to 1

17.
$^3_1H_2 \rightarrow ^3_2He_1 + \beta^- + \bar{\nu}_e$

19.
$^{50}_{25}M_{25} \rightarrow ^{50}_{24}Cr_{26} + \beta^+ + \nu_e$

21.
$^7_4Be_3 + e^- \rightarrow ^7_3Li_4 + \nu_e$

23.
$^{210}_{84}Po_{126} \rightarrow ^{206}_{82}Pb_{124} + ^4_2He_2$

25.
$^{137}_{55}Cs_{82} \rightarrow ^{137}_{56}Ba_{81} + \beta^- + \bar{\nu}_e$

27.
$^{232}_{90}Th_{142} \rightarrow ^{228}_{88}Ra_{140} + ^4_2He_2$

29.
(a) charge:(+1)+(−1)= 0; electron family number: (+1)+(−1)= 0; $A: 0 + 0 = 0$

(b) 0.511 MeV

(c) The two γ rays must travel in exactly opposite directions in order to conserve momentum, since initially there is zero momentum if the center of mass is initially at rest.

31.
$Z = (Z + 1) - 1; \quad A = A; \quad \text{efn}: 0 = (+1) + (-1)$

33.
$Z - 1 = Z - 1; \quad A = A; \quad \text{efn}: (+1) = (+1)$

35.
(a) $^{226}_{88}Ra_{138} \rightarrow ^{222}_{86}Rn_{136} + ^4_2He_2$

(b) 4.87 MeV

37.
(a) $n \rightarrow p + \beta^- + \bar{\nu}_e$

(b)) 0.783 MeV

39.
1.82 MeV

41.
(a) 4.274 MeV

(b) 1.927×10^{-5}

(c) Since U-238 is a slowly decaying substance, only a very small number of nuclei decay on human timescales; therefore, although those nuclei that decay lose a noticeable fraction of their mass, the change in the total mass of the sample is not detectable for a macroscopic sample.

43.
(a) $^{15}_8O_7 + e^- \rightarrow ^{15}_7N_8 + \nu_e$

(b) 2.754 MeV

44.
57,300 y

46.
(a) 0.988 Ci

(b) The half-life of ^{226}Ra is now better known.

48.
1.22×10^3 Bq

50.
(a) 16.0 mg

(b) 0.0114%

52.
1.48×10^{17} y

54.
5.6×10^4 y

56.
2.71 y

58.
(a) 1.56 mg

(b) 11.3 Ci

60.
(a) 1.23×10^{-3}

(b) Only part of the emitted radiation goes in the direction of the detector. Only a fraction of that causes a response in the detector. Some of the emitted radiation (mostly α particles) is observed within the source. Some is absorbed within the source, some is absorbed by the detector, and some does not penetrate the detector.

62.
(a) 1.68×10^{-5} Ci

(b) 8.65×10^{10} J

(c) $\$2.9 \times 10^3$

64.
(a) 6.97×10^{15} Bq

(b) 6.24 kW

(c) 5.67 kW

68.
(a) 84.5 Ci

(b) An extremely large activity, many orders of magnitude greater than permitted for home use.

(c) The assumption of $1.00\ \mu A$ is unreasonably large. Other methods can detect much smaller decay rates.

69.
1.112 MeV, consistent with graph

71.
7.848 MeV, consistent with graph

73.
(a) 7.680 MeV, consistent with graph

(b) 7.520 MeV, consistent with graph. Not significantly different from value for ^{12}C, but sufficiently lower to allow decay into another nuclide that is more tightly bound.

75.
(a) 1.46×10^{-8} u vs. 1.007825 u for ^1H

(b) 0.000549 u

(c) 2.66×10^{-5}

76.
(a) –9.315 MeV

(b) The negative binding energy implies an unbound system.

(c) This assumption that it is two bound neutrons is incorrect.

78.
22.8 cm

79.
(a) ${}^{235}_{92}U_{143} \rightarrow {}^{231}_{90}Th_{141} + {}^{4}_{2}He_{2}$

(b) 4.679 MeV

(c) 4.599 MeV

81.
a) 2.4×10^{8} u

(b) The greatest known atomic masses are about 260. This result found in (a) is extremely large.

(c) The assumed radius is much too large to be reasonable.

82.
(a) –1.805 MeV

(b) Negative energy implies energy input is necessary and the reaction cannot be spontaneous.

(c) Although all conversation laws are obeyed, energy must be supplied, so the assumption of spontaneous decay is incorrect.

84.

$$r = r_0 A^{1/3} = 1.2(235)^{1/3} = 7.4 \text{ fm}$$

(a) $V = \frac{4\pi r^3}{3} = 1700 \text{ fm}^3$

$$\rho = \frac{m}{v} = 0.14 \text{ u/fm}^3$$

(b) For barium: $r = r_0 A^{1/3} = 1.2(142)^{1/3} = 6.3 \text{ fm}$
$V = \frac{4\pi r^3}{3} = 1047 \text{ fm}^3$

$\rho = \frac{m}{v} = 0.14 \text{ u/fm}^3$
For krypton: $r = r_0 A^{1/3} = 1.2(92)^{1/3} = 5.4 \text{ fm}$
$V = \frac{4\pi r^3}{3} = 660 \text{ fm}^3$

$\rho = \frac{m}{v} = 0.14 \text{ u/fm}^3$
To two significant figures, they are all alike.

Test Prep for AP® Courses

1.
(c)

3.
(a)

5.
When ${}^{241}_{95}\text{Am}$ undergoes α decay, it loses 2 neutrons and 2 protons. The resulting nucleus is therefore ${}^{237}_{93}\text{Np}$.

7.
During this process, the nucleus emits a particle with -1 charge. In order for the overall charge of the system to remain constant, the charge of the nucleus must therefore increase by +1.

9.
a. No. Nucleon number is conserved (238 = 234 + 4), but the atomic number or charge is NOT conserved (92 ≠ 88+2).
b. Yes. Nucleon number is conserved (223 = 209 + 14), and atomic number is conserved (88 = 82 + 6).
c. Yes. Nucleon number is conserved (14 = 14), and charge is conserved if the electron's charge is properly counted (6 = 7 + (-1)).
d. No. Nucleon number is not conserved (24 ≠ 23). The positron released counts as a charge to conserve charge, but it doesn't count as a nucleon.

11.
This must be alpha decay since 4 nucleons (2 positive charges) are lost from the parent nucleus. The number remaining is found from:

$$\mathrm{N}(t) = \mathrm{N_0} e \left(\frac{-0.693t}{t_{\frac{1}{2}}} \right) = 3.4 \times 10^{17} e \left(\frac{-(0.693)(0.035)}{0.00173} \right)$$

$\mathrm{N}(t) = 4.1 \times 10^{11}$ nuclei

Chapter 32

Problems & Exercises

1.
5.701 MeV

3.
$^{99}_{42}\mathrm{Mo}_{57} \rightarrow {}^{99}_{43}\mathrm{Tc}_{56} + \beta^- + \bar{\upsilon}_e$

5.
1.43×10^{-9} g

7.
(a) 6.958 MeV

(b) 5.7×10^{-10} g

8.
(a) 100 mSv

(b) 80 mSv

(c) ~30 mSv

10.
~2 Gy

12.
1.69 mm

14.
1.24 MeV

16.
7.44×10^8

18.
4.92×10^{-4} Sv

20.

4.43 g

22.
0.010 g

24.
95%

26.
(a) A=1+1=2, Z=1+1=1+1, efn = 0 = −1 + 1

(b) A=1+2=3, Z=1+1=2, efn=0=0

(c) A=3+3=4+1+1, Z=2+2=2+1+1, efn=0=0

28.
$$\begin{aligned} E &= (m_i - m_f)c^2 \\ &= \left[4m\left({}^1\text{H}\right) - m\left({}^4\text{He}\right)\right]c^2 \\ &= [4(1.007825) - 4.002603](931.5\text{ MeV}) \\ &= 26.73\text{ MeV} \end{aligned}$$

30.
3.12×10^5 kg (about 200 tons)

32.
$$\begin{aligned} E &= (m_i - m_f)c^2 \\ E_1 &= (1.008665 + 3.016030 - 4.002603)(931.5\text{ MeV}) \\ &= 20.58\text{ MeV} \\ E_2 &= (1.008665 + 1.007825 - 2.014102)(931.5\text{ MeV}) \\ &= 2.224\text{ MeV} \end{aligned}$$

^{4}He is more tightly bound, since this reaction gives off more energy per nucleon.

34.
1.19×10^4 kg

36.
$2e^- + 4{}^1\text{H} \rightarrow {}^4\text{He} + 7\gamma + 2v_e$

38.
(a) A=12+1=13, Z=6+1=7, efn = 0 = 0

(b) A=13=13, Z=7=6+1, efn = 0 = −1 + 1

(c) A=13 + 1=14, Z=6+1=7, efn = 0 = 0

(d) A=14 + 1=15, Z=7+1=8, efn = 0 = 0

(e) A=15=15, Z=8=7+1, efn = 0 = −1 + 1

(f) A=15 + 1=12 + 4, Z=7+1=6 + 2, efn = 0 = 0

40.
$E_\gamma = 20.6\text{ MeV}$

$E_{{}^4\text{He}} = 5.68 \times 10^{-2}\text{ MeV}$

42.
(a) 3×10^9 y

(b) This is approximately half the lifetime of the Earth.

43.
(a) 177.1 MeV

(b) Because the gain of an external neutron yields about 6 MeV, which is the average BE/A for heavy nuclei.

(c) $A = 1 + 238 = 96 + 140 + 1 + 1 + 1,\ Z = 92 = 38 + 53,\ \text{efn} = 0 = 0$

45.
(a) 180.6 MeV

(b) $A = 1 + 239 = 96 + 140 + 1 + 1 + 1 + 1,\ Z = 94 = 38 + 56,\ \text{efn} = 0 = 0$

47.
$^{238}\text{U} + n \rightarrow {}^{239}\text{U} + \gamma$ 4.81 MeV

$^{239}\text{U} \rightarrow {}^{239}\text{Np} + \beta^- + v_e$ 0.753 MeV

$^{239}\text{Np} \rightarrow {}^{239}\text{Pu} + \beta^- + v_e$ 0.211 MeV

49.
(a) 2.57×10^3 MW

(b) 8.03×10^{19} fission/s

(c) 991 kg

51.
0.56 g

53.
4.781 MeV

55.
(a) Blast yields 2.1×10^{12} J to 8.4×10^{11} J, or 2.5 to 1, conventional to radiation enhanced.

(b) Prompt radiation yields 6.3×10^{11} J to 2.1×10^{11} J, or 3 to 1, radiation enhanced to conventional.

57.
(a) 1.1×10^{25} fissions , 4.4 kg

(b) 3.2×10^{26} fusions , 2.7 kg

(c) The nuclear fuel totals only 6 kg, so it is quite reasonable that some missiles carry 10 overheads. The mass of the fuel would only be 60 kg and therefore the mass of the 10 warheads, weighing about 10 times the nuclear fuel, would be only 1500 lbs. If the fuel for the missiles weighs 5 times the total weight of the warheads, the missile would weigh about 9000 lbs or 4.5 tons. This is not an unreasonable weight for a missile.

59.
7×10^4 g

61.
(a) 4.86×10^9 W

(b) 11.0 y

62.
(a) $(-0.500, 2.00, 3.00)$ and $(0.500, 2.00, 3.00)$

(b) $(0.000, 1.50, 3.00)$ and $(0.000, 2.50, 3.00)$

(c) They travel in opposite directions along the same line.

(d) Yes.

Test Prep for AP® Courses

1.
(b)

3.
(c)

5.
(d)

7.
(d)

9.
(b)

Chapter 33

Problems & Exercises

1.
3×10^{-39} s

3.
1.99×10^{-16} m (0.2 fm)

4.
(a) 10^{-11} to 1, weak to EM

(b) 1 to 1

6.
(a) 2.09×10^{-5} s

(b) 4.77×10^{4} Hz

8.
78.0 cm

10.
1.40×10^{6}

12.
100 GeV

13.
67.5 MeV

15.
(a) 1×10^{14}

(b) 2×10^{17}

17.
(a) 1671 MeV

(b) $Q = 1, Q' = 1 + 0 + 0 = 1.\ L_\tau = -1; L'\tau = -1; L\mu = 0; L'\mu = -1 + 1 = 0$

(c) $\tau^- \rightarrow \mu^- + \upsilon_\mu + \overline{\upsilon}_\tau$
$\Rightarrow \mu^-$ antiparticle of μ^+; υ_μ of $\overline{\upsilon}_\mu$; $\overline{\upsilon}_\tau$ of υ_τ

19.
(a) 3.9 eV

(b) 2.9×10^{-8}

21.
(a) The ***uud*** composition is the same as for a proton.

(b) 3.3×10^{-24} s

(c) Strong (short lifetime)

23.
a) $\Delta^{++}(uuu);\ B = \frac{1}{3} + \frac{1}{3} + \frac{1}{3} = 1$

b)

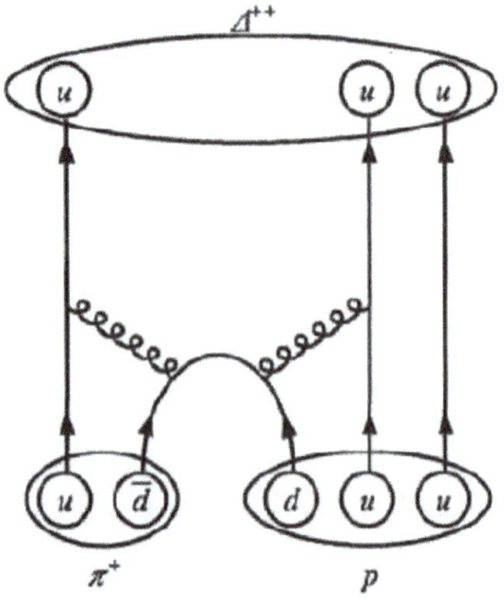

25.
(a) +1

(b) $B = 1 = 1 + 0,\ Z == 0+(- 1)$, all lepton numbers are 0 before and after

(c) $(sss) \rightarrow (uds)+(\overline{u}s)$

27.
(a) $(u\overline{u} + d\overline{d}) \rightarrow (u\overline{u} + d\overline{d}\ )+(\,u\overline{u} + d\overline{d})$

(b) 277.9 MeV

(c) 547.9 MeV

29.
No. Charge $= -1$ is conserved. $L_{e_{\text{i}}} = 0 \neq L_{e_{\text{f}}} = 2$ is not conserved. $L_{\mu} = 1$ is conserved.

31.
(a)Yes. $Z = -1 = 0+(- 1),\ B = 1 = 1 + 0$, all lepton family numbers are 0 before and after, spontaneous since mass greater before reaction.

(b) $dds \rightarrow udd + \overline{u}d$

33.
(a) 216

(b) There are more baryons observed because we have the 6 antiquarks and various mixtures of quarks (as for the π-meson) as well.

35.

$\Omega^+(\overline{s}\overline{s}\overline{s})$
$B = -\frac{1}{3} - \frac{1}{3} - \frac{1}{3} = -1,$
$L_e,\ \mu,\ \tau = 0 + 0 + 0 = 0,$
$Q = \frac{1}{3} + \frac{1}{3} + \frac{1}{3} = 1,$
$S = 1 + 1 + 1 = 3.$

37.
(a)803 MeV

(b) 938.8 MeV

(c) The annihilation energy of an extra electron is included in the total energy.

39.
$c\overline{d}$

41.
a)The antiproton

b) $\overline{p} \rightarrow \pi^0 + e^-$

43.
(a) 5×10^{10}

(b) 5×10^4 particles/m^2

45.
2.5×10^{-17} m

47.
(a) 33.9 MeV

(b) Muon antineutrino 29.8 MeV, muon 4.1 MeV (kinetic energy)

49.
(a) 7.2×10^5 kg

(b) 7.2×10^2 m^3

(c) 100 months

53.
(a) $2(1.67 \times 10^{-27}\text{ kg}) = 3.34 \times 10^{-27}\text{ kg}$

(b) $3.34 \times 10^{-27}(3.00 \times 10^8)^2$ joules $= 3.01 \times 10^{-10}$ joules

(c) 3.01×10^{-10} joules

(d) The proton has a positive charge, and the antiproton has a negative charge.

Test Prep for AP® Courses

1.
(d)

3.
(d)

5.
(b)

7.
(a)

9.
(c), though this comes from Einstein's special relativity

11.
(a)

13.
(d)

15.
(b)

17.
(b)

Chapter 34

Problems & Exercises

1.
$3 \times 10^{41}\ \text{kg}$

3.
(a) $3 \times 10^{52}\ \text{kg}$

(b) 2×10^{79}

(c) 4×10^{88}

5.
0.30 Gly

7.
(a) $2.0 \times 10^{5}\ \text{km/s}$

(b) $0.67c$

9.
$2.7 \times 10^{5}\ \text{m/s}$

11.
6×10^{-11} (an overestimate, since some of the light from Andromeda is blocked by gas and dust within that galaxy)

13.
(a) $2 \times 10^{-8}\ \text{kg}$

(b) 1×10^{19}

15.
(a) $30\ \text{km/s} \cdot \text{Mly}$

(b) $15\ \text{km/s} \cdot \text{Mly}$

17.
960 rev/s

19.
89.999773° (many digits are used to show the difference between 90°)

22.
23.6 km

24.
(a) $2.95 \times 10^{12}\ \text{m}$

(b) 3.12×10^{-4} ly

26.
(a) 1×10^{20}

(b) 10 times greater

27.
1.5×10^{15}
29.
$0.6\,\mathrm{m}^{-3}$
31.
$0.30\ \Omega$
32.
(a) $v = H_0 d = (20\ \mathrm{km/s})/\mathrm{Mly}\ (2.00 \times 10^2\ \mathrm{Mly}) = 4.00 \times 10^3\ \mathrm{km/s}$

(b)
$$d = \sqrt{(1.00 \times 10^2)^2 + (2.00 \times 10^2)^2}\ \mathrm{Mly}$$
$$= 2.24 \times 10^2\ \mathrm{Mly}$$
$$v = (20\ \mathrm{km/s})/\mathrm{Mly}\ (2.24 \times 10^2\ \mathrm{Mly}) = 4.48 \times 10^3\ \mathrm{km/s}$$

(c) The galaxies are separating mostly due to the expansion of space.

(d) Light from the third galaxy would have a red shift when detected in either of the other galaxies.

INDEX

Symbols

A

B

C

D

E

S

T

U

V

W

X

Y

Z